AP® Edition

Ninth Edition

CHEMISTRY & CHEMICAL REACTIVITY

John C. Kotz
State University of New York
College at Oneonta

Paul M. Treichel
University of Wisconsin–Madison

John R. Townsend
West Chester University of Pennsylvania

David A. Treichel
Nebraska Wesleyan University

CENGAGE Learning

Australia • Brazil • Mexico • Singapore • United Kingdom • United States

CENGAGE Learning

Chemistry & Chemical Reactivity,
Ninth Edition, AP® Edition
John C. Kotz, Paul M. Treichel,
John R. Townsend and David A. Treichel

Product Director: Mary Finch
Product Manager: Maureen Rosener
Managing Developers: Peter McGahey, Thomas Martin
Associate Developer: Elizabeth Woods
Product Assistant: Karolina Kiwak
Media Developer: Lisa Weber
Marketing Director: Nicole Hamm
Content Project Manager: Teresa L. Trego
Art Director: Maria Epes
Art Editor: Patrick Harman
Manufacturing Planner: Judy Inouye
Rights Acquisitions Specialist: Don Schlotman
Associate Content Developer, Advanced and Elective Products Program: Ashley Bargende
Senior Media Developer, Advanced and Elective Products Program: Philip Lanza
Production and Composition: Graphic World Inc.
Photo Researcher: QBS Learning
Text Researcher: QBS Learning
Copy Editor: Graphic World Inc.
Text Designer: Parallelogram Graphics
OWL Producers: Stephen Battisti, Cindy Stein, David Hart (Center for Educational Software Development, University of Massachusetts, Amherst)
Cover Designer: Irene Morris
Cover Image: Main image ©John C. Kotz, inset image ©Topic Photo Agency/Corbis

Library of Congress Control Number: 2013952168
ISBN-13: 978-1-285-45396-5
ISBN-10: 1-285-45396-4

Cengage Learning
200 First Stamford Place, 4th Floor
Stamford, CT 06902
USA

Cengage Learning is a leading provider of customized learning solutions with office locations around the globe, including Singapore, the United Kingdom, Australia, Mexico, Brazil, and Japan. Locate your local office at **www.cengage.com/global.**

Cengage Learning products are represented in Canada by Nelson Education, Ltd.

To find online supplements and other instructional support, please visit **www.cengagebrain.com.**

Printed in the United States of America
2 3 4 5 17 16 15 14

Brief Contents

Contents

PART FOUR ▶ THE CONTROL OF CHEMICAL REACTIONS

PART FIVE ▶ THE CHEMISTRY OF THE ELEMENTS

Preface

The first edition of this book was conceived over 30 years ago. Since that time there have been eight editions, and over 1 million students worldwide have used the book to begin their study of chemistry. Over the years, and the many editions, our goals have remained the same: to provide a broad overview of the principles of chemistry, the reactivity of the chemical elements and their compounds, and the applications of chemistry. To reach these goals, we have tried to show the close relation between the observations chemists make of chemical and physical changes in the laboratory and in nature and the way these changes are viewed at the atomic and molecular levels.

© Cengage Learning/Charles D. Winters

Sulfur burns in pure oxygen with a brilliant blue flame.

We have also tried to convey a sense that chemistry not only has a lively history but is also dynamic, with important new developments occurring every year. Furthermore, we have provided some insight into the chemical aspects of the world around us. Indeed, a major objective of this book has always been to provide the tools needed for our students to function as chemically literate citizens. Learning about the chemical world is just as important as understanding some basic mathematics and biology and as important as having an appreciation for history, music, and literature. For example, students should know something about the many materials that are important in our economy and in our daily lives. Furthermore, they should know how chemistry is important in understanding our environment. In this regard, one growing area of chemistry, highlighted throughout the previous edition and this one, is "green" or "sustainable" chemistry.

Looking back over the previous editions, we can see how the book has changed. There have been many new and exciting additions to the contents. In addition, there have been significant advances in the technology of communicating information, and we have taken advantage of those new developments. A desire to make the book even better for our students has been the impetus behind the preparation of each new edition. Over the last two editions we have introduced new approaches to problem solving, new ways to describe contemporary uses of chemistry, new technologies, and improved integration with existing technologies.

Audience for *Chemistry & Chemical Reactivity*

This textbook (both as a printed book and the digital versions) is designed for students interested in further study in science, whether that science is chemistry, biology, engineering, geology, physics, or related subjects. Our assumption is that students in a course using this book have had some preparation in algebra and in general science. Although undeniably helpful, a previous exposure to chemistry is neither assumed nor required.

Philosophy and Approach of *Chemistry & Chemical Reactivity*

We have had several major, but not independent, objectives since the first edition of the book. The first was to write a book that students would enjoy reading and that would offer, at a reasonable level of rigor, chemistry and chemical principles in a format and organization typical of college and university courses today. Second, we wanted to convey the utility and importance of chemistry by introducing the properties of the elements, their compounds, and their reactions.

The American Chemical Society has been urging educators to put "chemistry" back into introductory chemistry courses. We agree wholeheartedly. Therefore, we have tried to describe the elements, their compounds, and their reactions as early and as often as possible by:

- Bringing **material on the properties of elements and compounds** as early as possible into the Examples and Study Questions (and especially the *Applying Chemical Principles* questions) and introducing new principles using realistic chemical situations.
- Using numerous **photographs** of the elements and common compounds, of chemical reactions, and of common laboratory operations and industrial processes.

What's New in This Edition

General Comments

As we have done for all of the previous editions, we examined every paragraph for accuracy, clarity, and brevity. Where improvements could be made, paragraphs or entire sections were rewritten. We also wrote or rewrote many chapter-opening stories, *Closer Look* boxes, and *Case Studies*.

Some of the important additions from the 8th edition were retained. In particular, we kept and expanded

- the Review & Check questions.
- the organization of the Example problems.
- the Strategy Maps.
- an emphasis on green chemistry.
- the *Applying Chemical Principles* problems.

Changes from the 8th to the 9th Edition

A number of changes have been made for the 9th edition. This page *briefly* lists the most important; a more detailed list is given beginning on page xxi.

- Many of the illustrations have been redesigned with an emphasis on bringing information from the caption into the illustration itself.
- We have dropped the special topic coverage provided in the 8th edition from the interchapters and integrated the material into regular chapters.
  - Historical developments have been incorporated into Chapter 2 and elsewhere.
  - Material on solid state chemistry has been added to the chapter on solids (12).
  - The interchapters on fuels and energy and on environmental chemistry are incorporated into a new chapter (20), *Environmental Chemistry—Earth's Environment, Energy, and Sustainability.*
  - The topic of biochemistry has been expanded into a full chapter (24).
- Chapter goals or objectives for each chapter have been recast into three categories that most express what students should get out of the course. These goals are:
  - **UNDERSTAND** chapter concepts.
  - **DO**. Be able carry out calculations, draw molecular structures, and make chemical decisions.
  - **REMEMBER** important facts and chemical concepts.

  The objectives are repeated and amplified at the end of the chapter in the *Chapter Goals Revisited* section.
- Answers to questions in a chapter—Study Questions plus Check Your Understanding, Review & Check, *Case Studies,* and *Applying Chemical Principles*—are collected in Appendix N (rather than scattered over several appendices as in previous editions). This will allow students to more efficiently check their work.
- Over 100 new Study Questions have been added and a similar number have been revised.
- Example problems and end-of-chapter Study Questions that are interactive in OWL have been retained. All questions have been re-examined for clarity and relevance.
- *Applying Chemical Principles* questions have been moved from the very end of the chapter (following all of the Study Questions), to the last text material in the chapter.

Fluorite crystals (CaF_2).

- Introducing each chapter with a **discussion of contemporary chemistry** such as the use of copper surfaces in hospitals, energy in common foods, and lithium in car batteries.
- Using numerous ***Case Studies*** and ***Applying Chemical Principles*** study questions that delve into practical chemistry.
- New margin notes with AP®-specific content have been added where appropriate.
- Multiple-Choice and Free Response questions in AP® format have been added at the end of most chapters.
- A new Appendix has been added containing additional AP®-specific content and is referenced in the text where appropriate.

AP® Special Features

The AP® Chemistry course has been redesigned for the academic year 2013–2014. In order to help both teachers and students with the new course, there are several AP®-specific features in this edition.

- A correlation table connects AP® Learning Objectives to the page numbers in *Chemistry & Chemical Reactivity* where those topics are discussed.

General Organization

Through its many editions, *Chemistry & Chemical Reactivity* has had two broad themes: *Chemical Reactivity* and *Bonding and Molecular Structure*. The chapters on *Principles of Reactivity* introduce the factors that lead chemical reactions to be successful in converting reactants to products. Under this topic there is a discussion of common types of reactions, the energy involved in reactions, and the factors that affect the speed of a reaction. One reason for the enormous advances in chemistry and molecular biology in the last several decades has been an understanding of molecular structure. The sections of the book on *Principles of Bonding and Molecular Structure* lay the groundwork for understanding these developments. Particular attention is paid to an understanding of the structural aspects of such biologically important molecules as DNA.

Flexibility of Chapter Organization

A glance at the introductory chemistry texts currently available shows that there is a generally accepted order of topics used by most educators. With only minor variations, we have followed that order. That is not to say that the chapters in our book cannot be used in some other order. We have written this book to be as flexible as possible. An example is the **flexibility of covering the behavior of gases** (Chapter 10). It has been placed with chapters on liquids, solids, and solutions (Chapters 10–13) because it logically fits with those topics. However, it can easily be read and understood after covering only the first four chapters of the book.

Similarly, chapters on atomic and molecular structure (Chapters 6–9) could be used in an **atoms-first approach** before the chapters on stoichiometry and common reactions (Chapters 3 and 4). To facilitate this, there is an introduction to energy and its units in Chapter 1.

Also, the chapters on chemical equilibria (Chapters 15–17) can be covered before those on solutions and kinetics (Chapters 13 and 14).

Organic chemistry (Chapter 23) is one of the final chapters in the textbook. However, the topics of this chapter can also be presented to students following the chapters on structure and bonding.

A fireworks sparkler.

The order of topics in the text was also devised to introduce as early as possible the background required for the laboratory experiments usually performed in introductory chemistry courses. For this reason, chapters on chemical and physical properties, common reaction types, and stoichiometry begin the book. In addition, because an understanding of energy is so important in the study of chemistry, energy and its units are introduced in Chapter 1, and thermochemistry is introduced in Chapter 5.

Organization and Purposes of the Sections of the Book

PART ONE: The Basic Tools of Chemistry

The basic ideas and methods of chemistry are introduced in Part 1. Chapter 1 defines important terms, and the accompanying *Let's Review* section reviews units and mathematical methods. Chapter 2 introduces atoms, molecules, and ions, and the most important organizational device in chemistry, the periodic table. In Chapter 3, we begin to discuss the principles of chemical activity. Writing chemical equations is covered here, and there is a short introduction to equilibrium. Then, in Chapter 4, we describe the numerical methods used by chemists to extract quantitative information from chemical reactions. Chapter 5 is an introduction to the energy involved in chemical processes.

PART TWO: Atoms and Molecules

The current theories of the arrangement of electrons in atoms are presented in Chapters 6 and 7. This discussion is tied closely to the arrangement of elements in the periodic table and to periodic properties. In Chapter 8 we discuss the details of chemical bonding and the properties of these bonds. In addition, we show how to derive the three-dimensional structure of simple molecules. Finally, Chapter 9 considers the major theories of chemical bonding in more detail.

PART THREE: States of Matter

The behavior of the three states of matter—gases, liquids, and solids—is described in Chapters 10–12. The discussion of liquids and solids is tied to gases through the description of intermolecular forces in Chapter 11, with particular attention given to liquid and solid water. In Chapter 13 we describe the properties of solutions, intimate mixtures of gases, liquids, and solids.

PART FOUR: The Control of Chemical Reactions

This section is wholly concerned with the *Principles of Reactivity*. Chapter 14 examines the rates of chemical processes and the factors controlling these rates. Next, we move to Chapters 15–17, which describe chemical equilibrium. After an introduction to equilibrium in Chapter 15, we highlight the reactions involving acids and bases in water (Chapters 16 and 17) and reactions leading to slightly soluble salts (Chapter 17). To tie together the discussion of chemical equilibria and thermodynamics, we explore entropy and free energy in Chapter 18. As a final topic in this section we describe in Chapter 19 chemical reactions involving the transfer of electrons and the use of these reactions in electrochemical cells.

PART FIVE: The Chemistry of the Elements

Although the chemistry of the various elements is described throughout the book, Part 5 considers this topic in a more systematic way. Chapter 20 brings together many of the concepts in earlier chapters into a discussion of *Environmental Chemistry—Earth's Environment,*

Energy, and Sustainability. Chapter 21 is devoted to the chemistry of the main group elements, whereas Chapter 22 is a discussion of the transition elements and their compounds. Chapter 23 is a brief discussion of organic chemistry with an emphasis on molecular structure, basic reactions types, and polymers. Chapter 24 is an introduction to biochemistry, and Chapter 25 is an overview of nuclear chemistry.

Features of the Book

Some years ago a student of one of the authors, now an accountant, shared an interesting perspective with us. He said that, while general chemistry was one of his hardest subjects, it was also the most useful course he had taken because it taught him how to solve problems. We were gratified by this perspective. We have always thought that, for many students, an important goal in general chemistry was not only to teach students chemistry but also to help them learn critical thinking and problem-solving skills. Many of the features of the book are meant to support those goals.

Problem-Solving Approach: Organization and Strategy Maps

Worked-out examples are an essential part of each chapter. To better assist students in following the logic of a solution, these problems are organized around the following outline:

Problem
This is the statement of the problem.
What Do You Know?
The information given is outlined.
Strategy
The information available is combined with the objective and we begin to devise a pathway to a solution.
Solution
We work through the steps, both logical and mathematical, to the answer.
Think About Your Answer
We ask if the answer is reasonable or what it means.
Check Your Understanding
This is a similar problem for the student to try. A solution to the problem is in Appendix N.

For many students, a **visual strategy map** can be a useful tool in solving the problem. For example, on pages 42–43, we ask how thick the oil layer would be if you spread a given mass of oil on the surface of water in a dish. The density of the oil is also given. To help see the logic of the problem, the Example is accompanied by the Strategy Map given here. There are approximately 60 such Strategy Maps in the book accompanying Example problems.

Strategy Map for Example 5

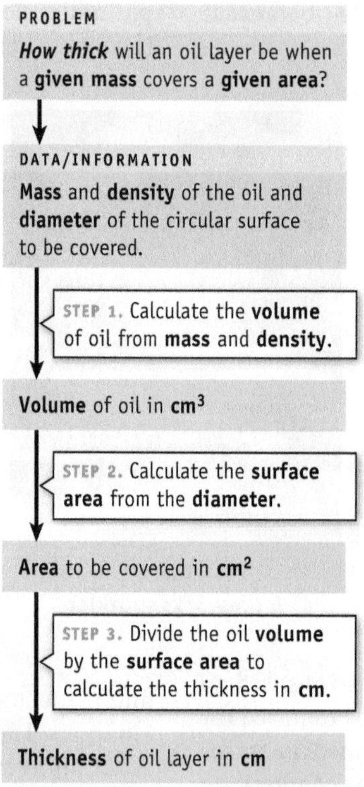

Review & Check: Quick Review Questions

In the 8th edition we added multiple choice *Review & Check* questions at the end of almost every section, and these have proved popular. Students can check their understanding of the section by attempting these brief questions. Answers to the questions are in Appendix N.

Chapter Goals/Revisited

The learning goals for each chapter are listed on the first page of each chapter. For this edition, we have organized these around the major tasks facing a student:

- What do you need to **UNDERSTAND** in the chapter.
- What do you need to be able to **DO**.
- What do you need to **REMEMBER** about the materials in the chapter.

The goals are revisited on the last page of the chapter. Each goal is given in more detail, and specific end-of-chapter Study Questions are listed that help students determine if they have met those goals.

End-of-Chapter Study Questions

There are 50 to over 150 Study Questions for each chapter (and answers to the odd-numbered questions are given in Appendix N). They are grouped as follows:

Practicing Skills: These questions are grouped by the topic covered by the questions.
General Questions: There is no indication regarding the type of question.
In the Laboratory: These are problems that may be encountered in a laboratory experiment on the chapter material.
Summary and Conceptual Questions: These questions use concepts from the current chapter as well as preceding chapters.

Study Questions are available in the OWL Online Web Learning system. The OWL system now has over 1900 of the roughly 2200 Study Questions in the book.

Finally, note that some questions are marked with a small red triangle (▲). These are meant to be more challenging than other questions.

Boxed Essays

As in the 8th edition, there are boxed essays titled *A Closer Look* (for a more in-depth look at relevant material), and *Problem Solving Tips*. We have added or revised a number of the *Case Studies*, some of which describe "green" or sustainable chemistry.

Changes for the 9th Edition

Significant changes from the 8th edition to this edition have been outlined in the section on "What's New." In addition, we have produced new photos and new illustrations and have continually tried to improve the writing throughout. The following chapter-by-chapter listing indicates specific changes from the 8th edition of the book to this edition.

Chapter 1 Basic Concepts of Chemistry and Let's Review: The Tools of Quantitative Chemistry

- The introductory story on gold has been rewritten.
- The figure on chemical and physical properties has been redone completely.

Chapter 2 Atoms, Molecules, and Ions

- There is a new introductory story on "seeing atoms" with a scanning-tunneling microscope.
- A new two-page spread *Key Experiments–How Do We Know the Nature of the Atom and Its Components?* has been added. This covers the main ideas from the interchapter on the history of chemistry from the 7th and 8th editions.
- The section in the 8th edition on hydrated compounds is now a *Closer Look* box.

Chapter 3 Chemical Reactions

- There is a new *Closer Look* box, *Alternative Organizations of Reaction Types*. Our reaction organization scheme is slightly different than the one used in Advanced Placement (AP®) chemistry, so this box relates our scheme to the AP® nomenclature.

© Cengage Learning/Charles D. Winters

Corundum crystal (Al_2O_3).

Chapter 4 Stoichiometry: Quantitative Information about Chemical Reactions

- The introduction to solving stoichiometry problems is laid out in a new way to help students better follow this vitally important topic.

Chapter 5 Principles of Chemical Reactivity: Energy and Chemical Reactions

- We expanded coverage of the first law of thermodynamics with more details on work. This includes a revised *Closer Look* box, a new Example problem, and new Study Questions.
- We updated the data on world energy usage and, in a *Closer Look* box, updated the information on ethanol in gasoline.

Chapter 6 The Structure of Atoms

- A new opening story on charge coupled devices has been added.
- There is a new *Example* problem on using Planck's law.
- A new *Closer Look* box on *Sunburn, Sunscreens, and Ultraviolet Radiation* has been added.
- Information on diamagnetism and paramagnetism has been moved to Chapter 7.

Chapter 7 The Structure of Atoms and Periodic Trends

- More on photoelectron spectroscopy has been incorporated with a new *Closer Look* box and four new Study Questions (33–36).

Chapter 8 Bonding and Molecular Structure

- There is a new *Closer Look* box, *A Triangular View of Chemical Bonding*. In this we introduce the van Arkel-Ketelaar diagram that shows the continuum of bonding models, an important concept in an introductory course.
- The introduction to electron dot structures has been changed to better show the steps involved in their construction, and new examples have been added.
- A new subsection has been added on drawing Lewis structures for organic molecules.

Chapter 9 Bonding and Molecular Structure: Orbital Hybridization and Molecular Orbitals

- Chemists have been rethinking the importance of *d* orbitals in bonding. As we state in Chapter 9, "current research indicates there is little evidence for *d* orbital participation in bonding in hypervalent molecules." This conclusion has been widely accepted in the chemical community, and has been integrated into our discussion of bonding in compounds such as PF_5 and SF_6.
- The *Applying Chemical Principles* question on photoelectron spectroscopy has been retained.

Chapter 10 Gases and Their Properties

- There is a new discussion on the behavior of real gases (Section 10-8).
- A new *Case Study, The Methane Mystery* has been added.
- A new *Closer Look* box was added: *Surface Science and the Need for Ultrahigh Vacuum Systems.*

Chapter 11 Intermolecular Forces and Liquids

- In 2011 the International Union of Pure and Applied Chemistry (IUPAC) redefined the concept of hydrogen bonding. The IUPAC perspective has been incorporated, and we have expanded our discussion on hydrogen bonding.
- The *Closer Look* box on supercritical CO_2 was extensively rewritten.

Chapter 12 The Solid State

- There is a new introductory story on jade, the subject of the cover photo.
- The *Case Study* on graphene was extensively rewritten to reflect research and development in this important new area.
- In the section on phase changes (12-6), there is a new *Closer Look* box on *New Memory for Your Computer Based on Phase Changes.*

Chapter 13 Solutions and Their Behavior

- There is a new chapter introduction on *Narcosis and the Bends.*
- A new *Closer Look* box on *Growing Crystals* was added. This is about growing large crystals, something students can do with alum from the supermarket.

Chapter 14 Chemical Kinetics: The Rates of Chemical Reactions

- A *Closer Look* box, *Rate Laws, Rate Constants, and Reaction Stoichiometry*, was added to the chapter.
- A new *Closer Look* box was added, *Thinking About Bond Energies*, which relates bond energies to kinetic parameters.
- Several changes have been made in Section 14-6, Reaction Mechanisms. Many students go on to organic chemistry, so a new *Closer Look* box covers *Organic Bimolecular Substitution Reactions.* A new subsection on chain reactions was added.
- New *Problem Solving Tip 14.1: Determining a Rate Equation.*

Sulfur-containing minerals.

Chapter 15 Principles of Chemical Reactivity: Equilibria

- The introductory story on equilibria in an aqueous solution of cobalt(II) ions was rewritten.

Chapter 16 Principles of Chemical Reactivity: The Chemistry of Acids and Bases

- New introductory story on *Alkaloids and Toxins.*

Chapter 17 Principles of Chemical Reactivity: Other Aspects of Aqueous Equilibria

- The introductory story on *Nature's Acids* was rewritten.
- There is increased emphasis on using the Henderson-Hasselbalch equation in buffer calculations.

Chapter 18 Principles of Chemical Reactivity: Entropy and Free Energy

- The introductory article on hydrogen was rewritten.
- The important section on Gibbs free energy (18.6) was carefully examined to reflect the exposition of free energy by J. Quilez in the *Journal of Chemical Education* ("First-Year University Chemistry Textbooks' Misrepresentation of Gibbs Energy," *Journal of Chemical Education*, Vol. 89, 87-93, 2012).
- There is a new *Example* (18.9) on calculating the Gibbs free energy change for a process run under nonstandard conditions. This clarifies the difference between $\Delta_r G$ and $\Delta_r G^\circ$.

Chapter 19 Principles of Chemical Reactivity: Electron Transfer Reactions

- There is a new introduction on lithium ion batteries.

Chapter 20 Environmental Chemistry—Earth's Environment, Energy, and Sustainability

- This new chapter uses concepts developed in earlier chapters to focus on the environment. Some material was taken from the 8th edition interchapters on energy and on the environment. However, all was rewritten and much new material was added.

Chapter 21 The Chemistry of the Main Group Elements

- The *Closer Look* box on *The Reducing Ability of the Alkali Metals* was rewritten.
- A new *Closer Look* box on *Green Cement* was added.
- The *Closer Look* box on *Iodine and Your Thyroid Gland* was moved into this chapter from the nuclear chemistry chapter in the 8th edition.
- A new section (21-11) on noble gases has been added as well as the *Closer Look* box *Predicting the Existence of Xenon Fluorides*.

Chapter 22 The Chemistry of the Transition Elements

- A new introductory story about *Life-Saving Copper* was written for this chapter.
- The *Case Study* on *High-Strength Steel* has been moved to this chapter from its location in the 8th edition (the solids chapter).
- New *Case Study* was added on *The Rare Earths*.
- The 8th edition section on organometallic chemistry has been dropped.
- The concept of chirality is introduced in this chapter (rather than in the organic chemistry chapter as in the 8th edition).

Chapter 23 Carbon: Not Just Another Element

- This introduction to organic chemistry was Chapter 10 in the 8th edition.
- A new *Closer Look* box was added on *Omega-3-Fatty Acids*.
- The information in the *Closer Look* box on glucose, which was in Chapter 10 in the 8th edition, is now included in the new biochemistry chapter (Chapter 24).
- A new *Closer Look* box *Green Chemistry: Recycling PET* was added.
- There is a new *Applying Chemical Principles* essay on BPA (*Bisphenol A*).

Chapter 24 Biochemistry

- This was an interchapter in the 8th edition. The material is now expanded to include a new section on carbohydrates.
- Many new Study Questions were added.
- There is a new introductory story on *Animal Cloning*.
- A new *Case Study, Antisense Therapy*, was added.
- The *Applying Chemical Principles* problem is about the *Polymerase Chain Reaction*.
- There are three new *Example* problems on drawing peptide structures, determining a complementary sequence of DNA, and determining the amino acid sequence selected by a sequence of DNA.
- There are new *Review & Check* Questions.

Chapter 25 Nuclear Chemistry

- In revising this chapter we incorporated the latest findings in nuclear chemistry and introduced the newest elements.

Anchoring Concepts in Chemistry

The American Chemical Society Examinations Institute has been writing assessment examinations for college chemistry for over 75 years. In 2012 the Institute published papers in *The Journal of Chemical Education* on "anchoring concepts" or "big ideas" in chemistry. The purpose was to provide college instructors with a fine-grained content map of chemistry so that instruction can be aligned better with the content of the American Chemical Society examinations. The ACS map begins with "anchoring concepts," which are subdivided into "enduring understandings" and then further broken down into detailed areas.

We believe these ideas are useful to both teachers and students of chemistry and are important enough to include them in this Preface.

The College Board, the publisher of Advanced Placement (AP®) examinations, has recently redesigned the AP® chemistry curriculum along many of the same ideas. This curriculum is also based on "big ideas" and then "enduring understandings." The latter are broken down into "essential knowledge" and "science practices" and finally into "learning objectives." We have made sure that the present edition of *Chemistry & Chemical Reactivity* has included material that meets many of the criteria of the College Board curriculum while basing the text largely on the "anchoring concepts" of the Examinations Institute.

American Chemical Society Examinations Institute's Anchoring Concepts

1. Atoms (Chapters 1, 2, 6, 7)
Atoms are the building blocks of chemistry. Chapters 1 and 2 describe the basic composition of atoms and the classic experiments that have defined atomic structure. The electronic structure of atoms is described in detail in Chapter 6 in which quantum numbers and atomic orbitals are introduced. This is followed in Chapter 7 by analysis of electron configurations, orbital energy level diagrams, and periodic trends in chemical and physical properties of the elements. We note that Coulomb's law is the underlying implicit and explicit principle in many of these discussions.

2. Bonding (Chapters 8, 9, 12, 23)
Two chapters on covalent bonding follow the discussion of atomic structure. Molecular structure is covered first in Chapter 8, which begins with Lewis structures and then moves on to the determination of electronic and molecular structures using VSEPR guidelines. A detailed discussion of valence bond theory and the introduction of hybridization comes next in Chapter 9, and this is followed by molecular orbital theory at a qualitative level. Bonding in ionic compounds and semiconductors is covered in the chapter on solids (Chapter 12). Bonding in organic compounds is re-emphasized in Chapter 23.

3. Structure and Function (Chapters 11, 12, 16, 24)
The most notable relationship of structure to function is in Chapter 24 (biochemistry) which includes interesting issues such as hemoglobin and sickle cell anemia, and the role of nucleic acids in protein synthesis. However, structure–function relationships are found throughout the book. Consider, for example, the properties of ice and water in Chapter 11, lattice energy and physical properties of ionic compounds in Chapter 12, and the relationships of acid strength and structure (Chapter 16).

4. Intermolecular Interactions (Chapters 10, 11, 24)
Chapter 11 is specifically devoted to this topic; introduced here are ion-dipole, dipole-dipole, and London forces, each based on coulombic (electrostatic) forces of attraction. Hydrogen bonding is given special attention. We also note the importance of intermolecular attractions in real gases (Chapter 10) and biochemical molecules (Chapter 24).

5. Reactions (Chapters 3, 4, 16, 17, 19–24)
Chemical reactivity is a major theme of this book. Chemistry is made up of a wide collection of chemical reactions. Types of reactions and principles of chemical equilibria are introduced in Chapter 3, and quantitative aspects of reactions (chemical stoichiometry) is covered in Chapter 4. In-depth analyses of Brønsted–Lowry acid–base reactions and precipitation reactions are presented in Chapter 16 and 17, and redox reactions are analyzed in depth in the chapter on electrochemistry (19). Reactions important in our environment are covered in Chapter 20, and the chemistry of the main group elements and transition elements is described in Chapters 21 and 22, respectively. Finally, the organic and biochemistry chapters (23 and 24) are organized around structures and reactions.

6. Energy and Thermodynamics (Chapters 1, 5–8, 12–13, 18, 20)
Energy is a pervasive theme of chemistry so some background information is incorporated in Chapter 1.

Thermochemistry and the first law of thermodynamics (heat and work) are presented in Chapter 5. Introduced in this chapter are important topics, including specific heat, internal energy, enthalpy, and experiments involving calorimetry. Energy is revisited in the discussion of atomic structure in Chapter 6, of ionization energy and electron attachment enthalpy in Chapter 7, and of bond energies in Chapter 8. It is once again important in the discussion of solids in Chapter 12 and solutions in Chapter 13.

The second and third laws of thermodynamics are developed in Chapter 18 in which we encounter entropy (briefly mentioned earlier in Chapter 13 on solutions) and especially free energy, which is tied to equilibrium.

Finally, energy resources and usage are key topics in the chapter on the environment (20).

7. Kinetics (Chapter 14, 24)

Chapter 14 is devoted to chemical kinetics. Here we define what is meant by rates and rate laws, and we illustrate examples where rate laws are determined from experimental data. Activation energy is also covered in this chapter. Enzyme kinetics is presented in Chapter 24.

8. Equilibrium (Chapters 3, 15–19)

We first mention equilibrium in Chapter 3, pointing out that all reactions proceed spontaneously to equilibrium and identifying the terms product-favored and reactant-favored. This subject is then covered in depth in a series of three chapters. Chapter 15 is an introduction to equilibrium principles. We describe solution and gas phase equilibria in terms of equilibrium constants. Le Chatelier's principle, which gives an intuitive sense of how stresses affect a system in equilibrium, is introduced here. In Chapters 16 and 17, we describe specific types of equilibria in aqueous solutions, with acid–base and solubility equilibria, and finally in Chapter 18 we tie equilibrium to the thermodynamic function Gibbs free energy. In Chapter 19, we introduce potentiometric measurements as a means of studying chemical equilibrium.

9. Experiments, Measurements, and Data (most chapters throughout the book)

Chemistry is built on experimental results, so it is important to realize that information on this topic occurs throughout the book. We will mention just a few here:

- the classic experiments that determined atomic structure in Chapter 2.
- calorimetry in Chapter 5.
- the use of experimental techniques such as mass spectrometry (Chapter 3) and photoelectron spectroscopy (Chapters 7 and 9) to define the composition and structure of molecules and energy levels in atoms.
- the development of the gas laws in Chapter 10.
- the measurement of rates of reactions in Chapter 14.
- and the measurement of electrochemical potentials in voltaic cells in Chapter 19.

In the end-of-chapter Study Questions there are *In the Laboratory* questions, questions that might occur in a laboratory experiment and that use material in the chapter. And don't overlook the *Applied Chemical Principles* questions, chapter-ending questions that are built around interesting and important experiments.

10. Visualizations (these appear throughout the book)

Visual learners will find this book exciting. Figures are used to illustrate concepts and examples are abundant in every chapter, and we have redesigned many figures to make these even more easily interpreted and informative. Representative examples include visualizations of electromagnetic radiation, colligative properties, dissolving precipitates, reaction mechanisms, chemical equilibria, atomic orbitals, and many, many molecular models.

More information:

K. Murphy, T. Holme, A. Zenisky, H. Caruthers, and K. Knaus, *Journal of Chemical Education*, Volume 89, pages 715-720, 2012. T. Holme and K. Murphy, *ibid.*, Volume 89, 721-723, 2012.

For Teachers

The following resources accompany this text.

AP® Teacher's Resource Guide (ISBN: 978-1-285-77862-4) This guide, written by Linda Wood, Lowndes High School, Valdosta, Georgia, includes an overview of the AP® exam, including guidelines and tips for teaching the course in relation to the AP® exam. For each chapter of the text the guide provides a chapter outline, objectives with a lesson plan, a glossary, a media menu, diagnostic quiz questions, and test bank questions.

AP® Instructor Resource Manual for Lab Manual Chemistry 9e (ISBN-13: 978-1-305-26610-0) This manual contains tips on running experiments and includes approximate times for each experiment. In addition, the manual contains answers to all prelab and postlab questions posed in the laboratory guide.

For Students

OWLv2 with Quick Prep and Fast Track to a 5 AP® Exam Prep (978-1-305-11515-6) OWLv2, the #1 online solution for chemistry, now features new enhanced functionality. OWLv2 includes powerful course management tools and advanced reporting and grade book features for teachers to track student progress. OWLv2 addresses different learning styles through a range of assignment types like algorithmically generated problems with instant answer-specific feedback—and it's easier to use. With OWLv2's mastery learning approach, students work at their own pace until they understand each concept and skill. For each attempt at a problem, OWLv2 changes the variables to ensure mastery and help prevent "gaming" the system. OWLv2 includes MindTap Reader™, a new iPad-compatible multimedia eBook. OWLv2 for Gen Chem, GOB, and Liberal Arts includes Quick Prep essential skills assignments. Finally, the OWLv2 subscription for this AP® Edition of *Chemistry & Chemical Reactivity* also includes Fast Track to a 5 AP® Exam Prep. This online product features a full review of the AP® chemistry course outline along with topic review questions, a diagnostic test, and two practice exams all with immediate feedback reinforced by links back to the MindTap Reader™.

Fast Track to a 5: Preparing for the AP® Chemistry Examination (ISBN-13: 978-1-285-76509-9) *Fast Track to a 5*, written by Laura Duncan, Boulder High School, Boulder, Colorado, and Kara Pezzi, Appleton East High School, Appleton, Wisconsin, will help students prepare for the AP® exam quickly, efficiently, and effectively. This comprehensive test-prep resource provides a diagnostic pre-test to assess prior knowledge, test-taking strategies, in-depth review and reinforcement of key concepts, and full-length practice exams—all specifically cross-referenced to *Chemistry & Chemical Reactivity*, Ninth Edition. Available for purchase either with the text or separately.

AP® Experimental Chemistry (ISBN-13: 978-1-285-77863-1) This lab manual contains 16 experiments adapted for the AP® class. All labs take into account considerations such as reduced class times and different uses of technology, materials, and equipment. Ask your sales representative about available discounts.

Acknowledgments

Preparing this new edition of *Chemistry & Chemical Reactivity* took over 2 years of continuous effort. As in our work on the first eight editions, we have had the support and encouragement of our colleagues at Cengage Publishing and of our families and wonderful friends, faculty colleagues, and students.

CENGAGE LEARNING

The eighth edition of this book was published by Cengage Learning, and we continue with much of the same excellent team we have had in place for several years.

The eighth edition of the book was very successful, in large part owing to the work of Lisa Lockwood as the Product Manager. She has an excellent sense of the market and worked with us in planning this new edition. Maureen Rosener assumed that role as this edition moved into production.

Peter McGahey has been our Content Developer since he joined us to work on the 5th edition. Peter is blessed with energy, creativity, enthusiasm, intelligence, and good humor. He is a trusted friend and confidant and cheerfully answers our many questions during almost-daily phone calls.

No book can be successful without proper marketing. Nicole Hamm (Marketing Director) and Janet del Munro (Market Development Manager) were a great help in marketing the previous edition, and they are back in that role for this edition. They are knowledgeable about the market and have worked tirelessly to bring the book to everyone's attention.

Our team at Cengage Learning is completed with Teresa Trego, Content Project Manager; Lisa Weber, Media Developer; and Elizabeth Woods, Associate Developer. Schedules are very demanding in textbook publishing, and Teresa has helped to keep us on schedule. We certainly appreciate her organizational skills.

Dan Fitzgerald of Graphic World Inc. guided the book through months of production, and Andy Vosburgh of that company was enormously helpful in getting us through the use of new software.

Jill Reichenbach of QBS Learning directed the photo research for the book and was successful in filling our sometimes offbeat requests for particular photos.

Art, Design, and Photography

Many of the color photographs in our book have been beautifully created by Charles D. Winters, and he produced almost 50 new images for this edition. Charlie's work gets better with each edition. We have worked with him for more than 30 years and have become close friends. We listen to his jokes, both new and old—and always forget them.

When the fifth edition was being planned some years ago, we brought in Patrick Harman as a member of the team. Pat designed the first edition of our *Interactive General Chemistry* CD-ROM (published in the 1990s), and we believe its success is in no small way connected to his design skill. For the fifth through the eighth editions of the book, Pat went over almost every figure, and almost every word, to bring a fresh perspective to ways to communicate chemistry. Once again he has worked on designing and producing new illustrations for this edition, and his creativity is obvious in their clarity. Pat has also become a good friend, and we share interests not only in books but in music.

Finally, another fine photographer, Steven Hyatt, has joined us in producing a number of new photos for this edition.

Other Collaborators

We have been fortunate to have a number of other colleagues who have played valuable roles in this project.

- Alton Banks (North Carolina State University) has also been involved for a number of editions preparing the *Student Solutions Manual*. Alton has been very helpful in ensuring the accuracy of the Study Question answers in the book, as well as in their respective manuals.

- John Vincent (University of Alabama-Tuscaloosa) again wrote the *Instructor's Resource Manual* and did an accuracy review.
- Greg Gellene (Texas Tech University) updated and revised the *Study Guide* for this text. Our textbook has had a history of excellent study guides, and this manual follows that tradition.
- Jay Freedman was the development editor for the first edition of the book and his work set the stage for the continuing success of the book. For several editions Jay has also done a masterful job compiling the index/glossary.
- Nathanael Fackler (Nebraska Wesleyan University) produced the *Test Bank* for this edition.
- Daniel Huchital (Florida Atlantic University) was the accuracy reviewer for this edition, and David Shinn of the U.S. Merchant Marine Academy was the accuracy reviewer for the *Student Solutions Manual* and *Instructor's Resource Manual.*
- Nathan Tice (Butler University) prepared a review of green chemistry for us.
- Professor J. Quilez (Departamento de Física y Química, IES Benicalap, Valencia, Spain) reviewed the free energy discussion in Chapter 18.

AP® Version

We would also like to thank those responsible for making the Advanced Placement (AP®) version of this textbook possible. In particular, we would like to thank Todd Abronowitz (Parish Episcopal High School) and Kristen Jones (College Station ISD) for their outstanding work on this project. They were responsible for authoring and reviewing the AP® Multiple-Choice and Free Response Review Questions at the end of various chapters in the AP® Edition. John Little (St. Mary's High School, Stockton, CA), Todd, and Kristen were also responsible for compiling the AP® correlations and review of content for its suitability for use in an AP® course. This correlation helped us to ensure that all of the learning objectives of the new AP® guidelines were met. It will also provide valuable help to instructors as they use this book in an AP® course.

In particular, we would like to thank Thomas Martin, Content Developer for the AP® version. Throughout this project, he patiently helped keep us on task regarding changes to make that would bring the book into compliance with the latest AP® guidelines and helped guide this project through to completion. Without his leadership in these areas, the AP® version would not be what it is today.

Finally, we would like to thank Alison Zetterquist, Vice-President, Director, Advanced and Elective Products Program, and Ashley Bargende, Associate Content Developer, Advanced and Elective Products Program, for the work that they do behind the scenes to ensure that this product will meet the market needs.

Participants in Development Surveys

The development of successful books depends on the help of many people within the publishing company as well as colleagues teaching chemistry. The following participated in surveys that gave us guidance in producing the book.

Dmitri Babikov, Marquette University

Yiyan Bai, Houston Community College–Central College

Dean Campbell, Bradley University

Susan Collins, California State University–Northridge

Christopher Collison, Rochester Institute of Technology

David Dearden, Brigham Young University

Emmanuel Ewane, Houston Community College–Northwest College

Mark Fritz, University of Cincinnati

Ron Garber, California State University–Long Beach

Luther Giddings, Salt Lake Community College

Brian Glute, University of Minnesota–Duluth

Donna Iannotti, Brevard Community College–Palm Bay Campus

Jason Jones, Francis Marion University

David Katz, Pima Community College–West Campus

Colleen Kelley, Pima Community College–West Campus

Kristine Miller, Anne Arundel Community College

Patricia Muisener, University of South Florida

Stacy O'Reilly, Butler University

Andrew Price, Temple University

Mark Scharf, West Virginia University

AP® Reviewers

Todd Abronowitz, Parish Episcopal High School

Kristen Jones, College Station ISD

John Little, St. Mary's High School, Stockton, CA

Correlation of Topics for the Chemistry AP® Course to *Chemistry & Chemical Reactivity*, Ninth Edition

AP® Course Topic	Correlation of Topics to *Chemistry & Chemical Reactivity*, Ninth Edition
Big Idea 1: The chemical elements are fundamental building materials of matter, and all matter can be understood in terms of arrangements of atoms. These atoms retain their identity in chemical reactions. **Enduring understanding 1.A:** All matter is made of atoms. There are a limited number of types of atoms; these are the elements. **Essential knowledge 1.A.1:** Molecules are composed of specific combinations of atoms; different molecules are composed of combinations of different elements and of combinations of the same elements in differing amounts and proportions.	Chap 1, Sec. 1.3–1.4, pp. 8–11 Chap 2, Sec. 2.1, pp. 45–46 Chap 2, Sec. 2.4, pp. 50–52 Chap 2, Sec. 2.10, p. 84
Essential knowledge 1.A.2: Chemical analysis provides a method for determining the relative number of atoms in a substance, which can be used to identify the substance or determine its purity.	Chap 2, Sec. 2.1–2.4, pp. 45–52
Essential knowledge 1.A.3: The mole is the fundamental unit for counting numbers of particles on the macroscopic level and allows quantitative connections to be drawn between laboratory experiments, which occur at the macroscopic level, and chemical processes, which occur at the atomic level.	Chap 2, Sec. 2.2–2.4, pp. 46–48 Chap 2, Sec. 2.9, pp. 77–84 Chap 3, Sec. 3.1–3.2, pp. 97–102
Enduring understanding 1.B: The atoms of each element have unique structures arising from interactions between electrons and nuclei. **Essential knowledge 1.B.1:** The atom is composed of negatively charged electrons, which can leave the atom, and a positively charged nucleus that is made of protons and neutrons. The attraction of the electrons to the nucleus is the basis of the structure of the atom. Coulomb's law is qualitatively useful for understanding the structure of the atom.	Chap 2, Sec. 2.7, pp. 65–66 Chap 7, Sec. 7.3–7.6, pp. 254–279 Chap 9, Sec. 9.3, p. 367
Essential knowledge 1.B.2: The electronic structure of the atom can be described using an electron configuration that reflects the concept of electrons in quantized energy levels or shells; the energetics of the electrons in the atom can be understood by consideration of Coulomb's law.	Chap 7, Sec. 7.3–7.6, pp. 254–279
Enduring understanding 1.C: Elements display periodicity in their properties when the elements are organized according to increasing atomic number. This periodicity can be explained by the regular variations that occur in the electronic structures of atoms. Periodicity is a useful principle for understanding properties and predicting trends in properties. Its modern-day uses range from examining the composition of materials to generating ideas for designing new materials. **Essential knowledge 1.C.1:** Many properties of atoms exhibit periodic trends that are reflective of the periodicity of electronic structure.	Chap 2, Sec. 2.7, pp. 65–66 Chap 7, Sec. 7.3–7.6, pp. 254–279 Chap 21, Sec. 21.2, pp. 804–809
Essential knowledge 1.C.2: The currently accepted best model of the atom is based on the quantum mechanical model.	Chap 6, Sec. 6.3–6.5, pp. 226–239 Chap 6, Sec. 6.7, p. 243
Enduring understanding 1.D: Atoms are so small that they are difficult to study directly; atomic models are constructed to explain experimental data on collections of atoms. **Essential knowledge 1.D.1:** As is the case with all scientific models, any model of the atom is subject to refinement and change in response to new experimental results. In that sense, an atomic model is not regarded as an exact description of the atom, but rather a theoretical construct that fits a set of experimental data.	Chap 6, Sec. 6.2–6.5, pp. 222–239 Chap 7, Sec. 7.3–7.6, pp. 254–279
Essential knowledge 1.D.2: An early model of the atom stated that all atoms of an element are identical. Mass spectrometry data demonstrate evidence that contradicts this early model.	Chap 2, Sec. 2.3–2.4, pp. 48–52

(continued)

AP® Course Topic	Correlation of Topics to *Chemistry & Chemical Reactivity,* Ninth Edition
Essential knowledge 1.D.3: The interaction of electromagnetic waves or light with matter is a powerful means to probe the structure of atoms and molecules, and to measure their concentration.	Chap 4, Sec. 4.8, pp. 172–177 Chap 6, Sec. 6.1–6.3, pp. 220–233
Enduring understanding 1.E: Atoms are conserved in physical and chemical processes. **Essential knowledge 1.E.1:** Physical and chemical processes can be depicted symbolically; when this is done, the illustration must conserve all atoms of all types.	Chap 3, Sec. 3.1–3.3, pp. 97–105 Chap 4, Sec. 4.1–4.2, pp. 139–147 Chap 5, Sec. 5.5, pp. 198–201
Essential knowledge 1.E.2: Conservation of atoms makes it possible to compute the masses of substances involved in physical and chemical processes. Chemical processes result in the formation of new substances, and the amount of these depends on the number and the types and masses of elements in the reactants, as well as the efficiency of the transformation.	Chap 2, Sec. 2.6, pp. 63–65 Chap 2, Sec. 2.9, pp. 77–84 Chap 3, Sec. 3.1–3.2, pp. 97–102 Chap 4, Sec. 4.1–4.2, pp. 139–147 Chap 4, Sec. 4.7, pp. 164–172 Chap 5, Sec. 5.5, pp. 198–201
Big Idea 2: Chemical and physical properties of materials can be explained by the structure and the arrangement of atoms, ions, or molecules and the forces between them. **Enduring understanding 2.A:** Matter can be described by its physical properties. The physical properties of a substance generally depend on the spacing between the particles (atoms, molecules, ions) that make up the substance and the forces of attraction among them. **Essential knowledge 2.A.1:** The different properties of solids and liquids can be explained by differences in their structures, both at the particulate level and in their supramolecular structures.	Chap 2, Sec. 2.6–2.9, pp. 63–84 Chap 3, Sec. 3.4–3.6, pp. 105–123 Chap 8, Sec. 8.1–8.10, pp. 283–332 Chap 11, Sec. 11.4, pp. 416–420 Chap 11, Sec. 11.6, pp. 421–432 Chap 12, Sec. 12.1–12.5, pp. 437–460 Chap 16, Sec. 16.9, pp. 617–622 Chap 23, Sec. 23.3, pp. 917–922
Essential knowledge 2.A.2: The gaseous state can be effectively modeled with a mathematical equation relating various macroscopic properties. A gas has neither a definite volume nor a definite shape; because the effects of attractive forces are minimal, we usually assume that the particles move independently.	Chap 2, Sec. 2.6–2.9, pp. 63–84 Chap 3, Sec. 3.4–3.6, pp. 105–123 Chap 8, Sec. 8.1, pp. 283–284 Chap 10, Sec. 10.2–10.8, pp. 374–401 Chap 11, Sec. 11.4, pp. 416–420 Chap 16, Sec. 16.9, pp. 617–622 Chap 23, Sec. 23.3, pp. 917–922
Essential knowledge 2.A.3: Solutions are homogenous mixtures in which the physical properties are dependent on the concentration of the solute and the strengths of all interactions among the particles of the solutes and solvent.	Chap 1, Sec. 1.3, pp. 9–10 Chap 2, Sec. 2.6–2.9, pp. 63–84 Chap 3, Sec. 3.4–3.6, pp. 105–123 Chap 4, Sec. 4.5, pp. 156–161 Chap 8, Sec. 8.1, pp. 283–284 Chap 11, Sec. 11.4, pp. 416–420 Chap 11, Sec. 11.6, pp. 432–433 Chap 13, Sec. 13.2, pp. 473–479 Chap 13, Sec. 13.5, pp. 498–502 Chap 16, Sec. 16.9, pp. 617–622 Chap 20, Sec. 20.2, pp. 771–777 Chap 23, Sec. 23.3, pp. 917–922
Enduring understanding 2.B: Forces of attraction between particles (including the noble gases and also different parts of some large molecules) are important in determining many macroscopic properties of a substance, including how the observable physical state changes with temperature. **Essential knowledge 2.B.1:** London dispersion forces are attractive forces present between all atoms and molecules. London dispersion forces are often the strongest net intermolecular force between large molecules.	Chap 2, Sec. 2.6–2.9, pp. 63–84 Chap 3, Sec. 3.4–3.6, pp. 105–123 Chap 8, Sec. 8.1, pp. 283–284 Chap 8, Sec. 8.10, pp. 332–333 Chap 11, Sec. 11.4, pp. 416–420 Chap 16, Sec. 16.9, pp. 617–622 Chap 23, Sec. 23.3, pp. 917–922

(*continued*)

AP® Course Topic	Correlation of Topics to *Chemistry & Chemical Reactivity,* Ninth Edition
Essential knowledge 2.B.2: Dipole forces result from the attraction among the positive ends and negative ends of polar molecules. Hydrogen bonding is a strong type of dipole-dipole force.	Chap 2, Sec. 2.6–2.9, pp. 63–84 Chap 3, Sec. 3.4–3.6, pp. 105–123 Chap 8, Sec. 8.1, pp. 283–284 Chap 8, Sec. 8.10, pp. 332–333 Chap 10, Sec. 10.8, pp. 399–401 Chap 11, Sec. 11.1–11.5, pp. 406–421 Chap 16, Sec. 16.9, pp. 617–622 Chap 23, Sec. 23.3, pp. 917–922
Essential knowledge 2.B.3: Intermolecular forces play a key role in determining the properties of substances, including biological structures and interactions.	Chap 2, Sec. 2.6–2.9, pp. 63–84 Chap 3, Sec. 3.4–3.6, pp. 105–123 Chap 8, Sec. 8.1, pp. 283–284 Chap 10, Sec. 10.8, pp. 399–401 Chap 11, Sec. 11.1–11.6, pp. 406–432 Chap 13, Sec. 13.2, pp. 473–479 Chap 13, Sec. 13.5, pp. 498–502 Chap 16, Sec. 16.9, pp. 617–622 Chap 23, Sec. 23.3, pp. 917–922 Chap 24, Sec. 24.1, pp. 946–953
Enduring understanding 2.C: The strong electrostatic forces of attraction holding atoms together in a unit are called chemical bonds.	Chap 2, Sec. 2.6–2.9, pp. 63–84 Chap 3, Sec. 3.4–3.6, pp. 105–123 Chap 8, Sec. 8.1, pp. 283–284 Chap 8, Sec. 8.7, pp. 314–319 Chap 11, Sec. 11.4, pp. 416–420 Chap 16, Sec. 16.9, pp. 617–622 Chap 23, Sec. 23.3, pp. 917–922
Essential knowledge 2.C.1: In covalent bonding, electrons are shared between the nuclei of two atoms to form a molecule or polyatomic ion. Electronegativity differences between the two atoms account for the distribution of the shared electrons and the polarity of the bond.	Chap 2, Sec. 2.6–2.9, pp. 63–84 Chap 3, Sec. 3.4–3.6, pp. 105–123 Chap 8, Sec. 8.1, pp. 283–284 Chap 8, Sec. 8.7–8.9, pp. 314–331 Chap 9, Sec. 9.2, pp. 340–354 Chap 11, Sec. 11.4, pp. 416–420 Chap 16, Sec. 16.9, pp. 617–622 Chap 23, Sec. 23.3, pp. 917–922
Essential knowledge 2.C.2: Ionic bonding results from the net attraction between oppositely charged ions, closely packed together in a crystal lattice.	Chap 2, Sec. 2.6–2.9, pp. 63–84 Chap 3, Sec. 3.4–3.6, pp. 105–123 Chap 8, Sec. 8.1, pp. 283–284 Chap 11, Sec. 11.4, pp. 416–420 Chap 12, Sec. 12.3, pp. 449–452 Chap 16, Sec. 16.9, pp. 617–622 Chap 23, Sec. 23.3, pp. 917–922
Essential knowledge 2.C.3: Metallic bonding describes an array of positively charged metal cores surrounded by a sea of mobile valence electrons.	Chap 2, Sec. 2.6–2.9, pp. 63–84 Chap 3, Sec. 3.4–3.6, pp. 105–123 Chap 8, Sec. 8.1, pp. 283–284 Chap 11, Sec. 11.4, pp. 416–420 Chap 12, Sec. 12.4, p. 452 Chap 16, Sec. 16.9, pp. 617–622 Chap 23, Sec. 23.3, pp. 917–922 Appendix O-1, pp. A-130–A-132

(continued)

AP® Course Topic	Correlation of Topics to *Chemistry & Chemical Reactivity,* Ninth Edition
Essential knowledge 2.C.4: The localized electron bonding model describes and predicts molecular geometry using Lewis diagrams and the VSEPR model.	Chap 2, Sec. 2.6–2.9, pp. 63–84 Chap 3, Sec. 3.4–3.6, pp. 105–123 Chap 8, Sec. 8.1–8.9, pp. 283–331 Chap 9, Sec. 9.1–9.3, pp. 340–369 Chap 11, Sec. 11.4, pp. 416–420 Chap 16, Sec. 16.9, pp. 617–622 Chap 23, Sec. 23.3, pp. 917–922
Enduring understanding 2.D: The type of bonding in the solid state can be deduced from the properties of the solid state.	Chap 2, Sec. 2.6–2.9, pp. 63–84 Chap 3, Sec. 3.4–3.6, pp. 105–123 Chap 8, Sec. 8.1, pp. 283–284 Chap 11, Sec. 11.4, pp. 416–420 Chap 12, Sec. 12.1–12.6, pp. 437–463 Chap 16, Sec. 16.9, pp. 617–622 Chap 23, Sec. 23.3, pp. 917–922
Essential knowledge 2.D.1: Ionic solids have high melting points, are brittle, and conduct electricity only when molten or in solution.	Chap 2, Sec. 2.6–2.9, pp. 63–84 Chap 3, Sec. 3.4–3.6, pp. 105–123 Chap 8, Sec. 8.1, pp. 283–284 Chap 11, Sec. 11.2, pp. 407–409 Chap 11, Sec. 11.4, pp. 416–420 Chap 12, Sec. 12.3, pp. 449–452 Chap 12, Sec. 12.6, p. 463 Chap 13, Sec. 13.2, pp. 473–479 Chap 16, Sec. 16.9, pp. 617–622 Chap 19, Sec. 19.2, pp. 723–729 Chap 19, Sec. 19.7, pp. 751–757 Chap 23, Sec. 23.3, pp. 917–922
Essential knowledge 2.D.2: Metallic solids are good conductors of heat and electricity; have a wide range of melting points; and are shiny, malleable, ductile, and readily alloyed.	Chap 2, Sec. 2.6–2.9, pp. 63–84 Chap 3, Sec. 3.4–3.6, pp. 105–123 Chap 8, Sec. 8.1, pp. 283–284 Chap 11, Sec. 11.4, pp. 416–420 Chap 12, Sec. 12.4, p. 453 Chap 16, Sec. 16.9, pp. 617–622 Chap 23, Sec. 23.3, pp. 917–922 Appendix O-1, pp. A-130–A-132
Essential knowledge 2.D.3: Covalent network solids generally have extremely high melting points, are hard, and are thermal insulators. Some conduct electricity.	Chap 2, Sec. 2.6–2.9, pp. 63–84 Chap 3, Sec. 3.4–3.6, pp. 105–123 Chap 8, Sec. 8.1, pp. 283–284 Chap 11, Sec. 11.4, pp. 416–420 Chap 12, Sec. 12.4–12.5, p. 452–460 Chap 16, Sec. 16.9, pp. 617–622 Chap 23, Sec. 23.3, pp. 917–922
Essential knowledge 2.D.4: Molecular solids with low molecular weight usually have low melting points and are not expected to conduct electricity as solids, in solution, or when molten.	Chap 2, Sec. 2.6–2.9, pp. 63–84 Chap 3, Sec. 3.4–3.6, pp. 105–123 Chap 8, Sec. 8.1, pp. 283–284 Chap 11, Sec. 11.3–11.4, pp. 409–420 Chap 12, Sec. 12.5, p. 456–460 Chap 16, Sec. 16.9, pp. 617–622 Chap 23, Sec. 23.3, pp. 917–922 Chap 23, Sec. 23.5, pp. 932–940 Chap 24, Sec. 24.1–24.3, pp. 946–964

(continued)

AP® Course Topic	Correlation of Topics to *Chemistry & Chemical Reactivity,* Ninth Edition
Big Idea 3: Changes in matter involve the rearrangement and/or reorganization of atoms and/or the transfer of electrons. **Enduring understanding 3.A:** Chemical changes are represented by a balanced chemical equation that identifies the ratios with which reactants react and products form.	Chap 3, Sec. 3.1–3.9, pp. 97–134 Chap 4, Sec. 4.1–4.4, pp. 139–156
Essential knowledge 3.A.1: A chemical change may be represented by a molecular, ionic, or net ionic equation.	Chap 3, Sec. 3.1–3.9, pp. 97–134 Chap 4, Sec. 4.1–4.4, pp. 139–156 Chap 4, Sec. 4.7, pp. 164–172 Chap 19, Sec. 19.1, pp. 715–723
Essential knowledge 3.A.2: Quantitative information can be derived from stoichiometric calculations that utilize the mole ratios from the balanced chemical equations. The role of stoichiometry in real-world applications is important to note, so that it does not seem to be simply an exercise done only by chemists.	Chap 4, Sec. 4.1–4.3, pp. 139–149 Chap 4, Sec. 4.7, pp. 164–172 Chap 10, Sec. 10.4, pp. 386–387
Enduring understanding 3.B: Chemical reactions can be classified by considering what the reactants are, what the products are, or how they change from one into the other. Classes of chemical reactions include synthesis, decomposition, acid–base, and oxidation–reduction reactions. **Essential knowledge 3.B.1:** Synthesis reactions are those in which atoms and/or molecules combine to form a new compound. Decomposition is the reverse of synthesis, a process whereby molecules are decomposed, often by the use of heat.	Chap 3, Sec. 3.1, pp. 97–99 Chap 3, Sec. 3.9, pp. 131–134
Essential knowledge 3.B.2: In a neutralization reaction, protons are transferred from an acid to a base.	Chap 3, Sec. 3.6, pp. 114–123 Chap 16, Sec. 16.1, pp. 586–589
Essential knowledge 3.B.3: In oxidation–reduction (redox) reactions, there is a net transfer of electrons. The species that loses electrons is oxidized, and the species that gains electrons is reduced.	Chap 3, Sec. 3.2, pp. 99–201 Chap 3, Sec. 3.8, pp. 125–131 Chap 4, Sec. 4.7, pp. 164–172 Chap 19, Sec. 19.1, pp. 715–723 Chap 19, Sec. 19.4, pp. 734–743 Chap 24, Sec. 24.5, pp. 968–971
Enduring understanding 3.C: Chemical and physical transformations may be observed in several ways and typically involve a change in energy. **Essential knowledge 3.C.1:** Production of heat or light, formation of a gas, and formation of a precipitate and/or a color change are possible evidences that a chemical change has occurred.	Chap 1, Sec. 1.6–1.7, pp. 13–16 Chap 3, Sec. 3.4–3.8, pp. 105–131
Essential knowledge 3.C.2: Net changes in energy for a chemical reaction can be endothermic or exothermic.	Chap 5, Sec. 5.1, pp. 182–184 Chap 5, Sec. 5.7, pp. 205–206
Essential knowledge 3.C.3: Electrochemistry shows the interconversion between chemical and electrical energy in galvanic and electrolytic cells.	Chap 19, pp. 713–715 Chap 19, Sec. 19.2, pp. 723–729 Chap 19, Sec. 19.4–19.8, pp. 734–758
Big Idea 4: Rates of chemical reactions are determined by details of the molecular collisions. **Enduring understanding 4.A:** Reaction rates that depend on temperature and other environmental factors are determined by measuring changes in concentrations of reactants or products over time. **Essential knowledge 4.A.1:** The rate of a reaction is influenced by the concentration or pressure of reactants, the phase of the reactants and products, and environmental factors such as temperature and solvent.	Chap 14, Sec. 14.1–14.3, pp. 508–520
Essential knowledge 4.A.2: The rate law shows how the rate depends on reactant concentrations.	Chap 14, Sec. 14.3–14.4, pp. 514–529

(continued)

AP® Course Topic	Correlation of Topics to *Chemistry & Chemical Reactivity,* Ninth Edition
Essential knowledge 4.A.3: The magnitude and temperature dependence of the rate of reaction is contained quantitatively in the rate constant.	Chap 14, Sec. 14.3–14.5, pp. 514–533 Chap 25, Sec. 25.4, pp. 987–992
Enduring understanding 4.B: Elementary reactions are mediated by collisions between molecules. Only collisions having sufficient energy and proper relative orientation of reactants lead to products. **Essential knowledge 4.B.1:** Elementary reactions can be unimolecular or involve collisions between two or more molecules.	Chap 14, Sec. 14.6, pp. 539–550
Essential knowledge 4.B.2: Not all collisions are successful. To get over the activation energy barrier, the colliding species need sufficient energy. Also, the orientations of the reactant molecules during the collision must allow for the rearrangement of reactant bonds to form product bonds.	Chap 14, Sec. 14.5–14.6, pp. 529–550
Essential knowledge 4.B.3: A successful collision can be viewed as following a reaction path with an associated energy profile.	Chap 14, Sec. 14.6, pp. 539–550
Enduring understanding 4.C: Many reactions proceed via a series of elementary reactions. **Essential knowledge 4.C.1:** The mechanism of a multistep reaction consists of a series of elementary reactions that add up to the overall reaction. **Essential knowledge 4.C.2:** In many reactions, the rate is set by the slowest elementary reaction, or rate-limiting step. **Essential knowledge 4.C.3:** Reaction intermediates, which are formed during the reaction but not present in the overall reaction, play an important role in multistep reactions.	Chap 14, Sec. 14.6, pp. 539–550
Enduring understanding 4.D: Reaction rates may be increased by the presence of a catalyst. **Essential knowledge 4.D.1:** Catalysts function by lowering the activation energy of an elementary step in a reaction mechanism and by providing a new and faster reaction mechanism.	Chap 14, Sec. 14.5, pp. 529–539
Essential knowledge 4.D.2: Important classes in catalysis include acid–base catalysis, surface catalysis, and enzyme catalysis.	Chap 14, Sec. 14.2, pp. 512–514 Chap 14, Sec. 14.5–14.6, pp. 529–550 Chap 15, Sec. 15.6, pp. 575–581 Chap 24, Sec. 24.1, pp. 946–953 Appendix O-2, pp. A-132–A-133
Big Idea 5: The laws of thermodynamics describe the essential role of energy and explain and predict the direction of changes in matter. **Enduring understanding 5.A:** Two systems with different temperatures that are in thermal contact will exchange energy. The quantity of thermal energy transferred from one system to another is called *heat.*	Chap 9, Sec. 9.2, pp. 340–354 Chap 11, Sec. 11.3, pp. 409–416
Essential knowledge 5.A.1: Temperature is a measure of the average kinetic energy of atoms and molecules.	Chap 5, Sec. 5.3, pp. 189–192 Chap 9, Sec. 9.2, pp. 340–354 Chap 10, Sec. 10.6, pp. 390–396 Chap 11, Sec. 11.3, pp. 409–416
Essential knowledge 5.A.2: The process of kinetic energy transfer at the particulate scale is referred to in this course as *heat transfer,* and the spontaneous direction of the transfer is always from a hot to a cold body.	Chap 5, Sec. 5.1–5.2, pp. 182–189 Chap 9, Sec. 9.2, pp. 340–354 Chap 11, Sec. 11.3, pp. 409–416
Enduring understanding 5.B: Energy is neither created nor destroyed, but only transformed from one form to another.	Chap 9, Sec. 9.2, pp. 340–354 Chap 11, Sec. 11.3, pp. 409–416
Essential knowledge 5.B.1: Energy is transferred between systems either through heat transfer or through one system doing work on the other system.	Chap 5, Sec. 5.4, pp. 193–197

(continued)

AP® Course Topic	Correlation of Topics to *Chemistry & Chemical Reactivity,* Ninth Edition
Essential knowledge 5.B.2: When two systems are in contact with each other and are otherwise isolated, the energy that comes out of one system is equal to the energy that goes into the other system. The combined energy of the two systems remains fixed. Energy transfer can occur through either heat exchange or work.	Chap 5, Sec. 5.1–5.3, pp. 182–192 Chap 5, Sec. 5.6, pp. 201–205 Chap 9, Sec. 9.2, pp. 340–354 Chap 11, Sec. 11.3, pp. 409–416
Essential knowledge 5.B.3: Chemical systems undergo three main processes that change their energy: heating/cooling, phase transitions, and chemical reactions.	Chap 5, Sec. 5.2–5.5, pp. 184–201 Chap 9, Sec. 9.2, pp. 340–354 Chap 11, Sec. 11.3, pp. 409–416 Chap 12, Sec. 12.6, pp. 460–463
Essential knowledge 5.B.4: Calorimetry is an experimental technique that is used to measure the change in energy of a chemical system.	Chap 5, Sec. 5.6, pp. 201–205 Chap 9, Sec. 9.2, pp. 340–354 Chap 11, Sec. 11.3, pp. 409–416
Enduring understanding 5.C: Breaking bonds requires energy, and making bonds releases energy.	Chap 9, Sec. 9.2, pp. 340–354 Chap 11, Sec. 11.3, pp. 409–416
Essential knowledge 5.C.1: Potential energy is associated with a particular geometric arrangement of atoms or ions and the electrostatic interactions between them.	Chap 8, Sec. 8.9, pp. 325–331 Chap 9, Sec. 9.2, pp. 340–354 Chap 11, Sec. 11.3, pp. 409–416 Chap 12, Sec. 12.3, pp. 449–452
Essential knowledge 5.C.2: The net energy change during a reaction is the sum of the energy required to break the bonds in the reactant molecules and the energy released in forming the bonds of the product molecules. The net change in energy may be positive for endothermic reactions where energy is required, or negative for exothermic reactions where energy is released.	Chap 5, Sec. 5.1, pp. 182–184 Chap 5, Sec. 5.5, pp. 198–201 Chap 5, Sec. 5.7, pp. 205–213 Chap 8, Sec. 8.9, pp. 325–331 Chap 9, Sec. 9.2, pp. 340–354 Chap 11, Sec. 11.3, pp. 409–416
Enduring understanding 5.D: Electrostatic forces exist between molecules as well as between atoms or ions, and breaking the resultant intermolecular interactions requires energy.	Chap 9, Sec. 9.2, pp. 340–354 Chap 11, Sec. 11.3, pp. 409–416
Essential knowledge 5.D.1: Potential energy is associated with the interaction of molecules; as molecules draw near each other, they experience an attractive force.	Chap 9, Sec. 9.2, pp. 340–354 Chap 11, Sec. 11.3, pp. 409–416
Essential knowledge 5.D.2: At the particulate scale, chemical processes can be distinguished from physical processes because chemical bonds can be distinguished from intermolecular interactions.	Chap 1, Sec. 1.7, pp. 15–16 Chap 5, Sec. 5.3, pp. 189–192 Chap 5, Sec. 5.5, pp. 198–201 Chap 9, Sec. 9.2, pp. 340–354 Chap 11, Sec. 11.3, pp. 409–416 Chap 13, Sec. 13.2, pp. 473–479
Essential knowledge 5.D.3: Noncovalent and intermolecular interactions play important roles in many biological and polymer systems.	Chap 9, Sec. 9.2, pp. 340–354 Chap 11, Sec. 11.3–11.4, pp. 409–420 Chap 23, Sec. 23.5, pp. 932–940 Chap 24, Sec. 24.1, pp. 946–953
Enduring understanding 5.E: Chemical or physical processes are driven by a decrease in enthalpy, an increase in entropy, or both.	Chap 9, Sec. 9.2, pp. 340–354 Chap 11, Sec. 11.3, pp. 409–416
Essential knowledge 5.E.1: Entropy is a measure of the dispersal of matter and energy.	Chap 9, Sec. 9.2, pp. 340–354 Chap 11, Sec. 11.3, pp. 409–416 Chap 18, Sec. 18.2–18.4, pp. 682–691
Essential knowledge 5.E.2: Some physical or chemical processes involve *both* a decrease in the internal energy of the components ($\Delta H° < 0$) under consideration *and* an increase in the entropy of those components ($\Delta S° > 0$). These processes are necessarily "thermodynamically favored" ($\Delta G° < 0$).	Chap 5, Sec. 5.4, p. 196 Chap 5, Sec. 5.6, p. 203 Chap 9, Sec. 9.2, pp. 340–354 Chap 11, Sec. 11.3, pp. 409–416 Chap 14, p. 507 Chap 18, Sec. 18.5–18.7, pp. 691–709 Appendix O-3, A-133–A-135

(continued)

AP® Course Topic	Correlation of Topics to *Chemistry & Chemical Reactivity,* Ninth Edition
Essential knowledge 5.E.3: If a chemical or physical process is not driven by *both* entropy and enthalpy changes, then the Gibbs free energy change can be used to determine whether the process is thermodynamically favored.	Chap 9, Sec. 9.2, pp. 340–354 Chap 11, Sec. 11.3, pp. 409–416 Chap 18, Sec. 18.5, pp. 691–696 Chap 18, Sec. 18.7, pp. 700–708
Essential knowledge 5.E.4: External sources of energy can be used to drive change in cases where the Gibbs free energy change is positive.	Chap 9, Sec. 9.2–9.3, pp. 340–367 Chap 11, Sec. 11.3, pp. 409–416 Chap 17, Sec. 17. 7, pp. 672–674 Chap 18, Sec. 18.7, pp. 700–708 Chap 19, Sec. 19.7, pp. 751–757 Chap 24, Sec. 24.5, pp. 968–971
Essential knowledge 5.E.5: A thermodynamically favored process may not occur due to kinetic constraints (kinetic versus thermodynamic control).	Chap 9, Sec. 9.2, pp. 340–354 Chap 11, Sec. 11.3, pp. 409–416 Chap 18, Sec. 18.6, p. 698 Appendix O-3, pp. A-133–A-135
Big Idea 6: Any bond or intermolecular attraction that can be formed can be broken. These two processes are in a dynamic competition, sensitive to initial conditions and external perturbations. **Enduring understanding 6.A:** Chemical equilibrium is a dynamic, reversible state in which rates of opposing processes are equal. **Essential knowledge 6.A.1:** In many classes of reactions, it is important to consider both the forward and reverse reaction.	Chap 11, Sec. 11.6, pp. 421–432 Chap 15, Sec. 15.1–15.6, pp. 556–575 Chap 16, Sec. 16.1, pp. 586–589
Essential knowledge 6.A.2: The current state of a system undergoing a reversible reaction can be characterized by the extent to which reactants have been converted to products. The relative quantities of reaction components are quantitatively described by the reaction quotient, Q.	Chap 15, Sec. 15.2, pp. 557–564 Chap 15, Sec. 15.5, pp. 571–575
Essential knowledge 6.A.3: When a system is at equilibrium, all macroscopic variables, such as concentrations, partial pressures, and temperature, do not change over time. Equilibrium results from an equality between the rates of the forward and reverse reactions, at which point $Q = K$.	Chap 3, Sec. 3.3, pp. 102–105 Chap 15, Sec. 15.1–15.4, pp. 556–571 Chap 15, Sec. 15.6, p. 575
Essential knowledge 6.A.4: The magnitude of the equilibrium constant, *K*, can be used to determine whether the equilibrium lies toward the reactant side or product side.	Chap 15, Sec. 15.2, pp. 557–564
Enduring understanding 6.B: Systems at equilibrium are responsive to external perturbations, with the response leading to a change in the composition of the system. **Essential knowledge 6.B.1:** Systems at equilibrium respond to disturbances by partially countering the effect of the disturbance (Le Châtelier's principle). **Essential knowledge 6.B.2:** A disturbance to a system at equilibrium causes Q to differ from *K*, thereby taking the system out of the original equilibrium state. The system responds by bringing Q back into agreement with *K*, thereby establishing a new equilibrium state.	Chap 15, Sec. 15.6, pp. 575–581 Chap 17, Sec. 17.1, pp. 632–635 Chap 20, Sec. 20.6, pp. 789–796
Enduring understanding 6.C: Chemical equilibrium plays an important role in acid–base chemistry and in solubility. **Essential knowledge 6.C.1:** Chemical equilibrium reasoning can be used to describe the proton-transfer reactions of acid-base chemistry.	Chap 3, Sec. 3.6, pp. 114–123 Chap 13, Sec. 13.2, pp. 473–479 Chap 16, Sec. 16.2–16.3, pp. 589–598 Chap 16, Sec. 16.5–16.9, pp. 601–622 Chap 17, Sec. 17.3, pp. 644–655
Essential knowledge 6.C.2: The pH is an important characteristic of aqueous solutions that can be controlled with buffers. Comparing pH to pKa allows one to determine the protonation state of a molecule with a labile proton.	Chap 17, Sec. 17.2, pp. 636–644

(*continued*)

AP® Course Topic	Correlation of Topics to *Chemistry & Chemical Reactivity,* Ninth Edition
Essential knowledge 6.C.3: The solubility of a substance can be understood in terms of chemical equilibrium.	Chap 3, Sec. 3.5, pp. 110–114 Chap 13, Sec. 13.2, pp. 473–479 Chap 17, Sec. 17.4–17.5, pp. 655–670 Chap 18, Sec. 18.6, pp. 696–700
Enduring understanding 6.D: The equilibrium constant is related to temperature and the difference in Gibbs free energy between reactants and products. **Essential knowledge 6.D.1:** When the difference in Gibbs free energy between reactants and products ($\Delta G°$) is much larger than the thermal energy (RT), the equilibrium constant is either very small (for $\Delta G° > 0$) or very large (for $\Delta G° < 0$). When $\Delta G°$ is comparable to the thermal energy (RT), the equilibrium constant is near 1.	Chap 18, Sec. 18.6, pp. 696–700 Chap 18, Sec. 18.7, p. 705 Appendix O-4, pp. A-135–A-136

Correlation of Learning Objectives for the Chemistry AP® Course to *Chemistry & Chemical Reactivity,* Ninth Edition

AP® Learning Objective	Correlation of Learning Objectives to *Chemistry & Chemical Reactivity,* Ninth Edition
Learning objective 1.1: The student can justify the observation that the ratio of the masses of the constituent elements in any pure sample of that compound is always identical on the basis of the atomic molecular theory. [*See* **SP 6.1; Essential knowledge 1.A.1**] **Learning objective 1.2:** The student is able to select and apply mathematical routines to mass data to identify or infer the composition of pure substances and/or mixtures. [*See* **SP 2.2; Essential knowledge 1.A.2**]	Chap 2, Sec. 2.1, pp. 45–46
Learning objective 1.3: The student is able to select and apply mathematical relationships to mass data in order to justify a claim regarding the identity and/or estimated purity of a substance. [*See* **SP 2.2, 6.1; Essential knowledge 1.A.2**]	Chap 2, Sec. 2.2–2.4, pp. 46–52
Learning objective 1.4: The student is able to connect the number of particles, moles, mass, and volume of substances to one another, both qualitatively and quantitatively. [*See* **SP 7.1; Essential knowledge 1.A.3**]	Chap 2, Sec. 2.9, pp. 77–84
Learning objective 1.5: The student is able to explain the distribution of electrons in an atom or ion based on data. [*See* **SP 1.5, 6.2; Essential knowledge 1.B.1**] **Learning objective 1.6:** The student is able to analyze data relating to electron energies for patterns and relationships. [*See* **SP 5.1; Essential knowledge 1.B.1**]	Chap 7, Sec. 7.3–7.6, pp. 254–279
Learning objective 1.7: The student is able to describe the electronic structure of the atom, using PES data, ionization energy data, and/or Coulomb's law to construct explanations of how the energies of electrons within shells in atoms vary. [*See* **SP 5.1, 6.2; Essential knowledge 1.B.2**] **Learning objective 1.8:** The student is able to explain the distribution of electrons using Coulomb's law to analyze measured energies. [*See* **SP 6.2; Essential knowledge 1.B.2**]	Chap 7, Sec. 7.3, pp. 254–263 Chap 7, Sec. 7.5, pp. 267–276
Learning objective 1.9: The student is able to predict and/or justify trends in atomic properties based on location on the periodic table and/or the shell model. [*See* **SP 6.4; Essential knowledge 1.C.1**]	Chap 7, Sec. 7.6, pp. 276–279
Learning objective 1.10: Students can justify with evidence the arrangement of the periodic table and can apply periodic properties to chemical reactivity. [*See* **SP 6.1; Essential knowledge 1.C.1**]	Chap 7, Sec. 7.3–7.6, pp. 254–279
Learning objective 1.11: The student can analyze data, based on periodicity and the properties of binary compounds, to identify patterns and generate hypotheses related to the molecular design of compounds for which data are not supplied. [*See* **SP 3.1, 5.1; Essential knowledge 1.C.1**]	Chap 2, Sec. 2.7, pp. 65–66 Chap 7, Sec. 7.4–7.6, pp. 263–279
Learning objective 1.12: The student is able to explain why a given set of data suggests, or does not suggest, the need to refine the atomic model from a classic shell model with the quantum mechanical model. [*See* **SP 6.3; Essential knowledge 1.C.2**]	Chap 6, Sec. 6.4–6.5, pp. 234–239
Learning objective 1.13: Given information about a particular model of the atom, the student is able to determine whether the model is consistent with specified evidence. [*See* **SP 5.3; Essential knowledge 1.D.1**]	Chap 7, Sec. 7.3–7.6, pp. 254–279
Learning objective 1.14: The student is able to use data from mass spectrometry to identify the elements and the masses of individual atoms of a specific element. [*See* **SP 1.4, 1.5; Essential knowledge 1.D.2**]	Chap 2, Sec. 2.3–2.4, pp. 48–52

(*continued*)

AP® Learning Objective	Correlation of Learning Objectives to *Chemistry & Chemical Reactivity,* Ninth Edition
Learning objective 1.15: The student can justify the selection of a particular type of spectroscopy to measure properties associated with vibrational or electronic motions of molecules. [*See* **SP 4.1; Essential knowledge 1.D.3**] **Learning objective 1.16:** The student can design and/or interpret the results of an experiment regarding the absorption of light to determine the concentration of an absorbing species in a solution. [*See* **SP 4.2, 5.1; Essential knowledge 1.D.3**]	Chap 4, Sec. 4.8, 172–177 Chap 6, Sec. 6.3, 226–233
Learning objective 1.17: The student is able to express the law of conservation of mass quantitatively and qualitatively using symbolic representations and particulate drawings. [*See* **SP 1.5; Essential knowledge 1.E.1**]	Chap 3, Sec. 3.1–3.2, pp. 97–102 Chap 4, Sec. 4.1–4.2, pp. 139–147 Chap 5, Sec. 5.5, pp. 198–201
Learning objective 1.18: The student is able to apply conservation of atoms to the rearrangement of atoms in various processes. [*See* **SP 1.4; Essential knowledge 1.E.2**]	Chap 2, Sec. 2.6, pp. 63–65 Chap 3, Sec. 3.1–3.2, pp. 97–102 Chap 4, Sec. 4.1–4.2, pp. 139–147 Chap 5, Sec. 5.5, pp. 198–201
Learning objective 1.19: The student can design, and/or interpret data from, an experiment that uses gravimetric analysis to determine the concentration of an analyte in a solution. [*See* **SP 4.2, 5.1; Essential knowledge 1.E.2**]	Chap 4, Sec. 4.7, pp. 164–172
Learning objective 1.20: The student can design, and/or interpret data from, an experiment that uses titration to determine the concentration of an analyte in a solution. [*See* **SP 4.2, 5.1; Essential knowledge 1.E.2**]	Chap 4, Sec. 4.7, pp. 164–172
Learning objective 2.1: Students can predict properties of substances based on their chemical formulas and provide explanations of their properties based on particle views. [*See* **SP 6.4, 7.1; Essential knowledge components of 2.A–2.D**]	Chap 2, Sec. 2.6–2.7, pp. 63–66 Chap 2, Sec. 2.8–2.9, pp. 76–84 Chap 3, Sec. 3.4–3.5, pp. 105–114 Chap 8, Sec. 8.1, pp. 283–284 Chap 11, Sec. 11.4, pp. 416–420 Chap 23, Sec. 23.3, pp. 917–922
Learning objective 2.2: The student is able to explain the relative strengths of acids and bases based on molecular structure, interparticle forces, and solution equilibrium. [*See* **SP 7.2,** *connects to* **Big Idea 5, Big Idea 6; Essential knowledge components of 2.A–2.D**]	Chap 3, Sec. 3.6, 114–123 Chap 16, Sec., 16.9, pp. 617–622
Learning objective 2.3: The student is able to use aspects of particulate models (i.e., particle spacing, motion, and forces of attraction) to reason about observed differences between solid and liquid phases and among solid and liquid materials. [*See* **SP 6.4, 7.1; Essential knowledge 2.A.1**]	Chap 5, Sec. 5.3, pp. 189–192 Chap 11, Sec. 11.6, pp. 421–432
Learning objective 2.4: The student is able to use KMT and concepts of intermolecular forces to make predictions about the macroscopic properties of gases, including both ideal and nonideal behaviors. [*See* **SP 1.4, 6.4; Essential knowledge 2.A.2**]	Chap 10, Sec. 10.6–10.7, pp. 390–399
Learning objective 2.5: The student is able to refine multiple representations of a sample of matter in the gas phase to accurately represent the effect of changes in macroscopic properties on the sample. [*See* **SP 1.3, 6.4, 7.2; Essential knowledge 2.A.2**] **Learning objective 2.6:** The student can apply mathematical relationships or estimation to determine macroscopic variables for ideal gases. [*See* **SP 2.2, 2.3; Essential knowledge 2.A.2**]	Chap 10, Sec. 10.2–10.3, pp. 374–386
Learning objective 2.7: The student is able to explain how solutes can be separated by chromatography based on intermolecular interactions. [*See* **SP 6.2; Essential knowledge 2.A.3**]	Chap 11, Sec. 11.6, pp. 432–433
Learning objective 2.8: The student can draw and/or interpret representations of solutions that show the interactions between the solute and solvent. [*See* **SP 1.1, 1.2, 6.4; Essential knowledge 2.A.3**]	Chap 1, Sec. 1.3, p. 9

(*continued*)

AP® Learning Objective	Correlation of Learning Objectives to *Chemistry & Chemical Reactivity,* Ninth Edition
Learning objective 2.9: The student is able to create or interpret representations that link the concept of molarity with particle views of solutions. [*See* **SP 1.1, 1.4; Essential knowledge 2.A.3**]	Chap 4, Sec. 4.5, pp. 156–161
Learning objective 2.10: The student can design and/or interpret the results of a separation experiment (filtration, paper chromatography, column chromatography, or distillation) in terms of the relative strength of interactions among and between the components. [*See* **SP 4.2, 5.1; Essential knowledge 2.A.3**]	Chap 11, Sec. 11.6, pp. 432–433 Chap 13, Sec. 13.5, p. 502
Learning objective 2.11: The student is able to explain the trends in properties and/or predict properties of samples consisting of particles with no permanent dipole on the basis of London dispersion forces. [*See* **SP 6.2, 6.4; Essential knowledge 2.B.1**]	Chap 11, Sec. 11.4, pp. 416–420
Learning objective 2.12: The student can qualitatively analyze data regarding real gases to identify deviations from ideal behavior and relate these to molecular interactions. [*See* **SP 5.1, 6.5; Essential knowledge 2.B.2,** *connects to* **2.A.2**]	Chap 10, Sec. 10.8, pp. 399–401 Chap 11, Sec. 11.1, pp. 406–407 Chap 11, Sec. 11.4, pp. 416–420
Learning objective 2.13: The student is able to describe the relationships between the structural features of polar molecules and the forces of attraction between the particles. [*See* **SP 1.4; Essential knowledge 2.B.2**]	Chap 11, Sec. 11.3, pp. 409–416
Learning objective 2.14: The student is able to apply Coulomb's law qualitatively (including using representations) to describe the interactions of ions and the attractions between ions and solvents to explain the factors that contribute to the solubility of ionic compounds. [*See* **SP 1.4, 6.4; Essential knowledge 2.B.2**]	Chap 2, Sec. 2.7, pp. 65–66 Chap 11, Sec. 11.2, pp. 407–409
Learning objective 2.15: The student is able to explain observations regarding the solubility of ionic solids and molecules in water and other solvents on the basis of particle views that include intermolecular interactions and entropic effects. [*See* **SP 1.4, 6.2; Essential knowledge 2.B.3,** *connects to* **5.E.1**]	Chap 11, Sec. 11.3–11.4, pp. 409–420 Chap 13, Sec. 13.2, pp. 473–479
Learning objective 2.16: The student is able to explain the properties (phase, vapor pressure, viscosity, etc.) of small and large molecular compounds in terms of the strengths and types of intermolecular forces. [*See* **SP 6.2; Essential knowledge 2.B.3**]	Chap 11, Sec. 11.3–11.6, pp. 409–432
Learning objective 2.17: The student can predict the type of bonding present between two atoms in a binary compound based on position in the periodic table and the electronegativity of the elements. [*See* **SP 6.4; Essential knowledge components of 2.C**]	Chap 8, Sec. 8.1, pp. 283–284 Chap 8, Sec. 8.7, pp. 314–319
Learning objective 2.18: The student is able to rank and justify the ranking of bond polarity on the basis of the locations of the bonded atoms in the periodic table. [*See* **SP 6.1; Essential knowledge 2.C.1**]	Chap 8, Sec. 8.7, pp. 314–319
Learning objective 2.19: The student can create visual representations of ionic substances that connect the microscopic structure to macroscopic properties, and/or use representations to connect the microscopic structure to macroscopic properties (e.g., boiling point, solubility, hardness, brittleness, low volatility, lack of malleability, ductility, or conductivity). [*See* **SP 1.1, 1.4, 7.1; Essential knowledge 2.C.2,** *connects to* **2.D.1, 2.D.2**]	Chap 2, Sec. 2.7, pp. 65–66 Chap 8, Sec. 8.1, pp. 283–284 Chap 12, Sec. 12.3, pp. 449–452
Learning objective 2.20: The student is able to explain how a bonding model involving delocalized electrons is consistent with macroscopic properties of metals (e.g., conductivity, malleability, ductility, and low volatility) and the shell model of the atom. [*See* **SP 6.2, 7.1; Essential knowledge 2.C.3,** *connects to* **2.D.2**]	Chap 12, Sec. 12.4, p. 452 Appendix O-1, A-130–A-132
Learning objective 2.21: The student is able to use Lewis diagrams and VSEPR to predict the geometry of molecules, identify hybridization, and make predictions about polarity. [*See* **SP 1.4; Essential knowledge 2.C.4**]	Chap 8, Sec. 8.2–8.9, pp. 285–331

(*continued*)

AP® Learning Objective	Correlation of Learning Objectives to *Chemistry & Chemical Reactivity*, Ninth Edition
Learning objective 2.22: The student is able to design or evaluate a plan to collect and/or interpret data needed to deduce the type of bonding in a sample of a solid. [*See* **SP 4.2; Essential knowledge components of 2.D**]	Chap 12, Sec. 12.1–12.6, pp. 437–463
Learning objective 2.23: The student can create a representation of an ionic solid that shows essential characteristics of the structure and interactions present in the substance. [*See* **SP 1.1; Essential knowledge 2.D.1**] **Learning objective 2.24:** The student is able to explain a representation that connects properties of an ionic solid to its structural attributes and to the interactions present at the atomic level. [*See* **SP 1.1, 6.2, 7.1; Essential knowledge 2.D.1**]	Chap 2, Sec. 2.7, pp. 65–66 Chap 12, Sec. 12.3, pp. 449–452
Learning objective 2.25: The student is able to compare the properties of metal alloys with their constituent elements to determine whether an alloy has formed, identify the type of alloy formed, and explain the differences in properties using particulate level reasoning. [*See* **SP 1.4, 7.2; Essential knowledge 2.D.2**] **Learning objective 2.26:** Students can use the electron sea model of metallic bonding to predict or make claims about the macroscopic properties of metals or alloys. [*See* **SP 6.4, 7.1; Essential knowledge 2.D.2**] **Learning objective 2.27:** The student can create a representation of a metallic solid that shows essential characteristics of the structure and interactions present in the substance. [*See* **SP 1.1; Essential knowledge 2.D.2**] **Learning objective 2.28:** The student is able to explain a representation that connects properties of a metallic solid to its structural attributes and to the interactions present at the atomic level. [*See* **SP 1.1, 6.2, 7.1; Essential knowledge 2.D.2**]	Chap 12, Sec. 12.4, p. 453 Appendix O-1, pp. A-130–A-132
Learning objective 2.29: The student can create a representation of a covalent solid that shows essential characteristics of the structure and interactions present in the substance. [*See* **SP 1.1; Essential knowledge 2.D.3**] **Learning objective 2.30:** The student is able to explain a representation that connects properties of a covalent solid to its structural attributes and to the interactions present at the atomic level. [*See* **SP 1.1, 6.2, 7.1; Essential knowledge 2.D.3**]	Chap 12, Sec. 12.5, pp. 456–460
Learning objective 2.31: The student can create a representation of a molecular solid that shows essential characteristics of the structure and interactions present in the substance. [*See* **SP 1.1; Essential knowledge 2.D.4**] **Learning objective 2.32:** The student is able to explain a representation that connects properties of a molecular solid to its structural attributes and to the interactions present at the atomic level. [*See* **SP 1.1, 6.2, 7.1; Essential knowledge 2.D.4**]	Chap 11, Sec. 11.3, pp. 409–416 Chap 12, Sec. 12.5, pp. 456–460
Learning objective 3.1: Students can translate among macroscopic observations of change, chemical equations, and particle views. [*See* **SP 1.5, 7.1; Essential knowledge components of 3.A–3.C**]	Chap 3, Sec. 3.1–3.9, pp. 97–134 Chap 4, Sec. 4.1–4.4, pp. 139–156
Learning objective 3.2: The student can translate an observed chemical change into a balanced chemical equation and justify the choice of equation type (molecular, ionic, or net ionic) in terms of utility for the given circumstances. [*See* **SP 1.5, 7.1; Essential knowledge 3.A.1**]	Chap 3, Sec. 3.1–3.9, pp. 97–134 Chap 19, Sec. 19.1, pp. 715–723
Learning objective 3.3: The student is able to use stoichiometric calculations to predict the results of performing a reaction in the laboratory and/or to analyze deviations from the expected results. [*See* **SP 2.2, 5.1; Essential knowledge 3.A.2**]	Chap 4, Sec. 4.1–4.3, pp. 139–149

(*continued*)

AP® Learning Objective	Correlation of Learning Objectives to *Chemistry & Chemical Reactivity,* Ninth Edition
Learning objective 3.4: The student is able to relate quantities (measured mass of substances, volumes of solutions, or volumes and pressures of gases) to identify stoichiometric relationships for a reaction, including situations involving limiting reactants and situations in which the reaction has not gone to completion. [*See* **SP 2.2, 5.1, 6.4; Essential knowledge 3.A.2**]	Chap 4, Sec. 4.1–4.3, pp. 139–149 Chap 10, Sec. 10.4, pp. 386–387
Learning objective 3.5: The student is able to design a plan in order to collect data on the synthesis or decomposition of a compound to confirm the conservation of matter and the law of definite proportions. [*See* **SP 2.1, 4.2; Essential knowledge 3.B.1**] **Learning objective 3.6:** The student is able to use data from synthesis or decomposition of a compound to confirm the conservation of matter and the law of definite proportions. [*See* **SP 2.2, 6.1; Essential knowledge 3.B.1**]	Chap 3, Sec. 3.1, pp. 97–99 Chap 3, Sec. 3.9, pp. 131–134
Learning objective 3.7: The student is able to identify compounds as Brønsted-Lowry acids, bases, and/or conjugate acid–base pairs, using proton-transfer reactions to justify the identification. [*See* **SP 6.1; Essential knowledge 3.B.2**]	Chap 3, Sec. 3.6, pp. 114–123 Chap 16, Sec. 16.1, pp. 586–589
Learning objective 3.8: The student is able to identify redox reactions and justify the identification in terms of electron transfer. [*See* **SP 6.1; Essential knowledge 3.B.3**]	Chap 3, Sec. 3.8, pp. 125–131 Chap 4, Sec. 4.7, pp. 164–172
Learning objective 3.9: The student is able to design and/or interpret the results of an experiment involving a redox titration. [*See* **SP 4.2, 5.1; Essential knowledge 3.B.3**]	Chap 3, Sec. 3.2, pp. 99–102 Chap 4, Sec. 4.7, pp. 164–172
Learning objective 3.10: The student is able to evaluate the classification of a process as a physical change, chemical change, or ambiguous change based on both macroscopic observations and the distinction between rearrangement of covalent interactions and noncovalent interactions. [*See* **SP 1.4, 6.1; Essential knowledge 3.C.1,** *connects to* **5.D.2**]	Chap 1, Sec. 1.6–1.7, pp. 13–16 Chap 3, Sec. 3.4–3.8, pp. 105–131
Learning objective 3.11: The student is able to interpret observations regarding macroscopic energy changes associated with a reaction or process to generate a relevant symbolic and/or graphical representation of the energy changes. [*See* **SP 1.5, 4.4; Essential knowledge 3.C.2**]	Chap 5, Sec. 5.7, pp. 205–206
Learning objective 3.12: The student can make qualitative or quantitative predictions about galvanic or electrolytic reactions based on half-cell reactions and potentials and/or Faraday's laws. [*See* **SP 2.2, 2.3, 6.4; Essential knowledge 3.C.3**] **Learning objective 3.13:** The student can analyze data regarding galvanic or electrolytic cells to identify properties of the underlying redox reactions. [*See* **SP 5.1; Essential knowledge 3.C.3**]	Chap 19, Sec. 19.2, pp. 723–729 Chap 19, Sec. 19.4–19.8, pp. 734–758
Learning objective 4.1: The student is able to design and/or interpret the results of an experiment regarding the factors (i.e., temperature, concentration, surface area) that may influence the rate of a reaction. [*See* **SP 4.2, 5.1; Essential knowledge 4.A.1**]	Chap 14, Sec. 14.2–14.3, pp. 512–520
Learning objective 4.2: The student is able to analyze concentration versus time data to determine the rate law for a zeroth-, first-, or second-order reaction. [*See* **SP 5.1; Essential knowledge 4.A.2,** *connects to* **4.A.3**]	Chap 14, Sec. 14.4, pp. 520–529
Learning objective 4.3: The student is able to connect the half-life of a reaction to the rate constant of a first-order reaction and justify the use of this relation in terms of the reaction being a first-order reaction. [*See* **SP 2.1, 2.2; Essential knowledge 4.A.3**]	Chap 14, Sec. 14.4, pp. 520–529 Chap 25, Sec. 25.4, pp. 987–992

(*continued*)

AP® Learning Objective	Correlation of Learning Objectives to *Chemistry & Chemical Reactivity,* Ninth Edition
Learning objective 4.4: The student is able to connect the rate law for an elementary reaction to the frequency and success of molecular collisions, including connecting the frequency and success to the order and rate constant, respectively. [*See* **SP 7.1; Essential knowledge 4.B.1,** *connects to* **4.A.3, 4.B.2**]	Chap 14, Sec. 14.6, pp. 539–550
Learning objective 4.5: The student is able to explain the difference between collisions that convert reactants to products and those that do not in terms of energy distributions and molecular orientation. [*See* **SP 6.2; Essential knowledge 4.B.2**]	Chap 14, Sec. 14.5, p. 538
Learning objective 4.6: The student is able to use representations of the energy profile for an elementary reaction (from the reactants, through the transition state, to the products) to make qualitative predictions regarding the relative temperature dependence of the reaction rate. [*See* **SP 1.4, 6.4; Essential knowledge 4.B.3**]	Chap 14, Sec. 14.5, pp. 528–539
Learning objective 4.7: The student is able to evaluate alternative explanations, as expressed by reaction mechanisms, to determine which are consistent with data regarding the overall rate of a reaction, and data that can be used to infer the presence of a reaction intermediate. [*See* **SP 6.5;** *connects to* **Essential knowledge 4.C.1, 4.C.2, 4.C.3**]	Chap 14, Sec. 14.6, pp. 539–550
Learning objective 4.8: The student can translate among reaction energy profile representations, particulate representations, and symbolic representations (chemical equations) of a chemical reaction occurring in the presence and absence of a catalyst. [*See* **SP 1.5; Essential knowledge 4.D.1**]	Chap 14, Sec. 14.5, pp. 529–539
Learning objective 4.9: The student is able to explain changes in reaction rates arising from the use of acid–base catalysts, surface catalysts, or enzyme catalysts, including selecting appropriate mechanisms with or without the catalyst present. [*See* **SP 6.2, 7.2; Essential knowledge 4.D.2**]	Chap 14, Sec. 14.6, pp. 539–550 Chap 24, Sec. 24.1, pp. 946–953 Appendix O-2, A-132–A-133
Learning objective 5.1: The student is able to create or use graphical representations in order to connect the dependence of potential energy to the distance between atoms and factors, such as bond order (for covalent interactions) and polarity (for intermolecular interactions), which influence the interaction strength. [*See* **SP 1.1, 1.4, 7.2,** *connects to* **Big Idea 2; Essential knowledge components of 5.A–5.E**]	Chap 9, Sec. 9.2, pp. 340–354 Chap 11, Sec. 11.3, pp. 409–416
Learning objective 5.2: The student is able to relate temperature to the motions of particles, either via particulate representations, such as drawings of particles with arrows indicating velocities, and/or via representations of average kinetic energy and distribution of kinetic energies of the particles, such as plots of the Maxwell-Boltzmann distribution. [*See* **SP 1.1, 1.4, 7.1; Essential knowledge 5.A.1**]	Chap 5, Sec. 5.3, pp. 189–192 Chap 10, Sec. 10.6, pp. 390–396
Learning objective 5.3: The student can generate explanations or make predictions about the transfer of thermal energy between systems based on this transfer being due to a kinetic energy transfer between systems arising from molecular collisions. [*See* **SP 7.1; Essential knowledge 5.A.2**]	Chap 5, Sec. 5.1, pp. 182–184
Learning objective 5.4: The student is able to use conservation of energy to relate the magnitudes of the energy changes occurring in two or more interacting systems, including identification of the systems, the type (heat versus work), or the direction of energy flow. [*See* **SP 1.4, 2.2,** *connects to* **Essential knowledge 5.B.1, 5.B.2**]	Chap 5, Sec. 5.2–5.3, pp. 184–192
Learning objective 5.5: The student is able to use conservation of energy to relate the magnitudes of the energy changes when two nonreacting substances are mixed or brought into contact with one another. [*See* **SP 2.2,** *connects to* **Essential knowledge 5.B.1, 5.B.2**]	Chap 5, Sec. 5.6, pp. 201–205

(*continued*)

AP® Learning Objective	Correlation of Learning Objectives to *Chemistry & Chemical Reactivity,* Ninth Edition
Learning objective 5.6: The student is able to use calculations or estimations to relate: energy changes associated with heating/cooling a substance to the heat capacity, energy changes associated with a phase transition to the enthalpy of fusion/vaporization, energy changes associated with a chemical reaction to the enthalpy of the reaction, and energy changes to $P\Delta V$ work. [*See* **SP 2.2, 2.3; Essential knowledge 5.B.3**]	Chap 5, Sec. 5.2–5.5, pp. 184–201 Chap 12, Sec. 12.6, pp. 460–463
Learning objective 5.7: The student is able to design and/or interpret the results of an experiment in which calorimetry is used to determine the change in enthalpy of a chemical process (heating/cooling, phase transition, or chemical reaction) at constant pressure. [*See* **SP 4.2, 5.1; Essential knowledge 5.B.4**]	Chap 5, Sec. 5.6, pp. 201–205
Learning objective 5.8: The student is able to draw qualitative and quantitative connections between the reaction enthalpy and the energies involved in the breaking and formation of chemical bonds. [*See* **SP 2.3, 7.1, 7.2; Essential knowledge 5.C.2**]	Chap 5, Sec. 5.5, pp. 198–201 Chap 8, Sec. 8.9, pp. 325–331
Learning objective 5.9: The student is able to make claims and/or predictions regarding relative magnitudes of the forces acting within collections of interacting molecules based on the distribution of electrons within the molecules and the types of intermolecular forces through which the molecules interact. [*See* **SP 6.4; Essential knowledge 5.D.1**]	Chap 11, Sec. 11.2–11.5, pp. 407–421
Learning objective 5.10: The student can support the claim about whether a process is a chemical or physical change (or may be classified as both) based on whether the process involves changes in intramolecular versus intermolecular interactions. [*See* **SP 5.1; Essential knowledge 5.D.2**]	Chap 1, Sec. 1.7, pp. 15–16 Chap 5, Sec. 5.3, pp. 189–192 Chap 5, Sec. 5.5, pp. 198–201
Learning objective 5.11: The student is able to identify the noncovalent interactions within and between large molecules, and/or connect the shape and function of the large molecule to the presence and magnitude of these interactions. [*See* **SP 7.2; Essential knowledge 5.D.3**]	Chap 11, Sec. 11.4, pp. 416–420 Chap 23, Sec. 23.5, pp. 932–940
Learning objective 5.12: The student is able to use representations and models to predict the sign and relative magnitude of the entropy change associated with chemical or physical processes. [*See* **SP 1.4; Essential knowledge 5.E.1**]	Chap 18, Sec. 18.2–18.4, pp. 682–691
Learning objective 5.13: The student is able to predict whether or not a physical or chemical process is thermodynamically favored by determination of (either quantitatively or qualitatively) the signs of both $\Delta H°$ and $\Delta S°$, and calculation or estimation of $\Delta G°$ when needed. [*See* **SP 2.2, 2.3, 6.4; Essential knowledge 5.E.2,** *connects to* **5.E.3**]	Chap 18, Sec. 18.5–18.6, pp. 691–700
Learning objective 5.14: The student is able to determine whether a chemical or physical process is thermodynamically favorable by calculating the change in standard Gibbs free energy. [*See* **SP 2.2; Essential knowledge 5.E.3,** *connects to* **5.E.2**]	Chap 18, Sec. 18.7, pp. 700–708
Learning objective 5.15: The student is able to explain how the application of external energy sources or the coupling of favorable with unfavorable reactions can be used to cause processes that are not thermodynamically favorable to become favorable. [*See* **SP 6.2; Essential knowledge 5.E.4**]	Chap 18, Sec. 18.7, pp. 700–708 Chap 19, Sec. 19.7, pp. 751–757 Chap 24, Sec. 24.5, pp. 968–971
Learning objective 5.16: The student can use Le Châtelier's principle to make qualitative predictions for systems in which coupled reactions that share a common intermediate drive formation of a product. [*See* **SP 6.4; Essential knowledge 5.E.4,** *connects to* **6.B.1**]	Chap 24, Sec. 24.5, pp. 968–971

(*continued*)

AP® Learning Objective	Correlation of Learning Objectives to *Chemistry & Chemical Reactivity,* Ninth Edition
Learning objective 5.17: The student can make quantitative predictions for systems involving coupled reactions that share a common intermediate, based on the equilibrium constant for the combined reaction. [*See* **SP 6.4; Essential knowledge 5.E.4,** *connects to* **6.A.2**]	Chap 17, Sec. 17.7, pp. 672–674
Learning objective 5.18: The student can explain why a thermodynamically favored chemical reaction may not produce large amounts of product (based on consideration of both initial conditions and kinetic effects), or why a thermodynamically unfavored chemical reaction can produce large amounts of product for certain sets of initial conditions. [*See* **SP 1.3, 7.2; Essential knowledge 5.E.5,** *connects to* **6.D.1**]	Chap 18, Sec. 18.6, p. 698 Appendix O-3, pp. A-133–A-135
Learning objective 6.1: The student is able to, given a set of experimental observations regarding physical, chemical, biological, or environmental processes that are reversible, construct an explanation that connects the observations to the reversibility of the underlying chemical reactions or processes. [*See* **SP 6.2; Essential knowledge 6.A.1**]	Chap 15, Sec. 15.1, pp. 556–557
Learning objective 6.2: The student can, given a manipulation of a chemical reaction or set of reactions (e.g., reversal of reaction or addition of two reactions), determine the effects of that manipulation on Q or K. [*See* **SP 2.2; Essential knowledge 6.A.2**]	Chap 15, Sec. 15.5, pp. 571–575
Learning objective 6.3: The student can connect kinetics to equilibrium by using reasoning about equilibrium, such as Le Châtelier's principle, to infer the relative rates of the forward and reverse reactions. [*See* **SP 7.2; Essential knowledge 6.A.3**]	Chap 15, Sec. 15.6, p. 575
Learning objective 6.4: The student can, given a set of initial conditions (concentrations or partial pressures) and the equilibrium constant, K, use the tendency of Q to approach K to predict and justify the prediction as to whether the reaction will proceed toward products or reactants as equilibrium is approached. [*See* **SP 2.2, 6.4; Essential knowledge 6.A.3**]	Chap 15, Sec. 15.2, pp. 557–564
Learning objective 6.5: The student can, given data (tabular, graphical, etc.) from which the state of a system at equilibrium can be obtained, calculate the equilibrium constant, K. [*See* **SP 2.2; Essential knowledge 6.A.3**]	Chap 15, Sec. 15.3, pp. 564–566
Learning objective 6.6: The student can, given a set of initial conditions (concentrations or partial pressures) and the equilibrium constant, K, use stoichiometric relationships and the law of mass action (Q equals K at equilibrium) to determine qualitatively and/or quantitatively the conditions at equilibrium for a system involving a single reversible reaction. [*See* **SP 2.2, 6.4; Essential knowledge 6.A.3**]	Chap 15, Sec. 15.4, pp. 567–571
Learning objective 6.7: The student is able, for a reversible reaction that has a large or small K, to determine which chemical species will have very large versus very small concentrations at equilibrium. [*See* **SP 2.2, 2.3; Essential knowledge 6.A.4**]	Chap 15, Sec. 15.2, pp. 557–564
Learning objective 6.8: The student is able to use Le Châtelier's principle to predict the direction of the shift resulting from various possible stresses on a system at chemical equilibrium. [*See* **SP 1.4, 6.4; Essential knowledge 6.B.1**]	Chap 15, Sec. 15.6, pp. 575–581 Chap 20, Sec. 20.6, pp. 789–796
Learning objective 6.9: The student is able to use Le Châtelier's principle to design a set of conditions that will optimize a desired outcome, such as product yield. [*See* **SP 4.2; Essential knowledge 6.B.1**] **Learning objective 6.10:** The student is able to connect Le Châtelier's principle to the comparison of Q to K by explaining the effects of the stress on Q and K. [*See* **SP 1.4, 7.2; Essential knowledge 6.B.2**]	Chap 15, Sec. 15.6, pp. 575–581

(continued)

AP® Learning Objective	Correlation of Learning Objectives to *Chemistry & Chemical Reactivity,* Ninth Edition
Learning objective 6.11: The student can generate or use a particulate representation of an acid (strong or weak or polyprotic) and a strong base to explain the species that will have large versus small concentrations at equilibrium. [*See* **SP 1.1, 1.4, 2.3; Essential knowledge 6.C.1**]	Chap 16, Sec. 16.3, pp. 592–598
Learning objective 6.12: The student can reason about the distinction between strong and weak acid solutions with similar values of pH, including the percent ionization of the acids, the concentrations needed to achieve the same pH, and the amount of base needed to reach the equivalence point in a titration. [*See* **SP 1.4; Essential knowledge 6.C.1,** *connects to* **1.E.2**]	Chap 16, Sec. 16.3, pp. 592–598 Chap 16, Sec. 16.5–16.6, pp. 601–605
Learning objective 6.13: The student can interpret titration data for monoprotic or polyprotic acids involving titration of a weak or strong acid by a strong base (or a weak or strong base by a strong acid) to determine the concentration of the titrant and the pK_a for a weak acid, or the pK_b for a weak base. [*See* **SP 5.1; Essential knowledge 6.C.1,** *connects to* **I.E.2**]	Chap 17, Sec. 17.3, pp. 644–655
Learning objective 6.14: The student can, based on the dependence of Kw on temperature, reason that neutrality requires $[H^+] = [OH^-]$ as opposed to requiring pH = 7, including especially the applications to biological systems. [*See* **SP 2.2, 6.2; Essential knowledge 6.C.1**]	Chap 16, Sec. 16.2, pp. 589–592
Learning objective 6.15: The student can identify a given solution as containing a mixture of strong acids and/or bases and calculate or estimate the pH (and concentrations of all chemical species) in the resulting solution. [*See* **SP 2.2, 2.3, 6.4; Essential knowledge 6.C.1**]	Chap 16, Sec. 16.6, pp. 603–605
Learning objective 6.16: The student can identify a given solution as being the solution of a monoprotic weak acid or base (including salts in which one ion is a weak acid or base), calculate the pH and concentration of all species in the solution, and/or infer the relative strengths of the weak acids or bases from given equilibrium concentrations. [*See* **SP 2.2, 6.4; Essential knowledge 6.C.1**]	Chap 16, Sec. 16.7, pp. 605–615
Learning objective 6.17: The student can, given an arbitrary mixture of weak and strong acids and bases (including polyprotic systems), determine which species will react strongly with one another (i.e., with $K > 1$) and what species will be present in large concentrations at equilibrium. [*See* **SP 6.4; Essential knowledge 6.C.1**]	Chap 16, Sec. 16.7–16.8, pp. 605–617
Learning objective 6.18: The student can design a buffer solution with a target pH and buffer capacity by selecting an appropriate conjugate acid–base pair and estimating the concentrations needed to achieve the desired capacity. [*See* **SP 2.3, 4.2, 6.4; Essential knowledge 6.C.2**] **Learning objective 6.19:** The student can relate the predominant form of a chemical species involving a labile proton (i.e., protonated/deprotonated form of a weak acid) to the pH of a solution and the pK_a associated with the labile proton. [*See* **SP 2.3, 5.1, 6.4; Essential knowledge 6.C.2**] **Learning objective 6.20:** The student can identify a solution as being a buffer solution and explain the buffer mechanism in terms of the reactions that would occur on addition of acid or base. [*See* **SP 6.4; Essential knowledge 6.C.2**]	Chap 17, Sec. 17.2, pp. 636–644
Learning objective 6.21: The student can predict the solubility of a salt, or rank the solubility of salts, given the relevant K_{sp} values. [*See* **SP 2.2, 2.3, 6.4; Essential knowledge 6.C.3**] **Learning objective 6.22:** The student can interpret data regarding solubility of salts to determine, or rank, the relevant K_{sp} values. [*See* **SP 2.2, 2.3, 6.4; Essential knowledge 6.C.3**] **Learning objective 6.23:** The student can interpret data regarding the relative solubility of salts in terms of factors (common ions, pH) that influence the solubility. [*See* **SP 5.1; Essential knowledge 6.C.3**]	Chap 17, Sec. 17.4, pp. 655–666

(*continued*)

AP® Learning Objective	Correlation of Learning Objectives to *Chemistry & Chemical Reactivity,* Ninth Edition
Learning objective 6.24: The student can analyze the enthalpic and entropic changes associated with the dissolution of a salt, using particulate level interactions and representations. [*See* **SP 1.4, 7.1; Essential knowledge 6.C.3,** *connects to* **5.E**]	Chap 13, Sec. 13.2, pp. 473–479
Learning objective 6.25: The student is able to express the equilibrium constant in terms of $\Delta G°$ and RT and use this relationship to estimate the magnitude of K and, consequently, the thermodynamic favorability of the process. [*See* **SP 2.3; Essential knowledge 6.D.1**]	Chap 18, Sec. 18.6, pp. 696–700

Preparing for the AP® Chemistry Examination

By Laura Duncan, Boulder High School, Boulder, Colorado, and Kara Pezzi, Appleton East High School, Appleton, Wisconsin

Advanced Placement can be exhilarating. Whether you are taking an AP® course at your school or you are working on AP® independently, the stage is set for a great intellectual experience.

When the examination begins to loom on a very real horizon, Advanced Placement can seem downright intimidating. The best way to deal with an AP® examination is to master it, not let it master you. If you can think of these examinations as a way to show how much chemistry you know, you have a leg up. Attitude and confidence *do* help. Focused review and practice time will help you master the examination so that you can walk in with confidence and score a 5.

What's in *Chemistry & Chemical Reactivity* That Will Help Your Preparation

As you study there are some features of the text that will assist you in maximizing your learning:

- Make use of the *Problem Solving Method* used throughout the text in which you break the problem down into four parts: (1) What Do You Know?, (2) Strategy, (3) Solution, and (4) Think About Your Answer.
- Make certain you understand the *Example Problems* with solutions in each chapter. These will often give you a guide to help develop your problem-solving skills.
- The *Interactive Examples* available online in MindTap Reader will help you think your way through examples and problems. This will be especially important in helping to prepare for the AP® Exam.
- The *Strategy Maps* will help you think your way through examples and problems. This will be especially important as you prepare for the AP® Exam.
- Try the *Review & Check* questions at the end of each section as a means to double check your understanding before you proceed.
- Answer the *Study Questions* at the end of each chapter as a measure of your understanding. This will give you instant feedback as to how much of the chapter you may need to study again.
- Do as many *Summary and Conceptual Questions* as you can. These questions are intended to incorporate many different concepts into the solution. Questions like this are particularly good practice for the free-response portion of the AP® exam.
- Answer the *AP® Multiple-Choice Review Questions* at the end of each chapter. They are tied to the *Learning Objectives,* which are part of the AP® format. Practice doing computations for these questions without a calculator. You are not allowed to use a calculator in the multiple-choice section of the test, so you need to be good at estimating. Some chapters will also have *AP® Free Response Questions.* These are also tied to Learning Objectives. Practice doing these questions, which will also be a great help in preparing for the AP® Exam.

Being successful in chemistry usually involves careful reading of the textbook and working as many different types of problems as possible. The successful student is not one who memorizes a bunch of facts but one who is able to synthesize and analyze the problem.

Before the Examination

By February, long before the exam, you need to make sure that you are registered to take the test. Many schools take care of the paperwork and handle the fees for their AP® students, but check with your teacher or the AP® coordinator to make sure that you are on the list. This is especially important if you have a documented disability and need test accommodations. If you are studying AP® independently, call AP® Services at the College Board for the name of the local AP® coordinator, who will help you through the registration process.

The evening before the exam is not a great time for partying. Nor is it a great time for cramming. If you like, look over class notes or drift through your textbook, concentrating on the broad outlines, not the small details, of the course. The evening before the exam *is* a great time to get your things together for the next day. Sharpen a fistful of no. 2 pencils with good erasers; bring a scientific calculator with fresh batteries. Certain types of calculators are not allowed, so be sure to verify with your teacher or the College Board that your model is acceptable. For example, you cannot use a calculator with a typewriter-style keyboard or a cell phone. Cell phones are not even allowed in the testing room, so you will need a watch and be certain to turn off the alarm if it has one. Bring a piece of fruit or a power bar and a bottle of water for the break. Make sure you have your Social Security number and whatever photo identification and admission ticket are required. Then relax. And get a good night's sleep.

On the day of the examination, plan to arrive early. It is wise not to skip breakfast—studies show that students who eat a hot breakfast before testing get higher grades. Be careful not to drink a lot of liquids, necessitating a trip to the bathroom during the exam. Breakfast will give you the energy you need to power through the exam—and more. You will spend some time waiting while everyone is seated in the right room for the right exam before the test has even begun. With a short break between Section I and Section II, the AP® Chemistry exam lasts for more than two and a half hours, so be prepared for a long morning. You do not want to be distracted by a growling stomach or hunger pangs.

Be sure to wear comfortable clothes, taking along a sweater in case the heating or air-conditioning is erratic. Be sure, too, to wear clothes you like—everyone performs better when they think they look better—and by all means wear your lucky socks.

You have been on the fast track. Now go get a 5!

Taking the AP® Chemistry Examination

The AP® Chemistry curriculum emphasizes the importance of inquiry and reasoning in science and requires depth of understanding more than the memorization of facts. On the exam you may be asked to do a range of tasks, such as interpreting lab data or making predictions based on your knowledge of chemical principles.

Some content in your text will not be tested in the examination, although your teacher may choose to include that material in your course.

The AP® Chemistry exam will consist of two sections. The sections are described below.

Section I: The main features of the multiple-choice sections are given in the following table.

	Format
Number of questions	60
Time to complete	90 minutes
Number of choices	4
Calculator	No
Weighting	50%

The questions will generally refer to "real-world" situations and may contain several parts. Some sample questions are given in the "Strategies for the Multiple-Choice Section" that follows.

Section II: After Section I is collected, you will have a short break. The main features of the free-response sections are given in the following table.

	Format
Number of questions	7 total. The questions are made up of 3 long questions (parts a-d or parts a-e) and 4 short questions (parts a-b).
Point value	This section is worth up to 46 points. Each long question is worth up to 10 points. Each short question is worth up to 4 points.
Types of long and short questions (at least one question from each type)	Lab I Lab II Representation I Representation II Quantitative
Time to complete	90 minutes
Calculator	Yes
Weighting	50%

In this section, you will be asked to:

- Design an experiment to test a hypothesis, given a specific set of laboratory equipment (Lab I)
- Interpret and draw conclusions from data (Lab II)
- Use models to describe physical phenomena (Representations I and II)
- Follow a logical or analytical pathway to solve a problem (Quantitative)

When answering these questions, you will need to be able to explain, say, what is happening at the atomic or molecular level when a substance changes from a solid, to a liquid, to a gas; but in addition, you may be asked to draw diagrams of the three phases to demonstrate that you can make models of systems.

The focus on laboratory work as a tool of scientific inquiry means that you will need to practice writing laboratory procedures, understand the correct use of laboratory equipment to gather data, and incorporate safe practices. Some example questions are given in the "Strategies for Answering Free-Response Questions" on page li.

Strategies for the Multiple-Choice Section

Each question in the multiple-choice section is worth 1 point, and since there is no penalty for guessing, you want to make the most educated guess! Here are some rules of thumb to help you:

- **Read the question carefully.** Pressured for time, many students make the mistake of reading the questions too quickly or merely skimming them. By reading a question carefully, you may already have some idea of the correct answer. You can then look for it in the responses.
- **Eliminate any answer you know is wrong.** You can write on the multiple-choice questions in the test book. As you read through the responses, draw a line through any answer you know is wrong.
- **Read all of the possible answers, then choose the most accurate response.** AP® examinations are written to test your precise knowledge of a subject. Some of the responses may be partially correct, but there will be only one response that is completely true.
- **Avoid absolute responses.** These answers often include the words "always" or "never." For example, the statement "all chlorides are always soluble in water" is incorrect because compounds, such as silver chloride and lead(II) chloride, are insoluble in water.
- **Mark tough questions.** If you are hung up on a question, make an educated guess, but mark it in the margin of the question book and come back to review it later if you have time.

Types of Multiple-Choice Questions

The exam will include long and short questions. The former will ask several questions about the same set of data. Here are some suggestions for approaching each of the various kinds of multiple-choice questions:

Classic/Best Answer Questions This is the most common type of multiple-choice question. It simply requires you to read the question and select the most correct answer. The example below is a short question.

1. Given the following reduction potentials, which metal would be best for a pipeline carrying dilute hydrochloric acid?

Reaction	$\mathcal{E}°$ (V)
$Ti^{3+} + 3e^- \rightarrow Ti$	+0.72
$Zn^{2+} + 2e^- \rightarrow Zn$	−0.76
$Cu^{2+} + 2e^- \rightarrow Cu$	+0.34
$Fe^{2+} + 2e^- \rightarrow Fe$	−0.44

(A) Ti
(B) Zn
(C) Cu
(D) Fe

ANSWER: A. You are looking for the metal that is least likely to be oxidized by the protons in a solution of the strong acid. The higher (most positive) the reduction potential, the less likely the metal will be oxidized. Eliminate (B) and (D) because their reduction potentials are negative, indicating that they are more likely to be oxidized. Of the two remaining, (A) has the largest positive value. **(Learning Objective 3.12: The student can make qualitative or quantitative predictions about galvanic or electrolytic reactions based on half-cell reactions and potentials and/or Faraday's laws.)**

Noncalculator Computations These questions require computation without the use of a calculator. Simple mathematics or the choice of the correct algebraic setup will be involved.

1. A weak acid, HA, has a K_a value of 1.0×10^{-6}. A student adds 10.0 mL of 0.200 *M* NaOH to 40.0 mL of 0.100 *M* HA and the two react completely. Calculate the final pH.

(A) 2.0
(B) 6.0
(C) 7.0
(D) 8.0

ANSWER: B. To answer this question, you must consider at what point in the titration the question is referring to. Because the base, NaOH, is twice as concentrated as the acid, HA, it will take half as much NaOH to reach the equivalence point, or 20.0 mL. We are not at the equivalence point. Half the amount of the NaOH, 10.0 mL, needed to reach the equivalence point has been added. Halfway to the equivalence point, the pH equals the pK_a, which equals $-\log(K_a)$ or 6.0. **(Learning Objective 6.13: The student can interpret titration data for monoprotic or polyprotic acids involving titration of a weak or strong acid by a strong base (or a weak or strong base by a strong acid) to determine the concentration of the titrant and the pK_a for a weak acid, or the pK_b for a weak base.)**

2. $2\,C(s) + O_2(g) \rightarrow 2\,CO(g)$

1.2 g of carbon (graphite) and 3.2 g oxygen gas are placed into a 3.0-L container at 25 °C.

If the carbon and the oxygen react completely to form CO(g), what will be the final pressure in the container at 25 °C?

(A) $\frac{0.05(0.082)(298)}{3.0}$ atm

(B) $\frac{0.10(0.082)(25)}{3.0}$ atm

(C) $\frac{0.15(0.082)(298)}{3.0}$ atm

(D) $\frac{0.10(0.082)(298)}{3.0}$ atm

ANSWER: C. To answer this question, 1.2 g of carbon is 0.10 mole of carbon (1 mole of carbon equals 12 g). Similarly, 3.2 g of O_2 is 0.10 mole of O_2. The limiting reactant is carbon producing 0.10 mole of CO. O_2 is present in excess (0.10 mole of CO requires 0.05 mole of O_2, leaving 0.05 mol of O_2). When the reaction is complete, there is 0.10 mole CO + 0.05 mole O_2 left, which equals 0.15 mole total. **(Learning Objective 2.6: The student can apply mathematical relationships or estimation to determine macroscopic variables for ideal gases; Learning Objective 3.4: The student is able to relate quantities [measured mass of substances, volumes of solutions, or volumes and pressures of gases] to identify stoichiometric relationships for a reaction, including situations involving limiting reactants and situations in which the reaction has not gone to completion.)**

Long Question

The following information is used to answer questions 1 and 2.

Nitroglycerine, $C_3H_5N_3O_9$, explodes with tremendous force due to the numerous gaseous products. The equation for the explosion of nitroglycerine is:

$$4\,C_3H_5N_3O_9(\ell) \rightarrow 12\,CO_2(g) + O_2(g) + 6\,N_2(g) + 10\,H_2O(g)$$

A scientist conducts an experiment to characterize a bomb containing nitroglycerine. She uses a steel, rigid container for the test.

Volume of rigid steel container	1.00 L
Molar mass of nitroglycerine	227 g/mol
Temperature	300. K
Amount of nitroglycerine tested	227 g
Value for ideal gas constant, *R*	$0.0821 \frac{\text{L atm}}{\text{mol K}}$

1. What is the total pressure produced in this explosion?

(A) 25.0 atm
(B) 52.0 atm
(C) 179 atm
(D) 435 atm

ANSWER: C. The 227 g of nitroglycerine corresponds to 1.00 mol of nitroglycerine. Based on the balanced chemical equation, we see that 4 mol of nitroglycerine produces 29 mol of gas. This stoichiometric factor can be used to predict the number of moles of gas produced.

$$1.00 \text{ mol } C_3H_5N_3O_9 \times \frac{29 \text{ mol gas}}{4 \text{ mol } C_3H_5N_3O_9} = 7.25 \text{ mol gas}$$

Because you will not have a calculator for this type of problem, the rest of the problem will be solved first using estimations. The amount of gas is a little more than seven moles. We know that one mole of an ideal gas will occupy 22.4 L at STP. Likewise, one mole of an ideal gas at 1.00 L volume and at 0 °C (273 K) will exert a pressure of 22.4 atm. The pressure exerted by 7 mol of an ideal gas at STP will be 7(22.4 atm) = 157 atm. We actually have a little more than seven moles of gas and we are at a slightly higher temperature than 0 °C, so we would expect that the total pressure would be a little higher than this. The only answer close to this value is 179 atm, the correct answer.

The exact solution would be obtained using the ideal gas law:

$$P = \frac{nRT}{V}$$
$$= \frac{(7.25 \text{ mol})(0.0821 \text{ L} \cdot \text{atm/K} \cdot \text{mol})(300.\text{ K})}{1.00 \text{ L}} = 179 \text{ atm}$$

(Learning Objective 2.6: The student can apply mathematical relationships or estimation to determine macroscopic variables for ideal gases.)

2. In a second experiment, the total pressure is observed to be 58 atm. What is the partial pressure of the water vapor produced?
   (A) 10. atm
   (B) 20. atm
   (C) 30. atm
   (D) 40. atm

ANSWER: B. The mole fraction of water in the gas mixture is 10 mol H_2O/29 mol gas. The total pressure is 58 atm. Based on Dalton's Law, the partial pressure of the water is given by the mole fraction of water multiplied by the total pressure.

$$\frac{10 \text{ mol } H_2O}{29 \text{ mol gas}}(58 \text{ mol atm}) = 20.\text{ atm}$$

This calculation is made easier by the fact that 58/29 is exactly 2. **(Learning Objective 2.6: The student can apply mathematical relationships or estimation to determine macroscopic variables for ideal gases.)**

Strategies for the Free-Response Section

Section II of the AP® exam comes with a periodic table and a table of equations and constants. The needed portions of the standard reduction potentials, $\mathscr{E}°_{red}$, will be provided within the questions.

- Scan all of the questions in the section you are working in and mark those that you know you can answer correctly. Do these problems first.
- Show all of your work and use units where requested. Partial credit will be awarded for problems if the correct work is shown but the answer is not present or is incorrect. In problems involving calculations, circle your final answer.
- Cross out incorrect answers with an "X" rather than spending time erasing.
- Be clear, neat, and organized in your work. If a grader cannot clearly understand your work, you may not receive full credit.
- Three of the questions will have several parts. Attempt to solve each part. Even if your answer to the first part is incorrect, you still may be awarded points for the remaining parts of the question if the work is correct for those parts.
- Units are important in your answer. Keeping track of your units throughout calculations and performing unit cancellation where possible will help guide you to your answer. Points will be deducted for missing or incorrect units in the answer. However, if the question does not specify the requirement of units, points will not be deducted for missing units, although they can be deducted for incorrect units.
- You do not need to work the questions in order. Make sure you put the number of the question in the corner of each page of your essay booklet. In addition, questions are sometimes broken into parts, such as (a) and (b). When this is the case, label each part of your response.

Strategies for Answering Free-Response Questions

Free-response questions will ask you to explain, compare, and predict. Minor calculations, showing mathematical relationships, or drawing graphs or structures, may also be involved. Usually these are not traditional essay questions. Most free-response questions do not require an introduction or conclusion. Most do not even require a thesis. Many of these questions may be written in a bulleted or short-answer format. Although this may sound easier than writing a traditional essay, it is important that you know the material very well because these are targeted questions. Examination readers want specifics. They are looking for accurate information presented in clear, concise prose. You cannot mask vague information with elegant prose. The use of appropriate vocabulary terms is strongly suggested, as this may make the difference between the awarding of a point or not.

To be successful in writing free-response answers for the AP® Chemistry exam, be sure to get straight to the answer and use key terms in your explanations. Sometimes, if you ramble on and on, you might accidentally state an incorrect fact. Points will be deducted for incorrect or extraneous information.

Techniques to write free-response questions include chart format, bullet format, and outline format. None of these styles requires that you write complete sentences. In each of these styles, restate the question in simple terms, using your own words. Restate each part (a, b, and so on) separately, not together. In your restatement and response, underline key words or concepts.

- **Fill in a chart to answer the question.** This style is helpful in answering questions about electronic and molecular structure.

- **In bullet or number format, make a list,** using a bullet (›) or number for each new concept. Leave room between concepts because you may want to come back later to fill them in.
- **Outline format** is more traditional, using Roman numerals, letters, etc. This takes more time to organize ideas, but it does show progression of ideas in a logical sequence. As in the bulleted format, leave room between concepts because you may want to come back later to fill them in.
- Last, **the freestyle method,** but this sometimes results in rambling and incomplete answers. Also, writing in paragraphs does not allow room for additional ideas to be added.

Types of Free-Response Questions

The free-response questions may be long or short. The long questions typically include four or five parts and are worth up to 10 points. The short questions include one or two parts and are worth up to 4 points. Samples and descriptions of the main categories of questions follow.

Sample Problem, Lab I: In this type of question, you will be asked to demonstrate your ability to plan and write a laboratory procedure based on your knowledge of chemical principles. The graders will also be looking for your knowledge of safe practices. These can be long or short questions but will often be long questions, as in the example below.

You are given a set of four clear liquids. One is ethanol, one is a dilute solution of acetic acid, one is water, and one is a dilute solution of sodium hydroxide. Design an experiment to identify the liquids. Describe the steps, the data you would collect, and how the data support the identifications. Laboratory equipment for your experiment should be taken from the list below. (You may not need all of the equipment.)

50-mL beakers	fume hood
hot plate	stirring rods
0.1 *M* $NaHCO_3$	phenolphthalein indicator
conductivity meter	safety glasses
thermometer	beaker tongs

ANSWER:

1. Work under a fume hood, because several of the liquids are volatile.
2. Wear safety glasses to protect your eyes from the acid, base, and alcohol.
3. Put approximately 5 mL of each liquid in each of four 50-mL beakers.
4. First test: Of the liquids, only sodium hydroxide will turn pink in the presence of phenolphthalein indicator. Add a drop of indicator to each solution and stir gently. The one that turns pink is sodium hydroxide solution. Clean off the stirring rods with distilled water so they will not cause contamination in subsequent tests. (**Learning Objective 6.15: The student can identify a given solution as containing a mixture of strong acids and/or bases and calculate or estimate the pH—and concentrations of all chemical species—in the resulting solution.**)
5. Second test: Of the remaining liquids, only acetic acid will react with sodium hydrogen carbonate to release carbon dioxide gas. The phenolphthalein indicator will not interfere with the test, so the same beakers can be used. Add approximately 5 mL of sodium hydrogen carbonate solution to the three remaining solutions and stir gently. The one that bubbles is the acetic acid being neutralized by the weak base to form water, carbon dioxide gas, and aqueous sodium acetate. (**Learning Objective 6.16: The student can identify a given solution as being the solution of a monoprotic weak acid or base [including salts in which one ion is a weak acid or base], calculate the pH and concentration of all species in the solution, and/or infer the relative strengths of the weak acids or bases from given equilibrium concentrations.**)
6. Third test: Of the remaining liquids, ethanol has a much lower boiling temperature than water because it has weaker intermolecular forces (it can make only one hydrogen bond per molecule, and water can make two). Put approximately 10 mL of each in two separate 50-mL beakers and put on a hot plate set at medium temperature. Check the temperatures of the liquids when they boil by placing a thermometer in the liquid, but not touching the bottom or sides of the beaker. The water should boil at around 90° to 100 °C; the ethanol will boil at a much lower temperature. Use the beaker tongs to remove the beakers from the hot plate as soon as you are done making measurements. (**Learning Objective 2.16: The student is able to explain the properties [phase, vapor pressure, viscosity, etc.] of small and large molecular compounds in terms of the strengths and types of intermolecular forces.**)
7. Dispose of all liquids in the designated liquid waste containers in your lab.

Solving this problem also involves the use of Science Practice 4: The student can plan and implement data collection strategies in relation to a particular scientific question. (*Note:* Data can be collected from many different sources, e.g., investigations, scientific observations, the findings of others, historic reconstruction, and/or archived data.) The problem also involves the use of Science Practice 5: The student can perform data analysis and evaluation of evidence.

Sample Problem, Lab II: Here, you will be given data and asked to draw conclusions based on these data. Your answers must demonstrate your knowledge of the specific chemical principles that relate to the observations. Using proper vocabulary is critical. These questions may be long or short. The example is a long question.

You are given a set of four vials of clear liquids, designated A, B, C, and D. One is ethanol, one is a dilute solution of acetic acid, one is mineral oil, and one is a dilute solution of sodium hydroxide. In a series of experiments, you collect the following data:

- Only A and B are strongly conductive.
- Only B turns pink when phenolphthalein indicator is added.
- When equal portions of each liquid are placed on thermocouples and the amount of cooling tracked over a 5-minute period, C shows the greatest change.

- When small portions of the liquids are mixed with water, all form homogeneous solutions except D, which forms a separate layer on the top.

Use this information to identify the contents of each vial. Explain clearly how you used the data to come to your conclusions.

ANSWER:

1. Compounds that ionize when dissolved in water form conductive solutions. Of the four liquids, only the sodium hydroxide solution (a base) and the acetic acid solution (an acid) consist of ions. A and B must be the acid and base. Since B turns pink when phenolphthalein is added and phenolphthalein is pink only in basic solutions, B must be sodium hydroxide and A must be acetic acid. **(Learning Objective 2.15: The student is able to explain observations regarding the solubility of ionic solids and molecules in water and other solvents on the basis of particle views that include intermolecular interactions and entropic effects; Learning Objective 2.16: The student is able to explain the properties [phase, vapor pressure, viscosity, etc.] of small and large molecular compounds in terms of the strengths and types of intermolecular forces.)**
2. Ethanol is completely soluble in water because it can form hydrogen bonds with water. Mineral oil is nonpolar and will not dissolve in water. D must be mineral oil because it forms a layer on top of the water. **(Learning Objective 2.15: The student is able to explain observations regarding the solubility of ionic solids and molecules in water and other solvents on the basis of particle views that include intermolecular interactions and entropic effects.)**
3. Although ethanol forms hydrogen bonds with itself, it can make only one hydrogen bond per molecule and water can make two. With fewer intermolecular forces per molecule, ethanol will be more volatile than water and the aqueous acid and base solutions. Mineral oil is nonpolar, but as a linear molecule has many contact points for London dispersion forces; it is also relatively nonvolatile. Ethanol will evaporate the most in a set period of time and therefore cool the thermocouple the most. C must be ethanol. **(Learning Objective 2.16: The student is able to explain the properties [phase, vapor pressure, viscosity, etc.] of small and large molecular compounds in terms of the strengths and types of intermolecular forces.)**

Solving this problem also demonstrates Science Practice 5: The student can perform data analysis and evaluation of evidence.

Scientists, chemists in particular, create models of atomic/molecular behavior that explain what is observed at "large" scale. In representation problems, you are asked to talk about the strengths and weaknesses of key models. There are two types of representation questions.

Sample Problem, Representation I: For representation I questions, you are asked to discuss how a model of particles behaves on the microscopic (particulate) level and explain macroscopic observations. You will need to understand the strengths and the weaknesses of various models. These can be long or short questions. The example below is a short question.

In kinetic molecular theory (KMT), gas atoms/molecules are depicted as particles with no appreciable volume, in constant random motion, that collide elastically with one another and do not interact with each other. What aspect(s) of this model break(s) down when a system's temperature decreases and pressure increases?

ANSWER:

1. In KMT, the number and size of molecules are so small relative to the size of the container that their volume can be neglected, and the system volume is essentially that of the "empty" container. The main way to increase pressure is to decrease the system volume. If the system volume decreases enough, the volume of the molecules themselves is no longer negligible and must be taken into account. Also, the molecules may get close enough for intermolecular forces to come into play, so the molecules now are able to interact with each other.
2. Temperature is a measure of molecular motion, so a lower temperature indicates that the molecules are moving more slowly. When they move more slowly, they can spend enough time near each other for intermolecular forces to become significant. **(Learning Objective 2.4: The student is able to use KMT and concepts of intermolecular forces to make predictions about the macroscopic properties of gases, including both ideal and nonideal behaviors.)**

Sample Problem, Representation II: This kind of problem is similar to representation I, except that your answer will contain diagrams as well as explanations. These can be long or short questions. This example is a short question.

Water is a liquid at room temperature, but hydrogen chloride and hydrogen are gases under the same conditions. Draw a particulate representation of each substance, clearly indicating the intermolecular forces that account for these observations, and name the primary intermolecular force for each.

ANSWER:

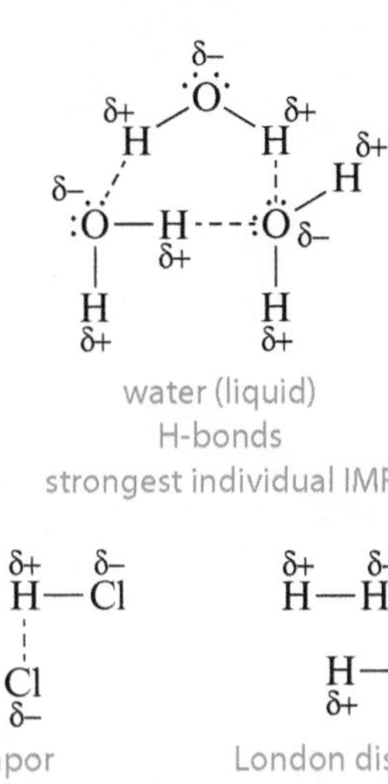

water (liquid)
H-bonds
strongest individual IMF

HCl vapor
dipole-dipole force

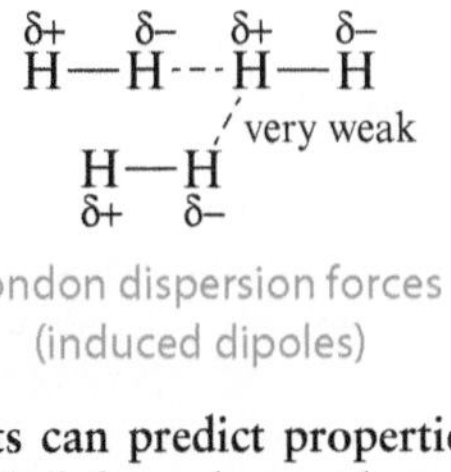

London dispersion forces
(induced dipoles)

(Learning Objective 2.1: Students can predict properties of substances based on their chemical formulas, and provide explanations of their properties based on particle views.

Learning Objective 2.4: The student is able to use KMT and concepts of intermolecular forces to make predictions about the macroscopic properties of gases, including both ideal and nonideal behaviors.)

Sample Problem, Quantitative: This type of question will ask you to follow a logical, analytical pathway to solve a problem. These can be long or short questions. The example given is a long question.

$$C_2H_4(g) + 3\ O_2(g) \rightarrow 2\ CO_2(g) + 2\ H_2O(g)$$

Information about the substances involved in the reaction presented above is tabulated below.

Substance	$S°$ (J/mol · K)	$\Delta G_f°$ (kJ/mol)
$C_2H_4(g)$	?	68
$O_2(g)$	205	0
$CO_2(g)$	213.6	−394
$H_2O(g)$	189	−229

Bond	Bond Energy (kJ/mol)
O—H	467
O—O	146
O=O	495
C—H	413
C—C	347
C=C	614
C≡C	839
C—O	358
C=O	799

(a) Calculate the value for the standard free energy change, $\Delta G°$, at 25 °C for the reaction. What does the sign of $\Delta G°$ indicate about the reaction?

(b) Calculate the value for the standard enthalpy change, $\Delta H°$, at 25 °C for the reaction. What does the sign of $\Delta H°$ indicate about the reaction?

(c) Calculate the value for the standard entropy change, $\Delta S°$, at 25 °C for the reaction. What does the sign of $\Delta S°$ indicate about the reaction?

(d) Calculate the value for the absolute entropy of $C_2H_4(g)$ at 25 °C.

ANSWER

(A) $\Delta G° = 2(-394) + 2(-229) - 68 = -1314$ kJ/mol. A negative standard free energy change indicates that the reaction is product-favored at equilibrium and therefore thermodynamically favored.

(B)

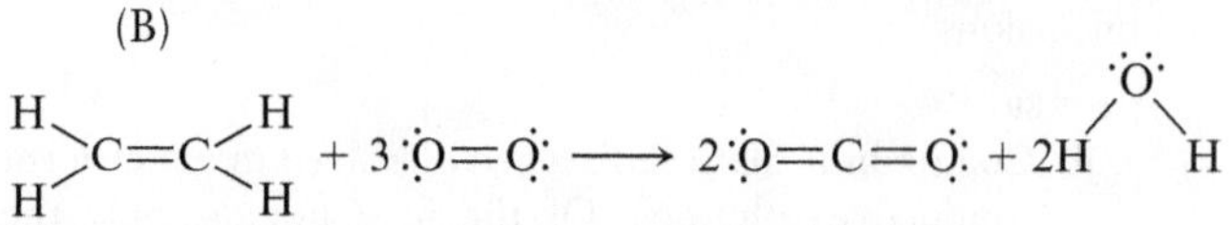

Bonds Broken		Bonds Formed	
4 C—H	4 (413)	4 C=O	4 (799)
1 C=C	1 (614)	4 O—H	4 (467)
3 O=O	3 (495)		−5064 kJ
	+3751 kJ		

$\Delta H° = 3751$ kJ $+ -5064$ kJ $= -1313$ kJ

The reaction is exothermic since $\Delta H°$ is negative.

(C) $\Delta G° = \Delta H° - T\Delta S°$; $\Delta S° = (\Delta H° - \Delta G°)/T$

$\Delta S° = -1313 - (-1314\text{ kJ})/298\text{ K} = 0.0034$ kJ/K

A positive sign for the entropy change of the system indicates that energy becomes more dispersed in the system.

(D) $\Delta S° = 2S°_{CO_2} + 2S°_{H_2O} - (S°_{C_2H_4} + 3S°_{O_2})$

$S°_{C_2H_4} = 2S°_{CO_2} + 2S°_{H_2O} - 3S°_{O_2} - \Delta S°$

$= 2(213.6) + 2(189) - 3(205) - 3.4 = 187$ J/K

(Learning Objective 5.8: The student is able to draw qualitative and quantitative connections between the reaction enthalpy and the energies involved in the breaking and formation of chemical bonds. Learning Objective 5.13: The student is able to predict whether or not a physical or chemical process is thermodynamically favored by determination of (either quantitatively or qualitatively) the signs of both $\Delta H°$ and $\Delta S°$, and calculation or estimation of $\Delta G°$ when needed. Learning Objective 5.14: The student is able to determine whether a chemical or physical process is thermodynamically favorable by calculating the change in standard Gibbs free energy.)

About the Authors

(Left to right) **John Kotz, John Townsend, David Treichel, Paul Treichel**

John C. Kotz, a State University of New York Distinguished Teaching Professor at the College at Oneonta, was educated at Washington and Lee University and Cornell University. He held National Institutes of Health postdoctoral appointments in England and at Indiana University.

He has coauthored three textbooks in several editions (*Inorganic Chemistry, Chemistry & Chemical Reactivity,* and *The Chemical World)* as well as the *General Chemistry Interactive CD-ROM.* His research on organometallic chemistry and electrochemistry has been published in scientific journals.

He has been a Fulbright Lecturer and Research Scholar in Portugal as well as a visiting professor at the University of Wisconsin, Auckland University in New Zealand, and Potchefstroom University in South Africa. He has also made invited presentations on chemistry and education at conferences in the United States, England, Brazil, South Africa, New Zealand, and Argentina.

He received a National Catalyst Award for Excellence in Teaching, the Visiting Scientist Award from the Western Connecticut Section of the American Chemical Society, and the Distinguished Education Award from the Binghamton (NY) Section of the American Chemical Society. In 1998 he was the Estee Lecturer in Chemical Education at the University of South Dakota and in 2007 was the Squibb Lecturer at the University of North Carolina-Asheville. Finally, he was a mentor for the U.S. National Chemistry Olympiad team. His email address is johnkotz@mac.com.

Paul M. Treichel received his B.S. degree from the University of Wisconsin in 1958 and a Ph.D. from Harvard University in 1962. After a year of postdoctoral study in London, he assumed a faculty position at the University of Wisconsin–Madison. He served as department chair from 1986 through 1995 and was awarded a Helfaer Professorship in 1996. He has held visiting faculty positions in South Africa (1975) and in Japan (1995). Retiring after 44 years as a faculty member in 2007, he is currently Emeritus Professor of Chemistry. During his faculty career he taught courses in general chemistry, inorganic chemistry, organometallic chemistry, and scientific ethics. Professor Treichel's research in organometallic and metal cluster chemistry and in mass spectrometry, aided by 75 graduate and undergraduate students, has led to more than 170 papers in scientific journals. He may be contacted by email at treichelpaul@me.com.

John R. Townsend, Professor of Chemistry at West Chester University of Pennsylvania, completed his B.A. in Chemistry as well as the Approved Program for Teacher Certification in Chemistry at the University of Delaware. After a career teaching high school science and mathematics, he earned his M.S. and Ph.D. in biophysical chemistry at Cornell University, where he also received the DuPont Teaching Award for his work as a teaching assistant. After teaching at Bloomsburg University, he joined the faculty at West Chester University, where he coordinates the chemistry education program for prospective high school teachers and the general chemistry lecture program for science majors. He has been the university supervisor for more than 60 prospective high school chemistry teachers during their student teaching semester. His research interests are in the fields of chemical education and biochemistry. He may be contacted by email at jtownsend@wcupa.edu.

David A. Treichel, Professor of Chemistry at Nebraska Wesleyan University, received a B.A. degree from Carleton College. He earned a M.S. and a Ph.D. in analytical chemistry at Northwestern University. After postdoctoral research at the University of Texas in Austin, he joined the faculty at Nebraska Wesleyan University. His research interests are in the fields of electrochemistry and surface-laser spectroscopy. He may be contacted by email at dat@nebrwesleyan.edu.

About the Cover

Steven Hyatt

The beautiful green stone on the cover of this book is a piece of jade carved in New Zealand. Jade is found in many parts of the world, and, because of its beauty, it has been used for centuries for decorative and religious items. In addition, because it is hard and withstands high temperatures, it has been used for tools such as axe blades. In China in the period from 200 BC to 200 AD, members of royalty were buried in suits made of jade panels sewn with gold thread. In New Zealand the stone is called "pounamu," the name given by the indigenous people of that country, the Maori. To the Maori pounamu has immense spiritual and material value; objects made of jade are among their most prized possessions.

The name "jade" comes from the Spanish *piedra de ijada,* which means "loin stone," a name given it because it was thought to cure kidney diseases.

There are actually two different minerals called jade: jadeite and nephrite. Jadeite is much rarer and a bit harder than nephrite. The two are difficult to tell apart visually, but nephrite has a "silkier" feel in the hand than jadeite, a feature that arises from differences in their underlying silicate structure.

The jade on the book cover and shown here is nephrite with the formula $Ca_2(Mg, Fe)_5(Si_4O_{11})_2(OH)_2$. The green color of nephrite comes from iron(II) ions. As the amount of iron(II) ions can vary from stone to stone, the color can vary from white (low iron content) to deep green (higher iron content).

The nature of jade and the origin of the color are discussed further in Chapters 12 and 22.

A scale used by gold miners; in an old mining shack in Arizona.

Basic Concepts of Chemistry

Chapter Outline

GOLD! Students beginning a chemistry course often tell us that they don't know anything about chemistry. However, there are many things in our lives that pertain to chemistry, and it's likely you know some things about at least one of the elements, gold.

Gold has been known and prized for millennia. It is one of the rarest of the elements. Wars have been fought over it, and humans have been enslaved to mine it. Gold is extracted from the Earth all over the world, and the oceans are estimated to contain more than 10 million tons.

Gold is a common investment commodity, but its most recognizable uses are in jewelry and dentistry. Statuary is often gilded, that is, covered by a thin layer of gold. We see its use in architecture; the dome of St. Isaac's Cathedral in St. Petersburg, Russia, for example, is covered with 220 pounds of gold in wafer-thin sheets.

Here are few facts about gold:

- Its name in German is the same as in English, but in Spanish it is *oro* and in French it is *l'or;* the chemical symbol for gold is Au, from the Latin word for gold, *aurum*.
- Most gold used in jewelry is not pure gold. Instead, gold is mixed with other metals to strengthen it and

Chapter Goals

See Chapter Goals Revisited (page 20) for Study Questions keyed to these goals.

UNDERSTAND

- Basic concepts applied in science: hypotheses, laws, and theories.
- The basic ideas of kinetic-molecular theory.
- Viewpoints of chemistry: macroscopic, microscopic, symbolic.
- Processes that involve energy changes and how they apply in chemical studies.

DO

- Classify matter.
- Identify physical and chemical properties and changes.

REMEMBER

- The characteristics of chemical building blocks: elements, atoms, compounds, and molecules.
- A list of common physical and chemical properties.
- The principles of green chemistry.

to change its color (and to make an article less expensive). The amount of gold in jewelry is identified by marks stamped on the article. Pure gold is 24 K (24 carat). The label 18 carat (18 K) means that the metal used is 18/24ths gold by weight; 9 K gold is 9/24ths gold.

- Gold is malleable, meaning it can be shaped by pounding. Gold leaf can be made as thin as 0.000127 mm, representing a thickness of about 500 atoms.
- Gold is unaffected by air, water, and most chemicals. This is why it doesn't tarnish. The chemical exception is aqua regia (Latin, *water of kings*), a mixture of hydrochloric and nitric acids, in which gold dissolves.
- Gold is one of the best conductors of electricity, the "gold standard" for use in electrical circuitry.

As you begin your study of chemistry, we encourage you to be aware of things you already know about chemistry. What do you know about elements such as iron, aluminum, copper, and oxygen, or about compounds such as water and carbon dioxide? Throughout this book we will have a lot to say about these and many other interesting and useful chemicals.

Study Questions Related to Chapter Introduction In each chapter there will be at least one Study Question related to the introductory essay. For Chapter 1 this is Study Question 1.47.

In 1991 a hiker in the Alps on the Austrian-Italian border found a well-preserved human body encased in ice. Although it was first thought to be a person who had recently died, a number of scientific studies over more than a decade concluded the man had lived 53 centuries ago and was about 46 years old when he died. He became known as Ötzi the Iceman.

The discovery of the Iceman's body, the oldest natural human mummy, set off innumerable scientific studies that brought together chemists, biologists, anthropologists,

(a) The Iceman before the body was removed from the ice within which he had been frozen for almost 53 centuries.

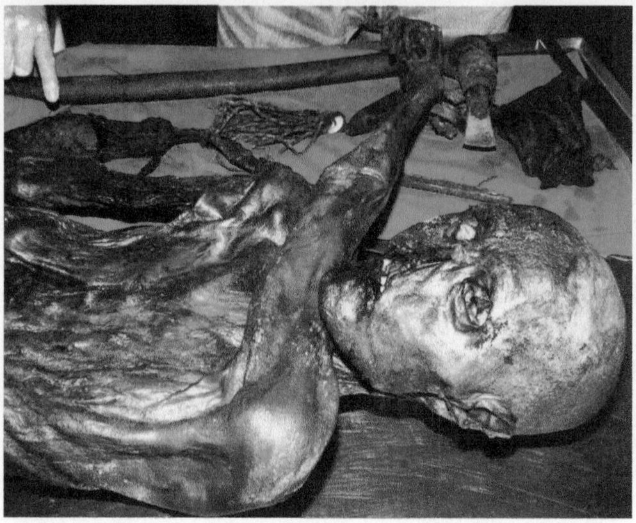

(b) The body of the Iceman now lies in the Archaeological Museum of South Tyrol in Bolzano, Italy.

Ötzi the Iceman. The name "Ötzi" comes from the Ötz valley, the region of Europe (on the Austrian-Italian border) where the man was found.

paleontologists, and others from all over the world. These studies give us a marvelous view of how science is done. Among the many discoveries made about the Iceman were the following:

- Some investigators looked for food residues in the Iceman's intestines. In addition to finding a few particles of grain, they located tiny flakes of mica believed to come from stones used to grind the grain the man ate. They analyzed these flakes and found their composition was like that of mica in a small area south of the Alps, thus establishing where the man lived in his later years. And, by analyzing animal fibers in his stomach, they determined his last meal was the meat of an Alpine ibex.
- High levels of copper and arsenic were found in his hair. These observations, combined with the discovery that his ax was nearly pure copper, led the investigators to conclude he had been involved in copper smelting.
- One fingernail was still present on his body. Based on its condition, scientists could conclude that he had been sick three times in the 6 months before he died and his last illness had lasted for 2 weeks. Finally, recent images of his teeth showed severe periodontal disease and cavities.
- Australian scientists took samples of blood residues from his stone-tipped knife, his arrows, and his coat. Using techniques developed to study ancient DNA, they found the blood came from four different individuals. The blood on one arrow tip was from two different individuals, suggesting that the man had killed two different people. Perhaps he had killed one person, retrieved the arrow, and used it to kill another.

The many different methods used to reveal the life of the Iceman and his environment are used by scientists around the world, including present-day forensic scientists in their study of accidents and crimes. As you study chemistry and the chemical principles in this book, keep in mind that many areas of science depend on chemistry and that many different careers in the sciences are available.

1-1 Chemistry and Its Methods

Chemistry is about change. It was once only about changing one natural substance into another—wood and oil burn, grape juice turns into wine, and cinnabar (Figure 1.1), a red mineral, ultimately changes into shiny quicksilver (mercury) when heated. The emphasis was largely on finding a recipe to carry out the desired transformation with little understanding of the underlying structure of the materials or explanations for why particular changes occurred. Chemistry is still about change, but now chemists focus on the change of one pure substance, whether natural or synthetic, into another and on understanding that change (Figure 1.2). As you will see, in modern chemistry, we now picture an exciting world of submicroscopic atoms and molecules interacting with each other. We have also developed ways to predict whether or not a particular reaction may occur.

Although chemistry is endlessly fascinating—at least to chemists—why should you study chemistry? Each person probably has a different answer, but many students take a chemistry course because someone else has decided it is an important part of preparing for a particular career. Chemistry is especially useful because it is central to our understanding of disciplines as diverse as biology, geology, materials science, medicine, physics, and some branches of engineering. In addition, chemistry plays a major role in the economy of developed nations, and chemistry and chemicals affect our daily lives in a wide variety of ways. Furthermore, a course in chemistry can help you see how a scientist thinks about the world and how to solve problems. The knowledge and skills developed in such a course will benefit you in many career paths and will help you become a better informed citizen in a world that is becoming technologically more complex—and more interesting.

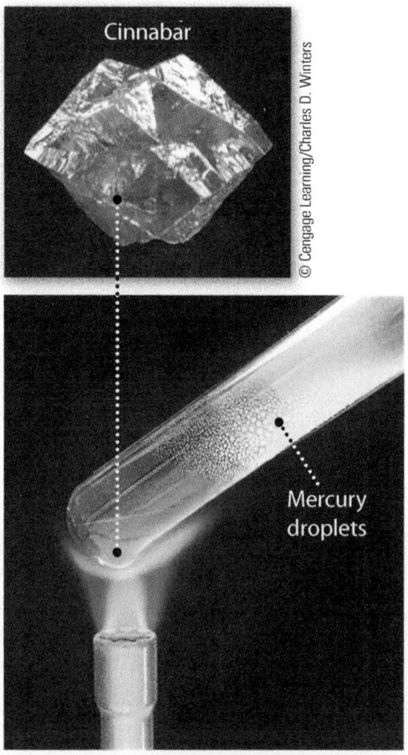

FIGURE 1.1 Cinnabar and mercury. Heating cinnabar (mercury(II) sulfide) in air changes it into orange mercury(II) oxide, which, on further heating, decomposes to the elements mercury and oxygen gas.

Hypotheses, Laws, and Theories

As scientists, we study questions of our own choosing or ones that someone else poses in the hope of finding an answer or discovering some useful information. When the Iceman was discovered, there were many questions that scientists could try to answer, such as where he was from. Considering what was known or assumed

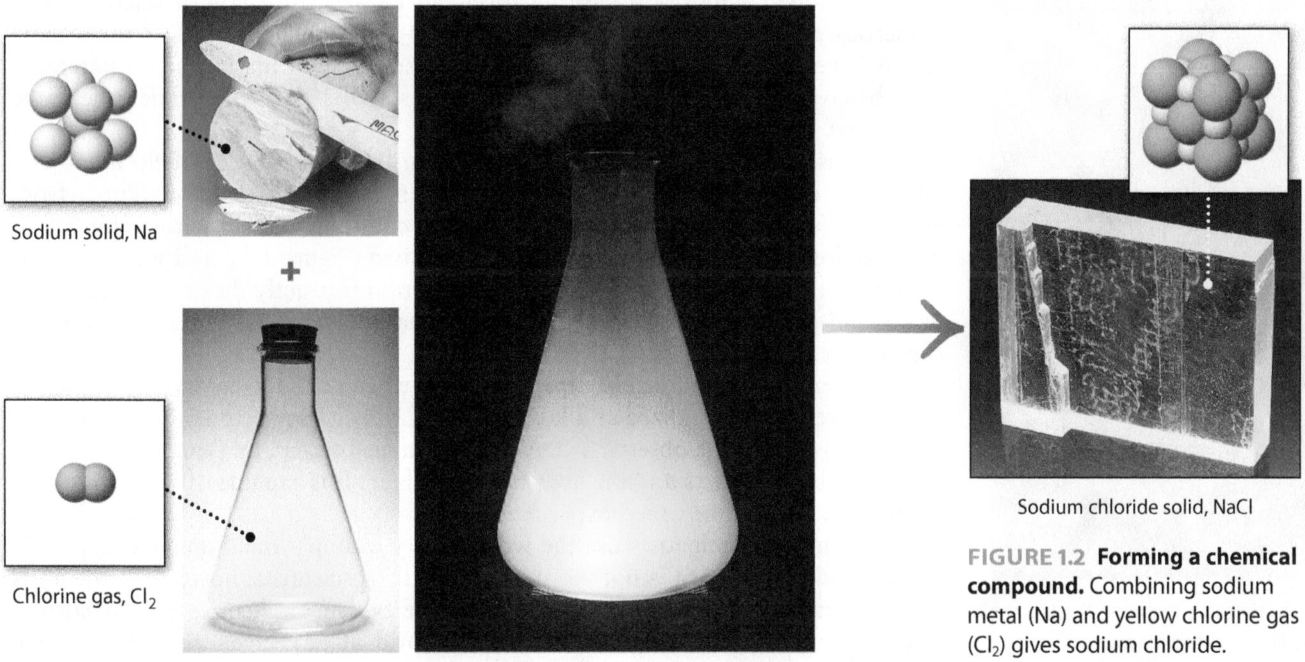

FIGURE 1.2 Forming a chemical compound. Combining sodium metal (Na) and yellow chlorine gas (Cl_2) gives sodium chloride.

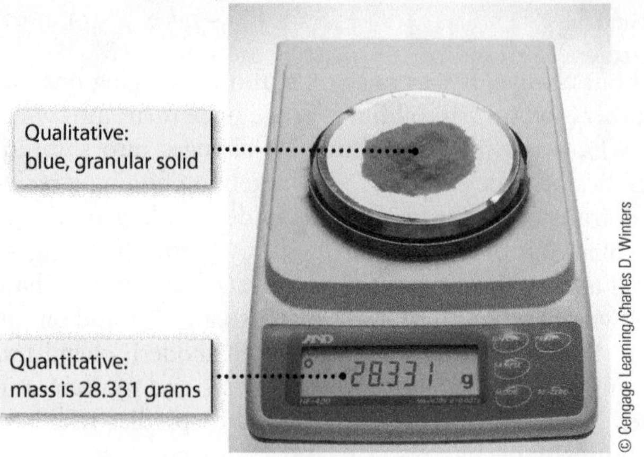

FIGURE 1.3 Qualitative and quantitative observations. Weighing a compound on a laboratory balance.

about humans living in that age, it seemed reasonable to assume that he was from an area on the border of what is now Austria and Italy. That is, regarding his origins, the scientists formed a **hypothesis**, a tentative explanation or prediction in accord with current knowledge.

After formulating one or more hypotheses, scientists perform experiments designed to give results that confirm or invalidate these hypotheses. In chemistry this usually requires that both quantitative and qualitative information be collected. **Quantitative** information is numerical data, such as the mass of a substance or temperature at which it melts (Figure 1.3). **Qualitative** information, in contrast, consists of nonnumerical observations, such as the color of a substance or its physical appearance.

In the case of the Iceman, scientists assembled a great deal of qualitative and quantitative information on his body, his clothing, and his weapons. Among this was information on the ratio of oxygen isotopes in his tooth enamel and bones. Scientists know that the ratio of oxygen isotopes in water and plants differs from place to place. This ratio of isotopes showed that the Iceman must have consumed water from a relatively small location within what is now Italy.

This analysis using oxygen isotopes could be done because it is well known that oxygen isotopes in water vary with altitude in predictable ways. That is, the variation in isotope composition with location can be deemed a law of science. After numerous experiments by many scientists over an extended period of time, these results have been summarized as a **law**—a concise verbal or mathematical statement of a behavior or a relation that seems always to be the same under the same conditions.

We base much of what we do in science on laws because they help us predict what may occur under a new set of circumstances. For example, we know from experience that if the chemical element sodium comes in contact with water, a violent reaction occurs and new substances are formed (Figure 1.4), and we know that the mass of the substances produced in the reaction is exactly the same as the mass of sodium and water used in the reaction. That is, *mass is always conserved in chemical reactions.*

FIGURE 1.4 The metallic element sodium reacts with water.

Once enough reproducible experiments have been conducted and experimental results have been generalized as a law or general rule, it may be possible to conceive a theory to explain the observation. A **theory** is a well-tested, unifying principle that explains a body of facts and the laws based on them. It is capable of suggesting new hypotheses that can be tested experimentally.

Sometimes nonscientists use the word *theory* to imply that someone has made a guess and that an idea is not yet substantiated. To scientists, however, a theory is based on carefully determined and reproducible evidence. Theories are the cornerstone of our understanding of the natural world at any given time. Remember, though, that theories are inventions of the human mind. Theories can and do change as new facts are uncovered.

Goals of Science

Scientists, including chemists, have several goals. Two of these are *prediction* and *control*. We do experiments and seek generalities because we want to be able to predict what may occur under other sets of circumstances. We also want to know how we might control the outcome of a chemical reaction or process.

Two further goals are *understanding* and *explaining*. We know, for example, that certain elements such as sodium react vigorously with water. But why should this be true? To explain and understand this, we need a background in chemical concepts that is developed throughout this book.

Dilemmas and Integrity in Science

You may think research in science is straightforward: Do experiments, collect information, and draw a conclusion. But, research is seldom that easy. Frustrations and disappointments are common enough, and results can be inconclusive. Experiments often contain some level of uncertainty, and spurious or contradictory data can be collected. For example, suppose you do an experiment expecting to find a direct relation between two experimental quantities. You collect six data sets. When plotted on a graph, four of the sets lie on a straight line, but two others lie far away from the line. Should you ignore the last two sets of data? Or should you do more experiments when you know the time they take will mean someone else could publish their results first and thus get the credit for a new scientific principle? Or should you consider that the two points not on the line might indicate that your original hypothesis is wrong and that you will have to abandon a favorite idea you have worked on for many months? Scientists have a responsibility to remain objective in these situations, but sometimes it is hard to do.

It is important to remember that a scientist is subject to the same moral pressures and dilemmas as any other person. To help ensure integrity in science, some simple principles have emerged over time that guide scientific practice:

- Experimental results should be reproducible. Furthermore, these results should be reported in the scientific literature in sufficient detail so that they can be used or reproduced by others.
- Research reports should be reviewed before publication by experts in the field to make sure that the experiments have been conducted properly and that the conclusions drawn are logical.
- Conclusions should be reasonable and unbiased.
- Credit should be given where it is due.

1-2 Sustainability and Green Chemistry

The world's population is about 7.2 billion people, with about 7 million added every month. Each of these new persons needs shelter, food, and medical care, and each uses increasingly scarce resources like fresh water and energy. And each produces by-products in the act of living and working that can affect our environment. With such a large population, these individual effects can have large consequences for our planet. The focus of scientists, planners, and politicians is increasingly turning to a concept of "sustainable development."

James Cusumano, a chemist and former president of a chemical company, said that "On one hand, society, governments, and industry seek economic growth to create greater value, new jobs, and a more enjoyable and fulfilling lifestyle. Yet, on the other, regulators, environmentalists, and citizens of the globe demand that we do

A CLOSER LOOK
Principles of Green Chemistry

Paul Anastas and John Warner enunciated the principles of green chemistry in their book *Green Chemistry: Theory and Practice* (Oxford, 1998). Among these are the ones stated below. As you read *Chemistry & Chemical Reactivity,* we will remind you of these principles, and others, and how they can be applied.

- "It is better to prevent waste than to treat or clean up waste after it is formed."
- New pharmaceuticals or consumer chemicals are synthesized, that is, made by a large number of chemical processes. Therefore, "synthetic methods should be designed to maximize the incorporation of all materials used in the final product."

©Charles Winters

- Synthetic methods "should be designed to use and generate substances that possess little or no toxicity to human health or the environment."
- "Chemical products should be designed to [function effectively] while still reducing toxicity."
- "Energy requirements should be recognized for their environmental and economic impacts and should be minimized. Synthetic methods should be conducted at ambient temperature and pressure."
- Raw materials "should be renewable whenever technically and economically practical."
- "Chemical products should be designed so that at the end of their function, they do not persist in the environment or break down into dangerous products."
- "Substances used in a chemical process should be chosen to minimize the potential for chemical accidents, including releases, explosions, and fires."

so with *sustainable development*—meeting today's global economic and environmental needs while preserving the options of future generations to meet theirs. How do nations resolve these potentially conflicting goals?" This is even more true now than it was in 1995 when Dr. Cusumano made this statement in the *Journal of Chemical Education.*

Much of the increase in life expectancy and quality of life, at least in the developed world, is derived from advances in science. But we have paid an environmental price for it, with increases in gases such as nitrogen oxides and sulfur oxides in the atmosphere, acid rain falling in many parts of the world, and waste pharmaceuticals entering the water supply. Among many others, chemists are seeking answers to these problems, and one response has been to practice *green chemistry.*

The concept of green chemistry began to take root more than 20 years ago and is now leading to new ways of doing things and to lower pollutant levels. By the time you finish this book, you will have been introduced to most of the underlying principles of green chemistry. As you can see in "A Closer Look: Principles of Green Chemistry," they are simple ideas. The challenge is to put them into practice.

Learning Objectives: LO 2.8

1-3 Classifying Matter

This chapter begins our discussion of how chemists think about science in general and about matter in particular. After looking at a way to classify matter, we will turn to some basic ideas about elements, atoms, compounds, and molecules and describe how chemists characterize these building blocks of matter.

States of Matter and Kinetic-Molecular Theory

An easily observed property of matter is its **state**—that is, whether a substance is a solid, liquid, or gas (Figure 1.5). You recognize a material as a solid because it has a rigid shape and a fixed volume that changes little as temperature and pressure change. Like solids, liquids have a fixed volume, but a liquid is fluid—it takes on the shape of its container and has no definite shape of its own. Gases are fluid as well, but the volume of a gas is determined by the size of its container. The volume of a gas varies more than the volume of a liquid with changes in temperature and pressure.

At low enough temperatures, virtually all matter is found in the solid state. As the temperature is raised, solids usually melt to form liquids. Eventually, if the temperature is high enough, liquids evaporate to form gases. Volume changes typically accompany changes in state. For a given mass of material, there is usually a small increase in volume on melting—water being a significant exception—and then a large increase in volume occurs upon evaporation.

The **kinetic-molecular theory of matter** helps us interpret the properties of solids, liquids, and gases. According to this theory, all matter consists of extremely tiny particles (atoms, molecules, or ions) that are in constant motion.

- In solids these particles are packed closely together, usually in a regular array. The particles vibrate back and forth about their average positions, but seldom do particles in a solid squeeze past their immediate neighbors to come into contact with a new set of particles.
- The particles in liquids are arranged randomly rather than in the regular patterns found in solids. Liquids and gases are fluid because the particles are not confined to specific locations and can move past one another.
- Under normal conditions, the particles in a gas are far apart. Gas molecules move extremely rapidly and are not constrained by their neighbors. The molecules of a gas fly about, colliding with one another and with the container walls. This random motion allows gas molecules to fill their container, so the volume of the gas sample is the volume of the container.
- There are net forces of attraction between particles in all states—generally small in gases and large in liquids and solids. These forces have a significant role in determining the properties of matter.

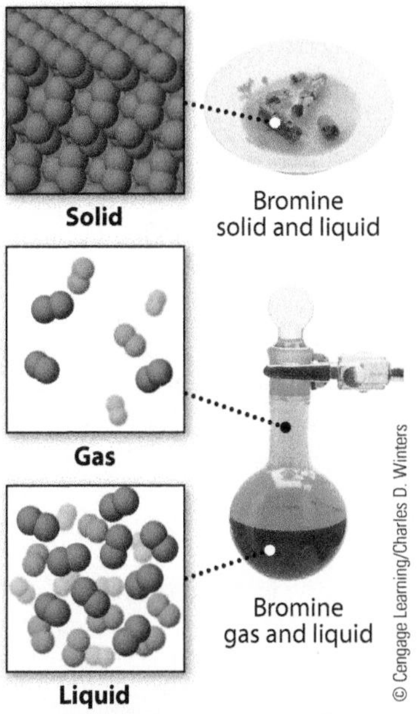

FIGURE 1.5 **States of matter—solid, liquid, and gas.** Elemental bromine exists in all three states near room temperature.

An important aspect of the kinetic-molecular theory is that the higher the temperature, the faster the particles move. The energy of motion of the particles (their **kinetic energy**, Section 1-8) acts to overcome the forces of attraction between particles. A solid melts to form a liquid when the temperature of the solid is raised to the point at which the particles vibrate fast enough and far enough to push one another out of the way and move out of their regularly spaced positions. As the temperature increases even more, the particles move even faster until finally they can escape the clutches of their comrades and enter the gaseous state. *Increasing temperature corresponds to faster and faster motions of atoms and molecules,* a general rule you will find useful in many future discussions.

Matter at the Macroscopic and Particulate Levels

The characteristic properties of gases, liquids, and solids are observed by the unaided human senses. They are determined using samples of matter large enough to be seen, measured, and handled. You can determine, for example, the color of a substance, whether it dissolves in water, whether it conducts electricity, and if it reacts with oxygen. Observations such as these generally take place in the **macroscopic** world of chemistry (Figure 1.6). This is the world of experiments and observations.

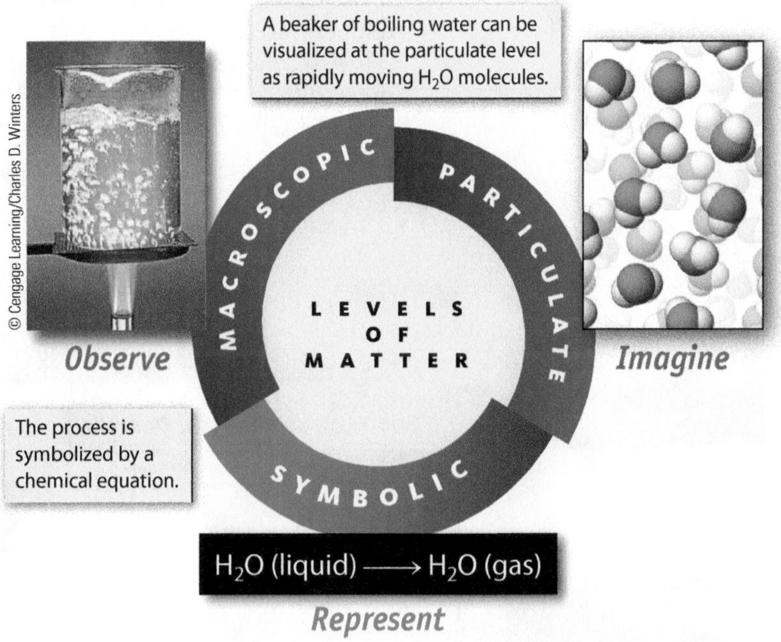

FIGURE 1.6 **Levels of matter.** We observe chemical and physical processes at the macroscopic level. To understand or illustrate these processes, scientists often imagine what has occurred at the particulate atomic and molecular levels and write symbols to represent these observations.

Now let us move to the level of atoms, molecules, and ions—a world of chemistry we cannot see. Take a macroscopic sample of material and divide it, again and again, past the point where the amount of sample can be seen by the naked eye, past the point where it can be seen using an optical microscope. Eventually you reach the level of individual particles that make up all matter, a level that chemists refer to as the **submicroscopic** or **particulate** world of atoms and molecules (see Figures 1.5 and 1.6).

Chemists are interested in the structure of matter at the particulate level. Atoms, molecules, and ions cannot be "seen" in the same way that one views the macroscopic world, but they are no less real. Chemists imagine what atoms must look like and how they might fit together to form molecules. They create models to represent atoms and molecules (see Figures 1.5 and 1.6)—where tiny spheres are used to represent atoms—and then use these models to think about chemistry and to explain the observations they have made about the macroscopic world.

It has been said that chemists carry out experiments at the macroscopic level, but they think about chemistry at the particulate level. They then write down their observations as "symbols," the formulas (such as H_2O for water or NH_3 for ammonia molecules) and drawings that signify the elements and compounds involved. This is a useful perspective that will help you as you study chemistry. Indeed, one of our goals is to help you make the connections in your own mind among the symbolic, particulate, and macroscopic worlds of chemistry.

Pure Substances

A chemist looks at a glass of drinking water and sees a liquid. This liquid could be the pure chemical compound water. However, it is also possible the liquid is actually a homogeneous mixture of water and dissolved substances—that is, a **solution.** Specifically, we can classify a sample of matter as being either a pure substance or a mixture (Figure 1.7).

A pure substance has a set of unique properties by which it can be recognized. Pure water, for example, is colorless and odorless. If you want to identify a substance conclusively as water, you would have to examine its properties carefully and compare them against the known properties of pure water. Melting point and boiling point serve the purpose well here. If you could show that the substance melts at 0 °C and boils at 100 °C at atmospheric pressure, you can be certain it is water. No other known substance melts and boils at precisely those temperatures.

A second feature of a pure substance is that it cannot be separated into two or more different species by any physical technique at ordinary temperatures. If it could be separated, our sample would be classified as a mixture.

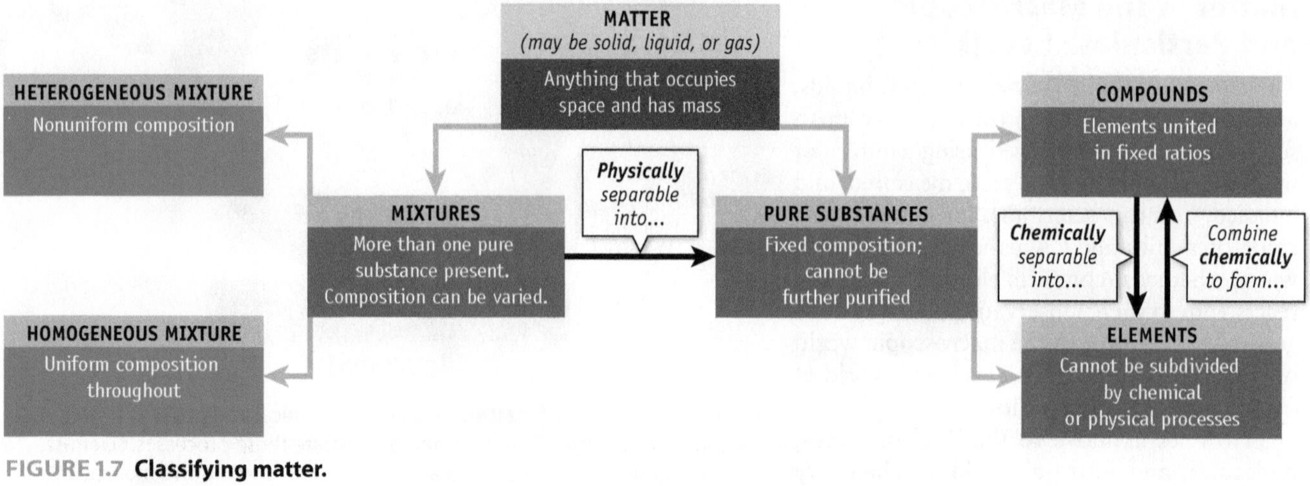

FIGURE 1.7 Classifying matter.

FIGURE 1.8 **Heterogeneous and homogeneous mixtures.**

Mixtures: Heterogeneous and Homogeneous

A mixture consists of two or more pure substances that can be separated by physical techniques. In a **heterogeneous** mixture the uneven texture of the material can often be detected by the naked eye (Figure 1.8). However, keep in mind there are heterogeneous mixtures that may appear completely uniform but on closer examination are not. Milk, for example, appears smooth in texture to the unaided eye, but magnification would reveal fat and protein globules within the liquid. In a heterogeneous mixture the properties in one region are different from those in another region.

A **homogeneous** mixture consists of two or more substances in the same phase (see Figure 1.8). No amount of optical magnification will reveal a homogeneous mixture to have different properties in different regions. Homogeneous mixtures are often called **solutions.** Common examples include air (mostly a mixture of nitrogen and oxygen gases), gasoline (a mixture of carbon- and hydrogen-containing compounds called *hydrocarbons*), and a soft drink in an unopened container.

When a mixture is separated into its pure components, the components are said to be **purified.** Efforts at separation are often not complete in a single step, however, and repetition almost always gives an increasingly pure substance. For example, soil particles can be separated from water by filtration (Figure 1.9). When the mixture

FIGURE 1.9 **Purifying a heterogeneous mixture by filtration.**

is passed through a filter, many of the particles are removed. Repeated filtrations will give water with a higher and higher state of purity. This purification process uses a property of the mixture, its clarity, to measure the extent of purification. When a perfectly clear sample of water is obtained, all of the soil particles are assumed to have been removed.

Review & Check At the end of almost all sections of each chapter there will be a set of multiple-choice questions to check your understanding. Answers to these questions are in Appendix N.

REVIEW & CHECK FOR SECTION 1-3

1. Which of the following is a pure substance?

   (a) dry ice (solid CO_2) (b) 9 K gold (c) dry air (d) blood

2. Which of the following is not characteristic of a pure substance?

   (a) Has a uniform composition throughout

   (b) Has a fixed melting temperature

   (c) Can be separated into two other pure substances

1-4 Elements

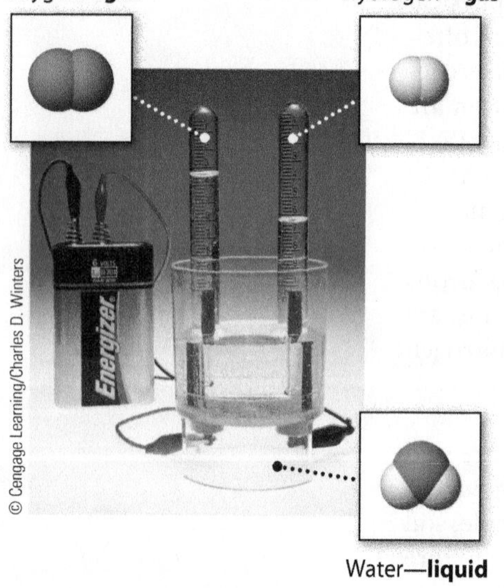

Passing an electric current through water can decompose it to gaseous hydrogen and oxygen. Substances like hydrogen and oxygen that are composed of *only one type of atom* are classified as **elements**. Currently 118 elements are known. Of these, only about 90—a few of which are illustrated in Figure 1.10—are found in nature. The remainder have been created by scientists. *Names and symbols for each element are listed in the tables at the front and back of this book.* Carbon (C), sulfur (S), iron (Fe), copper (Cu), silver (Ag), tin (Sn), gold (Au), mercury (Hg), and lead (Pb) were known to the early Greeks and Romans and to the alchemists of ancient China, the Arab world, and medieval Europe. However, many other elements—such as aluminum (Al), silicon (Si), iodine (I), and helium (He)—were not discovered until the 18th and 19th centuries. Finally, scientists in the 20th and 21st centuries have made elements that do not exist in nature, such as technetium (Tc), plutonium (Pu), and americium (Am).

The table inside the front cover of this book, in which the symbol and other information for the elements are enclosed in a box, is called the **periodic table**. We will describe this important tool of chemistry in more detail beginning in Chapter 2.

FIGURE 1.10 **Elements.** Chemical elements can often be distinguished by their color and their state at room temperature.

An **atom** is the smallest particle of an element that retains the characteristic chemical properties of that element. Modern chemistry is based on an understanding and exploration of nature at the atomic level, as you will see throughout the book.

REVIEW & CHECK FOR SECTION 1-4

Use the periodic table inside the front cover of this book to answer the following questions:

1. What is the symbol for the element sodium?

   (a) S (b) Na (c) So (d) Sm

2. What is the name of the element with the symbol Si?

   (a) silver (b) sulfur (c) selenium (d) silicon

1-5 Compounds

A pure substance like sugar, salt, or water, which is composed of two or more different elements held together by **chemical bonds**, is referred to as a **chemical compound**. Even though only 118 elements are known, there appears to be no limit to the number of compounds that can be made from those elements. In early 2012, 65 million different compounds were identified in *Chemical Abstracts*, a database created by the American Chemical Society.

When elements become part of a compound, their original properties, such as their color, hardness, and melting point, are replaced by the characteristic properties of the compound. Consider common table salt (sodium chloride), which is composed of two elements (see Figure 1.2):

- Sodium is a shiny metal that reacts violently with water. Its solid-state structure has sodium atoms tightly packed together.
- Chlorine is a light yellow gas that has a distinctive, suffocating odor and is a powerful irritant to lungs and other tissues. The element is composed of Cl_2 molecules in which two chlorine atoms are tightly bound together.
- Sodium chloride, or common salt (NaCl), is a colorless, crystalline solid composed of sodium and chlorine ions bound tightly together. Its properties are completely unlike those of the two elements from which it is made.

It is important to distinguish between a mixture of elements and a chemical compound of two or more elements. Pure metallic iron and yellow, powdered sulfur can be mixed in varying proportions. In the chemical compound iron pyrite, however, there is no variation in composition. Not only does iron pyrite exhibit properties peculiar to itself and different from those of either iron or sulfur, or a mixture of these two elements, but it also has a

© Cengage Learning/Charles D. Winters

The material in the dish is a **mixture** of iron chips and sulfur. The iron can be separated easily from the sulfur by using a magnet.

© Cengage Learning/Charles D. Winters

Iron pyrite is a **chemical compound** composed of iron and sulfur. It is often found in nature as perfect, golden cubes.

A CLOSER LOOK — Element Names and Symbols

The stories behind some of the names of the elements are fascinating. Many elements have names and symbols with Latin or Greek origins. Examples include helium (He), from the Greek word *helios* meaning "sun," and lead, whose symbol, Pb, comes from the Latin word for "heavy," *plumbum*. More recently discovered elements have been named for their place of discovery or place of significance. Americium (Am), californium (Cf), scandium (Sc), europium (Eu), francium (Fr), and polonium (Po) are examples.

A number of elements are named for their discoverers or famous scientists: curium (Cm), einsteinium (Es), fermium (Fm), mendeleevium (Md), nobelium (No), seaborgium (Sg), and meitnerium (Mt), among others. A recently named element, element 112, was given its official name, copernicium (Cn), in 2010. It was named after Nicolaus Copernicus (1473–1543), who first proposed that Earth and the other planets orbited the Sun. Some say his work was the beginning of the scientific revolution.

Nicolaus Copernicus (1473–1543). Element 112 was recently named for Copernicus.

What do you suppose is the origin of the names of the elements uranium, neptunium, and plutonium?

When writing the symbol for an element notice that the first letter (but not the second) of an element's symbol is capitalized. For example, cobalt is Co, not co or CO. The notation co has no chemical meaning, whereas CO represents the chemical compound carbon monoxide. Also note that the element name is not normally capitalized, except at the beginning of a sentence.

To learn more about element names, properties, and uses, there are a number of excellent references on the Internet.

- www.ptable.com
- www.chemeddl.org
- www.periodictable.com
- www.periodicvideos.com

definite percentage composition by mass (46.55% Fe and 53.45% S). Thus, two major differences exist between a mixture and a pure compound: A compound has distinctly different characteristics from its parent elements, and it has a definite percentage composition (by mass) of its combining elements.

The Law of Definite Proportions The statement that a chemical compound always has a definite percentage by mass is a basic principle of chemistry, often referred to as the "law of definite proportions" or the "law of constant composition."

Some compounds—such as table salt, NaCl—are composed of **ions**, which are electrically charged atoms or groups of atoms (▶ Chapter 2). Other compounds—such as water and sugar—consist of **molecules**, the smallest discrete units that retain the composition and chemical characteristics of the compound.

The composition of any compound is represented by its **chemical formula**. In the formula for water, H_2O, for example, the symbol for hydrogen, H, is followed by a subscript 2, indicating that two atoms of hydrogen occur in a single water molecule. The symbol for oxygen appears without a subscript, indicating that one oxygen atom occurs in the molecule.

As you shall see throughout this text, molecules can be represented with models that depict their composition and structure. Figure 1.11 illustrates the names, formulas, and models of the structures of a few common molecular compounds.

Name	Water	Methane	Ammonia	Carbon dioxide
Formula	H_2O	CH_4	NH_3	CO_2
Model	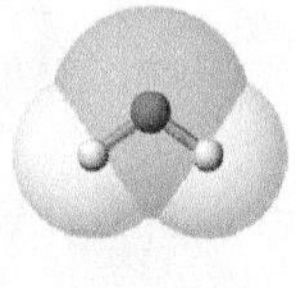	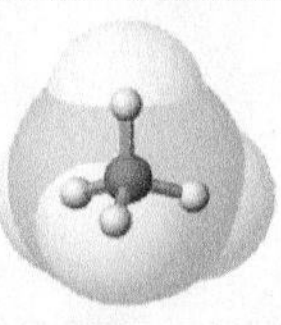	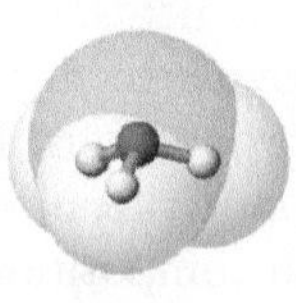	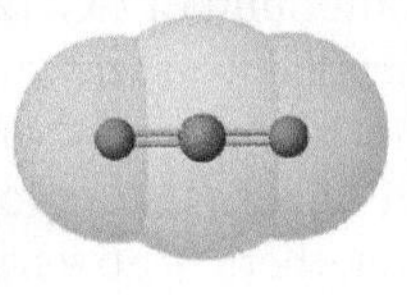

FIGURE 1.11 **Names, formulas, and models of some common molecular compounds.** A common color scheme is that C atoms are gray, H atoms are white, N atoms are blue, and O atoms are red.

REVIEW & CHECK FOR SECTION 1-5

1. Which of the following is NOT an element?

   (a) hydrogen (b) lithium (c) iron (d) water (e) silver

2. Which of the following is NOT a compound?

   (a) salt (b) water (c) potassium (d) sugar (e) alcohol

1-6 Physical Properties

Learning Objectives: LO 3.10 (see APEC Lab 9 "Actions, Reactions, and Interactions")

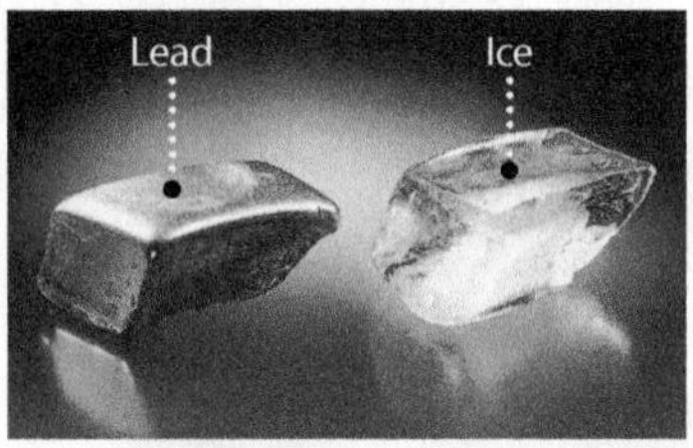

© Cengage Learning/ Charles D. Winters

You recognize your friends by their physical appearance: their height and weight and the color of their eyes and hair. The same is true of chemical substances. You can tell the difference between an ice cube and a cube of lead of the same size not only because of their appearance (one is clear and colorless, and the other is a lustrous metal), but also because one is more dense (lead) than the other (ice). Properties such as these, which can be observed and measured without changing the composition of a substance, are called **physical properties.** The chemical elements in Figure 1.10, for example, clearly differ in terms of their color, appearance, and state (solid, liquid, or gas). Physical properties allow us to classify and identify substances. Table 1.1 lists a few physical properties of matter that chemists commonly use.

Density, the ratio of the mass of an object to its volume, is a physical property useful for identifying substances.

$$\text{Density} = \frac{\text{mass}}{\text{volume}} \tag{1.1}$$

For example, you can readily tell the difference between an ice cube and a cube of lead of identical size because lead has a high density, 11.35 g/cm^3 (11.35 grams per

Units of Density As described in the later part of this chapter titled "The Tools of Quantitative Chemistry," the decimal system of units in the sciences is called the Systemé International d'Unites, often referred to as SI units. The SI unit of mass is the kilogram and the SI unit of length is the meter. Therefore, the SI unit of density is kg/m^3. In chemistry, the more commonly used unit is g/cm^3. To convert from kg/m^3 to g/cm^3, divide by 1000.

Table 1.1 Some Physical Properties

PROPERTY	USING THE PROPERTY TO DISTINGUISH SUBSTANCES
Color	Is the substance colored or colorless? What is the color, and what is its intensity?
State of matter	Is it a solid, liquid, or gas? If it is a solid, what is the shape of the particles?
Melting point	At what temperature does a solid melt?
Boiling point	At what temperature does a liquid boil (at 1 atmosphere pressure)?
Density	What is the substance's density (mass per unit volume)?
Solubility	What mass of substance can dissolve in a given volume of water or other solvent?
Electric conductivity	Does the substance conduct electricity?
Malleability	How easily can a solid be deformed?
Ductility	How easily can a solid be drawn into a wire?
Viscosity	How easily will a liquid flow?

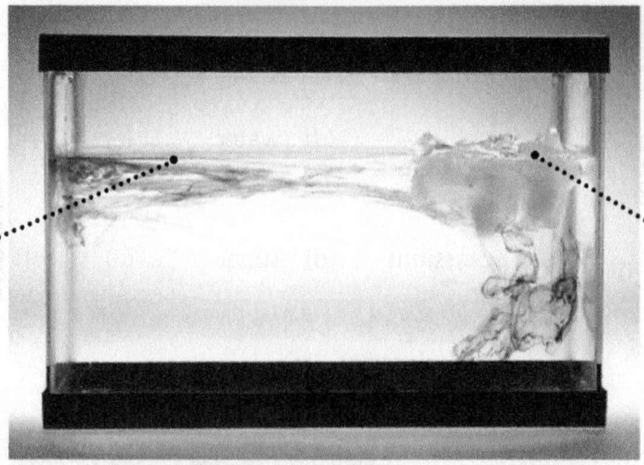

FIGURE 1.12 **Temperature dependence of physical properties.** Water and other substances change in density with temperature.

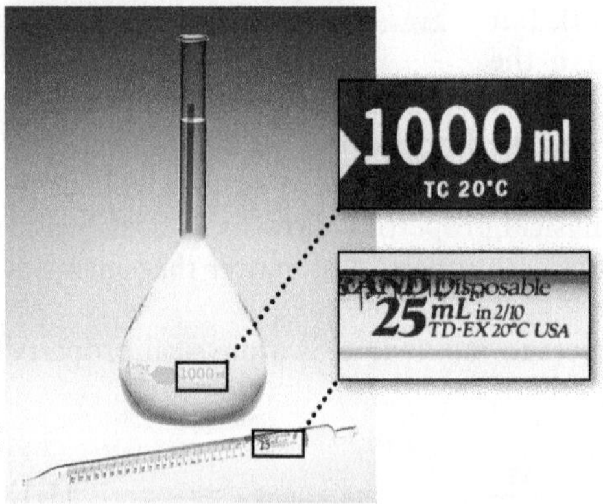

FIGURE 1.13 **Temperature dependence of density.** Water and other substances change in density with temperature so laboratory apparatus is calibrated for a particular temperature.

cubic centimeter), whereas ice has a density slightly less than 0.917 g/cm^3. An ice cube with a volume of 16.0 cm^3 has a mass of 14.7 g, whereas a cube of lead with the same volume has a mass of 182 g.

The **temperature** of a sample of matter often affects the numerical values of its properties. Density is a particularly important example. Although the change in water density with temperature seems small (Table 1.2), it affects our environment profoundly. For example, as the water in a lake cools, the density of the water increases and the denser water sinks as you see in Figure 1.12. This continues until the water temperature reaches 3.98 °C, the point at which water has its maximum density (0.999973 g/cm^3). If the water temperature drops further, the density decreases slightly and the colder water floats on top of water at 3.98 °C. If water is cooled below about 0 °C, solid ice forms. Water is unique among most substances in the universe: Its solid form is less dense than its liquid form, so ice floats on water.

Temperature Scales Scientists use the Celsius (°C) and Kelvin scales (K) for temperature. (▶ The Tools of Quantitative Chemistry; see page 24)

The volume of a given mass of liquid changes with temperature, so its density does as well. This is the reason laboratory glassware used to measure precise volumes of solutions always specifies the temperature at which it was calibrated (Figure 1.13).

Table 1.2 Temperature Dependence of Water Density

TEMPERATURE (°C)	DENSITY OF WATER (g/cm^3)
0 (ice)	0.917
0 (liq water)	0.99984
2	0.99994
4	0.99997
10	0.99970
25	0.99707
100	0.95836

Extensive and Intensive Properties

Extensive properties depend on the amount of a substance present. The mass and volume of the samples of elements in Figure 1.10, or the amount of energy transferred as heat from burning gasoline, are extensive properties, for example.

In contrast, **intensive properties** do *not* depend on the amount of substance. A sample of ice will melt at 0 °C, no matter whether you have an ice cube or an iceberg.

Although mass and volume are extensive properties, it is interesting that density (the quotient of these two quantities) is an intensive property. The density of gold, for example, is the same (19.3 g/cm^3 at 20 °C) whether you have a flake of pure gold or a solid gold ring.

Intensive properties are often useful in identifying a material. For example, the temperature at which a material melts (its melting point) is often so characteristic that it can be used to identify the solid (Figure 1.14).

REVIEW & CHECK FOR SECTION 1-6

1. Which of the following is NOT a physical property?
   (a) Liquid nitrogen boils at −196 °C.
   (b) Sugar dissolves in water.
   (c) Gasoline burns in air.
   (d) Gold melts at 1064 °C.
   (e) A copper compound is blue.

2. A piece of a polypropylene rope (used for water skiing) floats on water, whereas a terephthalate polymer from a soda bottle sinks in water. What is the order of increasing density of these substances?
   (a) water < polypropylene < soda bottle plastic
   (b) polypropylene < water < soda bottle plastic
   (c) polypropylene < soda bottle plastic < water
   (d) soda bottle plastic < polypropylene < water
   (e) soda bottle plastic < water < polypropylene

3. Which of the following is an extensive property of mercury (see Figure 1.10)?
   (a) shiny surface
   (b) melts at 234.22 K
   (c) density = 13.6 g/cm^3
   (d) volume = 13.6 cm^3

1-7 Physical and Chemical Changes

Learning Objectives: LO 3.10 (see APEC Lab 9 "Actions, Reactions, and Interactions"), LO 5.10

Changes in physical properties are called **physical changes**. In a physical change the identity of a substance is preserved even though it may have changed its physical state or the gross size and shape of its pieces. A physical change does not result in a new chemical substance being produced. The particles (atoms, molecules, or ions) present before and after the change are the same. An example of a physical change is the melting of a solid (see Figures 1.14) or the evaporation of a liquid (Figure 1.15). In either case, the same molecules are present both before and after the change. Their chemical identities have not changed.

A physical property of hydrogen gas (H_2) is its low density, so a balloon filled with H_2 floats in air. Suppose, however, that a lighted candle is brought up to the balloon. When the heat causes the skin of the balloon to rupture, the hydrogen mixes with the oxygen (O_2) in the air, and the heat of the candle sets off a chemical reaction, producing water, H_2O (see Figure 1.15). This reaction is an example of a **chemical change**, in which one or more substances (the **reactants**) are transformed into one or more different substances (the **products**).

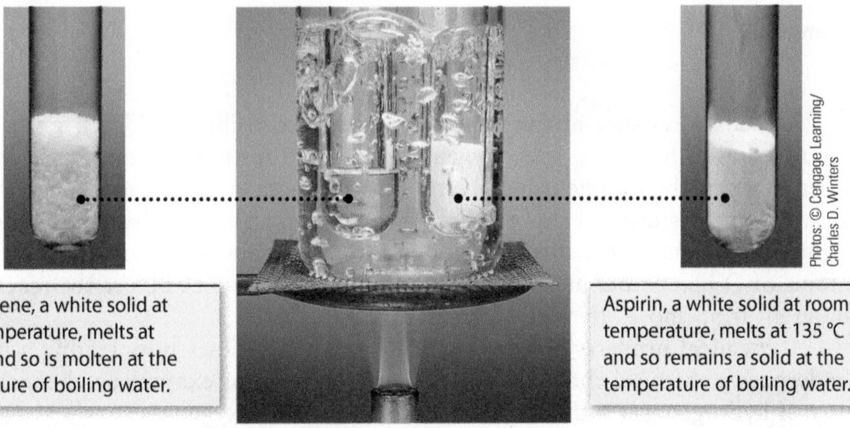

Naphthalene, a white solid at room temperature, melts at 80.2 °C and so is molten at the temperature of boiling water.

Aspirin, a white solid at room temperature, melts at 135 °C and so remains a solid at the temperature of boiling water.

FIGURE 1.14 A physical property used to distinguish compounds.

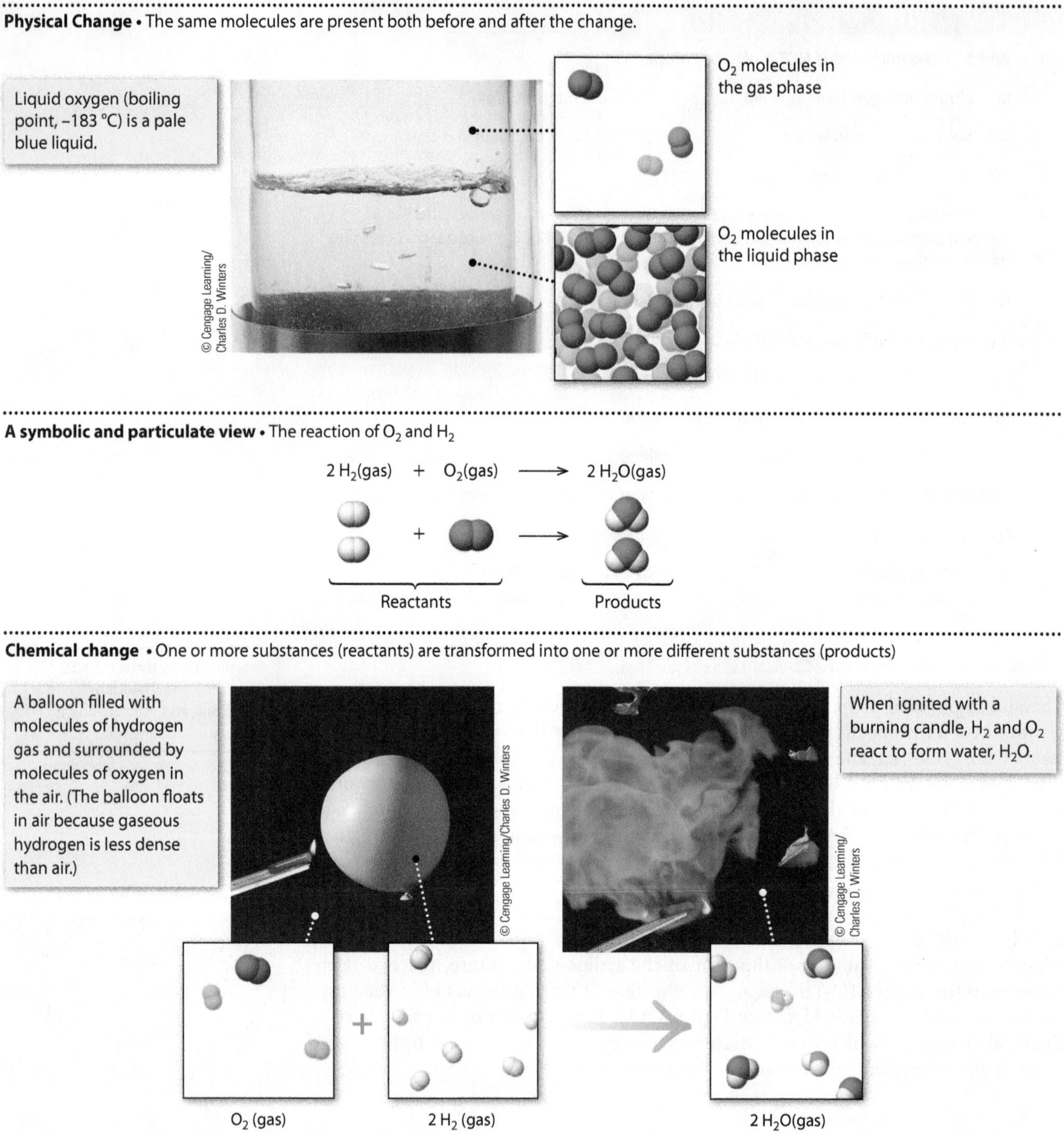

FIGURE 1.15 **Physical and chemical change.**

A chemical change at the particulate level is also illustrated in Figure 1.15 by the reaction of hydrogen and oxygen molecules to form water molecules. The representation of the change using chemical formulas is called a **chemical equation.** It shows that the substances on the left (the reactants) produce the substances on the right (the products). As this equation shows, there are four atoms of H and two atoms of O before *and* after the reaction, but the molecules before the reaction are different from those after the reaction.

A **chemical property** indicates whether and sometimes how readily a material undergoes a chemical change with another material. For example, a chemical property of hydrogen gas is that it reacts vigorously with oxygen gas.

REVIEW & CHECK FOR SECTION 1-7

1. When camping in the mountains, you boil a pot of water on a campfire to make tea. Which of the following is a chemical change?

   (a) The water boils.
   (b) The campfire wood burns.
   (c) The tea dissolves in the hot water.
   (d) The pot melts from the heat of the fire.

1-8 Energy: Some Basic Principles

Energy, a crucial part of many chemical and physical changes, is defined as the capacity to do work. You do work against the force of gravity when carrying yourself and hiking equipment up a mountain. The energy to do this is provided by the food you have eaten. Food is a source of chemical energy—energy stored in chemical compounds and released when the compounds undergo the chemical reactions of metabolism in your body. Chemical reactions almost always either release or absorb energy.

Units of Energy Energy in chemistry is measured in units of joules. See *The Tools of Quantitative Chemistry* and Chapter 5 for calculations involving energy units.

Energy can be classified as kinetic or potential. **Kinetic energy** is energy associated with motion, such as:

- The motion of atoms, molecules, or ions at the submicroscopic (particulate) level (*thermal energy*). All matter has thermal energy.
- The motion of macroscopic objects such as a moving tennis ball or automobile (*mechanical energy*).
- The movement of electrons in a conductor (*electrical energy*).
- The compression and expansion of the spaces between molecules in the transmission of sound (*acoustic energy*).

Potential energy results from an object's position or state and includes:

- Energy possessed by a ball held above the floor and by water at the top of a water wheel (*gravitational energy*) (Figure 1.16a).
- Energy stored in an extended spring.
- Energy stored in fuels (*chemical energy*) (Figure 1.16b).

(a) Potential energy is converted to mechanical energy.

(b) Chemical potential energy of a fuel and oxygen is converted to thermal and mechanical energy in a jet engine.

(c) Electrostatic energy is converted into radiant and thermal energy.

FIGURE 1.16 **Energy and its conversion.**

- Energy associated with the separation of electrical charges (*electrostatic energy*) (Figure 1.16c).

Potential energy and kinetic energy can be interconverted. For example, as water falls over a waterfall, its potential energy is converted into kinetic energy. Similarly, kinetic energy can be converted into potential energy: The kinetic energy of falling water can turn a turbine to produce electricity, which can then be used to convert water into H_2 and O_2 by electrolysis. Hydrogen gas contains stored chemical potential energy because it can be burned to produce heat and light or electricity.

Conservation of Energy

Standing on a diving board, you have considerable potential energy because of your position above the water. Once you dive off the board, some of that potential energy is converted into kinetic energy (Figure 1.17). During the dive, the force of gravity accelerates your body so that it moves faster and faster. Your kinetic energy increases and your potential energy decreases. At the moment you hit the water, your velocity is abruptly reduced and much of your kinetic energy is transferred to the water as your body moves it aside. Eventually you float to the surface, and the water becomes still again. If you could see them, however, you would find that the water molecules are moving a little faster in the vicinity of your entry into the water; that is, the kinetic energy of the water molecules is slightly higher.

This series of energy conversions illustrates the **law of conservation of energy,** which states that *energy can neither be created nor destroyed.* Or, to state this law differently, *the total energy of the universe is constant.* The law of conservation of energy summarizes the results of many experiments in which the amounts of energy transferred have been measured and in which the total energy content has been found to be the same before and after an event.

Let us examine this law in the case of a chemical reaction, the reaction of hydrogen and oxygen to form water (see Figure 1.15). In this reaction, the reactants (hydrogen and oxygen) have a certain amount of energy associated with them. When they react, some of this energy is released to their surroundings. If we were to add up all of the energy present before the reaction and all of the energy present after the reaction, we would find that the energy has only been redistributed; the total amount of energy in the universe has remained constant. Energy has been conserved.

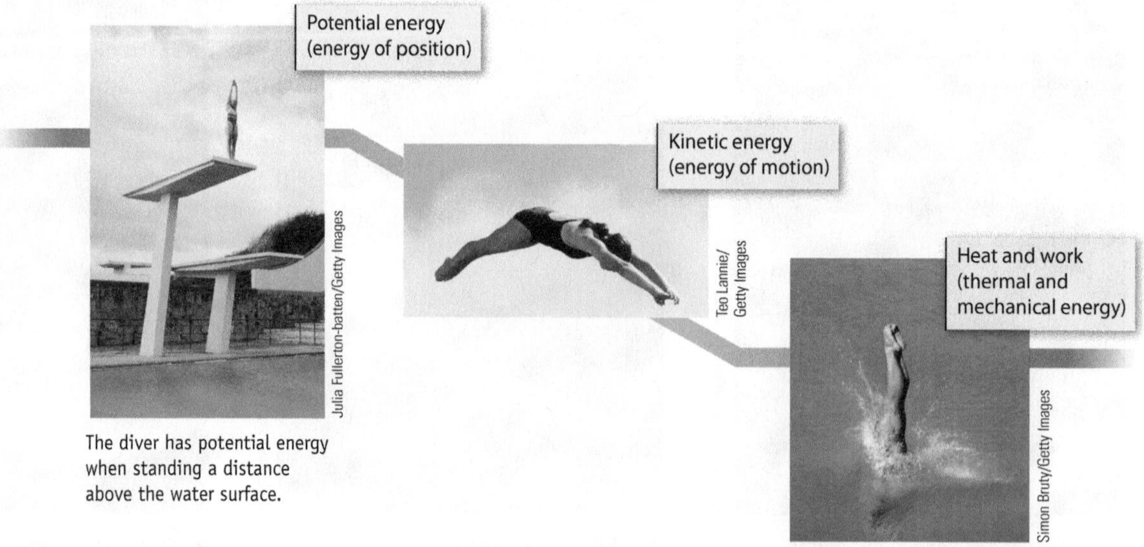

The diver has potential energy when standing a distance above the water surface.

The diver's potential energy is first converted to kinetic energy, which is then transferred to the water.

FIGURE 1.17 **The law of energy conservation.**

CASE STUDY — CO_2 in the Oceans

"Over the past 200 years, the oceans have absorbed approximately 550 billion tons of CO_2 from the atmosphere, or about a third of the total amount of anthropogenic emissions over that period." This amounts to about 22 million tons *per day*. This statement was made by R. A. Feely, a scientist at the National Oceanographic and Atmospheric Administration, in connection with studies on the effects of carbon dioxide on ocean chemistry.

The amount of CO_2 dissolved in the oceans is of great concern and interest to oceanographers because it affects the pH of the water, that is, its level of acidity. This in turn can affect the growth of marine systems such as corals and sea urchins and microscopic coccolithophores (single-cell phytoplankton).

Recent studies have indicated that, in water with a high CO_2 content, the spines of sea urchins are greatly impaired, the larvae of orange clown fish lose their homing ability, and the concentrations of calcium, copper, manganese, and iron in sea water are affected, sometimes drastically.

Finally, a recent investigation of the history of ocean acidification ended with the statement that "the current rate of (mainly fossil fuel) CO_2 release stands out as capable of driving a combination and magnitude of ocean geochemical changes potentially unparalleled in at least the last 300 million years of Earth history, raising the possibility that we are entering an unknown territory of marine ecosystem change." We will discuss this important issue in more detail in Chapter 20.

©David Mckee/Shutterstock.com

Clown fish. The larvae of the clown fish are affected by increased levels of CO_2 in the ocean.

Questions:

1. Much has been written about CO_2. What is its name?
2. Give the symbols for the four metals mentioned in this article.
3. Of the four metals mentioned here, which is the most dense? The least dense? (Use an Internet tool such as www.ptable.com to find this information.)
4. The spines of the sea urchin, corals, and coccolithophores all are built of the compound $CaCO_3$. What elements are involved in this compound? Do you know its name?

Answers to these questions are available in Appendix N.

Reference:

"Off-Balance Ocean: Acidification from absorbing atmospheric CO_2 is changing the ocean's chemistry," Rachel Petkewich, *Chemical and Engineering News,* February 23, 2009, page 56.

"The Geological Record of Ocean Acidification," B. Hönisch and others, *Science*, March 2, 2012, page 1058.

REVIEW & CHECK FOR SECTION 1-8

1. Which of the following has the highest thermal energy?
   (a) 1.0 g of ice at 0 °C
   (b) 1.0 g of liquid water at 25 °C
   (c) 1.0 g of liquid water at 100 °C
   (d) 1.0 g of water vapor at 100 °C
2. Which of the following is an incorrect statement?
   (a) A mixture of H_2 and O_2 has lower chemical potential energy than H_2O.
   (b) Input of energy is required to split an H_2 molecule into two H atoms.
   (c) Water at 30 °C has a higher thermal energy than the same amount of water at 20 °C.

CHAPTER GOALS REVISITED

Now that you have studied this chapter, you should ask whether you have met the chapter goals. In particular, you should be able to

UNDERSTAND

- Basic concepts applied in science: hypotheses, laws, and theories (Section 1-1).
  - **a.** Recognize the difference between a hypothesis and a theory and how laws are established.
- The basic ideas of kinetic-molecular theory (Section 1-3).
- Viewpoints of chemistry: macroscopic, microscopic, symbolic (Section 1-3).
  - **a.** Recognize the importance of representing matter at the macroscopic level and at the particulate level (Section 1-3). Study Questions: 25, 26.
- Processes that involve energy changes and how they apply in chemical studies (Section 1-8).
  - **a.** Identify types of potential and kinetic energy (Section 1-8). Study Questions: 13, 14.
  - **b.** Recognize and apply the law of conservation of energy (Section 1-8).

DO

- Classify matter (Section 1-3).
  - **a.** Recognize the different states of matter (solids, liquids, and gases) and give their characteristics. Study Question: 31.
  - **b.** Appreciate the difference between pure substances and mixtures and the difference between homogeneous and heterogeneous mixtures. Study Questions: 22, 29, 30.
- Identify physical and chemical properties and changes (Sections 1-5–1-7).
  - **a.** List commonly used physical properties of matter.
  - **b.** Identify several physical and chemical properties of common substances. Study Questions: 7–10, 17, 18, 20.
  - **c.** Relate density to the volume and mass of a substance. Study Questions: 15, 16, 27, 28, 33, 35, 39, 42, 43.
  - **d.** Explain the difference between chemical and physical changes. Study Questions: 8, 23, 24, 45.
  - **e.** Understand the difference between extensive and intensive properties and give examples of them. Study Questions: 15, 16.

REMEMBER

- The characteristics of chemical building blocks : elements, atoms, compounds, and molecules (Section 1-4).
  - **a.** Identify the name or symbol for an element, given its symbol or name, respectively. Study Questions: 1–4.
  - **b.** Use the terms *atom, element, molecule, and compound* correctly. Study Questions: 5, 6.
- A list of common physical and chemical properties (Sections 1-5 and 1-6).
- The principles of green chemistry (Section 1-2).

KEY EQUATION

Equation 1.1 (page 13) Density: In chemistry the common unit of density is g/cm^3, whereas kg/m^3 is commonly used in geology and oceanography.

$$\text{Density} = \frac{\text{mass}}{\text{volume}}$$

©Cengage Learning/Charles Winters

STUDY QUESTIONS

▲ denotes challenging questions.

Blue-numbered questions have answers in Appendix N and fully worked solutions in the *Student Solutions Manual.*

Practicing Skills

Matter: Elements and Atoms, Compounds, and Molecules

1. Give the name of each of the following elements:
   (a) C (b) K (c) Cl (d) P (e) Mg (f) Ni

2. Give the name of each of the following elements:
   (a) Mn (b) Cu (c) Na (d) Br (e) Xe (f) Fe

3. Give the symbol for each of the following elements:
   (a) barium (b) titanium (c) chromium (d) lead (e) arsenic (f) zinc

4. Give the symbol for each of the following elements:
   (a) silver (b) aluminum (c) plutonium (d) tin (e) technetium (f) krypton

5. In each of the following pairs, decide which is an element and which is a compound.
   (a) Na or NaCl
   (b) sugar or carbon
   (c) gold or gold chloride

6. In each of the following pairs, decide which is an element and which is a compound.
   (a) $Pt(NH_3)_2Cl_2$ or Pt
   (b) copper or copper(II) oxide
   (c) silicon or sand

Physical and Chemical Properties

7. In each case, decide if the underlined property is a physical or chemical property.
   (a) The color of elemental bromine is orange-red.
   (b) Iron turns to rust in the presence of air and water.
   (c) Hydrogen can explode when ignited in air (Figure 1.15).
   (d) The density of titanium metal is 4.5 g/cm^3.
   (e) Tin metal melts at 505 K.
   (f) Chlorophyll, a plant pigment, is green.

8. In each case, decide if the change is a chemical or physical change.
   (a) A cup of household bleach changes the color of your favorite T-shirt from purple to pink.
   (b) Water vapor in your exhaled breath condenses in the air on a cold day.
   (c) Plants use carbon dioxide from the air to make sugar.
   (d) Butter melts when placed in the Sun.

9. Which part of the description of a compound or element refers to its physical properties and which to its chemical properties?
   (a) The colorless liquid ethanol burns in air.
   (b) The shiny metal aluminum reacts readily with orange-red bromine.

10. Which part of the description of a compound or element refers to its physical properties and which to its chemical properties?
    (a) Calcium carbonate is a white solid with a density of 2.71 g/cm^3. It reacts readily with an acid to produce gaseous carbon dioxide.
    (b) Gray, powdered zinc metal reacts with purple iodine to give a white compound.

Energy

11. The flashlight in the photo does not use batteries. Instead, you move a lever, which turns a geared mechanism and finally results in light from the bulb. What type of energy is used to move the lever? What type or types of energy are produced?

A hand-operated flashlight

12. A solar panel is pictured in the photo. When light shines on the panel, it generates an electric current that can be used to recharge the batteries in an electric car. What types of energy are involved in this setup?

A solar panel

13. Determine which of the following represent potential energy and which represent kinetic energy.
    (a) thermal energy
    (b) gravitational energy
    (c) chemical energy
    (d) electrostatic energy

14. Determine whether kinetic energy is being converted to potential energy, or vice versa, in the following processes.
    (a) Water cascades downward in a waterfall.
    (b) A player kicks a football.
    (c) An electric current is generated by a chemical reaction in a battery.
    (d) Water boils when heated on a gas stove.

General Questions

These questions are not designated as to type or location in the chapter. They may combine several concepts.

15. A piece of turquoise is a blue-green solid; it has a density of 2.65 g/cm^3 and a mass of 2.5 g.
    (a) Which of these observations are qualitative and which are quantitative?
    (b) Which of the observations are extensive and which are intensive?
    (c) What is the volume of the piece of turquoise?

16. Iron pyrite (fool's gold, page 11) has a shiny golden metallic appearance. Crystals are often in the form of perfect cubes. A cube 0.40 cm on each side has a mass of 0.064 g.
    (a) Which of these observations are qualitative and which are quantitative?
    (b) Which of the observations are extensive and which are intensive?
    (c) What is the density of the sample of iron pyrite?

17. Which observations below describe chemical properties?
    (a) Sugar is soluble in water.
    (b) Water boils at 100 °C.
    (c) Ultraviolet light converts O_3 (ozone) to O_2 (oxygen).
    (d) Ice is less dense than water.

18. Which observations below describe chemical properties?
    (a) Sodium metal reacts violently with water.
    (b) The combustion of octane (a compound in gasoline) gives CO_2 and H_2O.
    (c) Chlorine is a green gas.
    (d) Heat is required to melt ice.

19. The mineral fluorite contains the elements calcium and fluorine and can have various colors, including blue, violet, green, and yellow.

The mineral fluorite, calcium fluoride

    (a) What are the symbols of these elements?
    (b) How would you describe the shape of the fluorite crystals in the photo? What can this tell us about the arrangement of the particles (ions) inside the crystal?

20. Azurite, a blue, crystalline mineral, is composed of copper, carbon, and oxygen.

Azurite is a deep blue crystalline mineral. It is surrounded by copper pellets and powdered carbon (in the dish).

(a) What are the symbols of the three elements that combine to make the mineral azurite?
(b) Based on the photo, describe some of the physical properties of the elements and the mineral. Are any the same? Are any properties different?

21. You have a solution of NaCl dissolved in water. Describe a method by which these two compounds could be separated.

22. Small chips of iron are mixed with sand (see photo). Is this a homogeneous or heterogeneous mixture? Suggest a way to separate the iron from the sand.

© Cengage Learning/Charles D. Winters

Chips of iron mixed with sand

23. Identify the following as either physical changes or chemical changes.
(a) Dry ice (solid CO_2) sublimes (converts directly from solid to gaseous CO_2).
(b) Mercury's density decreases as the temperature increases.
(c) Energy is given off as heat when natural gas (mostly methane, CH_4) burns.
(d) NaCl dissolves in water.

24. Identify the following as either physical changes or chemical changes.
(a) The desalination of sea water (separation of pure water from dissolved salts).
(b) The formation of SO_2 (an air pollutant) when coal containing sulfur is burned.
(c) Silver tarnishes.
(d) Iron is heated to red heat.

25. In Figure 1.2 you see a piece of salt and a representation of its internal structure. Which is the macroscopic view and which is the particulate view? How are the macroscopic and particulate views related?

26. In Figure 1.5 you see macroscopic and particulate views of the element bromine. Which are the macroscopic views and which are the particulate views? Describe how the particulate views explain properties of this element related to the state of matter.

27. Carbon tetrachloride, CCl_4, a common liquid compound, has a density of 1.58 g/cm^3. If you place a piece of a plastic soda bottle (d = 1.37 g/cm^3) and a piece of aluminum (d = 2.70 g/cm^3) in liquid CCl_4, will the plastic and aluminum float or sink?

28. The following photo shows copper balls, immersed in water, floating on top of mercury. What are the liquids and solids in this photo? Which substance is most dense? Which is least dense?

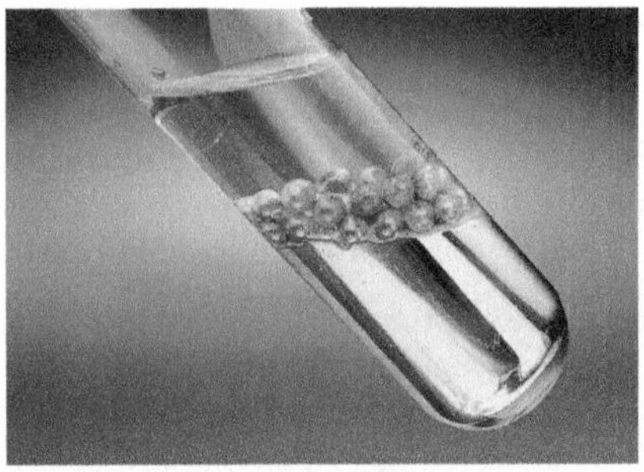
© Cengage Learning/Charles D. Winters

Water, copper, and mercury

29. Categorize each of the following as an element, a compound, or a mixture.
(a) sterling silver
(b) carbonated mineral water
(c) tungsten
(d) aspirin

30. Categorize each of the following as an element, a compound, or a mixture.
(a) air
(b) fluorite
(c) brass
(d) 18-carat gold

31. ▲ Make a drawing, based on the kinetic-molecular theory and the ideas about atoms and molecules presented in this chapter, of the arrangement of particles in each of the cases listed here. For each case, draw 10 particles of each substance. It is acceptable for your diagram to be two dimensional. Represent each atom as a circle, and distinguish each different kind of atom by shading.
(a) a sample of solid iron (which consists of iron atoms)
(b) a sample of *liquid* water (which consists of H_2O molecules)
(c) a sample of water *vapor*

32. ▲ Make a drawing, based on the kinetic-molecular theory and the ideas about atoms and molecules presented in this chapter, of the arrangement of particles in each of the cases listed here. For each case, draw 10 particles of each substance. It is acceptable for your diagram to be two dimensional. Represent each atom as a circle, and distinguish each different kind of atom by shading.
(a) a homogeneous mixture of water vapor and helium gas (which consists of helium atoms)
(b) a heterogeneous mixture consisting of liquid water and solid aluminum; show a region of the sample that includes both substances
(c) a sample of brass (which is a homogeneous solid mixture of copper and zinc)

33. Hexane (C_6H_{14}, density = 0.766 g/cm^3), perfluorohexane (C_6F_{14}, density = 1.669 g/cm^3), and water are immiscible liquids; that is, they do not dissolve in one another. You place 10 mL of each in a graduated cylinder, along with pieces of high-density polyethylene (HDPE, density =

0.97 g/cm^3), polyvinyl chloride (PVC, density = 1.36 g/cm^3), and Teflon (density = 2.3 g/cm^3). None of these common plastics dissolves in these liquids. Describe what you expect to see.

34. ▲ You have a sample of a white crystalline substance from your kitchen. You know that it is either salt or sugar. Although you could decide by taste, suggest another property that you could use to decide. (*Hint:* You may use the World Wide Web or a handbook of chemistry in the library to find some information.)

35. You can figure out whether a solid floats or sinks if you know its density and the density of the liquid. In which of the liquids listed below will high-density polyethylene (HDPE) float? (HDPE, a common plastic, has a density of 0.97 g/cm^3. It does not dissolve in any of these liquids.)

Substance	Density (g/cm^3)	Properties, Uses
Ethylene glycol	1.1088	Toxic; major component of automobile antifreeze
Water	0.9997	
Ethanol	0.7893	Alcohol in alcoholic beverages
Methanol	0.7914	Toxic; gasoline additive to prevent gas line freezing
Acetic acid	1.0492	Component of vinegar
Glycerol	1.2613	Solvent used in home care products

36. You are given a sample of a silvery metal. What information could you use to prove the metal is silver?

37. Milk in a glass bottle was placed in the freezing compartment of a refrigerator overnight. By morning, a column of frozen milk emerged from the bottle. Explain this observation.

© Cengage Learning/Charles D. Winters

Frozen milk in a glass bottle

38. Describe an experimental method that can be used to determine the density of an irregularly shaped piece of metal.

39. Diabetes can alter the density of urine, so urine density can be used as a diagnostic tool. Diabetics can excrete too much sugar or excrete too much water. What do you predict will happen to the density of urine under each of these conditions? (*Hint:* Water containing dissolved sugar is more dense than pure water.)

40. Suggest a way to determine if the colorless liquid in a beaker is water. How could you discover if there is salt dissolved in the water?

41. The following photo shows the element potassium reacting with water to form the element hydrogen, a gas, and a solution of the compound potassium hydroxide.

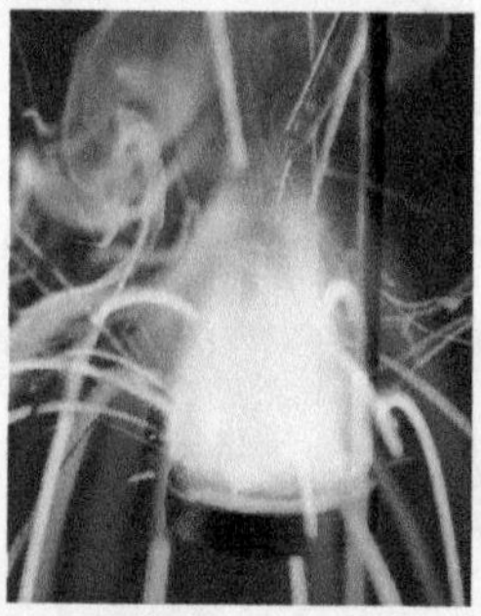

© Cengage Learning/Charles D. Winters

Potassium reacting with water to produce hydrogen gas and potassium hydroxide.

(a) What states of matter are involved in the reaction?
(b) Is the observed change chemical or physical?
(c) What are the reactants in this reaction, and what are the products?
(d) What qualitative observations can be made concerning this reaction?

42. Three liquids of different densities are mixed. Because they are not miscible (do not form a homogeneous solution with one another), they form discrete layers, one on top of the other. Sketch the result of mixing carbon tetrachloride (CCl_4, d = 1.58 g/cm^3), mercury (d = 13.546 g/cm^3), and water (d = 1.00 g/cm^3).

43. Four balloons are each filled with a different gas, each having a different density:

helium, d = 0.164 g/L   neon, d = 0.825 g/L

argon, d = 1.633 g/L   krypton, d = 4.425 g/L

If the density of dry air is 1.12 g/L, which balloon or balloons float in air?

44. A copper-colored metal is found to conduct an electric current. Can you say with certainty that it is copper? Why or why not? Suggest additional information that could provide unequivocal confirmation that it is copper.

45. The photo below shows elemental iodine dissolving in ethanol to give a solution. Is this a physical or chemical change?

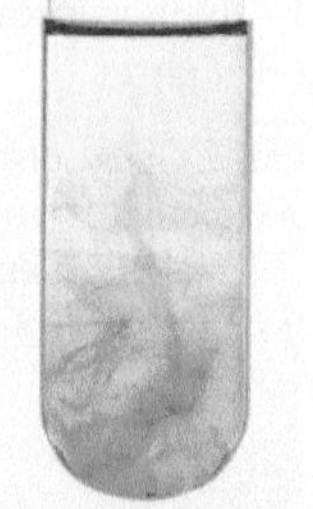

© Cengage Learning/Charles D. Winters

Elemental iodine dissolving in ethanol.

46. ▲ You want to determine the density of a compound but have only a tiny crystal, and it would be difficult to measure mass and volume accurately. There is another way to determine density, however, called the *flotation method.* If you placed the crystal in a liquid whose density is precisely that of the substance, it would be suspended in the liquid, neither sinking to the bottom of the beaker nor floating to the surface. However, for such an experiment you would need to have a liquid with the precise density of the crystal. You can accomplish this by mixing two liquids of different densities to create a liquid having the desired density.

(a) Consider the following: you mix 10.0 mL of $CHCl_3$ (d = 1.492 g/mL) and 5.0 mL of $CHBr_3$ (d = 2.890 g/mL), giving 15.0 mL of solution. What is the density of this mixture?

(b) Suppose now that you wanted to determine the density of a small yellow crystal to confirm that it is sulfur. From the literature, you know that sulfur has a density of 2.07 g/cm^3. How would you prepare 20.0 mL of the liquid mixture having that density from pure samples of $CHCl_3$ and $CHBr_3$? (*Note:* 1 mL = 1 cm^3.)

47. A few years ago a young chemist in Vienna, Austria, wanted to see just how permanent the gold was in his wedding band. The ring was 18-carat gold. (18-carat gold is 75% gold with the remainder copper and silver.) One week after his wedding day he took off the ring, cleaned it carefully, and weighed it. It had a mass of 5.58387 g. He weighed it weekly from then on, and after 1 year it had lost 6.15 mg just from normal wear and tear. He found that the activities that took the greatest toll on the gold were vacationing on a sandy beach and gardening.

(a) What are the symbols of the elements that make up 18-carat gold?

(b) Gold melts at 1064 °C. What is that temperature in kelvins? (See page 25.)

(c) The density of gold is 19.3 g/cm^3. Use one of the periodic tables on the Internet (such as www.ptable.com) to find out if gold is the most dense of all of the known elements. If it is not gold, then what element is the most dense [considering only the elements from hydrogen (H) through uranium (U)]?

(d) If a wedding band is 18-carat gold and has a mass of 5.58 g, what mass of gold is contained within the ring?

(e) Assume there are 56 million married couples in the United States, and each person has an 18-carat gold ring. What mass of gold is lost by all the wedding rings in the United States in 1 year (in units of grams) if each ring loses 6.15 mg of mass per year? Assuming gold is \$1620 per troy ounce (where 1 troy ounce = 31.1 g), what is the lost gold worth?

AP Multiple-Choice Review Questions

1. When each of the following is heated to 50 °C and the temperature is held constant for 5 minutes, which one undergoes *only* a physical change?

(A) egg
(B) steak
(C) ice cream
(D) cake batter

The following diagram is used for questions 2–4.

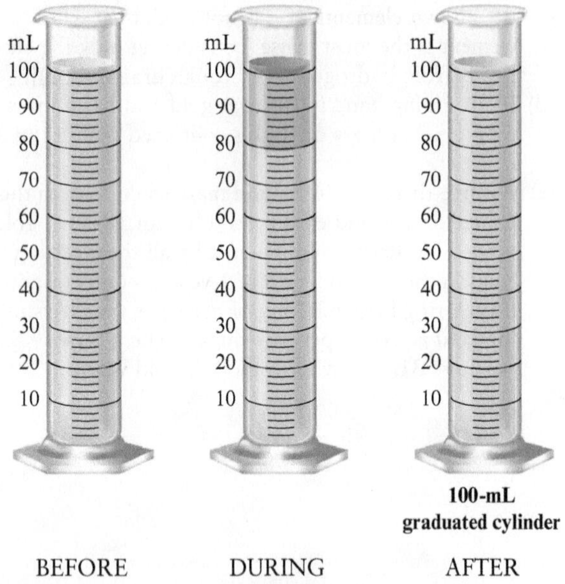

A 100-mL graduated cylinder is filled with 100 mL of water. A few drops of food coloring are added to the top of the water, without mixing. Initially, the top of the graduated cylinder appears to be very dark, while the bottom remains clear and colorless. After 5 minutes the liquid in the graduated cylinder appears to be uniformly colored.

2. Classify the contents in the graduated cylinder before any food coloring is added.

(A) element
(B) compound
(C) heterogeneous mixture
(D) homogeneous mixture

3. Classify the contents in the graduated cylinder just after the food coloring is added.

(A) element
(B) compound
(C) heterogeneous mixture
(D) homogeneous mixture

4. Classify the contents in the graduated cylinder after the 5 minutes have elapsed.

(A) element
(B) compound
(C) heterogeneous mixture
(D) homogeneous mixture

5. Several of Jupiter's moons are believed to have a liquid layer, possibly water, below their icy surfaces. NASA and the European Space Agency are planning several interplanetary probes that will visit the moons of Jupiter. It has been suggested that a probe could land on one of the moons and drill through the surface of ice to the liquid layer. The probe would then sample the liquid at five different depths. Why will the probe test the liquid at five different depths?

(A) to determine whether the liquid layer is water
(B) to determine whether the liquid layer could support life
(C) to determine the chemical composition of the liquid layer
(D) to determine whether the liquid layer is a homogeneous solution or heterogeneous mixture

6. A 10.00-g piece of metal is submerged in a graduated cylinder initially containing 20.00 mL of water. With the metal in the cylinder, the level of the water is recorded as 21.40 mL. Determine the identity of the metal.

(A) aluminum (density = 2.70 g/mL)
(B) zinc (density = 7.13 g/mL)
(C) silver (density = 10.49 g/mL)
(D) gold (density = 19.32 g/mL)

7. A graduated cylinder contains multiple different liquid layers.

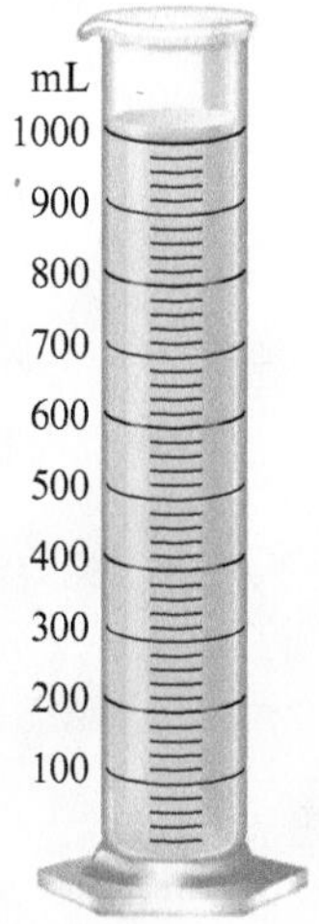

Very small samples are taken from the liquids at various heights and tested for density, viscosity, and boiling point. The data are listed in the following table.

mL Mark	Density (g/mL)	Viscosity (Pa · s)	Boiling Point (°C)
1000	0.83	0.72	242.4
900	0.83	0.71	242.3
800	1.07	0.93	99.7
700	1.08	0.92	99.8
600	1.08	0.93	99.7
500	2.05	1.86	153.5
400	2.06	1.87	153.5
300	2.05	1.85	153.6
200	2.04	1.86	153.6
100	2.05	1.86	153.5

How many different liquids are present in the graduated cylinder?

(A) 1

(B) 2

(C) 3

(D) 4

© Cengage Learning/Charles D. Winters

Native copper metal and copper-containing minerals.

Let's Review: The Tools of Quantitative Chemistry

COPPER Copper (Cu) is the 26th most abundant element in the Earth's crust (not too different from nickel and zinc, its near neighbors in the periodic table). Copper and its minerals are widely distributed, and obtaining the metal from its ores is relatively easy. As a result, elemental copper is used around the world for many useful items, from cooking pots to electric wires.

Pure copper (often called *native copper*) is found in nature, but more commonly it is found combined with other elements in minerals such as cuprite, azurite, or malachite.

Copper metal is relatively soft but, when combined in a ratio of about 2 to 1 with tin, it forms bronze. Bronze was important in early civilizations and gave its name to an epoch of human development, the Bronze Age, which started around 3000 BC and lasted until about 1000 BC. (The Iceman you learned about at the beginning of the chapter lived just before the Bronze Age and had an ax made of copper.) The development of bronze was significant because bronze is stronger than copper and can be shaped into a sharper edge. This improved the cutting edges of plows and weapons, thus giving cultures that possessed bronze advantages over those that did not.

Copper is used in electric wiring because it is a good conductor of electricity, and it is used in cooking pots because it conducts heat well. It is also one of the "coinage metals" (along with silver and gold) and has been used in coins for centuries.

Compounds of copper are common, and copper is one of the eight essential metals in our bodies, where it is needed for some enzymes to use oxygen more effectively. Fortunately, it is found in common foods (in meats such as lamb, duck, pork, and beef, and in nuts such as almonds and walnuts). The average person has about 72 mg of copper in his or her body.

You can learn more about copper and its properties in Study Questions 60 and 61 at the end of this *Let's Review* section.

At its core, chemistry is a quantitative science. Chemists make measurements of, among other things, size, mass, volume, time, and temperature. They then examine that information to search for relationships among properties and to provide insight into the molecular basis of matter.

This section reviews the units used in chemistry, briefly describes the proper treatment of numerical data, and reviews some mathematical skills you will need in chemical calculations. After studying this section you should be able to:

- Use the common units for measurements in chemistry and make unit conversions (such as from liters to milliliters).
- Express and use numbers in exponential or scientific notation.
- Incorporate quantitative information into an algebraic expression and solve that expression.
- Read information from graphs.
- Prepare and interpret graphs of numerical information, and, if a graph produces a straight line, find the slope and equation of the line.
- Recognize and express uncertainties in measurements.

1 Units of Measurement

Doing chemistry requires observing chemical reactions and physical changes. We make qualitative observations—such as changes in color or the evolution of heat—and quantitative measurements of temperature, time, volume, mass, and length or size. To record and report measurements, the scientific community has chosen a modified version of the **metric system**. This decimal system, used internationally in science, is called the Système International d'Unités (International System of Units), abbreviated **SI**.

All SI units are derived from base units, listed in Table 1. Larger and smaller quantities are expressed by using appropriate prefixes with the base unit (Table 2). The nanometer (nm), for example, is 1 billionth of a meter, that is, 1×10^{-9} m

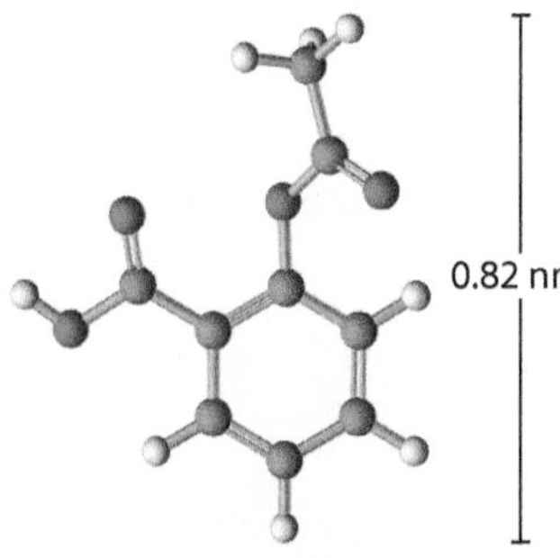

Structure of the aspirin molecule

Table 1 The Seven SI Base Units

Measured Property	Name of Unit	Abbreviation
Mass	Kilogram	kg
Length	Meter	m
Time	Second	s
Temperature	Kelvin	K
Amount of substance	Mole	mol
Electric current	Ampere	A
Luminous intensity	Candela	cd

The Kilogram, a New Standard Needed? Unlike the second and the meter, the kilogram is defined by a physical object: a block of platinum-iridium alloy in a building in Paris, France. The block has been mysteriously losing mass, so there is great interest in the scientific community to find a better way to define the kilogram. Two suggestions are now under consideration: defining the kilogram based on the mass of a given number of atoms, or defining it based on a fundamental constant of nature. The issue is a long way from resolution.

Common Conversion Factors
1000 g = 1 kg
1×10^9 nm = 1 m
10 mm = 1 cm
100 cm = 10 dm = 1 m
1000 m = 1 km
Conversion factors for SI units are given in Appendix C and inside the back cover of this book.

Table 2 Selected Prefixes Used in the Metric System

Prefix	Abbreviation	Meaning	Example
Giga-	G	10^9 (billion)	1 gigahertz = 1×10^9 Hz
Mega-	M	10^6 (million)	1 megaton = 1×10^6 tons
Kilo-	k	10^3 (thousand)	1 kilogram (kg) = 1×10^3 g
Deci-	d	10^{-1} (tenth)	1 decimeter (dm) = 1×10^{-1} m
Centi-	c	10^{-2} (one hundredth)	1 centimeter (cm) = 1×10^{-2} m
Milli-	m	10^{-3} (one thousandth)	1 millimeter (mm) = 1×10^{-3} m
Micro-	μ	10^{-6} (one millionth)	1 micrometer (μm) = 1×10^{-6} m
Nano-	n	10^{-9} (one billionth)	1 nanometer (nm) = 1×10^{-9} m
Pico-	p	10^{-12}	1 picometer (pm) = 1×10^{-12} m
Femto-	f	10^{-15}	1 femtometer (fm) = 1×10^{-15} m

(meter). Dimensions on the nanometer scale are common in chemistry and biology because, for example, a typical molecule is about 1 nm in length and a bacterium is about 1000 nm in length. The prefix *nano-* is also used in the name for a new area of science, *nanotechnology*, which involves the synthesis and study of materials having this tiny size.

Temperature Scales

Two temperature scales are commonly used in scientific work: Celsius and Kelvin (Figure 1). The Celsius scale is generally used worldwide for measurements in the laboratory. When calculations incorporate temperature data, however, the Kelvin scale is almost always used.

The Celsius Temperature Scale

The size of the Celsius degree is defined by assigning zero as the freezing point of pure water (0 °C) and 100 as its boiling point (100 °C). You may recognize that a comfortable room temperature is around 20 °C and your normal body temperature

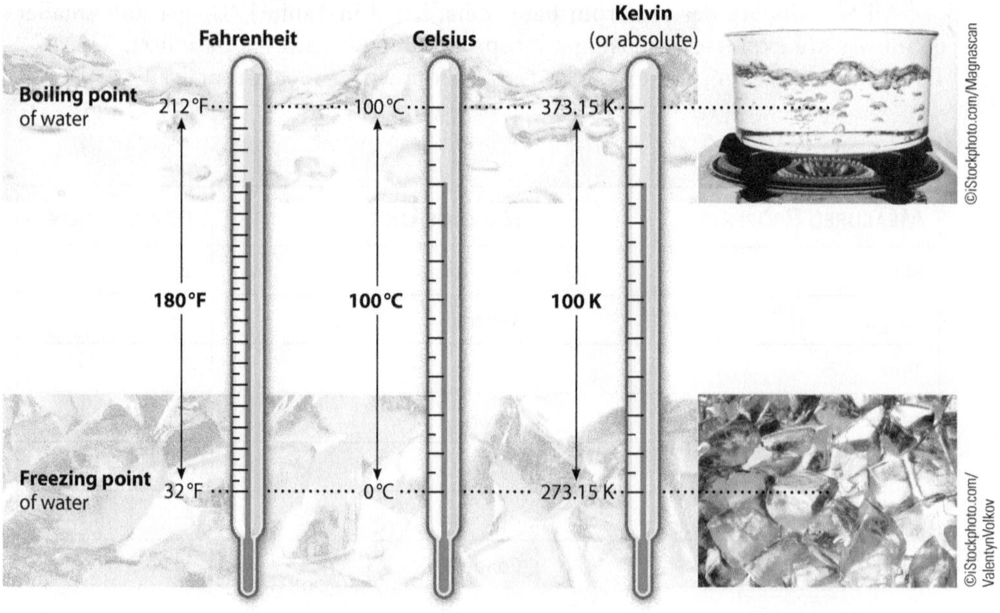

FIGURE 1 **Comparison of Fahrenheit, Celsius, and Kelvin scales.** Note that the degree sign (°) is not used with the Kelvin scale.

is 37 °C. We find that the warmest water we can stand to immerse a finger in is about 60 °C.

The Kelvin Temperature Scale

William Thomson, known as Lord Kelvin (1824–1907), first suggested the temperature scale that now bears his name. The Kelvin scale uses the same size unit as the Celsius scale, but it assigns zero as the lowest temperature that can be achieved, a point called **absolute zero.** Many experiments have found that this limiting temperature is −273.15 °C. *Kelvin units and Celsius degrees are the same size.* Thus, the freezing point of water is reached at 273.15 K; that is, 0 °C = 273.15 K. The normal boiling point of pure water is 373.15 K. Temperatures in Celsius degrees are readily converted to kelvins, and vice versa, using the relation

Lord Kelvin William Thomson (1824–1907), known as Lord Kelvin, was a professor of natural philosophy at the University in Glasgow, Scotland, from 1846 to 1899. He was best known for his study of heat and work, from which came the concept of the absolute temperature scale.

$$T\ (\mathrm{K}) = \frac{1\ \mathrm{K}}{1\ {}^\circ\mathrm{C}}\,(T\ {}^\circ\mathrm{C} + 273.15\ {}^\circ\mathrm{C}) \tag{1}$$

Using this equation, you can show that a common room temperature of 23.5 °C is equivalent to 296.7 K.

$$T\ (\mathrm{K}) = \frac{1\ \mathrm{K}}{1\ \cancel{{}^\circ\mathrm{C}}}\,(23.5\ \cancel{{}^\circ\mathrm{C}} + 273.15\ \cancel{{}^\circ\mathrm{C}}) = 296.7\ \mathrm{K}$$

There are three things to notice here:

- Converting from degrees Celsius to kelvins simply requires adding 273.15 to the temperature in Celsius, and converting from kelvins to degrees Celsius requires subtracting 273.15 from the value in kelvins.
- The degree symbol (°) is not used with Kelvin temperatures.
- The name of the unit on this scale is the *kelvin* (not capitalized), and such temperatures are designated with a capital K.

Length, Volume, and Mass

The meter is the standard unit of *length*, but objects observed in chemistry are frequently smaller than 1 meter. Measurements are often reported in units of centimeters (cm), millimeters (mm), or micrometers (μm) (Figure 2), and objects on

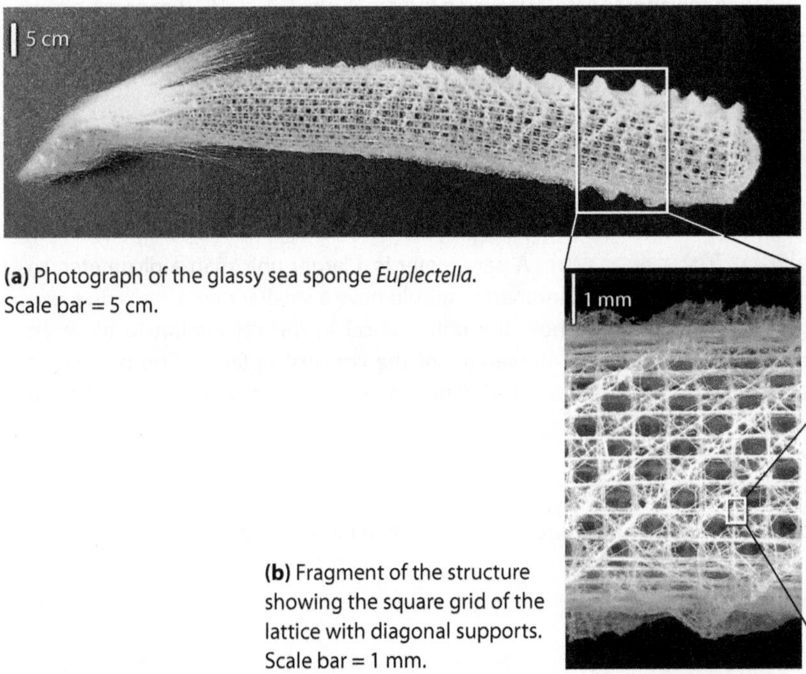

FIGURE 2 **Dimensions in chemistry and biology.** These photos are from the research of Professor Joanna Aizenberg of Harvard University.

(a) Photograph of the glassy sea sponge *Euplectella*. Scale bar = 5 cm.

(b) Fragment of the structure showing the square grid of the lattice with diagonal supports. Scale bar = 1 mm.

(c) Scanning electron microscope (SEM) image of a single strand showing its ceramic-composite structure. Scale bar = 20 μm.

Photos courtesy of Joanna Aizenberg, Bell Laboratories. Reference: J. Aizenberg, et al., Science, Vol. 309, pages 275-278, 2005

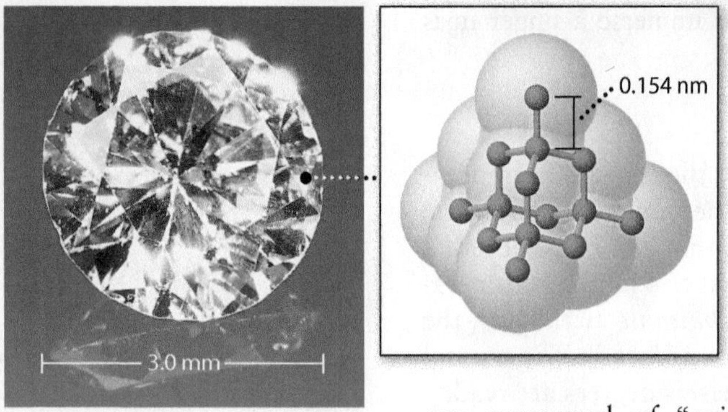

FIGURE 3 Dimensions in the molecular world. Dimensions on the molecular scale are often given in terms of nanometers ($1 \text{ nm} = 1 \times 10^{-9}$ m) or picometers ($1 \text{ pm} = 1 \times 10^{-12}$ m). Here, the distance between C atoms in diamond is 0.154 nm.

Ångstrom Units An older but often-used non-SI unit for molecular distances is the Ångstrom unit (Å), where $1 \text{ Å} = 1.0 \times 10^{-10}$ m. The C–C distance in diamond would be 1.54 Å.

the atomic and molecular scale have dimensions of nanometers (nm; $1 \text{ nm} = 1 \times 10^{-9}$ m) or picometers (pm; $1 \text{ pm} = 1 \times 10^{-12}$ m) (Figure 3).

To illustrate the range of dimensions used in science, let us look at a recent study of the glassy skeleton of a sea sponge. The sea sponge in Figure 2 is about 20 cm long and a few centimeters in diameter. A closer look shows more detail of the lattice-like structure. Scientists at Bell Laboratories found that each strand of the lattice is a ceramic-fiber composite of silica (SiO_2) and protein less than 100 μm in diameter. These strands are composed of "spicules," which, at the nanoscale level, consist of silica nanoparticles 50–200 nanometers in diameter.

EXAMPLE 1

Distances on the Molecular Scale

Problem The distance between an O atom and an H atom in a water molecule is 95.8 pm. What is this distance in nanometers (nm)?

What Do You Know? You know the interatomic O–H distance and the relationships of the metric units.

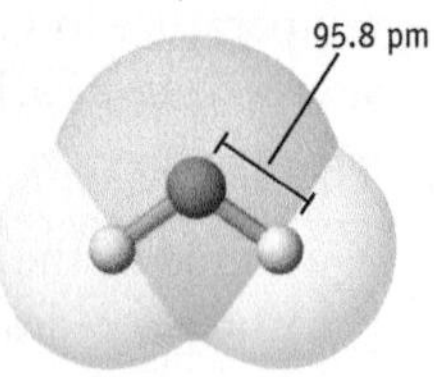

Strategy You can solve this problem by knowing the conversion factor between the units in the information you are given (picometers) and the desired units (meters or nanometers). (For more about conversion factors and their use in problem solving, see page 38.) There is no conversion factor given in Table 2 to change nanometers to picometers directly, but relationships are listed between meters and picometers and between meters and nanometers. Therefore, we first convert picometers to meters and then convert meters to nanometers.

$$\text{picometers} \xrightarrow{x \text{ m/pm}} \text{meters} \xrightarrow{y \text{ nm/m}} \text{nanometers}$$

Solution Using the appropriate conversion factors ($1 \text{ pm} = 1 \times 10^{-12}$ m and $1 \text{ nm} = 1 \times 10^{-9}$ m), we have

$$95.8 \text{ pm} \times \frac{1 \times 10^{-12} \text{ m}}{1 \text{ pm}} = 9.58 \times 10^{-11} \text{ m}$$

$$9.58 \times 10^{-11} \text{ m} \times \frac{1 \text{ nm}}{1 \times 10^{-9} \text{ m}} = 9.58 \times 10^{-2} \text{ nm or } 0.0958 \text{ nm}$$

Think about Your Answer A nanometer is a larger unit than a picometer, so the same distance expressed in nanometers should have a smaller numerical value. Our answer agrees with this. Notice how the units cancel in the calculation to leave an answer whose unit is that of the numerator of the conversion factor. The process of using units to guide a calculation is called *dimensional analysis*. It is explored further on pages 38–39.

Check Your Understanding

The C–C distance in diamond (Figure 3) is 0.154 nm. What is this distance in picometers (pm)? In centimeters (cm)?

Chemists often use glassware such as beakers, flasks, pipets, graduated cylinders, and burets, which are marked in volume units (Figure 4). Because the SI unit of volume [the cubic meter (m^3)] is too large for everyday laboratory use, chemists usually use the liter (L) or the milliliter (mL) for volume measurements. One liter is equivalent to the volume of a cube with sides equal to 10 cm [$V = (0.1\ m)^3 = 0.001\ m^3$].

$$1\ \text{liter (L)} = 1000\ cm^3 = 1000\ mL = 0.001\ m^3$$

Because there are exactly 1000 mL (= 1000 cm^3) in a liter, this means that

$$1\ mL = 0.001\ L = 1\ cm^3$$

The units *milliliter and cubic centimeter* (or "cc") *are interchangeable.* Therefore, a flask that contains exactly 125 mL has a volume of 125 cm^3.

Although not widely used in the United States, the cubic decimeter (dm^3) is a common unit in the rest of the world. A length of 10 cm is called a decimeter (dm). Because a cube 10 cm on a side defines a volume of 1 liter, *a liter is equivalent to a cubic decimeter:* 1 L = 1 dm^3. Products in Europe, Africa, and other parts of the world are often sold by the cubic decimeter.

The *deciliter, dL,* which is exactly equivalent to 1/10 of a liter (0.100 L) or 100 mL, is widely used in medicine. For example, standards for concentrations of environmental contaminants are often set as a certain mass per deciliter. For example, the U.S. Centers for Disease Control and Prevention recommends that children with more than 5 micrograms (5×10^{-6} g) of lead per deciliter of blood undergo further testing for lead poisoning.

Finally, when chemists prepare chemicals for reactions, they often take given masses of materials. The *mass* of a body is the fundamental measure of the quantity of matter, and the SI unit of mass is the kilogram (kg). Smaller masses are expressed in grams (g) or milligrams (mg).

$$1\ kg = 1000\ g \text{ and } 1\ g = 1000\ mg$$

© Cengage Learning/Charles D. Winters

FIGURE 4 Some common laboratory glassware. Volumes are marked in units of milliliters (mL). Remember that 1 mL is equivalent to 1 cm^3.

Energy Units

When expressing energy quantities, most chemists (and much of the world outside the United States) use the **joule** (J), the SI unit. The joule is related directly to the units used for mechanical energy: 1 J equals 1 kg · m^2/s^2. Because the joule is inconveniently small for most uses in chemistry, the kilojoule (kJ), equivalent to 1000 joules, is often the unit of choice.

To give you some feeling for joules, suppose you drop a six-pack of soft-drink cans, each full of liquid, on your foot. Although you probably will not take time to calculate the kinetic energy at the moment of impact, it is between 4 J and 10 J.

The calorie (cal) is an older energy unit. It is defined as the energy transferred as heat that is required to raise the temperature of 1.00 g of pure liquid water from 14.5 °C to 15.5 °C. A kilocalorie (kcal) is equivalent to 1000 calories. The conversion factor relating joules and calories is

$$\mathbf{1\ calorie\ (cal) = 4.184\ joules\ (J)}$$

The dietary Calorie (with a capital C) is often used in the United States to represent the energy content of foods. The dietary Calorie (Cal) is equivalent to the kilocalorie or 1000 calories. Thus, a breakfast cereal that gives you 100.0 Calories of nutritional energy per serving provides 100.0 kcal or 418.4 kJ.

Oesper Collection in the History of Chemistry/University of Cincinnati

James Joule The joule is named for James P. Joule (1818–1889), the son of a wealthy brewer in Manchester, England. The family wealth and a workshop in the brewery gave Joule the opportunity to pursue scientific studies. Among the topics that Joule studied was the issue of whether heat was a massless fluid. Scientists at that time referred to this idea as the caloric hypothesis. Joule's careful experiments showed that heat and mechanical work are related, providing evidence that heat is not a fluid. See Chapter 5 for more on this important topic.

A CLOSER LOOK Energy and Food

The U.S. Food and Drug Administration (FDA) mandates that nutritional data, including energy content, be included on almost all packaged food. The Nutrition Labeling and Education Act of 1990 requires that the total energy from protein, carbohydrates, fat, and alcohol be specified. How is this determined? Initially, the method used was calorimetry. In this method (described in Section 5-6), a food product is burned, and the energy transferred as heat in the combustion is measured. Now, however, energy contents are estimated using the Atwater system. This specifies the following average values for energy sources in foods:

1 g protein = 4 kcal (17 kJ)
1 g carbohydrate = 4 kcal (17 kJ)
1 g fat = 9 kcal (38 kJ)
1 g alcohol = 7 kcal (29 kJ)

Because carbohydrates may include some indigestible fiber, the mass of fiber is subtracted from the mass of carbohydrate when calculating the energy from carbohydrates.

As an example, one serving of cashew nuts (about 28 g) has

14 g fat = 126 kcal
6 g protein = 24 kcal
7 g carbohydrates − 1 g fiber = 24 kcal
Total = 174 kcal (728 kJ)

A value of 170 kcal is reported on the package.

You can find data on more than 6000 foods at the Nutrient Data Laboratory website (www.ars.usda.gov/ba/bhnrc/ndl).

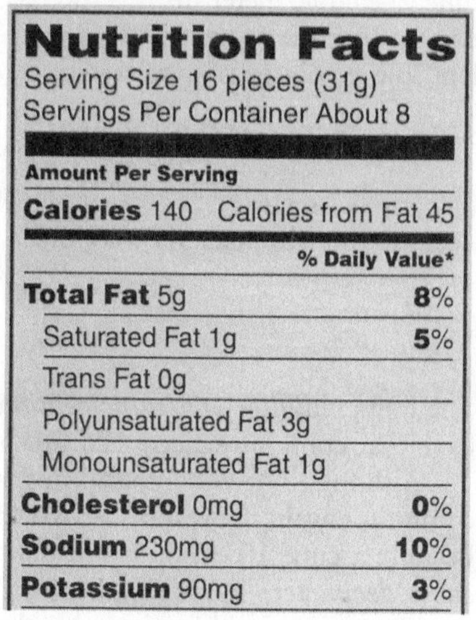

Energy and food labels. All packaged foods must have labels specifying nutritional values, with energy given in Calories (where 1 Cal = 1 kilocalorie).

Review & Check Answers to the Review & Check questions are given by chapter in Appendix N.

REVIEW & CHECK FOR SECTION 1

1. Liquid nitrogen boils at 77 K. What is this temperature in Celsius degrees?

   (a) 350 °C (b) −196 °C (c) 77 °C (d) −109 °C

2. A square platinum sheet has sides 2.50 cm long and a thickness of 0.25 mm. What is the volume of the platinum sheet (in cm^3)?

   (a) 16 cm^3 (b) 630 cm^3 (c) 0.16 cm^3 (d) 160 cm^3

3. A standard wine bottle has a volume of 750. mL. What volume, in liters, does this represent?

   (a) 0.750 L (b) 0.00750 L (c) 7.50 L (d) 75.0 L

4. One U.S. gallon is equivalent to 3.7865 L. What is the volume in liters of a 2.0-quart carton of milk? (There are 4 quarts in a gallon.)

   (a) 19 L (b) 3.8 L (c) 1.9 L (d) 0.95 L

5. A circulated U.S. quarter has a mass of 5.59 g. Express this mass in milligrams.

   (a) 5.59×10^3 mg (b) 5.59 mg (c) 55.9 mg (d) 559 mg

6. An environmental study of a river found a pesticide present to the extent of 0.02 microgram per liter of water. Express this amount in grams per liter.

   (a) 2 g/L (b) 0.02 g/L (c) 2×10^3 g/L (d) 2×10^{-8} g/L

7. The label on a cereal box indicates that one serving (with skim milk) provides 251 Cal. What is this energy in kilojoules (kJ)?

   (a) 251 kJ (b) 59.8 kJ (c) 1050 kJ (d) 4380 kJ

2 Making Measurements: Precision, Accuracy, Experimental Error, and Standard Deviation

The **precision** of a measurement indicates how well several determinations of the same quantity agree. This is illustrated by the results of throwing darts at a target. In Figure 5a, the dart thrower was apparently not skillful, and the precision of the dart's placement on the target is low. In Figures 5b and 5c, the darts are clustered together, indicating much better consistency on the part of the thrower—that is, greater precision.

Accuracy is the agreement of a measurement with the accepted value of the quantity. Figure 5c shows that our thrower was accurate as well as precise—the average of all shots is close to the targeted position, the bull's eye.

Figure 5b shows it is possible to be precise without being accurate—the thrower has consistently missed the bull's eye, although all the darts are clustered precisely around one point on the target. This is analogous to an experiment with some flaw (either in design or in a measuring device) that causes all results to differ from the correct value by the same amount.

The accuracy of a result in the laboratory is often expressed in terms of percent error relative to a standard or accepted value, whereas the precision is expressed as a standard deviation.

Accuracy and NIST The National Institute of Standards and Technology (NIST) is an important resource for the standards used in science. Comparison with NIST data is a test of the accuracy of the measurement (see www.nist.gov).

Experimental Error

If you measure a quantity in the laboratory, you may be required to report the error in the result, the difference between your result and the accepted value,

$$\text{Error in measurement} = \text{experimentally determined value} - \text{accepted value}$$

or the **percent error.**

$$\text{Percent error} = \frac{\text{error in measurement}}{\text{accepted value}} \times 100\%$$

(a) Poor precision and poor accuracy (b) Good precision and poor accuracy (c) Good precision and good accuracy

FIGURE 5 **Precision and accuracy.**

Percent Error Percent error can be positive or negative, indicating whether the experimental value is too high or too low compared to the accepted value. In Example 2, Student B's percent error is −0.2%, indicating it is 0.2% lower than the accepted value.

EXAMPLE 2

Precision, Accuracy, and Error

Problem Suppose a coin has an "accepted" diameter of 28.054 mm. In an experiment, two students measure this diameter. Student A makes four measurements of the diameter of the coin using a precision tool called a micrometer. Student B measures the same coin using a simple plastic ruler. The two students report the following results:

Student A	Student B
28.246 mm	27.9 mm
28.244	28.0
28.246	27.8
28.248	28.1

What is the average diameter and percent error obtained in each case? Which student's data are more accurate?

What Do You Know? You know the data collected by the two students and want to compare them with the "accepted" value by calculating the percent error.

Strategy For each set of values, we calculate the average of the results and then compare this average with 28.054 mm.

Solution The average for each set of data is obtained by summing the four values and dividing by 4.

Average value for Student A = 28.246 mm

Average value for Student B = 28.0 mm

Although Student A has four results very close to one another (and so of high precision), Student A's result is less accurate than that of Student B. The average diameter for Student A differs from the "accepted" value by 0.192 mm and has a percent error of 0.684%:

$$\text{Percent error} = \frac{28.246 \text{ mm} - 28.054 \text{ mm}}{28.054 \text{ mm}} \times 100\% = 0.684\%$$

Student B's measurement has a percent error of only about −0.2%.

Think about Your Answer Although Student A had less accurate results than Student B, they were more precise; the standard deviation for Student A is 2×10^{-3} (calculated as described below), in contrast to Student B's larger value (standard deviation = 0.14). Possible reasons for the error in Student A's result are incorrect use of the micrometer or a flaw in the instrument.

Check Your Understanding

Two students measured the freezing point of a sample of pure benzene. Student A used an ordinary laboratory thermometer calibrated in 0.1 °C units. Student B used a thermometer certified by NIST (National Institute of Standards and Technology) and calibrated in 0.01 °C units. Their results were as follows:

Student A: 5.2 °C, 5.7 °C, 5.5 °C, 5.2 °C

Student B: 5.48 °C, 5.52 °C, 5.50 °C, 5.54 °C

Calculate the average value for A and B and, knowing the freezing point of benzene is 5.50 °C (and using kelvins for temperature), calculate the percent error for each student. Which student has the smaller error?

Standard Deviation

Laboratory measurements can be in error for two basic reasons. First, "determinate" errors are caused by faulty instruments or human errors such as incorrect record keeping. Second, so-called indeterminate or random errors arise from uncertainties in a measurement. One way to judge the indeterminate error in a result is to calculate the standard deviation.

The **standard deviation** of a series of measurements is *equal to the square root of the sum of the squares of the deviations for each measurement from the average, divided by one less than the number of measurements.* It has a precise statistical significance: Assuming a large number of measurements is used to calculate the average, slightly more than 68% of the values collected are expected to be within one standard deviation of the value determined, and 95% are within two standard deviations.

Suppose you carefully measured the mass of water delivered by a 10-mL pipet. (A pipet containing a green solution is shown in Figure 4.) For five attempts at the measurement (shown in column 2 of the following table), the standard deviation is found as follows. First, the average of the measurements is calculated (here, 9.984). Next, the deviation of each individual measurement from this value is determined (column 3). These values are squared, giving the values in column 4, and the sum of these values is determined. The standard deviation is then calculated by dividing this sum by 4, the number of determinations minus 1, and taking the square root of the result.

Determination	Measured Mass (g)	Difference Between Measurement and Average (g)	Square of Difference
1	9.990	0.006	4×10^{-5}
2	9.993	0.009	8×10^{-5}
3	9.973	−0.011	12×10^{-5}
4	9.980	−0.004	2×10^{-5}
5	9.982	−0.002	0.4×10^{-5}

$$\text{Average mass} = 9.984 \text{ g}$$

$$\text{Sum of squares of differences} = 26 \times 10^{-5}$$

$$\text{Standard deviation} = \sqrt{\frac{26 \times 10^{-5}}{4}} = 0.008$$

The standard deviation calculation would tell a reader that if this experiment were repeated, a majority of the values would fall in the range from 9.976 g to 9.992 g (± 0.008 g from the average value).

REVIEW & CHECK FOR SECTION 2

Two students were assigned to determine the mass of a sample of an unknown liquid. Student A used an ordinary laboratory balance that could determine mass to ±0.01 g. Student B used an analytical balance that could measure mass to ±0.1 mg. Each made four measurements, giving the following results:

Student A: 8.19 g, 8.22 g, 8.21 g, 8.25 g

Student B: 8.2210 g, 8.2210 g, 8.2209 g, 8.2210 g

1. What is the standard deviation for Student A?

   (a) 0.2 g (b) 0.02 g (c) 0.03 g (d) 0.04 g

2. Which student is more precise?

   (a) A (b) B

Eiffel Tower (Paris, France).

3 Mathematics of Chemistry

Exponential or Scientific Notation

The Eiffel Tower, built in 1889, is the tallest building in Paris. It was designed by the French architect Gustave Eiffel to mark the centennial of the French Revolution. The Tower, constructed of very pure iron, is as tall as an 81-story building. It was supposed to be dismantled in 1909, but the building still stands as a symbol of Paris. Some quantitative information on the structure is collected in the following table:

Eiffel Tower Characteristics	**Quantitative Information**
Height	324 meters (m)
Mass of iron	6.6×10^3 kilograms (kg)
Volume of iron	7.5 cubic meters (m^3)
Number of iron pieces	1.8×10^4 pieces
Approximate number of visitors annually	6.6×10^6 people

Some of the data on the Tower are expressed in **fixed notation** (324 meters), whereas other data are expressed in **exponential,** or **scientific, notation** (6.6×10^3 kilograms). Scientific notation is a way of presenting very large or very small numbers in a compact and consistent form that simplifies calculations. Because of its convenience, scientific notation is widely used in sciences.

In scientific notation a number is expressed as the product of two numbers: $N \times 10^n$. N is the *digit term* and is a number between 1 and 9.9999. . . . The second number, 10^n, the *exponential term*, is some integer power of 10. For example, 1234 is written in scientific notation as 1.234×10^3, or 1.234 multiplied by 10 three times:

$$1234 = 1.234 \times 10^1 \times 10^1 \times 10^1 = 1.234 \times 10^3$$

Conversely, a number less than 1, such as 0.01234, is written as 1.234×10^{-2}. This notation tells us that 1.234 should be divided twice by 10 to obtain 0.01234:

$$0.01234 = \frac{1.234}{10^1 \times 10^1} = 1.234 \times 10^{-1} \times 10^{-1} = 1.234 \times 10^{-2}$$

When converting a number to scientific notation, notice that the exponent n is positive if the number is greater than 1 and negative if the number is less than 1. The value of n is the number of places by which the decimal is shifted to obtain the number in scientific notation:

$$1\,2\,3\,4\,5. = 1.2345 \times 10^4$$

(a) Decimal shifted four places to the left. Therefore, n is positive and equal to 4.

$$0.0\,0\,1\,2 = 1.2 \times 10^{-3}$$

(b) Decimal shifted three places to the right. Therefore, n is negative and equal to 3.

If you wish to convert a number in scientific notation to one using fixed notation (that is, not using powers of 10), the procedure is reversed:

$$6\,.\,2\,7\,3 \times 10^2 = 627.3$$

(a) Decimal point moved two places to the right because n is positive and equal to 2.

$$0\ 0\ 6.273 \times 10^{-3} = 0.006273$$

(b) Decimal point shifted three places to the left because n is negative and equal to 3.

In chemistry, you will often have to use numbers in exponential notation in mathematical operations. The following five operations are important:

- *Adding and Subtracting Numbers Expressed in Scientific Notation*
  When adding or subtracting two numbers, first convert them to the same powers of 10. The digit terms are then added or subtracted as appropriate:

$$(1.234 \times 10^{-3}) + (5.623 \times 10^{-2}) = (0.1234 \times 10^{-2}) + (5.623 \times 10^{-2})$$
$$= 5.746 \times 10^{-2}$$

- *Multiplication of Numbers Expressed in Scientific Notation*
  The digit terms are multiplied in the usual manner, and the exponents are added. The result is expressed with a digit term with only one nonzero digit to the left of the decimal place:

$$(6.0 \times 10^{23}) \times (2.0 \times 10^{-2}) = (6.0)(2.0 \times 10^{23-2}) = 12 \times 10^{21} = 1.2 \times 10^{22}$$

- *Division of Numbers Expressed in Scientific Notation*
  The digit terms are divided in the usual manner, and the exponents are subtracted. The quotient is written with one nonzero digit to the left of the decimal in the digit term:

$$\frac{7.60 \times 10^3}{1.23 \times 10^2} = \frac{7.60}{1.23} \times 10^{3-2} = 6.18 \times 10^1$$

- *Powers of Numbers Expressed in Scientific Notation*
  When raising a number in exponential notation to a power, treat the digit term in the usual manner. The exponent is then multiplied by the number indicating the power:

$$(5.28 \times 10^3)^2 = (5.28)^2 \times 10^{3\times2} = 27.9 \times 10^6 = 2.79 \times 10^7$$

- *Roots of Numbers Expressed in Scientific Notation*
  Unless you use an electronic calculator, the number must first be put into a form in which the exponent is exactly divisible by the root. For example, for a square root, the exponent should be divisible by 2. The root of the digit term is found in the usual way, and the exponent is divided by the desired root:

$$\sqrt{3.6 \times 10^7} = \sqrt{36 \times 10^6} = \sqrt{36} \times \sqrt{10^6} = 6.0 \times 10^3$$

Comparing Earth and a Plant Cell—Powers of 10
Earth = 12,760,000 meters wide
= 12.76 million meters
= 1.276×10^7 meters
Plant cell = 0.00001276 meter wide
= 12.76 millionths of a meter
= 1.276×10^{-5} meters

Significant Figures

In most experiments, several kinds of measurements must be made, and some can be made more precisely than others. It is common sense that a result calculated from experimental data can be no more precise than the least precise piece of information that went into the calculation. This is where the rules for significant figures come in. **Significant figures** are the digits in a measured quantity that are known exactly plus one digit that is inexact.

Determining Significant Figures

Suppose we place a new U.S. dime on the pan of a standard laboratory balance such as the one pictured in Figure 6 and observe a mass of 2.265 g. This number has four significant figures or digits because all four numbers are observed. However, you will learn from experience that the final digit (5) is somewhat uncertain because you may notice the balance readings can change slightly and give masses of 2.264, 2.265, and

FIGURE 6 **Standard laboratory balance and significant figures.** Such balances can determine the mass of an object to the nearest milligram. Thus, an object may have a mass of 13.456 g (13456 mg, five significant figures), 0.123 g (123 mg, three significant figures), or 0.072 g (72 mg, two significant figures).

PROBLEM SOLVING TIP 1
Using Your Calculator

You will be performing a number of calculations in general chemistry, most of them using an electronic calculator. Many different types of calculators are available, so be sure to consult your calculator manual for specific instructions to enter scientific notation and to find powers and roots of numbers.

1. Scientific Notation
When entering a number such as 1.23×10^{-4} into your calculator, you first enter 1.23 and then press a key marked EE or EXP (or something similar). This enters the "$\times$ 10" portion of the notation for you. You then complete the entry by keying in the exponent of the number, 4. (To change the exponent from +4 to −4, press the "+/−" key.)

A common error made by students is to enter 1.23, press the multiply key ($\times$), and then key in 10 before finishing by pressing EE or EXP followed by −4. This gives you an entry that is 10 times too large.

Two final points should be made concerning scientific notation. First, be aware that calculators and computers often express a number such as 1.23×10^3 as 1.23E3 or 6.45×10^{-5} as 6.45E-5. Second, some electronic calculators can readily convert numbers in fixed notation to scientific notation.

2. Powers of Numbers
Electronic calculators often offer two methods of raising a number to a power. To square a number, enter the number and then press the x^2 key. To raise a number to any power, use the y^x (or similar key such as ^). For example, to raise 1.42×10^2 to the fourth power:

1. Enter 1.42×10^2.
2. Press y^x.
3. Enter 4 (this should appear on the display).
4. Press =, and 4.0659×10^8 appears on the display.

3. Roots of Numbers
A general procedure for finding any root is to use the y^x key. For a square root, x is 0.5 (or 1/2), whereas x is 0.3333 (or 1/3) for a cube root, 0.25 (or 1/4) for a fourth root, and so on. For example, to find the fourth root of 5.6×10^{-10}:

1. Enter the number.
2. Press the y^x key.
3. Enter the desired root. Because we want the fourth root, enter 0.25.
4. Press =. The answer here is 4.9×10^{-3}.

To make sure you are using your calculator correctly, try these sample calculations:

1. $(6.02 \times 10^{23})(2.26 \times 10^{-5})/367$ (Answer = 3.71×10^{16})
2. $(4.32 \times 10^{-3})^3$ (Answer = 8.06×10^{-8})
3. $(4.32 \times 10^{-3})^{1/3}$ (Answer = 0.163)

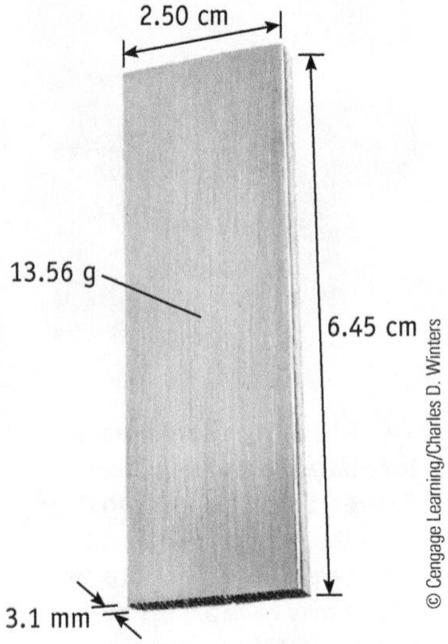

FIGURE 7 Data used to determine the density of a metal.

2.266, with the mass of 2.265 observed most of the time. Thus, of the four significant digits (2.265) the last (5) is uncertain. In general, *in a number representing a scientific measurement, the last digit to the right is taken to be inexact.* Unless stated otherwise, it is common practice to assign an uncertainty of ±1 to the last significant digit.

Suppose you want to calculate the density of a piece of metal (Figure 7). The mass and dimensions were determined by standard laboratory techniques. Most of these data have two digits to the right of the decimal, but they have different numbers of significant figures.

Measurement	Data Collected	Significant Figures
Mass of metal	13.56 g	4
Length	6.45 cm	3
Width	2.50 cm	3
Thickness	3.1 mm = 0.31 cm	2

The quantity 0.31 cm has two significant figures. The 3 in 0.31 is exactly known, but the 1 is uncertain. That is, the thickness of the metal piece may have been as small as 0.30 cm or as large as 0.32 cm. In the case of the width of the piece, you

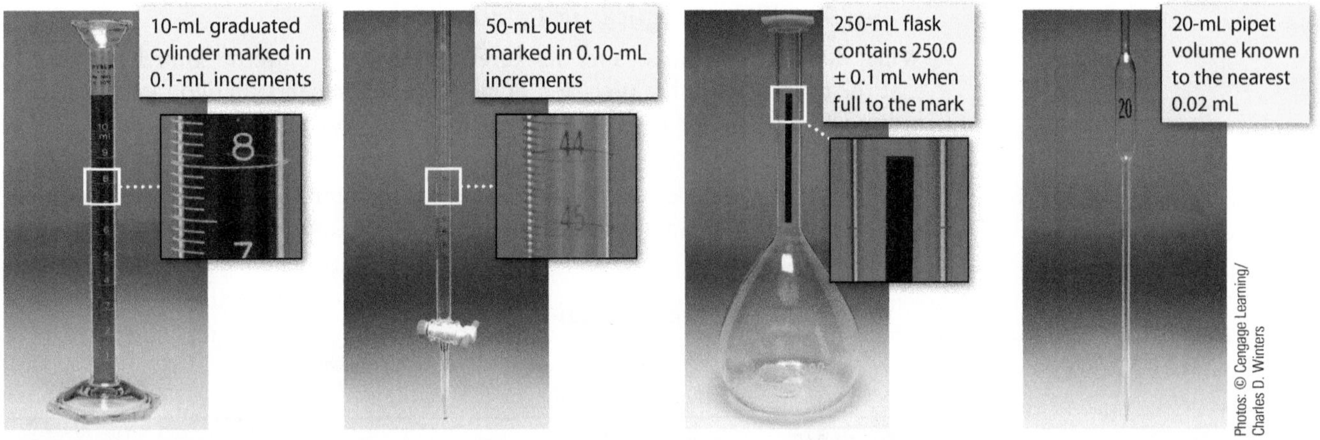

The 10-mL graduated cylinder is marked in 0.1-mL increments; its contents to be estimated to 0.01-mL. However, graduated cylinders are not precision glassware. You can expect no more than 2 significant figures when reading a volume.

A 50-mL buret is marked in 0.10-mL increments, but it may be read with greater precision (0.01 mL).

A volumetric flask is meant to be filled to the mark on the neck. For a 250-mL flask, the volume is known to the nearest 0.1 mL, so the flask contains 250.0 ± 0.1 mL when full to the mark (four significant figures).

A pipet is like a volumetric flask in that it is filled to the mark on its neck. For a 20-mL pipet the volume is known to the nearest 0.02 mL.

FIGURE 8 **Glassware and significant figures.**

found it to be 2.50 cm, where 2.5 is known with certainty, but the final 0 is uncertain. There are three significant figures in 2.50.

When you read a number in a problem or collect data in the laboratory (Figure 8), how do you determine which digits are significant?

First, is the number an exact number or a measured quantity? If it is an exact number, you don't have to worry about the number of significant figures. For example, there are exactly 100 cm in 1 m. We could add as many zeros after the decimal place as we want, and the expression would still be true. Using this number in a calculation will not affect how many significant figures you can report in your answer.

If, however, the number is a measured value, you must take into account significant figures. The number of significant figures in our data above is clear, with the possible exception of 0.31 and 2.50. Are the zeroes significant?

1. *Zeroes between two other significant digits are significant.* For example, the zero in 103 is significant.
2. *Zeroes to the right of a nonzero number, and also to the right of a decimal place, are significant.* For example, in the number 2.50 cm, the zero is significant.
3. *Zeroes that are placeholders are not significant.* There are two types of numbers that fall under this rule.
   (a) The first are decimal numbers with zeroes that occur *before* the first nonzero digit. For example, in 0.0013, only the 1 and the 3 are significant; the zeroes are not. This number has two significant figures.
   (b) The second are *numbers with trailing zeroes* that must be there to indicate the magnitude of the number. For example, the zeroes in the number 13,000 may or may not be significant; it depends on whether they were measured or not. To avoid confusion with regard to such numbers, *we shall assume in this book that trailing zeroes are significant when there is a decimal point to the right of the last zero.* Thus, we would say that 13,000 has only two significant figures but that 13,000. has five. The best way to be unambiguous when writing numbers with trailing zeroes is to use scientific notation. For example 1.300×10^4 indicates four significant figures, whereas 1.3×10^4 indicates two.

Zeroes and Common Laboratory Mistakes We often see students find the mass of a chemical on a balance and fail to write down trailing zeroes. For example, if you find the mass is 2.340 g, the final zero is significant and must be reported as part of the measured value. The number 2.34 g has only three significant figures and implies the 4 is uncertain, when in fact the balance reading indicated the 4 is certain.

Using Significant Figures in Calculations

When doing calculations using measured quantities, we follow some basic rules so that the results reflect the precision of all the measurements that go into the calculations. *The rules used for significant figures in this book are as follows:*

Rule 1. When adding or subtracting numbers, the number of decimal places in the answer is equal to the number of decimal places in the number with the fewest digits after the decimal.

0.12	2 decimal places
+ 1.9	1 decimal place
+10.925	3 decimal places
12.945	3 decimal places

The sum should be reported as 12.9, a number with one decimal place, because 1.9 has only one decimal place.

Rule 2. In multiplication or division, the number of significant figures in the answer is determined by the quantity with the fewest significant figures.

$$\frac{0.01208}{0.0236} = 0.512, \text{ or in scientific notation, } 5.12 \times 10^{-1}$$

Because 0.0236 has only three significant digits, while 0.01208 has four, the answer should have three significant digits.

Rule 3. When a number is rounded off, the last digit to be retained is increased by one only if the following digit is 5 or greater.

Full Number	Number Rounded to Three Significant Digits
12.696	12.7
16.349	16.3
18.35	18.4
18.351	18.4

Now let us apply these rules to calculate the density of the piece of metal in Figure 7.

$$\text{Length} \times \text{width} \times \text{thickness} = \text{volume}$$

$$6.45 \text{ cm} \times 2.50 \text{ cm} \times 0.31 \text{ cm} = 5.0 \text{ cm}^3$$

$$\text{Density} = \frac{\text{mass (g)}}{\text{volume (cm}^3)} = \frac{13.56 \text{ g}}{5.0 \text{ cm}^3} = 2.7 \text{ g/cm}^3$$

The calculated density has two significant figures because *a calculated result can be no more precise than the least precise data used*, and here the thickness has only two significant figures.

One last word on significant figures and calculations: When working problems, you should do the calculation with all the digits allowed by your calculator and round off only at the end of the calculation. *Rounding off in the middle of a calculation can introduce errors.*

EXAMPLE 3

Using Significant Figures

Problem An example of a calculation you will do later in the book (▶ Chapter 10) is

$$\text{Volume of gas (L)} = \frac{(0.120)(0.08206)(273.15 + 23)}{(230/760.0)}$$

Calculate the final answer to the correct number of significant figures.

What Do You Know? You know the rules for determining the number of significant figures for each number in the equation.

Strategy First decide on the number of significant figures represented by each number and then apply Rules 1–3.

Solution

NUMBER	NUMBER OF SIGNIFICANT FIGURES	COMMENTS
0.120	3	The trailing 0 is significant.
0.08206	4	The first 0 to the immediate right of the decimal is not significant.
273.15 + 23 = 296	3	23 has no decimal places, so the sum can have none.
230/760.0 = 0.30	2	230 has two significant figures because the last zero is not significant. In contrast, there is a decimal point in 760.0, so there are four significant digits. The quotient will have only two significant digits.

Multiplication and division gives 9.6363 ... L. However, analysis shows that one of the pieces of information is known to only two significant figures. Therefore, you should report the volume of gas as 9.6 L, a number with two significant figures.

Think about Your Answer Be especially careful when you add or subtract two numbers because it is easy to make significant figure errors when doing so.

Check Your Understanding

What is the result of the following calculation?

$$x = \frac{(110.7 - 64)}{(0.056)(0.00216)}$$

REVIEW & CHECK FOR SECTION 3

1. How many significant figures are indicated by 2.33×10^3?

   (a) 1 (b) 2 (c) 3 (d) 4

2. How many significant figures are indicated by 200?

   (a) 1 (b) 2 (c) 3

3. What is the sum of 10.26 g and 0.063 g?

   (a) 10.323 g (b) 10.32 g (c) 10.3 g (d) 10. g

4. What is the product of 10.26 cm and 0.063 cm?

(a) 0.6464 cm^2 (b) 0.646 cm^2 (c) 0.65 cm^2 (d) 0.6 cm^2

4 Problem Solving by Dimensional Analysis

Figure 7 illustrated the data that were collected to determine the density of a piece of metal. The thickness was measured in millimeters, whereas the length and width were measured in centimeters. To find the volume of the sample in cubic centimeters, we first had to have the length, width, and thickness in the same units, so we converted the thickness to centimeters.

$$3.1\ \cancel{\text{mm}} \times \frac{1\ \text{cm}}{10\ \cancel{\text{mm}}} = 0.31\ \text{cm}$$

Here, we multiplied the number we wished to convert (3.1 mm) by a *conversion factor* (1 cm/10 mm) to produce the result in the desired unit (0.31 cm). Notice that units are treated like numbers. Because the unit "mm" is in both the numerator and the denominator, the units are said to "cancel out." This leaves the answer in centimeters, the desired unit.

This approach to problem solving is often called **dimensional analysis** (or sometimes the **factor-label method**). *It is a general problem-solving approach that uses the dimensions or units of each value to guide us through calculations.*

Using Conversion Factors and Doing Calculations As you work problems in this book and read Example problems, notice that proceeding from given information to an answer very often involves a series of multiplications. That is, we multiply the given data by a conversion factor, multiply the answer of that step by another factor, and so on, to the answer.

A **conversion factor** expresses the equivalence of a measurement in two different units (1 cm ≡ 10 mm; 1 g ≡ 1000 mg; 12 eggs ≡ 1 dozen; 12 inches ≡ 1 foot). Because the numerator and the denominator describe the same quantity, the conversion factor is equivalent to the number 1. Therefore, multiplication by this factor does not change the measured quantity, only its units. A conversion factor is always written so that it has the form "new units divided by units of original number."

$$\underbrace{\text{Number in original unit}}_{\text{Quantity to express in new units}} \underbrace{\left[\frac{\text{new unit}}{\text{original unit}}\right]}_{\text{Conversion factor}} = \underbrace{\text{new number in new unit}}_{\text{Quantity now expressed in new units}}$$

EXAMPLE 4

Using Conversion Factors and Dimensional Analysis

Problem Oceanographers often express the density of sea water in units of kilograms per cubic meter. If the density of sea water is 1.025 g/cm^3 at 15 °C, what is its density in kilograms per cubic meter?

What Do You Know? You know the density in a unit involving mass in grams and volume in cubic centimeters. Each of these has to be changed to its equivalent in kilograms and cubic meters, respectively.

Strategy To simplify this problem, break it into three steps. First, change the mass in grams to kilograms. Next, convert the volume in cubic centimeters to cubic meters. Finally, calculate the density by dividing the mass in kilograms by the volume in cubic meters.

Solution First convert the mass in grams to a mass in kilograms.

$$1.025\ \cancel{g} \times \frac{1\ \text{kg}}{1000\ \cancel{g}} = 1.025 \times 10^{-3}\ \text{kg}$$

No conversion factor is available in one of our tables to directly change units of cubic centimeters to cubic meters. You can find one, however, by cubing (raising to the third power) the relation between the meter and the centimeter:

$$1\ \text{cm}^3 \times \left(\frac{1\ \text{m}}{100\ \text{cm}}\right)^3 = 1\ \cancel{\text{cm}^3} \times \left(\frac{1\ \text{m}^3}{1 \times 10^6\ \cancel{\text{cm}^3}}\right) = 1 \times 10^{-6}\ \text{m}^3$$

This tells us that 1 cm^3 is equivalent to $1 \times 10^{-6}\ \text{m}^3$. Therefore, the density of sea water is

$$\text{Density} = \frac{1.025 \times 10^{-3}\ \text{kg}}{1 \times 10^{-6}\ \text{m}^3} = 1025\ \text{kg/m}^3$$

Think about Your Answer Densities in units of kg/m^3 can often be large numbers. For example, the density of platinum is 21,450 kg/m^3, and dry air has a density of 1.204 kg/m^3.

Check Your Understanding

The density of gold is 19,320 kg/m^3. What is this density in g/cm^3?

Who Is Right—You or the Book?
If your answer to a problem in this book does not quite agree with the answers in Appendix N, the discrepancy may be the result of rounding the answer after each step and then using that rounded answer in the next step. This book follows these conventions:

(a) Final answers to numerical problems result from retaining several digits more than the number required by significant figures throughout the calculation and rounding only at the end.

(b) In Example problems, the answer to each step is given to the correct number of significant figures for that step, but more digits are carried to the next step. The number of significant figures in the final answer is dictated by the number of significant figures in the original data.

REVIEW & CHECK FOR SECTION 4

1. A lake has an area of $2.33 \times 10^7\ \text{m}^2$. What is this area in square kilometers?

   (a) 23.3 km^2 (b) $2.33 \times 10^{10}\ \text{km}^2$ (c) $23.3 \times 10^{-3}\ \text{km}^2$ (d) $2.33 \times 10^4\ \text{km}^2$

5 Graphs and Graphing

In a number of instances in this text, graphs are used when analyzing experimental data with a goal of obtaining a mathematical equation that may help us predict new results. The procedure used will often result in a straight line, which has the equation

$$y = mx + b$$

In this equation, y is usually referred to as the dependent variable; its value is determined from (that is, is dependent on) the values of x, m, and b. In this equation, x is called the independent variable, and m is the slope of the line. The parameter b is the y-intercept—that is, the value of y when $x = 0$. Let us use an example to investigate two things: (1) how to construct a graph from a set of data points and (2) how to derive an equation for the line generated by the data.

A set of data points to be graphed is presented in Figure 9. We first mark off each axis in increments of the values of x and y. Here, our x-data are within the range from −2 to 4, so the x-axis is marked off in increments of 1 unit. The *y-data fall within the range from 0 to 2.5, so we mark off the* y-axis in increments of 0.5. Each data point is marked as a circle on the graph.

After plotting the points on the graph (round circles), we draw a straight line that comes as close as possible to representing the trend in the data. (Do not just connect the dots!) Because there is always some inaccuracy in experimental data, the straight line we draw is unlikely to pass exactly through every point.

CASE STUDY Out of Gas!

On July 23, 1983, a new Boeing 767 jet aircraft was flying at 26,000 ft from Montreal to Edmonton as Air Canada Flight 143. Warning buzzers sounded in the cockpit. One of the world's largest planes was now a glider—the plane had run out of fuel!

How did this modern airplane, having the latest technology, run out of fuel? A simple mistake had been made in calculating the amount of fuel required for the flight!

Like all Boeing 767s, this plane had a sophisticated fuel gauge, but it was not working properly. The plane was still allowed to fly, however, because there is an alternative method of determining the quantity of fuel in the tanks. Mechanics can use a stick, much like the oil dipstick in an automobile engine, to measure the fuel level in each of the three tanks. The mechanics in Montreal read the dipsticks, which were calibrated in centimeters, and translated those readings to a volume in liters. According to this, the plane had a total of 7682 L of fuel.

Pilots always calculate fuel quantities in units of mass because they need to know the total mass of the plane before take-off. Air Canada pilots had always calculated the quantity of fuel in pounds, but the new 767's fuel consumption was given in kilograms. The pilots knew that 22,300 kg of fuel was required for the trip. If 7682 L of fuel remained in the tanks, how much had to be added? This involved using the fuel's density to convert 7682 L to a mass in kilograms. The mass of fuel to be added could then be calculated, and that mass converted to a volume of fuel to be added.

The First Officer of the plane asked a mechanic for the conversion factor to do the volume-to-mass conversion, and the mechanic replied "1.77." Using that number, the First Officer and the mechanics calculated that 4917 L of fuel should be added. But later calculations showed that this is only about one fourth of the required amount of fuel! Why? Because no one thought about the units of the number 1.77. They realized later that 1.77 has units of pounds per liter and not kilograms per liter.

Out of fuel, the plane could not make it to Winnipeg, so controllers directed them to the town of Gimli and to a small airport abandoned by the Royal Canadian Air Force. After gliding for almost 30 minutes, the plane approached the Gimli runway. The runway, however, had been converted to a race course for cars, and a race was underway. Furthermore, a steel barrier had been erected across the runway. Nonetheless, the pilot managed to touch down very near the end of the runway. The plane sped down the concrete strip; the nose wheel collapsed; several tires blew—and the plane skidded safely to a stop just before the barrier. The Gimli glider had made it! And somewhere an aircraft mechanic is paying more attention to units on numbers.

Wayne Glowacki/Winnipeg Free Press

The Gimli glider. After running out of fuel, Air Canada Flight 143 glided 29 minutes before landing on an abandoned airstrip at Gimli, Manitoba, near Winnipeg.

Questions:

1. What is the fuel density in units of kg/L?
2. What mass and what volume of fuel should have been loaded? (1 lb = 453.6 g) (See Study Question 62, page 43f.)

Answers to these questions are available in Appendix N.

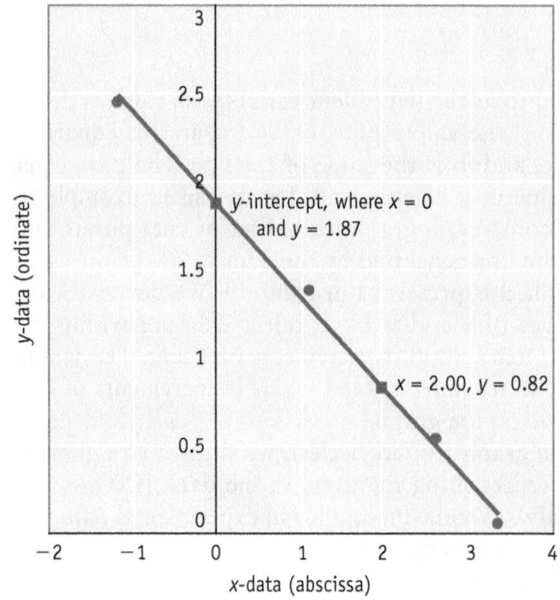

Experimental data

x	y
3.35	0.0565
2.59	0.520
1.08	1.38
−1.19	2.45

Using the points marked with a square, the slope of the line is:

$$\text{Slope} = \frac{\Delta y}{\Delta x} = \frac{0.82 - 1.87}{2.00 - 0.00} = -0.525$$

FIGURE 9 **Plotting data.** Using Microsoft Excel with these data and doing a linear regression analysis, we find $y = -0.525x + 1.87$.

To identify the specific equation corresponding to our data, we must determine the y-intercept (b) and slope (m) for the equation $y = mx + b$. The y-intercept is the point at which $x = 0$ and thus is the point where the line intersects the y-axis. The slope is determined by selecting two points *on the line* (marked with squares in Figure 9) and calculating the difference in values of y ($\Delta y = y_2 - y_1$) and x ($\Delta x = x_2 - x_1$). The slope of the line is then the ratio of these differences, $m = \Delta y/\Delta x$. With the slope and intercept now known, we can write the equation for the line

$$y = -0.525x + 1.87$$

and we can use this equation to calculate y-values for points that are not part of our original set of x–y data. For example, when $x = 1.50$, we find $y = 1.08$.

Determining the Slope with a Computer Program—Least-Squares Analysis Generally, the easiest method of determining the slope and intercept of a straight line (and thus the line's equation) is to use a program such as Microsoft Excel or Apple's Numbers. These programs perform a "least-squares" or "linear regression" analysis and give the best straight line based on the data. (This line is referred to in Excel or Numbers as a trendline.)

REVIEW & CHECK FOR SECTION 5

To find the mass of 32 jelly beans, we weighed several samples of beans.

Number of Beans	Mass (g)
5	12.82
11	27.14
16	39.30
24	59.04

Plot these data with the number of beans on the horizontal or x-axis and the mass of beans on the vertical or y-axis.

1. What is the approximate slope of the line?

   (a) 2.4 (b) 0.42 (c) 3.2 (d) 4.8

2. Use your graph or equation of a straight line to calculate the mass of 32 jelly beans.

   (a) 150 g (b) 100 g (c) 13 g (d) 78 g

6 Problem Solving and Chemical Arithmetic

Many aspects of chemistry involve analyzing quantitative information, so problem solving will be important in your success. In every chapter we will demonstrate how to work through problems step by step. However, as in any endeavor, careful planning is important, and our students usually find it helpful to follow a definite plan as illustrated in all of the examples in the book.

Strategy Maps Many Example problems in this book are accompanied by a Strategy Map that outlines a route to a solution.

STEP 1 *State the Problem.* Read it carefully—and then read it again.

STEP 2 *What Do You Know?* Determine specifically what you are trying to calculate or conclude and what information you are given. What key principles are involved? What information is known or not known? What information might be there just to place the question in the context of chemistry? Organize the information to see what is required and to discover the relationships among the data given. Try writing the information down in table form. If the information is numerical, be sure to include units.

STEP 3 *Strategy.* One of the greatest difficulties for a student in introductory chemistry is picturing what is being asked for. Try sketching a picture of the situation involved. For example, we sketched a picture of the piece of metal whose density we wanted to calculate and put the dimensions on the drawing (see Figure 7).

Develop a plan. Have you done a problem of this type before? If not, perhaps the problem is really just a combination of several simpler ones you have seen

General Strategy Map

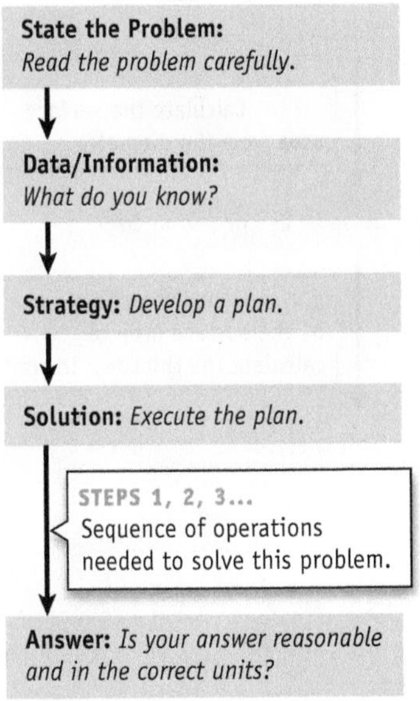

before. Break it down into those simpler components. Try reasoning backward from the units of the answer. What data do you need to find an answer in those units? Drawing a strategy map such as that shown in the margin may help you in planning how you will go about solving the problem.

STEP 4 *Solution.* Execute the plan. Carefully write down each step of the problem, being sure to keep track of the units on each number. (Do the units cancel to give you the answer in the desired units?) Don't skip steps. Don't do anything except the simplest steps in your head. Students often say they got a problem wrong because they "made a stupid mistake." Your instructors—and book authors—also make them, and it is usually because they don't take the time to write down the steps of the problem clearly.

STEP 5 *Think about Your Answer.* Ask yourself whether the answer is reasonable and if you obtained an answer in the correct units.

STEP 6 *Check Your Understanding.* In this text each Example is followed by another problem for you to try. (The solutions to those questions are given by chapter in Appendix N.) When doing homework Study Questions, try one of the *Practicing Skills* questions to see if you understand the basic ideas.

The steps we outline for problem solving are ones that many students have found to be successful, so try to conscientiously follow this scheme. But also be flexible. The "What Do You Know?" and "Strategy" steps often blend into a single set of ideas.

Strategy Map for Example 5

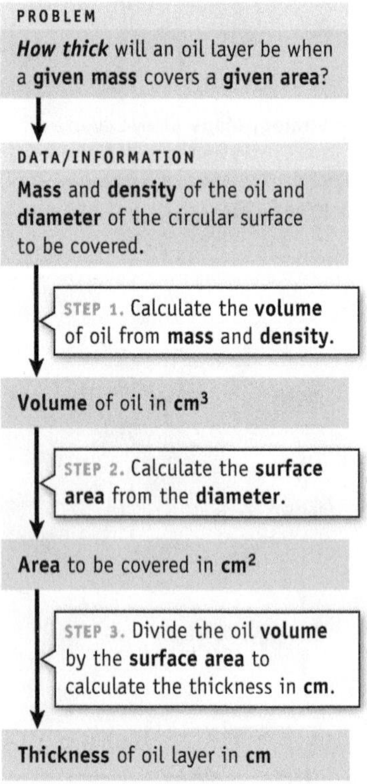

EXAMPLE 5

Problem Solving

Problem A mineral oil has a density of 0.875 g/cm^3. Suppose you spread 0.75 g of this oil over the surface of water in a large dish with an inner diameter of 21.6 cm. How thick is the oil layer? Express the thickness in centimeters.

What Do You Know? You know the mass and density of the oil and the diameter of the surface to be covered.

Strategy It is often useful to begin solving such problems by sketching a picture of the situation.

This helps you recognize that the solution to the problem is to find the volume of the oil on the water. If you know the volume, then you can find the thickness because

$$\text{Volume of oil layer} = (\text{thickness of layer}) \times (\text{area of oil layer})$$

So, you need two things: (1) the volume of the oil layer and (2) the area of the layer. The volume can be found using the mass and density of the oil. The area can be found because the oil will form a circle, which has an area equal to $\pi \times r^2$ (where r is the radius of the dish).

Solution First, calculate the volume of oil. The mass of the oil layer is known, so combining the mass of oil with its density gives the volume of the oil used:

$$0.75\ \cancel{g} \times \frac{1\ \text{cm}^3}{0.875\ \cancel{g}} = 0.86\ \text{cm}^3$$

Next, calculate the area of the oil layer. The oil is spread over a circular surface, whose area is given by

$$\text{Area} = \pi \times (\text{radius})^2$$

The radius of the oil layer is half its diameter (= 21.6 cm) or 10.8 cm, so

$$\text{Area of oil layer} = (3.142)(10.8\ \text{cm})^2 = 366\ \text{cm}^2$$

With the volume and the area of the oil layer known, the thickness can be calculated.

$$\text{Thickness} = \frac{\text{volume}}{\text{area}} = \frac{0.86\ \text{cm}^3}{366\ \text{cm}^2} = 0.0023\ \text{cm}$$

Think about Your Answer In the volume calculation, the calculator shows 0.857143. . . . The quotient should have two significant figures because 0.75 has two significant figures, so the result of this step is 0.86 cm^3. In the area calculation, the calculator shows 366.435. . . . The answer to this step should have three significant figures because 10.8 has three. When these interim results are combined in calculating thickness, however, the final result can have only two significant figures. Remember that premature rounding can lead to errors.

Check Your Understanding

A particular paint has a density of 0.914 g/cm^3. You need to cover a wall that is 7.6 m long and 2.74 m high with a paint layer 0.13 mm thick. What volume of paint (in liters) is required? What is the mass (in grams) of the paint layer?

REVIEW & CHECK FOR SECTION 6

1. A spool of copper wire has a mass of 4.26 kg. How long is the wire in the spool if the wire has a diameter of 2.2 mm? (The density of copper is 8.96 g/cm^3.)

   (a) 280 m (b) 220 m (c) 130 m (d) 14 m

© Cengage Learning/ Charles D. Winters

▲ denotes challenging questions.

Blue-numbered questions have answers in Appendix N and fully worked solutions in the *Student Solutions Manual.*

Practicing Skills

Temperature Scales

1. Many laboratories use 25 °C as a standard temperature. What is this temperature in kelvins?

2. The temperature on the surface of the Sun is 5.5×10^3 °C. What is this temperature in kelvins?

3. Make the following temperature conversions:

	°C	K
(a)	16	______
(b)	______	370
(c)	40	______

4. Make the following temperature conversions:

	°C	K
(a)	______	77
(b)	63	______
(c)	______	1450

Length, Volume, Mass, and Density

(See Example 1.)

5. A marathon distance race covers a distance of 42.195 km. What is this distance in meters? In miles?

6. The average lead pencil, new and unused, is 19 cm long. What is its length in millimeters? In meters?

7. A standard U.S. postage stamp is 2.5 cm long and 2.1 cm wide. What is the area of the stamp in square centimeters? In square meters?

8. A compact disc has a diameter of 11.8 cm. What is the surface area of the disc in square centimeters? In square meters? [Area of a circle = $(\pi)(\text{radius})^2$]

9. A typical laboratory beaker has a volume of 250. mL. What is its volume in cubic centimeters? In liters? In cubic meters? In cubic decimeters?

10. Some soft drinks are sold in bottles with a volume of 1.5 L. What is this volume in milliliters? In cubic centimeters? In cubic decimeters?

11. A book has a mass of 2.52 kg. What is this mass in grams?

12. A new U.S. dime has a mass of 2.265 g. What is its mass in kilograms? In milligrams?

13. Ethylene glycol, $C_2H_6O_2$, is an ingredient of automobile antifreeze. Its density is 1.11 g/cm^3 at 20 °C. If you need 500. mL of this liquid, what mass of the compound, in grams, is required?

14. A piece of silver metal has a mass of 2.365 g. If the density of silver is 10.5 g/cm^3, what is the volume of the silver?

15. You can identify a metal by carefully determining its density (d). An unknown piece of metal, with a mass of 2.361 g, is 2.35 cm long, 1.34 cm wide, and 1.05 mm thick. Which of the following is the element?
    (a) nickel, d = 8.91 g/cm^3
    (b) titanium, d = 4.50 g/cm^3
    (c) zinc, d = 7.14 g/cm^3
    (d) tin, d = 7.23 g/cm^3

16. Which occupies a larger volume, 600 g of water (with a density of 0.995 g/cm^3) or 600 g of lead (with a density of 11.35 g/cm^3)?

Energy Units

17. You are on a diet that calls for eating no more than 1200 Cal/day. What is this energy in joules?

18. A 2-in. piece of chocolate cake with frosting provides 1670 kJ of energy. What is this in dietary Calories (Cal)?

19. One food product has an energy content of 170 kcal per serving, and another has 280 kJ per serving. Which food provides the greater energy per serving?

20. A can of soft drink (335 mL) provides 130 Calories. A bottle of mixed berry juice (295 mL) provides 630 kJ. Which provides the greater total energy? Which provides the greater energy per milliliter?

Accuracy, Precision, Error, and Standard Deviation

(See Example 2.)

21. You and your lab partner are asked to determine the density of an aluminum bar. The mass is known accurately (to four significant figures). You use a simple metric ruler to measure its dimensions and obtain the results for Method A. Your partner uses a precision micrometer and obtains the results for Method B.

Method A (g/cm^3)	Method B (g/cm^3)
2.2	2.703
2.3	2.701
2.7	2.705
2.4	5.811

The accepted density of aluminum is 2.702 g/cm^3.

(a) Calculate the average density for each method. Should all the experimental results be included in your calculations? If not, justify any omissions.
(b) Calculate the percent error for each method's average value.
(c) Calculate the standard deviation for each set of data.
(d) Which method's average value is more precise? Which method is more accurate?

22. The accepted value of the melting point of pure aspirin is 135 °C. Trying to verify that value, you obtain 134 °C, 136 °C, 133 °C, and 138 °C in four separate trials. Your partner finds 138 °C, 137 °C, 138 °C, and 138 °C.

(a) Calculate the average value and percent error for your data and your partner's data.
(b) Which of you is more precise? More accurate?

Exponential Notation and Significant Figures

(See Example 3.)

23. Express the following numbers in exponential or scientific notation, and give the number of significant figures in each.

(a) 0.054 g
(b) 5462 g
(c) 0.000792 g
(d) 1600 mL

24. Express the following numbers in fixed notation (e.g., $1.23 \times 10^2 = 123$), and give the number of significant figures in each.

(a) 1.623×10^3
(b) 2.57×10^{-4}
(c) 6.32×10^{-2}
(d) 3.404×10^3

25. Carry out the following operations. Provide the answer with the correct number of significant figures.

(a) $(1.52)(6.21 \times 10^{-3})$
(b) $(6.217 \times 10^3) - (5.23 \times 10^2)$
(c) $(6.217 \times 10^3) \div (5.23 \times 10^2)$
(d) $(0.0546)(16.0000)\left[\frac{7.779}{55.85}\right]$

26. Carry out the following operations. Provide the answer with the correct number of significant figures.

(a) $(6.25 \times 10^2)^3$
(b) $\sqrt{2.35 \times 10^{-3}}$
(c) $(2.35 \times 10^{-3})^{1/3}$
(d) $(1.68)\left[\frac{23.56 - 2.3}{1.248 \times 10^3}\right]$

Graphing

27. To determine the average mass of a popcorn kernel, you collect the following data:

Number of kernels	Mass (g)
5	0.836
12	2.162
35	5.801

Plot the data with number of kernels on the x-axis and mass on the y-axis. Draw the best straight line using the points on the graph (or do a least-squares or linear regression analysis using a computer program), and then write the equation for the resulting straight line. What is the slope of the line? What does the slope of the line signify about the mass of a popcorn kernel? What is the mass of 20 popcorn kernels? How many kernels are there in a handful of popcorn with a mass of 20.88 g?

28. Use the following graph to answer the following questions:

(a) What is the value of x when $y = 4.0$?
(b) What is the value of y when $x = 0.30$?
(c) What are the slope and the y-intercept of the line?
(d) What is the value of y when $x = 1.0$?

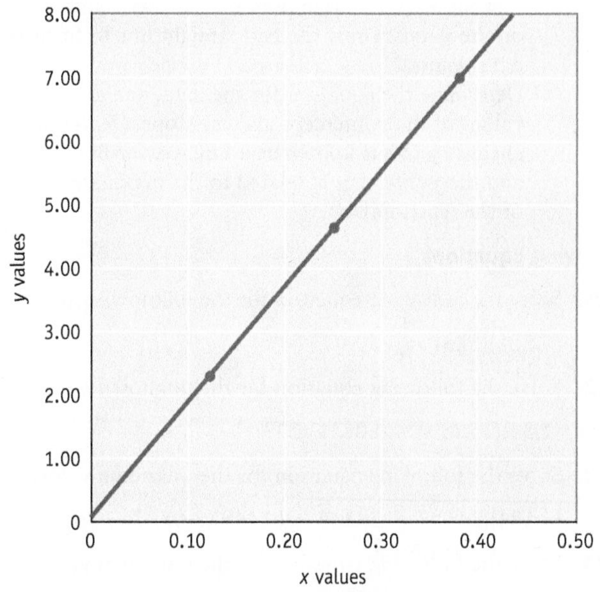

29. Use the graph below to answer the following questions.

(a) Derive the equation for the straight line, $y = mx + b$.
(b) What is the value of y when $x = 6.0$?

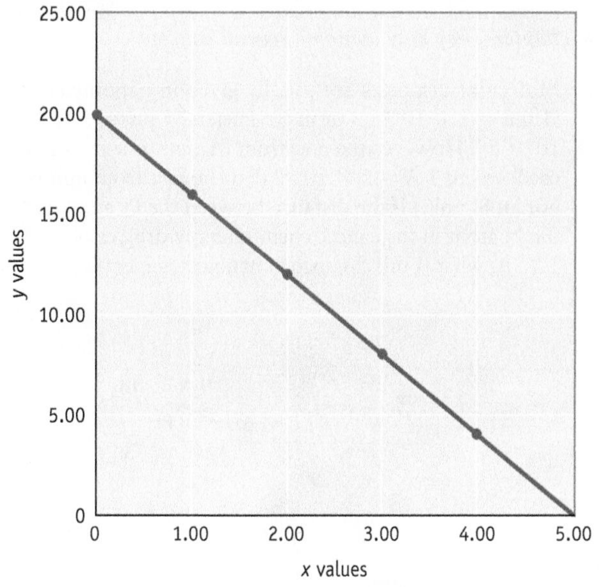

30. The following data were collected in an experiment to determine how an enzyme works in a biochemical reaction.

Amount of H_2O_2	Reaction Speed (amount/second)
1.96	4.75×10^{-5}
1.31	4.03×10^{-5}
0.98	3.51×10^{-5}
0.65	2.52×10^{-5}
0.33	1.44×10^{-5}
0.16	0.585×10^{-5}

(a) Plot these data as 1/amount on the y-axis and 1/speed on the x-axis. Draw the best straight line to fit these data points.
(b) Determine the equation for the data, and give the values of the y-intercept and the slope. (*Note:* In biochemistry this is known as a Lineweaver-Burk plot, and the y-intercept is related to the maximum speed of the reaction.)

Solving Equations

31. Solve the following equation for the unknown value, C.

$$(0.502)(123) = (750.)C$$

32. Solve the following equation for the unknown value, n.

$$(2.34)(15.6) = n(0.0821)(273)$$

33. Solve the following equation for the unknown value, T.

$$(4.184)(244)(T - 292.0) + (0.449)(88.5)(T - 369.0) = 0$$

34. Solve the following equation for the unknown value, n.

$$-246.0 = 1312\left[\frac{1}{2^2} - \frac{1}{n^2}\right]$$

General Questions

These questions are not designated as to type or location in the chapter. They may combine several concepts.

35. Molecular distances are usually given in nanometers ($1 \text{ nm} = 1 \times 10^{-9}$ m) or in picometers ($1 \text{ pm} = 1 \times 10^{-12}$ m). However, the angstrom (Å) unit is sometimes used, where $1 \text{ Å} = 1 \times 10^{-10}$ m. (The angstrom unit is not an SI unit.) If the distance between the Pt atom and the N atom in the cancer chemotherapy drug cisplatin is 1.97 Å, what is this distance in nanometers? In picometers?

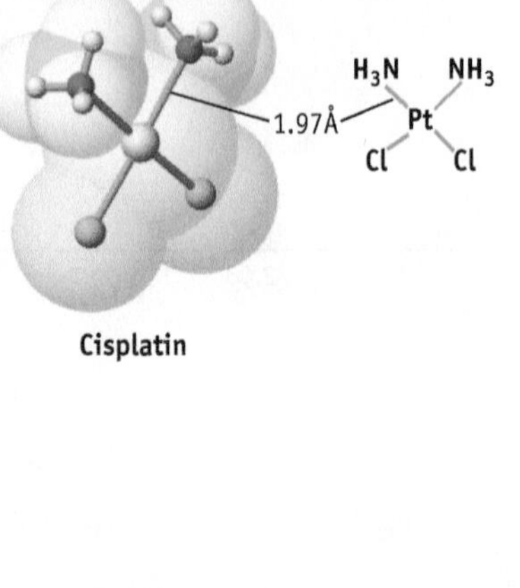

Cisplatin

36. The separation between carbon atoms in diamond is 0.154 nm. What is their separation in meters? In picometers (pm)? In Angstroms (Å)?

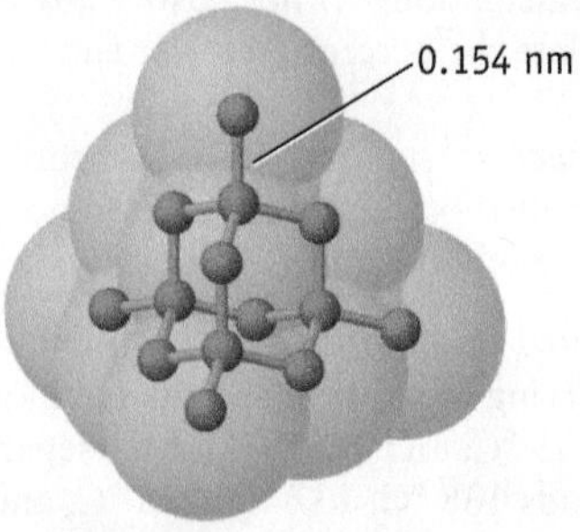

A portion of the diamond structure

37. A red blood cell has a diameter of 7.5 μm (micrometers). What is this dimension in (a) meters, (b) nanometers, and (c) picometers?

38. The platinum-containing cancer drug cisplatin (Study Question 35) contains 65.0 mass-percent of the metal. If you have 1.53 g of the compound, what mass of platinum (in grams) is contained in this sample?

39. The anesthetic procaine hydrochloride is often used to deaden pain during dental surgery. The compound is packaged as a 10.% solution (by mass; $d = 1.0$ g/mL) in water. If your dentist injects 0.50 mL of the solution, what mass of procaine hydrochloride (in milligrams) is injected?

40. You need a cube of aluminum with a mass of 7.6 g. What must be the length of the cube's edge (in cm)? (The density of aluminum is 2.698 g/cm^3.)

41. You have a 250.0-mL graduated cylinder containing some water. You drop three marbles with a total mass of 95.2 g into the water. What is the average density of a marble?

(a) (b)

Determining density. (a) A graduated cylinder with 61 mL of water. **(b)** Three marbles are added to the cylinder.

42. You have a white crystalline solid, known to be one of the potassium compounds listed below. To determine which, you measure its density. You measure out 18.82 g and transfer it to a graduated cylinder containing kerosene (in which these compounds will not dissolve). The level of liquid kerosene rises from 8.5 mL to 15.3 mL. Calculate the density of the solid, and identify the compound from the following list.
   (a) KF, d = 2.48 g/cm^3
   (b) KCl, d = 1.98 g/cm^3
   (c) KBr, d = 2.75 g/cm^3
   (d) KI, d = 3.13 g/cm^3

43. ▲ The smallest repeating unit of a crystal of common salt is a cube (called a unit cell) with an edge length of 0.563 nm.

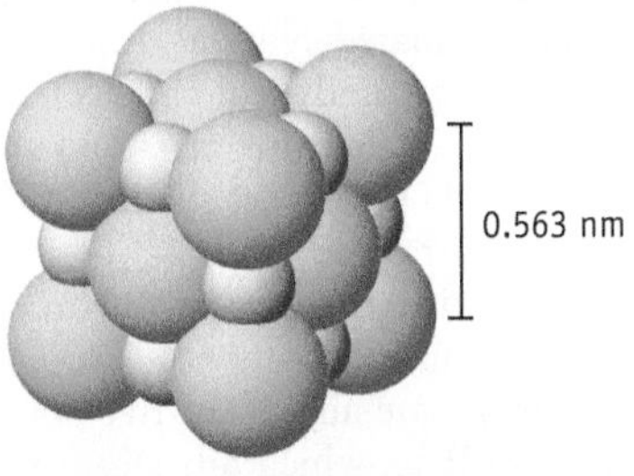

Sodium chloride, NaCl

   (a) What is the volume of this cube in cubic nanometers? In cubic centimeters?
   (b) The density of NaCl is 2.17 g/cm^3. What is the mass of this smallest repeating unit ("unit cell")?
   (c) Each repeating unit is composed of four NaCl units. What is the mass of one NaCl formula unit?

44. Diamond has a density of 3.513 g/cm^3. The mass of diamonds is often measured in "carats," where 1 carat equals 0.200 g. What is the volume (in cubic centimeters) of a 1.50-carat diamond?

45. The element gallium has a melting point of 29.8 °C. If you hold a sample of gallium in your hand, should it melt? Explain briefly.

Gallium metal

46. ▲ The density of pure water at various temperatures is given below.

T(°C)	d (g/cm^3)
4	0.99997
15	0.99913
25	0.99707
35	0.99406

Suppose your laboratory partner tells you the density of water at 20 °C is 0.99910 g/cm^3. Is this a reasonable number? Why or why not?

47. When you heat popcorn, it pops because it loses water explosively. Assume a kernel of corn, with a mass of 0.125 g, has a mass of only 0.106 g after popping.
   (a) What percentage of its mass did the kernel lose on popping?
   (b) Popcorn is sold by the pound in the United States. Using 0.125 g as the average mass of a popcorn kernel, how many kernels are there in a pound of popcorn? (1 lb = 453.6 g)

48. ▲ The aluminum in a package containing 75 ft^2 of kitchen foil weighs approximately 12 ounces. Aluminum has a density of 2.70 g/cm^3. What is the approximate thickness of the aluminum foil in millimeters? (1 ounce = 28.4 g)

49. ▲ Fluoridation of city water supplies has been practiced in the United States for several decades. It is done by continuously adding sodium fluoride to water as it comes from a reservoir. Assume you live in a medium-sized city of 150,000 people and that 660 L (170 gal) of water is used per person per day. What mass of sodium fluoride (in kilograms) must be added to the water supply each year (365 days) to have the required fluoride concentration of 1 ppm (part per million)—that is, 1 kilogram of fluoride per 1 million kilograms of water? (Sodium fluoride is 45.0% fluoride, and water has a density of 1.00 g/cm^3.)

50. ▲ About two centuries ago, Benjamin Franklin showed that 1 teaspoon of oil would cover about 0.5 acre of still water. If you know that 1.0×10^4 m^2 = 2.47 acres and that there is approximately 5 cm^3 in a teaspoon, what is the thickness of the 0.5-acre layer of oil? How might this thickness be related to the sizes of molecules?

51. ▲ Automobile batteries are filled with an aqueous solution of sulfuric acid. What is the mass of the acid (in grams) in 500. mL of the battery acid solution if the density of the solution is 1.285 g/cm^3 and the solution is 38.08% sulfuric acid by mass?

52. A 26-meter-tall statue of Buddha in Tibet is covered with 279 kg of gold. If the gold was applied to a thickness of 0.0015 mm, what surface area is covered (in square meters)? (Gold density = 19.3 g/cm^3)

53. At 25 °C, the density of water is 0.997 g/cm^3, whereas the density of ice at −10 °C is 0.917 g/cm^3.
(a) If a soft-drink can (volume = 250. mL) is filled completely with pure water at 25 °C and then frozen at −10 °C, what volume does the ice occupy?
(b) Can the ice be contained within the can?

54. Suppose your bedroom is 18 ft long and 15 ft wide, and the distance from floor to ceiling is 8 ft 6 in. You need to know the volume of the room in metric units for some scientific calculations.
(a) What is the room's volume in cubic meters? In liters?
(b) What is the mass of air in the room in kilograms? In pounds? (Assume the density of air is 1.2 g/L and that the room is empty of furniture.)

55. A spherical steel ball has a mass of 3.475 g and a diameter of 9.40 mm. What is the density of the steel? [The volume of a sphere = $(4/3)\pi r^3$ where r = radius.]

56. ▲ You are asked to identify an unknown liquid that is known to be one of the liquids listed below. You pipet a 3.50-mL sample into a beaker. The empty beaker had a mass of 12.20 g, and the beaker plus the liquid weighed 16.08 g.

Substance	Density at 25 °C (g/cm^3)
Ethylene glycol	1.1088 (major component of automobile antifreeze)
Water	0.9971
Ethanol	0.7893 (alcohol in alcoholic beverages)
Acetic acid	1.0492 (active component of vinegar)
Glycerol	1.2613 (solvent used in home care products)

(a) Calculate the density and identify the unknown.
(b) If you were able to measure the volume to only two significant figures (that is, 3.5 mL, not 3.50 mL), will the results be sufficiently accurate to identify the unknown? Explain.

57. ▲ You have an irregularly shaped piece of an unknown metal. To identify it, you determine its density and then compare this value with known values that you look up in the chemistry library. The mass of the metal is 74.122 g. Because of the irregular shape, you measure the volume by submerging the metal in water in a graduated cylinder. When you do this, the water level in the cylinder rises from 28.2 mL to 36.7 mL.
(a) What is the density of the metal? (Use the correct number of significant figures in your answer.)
(b) The unknown is one of the seven metals listed below. Is it possible to identify the metal based on the density you have calculated? Explain.

Metal	Density (g/cm^3)	Metal	Density (g/cm^3)
Zinc	7.13	Nickel	8.90
Iron	7.87	Copper	8.96
Cadmium	8.65	Silver	10.50
Cobalt	8.90		

58. ▲ There are five hydrocarbon compounds (compounds of C and H) that have the formula C_6H_{14}. (These are isomers; they differ in the way that C and H atoms are attached. ▶ Chapter 23.) All are liquids at room temperature but have slightly different densities.

Hydrocarbon	Density (g/mL)
Hexane	0.6600
2,3-Dimethylbutane	0.6616
1-Methylpentane	0.6532
2,2-Dimethylbutane	0.6485
2-Methylpentane	0.6645

(a) You have a pure sample of one of these hydrocarbons, and to identify it you decide to measure its density. You determine that a 5.0-mL sample (measured in a graduated cylinder) has a mass of 3.2745 g (measured on an analytical balance). Assume that the accuracy of the values for mass and volume is plus or minus one (±1) in the last significant figure. What is the density of the liquid?
(b) Can you identify the unknown hydrocarbon based on your experiment?
(c) Can you eliminate any of the five possibilities based on the data? If so, which one(s)?
(d) You need a more accurate volume measurement to solve this problem, and you redetermine the volume to be 4.93 mL. Based on these new data, what is the unknown compound?

59. ▲ Suppose you have a cylindrical glass tube with a thin capillary opening, and you wish to determine the diameter of the opening. You can do this experimentally by weighing a piece of the tubing before and after filling a portion of the capillary with mercury. Using the following information, calculate the diameter of the opening.

Mass of tube before adding mercury = 3.263 g

Mass of tube after adding mercury = 3.416 g

Length of capillary filled with mercury = 16.75 mm

Density of mercury = 13.546 g/cm^3

Volume of cylindrical capillary filled with mercury = $(\pi)(\text{radius})^2(\text{length})$

60. COPPER: Copper has a density of 8.96 g/cm^3. An ingot of copper with a mass of 57 kg (126 lb) is drawn into wire with a diameter of 9.50 mm. What length of wire (in meters) can be produced? [Volume of wire = $(\pi)(\text{radius})^2(\text{length})$]

61. ▲ COPPER:
(a) Suppose you have a cube of copper metal that is 0.236 cm on a side with a mass of 0.1206 g. If you know that each copper atom (radius = 128 pm) has a mass of 1.055×10^{-22} g (you will learn in Chapter 2 how to find the mass of one atom), how many atoms are there in this cube? What fraction of the cube is filled with atoms? (Or conversely, how much of the lattice is empty space?) Why is there "empty" space in the lattice?

(b) Now look at the smallest, repeating unit of the crystal lattice of copper.

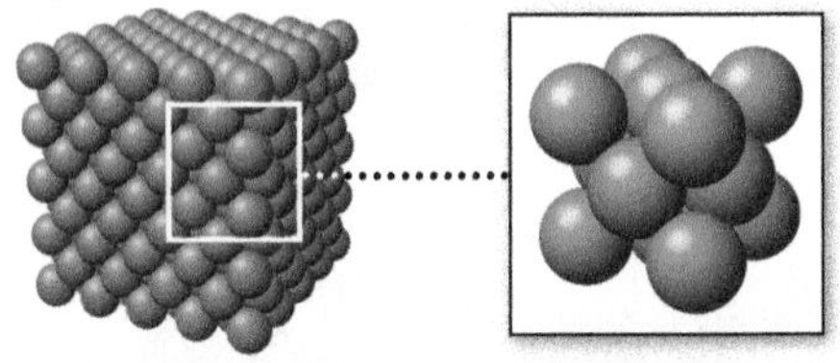

Cube of copper atoms Smallest repeating unit

Knowing that an edge of this cube is 361.47 pm and the density of copper is 8.960 g/cm³, calculate the number of copper atoms in this smallest, repeating unit.

62. ▲ CASE STUDY: In July 1983, an Air Canada Boeing 767 ran out of fuel over central Canada on a trip from Montreal to Edmonton. (The plane glided safely to a landing at an abandoned airstrip.) The pilots knew that 22,300 kg of fuel was required for the trip, and they knew that 7682 L of fuel was already in the tank. The ground crew added 4916 L of fuel, which was only about one fourth of what was required. The crew members used a factor of 1.77 for the fuel density—the problem is that 1.77 has units of pounds per liter and not kilograms per liter! What is the fuel density in units of kg/L? What mass and what volume of fuel should have been loaded? (1 lb = 453.6 g)

In the Laboratory

63. A sample of unknown metal is placed in a graduated cylinder containing water. The mass of the sample is 37.5 g, and the water levels before and after adding the sample to the cylinder are as shown in the figure. Which metal in the following list is most likely the sample? (*d* is the density of the metal.)

(a) Mg, d = 1.74 g/cm³ (d) Al, d = 2.70 g/cm³
(b) Fe, d = 7.87 g/cm³ (e) Cu, d = 8.96 g/cm³
(c) Ag, d = 10.5 g/cm³ (f) Pb, d = 11.3 g/cm³

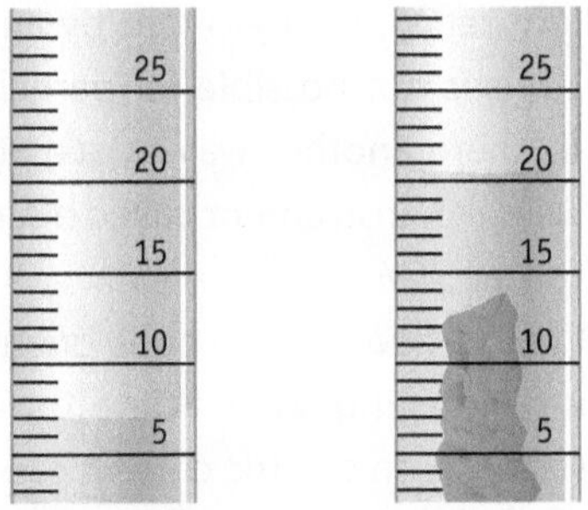

Graduated cylinders with unknown metal *(right)*

64. Iron pyrite is often called "fool's gold" because it looks like gold (see page 11). Suppose you have a solid that looks like gold, but you believe it to be fool's gold. The sample has a mass of 23.5 g. When the sample is lowered into the water in a graduated cylinder (see Study Question 63), the water level rises from 47.5 mL to 52.2 mL. Is the sample fool's gold (d = 5.00 g/cm³) or "real" gold (d = 19.3 g/cm³)?

65. You can analyze for a copper compound in water using an instrument called a spectrophotometer. [A spectrophotometer is a scientific instrument that measures the amount of light (of a given wavelength) that is absorbed by the solution.] The amount of light absorbed at a given wavelength of light (A) depends directly on the mass of compound per liter of solution. To calibrate the spectrophotometer, you collect the following data:

Absorbance (A)	Mass per Liter of Copper Compound (g/L)
0.000	0.000
0.257	1.029×10^{-3}
0.518	2.058×10^{-3}
0.771	3.087×10^{-3}
1.021	4.116×10^{-3}

Plot the absorbance (A) against the mass of copper compound per liter (g/L), and find the slope (m) and intercept (b) (assuming that A is y and the amount in solution is x in the equation for a straight line, $y = mx + b$). What is the mass of copper compound in the solution in g/L and mg/mL when the absorbance is 0.635?

66. A gas chromatograph is calibrated for the analysis of isooctane (a major gasoline component) using the following data:

Percent Isooctane (*x*-data)	Instrument Response (*y*-data)
0.352	1.09
0.803	1.78
1.08	2.60
1.38	3.03
1.75	4.01

If the instrument response is 2.75, what percentage of isooctane is present? (Data are taken from *Analytical Chemistry, An Introduction,* by D.A. Skoog, D.M. West, F.J. Holler, and S.R. Crouch, Cengage Learning, Brooks/Cole, Belmont, CA, 7th Edition, 2000.)

67. A general chemistry class carried out an experiment to determine the percentage (by mass) of acetic acid in vinegar. Ten students reported the following values: 5.22%, 5.28%, 5.22%, 5.30%, 5.19%, 5.23%, 5.33%, 5.26%, 5.15%, 5.22%. Determine the average value and the standard deviation from these data. How many of these results fell within one standard deviation of this average value?

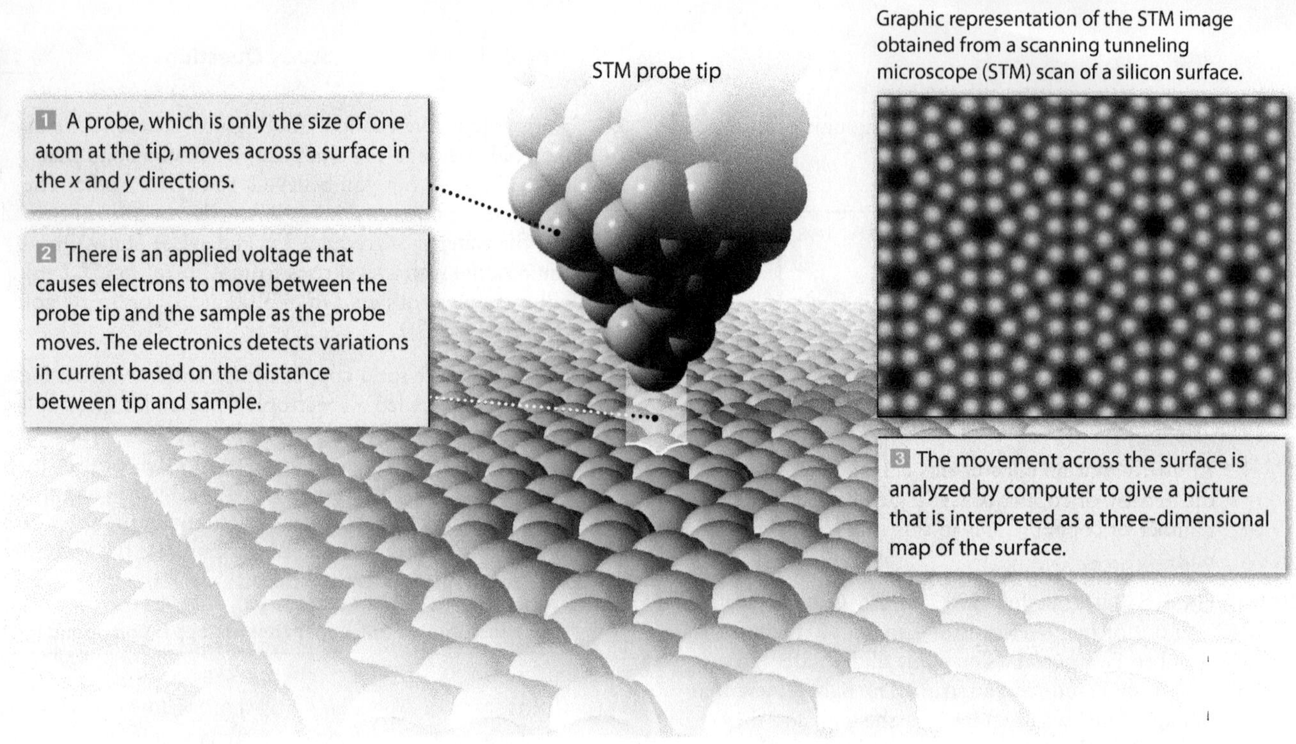

Sample of silicon atoms on a surface.

Atoms, Molecules, and Ions

Chapter Outline

- 2-1 Atomic Structure—Protons, Electrons, and Neutrons
- 2-2 Atomic Number and Atomic Mass
- 2-3 Isotopes
- 2-4 Atomic Weight
- 2-5 The Periodic Table
- 2-6 Molecules, Compounds, and Formulas
- 2-7 Ionic Compounds: Formulas, Names, and Properties
- 2-8 Molecular Compounds: Formulas and Names
- 2-9 Atoms, Molecules, and the Mole
- 2-10 Chemical Analysis: Determining Compound Formulas

"SEEING" ATOMS In Chapter 1 we described a thought experiment: "Take a macroscopic sample of material and divide it, again and again, past the point where the amount of sample can be seen by the naked eye, past the point where it can be seen using an optical microscope. Eventually you reach the level of individual particles—the atoms—that make up all matter. . . ." But can you "see" those ultimate particles? This has been an objective for scientists for many years.

In the traditional sense "seeing" atoms refers to visual processes: light reflected or emitted by an object reaching the eye. This is not possible for particles as small as atoms. But, is there another way to see atoms? The answer is yes, using an instrument called a *scanning tunneling microscope*, or STM.

An STM uses a needle-like probe oriented above the surface of a conducting solid. When the probe is very close to the surface, an electric current can flow from the probe to the surface. The current depends on the distance between the probe tip and the atoms on the surface. Variations in current are measured as the probe

Chapter Goals

See Chapter Goals Revisited (page 93) for Study Questions keyed to these goals.

UNDERSTAND

- The composition and structure of atoms (protons, neutrons, electrons) and the terms atomic number and mass number.
- The various representations of masses of atoms: atomic mass, atomic weight (relative atomic mass), and their interrelationships.
- The composition of isotopes.
- The importance of Coulomb's law in chemistry.
- The mole concept and molar mass and their application.
- How mass spectrometry is used (in determining isotopic abundances, isotopic masses, and molecular formulas).

DO

- Carry out calculations relating atomic weights, isotopic masses, and isotopic abundances.
- Carry out calculations involving masses, moles, and numbers of particles.
- Interpret, predict, and write formulas for ionic and molecular compounds.
- Determine empirical and molecular formulas and percent composition of compounds from experimental data.

REMEMBER

- The terminology of the periodic table (periods, groups) and know how to use the information given in the periodic table.
- Some common elements and identify some of their properties.
- Formulas and names of ions and ionic compounds and of common molecular compounds.
- Common properties of ionic compounds.

moves across the surface. These data are then plotted graphically, giving a map of the atoms on the surface of the solid.

This is a remarkably sophisticated experiment. For it to work, the tip of the needle must be very small (ideally, one atom in size), and the probe must be only an atom's distance away from the surface. Successfully carried out, the experiment gives a picture of the solid's surface, which can show individual atoms.

The chemical elements are forged in stars and, from these elements, molecules such as water and ammonia are made in outer space. These simple molecules and much more complex ones such as DNA and hemoglobin are found on Earth. To comprehend the burgeoning field of molecular biology as well as all of modern chemistry, we have to understand the nature of the chemical elements and the properties and structures of molecules. This chapter begins our exploration of the chemistry of the elements, the building blocks of chemistry, and the compounds they form.

2-1 Atomic Structure—Protons, Electrons, and Neutrons

Learning Objectives: LO 1.1, LO 1.2

Around 1900 a series of experiments done by scientists in England such as Sir Joseph John Thomson (1856–1940) and Ernest Rutherford (1871–1937) established a model of the atom that is still the basis of modern atomic theory. Atoms themselves are made of subatomic particles, three of which are important in chemistry: electrically positive protons, electrically negative electrons, and, in all except one type of hydrogen atom, electrically neutral neutrons. The model places the

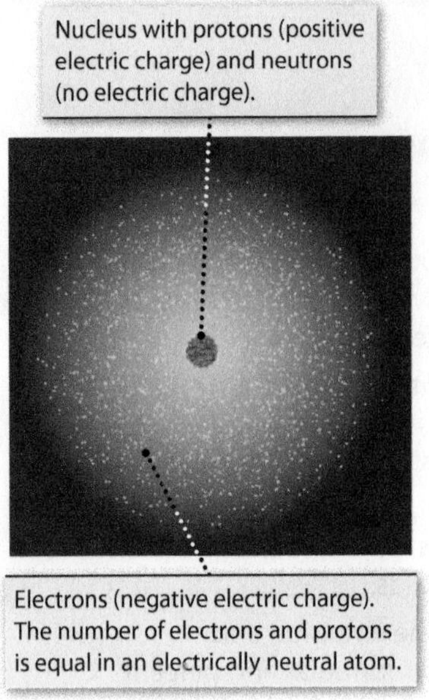

FIGURE 2.1 **The structure of the atom.** This figure is not drawn to scale. If the nucleus were really the size depicted here, the electron cloud would extend over 200 m. The atom is mostly empty space! In this illustration, the electrons are depicted as a "cloud" around the nucleus. This is a more accurate view of the atom (Chapter 6) than the traditional view of electrons as tiny particles orbiting the nucleus.

more massive protons and neutrons in a very small nucleus (Figure 2.1), which contains all the positive charge and almost all the mass of an atom. Electrons, with a much smaller mass than protons or neutrons, surround the nucleus and occupy most of the volume. In an electrically neutral atom, the number of electrons equals the number of protons.

The chemical properties of elements and molecules depend largely on the electrons in atoms. We shall look more carefully at their arrangement and how they influence atomic properties in Chapters 6 and 7. In this chapter, however, we first want to describe how the composition of the atom relates to its mass and then to the mass of compounds. This is crucial information when we consider the quantitative aspects of chemical reactions in later chapters.

Learning Objectives: LO 1.3

2-2 Atomic Number and Atomic Mass

Atomic Number

All atoms of a given element have the same number of protons in the nucleus. Hydrogen is the simplest element, with one nuclear proton. All helium atoms have two protons, all lithium atoms have three protons, and all beryllium atoms have four protons. The number of protons in the nucleus of an element is given by its **atomic number**, which is generally indicated by the symbol Z.

Currently known elements are listed in the periodic table inside the front cover of this book and on the list inside the back cover. The integer number at the top of the box for each element in the periodic table is its atomic number. A copper atom (Cu), for example, has an atomic number of 29, so its nucleus contains 29 protons. A uranium atom (U) has 92 nuclear protons and $Z = 92$.

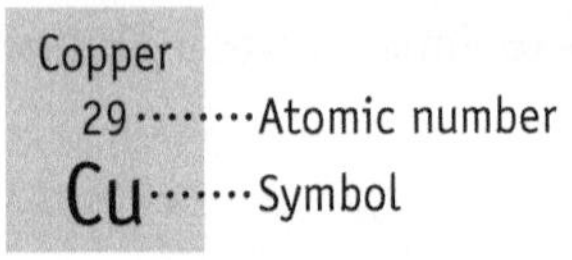

Relative Atomic Mass and the Atomic Mass Unit

Historical Perspective on the Development of Our Understanding of Atomic Structure
A brief history of important experiments and the scientists involved in developing the modern view of the atom is on pages 54–55.

With the quantitative work of the great French chemist Antoine Laurent Lavoisier (1743–1794), chemistry began to change from medieval alchemy to a modern field of study (Section 3-1). As 18th- and 19th-century chemists tried to understand how the elements combined, they carried out increasingly quantitative studies aimed at learning, for example, how much of one element would combine with another. Based on this work, they learned that the substances they produced had a constant composition, so they could define the relative masses of elements that would combine to produce a new substance. At the beginning of the 19th century, John Dalton (1766–1844) suggested that the combinations of elements involve atoms, and he proposed a relative scale of atom masses. Apparently for simplicity, Dalton chose a mass of 1 for hydrogen on which to base his scale.

The atomic mass scale has changed since 1800. Like the 19th-century chemists, we still use *relative* masses, but the standard today is carbon. A carbon atom having six protons and six neutrons in the nucleus is assigned a mass value of exactly 12. From chemical experiments and physical measurements, we know an oxygen atom having eight protons and eight neutrons has 1.33291 times the mass of carbon, so it has a relative mass of 15.9949. Masses of atoms of other elements are assigned in a similar manner.

Table 2.1 Properties of Subatomic Particles*

	MASS			
PARTICLE	GRAMS	ATOMIC MASS UNITS	CHARGE	SYMBOL
Electron	9.109383×10^{-28}	0.0005485799	1−	$_{-1}^{0}e$ or e^-
Proton	1.672622×10^{-24}	1.007276	1+	$_{1}^{1}p$ or p^+
Neutron	1.674927×10^{-24}	1.008665	0	$_{0}^{1}n$ or n

*These values and others in the book are taken from the National Institute of Standards and Technology website at http://physics.nist.gov/cuu/Constants/index.html

Masses of fundamental atomic particles are often expressed in **atomic mass units (u)**. *One atomic mass unit, 1 u, is one-twelfth of the mass of an atom of carbon with six protons and six neutrons*. Thus, such a carbon atom has a mass of exactly 12 u. The atomic mass unit can be related to other units of mass using the conversion factor 1 atomic mass unit (u) = 1.661×10^{-24} g.

Mass Number

Because proton and neutron masses are so close to 1 u, while the mass of an electron is only about 1/2000 of this value (Table 2.1), the approximate mass of an atom can be estimated if the number of neutrons and protons is known. The sum of the number of protons and neutrons for an atom is called its **mass number** and is given the symbol *A*.

$$A = \text{mass number} = \text{number of protons} + \text{number of neutrons}$$

For example, a sodium atom, which has 11 protons and 12 neutrons in its nucleus, has a mass number of 23 (A = 11 p + 12 n). The most common atom of uranium has 92 protons and 146 neutrons, and a mass number of $A = 238$. Using this information, we often symbolize atoms with the following notation:

$$\text{Mass number} \rightarrow {}^{A}_{Z}\text{X} \leftarrow \text{Element symbol}$$
$$\text{Atomic number} \rightarrow Z$$

The subscript Z is optional because the element's symbol tells us what the atomic number must be. For example, the atoms described previously have the symbols $^{23}_{11}Na$ and $^{238}_{92}U$, or just ^{23}Na and ^{238}U. In words, we say "sodium-23" or "uranium-238."

How Small Is an Atom? The radius of the typical atom is between 30 and 300 pm (3×10^{-11} m to 3×10^{-10} m). To get a feeling for the incredible smallness of an atom, consider that 1 cm^3 of water contains about three times as many atoms as the Atlantic Ocean contains teaspoons of water.

EXAMPLE 2.1

Atomic Composition

Problem What is the composition of an atom of phosphorus with 16 neutrons? What is its mass number? What is the symbol for such an atom? If the atom has an actual mass of 30.9738 u, what is its mass in grams? Finally, what is the mass of this phosphorus atom relative to the mass of a carbon atom with a mass number of 12?

What Do You Know? You know the name of the element and the number of neutrons. You also know the actual mass, so you can determine its mass relative to carbon-12.

Strategy The symbol for phosphorus is P, and, from the periodic table, you know its atomic number is 15. The mass number is the sum of the number of protons and neutrons. The mass of the atom in grams can be obtained from the mass in atomic mass units using

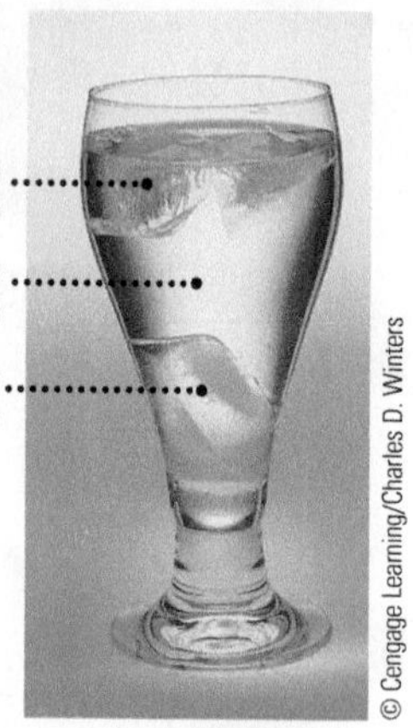

FIGURE 2.2 **Ice made from "heavy water" sinks in "ordinary" water.** Water containing ordinary hydrogen (^1_1H, protium) forms a solid that is less dense than liquid H_2O, so it floats in the liquid. (Water is different in this regard. The solid phase of almost all other substances sinks in the liquid phase of that substance.) Similarly, "heavy ice" (D_2O, deuterium oxide) floats in "heavy water." D_2O-ice is denser than liquid H_2O, however, so solid D_2O sinks in liquid H_2O.

the conversion factor 1 u = 1.661×10^{-24} g. The relative mass of an atom of P compared to ^{12}C can be determined by dividing the mass of the P atom in atomic mass units by the mass of a ^{12}C atom, 12.0000 u.

Solution A phosphorus atom has 15 protons and, because it is electrically neutral, also has 15 electrons. A phosphorus atom with 16 neutrons has a mass number of 31.

$$\text{Mass number} = \text{number of protons} + \text{number of neutrons} = 15 + 16 = 31$$

The atom's complete symbol is $^{31}_{15}P$.

$$\text{Mass of one } ^{31}P \text{ atom} = (30.9738\ u) \times (1.661 \times 10^{-24}\ g/u) = 5.145 \times 10^{-23}\ g$$

Mass of ^{31}P relative to the mass of an atom of ^{12}C: 30.9738/12.0000 = 2.58115

Think about Your Answer Because phosphorus has an atomic number greater than carbon's, you expect its mass to be greater than 12.

Check Your Understanding

1. What is the mass number of an iron atom with 30 neutrons?
2. A nickel atom with 32 neutrons has a mass of 59.930788 u. What is its mass in grams?
3. How many protons, neutrons, and electrons are in a ^{64}Zn atom?

REVIEW & CHECK FOR SECTION 2-2

1. The mass of an atom of manganese is 54.9380 u. How many neutrons are contained in one atom of this element?

   (a) 25 (b) 30 (c) 29 (d) 55

2. An atom contains 12 neutrons and has a mass number of 23. Identify the element.

   (a) C (b) Mg (c) Na (d) Cl

Learning Objectives: LO 1.3, LO 1.14

2-3 Isotopes

All the atoms in a naturally occurring sample of a given element have the same mass in only a few instances (for example, aluminum, fluorine, and phosphorus). Most elements consist of atoms having several different mass numbers. For example, there are two kinds of boron atoms, one with a mass of about 10 (^{10}B) and a second with a mass of about 11 (^{11}B). Atoms of tin can have any of 10 different masses ranging from 112 to 124. Atoms with the same atomic number but different mass numbers are called **isotopes.**

All atoms of an element have the same number of protons—five in the case of boron. To have different masses, isotopes must have different numbers of neutrons. The nucleus of a ^{10}B atom ($Z = 5$) contains five protons and five neutrons, whereas the nucleus of a ^{11}B atom contains five protons and six neutrons.

Scientists often refer to a particular isotope by giving its mass number (for example, uranium-238, ^{238}U), but the isotopes of hydrogen are so important that they have special names and symbols. All hydrogen atoms have one proton. When that is the only nuclear particle, the isotope is called *protium*, or just "hydrogen." The isotope of hydrogen with one neutron, ^2_1H, is called *deuterium*, or "heavy hydrogen" (symbol = D). The nucleus of radioactive hydrogen-3, ^3_1H, or *tritium* (symbol = T), contains one proton and two neutrons.

The substitution of one isotope of an element for another isotope of the same element in a compound sometimes can have an effect on chemical and physical properties (Figure 2.2). This is especially true when deuterium is substituted for hydrogen because the mass of deuterium is double that of hydrogen.

Isotope Abundance

A sample of water from a lake will consist almost entirely of H_2O where the H atoms are the ^1H isotope. A few molecules, however, will have deuterium (^2H) substituted for ^1H. We can predict this outcome because we know that 99.985% of all hydrogen atoms on Earth are ^1H atoms. That is, the abundance of ^1H atoms is 99.985%.

$$\text{Percent abundance} = \frac{\text{number of atoms of a given isotope}}{\text{total number of atoms of all isotopes of that element}} \times 100\% \quad \textbf{(2.1)}$$

The remainder of naturally occurring hydrogen is deuterium, whose abundance is only 0.015% of the total hydrogen atoms. Tritium, the radioactive ^3H isotope, occurs naturally in only trace amounts.

Consider again the two isotopes of boron. The boron-10 isotope has an abundance of 19.91%; the abundance of boron-11 is 80.09%. Thus, if you could count out 10,000 boron atoms from an "average" natural sample, 1991 of them would be boron-10 atoms and 8009 of them would be boron-11 atoms.

Isotopic Masses and the Mass Defect Actual masses of atoms are always less than the sum of the masses of the subatomic particles composing that atom. This is called the *mass defect*, and the reason for it is discussed in Chapter 25.

Determining Atomic Mass and Isotope Abundance

The masses of isotopes and their abundances are determined experimentally by mass spectrometry (Figure 2.3). A gaseous sample of an element is introduced into the evacuated chamber of the spectrometer, and the atoms are converted to positively charged particles (called *ions*). The cloud of ions forms a beam as they are attracted to negatively charged plates within the instrument. As the ions stream toward the negatively charged detector, they fly through a magnetic field, which causes the paths of the ions to be deflected. The extent of deflection depends on particle mass: Lighter ions are deflected more than heavier ions. The ions, now separated by mass, are detected at the end of the chamber. Modern spectrometers can measure isotopic masses to as many as nine significant figures.

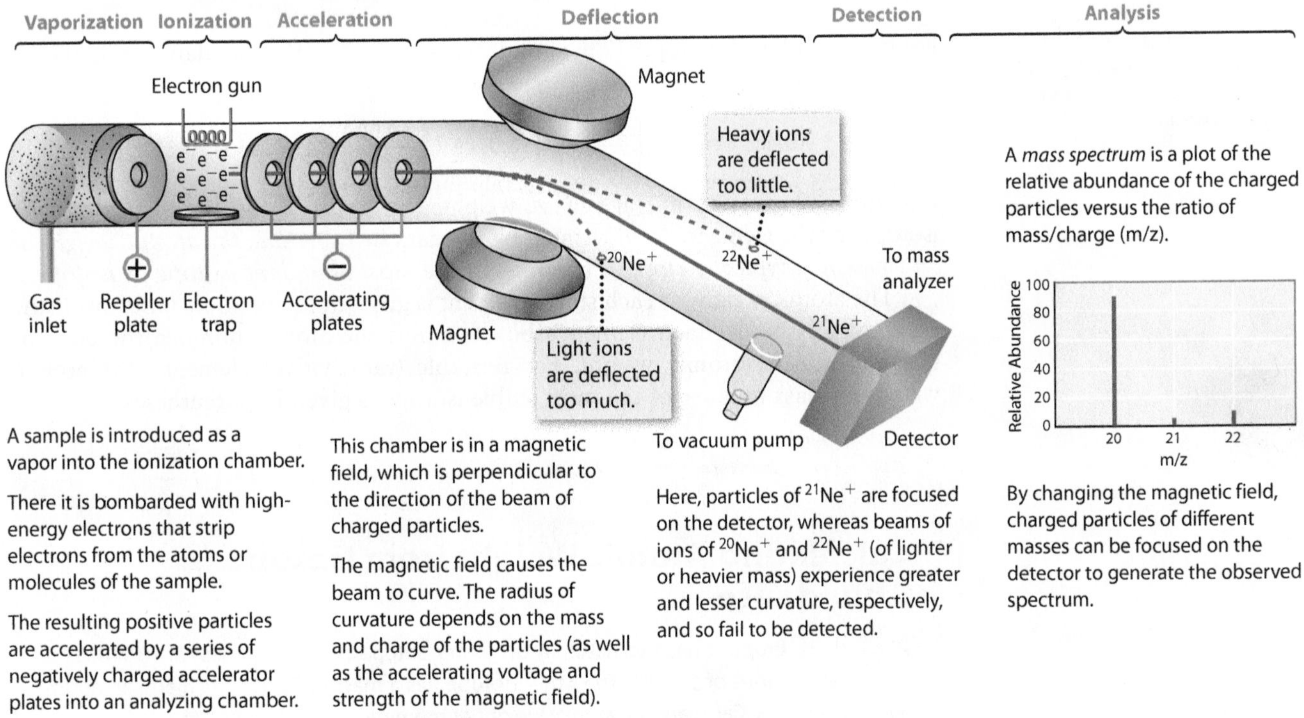

FIGURE 2.3 **Mass spectrometer.** A mass spectrometer will separate ions of different mass and charge in a gaseous sample of ions. The instrument allows the researcher to determine the accurate mass of each ion, whether the ions are composed of individual atoms, molecules, or molecular fragments.

Except for carbon-12, whose mass is defined to be exactly 12 u, isotopic masses do not have integer values. However, the isotopic masses are always very close to the mass numbers for the isotope. For example, the mass of an atom of boron-11 (^{11}B, 5 protons and 6 neutrons) is 11.0093 u, and the mass of an atom of iron-58 (^{58}Fe, 26 protons and 32 neutrons) is 57.9333 u.

REVIEW & CHECK FOR SECTION 2-3

1. Silver has two isotopes, one with 60 neutrons (percent abundance = 51.839%) and the other with 62 neutrons. What is the symbol of the isotope with 62 neutrons, and what is its percent abundance?

   (a) $^{107}_{47}Ag$, 51.839% (b) $^{107}_{47}Ag$, 48.161% (c) $^{109}_{47}Ag$, 51.839% (d) $^{109}_{47}Ag$, 48.161%

2. A naturally occurring sample of argon contains 2696 atoms of ^{36}Ar, 504 atoms of ^{38}Ar, and 7.968×10^5 atoms of ^{40}Ar. What is the percent abundance of the most abundant isotope?

   (a) 99.60% (b) 95.08% (c) 71.35% (d) 99.92%

Learning Objectives: LO 1.3, LO 1.14

2-4 Atomic Weight

Every sample of boron has some atoms with a mass of 10.0129 u and others with a mass of 11.0093 u. The **atomic weight** of the element, the average mass of a representative sample of boron atoms, is somewhere between these values. For boron, for example, the atomic weight is 10.811. If isotope masses and abundances are known, the atomic weight of an element can be calculated using Equation 2.2.

Atomic Weight We will continue to use the term atomic weight but note that this term is being slowly phased out. The preferred term is *relative atomic mass* (symbol, A_r), which is defined as the ratio of the average mass per atom of an element to 1/12th of the mass of an atom of ^{12}C. The relative atomic mass does not have units because it is a ratio.

$$\text{Atomic weight} = \left(\frac{\%\text{ abundance isotope 1}}{100}\right)(\text{mass of isotope 1}) + \left(\frac{\%\text{ abundance isotope 2}}{100}\right)(\text{mass of isotope 2}) + \ldots \quad (2.2)$$

For boron with two isotopes (^{10}B, abundance = 19.91%; ^{11}B, abundance = 80.09%), we find

$$\text{Atomic weight} = \left(\frac{19.91}{100}\right) \times 10.0129 + \left(\frac{80.09}{100}\right) \times 11.0093 = 10.811$$

Equation 2.2 gives an average mass, weighted in terms of the abundance of each isotope for the element. As illustrated by the data in Table 2.2, *the atomic weight of an element is typically close to the mass of the most abundant isotope or isotopes.*

The atomic weight of each stable element is given in the periodic table inside the cover of this book. Each element's box contains the atomic number, the element symbol, and the atomic weight. For unstable (radioactive) elements, the atomic weight or mass number of the most stable isotope is given in parentheses.

EXAMPLE 2.2

Calculating Atomic Weight from Isotope Abundance

Problem Bromine has two naturally occurring isotopes. One has a mass of 78.918338 u and an abundance of 50.69%. The other isotope has a mass of 80.916291 u and an abundance of 49.31%. Calculate the atomic weight of bromine.

What Do You Know? You know the mass and abundance of each of the two isotopes.

Table 2.2 Isotope Abundance and Atomic Weight

Element	Symbol	Atomic Weight	Mass Number	Isotopic Mass	Natural Abundance (%)
Hydrogen	H	1.00794	1	1.0078	99.985
	D*		2	2.0141	0.015
	T†		3	3.0161	0
Boron	B	10.811	10	10.0129	19.91
			11	11.0093	80.09
Neon	Ne	20.1797	20	19.9924	90.48
			21	20.9938	0.27
			22	21.9914	9.25
Magnesium	Mg	24.3050	24	23.9850	78.99
			25	24.9858	10.00
			26	25.9826	11.01

*D = deuterium; †T = tritium, radioactive.

Strategy The atomic weight of any element is the weighted average of the masses of the isotopes in a representative sample. To calculate the atomic weight, multiply the mass of each isotope by its percent abundance divided by 100 (Equation 2.2).

Solution

Atomic weight of bromine =

$$(50.69/100)(78.918338) + (49.31/100)(80.916291) = 79.90$$

Think about Your Answer You can also estimate the atomic weight from the data given. There are two isotopes, mass numbers of 79 and 81, in approximately equal abundance. From this, we would expect the average mass to be about 80, midway between the two mass numbers. The calculation bears this out.

Check Your Understanding

Verify that the atomic weight of chlorine is 35.45, given the following information:

$$^{35}\text{Cl mass} = 34.96885 \text{ u; percent abundance} = 75.77\%$$

$$^{37}\text{Cl mass} = 36.96590 \text{ u; percent abundance} = 24.23\%$$

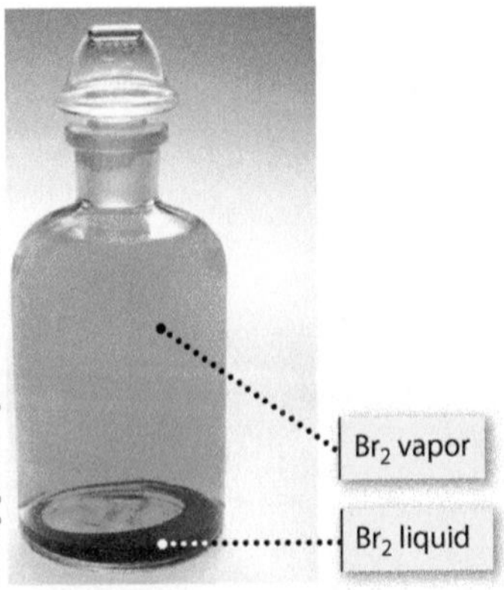

© Cengage Learning/Charles D. Winters

Elemental bromine. Bromine is a deep orange-red, volatile liquid at room temperature. It consists of Br_2 molecules in which two bromine atoms are chemically bonded together. There are two, stable, naturally occurring isotopes of bromine atoms: ^{79}Br (50.69% abundance) and ^{81}Br (49.31% abundance).

EXAMPLE 2.3

Calculating Isotopic Abundances

Problem Antimony, Sb, has two stable isotopes: ^{121}Sb, 120.904 u, and ^{123}Sb, 122.904 u. What are the relative abundances of these isotopes?

What Do You Know? You know the masses of the two isotopes of the element and know that their weighted average, the atomic weight, is 121.760 (see the periodic table).

Strategy To calculate the abundances recognize there are two unknown but related quantities, and you can write the following expression (where the fractional abundance of an isotope is the percent abundance of the isotope divided by 100)

$$\text{Atomic weight} = 121.760 = (\text{fractional abundance of } ^{121}\text{Sb})(120.904) + (\text{fractional abundance of } ^{123}\text{Sb})(122.904)$$

© Paul Degginger/Alamy

A sample of the metalloid antimony. The element has two stable isotopes, ^{121}Sb and ^{123}Sb.

or

$$121.760 = x(120.904) + y(122.904)$$

where x = fractional abundance of ^{121}Sb and y = fractional abundance of ^{123}Sb. Because you know that the sum of fractional abundances of the isotopes must equal 1 ($x + y = 1$), you can solve the two equations simultaneously for x and y.

Solution Because y = fractional abundance of ^{123}Sb $= 1 - x$, you can make a substitution for y.

$$121.760 = x(120.904) + (1 - x)(122.904)$$

Expanding this equation, you have

$$121.760 = 120.904x + 122.904 - 122.904x$$

Finally, solving for x, you find

$$121.760 - 122.904 = (120.904 - 122.904)x$$

$$x = 0.5720$$

The fractional abundance of ^{121}Sb is 0.5720 and its percent abundance is 57.20%. This means that the percent abundance of ^{123}Sb must be 42.80%.

Think about Your Answer You might have predicted that the lighter isotope (^{121}Sb) must be the more abundant because the atomic weight is closer to 121 than to 123.

Check Your Understanding

Neon has three stable isotopes, one with a small abundance. What are the abundances of the other two isotopes?

^{20}Ne, mass = 19.992435 u; percent abundance = ?

^{21}Ne, mass = 20.993843 u; percent abundance = 0.27%

^{22}Ne, mass = 21.991383 u; percent abundance = ?

REVIEW & CHECK FOR SECTION 2-4

1. Which is the more abundant isotope of copper, ^{63}Cu or ^{65}Cu?

   (a) ^{63}Cu (b) ^{65}Cu

2. Which of the following is closest to the observed abundance of ^{71}Ga, one of two stable gallium isotopes (^{69}Ga and ^{71}Ga)?

   (a) 20% (b) 40% (c) 60% (d) 70%

3. An element X has four stable isotopes, ^{204}X (mass 203.97 u, 1.4%), ^{206}X (mass 205.97 u, 24.1%), ^{207}X (mass 206.98 u, 22.1%), and ^{208}X (mass 207.98 u, 52.4%). Identify the element by calculating the atomic weight from these data.

   (a) Tl (b) Pb (c) Bi (d) Po

2-5 The Periodic Table

The periodic table of elements (inside the book cover) is one of the most useful tools in modern chemistry. Not only does it contain a wealth of information, but it can also be used to organize many of the ideas of chemistry. It is important to become familiar with its main features and terminology.

CASE STUDY Using Isotopes: Ötzi, the Iceman of the Alps

In 1991 a hiker in the Alps on the Austrian-Italian border found the well-preserved remains of an approximately 46-year-old man, now nicknamed "The Iceman," who lived about 5200 years ago (Chapter 1). Studies using isotopes of oxygen, strontium, lead, and argon, among others, have helped scientists paint a detailed picture of the man and his life.

The abundance of the ^{18}O isotope of oxygen is related to the latitude and altitude at which a person was born and raised. Oxygen in biominerals such as teeth and bones comes primarily from ingested water. The lakes and rivers on the northern side of the Alps are known to have a lower ^{18}O content than those on the southern side of the mountains. The ^{18}O content of the teeth and bones of the Iceman was found to be relatively high and characteristic of the watershed south of the Alps. He had clearly been born and raised in that area.

The relative abundance of isotopes of heavier elements also varies slightly from place to place and in their incorporation into different minerals. Strontium, a member of the same periodic group as calcium, is incorporated into teeth and bones. The ratio of strontium isotopes, $^{87}Sr/^{86}Sr$, and of lead isotopes, $^{206}Pb/^{204}Pb$, in the Iceman's teeth and bones was characteristic of soils from a narrow region of Italy south of the Alps, which established more clearly where he was born and lived most of his life.

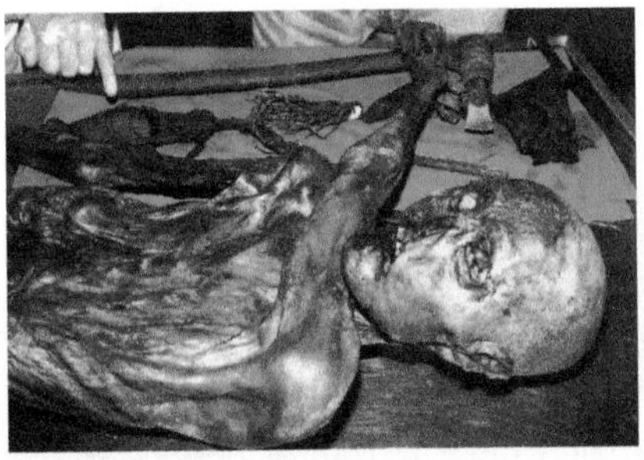

Ötzi the Iceman. A well-preserved mummy of a man who lived in northern Italy about 5000 years ago.

The investigators also looked for food residues in the Iceman's intestines. Although a few grains of cereal were found, they located tiny flakes of mica believed to have broken off stones used to grind grain and that were therefore eaten when the man ate the grain. They analyzed these flakes using argon isotopes, ^{40}Ar and ^{39}Ar, and found their signature was like that of mica in an area south of the Alps, thus establishing where he lived in his later years.

The overall result of the many isotope studies showed that the Iceman lived thousands of years ago in a small area about 10–20 kilometers west of Merano in northern Italy.

For details of the isotope studies, see W. Müller, et al., *Science*, Volume 302, October 31, 2003, pages 862–866.

Questions:

1. How many neutrons are there in atoms of ^{18}O? In each of the two isotopes of lead?
2. There are three stable isotopes of oxygen (^{16}O, mass 15.9949 u, 99.763%, ^{17}O, mass 16.9991 u, 0.0375%, and ^{18}O, 17.9991, 0.1995%). Use these data to calculate the atomic weight of oxygen.

Answers to these questions are available in Appendix N.

Features of the Periodic Table

The main organizational features of the periodic table are the following (Figure 2.4):

- Elements with similar chemical and physical properties lie in vertical columns called **groups** or **families**. The periodic table commonly used in the United States has groups numbered 1 through 8, with each number followed by the letter A or B. The A groups are often called the **main group elements** and the B groups are the **transition elements**. In other parts of the world, the groups are numbered 1–18.
- The horizontal rows of the table are called **periods**, and they are numbered beginning with 1 for the period containing only H and He. For example, sodium, Na, in Group 1A, is the first element in the third period. Mercury, Hg, in Group 2B, is in the sixth period (or sixth row).

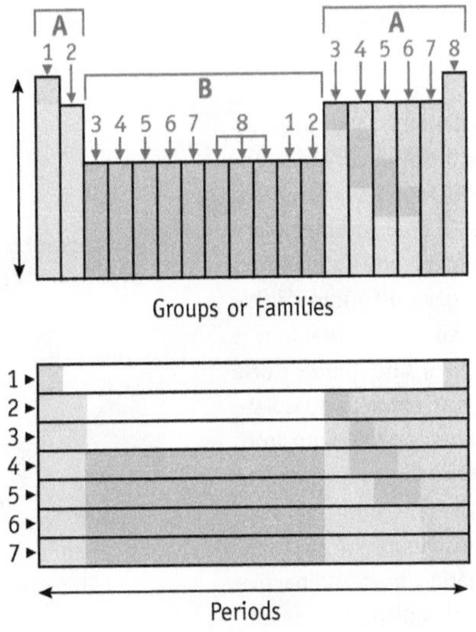

FIGURE 2.4 **Periods and groups in the periodic table.** In the United States the system predominantly used to designate groups labels main group elements as Groups 1A–8A and transition elements as Groups 1B–8B. Alternatively, they are numbered 1 through 18 from left to right. The latter notation is generally used outside the United States.

Main Group Metals · Transition Metals · Metalloids · Nonmetals

The periodic table can be divided into several regions according to the properties of the elements. On the table inside the cover of this book (and in Figure 2.4), *metals* are indicated in shades of blue, *nonmetals* are indicated in orange, and elements called *metalloids* appear in green. Elements gradually become less metallic as one moves from left to right across a period, and the metalloids lie along the metal-nonmetal boundary. A few of the 118 elements are pictured in Figure 2.5.

KEY EXPERIMENTS

How Do We Know the Nature of the Atom and Its Components?

The idea that atoms are the building blocks for matter was set on the right track by the English chemist John Dalton in the early 1800s, but little was known about atoms at that time and for a long time after. Dalton proposed that an atom was a "solid, massy, hard, impenetrable, moveable particle," far from the description we have today. To reach the current model involving a nuclear atom with protons, neutrons, and electrons required ingenious experiments, carried out in the late 1800s and early 1900s. This section describes the main ideas for a few of these experiments.

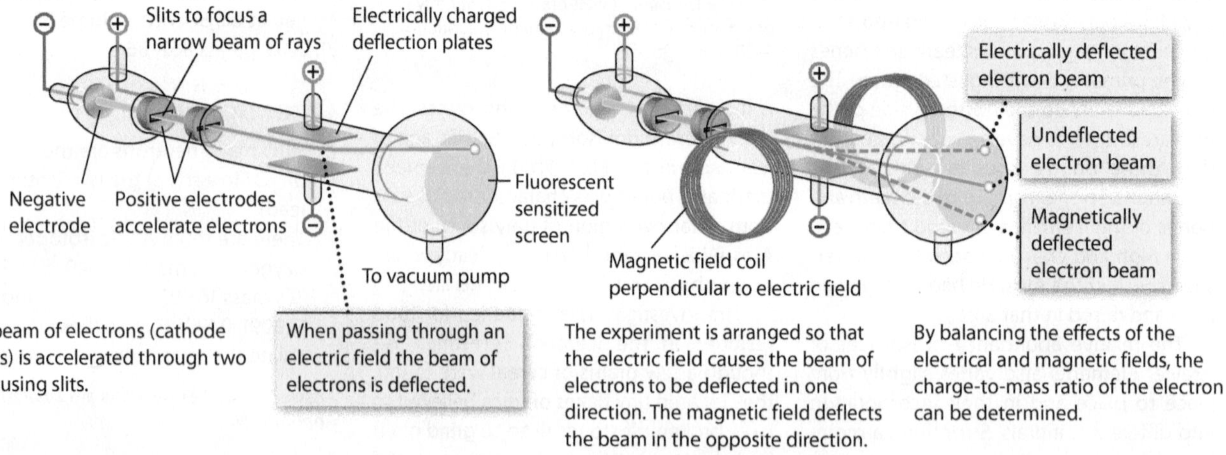

FIGURE 1 Cathode rays. Thomson's experiment to measure the electron's charge-to-mass ratio. The second half of the 19th century saw a series of experiments involving cathode ray tubes. First described in 1869 by William Crookes (1832–1919), a cathode ray tube is an evacuated container with two electrodes. When a high voltage is applied, particles (cathode rays) flow from the negative electrode (the cathode) to the anode. These particles were deflected by electric and magnetic fields, and by balancing these effects, it was possible to determine their charge-to-mass ratio (e/m). In 1897, J. J. Thomson (1856–1940) at the University of Cambridge in England reported that these particles were about 1/2000th of the mass of a hydrogen atom. They became known as electrons, a term already invented to describe the smallest particle of electricity. Thomson reasoned that electrons must originate from the atoms of the cathode, and he speculated that an atom was a uniform sphere of positively charged matter in which negative electrons were embedded, a model that we now know is incorrect.

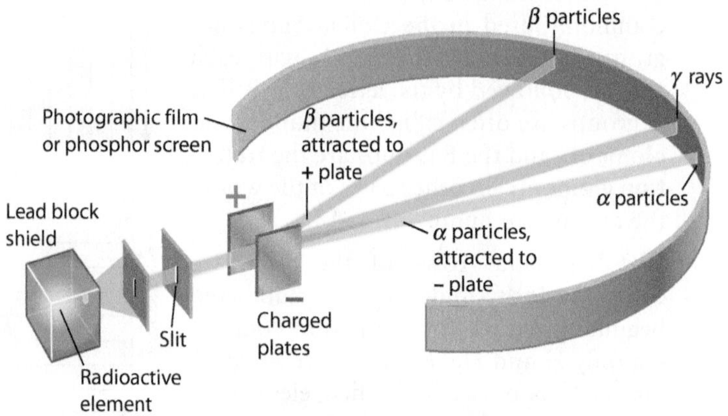

FIGURE 2 Radioactivity. Evidence that atoms were made up from smaller particles was also inferred by the discovery of radioactivity. In 1896 Henri Becquerel (1852–1908) found that uranium emitted invisible rays that caused a covered photographic plate to darken. Further study showed that pitchblende (a common uranium ore) contained substances that gave off more of this invisible radiation than could be explained by the uranium it contained. This led Pierre Curie (1859–1906) and Marie Curie (1867–1934), working in an old shed in Paris, to extract and isolate the previously unknown elements polonium and radium from uranium ore. Radioactivity was the word the Curies invented to describe the new phenomenon of invisible rays, and they concluded the radiation was the result of the disintegration of atoms.

Identification of the radiation emanating from radioactive substances soon followed. Three types of radiation were observed and given the labels alpha, beta, and gamma. Charge-to-mass studies revealed that alpha rays are helium nuclei (He^{2+}) and beta rays are electrons. Gamma rays have neither mass nor charge; they are now known to be a highly energetic form of electromagnetic radiation.

Marie Curie is one of very few people and the only woman to have ever received two Nobel Prizes. She was born in Poland but studied and carried out her research in Paris. In 1903, she shared the Nobel Prize in Physics with H. Becquerel and her husband Pierre for their discovery of radioactivity. In 1911 she received the Nobel Prize in Chemistry for the discovery of two new chemical elements, radium and polonium (the latter named for her homeland, Poland). A unit of radioactivity (curie, Ci) and an element (curium, Cm) are named in her honor. Pierre, who died in an accident in 1906, was also well known for his research on magnetism. One of their daughters, Irène, married Frédèric Joliot, and they shared in the 1935 Nobel Prize in Chemistry for their discovery of artificial radioactivity.

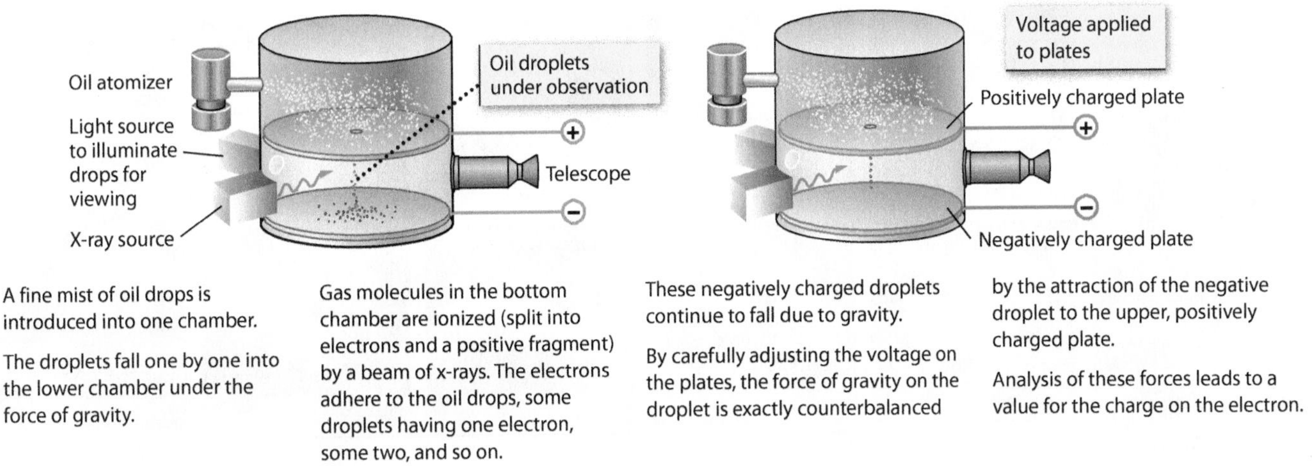

FIGURE 3 **Millikan's experiment to determine the electron charge.** Cathode ray experiments allow measurement of the charge-to-mass ratio of a charged particle, but not the charge or mass individually. In 1908, the American physicist Robert Millikan (1868–1953), at California Institute of Technology, carried out an experiment to measure the charge on the electron. In his experiment, tiny oil droplets were sprayed into a chamber and then subjected to x-rays, causing them to take on a negative charge. The drops could be suspended in air if the force of gravity was balanced against an electric field, and from an analysis of these forces on the droplet the charge could be calculated. Millikan determined that the electronic charge was 1.592×10^{-19} coulombs (C), not far from today's accepted value of 1.602×10^{-19} C. Millikan rightly assumed this was the fundamental unit of charge. Knowing this value and the charge-to-mass ratio determined by Thomson, the mass of an electron could be calculated.

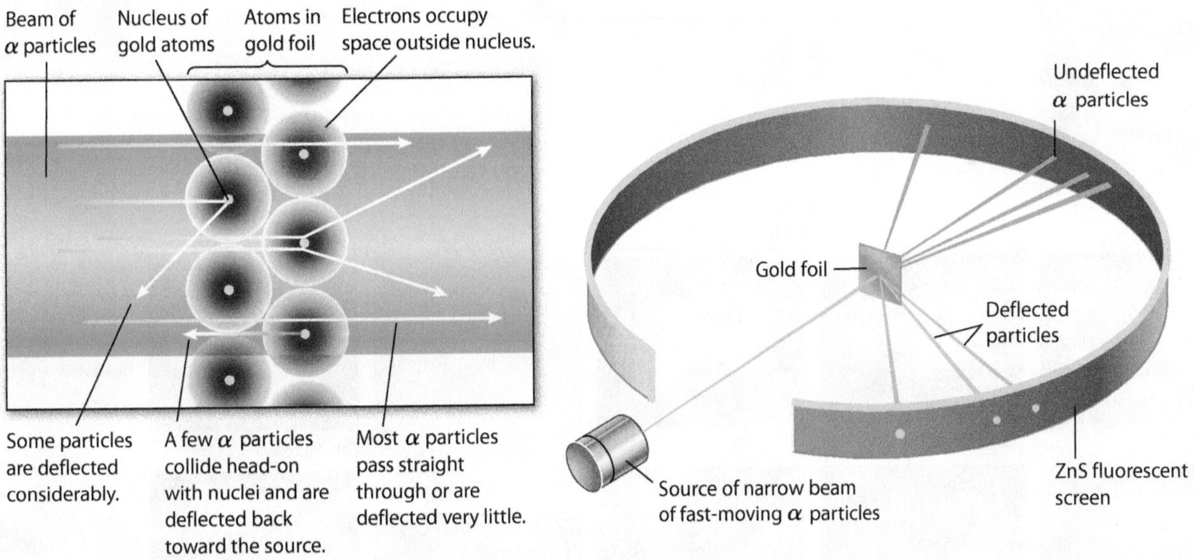

FIGURE 4 **Rutherford's experiment to determine the structure of the atom.** Although it was recognized that atoms were made up of smaller particles, it was not clear how these particles fit together. The experiments by Ernest Rutherford (1871–1937) established the model that we now accept. Around 1910, Rutherford and his students—Hans Geiger (1882–1945) and Ernest Marsden (1889–1970)—bombarded thin gold foil with α particles. Almost all the particles passed straight through the gold foil as if there was nothing there. However, a few α particles were deflected sideways and some even bounced right back. This experiment proved that an atom of gold is mostly empty space with a tiny nucleus at its center. The electrons surround the nucleus and account for most of the volume of the atom. Rutherford calculated that the central nucleus of an atom occupied only 1/10,000th of its volume. He also estimated that a gold nucleus had a positive charge of around 100 units and a radius of about 10^{-12} cm. (The values are now known to be +79 for atomic charge and 10^{-13} cm for the radius.)

The final piece of the picture of atomic structure was not established for another decade. It had been known for some time that there had to be something else in the nucleus, and it had to be a heavy particle to account for the mass of an element. In 1932, the British physicist James Chadwick (1891–1974) found the missing particle. These particles, now known as neutrons, had no electric charge and a mass of 1.675×10^{-24} g, slightly greater than the mass of a proton.

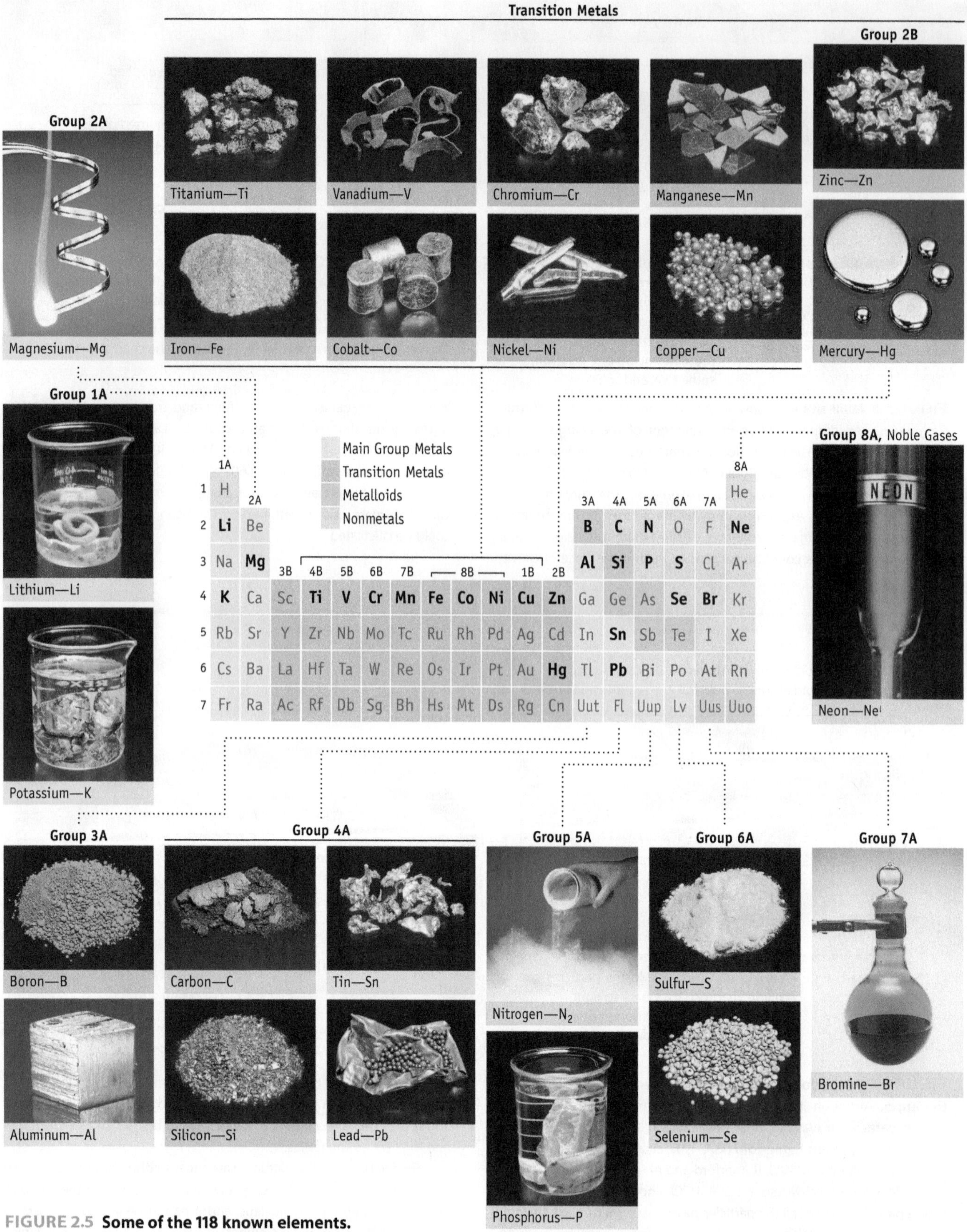

FIGURE 2.5 Some of the 118 known elements.

A CLOSER LOOK

Mendeleev and the Periodic Table

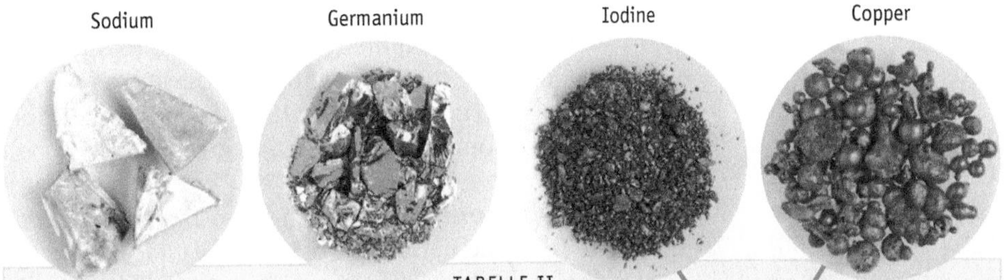

TABELLE II.

REIHEN	GRUPPE I. — R^2O	GRUPPE II. — RO	GRUPPE III. — R^2O^3	GRUPPE IV. RH^4 RO^2	GRUPPE V. RH^3 R^2O^5	GRUPPE VI. RH^2 RO^3	GRUPPE VII. RH R^2O^7	GRUPPE VIII. — RO^4
1	H=1							
2	Li=7	Be=9,4	B=11	C=12	N=14	O=16	F=19	
3	Na=23	Mg=24	Al=27,3	Si=28	P=31	S=32	Cl=35,5	
4	K=39	Ca=40	—=44	Ti=48	V=51	Cr=52	Mn=55	Fe=56, Co=59, Ni=59, Cu=63.
5	(Cu=63)	Zn=65	—=68	—=72	As=75	Se=78	Br=80	
6	Rb=85	Sr=87	?Yt=88	Zr=90	Nb=94	Mo=96	—=100	Ru=104, Rh=104, Pd=106, Ag=108.
7	(Ag=108)	Cd=112	In=113	Sn=118	Sb=122	Te=125	J=127	
8	Cs=133	Ba=137	?Di=138	?Ce=140	—	—	—	— — — —
9	(—)	—	—	—	—	—	—	
10	—	—	?Er=178	?La=180	Ta=182	W=184	—	Os=195, Ir=197, Pt=198, Au=199.
11	(Au=199)	Hg=200	Tl=204	Pb=207	Bi=208	—	—	
12	—	—	—	Th=231	—	U=240	—	— — — —

Photos: © Cengage Learning/Charles D. Winters

The original Mendeleev table showing the places he left for as yet-undiscovered elements.

Although the arrangement of elements in the periodic table is now understood on the basis of atomic structure, the table was originally developed from many experimental observations of the chemical and physical properties of elements and is the result of the ideas of a number of chemists in the 18th and 19th centuries.

In 1869, at the University of St. Petersburg in Russia, Dmitri Ivanovitch Mendeleev (1834–1907) wrote a textbook on chemistry. As he pondered the chemical and physical properties of the elements, he realized that, if the elements were arranged in order of increasing atomic mass, elements with similar properties appeared in a regular pattern. That is, he saw a **periodicity** or periodic repetition of the properties of elements. Mendeleev organized the known elements into a table by lining them up in horizontal rows in order of increasing atomic mass. When he came to an element with properties similar to one already in the row, he started a new row. For example, the elements Li, Be, B, C, N, O, and F were in a row. Sodium was the next element then known; because its properties closely resembled those of Li, Mendeleev started a new row. As more and more elements were added to the table, new rows were begun, and elements with similar properties (such as Li, Na, and K) were placed in the same vertical column.

John C. Kotz

Statue of Dmitri Mendeleev and a periodic table. This statue and mural are at the Institute of Metrology in St. Petersburg, Russia.

An important feature of Mendeleev's table—and a mark of his genius—was that he left an empty space in a column when he believed an element was not known but should exist and have properties similar to the elements above and below it in his table. He deduced that these spaces would be filled by undiscovered elements. For example, he left a space between Si (silicon) and Sn (tin) in Group 4A for an element he called *eka-silicon*. Based on the progression of properties in this group, Mendeleev was able to predict the properties of the missing element. With the discovery of germanium (Ge) in 1886, Mendeleev's prediction was confirmed.

In Mendeleev's table the elements were ordered by increasing mass. A glance at a modern table, however, shows that, if listed in order of increasing mass and not based on their properties, three pairs of elements (Ni and Co, Ar and K, and Te and I) would be out of order. Mendeleev recognized these discrepancies and simply assumed the atomic masses known at that time were inaccurate—not a bad assumption based on the analytical methods then in use. In fact, his order is correct and what was wrong was his assumption that element properties were a function of their mass.

In 1913 H. G. J. Moseley (1887–1915), a young English scientist working with Ernest Rutherford (1871–1937), bombarded many different metals with electrons in a cathode-ray tube (see "Key Experiments") and examined the x-rays emitted in the process. Moseley realized the wavelength of the x-rays emitted by a given element was related in a precise manner to the positive charge in the nucleus of the element and that this provided a way to experimentally determine the atomic number of a given element. Indeed, once atomic numbers could be determined, chemists recognized that organizing the elements in a table by increasing atomic number corrected the inconsistencies in Mendeleev's table. The **law of chemical periodicity** is now stated as *the properties of the elements are periodic functions of atomic number.*

For more on the periodic table, see:

- J. Emsley: *Nature's Building Blocks—An A-Z Guide to the Elements*, New York, Oxford University Press, 2001.
- E. Scerri, *The Periodic Table*, New York, Oxford University Press, 2007.

You are probably familiar with many properties of **metals** from your own experience. At room temperature and normal atmospheric pressure metals are solids (except for mercury), can conduct electricity, are usually ductile (can be drawn into wires) and malleable (can be rolled into sheets), and can form alloys (mixtures of one or more metals in another metal). Iron (Fe) and aluminum (Al) are used in automobile parts because of their ductility, malleability, and low cost relative to other metals. Copper (Cu) is used in electric wiring because it conducts electricity better than most other metals.

© Cengage Learning/Charles D. Winters

Silicon—a metalloid. Only six elements are generally classified as metalloids or semimetals. This photograph shows solid silicon in various forms, including a wafer that holds printed electronic circuits.

The **nonmetals**, which lie to the right of a diagonal line that stretches from B to Te in the periodic table, have a wide variety of properties. Some are solids (carbon, sulfur, phosphorus, and iodine). Ten elements are gases at room temperature (hydrogen, oxygen, nitrogen, fluorine, chlorine, helium, neon, argon, krypton, and xenon). One nonmetal, bromine, is a liquid at room temperature. With the exception of carbon in the form of graphite, nonmetals do not conduct electricity, which is one of the main features that distinguishes them from metals.

The elements along the diagonal line from boron (B) to tellurium (Te) have properties that make them difficult to classify as metals or nonmetals. Chemists call them **metalloids** or, sometimes, **semimetals** (see Figure 2.5). You should know, however, that chemists often disagree about which elements fit this category. We will define a metalloid as an element that has some of the physical characteristics of a metal but some of the chemical characteristics of a nonmetal; we include only B, Si, Ge, As, Sb, and Te in this category. This definition reflects the ambiguity in the behavior of these elements. Antimony (Sb), for example, conducts electricity as well as many elements that are true metals. Its chemistry, however, resembles that of a nonmetal such as phosphorus, an element also in Group 5A.

A Brief Overview of the Periodic Table and the Chemical Elements

Elements in the leftmost column, **Group 1A**, are known as the **alkali metals** (except H). The word *alkali* comes from the Arabic language. Ancient Arabian chemists discovered that ashes of certain plants, which they called al-qali, gave water solutions that felt slippery and burned the skin. These ashes contain compounds of Group 1A elements that produce alkaline (basic) solutions.

All the alkali metals are solids at room temperature and all are reactive. For example, they react with water to produce hydrogen and alkaline solutions (Figure 2.6). Because of their reactivity, these metals are only found in nature combined in compounds (such as NaCl) (◀ Figure 1.2), never as free elements.

The second group in the periodic table, **Group 2A**, is also composed entirely of metals that occur naturally only in compounds. Except for beryllium (Be), these

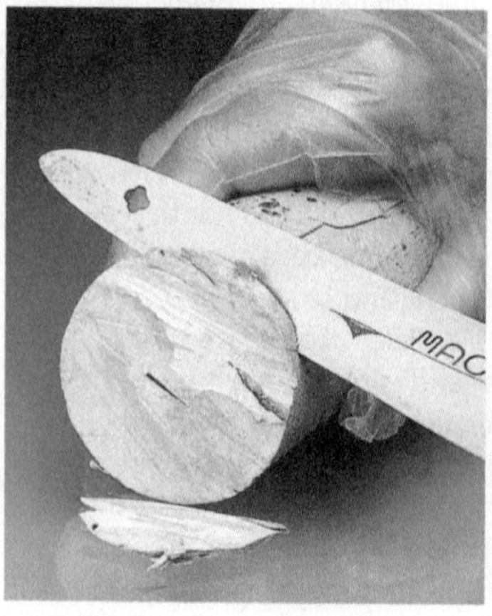
© Cengage Learning/Charles D. Winters

(a) Cutting sodium.

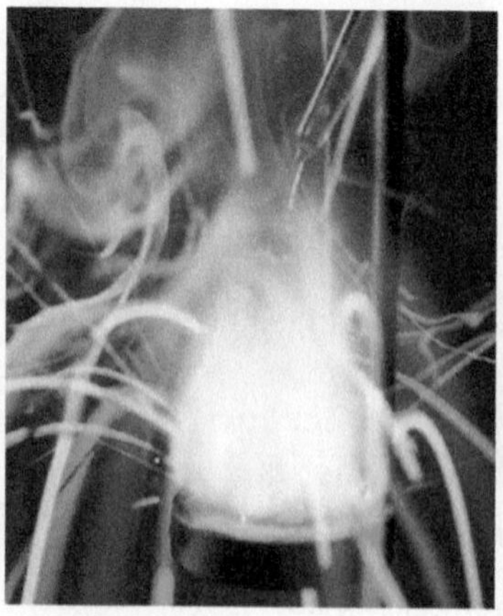
© Cengage Learning/Charles D. Winters

(b) Potassium reacts with water.

FIGURE 2.6 **Properties of the alkali metals.**

elements react with water to produce alkaline solutions, and most of their oxides (such as lime, CaO) form alkaline solutions; hence, they are known as the **alkaline earth metals**. Magnesium (Mg) and calcium (Ca) are the seventh and fifth most abundant elements in the Earth's crust, respectively (Table 2.3). Calcium, one of the important elements in teeth and bones, occurs naturally in vast limestone deposits. Calcium carbonate ($CaCO_3$) is the chief constituent of limestone and of corals, sea shells, marble, and chalk. Radium (Ra), the heaviest alkaline earth element, is radioactive and is used to treat some cancers by radiation.

Gallium melts (melting point = 29.8 °C) when held in the hand.

Liquid gallium. Bromine and mercury are the only elements that are liquids under ambient conditions. Gallium and cesium melt slightly above room temperature.

Aluminum, an element of great commercial importance, is in **Group 3A** (see Figure 2.5). This element and three others of Group 3A (gallium, indium, and thallium) are metals, whereas boron (B) is a metalloid. Aluminum (Al) is the most abundant metal in the Earth's crust at 8.2% by mass. It is exceeded in abundance only by the nonmetal oxygen and metalloid silicon and is usually found in minerals and clays. Boron occurs in the mineral borax, a compound used as a cleaning agent, antiseptic, and flux for metal work.

As a metalloid, boron has a different chemistry than the other elements of Group 3A, all of which are metals. Nonetheless, all form compounds with analogous formulas such as BCl_3 and $AlCl_3$, and this similarity marks them as members of the same periodic group.

Thus far all the elements we have described, except boron, have been metals. Beginning with **Group 4A**, however, the groups contain more and more nonmetals. In Group 4A there is a nonmetal, carbon (C), two metalloids, silicon (Si) and germanium (Ge), and two metals, tin (Sn) and lead (Pb) (see Figure 2.5). Because of the change from nonmetallic to metallic behavior, more variation occurs in the properties of the elements of this group than in most others. Nonetheless, there are similarities. For example, these elements form compounds with analogous formulas such as CO_2, SiO_2, GeO_2, and PbO_2.

Placing H in the Periodic Table Where to place H? Tables often show it in Group 1A even though it is clearly not an alkali metal. However, in its reactions it forms a 1+ ion just like the alkali metals. For this reason, H is often placed in Group 1A.

One interesting aspect of the chemistry of the nonmetals is that a particular element can often exist in several different and distinct forms, called **allotropes**, each having its own properties. Carbon has many allotropes, the best known of which are graphite and diamond. Graphite consists of flat sheets in which each carbon atom is connected to three others (Figure 2.7 *left*). Because the sheets of carbon atoms cling only weakly to one another, one layer can slip easily over another. This explains why graphite is soft, is a good lubricant, and is used in pencil lead. [Pencil "lead" is not the element lead (Pb) but a composite of clay and graphite that leaves a trail of graphite on the page as you write.]

In diamond each carbon atom is connected to four others at the corners of a tetrahedron, and this extends throughout the solid (Figure 2.7 *middle*). This structure causes diamonds to be extremely hard, denser than graphite (d = 3.51 g/cm^3 for diamond versus d = 2.22 g/cm^3 for graphite), and chemically less reactive. Because diamonds are not only hard but are excellent conductors of heat, they are used on the tips of metal- and rock-cutting tools.

In the late 1980s another form of carbon was identified as a component of black soot, the stuff that collects when carbon-containing materials are burned in a deficiency of oxygen. This substance is made up of molecules with 60 carbon atoms arranged as a spherical "cage" (Figure 2.7 *right*). You may recognize that the surface is made up of five- and six-member rings and resembles a hollow soccer ball. The shape also reminded its discoverers of an architectural dome conceived over 50 years ago by the American philosopher and engineer, R. Buckminster Fuller. This led to the official name of the

Table 2.3 The 10 Most Abundant Elements in the Earth's Crust

Rank	Element	Abundance (ppm)*
1	Oxygen	474,000
2	Silicon	277,000
3	Aluminum	82,000
4	Iron	41,000
5	Calcium	41,000
6	Sodium	23,000
7	Magnesium	23,000
8	Potassium	21,000
9	Titanium	5,600
10	Hydrogen	1,520

*ppm = parts per million = g per 1000 kg.

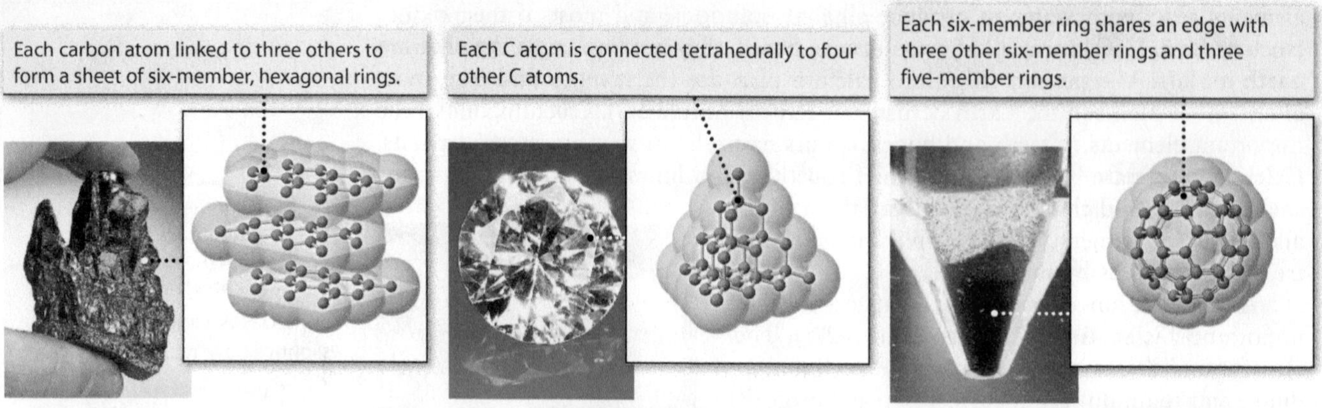

(a) Graphite. Graphite consists of layers of carbon atoms.

(b) Diamond. In diamond the carbon atoms are also arranged in six-member rings, but the rings are not planar.

(c) Buckyballs. A member of the family called buckminsterfullerenes, C_{60} is an allotrope of carbon. Sixty carbon atoms are arranged in a spherical cage that resembles a hollow soccer ball. Chemists call this molecule a "buckyball." C_{60} is a black powder; it is shown here in the tip of a pointed glass tube.

FIGURE 2.7 **The allotropes of carbon.**

allotrope, buckminsterfullerene, although chemists often just call these molecules "buckyballs."

Oxides of silicon are the basis of many minerals such as clay, quartz, and beautiful gemstones like amethyst. Tin and lead have been known for centuries because they are easily smelted from their ores. Tin alloyed with copper makes bronze, which was used in ancient times in utensils and weapons. Lead has been used in water pipes and paint, even though the element is toxic to humans.

FIGURE 2.8 **Elements that exist as diatomic or triatomic molecules.** Seven of the known elements exist as diatomic, or two-atom, molecules. Oxygen has an additional allotrope, ozone, with three O atoms in each molecule.

Nitrogen in **Group 5A** occurs naturally in the form of the diatomic molecule N_2 (Figures 2.8) and makes up about three-fourths of Earth's atmosphere. It is also found in biochemically important substances such as chlorophyll, proteins, and DNA. Scientists have long studied ways to make compounds from atmospheric nitrogen, a process referred to as "nitrogen fixation." Nature accomplishes this easily in some prokaryotic organisms, but severe conditions (high temperatures, for example) must be used in the laboratory and in industry to cause N_2 to react with other elements (such as H_2 to make ammonia, NH_3, which is widely used as a fertilizer).

Phosphorus is also essential to life. It is an important constituent in bones, teeth, and DNA. The element glows in the dark if it is in the air (owing to its reaction with O_2), and its name, based on Greek words meaning "light-bearing," reflects this. This element also has several allotropes, the most important being white (see Figure 2.5) and red phosphorus. White phosphorus (which is composed of P_4 molecules) ignites spontaneously in air, so it is normally stored under water. When it does react with air, it forms P_4O_{10}, which can react with water to form phosphoric acid (H_3PO_4), a compound used in food products such as soft drinks. Red phosphorus is used in the striking strips on match books. When a match is struck, potassium chlorate in the match head mixes with some red phosphorus on the striking strip, and the friction is enough to ignite the mixture.

As with Group 4A, we again see nonmetals (N and P), metalloids (As and Sb), and a metal (Bi) in Group 5A. In spite of these variations, they also form analogous compounds such as the oxides N_2O_5, P_4O_{10}, and As_2O_5.

Oxygen, which constitutes about 20% of Earth's atmosphere and which combines readily with most other elements, is at the top of **Group 6A**. Most of the energy that powers life on Earth is derived from reactions in which oxygen combines with other substances.

Sulfur has been known in elemental form since ancient times as brimstone or "burning stone" (Figure 2.9). Sulfur, selenium, and tellurium are often referred to collectively as *chalcogens* (from the Greek word, *khalkos*, for copper) because most copper ores contain these elements. Their compounds can be foul-smelling and poisonous; nevertheless, sulfur and selenium are essential components of the human diet. By far the most important compound of sulfur is sulfuric acid (H_2SO_4), which is manufactured in larger amounts than any other compound.

As in Group 5A, the second- and third-period elements of Group 6A have different structures. Like nitrogen, oxygen is also a diatomic molecule (see Figure 2.8). Unlike nitrogen, however, oxygen has an allotrope, the triatomic molecule ozone, O_3. Sulfur, which can be found in nature as a yellow solid, has many allotropes, the most common of which consists of eight-member, crown-shaped rings of sulfur atoms (see Figure 2.9).

Polonium, the radioactive element in Group 6A, was isolated in 1898 by Marie and Pierre Curie, who separated a small amount from tons of a uranium-containing ore and named it for Madame Curie's native country, Poland.

In Group 6A we once again observe a variation of properties. Oxygen, sulfur, and selenium are nonmetals, tellurium is a metalloid, and polonium is a metal. Nonetheless, there is a family resemblance in their chemistries. All of oxygen's fellow group members form oxygen-containing compounds (SO_2, SeO_2, and TeO_2), and all form sodium-containing compounds (Na_2O, Na_2S, Na_2Se, and Na_2Te).

At the far right of the periodic table are two groups composed entirely of nonmetals. The **Group 7A** elements—fluorine, chlorine, bromine, iodine, and radioactive astatine—are nonmetals and all exist as diatomic molecules. At room temperature fluorine (F_2) and chlorine (Cl_2) are gases. Bromine (Br_2) is a liquid and iodine (I_2) is a solid, but bromine and iodine vapor are clearly visible over the liquid or solid (Figure 2.10).

The Group 7A elements are among the most reactive of all elements, and all combine violently with alkali metals to form salts such as table salt, NaCl (◀ Figure 1.2). The name for this group, the **halogens**, comes from the Greek words *hals*, meaning "salt," and *genes*, for "forming."

The **Group 8A** elements—helium, neon, argon, krypton, xenon, and radioactive radon—are the least reactive elements. All are gases, and none is abundant on Earth or in the Earth's atmosphere (although argon is the third most abundant gas in dry air at 0.9%). Because of this, they were not discovered until the end of the 19th century (see page 92). A common name for this group, the **noble gases**, denotes their general lack of reactivity.

Helium, the second most abundant element in the universe after hydrogen, was detected in the Sun in 1868 by analysis of the solar spectrum but was not found on

FIGURE 2.9 **Sulfur.** The most common allotrope of sulfur consists of S atoms arranged in eight-member, crown-shaped rings.

Special Group Names Some groups have common and widely used names.

Group 1A: Alkali metals
Group 2A: Alkaline earth metals
Group 7A: Halogens
Group 8A: Noble (or rare) gases

FIGURE 2.10 **The halogens, bromine and iodine.**

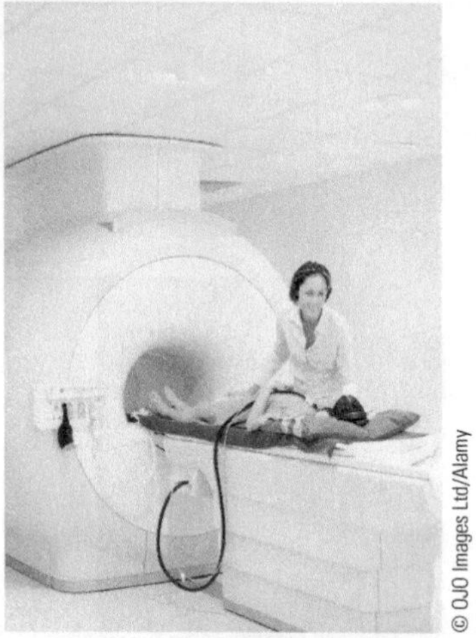

© OJO Images Ltd/Alamy

FIGURE 2.11 **Helium, a noble gas, and MRI units.** The magnets of MRI units need to be cooled to 4 K with liquid helium in order to be able to generate the high magnetic field required. This is the largest use of this noble gas.

Earth until 1895. It is now widely used, with worldwide demand currently about 170 billion liters per year. The biggest single use of helium is to cool the magnets found in MRI units in hospitals, and nuclear magnetic resonance spectrometers in research laboratories (Figure 2.11). These magnets need to be cooled with liquid helium to 4 K because, at this extremely low temperature, the magnets are superconductors of electricity. They can then generate the high magnetic fields needed to produce an image of your body, for example. In addition, helium gas is used to fill weather balloons (and party balloons) and in the semiconductor industry. The United States supplies most of the helium, but there are periodic shortages that seriously disrupt commerce and research.

Stretching between Groups 2A and 3A in the periodic table is a series of elements called the **transition elements**. These fill the B-groups (1B through 8B) in the fourth through the seventh periods in the center of the periodic table. All are metals (see Figure 2.5), and 13 of them are in the top 30 elements in terms of abundance in the Earth's crust. Most occur naturally in combination with other elements, but a few—copper (Cu), silver (Ag), gold (Au), and platinum (Pt)—can be found in nature as pure elements.

Virtually all of the transition elements have commercial uses. They are used as structural materials (iron, titanium, chromium, copper); in paints (titanium, chromium); in the catalytic converters in automobile exhaust systems (platinum and rhodium); in coins (copper, nickel, zinc); and in batteries (manganese, nickel, zinc, cadmium, mercury).

Two rows at the bottom of the table accommodate the **lanthanides** [the series of elements between the elements lanthanum ($Z = 57$) and hafnium ($Z = 72$)] and the **actinides** [the series of elements between actinium ($Z = 89$) and rutherfordium ($Z = 104$)].

The lanthanides are often referred to as **rare earth elements** (Figure 2.12). In fact, they are not that rare but are geologically widely dispersed. In spite of the difficulty in mining rare earth–containing minerals, they have become very important commercially. They are used in magnets (neodymium), in LCD screens, in hybrid car batteries, and in polishing glass. Minerals containing rare earth elements are presently mined largely in China, and there is concern that a worldwide shortage looms.

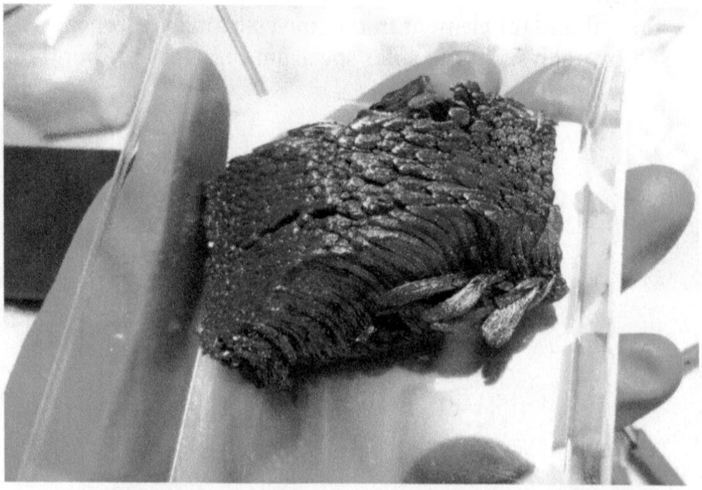

© Heinrich Pniok (www.pse-mendelejew.de)

FIGURE 2.12 **A sample of the rare earth element europium.** It is among the rarest of the lanthanides, but its abundance on Earth is about the same as tin and uranium, and it is more abundant than arsenic.

REVIEW & CHECK FOR SECTION 2-5

1. Which of the following elements is a metalloid?

   (a) Ge (b) S (c) Be (d) Al

2. What is the symbol for the element in the third period and the fourth group?

   (a) Si (b) Sc (c) V (d) Sn

3. What is the most abundant element in the Earth's crust?

   (a) Fe (b) C (c) O (d) N

4. What is the name given to elements that exist in different forms, such as graphite, diamond, and buckyballs?

   (a) isotopes (b) isomers (c) allotropes (d) nonmetals

2-6 Molecules, Compounds, and Formulas

Learning Objectives: LO 1.18, LO 2.1

A molecule is the smallest identifiable unit into which some pure substances like sugar and water can be divided and still retain the composition and chemical properties of the substance. Such substances are composed of identical molecules consisting of two or more atoms bound firmly together. In the reaction below and in Figure 2.13, molecules of sulfur, S_8, combine with molecules of oxygen, O_2, to produce molecules of the compound sulfur dioxide, SO_2.

$$S_8(s) + 8\ O_2(g) \rightarrow 8\ SO_2(g)$$

$$\text{sulfur} + \text{oxygen} \rightarrow \text{sulfur dioxide}$$

To describe this chemical change (or chemical reaction) on paper, the composition of each element and compound is represented by a symbol or formula. Here one molecule of SO_2 is composed of one S atom and two O atoms.

Formulas

There is often more than one way to write the formula of a compound. For example, the formula of ethanol (also called ethyl alcohol) can be represented as C_2H_6O (Figure 2.14). This **molecular formula** describes the composition of ethanol

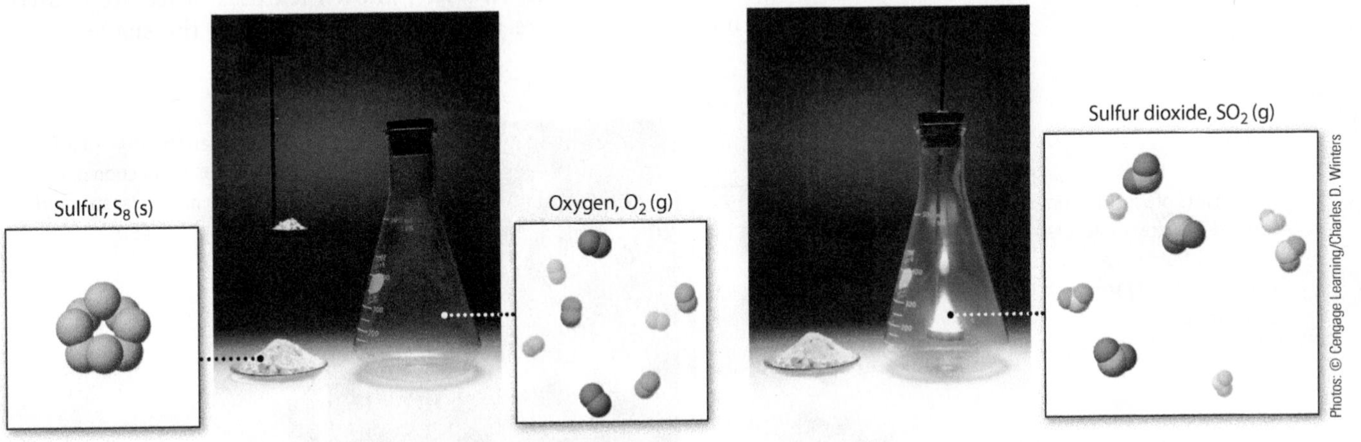

FIGURE 2.13 **The reaction of the elements sulfur and oxygen to give the compound sulfur dioxide.**

Standard Colors for Atoms in Molecular Models The colors listed here are used for molecular models in this book and are generally used by chemists.

NAME	MOLECULAR FORMULA	CONDENSED FORMULA	STRUCTURAL FORMULA	MOLECULAR MODEL
Ethanol	C_2H_6O	CH_3CH_2OH	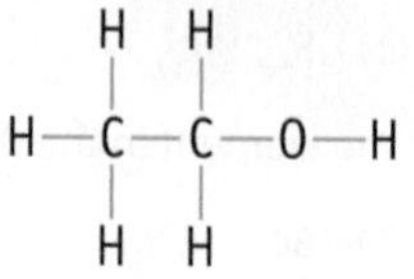	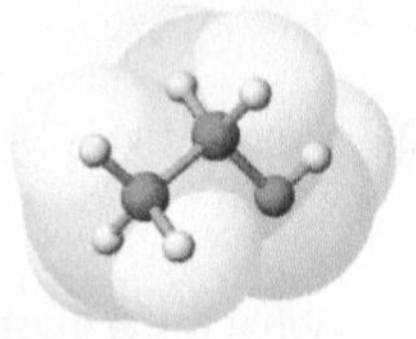
Dimethyl ether	C_2H_6O	CH_3OCH_3	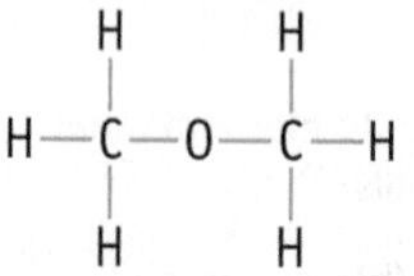	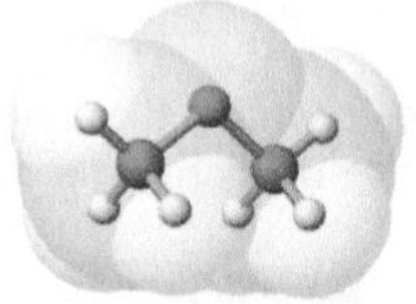

FIGURE 2.14 **Four approaches to showing molecular formulas.** Here the two molecules have the same molecular formula. Condensed or structural formulas, or a molecular model, clearly show these molecules are different.

molecules—two carbon atoms, six hydrogen atoms, and one atom of oxygen per molecule—but it gives us no structural information. Structural information—how the atoms are connected and how the molecule fills space—is important because it helps us understand how a molecule can interact with other molecules, which is the essence of chemistry.

To provide some structural information, it is useful to write a **condensed formula**, which indicates how certain atoms are grouped together. For example, the condensed formula of ethanol, CH_3CH_2OH (see Figure 2.14), tells us that the molecule consists of three "groups": a CH_3 group, a CH_2 group, and an OH group. Writing the formula as CH_3CH_2OH also shows that the compound is not dimethyl ether, CH_3OCH_3, a compound with the same molecular formula but with a different structure and distinctly different properties.

Writing Formulas When writing molecular formulas of organic compounds (compounds with C, H, and other elements) the convention is to write C first, then H, and finally other elements in alphabetical order. For example, acrylonitrile, a compound used to make consumer plastics, has the condensed formula CH_2CHCN. Its molecular formula would be C_3H_3N.

That ethanol and dimethyl ether are different molecules is further apparent from their **structural formulas** (see Figure 2.14). This type of formula gives us an even higher level of structural detail, showing how all of the atoms are attached within a molecule. The lines between atoms represent the chemical bonds that hold atoms together in this molecule [▶ Chapter 8].

Molecular Models

The physical and chemical properties of a molecular compound are often closely related to its structure. For example, two well-known features of ice are related to its underlying molecular structure (Figure 2.15). The first is the shape of ice

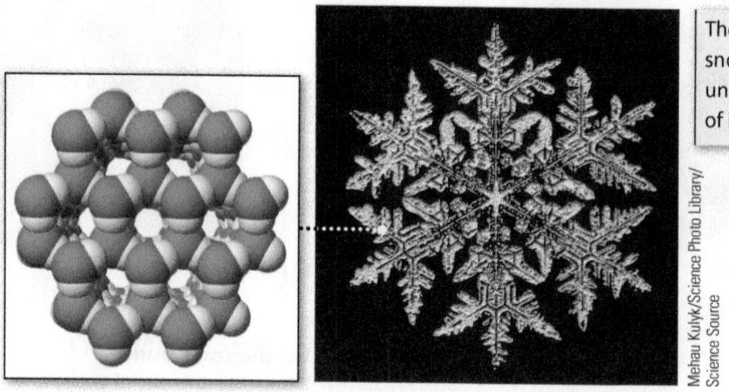

FIGURE 2.15 **Ice.** Snowflakes reflect the underlying structure of ice.

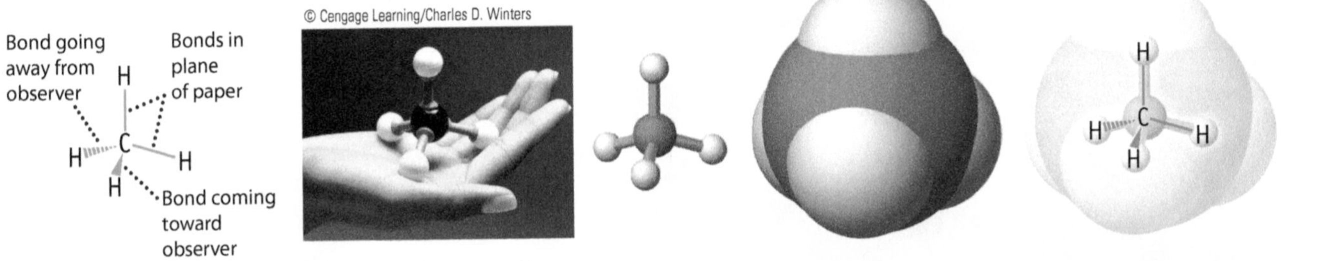

Simple perspective drawing | Plastic model | Ball-and-stick model | Space-filling model | All visualizing techniques represent the same molecule.

FIGURE 2.16 **Ways of depicting a molecule, here the methane (CH_4) molecule.**

crystals: The sixfold symmetry of macroscopic ice crystals also appears at the particulate level in the form of six-sided rings of hydrogen and oxygen atoms. The second is water's unusual property of being less dense when it is solid than when it is liquid. The lower density of ice, which has enormous consequences for Earth's climate, results from the fact that molecules of water are not packed together tightly in ice.

Because molecules are three dimensional, it is often difficult to represent their structures on paper. Certain conventions have been developed, however, that help represent three-dimensional structures on two-dimensional surfaces. Simple perspective drawings are often used (Figure 2.16).

Molecular models are very useful for visualizing structures. These models make it easy to see how atoms are attached to one another and show the molecule's overall three-dimensional structure. In the **ball-and-stick model**, spheres of different colors represent the atoms, and sticks represent the bonds holding them together. Molecules can also be represented using **space-filling models**. These models are a better representation of relative sizes of atoms and their proximity to each other. A disadvantage of pictures of space-filling models is that atoms can often be hidden from view.

REVIEW & CHECK FOR SECTION 2-6

1. Cysteine, whose molecular model and structural formula are illustrated here, is an important amino acid and a constituent of many living things. What is its molecular formula?

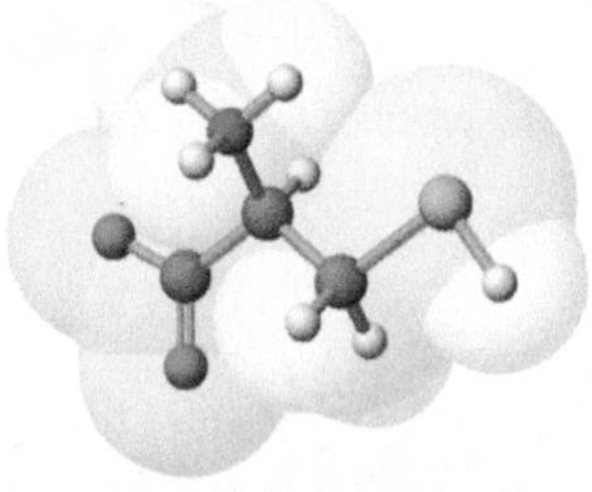

Molecular model

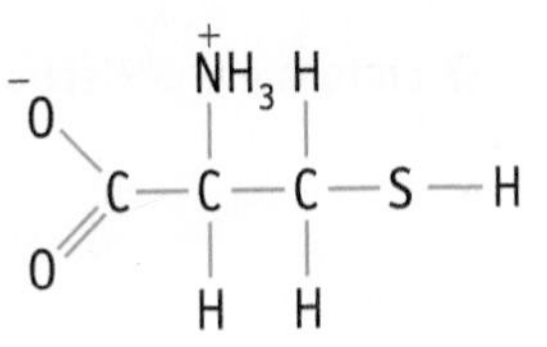

Structural formula

(a) $C_3H_6O_2S$ (b) $C_3H_7NO_2S$ (c) $C_3H_7N_2OS$ (d) $C_3H_7NO_2$

2-7 Ionic Compounds: Formulas, Names, and Properties

Learning Objectives: LO 1.11, LO 2.1, LO 2.14, LO 2.19, LO 2.23, LO 2.24

The compounds you have encountered so far in this chapter are **molecular compounds**, that is, compounds that consist of discrete molecules at the particulate level. **Ionic compounds** make up another major class of compounds, and many are

FIGURE 2.17 **Some common ionic compounds.**

Common Name	Name	Formula	Ions Involved
Calcite	Calcium carbonate	$CaCO_3$	Ca^{2+}, CO_3^{2-}
Fluorite	Calcium fluoride	CaF_2	Ca^{2+}, F^-
Gypsum	Calcium sulfate dihydrate	$CaSO_4 \cdot 2\ H_2O$	Ca^{2+}, SO_4^{2-}
Hematite	Iron(III) oxide	Fe_2O_3	Fe^{3+}, O^{2-}
Orpiment	Arsenic sulfide	As_2S_3	As^{3+}, S^{2-}

probably familiar to you (Figure 2.17). Table salt, or sodium chloride (NaCl), and lime (CaO) are just two. It is important for you to be able to recognize ionic compounds, to name them, and to write their formulas.

Ions

Ionic compounds consist of ions, atoms or groups of atoms that bear a positive or negative electric charge. Atoms of many elements can lose or gain electrons to form monatomic ions, and commonly encountered ions are listed in Figure 2.18. How do you know if an atom is likely to gain or lose electrons? It depends on whether the element is a metal or nonmetal. In reactions,

- Metals generally lose one or more electrons.
- Nonmetals frequently gain one or more electrons.

Monatomic Cations

If an atom loses an electron (which is transferred to an atom of another element in the course of a reaction), the atom now has one less negative electron than it has positive protons in the nucleus. The result is a positively charged ion called a **cation** (see Figure 2.18). (The name is pronounced "cat′-i-on.") For example, the loss of an electron from the Group 1A element lithium results in the formation of the Li^+ ion.

$$\text{Li atom} \rightarrow e^- + \text{Li}^+ \text{ cation}$$

(3 protons and 3 electrons) (3 protons and 2 electrons)

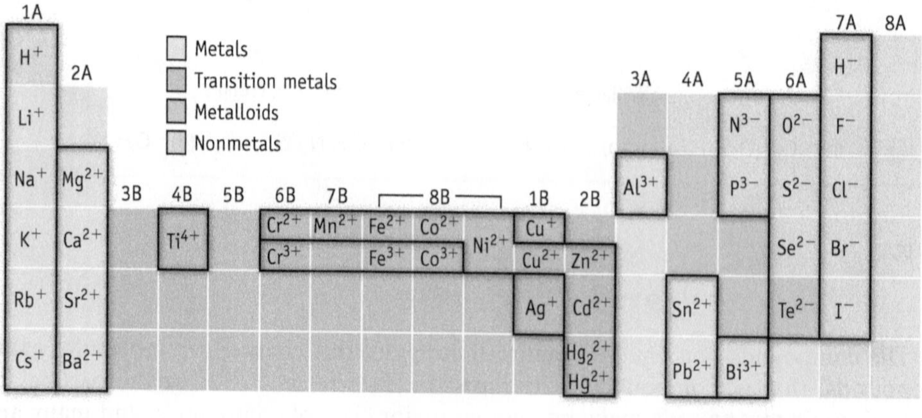

FIGURE 2.18 **Charges on some common monatomic cations and anions.** Metals usually form cations and nonmetals usually form anions. (The boxed areas show ions of identical charge.) **NOTE:** It is important to recognize that transition metals (and a few main group metals) form cations of several charges. Examples include Cr^{2+} and Cr^{3+}, Fe^{2+} and Fe^{3+}, and Cu^+ and Cu^{2+}. As explained, their names must reflect this.

Elements of Group 2A will lose two electrons in reactions,

$$\text{Ca atom} \rightarrow 2\ e^- + Ca^{2+}\ \text{cation}$$

(20 protons and 20 electrons) (20 protons and 18 electrons)

Writing Ion Formulas When writing the formula of an ion, the charge on the ion **must** be included.

and elements of Group 3A will lose three electrons.

$$\text{Al atom} \rightarrow 3\ e^- + Al^{3+}\ \text{cation}$$

(13 protons and 13 electrons) (13 protons and 10 electrons)

How can you predict the number of electrons gained or lost in reactions of elements in Groups 1A through 3A?

- Metals of Groups 1A–3A lose one or more electrons to form positive ions having a charge equal to the group number of the metal.
- The number of electrons remaining on the cation is the same as the number of electrons in an atom of the noble gas that precedes it in the periodic table.

Transition metals (B-group elements) also form cations, but unlike the A-group metals, there is no easily predictable pattern of behavior. In addition, transition metals often form several different ions. Iron, for example, may form either Fe^{2+} or Fe^{3+} ions in its reactions. Indeed, formation of 2+ and 3+ ions is typical of many transition metals (see Figure 2.18).

$$\text{Fe atom} \rightarrow 3\ e^- + Fe^{3+}\ \text{cation}$$

(26 protons and 26 electrons) (26 protons and 23 electrons)

Monatomic Anions

Nonmetals can gain electrons to form negatively charged ions. If an atom gains one or more electrons, there will now be one or more negatively charged electrons than protons (Figure 2.18). A negatively charged ion is called an anion (pronounced

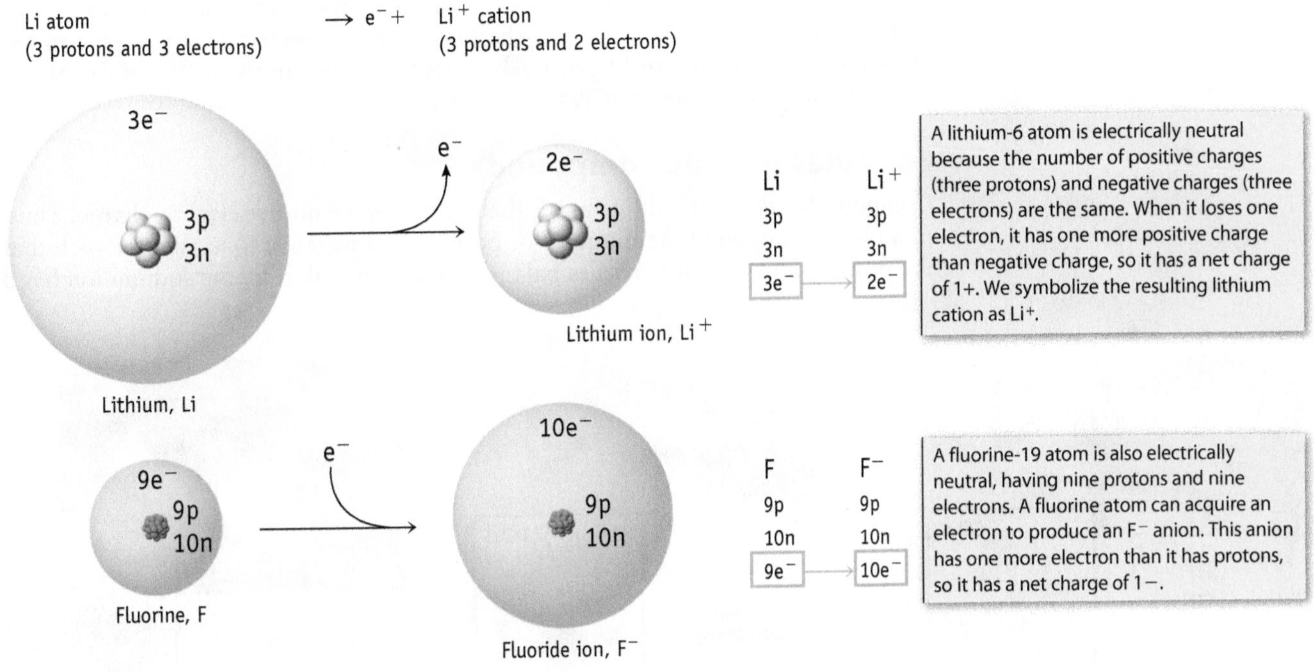

FIGURE 2.19 **Ions.**

"an′-i-on"). An oxygen atom, for example, can gain two electrons in a reaction to form an ion with the formula O^{2-}:

$$\text{O atom} + 2\,e^- \rightarrow O^{2-}\text{ anion}$$
$$\text{(8 protons and 8 electrons)} \qquad \text{(8 protons and 10 electrons)}$$

A chlorine atom can add a single electron to form Cl^-.

$$\text{Cl atom} + e^- \rightarrow Cl^-\text{ anion}$$
$$\text{(17 protons and 17 electrons)} \qquad \text{(17 protons and 18 electrons)}$$

We can make at least two general observations concerning the formation of anions from nonmetals.

- Nonmetals of Groups 5A–7A form negative ions having a charge equal to the group number of the metal minus 8.
- The number of electrons on the anion is the same as the number of electrons in an atom of the noble gas that follows it in the periodic table.

Notice that hydrogen appears at two locations in Figure 2.18. The H atom can either lose or gain electrons, depending on the other atoms it encounters.

Electron lost: H (1 proton, 1 electron) $\rightarrow$ H^+ (1 proton, 0 electrons) + e^-

Electron gained: H (1 proton, 1 electron) + e^- $\rightarrow$ H^- (1 proton, 2 electrons)

Finally, the noble gases very rarely form monatomic cations and never form monatomic anions in chemical reactions.

Polyatomic Ions

Polyatomic ions are made up of two or more atoms, and the collection has an electric charge (Figure 2.20 and Table 2.4). For example, carbonate ion, CO_3^{2-}, a common polyatomic anion, consists of one C atom and three O atoms. The ion has two units of negative charge because there are two more electrons (a total of 32) in the ion than there are protons (a total of 30) in the nuclei of one C atom and three O atoms.

The ammonium ion, NH_4^+, is a common polyatomic cation. In this case, four H atoms surround an N atom, and the ion has a 1+ electric charge. This ion has 10 electrons, but there are 11 positively charged protons in the nuclei of the N and H atoms (seven and one each, respectively).

Formulas of Ionic Compounds

Compounds are electrically neutral; that is, they have no net electric charge. Thus, in an ionic compound the numbers of positive and negative ions must be such that the positive and negative charges balance. In sodium chloride, the sodium ion has a

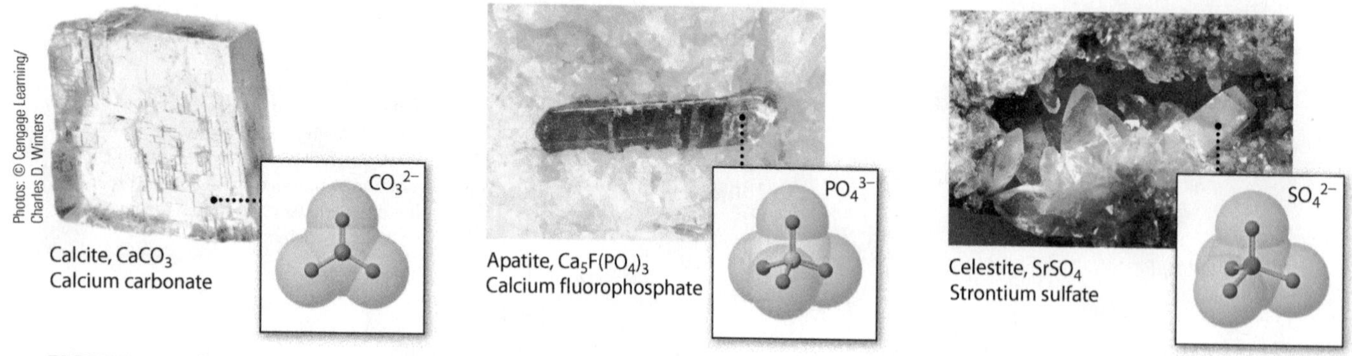

FIGURE 2.20 Common ionic compounds containing polyatomic ions.

Table 2.4 Formulas and Names of Some Common Polyatomic Ions

FORMULA	NAME	FORMULA	NAME
CATION: POSITIVE ION			
NH_4^+	Ammonium ion		
ANIONS: NEGATIVE IONS			
BASED ON A GROUP 4A ELEMENT		**BASED ON A GROUP 7A ELEMENT**	
CN^-	Cyanide ion	ClO^-	Hypochlorite ion
$CH_3CO_2^-$	Acetate ion	ClO_2^-	Chlorite ion
CO_3^{2-}	Carbonate ion	ClO_3^-	Chlorate ion
HCO_3^-	Hydrogen carbonate ion (or bicarbonate ion)	ClO_4^-	Perchlorate ion
$C_2O_4^{2-}$	Oxalate ion		
BASED ON A GROUP 5A ELEMENT		**BASED ON A TRANSITION METAL**	
NO_2^-	Nitrite ion	CrO_4^{2-}	Chromate ion
NO_3^-	Nitrate ion	$Cr_2O_7^{2-}$	Dichromate ion
PO_4^{3-}	Phosphate ion	MnO_4^-	Permanganate ion
HPO_4^{2-}	Hydrogen phosphate ion		
$H_2PO_4^-$	Dihydrogen phosphate ion		
BASED ON A GROUP 6A ELEMENT			
OH^-	Hydroxide ion		
SO_3^{2-}	Sulfite ion		
SO_4^{2-}	Sulfate ion		
HSO_4^-	Hydrogen sulfate ion (or bisulfate ion)		

1+ charge (Na^+) and the chloride ion has a 1− charge (Cl^-). These ions must be present in a 1:1 ratio, and so the formula is NaCl.

The gemstone ruby is largely the compound formed from aluminum ions (Al^{3+}) and oxide ions (O^{2-}). Here the ions have positive and negative charges that are of different absolute value. To have a compound with the same number of positive and negative charges, two Al^{3+} ions [total charge = 2 × (3+) = 6+] must combine with three O^{2-} ions [total charge = 3 × (2−) = 6−] to give a formula of Al_2O_3.

The Color of Rubies The beautiful red color of a ruby comes from a trace of Cr^{3+} ions that take the place of a few of the Al^{3+} ions in the solid.

Calcium, a Group 2A metal, forms a cation having a 2+ charge. It can combine with a variety of anions to form ionic compounds such as those in the following table:

COMPOUND	ION COMBINATION	OVERALL CHARGE ON COMPOUND
$CaCl_2$	$Ca^{2+} + 2\ Cl^-$	(2+) + 2 × (1−) = 0
$CaCO_3$	$Ca^{2+} + CO_3^{2-}$	(2+) + (2−) = 0
$Ca_3(PO_4)_2$	$3\ Ca^{2+} + 2\ PO_4^{3-}$	3 × (2+) + 2 × (3−) = 0

In writing formulas of ionic compounds, the convention is that *the symbol of the cation is given first, followed by the anion symbol.* Also notice the use of parentheses when more than one polyatomic ion of a given kind is present [as in $Ca_3(PO_4)_2$]. (None, however, are used when only one polyatomic ion is present, as in $CaCO_3$.)

EXAMPLE 2.4

Ionic Compound Formulas

Problem For each of the following ionic compounds, write the symbols for the ions present and give the relative number of each: (a) Li_2CO_3, and (b) $Fe_2(SO_4)_3$.

What Do You Know? You know the formulas of the ionic compounds, the predicted charges on monatomic ions (see Figure 2.18), and the formulas and charges of polyatomic ions (see Table 2.4).

Strategy Divide the formula of the compound into the cations and anions. To accomplish this you will have to recognize, and remember, the composition and charges of common ions.

Solution

(a) Li_2CO_3 is composed of two lithium ions, Li^+, for each carbonate ion, CO_3^{2-}. Li is a Group 1A element and always has a 1+ charge in its compounds. Because the two 1+ charges balance the negative charge of the carbonate ion, the latter must be 2−.

(b) $Fe_2(SO_4)_3$ contains two iron(III) ions, Fe^{3+}, for every three sulfate ions, SO_4^{2-}. The way to recognize this is to recall that sulfate has a 2− charge. Because three sulfate ions are present (with a total charge of 6−), the two iron cations must have a total charge of 6+. This is possible only if each iron cation has a charge of 3+.

Think about Your Answer Remember that the formula for an ion must include its composition and its charge. Formulas for ionic compounds are always written with the cation first and then the anion, but ion charges are ***not*** included.

Check Your Understanding

Give the number and identity of the constituent ions in each of the following ionic compounds: NaF, $Cu(NO_3)_2$, and $NaCH_3CO_2$.

EXAMPLE 2.5

Ionic Compound Formulas

Problem Write formulas for ionic compounds composed of an aluminum cation and each of the following anions: (a) fluoride ion, (b) sulfide ion, and (c) nitrate ion.

What Do You Know? You know the names of the ions involved, the predicted charges on monatomic ions (see Figure 2.18), and the names of polyatomic ions (see Table 2.4).

Strategy First decide on the formula of the Al cation and the formula of each anion. Combine the Al cation with each type of anion to form electrically neutral compounds.

Solution An aluminum cation is predicted to have a charge of 3+ because Al is a metal in Group 3A.

(a) Fluorine is a Group 7A element. The charge of the fluoride ion is predicted to be 1− (from 7 − 8 = 1−). Therefore, we need 3 F^- ions to combine with one Al^{3+}. The formula of the compound is AlF_3.

(b) Sulfur is a nonmetal in Group 6A, so it forms a 2− anion. Thus, we need to combine two Al^{3+} ions [total charge is 6+ = 2 × (3+)] with three S^{2-} ions [total charge is 6− = 3 × (2−)]. The compound has the formula Al_2S_3.

(c) The nitrate ion has the formula NO_3^- (see Table 2.4). The answer here is therefore similar to the AlF_3 case, and the compound has the formula $Al(NO_3)_3$. Here we place parentheses around NO_3 to show that three polyatomic NO_3^- ions are involved.

Think about Your Answer The most common error students make is not knowing the correct charge on an ion.

Check Your Understanding

(a) Write the formulas of all neutral ionic compounds that can be formed by combining the cations Na^+ and Ba^{2+} with the anions S^{2-} and PO_4^{3-}.

(b) Iron, a transition metal, forms ions having 2+ and 3+ charges. Write the formulas of the compounds formed between chloride ions and these two different iron cations.

Names of Ions

Naming Positive Ions (Cations)

With a few exceptions (such as NH_4^+), the positive ions described in this text are metal ions. Positive ions are named by the following rules:

1. For a monatomic positive ion (that is, a metal cation) the name is that of the metal plus the word "cation." For example, we have already referred to Al^{3+} as the aluminum cation.
2. In the transition series, a metal can form more than one type of positive ion. So that the name specifies which ion is involved, the charge of transition metal cations is indicated by a Roman numeral in parentheses immediately following the ion's name. For example, Co^{2+} is the cobalt(II) cation, and Co^{3+} is the cobalt(III) cation.

Finally, you will encounter the ammonium cation, NH_4^+, many times in this book and in the laboratory. Do not confuse the ammonium cation with the ammonia molecule, NH_3, which has no electric charge and one less H atom.

Elements with Multiple Ion Charges This is especially the case in the transition metals. However, it is also true of some main group metals such as tin (Sn^{2+} and Sn^{4+}) and lead (Pb^{2+} and Pb^{4+}). It is our practice to always indicate the ion charge with a Roman numeral in the transition metal elements and in other cases when multiple charges are possible.

Naming Negative Ions (Anions)

There are two types of negative ions: those having only one atom (*monatomic*) and those having several atoms (*polyatomic*).

1. A monatomic negative ion is named by adding *-ide* to the stem of the name of the nonmetal element from which the ion is derived (Figure 2.21). The anions of the Group 7A elements, the halogens, are known as fluoride, chloride, bromide, and iodide ions and as a group are called **halide ions**.
2. Polyatomic negative ions are common, especially those containing oxygen (called **oxoanions**). The names of some of the most common oxoanions are given in Table 2.4. Although most of these names must simply be learned, some guidelines can help. For example, consider the following pairs of ions:

NO_3^- is the nitrate ion, whereas NO_2^- is the nitrite ion.

SO_4^{2-} is the sulfate ion, whereas SO_3^{2-} is the sulfite ion.

The oxoanion having the greater number of oxygen atoms is given the suffix -ate, and the oxoanion having the smaller number of oxygen atoms has the suffix -ite. For a series of oxoanions having more than two members, the ion with the largest number of oxygen atoms has the prefix *per-* and the suffix *-ate*. The ion having

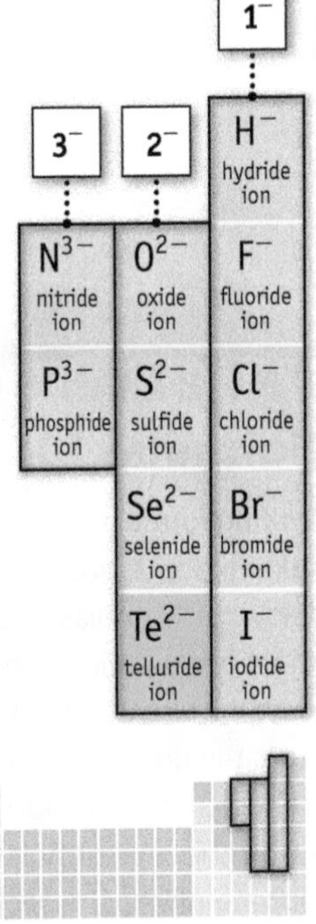

FIGURE 2.21 Names and charges of some common monatomic ions.

the smallest number of oxygen atoms has the prefix *hypo-* and the suffix *-ite*. The chlorine oxoanions are the most commonly encountered example.

ClO_4^-	*Perchlorate* ion	per . . . ate
ClO_3^-	Chlor*ate* ion	. . . ate
ClO_2^-	Chlor*ite* ion	. . . ite
ClO^-	*Hypo*chlor*ite* ion	hypo . . . ite

↑ increasing oxygen content

Oxoanions that contain hydrogen are named by adding the word "hydrogen" before the name of the oxoanion. If two hydrogens are in the anion, we say "dihydrogen." Many hydrogen-containing oxoanions have common names that are used as well. For example, the hydrogen carbonate ion, HCO_3^-, is called the bicarbonate ion.

Ion	**Systematic Name**	**Common Name**
HPO_4^{2-}	Hydrogen phosphate ion	
$H_2PO_4^-$	Dihydrogen phosphate ion	
HCO_3^-	Hydrogen carbonate ion	Bicarbonate ion
HSO_4^-	Hydrogen sulfate ion	Bisulfate ion
HSO_3^-	Hydrogen sulfite ion	Bisulfite ion

Names of Ionic Compounds

The name of an ionic compound is built from the names of the positive and negative ions in the compound. The name of the positive cation is given first, followed by the name of the negative anion. Examples of ionic compound names are given below.

Names of Compounds Containing Transition Metal Cations
Be sure to notice that the charge on a transition metal cation is indicated by a Roman numeral and is included in the name.

Ionic Compound	**Ions Involved**	**Name**
$CaBr_2$	Ca^{2+} and 2 Br^-	Calcium bromide
$NaHSO_4$	Na^+ and HSO_4^-	Sodium hydrogen sulfate
$(NH_4)_2CO_3$	2 NH_4^+ and CO_3^{2-}	Ammonium carbonate
$Mg(OH)_2$	Mg^{2+} and 2 OH^-	Magnesium hydroxide
$TiCl_2$	Ti^{2+} and 2 Cl^-	Titanium(II) chloride
Co_2O_3	2 Co^{3+} and 3 O^{2-}	Cobalt(III) oxide

PROBLEM SOLVING TIP 2.1
Formulas for Ions and Ionic Compounds

Writing formulas for ionic compounds takes practice, and it requires that you know the formulas and charges of the most common ions. The charges on monatomic ions are often evident from the position of the element in the periodic table, but you simply have to remember the formulas and charges of polyatomic ions, especially the most common ones such as nitrate, sulfate, carbonate, phosphate, and acetate.

If you cannot remember the formula of a polyatomic ion or if you encounter an ion you have not seen before, you may be able to figure out its formula. For example, suppose you are told that $NaCHO_2$ is sodium formate. You know that the sodium ion is Na^+, so the formate ion must be the remaining portion of the compound; it must have a charge of 1− to balance the 1+ charge on the sodium ion. Thus, the formate ion must be CHO_2^-.

Finally, when writing the formulas of ions, you *must* include the charge on the ion (except in the formula of an ionic compound). Writing Na when you mean sodium ion is incorrect. There is a vast difference in the properties of the element sodium (Na) and those of its ion (Na^+).

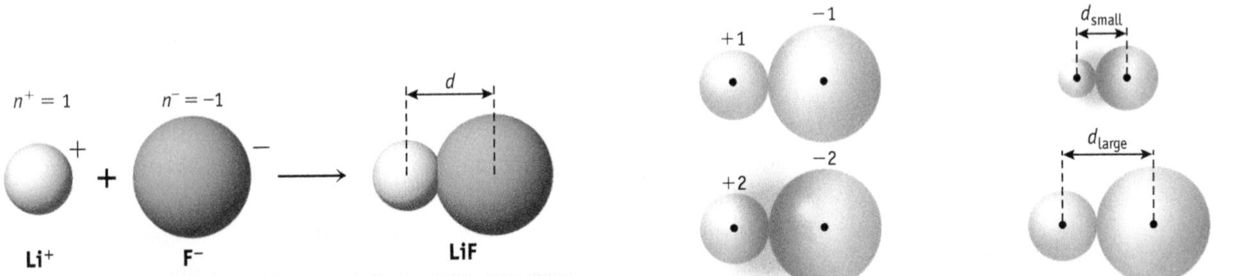

Ions such as Li^+ and F^- are held together by a coulombic force of attraction. Here a lithium ion is attracted to a fluoride ion, and the distance between the nuclei of the two ions is d.

(a)

As **ion charge** increases, **force of attraction** increases

As **distance** increases, **force of attraction** decreases

(b)

FIGURE 2.22 **Coulomb's law and electrostatic forces.**

Properties of Ionic Compounds

When a particle having a negative electric charge is brought near another particle having a positive electric charge, there is a force of attraction between them (Figure 2.22). In contrast, there is a repulsive force when two particles with the same charge—both positive or both negative—are brought together. These forces are called **electrostatic** forces, and the force of attraction (or repulsion) between ions is given by **Coulomb's law** (Equation 2.3):

charge on + and − ions; charge on electron

$$\text{Force} = -k\frac{(n^+e)(n^-e)}{d^2} \tag{2.3}$$

proportionality constant; distance between ions

where, for example, n^+ is +3 for Al^{3+} and n^- is −2 for O^{2-}. Based on Coulomb's law, the force of attraction between oppositely charged ions increases

- as the ion charges (n^+ and n^-) increase. Thus, the attraction between ions having charges of 2+ and 2− is greater than that between ions having 1+ and 1− charges (see Figure 2.22).
- as the distance between the ions becomes smaller (see Figure 2.22).

Ionic compounds do not consist of simple pairs or small groups of positive and negative ions. The simplest ratio of cations to anions in an ionic compound is represented by its formula, but an ionic solid consists of millions upon millions of ions arranged in an extended three-dimensional network called a **crystal lattice**. A portion of the lattice for NaCl, illustrated in Figure 2.23, represents a common way of arranging ions for compounds that have a 1:1 ratio of cations to anions.

Ionic compounds have characteristic properties that can be understood in terms of the charges of the ions and their arrangement in the lattice. Because each ion is surrounded by oppositely charged nearest neighbors, it is held tightly in its allotted location. At room temperature each ion can move just a bit around its average position, but considerable energy must be added before an ion can escape the attraction of its neighboring ions. Only if enough energy is added will the lattice structure collapse and the substance melt. Greater attractive forces mean that ever more energy—and higher and higher temperatures—is required to cause melting. Thus, Al_2O_3, a solid composed of Al^{3+} and O^{2-} ions, melts at a much higher temperature (2072 °C) than NaCl (801 °C), a solid composed of Na^+ and Cl^- ions.

Most ionic compounds are "hard" solids. That is, the solids are not pliable or soft. The reason for this characteristic is again related to the lattice of ions. The nearest neighbors of a cation in a lattice are anions, and the force of attraction

The Importance of Coulomb's Law Coulomb's law is the basis for understanding many fundamental concepts of chemistry. Among the chapters where this is important are:

Chapter 3: dissolving compounds in water.
Chapters 6 & 7: the interaction of electrons and the atomic nucleus.
Chapters 8 & 9: the interaction of atoms to form molecules.
Chapter 11: the interactions between molecules (intermolecular forces).
Chapter 12: the formation of ionic solids.
Chapter 13: the solution process.

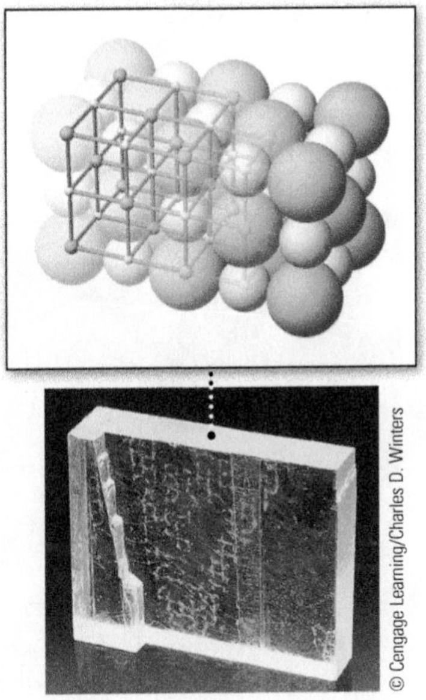

FIGURE 2.23 **Sodium chloride.** A crystal of NaCl consists of an extended lattice of sodium ions and chloride ions in a 1:1 ratio. When melted, the crystal lattice collapses and the ions move freely and can conduct an electrical current.

PROBLEM SOLVING TIP 2.2

Is a Compound Ionic?

Students often ask how to know whether a compound is ionic. Here are some useful guidelines.

1. Most metal-containing compounds are ionic. So, if a metal atom appears in the formula of a compound and especially when it is the element listed first, a good first guess is that the compound is ionic. (There are interesting exceptions, but few come up in introductory chemistry.) It is helpful in this regard to recall trends in metallic behavior: All elements to the left of a diagonal line running from boron (B) to tellurium (Te) in the periodic table are metallic.
2. If there is no metal in the formula, it is likely that the compound is not ionic. The exceptions here are compounds composed of polyatomic cations based on nonmetals (e.g., NH_4Cl or NH_4NO_3).
3. Learn to recognize the formulas of polyatomic ions (see Table 2.4).

Chemists write the formula of ammonium nitrate as NH_4NO_3 (not as $N_2H_4O_3$) to alert others to the fact that it is an ionic compound composed of the common polyatomic ions NH_4^+ and NO_3^-.

As an example of these guidelines, you can be sure that $MgBr_2$ (Mg^{2+} with Br^-) and K_2S (K^+ with S^{2-}) are ionic compounds. On the other hand, the compound CCl_4, formed from two nonmetals, C and Cl, is not ionic.

makes the lattice rigid. However, a blow with a hammer can cause the lattice to break cleanly along a sharp boundary. The hammer blow displaces layers of ions just enough to cause ions of like charge to become nearest neighbors, and the repulsion between these like-charged ions forces the lattice apart (Figure 2.24).

REVIEW & CHECK FOR SECTION 2-7

1. What is the most likely charge on an ion of barium?

   (a) 2− (b) 2+ (c) 3+ (d) 1−

An ionic solid is normally rigid owing to the forces of attraction between oppositely charged ions. When struck sharply, however, the crystal can cleave cleanly.

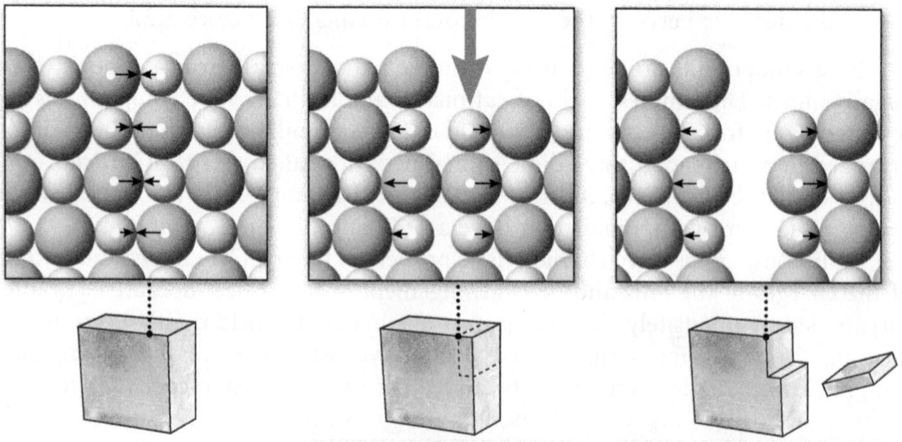

When a crystal is struck, layers of ions move slightly, and ions of like charge become nearest neighbors.

Repulsions between ions of similar charge cause the crystal to cleave.

FIGURE 2.24 **Ionic solids.**

2. When a gallium atom forms an ion, it
   (a) loses 3 electrons
   (b) gains 3 electrons
   (c) loses 2 electrons
   (d) gains 2 electrons
3. The name of the compound $(NH_4)_2S$ is
   (a) nitrohydrogen sulfide
   (b) ammonium sulfide
   (c) ammonium sulfur
   (d) ammonia sulfide
4. The formula of barium acetate is
   (a) $Ba(CH_3CO_2)_2$
   (b) $BaCH_3CO_2$
   (c) $BaMnO_4$
   (d) $BaCO_3$
5. The name of the compound with the formula V_2O_3 is
   (a) vanadium(III) oxide
   (b) vanadium oxide
   (c) divanadium trioxide
   (d) vanadium trioxide
6. Which should have the higher melting point, MgO or NaCl?
   (a) MgO
   (b) NaCl

A CLOSER LOOK — Hydrated Ionic Compounds

If ionic compounds are prepared in water solution and then isolated as solids, the crystals often retain molecules of water. These compounds are called **hydrated compounds**. For example, crystals of the red cobalt(II) compound in the Figure have six water molecules per $CoCl_2$. By convention, the formula for this compound is written as $CoCl_2 \cdot 6\,H_2O$. The dot between $CoCl_2$ and 6 H_2O indicates that 6 molecules of water are associated with every $CoCl_2$. The name of the compound is cobalt(II) chloride hexahydrate.

Hydrated cobalt(II) chloride, the red solid in the Figure, turns purple and then deep blue as it is heated and loses water to form anhydrous $CoCl_2$; "anhydrous" means a substance without water. On exposure to moist air, anhydrous $CoCl_2$ takes up water and is converted back into the red hydrated compound. It is this property that allows crystals of the blue compound to be used as a humidity indicator. You may have seen them in small bags packed with a piece of electronic equipment.

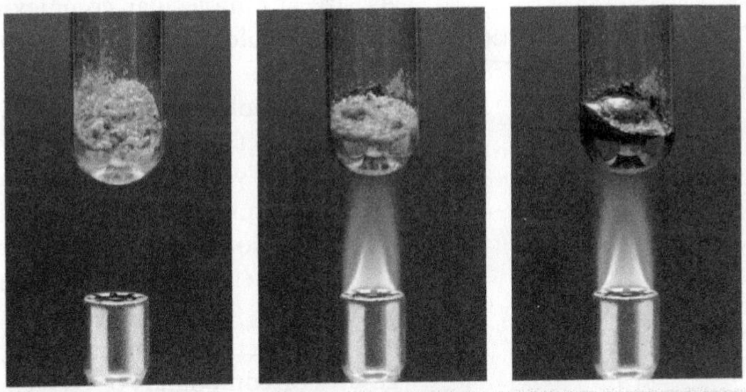

Cobalt(II) chloride hexahydrate $[CoCl_2 \cdot 6\,H_2O]$ is deep red.

When it is heated, the compound loses some of the water of hydration.

Heating ultimately leads to the deep blue compounds $CoCl_2 \cdot 2\,H_2O$ and $CoCl_2$. (Experiments show that some also decomposes to black CoO and HCl.)

Photos: © Cengage Learning/Charles D. Winters

Hydrated compounds are common. The walls of your home are probably covered with wallboard, or "plaster board" which contains hydrated calcium sulfate (gypsum, $CaSO_4 \cdot 2\,H_2O$), as well as anhydrous $CaSO_4$, sandwiched between paper. If gypsum is heated between 120 and 180 °C, the water is partly driven off to give $CaSO_4 \cdot 1/2\,H_2O$, a compound commonly called "plaster of Paris." If you have ever broken an arm or leg and had to have a cast, the cast may have been made of this compound. It is an effective casting material because, when added to water, it forms a thick slurry that can be poured into a mold or spread out over a part of the body. As it takes on more water, the material increases in volume and forms a hard, inflexible solid. Plaster of Paris is also a useful material for artists, because the expanding compound fills a mold completely and makes a high-quality reproduction.

FIGURE 2.25 Molecular compounds. Ionic compounds are generally solids at room temperature. In contrast, molecular compounds can be gases, liquids, or solids.

Learning Objectives: LO 2.1

2-8 Molecular Compounds: Formulas and Names

Many familiar compounds are not ionic, they are molecular: the water you drink, the sugar in your coffee or tea, or the aspirin you take for a headache.

Ionic compounds are generally solids, whereas molecular compounds can range from gases to liquids to solids at ordinary temperatures (Figure 2.25). As size and molecular complexity increase, compounds generally exist as solids. We will explore some of the underlying causes of these general observations in Chapter 11.

Some molecular compounds have complicated formulas that you cannot, at this stage, predict or even decide if they are correct. However, there are many simple compounds you will encounter often, and you should understand how to name them and, in many cases, know their formulas.

Let us look first at molecules formed from combinations of two nonmetals. These "two-element" or **binary compounds** of nonmetals can be named in a systematic way.

Hydrogen forms binary compounds with all of the nonmetals except the noble gases. For compounds of oxygen, sulfur, and the halogens, the H atom is generally written first in the formula and is named first. The other nonmetal is named as if it were a negative ion.

Formulas of Binary Nonmetal Compounds Containing Hydrogen Simple hydrocarbons (compounds of C and H) such as methane (CH_4) and ethane (C_2H_6) have formulas written with H following C, and the formulas of ammonia and hydrazine have H following N. Water and the hydrogen halides, however, have the H atom preceding O or the halogen atom. Tradition is the only explanation for such irregularities in writing formulas.

Compound	Name
HF	Hydrogen fluoride
HCl	Hydrogen chloride
H_2S	Hydrogen sulfide

Although there are exceptions, *most binary molecular compounds are a combination of nonmetallic elements from Groups 4A–7A with one another or with hydrogen.* The formula is generally written by putting the elements in order of increasing group number. When naming the compound, the number of atoms of a given type in the compound is designated with a prefix, such as "di-," "tri-," "tetra-," "penta-," and so on.

Compound	Systematic Name
NF_3	Nitrogen trifluoride
NO	Nitrogen monoxide
NO_2	Nitrogen dioxide
N_2O	Dinitrogen monoxide
N_2O_4	Dinitrogen tetraoxide
PCl_3	Phosphorus trichloride
PCl_5	Phosphorus pentachloride
SF_6	Sulfur hexafluoride
S_2F_{10}	Disulfur decafluoride

Hydrocarbons Compounds such as methane, ethane, propane, and butane belong to a class of hydrocarbons called *alkanes*.

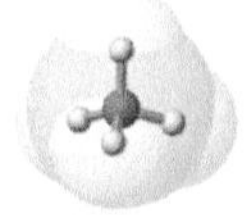
methane, CH_4

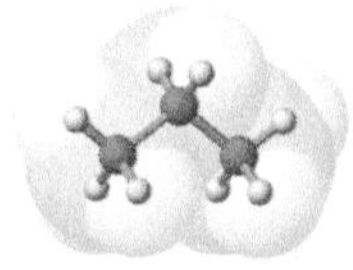
propane, C_3H_8

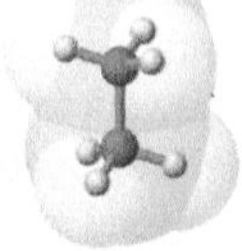
ethane, C_2H_6

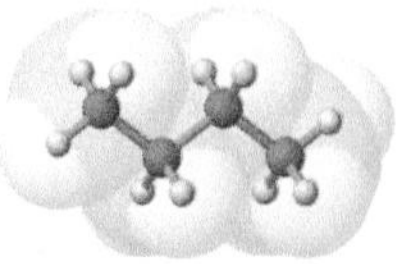
butane, C_4H_{10}

Finally, many of the binary compounds of nonmetals were discovered years ago and have common names.

Compound	Common Name	Compound	Common Name
CH_4	Methane	N_2H_4	Hydrazine
C_2H_6	Ethane	PH_3	Phosphine
C_3H_8	Propane	NO	Nitric oxide
C_4H_{10}	Butane	N_2O	Nitrous oxide ("laughing gas")
NH_3	Ammonia	H_2O	Water

REVIEW & CHECK FOR SECTION 2-8

1. What is the formula for dioxygen difluoride?

   (a) O_2F_2 (b) OF (c) O_2F (d) OF_2

2. Compound names and formulas are listed below. Which name is incorrect?

   (a) carbon disulfide, CS_2
   (b) nitrogen pentaoxide, N_2O_5
   (c) boron trifluoride, BF_3
   (d) sulfur tetrafluoride, SF_4

3. The name of the compound with the formula N_2F_4 is

   (a) nitrogen fluoride
   (b) dinitrogen fluoride
   (c) dinitrogen tetrafluoride
   (d) nitrogen tetrafluoride

4. The name of the compound with the formula P_4O_{10} is

   (a) phosphorus oxide
   (b) tetraphosphorus decaoxide
   (c) tetraphosphorus oxide
   (d) phosphorus decaoxide

2-9 Atoms, Molecules, and the Mole

Learning Objectives: LO 1.4, LO 2.1

One of the most exciting aspects of chemical research is the discovery of some new substance, and part of this process of discovery involves quantitative experiments. When two chemicals react with each other, we want to know how many atoms or molecules of each are used so that formulas can be established for the reaction's products. To do this, we need a method of counting atoms and molecules. That is, we must discover a way of connecting the macroscopic world, the world we can see, with the particulate world of atoms, molecules, and ions. The solution to this

A CLOSER LOOK — Amedeo Avogadro and His Number

Amedeo Avogadro, conte di Quaregna (1776–1856), was an Italian nobleman and a lawyer. In about 1800, he turned to science and was the first professor of mathematical physics in Italy.

Avogadro did not himself propose the notion of a fixed number of particles in a chemical unit. Rather, the number was named in his honor because he had performed experiments in the 19th century that laid the groundwork for the concept.

Just how large is Avogadro's number? One mole of unpopped popcorn kernels would cover the continental United States to a depth of about 9 miles. One mole of pennies divided equally among every man, woman, and child in the United States would allow each person to pay off the national debt (\$15.5 trillion or 15.5×10^{12} dollars in 2012), and there would still be about \$3 trillion left over per person!

Is the number a unique value like π? No. It is fixed by the definition of the mole as exactly 12 g of carbon-12. If one mole of carbon were defined to have some other mass, then Avogadro's number would have a different value. Furthermore, it is determined experimentally, and, as experimental techniques improve, the value is determined with more and more accuracy. From the 8th edition of this book to this edition the value changed slightly in the 8th digit.

Amedeo Avogadro

E. F. Smith Collection/VanPelt Library/University of Pennsylvania

problem is to define a unit of matter that contains a known number of particles. That chemical unit is the mole.

The "Mole" The term *mole* was introduced about 1895 by Wilhelm Ostwald (1853–1932), who derived the term from the Latin word *moles*, meaning a "heap" or a "pile."

The **mole** (abbreviated mol) is the SI base unit for measuring an *amount of a substance* (◀ Table 1, page 23) and is defined as follows:

A **mole** is the amount of a substance that contains as many elementary entities (atoms, molecules, or other particles) as there are atoms in exactly 12 g of the carbon-12 isotope.

The key to understanding the concept of the mole is recognizing that *one mole always contains the same number of particles, no matter what the substance.* One mole of sodium contains the same number of atoms as one mole of iron and the same as the number of molecules in one mole of water. How many particles? Many, many experiments over the years have established that number as

$$\textbf{1 mole} = \mathbf{6.02214129 \times 10^{23}}\ \textbf{particles}$$

This value is known as **Avogadro's number** (symbolized by N_A) in honor of Amedeo Avogadro, an Italian lawyer and physicist (1776–1856) who conceived the basic idea (but never determined the number).

An Important Difference Between the Terms *Amount* and *Quantity* The terms "amount" and "quantity" are used in a specific sense by chemists. The amount of a substance is the number of moles of that substance. In contrast, quantity refers, for example, to the mass or volume of the substance. See W. G. Davies and J. W. Moore. *Journal of Chemical Education*, Vol. 57, p. 303, 1980. See also http://physics.nist.gov

Atoms and Molar Mass

The mass in grams of one mole of any element ($6.02214129 \times 10^{23}$ atoms of that element) is the **molar mass** of that element. Molar mass is abbreviated with a capital italicized M and has units of grams per mole (g/mol). *An element's molar mass is the quantity in grams numerically equal to its atomic weight.* Using sodium and lead as examples,

$$\begin{aligned}\text{Molar mass of sodium (Na)} &= \text{mass of 1.000 mol of Na atoms}\\ &= 22.99\ \text{g/mol}\\ &= \text{mass of } 6.022 \times 10^{23}\ \text{Na atoms}\\ \text{Molar mass of lead (Pb)} &= \text{mass of 1.000 mol of Pb atoms}\\ &= 207.2\ \text{g/mol}\\ &= \text{mass of } 6.022 \times 10^{23}\ \text{Pb atoms}\end{aligned}$$

Figure 2.26 shows one mole of some common elements. Although each of these "piles of atoms" has a different volume and different mass, each contains 6.022×10^{23} atoms.

FIGURE 2.26 One mole of common elements. (*Left to right*) Sulfur powder, magnesium chips, tin, and silicon. (*Above*) Copper beads.

The mole concept is the cornerstone of quantitative chemistry. It is essential to be able to convert from moles to mass and from mass to moles. Dimensional analysis, which is described in Let's Review, page 38, shows that this can be done in the following way:

MASS ⟷ MOLES CONVERSION

Moles to Mass	*Mass to Moles*
$\text{Moles} \times \dfrac{\text{grams}}{1\text{ mol}} = \text{grams}$ (↑ molar mass)	$\text{Grams} \times \dfrac{1\text{ mol}}{\text{grams}} = \text{moles}$ (↑ 1/molar mass)

For example, what mass, in grams, is represented by 0.35 mol of aluminum? Using the molar mass of aluminum (27.0 g/mol), you can determine that 0.35 mol of Al has a mass of 9.5 g.

$$0.35\ \cancel{\text{mol Al}} \times \frac{27.0\text{ g Al}}{1\ \cancel{\text{mol Al}}} = 9.5\text{ g Al}$$

Molar masses of the elements are generally known to at least four significant figures. The convention followed in calculations in this book is to use a value of the molar mass with at least one more significant figure than in any other number in the problem. For example, if you weigh out 16.5 g of carbon, you use 12.01 g/mol for the molar mass of C to find the amount of carbon present.

$$16.5\ \cancel{\text{g C}} \times \frac{1\text{ mol C}}{12.01\ \cancel{\text{g C}}} = 1.37\text{ mol C}$$

↑ Note that four significant figures are used in the molar mass, but there are three in the sample mass.

Using one more significant figure for the molar mass than in the data means the accuracy of this value will not affect the accuracy of the result.

EXAMPLE 2.6

Mass, Moles, and Atoms

Problem Consider two elements in the same vertical column of the periodic table, lead and tin.

(a) What mass of lead, in grams, is equivalent to 2.50 mol of lead (Pb)?

(b) What amount of tin, in moles, is represented by 36.6 g of tin (Sn)? How many atoms of tin are in the sample?

What Do You Know? You know the amount of lead and the mass of tin. You also know, from the periodic tables in this book, the molar masses of lead (207.2 g/mol) and tin (118.7 g/mol). For part (b) Avogadro's number is needed.

Strategy

Part (a) Multiply the amount of Pb by the molar mass.

Part (b) Multiply the mass of tin by (1/molar mass). To determine the number of atoms, multiply the amount of tin by Avogadro's number.

Solution

(a) Convert the amount of lead in moles to mass in grams.

$$2.50 \text{ mol Pb} \times \frac{207.2 \text{ g}}{1 \text{ mol Pb}} = 518 \text{ g Pb}$$

(b) Convert the mass of tin to the amount in moles,

$$36.6 \text{ g Sn} \times \frac{1 \text{ mol Sn}}{118.7 \text{ g Sn}} = 0.308 \text{ mol Sn}$$

and then use Avogadro's number to find the number of atoms in the sample.

$$0.308 \text{ mol Sn} \times \frac{6.022 \times 10^{23} \text{ atoms Sn}}{1 \text{ mol Sn}} = 1.86 \times 10^{23} \text{ atoms Sn}$$

Think about Your Answer These problems were solved using *g/mol* or *mol/g* as conversion factors. To be sure you have used them correctly you should keep track of the units of each term (page 38). Also, you should think about your answers. For example, in part (b), if you had inverted the conversion factor (*mol/atoms* instead of *atoms/mol*), you would have calculated that there was less than one atom in 0.308 mol of Sn, clearly an unreasonable answer.

Check Your Understanding

The density of gold, Au, is 19.32 g/cm^3. What is the volume (in cubic centimeters) of a piece of gold that contains 2.6×10^{24} atoms?

© Cengage Learning/Charles D. Winters

Lead. A 150-mL beaker containing 2.50 mol or 518 g of lead.

© Cengage Learning/Charles D. Winters

Tin. A sample of tin having a mass of 36.6 g (or 1.86×10^{23} atoms).

Molecules, Compounds, and Molar Mass

Molecular Weight and Molar Mass The old term *molecular weight* is sometimes encountered. This is the sum of the atomic weights of the constituent elements.

The formula of a compound tells you the type of atoms or ions in the compound and the relative number of each. For example, one molecule of methane, CH_4, is made up of one atom of C and four atoms of H. But suppose you have Avogadro's number of C atoms (6.022×10^{23}) combined with the proper number of H atoms. (For CH_4 this means there are $4 \times 6.022 \times 10^{23}$ H atoms per mole of C atoms.) What masses of atoms are combined, and what is the mass of this many CH_4 molecules?

A CLOSER LOOK The Mole, a Counting Unit

Students studying chemistry for the first time are often perplexed by the idea of the mole. But you should recognize it is just an odd name for a counting unit. Pairs and dozens are two other common counting units. For example, a pair of objects has two of the same things (two shoes or two gloves), and there are always 12 eggs or apples in a dozen. In the same way, a mole of atoms or a mole of jelly beans has 6.022×10^{23} objects.

The great advantage of counting units is that if you know the number of units you also know the number of objects. If you know there are 3.5 dozen apples in a box, you know there are 42 apples. And, if you have 0.308 mol of tin (36.6 g), you know you have 1.86×10^{23} atoms of tin.

In the chemistry lab when we do a reaction, we need to know how many "chemical units" of an element are involved. Atoms obviously cannot be counted out one by one. Instead, we weigh a given mass of the element, and, from the molar mass, we know the number of "chemical units" or moles. And, if we really wanted to know the information, we could calculate the number of atoms involved.

© Cengage Learning/Charles D. Winters

Counting Units. The unit "dozen," which refers to 12 objects, is a common counting unit. Similarly, the mole is a chemical counting unit. Just as a dozen always has 12 objects, a mole always has 6.022×10^{23} objects.

C	+ 4 H	→ CH_4
6.022×10^{23} C atoms	$4 \times 6.022 \times 10^{23}$ H atoms	6.022×10^{23} CH_4 molecules
= 1.000 mol of C	= 4.000 mol of H atoms	= 1.000 mol of CH_4 molecules
= 12.01 g of C atoms	= 4.032 g of H atoms	= 16.04 g of CH_4 molecules

Because you know the number of moles of C and H atoms in 1 mol of CH_4, you can calculate the masses of carbon and hydrogen that must be combined. It follows that the mass of CH_4 is the sum of these masses. That is, 1 mol of CH_4 has a mass equal to the mass of 1 mol of C atoms (12.01 g) plus 4 mol of H atoms (4.032 g). Thus, the *molar mass, M*, of CH_4 is 16.04 g/mol.

Because you know the mass of one mole of methane, 16.04 g, and that there are 6.022×10^{23} molecules present in one mole, you can also calculate the mass of an average molecule of CH_4. (This is an average mass; because there are several isotopes of carbon and hydrogen, and the mass of a given molecule will be determined by which isotopes make up that molecule.)

$$\text{Average molecular mass} = \frac{16.04\text{ g}}{\text{mol}} \times \frac{1\text{ mol}}{6.022 \times 10^{23}\text{ molecule}} = 2.664 \times 10^{-23}\text{ g/molecule}$$

Ionic compounds such as NaCl do not exist as individual molecules. Thus, for ionic compounds we write the simplest formula that shows the relative number of each kind of atom in a "formula unit" of the compound, and the molar mass is calculated from this formula (M for NaCl = 58.44 g/mol). To differentiate substances like NaCl that do not contain molecules, chemists sometimes refer to their *formula mass* instead of their molar mass.

Figure 2.27 illustrates 1-mol quantities of several common compounds. To find the molar mass of any compound, you need only to add up the atomic masses for each element in the compound, taking into account any subscripts on elements. As an example, let us find the molar mass of aspirin, $C_9H_8O_4$. In one mole of aspirin there are 9 mol of carbon atoms, 8 mol of hydrogen atoms, and 4 mol of oxygen atoms, which add up to 180.2 g/mol of aspirin.

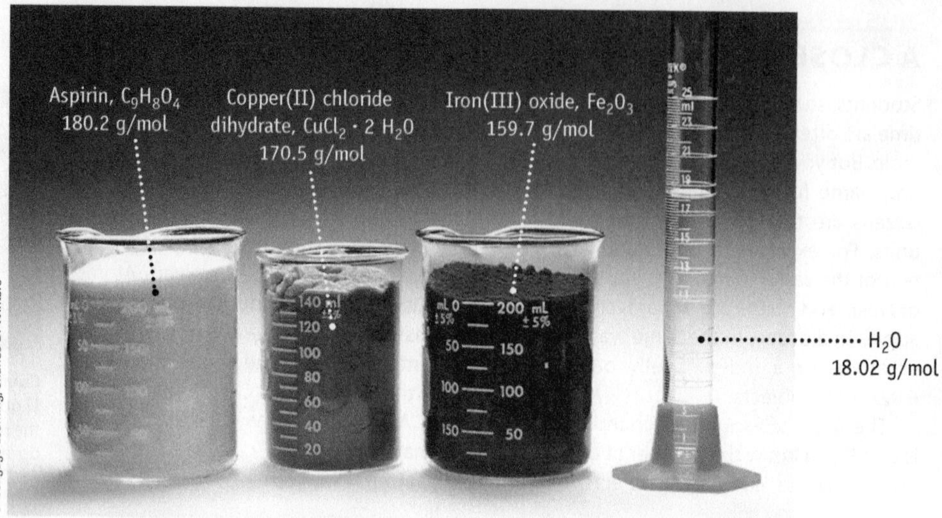

FIGURE 2.27 One-mole quantities of some compounds. The second compound, $CuCl_2 \cdot 2\ H_2O$, is called a *hydrated compound* because water is associated with the $CuCl_2$ (see page 75). Thus, one "formula unit" consists of one Cu^{2+} ion, two Cl^- ions, and two water molecules. The molar mass is the sum of the mass of 1 mol of Cu, 2 mol of Cl, and 2 mol of H_2O.

$$\text{Mass of C in 1 mol } C_9H_8O_4 = 9\ \text{mol C} \times \frac{12.01\ \text{g C}}{1\ \text{mol C}} = 108.09\ \text{g C}$$

$$\text{Mass of H in 1 mol } C_9H_8O_4 = 8\ \text{mol H} \times \frac{1.008\ \text{g H}}{1\ \text{mol H}} = 8.064\ \text{g H}$$

$$\text{Mass of O in 1 mol } C_9H_8O_4 = 4\ \text{mol O} \times \frac{16.00\ \text{g O}}{1\ \text{mol O}} = 64.00\ \text{g O}$$

$$\text{Total mass of 1 mol of } C_9H_8O_4 = \text{molar mass of } C_9H_8O_4 = 180.2\ \text{g}$$

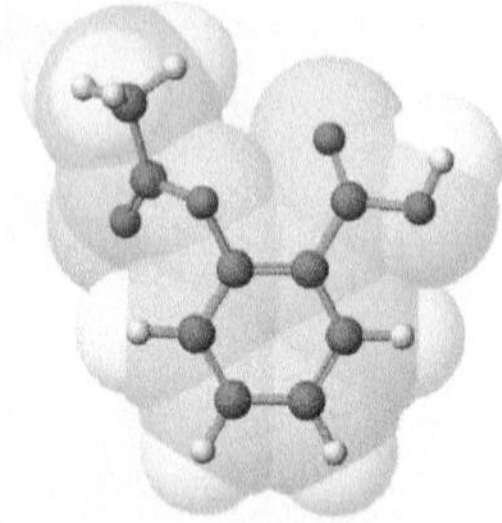

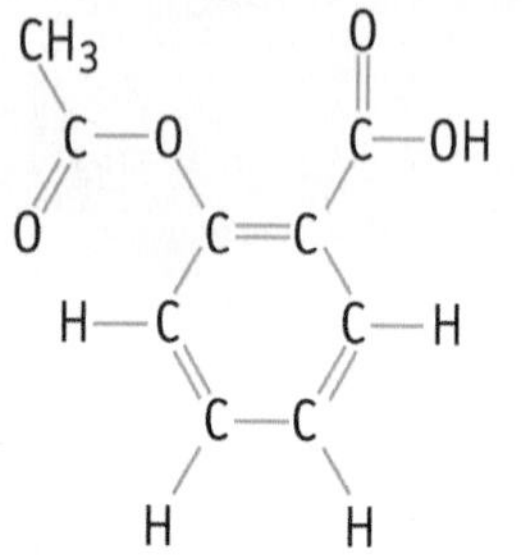

Aspirin Formula Aspirin has the molecular formula $C_9H_8O_4$ and a molar mass of 180.2 g/mol. Aspirin is the common name of the compound acetylsalicylic acid.

As was the case with elements, it is important to be able to convert between amounts (moles) and mass (grams). For example, if you take 325 mg (0.325 g) of aspirin in one tablet, what amount of the compound have you ingested? Based on a molar mass of 180.2 g/mol, there is 0.00180 mol of aspirin per tablet.

$$0.325\ \text{g aspirin} \times \frac{1\ \text{mol aspirin}}{180.2\ \text{g aspirin}} = 0.00180\ \text{mol aspirin}$$

Using the molar mass of a compound it is possible to determine the number of molecules in any sample from the sample mass and to determine the mass of one molecule. For example, the number of aspirin molecules in one tablet is

$$0.00180\ \text{mol aspirin} \times \frac{6.022 \times 10^{23}\ \text{molecules}}{1\ \text{mol aspirin}} = 1.09 \times 10^{21}\ \text{molecules}$$

and the mass of one molecule is

$$\frac{180.2\ \text{g aspirin}}{1\ \text{mol aspirin}} \times \frac{1\ \text{mol aspirin}}{6.022 \times 10^{23}\ \text{molecules}} = 2.99 \times 10^{-22}\ \text{g/molecule}$$

EXAMPLE 2.7

Molar Mass and Moles

Problem You have 16.5 g of oxalic acid, $H_2C_2O_4$.

(a) What amount is represented by 16.5 g of oxalic acid?

(b) How many molecules of oxalic acid are in 16.5 g of the acid?

(c) How many atoms of carbon are in 16.5 g of oxalic acid?

What Do You Know? You know the mass and formula of oxalic acid. The molar mass of the compound can be calculated based on the formula.

Strategy The strategy is outlined in the strategy map.

- The molar mass is the sum of the masses of the component atoms.
- Part (a) Use the molar mass to convert mass to amount.
- Part (b) Use Avogadro's number to calculate the number of molecules from the amount.
- Part (c) From the formula you know there are two atoms of carbon in each molecule.

Solution

(a) *Moles represented by 16.5 g* Let us first calculate the molar mass of oxalic acid:

$$2 \text{ mol C per mol } H_2C_2O_4 \times \frac{12.01 \text{ g C}}{1 \text{ mol C}} = 24.02 \text{ g C per mol } H_2C_2O_4$$

$$2 \text{ mol H per mol } H_2C_2O_4 \times \frac{1.008 \text{ g H}}{1 \text{ mol H}} = 2.016 \text{ g H per mol } H_2C_2O_4$$

$$4 \text{ mol O per mol } H_2C_2O_4 \times \frac{16.00 \text{ g O}}{1 \text{ mol O}} = 64.00 \text{ g O per mol } H_2C_2O_4$$

$$\text{Molar mass of } H_2C_2O_4 = 90.04 \text{ g per mol } H_2C_2O_4$$

Now calculate the amount in moles. The molar mass (expressed here in units of 1 mol/90.04 g) is used in all mass-mole conversions.

$$16.5 \text{ g } H_2C_2O_4 \times \frac{1 \text{ mol}}{90.04 \text{ g } H_2C_2O_4} = 0.183 \text{ mol } H_2C_2O_4$$

(b) *Number of molecules* Use Avogadro's number to find the number of oxalic acid molecules in 0.183 mol of $H_2C_2O_4$.

$$0.183 \text{ mol} \times \frac{6.022 \times 10^{23} \text{ molecules}}{1 \text{ mol}} = 1.10 \times 10^{23} \text{ molecules}$$

(c) *Number of C atoms* Because each molecule contains two carbon atoms, the number of carbon atoms in 16.5 g of the acid is

$$1.10 \times 10^{23} \text{ molecules} \times \frac{2 \text{ C atoms}}{1 \text{ molecule}} = 2.21 \times 10^{23} \text{ C atoms}$$

Think about Your Answer The mass of oxalic acid is 16.5 g, much less than the mass of a mole, so check to make sure your answer reflects this. The number of molecules of the acid should be many fewer than in one mole of molecules.

Check Your Understanding

If you have 454 g of citric acid ($H_3C_6H_5O_7$), what amount (moles) does this represent? How many molecules? How many atoms of carbon?

Strategy Map 2.7

PROBLEM
Find **amount of oxalic acid** in a **given mass.** Then find **number of molecules** and **number of C atoms** in the sample.

↓

DATA/INFORMATION KNOWN
- **Mass** of sample
- **Formula** of compound
- **Avogadro's number**

↓ STEP 1. Calculate **molar mass** of oxalic acid.

Molar mass of oxalic acid **(g/mol)**

↓ STEP 2. Use molar mass to calculate **amount** (multiply **mass** by **1/molar mass**).

Amount (mol) of oxalic acid

↓ STEP 3. Multiply by **Avogadro's number.**

Number of molecules

↓ STEP 4. Multiply by number of **C atoms** per molecule.

Number of **C** atoms in sample

REVIEW & CHECK FOR SECTION 2-9

1. What is the molar mass of calcium nitrate?

   (a) 150.08 g/mol (c) 164.09 g/mol

   (b) 102.08 g/mol (d) 68.09 g/mol

2. Which of the following contains the largest number of molecules?

   (a) 24 g of O_2 (b) 4.0 g of H_2 (c) 19 g of F_2 (d) 28 g of N_2

3. Which of the following has the largest mass?

(a) 0.50 mol Na (b) 0.20 mol K (c) 0.40 mol Ca (d) 0.60 mol Mg

4. Which quantity represents the largest amount (moles) of the indicated substance?

(a) 6.02×10^{23} molecules of H_2O
(b) 22 g of CO_2
(c) 3.01×10^{23} molecules of Br_2
(d) 30 g of HF

5. How many atoms of oxygen are contained in 16 g of O_2?

(a) 6.0×10^{23} atoms of O
(b) 3.0×10^{23} atoms of O
(c) 1.5×10^{23} atoms of O
(d) 1.2×10^{24} atoms of O

2-10 Chemical Analysis: Determining Compound Formulas

Given a sample of an unknown compound, how can its formula be determined? The answer lies in *chemical analysis*, a major branch of chemistry that deals with the determination of formulas and structures.

Percent Composition

A central principle of chemistry is that any sample of a pure compound always consists of the same elements combined in the same proportion by mass. This means molecular composition can be expressed in at least three ways:

- in terms of the number of atoms of each type per molecule or per formula unit—that is, by giving the formula of the compound
- in terms of the mass of each element per mole of compound
- in terms of the mass of each element in the compound relative to the total mass of the compound—that is, as a mass percent

Molecular Composition Molecular composition can be expressed as a percent (mass of an element in a 100-g sample). For example, NH_3 is 82.244% N. Therefore, it has 82.244 g of N in 100.000 g of compound.

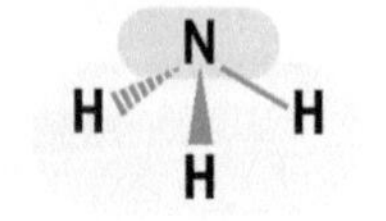

Suppose you have 1.0000 mol of NH_3 or 17.031 g. This mass of NH_3 is composed of 14.007 g of N (1.0000 mol) and 3.0237 g of H (3.0000 mol). If you compare the mass of N to the total mass of compound, 82.244% of the total mass is N and 17.755% is H.

$$\text{Mass percent N in } NH_3 = \frac{\text{mass of N in 1 mol } NH_3}{\text{mass of 1 mol } NH_3} \times 100\%$$
$$= \frac{14.007 \text{ g N}}{17.031 \text{ g } NH_3} \times 100\%$$
$$= 82.244\% \text{ (or 82.244 g N in 100.000 g } NH_3)$$

$$\text{Mass percent H in } NH_3 = \frac{\text{mass of H in 1 mol } NH_3}{\text{mass of 1 mol } NH_3} \times 100\%$$
$$= \frac{3.0237 \text{ g H}}{17.031 \text{ g } NH_3} \times 100\%$$
$$= 17.755\% \text{ (or 17.755 g H in 100.000 g } NH_3)$$

Compound Formulas and Mass Percent The "Law of Multiple Proportions" was proposed by John Dalton in 1804. It states that when two elements A and B form two different compounds, the masses of element B in the two compounds that will combine with a given amount of element A can be expressed as the ratio of two whole numbers. For example, in CO, 1.33 g of O combines with 1.0 g of C, whereas, in CO_2, 2.66 g of O combines with 1.0 g of C. The mass of O combining with C is in the ratio of 1 to 2.

These values tell you that in a 100.00-g sample there are 82.244 g of N and 17.755 g of H.

EXAMPLE 2.8

Using Percent Composition

Problem What is the mass percent of each element in propane, C_3H_8? What mass of carbon is contained in 454 g of propane?

What Do You Know? You know the formula of propane. You will need the atomic weights of C and H to calculate the mass percent of each element.

Strategy

- Calculate the molar mass of propane.
- From the formula, you know there are 3 moles of C and 8 moles of H per mole of C_3H_8. Determine the mass of C and H represented by these amounts. The percent of each element is the mass of the element divided by the molar mass and multiplied by 100.
- The mass of C in 454 g of C_3H_8 is obtained by multiplying this mass by the % C/100 (that is, by the decimal fraction of C in the compound).

Solution

(a) The molar mass of C_3H_8 is 44.09 g/mol.

(b) Mass percent of C and H in C_3H_8:

$$\frac{3 \text{ mol C}}{1 \text{ mol } C_3H_8} \times \frac{12.01 \text{ g C}}{1 \text{ mol C}} = 36.03 \text{ g C/1 mol } C_3H_8$$

$$\text{Mass percent of C in } C_3H_8 = \frac{36.03 \text{ g C}}{44.09 \text{ g } C_3H_8} \times 100\% = 81.72\% \text{ C}$$

$$\frac{8 \text{ mol H}}{1 \text{ mol } C_3H_8} \times \frac{1.008 \text{ g H}}{1 \text{ mol H}} = 8.064 \text{ g H/1 mol } C_3H_8$$

$$\text{Mass percent of H in } C_3H_8 = \frac{8.064 \text{ g H}}{44.09 \text{ g } C_3H_8} \times 100\% = 18.29\% \text{ H}$$

(c) Mass of C in 454 g of C_3H_8:

$$454 \text{ g } C_3H_8 \times \frac{81.72 \text{ g C}}{100.0 \text{ g } C_3H_8} = 371 \text{ g C}$$

Think about Your Answer Once you know the percent C in the sample, you could calculate the percent H from it using the formula %H = 100% − %C.

Check Your Understanding

1. Express the composition of ammonium carbonate, $(NH_4)_2CO_3$, in terms of the mass of each element in 1.00 mol of compound and the mass percent of each element.
2. What is the mass of carbon in 454 g of octane, C_8H_{18}?

Empirical and Molecular Formulas from Percent Composition

Now consider the reverse of the procedure just described. That is, let us use relative mass or percent composition data to find a molecular formula. Suppose you know the identity of the elements in a sample and have determined the mass of each element in a given mass of compound by chemical analysis (▶ Section 4-4). You can then calculate the relative amount (moles) of each element, which is also the relative number of atoms of each element in the formula of the compound. For example, for a compound composed of atoms of A and B, the steps from percent composition to a formula are as follows:

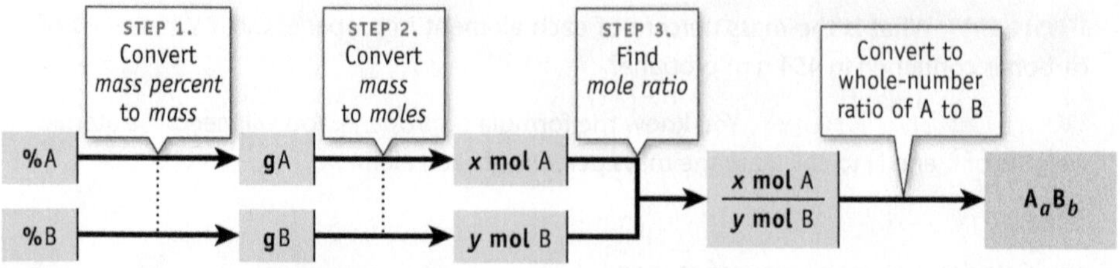

As an example, let us derive the formula for hydrazine, a compound used to remove oxygen from water in heating and cooling systems and a close relative of ammonia. Hydrazine is composed of 87.42% N and 12.58% H.

Deriving a Formula Percent composition gives the mass of an element in 100 g of a sample. However, in deriving a formula, any amount of sample is appropriate if you know the mass of each element in that sample mass.

STEP 1 *Convert mass percent to mass.* The mass percentages of N and H in hydrazine tell us there are 87.42 g of N and 12.58 g of H in a 100.00-g sample.

STEP 2 *Convert the mass of each element to moles.* The amount of each element in the 100.00-g sample is

$$87.42 \text{ g N} \times \frac{1 \text{ mol N}}{14.007 \text{ g N}} = 6.241 \text{ mol N}$$

$$12.58 \text{ g H} \times \frac{1 \text{ mol H}}{1.0079 \text{ g H}} = 12.48 \text{ mol H}$$

STEP 3 *Find the mole ratio of elements.* Use the amount (moles) of each element in the 100.00-g of sample to find the amount of one element relative to the other. (To do this it is usually best to divide the larger amount by the smaller amount.) For hydrazine, this ratio is 2 mol of H to 1 mol of N,

$$\frac{12.48 \text{ mol H}}{6.241 \text{ mol N}} = \frac{2.000 \text{ mol H}}{1.000 \text{ mol N}} \longrightarrow NH_2$$

showing that there are 2 mol of H atoms for every 1 mol of N atoms in hydrazine. Thus, in one molecule, two atoms of H occur for every atom of N; that is, the formula is NH_2. This simplest, whole-number atom ratio of atoms in a formula is called the **empirical formula**.

PROBLEM SOLVING TIP 2.3
Finding Empirical and Molecular Formulas

- The experimental data available to find a formula may be in the form of percent composition or the masses of elements combined in some mass of compound. No matter what the starting point, the first step is always to convert masses of elements to moles.
- Be sure to use *at least* three significant figures when calculating empirical formulas. Using fewer significant figures can give a misleading result.
- When finding atom ratios, always divide the larger number of moles by the smaller one.
- Empirical and molecular formulas can differ for molecular compounds. In contrast, there is no "molecular" formula for an ionic compound; all that can be recorded is the empirical formula.
- Determining the molecular formula of a compound after calculating the empirical formula requires knowing the molar mass.
- When *both* the percent composition and the molar mass are known for a compound, the alternative method mentioned in *Think about Your Answer* in Example 2.9 could be used.

Percent composition data allow us to calculate the atom ratios in a compound. A *molecular formula*, however, must convey two pieces of information: (1) the relative numbers of atoms of each element in a molecule (the atom ratios) and (2) the total number of atoms in the molecule. For hydrazine there are twice as many H atoms as N atoms, so the molecular formula could be NH_2. Recognize, however, that NH_2 is only the simplest possible ratio of atoms in a molecule. The empirical formula of hydrazine is NH_2, but the true molecular formula could be NH_2, N_2H_4, N_3H_6, N_4H_8, or any other formula having a 1:2 ratio of N to H.

To determine the molecular formula from the empirical formula, the molar mass must be obtained from experiment. For example, experiments show that the molar mass of hydrazine is 32.0 g/mol, twice the formula mass of NH_2, which is 16.0 g/mol. Thus, the molecular formula of hydrazine is two times the empirical formula of NH_2, that is, N_2H_4.

EXAMPLE 2.9

Calculating a Formula from Percent Composition

Problem Many soft drinks contain sodium benzoate as a preservative. When you consume the sodium benzoate, it reacts with the amino acid glycine in your body to form hippuric acid, which is then excreted in the urine. Hippuric acid has a molar mass of 179.17 g/mol and is 60.33% C, 5.06% H, and 7.82% N; the remainder is oxygen. What are the empirical and molecular formulas of hippuric acid?

What Do You Know? You know the mass percent of C, H, and N. The mass percent of oxygen is not known but is obtained by difference. You know the molar mass but will need atomic weights of C, H, N, and O for the calculation.

Strategy Assume the mass percent of each element is equivalent to its mass in grams, and convert each mass to moles. The ratio of moles gives the empirical formula. The mass of a mole of compound having the calculated empirical formula is compared with the actual, experimental molar mass to find the true molecular formula.

Solution The mass of oxygen in a 100.0-g sample of hippuric acid is

$$100.00 \text{ g} = 60.33 \text{ g C} + 5.06 \text{ g H} + 7.82 \text{ g N} + \text{mass of O}$$

$$\text{Mass of O} = 26.79 \text{ g O}$$

The amount of each element in 100.0 g is

$$60.33 \text{ g C} \times \frac{1 \text{ mol C}}{12.011 \text{ g C}} = 5.023 \text{ mol C}$$

$$5.06 \text{ g H} \times \frac{1 \text{ mol H}}{1.008 \text{ g H}} = 5.02 \text{ mol H}$$

$$7.82 \text{ g N} \times \frac{1 \text{ mol N}}{14.01 \text{ g N}} = 0.558 \text{ mol N}$$

$$26.79 \text{ g O} \times \frac{1 \text{ mol O}}{15.999 \text{ g O}} = 1.674 \text{ mol O}$$

To find the mole ratio, the best approach is to base the ratios on the smallest number of moles present—in this case, nitrogen.

$$\frac{\text{mol C}}{\text{mol N}} = \frac{5.023 \text{ mol C}}{0.558 \text{ mol N}} = \frac{9.00 \text{ mol C}}{1.00 \text{ mol N}} = 9 \text{ mol C/1 mol N}$$

$$\frac{\text{mol H}}{\text{mol N}} = \frac{5.02 \text{ mol H}}{0.558 \text{ mol N}} = \frac{9.00 \text{ mol H}}{1.00 \text{ mol N}} = 9 \text{ mol H/1 mol N}$$

$$\frac{\text{mol O}}{\text{mol N}} = \frac{1.674 \text{ mol O}}{0.558 \text{ mol N}} = \frac{3.00 \text{ mol O}}{1.00 \text{ mol N}} = 3 \text{ mol O/1 mol N}$$

Strategy Map 2.9

PROBLEM
Determine **empirical** and **molecular formulas** based on ***known composition*** and ***known molar mass.***

DATA/INFORMATION KNOWN
- Molar mass
- Percent composition

STEP 1. Assume each **atom %** is equivalent to **mass in grams** in **100-g** sample.

Mass of each element in a **100-g** sample of the compound

STEP 2. Use **atomic weight** of each element to calculate **amount** of each element in 100-g sample (multiply **mass** by **mol/g**).

Amount (mol) of each element in **100-g** sample

STEP 3. Divide the *amount of each element* by the *amount of the element present* ***in the least amount.***

Whole-number ratio of the *amount of each element* to the *amount of element present in the least amount* = **empirical formula**

STEP 4. Divide *known* **molar mass** by **empirical formula mass.**

Molecular formula

Now we know there are 9 mol of C, 9 mol of H, and 3 mol of O for each mol of N. Thus, the empirical formula is $C_9H_9NO_3$. The experimentally determined molar mass of hippuric acid is 179.17 g/mol. This is the same as the empirical formula weight, so the molecular formula is $C_9H_9NO_3$.

Think about Your Answer There is another approach to finding the molecular formula here. Knowing the percent composition of hippuric acid and its molar mass, you could calculate that in 179.17 g of hippuric acid there are 108.06 g of C (8.997 mol of C), 9.06 g of H (8.99 mol of H), 14.01 g N (1.000 mol N), and 48.00 g of O (3 mol of O). This gives us a molecular formula of $C_9H_9NO_3$. However, you must recognize that *this approach can only be used when you know **both** the percent composition and the molar mass.*

Check Your Understanding

1. What is the empirical formula of naphthalene, $C_{10}H_8$?
2. The empirical formula of acetic acid is CH_2O. If its molar mass is 60.05 g/mol, what is the molecular formula of acetic acid?
3. Isoprene is a liquid compound that can be polymerized to form natural rubber. It is composed of 88.17% carbon and 11.83% hydrogen. Its molar mass is 68.11 g/mol. What are its empirical and molecular formulas?
4. Camphor is found in camphor wood, much prized for its wonderful odor. It is composed of 78.90% carbon and 10.59% hydrogen. The remainder is oxygen. What is its empirical formula?

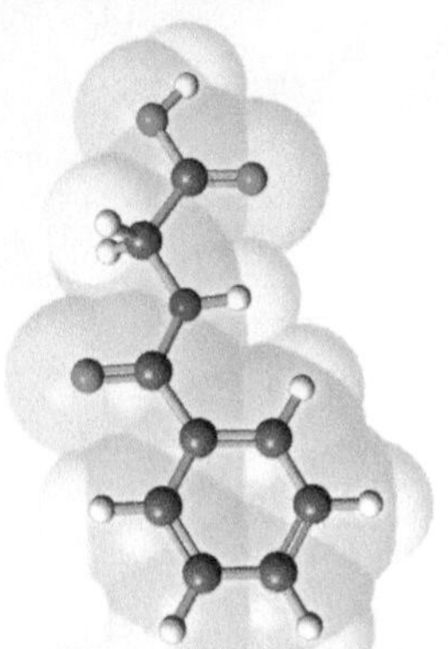

Hippuric Acid, $C_9H_9NO_3$ This substance, which can be isolated as white crystals, is found in the urine of humans and of herbivorous animals.

Determining a Formula from Mass Data

The composition of a compound in terms of mass percent gives us the mass of each element in a 100.0-g sample. In the laboratory we often collect information on the composition of compounds slightly differently. We can

1. Combine known masses of elements to give a sample of the compound of known mass. Element masses can be converted to amounts (moles), and the ratio of amounts gives the combining ratio of atoms—that is, the empirical formula. This approach is described in Example 2.10.
2. Decompose a known mass of an unknown compound into "pieces" of known composition. If the masses of the "pieces" can be determined, the ratio of moles of the "pieces" gives the formula. An example is a decomposition such as

$$Ni(CO)_4(\ell) \rightarrow Ni(s) + 4\ CO(g)$$

The masses of Ni and CO can be converted to moles, whose 1:4 ratio would reveal the formula of the compound. We will describe this approach in Example 2.11.

Strategy Map 2.10

PROBLEM
Determine **empirical formula** based on ***masses of combining elements.***

DATA/INFORMATION KNOWN
- Mass of one element in binary compound
- Mass of product

STEP 1. Find *mass of second element* by **difference.**

Mass of each element in a sample of the compound

STEP 2. Use **atomic weight** of each element to calculate **amount** of each element in sample (multiply mass by mol/g).

Amount (mol) of each element in sample

STEP 3. Divide the *amount of each element* by the *amount of the element present* ***in the least amount.***

Whole-number ratio of the *amount of each element to the amount of element present in the least amount* = **empirical formula**

EXAMPLE 2.10

Formula of a Compound from Combining Masses

Problem Oxides of virtually every element are known. Bromine, for example, forms several oxides when treated with ozone. Suppose you allow 1.250 g of bromine, Br_2, to react with ozone and obtain 1.876 g of Br_xO_y. What is the empirical formula of the product?

What Do You Know? You know that you begin with a given mass of bromine and that all of the bromine becomes part of bromine oxide of unknown formula. You also know the mass of the product, and because you know the mass of Br in this product, you can determine the mass of O in the product.

Strategy

- The mass of oxygen is determined as the difference between the product mass and the mass of bromine used.
- Calculate the amounts of Br and O from the masses of each element.
- Find the lowest whole number ratio between the moles of Br and moles of O. This defines the empirical formula.

Solution You already know the mass of bromine in the compound, so you can calculate the mass of oxygen in the compound by subtracting the mass of bromine from the mass of the product.

$$1.876 \text{ g product} - 1.250 \text{ g } Br_2 = 0.626 \text{ g O}$$

Next, calculate the amount of each reactant. Notice that, although Br_2 was the reactant, we need to know the amount of Br in the product.

$$1.250 \text{ g } Br_2 \times \frac{1 \text{ mol } Br_2}{159.81 \text{ g}} = 0.007822 \text{ mol } Br_2$$

$$0.007822 \text{ mol } Br_2 \times \frac{2 \text{ mol Br}}{1 \text{ mol } Br_2} = 0.01564 \text{ mol Br}$$

$$0.626 \text{ g O} \times \frac{1 \text{ mol O}}{16.00 \text{ g O}} = 0.0391 \text{ mol O}$$

Find the ratio of moles of O to moles of Br:

$$\text{Mole ratio} = \frac{0.0391 \text{ mol O}}{0.01564 \text{ mol Br}} = \frac{2.50 \text{ mol O}}{1.00 \text{ mol O}}$$

The atom ratio is 2.5 mol O/1.0 mol Br. However, atoms combine in the ratio of small whole numbers, so we double this to give a ratio of 5 mol O to 2 mol Br. Thus, the product is Br_2O_5 (dibromine pentaoxide).

Think about Your Answer The whole number ratio of 5 : 2 was found by realizing that 2.5 = 2 1/2 = 5/2. The calculation gave the empirical formula for this compound. To determine whether this is also the molecular formula the molar mass of the compound would have to be determined.

Check Your Understanding

Gallium oxide, Ga_xO_y, forms when gallium is combined with oxygen. Suppose you allow 1.25 g of gallium (Ga) to react with oxygen and obtain 1.68 g of Ga_xO_y. What is the formula of the product?

EXAMPLE 2.11

Determining the Formula of a Hydrated Compound

Problem You want to know the value of *x* in blue, hydrated copper(II) sulfate, $CuSO_4 \cdot x\,H_2O$, that is, the number of water molecules for each unit of $CuSO_4$. In the laboratory you weigh out 1.023 g of the solid. After heating the solid thoroughly in a porcelain crucible (Figure), 0.654 g of nearly white, anhydrous copper(II) sulfate, $CuSO_4$, remains.

$$1.023 \text{ g } CuSO_4 \cdot x\,H_2O + \text{heat} \rightarrow$$
$$0.654 \text{ g } CuSO_4 + ? \text{ g } H_2O$$

© Cengage Learning/Charles D. Winters

Strategy Map 2.11

PROBLEM

Determine **formula of hydrated salt** based on ***masses of water and dehydrated salt.***

DATA/INFORMATION KNOWN

- Mass of sample before and after heating to dehydrate

STEP 1. Find *masses of salt and water* by **difference.**

Mass of salt and water in a sample of the hydrated compound

STEP 2. Use **molar mass** of salt and water to calculate **amount** of each in sample (multiply **mass** by **mol/g**).

Amount (mol) of salt and water in sample

STEP 3. Divide the *amount of water* by the *amount of the dehydrated salt.*

Formula = *ratio of the amount of water to the amount of salt* in dehydrated sample

What Do You Know? You know the mass of the copper(II) sulfate sample including water (before heating) and with no water (after heating). Therefore, you know the mass of water in the sample and the mass of $CuSO_4$.

Strategy To find *x* you need to know the amount of H_2O per mole $CuSO_4$.

- Determine the mass of water released on heating the hydrated compound.
- Calculate the amount (moles) of $CuSO_4$ and H_2O from their masses and molar masses.
- Determine the smallest whole number ratio (amount H_2O/amount $CuSO_4$).

Solution Find the mass of water.

Mass of hydrated compound	1.023 g
− Mass of anhydrous compound, $CuSO_4$	−0.654
Mass of water	0.369 g

Next convert the masses of $CuSO_4$ and H_2O to moles.

$$0.369 \text{ g } H_2O \times \frac{1 \text{ mol } H_2O}{18.02 \text{ g } H_2O} = 0.0205 \text{ mol } H_2O$$

$$0.654 \text{ g } CuSO_4 \times \frac{1 \text{ mol } CuSO_4}{159.6 \text{ g } CuSO_4} = 0.00410 \text{ mol } CuSO_4$$

The value of *x* is determined from the mole ratio.

$$\frac{0.0205 \text{ mol } H_2O}{0.00410 \text{ mol } CuSO_4} = \frac{5.00 \text{ mol } H_2O}{1.00 \text{ mol } CuSO_4}$$

The water-to-$CuSO_4$ ratio is 5 : 1, so the formula of the hydrated compound is $CuSO_4 \cdot 5\,H_2O$. Its name is copper(II) sulfate pentahydrate.

Think about Your Answer The ratio of the amount of water to the amount of $CuSO_4$ is a whole number. This is almost always the case with hydrated compounds.

Check Your Understanding

Hydrated nickel(II) chloride is a beautiful green, crystalline compound. When heated strongly, the compound is dehydrated. If 0.235 g of $NiCl_2 \cdot x\,H_2O$ gives 0.128 g of $NiCl_2$ on heating, what is the value of *x*?

CASE STUDY — Arsenic, Medicine, and the Formula of Compound 606

The practice in medicine for some centuries has been to find compounds that are toxic to certain organisms but not so toxic that the patient is harmed. In the early part of the 20th century, Paul Ehrlich set out to find just such a compound that would cure syphilis, a sexually transmitted disease that was rampant at the time. He screened hundreds of compounds, and found that his 606th compound was effective: an arsenic-containing drug now called salvarsan. It was used for some years for syphilis treatment until penicillin was discovered in the 1930s.

Salvarsan was a forerunner of the modern drug industry. Interestingly, what chemists long thought to be a single compound was in fact discovered to be a mixture of compounds. Question 2 below will lead you to the molecular formula for each of them.

Questions:

1. Arsenic is found widely in the environment and is a major problem in the ground water supply in Bangladesh. Orpiment is one arsenic-containing mineral and enargite is another. The latter has 19.024% As, 48.407% Cu, and 32.569% S. What is the empirical formula of the mineral?
2. Salvarsan was long thought to be a single substance. Recently, however, a mass spectrometry study of the compound shows it to be a mixture of two molecules with the same empirical formula. Each has the composition 39.37% C, 3.304% H, 8.741% O, 7.652% N, and 40.932% As. One has a molar mass of 549 g/mol and the other has a molar mass of 915 g/mol. What are the molecular formulas of the compounds?

John C. Kotz

A sample of orpiment, a common arsenic-containing mineral (As_2S_3). The name of the element is thought to come from the Greek word for this mineral, which was long favored by 17th century Dutch painters as a pigment.

Answers to these questions are available in Appendix N.

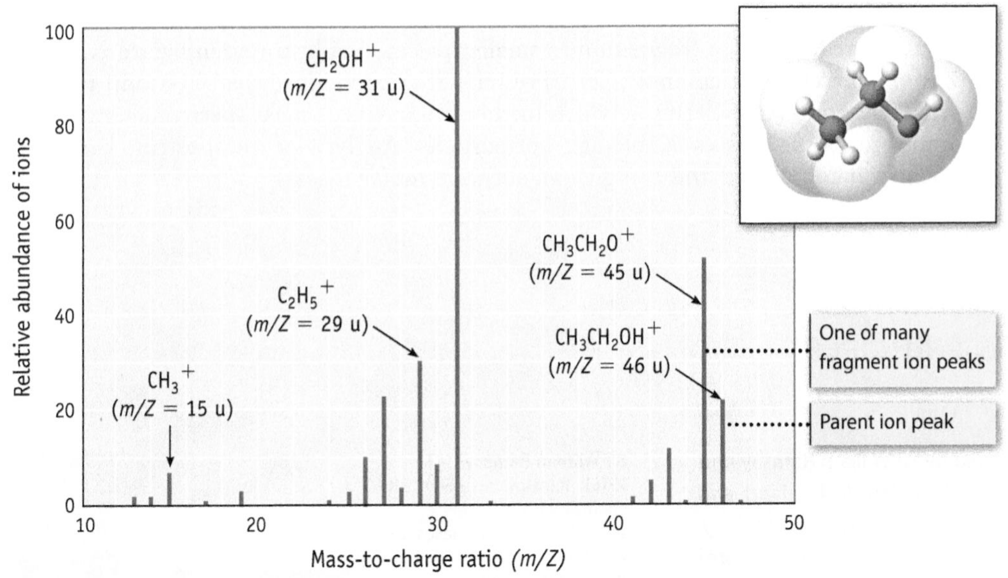

FIGURE 2.28 Mass spectrum of ethanol, CH_3CH_2OH. A prominent peak or line in the spectrum is the "parent" ion ($CH_3CH_2OH^+$) at mass 46. (The parent ion is the heaviest ion observed.) The mass designated by the peak for the parent ion confirms the formula of the molecule. Other peaks are for "fragment" ions. This pattern of lines can provide further, unambiguous evidence of the formula of the compound. (The horizontal axis is the mass-to-charge ratio of a given ion. Because almost all observed ions have a charge of $Z = +1$, the value observed is the mass of the ion.) (See *"A Closer Look: Mass Spectrometry, Molar Mass, and Isotopes."*)

Determining a Formula by Mass Spectrometry

We have described chemical methods of determining a molecular formula, but there are many instrumental methods as well. One of them is *mass spectrometry* (see Figure 2.28). We introduced this technique earlier when discussing the existence of isotopes and their relative abundance (see Figure 2.3). If a compound can be vaporized, the vapor can be passed through an electron beam in a mass spectrometer where high-energy electrons collide with the gas phase molecules. These high-energy

A CLOSER LOOK Mass Spectrometry, Molar Mass, and Isotopes

Bromobenzene, C_6H_5Br, has a molar mass of 157.010 g/mol. Why, then, are there two prominent lines at mass-to-charge ratios (m/Z) of 156 and 158 in the mass spectrum of the compound (when $Z = +1$)? The answer shows us the influence of isotopes on molar mass.

Bromine has two naturally occurring isotopes, ^{79}Br and ^{81}Br. They are 50.7% and 49.3% abundant, respectively. What is the mass of C_6H_5Br based on each isotope? If we use the most abundant isotopes of C and H (^{12}C and ^{1}H), the mass of the molecule having the ^{79}Br isotope, $C_6H_5{}^{79}Br$, is 156. The mass of the molecule containing the ^{81}Br isotope, $C_6H_5{}^{81}Br$, is 158. The relative size of these two peaks in the spectrum reflects the relative abundances of the two bromine isotopes.

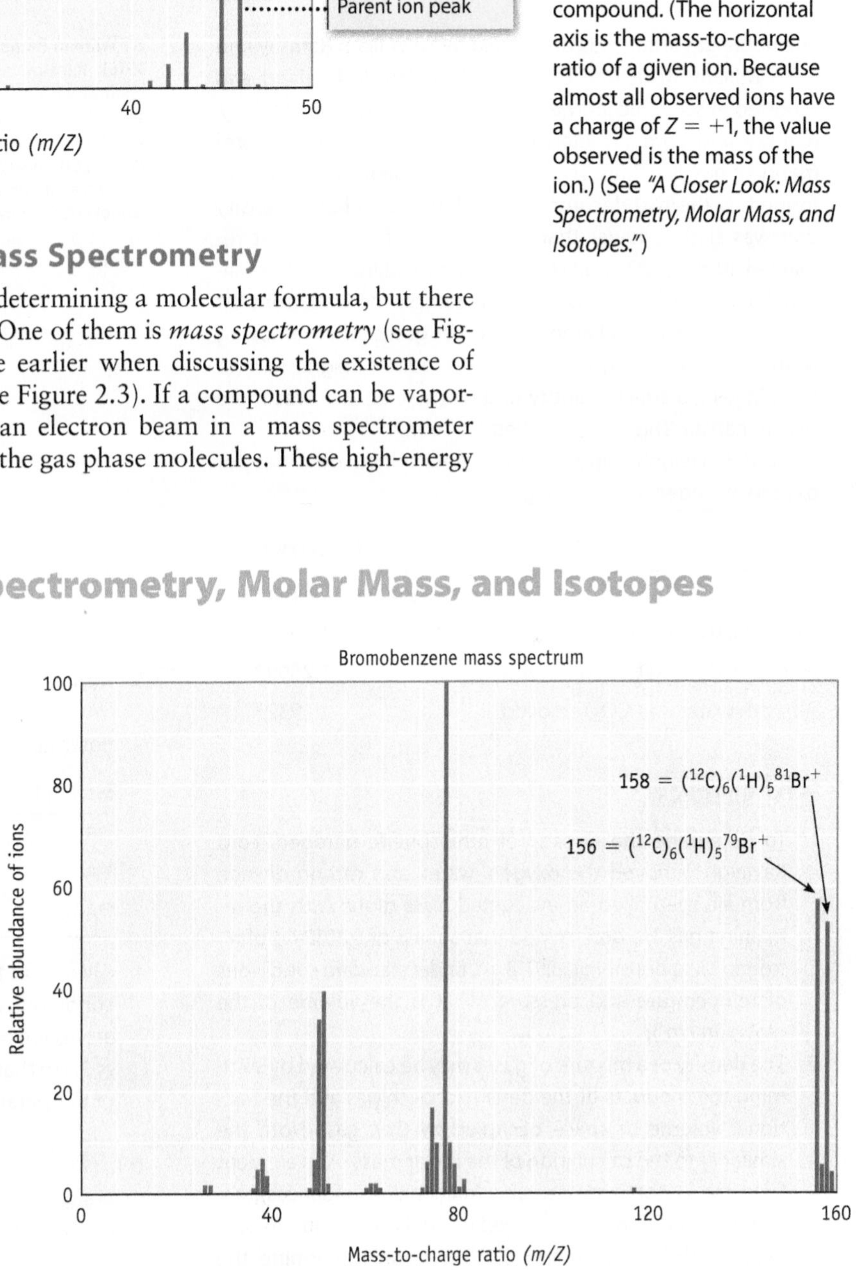

The calculated molar mass of bromobenzene (157.010 g/mol) reflects the abundances of all of the isotopes. In contrast, the mass spectrum has a line for each possible combination of isotopes. This also explains why there are also small lines at the mass-to-charge ratios of 157 and 159. They arise from various combinations of ^{1}H, ^{12}C, ^{13}C, ^{79}Br, and ^{81}Br atoms. In fact careful analysis of such patterns can identify a molecule unambiguously.

collisions cause molecules to lose electrons and become positive ions. These ions usually break apart or fragment into smaller pieces. As illustrated in Figure 2.28 the cation created from ethanol ($CH_3CH_2OH^+$) fragments (losing an H atom) to give another cation ($CH_3CH_2O^+$), which further fragments. A mass spectrometer detects and records the masses of the different particles. Analysis of the spectrum can help identify a compound and can give an accurate molar mass.

APPLYING CHEMICAL PRINCIPLES

Argon—An Amazing Discovery

The noble gas argon was discovered by Sir William Ramsay and John William Strutt (the third Lord Rayleigh) in England and reported in scientific journals in 1895. In making this discovery, Ramsay and Lord Rayleigh made highly accurate measurements of gas densities. They found that gaseous nitrogen (N_2) formed by thermal decomposition of ammonia had a density that was slightly lower than the density of the gas that remained after O_2, CO_2, and H_2O were removed from air. The reason for the difference is that the sample derived from air contained a very small amount of other gases. After removing N_2 from the sample by reacting it with red hot magnesium (to form Mg_3N_2), a small quantity of gas remained that was more dense than air. This was identified as argon.

Lord Rayleigh's experimentally determined densities for oxygen, nitrogen, and air are given below:

Gas	Density (g/L)
Oxygen	1.42952
Nitrogen, derived from air	1.25718
Nitrogen, derived from ammonia	1.25092
Air, with water and CO_2 removed	1.29327

Sir William Ramsay (1852–1916). Ramsay was a Scottish chemist who discovered several of the noble gases (for which he received the Nobel Prize in Chemistry in 1904). Lord Rayleigh received the Nobel Prize in Physics, also in 1904, for the discovery of argon.

AFPPhoto/Toshifumi KITAMURA/Newscom

QUESTIONS:

1. To determine the density of atmospheric nitrogen, Lord Rayleigh removed the oxygen, water, and carbon dioxide from air, then filled an evacuated glass globe with the remaining gas. He determined that a mass of 0.20389 g of nitrogen has a density of 1.25718 g/L under standard conditions of temperature and pressure. What is the volume of the globe (in cm^3)?
2. The density of a mixture of gases may be calculated by summing the products of the density of each gas and the fractional volume of space occupied by that gas. (Note the similarity to the calculation of the molar mass of an element from the isotopic masses and fractional abundances). Assume dry air with CO_2 removed is 20.96% (by volume) oxygen, 78.11% nitrogen, and 0.930% argon. Determine the density of argon.
3. Atmospheric argon is a mixture of three stable isotopes, ^{36}Ar, ^{38}Ar, and ^{40}Ar. Use the information in the table below to determine the atomic mass and natural abundance of ^{40}Ar.

Isotope	Atomic Mass (u)	Abundance (%)
^{36}Ar	35.967545	0.337
^{38}Ar	37.96732	0.063
^{40}Ar	?	?

4. Given that the density of argon is 1.78 g/L under standard conditions of temperature and pressure, how many argon atoms are present in a room with dimensions 4.0 m × 5.0 m × 2.4 m that is filled with pure argon under these conditions of temperature and pressure?

REFERENCES:

1. *Proceedings of the Royal Society of London*, Vol. 57, (1894–1895), pp. 265–287.
2. *The Gases of the Atmosphere and Their History*, 4th ed., William Ramsay, MacMillan and Co., Limited, London, 1915.

REVIEW & CHECK FOR SECTION 2-10

1. Which of the following hydrocarbons has the highest mass percentage of carbon?

   (a) methane, CH_4 (b) ethane, C_2H_6 (c) propane, C_3H_8 (d) butane, C_4H_{10}

2. An organic compound has an empirical formula CH_2O and a molar mass of 180 g/mol. What is its molecular formula?

   (a) CH_2O (b) $C_6H_{12}O_6$ (c) $C_2H_4O_2$ (d) $C_5H_{10}O_5$

3. Eugenol is the major component in oil of cloves. It has a molar mass of 164.2 g/mol and is 73.14% C and 7.37% H; the remainder is oxygen. What are the empirical and molecular formulas of eugenol?

   (a) C_5H_6O, C_5H_6O (b) C_5H_6O, $C_{10}H_{12}O_2$ (c) C_6H_5O, $C_{12}H_{10}O_2$ (d) C_3H_6O, $C_6H_{12}O_2$

4. Epsom salt is $MgSO_4 \cdot 7H_2O$. When heated to 70 to 80 °C it loses some, but not all, of its water of hydration. Suppose you heat 2.465 g of Epsom salt to 75 °C and find that the mass is now only 1.744 g. What is the formula of the slightly dehydrated salt?

   (a) $MgSO_4 \cdot 6H_2O$ (b) $MgSO_4 \cdot 5H_2O$ (c) $MgSO_4 \cdot 4H_2O$ (d) $MgSO_4 \cdot 3H_2O$

CHAPTER GOALS REVISITED

Now that you have studied this chapter, you should ask whether you have met the chapter goals. In particular, you should be able to

UNDERSTAND

- The composition and structure of atoms (protons, neutrons, electrons) and the terms atomic number and mass number (Sections 2-1 and 2-2). Study Questions: 1, 6, 7.
- The various representations of masses of atoms: atomic mass, atomic weight (relative atomic mass), and their interrelationships (Sections 2-2 and 2-3).
- The composition of isotopes (Section 2-3). Study Questions: 5, 7, 97.
- The importance of Coulomb's Law in chemistry (Equation 2.3). (This law describes the electrostatic forces of attraction and repulsion of ions. Coulomb's Law states that the force of attraction between oppositely charged species increases with electric charge and with decreasing distance between the species.) Study Question: 55.
- The mole concept and molar mass and their application (Sections 2-9 and 2-10). Study Questions: 61, 62, 65, 105.
- How mass spectrometry is used (in determining isotopic abundances, isotopic masses, and molecular formulas) (Section 2-10). Study Question: 155.

DO

- Carry out calculations relating atomic weights, isotopic masses, and isotopic abundances.
  - **a.** Give the mass number and number of neutrons for a specific isotope (Sections 2-2 and 2-3). Study Questions: 5, 6, 8, 16, 97.
  - **b.** Do calculations that relate the atomic weight (atomic mass) of an element and isotopic abundances and masses (Section 2-4). Study Questions: 19–24, 98, 154.

- Carry out calculations involving masses, moles, and numbers of particles.
  - **a.** Use the molar mass of an element and Avogadro's number in calculations (Section 2-9). Study Questions: 63, 67, 106, 107.
  - **b.** Calculate the molar mass of a compound from its formula and a table of atomic weights (Section 2-9). Study Questions: 69, 71.
  - **c.** Calculate the number of moles of a compound that is represented by a given mass, and vice versa (Section 2-9). Study Questions: 73–75, 117
- Interpret, predict, and write formulas for ionic and molecular compounds.
  - **a.** Recognize and interpret molecular formulas, condensed formulas, and structural formulas (Section 2-6). Study Questions: 33, 74.
  - **b.** Recognize that metal atoms commonly lose one or more electrons to form positive ions, called cations, and nonmetal atoms often gain electrons to form negative ions, called anions (Figure 2.18).
  - **c.** Predict the charge on a metal cation: for Groups 1A, 2A, and 3A ions, the charge is equal to the group number in which the element is found in the periodic table (M^{n+}, n = Group number) (Section 2-7); for transition metal cations, the charges are often 2+ or 3+, but other charges are observed. Study Questions: 35, 37, 39.
  - **d.** Recognize that the negative charge on a single-atom or monatomic anion, X^{n-}, is given by n = Group number − 8 (Section 2-7). Study Questions: 36, 40.
  - **e.** Write formulas for ionic compounds by combining ions in the proper ratio to give no overall charge (Section 2-7). Study Questions: 41, 43, 45, 47.
- Determine empirical and molecular formulas and percent composition of compounds from experimental data.
  - **a.** Express the composition of a compound in terms of percent composition (Section 2-10). Study Questions: 79, 81, 113.
  - **b.** Use percent composition or other experimental data to determine the empirical formula of a compound (Section 2-10). Study Questions: 87, 88, 89, 91.
  - **c.** Use experimental data to find the number of water molecules in a hydrated compound (Section 2-11). Study Questions: 157, 158.

REMEMBER

- The terminology of the periodic table (periods, groups) and know how to use the information given in the periodic table (Section 2-5). Study Questions: 25, 28–30, 103.
- Some common elements and identify some of their properties.
- Formulas and names of ions and ionic compounds and of common molecular compounds.
  - **a.** Polyatomic ions (Table 2.4 and Section 2-7). Study Questions: 37, 38.
  - **b.** Ionic compounds and simple binary compounds of the nonmetals (Sections 2-7 and 2-8). Study Questions: 49, 57–60, 128.
- Common properties of ionic compounds (Section 2-7).

KEY EQUATIONS

Equation 2.1 (page 49) Percent abundance of an isotope.

$$\text{Percent abundance} = \frac{\text{number of atoms of a given isotope}}{\text{total number of atoms of all isotopes of that element}} \times 100\%$$

Equation 2.2 (page 50) Calculate the atomic weight from isotope abundances and the exact atomic mass of each isotope of an element.

$$\text{Atomic weight} = \left(\frac{\%\text{ abundance isotope 1}}{100}\right)(\text{mass of isotope 1}) + \left(\frac{\%\text{ abundance isotope 2}}{100}\right)(\text{mass of isotope 2}) + \ldots$$

Equation 2.3 (page 73) **Coulomb's Law**, the force of attraction between oppositely charged ions.

$$\text{Force} = -k\frac{(n^{+}e)(n^{-}e)}{d^2}$$

charge on + and − ions (n^+, n^-); charge on electron (e); proportionality constant (k); distance between ions (d)

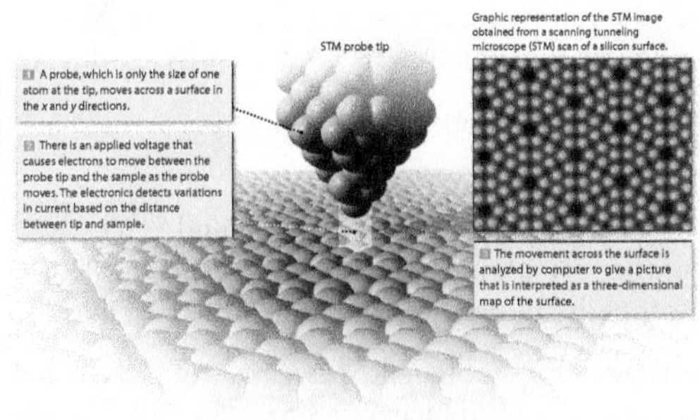

STUDY QUESTIONS

▲ denotes challenging questions.

Blue-numbered questions have answers in Appendix N and fully worked solutions in the *Student Solutions Manual.*

Practicing Skills

Atoms: Their Composition and Structure

1. What are the three fundamental particles from which atoms are built? What are their electric charges? Which of these particles constitute the nucleus of an atom? Which is the least massive particle of the three?

2. Define mass number. What is the difference between mass number and atomic mass?

3. An atom has a very small nucleus surrounded by an electron "cloud." Figure 2.1 represents the nucleus with a diameter of about 2 mm and describes the electron cloud as extending over 200 m. If the diameter of an atom is 1×10^{-8} cm, what is the approximate diameter of its nucleus?

4. A gold atom has a radius of 145 pm. If you could string gold atoms like beads on a thread, how many atoms would you need to have a necklace 36 cm long?

5. Give the complete symbol (^A_ZX), including atomic number and mass number, for each of the following atoms: (a) magnesium with 15 neutrons, (b) titanium with 26 neutrons, and (c) zinc with 32 neutrons.

6. Give the complete symbol (^A_ZX), including atomic number and mass number, of (a) a nickel atom with 31 neutrons, (b) a plutonium atom with 150 neutrons, and (c) a tungsten atom with 110 neutrons.

7. How many electrons, protons, and neutrons are there in each of the following atoms?
   (a) magnesium-24, ^{24}Mg
   (b) tin-119, ^{119}Sn
   (c) thorium-232, ^{232}Th
   (d) carbon-13, ^{13}C
   (e) copper-63, ^{63}Cu
   (f) bismuth-205, ^{205}Bi

8. Atomic structure.
   (a) The synthetic radioactive element technetium is used in many medical studies. Give the number of electrons, protons, and neutrons in an atom of technetium-99.
   (b) Radioactive americium-241 is used in household smoke detectors and in bone mineral analysis. Give the number of electrons, protons, and neutrons in an atom of americium-241.

Key Experiments Developing Atomic Structure

(See pages 54–55.)

9. From cathode ray experiments, J. J. Thomson estimated that the mass of an electron was "about a thousandth" of the mass of a proton. How accurate is that estimate? Calculate the ratio of the mass of an electron to the mass of a proton.

10. In 1886 Eugene Goldstein observed positively charged particles moving in the opposite direction to electrons in a cathode ray tube (illustrated below). From their mass, he concluded that these particles were formed from residual gas in the tube. For example, if the cathode ray tube contained helium, the canal rays consisted of He^+ ions. Describe a process that could lead to these ions.

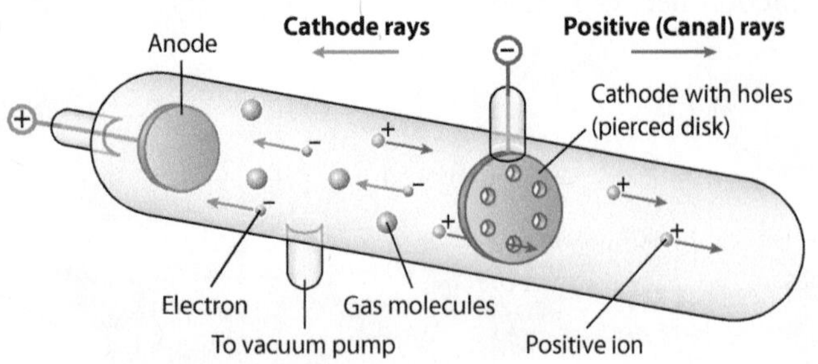

Canal rays. In 1886, Eugene Goldstein detected a stream of particles traveling in the direction opposite to that of the negatively charged cathode rays (electrons). He called this stream of positive particles "canal rays."

11. Marie Curie was born in Poland but studied and carried out her research in Paris. In 1903, she shared the Nobel Prize in Physics with H. Becquerel and her husband Pierre for their discovery of radioactivity. (In 1911 she received the Nobel Prize in Chemistry for the discovery of two new chemical elements, radium and polonium, the latter named for her homeland, Poland.) They and others observed that a radioactive substance could emit three types of radiation: alpha (α), beta (β), and gamma (γ). If the radiation from a radioactive source is passed between electrically charged plates, some particles are attached to the positive plate, some to the negative plate, and others feel no attraction. Which particles are positively charged, which are negatively charged, and which have no charge? Of the two charged particles, which has the most mass?

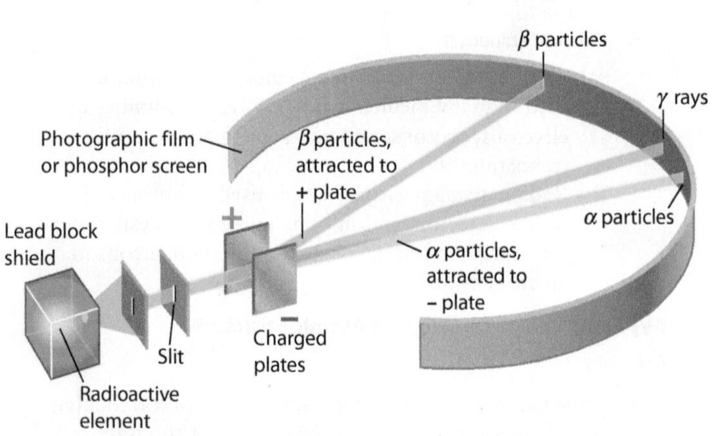

Radioactivity. Alpha (α), beta (β), and gamma (γ) rays from a radioactive element are separated by passing them between electrically charged plates.

12. Early in the 1800's John Dalton proposed that an atom was a "solid, massy, hard, impenetrable, moveable particle." Critique this description. How does this description misrepresent atomic structure?

Isotopes

13. The mass of an ^{16}O atom is 15.995 u. What is its mass relative to the mass of an atom of ^{12}C?

14. What is the mass of one ^{16}O atom, in grams?

15. Cobalt has three radioactive isotopes used in medical studies. Atoms of these isotopes have 30, 31, and 33 neutrons, respectively. Give the complete symbol for each of these isotopes.

16. Naturally occurring silver exists as two isotopes having mass numbers 107 and 109. How many protons, neutrons, and electrons are there in each of these isotopes?

17. Name and describe the composition of the three hydrogen isotopes.

18. Which of the following are isotopes of element X, the atomic number for which is 9: $^{19}_{9}X$, $^{20}_{9}X$, $^{9}_{18}X$, and $^{21}_{9}X$?

Isotope Abundance and Atomic Weight

(See Examples 2.2 and 2.3.)

19. Thallium has two stable isotopes, ^{203}Tl and ^{205}Tl. Knowing that the atomic weight of thallium is 204.4, which isotope is the more abundant of the two?

20. Strontium has four stable isotopes. Strontium-84 has a very low natural abundance, but ^{86}Sr, ^{87}Sr, and ^{88}Sr are all reasonably abundant. Knowing that the atomic weight of strontium is 87.62, which of the more abundant isotopes predominates?

21. Verify that the atomic weight of lithium is 6.94, given the following information:
^{6}Li, mass = 6.015121 u; percent abundance = 7.50%
^{7}Li, mass = 7.016003 u; percent abundance = 92.50%

22. Verify that the atomic weight of magnesium is 24.31, given the following information:
^{24}Mg, mass = 23.985042 u; percent abundance = 78.99%
^{25}Mg, mass = 24.985837 u; percent abundance = 10.00%
^{26}Mg, mass = 25.982593 u; percent abundance = 11.01%

23. Gallium has two naturally occurring isotopes, ^{69}Ga and ^{71}Ga, with masses of 68.9257 u and 70.9249 u, respectively. Calculate the percent abundances of these isotopes of gallium.

24. Europium has two stable isotopes, ^{151}Eu and ^{153}Eu, with masses of 150.9197 u and 152.9212 u, respectively. Calculate the percent abundances of these isotopes of europium.

The Periodic Table

(See Section 2-5.)

25. Titanium and thallium have symbols that are easily confused with each other. Give the symbol, atomic number, atomic weight, and group and period number of each element. Are they metals, metalloids, or nonmetals?

26. In Groups 4A–6A, there are several elements whose symbols begin with S. Name these elements, and for each one give its symbol, atomic number, group number, and period. Describe each as a metal, metalloid, or nonmetal.

27. How many periods of the periodic table have 8 elements, how many have 18 elements, and how many have 32 elements?

28. How many elements occur in the seventh period? What is the name given to the majority of these elements, and what well-known property characterizes them?

29. Select answers to the questions listed below from the following list of elements whose symbols start with the letter C: C, Ca, Cr, Co, Cd, Cl, Cs, Ce, Cm, Cu, and Cf. (You should expect to use some symbols more than once.)
   (a) Which are nonmetals?
   (b) Which are main group elements?
   (c) Which are lanthanides?
   (d) Which are transition elements?
   (e) Which are actinides?
   (f) Which are gases?

30. Give the name and chemical symbol for the following.
   (a) a nonmetal in the second period
   (b) an alkali metal in the fifth period
   (c) the third-period halogen
   (d) an element that is a gas at 20°C and 1 atmosphere pressure

31. Classify the following elements as metals, metalloids, or nonmetals: N, Na, Ni, Ne, and Np.

32. Here are symbols for five of the seven elements whose names begin with the letter B: B, Ba, Bk, Bi, and Br. Match each symbol with one of the descriptions below.
   (a) a radioactive element
   (b) a liquid at room temperature
   (c) a metalloid
   (d) an alkaline earth element
   (e) a group 5A element

Molecular Formulas and Models

33. A model of nitric acid is illustrated here. Write the molecular formula for nitric acid, and draw the structural formula. Describe the structure of the molecule. Is it flat? That is, are all the atoms in the plane of the paper? (Color code: nitrogen atoms are blue; oxygen atoms are red; and hydrogen atoms are white.)

Nitric acid

34. A model of the amino acid asparagine is illustrated here. Write the molecular formula for the compound, and draw its structural formula.

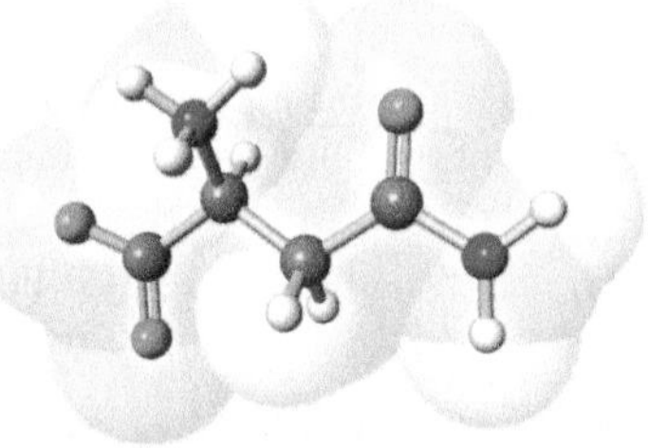

Asparagine, an amino acid

Ions and Ion Charges

(See Figure 2.18 and Table 2.4.)

35. What is the charge on the common monatomic ions of the following elements?
   (a) magnesium
   (b) zinc
   (c) nickel
   (d) gallium

36. What is the charge on the common monatomic ions of the following elements?
   (a) selenium
   (b) fluorine
   (c) iron
   (d) nitrogen

37. Give the symbol, including the correct charge, for each of the following ions:
   (a) barium ion
   (b) titanium(IV) ion
   (c) phosphate ion
   (d) hydrogen carbonate ion
   (e) sulfide ion
   (f) perchlorate ion
   (g) cobalt(II) ion
   (h) sulfate ion

38. Give the symbol, including the correct charge, for each of the following ions:
   (a) permanganate ion
   (b) nitrite ion
   (c) dihydrogen phosphate ion
   (d) ammonium ion
   (e) phosphate ion
   (f) sulfite ion

39. When a potassium atom becomes a monatomic ion, how many electrons does it lose or gain? What noble gas atom has the same number of electrons as a potassium ion?

40. When oxygen and sulfur atoms become monatomic ions, how many electrons does each lose or gain? Which noble gas atom has the same number of electrons as an oxide ion? Which noble gas atom has the same number of electrons as a sulfide ion?

Ionic Compounds

(See Examples 2.4 and 2.5.)

41. What are the charges on the ions in an ionic compound containing the elements barium and bromine? Write the formula for the compound.

42. What are the charges of the ions in an ionic compound containing cobalt(III) and fluoride ions? Write the formula for the compound.

43. Give the formula and the number of each ion that makes up each of the following compounds:

(a) K_2S
(b) $CoSO_4$
(c) $KMnO_4$
(d) $(NH_4)_3PO_4$
(e) $Ca(ClO)_2$
(f) $NaCH_3CO_2$

44. Give the formula and the number of each ion that makes up each of the following compounds:

(a) $Mg(CH_3CO_2)_2$
(b) $Al(OH)_3$
(c) $CuCO_3$
(d) $Ti(SO_4)_2$
(e) KH_2PO_4
(f) $CaHPO_4$

45. Cobalt forms Co^{2+} and Co^{3+} ions. Write the formulas for the two cobalt oxides formed by these transition metal ions.

46. Platinum is a transition element and forms Pt^{2+} and Pt^{4+} ions. Write the formulas for the compounds of each of these ions with (a) chloride ions and (b) sulfide ions.

47. Which of the following are correct formulas for ionic compounds? For those that are not, give the correct formula.

(a) $AlCl_2$
(b) KF_2
(c) Ga_2O_3
(d) MgS

48. Which of the following are correct formulas for ionic compounds? For those that are not, give the correct formula.

(a) Ca_2O
(b) $SrBr_2$
(c) Fe_2O_5
(d) Li_2O

Naming Ionic Compounds

49. Name each of the following ionic compounds:

(a) K_2S
(b) $CoSO_4$
(c) $(NH_4)_3PO_4$
(d) $Ca(ClO)_2$

50. Name each of the following ionic compounds:

(a) $Ca(CH_3CO_2)_2$
(b) $Ni_3(PO_4)_2$
(c) $Al(OH)_3$
(d) KH_2PO_4

51. Give the formula for each of the following ionic compounds:

(a) ammonium carbonate
(b) calcium iodide
(c) copper(II) bromide
(d) aluminum phosphate
(e) silver(I) acetate

52. Give the formula for each of the following ionic compounds:

(a) calcium hydrogen carbonate
(b) potassium permanganate
(c) magnesium perchlorate
(d) potassium hydrogen phosphate
(e) sodium sulfite

53. Write the formulas for the four ionic compounds that can be made by combining each of the cations Na^+ and Ba^{2+} with the anions CO_3^{2-} and I^-. Name each of the compounds.

54. Write the formulas for the four ionic compounds that can be made by combining the cations Mg^{2+} and Fe^{3+} with the anions PO_4^{3-} and NO_3^-. Name each compound formed.

Coulomb's Law

(See Equation 2.3 and Figure 2.22.)

55. Sodium ions, Na^+, form ionic compounds with fluoride ions, F^-, and iodide ions, I^-. The radii of these ions are as follows: $Na^+ = 116$ pm; $F^- = 119$ pm; and $I^- = 206$ pm. In which ionic compound, NaF or NaI, are the forces of attraction between cation and anion stronger? Explain your answer.

56. Consider the two ionic compounds NaCl and CaO. In which compound are the cation–anion attractive forces stronger? Explain your answer.

Naming Binary, Molecular Compounds

57. Name each of the following binary, nonionic compounds:

(a) NF_3
(b) HI
(c) BI_3
(d) PF_5

58. Name each of the following binary, nonionic compounds:

(a) N_2O_5
(b) P_4S_3
(c) OF_2
(d) XeF_4

59. Give the formula for each of the following compounds:

(a) sulfur dichloride
(b) dinitrogen pentaoxide
(c) silicon tetrachloride
(d) diboron trioxide (commonly called boric oxide)

60. Give the formula for each of the following compounds:

(a) bromine trifluoride
(b) xenon difluoride
(c) hydrazine
(d) diphosphorus tetrafluoride
(e) butane

Atoms and the Mole

(See Example 2.6.)

61. Calculate the mass, in grams, of each the following:

(a) 2.5 mol of aluminum
(b) 1.25×10^{-3} mol of iron
(c) 0.015 mol of calcium
(d) 653 mol of neon

62. Calculate the mass, in grams, of each the following:

(a) 4.24 mol of gold
(b) 15.6 mol of He
(c) 0.063 mol of platinum
(d) 3.63×10^{-4} mol of Pu

63. Calculate the amount (moles) represented by each of the following:

(a) 127.08 g of Cu
(b) 0.012 g of lithium
(c) 5.0 mg of americium
(d) 6.75 g of Al

64. Calculate the amount (moles) represented by each of the following:

(a) 16.0 g of Na
(b) 0.876 g of tin
(c) 0.0034 g of platinum
(d) 0.983 g of Xe

65. You are given 1.0-g samples of He, Fe, Li, Si, and C. Which sample contains the largest number of atoms? Which contains the smallest?

66. You are given 0.10-g samples of K, Mo, Cr, and Al. List the samples in order of the amount (moles), from smallest to largest.

67. Analysis of a 10.0-g sample of apatite (a major component of tooth enamel) showed that it was made up of 3.99 g Ca, 1.85 g P, 4.14 g O, and 0.020 g H. List these elements based on relative amounts (moles), from smallest to largest.

68. A semiconducting material is composed of 52 g of Ga, 9.5 g of Al, and 112 g of As. Which element has the largest number of atoms in this material?

Molecules, Compounds, and the Mole

(See Example 2.7.)

69. Calculate the molar mass of each of the following compounds:
   (a) Fe_2O_3, iron(III) oxide
   (b) BCl_3, boron trichloride
   (c) $C_6H_8O_6$, ascorbic acid (vitamin C)

70. Calculate the molar mass of each of the following compounds:
   (a) $Fe(C_6H_{11}O_7)_2$, iron(II) gluconate, a dietary supplement
   (b) $CH_3CH_2CH_2CH_2SH$, butanethiol, has a skunk-like odor
   (c) $C_{20}H_{24}N_2O_2$, quinine, used as an antimalarial drug

71. Calculate the molar mass of each hydrated compound. Note that the water of hydration is included in the molar mass. (See page 82.)
   (a) $Ni(NO_3)_2 \cdot 6\ H_2O$
   (b) $CuSO_4 \cdot 5\ H_2O$

72. Calculate the molar mass of each hydrated compound. Note that the water of hydration is included in the molar mass. (See page 82.)
   (a) $H_2C_2O_4 \cdot 2\ H_2O$
   (b) $MgSO_4 \cdot 7\ H_2O$, Epsom salt

73. What mass is represented by 0.0255 mol of each of the following compounds?
   (a) C_3H_7OH, 2-propanol, rubbing alcohol
   (b) $C_{11}H_{16}O_2$, an antioxidant in foods, also known as BHA (butylated hydroxyanisole)
   (c) $C_9H_8O_4$, aspirin
   (d) $(CH_3)_2CO$, acetone, an important industrial solvent

74. Assume you have 0.123 mol of each of the following compounds. What mass of each is present?
   (a) $C_{14}H_{10}O_4$, benzoyl peroxide, used in acne medications
   (b) Dimethylglyoxime, used in the laboratory to test for nickel(II) ions

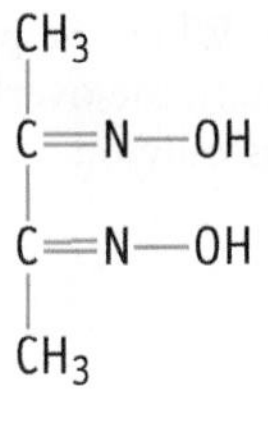

   (c) The compound below, responsible for the "skunky" taste in poorly made beer.

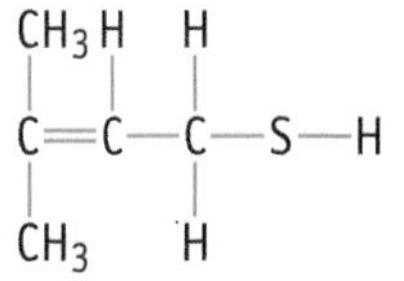

   (d) DEET, a mosquito repellent

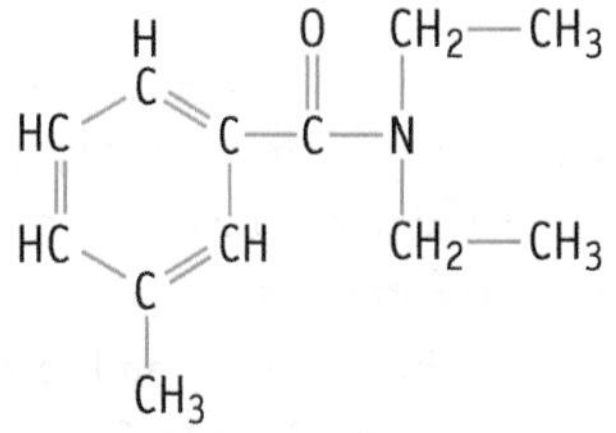

75. Sulfur trioxide, SO_3, is made industrially in enormous quantities by combining oxygen and sulfur dioxide, SO_2. What amount (moles) of SO_3 is represented by 1.00 kg of sulfur trioxide? How many molecules? How many sulfur atoms? How many oxygen atoms?

76. How many ammonium ions and how many sulfate ions are present in a 0.20 mol sample of $(NH_4)_2SO_4$? How many atoms of N, H, S and O are contained in this sample?

77. Acetaminophen, whose structure is drawn below, is the active ingredient in some nonprescription pain killers. The recommended dose for an adult is two 500 mg caplets. How many molecules make up one dose of this drug?

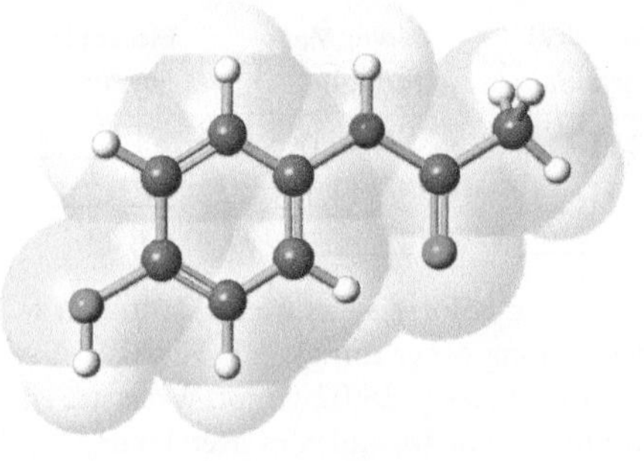

Acetaminophen

78. An Alka-Seltzer tablet contains 324 mg of aspirin ($C_9H_8O_4$), 1904 mg of $NaHCO_3$, and 1000. mg of citric acid ($H_3C_6H_5O_7$). (The last two compounds react with each other to provide the "fizz," bubbles of CO_2, when the tablet is put into water.)
   (a) Calculate the amount (moles) of each substance in the tablet.
   (b) If you take one tablet, how many molecules of aspirin are you consuming?

Percent Composition

(See Example 2.8.)

79. Calculate the mass percent of each element in the following compounds:
   (a) PbS, lead(II) sulfide, galena
   (b) C_3H_8, propane
   (c) $C_{10}H_{14}O$, carvone, found in caraway seed oil

80. Calculate the mass percent of each element in the following compounds:

(a) $C_8H_{10}N_2O_2$, caffeine
(b) $C_{10}H_{20}O$, menthol
(c) $CoCl_2 \cdot 6\ H_2O$

81. Calculate the mass percent of copper in CuS, copper(II) sulfide. If you wish to obtain 10.0 g of copper metal from copper(II) sulfide, what mass of CuS (in grams) must you use?

82. Calculate the mass percent of titanium in the mineral ilmenite, $FeTiO_3$. What mass of ilmenite (in grams) is required if you wish to obtain 750 g of titanium?

Empirical and Molecular Formulas

(See Example 2.9.)

83. Succinic acid occurs in fungi and lichens. Its empirical formula is $C_2H_3O_2$, and its molar mass is 118.1 g/mol. What is its molecular formula?

84. An organic compound has the empirical formula C_2H_4NO. If its molar mass is 116.1 g/mol, what is the molecular formula of the compound?

85. Complete the following table:

Empirical Formula	Molar Mass (g/mol)	Molecular Formula
(a) CH	26.0	______
(b) CHO	116.1	______
(c) ______	______	C_8H_{16}

86. Complete the following table:

Empirical Formula	Molar Mass (g/mol)	Molecular Formula
(a) $C_2H_3O_3$	150.0	______
(b) C_3H_8	44.1	______
(c) ______	______	B_4H_{10}

87. Acetylene is a colorless gas used as a fuel in welding torches, among other things. It is 92.26% C and 7.74% H. Its molar mass is 26.02 g/mol. What are the empirical and molecular formulas of acetylene?

88. A large family of boron-hydrogen compounds has the general formula B_xH_y. One member of this family contains 88.5% B; the remainder is hydrogen. What is its empirical formula?

89. Cumene, a hydrocarbon, is a compound composed only of C and H. It is 89.94% carbon, and its molar mass is 120.2 g/mol. What are the empirical and molecular formulas of cumene?

90. In 2006, a Russian team discovered an interesting molecule they called "sulflower" because of its shape and because it was based on sulfur. It is composed of 57.17% S and 42.83% C and has a molar mass of 448.70 g/mol. Determine the empirical and molecular formulas of "sulflower."

91. Mandelic acid is an organic acid composed of carbon (63.15%), hydrogen (5.30%), and oxygen (31.55%). Its molar mass is 152.14 g/mol. Determine the empirical and molecular formulas of the acid.

92. Nicotine, a poisonous compound found in tobacco leaves, is 74.0% C, 8.65% H, and 17.35% N. Its molar mass is 162 g/mol. What are the empirical and molecular formulas of nicotine?

Determining Formulas from Mass Data

(See Examples 2.10 and 2.11.)

93. A compound containing xenon and fluorine was prepared by shining sunlight on a mixture of Xe (0.526 g) and excess F_2 gas. If you isolate 0.678 g of the new compound, what is its empirical formula?

94. Elemental sulfur (1.256 g) is combined with fluorine, F_2, to give a compound with the formula SF_x, a very stable, colorless gas. If you have isolated 5.722 g of SF_x, what is the value of x?

95. Epsom salt is used in tanning leather and in medicine. It is hydrated magnesium sulfate, $MgSO_4 \cdot 7\ H_2O$. The water of hydration is lost on heating, with the number lost depending on the temperature. Suppose you heat a 1.394-g sample at 100 °C and obtain 0.885 g of a partially hydrated sample, $MgSO_4 \cdot x\ H_2O$. What is the value of x?

96. You combine 1.25 g of germanium, Ge, with excess chlorine, Cl_2. The mass of product, Ge_xCl_y, is 3.69 g. What is the formula of the product, Ge_xCl_y?

General Questions

These questions are not designated as to type or location in the chapter. They may combine several concepts.

97. Fill in the blanks in the table (one column per element).

Symbol	^{58}Ni	^{33}S	______	______
Number of protons	______	______	10	______
Number of neutrons	______	______	10	30
Number of electrons in the neutral atom	______	______	______	25
Name of element	______	______	______	______

98. Potassium has three naturally occurring isotopes (^{39}K, ^{40}K, and ^{41}K), but ^{40}K has a very low natural abundance. Which of the other two isotopes is more abundant? Briefly explain your answer.

99. Crossword Puzzle: In the 2 × 2 box shown here, each answer must be correct four ways: horizontally, vertically, diagonally, and by itself. Instead of words, use symbols of elements. When the puzzle is complete, the four spaces will contain the overlapping symbols of 10 elements. There is only one correct solution.

1	2
3	4

Horizontal
1–2: two-letter symbol for a metal used in ancient times
3–4: two-letter symbol for a metal that burns in air and is found in Group 5A

Vertical
1–3: two-letter symbol for a metalloid
2–4: two-letter symbol for a metal used in U.S. coins

Single squares: All one-letter symbols
1: a colorful nonmetal
2: colorless, gaseous nonmetal
3: an element that makes fireworks green
4: an element that has medicinal uses

Diagonal
1–4: two-letter symbol for an element used in electronics
2–3: two-letter symbol for a metal used with Zr to make wires for superconducting magnets

This puzzle first appeared in *Chemical & Engineering News*, p. 86, December 14, 1987 (submitted by S. J. Cyvin) and in *Chem Matters*, October 1988.

100. The chart below shows a general decline in abundance with increasing mass among the first 30 elements. The decline continues beyond zinc. (Notice that the scale on the vertical axis is logarithmic, that is, it progresses in powers of 10. The abundance of nitrogen, for example, is 1/10,000 ($1/10^4$) of the abundance of hydrogen. All abundances are plotted as the number of atoms per 10^{12} atoms of H. (The fact that the abundances of Li, Be, and B, as well as those of the elements near Fe, do not follow the general decline is a consequence of the way that elements are synthesized in stars.)

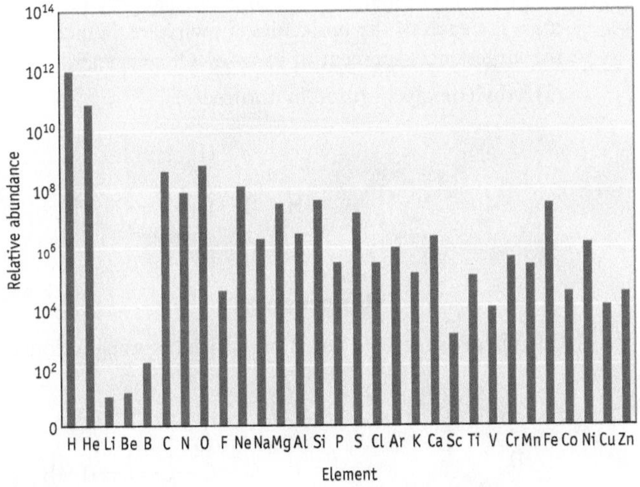

The abundance of the elements in the solar system from H to Zn

(a) What is the most abundant main group metal?
(b) What is the most abundant nonmetal?
(c) What is the most abundant metalloid?
(d) Which of the transition elements is most abundant?
(e) Which halogens are included on this plot, and which is the most abundant?

101. Copper atoms.

(a) What is the average mass of one copper atom?
(b) Students in a college computer science class once sued the college because they were asked to calculate the cost of one atom and could not do it. But you are in a chemistry course, and you can do this. (See E. Felsenthal, *Wall Street Journal*, May 9, 1995.) If the cost of 2.0-mm diameter copper wire (99.999% pure) is currently \$41.70 for 7.0 g, what is the cost of one copper atom?

102. Which of the following is impossible?

(a) silver foil that is 1.2×10^{-4} m thick
(b) a sample of potassium that contains 1.784×10^{24} atoms
(c) a gold coin of mass 1.23×10^{-3} kg
(d) 3.43×10^{-27} mol of S_8 molecules

103. Reviewing the periodic table.

(a) Name the element in Group 2A and the fifth period.
(b) Name the element in the fifth period and Group 4B.
(c) Which element is in the second period in Group 4A?
(d) Which element is in the fourth period in Group 5A?
(e) Which halogen is in the fifth period?
(f) Which alkaline earth element is in the third period?
(g) Which noble gas element is in the fourth period?
(h) Name the nonmetal in Group 6A and the third period.
(i) Name a metalloid in the fourth period.

104. Identify two nonmetallic elements that have allotropes and describe the allotropes of each.

105. In each case, decide which represents more mass:

(a) 0.5 mol of Na, 0.5 mol of Si, or 0.25 mol of U
(b) 9.0 g of Na, 0.50 mol of Na, or 1.2×10^{22} atoms of Na
(c) 10 atoms of Fe or 10 atoms of K

106. The recommended daily allowance (RDA) of iron for women 19–30 years old is 18 mg. How many moles is this? How many atoms?

107. Put the following elements in order from smallest to largest mass:

(a) 3.79×10^{24} atoms Fe
(b) 19.921 mol H_2
(c) 8.576 mol C
(d) 7.4 mol Si
(e) 9.221 mol Na
(f) 4.07×10^{24} atoms Al
(g) 9.2 mol Cl_2

108. ▲ When a sample of phosphorus burns in air, the compound P_4O_{10} forms. One experiment showed that 0.744 g of phosphorus formed 1.704 g of P_4O_{10}. Use this information to determine the ratio of the atomic weights of phosphorus and oxygen (mass P/mass O). If the atomic weight of oxygen is assumed to be 16.000, calculate the atomic weight of phosphorus.

109. ▲ Although carbon-12 is now used as the standard for atomic weights, this has not always been the case. Early attempts at classification used hydrogen as the standard, with the weight of hydrogen being set equal to 1.0000. Later attempts defined atomic weights using oxygen (with a weight of 16.0000). In each instance, the atomic weights of the other elements were defined relative to these masses. (To answer this question, you need more precise data on current atomic weights: H, 1.00794; O, 15.9994.)

(a) If H = 1.0000 u was used as a standard for atomic weights, what would the atomic weight of oxygen be? What would be the value of Avogadro's number under these circumstances?

(b) Assuming the standard is O = 16.0000, determine the value for the atomic weight of hydrogen and the value of Avogadro's number.

110. A reagent occasionally used in chemical synthesis is sodium–potassium alloy. (Alloys are mixtures of metals, and Na-K has the interesting property that it is a liquid.) One formulation of the alloy (the one that melts at the lowest temperature) contains 68 atom percent K; that is, out of every 100 atoms, 68 are K and 32 are Na. What is the mass percent of potassium in sodium–potassium alloy?

111. Write formulas for all of the compounds that can be made by combining the cations NH_4^+ and Ni^{2+} with the anions CO_3^{2-} and SO_4^{2-}.

112. How many electrons are in a strontium atom (Sr)? Does an atom of Sr gain or lose electrons when forming an ion? How many electrons are gained or lost by the atom? When Sr forms an ion, the ion has the same number of electrons as which one of the noble gases?

113. Which of the following compounds has the highest mass percent of chlorine?

(a) BCl_3
(b) $AsCl_3$
(c) $GaCl_3$
(d) $AlCl_3$
(e) PCl_3

114. Which of the following samples has the largest number of ions?

(a) 1.0 g of $BeCl_2$
(b) 1.0 g of $MgCl_2$
(c) 1.0 g of CaS
(d) 1.0 g of $SrCO_3$
(e) 1.0 g of $BaSO_4$

115. The structure of one of the bases in DNA, adenine, is shown here. Which represents the greater mass: 40.0 g of adenine or 3.0×10^{23} molecules of the compound?

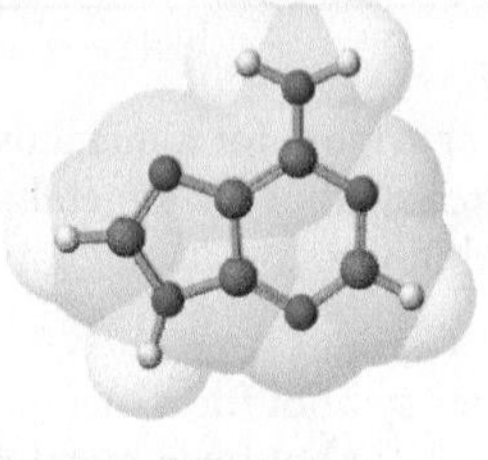

Adenine

116. Ionic and molecular compounds of the halogens.

(a) What are the names of BaF_2, $SiCl_4$, and $NiBr_2$?

(b) Which of the compounds in part (a) are ionic, and which are molecular?

(c) Which has the largest mass, 0.50 mol of BaF_2, 0.50 mol of $SiCl_4$, or 1.0 mol of $NiBr_2$?

117. A drop of water has a volume of about 0.050 mL. How many molecules of water are in a drop of water? (Assume water has a density of 1.00 g/cm^3.)

118. Capsaicin, the compound that gives the hot taste to chili peppers, has the formula $C_{18}H_{27}NO_3$.

(a) Calculate its molar mass.

(b) If you eat 55 mg of capsaicin, what amount (moles) have you consumed?

(c) Calculate the mass percent of each element in the compound.

(d) What mass of carbon (in milligrams) is there in 55 mg of capsaicin?

119. Calculate the molar mass and the mass percent of each element in the blue solid compound $Cu(NH_3)_4SO_4 \cdot H_2O$. What is the mass of copper and the mass of water in 10.5 g of the compound?

120. Write the molecular formula and calculate the molar mass for each of the molecules shown here. Which has the largest mass percent of carbon? Of oxygen?

(a) ethylene glycol (used in antifreeze)

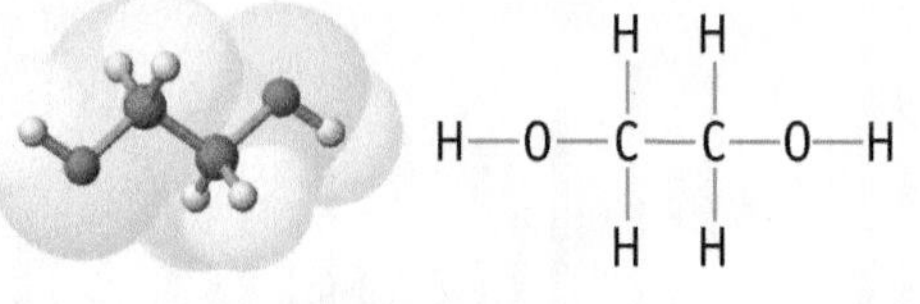

Ethylene glycol

(b) dihydroxyacetone (used in artificial tanning lotions)

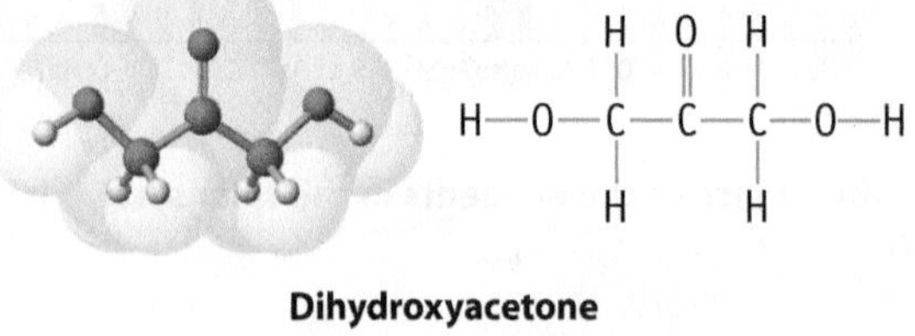

Dihydroxyacetone

(c) ascorbic acid, commonly known as vitamin C

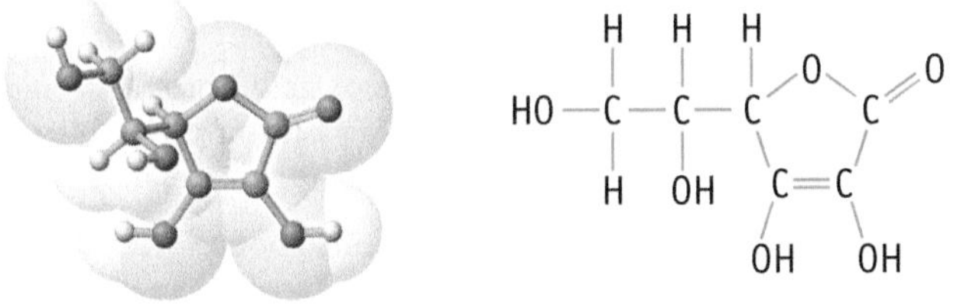

Ascorbic acid, vitamin C

121. Malic acid, an organic acid found in apples, contains C, H, and O in the following ratios: $C_1H_{1.50}O_{1.25}$. What is the empirical formula of malic acid?

122. Your doctor has diagnosed you as being anemic—that is, as having too little iron in your blood. At the drugstore, you find two iron-containing dietary supplements: one with iron(II) sulfate, $FeSO_4$, and the other with iron(II) gluconate, $Fe(C_6H_{11}O_7)_2$. If you take 100. mg of each compound, which will deliver more atoms of iron?

123. A compound composed of iron and carbon monoxide, $Fe_x(CO)_y$, is 30.70% iron. What is the empirical formula for the compound?

124. Ma huang, an extract from the ephedra species of plants, contains ephedrine. The Chinese have used this herb for more than 5000 years to treat asthma. More recently, ephedrine has been used in diet pills that can be purchased over the counter in herbal medicine shops. However, very serious concerns have been raised regarding these pills following reports that their use led to serious heart problems.

(a) A molecular model of ephedrine is drawn below. From this determine the molecular formula for ephedrine and calculate its molar mass.
(b) What is the weight percent of carbon in ephedrine?
(c) Calculate the amount (moles) of ephedrine in a 0.125 g sample.
(d) How many molecules of ephedrine are there in 0.125 g? How many C atoms?

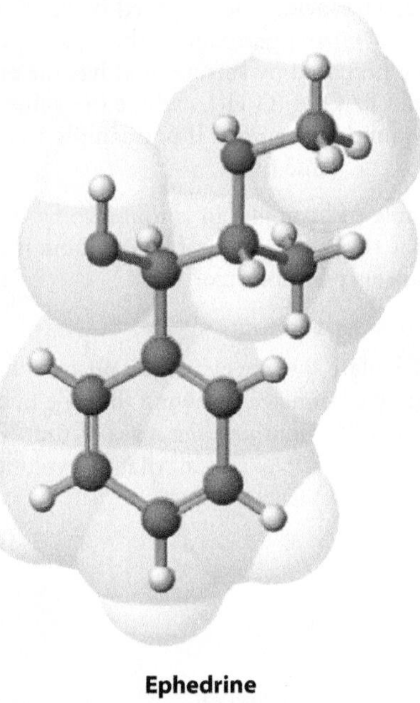

Ephedrine

125. Saccharin, a molecular model of which is shown below, is more than 300 times sweeter than sugar. It was first made in 1897, when it was common practice for chemists to record the taste of any new substances they synthesized.

(a) Write the molecular formula for the compound, and draw its structural formula. (S atoms are yellow.)
(b) If you ingest 125 mg of saccharin, what amount (moles) of saccharin have you ingested?
(c) What mass of sulfur is contained in 125 mg of saccharin?

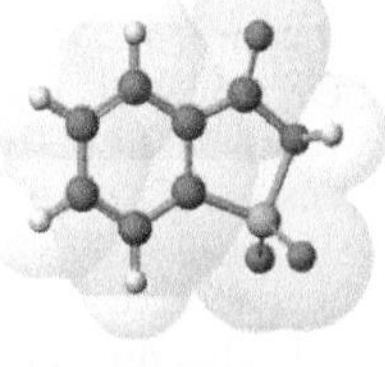

Saccharin

126. Name each of the following compounds and indicate which ones are best described as ionic:

(a) ClF_3
(b) NCl_3
(c) $SrSO_4$
(d) $Ca(NO_3)_2$
(e) XeF_4
(f) OF_2
(g) KI
(h) Al_2S_3
(i) PCl_3
(j) K_3PO_4

127. Write the formula for each of the following compounds and indicate which ones are best described as ionic:

(a) sodium hypochlorite
(b) boron triiodide
(c) aluminum perchlorate
(d) calcium acetate
(e) potassium permanganate
(f) ammonium sulfite
(g) potassium dihydrogen phosphate
(h) disulfur dichloride
(i) chlorine trifluoride
(j) phosphorus trifluoride

128. Complete the table by placing symbols, formulas, and names in the blanks.

Cation	Anion	Name	Formula
____	____	ammonium bromide	____
Ba^{2+}	____	____________	BaS
____	Cl^-	iron(II) chloride	____
____	F^-	____________	PbF_2
Al^{3+}	CO_3^{2-}	____________	____
____	____	iron(III) oxide	____

129. Empirical and molecular formulas.

(a) Fluorocarbonyl hypofluorite is composed of 14.6% C, 39.0% O, and 46.3% F. The molar mass of the compound is 82 g/mol. Determine the empirical and molecular formulas of the compound.
(b) Azulene, a beautiful blue hydrocarbon, is 93.71% C and has a molar mass of 128.16 g/mol. What are the empirical and molecular formulas of azulene?

130. Cacodyl, a compound containing arsenic, was reported in 1842 by the German chemist Robert Wilhelm Bunsen. It has an almost intolerable garlic-like odor. Its molar mass is 210 g/mol, and it is 22.88% C, 5.76% H, and 71.36% As. Determine its empirical and molecular formulas.

131. The action of bacteria on meat and fish produces a compound called cadaverine. As its name and origin imply, it stinks! (It is also present in bad breath and adds to the odor of urine.) It is 58.77% C, 13.81% H, and 27.40% N. Its molar mass is 102.2 g/mol. Determine the molecular formula of cadaverine.

132. ▲ In the laboratory you combine 0.125 g of nickel with CO and isolate 0.364 g of $Ni(CO)_x$. What is the value of x?

133. ▲ A compound called MMT was once used to boost the octane rating of gasoline. What is the empirical formula of MMT if it is 49.5% C, 3.2% H, 22.0% O, and 25.2% Mn?

134. ▲ Elemental phosphorus is made by heating calcium phosphate with carbon and sand in an electric furnace. What is the mass percent of phosphorus in calcium phosphate? Use this value to calculate the mass of calcium phosphate (in kilograms) that must be used to produce 15.0 kg of phosphorus.

135. ▲ Chromium is obtained by heating chromium(III) oxide with carbon. Calculate the mass percent of chromium in the oxide, and then use this value to calculate the quantity of Cr_2O_3 required to produce 850 kg of chromium metal.

136. ▲ Stibnite, Sb_2S_3, is a dark gray mineral from which antimony metal is obtained. What is the mass percent of antimony in the sulfide? If you have 1.00 kg of an ore that contains 10.6% antimony, what mass of Sb_2S_3 (in grams) is in the ore?

137. ▲ Direct reaction of iodine (I_2) and chlorine (Cl_2) produces an iodine chloride, I_xCl_y, a bright yellow solid. If you completely consume 0.678 g of I_2 in a reaction with excess Cl_2 and produce 1.246 g of I_xCl_y, what is the empirical formula of the compound? A later experiment showed that the molar mass of I_xCl_y was 467 g/mol. What is the molecular formula of the compound?

138. ▲ In a reaction, 2.04 g of vanadium combined with 1.93 g of sulfur to give a pure compound. What is the empirical formula of the product?

139. ▲ Iron pyrite, often called "fool's gold," has the formula FeS_2. If you could convert 15.8 kg of iron pyrite to iron metal, what mass of the metal would you obtain?

140. Which of the following statements about 57.1 g of octane, C_8H_{18}, is (are) *not* true?

(a) 57.1 g is 0.500 mol of octane.
(b) The compound is 84.1% C by weight.
(c) The empirical formula of the compound is C_4H_9.
(d) 57.1 g of octane contains 28.0 g of hydrogen atoms.

141. The formula of barium molybdate is $BaMoO_4$. Which of the following is the formula of sodium molybdate?

(a) Na_4MoO (b) $NaMoO$ (c) Na_2MoO_3 (d) Na_2MoO_4 (e) Na_4MoO_4

142. ▲ A metal M forms a compound with the formula MCl_4. If the compound is 74.75% chlorine, what is the identity of M?

143. Pepto-Bismol, which can help provide relief for an upset stomach, contains 300. mg of bismuth subsalicylate, $C_{21}H_{15}Bi_3O_{12}$, per tablet. If you take two tablets for your stomach distress, what amount (in moles) of the "active ingredient" are you taking? What mass of Bi are you consuming in two tablets?

144. ▲ The weight percent of oxygen in an oxide that has the formula MO_2 is 15.2%. What is the molar mass of this compound? What element or elements are possible for M?

145. The mass of 2.50 mol of a compound with the formula ECl_4, in which E is a nonmetallic element, is 385 g. What is the molar mass of ECl_4? What is the identity of E?

146. ▲ The elements A and Z combine to produce two different compounds: A_2Z_3 and AZ_2. If 0.15 mol of A_2Z_3 has a mass of 15.9 g and 0.15 mol of AZ_2 has a mass of 9.3 g, what are the atomic weights of A and Z?

147. ▲ Polystyrene can be prepared by heating styrene with tribromobenzoyl peroxide in the absence of air. A sample prepared by this method has the empirical formula $Br_3C_6H_3(C_8H_8)_n$, where the value of n can vary from sample to sample. If one sample has 0.105% Br, what is the value of n?

148. A sample of hemoglobin is found to be 0.335% iron. What is the molar mass of hemoglobin if there are four iron atoms per molecule?

149. ▲ Consider an atom of ^{64}Zn.

(a) Calculate the density of the nucleus in grams per cubic centimeter, knowing that the nuclear radius is 4.8×10^{-6} nm and the mass of the ^{64}Zn atom is 1.06×10^{-22} g. (Recall that the volume of a sphere is $[4/3]\pi r^3$.)

(b) Calculate the density of the space occupied by the electrons in the zinc atom, given that the atomic radius is 0.125 nm and the electron mass is 9.11×10^{-28} g.

(c) Having calculated these densities, what statement can you make about the relative densities of the parts of the atom?

150. ▲ Estimating the radius of a lead atom.

(a) You are given a cube of lead that is 1.000 cm on each side. The density of lead is 11.35 g/cm^3. How many atoms of lead are in the sample?

(b) Atoms are spherical; therefore, the lead atoms in this sample cannot fill all the available space. As an approximation, assume that 60% of the space of the cube is filled with spherical lead atoms. Calculate the volume of one lead atom from this information. From the calculated volume (V) and the formula $(4/3)\pi r^3$ for the volume of a sphere, estimate the radius (r) of a lead atom.

151. A piece of nickel foil, 0.550 mm thick and 1.25 cm square, is allowed to react with fluorine, F_2, to give a nickel fluoride.

(a) How many moles of nickel foil were used? (The density of nickel is 8.902 g/cm^3.)

(b) If you isolate 1.261 g of the nickel fluoride, what is its formula?

(c) What is its complete name?

152. ▲ Uranium is used as a fuel, primarily in the form of uranium(IV) oxide, in nuclear power plants. This question considers some uranium chemistry.

(a) A small sample of uranium metal (0.169 g) is heated to between 800 and 900 °C in air to give 0.199 g of a dark green oxide, U_xO_y. How many moles of uranium metal were used? What is the empirical formula of the oxide, U_xO_y? What is the name of the oxide? How many moles of U_xO_y must have been obtained?

(b) The naturally occurring isotopes of uranium are ^{234}U, ^{235}U, and ^{238}U. Knowing that uranium's atomic weight is 238.02 g/mol, which isotope must be the most abundant?

(c) If the hydrated compound $UO_2(NO_3)_2 \cdot z\, H_2O$ is heated gently, the water of hydration is lost. If you have 0.865 g of the hydrated compound and obtain 0.679 g of $UO_2(NO_3)_2$ on heating, how many waters of hydration are in each formula unit of the original compound? (The oxide U_xO_y is obtained if the hydrate is heated to temperatures over 800°C in the air.)

153. In an experiment, you need 0.125 mol of sodium metal. Sodium can be cut easily with a knife (Figure 2.6), so if you cut out a block of sodium, what should the volume of the block be in cubic centimeters? If you cut a perfect cube, what is the length of the edge of the cube? (The density of sodium is 0.97 g/cm^3.)

154. Mass spectrometric analysis showed that there are four isotopes of an unknown element having the following masses and abundances:

Isotope	Mass Number	Isotope Mass	Abundance (%)
1	136	135.9090	0.193
2	138	137.9057	0.250
3	140	139.9053	88.48
4	142	141.9090	11.07

Three elements in the periodic table that have atomic weights near these values are lanthanum (La), atomic number 57, atomic weight 138.9055; cerium (Ce), atomic number 58, atomic weight 140.115; and praseodymium (Pr), atomic number 59, atomic weight 140.9076. Using the data above, calculate the atomic weight, and identify the element if possible.

155. The mass spectrum of CH_3Cl is illustrated here. You know that carbon has two stable isotopes, ^{12}C and ^{13}C with relative abundances of 98.9% and 1.1%, respectively, and chlorine has two isotopes, ^{35}Cl and ^{37}Cl with abundances of 75.77% and 24.23%, respectively.

(a) What molecular species gives rise to the lines at m/Z of 50 and 52? Why is the line at 52 about 1/3 the height of the line at 50?

(b) What species might be responsible for the line at $m/Z = 51$?

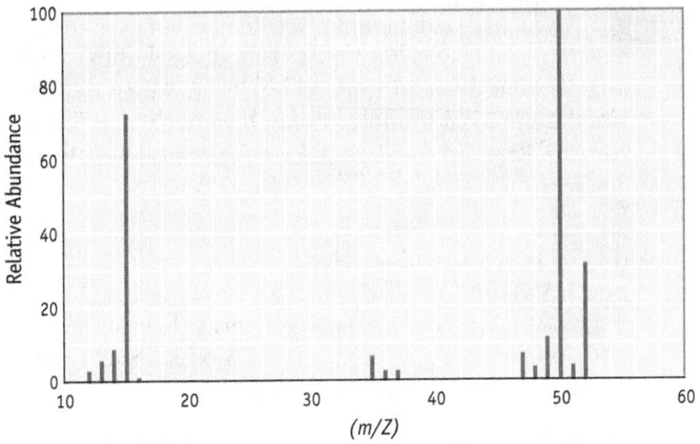

156. The highest mass peaks in the mass spectrum of Br_2 occur at m/Z 158, 160, and 162. The ratio of intensities of these peaks is approximately 1:2:1. Bromine has two stable isotopes, ^{79}Br (50.7% abundance) and ^{81}Br (49.3% abundance).

(a) What molecular species gives rise to each of these peaks?

(b) Explain the relative intensities of these peaks. (*Hint:* Consider the probabilities of each atom combination.)

In the Laboratory

157. If Epsom salt, $MgSO_4 \cdot x\ H_2O$, is heated to 250 °C, all the water of hydration is lost. On heating a 1.687-g sample of the hydrate, 0.824 g of $MgSO_4$ remains. How many molecules of water occur per formula unit of $MgSO_4$?

158. The "alum" used in cooking is potassium aluminum sulfate hydrate, $KAl(SO_4)_2 \cdot x\ H_2O$. To find the value of x, you can heat a sample of the compound to drive off all of the water and leave only $KAl(SO_4)_2$. Assume you heat 4.74 g of the hydrated compound and that the sample loses 2.16 g of water. What is the value of x?

159. Tin metal (Sn) and purple iodine (I_2) combine to form orange, solid tin iodide with an unknown formula.

$$\text{Sn metal} + \text{solid } I_2 \rightarrow \text{solid } Sn_xI_y$$

Weighed quantities of Sn and I_2 are combined, where the quantity of Sn is more than is needed to react with all of the iodine. After Sn_xI_y has been formed, it is isolated by filtration. The mass of excess tin is also determined. The following data were collected:

Mass of tin (Sn) in the original mixture	1.056 g
Mass of iodine (I_2) in the original mixture	1.947 g
Mass of tin (Sn) recovered after reaction	0.601 g

What is the empirical formula of the tin iodide obtained?

160. ▲ When analyzed, an unknown compound gave these experimental results: C, 54.0%; H, 6.00%; and O, 40.0%. Four different students used these values to calculate the empirical formulas shown here. Which answer is correct? Why did some students not get the correct answer?

(a) $C_4H_5O_2$
(b) $C_5H_7O_3$
(c) $C_7H_{10}O_4$
(d) $C_9H_{12}O_5$

161. ▲ Two general chemistry students working together in the lab weigh out 0.832 g of $CaCl_2 \cdot 2\ H_2O$ into a crucible. After heating the sample for a short time and allowing the crucible to cool, the students determine that the sample has a mass of 0.739 g. They then do a quick calculation. On the basis of this calculation, what should they do next?

(a) Congratulate themselves on a job well done.
(b) Assume the bottle of $CaCl_2 \cdot 2\ H_2O$ was mislabeled; it actually contained something different.
(c) Heat the crucible again, and then reweigh it.

162. To find the empirical formula of tin oxide, you first react tin metal with nitric acid in a porcelain crucible. The metal is converted to tin nitrate, but, on heating the nitrate strongly, brown nitrogen dioxide gas is evolved and tin oxide is formed. In the laboratory you collect the following data:

Mass of crucible	13.457 g
Mass of crucible plus tin	14.710 g
Mass of crucible after heating	15.048 g

What is the empirical formula of tin oxide?

Summary and Conceptual Questions

The following questions may use concepts from this and the previous chapter.

163. ▲ Identify, from the list below, the information needed to calculate the number of atoms in 1.00 cm^3 of iron. Outline the procedure used in this calculation.

(a) the structure of solid iron
(b) the molar mass of iron
(c) Avogadro's number
(d) the density of iron
(e) the temperature
(f) iron's atomic number
(g) the number of iron isotopes

164. Consider the plot of relative element abundances on page 95f. Is there a relationship between abundance and atomic number? Is there any difference between the relative abundance of an element of even atomic number and the relative abundance of an element of odd atomic number?

165. The photo here depicts what happens when a coil of magnesium ribbon and a few calcium chips are placed in water.

(a) Based on these observations, what might you expect to see when barium, another Group 2A element, is placed in water?

(b) Give the period in which each element (Mg, Ca, and Ba) is found; what correlation do you think you might find between the reactivity of these elements and their positions in the periodic table?

© Cengage Learning/Charles D. Winters

Magnesium *(left)* and calcium *(right)* in water

166. A jar contains some number of jelly beans. To find out precisely how many are in the jar, you could dump them out and count them. How could you estimate their number without counting each one? (Chemists need to do just this kind of "bean counting" when they work with atoms and molecules. Atoms and molecules are too small to count one by one, so chemists have worked out other methods to determine the number of atoms in a sample.)

© Cengage Learning/Charles D. Winters

How many jelly beans are in the jar?

AP Multiple-Choice Review Questions

1. Which of the following choices consists of a pair of isotopes?
(A) ^{14}C and ^{14}N
(B) ^{23}Na and $^{23}Na^+$
(C) ^{2}H and ^{1}H
(D) ^{35}Cl and $^{35}Cl^-$

2. What is the correct name for $CaCl_2$?
(A) calcium chloride
(B) calcium chlorine
(C) calcium chlorite
(D) calcium(II) chloride

3. What is the correct name for Fe_2S_3?
(A) diiron trisulfide
(B) iron sulfide
(C) iron(II) sulfide
(D) iron(III) sulfide

4. What is the correct name for NO_2?
(A) nitrite
(B) nitrogen oxide
(C) nitrogen dioxide
(D) dinitrogen monoxide

5. When a sample of an unknown element is vaporized and injected into a mass spectrometer, the results shown below are obtained. Use these data to estimate the average atomic mass of this element.

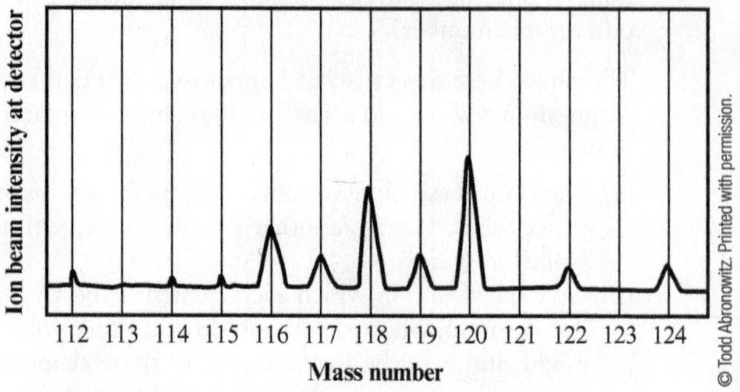

(A) 117 amu
(B) between 117 and 118 amu
(C) between 118 and 119 amu
(D) between 119 and 120 amu

6. An unnamed element with an atomic number of 130 is vaporized and injected into a mass spectrometer. The results are shown below. Use these data to calculate the average atomic mass of this element.

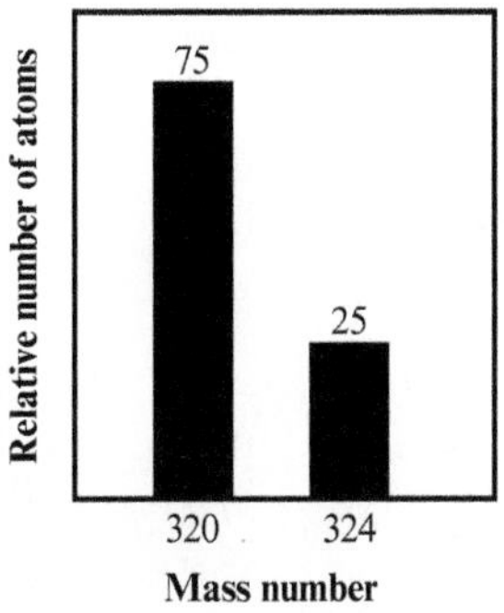

(A) 320 amu
(B) 321 amu
(C) 322 amu
(D) 324 amu

7. The simplest formula for a compound made from element X (molar mass = 79.0 g/mol) that is 21.0% nitrogen by mass is
(A) XN
(B) XN_2
(C) X_2N_3
(D) X_3N_2

8. Which of the following combinations of elements is likely to produce an ionic bond?
(A) Li and Cl
(B) Li and Rb
(C) N and S
(D) N and O

The following information is used for Questions 9 and 10.

A 20.0-g sample of a hydrated compound is placed into a crucible and heated. The data table for this laboratory investigation is shown below.

Mass of crucible	15.5867 g
Mass of crucible and hydrated sample	19.7644 g
Mass of crucible and anhydrous sample after first heating	18.4388 g
Mass of crucible and anhydrous sample after second heating	18.0244 g
Mass of crucible and anhydrous sample after third heating	18.0242 g

9. Why can we conclude that all of the water of hydration has been removed?
(A) The mass of the crucible and sample increased then decreased.
(B) The mass of the crucible and sample decreased after each heating.
(C) The mass of the crucible and sample decreased due to the water of hydration being "driven off" by the heating.
(D) The mass of the crucible and sample remained relatively constant after the second heating.

10. What is the mass of the water of hydration in the hydrate?
(A) 0.4146 g
(B) 1.7402 g
(C) 2.4325 g
(D) 4.1777 g

11. A compound is analyzed and found to contain 1.30 moles of Na, 0.65 moles of Te, and 2.60 moles of O. What is the simplest formula of this compound?

(A) $NaTeO_2$

(B) Na_2TeO_4

(C) Na_2Te_2O

(D) Na_2Te_4O

12. The average atomic mass of a chlorine atom is 35.45 amu. Chlorine consists of two isotopes, ^{35}Cl and ^{37}Cl. Which of the following most closely approximates the relative abundance of these isotopes?

(A) 25% ^{35}Cl and 75% ^{37}Cl

(B) 50% ^{35}Cl and 50% ^{37}Cl

(C) 75% ^{35}Cl and 25% ^{37}Cl

(D) 90% ^{35}Cl and 10% ^{37}Cl

13. Which of the following compounds contains the greatest percent by mass of nitrogen?

(A) NH_3

(B) HCN

(C) N_2O

(D) NI_3

14. Substance AB_2 is 60.0% A by mass. What is the percent A by mass for substance AB?

(A) 20.0%

(B) 40.0%

(C) 60.0%

(D) 75.0%

AP Free Response Review Questions

Question Format: Short

Category of Question: Quantitative

Tagatose is a new *sweetener* that may soon appear as an ingredient in some "lower calorie" foods for diabetics. It is used for these because it is 92% as sweet as *sucrose (table sugar),* contains only 38% as many *calories* per gram, and does not increase blood sugar levels to any appreciable extent. Tagatose has a molar mass of 180.15 g/mol and analysis finds that it is 40.00% carbon, 6.73% hydrogen, and 53.27% oxygen.

Questions

(a) Find the empirical formula for tagatose.

(b) Find the molecular formula for tagatose.

Question Format: Long

Category of Question: Lab 1

Design an experiment to determine the number of water molecules in one formula unit of hydrated nickel(II) chloride.

Available Equipment and Materials (not all are necessarily used):

Bunsen burner	electronic balance
crucible and cover	funnel and filter paper
ring stand and ring	clay triangle
test tubes	test tube clamp
hot plate	crucible tongs
6.00 g hydrated nickel(II) chloride	

(a) List and describe the steps involved in your procedure.

(b) Construct a data table showing all data that needs to be collected. Include units where appropriate (leaving values blank).

(c) Show the calculations that are needed to determine the formula of the hydrated compound. Actual calculations are not needed.

(d) A common error results if a student handles the cooled crucible with their fingers before the final weighing. Why and how would this affect the experimental results?

(e) List and describe two other common sources of experimental error that may occur with this procedure. Describe how each may be avoided. Also, state whether each would result in the experimentally determined number of water molecules being too high or too low.

Metal sulfides from a black smoker. A "black smoker" photographed deep in the Pacific Ocean along the East Pacific Rise. The "smoke" is a cloud of insoluble metal sulfides formed when the molten material is forced from the Earth's interior.

Chemical Reactions

Chapter Outline

BLACK SMOKERS AND VOLCANOES

In 1977, scientists were exploring the junction of two of the tectonic plates that form the floor of the Pacific Ocean. There they found thermal springs gushing a hot, black soup of minerals. Seawater seeps into cracks in the ocean floor and, as it sinks deeper into the Earth's crust, the water is superheated to between 300 °C and 400 °C by the hot magma just below the Earth's crust. This superhot water dissolves minerals in the crust and is pushed back to the surface. When this hot water, now laden with dissolved metal cations and rich in anions such as sulfide and sulfate, gushes through the surface, it cools, and metal sulfates—such as calcium sulfate—and metal sulfides—such as those of copper, manganese, iron, zinc, and nickel—precipitate. Many metal sulfides are black, and the plume of material coming from the sea bottom looks like black "smoke;" thus, the vents have been called "black smokers." The solid sulfides and other minerals settle around the edges of the vent on the sea floor and eventually form a "chimney" of precipitated minerals. You can see the same deposits of metal sulfides around steam vents from volcanoes and in the water flowing away from a volcano or steam vent.

Chapter Goals

See Chapter Goals Revisited (page 136) for Study Questions keyed to these goals.

UNDERSTAND

- The significance and uses of balanced chemical equations.
- The nature and characteristics of chemical equilibrium.
- The nature of ionic substances dissolved in water.
- Oxidation–reduction reactions and the three types of exchange reactions.
- Acid–base reactions involve the transfer of hydrogen ions.
- Oxidation–reduction reactions involve the transfer of electrons.

DO

- Balance chemical equations, given formulas for reactants and products.
- Predict the solubility of ionic compounds in water and the species present in aqueous solutions of ionic and molecular compounds.
- Recognize common types of chemical reactions in aqueous solution and predict products of precipitation, acid–base, and gas-forming exchange reactions.
- Know the names and formulas of common acids and bases and understand their nature in aqueous solution.
- Write a net ionic equation, given the overall balanced equation for a chemical reaction.
- Determine oxidation numbers for elements in a compound and use them to identify oxidation–reduction reactions.

REMEMBER

- The guidelines for the solubility of ionic compounds.
- The names and formulas of common acids and bases.
- Common oxidizing and reducing agents.

Scientists were amazed to discover that the deep sea vents were surrounded by peculiar animals living in the hot, sulfide-rich environment. Because black smokers are under hundreds of feet of water and sunlight does not penetrate to these depths, the animals have developed a way to live without the energy from sunlight. In a terrestrial environment, plants use the energy of the Sun to synthesize organic molecules by the process of photosynthesis. In the lightless ecosystem deep in the ocean, energy is derived from the oxidation of sulfides. With this source of energy, microbes are able to make the organic molecules that are the basis of life.

Chemical reactions are the major focus of this chapter. We will present guidelines for organizing information on chemical reactions, for predicting the products of reactions, and for representing this information in the form of chemical equations.

Chemical reactions are at the heart of chemistry. We begin a chemical reaction with one set of materials and end up with different materials. Just reading this sentence involves an untold number of chemical reactions in your body. Indeed, every activity of living things depends on carefully regulated chemical reactions. Our objective in this chapter is to introduce you to the symbolism used to represent chemical reactions and to describe several common types of chemical reactions.

3-1 Introduction to Chemical Equations

Learning Objectives: LO 1.17, LO 1.18, LO 3.1, LO 3.2, LO 3.5 (see APEC Lab 7 "Hydrates and Thermal Decomposition"), LO 3.6

When a stream of chlorine gas, Cl_2, is directed onto solid phosphorus, P_4, the mixture bursts into flame, and a chemical reaction produces liquid phosphorus trichloride, PCl_3 (Figure 3.1). We can depict this reaction using a **balanced chemical equation**.

$$\underbrace{P_4(s) + 6\,Cl_2(g)}_{\text{reactants}} \longrightarrow \underbrace{4\,PCl_3(\ell)}_{\text{product}}$$

Photos: © Cengage Learning/Charles D. Winters

$$\underbrace{P_4(s) + 6\ Cl_2(g)}_{\text{REACTANTS}} \longrightarrow \underbrace{4\ PCl_3(\ell)}_{\text{PRODUCT}}$$

FIGURE 3.1 **Reaction of solid white phosphorus with chlorine gas.** The product is liquid phosphorus trichloride.

States of Reactants and Products Including the states of each species (s, ℓ, g, aq) provides useful information to the reader. This practice is optional, however, and you will see equations written without this information elsewhere in this text.

In a chemical equation, the formulas for the **reactants** (the substances combined in the reaction) are written to the left of the arrow and the formulas of the **products** (the substances produced) are written to the right of the arrow. The physical states of reactants and products can also be indicated. The symbol (s) indicates a solid, (g) a gas, and (ℓ) a liquid. A substance dissolved in water, that is, in an *aq*ueous solution, is indicated by (aq).

In the 18th century, the French scientist Antoine Lavoisier (1743–1794) introduced the **law of conservation of matter**, which states that *matter can neither be created nor destroyed.* This means that if the total mass of reactants is 10 g, and if the reaction completely converts reactants to products, you must end up with 10 g of products. This also means that if 1000 atoms of a particular element are contained in the reactants, then those 1000 atoms must appear in the products in some fashion. *Atoms, and thus mass, are conserved in chemical reactions.*

When applied to the reaction of phosphorus and chlorine, the law of conservation of matter tells us that 1 molecule of phosphorus, P_4 (with 4 phosphorus atoms), and 6 diatomic molecules of Cl_2 (with 12 atoms of Cl) will produce four molecules of PCl_3. Because each PCl_3 molecule contains 1 P atom and 3 Cl atoms, the four PCl_3 molecules are needed to account for 4 P atoms and 12 Cl atoms in the product. The equation is *balanced*; the same number of P and Cl atoms appear on each side of the equation.

$$\overset{}{\underset{\text{4 P atoms}}{P_4(s)}} + \overset{6 \times 2 = \text{12 Cl atoms}}{6\ Cl_2(g)} \longrightarrow \underset{\text{4 P atoms}}{\overset{4 \times 3 = \text{12 Cl atoms}}{4\ PCl_3(\ell)}}$$

In a chemical reaction, the relationship between the amounts of chemical reactants and products is called **stoichiometry** (pronounced "stoy-key-AHM-uh-tree"). The coefficients in a balanced equation are called **stoichiometric coefficients.** (In the P_4 and Cl_2 reaction, these are 1, 6, and 4.) They can be interpreted as a number of atoms or molecules: one molecule of P_4 and 6 molecules of Cl_2. They can refer equally well to amounts of reactants and products: one mole of P_4 combines with 6 moles of Cl_2 to produce 4 moles of PCl_3.

A CLOSER LOOK

Antoine Laurent Lavoisier, 1743–1794

On Monday, August 7, 1774, the Englishman Joseph Priestley (1733–1804) isolated oxygen. (The Swedish chemist Carl Scheele [1742–1786] also discovered the element, perhaps in 1773, but did not publish his results until later.) To obtain oxygen, Priestley heated mercury(II) oxide, HgO, causing it to decompose to mercury and oxygen.

$$2\ HgO(s) \rightarrow 2\ Hg(\ell) + O_2(g)$$

Priestley did not immediately understand the significance of the discovery, but he mentioned it to the French chemist Antoine Lavoisier in October 1774. One of Lavoisier's contributions to science was his recognition of the importance of exact scientific measurements and of carefully planned experiments, and he applied these methods to the study of oxygen. From this work, Lavoisier proposed that oxygen was an element, that it was one of the constituents of the compound water, and that burning involved a reaction with oxygen. He also mistakenly came to believe Priestley's gas was present in all acids, so he named it "oxygen" from the Greek words meaning "to form an acid."

In other experiments, Lavoisier observed that the heat produced by a guinea pig when exhaling a given amount of carbon dioxide is similar to the quantity of heat produced by burning carbon to give the same amount of carbon dioxide. From these and other experiments he concluded that, "Respiration is a combustion, slow it is true, but otherwise perfectly similar to that of charcoal." Although he did not understand the details of the process, this was an important step in the development of biochemistry.

Lavoisier was a prodigious scientist, and the principles of naming chemical substances that he introduced are still in use today. Furthermore, he wrote a textbook in which he applied the principles of the conservation of matter to chemistry, and he used the idea to write early versions of chemical equations.

Because Lavoisier was an aristocrat, he came under suspicion during the Reign of Terror of the French Revolution in 1794. He was an investor in the Ferme Générale, the infamous tax-collecting organization in 18th-century France. Tobacco was a monopoly product of the Ferme Générale, and it was common to cheat the purchaser by adding water to the tobacco, a practice that Lavoisier opposed. Nonetheless, because of his involvement with the Ferme, his career was cut short by the guillotine on May 8, 1794, on the charge of "adding water to the people's tobacco."

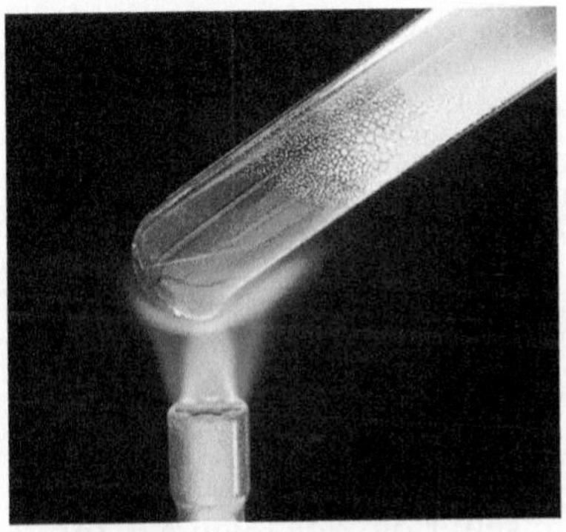

The decomposition of red mercury(II) oxide. The decomposition reaction gives mercury metal and oxygen gas. The mercury is seen as a film on the surface of the test tube.

Lavoisier and his wife, as painted in 1788 by Jacques-Louis David. Lavoisier was then 45, and his wife, Marie Anne Pierrette Paulze, was 30.

REVIEW & CHECK FOR SECTION 3-1

The reaction of aluminum with bromine is shown here. The equation for the reaction is

$$2\ Al(s) + 3\ Br_2(\ell) \rightarrow Al_2Br_6(s)$$

1. What are the stoichiometric coefficients in this equation?

   (a) 1, 3, 4 (b) 2, 3, 1 (c) 1, 6, 8 (d) 1, 1, 1

2. If you were to use 8000 atoms of Al, how many molecules of Br_2 are required to consume the Al completely?

   (a) 5333 (b) 8000 (c) 12,000 (d) 20,000

The reaction of aluminum metal [Al(s)] with bromine [$Br_2(\ell)$].

3-2 Balancing Chemical Equations

Learning Objectives: LO 1.17, LO 1.18, LO 3.1, LO 3.2, LO 3.9 (see APEC Lab 8 "Analysis by Oxidation-Reduction Titration")

A balanced equation is one in which the same number of atoms of each element appears on each side of the equation. The process of balancing equations involves assigning the correct stoichiometric coefficients. Many chemical equations can be balanced by trial and error, and this is the method that will often be used. However,

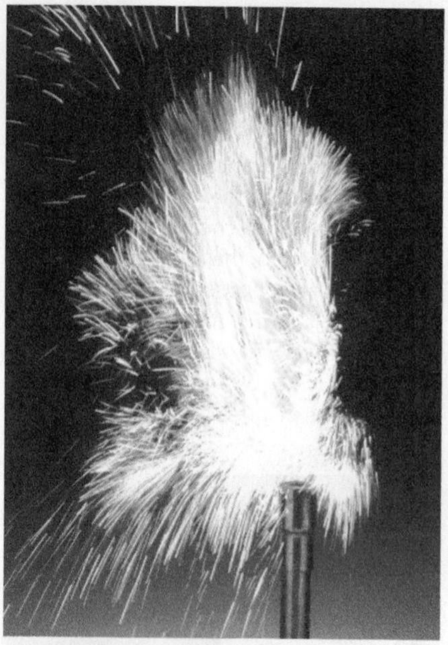

(a) Reaction of iron and oxygen to give iron(III) oxide, Fe_2O_3.

(b) Reaction of sulfur (in the spoon) with oxygen to give sulfur dioxide, SO_2.

(c) Reaction of phosphorus and oxygen to give tetraphosphorus decaoxide, P_4O_{10}.

FIGURE 3.2 **Reactions of a metal and two nonmetals with oxygen.**

more systematic methods are also available, and are especially useful if reactions are complicated.

One general class of chemical reactions is the reaction of metals or nonmetals with oxygen to give oxides of the general formula M_xO_y. For example, iron reacts with oxygen to give iron(III) oxide (Figure 3.2a).

$$4\ Fe(s) + 3\ O_2(g) \rightarrow 2\ Fe_2O_3(s)$$

The nonmetals sulfur and oxygen react to form sulfur dioxide (Figure 3.2b),

$$S(s) + O_2(g) \rightarrow SO_2(g)$$

and phosphorus, P_4, reacts vigorously with oxygen to give tetraphosphorus decaoxide, P_4O_{10} (Figure 3.2c).

$$P_4(s) + 5\ O_2(g) \rightarrow P_4O_{10}(s)$$

The equations written above are balanced. The same number of iron, sulfur, or phosphorus atoms and oxygen atoms occurs on each side of these equations.

When balancing chemical equations, there are two important things to remember:

- Formulas for reactants and products must be correct or the equation is meaningless. Once the correct formulas for the reactants and products have been determined, the subscripts in their formulas cannot be changed to balance an equation. Changing the subscripts changes the identity of the substance. For example, you cannot change CO_2 to CO to balance an equation; carbon monoxide, CO, and carbon dioxide, CO_2, are different compounds.
- Chemical equations are balanced using stoichiometric coefficients. The entire chemical formula of a substance is multiplied by the stoichiometric coefficient.

FIGURE 3.3 **A combustion reaction.** Here, propane, C_3H_8, burns to give CO_2 and H_2O. These simple oxides are always the products of the complete combustion of a hydrocarbon.

Every day, you encounter **combustion** reactions, the burning of a fuel in oxygen accompanied by the evolution of energy as heat (Figure 3.3). One of the most familiar is the combustion of octane, C_8H_{18}, a component of gasoline, in an automobile engine:

$$2\ C_8H_{18}(\ell) + 25\ O_2(g) \rightarrow 16\ CO_2(g) + 18\ H_2O(g)$$

In all combustion reactions, some or all of the elements in the reactants end up as oxides, compounds containing oxygen. When the reactant is a hydrocarbon (a compound that contains only C and H, such as octane, a hydrocarbon in gasoline), the products of complete combustion are always carbon dioxide and water.

As an example of equation balancing, let us write the balanced equation for the complete combustion of propane, C_3H_8, a common fuel.

STEP 1 *Write correct formulas for the reactants and products.* Here propane and oxygen are the reactants, and carbon dioxide and water are the products.

$$C_3H_8(g) + O_2(g) \xrightarrow{\text{unbalanced equation}} CO_2(g) + H_2O(g)$$

STEP 2 *Balance the C atoms.* In combustion reactions such as this it is usually best to balance the carbon atoms first and leave the oxygen atoms until the end (because oxygen atoms are often found in more than one product). In this case three carbon atoms are in the reactants, so three must occur in the products. Three CO_2 molecules are therefore required on the right side.

$$C_3H_8(g) + O_2(g) \xrightarrow{\text{unbalanced equation}} 3\ CO_2(g) + H_2O(g)$$

STEP 3 *Balance the H atoms.* A molecule of propane contains 8 H atoms. Each molecule of water has two hydrogen atoms, so four molecules of water account for the required eight hydrogen atoms on the right side.

$$C_3H_8(g) + O_2(g) \xrightarrow{\text{unbalanced equation}} 3\ CO_2(g) + 4\ H_2O(g)$$

STEP 4 *Balance the O atoms.* Ten oxygen atoms are on the right side ($3 \times 2 = 6$ in CO_2 plus $4 \times 1 = 4$ in H_2O). Five O_2 molecules are needed to supply the required ten oxygen atoms.

$$C_3H_8(g) + 5\ O_2(g) \xrightarrow{\text{unbalanced equation}} 3\ CO_2(g) + 4\ H_2O(g)$$

STEP 5 *Verify that the number of atoms of each element is balanced.* There are three carbon atoms, eight hydrogen atoms, and ten oxygen atoms on each side of the equation.

EXAMPLE 3.1

Balancing an Equation for a Combustion Reaction

Problem Write the balanced equation for the combustion of ammonia gas (NH_3) to give water vapor and nitrogen monoxide gas (NO).

What Do You Know? You know the correct formulas and/or names for the reactants (NH_3 and oxygen, O_2) and the products (H_2O and nitrogen monoxide, NO). You also know their states.

Strategy First write the unbalanced equation. Next balance the N atoms, then the H atoms, and finally the O atoms.

Solution

Step 1. *Write out the equation using correct formulas for the reactants and products.* The reactants are $NH_3(g)$ and $O_2(g)$, and the products are NO(g) and $H_2O(g)$.

$$NH_3(g) + O_2(g) \xrightarrow{\text{unbalanced equation}} NO(g) + H_2O(g)$$

Step 2. *Balance the N atoms.* There is one N atom on each side of the equation. The N atoms are in balance, at least for the moment.

$$NH_3(g) + O_2(g) \xrightarrow{\text{unbalanced equation}} NO(g) + H_2O(g)$$

Strategy Map 3.1

PROBLEM

Balance the equation for the reaction of NH_3 and O_2

DATA/INFORMATION

The **formulas** of the **reactants** and **products** are given

Balance **N** atoms.

N atoms balanced but overall equation not balanced

Balance **H** atoms.

N and H atoms balanced but overall equation not balanced

Balance **O** atoms. Best left to final step.

N, H, and O atoms balanced. *Overall equation now balanced.*

Step 3. *Balance the H atoms.* There are three H atoms on the left and two on the right. To have the same number on each side (6), use two molecules of NH_3 on the left and three molecules of H_2O on the right (which gives us six H atoms on each side).

$$2\ NH_3(g) + O_2(g) \xrightarrow{\text{unbalanced equation}} NO(g) + 3\ H_2O(g)$$

Notice that when we balance the H atoms, the N atoms are no longer balanced. To bring them into balance, use 2 NO molecules on the right.

$$2\ NH_3(g) + O_2(g) \xrightarrow{\text{unbalanced equation}} 2\ NO(g) + 3\ H_2O(g)$$

Step 4. *Balance the O atoms.* After Step 3, there is an even number of O atoms (two) on the left and an odd number (five) on the right. Because there cannot be an odd number of O atoms on the left (O atoms are paired in O_2 molecules), multiply each coefficient on both sides of the equation by 2 so that an even number of oxygen atoms (10) now occurs on the right side:

$$4\ NH_3(g) + O_2(g) \xrightarrow{\text{unbalanced equation}} 4\ NO(g) + 6\ H_2O(g)$$

Now the oxygen atoms can be balanced by having five O_2 molecules on the left side of the equation:

$$4\ NH_3(g) + 5\ O_2(g) \xrightarrow{\text{balanced equation}} 4\ NO(g) + 6\ H_2O(g)$$

Step 5. *Verify the result.* Four N atoms, 12 H atoms, and 10 O atoms occur on each side of the equation.

Think about Your Answer An alternative way to write this equation is

$$2\ NH_3(g) + {}^5/_2\ O_2(g) \rightarrow 2\ NO(g) + 3\ H_2O(g)$$

where a fractional coefficient has been used. This equation is correctly balanced. In general, however, we balance equations with whole-number coefficients.

Check Your Understanding

(a) Butane gas, C_4H_{10}, can burn completely in air [use $O_2(g)$ as the other reactant] to give carbon dioxide gas and water vapor. Write a balanced equation for this combustion reaction.

(b) Write a balanced chemical equation for the complete combustion of $C_3H_7BO_3$, a gasoline additive. The products of combustion are $CO_2(g)$, $H_2O(g)$, and $B_2O_3(s)$.

Art Palmer

FIGURE 3.4 Cave chemistry. Calcium carbonate stalactites cling to the roof of a cave, and stalagmites grow up from the cave floor. The chemistry producing these formations is a good example of the reversibility of chemical reactions.

REVIEW & CHECK FOR SECTION 3-2

1. The (unbalanced) equation describing the oxidation of propanol is

$$2\ C_3H_7OH(\ell) + \_\_O_2(g) \rightarrow 6\ CO_2(g) + \_\_H_2O(g)$$

What are the two missing stoichiometric coefficients?

(a) 4.5 O_2, 4 H_2O (b) 9 O_2, 8 H_2O (c) 5 O_2, 4 H_2O (d) 5 O_2, 7 H_2O

Learning Objectives: LO 3.1, LO 3.2

3-3 Introduction to Chemical Equilibrium

To this point, we have treated chemical reactions as proceeding in one direction only, with reactants being converted *completely* to products. Nature, however, is more complex than this. All chemical reactions are reversible, in principle, and many reactions lead to incomplete conversion of reactants to products.

The formation of stalactites and stalagmites in a limestone cave is an example of a system that depends on the reversibility of a chemical reaction (Figure 3.4).

Stalactites and stalagmites are made chiefly of calcium carbonate, a mineral found in underground deposits in the form of limestone, a leftover from ancient oceans. If water seeping through the limestone contains dissolved CO_2, a reaction occurs in which the mineral dissolves, giving an aqueous solution of $Ca(HCO_3)_2$.

$$CaCO_3(s) + CO_2(aq) + H_2O(\ell) \rightarrow Ca(HCO_3)_2(aq)$$

When the mineral-laden water reaches a cave, the reverse reaction occurs, with CO_2 being evolved into the cave and solid $CaCO_3$ being deposited.

$$Ca(HCO_3)_2(aq) \rightarrow CaCO_3(s) + CO_2(g) + H_2O(\ell)$$

As illustrated in Figure 3.5, these reactions can be done in a laboratory.

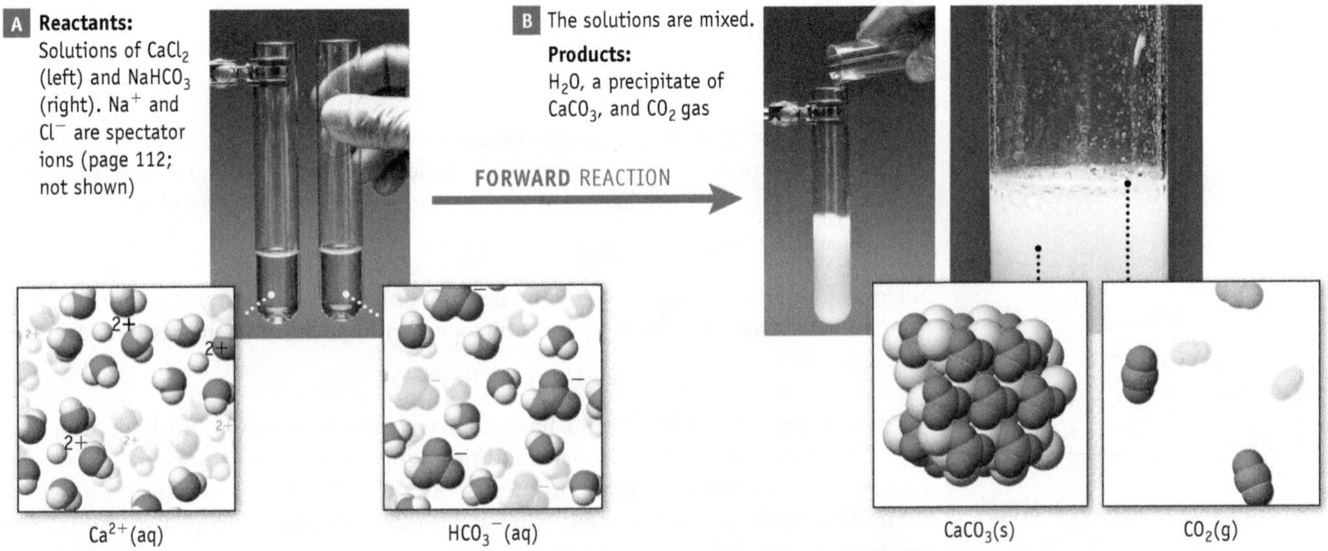

Solutions of $CaCl_2$ (a source of Ca^{2+} ions) and $NaHCO_3$ (a source of HCO_3^- ions) are mixed and produce a precipitate of $CaCO_3$ and CO_2 gas.

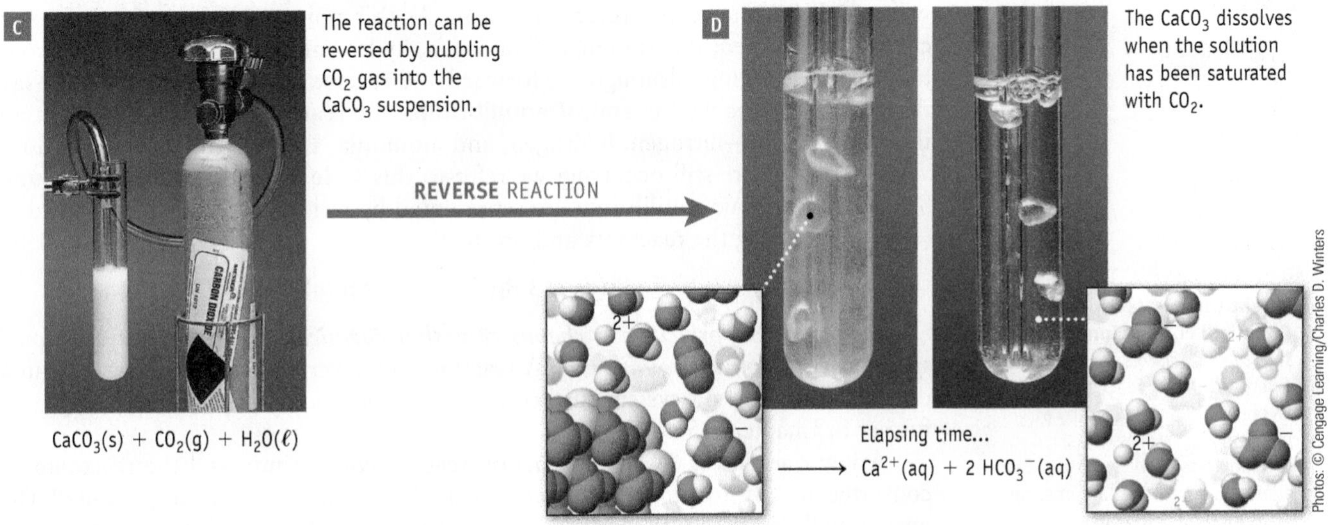

If CO_2 gas is bubbled into a suspension of $CaCO_3$, the reverse reaction occurs. That is, solid $CaCO_3$ and gaseous CO_2 react to produce Ca^{2+} and HCO_3^- ions in solution.

FIGURE 3.5 **The reversibility of chemical reactions.** The experiments here demonstrate the reversibility of chemical reactions.

$$Ca^{2+}(aq) + 2\,HCO_3^-(aq) \rightleftharpoons CaCO_3(s) + CO_2(g) + H_2O(\ell)$$

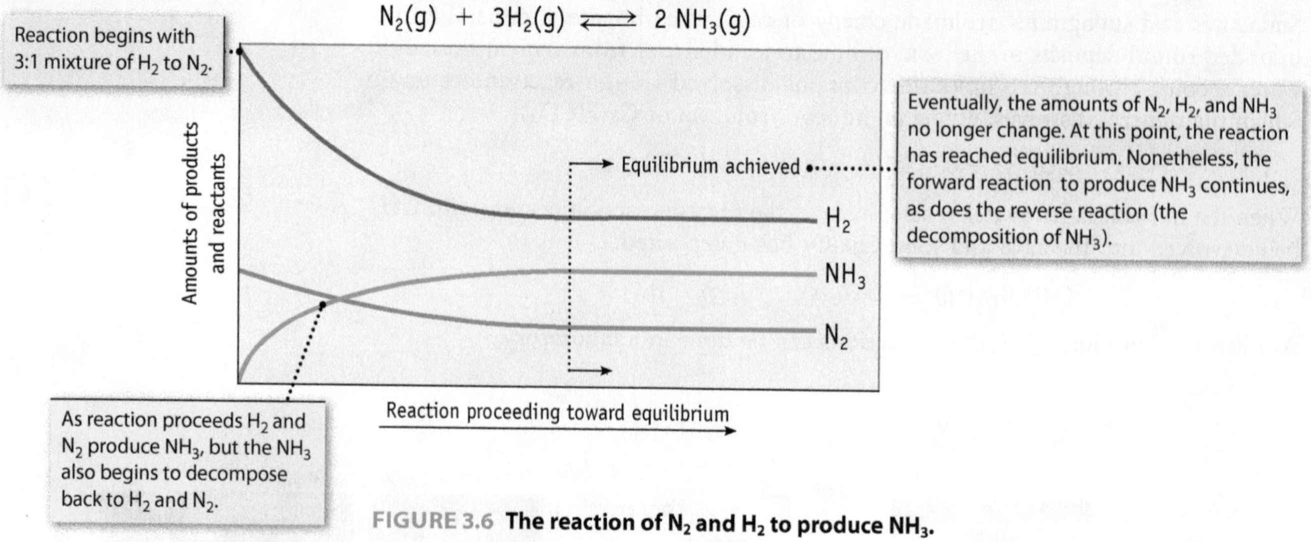

FIGURE 3.6 The reaction of N_2 and H_2 to produce NH_3.

Another example of a reversible reaction is the reaction of nitrogen with hydrogen to form ammonia gas, a compound made industrially in enormous quantities and used directly as a fertilizer and in the production of other chemicals.

$$N_2(g) + 3\ H_2(g) \rightarrow 2\ NH_3(g)$$

Nitrogen and hydrogen react to form ammonia, but, under the conditions of the reaction, ammonia also breaks down into nitrogen and hydrogen in the reverse reaction.

$$2\ NH_3(g) \rightarrow N_2(g) + 3\ H_2(g)$$

Let us consider what would happen if we mixed nitrogen and hydrogen in a closed container under the proper conditions for the reaction to occur. At first, N_2 and H_2 react to produce some ammonia. As the ammonia is produced, however, some NH_3 molecules decompose to re-form nitrogen and hydrogen in the reverse reaction (Figure 3.6). At the beginning of the process, the forward reaction to give NH_3 predominates, but, as the reactants are consumed, the rate (or speed) of the forward reaction progressively slows. At the same time, the reverse reaction speeds up as the amount of ammonia increases. Eventually, the rate of the forward reaction will equal the rate of the reverse reaction. At this point, no further *macroscopic* change is observed; the amounts of nitrogen, hydrogen, and ammonia in the container stop changing (although the forward and reverse reactions continue). We say the system has reached **chemical equilibrium**. The reaction vessel will contain all three substances—nitrogen, hydrogen, and ammonia. Because the forward and reverse processes are still occurring we refer to this state as a **dynamic equilibrium**. Systems in dynamic equilibrium are represented by writing a double arrow symbol ($\rightleftharpoons$) connecting the reactants and products.

$$N_2(g) + 3\ H_2(g) \rightleftharpoons 2\ NH_3(g)$$

An important principle in chemistry is that chemical reactions always proceed spontaneously toward equilibrium. A reaction will never proceed spontaneously in a direction that takes a system further from equilibrium. (This principle is explored further in Chapters 15 and 18.)

A key question is "When a reaction reaches equilibrium, will the reactants be converted largely to products or will most of the reactants still be present?" The answer will depend on the nature of the substances involved, the temperature, and other factors, and that is also the subject of later chapters (▶ Chapters 15–18). For the present, though, it is useful to define **product-favored reactions** as *reactions in which reactants are completely or largely converted to products when equilibrium is reached.* The combustion reactions we have been studying are examples of reactions

Quantitative Description of Chemical Equilibrium As you shall see in Chapters 15–18, the extent to which a reaction is product-favored can be described by a mathematical expression called the *equilibrium constant expression*. Each chemical reaction has a numerical value for the equilibrium constant, symbolized by *K*. Product-favored reactions have large values of *K*; small *K* values indicate reactant-favored reactions. For the ionization of acetic acid in water, $K = 1.8 \times 10^{-5}$.

that are product-favored at equilibrium. In fact, most of the reactions you will study in the rest of this chapter are product-favored reactions at equilibrium. We usually write the equations for reactions that are very product-favored using a single arrow (→) connecting reactants and products.

The opposite of a product-favored reaction is one that is **reactant-favored** at equilibrium. Such reactions lead to the conversion of only a small amount of the reactants to products. An example of a reactant-favored reaction is the ionization of acetic acid in water where only a tiny fraction of the acid produces ions.

$$CH_3CO_2H(aq) \quad + \quad H_2O(\ell) \quad \rightleftharpoons \quad CH_3CO_2^-(aq) \quad + \quad H_3O^+(aq)$$

Acetic acid is an example of a large number of acids called "weak acids" because the reaction with water is reactant-favored at equilibrium and only a few percent of the molecules react with water to form ionic products. You will learn more about this in Section 3-6 and Chapters 15–18.

REVIEW & CHECK FOR SECTION 3-3

1. Which of the following statements about chemical equilibrium is *not* true?
   (a) At equilibrium the rates of the forward and reverse reactions are equal.
   (b) There is no observable change in a chemical system at equilibrium.
   (c) Chemical reactions always proceed toward equilibrium.
   (d) All chemical reactions are product-favored at equilibrium.

3-4 Aqueous Solutions

Learning Objectives: LO 2.1, LO 3.1, LO 3.2, LO 3.10 (see APEC Lab 9 "Actions, Reactions, and Interactions")

Many of the reactions you will study in your chemistry course and almost all of the reactions that occur in living things are carried out in solutions in which the reacting substances are dissolved in water. In Chapter 1, we defined a **solution** as a homogeneous mixture of two or more substances. One substance is generally considered the **solvent**, the medium in which another substance—the **solute**—is dissolved. The remainder of this chapter is an introduction to some of the types of reactions that occur in **aqueous solutions**, solutions in which *water* is the solvent. First, it is important to understand something about the behavior of compounds dissolved in water (Figure 3.7).

Ions and Molecules in Aqueous Solutions

Dissolving an ionic solid requires separating each ion from the oppositely charged ions that surround it in the solid state (see Figure 3.7). Water is especially good at dissolving ionic compounds because each water molecule has a positively charged end and a negatively charged end. When an ionic compound dissolves in water, each negative ion becomes surrounded by water molecules with the positive ends of water molecules pointing toward it, and each positive ion becomes surrounded by the negative ends of several water molecules. The forces involved are best described by Coulomb's Law (Equation 2.3).

The water-encased ions produced by dissolving an ionic compound are free to move about in solution. Under normal conditions, the movement of ions is random,

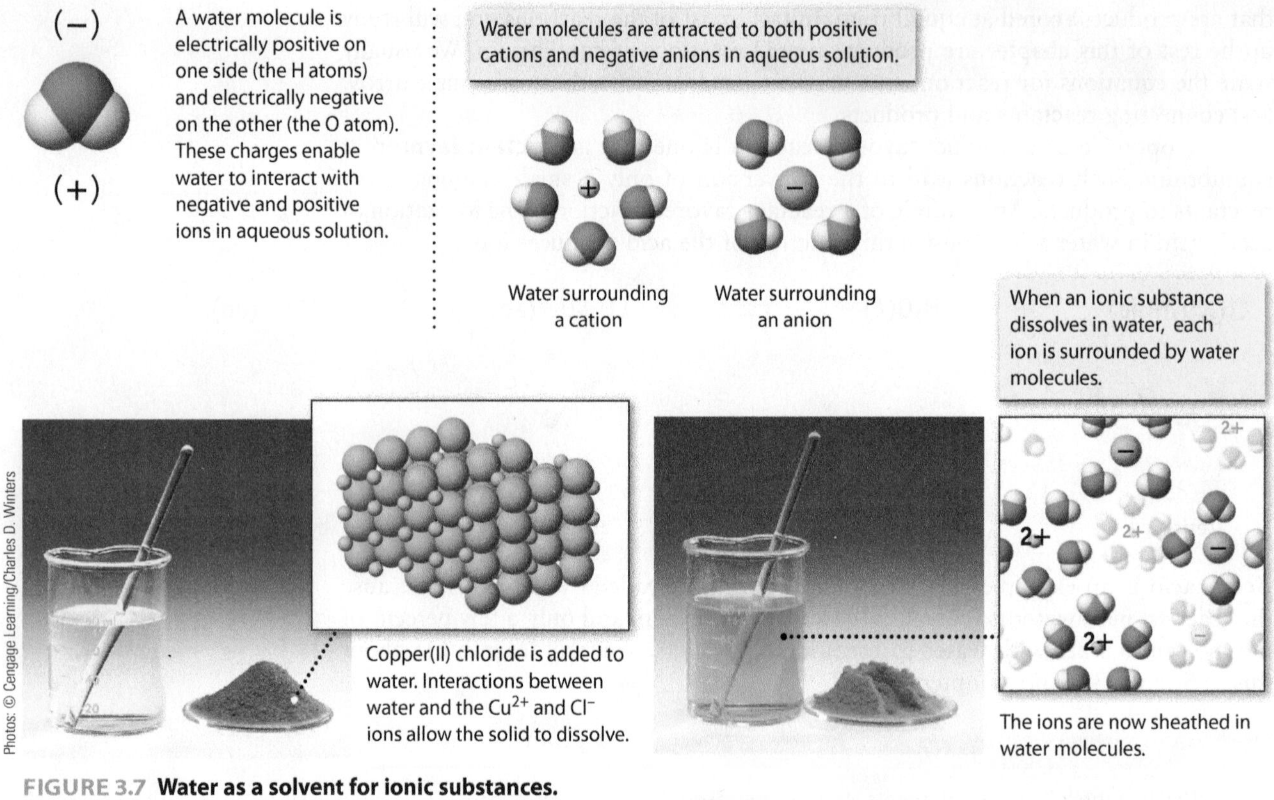

FIGURE 3.7 Water as a solvent for ionic substances.

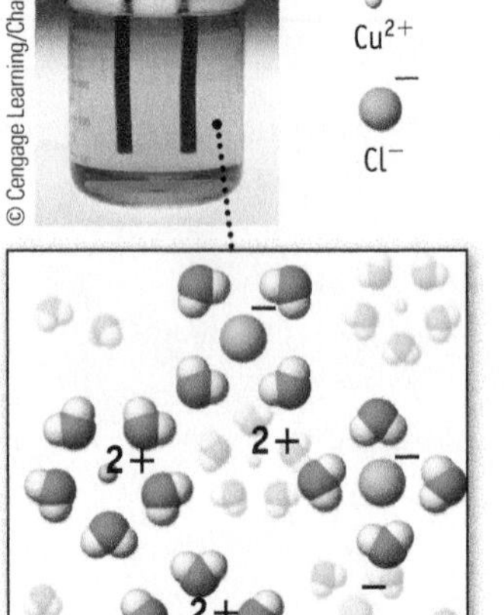

FIGURE 3.8a A **strong electrolyte** conducts electricity. $CuCl_2$ is completely dissociated into Cu^{2+} and Cl^- ions.

and the cations and anions from a dissolved ionic compound are dispersed uniformly throughout the solution. However, if two **electrodes** (conductors of electricity such as copper wire) are placed in the solution and connected to a battery, positive cations are drawn toward the negative electrode and negative anions are drawn toward the positive electrode (Figure 3.8).

Compounds whose aqueous solutions conduct electricity are called **electrolytes.** *All ionic compounds that are soluble in water are electrolytes.* The extent to which a solution conducts electricity, its conductivity, depends on the ion concentration. You can test the conductivity of a solution by inserting a lightbulb in the circuit, as was done in Figure 3.8. The greater the ion concentration, the greater the conductivity, and the brighter the bulb will glow.

For every mole of NaCl that dissolves, 1 mol of Na^+ and 1 mol of Cl^- ions enter the solution.

$$\mathrm{NaCl(s)} \rightarrow \mathrm{Na^+(aq)} + \mathrm{Cl^-(aq)}$$

100% Dissociation → strong electrolyte

Because the solute has dissociated (broken apart) completely into ions, there will be a significant concentration of ions in the solution, and the solution will be a good conductor of electricity. Substances whose solutions are good electrical conductors are called **strong electrolytes** (see Figure 3.8a). The ions into which an ionic compound will dissociate are given by the compound's name, and the relative amounts of these ions are given by its formula. For example, as we have seen, sodium chloride yields sodium ions (Na^+) and chloride ions (Cl^-) in solution in a 1 : 1 ratio. The ionic compound barium chloride, $BaCl_2$, is also a strong electrolyte. In this case there are two chloride ions for each barium ion in solution.

$$\mathrm{BaCl_2(s)} \rightarrow \mathrm{Ba^{2+}(aq)} + 2\ \mathrm{Cl^-(aq)}$$

Notice that the two chloride ions per formula unit are present as two separate particles in solution; they are not present as diatomic particles, Cl_2^{2-}. In yet another example, the ionic compound barium nitrate yields barium ions and nitrate ions in solution. For each Ba^{2+} ion in solution, there are two NO_3^- ions.

$$Ba(NO_3)_2(s) \rightarrow Ba^{2+}(aq) + 2\ NO_3^-(aq)$$

Notice also that NO_3^-, a polyatomic ion, does not dissociate further; the ion exists as one unit in aqueous solution.

Compounds whose aqueous solutions do not conduct electricity are called **nonelectrolytes** (see Figure 3.8b). The solute particles present in these aqueous solutions are molecules, not ions. *Most molecular compounds that dissolve in water are nonelectrolytes.* For example, when the molecular compound ethanol (C_2H_5OH) dissolves in water, each molecule of ethanol stays together as a single unit. We do not get ions in the solution. Other examples of nonelectrolytes are sucrose ($C_{12}H_{22}O_{11}$) and antifreeze (ethylene glycol, $HOCH_2CH_2OH$).

Some molecular compounds (strong acids, weak acids, and weak bases) can react with water to produce ions in aqueous solutions and are thus electrolytes. One example is gaseous hydrogen chloride, a molecular compound, which reacts with water to form ions. The solution is referred to as hydrochloric acid.

$$HCl(g) + H_2O(\ell) \rightarrow H_3O^+(aq) + Cl^-(aq)$$

This reaction is very product-favored. Each molecule of HCl produces ions in solution, so hydrochloric acid is a strong electrolyte.

Some molecular compounds are **weak electrolytes** (see Figure 3.8c). When these compounds dissolve in water only a small fraction of the molecules dissociate to form ions; the majority remains intact. These aqueous solutions are poor conductors of electricity (see Figure 3.8c). As described on page 105, the reaction of acetic acid with water is reactant-favored. In vinegar, an aqueous solution of acetic acid, only about 0.5% of the molecules of acetic acid are ionized to form acetate ($CH_3CO_2^-$) and hydronium (H_3O^+) ions. Thus, aqueous acetic acid is a weak electrolyte.

$$CH_3CO_2H(aq) + H_2O(\ell) \rightleftharpoons CH_3CO_2^-(aq) + H_3O^+(aq)$$

Figure 3.9 summarizes whether a given type of solute will be present in aqueous solution as ions, molecules, or a combination of ions and molecules.

Solubility of Ionic Compounds in Water

Many ionic compounds are soluble in water, but some dissolve only to a small extent; still others are essentially insoluble. Fortunately, we can make some general statements about which ionic compounds are water-soluble. In this chapter, we consider solubility as an "either-or" question, referring to those materials that are soluble beyond a certain extent as "soluble" and to those that do not dissolve to that extent as "insoluble." Solubilities vary widely, and to get a better idea of the amounts that will actually dissolve in a given quantity of water, we would need to do an experiment or perform a calculation that uses the concept of equilibrium (▶ Chapters 15–17).

Figure 3.10 gives broad guidelines that can help you to predict whether a particular ionic compound is soluble in water. For example, sodium nitrate, $NaNO_3$, contains an alkali metal cation, Na^+, and the nitrate anion, NO_3^-. The presence of *either* of these ions ensures that the compound is soluble in water; at 20 °C, over 90 g of $NaNO_3$ will dissolve in 100 mL of water. In contrast, calcium hydroxide is poorly soluble in water. If a spoonful of solid $Ca(OH)_2$ is added to 100 mL of water, less than one gram will dissolve at 20 °C. Nearly all of the $Ca(OH)_2$ remains as a solid (Figure 3.10c).

Nonelectrolyte

Bulb is not lit, showing solution does not conduct.

FIGURE 3.8B A **nonelectrolyte** does not conduct electricity because no ions are present in solution.

Weak Electrolyte

Bulb is dimly lit, showing solution conducts electricity poorly.

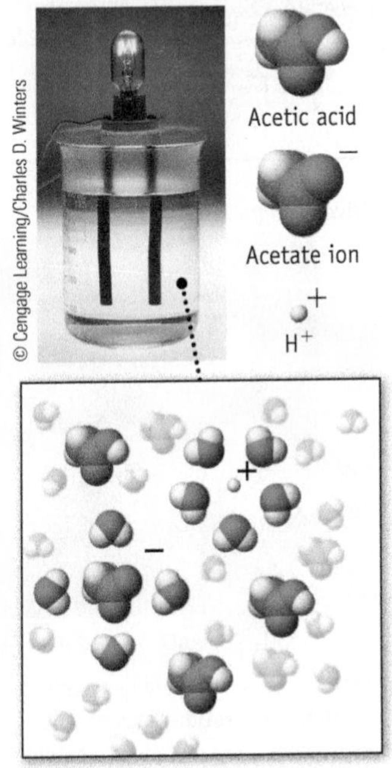

FIGURE 3.8C A **weak electrolyte** conducts electricity poorly because only a few ions are present in solution.

FIGURE 3.9 **Predicting the species present in aqueous solution.** When compounds dissolve in aqueous solution, ions may result from ionic or molecular compounds. Some molecular compounds may remain intact as molecules in solution. (Note that hydroxide-containing strong bases are ionic compounds.)

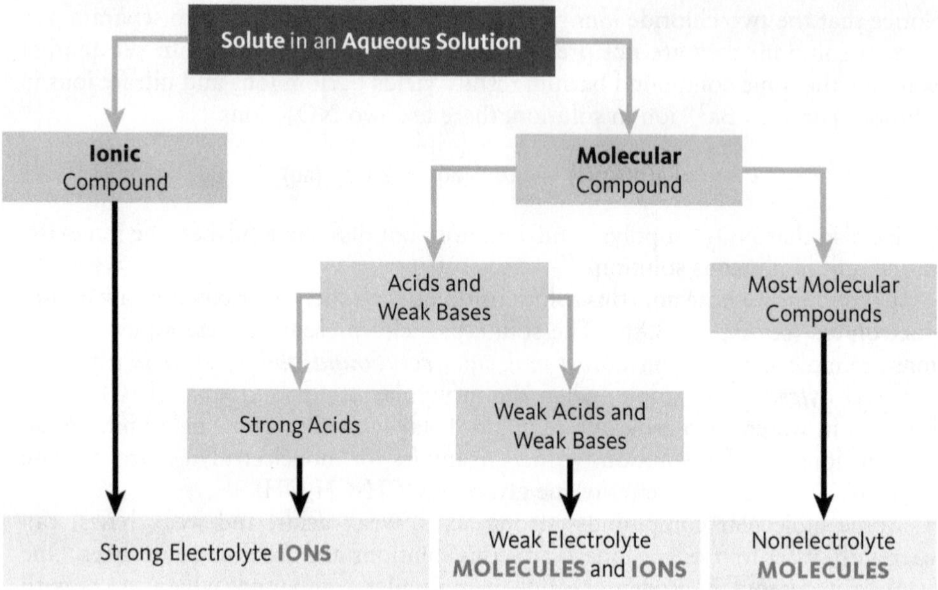

Soluble compounds				**Insoluble compounds**	
Almost all salts of Na^+, K^+, NH_4^+ *Salts of* nitrate, NO_3^- chlorate, ClO_3^- perchlorate, ClO_4^- acetate, $CH_3CO_2^-$	*Almost all salts of* Cl^-, Br^-, I^-	*Salts containing* F^-	*Salts of* sulfate, SO_4^{2-}	*Most salts of* carbonate, CO_3^{2-} phosphate, PO_4^{3-} oxalate, $C_2O_4^{2-}$ chromate, CrO_4^{2-} sulfide, S^{2-}	Most metal hydroxides and oxides
	Exceptions (not soluble) Halides of Ag^+, Hg_2^{2+}, Pb^{2+}	***Exceptions (not soluble)*** Fluorides of Mg^{2+}, Ca^{2+}, Sr^{2+}, Ba^{2+}, Pb^{2+}	***Exceptions (not soluble)*** Sulfates of Ca^{2+}, Sr^{2+}, Ba^{2+}, Pb^{2+}, Ag^+	***Exceptions (soluble)*** Salts of NH_4^+ and the alkali metal cations	***Exceptions (soluble)*** Alkali metal hydroxides and $Ba(OH)_2$ and $Sr(OH)_2$

Silver compounds **Sulfides** **Hydroxides**

$AgNO_3$ AgCl AgOH

(a) Nitrates are generally soluble, as are chlorides (exceptions include AgCl). Hydroxides are generally not soluble.

$(NH_4)_2S$ CdS Sb_2S_3 PbS

(b) Sulfides are generally not soluble (exceptions include salts with NH_4^+ and Na^+).

NaOH $Ca(OH)_2$ $Fe(OH)_3$ $Ni(OH)_2$

(c) Hydroxides are generally not soluble, except when the cation is a Group 1A metal (or Sr^{2+} or Ba^{2+}).

FIGURE 3.10 **Guidelines to predict the solubility of ionic compounds.** If a compound contains one of the ions in the column on the left in the top chart, it is predicted to be at least moderately soluble in water. Exceptions to the guidelines are highlighted.

EXAMPLE 3.2

Solubility Guidelines

Problem Predict whether the following ionic compounds are likely to be water-soluble. For soluble compounds, list the ions present in solution.

(a) KCl (b) $MgCO_3$ (c) Fe_2O_3 (d) $Cu(NO_3)_2$

What Do You Know? You know the formulas of the compounds but need to be able to identify the ions that make up each of them in order to use the solubility guidelines in Figure 3.10.

Strategy Decide the probable water solubility based on the solubility guidelines (see Figure 3.10). Soluble compounds will dissociate into their respective ions in solution.

Solution

(a) KCl is composed of K^+ and Cl^- ions. The presence of *either* of these ions means that the compound is likely to be soluble in water. The solution contains K^+ and Cl^- ions dissolved in water.

$$KCl(s) \rightarrow K^+(aq) + Cl^-(aq)$$

(The solubility of KCl is about 35 g in 100 mL of water at 20 °C.)

(b) Magnesium carbonate is composed of Mg^{2+} and CO_3^{2-} ions. Salts containing the carbonate ion usually are insoluble, unless combined with an ion like Na^+ or NH_4^+. Therefore, $MgCO_3$ is predicted to be insoluble in water. (The solubility of $MgCO_3$ is less than 0.2 g/100 mL of water.)

(c) Iron(III) oxide is composed of Fe^{3+} and O^{2-} ions. Oxides are soluble only when O^{2-} is combined with an alkali metal ion; Fe^{3+} is a transition metal ion, so Fe_2O_3 is insoluble.

(d) Copper(II) nitrate is composed of Cu^{2+} and NO_3^- ions. Nitrate salts are soluble, so this compound dissolves in water, giving ions in solution as shown in the equation below.

$$Cu(NO_3)_2(s) \rightarrow Cu^{2+}(aq) + 2\ NO_3^-(aq)$$

Think about Your Answer For chemists, a set of guidelines like those in Figure 3.10 is useful. If needed, accurate solubility information is available for many compounds in chemical resource books or online databases.

Check Your Understanding

Predict whether each of the following ionic compounds is likely to be soluble in water. If it is soluble, write the formulas of the ions present in aqueous solution.

(a) $LiNO_3$ (b) $CaCl_2$ (c) CuO (d) $NaCH_3CO_2$

Solubility Guidelines Observations such as those shown in Figure 3.10 were used to create the solubility guidelines. Note, however, that these are general guidelines. There are exceptions, but the guidelines are a good place to begin. See B. Blake, *Journal of Chemical Education*, Vol. 80, pp. 1348–1350, 2003.

REVIEW & CHECK FOR SECTION 3-4

1. Which of the compounds listed below is water-soluble?

   (a) $Ba(NO_3)_2$ (b) CuS (c) $Fe_3(PO_4)_2$ (d) $Mg(OH)_2$

2. Calcium nitrate dihydrate is dissolved in water. What ions are present in solution?

   (a) Ca^{2+} and $(NO_3)_2^{2-}$ (c) Ca^{2+} and NO_3^{2-}

   (b) Ca^{2+} and 2 NO_3^- (d) Ca^+ and NO_3^-

3. A 1-g sample of each of the four compounds listed below was placed in a beaker with 100 mL of water. The mixture was then tested to see if it conducted an electric current. Which solution was a weak conductor of electricity?

   (a) ethanol (b) acetic acid (c) NaCl (d) NaOH

Learning Objectives: LO 2.1, LO 3.1, LO 3.2, LO 3.10 (see APEC Lab 9 "Actions, Reactions, and Interactions")

3-5 Precipitation Reactions

Now that you can predict whether compounds will yield ions or molecules when they dissolve in water and whether ionic compounds are soluble or insoluble in water, we can begin to discuss the chemical reactions that occur in aqueous solutions. We will introduce you to four major categories of reactions: precipitation, acid–base, gas-forming, and oxidation–reduction reactions.

As you learn about these reactions, it will be useful to look for patterns that can help you to predict the reaction products. You will notice that precipitation, acid–base, and many gas-forming (but not oxidation–reduction) reactions are **exchange reactions** (sometimes called double displacement, double replacement, or metathesis reactions) in which *the ions of the reactants exchange partners.*

$$A^+B^- + C^+D^- \longrightarrow A^+D^- + C^+B^-$$

For example, aqueous solutions of silver nitrate and potassium chloride react to produce solid silver chloride and aqueous potassium nitrate (Figure 3.11).

$$AgNO_3(aq) + KCl(aq) \rightarrow AgCl(s) + KNO_3(aq)$$

Reactants	**Products**
$Ag^+(aq) + NO_3^-(aq)$	Insoluble $AgCl(s)$
$K^+(aq) + Cl^-(aq)$	$K^+(aq) + NO_3^-(aq)$

This particular reaction is an example of a **precipitation reaction**, because the reaction produces a **precipitate**, a water-insoluble solid product. The reactants in such reactions are generally water-soluble ionic compounds. If the cation from one reactant can form an insoluble compound with the anion from the other reactant, precipitation occurs when they are mixed.

Predicting the Outcome of a Precipitation Reaction

Many combinations of positive and negative ions give insoluble substances. For example, the solubility guidelines in Figure 3.10 indicate that most compounds

FIGURE 3.11 Precipitation of silver chloride.

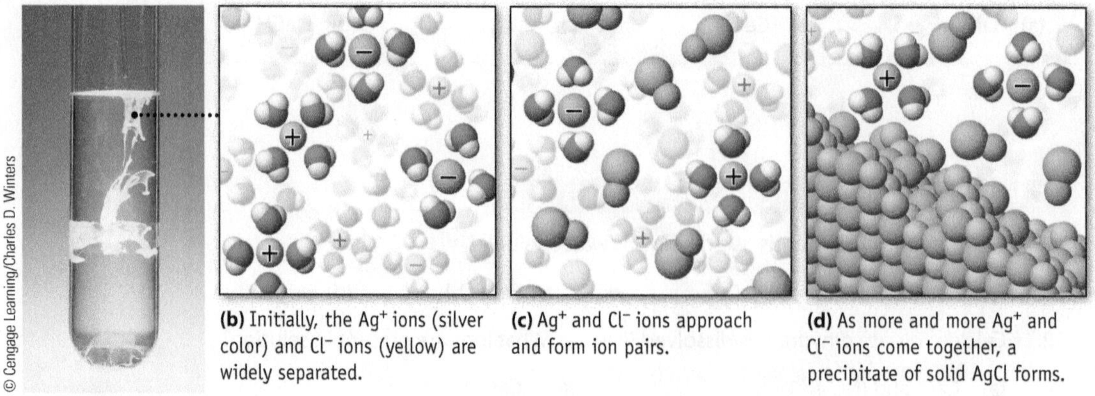

(b) Initially, the Ag^+ ions (silver color) and Cl^- ions (yellow) are widely separated.

(c) Ag^+ and Cl^- ions approach and form ion pairs.

(d) As more and more Ag^+ and Cl^- ions come together, a precipitate of solid AgCl forms.

(a) Mixing aqueous solutions of silver nitrate and potassium chloride produces white, insoluble silver chloride, AgCl.

FIGURE 3.12 Precipitation reactions.

Photos: © Cengage Learning/Charles D. Winters

$PbCrO_4$ from $Pb(NO_3)_2$ and K_2CrO_4 | **PbS** from $Pb(NO_3)_2$ and $(NH_4)_2S$ | **$Fe(OH)_3$** from $FeCl_3$ and NaOH | **Ag_2CrO_4** from $AgNO_3$ and K_2CrO_4

containing the chromate ion. CrO_4^{2-} are not soluble (alkali metal chromates and ammonium chromate are exceptions). Thus, we can predict that solid yellow lead(II) chromate will precipitate when a water-soluble lead(II) compound is combined with a water-soluble chromate compound (Figure 3.12).

$$Pb(NO_3)_2(aq) + K_2CrO_4(aq) \rightarrow PbCrO_4(s) + 2\ KNO_3(aq)$$

Reactants	**Products**
$Pb^{2+}(aq) + 2\ NO_3^-(aq)$	Insoluble $PbCrO_4(s)$
$2\ K^+(aq) + CrO_4^{2-}(aq)$	$2\ K^+(aq) + 2\ NO_3^-(aq)$

Similarly, we know from the solubility guidelines that almost all metal sulfides are insoluble in water (see Figure 3.12). If a solution of a soluble metal compound comes in contact with a source of sulfide ions, the metal sulfide precipitates.

$$Pb(NO_3)_2(aq) + (NH_4)_2S(aq) \rightarrow PbS(s) + 2\ NH_4NO_3(aq)$$

Reactants	**Products**
$Pb^{2+}(aq) + 2\ NO_3^-(aq)$	Insoluble $PbS(s)$
$2\ NH_4^+(aq) + S^{2-}(aq)$	$2\ NH_4^+(aq) + 2\ NO_3^-(aq)$

In yet another example, the solubility guidelines indicate that with the exception of the alkali metal cations (and Sr^{2+} and Ba^{2+}), metal cations form insoluble hydroxides. Thus, water-soluble iron(III) chloride and sodium hydroxide react to give insoluble iron(III) hydroxide (see Figures 3.10c and 3.12).

$$FeCl_3(aq) + 3\ NaOH(aq) \rightarrow Fe(OH)_3(s) + 3\ NaCl(aq)$$

Reactants	**Products**
$Fe^{3+}(aq) + 3\ Cl^-(aq)$	Insoluble $Fe(OH)_3(s)$
$3\ Na^+(aq) + 3\ OH^-(aq)$	$3\ Na^+(aq) + 3\ Cl^-(aq)$

EXAMPLE 3.3

Writing the Equation for a Precipitation Reaction

Problem Is an insoluble product formed when aqueous solutions of potassium chromate and silver nitrate are mixed? If so, write the balanced equation.

What Do You Know? Names of the two reactants are given. You should recognize that this is an exchange reaction, and you will need the information on solubilities in Figure 3.10.

Strategy

- Determine the formulas from the names of the reactants and identify the ions that make up these compounds.
- Write formulas for the products in this reaction by exchanging cations and anions and determine whether either product is insoluble using information in Figure 3.10.
- Write and balance the equation.

Solution The reactants are $AgNO_3$ and K_2CrO_4. The possible products of the exchange reaction are silver chromate (Ag_2CrO_4) and potassium nitrate (KNO_3). Based on the solubility guidelines, we know that silver chromate is an insoluble compound (chromates are insoluble except for those with Group 1A metals), and potassium nitrate is soluble in water. A precipitate of silver chromate will therefore form if these reactants are mixed.

$$2\ AgNO_3(aq) + K_2CrO_4(aq) \rightarrow Ag_2CrO_4(s) + 2\ KNO_3(aq)$$

Think about Your Answer This reaction is illustrated in Figure 3.12.

Check Your Understanding

In each of the following cases, does a precipitation reaction occur when solutions of the two water-soluble reactants are mixed? Give the formula of any precipitate that forms, and write a balanced chemical equation for the precipitation reactions that occur.

(a) sodium carbonate and copper(II) chloride

(b) potassium carbonate and sodium nitrate

(c) nickel(II) chloride and potassium hydroxide

Net Ionic Equations

We have seen that when aqueous solutions of silver nitrate and potassium chloride are mixed, insoluble silver chloride forms, leaving potassium nitrate in solution (see Figure 3.11). The balanced chemical equation for this process is

$$AgNO_3(aq) + KCl(aq) \rightarrow AgCl(s) + KNO_3(aq)$$

We can represent this reaction in another way by writing an equation in which we show that the *soluble* ionic compounds are present in solution as dissociated ions. An aqueous solution of silver nitrate contains Ag^+ and NO_3^- ions, and an aqueous solution of potassium chloride contains K^+ and Cl^- ions. In the products, potassium nitrate is present in solution as K^+ and NO_3^- ions. Silver chloride, however, is insoluble and thus is not present in the solution as dissociated ions. It is shown in the equation by AgCl(s).

$$\underbrace{Ag^+(aq) + NO_3^-(aq) + K^+(aq) + Cl^-(aq)}_{\text{before reaction}} \longrightarrow \underbrace{AgCl(s) + K^+(aq) + NO_3^-(aq)}_{\text{after reaction}}$$

This type of equation is called a **complete ionic equation**.

The K^+ and NO_3^- ions are present in solution both before and after reaction, so they appear on both the reactant and product sides of the complete ionic equation. Such ions are often called **spectator ions** because they do not participate in the net reaction; they only "look on" from the sidelines. Little chemical information is lost if the equation is written without them, so we can simplify the equation to

$$Ag^+(aq) + Cl^-(aq) \rightarrow AgCl(s)$$

The balanced equation that results from leaving out spectator ions is the **net ionic equation** for the reaction.

Leaving out spectator ions does not mean that K^+ and NO_3^- ions are unimportant in the $AgNO_3$ + KCl reaction. Indeed, Ag^+ ions cannot exist alone in solution;

Net Ionic Equations All chemical equations, including net ionic equations, must be balanced. The same number of atoms of each kind must appear on both the product and reactant sides. In addition, *the sum of positive and negative charges must be the same on both sides of the equation.*

PROBLEM SOLVING TIP 3.1
Writing Net Ionic Equations

Net ionic equations are commonly written for chemical reactions in aqueous solution because they describe the actual chemical species involved in a reaction. To write net ionic equations you must know which compounds exist as ions in solution.

1. Strong acids, strong bases, and soluble salts exist as ions in solution. Examples include the acids HCl and HNO_3, a base such as NaOH, and salts such as NaCl and $CuCl_2$.
2. All other species should be represented by their complete formulas. Weak acids such as acetic acid (CH_3CO_2H) exist in aqueous solutions primarily as molecules. (See Section 3-6.) Insoluble salts such as $CaCO_3$(s) or insoluble bases such as $Mg(OH)_2$(s) should not be written in ionic form, even though they are ionic compounds.

The best way to approach writing net ionic equations is to follow precisely a set of steps.

1. Write a complete, balanced equation. Indicate the state of each substance (aq, s, ℓ, g).
2. Next rewrite the whole equation, writing all strong acids, strong bases, and soluble salts as ions. (Consider only species labeled "(aq)" in this step.)
3. Some ions may remain unchanged in the reaction (the ions that appear in the equation both as reactants and products). These "spectator ions" are not part of the chemistry that is going on, and you can strike them from each side of the equation.
4. Net ionic equations must be balanced. The same number of atoms appears on each side of the arrow, and the sum of the ion charges on the two sides must also be equal.

a negative ion, in this case NO_3^-, must be present to balance the positive charge of Ag^+. Any anion will do, however, as long as it forms a water-soluble compound with Ag^+. Thus, we could have used $AgClO_4$ instead of $AgNO_3$. Similarly, there must be a positive ion present to balance the negative charge of Cl^-. In this case, the positive ion present is K^+ in KCl, but we could have used NaCl instead of KCl. The net ionic equation would have been the same.

Finally, notice that there must always be a *charge balance* as well as a mass balance in a balanced chemical equation. Thus, in the $Ag^+ + Cl^-$ net ionic equation, the cation and anion charges on the left add together to give a net charge of zero, the same as the zero charge on AgCl(s) on the right.

EXAMPLE 3.4
Writing and Balancing Net Ionic Equations

Problem Write a balanced, net ionic equation for the reaction of aqueous solutions of $BaCl_2$ and Na_2SO_4.

What Do You Know? The formulas for the reactants are given. You should recognize that this is an exchange reaction, and that you will need the information on solubilities in Figure 3.10.

Strategy Follow the strategy outlined in Problem Solving Tip 3.1.

Solution

Step 1. In this *exchange reaction*, the Ba^{2+} and Na^+ cations exchange anions (Cl^- and SO_4^{2-}) to give $BaSO_4$ and NaCl. Now that the reactants and products are known, we can write an equation for the reaction. To balance the equation, we place a 2 in front of the NaCl.

$$BaCl_2 + Na_2SO_4 \rightarrow BaSO_4 + 2\ NaCl$$

© Cengage Learning/Charles D. Winters

Precipitation reaction. The reaction of barium chloride and sodium sulfate produces insoluble barium sulfate and water-soluble sodium chloride. See Example 3.4.

Strategy Map 3.4

PROBLEM

Write **balanced net ionic equation** for the reaction of **$BaCl_2$ + Na_2SO_4**.

DATA/INFORMATION

The **formulas** of the **reactants** are given

STEP 1. Decide on **products** and then write **complete balanced equation.**

Complete balanced equation with ***reactants*** and ***products***

STEP 2. Decide if each reactant and product is **solid, liquid, gas,** or **dissolved in water.**

Complete balanced equation with **indication of state** of each reactant and product

STEP 3. Identify ions in solution.

Complete ionic equation with reactants and products **dissociated into ions** if appropriate

STEP 4. Eliminate spectator ions.

Balanced net ionic equation

Step 2. Decide on the solubility of each compound (see Figure 3.10). Compounds containing sodium ions are always water-soluble, as are those containing chloride ions (with some important exceptions). Sulfate salts are also usually soluble, one important exception being $BaSO_4$. We can therefore write

$$BaCl_2(aq) + Na_2SO_4(aq) \rightarrow BaSO_4(s) + 2\ NaCl(aq)$$

Step 3. Identify the ions in solution. All soluble ionic compounds dissociate to form ions in aqueous solution. Writing the soluble substances as ions in solution results in the following complete ionic equation:

$$Ba^{2+}(aq) + 2\ Cl^-(aq) + 2\ Na^+(aq) + SO_4^{2-}(aq) \rightarrow BaSO_4(s) + 2\ Na^+(aq) + 2\ Cl^-(aq)$$

Step 4. Identify and eliminate the spectator ions (Na^+ and Cl^-) to give the net ionic equation.

$$Ba^{2+}(aq) + SO_4^{2-}(aq) \rightarrow BaSO_4(s)$$

Think about Your Answer Notice that the sum of ion charges is the same on both sides of the equation. On the left, 2+ and 2− sum to zero; on the right the charge on $BaSO_4$ is also zero.

Check Your Understanding

In each of the following cases, aqueous solutions containing the compounds indicated are mixed. Write balanced net ionic equations for the reactions that occur.

(a) $CaCl_2 + Na_3PO_4$

(b) iron(III) chloride and potassium hydroxide (a similar reaction is shown in Figure 3.12)

(c) lead(II) nitrate and potassium chloride

REVIEW & CHECK FOR SECTION 3-5

1. Aqueous solutions of the two reactants listed below are mixed. In which solutions will a precipitate form?

   (1) $NaI(aq) + Pb(NO_3)_2(aq)$

   (2) $CaCl_2(aq) + Na_2CO_3(aq)$

   (3) $H_2SO_4(aq) + BaCl_2(aq)$

   (4) $NaOH(aq) + AgNO_3(aq)$

   (a) 1, 2, and 3 (b) 2 and 3 (c) 1, 2, and 4 (d) 1, 2, 3, and 4

2. What is the net ionic equation for the reaction of $AgNO_3(aq)$ and $Na_2CO_3(aq)$?

   (a) $Ag^+(aq) + CO_3^{2-}(aq) \rightarrow AgCO_3(s)$

   (b) $Na^+(aq) + NO_3^-(aq) \rightarrow NaNO_3(s)$

   (c) $2\ Ag^+(aq) + CO_3^{2-}(aq) \rightarrow Ag_2CO_3(s)$

   (d) $AgNO_3(aq) + Na_2CO_3(aq) \rightarrow 2\ NaNO_3(aq) + Ag_2CO_3(s)$

3-6 Acids and Bases

Learning Objectives: LO 2.2, LO 3.1, LO 3.2, LO 3.7, LO 3.10 (see APEC Lab 9 "Actions, Reactions, and Interactions")

Acids and bases are two important classes of compounds. You may already be familiar with some common properties of acids. They produce bubbles of CO_2 gas when added to a metal carbonate such as $CaCO_3$ (Figure 3.13a), and they react with many metals to produce hydrogen gas (H_2) (Figure 3.13b). Although tasting substances is *never* done in a chemistry laboratory, you have probably experienced the sour taste of acids such as acetic acid in vinegar and citric acid (commonly found in fruits and added to candies and soft drinks).

Photos: © Cengage Learning/Charles D. Winters

(a) A piece of coral (mostly $CaCO_3$) dissolves in acid to give CO_2 gas.

(b) Zinc reacts with hydrochloric acid to produce zinc chloride and hydrogen gas.

(c) An extract of red rose petals turns deep red on adding acid but turns green on adding base.

FIGURE 3.13 **Some properties of acids and bases.**

Acids and bases have some related properties. Solutions of acids or bases, for example, can change the colors of natural pigments (Figure 3.13c). You may have seen acids change the color of litmus, a dye derived from certain lichens, from blue to red. Adding a base reverses the effect, making the litmus blue again. Thus, acids and bases seem to be opposites. A base can neutralize the effect of an acid, and an acid can neutralize the effect of a base. Table 3.1 lists common acids and bases.

Table 3.1 Common Acids and Bases*

Strong Acids (Strong Electrolytes)		**Soluble Strong Bases (Strong Electrolytes)****	
HCl	Hydrochloric acid	LiOH	Lithium hydroxide
HBr	Hydrobromic acid	NaOH	Sodium hydroxide
HI	Hydroiodic acid	KOH	Potassium hydroxide
HNO_3	Nitric acid	$Ba(OH)_2$	Barium hydroxide
$HClO_4$	Perchloric acid	$Sr(OH)_2$	Strontium hydroxide
H_2SO_4	Sulfuric acid		
Weak Acids (Weak Electrolytes)		**Weak Base (Weak Electrolyte)**	
HF	Hydrofluoric acid	NH_3	Ammonia
H_3PO_4	Phosphoric acid		
H_2CO_3	Carbonic acid		
CH_3CO_2H	Acetic acid		
$H_2C_2O_4$	Oxalic acid		
$H_2C_4H_4O_6$	Tartaric acid		
$H_3C_6H_5O_7$	Citric acid		
$HC_9H_7O_4$	Aspirin		

*The electrolytic behavior refers to aqueous solutions of these acids and bases.

**$Mg(OH)_2$ and $Ca(OH)_2$ are often listed as strong bases, although they are poorly soluble.

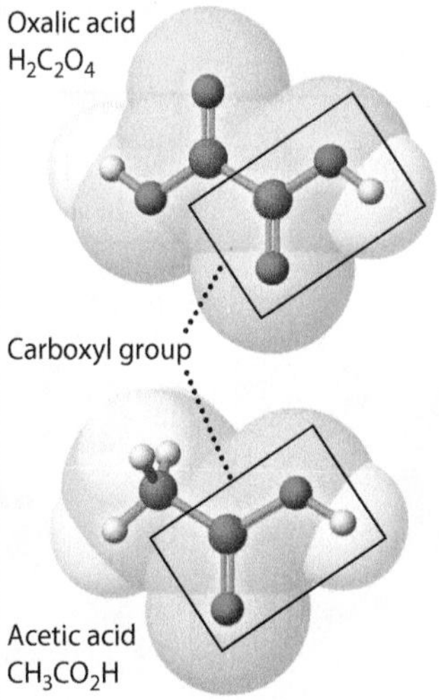

Weak Acids Common acids and bases are listed in Table 3.1. There are numerous other weak acids and bases, and many are natural substances. Many of the natural acids such as oxalic and acetic acids, contain CO_2H or carboxyl groups. (The H of this group is lost as H^+.)

Over the years, chemists have examined the properties, chemical structures, and reactions of acids and bases and have proposed different definitions of the terms *acid* and *base*. In this section, we shall examine the two most commonly used definitions, one proposed by Svante Arrhenius (1859–1927) and another proposed by Johannes N. Brønsted (1879–1947) and Thomas M. Lowry (1874–1936).

Acids and Bases: The Arrhenius Definition

In the late 1800s, the Swedish chemist Svante Arrhenius proposed that acids and bases dissolve in water and ultimately form ions. This theory predated any knowledge of the composition and structure of atoms and was not well accepted initially. With a knowledge of atomic structure, however, we now take it for granted.

The Arrhenius definition for acids and bases focuses on formation of H^+ and OH^- ions in aqueous solutions.

- An acid is a substance that, when dissolved in water, increases the concentration of hydrogen ions, H^+, in solution.

$$HCl(g) \rightarrow H^+(aq) + Cl^-(aq)$$

- A base is a substance that, when dissolved in water, increases the concentration of hydroxide ions, OH^-, in the solution.

$$NaOH(s) \rightarrow Na^+(aq) + OH^-(aq)$$

- The reaction of an acid and a base produces a salt and water. Because the characteristic properties of an acid are lost when a base is added, and vice versa, acid–base reactions were logically described as resulting from the combination of H^+ and OH^- to form water.

$$HCl(aq) + NaOH(aq) \rightarrow NaCl(aq) + H_2O(\ell)$$

Arrhenius further proposed that acid strength was related to the extent to which the acid ionized. Some acids such as hydrochloric acid (HCl) and nitric acid (HNO_3) ionize completely in water; they are strong electrolytes, and we now call them **strong acids**. Other acids such as acetic acid and hydrofluoric acid are incompletely ionized; they are weak electrolytes and are **weak acids**. Weak acids exist in solution primarily as molecules, and only a fraction of these molecules ionize to produce $H^+(aq)$ ions along with the appropriate anion.

Water-soluble compounds that contain hydroxide ions, such as sodium hydroxide (NaOH) and potassium hydroxide (KOH), are strong electrolytes and **strong bases**.

Aqueous ammonia, $NH_3(aq)$, is a weak electrolyte. Even though it does not have an OH^- ion as part of its formula, it does produce ammonium ions and hydroxide ions from its reaction with water and so is a base (Figure 3.14). The fact that this is a weak electrolyte indicates that this reaction with water to form ions is reactant-favored at equilibrium. Most of the ammonia remains in solution in molecular form.

$$NH_3(aq) + H_2O(\ell) \rightleftharpoons NH_4^+(aq) + OH^-(aq)$$

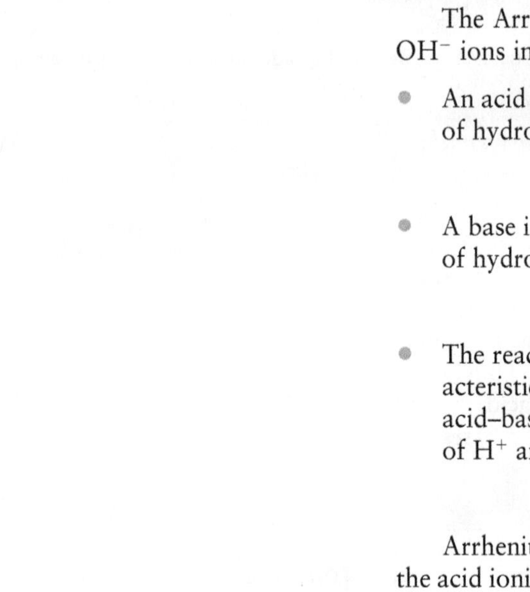

FIGURE 3.14 **Ammonia, a weak electrolyte.** The name on the bottle, ammonium hydroxide, is misleading. The solution consists almost entirely of NH_3 molecules dissolved in water. It is better referred to as "aqueous ammonia."

Although the Arrhenius theory is still used to some extent and is interesting in an historical context, modern concepts of acid–base chemistry such as the Brønsted–Lowry theory have gained preference among chemists.

Acids and Bases: The Brønsted–Lowry Definition

In 1923, Johannes Brønsted (1879–1947) in Copenhagen, Denmark, and Thomas Lowry (1874–1936) in Cambridge, England, independently suggested a new concept of acid and base behavior. They viewed acids and bases in terms of the transfer of a proton (H^+) from one species to another, and they described all acid–base reactions in terms of equilibria. The Brønsted–Lowry theory expanded the scope of the definition of acids and bases and helped chemists make predictions of product- or reactant-favorability based on acid and base strength. We will describe this theory here qualitatively; a more complete discussion will be given in Chapter 16.

The main concepts of the Brønsted–Lowry theory are the following:

- *An acid is a proton donor.* This is similar to the Arrhenius definition.
- *A base is a proton acceptor.* This definition includes the OH^- ion but it also broadens the number and type of bases to include anions derived from acids as well as neutral compounds such as ammonia.
- *An acid–base reaction involves the transfer of a proton from an acid to a base to form a new acid and a new base.*

From the point of view of the Brønsted–Lowry theory, the behavior of acids such as HCl or CH_3CO_2H in water is written as an acid–base reaction. Both species (both Brønsted acids) donate a proton to water (a Brønsted base) forming $H_3O^+(aq)$, the hydronium ion.

Hydrochloric acid, HCl(aq), which we know to be a strong electrolyte and a strong acid, ionizes completely in aqueous solution; it is classified as a strong acid.

Hydrochloric acid, a strong acid. 100% ionized. Equilibrium strongly favors products.

$$HCl(aq) + H_2O(\ell) \rightleftharpoons H_3O^+(aq) + Cl^-(aq)$$

In contrast, CH_3CO_2H, a weak electrolyte and weak acid, ionizes only to a small extent.

Acetic acid, a weak acid, << 100% ionized. Equilibrium favors reactants.

$$CH_3CO_2H(aq) + H_2O(\ell) \rightleftharpoons CH_3CO_2^-(aq) + H_3O^+(aq)$$

Sulfuric acid, a *diprotic acid* (an acid capable of transferring two H^+ ions), reacts with water in two steps. The first step strongly favors products, whereas the second step is reactant-favored.

Strong acid: $H_2SO_4(aq) + H_2O(\ell) \rightleftharpoons H_3O^+(aq) + HSO_4^-(aq)$

sulfuric acid, 100% ionized; hydronium ion; hydrogen sulfate ion

Weak acid: $HSO_4^-(aq) + H_2O(\ell) \rightleftharpoons H_3O^+(aq) + SO_4^{2-}(aq)$

hydrogen sulfate ion, <100% ionized; hydronium ion; sulfate ion

Ammonia, a weak base, reacts with water to produce $OH^-(aq)$ ions. The reaction is reactant-favored at equilibrium.

A CLOSER LOOK

The Hydronium Ion—The H^+ Ion in Water

The term "hydrogen ion" and the symbol H^+ are sometimes used when discussing acids. In aqueous solution, however, a better representation is H_3O^+, called the **hydronium ion.** This ion is formed by combining H^+ and H_2O. Experiments show that other forms of the ion also exist in water, one example being $[H_3O(H_2O)_3]^+$.

There will be instances when, for simplicity, we will use $H^+(aq)$. However, in this book we will usually use the $H_3O^+(aq)$ symbol to represent the hydrogen ion in water. Thus, what we call hydrochloric acid, HCl(aq), is better represented as a solution of H_3O^+ and Cl^- with both ions cloaked in a sheath of water molecules.

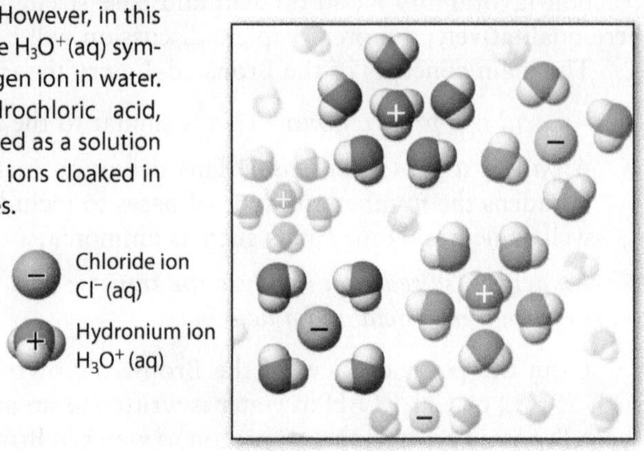

Representation of a solution of the strong acid HCl.

Ammonia, a weak base, << 100% ionized. Equilibrium favors reactants.

$$NH_3(aq) + H_2O(\ell) \rightleftharpoons NH_4^+(aq) + OH^-(aq)$$

ammonia, base weak electrolyte < 100% ionized | water | ammonium ion | hydroxide ion

According to the Brønsted-Lowry theory, anions can add a proton and are thus classified as bases. In particular, anions of weak acids typically behave as weak bases, and basic solutions result from dissolving a salt containing the anion of a weak acid in water. For example, an aqueous solution of sodium acetate is basic because of the following reaction:

Acetate ion, weak base; equilibrium favors reactants.

$$CH_3CO_2^-(aq) + H_2O(\ell) \rightleftharpoons CH_3CO_2H(aq) + OH^-(aq)$$

acetate ion, a weak base | water | acetic acid molecules | hydroxide ion

Some species are described as **amphiprotic**, that is, they can function either as acids or as bases depending on the reaction. In the examples above, water functions as a base in reactions with acids (it accepts a proton) and as an acid in its reaction with ammonia (where it donates a proton to ammonia, forming the ammonium ion).

EXAMPLE 3.5

Brønsted Acids and Bases

Problem Write a balanced net ionic equation for the reaction that occurs when the cyanide ion, CN^-, accepts a proton (H^+) from water to form HCN. Is CN^- a Brønsted acid or base?

What Do You Know? You know the formulas of the reactants (CN^- and H_2O) and of one of the products, (HCN). You also know a proton transfer occurs from water to CN^-.

Strategy As it is a proton transfer, you should move an H^+ ion from H_2O to CN^- to give the products.

Solution

$$H_2O(\ell) + CN^-(aq) \rightleftharpoons OH^-(aq) + HCN(aq)$$

In this reaction water is the Brønsted acid and the CN^- ion is the Brønsted base.

Think about Your Answer The CN^- ion is a Brønsted base and so produces the OH^- ion in aqueous solution. In general, anions derived from weak acids produce basic solutions in water. This is described in more detail in Chapter 16.

Check Your Understanding

(a) Write a balanced equation for the reaction that occurs when H_3PO_4, phosphoric acid, donates a proton to water to form the dihydrogen phosphate ion.

(b) Write a net ionic equation showing the dihydrogen phosphate ion acting as a Brønsted acid in a reaction with water. Write another net ionic equation showing the dihydrogen phosphate ion acting as a Brønsted base in a reaction with water. What term is used to describe a species such as the dihydrogen phosphate ion that can act both as an acid or as a base?

Reactions of Acids and Bases

Acids and bases in aqueous solution usually react to produce a salt and water. For example (Figure 3.15),

$$\underset{\text{hydrochloric acid}}{HCl(aq)} + \underset{\text{sodium hydroxide}}{NaOH(aq)} \longrightarrow \underset{\text{water}}{H_2O(\ell)} + \underset{\text{sodium chloride}}{NaCl(aq)}$$

The word "salt" has come into the language of chemistry to describe any ionic compound whose cation comes from a base (here Na^+ from NaOH) and whose anion comes from an acid (here Cl^- from HCl). The reaction of any of the acids listed in Table 3.1 with any of the listed hydroxide-containing bases produces a salt and water.

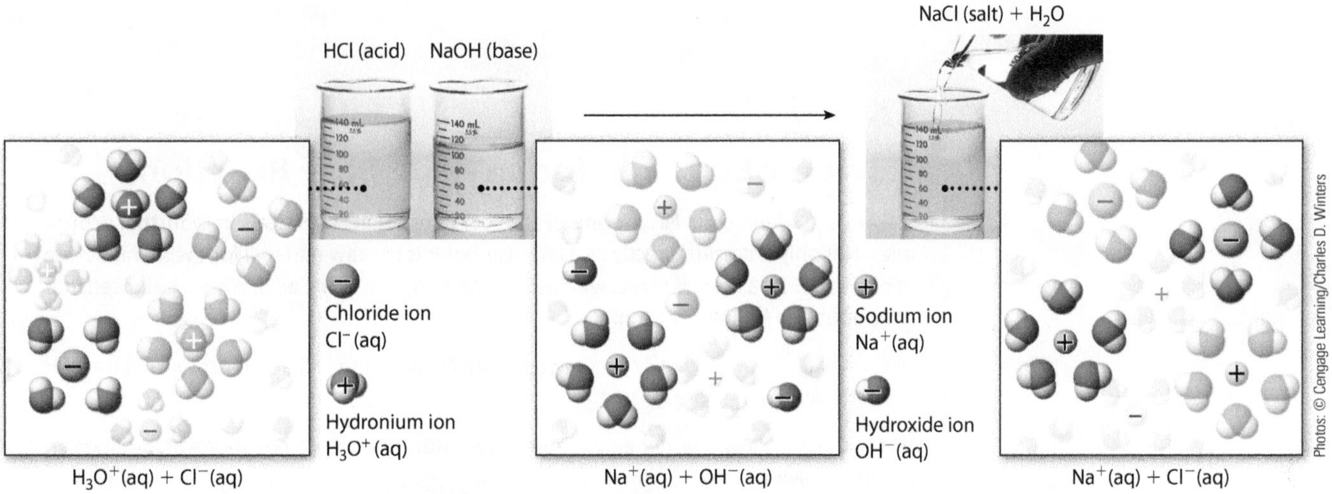

FIGURE 3.15 An acid-base reaction, HCl and NaOH. On mixing, the H_3O^+ and OH^- ions combine to produce H_2O, whereas the ions Na^+ and Cl^- remain in solution.

Hydrochloric acid and sodium hydroxide are strong electrolytes in water (see Figure 3.15 and Table 3.1), so the complete ionic equation for the reaction of HCl(aq) and NaOH(aq) is written as

$$\underbrace{H_3O^+(aq) + Cl^-(aq)}_{\text{from HCl(aq)}} + \underbrace{Na^+(aq) + OH^-(aq)}_{\text{from NaOH(aq)}} \longrightarrow \underset{\text{water}}{2\ H_2O(\ell)} + \underbrace{Na^+(aq) + Cl^-(aq)}_{\text{from salt}}$$

Because Na^+ and Cl^- ions appear on both sides of the equation they can be cancelled out, and the *net ionic equation* is just the combination of the ions H_3O^+ and OH^- to give water.

$$H_3O^+(aq) + OH^-(aq) \rightarrow 2\ H_2O(\ell)$$

This is always the net ionic equation when a strong acid reacts with a strong base.

Reactions between strong acids *and* strong bases are called **neutralization reactions** because, on completion of the reaction, the solution is neither acidic nor basic if exactly the same amounts (number of moles) of the acid and base are mixed. The other ions (the cation of the base and the anion of the acid) remain unchanged. If the water is evaporated, however, the cation and anion form a solid salt. If you mix NaOH and HCl, NaCl can be obtained. If nitric acid, HNO_3, and NaOH were allowed to react, the salt sodium nitrate, $NaNO_3$, (and water) would be the result.

$$HNO_3(aq) + NaOH(aq) \rightarrow NaNO_3(aq) + H_2O(\ell)$$

If acetic acid and sodium hydroxide are mixed, the following reaction will take place.

$$CH_3CO_2H(aq) + NaOH(aq) \rightarrow NaCH_3CO_2(aq) + H_2O(\ell)$$

Because acetic acid is a weak acid and ionizes to such a small extent (Figure 3.8c), the molecular species is the predominant form in aqueous solutions. In ionic equations, therefore, acetic acid is shown as molecular $CH_3CO_2H(aq)$. The *complete ionic equation* for this reaction is

$$CH_3CO_2H(aq) + Na^+(aq) + OH^-(aq) \rightarrow Na^+(aq) + CH_3CO_2^-(aq) + H_2O(\ell)$$

The only spectator ions in this equation are the sodium ions, so the *net ionic equation* is

$$CH_3CO_2H(aq) + OH^-(aq) \rightarrow CH_3CO_2^-(aq) + H_2O(\ell)$$

EXAMPLE 3.6

Net Ionic Equation for an Acid–Base Reaction

Problem Ammonia, NH_3, is one of the most important chemicals in industrial economies. Not only is it used directly as a fertilizer but it is the raw material for the manufacture of nitric acid. As a base, it reacts with acids such as hydrochloric acid. Write a balanced, net ionic equation for this reaction.

What Do You Know? The reactants are $NH_3(aq)$ and HCl(aq). A proton will transfer from the acid to the base.

Strategy Follow the general strategy for writing net ionic equations as outlined in Problem Solving Tip 3.1.

Solution A proton transfers from HCl to NH_3, a weak Brønsted base, to form the ammonium ion, NH_4^+. This positive ion must have a negative counterion from the acid, Cl^-, so the reaction product is NH_4Cl, and the complete balanced equation is

$$\underset{\text{ammonia}}{NH_3(aq)} + \underset{\text{hydrochloric acid}}{HCl(aq)} \rightarrow \underset{\text{ammonium chloride}}{NH_4Cl(aq)}$$

Hydrochloric acid is a strong acid and produces H_3O^+ and Cl^- ions in water. NH_4Cl is quite soluble and exists as NH_4^+ and Cl^- ions in solution. On the other hand, ammonia is a weak base and so is predominantly present in the solution as the molecular species, NH_3. The complete ionic equation for this reaction is

$$NH_3(aq) + H_3O^+(aq) + Cl^-(aq) \rightarrow NH_4^+(aq) + Cl^-(aq) + H_2O(\ell)$$

Eliminating the spectator ion, Cl^-, we have

$$NH_3(aq) + H_3O^+(aq) \rightleftharpoons NH_4^+(aq) + H_2O(\ell)$$

Think about Your Answer The net ionic equation shows that the important aspect of the reaction between the weak base ammonia and the strong acid HCl is the transfer of an H^+ ion from the acid to the NH_3. Any strong acid could be used here (HBr, HNO_3, $HClO_4$, H_2SO_4) and the net ionic equation would be the same. Also notice that, even though H_2O is not in the overall balanced equation, it is present in the net ionic equation because the H^+ from the acid is present in the initial solution as H_3O^+.

Check Your Understanding

Write the balanced, overall equation and the net ionic equation for the reaction of magnesium hydroxide with hydrochloric acid. (*Hint:* Think about the solubility guidelines.)

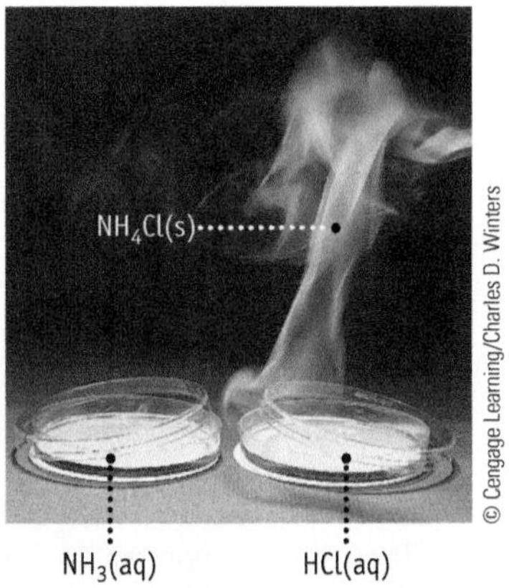

Reaction of gaseous HCl and NH_3. Open dishes of aqueous ammonia and hydrochloric acid were placed side by side. When molecules of NH_3 and HCl escape from solution to the atmosphere and encounter one another, a cloud of solid ammonium chloride, NH_4Cl, is observed.

Oxides of Nonmetals and Metals

Each acid shown in Table 3.1 has one or more H atoms that ionize in water to form H_3O^+ ions. There are, however, less obvious compounds that form acidic solutions. Carbon dioxide and sulfur trioxide, oxides of nonmetals, have no H atoms but both react with water to produce H_3O^+ ions. Carbon dioxide, for example, dissolves in water to a small extent, and a few of the dissolved molecules react with water to form the weak acid, carbonic acid. This acid then ionizes to a small extent to form the hydronium ion, H_3O^+, and the hydrogen carbonate (bicarbonate) ion, HCO_3^-.

$$CO_2(g) + H_2O(\ell) \rightleftharpoons H_2CO_3(aq)$$

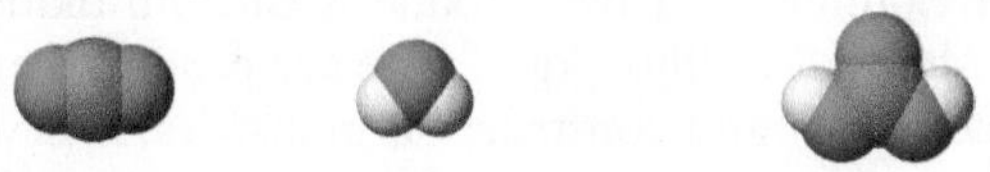

$$H_2CO_3(aq) + H_2O(\ell) \rightleftharpoons HCO_3^-(aq) + H_3O^+(aq)$$

The HCO_3^- ion can also function as an acid, ionizing to produce H_3O^+ and the carbonate ion, CO_3^{2-}.

$$HCO_3^-(aq) + H_2O(\ell) \rightleftharpoons CO_3^{2-}(aq) + H_3O^+(aq)$$

A CLOSER LOOK

Sulfuric Acid

For many years sulfuric acid has been the chemical produced in the largest quantity in the United States (as well as in many other industrialized countries). About 40–50 billion kilograms (40–50 million metric tons) is made annually in the United States. The acid is so important to the economy of industrialized nations that some economists have said sulfuric acid production is a measure of a nation's industrial strength.

© imagebroker/Alamy

Sulfur. Much of the sulfur used in the United States used to be mined, but it is now largely a by-product from natural gas and oil-refining processes. It takes about 1 ton of sulfur to make 3 tons of sulfuric acid.

Sulfuric acid is a colorless, syrupy liquid with a density of 1.84 g/mL and a boiling point of 337 °C. It has several desirable properties that have led to its widespread use: it is generally less expensive to produce than other acids, is a strong acid, and can be handled in steel containers. It reacts readily with many organic compounds to produce useful products and reacts readily with lime (CaO), the least expensive and most readily available base, to give calcium sulfate, a compound used to make wall board for the construction industry.

The first step in the industrial preparation of sulfuric acid is the production of sulfur dioxide from the combustion of sulfur in air,

$$S(s) + O_2(g) \rightarrow SO_2(g)$$

or using the SO_2 produced in smelting sulfur-containing copper, nickel, or other metal ores. The SO_2 is then combined with more oxygen, in the presence of a catalyst (a substance that speeds up the reaction), to give sulfur trioxide,

$$2\ SO_2(g) + O_2(g) \rightarrow 2\ SO_3(g)$$

which then gives sulfuric acid when dissolved in water.

$$SO_3(g) + H_2O(\ell) \rightarrow H_2SO_4(aq)$$

Currently, over two thirds of the production is used in the fertilizer industry. The remainder is used to make pigments, explosives, pulp and paper, detergents, and as a component in storage batteries.

"The Acid Touch," *Chemical and Engineering News,* April 14, 2008, p. 27.

These reactions are important in our environment and in the human body. Carbon dioxide is found in small amounts in the atmosphere, so rainwater is always slightly acidic. In the human body, carbon dioxide is dissolved in body fluids where the HCO_3^- and CO_3^{2-} ions perform an important "buffering" action that keeps our body stable (▶ Chapter 17).

Oxides of nonmetals such as CO_2, SO_2, SO_3, and NO_2 that react with water to produce an acidic solution are called **acidic oxides**. In contrast, oxides of metals are called **basic oxides** because they produce basic solutions if they dissolve appreciably in water. Perhaps the best example of a basic oxide is calcium oxide, CaO, often called *lime*, or *quicklime*. Almost 20 billion kg of lime are produced annually in the United States for use in the metals and construction industries, in sewage and pollution control, in water treatment, and in agriculture. Calcium oxide reacts with water to give calcium hydroxide, commonly called *slaked lime*. Although only slightly soluble in water (about 0.2 g/100 g H_2O at 10 °C), $Ca(OH)_2$ is widely used in industry as a base because it is inexpensive.

$$\underset{\text{lime}}{CaO(s)} + H_2O(\ell) \rightarrow \underset{\text{slaked lime}}{Ca(OH)_2(s)}$$

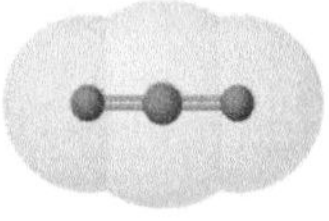

CO_2

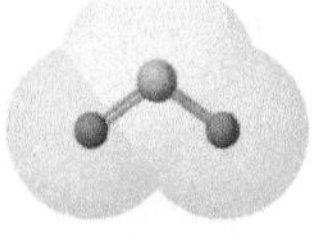

SO_2

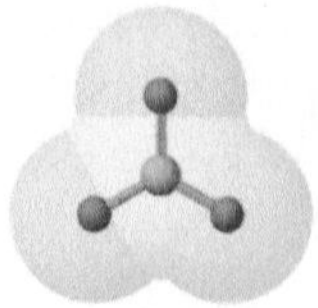

SO_3

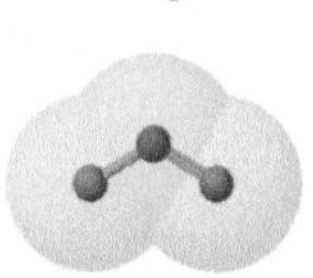

NO_2

Some common nonmetal oxides that form acids in water.

REVIEW & CHECK FOR SECTION 3-6

1. Which of the following is a strong acid in aqueous solution?

   (a) HF (b) H_2CO_3 (c) CH_3CO_2H (d) H_2SO_4

2. The hydrogen phosphate ion is amphiprotic. Identify the product formed from this ion when it reacts with a base.

   (a) H_3PO_4 (b) $H_2PO_4^-$ (c) HPO_4^{2-} (d) PO_4^{3-}

3. What is the net ionic equation for the reaction of acetic acid and sodium hydroxide?

   (a) $H_3O^+(aq) + OH^-(aq) \rightarrow 2\ H_2O(\ell)$

   (b) $Na^+(aq) + CH_3CO_2^-(aq) \rightarrow NaCH_3CO_2(aq)$

   (c) $CH_3CO_2H(aq) + OH^-(aq) \rightarrow H_2O(\ell) + CH_3CO_2^-(aq)$

   (d) $CH_3CO_2H(aq) + NaOH(aq) \rightarrow H_2O(\ell) + NaCH_3CO_2(aq)$

4. Identify the basic oxide from those listed below.

   (a) SO_2 (b) BaO (c) P_4O_{10} (d) CO_2

3-7 Gas-Forming Reactions

Learning Objectives: LO 3.1, LO 3.2, LO 3.10 (see APEC Lab 9 "Actions, Reactions, and Interactions")

Reactions that produce a gas represent another type of chemical reaction, and there are several commonly encountered examples in a chemical laboratory. The odor of rotten eggs will be very noticeable when you produce hydrogen sulfide, $H_2S(g)$, from a metal sulfide and an acid. Probably the most commonly encountered examples of gas forming reactions, however, involve the formation of $CO_2(g)$ when either metal carbonates or metal hydrogen carbonates are treated with acid (Figure 3.16) Equations for several types of gas-forming reactions are given in Table 3.2.

Although we usually write a single equation for the formation of $CO_2(g)$ for the reaction between a metal carbonate (or hydrogen carbonate), the formation of $CO_2(g)$ actually occurs in two distinct steps. Consider the reaction of $CaCO_3$ and hydrochloric acid. The first step is an exchange reaction in which hydrogen ions are exchanged for the cation(s) in the metal carbonate.

$$CaCO_3(s) + 2\ HCl(aq) \rightarrow CaCl_2(aq) + H_2CO_3(aq)$$

The product formed in this reaction is carbonic acid, H_2CO_3. This compound is unstable, however, and decomposes to CO_2 and H_2O.

$$H_2CO_3(aq) \rightarrow H_2O(\ell) + CO_2(g)$$

Carbon dioxide bubbles then escape the solution because CO_2 is not very soluble in water. The overall equation is obtained by adding the two equations.

$$\text{Overall reaction:}\quad CaCO_3(s) + 2\ HCl(aq) \rightarrow CaCl_2(aq) + H_2O(\ell) + CO_2(g)$$

Calcium carbonate is a common residue from hard water in home heating systems and cooking utensils. Washing with vinegar is a good way to clean the system or utensils because insoluble calcium carbonate is turned into water-soluble calcium acetate in the following gas-forming reaction (see Figure 3.16).

$$2\ CH_3CO_2H(aq) + CaCO_3(s) \rightarrow Ca(CH_3CO_2)_2(aq) + H_2O(\ell) + CO_2(g)$$

FIGURE 3.16 **Dissolving limestone (calcium carbonate, $CaCO_3$) in vinegar.** Notice the bubbles of CO_2 rising from the surface of the limestone. This reaction shows why vinegar can be used as a household cleaning agent. It can be used, for example, to clean the calcium carbonate deposited from hard water.

Table 3.2 Gas-Forming Reactions

Metal carbonate or hydrogen carbonate + acid → metal salt + $CO_2(g)$ + $H_2O(\ell)$
$Na_2CO_3(aq) + 2\ HCl(aq) \rightarrow 2\ NaCl(aq) + CO_2(g) + H_2O(\ell)$
$NaHCO_3(aq) + HCl(aq) \rightarrow NaCl(aq) + CO_2(g) + H_2O(\ell)$
Metal sulfide + acid → metal salt + $H_2S(g)$
$Na_2S(aq) + 2\ HCl(aq) \rightarrow 2\ NaCl(aq) + H_2S(g)$
Metal sulfite + acid → metal salt + $SO_2(g)$ + $H_2O(\ell)$
$Na_2SO_3(aq) + 2\ HCl(aq) \rightarrow 2\ NaCl(aq) + SO_2(g) + H_2O(\ell)$
Ammonium salt + strong base → metal salt + $NH_3(g)$ + $H_2O(\ell)$
$NH_4Cl(aq) + NaOH(aq) \rightarrow NaCl(aq) + NH_3(g) + H_2O(\ell)$

PROBLEM SOLVING TIP 3.2

Recognizing Gas-Forming Reactions

How can you recognize that a particular reaction will lead to gas formation? After you predict the products of the exchange reaction, be alert for certain products:

(a) H_2CO_3: This will decompose into carbon dioxide gas and water.

(b) H_2SO_3: This will decompose into sulfur dioxide gas and water.

(c) H_2S: This is already a gaseous product.

(d) If NH_4^+ and OH^- ions are produced, they will form NH_3 and water.

What is the net ionic equation for this reaction? Acetic acid is a weak acid, and calcium carbonate is insoluble in water. Therefore, the reactants are simply $CH_3CO_2H(aq)$ and $CaCO_3(s)$. On the products side, calcium acetate is water-soluble and so is present in solution as aqueous calcium and acetate ions. Water and carbon dioxide are molecular compounds, so the net ionic equation is

$$2\ CH_3CO_2H(aq) + CaCO_3(s) \rightarrow Ca^{2+}(aq) + 2\ CH_3CO_2^-(aq) + H_2O(\ell) + CO_2(g)$$

There are no spectator ions in this reaction.

Have you ever made biscuits or muffins? As you bake the dough, it rises in the oven because a gas-forming reaction occurs between an acid and baking soda, sodium hydrogen carbonate (bicarbonate of soda, $NaHCO_3$). One acid used for this purpose is tartaric acid, a weak acid found in many foods. The net ionic equation for a typical reaction is

$$\underset{\text{tartaric acid}}{H_2C_4H_4O_6(aq)} + \underset{\text{hydrogen carbonate ion}}{HCO_3^-(aq)} \longrightarrow \underset{\text{hydrogen tartrate ion}}{HC_4H_4O_6^-(aq)} + H_2O(\ell) + CO_2(g)$$

EXAMPLE 3.7

Gas-Forming Reactions

Problem Write a balanced equation for the reaction that occurs when nickel(II) carbonate is treated with sulfuric acid.

What Do You Know? You know the names of the reactants and therefore their formulas. You should recognize that the reaction of a metal carbonate with an acid is a gas-forming reaction (CO_2 is formed in these reactions).

Strategy

- Write the formulas for the reactants.
- Determine the products of the reaction and their formulas.
- Write and balance the equation.

Solution The reactants are $NiCO_3$ and H_2SO_4, and the products of the reaction are $NiSO_4$, CO_2, and H_2O. The complete, balanced equation is

$$NiCO_3(s) + H_2SO_4(aq) \rightarrow NiSO_4(aq) + H_2O(\ell) + CO_2(g)$$

Think about Your Answer The products in this reaction were determined by first exchanging cations (Ni^{2+} and 2 H^+) and anions (CO_3^{2-} and SO_4^{2-}). This exchange reaction is then followed by a second reaction in which one product, H_2CO_3, decomposes to give CO_2 and H_2O.

Check Your Understanding

Barium carbonate, $BaCO_3$, is used in the brick, ceramic, glass, and chemical manufacturing industries. Write a balanced equation that shows what happens when barium carbonate is treated with nitric acid. Give the name of each of the reaction products.

REVIEW & CHECK FOR SECTION 3-7

1. Which of the following compounds, when treated with acid, results in gas evolution?

   (a) NH_4Cl (b) Na_2CO_3 (c) Na_2SO_4 (d) Na_3PO_4

Learning Objectives: LO 3.1, LO 3.2, LO 3.8, LO 3.10 (see APEC Lab 9 "Actions, Reactions, and Interactions")

3-8 Oxidation–Reduction Reactions

The terms *oxidation* and *reduction* come from reactions that have been known for centuries. Ancient civilizations learned how to change metal oxides and sulfides into the metal, that is, how to "reduce" ore to the metal. A modern example is the reduction of iron(III) oxide with carbon monoxide to give iron metal.

Fe_2O_3 loses oxygen and is reduced.

$$Fe_2O_3(s) + 3\,CO(g) \longrightarrow 2\,Fe(s) + 3\,CO_2(g)$$

CO is the reducing agent. It gains oxygen and is oxidized.

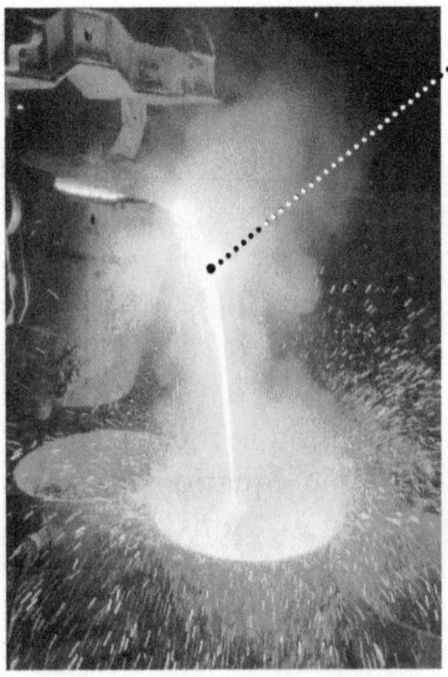

Jan Halaska/Science Source

Iron ore, which is largely Fe_2O_3, is reduced to metallic iron with carbon (C) or carbon monoxide (CO) in a blast furnace. The C or CO is oxidized to CO_2.

In this reaction carbon monoxide is the agent that brings about the reduction of iron ore to iron metal, so carbon monoxide is called the **reducing agent.**

When Fe_2O_3 is reduced by carbon monoxide, oxygen is removed from the iron ore and added to the carbon monoxide. The carbon monoxide, therefore, is "oxidized" by the addition of oxygen to give carbon dioxide. *Any process in which oxygen is added to another substance is an oxidation.*

Magnesium metal and oxygen produce magnesium oxide. In such oxidations, oxygen is called the **oxidizing agent** because it is the substance responsible for the oxidation of the metal.

Mg combines with oxygen and is oxidized.

$$2\,Mg(s) + O_2(g) \longrightarrow 2\,MgO(s)$$

O_2 is the oxidizing agent.

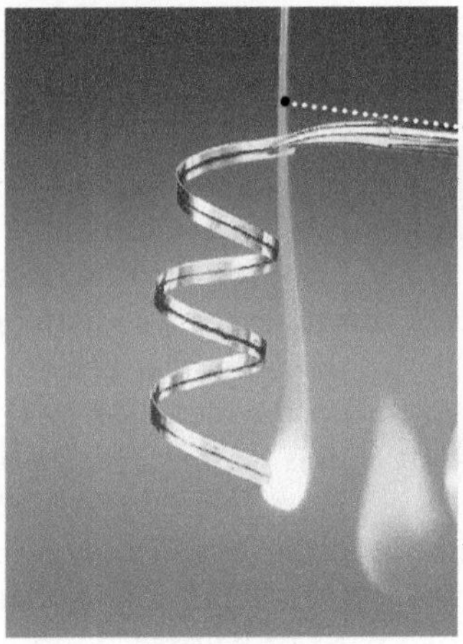

© Cengage Learning/Charles D. Winters

Burning magnesium metal in air produces magnesium oxide. The magnesium is oxidized by the oxidizing agent O_2. Oxygen is reduced by the reducing agent Mg.

Oxidation–Reduction Reactions and Electron Transfer

The concept of oxidation–reduction reactions can be extended to a vast number of other reactions, many of which do not involve oxygen. Rather than concentrate on whether oxygen is gained or lost, let us look at what is going on with electrons

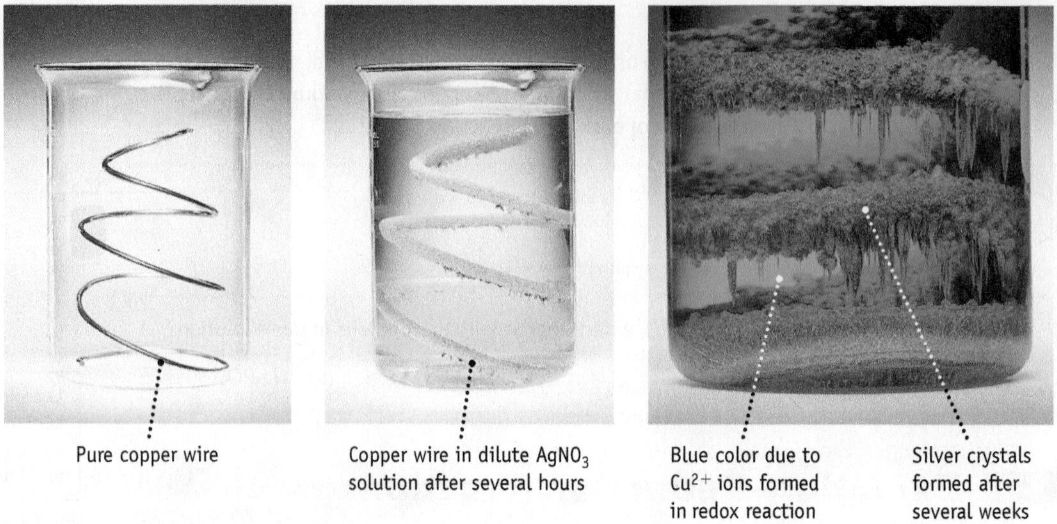

FIGURE 3.17 The oxidation of copper metal by silver ions. A clean piece of copper wire is placed in a solution of silver nitrate, $AgNO_3$. Over time, the copper reduces Ag^+ ions, forming silver crystals, and the copper metal is oxidized to copper ions, Cu^{2+}. The blue color of the solution is due to the presence of aqueous copper(II) ions.

during the course of the reaction. All oxidation and reduction reactions can be accounted for by considering them to occur by a transfer of electrons between substances. When a substance accepts electrons, it is said to be reduced because there is a reduction in the numerical value of the charge on an atom of the substance. In the net ionic equation for the reaction of a silver salt with copper metal, positively charged Ag^+ ions accept electrons from copper metal and are reduced to uncharged silver atoms (Figure 3.17).

Ag^+ ions accept electrons from Cu and are reduced to Ag. Ag^+ is the oxidizing agent.
$Ag^+(aq) + e^- \rightarrow Ag(s)$

$$2\ Ag^+(aq) + Cu(s) \longrightarrow 2\ Ag(s) + Cu^{2+}(aq)$$

Cu donates electrons to Ag^+ and is oxidized to Cu^{2+}.
Cu is the reducing agent.
$Cu(s) \rightarrow Cu^{2+}(aq) + 2\ e^-$

Because copper metal supplies the electrons that cause Ag^+ ions to be reduced, Cu is the *reducing agent.*

Balancing Equations for Redox Reactions The notion that a redox reaction can be divided into a reduction portion and an oxidation portion will lead us to a method of balancing more complex equations for redox reactions described in Chapter 19.

When a substance *loses electrons*, the numerical value of the charge on an atom of the substance increases. The substance is said to have been **oxidized.** In our example, copper metal releases electrons on going to Cu^{2+}, so the metal is oxidized. For this to happen, something must be available to accept the electrons from copper. In this case, Ag^+ is the electron acceptor; its charge is reduced to zero in silver metal, so we say the metal ion has been **reduced.** Furthermore, because Ag^+ is the "agent" that causes Cu metal to be oxidized, we say Ag^+ is the *oxidizing agent.*

In every oxidation–reduction reaction, one reactant is reduced (and therefore is the oxidizing agent) and one reactant is oxidized (and therefore is the reducing agent). We can show this by dividing the general redox reaction $X + Y \rightarrow X^{n+} + Y^{n-}$ into two parts or *half-reactions*:

Half-Reaction	Electron Transfer	Result
$X \rightarrow X^{n+} + n\,e^-$	X transfers electrons to Y	X is oxidized to X^{n+}. X is the reducing agent.
$Y + n\,e^- \rightarrow Y^{n-}$	Y accepts electrons from X	Y is reduced to Y^{n-}. Y is the oxidizing agent.

In the reaction of magnesium and oxygen, the oxidizing agent, O_2, is reduced because it gains electrons (four electrons per molecule) on going to two oxide ions.

Mg releases 2 e^- per atom. Mg is oxidized to Mg^{2+} and is the reducing agent.

$$2\ Mg(s) + O_2(g) \longrightarrow 2\ MgO(s)$$

O_2 gains 4 e^- per molecule to form 2 O^{2-}. O_2 is reduced and is the oxidizing agent.

In the same reaction, magnesium is the reducing agent because it releases two electrons per atom on being oxidized to the Mg^{2+} ion (and so two Mg atoms are required to supply the four electrons required by one O_2 molecule). All oxidation–reduction reactions can be analyzed in a similar manner.

An important principle to remember concerning oxidation–reduction reactions is that in a balanced equation the extents of oxidation and reduction must be the same. This is easy to see in the Mg/O_2 equation. Here, four electrons are released when two magnesium atoms are oxidized, so four electrons must be taken up by the oxidizing agent, in this example one molecule of O_2.

The observations outlined so far lead to several important conclusions:

- If one substance is oxidized, another substance in the same reaction must be reduced. For this reason, such reactions are called *oxidation–reduction reactions,* or **redox reactions** for short.
- The reducing agent is itself oxidized, and the oxidizing agent is reduced.
- The gain of electrons is reduction and the loss of electrons is oxidation.
- The extents of oxidation and reduction in a reaction must be the same. This means that the number of electrons released when a substance is oxidized must equal the number of electrons gained by the substance being reduced.

Oxidation Numbers

How can you tell an oxidation–reduction reaction when you see one? How can you tell which substance has gained or lost electrons and so decide which substance is the oxidizing (or reducing) agent? Sometimes it is obvious. For example, if an uncombined element becomes part of a compound (Mg becomes part of MgO, for example), the reaction is definitely a redox process. If it's not obvious, then the answer is to *look for a change in the oxidation number of an element in the course of the reaction.* The **oxidation number** of an atom in a molecule or ion is defined as the charge an atom has, *or appears to have,* as determined by the following guidelines for assigning oxidation numbers.

Writing Charges and Oxidation Numbers on Ions Conventionally, charges on ions are written as (number, sign), whereas oxidation numbers are written as (sign, number). For example, the oxidation number of the Cu^{2+} ion is +2 and its charge is 2+.

1. **Each atom in a pure element has an oxidation number of zero.** The oxidation number of Cu in metallic copper is 0, and it is 0 for each atom in I_2 and S_8.
2. **For monatomic ions, the oxidation number is equal to the charge on the ion.** You know that magnesium forms ions with a 2+ charge (Mg^{2+}); the oxidation number of magnesium in this ion is therefore +2.
3. **When combined with another element, fluorine always has an oxidation number of −1.**
4. **The oxidation number of O is −2 in most compounds.** Exceptions to this rule occur
   (a) when oxygen is combined with fluorine (where oxygen takes on a positive oxidation number),
   (b) in compounds called *peroxides* (such as Na_2O_2) and *superoxides* (such as KO_2) in which oxygen has an oxidation number of −1 and −1/2, respectively.
5. **Cl, Br, and I have oxidation numbers of −1 in compounds, except when combined with oxygen and fluorine.** This means that Cl has an oxidation number of −1 in NaCl (in which Na's oxidation number is +1, as predicted by the fact

Peroxides In peroxides, the oxidation number of oxygen is −1. For example, in hydrogen peroxide (H_2O_2), each hydrogen atom has an oxidation number of +1. To balance this, each oxygen must have an oxidation number of −1. A 3% aqueous solution of H_2O_2 is sometimes used as an antiseptic because it is a good oxidizing agent.

that it is an element of Group 1A). In the ion ClO^-, however, the Cl atom has an oxidation number of +1 (and O has an oxidation number of −2; see Guideline 4).

6. **The oxidation number of H is +1 in most compounds.** The key exception to this guideline occurs when H forms a binary compound with a metal. In such cases, the metal forms a positive ion and H becomes a hydride ion, H^-. Thus, in CaH_2 the oxidation number of Ca is +2 (equal to the group number) and that of H is −1.
7. **The algebraic sum of the oxidation numbers for the atoms in a neutral compound must be zero; in a polyatomic ion, the sum must equal the ion charge.** For example, in $HClO_4$ the H atom is assigned +1 and each O atom is assigned −2. This means the Cl atom must be +7. In ClO_4^-, the sum of the oxidation states of O ($-2 \times 4 = -8$) and Cl (+7) is the charge on the ion, −1.

EXAMPLE 3.8

Determining Oxidation Numbers

Problem Determine the oxidation number of the indicated element in each of the following compounds or ions:

(a) aluminum in aluminum oxide, Al_2O_3

(b) phosphorus in phosphoric acid, H_3PO_4

(c) sulfur in the sulfate ion, SO_4^{2-}

(d) each Cr atom in the dichromate ion, $Cr_2O_7^{2-}$

What Do You Know? Correct formulas for each species are given.

Strategy Follow the guidelines in the text, paying particular attention to Guidelines 4, 6, and 7.

Solution

(a) Al_2O_3 is a neutral compound. Assuming that oxygen has its usual oxidation number of −2, we can solve the following algebraic equation for the oxidation number of aluminum.

Net charge on Al_2O_3 = sum of oxidation numbers for two Al atoms + three O atoms

$$0 = 2(x) + 3(-2) \text{ and so } x = +3$$

The oxidation number of Al must be +3, in agreement with its position in the periodic table.

(b) H_3PO_4 has an overall charge of 0. If each of the oxygen atoms has an oxidation number of −2 and each of the H atoms is +1, then the oxidation number of phosphorus is +5.

Net charge on H_3PO_4 = sum of oxidation numbers for three H atoms + one P atom + four O atoms

$$0 = 3(+1) + (x) + 4(-2) \text{ and so } x = +5$$

(c) The sulfate ion, SO_4^{2-}, has an overall charge of 2−. Oxygen is assigned its usual oxidation number of −2, and so sulfur in this ion has an oxidation number of +6.

Net charge on SO_4^{2-} = sum of oxidation number of one S atom + four O atoms

$$-2 = (x) + 4(-2) \text{ and so } x = +6$$

A CLOSER LOOK — Are Oxidation Numbers "Real"?

Do oxidation numbers reflect the actual electric charge on an atom in a molecule or ion? With the exception of monatomic ions such as Cl^- or Na^+, the answer is generally no.

Oxidation numbers assume that all atoms in a molecule are positive or negative ions, which is not true. For example, in H_2O, the H atoms are not H^+ ions and the O atoms are not O^{2-} ions. This is not to say, however, that atoms in molecules do not bear an electric charge of any kind. Advanced calculations indicate the O atom in water actually has a charge of about 0.4− (or 40% of the electron charge) and the H atoms are each about 0.2+.

So why use oxidation numbers? Oxidation numbers provide a convenient way of dividing up the electrons among the atoms in a molecule or polyatomic ion. Because the distribution of electrons changes in a redox reaction, we use this method as a way to decide whether a redox reaction has occurred and to distinguish the oxidizing and reducing agents.

(d) The net charge on the $Cr_2O_7^{2-}$ ion is 2−. Oxygen is assigned its usual oxidation number of −2.

Net charge on $Cr_2O_7^{2-}$ = sum of oxidation numbers for two Cr atoms + seven O atoms

$$-2 = 2(x) + 7(-2) \text{ and so } x = +6$$

The oxidation number of each chromium in this polyatomic ion is +6.

Think about Your Answer Notice that in each of these examples, the oxidation number of Al, S, P, and Cr matched the number of the periodic group in which the element is found. This is often (but not always) the case. For example, S, P, and Cr have a range of oxidation numbers, depending on the compound.

Check Your Understanding

Assign an oxidation number to the underlined atom in each ion or molecule.

(a) $\underline{Fe}_2O_3$ (b) $H_2\underline{S}O_4$ (c) $\underline{C}O_3^{2-}$ (d) $\underline{N}O_2^+$

Recognizing Oxidation–Reduction Reactions

You can always tell whether a reaction involves oxidation and reduction by assessing the oxidation number of each element and noting whether any of these numbers change in the course of the reaction. In many cases, however, this will not be necessary. For example, it will be obvious that a redox reaction has occurred if an uncombined element is converted to a compound or if a well-known oxidizing or reducing agent is involved.

The halogens and oxygen (see Figures 3.1 and 3.2) are oxidizing agents, and another common oxidizing agent is nitric acid, HNO_3. In Figure 3.18 copper metal is oxidized by the acid to give copper(II) nitrate, and the nitrate ion is reduced to the brown gas NO_2. The net ionic equation for the reaction is

Oxidation number of Cu changes from 0 to +2. Cu is oxidized to Cu^{2+} and is the reducing agent.

$$Cu(s) + 2\ NO_3^-(aq) + 4\ H_3O^+(aq) \longrightarrow Cu^{2+}(aq) + 2\ NO_2(g) + 6\ H_2O(\ell)$$

N in NO_3^- changes from +5 to +4 in NO_2. NO_3^- is reduced to NO_2 and is the oxidizing agent.

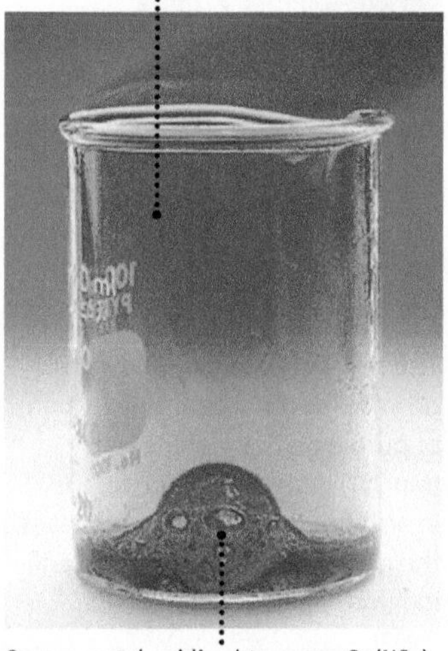

FIGURE 3.18 Oxidizing and reducing agents. The reaction of copper with nitric acid. Copper (a reducing agent) reacts vigorously with concentrated nitric acid (an oxidizing agent) to give the brown gas NO_2 and a deep blue-green solution of copper(II) nitrate.

Table 3.3 Common Oxidizing and Reducing Agents

OXIDIZING AGENT	REACTION PRODUCT	REDUCING AGENT	REACTION PRODUCT
O_2, oxygen	O^{2-}, oxide ion or O combined in H_2O or other molecule	H_2, hydrogen	H^+(aq), hydrogen ion or H combined in H_2O or other molecule
Halogen, F_2, Cl_2, Br_2, or I_2	Halide ion, F^-, Cl^-, Br^-, or I^-	M, metals such as Na, K, Fe, and Al	M^{n+}, metal ions such as Na^+, K^+, Fe^{2+} or Fe^{3+}, and Al^{3+}
HNO_3, nitric acid	Nitrogen oxides* such as NO and NO_2	C, carbon (used to reduce metal oxides)	CO and CO_2
$Cr_2O_7^{2-}$, dichromate ion	Cr^{3+}, chromium(III) ion (in acid solution)		
MnO_4^-, permanganate ion	Mn^{2+}, manganese(II) ion (in acid solution)		

*NO is produced with dilute HNO_3, whereas NO_2 is a product of concentrated acid.

Nitrogen has been reduced from +5 (in the NO_3^- ion) to +4 (in NO_2); therefore, the nitrate ion in acid solution is the oxidizing agent. Copper metal is the reducing agent; each metal atom has given up two electrons to produce the Cu^{2+} ion.

Tables 3.3 and 3.4 may help you organize your thinking as you look for oxidation–reduction reactions and use their terminology.

Oxidizing and reducing agents. The reaction of iron(II) ion and permanganate ion. The reaction of purple permanganate ion (MnO_4^-) with the iron(II) ion (Fe^{2+}) in acidified aqueous solution gives the nearly colorless manganese(II) ion (Mn^{2+}) and the iron(III) ion (Fe^{3+}).

EXAMPLE 3.9

Oxidation–Reduction Reaction

Problem For the reaction of the iron(II) ion with permanganate ion in aqueous acid,

$$5\ Fe^{2+}(aq) + MnO_4^-(aq) + 8\ H_3O^+(aq) \rightarrow 5\ Fe^{3+}(aq) + Mn^{2+}(aq) + 12\ H_2O(\ell)$$

decide which atoms are undergoing a change in oxidation number and identify the oxidizing and reducing agents.

What Do You Know? The equation given here is balanced (but, for practice, you might verify this). Based on the reactants and products you can quickly decide this is an oxidation–reduction reaction. Here you know MnO_4^- is a common oxidizing agent (see Table 3.3), and you see that iron changes from Fe^{2+} to Fe^{3+}.

Strategy Determine the oxidation number of the atoms in each molecule or ion in the equation and identify which atoms change oxidation number.

Table 3.4 Recognizing Oxidation–Reduction Reactions

	OXIDATION	REDUCTION
In terms of oxidation number	Increase in oxidation number of an atom	Decrease in oxidation number of an atom
In terms of electrons	Loss of electrons by an atom	Gain of electrons by an atom
In terms of oxygen	Gain of one or more O atoms	Loss of one or more O atoms

Solution The Mn oxidation number in MnO_4^- is +7, and it decreases to +2 in the product, the Mn^{2+} ion. Thus, the MnO_4^- ion has been reduced and is the oxidizing agent (see Table 3.3).

$$\underset{+2}{5\ Fe^{2+}(aq)} + \underset{+7,\ -2}{MnO_4^-(aq)} + \underset{+1,\ -2}{8\ H_3O^+(aq)} \rightarrow \underset{+3}{5\ Fe^{3+}(aq)} + \underset{+2}{Mn^{2+}(aq)} + \underset{+1,\ -2}{12\ H_2O(\ell)}$$

The oxidation number of iron has increased from +2 to +3, so each Fe^{2+} ion has lost one electron upon being oxidized to Fe^{3+} (see Table 3.4). This means the Fe^{2+} ion is the reducing agent.

Think about Your Answer If one of the reactants in a redox reaction is a simple substance such as an element or a monoatomic ion (here Fe^{2+}), it usually is obvious whether its oxidation number has increased or decreased. Once a species has been established as having been reduced (or oxidized), you know another species has undergone the opposite process. It is also helpful to recognize common oxidizing and reducing agents (see Table 3.3).

Check Your Understanding

The following reaction is used in a device for testing the breath of a person for the presence of ethanol. Identify the oxidizing and reducing agents, the substance oxidized, and the substance reduced.

$$\underset{\text{ethanol}}{3\ CH_3CH_2OH(aq)} + \underset{\text{dichromate ion; orange-red}}{2\ Cr_2O_7^{2-}(aq)} + 16\ H_3O^+(aq) \rightarrow \underset{\text{acetic acid}}{3\ CH_3CO_2H(aq)} + \underset{\text{chromium(III) ion; green}}{4\ Cr^{3+}(aq)} + 27\ H_2O(\ell)$$

REVIEW & CHECK FOR SECTION 3-8

1. What is the oxidation number of Mn in $BaMnO_4$?

   (a) 0 (b) +3 (c) +6 (d) +12

2. Which of the following reactions are oxidation–reduction reactions?

   (1) $NaOH(aq) + HNO_3(aq) \rightarrow NaNO_3(aq) + H_2O(\ell)$

   (2) $Cu(s) + Cl_2(g) \rightarrow CuCl_2(s)$

   (3) $Na_2CO_3(aq) + 2\ HClO_4(aq) \rightarrow CO_2(g) + H_2O(\ell) + 2\ NaClO_4(aq)$

   (4) $2\ S_2O_3^{2-}(aq) + I_2(aq) \rightarrow S_4O_6^{2-}(aq) + 2\ I^-(aq)$

   (a) all of them (b) 2, 3, and 4 (c) 2 and 4 (d) 2 only

3. In which of the manganese compounds below does Mn have the highest oxidation number?

   (a) MnO_2 (b) Mn_2O_3 (c) $KMnO_4$ (d) $MnCl_2$

© Cengage Learning/Charles D. Winters

FIGURE 3.19 A gas-forming reaction. An Alka-Seltzer tablet contains an acid (citric acid) and sodium hydrogen carbonate ($NaHCO_3$), the reactants in a gas-forming reaction.

3-9 Classifying Reactions in Aqueous Solution

Learning Objectives: LO 3.1, LO 3.2, LO 3.5 (see APEC Lab 7 "Hydrates and Thermal Decomposition"), LO 3.6

One goal of this chapter has been to explore the most common types of reactions that can occur in aqueous solution. This helps you decide, for example, that a gas-forming reaction occurs when an Alka-Seltzer tablet (containing citric acid and $NaHCO_3$) is dropped into water (Figure 3.19).

$$\underset{\text{citric acid}}{H_3C_6H_5O_7(aq)} + \underset{\text{hydrogen carbonate ion}}{HCO_3^-(aq)} \longrightarrow \underset{\text{dihydrogen citrate ion}}{H_2C_6H_5O_7^-(aq)} + H_2O(\ell) + CO_2(g)$$

CASE STUDY Killing Bacteria with Silver

There is a washing machine on the market that injects silver ions into the wash water, the purpose being to kill bacteria in the wash water. The advertisement for the machine tells us that "100 quadrillion silver ions" are injected into a wash load. How does this machine work? Is 100 quadrillion silver ions a lot? Does the silver kill bacteria?

The washing machine works by using electrical energy to oxidize silver metal to give silver ions.

$$Ag(s) \rightarrow Ag^+(aq) + e^-$$

This is a simple electrolysis procedure. (More about that in Chapter 19.) And 100 quadrillion silver ions? This is 100×10^{15} ions.

Do silver ions act as a bacteriocide? There is plenty of medical evidence for this property. In fact, when you were born, the physician or nurse may have put drops of a very dilute silver nitrate solution in your eyes to guard against neonatal conjunctivitis. And severely burned patients are treated with silver sulfadiazine ($C_{10}H_9AgN_4O_2S$) to prevent bacterial or fungal infections.

Silver ions as a bacteriocide in dental floss.

The use of silver to prevent infections has a long history. Phoenicians kept wine, water, and vinegar in silver vessels. Early settlers in America put silver coins into water barrels. And you might have been born with a "silver spoon in your mouth." Babies in wealthier homes, who were fed from silver spoons and used a silver pacifier, were found to be healthier.

The historical uses of silver carry over to modern society. One can buy many different kinds of silver-containing water purifiers for the home, and dental floss coated with silver nitrate is available.

Although silver does have health benefits, beware of fraudulent claims. For example, consuming large amounts of "colloidal silver" (nanosized particles of silver suspended in water) is claimed to have health-giving properties. One person who tried this, Stan Jones, ran for the U.S. Congress in 2002 and 2006. From consuming silver, he acquired argyria, a medically irreversible condition in which the skin turns a gray-blue color.

Questions:

1. How many moles of silver are used in a wash cycle?
2. What mass of silver is used?

Answers to these questions are available in Appendix N.

We have examined four types of reactions in aqueous solution: precipitation, acid–base, gas-forming, and oxidation–reduction. Three of these four (precipitation, acid–base, and gas-forming) fall into the category of exchange reactions.

Precipitation Reactions (see Figure 3.12): Ions combine in solution to form an insoluble reaction product.

Overall Equation

$$Pb(NO_3)_2(aq) + 2\ KI(aq) \rightarrow PbI_2(s) + 2\ KNO_3(aq)$$

Net Ionic Equation

$$Pb^{2+}(aq) + 2\ I^-(aq) \rightarrow PbI_2(s)$$

Acid–Base Reactions (see Figures 3.13 and 3.15): Water is a product of many acid–base reactions, and the cation of the base and the anion of the acid form a salt.

Overall Equation for the Reaction of a Strong Acid and a Strong Base

$$HNO_3(aq) + KOH(aq) \rightarrow HOH(\ell) + KNO_3(aq)$$

Net Ionic Equation for the Reaction of a Strong Acid and a Strong Base

$$H_3O^+(aq) + OH^-(aq) \rightarrow 2\ H_2O(\ell)$$

Overall Equation for the Reaction of a Weak Acid and a Strong Base

$$CH_3CO_2H(aq) + NaOH(aq) \rightarrow NaCH_3CO_2(aq) + HOH(\ell)$$

Net Ionic Equation for the Reaction of a Weak Acid and a Strong Base

$$CH_3CO_2H(aq) + OH^-(aq) \rightarrow CH_3CO_2^-(aq) + H_2O(\ell)$$

A CLOSER LOOK

Alternative Organizations of Reaction Types

As we said in Chapter 1, chemistry is about the transformation of one or more substances into other substances. This is done by chemical reactions, and thousands upon thousands of reactions have been carried out by chemists over the past few hundred years. Although students beginning their study of chemistry can be bewildered by the apparent infinite variety of these reactions, there are some common reaction types. We have classified them as oxidation–reduction reactions and exchange reactions. The latter include precipitation, acid–base, and gas-forming reactions. Classifying reactions is useful because it helps to see their common features and to predict what might happen if you see a new set of reactants.

There are two other terms that are commonly used when describing chemical reactions: synthesis and decomposition. **Synthesis** describes the preparation of a compound from elements or other compounds. You have already seen synthesis reactions such as the preparation of ammonium chloride, which is widely used in fertilizers, in medicines, in consumer products such as shampoo, and in explosives. The synthesis of ammonium chloride can be carried out using an acid–base reaction.

$$NH_3(aq) + HCl(aq) \rightarrow NH_4Cl(aq)$$

Decomposition describes a reaction in which a compound is taken apart into smaller constituents. One such reaction is the decomposition of hydrogen peroxide to water and oxygen, an oxidation-reduction reaction seen in the Figure.

$$2\ H_2O_2(aq) \rightarrow 2\ H_2O(\ell) + O_2(g)$$

The terms synthesis and decomposition are widely used in chemistry because they are useful in describing the outcome of a reaction. The reaction classification scheme adopted in this book is also useful because it describes the kinds of reactants and products involved in many different types of reactions, which can include synthesis and decomposition reactions.

© Cengage Learning/Charles D. Winters

The decomposition of hydrogen peroxide, H_2O_2. This can also be classified as an oxidation–reduction reaction.

Gas-Forming Reactions (see Figures 3.16 and 3.19): The most common examples involve metal carbonates and acids but others exist (see Table 3.2). The reaction of a metal carbonate and acid produces carbonic acid, H_2CO_3, which decomposes to H_2O and CO_2. Carbon dioxide is the gas in the bubbles you see during these reactions.

Overall Equation:

$$CuCO_3(s) + 2\ HNO_3(aq) \rightarrow Cu(NO_3)_2(aq) + CO_2(g) + H_2O(\ell)$$

Net Ionic Equation

$$CuCO_3(s) + 2\ H_3O^+(aq) \rightarrow Cu^{2+}(aq) + CO_2(g) + 3\ H_2O(\ell)$$

Oxidation–Reduction Reactions (see Figure 3.17): These reactions are *not* ion exchange reactions. Rather, electrons are transferred from one material to another.

Overall Equation

$$Cu(s) + 2\ AgNO_3(aq) \rightarrow Cu(NO_3)_2(aq) + 2\ Ag(s)$$

Net Ionic Equation

$$Cu(s) + 2\ Ag^+(aq) \rightarrow Cu^{2+}(aq) + 2\ Ag(s)$$

The four types of reactions usually are easy to recognize, but keep in mind that a reaction can fall into more than one category. For example, barium hydroxide reacts readily with sulfuric acid to give barium sulfate and water, a reaction that is both a precipitation and an acid–base reaction.

$$Ba(OH)_2(aq) + H_2SO_4(aq) \rightarrow BaSO_4(s) + 2\ H_2O(\ell)$$

Strategy Map 3.10a

PROBLEM

Write equation for the reaction of Na_2S and $Cu(NO_3)_2$ and decide on *reaction type*

↓

DATA/INFORMATION

The **formulas** of the **reactants** are given

STEP 1. Decide on **products** and then write **complete balanced equation.**

↓

Complete balanced equation with *reactants* and *products*

STEP 2. Decide if each reactant and product is **solid, liquid, gas,** or **dissolved in water.**

↓

Complete balanced equation with **indication of state** of each reactant and product

STEP 3. Decide on **reaction type.**

↓

One product is ***insoluble in water***, so this is a **precipitation reaction.**

EXAMPLE 3.10

Types of Reactions

Problem Complete and balance each of the following equations and classify each as a precipitation, acid–base, or gas-forming reaction.

(a) $Na_2S(aq) + Cu(NO_3)_2(aq) \rightarrow$

(b) $Na_2SO_3(aq) + HCl(aq) \rightarrow$

(c) $HClO_4(aq) + NaOH(aq) \rightarrow$

What Do You Know? You know the formulas for the reactants and that these are all exchange reactions.

Strategy

- Recognize that these are exchange reactions. The products of each reaction can be found by exchanging cations and anions between the two reactants.
- Write and balance each equation.
- To determine the kind of reaction examine the reactants and products. Look specifically for common acids and bases, for a product that is insoluble, and for anions that react with acid to give a gas (CO_3^{2-}, S^{2-}, SO_3^{2-}).

Solution

(a) The products of the exchange reaction are predicted to be $NaNO_3$ and CuS. The first of these is water-soluble, but the second is an insoluble salt. Thus, this is a precipitation reaction. The balanced chemical equation is

$$Na_2S(aq) + Cu(NO_3)_2(aq) \rightarrow 2\ NaNO_3(aq) + CuS(s)$$

(b) The products of the exchange reaction are predicted to be NaCl and H_2SO_3. The H_2SO_3 should immediately alert us to the fact that this is a gas-forming reaction because it will decompose into $SO_2(g)$ and $H_2O(\ell)$ (see Table 3.2). The balanced equation is

$$Na_2SO_3(aq) + 2\ HCl\ (aq) \rightarrow 2\ NaCl(aq) + SO_2\ (g) + H_2O(\ell)$$

(c) The products of the exchange reaction are predicted to be $NaClO_4$ and H_2O, a salt and water; this is an acid–base reaction. The balanced equation is

$$HClO_4(aq) + NaOH(aq) \rightarrow NaClO_4(aq) + H_2O(\ell)$$

Think about Your Answer As practice, try writing the net ionic equations for each of the preceding reactions. The answers are:

(a) $S^{2-}(aq) + Cu^{2+}(aq) \rightarrow CuS(s)$

(b) $SO_3^{2-}(aq) + 2\ H_3O^+(aq) \rightarrow 3\ H_2O(\ell) + SO_2(g)$

(c) $H_3O^+(aq) + OH^-(aq) \rightarrow 2\ H_2O(\ell)$

Check Your Understanding

Classify each of the following reactions as a precipitation, acid–base, gas-forming, or oxidation–reduction reaction. Predict the products of the reaction, and then balance the completed equation. Write the net ionic equation for each.

(a) $CuCO_3(s) + H_2SO_4(aq) \rightarrow$

(b) $Ga(s) + O_2(g) \rightarrow$

(c) $Ba(OH)_2(s) + HNO_3(aq) \rightarrow$

(d) $CuCl_2(aq) + (NH_4)_2S(aq) \rightarrow$

REVIEW & CHECK FOR SECTION 3-9

1. Sometimes a reaction can fall in more than one category. Into what category (or categories) does the reaction of $Ba(OH)_2(aq) + H_3PO_4(aq)$ fit?

   (a) acid–base and oxidation–reduction
   (b) oxidation–reduction
   (c) acid–base and precipitation
   (d) precipitation

APPLYING CHEMICAL PRINCIPLES

Superconductors

In 1987, the Nobel Prize in Physics was awarded to Georg Benorz and Karl Müller (IBM Labs, Zurich, Switzerland) for their pioneering work in superconductivity, including their discovery of a new class of superconductors based on a lanthanum, barium, copper, and oxygen compound. The superconductor was identified as $La_{2-x}Ba_xCuO_4$, where the value of x varied from 0.10 to 0.20. In the same year, researchers at the University of Alabama at Huntsville synthesized $YBa_2Cu_3O_{7-x}$ (or YBCO), where x varies from 0 to 0.50. YBCO was the first material discovered to superconduct at temperatures above the boiling point of liquefied nitrogen (77 K). Further research determined that the critical temperature for superconductivity of YBCO varies with changes to the ratios of its components. The highest superconducting temperature, 95 K, is found for $YBa_2Cu_3O_{6.93}$.

Superconductors are important because these materials have no resistance to the flow of electric current. Once a current (that is, a flow of electrons) is induced in a superconductor, it will continue indefinitely with no energy loss. A potential application for superconductors is electricity storage. Currently, electricity produced at power plants must be used as it is produced. If unused electricity could be fed into a superconducting storage ring, the current could be stored indefinitely. For a storage ring to be feasible, the superconductor must operate at a temperature where refrigeration is not cost prohibitive, and the superconductor must support high currents. YCBO meets the first criterion but not the second. To date, no superconductor has been discovered that can carry large currents at temperatures greater than 77 K.

Compound formulas containing subscripts that are not whole numbers are common for a variety of compounds, including high-temperature superconductors. Answer the following questions concerning a couple of these superconductors.

Superconductivity. When a superconducting material is cooled to a low temperature, say in liquid nitrogen (boiling point 77 K), and is placed in a magnetic field, the field does not penetrate the superconductor but rather is rejected from the superconductor. The effect is seen here where a magnet floats above cooled superconductors.

QUESTIONS:

1. Use the following mass percentages to determine the value of x in a sample of $La_{2-x}Ba_xCuO_4$: %La = 63.43, %Ba = 5.085, %Cu = 15.69, and %O = 15.80.
2. What is the percent by mass of each element in YBCO when $x = 0.07$?
3. Assuming the charges on the yttrium and barium ions are 3+ and 2+, respectively, what charges are present on the copper ions in $YBa_2Cu_3O_7$? (Note: Although most copper compounds are based on Cu^{2+}, charges of 1+ and 3+ are also possible. Assume at least one copper ion in this substance is Cu^{2+}.)
4. The reaction of Y_2O_3, $BaCO_3$, and CuO produces $YBa_2Cu_3O_{7-x}$ with $CO_2(g)$ as the only byproduct. Write a balanced chemical equation of this reaction and determine the value of x.
5. The percentage of oxygen in YBCO is adjusted by heating it in the presence of elemental oxygen. What mass of oxygen is required to convert 1.00 g $YBa_2Cu_3O_{6.50}$ to $YBa_2Cu_3O_{6.93}$?

REFERENCES:

1. M. K. Wu, et al., *Phys. Rev. Lett.*, Vol. 58, page 908, 1987.
2. J. W. Cochrane and G. J. Russell, *Supercond. Sci. Technol.*, Vol. 11, page 1105, 1998.

CHAPTER GOALS REVISITED

Now that you have studied this chapter, you should ask if you have met the chapter goals. In particular, you should be able to

UNDERSTAND

- The significance and uses of balanced chemical equations (Sections 3-1, 3-2).
- The nature and characteristics of chemical equilibrium (Section 3-3).
  - **a.** Recognize that chemical reactions are reversible.
  - **b.** Describe what is meant by the term *dynamic equilibrium*. Study Question: 80.
  - **c.** Recognize the difference between reactant-favored and product-favored reactions at equilibrium. Study Questions: 7, 8.
- The nature of ionic substances dissolved in water (Section 3-4). Study Questions: 13, 15.
- Oxidation–reduction reactions and the three types of exchange reactions (Sections 3-5, 3-6, 3-7, 3-8).
- Acid–base reactions involve the transfer of hydrogen ions (Section 3-6). Study Question: 23.
- Oxidation–reduction reactions involve the transfer of electrons (Section 3-8).

DO

- Balance chemical equations, given formulas for reactants and products. Study Questions: 1, 3, 5, 51, 60.
- Predict the solubility of ionic compounds in water and the species present in aqueous solutions of ionic and molecular compounds.
  - **a.** Explain the difference between electrolytes and nonelectrolytes and recognize examples of each (Section 3-4 and Figure 3.8). Study Question: 9.
  - **b.** Predict the solubility of ionic compounds in water (Sections 3-4 and Figure 3.10). Study Questions: 11, 15, 61, 63, 66, 72.
  - **c.** Recognize what ions are formed when an ionic compound or acid or base dissolves in water (Sections 3-4–3-6). Study Questions: 13, 15, 66, 69.
- Recognize common types of chemical reactions in aqueous solution and predict products of precipitation, acid–base, and gas-forming exchange reactions.
  - **a.** Recognize the key characteristics of four types of reactions in aqueous solution.

Reaction Type	Key Characteristic
Precipitation	Formation of an insoluble compound
Acid–base	Formation of a salt and water
Gas-forming	Evolution of a water-insoluble gas such as CO_2
Oxidation–reduction	Transfer of electrons (with changes in oxidation numbers)

  Study Questions: 51, 52, 55, 56, 82.
  - **b.** Predict the products of precipitation reactions (Section 3-5), acid–base reactions (Section 3-6), and gas-forming reactions (Section 3-7). These are all examples of exchange reactions, which involve the exchange of anions between the cations involved in the reaction. Study Questions: 19, 27, 29, 41–43, 83.
  - **c.** Write overall balanced equations for exchange reactions. Study Questions: 17, 19, 27, 29, 41, 43, 73.

- Know the names and formulas of common acids and bases and understand their nature in aqueous solution.
  - **a.** Know the names and formulas of common acids and bases (Section 3-6 and Table 3.1). Study Questions: 21, 27, 30.
  - **b.** Categorize acids and bases as strong or weak.
  - **c.** Define and use the Arrhenius concept of acids and bases.
  - **d.** Define and use the Brønsted–Lowry concept of acids and bases.
  - **e.** Recognize substances that are amphiprotic. Study Question: 33.
  - **f.** Identify the Brønsted acid and base in a reaction. Study Questions: 21, 27, 28, 32.
  - **g.** Understand that the net ionic equation for the reaction of a strong acid with a strong base is $H_3O^+(aq) + OH^-(aq) \rightarrow 2\ H_2O(\ell)$ (Section 3-6).
- Write a net ionic equation, given the overall balanced equation for a chemical reaction (Sections 3-5–3-7). Study Questions: 17, 19, 35, 37, 39, 69, 73, 74.
- Determine oxidation numbers for elements in a compound and use them to identify oxidation–reduction reactions.
  - **a.** Determine oxidation numbers of elements in a compound and understand that these numbers represent the charge an atom has, or appears to have, when the electrons of the compound are counted according to a set of guidelines (Section 3-8). Study Questions: 45, 46, 81.
  - **b.** Identify oxidation–reduction reactions (often called *redox reactions*) and identify the oxidizing and reducing agents and substances oxidized and reduced in the reaction (Section 3-8 and Tables 3.3 and 3.4). Study Questions: 47–50, 67, 85.

REMEMBER

- The guidelines for the solubility of ionic compounds (Figure 3.10).
- The names and formulas of common acids and bases (Table 3.1).
- Common oxidizing and reducing agents (Table 3.3).

B. Murton/Science Source

STUDY QUESTIONS

▲ denotes challenging questions.

Blue-numbered questions have answers in Appendix N and fully worked solutions in the *Student Solutions Manual.*

Practicing Skills

Balancing Equations

(See Example 3.1.)

1. Write balanced chemical equations for the following reactions.
   (a) The reaction of aluminum and iron(III) oxide to form iron and aluminum oxide (known as the thermite reaction).

© Cengage Learning/Charles D. Winters

Thermite reaction

   (b) The reaction of carbon and water at high temperature to form a mixture of gaseous CO and H_2 (known as water gas and once used as a fuel).
   (c) The reaction of liquid silicon tetrachloride and magnesium forming silicon and magnesium chloride. This is one step in the preparation of ultrapure silicon used in the semiconductor industry.

2. Write balanced chemical equations for the following reactions:
   (a) production of ammonia, $NH_3(g)$, by combining $N_2(g)$ and $H_2(g)$
   (b) production of methanol, $CH_3OH(\ell)$ by combining $H_2(g)$ and $CO(g)$
   (c) production of sulfuric acid by combining sulfur, oxygen, and water

3. Balance the following equations:
   (a) $Cr(s) + O_2(g) \rightarrow Cr_2O_3(s)$
   (b) $Cu_2S(s) + O_2(g) \rightarrow Cu(s) + SO_2(g)$
   (c) $C_6H_5CH_3(\ell) + O_2(g) \rightarrow H_2O(\ell) + CO_2(g)$

4. Balance the following equations:
   (a) $Cr(s) + Cl_2(g) \rightarrow CrCl_3(s)$
   (b) $SiO_2(s) + C(s) \rightarrow Si(s) + CO(g)$
   (c) $Fe(s) + H_2O(g) \rightarrow Fe_3O_4(s) + H_2(g)$

5. Balance the following equations, and name each reactant and product:
   (a) $Fe_2O_3(s) + Mg(s) \rightarrow MgO(s) + Fe(s)$
   (b) $AlCl_3(s) + NaOH(aq) \rightarrow Al(OH)_3(s) + NaCl(aq)$
   (c) $NaNO_3(s) + H_2SO_4(aq) \rightarrow Na_2SO_4(s) + HNO_3(aq)$
   (d) $NiCO_3(s) + HNO_3(aq) \rightarrow Ni(NO_3)_2(aq) + CO_2(g) + H_2O(\ell)$

6. Balance the following equations, and name each reactant and product:
   (a) $SF_4(g) + H_2O(\ell) \rightarrow SO_2(g) + HF(\ell)$
   (b) $NH_3(aq) + O_2(aq) \rightarrow NO(g) + H_2O(\ell)$
   (c) $BF_3(g) + H_2O(\ell) \rightarrow HF(aq) + H_3BO_3(aq)$

Chemical Equilibrium

(See Section 3-3.)

7. Equal amounts of two acids—HCl and HCO_2H (formic acid)—are placed in aqueous solution. When equilibrium has been achieved, the HCl solution has a much greater electrical conductivity than the HCO_2H solution. Which reaction is more product-favored at equilibrium?

$$HCl(aq) + H_2O(\ell) \rightleftharpoons H_3O^+(aq) + Cl^-(aq)$$

$$HCO_2H(aq) + H_2O(\ell) \rightleftharpoons H_3O^+(aq) + HCO_2^-(aq)$$

8. Two aqueous solutions were prepared, one containing 0.10 mol of boric acid (H_3BO_3) in 200 mL and the second containing 0.10 mol phosphoric acid (H_3PO_4) in 200 mL. Both were weak conductors of electricity, but the H_3PO_4 solution was a noticeably stronger conductor. Write equations to describe the equilibrium in each solution, and explain the observed difference in conductivity.

Ions and Molecules in Aqueous Solution

(See Section 3-4 and Example 3.2.)

9. What is an electrolyte? How can you differentiate experimentally between a weak electrolyte and a strong electrolyte? Give an example of each.

10. Name and give the formulas of two acids that are strong electrolytes and one acid that is a weak electrolyte. Name and give formulas of two bases that are strong electrolytes and one base that is a weak electrolyte.

11. Which compound or compounds in each of the following groups is (are) soluble in water?
(a) CuO, $CuCl_2$, $FeCO_3$
(b) AgI, Ag_3PO_4, $AgNO_3$
(c) K_2CO_3, KI, $KMnO_4$

12. Which compound or compounds in each of the following groups is (are) soluble in water?
(a) $BaSO_4$, $Ba(NO_3)_2$, $BaCO_3$
(b) Na_2SO_4, $NaClO_4$, $NaCH_3CO_2$
(c) $AgBr$, KBr, Al_2Br_6

13. The following compounds are water-soluble. What ions are produced by each compound in aqueous solution?
(a) KOH (c) $LiNO_3$
(b) K_2SO_4 (d) $(NH_4)_2SO_4$

14. The following compounds are water-soluble. What ions are produced by each compound in aqueous solution?
(a) KI (c) K_2HPO_4
(b) $Mg(CH_3CO_2)_2$ (d) $NaCN$

15. Decide whether each of the following is water-soluble. If soluble, tell what ions are produced when the compound dissolves in water.
(a) Na_2CO_3 (c) NiS
(b) $CuSO_4$ (d) $BaBr_2$

16. Decide whether each of the following is water-soluble. If soluble, tell what ions are produced when the compound dissolves in water.
(a) $NiCl_2$ (c) $Pb(NO_3)_2$
(b) $Cr(NO_3)_3$ (d) $BaSO_4$

Precipitation Reactions and Net Ionic Equations

(See Section 3-5 and Examples 3.3 and 3.4.)

17. Balance the equation for the following precipitation reaction, and then write the net ionic equation. Indicate the state of each species (s, ℓ, aq, or g).

$$CdCl_2 + NaOH \rightarrow Cd(OH)_2 + NaCl$$

18. Balance the equation for the following precipitation reaction, and then write the net ionic equation. Indicate the state of each species (s, ℓ, aq, or g).

$$Ni(NO_3)_2 + Na_2CO_3 \rightarrow NiCO_3 + NaNO_3$$

19. Predict the products of each precipitation reaction. Balance the equation, and then write the net ionic equation.
(a) $NiCl_2(aq) + (NH_4)_2S(aq) \rightarrow$
(b) $Mn(NO_3)_2(aq) + Na_3PO_4(aq) \rightarrow$

20. Predict the products of each precipitation reaction. Balance the equation, and then write the net ionic equation.
(a) $Pb(NO_3)_2(aq) + KBr(aq) \rightarrow$
(b) $Ca(NO_3)_2(aq) + KF(aq) \rightarrow$
(c) $Ca(NO_3)_2(aq) + Na_2C_2O_4(aq) \rightarrow$

Acids and Bases and Their Reactions

(See Section 3-6 and Example 3.5.)

21. Write a balanced equation for the ionization of nitric acid in water.

22. Write a balanced equation for the ionization of perchloric acid in water.

23. Oxalic acid, $H_2C_2O_4$, which is found in certain plants, can provide two hydronium ions in water. Write balanced equations (like those for sulfuric acid on page 117) to show how oxalic acid can supply one and then a second H_3O^+ ion.

24. Phosphoric acid can supply one, two, or three H_3O^+ ions in aqueous solution. Write balanced equations (like those for sulfuric acid on page 117) to show this successive loss of hydrogen ions.

25. Write a balanced equation for reaction of the basic oxide, magnesium oxide, with water.

26. Write a balanced equation for the reaction of sulfur trioxide gas with water.

27. Complete and balance the equations for the following acid–base reactions. Name the reactants and products.
(a) $CH_3CO_2H(aq) + Mg(OH)_2(s) \rightarrow$
(b) $HClO_4(aq) + NH_3(aq) \rightarrow$

28. Complete and balance the equations for the following acid–base reactions. Name the reactants and products.
(a) $H_3PO_4(aq) + KOH(aq) \rightarrow$
(b) $H_2C_2O_4(aq) + Ca(OH)_2(s) \rightarrow$
($H_2C_2O_4$ is oxalic acid, an acid capable of donating two H^+ ions. See Study Question 23.)

29. Write a balanced equation for the reaction of barium hydroxide with nitric acid.

30. Write a balanced equation for the reaction of aluminum hydroxide with sulfuric acid.

31. Write an equation that describes the equilibrium that exists when nitric acid dissolves in water. Identify each of the four species in solution as either Brønsted acids or Brønsted bases. Does the equilibrium favor the products or the reactants?

32. Write an equation that describes the equilibrium that exists when the weak acid benzoic acid ($C_6H_5CO_2H$) dissolves in water. Identify each of the four species in solution as either Brønsted acids or Brønsted bases. Does the equilibrium favor the products or the reactants? (In acting as an acid, the —CO_2H group supplies H^+ to form H_3O^+.)

33. Write two chemical equations, one that shows H_2O reacting (with HBr) as a Brønsted base and a second that shows H_2O reacting (with NH_3) as a Brønsted acid.

34. Write two chemical equations, one in which $H_2PO_4^-$ is a Brønsted acid (in reaction with the carbonate ion, CO_3^{2-}), and a second in which HPO_4^{2-} is a Brønsted base (in reaction with acetic acid, CH_3CO_2H).

Writing Net Ionic Equations

(See Examples 3.4 and 3.6.)

35. Balance the following equations, and then write the net ionic equation.

(a) $(NH_4)_2CO_3(aq) + Cu(NO_3)_2(aq) \rightarrow CuCO_3(s) + NH_4NO_3(aq)$

(b) $Pb(OH)_2(s) + HCl(aq) \rightarrow PbCl_2(s) + H_2O(\ell)$

(c) $BaCO_3(s) + HCl(aq) \rightarrow BaCl_2(aq) + H_2O(\ell) + CO_2(g)$

(d) $CH_3CO_2H(aq) + Ni(OH)_2(s) \rightarrow Ni(CH_3CO_2)_2(aq) + H_2O(\ell)$

36. Balance the following equations, and then write the net ionic equation:

(a) $Zn(s) + HCl(aq) \rightarrow H_2(g) + ZnCl_2(aq)$

(b) $Mg(OH)_2(s) + HCl(aq) \rightarrow MgCl_2(aq) + H_2O(\ell)$

(c) $HNO_3(aq) + CaCO_3(s) \rightarrow Ca(NO_3)_2(aq) + H_2O(\ell) + CO_2(g)$

(d) $(NH_4)_2S(aq) + FeCl_2(aq) \rightarrow NH_4Cl(aq) + FeS(s)$

37. Balance the following equations, and then write the net ionic equation. Show states for all reactants and products (s, ℓ, g, aq).

(a) the reaction of silver nitrate and potassium iodide to give silver iodide and potassium nitrate

(b) the reaction of barium hydroxide and nitric acid to give barium nitrate and water

(c) the reaction of sodium phosphate and nickel(II) nitrate to give nickel(II) phosphate and sodium nitrate

38. Balance each of the following equations, and then write the net ionic equation. Show states for all reactants and products (s, ℓ, g, aq).

(a) the reaction of sodium hydroxide and iron(II) chloride to give iron(II) hydroxide and sodium chloride

(b) the reaction of barium chloride with sodium carbonate to give barium carbonate and sodium chloride

(c) the reaction of ammonia with phosphoric acid

39. Write balanced net ionic equations for the following reactions:

(a) the reaction of nitrous acid (a weak acid) and sodium hydroxide in aqueous solution

(b) the reaction of calcium hydroxide and hydrochloric acid

40. Write balanced net ionic equations for the following reactions:

(a) the reaction of aqueous solutions of silver nitrate and sodium iodide

(b) the reaction of aqueous solutions of barium chloride and potassium carbonate

Gas-Forming Reactions

(See Section 3-7 and Example 3.7.)

41. Siderite is a mineral consisting largely of iron(II) carbonate. Write an overall, balanced equation for its reaction with nitric acid, and name the products.

42. The mineral rhodochrosite is manganese(II) carbonate. Write an overall, balanced equation for the reaction of the mineral with hydrochloric acid, and name the products.

Rhodochrosite, a mineral consisting largely of $MnCO_3$

43. Write an overall, balanced equation for the reaction of $(NH_4)_2S$ with HBr, and name the reactants and products.

44. Write an overall, balanced equation for the reaction of Na_2SO_3 with CH_3CO_2H, and name the reactants and products.

Oxidation Numbers

(See Section 3-8 and Example 3.8.)

45. Determine the oxidation number of each element in the following ions or compounds.

(a) BrO_3^- (d) CaH_2

(b) $C_2O_4^{2-}$ (e) H_4SiO_4

(c) F^- (f) HSO_4^-

46. Determine the oxidation number of each element in the following ions or compounds.

(a) PF_6^- (d) N_2O_5

(b) $H_2AsO_4^-$ (e) $POCl_3$

(c) UO^{2+} (f) XeO_4^{2-}

Oxidation–Reduction Reactions

(See Section 3-8 and Example 3.9.)

47. Which two of the following reactions are oxidation–reduction reactions? Explain your answer in each case. Classify the remaining reaction.

(a) $Zn(s) + 2\ NO_3^-(aq) + 4\ H_3O^+(aq) \rightarrow Zn^{2+}(aq) + 2\ NO_2(g) + 6\ H_2O(\ell)$

(b) $Zn(OH)_2(s) + H_2SO_4(aq) \rightarrow ZnSO_4(aq) + 2\ H_2O(\ell)$

(c) $Ca(s) + 2\ H_2O(\ell) \rightarrow Ca(OH)_2(s) + H_2(g)$

48. Which two of the following reactions are oxidation–reduction reactions? Explain your answer briefly. Classify the remaining reaction.

(a) $CdCl_2(aq) + Na_2S(aq) \rightarrow CdS(s) + 2\ NaCl(aq)$

(b) $2\ Ca(s) + O_2(g) \rightarrow 2\ CaO(s)$

(c) $4\ Fe(OH)_2(s) + 2\ H_2O(\ell) + O_2(g) \rightarrow 4\ Fe(OH)_3(s)$

49. In the following reactions, decide which reactant is oxidized and which is reduced. Designate the oxidizing agent and the reducing agent.

(a) $C_2H_4(g) + 3\ O_2(g) \rightarrow 2\ CO_2(g) + 2\ H_2O(\ell)$
(b) $Si(s) + 2\ Cl_2(g) \rightarrow SiCl_4(\ell)$

50. In the following reactions, decide which reactant is oxidized and which is reduced. Designate the oxidizing agent and the reducing agent.

(a) $Cr_2O_7^{2-}(aq) + 3\ Sn^{2+}(aq) + 14\ H_3O^+(aq) \rightarrow 2\ Cr^{3+}(aq) + 3\ Sn^{4+}(aq) + 21\ H_2O(\ell)$
(b) $FeS(s) + 3\ NO_3^-(aq) + 4\ H_3O^+(aq) \rightarrow 3\ NO(g) + SO_4^{2-}(aq) + Fe^{3+}(aq) + 6\ H_2O(\ell)$

Types of Reactions in Aqueous Solution

(See Section 3-9 and Example 3.10.)

51. Balance the following equations, and then classify each as a precipitation, acid–base, or gas-forming reaction.

(a) $Ba(OH)_2(aq) + HCl(aq) \rightarrow BaCl_2(aq) + H_2O(\ell)$
(b) $HNO_3(aq) + CoCO_3(s) \rightarrow Co(NO_3)_2(aq) + H_2O(\ell) + CO_2(g)$
(c) $Na_3PO_4(aq) + Cu(NO_3)_2(aq) \rightarrow Cu_3(PO_4)_2(s) + NaNO_3(aq)$

52. Balance the following equations, and then classify each as a precipitation, acid–base, or gas-forming reaction.

(a) $K_2CO_3(aq) + Cu(NO_3)_2(aq) \rightarrow CuCO_3(s) + KNO_3(aq)$
(b) $Pb(NO_3)_2(aq) + HCl(aq) \rightarrow PbCl_2(s) + HNO_3(aq)$
(c) $MgCO_3(s) + HCl(aq) \rightarrow MgCl_2(aq) + H_2O(\ell) + CO_2(g)$

53. Balance the following equations, and then classify each as a precipitation, acid–base, or gas-forming reaction. Show states for the products (s, ℓ, g, aq), and then balance the completed equation. Write the net ionic equation.

(a) $MnCl_2(aq) + Na_2S(aq) \rightarrow MnS + NaCl$
(b) $K_2CO_3(aq) + ZnCl_2(aq) \rightarrow ZnCO_3 + KCl$

54. Balance the following equations, and then classify each as a precipitation, acid–base, or gas-forming reaction. Show states for the products (s, ℓ, g, aq), and then balance the completed equation. Write the net ionic equation.

(a) $Fe(OH)_3(s) + HNO_3(aq) \rightarrow Fe(NO_3)_3 + H_2O$
(b) $FeCO_3(s) + HNO_3(aq) \rightarrow Fe(NO_3)_2 + CO_2 + H_2O$

55. Balance each of the following equations, and classify them as precipitation, acid–base, gas-forming, or oxidation–reduction reactions. Show states for the products (s, ℓ, g, aq).

(a) $CuCl_2 + H_2S \rightarrow CuS + HCl$
(b) $H_3PO_4 + KOH \rightarrow H_2O + K_3PO_4$
(c) $Ca + HBr \rightarrow H_2 + CaBr_2$
(d) $MgCl_2 + NaOH \rightarrow Mg(OH)_2 + NaCl$

56. ▲ Complete and balance the equations below, and classify them as precipitation, acid–base, gas-forming, or oxidation–reduction reactions. Show states for the products (s, ℓ, g, aq).

(a) $NiCO_3 + H_2SO_4 \rightarrow$
(b) $Co(OH)_2 + HBr \rightarrow$
(c) $AgCH_3CO_2 + NaCl \rightarrow$
(d) $NiO + CO \rightarrow$

57. The products formed in several reactions are given below. Identify the reactants (labeled *x* and *y*) and write the complete balanced equation for each reaction.

(a) $x + y \rightarrow H_2O(\ell) + CaBr_2(aq)$
(b) $x + y \rightarrow Mg(NO_3)_2(aq) + CO_2(g) + H_2O(\ell)$
(c) $x + y \rightarrow BaSO_4(s) + NaCl(aq)$
(d) $x + y \rightarrow NH_4^+(aq) + OH^-(aq)$

58. The products formed in several reactions are given below. Identify the reactants (labeled *x* and *y*) and write the complete balanced equation for each reaction.

(a) $x + y \rightarrow (NH_4)_2SO_4(aq)$
(b) $x + y \rightarrow CaCl_2(aq) + CO_2(g) + H_2O(\ell)$
(c) $x + y \rightarrow Ba(NO_3)_2(aq) + AgCl(s)$
(d) $x + y \rightarrow H_3O^+(aq) + ClO_4^-(aq)$

General Questions

These questions are not designated as to type or location in the chapter. They may combine concepts.

59. Balance the following equations:

(a) for the synthesis of urea, a common fertilizer

$$CO_2(g) + NH_3(g) \rightarrow NH_2CONH_2(s) + H_2O(\ell)$$

(b) for the reactions used to make uranium(VI) fluoride for the enrichment of natural uranium

$$UO_2(s) + HF(aq) \rightarrow UF_4(s) + H_2O(\ell)$$

$$UF_4(s) + F_2(g) \rightarrow UF_6(s)$$

(c) for the reaction to make titanium(IV) chloride, which is then converted to titanium metal

$$TiO_2(s) + Cl_2(g) + C(s) \rightarrow TiCl_4(\ell) + CO(g)$$

$$TiCl_4(\ell) + Mg(s) \rightarrow Ti(s) + MgCl_2(s)$$

60. Balance the following equations:

(a) for the reaction to produce "superphosphate" fertilizer

$$Ca_3(PO_4)_2(s) + H_2SO_4(aq) \rightarrow Ca(H_2PO_4)_2(aq) + CaSO_4(s)$$

(b) for the reaction to produce diborane, B_2H_6

$$NaBH_4(s) + H_2SO_4(aq) \rightarrow B_2H_6(g) + H_2(g) + Na_2SO_4(aq)$$

(c) for the reaction to produce tungsten metal from tungsten(VI) oxide

$$WO_3(s) + H_2(g) \rightarrow W(s) + H_2O(\ell)$$

(d) for the decomposition of ammonium dichromate

$$(NH_4)_2Cr_2O_7(s) \rightarrow N_2(g) + H_2O(\ell) + Cr_2O_3(s)$$

61. Give a formula for each of the following compounds:
(a) a soluble compound containing the bromide ion
(b) an insoluble hydroxide
(c) an insoluble carbonate
(d) a soluble nitrate-containing compound
(e) a weak Brønsted acid

62. Give the formula for each of the following compounds:
(a) a soluble compound containing the acetate ion
(b) an insoluble sulfide
(c) a soluble hydroxide
(d) an insoluble chloride
(e) a strong Brønsted base

63. Indicate which of the following copper(II) salts are soluble in water and which are insoluble: $Cu(NO_3)_2$, $CuCO_3$, $Cu_3(PO_4)_2$, $CuCl_2$.

64. Name two anions that combine with Al^{3+} ion to produce water-soluble compounds.

65. Write the net ionic equation and identify the spectator ion or ions in the reaction of nitric acid and magnesium hydroxide. What type of reaction is this?

$$2\ H_3O^+(aq) + 2\ NO_3^-(aq) + Mg(OH)_2(s) \rightarrow 4\ H_2O(\ell) + Mg^{2+}(aq) + 2\ NO_3^-(aq)$$

66. Identify and name the water-insoluble product in each reaction and write the net ionic equation:
(a) $CuCl_2(aq) + H_2S(aq) \rightarrow CuS + 2\ HCl$
(b) $CaCl_2(aq) + K_2CO_3(aq) \rightarrow 2\ KCl + CaCO_3$
(c) $AgNO_3(aq) + NaI(aq) \rightarrow AgI + NaNO_3$

67. Bromine is obtained from sea water by the following redox reaction:

$$Cl_2(g) + 2\ NaBr(aq) \rightarrow 2\ NaCl(aq) + Br_2(\ell)$$

(a) What has been oxidized? What has been reduced?
(b) Identify the oxidizing and reducing agents.

68. Identify each of the following substances as a likely oxidizing or reducing agent: HNO_3, Na, Cl_2, O_2, $KMnO_4$.

69. The mineral dolomite contains magnesium carbonate. This reacts with hydrochloric acid.

$$MgCO_3(s) + 2\ HCl(aq) \rightarrow CO_2(g) + MgCl_2(aq) + H_2O(\ell)$$

(a) Write the net ionic equation for this reaction and identify the spectator ions.
(b) What type of reaction is this?

70. Aqueous solutions of ammonium sulfide, $(NH_4)_2S$, and $Hg(NO_3)_2$ react to produce HgS and NH_4NO_3.
(a) Write the overall, balanced equation for the reaction. Indicate the state (s, aq) for each compound.
(b) Name each compound.
(c) What type of reaction is this?

71. Identify the primary species (atoms, molecules, or ions) present in an aqueous solution of each of the following compounds. Decide which species are Brønsted acids or bases and whether they are strong or weak.
(a) NH_3
(b) CH_3CO_2H
(c) NaOH
(d) HBr

72. (a) Name and give formulas for two water-soluble compounds containing the Cu^{2+} ion. Name two water-insoluble compounds containing the Cu^{2+} ion.
(b) Name and give formulas for two water-soluble compounds containing the Ba^{2+} ion. Name two water-insoluble compounds containing the Ba^{2+} ion.

73. Balance equations for these reactions that occur in aqueous solution, and then classify each as a precipitation, acid–base, or gas-forming reaction. Show states for the products (s, ℓ, g, aq), give their names, and write the net ionic equation.
(a) $K_2CO_3 + HClO_4 \rightarrow KClO_4 + CO_2 + H_2O$
(b) $FeCl_2 + (NH_4)_2S \rightarrow FeS + NH_4Cl$
(c) $Fe(NO_3)_2 + Na_2CO_3(aq) \rightarrow FeCO_3 + NaNO_3$
(d) $NaOH + FeCl_3 \rightarrow NaCl + Fe(OH)_3$

74. For each reaction, write an overall, balanced equation and the net ionic equation.
(a) the reaction of aqueous lead(II) nitrate and aqueous potassium hydroxide
(b) the reaction of aqueous copper(II) nitrate and aqueous sodium carbonate

75. You are given mixtures containing the following compounds. Which compound in each pair could be separated by stirring the solid mixture with water?
(a) NaOH and $Ca(OH)_2$
(b) $MgCl_2$ and MgF_2
(c) AgI and KI
(d) NH_4Cl and $PbCl_2$

76. Identify, from each list below, the compound or compounds that will dissolve in water to give a solution that strongly conducts electricity.
(a) $CuCO_3$, $Cu(OH)_2$, $CuCl_2$, CuO
(b) HCl, $H_2C_2O_4$, H_3PO_4, H_2SO_4

77. Identify, from each list below, the compound or compounds that will dissolve in water to give a solution that is only a very weak conductor of electricity.
(a) NH_3, NaOH, $Ba(OH)_2$, $Fe(OH)_3$
(b) CH_3CO_2H, Na_3PO_4, HF, HNO_3

78. Write net ionic equations for the following reactions:
(a) The reaction of acetic acid, a weak acid, and $Sr(OH)_2(aq)$.
(b) The reaction of zinc and hydrochloric acid to form zinc(II) chloride and hydrogen gas.

79. Gas evolution was observed when a solution of Na_2S was treated with acid. The gas was bubbled into a solution containing $Pb(NO_3)_2$, and a black precipitate formed. Write net ionic equations for the two reactions.

80. Heating HI(g) at 425 °C causes some of this compound to decompose, forming H_2(g) and I_2(g). Eventually, the amounts of the three species do not change further; the system has reached equilibrium. (At this point, approximately 22% of the HI has decomposed.) Describe what is happening in this system at the molecular level.

In the Laboratory

81. The following reaction can be used to prepare iodine in the laboratory.

$$2\ NaI(s) + 2\ H_2SO_4(aq) + MnO_2(s) \rightarrow Na_2SO_4(aq) + MnSO_4(aq) + I_2(g) + 2\ H_2O(\ell)$$

(a) Determine the oxidation number of each atom in the equation.
(b) What is the oxidizing agent, and what has been oxidized? What is the reducing agent, and what has been reduced?
(c) Is the reaction product-favored or reactant-favored?
(d) Name the reactants and products.

Photos: © Cengage Learning/Charles D. Winters

Preparation of iodine. A mixture of NaI and MnO_2 was placed in a flask *(left)*. On adding concentrated H_2SO_4 *(right)*, brown gaseous I_2 evolved.

82. ▲ If you have "silverware" in your home, you know it tarnishes easily. Tarnish is from the oxidation of silver in the presence of sulfur-containing compounds (in the atmosphere or in your food) to give black Ag_2S. To remove the tarnish, you can warm the tarnished object with some aluminum foil in water with a small amount of baking soda. Silver sulfide reacts with aluminum to produce silver as well as aluminum oxide and hydrogen sulfide.

$$3\ Ag_2S(s) + 2\ Al(s) + 3\ H_2O(\ell) \rightarrow 6\ Ag(s) + Al_2O_3(s) + 3\ H_2S(aq)$$

Hydrogen sulfide is foul smelling, but it is removed by reaction with the baking soda.

$$NaHCO_3(aq) + H_2S(aq) \rightarrow NaHS(aq) + H_2O(\ell) + CO_2(g)$$

Classify the two reactions, and identify any acids, bases, oxidizing agents, or reducing agents.

Photos: © Cengage Learning/Charles D. Winters

(a) (b)

Removing silver tarnish. (a) A badly tarnished piece of silver is placed in a dish with aluminum foil and aqueous sodium hydrogen carbonate. **(b)** The portion of the silver in contact with the solution is now free of tarnish.

83. ▲ Suppose you wish to prepare a sample of magnesium chloride. One way to do this is to use an acid–base reaction, the reaction of magnesium hydroxide with hydrochloric acid.

$$Mg(OH)_2(s) + 2\ HCl(aq) \rightarrow MgCl_2(aq) + 2\ H_2O(\ell)$$

When the reaction is complete, evaporating the water will give solid magnesium chloride. Suggest another way to prepare $MgCl_2$.

84. ▲ Suggest a laboratory method for preparing barium phosphate. (See Study Question 89 for a way to approach this question.)

85. The Tollen's test for the presence of reducing sugars (say, in a urine sample) involves treating the sample with silver ions in aqueous ammonia. The result is the formation of a silver mirror within the reaction vessel if a reducing sugar is present. Using glucose, $C_6H_{12}O_6$, to illustrate this test, the oxidation–reduction reaction occurring is

$$C_6H_{12}O_6\ (aq) + 2\ Ag^+(aq) + 2\ OH^-(aq) \rightarrow C_6H_{12}O_7(aq) + 2\ Ag(s) + H_2O(\ell)$$

What has been oxidized, and what has been reduced? What is the oxidizing agent, and what is the reducing agent?

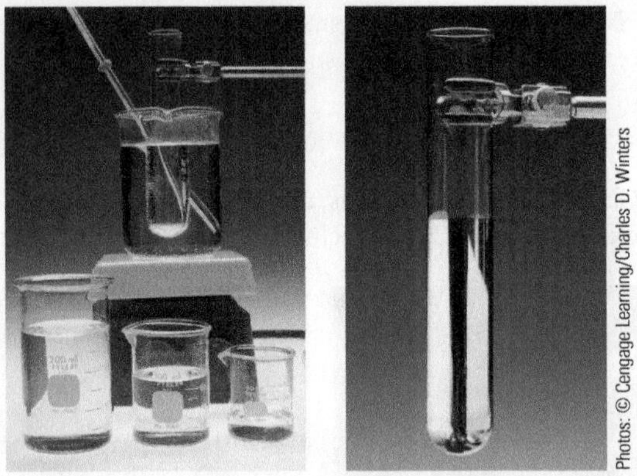

(a) (b)

Tollen's test. The reaction of silver ions with a sugar such as glucose produces metallic silver. **(a)** The set-up for the reaction. **(b)** The silvered test tube.

Summary and Conceptual Questions

The following questions may use concepts from this and previous chapters.

86. There are many ionic compounds that dissolve in water to a very small extent. One example is lead(II) chloride. When it dissolves an equilibrium is established between the solid salt and its component ions. Suppose you stir some solid $PbCl_2$ into water. Explain how you would prove that the compound dissolves but to a small extent? Is the dissolving process product-favored or reactant-favored?

$$PbCl_2(s) \rightleftharpoons Pb^{2+}(aq) + 2\ Cl^-(aq)$$

87. ▲ Most naturally occurring acids are weak acids. Lactic acid is one example.

$$CH_3CH(OH)CO_2H(s) + H_2O(\ell) \rightleftharpoons H_3O^+(aq) + CH_3CH(OH)CO_2^-(aq)$$

If you place some lactic acid in water, it will ionize to a small extent, and an equilibrium will be established. Suggest some experiments to prove that this is a weak acid and that the establishment of equilibrium is a reversible process.

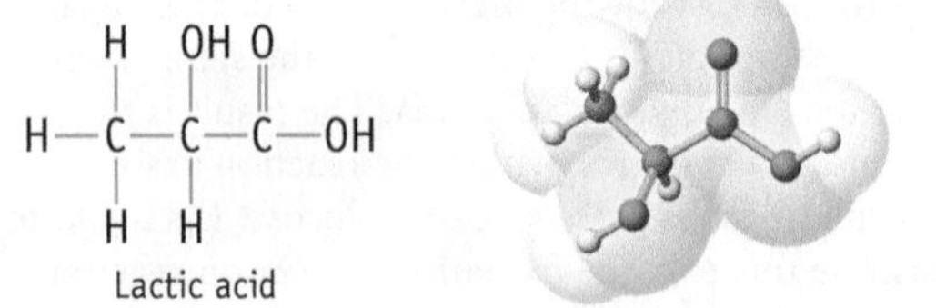

Lactic acid

88. ▲ You want to prepare barium chloride, $BaCl_2$, using an exchange reaction of some type. To do so, you have the following reagents from which to select the reactants: $BaSO_4$, $BaBr_2$, $BaCO_3$, $Ba(OH)_2$, HCl, $HgSO_4$, $AgNO_3$, and HNO_3. Write a complete, balanced equation for the reaction chosen. (*Note:* There are several possibilities.)

89. ▲ Describe how to prepare $BaSO_4$, barium sulfate, by (a) a precipitation reaction and (b) a gas-forming reaction. The available starting materials are $BaCl_2$, $BaCO_3$, $Ba(OH)_2$, H_2SO_4, and Na_2SO_4. Write complete, balanced equations for the reactions chosen. (See page 113 for an illustration of the preparation of the compound.)

90. ▲ Describe how to prepare zinc chloride by (a) an acid–base reaction, (b) a gas-forming reaction, and (c) an oxidation–reduction reaction. The available starting materials are $ZnCO_3$, HCl, Cl_2, HNO_3, $Zn(OH)_2$, NaCl, $Zn(NO_3)_2$, and Zn. Write complete, balanced equations for the reactions chosen.

91. A common method for analyzing for the nickel content of a sample is to use a precipitation reaction. Adding the organic compound dimethylglyoxime to a solution containing Ni^{2+} ions precipitates a red solid.

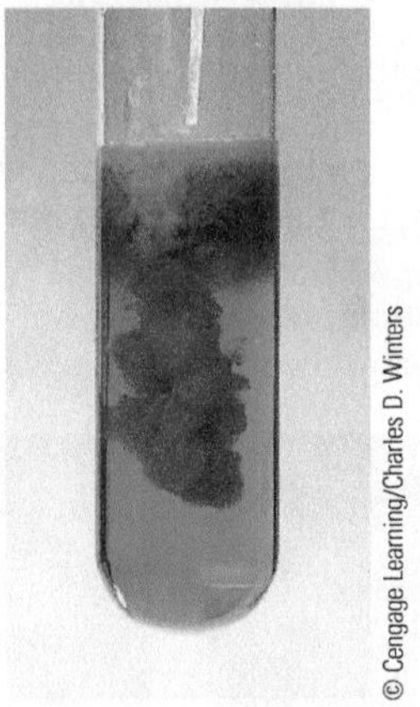

Derive the empirical formula for the red solid based on the following composition: Ni, 20.315%; C, 33.258%; H, 4.884%; O, 22.151%; and N, 19.392%.

92. The lanthanide elements react with oxygen to give, generally, compounds of the type Ln_2O_3 (where Ln stands for a lanthanide element). However, there are interesting exceptions, such as a common oxide of terbium, Tb_xO_y. Given that the compound is 73.945% Tb, what is its formula? What is the oxidation number of terbium in this compound? Write a balanced equation for the reaction of terbium and oxygen to give this oxide.

93. The presence of arsenic in a sample that may also contain another Group 5A element, antimony, can be confirmed by first precipitating the As^{3+} and Sb^{3+} ions as yellow solid As_2S_3 and orange solid Sb_2S_3. If aqueous HCl is then added, only Sb_2S_3 dissolves, leaving behind solid As_2S_3. The As_2S_3 can then be dissolved using aqueous HNO_3.

$$3\ As_2S_3(s) + 10\ HNO_3(aq) + 4\ H_2O(\ell) \rightarrow 6\ H_3AsO_4(aq) + 10\ NO(g) + 9\ S(s)$$

Finally, the presence of arsenic is confirmed by adding $AgNO_3$ to the solution of H_3AsO_4 to precipitate a reddish brown solid Ag_xAsO_y. The composition of this solid is As, 16.199% and Ag, 69.964%.

(a) What are the oxidation numbers of As, S, and N in the reaction of As_2S_3 with nitric acid?

(b) What is the formula of the reddish brown solid Ag_xAsO_y?

94. You have a bottle of solid barium hydroxide and some dilute sulfuric acid. You place some of the barium hydroxide in water and slowly add sulfuric acid to the mixture. While adding the sulfuric acid, you measure the conductivity of the mixture.

(a) Write the complete, balanced equation for the reaction occurring when barium hydroxide and sulfuric acid are mixed.

(b) Write the net ionic equation for the barium hydroxide and sulfuric acid reaction.

(c) Which diagram represents the change in conductivity as the acid is added to the aqueous barium hydroxide? Explain briefly.

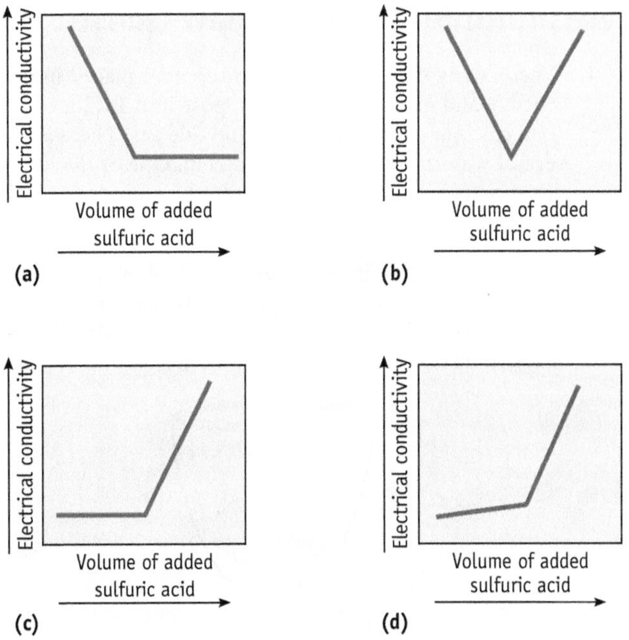

AP Multiple-Choice Review Questions

1. When 20.0 g of solid calcium carbonate is placed into a crucible and heated, it will decompose into 11.2 g of solid calcium oxide and carbon dioxide gas. There are several ways to represent this reaction. One of the most common is by a chemical equation, shown here:

$$CaCO_3(s) \rightarrow CaO(s) + CO_2(g)$$

Another way is to draw it. The crucible shown below illustrates what it looks like before any reaction has taken place. What will the crucible look like after the reaction has taken place?

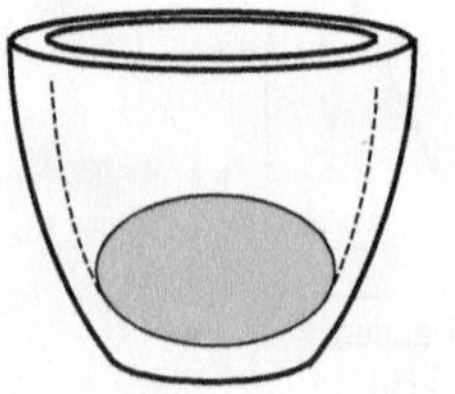

20.0 g $CaCO_3(s)$

(A) 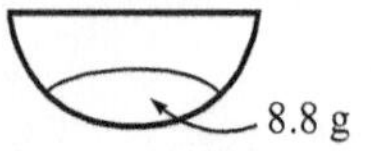

(B) 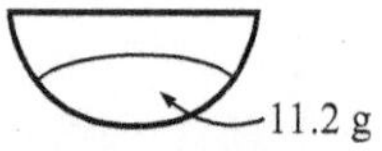

(C) 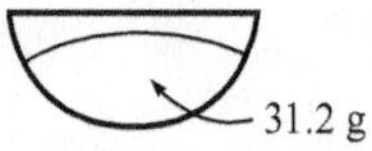

(D) 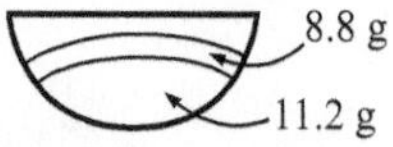

2. When fossil fuels are burned, carbon is released into the air in the form of carbon dioxide (CO_2) gas. Carbon dioxide is known as a greenhouse gas, because it traps heat in the atmosphere and has been implicated as a contributor to global warming. One method of reducing global warming is to plant trees. What role do trees play in reducing global warming?

(A) Trees absorb carbon dioxide and use the carbon to grow.

(B) Trees absorb sunlight as they grow, reducing the temperature.

(C) Trees produce oxygen, which reacts with the carbon dioxide in the air.

(D) Tree leaves reflect the sun's light back into space, thus less is available to heat up the atmosphere.

3.

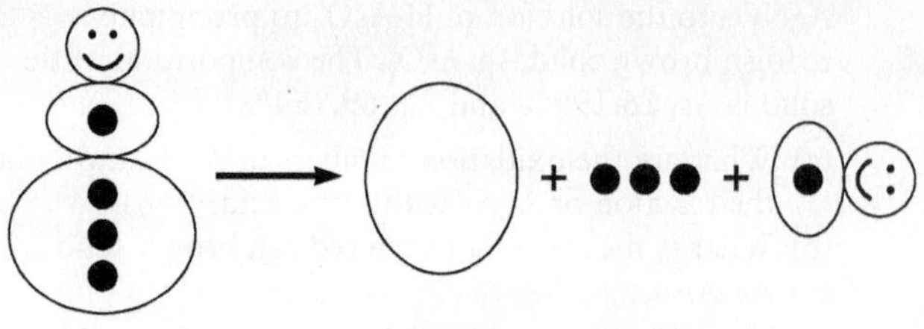

The diagram shown above best represents which of the following?

(A) Dalton's atomic theory

(B) law of definite proportions

(C) law of multiple proportions

(D) law of conservation of mass

4. Consider the reaction between hydrogen (H_2) gas and oxygen (O_2) gas to form water (H_2O).

$$2H_2(g) + O_2(g) \rightarrow 2H_2O(g)$$

Which of the following is a correct representation of this reaction?

(A) 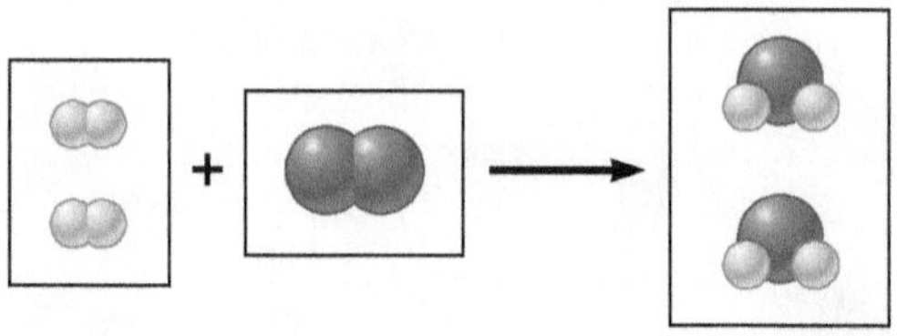

(B) 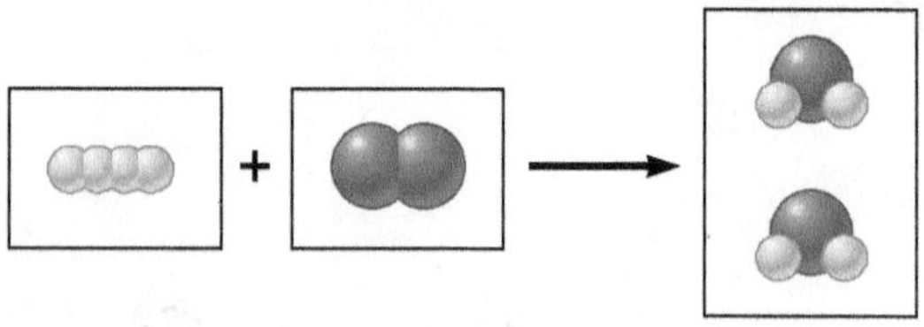

(C)

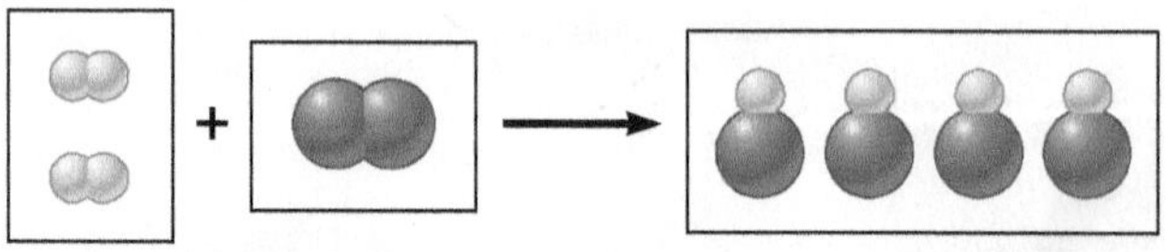

(D) 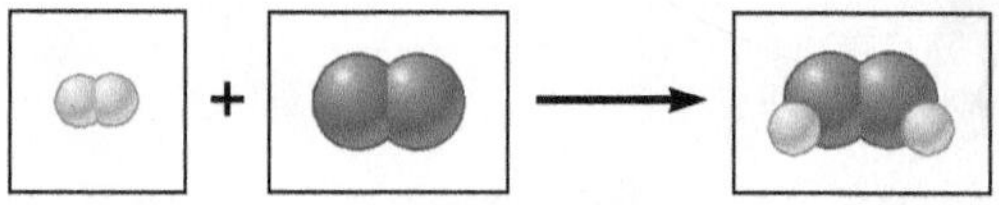

5. Which of the following equations satisfies the law of conservation of mass?
   (A) $H_2(g) + O_2(g) \rightarrow H_2O(g)$
   (B) $Na(s) + Cl_2(g) \rightarrow NaCl(s)$
   (C) $N_2(g) + H_2(g) \rightarrow NH_3(g)$
   (D) $C(s) + O_2(g) \rightarrow CO_2(g)$

6. Phosphorus can be produced by reacting calcium phosphate, silicon dioxide, and carbon at high temperatures according to the following equation:

$$Ca_3(PO_4)_2(s) + SiO_2(s) + C(s) \rightarrow CaSiO_3(s) + P_4(s) + CO(g)$$

   What is the sum of the coefficients when the equation is balanced in standard form (lowest multiple whole numbers)?
   (A) 16
   (B) 25
   (C) 32
   (D) 35

7. Nitroglycerine, $C_3H_5N_3O_9$, explodes with tremendous force due to the numerous gaseous products. The *unbalanced* equation for the explosion of nitroglycerine is shown below. What is the coefficient of the $CO_2(g)$ when the equation is balanced using the lowest whole number coefficients?

$$C_3H_5N_3O_9(\ell) \rightarrow CO_2(g) + O_2(g) + N_2(g) + H_2O(g)$$

   (A) 8
   (B) 10
   (C) 12
   (D) 14

8. What is the sum of the coefficient integers when the following equation is balanced in standard form (lowest multiple whole numbers)?

$$FeCr_2O_7(s) + K_2CO_3(s) + O_2(g) \rightarrow K_2CrO_4(s) + Fe_2O_3(s) + CO_2(g)$$

   (A) 9
   (B) 15
   (C) 24
   (D) 31

9. When iron(III) oxide is heated with carbon, the products are iron metal and carbon monoxide. Balance the equation in standard form and determine the sum of the coefficients.
   (A) 4
   (B) 5
   (C) 6
   (D) 9

Use the following information to answer questions 10 and 11.

For a laboratory investigation, a student is instructed to place a 2.4-g sample of magnesium ribbon into 500 mL of a 2.0 *M* solution of hydrochloric acid. The student then records the following observations:

1) The magnesium ribbon is a bright, shiny, silvery metal.
2) The hydrochloric acid is clear and colorless with no detectable odor.
3) As soon as the magnesium ribbon is dropped into the hydrochloric acid:
   a. bubbles form,
   b. a sizzling sound is heard, and
   c. a clear, colorless gas with no detectable odor appears to be coming from the reaction vessel.
4) After 32 seconds, the magnesium ribbon has completely disappeared.
5) There appears to be only a clear, colorless solution after the reaction has taken place.

10. What is the balanced chemical equation for this reaction?
   (A) $Mg + HCl \rightarrow MgCl + H$
   (B) $Mg + 2HCl \rightarrow MgH_2 + Cl_2$
   (C) $Mg + 2HCl \rightarrow MgCl_2 + H_2$
   (D) $Mg + 2HCl \rightarrow Mg + Cl_2 + H_2$

11. Identify which substance is being oxidized and which substance is being reduced in this laboratory investigation.

(A) Magnesium is being oxidized, and the chloride ion is being reduced.

(B) Magnesium is being reduced, and the chloride ion is being oxidized.

(C) Magnesium is being oxidized, and the hydrogen ion is being reduced.

(D) Magnesium is being reduced, and the hydrogen ion is being oxidized.

Use the following information to answer questions 12 and 13.

Solutions of lead(II) nitrate and potassium iodide react according to the following equation:

$$Pb(NO_3)_2(aq) + 2KI(aq) \rightarrow PbI_2(s) + 2KNO_3(aq)$$

A molecular-level representation illustrating solutions of the reactants lead(II) nitrate and potassium iodide is shown below.

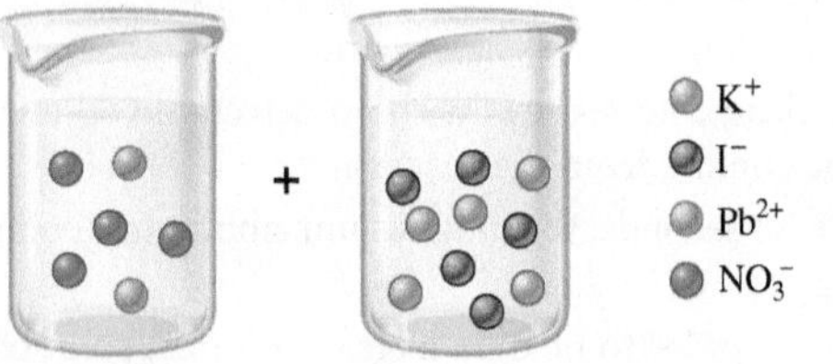

12. Which of the following would be the best molecular-level representation after the reaction has taken place?

(A)
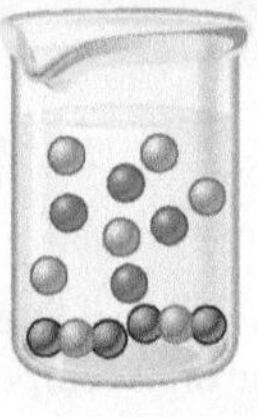

(B)
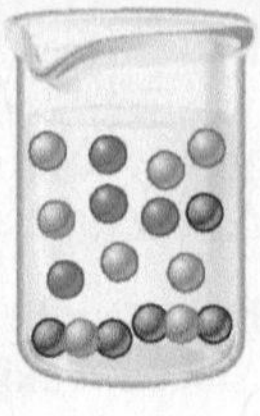

(C)
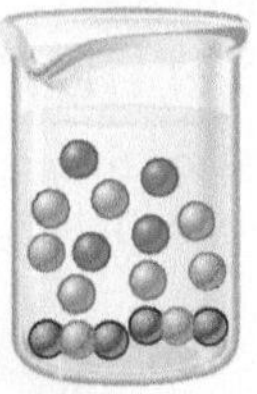

(D)
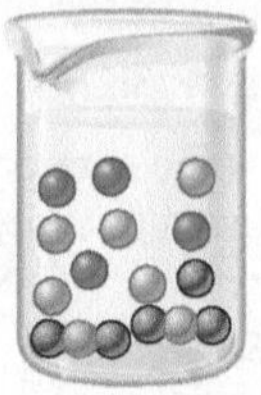

13. Which species acts exclusively as spectator ions in this reaction?

(A) K^+ and NO_3^-

(B) Pb^{2+} and I^-

(C) K^+ and Pb^{2+}

(D) I^- and NO_3^-

Use the following information to answer questions 14 and 15. The photos of a reaction along with the molecular-level representations are shown below.

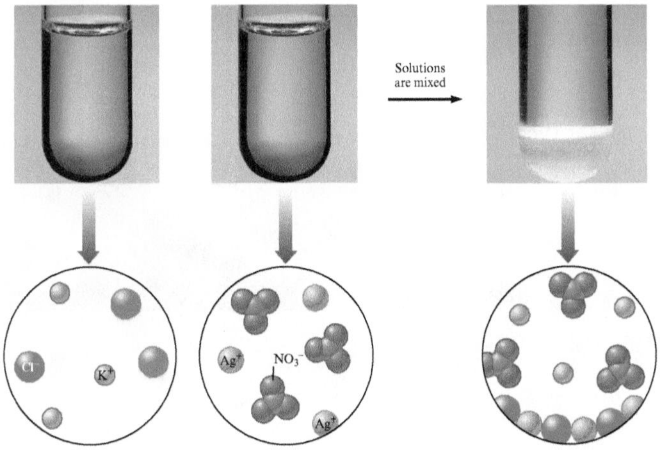

14. What is the correct balanced net ionic equation for the reaction illustrated?

(A) $KCl + AgNO_3 \rightarrow KNO_3 + AgCl$

(B) $K^+ + NO_3^- \rightarrow KNO_3$

(C) $Ag^+ + NO_3^- \rightarrow AgNO_3$

(D) $Ag^+ + Cl^- \rightarrow AgCl$

15. Which species are the spectator ions in this reaction?

(A) K^+ and NO_3^-

(B) K^+ and Cl^-

(C) Ag^+ and NO_3^-

(D) Ag^+ and Cl^-

16. In which of the following species is the oxidation state for nitrogen the greatest?

(A) NO

(B) NO_2

(C) N_2O

(D) N_2O_5

© Cengage Learning/Charles D. Winters

Thermite reaction.

Stoichiometry: Quantitative Information about Chemical Reactions

Chapter Outline

THERMITE One of the most spectacular chemical reactions is the thermite reaction, the reduction of iron(III) oxide with metallic aluminum.

$$Fe_2O_3(s) + 2\ Al(s) \rightarrow 2\ Fe(\ell) + Al_2O_3(s)$$

This reaction generates an enormous amount of energy, sufficient to produce iron in the molten state. Although the thermite reaction was originally developed as a way of producing metals from their oxides (copper, uranium, and others also work well), it was quickly realized that it can be used for welding. For some years the iron(III) oxide/aluminum reaction was used to weld the rails of railroad train tracks.

The most important objective of this chapter is to discuss the quantitative relationships between reactants and products. For example, you will learn how to predict the mass of iron that can be produced from known masses of iron(III) oxide and aluminum.

Study Questions related to this story are: 4.1 and 4.17.

Chapter Goals

See Chapter Goals Revisited (page 178) for Study Questions keyed to these goals.

UNDERSTAND

- The law of the conservation of matter, which forms the basis of chemical stoichiometry.
- The meaning of a limiting reactant in a chemical reaction.

DO

- Perform stoichiometric calculations using balanced chemical equations.
- Calculate the theoretical and percent yields of chemical reactions.
- Use stoichiometry to analyze a mixture of compounds or to determine the formula of a compound.
- Define and use concentration in solution stoichiometry.
- Use the relationship of pH and hydronium ion concentration.
- Use spectrophotometry to determine the concentration of a species in solution.

REMEMBER

- That concentration (as molarity) is the amount of solute per liter of solution.
- That pH is a measure of hydronium ion concentration.

The objective of this chapter is to introduce the quantitative study of chemical reactions. Quantitative studies are needed to determine, for example, how much oxygen is required for the complete combustion of a given quantity of gasoline and what masses of carbon dioxide and water can be obtained. This part of chemistry is fundamental to much of what chemists, chemical engineers, biochemists, molecular biologists, geochemists, and many others do.

4-1 Mass Relationships in Chemical Reactions: Stoichiometry

Learning Objectives: LO 1.17, LO 1.18, LO 3.1, LO 3.3, LO 3.4

A balanced chemical equation shows the quantitative relationship between reactants and products in a chemical reaction. On the submicroscopic scale, the stoichiometric coefficients in the equation refer to atoms, molecules, or formula units. On the macroscopic level on which we work in the laboratory, the coefficients refer to the number of moles of each reactant and product. The coefficients in a balanced chemical equation thus allow us to relate the amount (moles) of one substance involved in a chemical reaction to the amount (moles) of another substance involved in that chemical reaction.

Let us apply this concept to the reaction of phosphorus and chlorine.

$$P_4(s) + 6\ Cl_2(g) \rightarrow 4\ PCl_3(\ell)$$

$P_4(s)$	$6\ Cl_2(g)$	$4\ PCl_3(\ell)$
1 mol	6 mol	4 mol
124 g	425 g	549 g

The chemical equation for this reaction indicates that 1 mol (124 g) of solid phosphorus (P_4) can react with 6 mol (425 g) of chlorine gas (Cl_2) to form 4 mol (549 g) of liquid phosphorus trichloride (PCl_3).

Now, suppose you want to use less P_4 in the reaction, only 1.45 g. What mass of Cl_2 gas would be required and what mass of PCl_3 could be produced? This is an example of a situation common in chemistry and chemical engineering, so let us

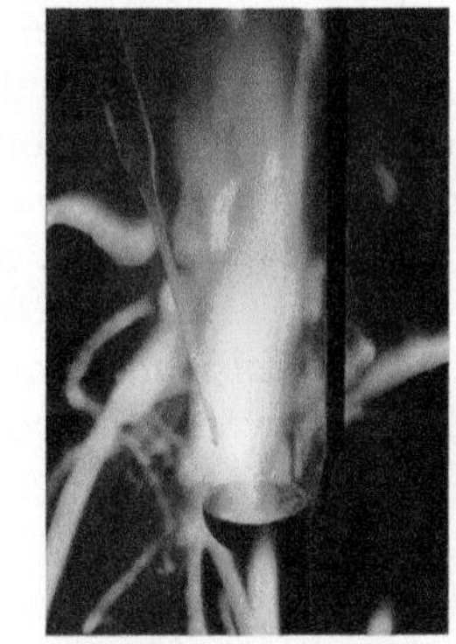

© Cengage Learning/Charles D. Winters

Reaction of P_4 and Cl_2. When white phosphorus comes into contact with chlorine, a reaction occurs spontaneously. See Figure 3.1 for more on this reaction.

work carefully through the steps you should follow when solving a stoichiometry problem.

Part (a): Calculate the mass of Cl_2 required by 1.45 g of P_4

STEP 1 *Write the balanced equation* (using correct formulas for reactants and products). This is *always* the first step when dealing with chemical reactions.

$$P_4(s) + 6\ Cl_2(g) \rightarrow 4\ PCl_3(\ell)$$

STEP 2 *Calculate amount (moles) from mass (grams).* Recall that chemical equations reflect the relative amounts of reactants and products, not their masses. Therefore, calculate the amount (moles) of P_4 available.

$$1.45\ \text{g P}_4 \times \frac{1\ \text{mol P}_4}{123.9\ \text{g P}_4} = 0.0117\ \text{mol P}_4$$

↑ 1/molar mass of P_4

STEP 3a *Use a stoichiometric factor.* The next step is to use the balanced equation to relate the amount of P_4 available to the amount of Cl_2 required to completely consume the P_4. This relationship is a **stoichiometric factor**, a mole ratio based on the stoichiometric coefficients in the balanced equation. Here the balanced equation specifies that 6 mol of Cl_2 is required for each mole of P_4, so the stoichiometric factor is (6 mol Cl_2/1 mol P_4).

$$0.0117\ \text{mol P}_4 \times \frac{6\ \text{mol Cl}_2\ \text{required}}{1\ \text{mol P}_4\ \text{available}} = 0.0702\ \text{mol Cl}_2\ \text{required}$$

↑ stoichiometric factor from balanced equation

STEP 4a *Calculate mass from amount.* Convert the amount (moles) of Cl_2 calculated in Step 3 to the mass of Cl_2 required.

$$0.0702\ \text{mol Cl}_2 \times \frac{70.91\ \text{g Cl}_2}{1\ \text{mol Cl}_2} = 4.98\ \text{g Cl}_2$$

Part (b): Calculate mass of PCl_3 produced from 1.45 g of P_4 and 4.98 g of Cl_2

From part (a), we know that 1.45 g of P_4 and 4.98 g of Cl_2 are the correct quantities needed for complete reaction. Because mass is conserved, the answer can be obtained by adding the masses of P_4 and Cl_2 used (giving 1.45 g + 4.98 g = 6.43 g of PCl_3 produced). Alternatively, Steps 3 and 4 can be repeated, but with the appropriate stoichiometric factor and molar mass.

STEP 3b *Use a stoichiometric factor.* Convert the amount of available P_4 to the amount of PCl_3 produced. Here the balanced equation specifies that 4 mol of PCl_3 is produced for each mole of P_4 used, so the stoichiometric factor is (4 mol PCl_3/1 mol P_4).

$$0.0117\ \text{mol P}_4 \times \frac{4\ \text{mol PCl}_3\ \text{produced}}{1\ \text{mol P}_4\ \text{available}} = 0.0468\ \text{mol PCl}_3\ \text{produced}$$

↑ stoichiometric factor from balanced equation

STEP 4b *Calculate the mass of product from its amount.* Convert the amount of PCl_3 produced to its mass in grams.

$$0.0468\ \text{mol PCl}_3 \times \frac{137.3\ \text{g PCl}_3}{1\ \text{mol PCl}_3} = 6.43\ \text{g PCl}_3$$

We find it useful to summarize the mole relationships of reactants and products in a reaction in an **amounts table.**

Amounts Tables The mole (and mass) relationships of reactants and products in a reaction can be summarized in an *amounts table.* Such tables will be used extensively when studying chemical equilibria in Chapters 15–17.

EQUATION	$P_4(s)$	+	$6\ Cl_2(g)$	→	$4\ PCl_3(\ell)$
Initial amount (mol)	0.0117 mol		0.0702 mol		0 mol
Change in amount upon reaction (mol)	−0.0117 mol		−0.0702 mol		+0.0468 mol
Amount after complete reaction (mol)	0 mol		0 mol		0.0468 mol

PROBLEM SOLVING TIP 4.1

Stoichiometry Calculations

You are asked to determine what mass of product can be formed from a given mass of reactant. It is not possible to calculate the mass of product in a single step. Instead, you must follow a route such as that illustrated in the strategy map here for the reaction of reactant A to give the product B according to an equation such as $x\text{ A} \rightarrow y\text{ B}$.

- The mass (g) of reactant A is converted to the amount (moles) of A using the molar mass of A.
- Next, using the stoichiometric factor, you find the amount (moles) of B.
- Finally, the mass (g) of B is obtained by multiplying amount of B by its molar mass.

When solving a stoichiometry problem, remember that you will always use a stoichiometric factor at some point.

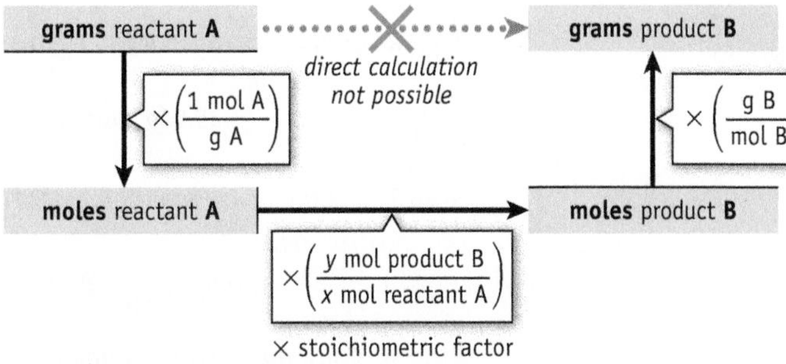

The balanced chemical equation is written across the top of the table. The next three lines indicate the following:

- *Initial* amount (moles) of each reactant and product present.
- *Change* in amount that occurs during the reaction.
- *Final* amount of each reactant and product present after the reaction.

The completed amounts table for the example just worked indicates that the reactants P_4 and Cl_2 were initially present in the correct stoichiometric ratio but no PCl_3 was present. During the course of the reaction, all of the reactants were consumed and formed the product. The total mass of reactants consumed (1.45 g of P_4 and 4.98 g of Cl_2) is always the same as the total mass of products (6.43 g of PCl_3).

Strategy Map 4.1

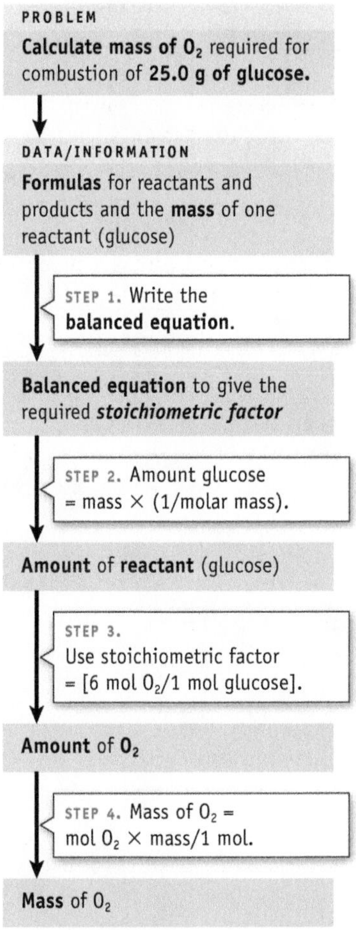

EXAMPLE 4.1

Mass Relations in Chemical Reactions

Problem Glucose, $C_6H_{12}O_6$, reacts with oxygen to give CO_2 and H_2O. What mass of oxygen (in grams) is required for complete reaction of 25.0 g of glucose? What masses of carbon dioxide and water (in grams) are formed?

What Do You Know? This is a stoichiometry problem because you are given the mass of one of the reactants (glucose) and are asked to determine the masses of the other substances involved in the chemical reaction. In addition, you know formulas for the reactants and products and the mass of one of the reactants (glucose). You will need the molar masses of the reactants and products for the calculation.

Strategy Write the balanced chemical equation for this reaction. Then, follow the scheme outlined in Problem Solving Tip 4.1 and in the Strategy Map 4.1.

- Write the balanced chemical equation for the reaction of glucose and oxygen to form carbon dioxide and water.

- Find the amount (moles) of glucose available.
- Find the amount (moles) of O_2 required. Relate the amount of glucose to the amount of O_2 required using the stoichiometric factor based on the coefficients in the balanced equation.
- Find the mass (g) of O_2 required from the amount of O_2.
- Follow the same procedure to calculate the masses of carbon dioxide and water.

Solution

Step 1. *Write a balanced equation.*

$$C_6H_{12}O_6(s) + 6\ O_2(g) \rightarrow 6\ CO_2(g) + 6\ H_2O(\ell)$$

Step 2. *Convert the mass of glucose to amount of glucose.*

$$25.0\ \text{g glucose} \times \frac{1\ \text{mol}}{180.2\ \text{g}} = 0.139\ \text{mol glucose}$$

Step 3. *Use the stoichiometric factor to calculate the amount of O_2 required.*

$$0.139\ \text{mol glucose} \times \frac{6\ \text{mol}\ O_2}{1\ \text{mol glucose}} = 0.832\ \text{mol}\ O_2$$

Step 4. *Calculate mass from amount.* Convert the required amount of O_2 to a mass in grams.

$$0.832\ \text{mol}\ O_2 \times \frac{32.00\ \text{g}}{1\ \text{mol}\ O_2} = 26.6\ \text{g}\ O_2$$

Repeat Steps 3 and 4 to find the mass of CO_2 produced in the combustion. First, relate the amount (moles) of glucose available to the amount of CO_2 produced using a stoichiometric factor. Then convert the amount of CO_2 to its mass in grams.

$$0.139\ \text{mol glucose} \times \frac{6\ \text{mol}\ CO_2}{1\ \text{mol glucose}} \times \frac{44.01\ \text{g}\ CO_2}{1\ \text{mol}\ CO_2} = 36.6\ \text{g}\ CO_2$$

Now, how can you find the mass of H_2O produced? You could go through Steps 3 and 4 again. However, recognize that the total mass of reactants

$$25.0\ \text{g}\ C_6H_{12}O_6 + 26.6\ \text{g}\ O_2 = 51.6\ \text{g reactants}$$

must be the same as the total mass of products. The mass of water that can be produced is therefore

$$\text{Total mass of products} = 51.6\ \text{g} = 36.6\ \text{g}\ CO_2\ \text{produced} + ?\ \text{g}\ H_2O$$

$$\text{Mass of}\ H_2O\ \text{produced} = 15.0\ \text{g}$$

Think about Your Answer The results of this calculation can be summarized in an amounts table.

EQUATION	$C_6H_{12}O_6(s)$ +	$6\ O_2(g)$	→ $6\ CO_2(g)$ +	$6\ H_2O(\ell)$
Initial amount (mol)	0.139 mol	6(0.139 mol) = 0.832 mol	0	0
Change in amount upon reaction (mol)	−0.139 mol	−0.832 mol	+0.832 mol	+0.832 mol
Amount after complete reaction (mol)	0	0	0.832 mol	0.832 mol

When you know the mass of all but one of the chemicals in a reaction, you can find the unknown mass using the principle of mass conservation (the total mass of reactants must equal the total mass of products; page 141).

Check Your Understanding

What mass of oxygen, O_2, is required to completely combust 454 g of propane, C_3H_8? What masses of CO_2 and H_2O are produced?

REVIEW & CHECK FOR SECTION 4-1

1. Aluminum reacts with Cl_2 to form $AlCl_3$. If you have 0.40 mol of Al, what amount (moles) of Cl_2 is needed for a complete reaction?

   (a) 0.40 moles Cl_2 (b) 0.60 moles Cl_2 (c) 1.0 moles Cl_2 (d) 1.2 moles Cl_2

2. The equation for the reaction of Mg and O_2 is $2\ Mg(s) + O_2(g) \rightarrow 2\ MgO(s)$. If you want to prepare 1.0 g of MgO, what mass of magnesium should you use?

   (a) 0.60 g Mg (b) 0.30 g Mg (c) 0.20 g Mg (d) 0.40 g Mg

4-2 Reactions in Which One Reactant Is Present in Limited Supply

Learning Objectives: LO 1.17, LO 1.18, LO 3.1, LO 3.3, LO 3.4

Reactions are often carried out with an excess of one reactant over that required by stoichiometry. This is usually done to make sure that one of the reactants is consumed completely, even though some of another reactant remains unused.

Suppose you burn a toy sparkler, a wire coated with a mixture of aluminum or iron powder and potassium chlorate (Figure 4.1). The aluminum or iron burns, consuming oxygen from the air or from the potassium salt and producing a metal oxide.

$$4\ Al(s) + 3\ O_2(g) \rightarrow 2\ Al_2O_3(s)$$

The sparkler burns until the metal powder is consumed completely. What about the oxygen? Four moles of aluminum require three moles of oxygen, but there is much, much more O_2 available in the air than is needed to consume the metal in a sparkler. How much metal oxide is produced? That depends on the quantity of metal powder in the sparkler, not on the quantity of O_2 in the atmosphere. The metal powder in this example is called the **limiting reactant** because its amount determines, or limits, the amount of product formed.

FIGURE 4.1 **Burning aluminum and iron powder.** A toy sparkler contains a metal powder such as Al or Fe and other chemicals such as $KClO_3$. When ignited, the metal burns with a brilliant white light.

Now let us see how these same principles apply to another example, the reaction of oxygen and carbon monoxide to give carbon dioxide. The balanced equation for the reaction is

$$2\ CO(g) + O_2(g) \rightarrow 2\ CO_2(g)$$

Suppose you have a mixture of four CO molecules and three O_2 molecules. The four CO molecules require only two O_2 molecules (and produce four CO_2 molecules). This means that one O_2 molecule remains after reaction is complete.

Reactants: 4 **CO** and 3 $\mathbf{O_2}$ ⟶ Products: 4 $\mathbf{CO_2}$ and 1 $\mathbf{O_2}$

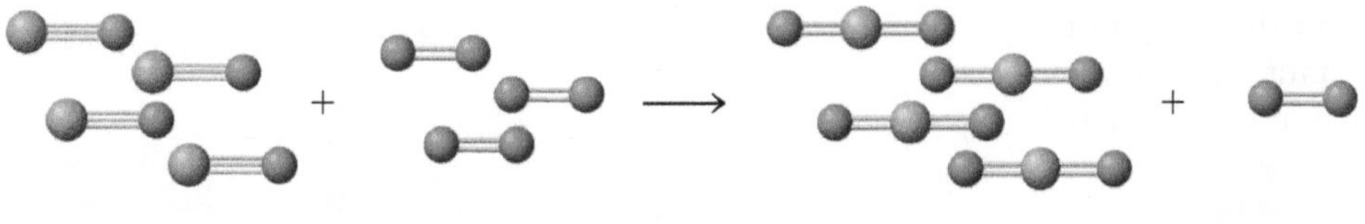

FIGURE 4.2 **Oxidation of ammonia.** Billions of kilograms of HNO_3 are made annually starting with the oxidation of ammonia over a wire gauze containing platinum.

Because more O_2 molecules are available than are required, the number of CO_2 molecules produced is determined by the number of CO molecules available. Carbon monoxide, CO, is therefore the limiting reactant in this case.

A Stoichiometry Calculation with a Limiting Reactant

The first step in the manufacture of nitric acid is the oxidation of ammonia to NO over a platinum-wire gauze (Figure 4.2).

$$4\ NH_3(g) + 5\ O_2(g) \rightarrow 4\ NO(g) + 6\ H_2O(\ell)$$

Suppose equal masses of NH_3 and O_2 are mixed (750. g of each). Are these reactants mixed in the correct stoichiometric ratio or is one of them in short supply? That is, will one of them limit the quantity of NO that can be produced? How much NO can be formed if the reaction using this reactant mixture goes to completion? And how much of the excess reactant is left over when the maximum amount of NO has been formed?

STEP 1 *Find the amount of each reactant.*

$$750.\ \text{g NH}_3 \times \frac{1\ \text{mol NH}_3}{17.03\ \text{g NH}_3} = 44.0\ \text{mol NH}_3\ \text{available}$$

$$750.\ \text{g O}_2 \times \frac{1\ \text{mol O}_2}{32.00\ \text{g O}_2} = 23.4\ \text{mol O}_2\ \text{available}$$

STEP 2 *What is the limiting reactant?* Examine the ratio of amounts of reactants. Are the reactants present in the correct stoichiometric ratio as given by the balanced equation?

Dividing moles of O_2 available by moles of NH_3 available shows that the ratio of available reactants is much smaller than the 5 mol O_2/4 mol NH_3 ratio required by the balanced equation. Thus, there is not sufficient O_2 available to react with all of the NH_3. In this case, oxygen, O_2, is the limiting reactant. That is, 1 mol of NH_3 requires 1.25 mol of O_2, but we have only 0.532 mol of O_2 available.

$$\text{Required ratio of reactants} = \frac{5\ \text{mol O}_2}{4\ \text{mol NH}_3} = \frac{1.25\ \text{mol O}_2}{1\ \text{mol NH}_3}$$

$$\text{Ratio of reactants available} = \frac{23.4\ \text{mol O}_2}{44.0\ \text{mol NH}_3} = \frac{0.532\ \text{mol O}_2}{1\ \text{mol NH}_3}$$

STEP 3 *Calculate the mass of product.* We can now calculate the expected mass of product, NO, based on the amount of the limiting reactant, O_2.

$$23.4 \text{ mol } O_2 \times \frac{4 \text{ mol NO}}{5 \text{ mol } O_2} \times \frac{30.01 \text{ g NO}}{1 \text{ mol NO}} = 562 \text{ g NO}$$

STEP 4 *Calculate the mass of excess reactant.* Ammonia is the "excess reactant" in this NH_3/O_2 reaction because more than enough NH_3 is available to react with 23.4 mol of O_2. Let us calculate the quantity of NH_3 remaining after all the O_2 has been used. To do so, we first need to know the amount of NH_3 required to consume all the limiting reactant, O_2.

$$23.4 \text{ mol } O_2 \text{ available} \times \frac{4 \text{ mol } NH_3 \text{ required}}{5 \text{ mol } O_2} = 18.8 \text{ mol } NH_3 \text{ required}$$

Because 44.0 mol of NH_3 is available, the amount of excess NH_3 can be calculated.

$$\text{Excess } NH_3 = 44.0 \text{ mol } NH_3 \text{ available} - 18.8 \text{ mol } NH_3 \text{ required} = 25.2 \text{ mol } NH_3 \text{ remaining}$$

Finally, the amount of excess NH_3 can be converted to a mass. Because 429 g of NH_3 is left over, this means that 321 g of the initial 750.0 g of NH_3 has been consumed.

$$25.2 \text{ mol } NH_3 \times \frac{17.03 \text{ g } NH_3}{1 \text{ mol } NH_3} = 429 \text{ g } NH_3 \text{ in excess}$$

The information in this example can be organized in an amounts table.

Equation	$4\,NH_3(g)$	+ $5\,O_2(g)$	→ $4\,NO(g)$	+ $6\,H_2O(g)$
Initial amount (mol)	44.0	23.4	0	0
Change in amount upon reaction (mol)	−(4/5)(23.4) = −18.8	−23.4	+(4/5)(23.4) = +18.8	+(6/5)(23.4) = +28.1
Amount after complete reaction (mol)	44.0 − 18.8 = 25.2	0	18.8	28.1

All of the limiting reactant, O_2, is consumed. Of the original 44.0 mol of NH_3, 18.8 mol is consumed and 25.2 mol remains. The balanced equation indicates that the amount of NO produced is equal to the amount of NH_3 consumed, so 18.8 mol of NO is produced from 18.8 mol of NH_3. In addition, 28.1 mol of H_2O is produced.

EXAMPLE 4.2

A Reaction with a Limiting Reactant

Problem Methanol, CH_3OH, which can be used as a fuel in racing cars and in fuel cells, can be made by the reaction of carbon monoxide and hydrogen.

$$CO(g) + 2\,H_2(g) \rightarrow \underset{\text{methanol}}{CH_3OH(\ell)}$$

Suppose 356 g of CO and 65.0 g of H_2 are mixed and allowed to react.

(a) What mass of methanol can be produced?

(b) What mass of the excess reactant remains after the limiting reactant has been consumed?

What Do You Know? You should suspect this problem might involve a limiting reactant because the masses of two reactants are given, and you are asked to determine the mass of the product. The equation for the reaction is given, and you know the masses

SRA Photo

Methanol as a fuel. Methanol can be used as an automotive fuel when blended with gasoline (in M85, which contains 85% methanol). Small fuel cells using methanol to produce electricity are also on the market.

Strategy Map 4.2

PROBLEM

Calculate **mass** of **product** from a reaction.

DATA/INFORMATION

- **Masses** of two reactants.
- Recognize as a **limiting reactant** problem.

STEP 1. Write the **balanced equation.**

Balanced equation gives **stoichiometric ratio.**

STEP 2. Calculate **amount** of each **reactant** = mass × (1 mol/molar mass).

Amount of each **reactant**

STEP 3. Decide which reactant is **limiting.** Is ratio of reactant amounts ***greater than*** or ***less than*** stoichiometric ratio?

Limiting reactant now known

STEP 4. Calculate **amount** of **product** based on amount of limiting reactant. Product amount = mol reactant × stoichiometric factor.

Amount of product expected based on amount of limiting reactant

STEP 5. Calculate **mass** of **product** = mol product × (molar mass/1 mol).

Mass of product

of CO and H_2 that are available. You will need the molar masses of the two reactants and the product to solve the problem.

Strategy

- Calculate the amounts of each reactant.
- Compare the ratio of reactant amounts to the stoichiometric ratio defined by the equation, here (2 mol H_2/1 mol CO). If (mol H_2 available/mol CO available) is greater than 2/1, then CO is the limiting reactant. If (mol H_2 available/mol CO available) is less than 2/1, then H_2 is the limiting reactant.
- Use the amount of the limiting reactant to calculate the mass of product formed, following the scheme in Problem Solving Tip 4.1.
- Determine the mass of the second reactant required in the reaction from the limiting reactant in a similar calculation. The mass of excess reagent is the difference between its starting mass and what was used in the reaction.

Solution

What is the limiting reactant? The amount of each reactant is

$$\text{Amount of CO} = 356 \text{ g CO} \times \frac{1 \text{ mol CO}}{28.01 \text{ g CO}} = 12.7 \text{ mol CO}$$

$$\text{Amount of } H_2 = 65.0 \text{ g } H_2 \times \frac{1 \text{ mol } H_2}{2.016 \text{ g } H_2} = 32.2 \text{ mol } H_2$$

Are these reactants present in a perfect stoichiometric ratio?

$$\frac{\text{Mol } H_2 \text{ available}}{\text{Mol CO available}} = \frac{32.2 \text{ mol } H_2}{12.7 \text{ mol CO}} = \frac{2.54 \text{ mol } H_2}{1.00 \text{ mol CO}}$$

The required mole ratio is 2 mol of H_2 to 1 mol of CO. Here you see that more hydrogen is available than is required to consume all the CO. Therefore, because not enough CO is present to use up all of the hydrogen, CO is the limiting reactant.

(a) *What is the maximum mass of CH_3OH that can be formed?* This calculation must be based on the amount of the limiting reactant.

$$12.7 \text{ mol CO} \times \frac{1 \text{ mol } CH_3OH \text{ formed}}{1 \text{ mol CO available}} \times \frac{32.04 \text{ g } CH_3OH}{1 \text{ mol } CH_3OH} = 407 \text{ g } CH_3OH$$

(b) *What mass of H_2 remains when all the CO has been converted to product?* First, you must find the mass of H_2 required to react with all the CO.

$$12.7 \text{ mol CO} \times \frac{2 \text{ mol } H_2}{1 \text{ mol CO}} \times \frac{2.016 \text{ g } H_2}{1 \text{ mol } H_2} = 51.2 \text{ g } H_2 \text{ required}$$

You began with 65.0 g of H_2, but only 51.2 g is required by the limiting reactant; thus, the mass that is present in excess is

$$65.0 \text{ g } H_2 \text{ present} - 51.2 \text{ g } H_2 \text{ required} = 13.8 \text{ g } H_2 \text{ left}$$

Think about Your Answer The amounts table for this reaction is as follows.

EQUATION	**CO(g)**	**+**	**$2\,H_2(g)$**	**→**	**$CH_3OH(\ell)$**
Initial amount (mol)	12.7		32.2		0
Change in amount upon reaction (mol)	−12.7		−2(12.7)		+12.7
Amount after complete reaction (mol)	0		6.8		12.7

The mass of product formed plus the mass of H_2 remaining after reaction (407 g CH_3OH produced + 14 g H_2 remaining = 421 g) is equal to the mass of reactants present before reaction (356 g CO + 65.0 g H_2 = 421 g).

Check Your Understanding

The thermite reaction produces iron metal and aluminum oxide from a mixture of powdered aluminum metal and iron(III) oxide (page 138).

$$Fe_2O_3(s) + 2\ Al(s) \rightarrow 2\ Fe(\ell) + Al_2O_3(s)$$

A mixture of 50.0 g each of Fe_2O_3 and Al is used. Which is the limiting reactant? What mass of iron metal can be produced?

REVIEW & CHECK FOR SECTION 4-2

1. The equation for the combustion of methanol is $2\ CH_3OH(\ell) + 3\ O_2(g) \rightarrow 2\ CO_2(g) + 4\ H_2O(\ell)$. If equal masses of the two reactants are allowed to react, which is the limiting reactant?

   (a) CH_3OH

   (b) O_2

   (c) Neither. The reactants are present in the correct stoichiometric ratio.

4-3 Percent Yield

Learning Objectives: LO 3.1, LO 3.3, LO 3.4

The maximum mass of product that can be obtained from a chemical reaction is called the **theoretical yield**. The **actual yield** of the product—the mass of material that is actually obtained in the laboratory or a chemical plant—is almost always less than the theoretical yield. Loss of product usually occurs during the isolation and purification steps. In addition, some reactions do not go completely to products, and reactions are sometimes complicated by giving more than one set of products.

To provide information to other chemists who might want to carry out a reaction, it is customary to report a percent yield (Figure 4.3). **Percent yield**, which specifies how much of the theoretical yield was obtained, is defined as

$$\text{Percent yield} = \frac{\text{actual yield}}{\text{theoretical yield}} \times 100\% \quad (4.1)$$

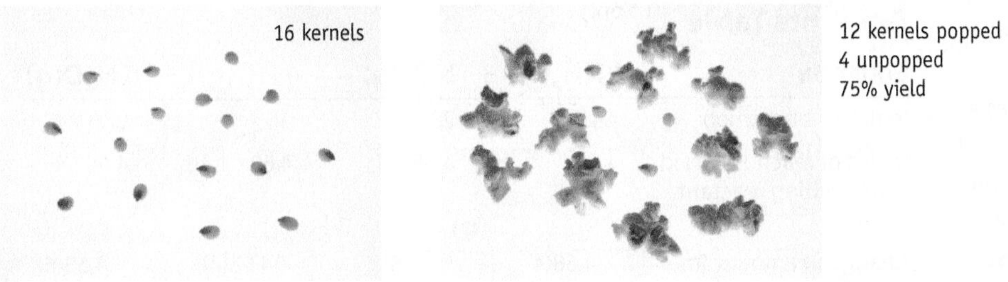

FIGURE 4.3 **Percent yield.** Although not a chemical reaction, popping corn is a good analogy to the difference between a theoretical yield and an actual yield. Here, we began with 16 popcorn kernels and found that only 12 of them popped. The percent yield from our "reaction" was (12/16) × 100%, or 75%.

PROBLEM SOLVING TIP 4.2
Moles of Reaction and Limiting Reactants

There is another method for solving stoichiometry problems that applies especially well to limiting reactant problems. This involves the useful concept of "moles of reaction."

One "mole of reaction" is said to have occurred when the reaction has taken place according to the number of moles given by the coefficients in the equation. For example, for the reaction of CO and O_2,

$$2\ CO(g) + O_2(g) \rightarrow 2\ CO_2(g)$$

1 mole of reaction occurs when 2 mol of CO and 1 mol of O_2 produce 2 mol of CO_2.

Now, suppose 9.5 g of CO and excess O_2 are combined. What amount of CO_2 (moles) can be produced?

$$9.5\text{ g CO} \times \frac{1\text{ mol CO}}{28.0\text{ g CO}} \times \frac{1\text{ mol-rxn}}{2\text{ mol CO}} = 0.17\text{ mol-rxn}$$

$$0.17\text{ mol-rxn} \times \frac{2\text{ mol }CO_2}{1\text{ mol-rxn}} = 0.34\text{ mol }CO_2$$

The first equation above shows that the number of moles of reaction is calculated by multiplying the amount (moles) of the reactant CO by the factor, 1 mol-rxn/2 mol CO.

All reactants and products involved in a chemical reaction undergo the same number of moles of reaction because the reaction can only occur a certain number of times before one or more of the reactants are consumed and the reaction reaches completion.

If one of the reactants is in short supply the actual number of times a reaction can be carried out—the number of "moles of reaction"—will be determined by the limiting reactant. To use this approach you first calculate the amount of each reactant initially present and then calculate the moles of reaction that could occur with each amount of reactant. [This is equivalent to dividing the amount (moles) of each reactant by its stoichiometric coefficient.] The reactant producing the smaller number of moles of reaction is the limiting reactant. Once the limiting reactant is known, you proceed as before.

As an example, consider again the NH_3/O_2 reaction on page 144:

$$4\ NH_3(g) + 5\ O_2(g) \rightarrow 4\ NO(g) + 6\ H_2O(\ell)$$

1. *Calculate the moles of reaction predicted for each reactant and decide on the limiting reactant.*

In the case of the NH_3/O_2 reaction, 1 "mole of reaction" uses 4 mol of NH_3 and 5 mol of O_2 and produces 4 mol of NO and 6 mol of H_2O. In the example on page 144, we started with 44.0 mol of NH_3, so 11.0 mol of reaction could result.

$$44.0\text{ mol }NH_3 \times \frac{1\text{ mol-rxn}}{4\text{ mol }NH_3} = 11.0\text{ mol-rxn}$$

Based on the amount of O_2 available, 4.68 mol of reaction could occur.

$$23.4\text{ mol }O_2 \times \frac{1\text{ mol-rxn}}{5\text{ mol }O_2} = 4.68\text{ mol-rxn}$$

Fewer moles of reaction can occur with the amount of O_2 available, so O_2 is the limiting reactant.

2. *Calculate the change in amount and the amount upon completion of the reaction for each reactant and product.* The number of moles of reaction predicted by the limiting reactant corresponds to the number of moles of reaction that can *actually* occur. Each reactant and product will undergo this number of moles of reaction, 4.68 mol-rxn in this case. To calculate the *change* in amount for a given reactant or product, multiply this number of moles of reaction by the stoichiometric coefficient of the reactant or product. To illustrate this step, for NH_3 this corresponds to the following calculation:

$$4.68\text{ mol-rxn} \times \frac{4\text{ mole }NH_3}{1\text{ mol-rxn}} = 18.8\text{ mol }NH_3$$

The amount of each reactant and product after reaction is calculated as usual.

You may find this approach easier to use particularly when there are more than two reactants, each present initially in some designated quantity.

Note: The concept of "moles of reaction" will be applied in this text in the discussion of thermochemistry in Chapters 5 and 18.

Amounts Table

EQUATION	$4\ NH_3(g)$ +	$5\ O_2(g)$ →	$4\ NO(g)$ +	$6\ H_2O(g)$
Initial amount (mol)	44.0	23.4	0	0
Moles of reaction based on limiting reactant (mol)	4.68	4.68	4.68	4.68
Change in amount (mol)*	−4.68(4) = −18.8	−4.68(5) = −23.4	+4.68(4) = +18.8	+4.68(6) = +28.1
Amount after complete reaction (mol)	25.2	0	18.8	28.1

*Moles of reaction are multiplied by the stoichiometric coefficient for each reactant and product.

Suppose you made aspirin in the laboratory by the following reaction:

$$\underset{\text{salicylic acid}}{C_7H_6O_3(s)} + \underset{\text{acetic anhydride}}{C_4H_6O_3(\ell)} \longrightarrow \underset{\text{aspirin}}{C_9H_8O_4(s)} + \underset{\text{acetic acid}}{CH_3CO_2H(\ell)}$$

and that you began with 14.4 g of salicylic acid ($C_7H_6O_3$) and an excess of acetic anhydride. That is, salicylic acid is the limiting reactant. If you obtain 6.26 g of aspirin, what is the percent yield of this product? The first step is to find the amount of the limiting reactant, salicylic acid.

$$14.4 \text{ g } C_7H_6O_3 \times \frac{1 \text{ mol } C_7H_6O_3}{138.1 \text{ g } C_7H_6O_3} = 0.104 \text{ mol } C_7H_6O_3$$

Next, use the stoichiometric factor from the balanced equation to find the amount of aspirin expected based on the limiting reactant, $C_7H_6O_3$.

$$0.104 \text{ mol } C_7H_6O_3 \times \frac{1 \text{ mol aspirin}}{1 \text{ mol } C_7H_6O_3} = 0.104 \text{ mol aspirin}$$

The maximum amount of aspirin that can be produced—the theoretical yield—is 0.104 mol. Next, express the theoretical yield as a mass in grams.

$$0.104 \text{ mol aspirin} \times \frac{180.2 \text{ g aspirin}}{1 \text{ mol aspirin}} = 18.8 \text{ g aspirin}$$

Finally, with the actual yield known to be only 6.26 g, the percent yield of aspirin can be calculated.

$$\text{Percent yield} = \frac{6.26 \text{ g aspirin obtained (actual yield)}}{18.8 \text{ g aspirin expected (theoretical yield)}} \times 100\% = 33.3\% \text{ yield}$$

REVIEW & CHECK FOR SECTION 4-3

Aluminum carbide, Al_4C_3, reacts with water to produce methane, CH_4.

$$Al_4C_3(s) + 12\ H_2O(\ell) \rightarrow 4\ Al(OH)_3(s) + 3\ CH_4(g)$$

1. If 125 g of aluminum carbide is decomposed, what is the theoretical yield of methane?

   (a) 4.64 g (b) 13.9 g (c) 41.8 g (d) 154 g

2. If only 13.6 g of methane is obtained, what is the percent yield of this gas?

   (a) 34.1% (b) 97.8% (c) 32.5% (d) 8.83%

CASE STUDY

Green Chemistry and Atom Economy

Chemists and chemical industries are increasingly following the principles of "green chemistry." One of these principles is to try to convert all of the atoms of the reactants into the product; nothing should be wasted.

One way to evaluate the efficiency of a reaction is to calculate the "atom economy."

$$\% \text{ atom economy} = \frac{\text{molar mass of atoms utilized}}{\text{molar mass of reactants}} \times 100\%$$

A simple example of the concept is the reaction of methanol and carbon monoxide to produce acetic acid. The atom economy is 100% because all of the atoms of the reactants appear in the product.

$$CH_3OH + CO \rightarrow CH_3CO_2H$$

Ibuprofen is a widely used nonsteroidal anti-inflammatory drug, which is used in the United States in products under tradenames such as Motrin and Advil. A recently developed synthesis of ibuprofen involves the collection of compounds below (which combine in three reaction steps to give ibuprofen and, as a by-product, acetic acid).

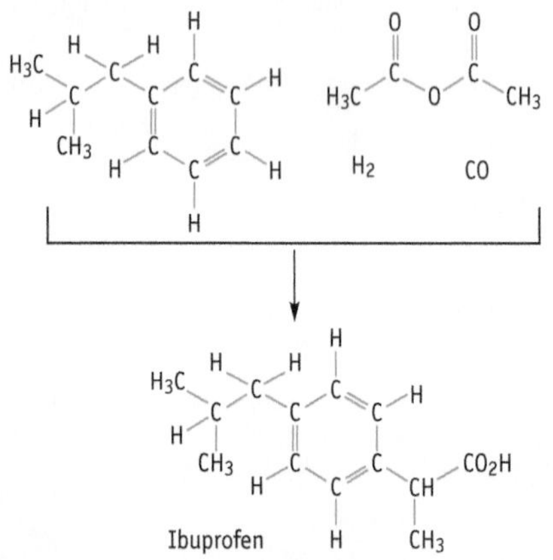

What is the atom economy for this reaction? The reactants, collectively, have 15 C atoms, 22 H atoms, and 4 O atoms. The "molar mass" of this collection is 266 g/mol. In contrast, ibuprofen has a molar mass of 206 g/mol. Therefore, the atom economy is 77%. This is far superior to a competing commercial process for the synthesis of ibuprofen that has an atom economy of only 40%.

Question:

Methyl methacrylate is the reactant used to prepare plastics you may know as Lucite or some other tradename. The substance was first introduced in 1933, but chemists have long sought better (and less costly) ways to make the compound. In a newly developed process, ethylene (C_2H_4), methanol (CH_3OH), CO, and formaldehyde (CH_2O) combine in two steps to give methyl methacrylate and water. What is the atom economy of this new process? (Not only does the new process have a much better atom economy than the previously used process, it also does not involve HCN, a toxic substance used in another method of making this compound.)

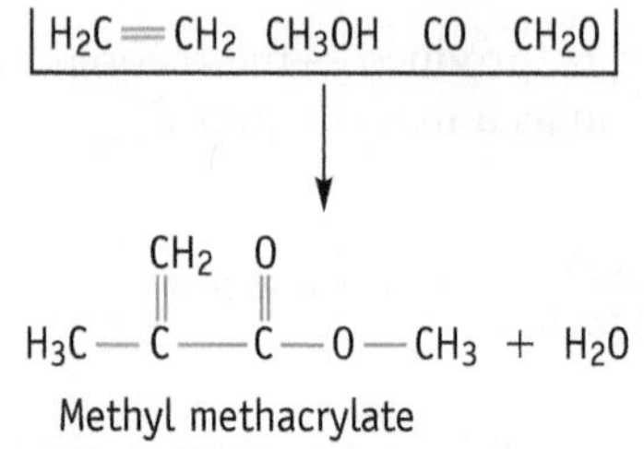

The answer to this question is available in Appendix N.

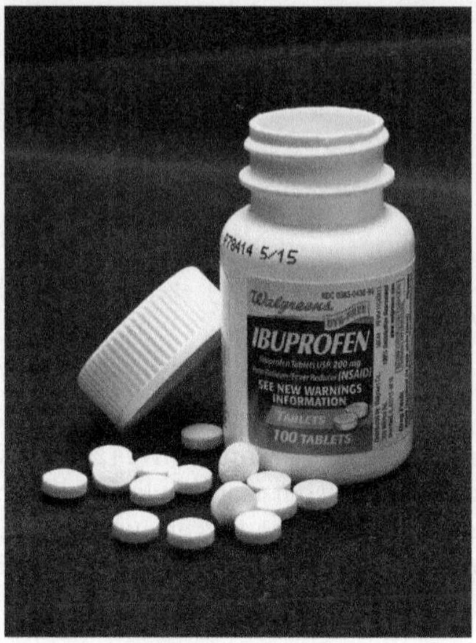

© Cengage Learning/Charles D. Winters

Ibuprofen is one over-the-counter drug made by a green chemistry approach.

Reference:

M. C. Cann and M. E. Connelly, *Real-World Cases in Green Chemistry,* American Chemical Society, 2000.

Learning Objectives: LO 3.1

4-4 Chemical Equations and Chemical Analysis

Analytical chemists use a variety of approaches to identify substances as well as to measure the quantities of components of mixtures. Analytical chemistry is often done now using instrumental methods, but classical chemical reactions and stoichiometry still play a central role.

Quantitative Analysis of a Mixture

Quantitative chemical analysis generally depends on one of the following basic ideas:

- A substance, present in an unknown amount, can be allowed to react with a known amount of another substance. If the stoichiometric ratio for their reaction is known, the unknown amount can be determined.

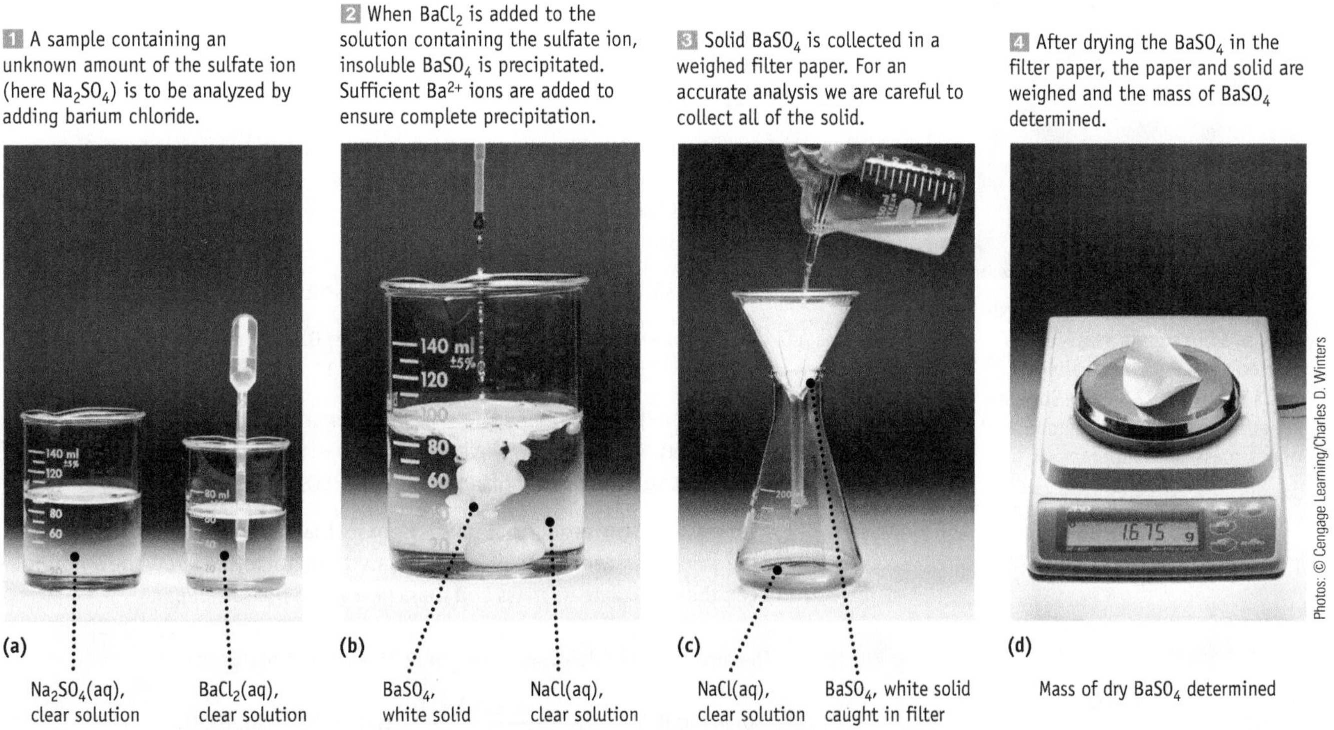

FIGURE 4.4 **The procedure for analyzing a solution for the sulfate ion content by precipitation.** Using the mass of a precipitate to determine the composition of an unknown sample is often called "gravimetric analysis."

- A material of unknown composition can be converted to one or more substances of known composition. Those substances can be identified, their amounts determined, and these amounts related to the amount of the original, unknown substance.

An example of the first type of analysis is the analysis of a sample of vinegar containing an unknown amount of acetic acid, the ingredient that makes vinegar acidic. The acid reacts readily and completely with sodium hydroxide.

$$\underset{\text{acetic acid}}{CH_3CO_2H(aq)} + NaOH(aq) \rightarrow CH_3CO_2Na(aq) + H_2O(\ell)$$

If the exact amount of sodium hydroxide used in the reaction can be measured, the amount of acetic acid present can be calculated. This type of analysis is the subject of a later section in this chapter (▶ Section 4-7).

An example of the second type of analysis is the analysis of a sample of a mineral, thenardite, which is largely sodium sulfate, Na_2SO_4. Sodium sulfate is soluble in water. To find the quantity of Na_2SO_4 in an impure mineral sample, the sample is crushed into a powder and then washed with water to dissolve the sodium sulfate. Next, the solution of sodium sulfate is treated with aqueous barium chloride to precipitate the water-insoluble compound barium sulfate. The barium sulfate is collected on a filter and weighed (Figure 4.4).

$$Na_2SO_4(aq) + BaCl_2(aq) \rightarrow BaSO_4(s) + 2\ NaCl(aq)$$

We can then find the amount of sodium sulfate in the mineral sample because it is directly related to the amount of $BaSO_4$. For more on this analysis, see Example 4.3.

Thenardite. The mineral thenardite is sodium sulfate, Na_2SO_4. It is named after the French chemist Louis Thenard (1777–1857). Sodium sulfate is used in making detergents, glass, and paper.

EXAMPLE 4.3

Mineral Analysis

Problem Sodium sulfate, Na_2SO_4, occurs naturally as the mineral thenardite. To analyze an impure mineral sample for the quantity of Na_2SO_4, the sample is crushed, then dissolved in water to form a solution of Na_2SO_4. Next, the aqueous solution is treated with aqueous barium chloride, $BaCl_2$, to give solid $BaSO_4$ (see Figure 4.4).

$$Na_2SO_4(aq) + BaCl_2(aq) \rightarrow BaSO_4(s) + 2\ NaCl(aq)$$

Suppose a 0.498-g sample containing thenardite produces 0.541 g of solid $BaSO_4$. What is the mass percent of Na_2SO_4 in the sample?

What Do You Know? You know the mass of thenardite and the mass of $BaSO_4$ produced in the reaction. You also know the balanced equation for the reaction leading to the formation of $BaSO_4$. You will need molar masses of Na_2SO_4 and $BaSO_4$.

Strategy First calculate the amount of $BaSO_4$ from its mass. Because 1 mol of Na_2SO_4 was present in the sample for each mole of $BaSO_4$ isolated, you therefore know the amount of Na_2SO_4 and can then calculate its mass and mass percent in the sample.

Solution The molar mass of $BaSO_4$ is 233.4 g/mol. The amount of this solid is

$$0.541\ \text{g BaSO}_4 \times \frac{1\ \text{mol BaSO}_4}{233.4\ \text{g BaSO}_4} = 2.32 \times 10^{-3}\ \text{mol BaSO}_4$$

Because 1 mol of $BaSO_4$ is produced from 1 mol of Na_2SO_4, the amount of Na_2SO_4 in the sample must also have been 2.32×10^{-3} mol.

With the amount of Na_2SO_4 known, the mass of Na_2SO_4 can be calculated.

$$2.32 \times 10^{-3}\ \text{mol Na}_2\text{SO}_4 \times \frac{142.0\ \text{g Na}_2\text{SO}_4}{1\ \text{mol Na}_2\text{SO}_4} = 0.329\ \text{g Na}_2\text{SO}_4$$

Finally, the mass percent of Na_2SO_4 in the 0.498-g sample is

$$\text{Mass percent Na}_2\text{SO}_4 = \frac{0.329\ \text{g Na}_2\text{SO}_4}{0.498\ \text{g sample}} \times 100\% = 66.1\%\ \text{Na}_2\text{SO}_4$$

Think about Your Answer For an analytical procedure to be used, the reactants must be completely converted to product and the product being measured must be isolated without losses in handling. This calls for very careful experimental techniques.

Check Your Understanding

One method for determining the purity of a sample of titanium(IV) oxide, TiO_2, an important industrial chemical, is to react the sample with bromine trifluoride.

$$3\ TiO_2(s) + 4\ BrF_3(\ell) \rightarrow 3\ TiF_4(s) + 2\ Br_2(\ell) + 3\ O_2(g)$$

This reaction is known to occur completely and quantitatively. That is, all of the oxygen in TiO_2 is evolved as O_2. Suppose 2.367 g of a TiO_2-containing sample evolves 0.143 g of O_2. What is the mass percent of TiO_2 in the sample?

Determining the Formula of a Compound by Combustion

The empirical formula of a compound can be determined if the percent composition of the compound is known (◀ Section 2-10). But where do the percent composition data come from? One chemical method that works well for compounds that burn in oxygen is analysis by combustion. In this technique, each element in the compound combines with oxygen to produce the appropriate oxide.

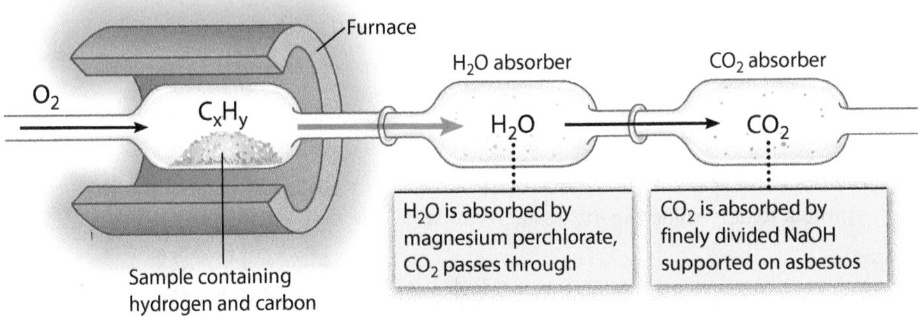

FIGURE 4.5 **Combustion analysis of a hydrocarbon.** If a compound containing C and H is burned in oxygen, CO_2 and H_2O are formed, and the mass of each can be determined. The mass of each absorbent before and after combustion gives the masses of CO_2 and H_2O. Only a few milligrams of a combustible compound are needed for analysis.

Consider an analysis of the hydrocarbon methane, CH_4. A balanced equation for the combustion of methane shows that every carbon atom in the original compound appears as CO_2 and every hydrogen atom appears in the form of water. In other words, for every mole of CO_2 observed, there must have been one mole of carbon in the unknown compound. Similarly, for every mole of H_2O observed from combustion, there must have been *two* moles of H atoms in the unknown compound.

$$CH_4(g) + 2\,O_2(g) \longrightarrow CO_2(g) + 2\,H_2O(\ell)$$

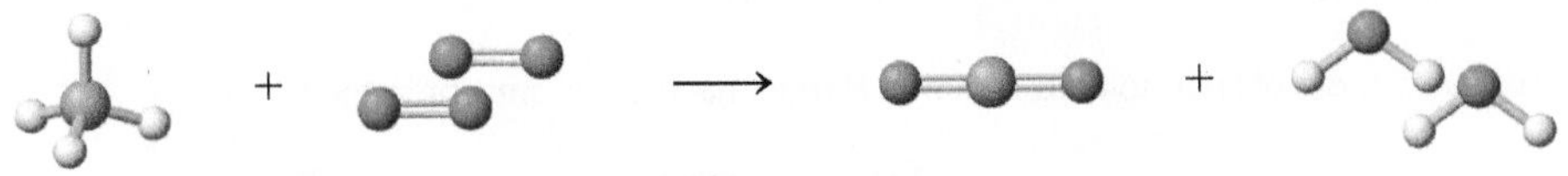

In the combustion experiment gaseous carbon dioxide and water are separated (as illustrated in Figure 4.5) and their masses determined. From these masses it is possible to calculate the amounts of C and H in CO_2 and H_2O, respectively, and the ratio of amounts of C and H in a sample of the original compound can then be found. This ratio gives the empirical formula. If the molar mass is known from a separate experiment, the molecular formula can also be determined.

EXAMPLE 4.4

Using Combustion Analysis to Determine the Formula of a Hydrocarbon

Problem When 1.125 g of a liquid hydrocarbon, C_xH_y, was burned in an apparatus like that shown in Figure 4.5, 3.447 g of CO_2 and 1.647 g of H_2O were produced. In a separate experiment the molar mass of the compound was found to be 86.2 g/mol. Determine the empirical and molecular formulas for the unknown hydrocarbon, C_xH_y.

What Do You Know? You know the mass of the hydrocarbon, the fact that it contains only C and H, and the molar mass of this compound. You are also provided with the masses of H_2O and CO_2 formed when the hydrocarbon is burned.

Strategy The strategy to solve this problem is outlined in the diagram below and Strategy Map 4.4.

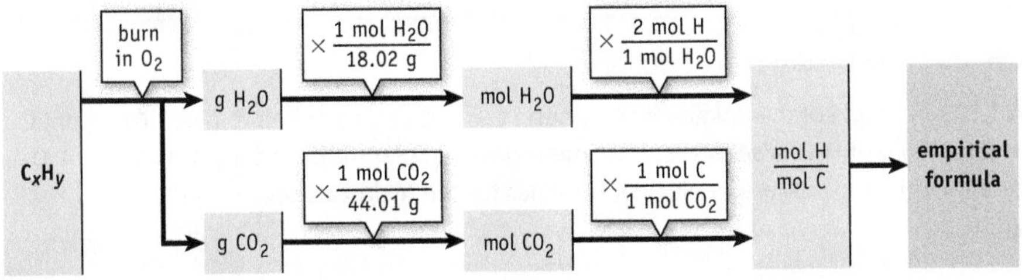

Strategy Map 4.4

PROBLEM

Determine **empirical** and **molecular formulas** of a hydrocarbon.

DATA/INFORMATION

- **Masses** of CO_2 and H_2O from combustion of given mass of C_xH_y
- **Molar mass** of **unknown**

STEP 1. Calculate **amounts** of CO_2 and H_2O.

Amounts of CO_2 and H_2O

STEP 2. Calculate **amount** of C and H from amounts of CO_2 and H_2O, respectively.

Amounts of **C** and **H** in unknown compound

STEP 3. Find **whole-number ratio** of amounts of **C** and **H**.

C_xH_y = empirical formula

STEP 4. Determine ratio of **experimental molar mass** to **empirical formula mass.**

Molecular formula $[C_xH_y]_n$

Finding an Empirical Formula by Chemical Analysis Finding the empirical formula of a compound by chemical analysis always uses the following procedure:

1. The unknown but pure compound is converted in a chemical reaction into known products.
2. The reaction products are isolated, and the amount of each is determined.
3. The amount of each product is related to the amount of each element in the original compound.
4. The empirical formula is determined from the relative amounts of elements in the original compound.

The steps in sequence are as follows:

- Calculate the amounts of CO_2 and H_2O from the given masses.
- Calculate the amounts of C and H from the amounts of CO_2 and H_2O, respectively.
- Determine the lowest whole-number ratio of amounts of C and H. This gives the subscripts for C and H in the empirical formula.
- Compare the experimental molar mass of the hydrocarbon with that of the empirical formula to determine the molecular formula.

Solution The amounts of CO_2 and H_2O isolated from the combustion are

$$3.447\ \cancel{\text{g CO}_2} \times \frac{1\ \text{mol CO}_2}{44.010\ \cancel{\text{g CO}_2}} = 0.07832\ \text{mol CO}_2$$

$$1.647\ \cancel{\text{g H}_2\text{O}} \times \frac{1\ \text{mol H}_2\text{O}}{18.015\ \cancel{\text{g H}_2\text{O}}} = 0.09142\ \text{mol H}_2\text{O}$$

For every mole of CO_2 isolated, 1 mol of C must have been present in the unknown compound.

$$0.07832\ \cancel{\text{mol CO}_2} \times \frac{1\ \text{mol C in unknown}}{1\ \cancel{\text{mol CO}_2}} = 0.07832\ \text{mol C}$$

For every mole of H_2O isolated, 2 mol of H must have been present in the unknown.

$$0.09142\ \cancel{\text{mol H}_2\text{O}} \times \frac{2\ \text{mol H in unknown}}{1\ \cancel{\text{mol H}_2\text{O}}} = 0.1828\ \text{mol H}$$

The original 1.125-g sample of compound therefore contained 0.07832 mol of C and 0.1828 mol of H. To determine the empirical formula of the unknown, we find the ratio of moles of H to moles of C (◀ Section 2-10).

$$\frac{0.1828\ \text{mol H}}{0.07832\ \text{mol C}} = \frac{2.335\ \text{mol H}}{1.000\ \text{mol C}}$$

The empirical formula gives the simplest *whole-number* ratio. The translation of this ratio (2.335/1) to a whole-number ratio can usually be done quickly by trial and error. Multiplying the numerator and denominator by 3 gives 7/3. So, we know the ratio is 7 mol H to 3 mol C, which means the empirical formula of the hydrocarbon is C_3H_7.

Comparing the experimental molar mass with the molar mass calculated for the empirical formula,

$$\frac{\text{Experimental molar mass}}{\text{Molar mass of C}_3\text{H}_7} = \frac{86.2\ \text{g/mol}}{43.1\ \text{g/mol}} = \frac{2}{1}$$

we find that the molecular formula is twice the empirical formula. That is, the molecular formula is $(C_3H_7)_2$, or C_6H_{14}.

Think about Your Answer As noted in Problem Solving Tip 2.3 (page 86), for problems of this type be sure to use data with enough significant figures to give accurate atom ratios.

Check Your Understanding

A 0.523-g sample of the unknown compound C_xH_y was burned in air to give 1.612 g of CO_2 and 0.7425 g of H_2O. A separate experiment gave a molar mass for C_xH_y of 114 g/mol. Determine the empirical and molecular formulas for the hydrocarbon.

It is also possible to determine the empirical formula of an oxygenated hydrocarbon, such as ethanol (C_2H_6O), from combustion analysis. The amount of carbon and hydrogen can be determined from the masses of collected carbon dioxide and water. By calculating the mass of carbon and hydrogen from the amounts of those elements and then subtracting these masses from the mass of the combusted compound, the mass of oxygen, and ultimately the amount of oxygen, may be determined.

EXAMPLE 4.5

Using Combustion Analysis to Determine an Empirical Formula of a Compound Containing C, H, and O

Problem Suppose you isolate an acid from clover leaves and know that it contains only the elements C, H, and O. Heating 0.513 g of the acid in oxygen produces 0.501 g of CO_2 and 0.103 g of H_2O. What is the empirical formula of the acid, $C_xH_yO_z$?

What Do You Know? You know the mass of the compound and the fact that it contains only C, H, and O. You are also provided with the masses of H_2O and CO_2 formed when the hydrocarbon is burned.

Strategy In order to determine the empirical formula, you need to determine the amounts (moles) of C, H, and O in the unknown compound. Follow the steps outlined below.

- Determine the amounts of C and H following the procedure in Example 4.4.
- Determine the masses of C and H from the amounts of C and H.
- The mass of O is the mass of the sample minus the masses of C and H.
- From the mass of O determine the amount of O.
- Finally, determine the smallest whole number ratio between the amounts of the three elements. This determines the subscripts for the elements in the empirical formula.

Solution The first step is to determine the amounts of C and H in the sample.

$$0.501 \text{ g } CO_2 \times \frac{1 \text{ mol } CO_2}{44.01 \text{ g } CO_2} \times \frac{1 \text{ mol C}}{1 \text{ mol } CO_2} = 0.0114 \text{ mol C}$$

$$0.103 \text{ g } H_2O \times \frac{1 \text{ mol } H_2O}{18.02 \text{ g } H_2O} \times \frac{2 \text{ mol H}}{1 \text{ mol } H_2O} = 0.0114 \text{ mol H}$$

From these amounts, you can determine the mass of C and the mass of H in the sample.

$$0.0114 \text{ mol C} \times \frac{12.01 \text{ g C}}{1 \text{ mol C}} = 0.137 \text{ g C}$$

$$0.0114 \text{ mol H} \times \frac{1.008 \text{ g H}}{1 \text{ mol H}} = 0.0115 \text{ g H}$$

Using the mass of the original sample and the masses of C and H in the sample, you can now determine the mass of O in the sample. From this, you can find the amount of O in the sample.

$$\text{Mass of sample} = 0.513 \text{ g} = 0.137 \text{ g C} + 0.0115 \text{ g H} + x \text{ g O}$$

$$\text{Mass of O} = 0.365 \text{ g O}$$

$$0.365 \text{ g O} \times \frac{1 \text{ mol O}}{16.00 \text{ g O}} = 0.0228 \text{ mol O}$$

To find the mole ratios of elements, divide the number of moles of each element by the smallest amount present. Because both C and H are present in the same amount in the sample, you know their ratio is 1 C:1 H. What about O?

$$\frac{0.0228 \text{ mol O}}{0.0114 \text{ mol C}} = \frac{2 \text{ mol O}}{1 \text{ mol C}}$$

The mole ratios show that, for every C atom in the molecule, one H atom and two O atoms occur. The empirical formula of the acid is therefore CHO_2.

Think about Your Answer If the molar mass of the unknown compound were known, you would then be able to derive the molecular formula of the compound.

Check Your Understanding

A 0.1342-g sample of a compound composed of C, H, and O was burned in oxygen and 0.240 g of CO_2 and 0.0982 g of H_2O was isolated. What is the empirical formula of the compound? If the experimentally determined molar mass is 74.1 g/mol, what is the molecular formula of the compound?

REVIEW & CHECK FOR SECTION 4-4

1. A 0.509-g sample of an unknown organic compound containing C, H, and O was burned in air to give 1.316 g of CO_2 and 0.269 g of H_2O. What is the empirical formula for this compound?

   (a) CHO (b) C_2H_2O (c) C_4H_4O (d) CHO_4

Learning Objectives: LO 2.9

4-5 Measuring Concentrations of Compounds in Solution

Moles Versus Molarity The amount of a substance is an extensive property. Molarity is an intensive property; the amount of substance (moles) per liter of solution is independent of the quantity of solution.

Most chemical studies require quantitative measurements, including experiments involving aqueous solutions. When doing such experiments, we continue to use balanced equations and moles, but we measure volumes of solutions rather than masses of solids, liquids, or gases. Solution concentration, expressed as molarity, relates the volume of solution in liters to the amount of solute. A solute is any substance (solid, liquid, or gas) that is dissolved in a solvent.

Solution Concentration: Molarity

A useful unit of solute concentration, c, is **molarity**, which is defined as amount of solute per liter of solution.

$$\text{Molarity of } x\ (c_x) = \frac{\text{amount of solute } x \text{ (mol)}}{\text{volume of solution (L)}} \quad \textbf{(4.2)}$$

For example, if 58.4 g (1.00 mol) of NaCl is dissolved in enough water to give a total solution volume of 1.00 L, the molarity, c, is 1.00 mol/L. This is often abbreviated as 1.00 M, where the capital "M" stands for "moles per liter." Another common notation is to place the formula of the compound in square brackets (for example, [NaCl]); this notation indicates that the concentration of the solute in moles per liter of solution is being specified.

$$c_{NaCl} = [NaCl] = 1.00 \text{ mol/L} = 1.00 \text{ M}$$

It is important to notice that molarity refers to the amount of solute *per liter of solution* and not per liter of solvent. If one liter of water is added to one mole of a solid compound, the final volume will not be exactly one liter, and the final concentration will not be exactly one mol/L (Figure 4.6). When making solutions of a given

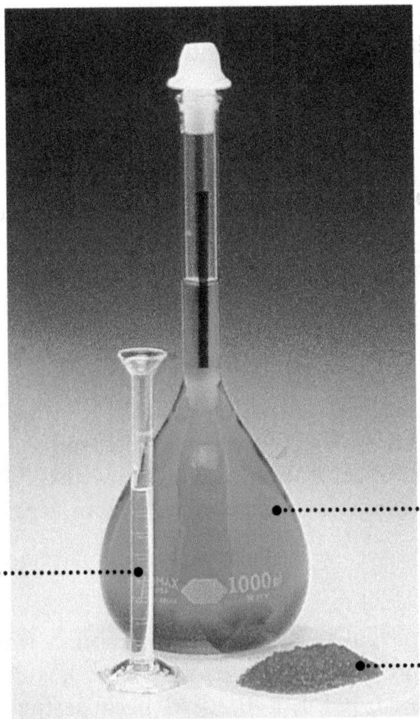

FIGURE 4.6 Volume of solution versus volume of solvent. This figure emphasizes that molar concentrations are defined as moles of solute per liter of solution and not per liter of water or other solvent.

concentration, it is always the case that we dissolve the solute in a volume of solvent smaller than the desired volume of solution, then add solvent until the final solution volume is reached.

Potassium permanganate, $KMnO_4$, which was used at one time as a germicide in the treatment of burns, is a shiny, purple-black solid that dissolves readily in water to give a deep purple solution. Suppose 0.435 g of $KMnO_4$ has been dissolved in enough water to give 250. mL of solution (Figure 4.7). What is the concentration of $KMnO_4$? The first step is to convert the mass of $KMnO_4$ to an amount.

$$0.435\ \cancel{\text{g KMnO}_4} \times \frac{1\ \text{mol KMnO}_4}{158.0\ \cancel{\text{g KMnO}_4}} = 0.00275\ \text{mol KMnO}_4$$

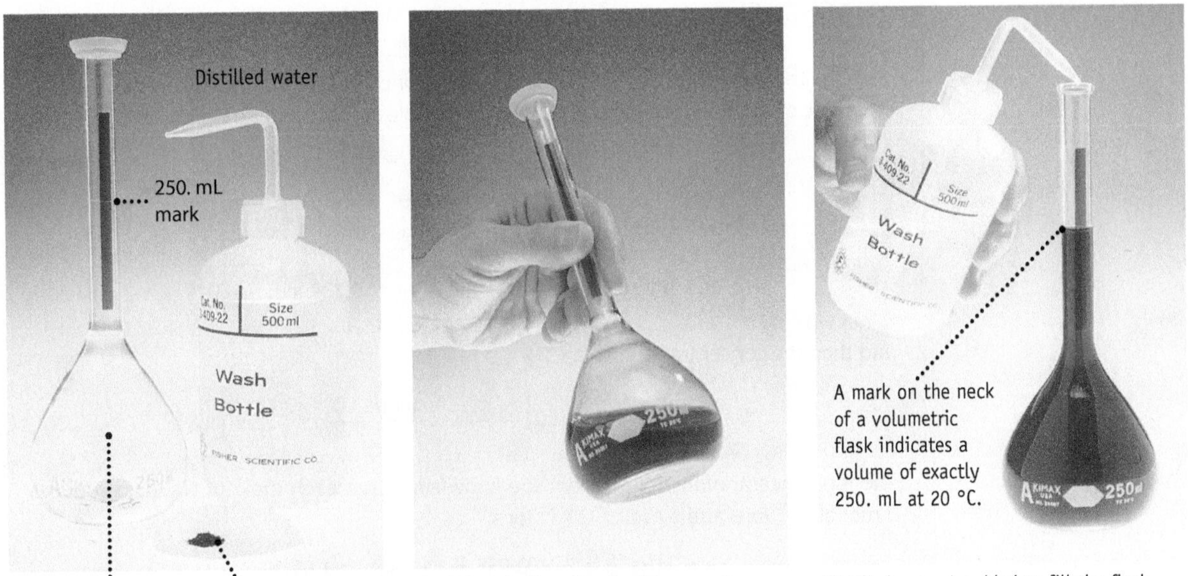

FIGURE 4.7 Making a solution. A 0.0110 M solution of $KMnO_4$ is made by adding enough water to 0.435 g of $KMnO_4$ to make 0.250 L of solution.

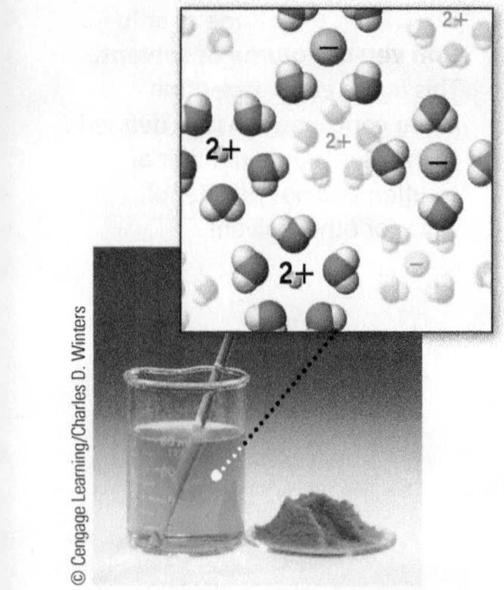

© Cengage Learning/Charles D. Winters

Ion concentrations for a soluble ionic compound. Here, 1 mol of $CuCl_2$ dissociates to 1 mol of Cu^{2+} ions and 2 mol of Cl^- ions. Therefore, the Cl^- concentration is twice the concentration calculated for $CuCl_2$.

Next, the amount of $KMnO_4$ is combined with the volume of solution—which must be in liters—to give the concentration. Because 250. mL is equivalent to 0.250 L,

$$\text{Concentration of } KMnO_4 = c_{KMnO_4} = [KMnO_4] = \frac{0.00275 \text{ mol } KMnO_4}{0.250 \text{ L}} = 0.0110 \text{ M}$$

The $KMnO_4$ concentration is 0.0110 mol/L, or 0.0110 M. This is useful information, but it is often equally useful to know the concentration of each type of ion in a solution. Like all soluble ionic compounds, $KMnO_4$ dissociates completely into its ions, K^+ and MnO_4^-, when dissolved in water.

$$\underset{\text{100\% dissociation}}{KMnO_4(aq)} \longrightarrow K^+(aq) + MnO_4^-(aq)$$

One mole of $KMnO_4$ provides 1 mol of K^+ ions and 1 mol of MnO_4^- ions. Accordingly, 0.0110 M $KMnO_4$ gives a concentration of K^+ in the solution of 0.0110 M; similarly, the concentration of MnO_4^- is also 0.0110 M.

Another example of ion concentrations is provided by the dissociation of $CuCl_2$.

$$\underset{\text{100\% dissociation}}{CuCl_2(aq)} \longrightarrow Cu^{2+}(aq) + 2\ Cl^-(aq)$$

If 0.10 mol of $CuCl_2$ is dissolved in enough water to make 1.0 L of solution, the concentration of the copper(II) ion, $[Cu^{2+}]$, is 0.10 M. However, the concentration of chloride ions, $[Cl^-]$, is 0.20 M because the compound dissociates in water to provide 2 mol of Cl^- ions for each mole of $CuCl_2$.

EXAMPLE 4.6

Concentration

Problem If 25.3 g of sodium carbonate, Na_2CO_3, is dissolved in enough water to make 250. mL of solution, what is the concentration of Na_2CO_3? What are the concentrations of the Na^+ and CO_3^{2-} ions?

What Do You Know? You know the mass of the solute, Na_2CO_3, and the volume of the solution. You will need the molar mass of Na_2CO_3 to calculate the amount of this compound.

Strategy The concentration (moles/L) of Na_2CO_3 is the amount of Na_2CO_3 (moles) divided by the volume (in liters). To determine the concentrations of the ions, recognize that one mole of this ionic compound contains two moles of Na^+ and one mole of CO_3^{2-} ions.

$$Na_2CO_3(s) \longrightarrow 2\ Na^+(aq) + CO_3^{2-}(aq)$$

Solution Let us first find the amount of Na_2CO_3.

$$25.3 \text{ g } Na_2CO_3 \times \frac{1 \text{ mol } Na_2CO_3}{106.0 \text{ g } Na_2CO_3} = 0.239 \text{ mol } Na_2CO_3$$

and then the concentration of Na_2CO_3,

$$\text{Concentration of } Na_2CO_3 = \frac{0.239 \text{ mol } Na_2CO_3}{0.250 \text{ L}} = 0.955 \text{ mol/L}$$

The ion concentrations follow from the knowledge that each mole of Na_2CO_3 produces 2 mol of Na^+ ions and 1 mol of CO_3^{2-} ions.

$$[Na^+] = 2 \times 0.955 \text{ M } Na^+(aq) = 1.91 \text{ M}$$

$$[CO_3^{2-}] = 0.955 \text{ M}$$

Think about Your Answer While we refer to this solution as 0.955 M Na_2CO_3, there are no actual particles of Na_2CO_3 present. This soluble ionic compound is present in solution as dissociated sodium and carbonate ions.

Check Your Understanding

Sodium bicarbonate, $NaHCO_3$, is used in baking powder formulations and in the manufacture of plastics and ceramics, among other things. If 26.3 g of the compound is dissolved in enough water to make 200. mL of solution, what is the concentration of $NaHCO_3$? What are the concentrations of the ions in solution?

Preparing Solutions of Known Concentration

Chemists often have to prepare a given volume of solution of known concentration. There are two generally used ways to do this.

Combining a Weighed Solute with the Solvent

Suppose you need to prepare 2.00 L of a 1.50 M solution of aqueous Na_2CO_3. You have some solid Na_2CO_3 and distilled water. You also have a 2.00-L volumetric flask. To make the solution, you must weigh the required quantity of Na_2CO_3 as accurately as possible considering the number of significant figures desired for the concentration, carefully place all the solid in the volumetric flask, and then add some water to dissolve the solid. After the solid has dissolved completely, more water is added to bring the solution volume to 2.00 L. The solution then has the desired concentration and the volume specified.

Volumetric Flask A volumetric flask is a special flask with a line marked on its neck (see page 35 and Figures 4.6–4.8). If the flask is filled with a solution to this line (at a given temperature), it contains precisely the volume of solution specified.

But what mass of Na_2CO_3 is required to make 2.00 L of 1.50 M Na_2CO_3? First, calculate the amount of Na_2CO_3 required,

$$2.00\ \cancel{L} \times \frac{1.50\ \text{mol Na}_2\text{CO}_3}{1.00\ \cancel{L}\ \text{solution}} = 3.00\ \text{mol Na}_2\text{CO}_3\ \text{required}$$

and then the mass in grams.

$$3.00\ \cancel{\text{mol Na}_2\text{CO}_3} \times \frac{106.0\ \text{g Na}_2\text{CO}_3}{1\ \cancel{\text{mol Na}_2\text{CO}_3}} = 318\ \text{g Na}_2\text{CO}_3$$

Thus, to prepare the desired solution, you should dissolve 318 g of Na_2CO_3 in enough water to make 2.00 L of solution.

Diluting a More Concentrated Solution

Another method of making a solution of a given concentration is to begin with a concentrated solution and add more solvent (usually water) until the desired, lower concentration is reached (Figure 4.8). Many of the solutions prepared for your laboratory course are probably made by this dilution method. It is more efficient to store a small volume of a concentrated solution and then, when needed, add water to make a much larger volume of a dilute solution.

Suppose you need 500. mL of aqueous 0.0010 M potassium dichromate, $K_2Cr_2O_7$, for use in chemical analysis. You have some 0.100 M $K_2Cr_2O_7$ solution available. To make the required 0.0010 M solution, place a measured volume of the more concentrated $K_2Cr_2O_7$ solution in a flask and then add water until the $K_2Cr_2O_7$ is contained in the appropriate, larger volume of water (see Figure 4.8).

What volume of a 0.100 M $K_2Cr_2O_7$ solution must be diluted to make the 0.0010 M solution? If the volume and concentration of a solution are known, the

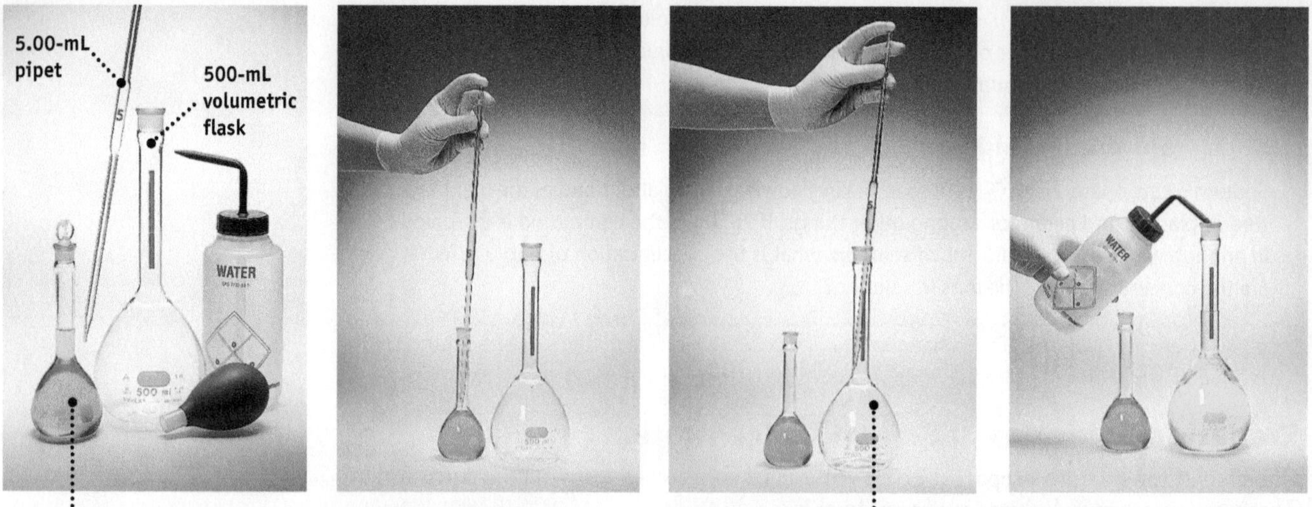

0.100 M $K_2Cr_2O_7$

Use a 5.00-mL pipet to withdraw 5.00 mL of 0.100 M $K_2Cr_2O_7$ solution.

Add the 5.00-mL sample of 0.100 M $K_2Cr_2O_7$ solution to a 500-mL volumetric flask.

Fill the flask to the mark with distilled water to give 0.00100 M $K_2Cr_2O_7$ solution.

FIGURE 4.8 **Making a solution by dilution.** Here, 5.00 mL of a 0.100 M $K_2Cr_2O_7$ solution is diluted to 500. mL. This means the solution is diluted by a factor of 100, from 0.100 M to 0.00100 M.

amount of solute is also known. Therefore, the amount of $K_2Cr_2O_7$ that must be in the final dilute solution is

$$\text{Amount of } K_2Cr_2O_7 \text{ in dilute solution} = c_{K_2Cr_2O_7} \times V_{K_2Cr_2O_7} = \left(\frac{0.0010 \text{ mol}}{\cancel{L}}\right) \times (0.500 \cancel{L})$$
$$= 0.00050 \text{ mol } K_2Cr_2O_7$$

The more concentrated solution containing this amount of $K_2Cr_2O_7$ is placed in a 500.-mL flask and then diluted to the final volume. The volume of 0.100 M $K_2Cr_2O_7$ required is 5.0 mL.

$$0.00050 \cancel{\text{mol } K_2Cr_2O_7} \times \frac{1.00 \text{ L}}{0.100 \cancel{\text{mol } K_2Cr_2O_7}} = 0.0050 \text{ L or } 5.0 \text{ mL}$$

Thus, to prepare 500. mL of 0.0010 M $K_2Cr_2O_7$, place 5.0 mL of 0.100 M $K_2Cr_2O_7$ in a 500.-mL flask and add water until a volume of 500. mL is reached (see Figure 4.8).

PROBLEM SOLVING TIP 4.3
Preparing a Solution by Dilution

There is a straightforward method to use for problems involving dilution. The central idea is that the amount of solute in the final, dilute solution has to be equal to the amount of solute taken from the more concentrated solution. If *c* is the concentration (molarity) and *V* is the volume (and the subscripts *d* and *c* identify the dilute and concentrated solutions, respectively), then the amount of solute in either solution (in the case of the $K_2Cr_2O_7$ example in the text) can be calculated as follows:

(a) Amount of $K_2Cr_2O_7$ in the final dilute solution is

$$c_d \times V_d = 0.00050 \text{ mol}$$

(b) Amount of $K_2Cr_2O_7$ taken from the more concentrated solution is

$$c_c \times V_c = 0.00050 \text{ mol}$$

Both the concentrated and dilute solutions contain the same amount of solute. Therefore, we can use the following equation:

Amount in concentrated solution = Amount in dilute solution

$$c_c \times V_c = c_d \times V_d$$

This equation is valid for all cases in which a more concentrated solution is used to make a more dilute one.

EXAMPLE 4.7

Preparing a Solution by Dilution

Problem What is the concentration of iron(III) ions in a solution prepared by diluting 1.00 mL of a 0.236 M solution of iron(III) nitrate to a volume of 100.0 mL?

What Do I Know? You know the initial concentration and volume and the final volume after dilution.

Strategy First calculate the amount of iron(III) ions in the 1.00-mL sample (amount = concentration × volume). The concentration of the iron(III) ions in the final, dilute solution is equal to this amount of iron(III) ions divided by the new volume.

Solution The amount of iron(III) ion in the 1.00 mL sample is

$$\text{Amount of } Fe^{3+} = c_{Fe^{3+}} \times V_{Fe^{3+}} = \frac{0.236 \text{ mol } Fe^{3+}}{\cancel{L}} \times 1.00 \times 10^{-3} \cancel{L} = 2.36 \times 10^{-4} \text{ mol } Fe^{3+}$$

This amount of iron(III) ion is contained in the new volume of 100.0 mL, so the final concentration of the diluted solution is

$$c_{Fe^{3+}} = [Fe^{3+}] = \frac{2.36 \times 10^{-4} \text{ mol } Fe^{3+}}{0.1000 \text{ L}} = 2.36 \times 10^{-3} \text{ M}$$

Think about Your Answer The sample has been diluted 100-fold, so we would expect the final concentration to be 1/100th of the initial value. See also Problem Solving Tip 4.3, which gives a quick and easy-to-use method for this calculation.

Check Your Understanding

An experiment calls for you to use 250. mL of 1.00 M NaOH, but you are given a large bottle of 2.00 M NaOH. Describe how to make the desired volume of 1.00 M NaOH.

REVIEW & CHECK FOR SECTION 4-5

1. A 1.71-g sample of $Ba(OH)_2$(s) was dissolved in water to give 250 mL of solution. What is the OH^- concentration in this solution?

   (a) 0.010 M (b) 0.040 M (c) 0.080 M (d) 0.10 M

2. You have a 100.-mL volumetric flask containing 0.050 M HCl. A 2.0-mL sample of this solution was diluted to 10.0 mL. What is the concentration of HCl in the dilute solution?

   (a) 0.10 M (b) 0.010 M (c) 1.0×10^{-3} M (d) 0.25 M

3. What volume of 0.250 M $KMnO_4$(aq) contains 0.500 g $KMnO_4$?

   (a) 0.791 mL (b) 2.00 mL (c) 12.7 mL (d) 125 mL

4-6 pH, a Concentration Scale for Acids and Bases

A sample of vinegar, which contains the weak acid acetic acid, has a hydronium ion concentration of 1.6×10^{-3} M and "pure" rainwater has $[H_3O^+] = 2.5 \times 10^{-6}$ M. These small values can be expressed using scientific notation, but a more convenient way to express such numbers is the logarithmic pH scale.

The pH of a solution is the negative of the base-10 logarithm of the hydronium ion concentration.

$$pH = -\log[H_3O^+] \tag{4.3}$$

Logarithms Numbers less than 1 have negative logs. Defining pH as $-\log[H_3O^+]$ produces a positive number. See Appendix A for a discussion of logs.

A CLOSER LOOK

Serial Dilutions

We often find in the laboratory that a solution is too concentrated for the analytical technique we want to use. You might want to analyze a seawater sample for its chloride ion content, for instance. To obtain a solution with a chloride concentration of the proper magnitude for analysis by the Mohr method (Case Study, page 172), for example, you might want to dilute the sample, not once but several times.

Suppose you have 100.0 mL of a seawater sample that has an NaCl concentration of 0.550 mol/L. You transfer 10.00 mL of that sample to a 100.0-mL volumetric flask and fill to the mark with distilled water. After thoroughly mixing the diluted sample, you then transfer 5.00 mL of that sample to another 100.0-mL flask and fill to the mark with distilled water. What is the NaCl concentration in the final 100.0-mL sample?

The original solution contains 0.550 mol/L of NaCl. If you remove 10.00 mL, you have removed

$$0.01000 \text{ L} \times 0.550 \text{ mol/L} = 5.50 \times 10^{-3} \text{ mol NaCl}$$

and the concentration in 100.0 mL of the diluted solution is

$$c_{NaCl} = 5.50 \times 10^{-3} \text{ mol}/0.1000 \text{ L} = 5.50 \times 10^{-2} \text{ M}$$

or 1/10 of the concentration of the original solution (because we diluted the sample by a factor of 10).

Now we take 5.00 mL of the diluted solution and dilute that once again to 100.0 mL. The final concentration is

$$0.00500 \text{ L} \times 5.50 \times 10^{-2} \text{ mol/L} = 2.75 \times 10^{-4} \text{ mol NaCl}$$

$$c_{NaCl} = 2.75 \times 10^{-4} \text{ mol}/0.1000 \text{ L} = 2.75 \times 10^{-3} \text{ M}$$

This is 1/200 of the concentration of the original solution.

A fair question at this point is why we did not just take 1 mL of the original solution and dilute to 200 mL. The answer is that there is less error in using larger pipets such as 5.00- or 10.00-mL pipets rather than a 1.00-mL pipet. And then there is a limitation in available glassware. A 200.00-mL volumetric flask is not often available.

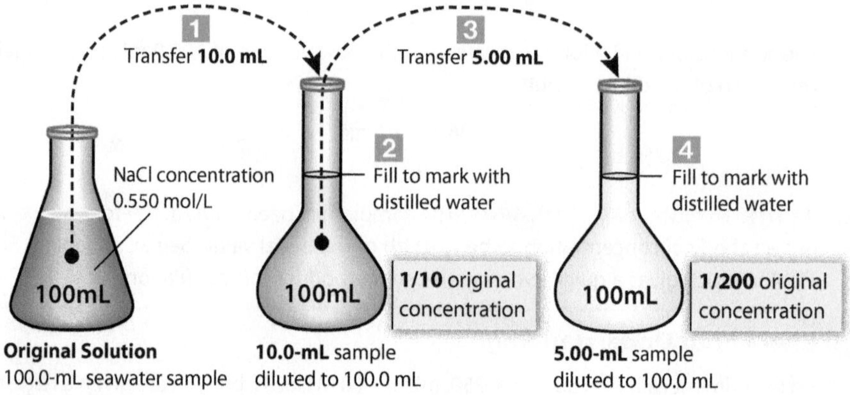

Taking vinegar, pure water, blood, and ammonia as examples,

pH of vinegar	$= -\log(1.6 \times 10^{-3} \text{ M})$	$= -(-2.80)$	$= 2.80$	acidic
pH of pure water (at 25 °C)	$= -\log(1.0 \times 10^{-7} \text{ M})$	$= -(-7.00)$	$= 7.00$	neutral
pH of blood	$= -\log(4.0 \times 10^{-8} \text{ M})$	$= -(-7.40)$	$= 7.40$	basic
pH of household ammonia	$= -\log(4.3 \times 10^{-12} \text{ M})$	$= -(-11.37)$	$= 11.37$	basic

you see that something you recognize as acidic has a relatively low pH, whereas ammonia, a common base, has a very low hydronium ion concentration and a high pH. *For aqueous solutions at 25 °C, acids have pH values less than 7, bases have values greater than 7, and a pH of 7 represents a neutral solution* (Figure 4.9). Blood, which your common sense tells you is likely to be neither acidic nor basic, has a pH slightly greater than 7.

Logs and Your Calculator All scientific calculators have a key marked "log." To find an antilog, use the key marked "10^x" or the inverse log. In determining $[H_3O^+]$ from a pH, when you enter the value of *x* for 10^x, make sure it has a negative sign.

Suppose you know the pH of a solution. To find the hydronium ion concentration you take the antilog of the pH. That is,

$$[H_3O^+] = 10^{-pH} \quad \textbf{(4.4)}$$

For example, the pH of a diet soda is 3.12, and the hydronium ion concentration of the solution is

$$[H_3O^+] = 10^{-3.12} = 7.6 \times 10^{-4} \text{ M}$$

The approximate pH of a solution may be determined using any of a variety of dyes. Litmus paper contains a dye extracted from a type of lichen, but many other dyes are also available (Figure 4.10a). A more accurate measurement of pH is done with a pH meter such as that shown in Figure 4.10b. Here, a pH electrode is immersed in the solution to be tested, and the pH is read from the instrument.

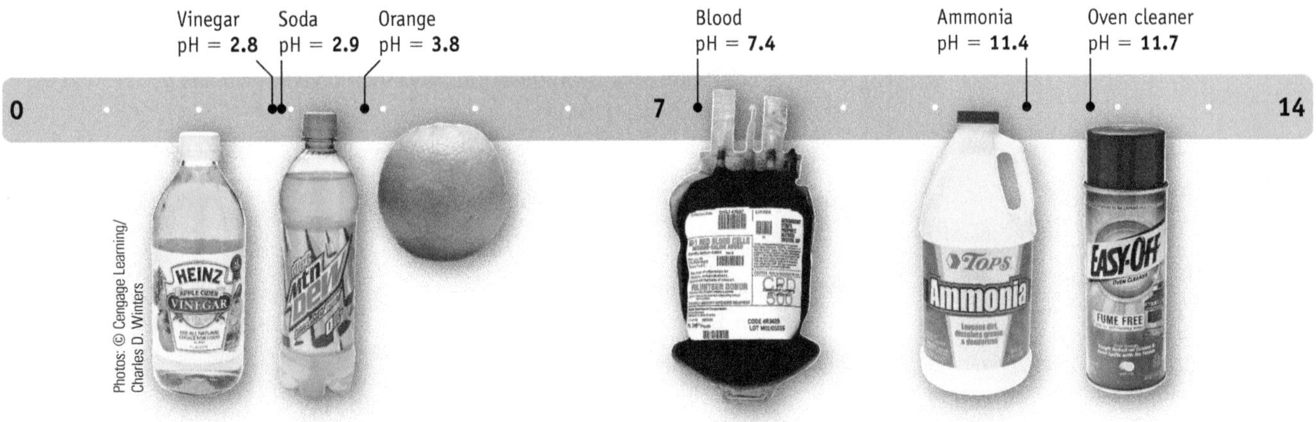

Photos: © Cengage Learning/
Charles D. Winters

FIGURE 4.9 **pH values of some common substances.** Here, the "bar" is colored red at one end and blue at the other. These are the colors of litmus paper, commonly used in the laboratory to decide whether a solution is acidic (litmus is red) or basic (litmus is blue).

EXAMPLE 4.8

pH of Solutions

Problem

(a) Lemon juice has $[H_3O^+] = 0.0032$ M. What is its pH?

(b) Seawater has a pH of 8.07. What is the hydronium ion concentration of this solution?

(c) A solution of nitric acid has a concentration of 0.0056 mol/L. What is the pH of this solution?

What Do You Know? In part (a) you are given a concentration and asked to calculate the pH, whereas the opposite is true in (b). For part (c), however, you first must recognize that HNO_3 is a strong acid and is 100% ionized in water.

Strategy Use Equation 4.3 to calculate pH from the H_3O^+ concentration and Equation 4.4 to find $[H_3O^+]$ from the pH.

Weak and Strong Acids and Hydronium Ion Concentration
Because a weak acid (e.g., acetic acid) does not ionize completely in water, the hydronium ion concentration in an aqueous solution of a weak acid is less than the concentration of the acid. In contrast, the hydronium ion concentration in strong acids is the same as the acid concentration.

Photos: © Cengage Learning/Charles D. Winters

FIGURE 4.10 **Determining pH.**

(a) Some household products. Each solution contains a few drops of an acid–base indicator. A color of yellow or red indicates a pH less than 7. A green to purple color indicates a pH greater than 7.

(b) The pH of a soda is measured with a modern pH meter. Soft drinks are often quite acidic, owing to dissolved CO_2 and other ingredients.

Solution

(a) Lemon juice: Because the hydronium ion concentration is known, the pH is found using Equation 4.3.

$$pH = -\log [H_3O^+] = -\log (3.2 \times 10^{-3}) = -(-2.49) = 2.49$$

(b) Seawater: Here pH = 8.07. Therefore,

$$[H_3O^+] = 10^{-pH} = 10^{-8.07} = 8.5 \times 10^{-9} \text{ M}$$

(c) Nitric acid: Nitric acid, a strong acid (Table 3.1, page 115), is completely ionized in aqueous solution. Because the concentration of HNO_3 is 0.0056 mol/L, the ion concentrations are also 0.0056 mol/L.

$$[H_3O^+] = [NO_3^-] = 0.0056 \text{ M}$$

$$pH = -\log [H_3O^+] = -\log (0.0056 \text{ M}) = 2.25$$

Think about Your Answer A comment on logarithms and significant figures (Appendix A) is useful. The number to the left of the decimal point in a logarithm is called the *characteristic*, and the number to the right is the *mantissa*. The mantissa has as many significant figures as the number whose log was found. For example, the logarithm of 3.2×10^{-3} (two significant figures) is 2.49. (The significant figures are the two numbers to the right of the decimal point.)

Check Your Understanding

(a) What is the pH of a solution of HCl in which [HCl] = 2.6×10^{-2} M?

(b) What is the hydronium ion concentration in orange juice with a pH of 3.80?

REVIEW & CHECK FOR SECTION 4-6

1. Which of the solutions listed below has the lowest pH?

   (a) 0.10 M HCl
   (b) 0.10 M NaOH
   (c) 2.5×10^{-5} M HNO_3
   (d) pure H_2O

2. A 0.365-g sample of HCl is dissolved in enough water to give 2.00×10^2 mL of solution. What is the pH?

   (a) 2.000
   (b) 0.0500
   (c) 1.301
   (d) 1.000

3. A solution has a pH of 10.54. What is the hydronium ion concentration?

   (a) 2.9×10^{-11} M
   (b) 2.7×10^{-5} M
   (c) 10.54 M
   (d) 3.5×10^{10} M

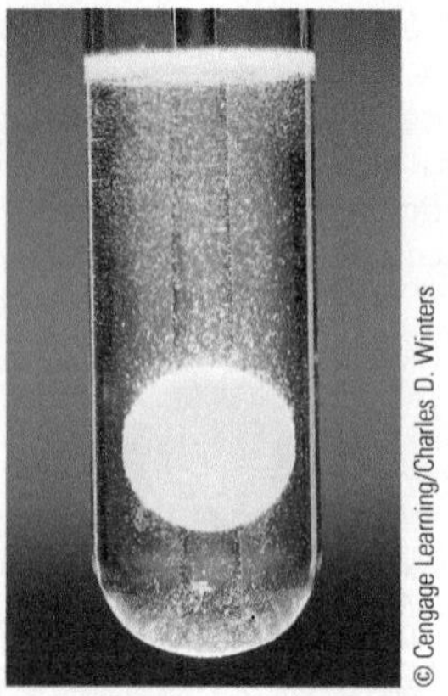

FIGURE 4.11 A commercial remedy for excess stomach acid. The tablet contains calcium carbonate, which reacts with hydrochloric acid, the acid present in the digestive system. The most obvious product is CO_2 gas, but $CaCl_2$(aq) is also produced.

Learning Objectives: LO 1.19 (see APEC Lab 3 "Gravimetric Analysis of a Sulfate Mixture"), LO 1.20 (see APEC Lab 4 "Analysis of Vinegar"), LO 3.8, LO 3.9 (see APEC Lab 8 "Analysis by Oxidation-Reduction Titration")

4-7 Stoichiometry of Reactions in Aqueous Solution

Solution Stoichiometry

Suppose we want to know what mass of $CaCO_3$ is required to react completely with 25 mL of 0.750 M HCl. The first step in finding the answer is to write a balanced equation. In this case, we have a gas-forming exchange reaction involving a metal carbonate and an aqueous acid (Figure 4.11).

$$\underset{\text{metal carbonate}}{CaCO_3(s)} + \underset{\text{acid}}{2\,HCl(aq)} \rightarrow \underset{\text{salt}}{CaCl_2(aq)} + \underset{\text{water}}{H_2O(\ell)} + \underset{\text{carbon dioxide}}{CO_2(g)}$$

This problem differs from the previous stoichiometry problems in that the quantity of one reactant (HCl) is given as a volume of a solution of known concentration instead of as a mass in grams. Because our balanced equation is written in terms of amounts (moles), our first step will be to determine the amount of HCl present from the given information so that we can relate the amount of HCl available to the amount of $CaCO_3$.

$$\text{Amount of HCl} = c_{HCl} \times V_{HCl} = \frac{0.750 \text{ mol HCl}}{1 \cancel{\text{ L HCl}}} \times 0.025 \cancel{\text{ L HCl}} = 0.019 \text{ mol HCl}$$

This is then related to the amount of $CaCO_3$ required using the stoichiometric factor from the balanced equation.

$$0.019 \cancel{\text{ mol HCl}} \times \frac{1 \text{ mol CaCO}_3}{2 \cancel{\text{ mol HCl}}} = 0.0094 \text{ mol CaCO}_3$$

Finally, the amount of $CaCO_3$ is converted to a mass in grams using the molar mass of $CaCO_3$ as the conversion factor.

$$0.0094 \cancel{\text{ mol CaCO}_3} \times \frac{100. \text{ g CaCO}_3}{1 \cancel{\text{ mol CaCO}_3}} = 0.94 \text{ g CaCO}_3$$

If you follow the general scheme outlined in Problem Solving Tip 4.4 and pay attention to the units on the numbers, you can successfully carry out any kind of stoichiometry calculations involving concentrations.

EXAMPLE 4.9

Stoichiometry of a Reaction in Solution

Problem Metallic zinc reacts with aqueous HCl (Figure 3.13).

$$\text{Zn(s)} + 2 \text{ HCl(aq)} \rightarrow \text{ZnCl}_2\text{(aq)} + \text{H}_2\text{(g)}$$

What volume of 2.50 M HCl, in milliliters, is required to convert 11.8 g of Zn completely to products?

What Do You Know? The balanced equation for the reaction of Zn and HCl(aq) is provided. You know the mass of zinc and the concentration of HCl(aq).

Strategy

- Calculate the amount of zinc.
- Use a stoichiometric factor (= 2 mol HCl/1 mol Zn) to relate amount of HCl required to amount of Zn available.
- Calculate the volume of HCl solution from the amount of HCl and its concentration.

Solution Begin by calculating the amount of Zn.

$$11.8 \cancel{\text{ g Zn}} \times \frac{1 \text{ mol Zn}}{65.38 \cancel{\text{ g Zn}}} = 0.180 \text{ mol Zn}$$

Use the stoichiometric factor to calculate the amount of HCl required.

$$0.180 \cancel{\text{ mol Zn}} \times \frac{2 \text{ mol HCl}}{1 \cancel{\text{ mol Zn}}} = 0.360 \text{ mol HCl}$$

Use the amount of HCl and the solution concentration to calculate the volume.

$$0.360 \cancel{\text{ mol HCl}} \times \frac{1.00 \text{ L solution}}{2.50 \cancel{\text{ mol HCl}}} = 0.144 \text{ L HCl}$$

Strategy Map 4.9

PROBLEM
Calculate **volume of HCl solution** required to consume ***given mass*** of a **reactant (Zn)**

DATA/INFORMATION
- **Mass** of **Zn**
- **Concentration** of **HCl**
- Balanced equation

STEP 1. Write balanced equation.

Balanced equation is **given**

STEP 2. Amount reactant (mol) = mass × (1 mol/molar mass).

Amount of **Zn**

STEP 3. Use **stoichiometric factor** to relate moles Zn to amount (mol) acid required.

Amount of acid required **(mol)**

STEP 4. Volume of acid required = mol HCl required × (1 L/mol HCl).

Volume of acid required **(L)**

The answer is requested in units of milliliters, so we convert the volume to milliliters and find that 144 mL of 2.50 M HCl is required to convert 11.8 g of Zn completely to products.

Think about Your Answer You began with 0.180 mol of zinc. Because the concentration of the HCl solution is 2.50 mol/L, it makes sense that significantly less than 1 L of HCl solution is needed. Notice also that this is a redox reaction in which zinc is oxidized (oxidation number changes from 0 to +2) and hydrogen, in HCl(aq), is reduced (its oxidation number changes from +1 to 0).

Check Your Understanding

If you combine 75.0 mL of 0.350 M HCl and an excess of Na_2CO_3, what mass of CO_2, in grams, is produced?

$$Na_2CO_3(s) + 2\ HCl(aq) \rightarrow 2\ NaCl(aq) + H_2O(\ell) + CO_2(g)$$

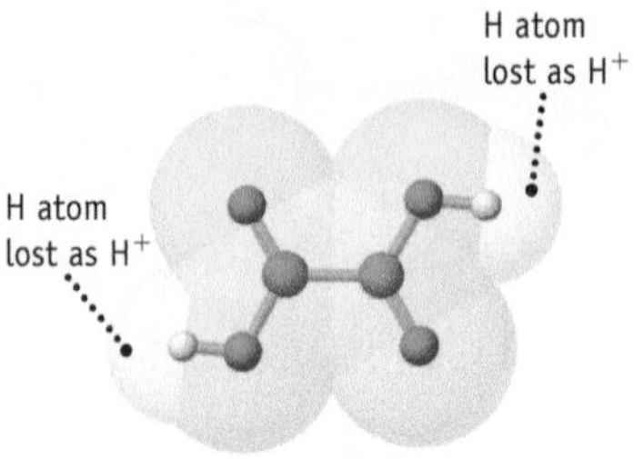

oxalic acid $H_2C_2O_4$

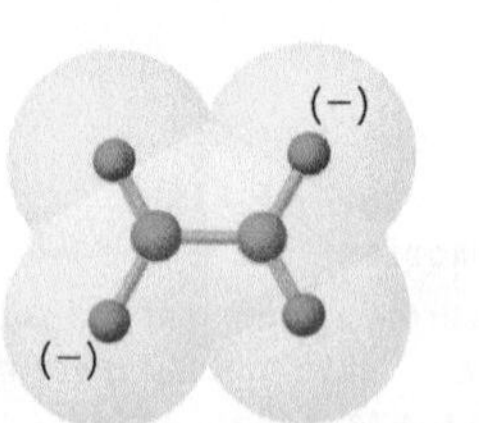

oxalate anion $C_2O_4^{2-}$

Oxalic acid. Oxalic acid has two groups that can supply an H^+ ion to solution. Hence, 1 mol of the acid requires 2 mol of NaOH for complete reaction.

Titration: A Method of Chemical Analysis

Oxalic acid, $H_2C_2O_4$, is a naturally occurring acid. Suppose you are asked to determine the mass of this acid in an impure sample. Because the compound is an acid, it reacts with a base such as sodium hydroxide.

$$H_2C_2O_4(aq) + 2\ NaOH(aq) \rightarrow Na_2C_2O_4(aq) + 2\ H_2O(\ell)$$

You can use this reaction to determine the quantity of oxalic acid present in a given mass of sample if the following conditions are met:

- You can determine when the amount of sodium hydroxide added is exactly enough to react with all the oxalic acid present in solution.
- You know the concentration of the sodium hydroxide solution and volume that has been added at exactly the point of complete reaction.

These conditions are fulfilled in a titration, a procedure illustrated in Figure 4.12. The solution containing oxalic acid is placed in a flask along with an acid–base indicator, a dye that changes color when the pH of the reaction solution reaches a certain value. Aqueous sodium hydroxide of accurately known concentration is placed in a buret. The sodium hydroxide in the buret is added slowly to the acid solution in the flask. As long as some acid is present in solution, all the base supplied from the buret is consumed, the solution remains acidic, and the indicator color is unchanged. At some point, however, the amount of OH^- added exactly equals the

PROBLEM SOLVING TIP 4.4
Stoichiometry Calculations Involving Solutions

In Problem Solving Tip 4.1, you learned about a general approach to stoichiometry problems. We can now modify that scheme for a reaction involving solutions such as $x\,A(aq) + y\,B(aq) \rightarrow$ products.

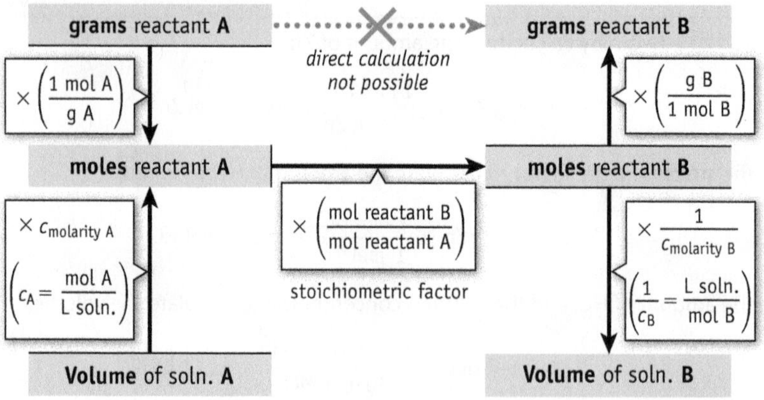

1 A buret, a volumetric measuring device calibrated in divisions of 0.1 mL (and consequently read to the nearest 0.01 mL), is filled with an aqueous solution of a base of known concentration.

2 Base is added slowly from the buret to the solution containing the acid being analyzed and an indicator.

3 When the amount of NaOH added from the buret equals the amount of H_3O^+ supplied by the acid (the equivalence point), the dye (the indicator) changes color. (The indicator used here is phenolphthalein.)

FIGURE 4.12 **Titration of an acid in aqueous solution with a base.**

amount of H_3O^+ that can be supplied by the acid. This is called the **equivalence point**. As soon as the slightest excess of base has been added beyond the equivalence point, the solution becomes basic, and the indicator changes color (see Figure 4.12). Example 4.10 shows how to use the equivalence point and the other information to determine the percentage of oxalic acid in a mixture.

EXAMPLE 4.10

Acid–Base Titration

Problem A 1.034-g sample of impure oxalic acid is dissolved in water and an acid–base indicator added. The sample requires 34.47 mL of 0.485 M NaOH to reach the equivalence point. What is the mass of oxalic acid in the sample, and what is its mass percent?

What Do You Know? You know the mass of impure oxalic acid and the volume and concentration of NaOH solution used in the titration.

Strategy

- Write a balanced chemical equation for this acid–base reaction.
- Calculate the amount of NaOH used in the titration from its volume and concentration.
- Use the stoichiometric factor defined by the equation to determine the amount of $H_2C_2O_4$.
- Calculate the mass of $H_2C_2O_4$ from the amount and its molar mass.
- Determine the percent by mass of $H_2C_2O_4$ in the sample.

Strategy Map 4.10

PROBLEM

Calculate the **mass percent of acid** in an impure sample. Determine the **acid content** using an *acid–base titration.*

DATA/INFORMATION

- **Mass** of impure sample containing ***acid.***
- **Volume** and **concentration** of ***base*** used in titration.

STEP 1. Write balanced equation.

Balanced equation for reaction of **acid** (oxalic acid) with **base** (NaOH)

STEP 2. **Amount** of base (mol) = volume (L) × (mol/L).

Amount of base (mol)

STEP 3. Use a **stoichiometric factor** to relate amount of base (mol) to amount (mol) of acid.

Amount of acid (mol) in impure sample

STEP 4. **Mass** of acid in sample = mol acid × (g/mol).

Mass of acid in impure sample

STEP 5. **Mass %** of acid in sample = (g acid/g sample)100%.

Mass % acid in impure sample

Solution The balanced equation for the reaction of NaOH and $H_2C_2O_4$ is

$$H_2C_2O_4(aq) + 2\ NaOH(aq) \rightarrow Na_2C_2O_4(aq) + 2\ H_2O(\ell)$$

and the amount of NaOH is given by

$$\text{Amount of NaOH} = c_{NaOH} \times V_{NaOH} = \frac{0.485 \text{ mol NaOH}}{\cancel{L}} \times 0.03447\ \cancel{L} = 0.0167 \text{ mol NaOH}$$

The balanced equation for the reaction shows that 1 mol of oxalic acid requires 2 mol of sodium hydroxide. This is the required stoichiometric factor to obtain the amount of oxalic acid present.

$$0.0167\ \cancel{\text{mol NaOH}} \times \frac{1 \text{ mol } H_2C_2O_4}{2\ \cancel{\text{mol NaOH}}} = 0.00836 \text{ mol } H_2C_2O_4$$

The mass of oxalic acid is found from the amount of the acid and its molar mass.

$$0.00836\ \cancel{\text{mol } H_2C_2O_4} \times \frac{90.04 \text{ g } H_2C_2O_4}{1\ \cancel{\text{mol } H_2C_2O_4}} = 0.753 \text{ g } H_2C_2O_4$$

This mass of oxalic acid represents 72.8% of the total sample mass.

$$\frac{0.753 \text{ g } H_2C_2O_4}{1.034 \text{ g sample}} \times 100\% = 72.8\%\ H_2C_2O_4$$

Think about Your Answer Problem Solving Tip 4.4 outlines the procedure used to solve this problem.

Check Your Understanding

A 25.0-mL sample of vinegar (which contains the weak acid acetic acid, CH_3CO_2H) requires 28.33 mL of a 0.953 M solution of NaOH for titration to the equivalence point. What is the mass of acetic acid, in grams, in the vinegar sample, and what is the concentration of acetic acid in the vinegar?

$$CH_3CO_2H(aq) + NaOH(aq) \rightarrow NaCH_3CO_2(aq) + H_2O(\ell)$$

Standardizing an Acid or Base

In Example 4.10 the concentration of the base used in the titration was given. In actual practice this usually has to be found by a prior measurement. The procedure by which the concentration of an analytical reagent is determined accurately is called **standardization**, and there are two general approaches.

One approach is to weigh accurately a sample of a pure, solid acid or base (known as a *primary standard*) and then titrate this sample with a solution of the base or acid to be standardized (Example 4.11). An alternative approach to standardizing a solution is to titrate it with another solution that is already standardized (see "Check Your Understanding" in Example 4.11). This is often done using standard solutions purchased from chemical supply companies.

EXAMPLE 4.11

Standardizing an Acid by Titration

Problem Sodium carbonate, Na_2CO_3, is a base, and an accurately weighed sample can be used to standardize an acid. A sample of sodium carbonate (0.263 g) requires 28.35 mL of aqueous HCl for titration to the equivalence point. What is the concentration of the HCl?

What Do You Know? The concentration of the HCl(aq) solution is the unknown in this problem. You know the mass of Na_2CO_3 and the volume of HCl(aq) solution needed to react completely with the Na_2CO_3. You need the molar mass of Na_2CO_3 and a balanced equation for the reaction.

Strategy

- Write a balanced equation for this acid–base reaction.
- Calculate the amount of Na_2CO_3 from its mass and molar mass.
- Use the stoichiometric factor (from the equation) to find the amount of HCl(aq).
- The amount of HCl divided by the volume of solution (in liters) gives its concentration (mol/L).

Solution The balanced equation for the reaction is written first.

$$Na_2CO_3(aq) + 2\ HCl(aq) \rightarrow 2\ NaCl(aq) + H_2O(\ell) + CO_2(g)$$

Calculate the amount of the base, Na_2CO_3, from its mass and molar mass.

$$0.263\ \text{g}\ Na_2CO_3 \times \frac{1\ \text{mol}\ Na_2CO_3}{106.0\ \text{g}\ Na_2CO_3} = 0.00248\ \text{mol}\ Na_2CO_3$$

Next, use the stoichiometric factor to calculate the amount of HCl in 28.35 mL.

$$0.00248\ \text{mol}\ Na_2CO_3 \times \frac{2\ \text{mol HCl required}}{1\ \text{mol}\ Na_2CO_3\ \text{available}} = 0.00496\ \text{mol HCl}$$

Calculate the concentration of HCl solution by dividing the amount of HCl by the volume of HCl used in the titration.

$$[HCl] = \frac{0.00496\ \text{mol HCl}}{0.02835\ \text{L}} = 0.175\ \text{M HCl}$$

Think about Your Answer Sodium carbonate is commonly used as a primary standard. It can be obtained in pure form, can be weighed accurately, and it reacts completely with strong acids.

Check Your Understanding

Hydrochloric acid, HCl, with a concentration of 0.100 M can be purchased from chemical supply houses, and this solution can be used to standardize the solution of a base. If titrating 25.00 mL of a sodium hydroxide solution to the equivalence point requires 29.67 mL of 0.100 M HCl, what is the concentration of the base?

Determining Molar Mass by Titration

In Chapter 2 and in this chapter we used analytical data to determine the empirical formula of a compound. The molecular formula could then be derived if the molar mass were known. If the unknown substance is an acid or a base, it is possible to determine the molar mass by titration.

EXAMPLE 4.12

Determining the Molar Mass of an Acid by Titration

Problem To determine the molar mass of an unknown organic acid, HA, a 1.056-g sample of HA is titrated with standardized NaOH (that is, with a NaOH solution whose concentration is accurately known). Calculate the molar mass of HA assuming the acid reacts with 33.78 mL of 0.256 M NaOH according to the equation

$$HA(aq) + NaOH(aq) \rightarrow NaA(aq) + H_2O(\ell)$$

Strategy Map 4.12

PROBLEM

Calculate the **molar mass** of an acid, **HA,** using an *acid–base titration.*

↓

DATA/INFORMATION

- **Mass** of ***acid*** sample.
- **Volume** and **concentration** of ***base*** used in titration

STEP 1. Write balanced equation.

Balanced equation for reaction of **acid** (HA) with **base** (NaOH)

STEP 2. **Amount** of base (mol) = volume (L) × (mol/L).

Amount of base (mol)

STEP 3. Use a **stoichiometric factor** to relate amount of base (mol) to amount (mol) of acid.

Amount of acid **HA** (mol)

STEP 4. **Molar mass** = mass of acid in sample/amount of acid in sample.

Molar mass of acid **HA**

What Do You Know? You know the mass of the sample of unknown acid, and the volume and concentration of NaOH(aq). From the equation given, you know that the acid and base react in a 1 : 1 fashion.

Strategy The key to this problem is to recognize that the molar mass of a substance is the ratio of the mass of the sample (g) to its amount (mol). You know the mass, but you need to determine the amount equivalent to that mass. The equation informs you that 1 mol of HA reacts with 1 mol of NaOH, so the amount of HA equals the amount of NaOH used in the titration. And, the amount of NaOH can be calculated from its concentration and volume.

Solution Let us first calculate the amount of NaOH used in the titration.

$$\text{Amount of NaOH} = c_{\text{NaOH}} \times V_{\text{NaOH}} = \frac{0.256 \text{ mol}}{\cancel{\text{L}}} \times 0.03378 \ \cancel{\text{L}} = 8.65 \times 10^{-3} \text{ mol NaOH}$$

The amount of NaOH used in the titration is the same as the amount of acid titrated. That is,

$$8.65 \times 10^{-3} \ \cancel{\text{mol NaOH}} \times \frac{1 \text{ mol HA}}{1 \ \cancel{\text{mol NaOH}}} = 8.65 \times 10^{-3} \text{ mol HA}$$

Finally, calculate the molar mass of HA.

$$\text{Molar mass of acid} = \frac{1.056 \text{ g HA}}{8.65 \times 10^{-3} \text{ mol HA}} = 122 \text{ g/mol}$$

Think about Your Answer The molar masses of water-soluble acids range from 20 g/mol (for HF) to a few hundred grams per mole.

Check Your Understanding

An unknown monoprotic acid reacts with NaOH according to the net ionic equation

$$HA(aq) + OH^-(aq) \rightarrow A^-(aq) + H_2O(\ell)$$

Calculate the molar mass of HA if 0.856 g of the acid requires 30.08 mL of 0.323 M NaOH.

Titrations Using Oxidation–Reduction Reactions

Analysis by titration is not limited to acid–base chemistry. Many oxidation–reduction reactions go rapidly to completion in aqueous solution, and methods exist to determine their equivalence points.

EXAMPLE 4.13

Using an Oxidation–Reduction Reaction in a Titration

Problem The iron in a sample of an iron ore can be converted quantitatively to the iron(II) ion, Fe^{2+}, in aqueous solution, and this solution can then be titrated with aqueous potassium permanganate, $KMnO_4$. The balanced, net ionic equation for the reaction occurring in this titration is

$$\underset{\text{purple}}{MnO_4^-(aq)} + \underset{\text{colorless}}{5\,Fe^{2+}(aq)} + 8\,H_3O^+(aq) \rightarrow \underset{\text{colorless}}{Mn^{2+}(aq)} + \underset{\text{pale yellow}}{5\,Fe^{3+}(aq)} + 12\,H_2O(\ell)$$

A 1.026-g sample of iron-containing ore requires 24.35 mL of 0.0195 M $KMnO_4$ to reach the equivalence point. What is the mass percent of iron in the ore?

What Do You Know? You know the concentration and volume of the $KMnO_4$ solution used to titrate Fe^{2+}(aq) to the equivalence point. The stoichiometric factor relating amounts of $KMnO_4$ and Fe^{2+}(aq) is derived from the balanced equation.

Strategy

- Use the volume and concentration of the $KMnO_4$ solution to calculate the amount of $KMnO_4$ used in the titration.
- Use the stoichiometric factor to determine the amount of Fe^{2+} from the amount of $KMnO_4$.
- Convert the amount of Fe^{2+} to mass of iron using the molar mass of iron.
- Calculate the mass percent of iron in the sample.

Solution First, calculate the amount of $KMnO_4$.

$$\text{Amount of KMnO}_4 = c_{KMnO_4} \times V_{KMnO_4} = \frac{0.0195 \text{ mol KMnO}_4}{\text{L}} \times 0.02435 \text{ L} = 0.000475 \text{ mol}$$

Use the stoichiometric factor to calculate the amount of iron(II) ion.

$$0.000475 \text{ mol KMnO}_4 \times \frac{5 \text{ mol Fe}^{2+}}{1 \text{ mol KMnO}_4} = 0.00237 \text{ mol Fe}^{2+}$$

Next, calculate the mass of iron.

$$0.00237 \text{ mol Fe}^{2+} \times \frac{55.85 \text{ g Fe}^{2+}}{1 \text{ mol Fe}^{2+}} = 0.133 \text{ g Fe}^{2+}$$

Finally, determine the mass percent.

$$\frac{0.133 \text{ g Fe}^{2+}}{1.026 \text{ g sample}} \times 100\% = 12.9\% \text{ iron}$$

Think about Your Answer The reaction of iron(II) ions with $KMnO_4$ is well suited for use in a titration because it is easy to detect when all the iron(II) ion has reacted. The MnO_4^- ion is a deep purple color, but when it reacts with Fe^{2+} the color disappears because the reaction product, Mn^{2+}, is colorless. Therefore, $KMnO_4$ solution is added from a buret until the initially colorless, Fe^{2+}-containing solution just turns a faint purple color (due to unreacted $KMnO_4$), the signal that the equivalence point has been reached.

Check Your Understanding

Vitamin C, ascorbic acid ($C_6H_8O_6$), is a reducing agent. One way to determine the ascorbic acid content of a sample is to mix the acid with an excess of iodine,

$$C_6H_8O_6(aq) + I_2(aq) + 2\ H_2O(\ell) \rightarrow C_6H_6O_6(aq) + 2\ H_3O^+(aq) + 2\ I^-(aq)$$

and then titrate the iodine that did not react with the ascorbic acid with sodium thiosulfate. The balanced, net ionic equation for the reaction occurring in this titration is

$$I_2(aq) + 2\ S_2O_3^{2-}(aq) \rightarrow 2\ I^-(aq) + S_4O_6^{2-}(aq)$$

Suppose 50.00 mL of 0.0520 M I_2 was added to the sample containing ascorbic acid. After the ascorbic acid/I_2 reaction was complete, the I_2 not used in this reaction required 20.30 mL of 0.196 M $Na_2S_2O_3$ for titration to the equivalence point. Calculate the mass of ascorbic acid in the unknown sample.

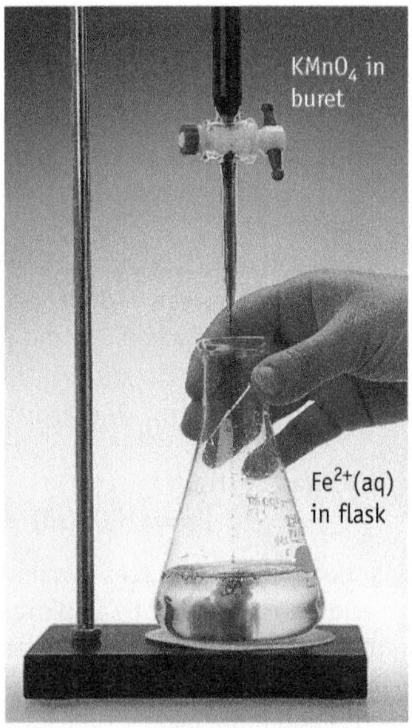

Using an oxidation–reduction reaction for analysis by titration. Purple, aqueous $KMnO_4$ is added to a solution containing Fe^{2+}. As $KMnO_4$ drops into the solution, colorless Mn^{2+} and pale yellow Fe^{3+} form.

CASE STUDY How Much Salt Is There in Seawater?

Saltiness is one of the basic taste sensations, and a taste of seawater quickly reveals it is salty. How did the oceans become salty?

Dissolved CO_2 reacts with water to produce H_2CO_3, a weak acid that partially dissociates to form hydronium and bicarbonate ions.

$$CO_2(g) + H_2O(\ell) \rightarrow H_2CO_3(aq)$$

$$H_2CO_3(aq) + H_2O(\ell) \rightleftharpoons H_3O^+(aq) + HCO_3^-(aq)$$

Indeed, this is the reason rain is normally acidic, and this slightly acidic rainwater can then cause substances such as limestone or corals to dissolve, producing calcium ions and more bicarbonate ions.

$$CaCO_3(s) + H_3O^+(aq) \rightarrow Ca^{2+}(aq) + HCO_3^-(aq) + H_2O(\ell)$$

Sodium ions arrive in the oceans by a similar reaction with sodium-bearing minerals such as albite, $NaAlSi_3O_6$. Acidic rain falling on the land extracts sodium ions that are then carried by rivers to the ocean.

The average chloride content of rocks in the Earth's crust is only 0.01%, so only a minute proportion of the chloride ion in the oceans can come from the weathering of rocks and minerals. What then is the origin of the chloride ions in seawater? The answer is volcanoes. Hydrogen chloride gas, HCl, is a constituent of volcanic gases. Early in Earth's history, the planet was

Courtesy Jack Kotz

much hotter, and volcanoes were much more widespread. The HCl gas emitted from these volcanoes is very soluble in water and quickly dissolves to give a dilute solution of hydrochloric acid. The chloride ions from dissolved HCl gas and sodium ions from weathered rocks are the source of the salt in the sea.

Suppose you are an oceanographer, and you want to determine the concentration of chloride ions in a sample of seawater. How can you do this? And what results might you find?

There are several ways to analyze a solution for its chloride ion content; among them is the classic "Mohr method" in which a solution containing chloride ions is titrated with standardized silver nitrate. The following reaction will occur:

$$Ag^+(aq) + Cl^-(aq) \rightarrow AgCl(s)$$

The reaction will continue until the chloride ions have been precipitated completely. To detect the equivalence point of the titration of Cl^- with Ag^+, the Mohr method involves the addition of a few drops of a solution of potassium chromate. This "indicator" works because silver chromate is slightly more soluble than AgCl, so the red Ag_2CrO_4 precipitates only after all of the AgCl is precipitated.

$$2\ Ag^+(aq) + CrO_4^{2-}(aq) \rightarrow Ag_2CrO_4(s)$$

The appearance of the red color of Ag_2CrO_4 (◀ Figure 3.12) signals the equivalence point.

Question:

Using the following information, calculate the chloride ion concentration in a sample of seawater.

a. Volume of original seawater sample = 100.0 mL.
b. A 10.00-mL sample of the seawater was diluted to 100.0 mL with distilled water.
c. 10.00 mL of the diluted sample was again diluted to 100.0 mL.
d. A Mohr titration was performed on 50.00 mL of the diluted sample (from step c) and required 26.25 mL of 0.100 M $AgNO_3$. What was the chloride ion concentration in the original seawater sample?

The answer to this question is available in Appendix N.

REVIEW & CHECK FOR SECTION 4-7

1. A 25-mL sample of 0.40 M HCl is added to 32 mL of 0.30 M NaOH. Is the resulting solution acidic, basic, or neutral?

   (a) acidic (b) basic (c) neutral

2. What volume of 0.250 M NaOH is required to react *completely* with 0.0100 moles of H_2SO_4?

   (a) 80.0 mL (b) 60.0 mL (c) 40.0 mL (d) 125 mL

Learning Objectives: LO 1.15 (see APEC Lab 1 "Energy Levels and Electron Transitions"), LO 1.16 (see APEC Lab 2 "The Percentage of Copper in Brass")

4-8 Spectrophotometry

Solutions of many compounds are colored, a consequence of the absorption of light (Figure 4.13). It is possible to measure, quantitatively, the extent of light absorption and to relate this to the concentration of the dissolved solute. This kind of experiment, called **spectrophotometry**, is an important analytical method and you may use it in your laboratory course. Spectrophotometry is one of the most frequently used methods of quantitative analysis. It is applicable to many industrial, clinical, and forensic problems involving the quantitative determination of compounds that are colored or that react to form a colored product.

CASE STUDY Forensic Chemistry: Titrations and Food Tampering

The U.S. Food and Drug Administration (FDA) has discovered cases of product tampering involving the addition of bleach to products such as soup, infant formula, and soft drinks. Household bleach is a dilute solution of sodium hypochlorite (NaClO), a compound that is an oxidizing agent and is dangerous if swallowed.

One method of detecting bleach uses starch-iodide paper. The bleach oxidizes the iodide ion to iodine in an acid solution,

$$2\ I^-(aq) + HClO(aq) + H_3O^+(aq) \rightarrow I_2(aq) + 2\ H_2O(\ell) + Cl^-(aq)$$

and the presence of I_2 is detected by a deep blue color in the presence of starch.

This reaction is also used in the quantitative analysis of solutions containing bleach. Excess iodide ion (in the form of KI) is added to the sample. The bleach in the sample (which forms HClO in acid solution) oxidizes I^- in a ratio of 1 mol HClO to 2 mol I^-. The iodine formed in the reaction is then titrated with sodium thiosulfate, $Na_2S_2O_3$ in another oxidation-reduction reaction (as in "Check Your Understanding" in Example 4.13).

$$I_2(aq) + 2\ S_2O_3^{2-}(aq) \rightarrow 2\ I^-(aq) + S_4O_6^{2-}(aq)$$

The amount of $Na_2S_2O_3$ used in the titration can then be used to determine the amount of NaClO in the original sample.

Question:

Excess KI is added to a 100.0-mL sample of a soft drink that had been contaminated with bleach, NaClO. The iodine (I_2) generated in the solution is then titrated with 0.0425 M $Na_2S_2O_3$ and requires 25.3 mL to reach the equivalence point. What mass of NaClO was contained in the 100.0-mL sample of adulterated soft drink?

The answer to this question is available in Appendix N.

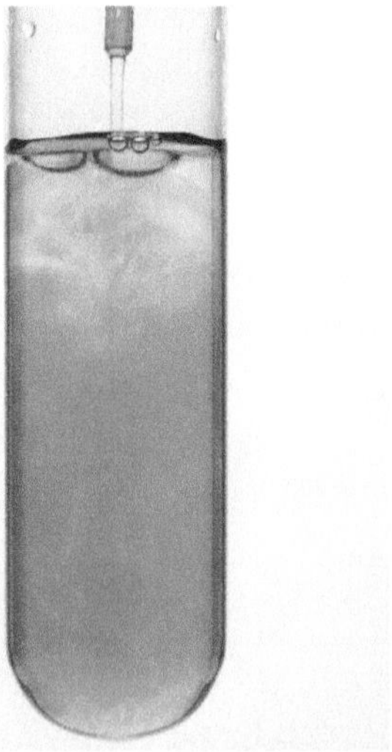

© Cengage Learning/Charles D. Winters

A distinctive blue color is generated when iodine reacts with water-soluble starch.

Every substance absorbs or transmits certain wavelengths of radiant energy but not others (Figures 4.13 and 4.14). For example, nickel(II) ions (and chlorophyll) absorb red and blue/violet light while they transmit green light. Your eyes "see" the transmitted or reflected light as the color green. Furthermore, the specific wavelengths of light absorbed and transmitted are characteristic for a substance, so a spectrum serves as a "fingerprint" of the substance that can help identify an unknown.

Now suppose you look at two solutions containing copper(II) ions, one a deeper color than the other. Your common sense tells you that the intensely colored one is the more concentrated (Figure 4.15a). This is true: the intensity of the color is a measure of the concentration of the material in the solution.

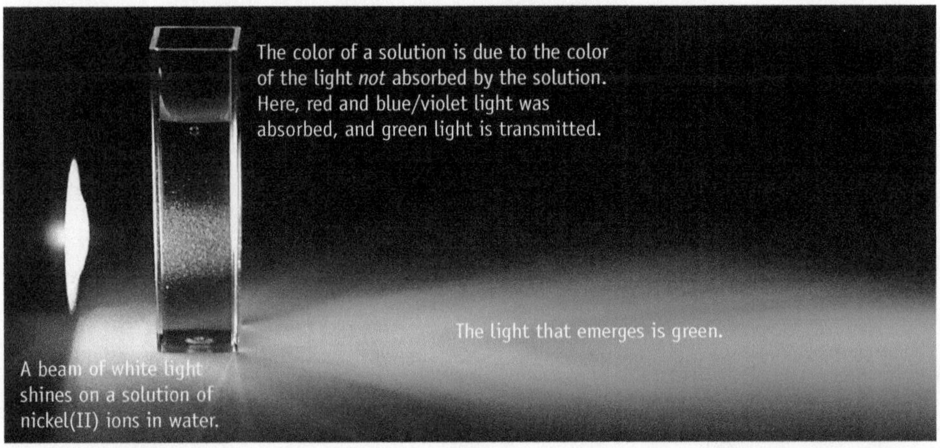

© Cengage Learning/Charles D. Winters

FIGURE 4.13 Light absorption and color.

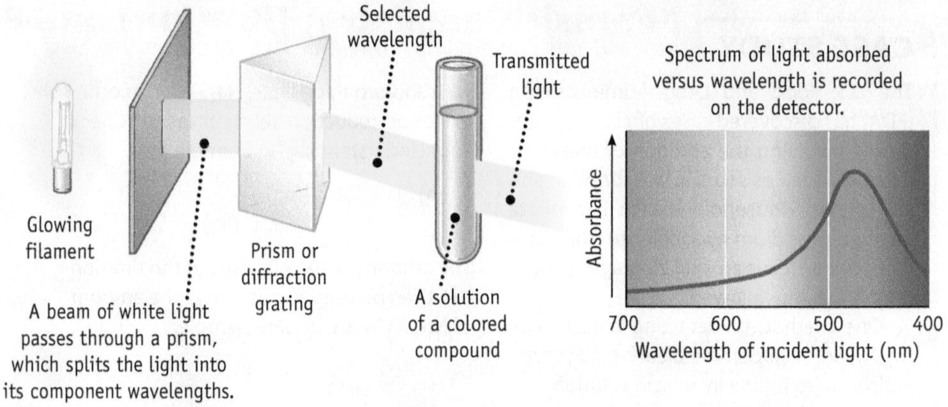

FIGURE 4.14 **An absorption spectrophotometer.** The detector in the spectrophotometer "scans" all wavelengths of light and determines the absorbance at each wavelength. The output is a *spectrum*, a plot of absorbance as a function of the wavelength or frequency of the incoming or incident light. Here, the sample absorbs light in the green-blue part of the spectrum and transmits light in the remaining wavelengths. The sample would appear red to orange to your eye.

Transmittance, Absorbance, and the Beer–Lambert Law

To understand the exact relationship of light absorption and solution concentration, we need to define several terms. **Transmittance** (T) is the ratio of the amount of light transmitted by or passing through the sample(P) relative to the amount of light that initially fell on the sample (the incident light, P_0).

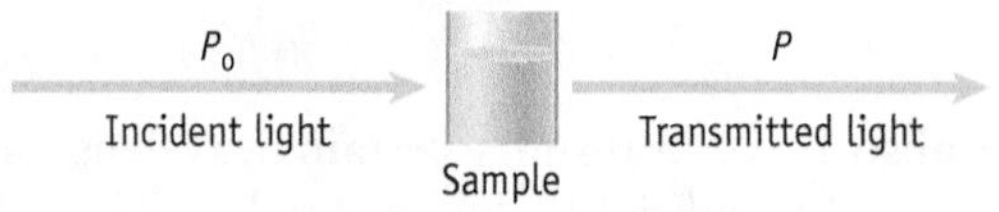

$$\text{Transmittance } (T) = \frac{P}{P_0} = \frac{\text{intensity of transmitted light}}{\text{intensity of incident light}}$$

The **absorbance** of a sample is defined as the negative logarithm of its transmittance. That is, absorbance and transmittance have an inverse relationship. As the absorbance of a solution increases, the transmittance decreases

$$\text{Absorbance} = -\log T = -\log P/P_0$$

FIGURE 4.15 **Light absorption, concentration, and path length.**

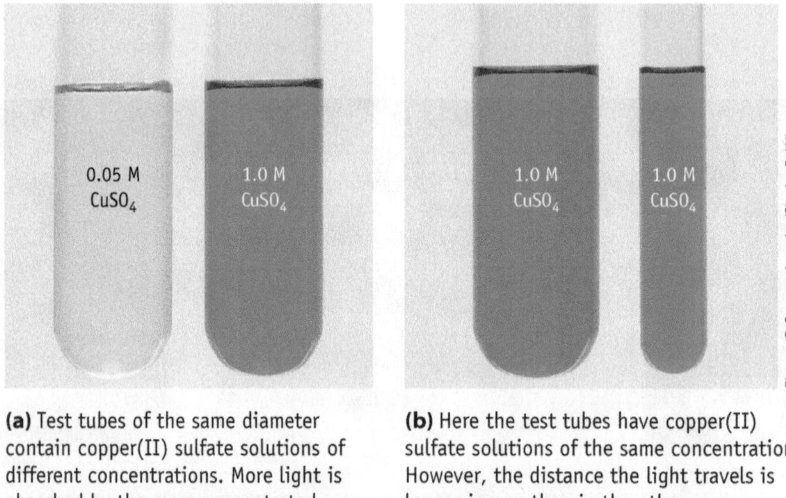

(a) Test tubes of the same diameter contain copper(II) sulfate solutions of different concentrations. More light is absorbed by the more concentrated solution, and it appears more blue.

(b) Here the test tubes have copper(II) sulfate solutions of the same concentration. However, the distance the light travels is longer in one than in the other.

Going back to our example of an aqueous solution of copper(II) ions in Figure 4.15a, if you have two solutions of copper(II) sulfate, you may deduce that the bluer solution appears more blue because this solution has a greater concentration of copper(II) sulfate. That is, the *absorbance, A, of a sample increases as the concentration increases.*

Next, suppose that there are two test tubes, both containing the same solution at the same concentration. The only difference is that one of the test tubes has a smaller diameter than the other (Figure 4.15b). We shine light of the same intensity (P_0) on both test tubes. In the narrower-diameter tube, the light has to travel only a short distance through the sample before its strikes your eyes, whereas in the other tube it has to pass through more of the sample. In the wider-diameter tube more of the light will be absorbed because the path length is longer. In other words, *absorbance increases as path length increases.*

The two observations described above constitute the **Beer–Lambert law:**

$$\text{Absorbance } (A) \propto \text{path length } (\ell) \times \text{concentration } (c)$$
$$A = \varepsilon \times \ell \times c \qquad (4.5)$$

where

- A, the absorbance of the sample, is a dimensionless number.
- ε, a proportionality constant, is called the *molar absorptivity*. It is a constant for a given substance, provided the temperature and wavelength are constant. It has units of L/mol · cm.
- ℓ and c have the units of length (cm) and concentration (mol/L), respectively.

The important point is that the Beer–Lambert law shows *there is a linear relationship between a sample's absorbance and its concentration for a given path length.*

Beer–Lambert Law The Beer–Lambert law applies strictly to relatively dilute solutions. At higher solute concentrations, the dependence of absorbance on concentration may not be linear.

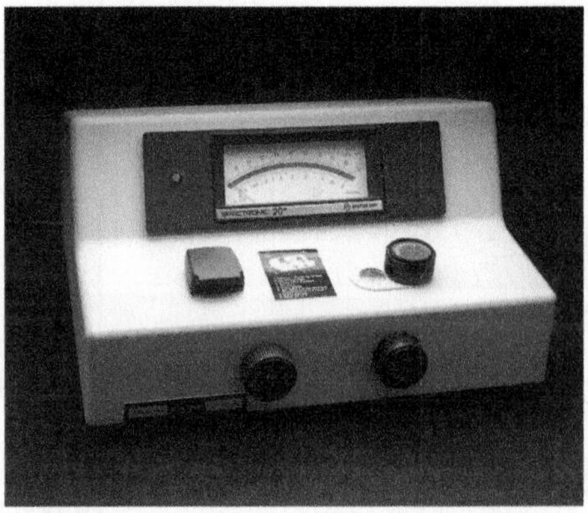

© Cengage Learning/Charles D. Winters

FIGURE 4.16 **Spectrophotometer.** This instrument is often found in introductory chemistry laboratories.

Spectrophotometric Analysis

There are usually four steps in carrying out a spectrophotometric analysis.

1. **Record the absorption spectrum of the substance to be analyzed.** In introductory chemistry laboratories, this is often done using instruments such as the one shown in Figure 4.16. The result is a spectrum such as that for aqueous permanganate ions (MnO_4^-) in Figure 4.17. The spectrum is a plot of the absorbance of the sample versus the wavelength of the incident light. Here, the maximum in absorbance is at about 525 nm.
2. **Choose the wavelength for the measurement.** The absorbance at each wavelength is proportional to concentration. Therefore, in theory you could choose any wavelength for quantitative estimations of concentration. However, the magnitude of the absorbance is important, especially when you are trying to detect very small amounts of material. In the spectra of permanganate ions in Figure 4.17, note that the difference in absorbance between curves 1 and 2 is largest at about 525 nm, and at this wavelength the change in absorbance is greatest for a given change in concentration. That is, the measurement of concentration as a function of concentration is most sensitive at this wavelength. For this reason, *the wavelength of maximum absorbance is selected for our measurements.*
3. **Prepare a calibration plot.** Once you have chosen the wavelength, the next step is to construct a **calibration curve** or **calibration plot** at this wavelength. This consists of a plot of absorbance versus concentration for a series of standard solutions whose concentrations are accurately known. Because of the linear relation between concentration and absorbance (at a given wavelength and path length), this plot is a straight line with a positive slope. (You will prepare a calibration plot in Example 4.14.)

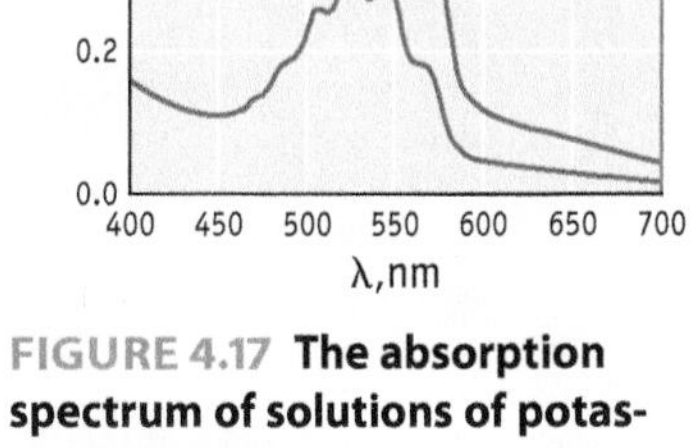

FIGURE 4.17 **The absorption spectrum of solutions of potassium permanganate ($KMnO_4$) at different concentrations.** The solution for curve 1 has a higher concentration than that for curve 2.

4 **Determine the concentration of the species of interest in other solutions.** Once the calibration plot has been made, and the equation for the line is known, you can find the concentration of an unknown sample from its absorbance.

EXAMPLE 4.14

Using Spectrophotometry in Chemical Analysis

Problem A solution of $KMnO_4$ has an absorbance of 0.539 when measured at 540 nm in a 1.0-cm cell. What is the concentration of the $KMnO_4$? Prior to determining the absorbance for the unknown solution, the following calibration data were collected for the spectrophotometer.

Concentration of $KMnO_4$ (M)	Absorbance
0.0300	0.162
0.0600	0.330
0.0900	0.499
0.120	0.670
0.150	0.840

What Do You Know? The table relates concentration and absorbance for aqueous solutions of $KMnO_4$. The absorbance of the unknown sample (at 540 nm in a 1.0-cm cell) is given.

Strategy Prepare a calibration plot from the data given above, and then use this plot to estimate the concentration of the unknown from its absorbance. A more accurate value of the concentration can be obtained if you find the equation for the straight line in the calibration plot and calculate the unknown concentration using this equation.

Solution Using Microsoft Excel (or equivalent software) or a calculator, prepare a calibration plot from the experimental data.

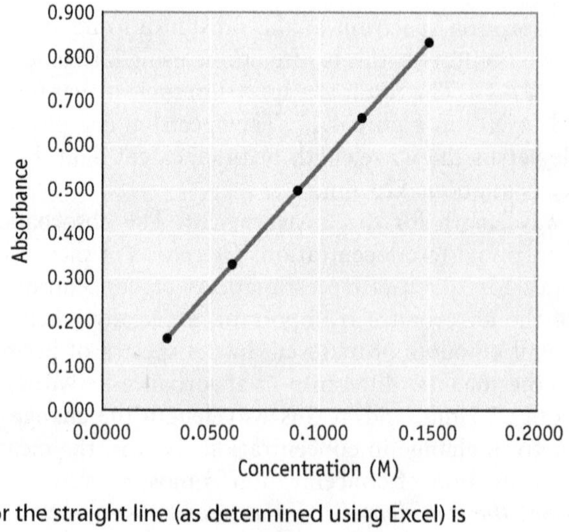

The equation for the straight line (as determined using Excel) is

$$y = 5.653x - 0.009$$

$$\text{Absorbance} = 5.653\ c - 0.009$$

If we put in the absorbance for the unknown solution,

$$0.539 = 5.653\ c - 0.009$$

$$\text{Unknown concentration} = 0.0969\ \text{M}$$

Think about Your Answer The absorbance of the unknown was 0.539. Looking back at our calibration data, we can see that this absorbance falls between the data points for absorbances of 0.499 and 0.670. Our answer determined for the concentration of $KMnO_4$ in the unknown (0.0969 M) falls between the concentrations for these two data points of 0.0900 M and 0.120 M, as it should. (See pages 39–41 for information on graphing.)

Check Your Understanding

A solution of copper(II) ions has an absorbance of 0.418 when measured at 645 nm in a 1.0-cm cell. Using the following data, calculate the concentration of copper(II) ions in an unknown solution.

CALIBRATION DATA

CONCENTRATION OF CU^{2+} (M)	ABSORBANCE
0.0562	0.720
0.0337	0.434
0.0281	0.332
0.0169	0.219

REVIEW & CHECK FOR SECTION 4-8

1. How is the absorbance (*A*) of a solution affected if a solution is diluted to twice the initial volume?

   (a) *A* is doubled. (c) *A* is not changed.

   (b) *A* is reduced to half the original value.

2. A plot of absorbance versus concentration of a series of solutions of $KMnO_4$ gives a straight line with the equation: $y = 2.50x + 0.02$. What is the concentration of a $KMnO_4$ in a solution that has an absorbance of 0.442?

   (a) 0.157 M (b) 0.169 M (c) 0.442 M (d) 1.08 M

APPLYING CHEMICAL PRINCIPLES

Antacids

Antacids are chemical compounds that relieve indigestion and heartburn. Antacids that advertise immediate relief from indigestion or heartburn contain carbonate or hydroxide ions that neutralize stomach acids. Some common active ingredients include $NaHCO_3$, $KHCO_3$, $CaCO_3$, $Mg(OH)_2$, and $Al(OH)_3$. Although these compounds give quick relief, they are not recommended for prolonged consumption. Calcium carbonate may contribute to the growth of kidney stones. In addition, calcium carbonate and aluminum hydroxide may cause constipation. Magnesium hydroxide, on the other hand, is a mild laxative that can cause diarrhea. Antacids containing magnesium, therefore, are often combined with aluminum hydroxide since the aluminum counteracts the laxative properties of the magnesium.

© Cengage Learning/Charles D. Winters

Antacids. Antacids are chemical compounds such as $CaCO_3$, $MgCO_3$, $Mg(OH)_2$, and $Al(OH)_3$ that can relieve indigestion and heartburn.

QUESTIONS:

1. Which of the compounds listed above produce gas-forming reactions when combined with HCl?
2. One tablet of Tums Regular Strength Antacid™ contains 500. mg $CaCO_3$.
   a. Write a balanced chemical equation for the reaction of $CaCO_3$ and stomach acid (HCl).
   b. What volume (in mL) of 0.500 M HCl(aq) will react completely with one tablet of Tums™?
3. The active ingredients in Rolaids™ are $CaCO_3$ and $Mg(OH)_2$.
   a. Write a balanced chemical equation for the reaction of $Mg(OH)_2$ and HCl.
   b. If 29.52 mL of 0.500 M HCl is required to titrate one tablet of Rolaids™ and the tablet contains 550 mg of $CaCO_3$, what mass of $Mg(OH)_2$ is present in one tablet?
4. Maalox™ may be purchased in either a liquid or solid form. One teaspoon of the liquid form of Maalox™ contains a mixture of 200. mg of $Al(OH)_3$ and 200. mg of $Mg(OH)_2$. What volume of 0.500 M HCl(aq) will react completely with one teaspoon of Maalox™?
5. Which product neutralizes the greatest amount of acid when taken in the quantities presented above: one tablet of Tums™ or Rolaids™ or one teaspoon of Maalox™?

CHAPTER GOALS REVISITED

Now that you have studied this chapter, you should ask whether you have met the chapter goals. In particular, you should be able to

UNDERSTAND

- The law of the conservation of matter, which forms the basis of chemical stoichiometry. Study Question: 135.
- The meaning of a limiting reactant in a chemical reaction. Study Questions: 136–138.

DO

- Perform stoichiometric calculations using balanced chemical equations.
  a. Calculate the mass of one reactant or product from the mass of another reactant or product by using the balanced chemical equation (Section 4-1). Study Questions: 2–6, 79, 81, 83, 97, 99, 102.
  b. Use amounts tables to organize stoichiometric information. Study Questions: 7–10.
  c. Determine which of two reactants is the limiting reactant (Section 4-2). Study Questions: 11–18, 98.
  d. Determine the yield of a product based on the limiting reactant. Study Questions: 11–18, 85.
- Calculate the theoretical and percent yields of chemical reactions.
  a. Explain the differences among actual yield, theoretical yield, and percent yield, and calculate percent yield (Section 4-3). Study Questions: 21, 22.
- Use stoichiometry to analyze a mixture of compounds or to determine the formula of a compound.
  a. Use stoichiometric principles to analyze a mixture (Section 4-4). Study Questions: 25–30, 129, 130.
  b. Find the empirical formula of an unknown compound using chemical stoichiometry (Section 4-4). Study Questions: 31–38.
- Define and use concentration in solution stoichiometry.
  a. Calculate the concentration of a solute in a solution in units of moles per liter (molarity), and use concentrations in calculations (Section 4-5). Study Questions: 39, 40, 42.
  b. Describe how to prepare a solution of a given concentration from the solute and a solvent or by dilution from a more concentrated solution (Section 4-5). Study Questions: 47–54.

c. Solve stoichiometry problems using solution concentrations (Section 4-7). Study Questions: 61–68, 106, 107.
d. Explain how a titration is carried out, explain the procedure of standardization, and calculate concentrations or amounts of reactants from titration data (Section 4-7). Study Questions: 69–76.

- Use the relationship of pH and hydronium ion concentration.
  a. Calculate the pH of a solution from the concentration of hydronium ion in the solution. Calculate the hydronium ion concentration of a solution from the pH (Section 4-6). Study Questions: 55–60.
- Use spectrophotometry to determine the concentration of a species in solution.
  a. Construct an absorbance versus concentration plot, and determine the slope and intercept (Section 4-8). Study Questions: 77, 78, 133.
  b. Use an absorbance versus concentration plot to determine the concentration of unknown solution. Study Questions: 77, 78, 133.

REMEMBER

- That concentration (as molarity) is the amount of solute per liter of solution.
- That pH is a measure of hydronium ion concentration.

KEY EQUATIONS

Equation 4.1 (page 147) Percent yield.

$$\text{Percent yield} = \frac{\text{actual yield}}{\text{theoretical yield}} \times 100\%$$

Equation 4.2 (page 156) Definition of molarity, a measure of the concentration of a solute in a solution.

$$\text{Molarity of } x\ (c_x) = \frac{\text{amount of solute } x \text{ (mol)}}{\text{volume of solution (L)}}$$

A useful form of this equation is

$$\text{Amount of solute } x \text{ (mol)} = c_x \text{ (mol/L)} \times \text{volume of solution (L)}$$

Dilution Equation (page 160) This is a shortcut to find, for example, the concentration of a solution (c_d) after diluting some volume (V_c) of a more concentrated solution (c_c) to a new volume (V_d).

$$c_c \times V_c = c_d \times V_d$$

Equation 4.3 (page 161) pH. The pH of a solution is the negative logarithm of the hydronium ion concentration.

$$\text{pH} = -\log[H_3O^+]$$

Equation 4.4 (page 162) Calculating $[H_3O^+]$ from pH. The equation for calculating the hydronium ion concentration of a solution from the pH of the solution.

$$[H_3O^+] = 10^{-\text{pH}}$$

Equation 4.5 (page 175) Beer–Lambert law. The absorbance of light (A) by a substance in solution is equal to the product of the molar absorptivity of the substance (ε), the path length of the cell (ℓ), and the concentration of the solute (c).

$$\text{Absorbance } (A) \propto \text{path length } (\ell) \times \text{concentration } (c)$$

$$A = \varepsilon \times \ell \times c$$

STUDY QUESTIONS

▲ denotes challenging questions.

Blue-numbered questions have answers in Appendix N and fully worked solutions in the *Student Solutions Manual.*

Practicing Skills

Mass Relationships in Chemical Reactions: Basic Stoichiometry

(See Example 4.1.)

1. In a reaction known as the thermite reaction, iron(III) oxide reacts with aluminum to give molten iron.

$$Fe_2O_3(s) + 2\ Al(s) \rightarrow 2\ Fe(\ell) + Al_2O_3(s)$$

What amount of Al, in moles, is needed for complete reaction with 3.0 mol of Fe_2O_3? What mass of Fe, in grams, can be produced?

2. What mass of HCl, in grams, is required to react with 0.750 g of $Al(OH)_3$? What mass of water, in grams, is produced?

$$Al(OH)_3(s) + 3\ HCl(aq) \rightarrow AlCl_3(aq) + 3\ H_2O(\ell)$$

3. Like many metals, aluminum reacts with a halogen to give a metal halide (page 99).

$$2\ Al(s) + 3\ Br_2(\ell) \rightarrow Al_2Br_6(s)$$

What mass of Br_2, in grams, is required for complete reaction with 2.56 g of Al? What mass of white, solid Al_2Br_6 is expected?

4. The balanced equation for the reduction of iron ore to the metal using CO is

$$Fe_2O_3(s) + 3\ CO(g) \rightarrow 2\ Fe(s) + 3\ CO_2(g)$$

(a) What is the maximum mass of iron, in grams, that can be obtained from 454 g (1.00 lb) of iron(III) oxide?
(b) What mass of CO is required to react with 454 g of Fe_2O_3?

5. Methane, CH_4, burns in oxygen.
(a) What are the products of the reaction?
(b) Write the balanced equation for the reaction.
(c) What mass of O_2, in grams, is required for complete combustion of 25.5 g of methane?
(d) What is the total mass of products expected from the combustion of 25.5 g of methane?

6. The formation of water-insoluble silver chloride is useful in the analysis of chloride-containing substances. Consider the following *unbalanced* equation:

$$BaCl_2(aq) + AgNO_3(aq) \rightarrow AgCl(s) + Ba(NO_3)_2(aq)$$

(a) Write the balanced equation.
(b) What mass of $AgNO_3$, in grams, is required for complete reaction with 0.156 g of $BaCl_2$? What mass of AgCl is produced?

Amounts Tables and Chemical Stoichiometry

For each question below, set up an amounts table that lists the initial amount or amounts of reactants, the changes in amounts of reactants and products, and the amounts of reactants and products after reaction (see page 140 and Example 4.1).

7. The metals industry was a major source of air pollution years ago. One common process involved "roasting" metal sulfides in the air:

$$2\ PbS(s) + 3\ O_2(g) \rightarrow 2\ PbO(s) + 2\ SO_2(g)$$

If 2.50 mol of PbS is heated in air, what amount of O_2 is required for complete reaction? What amounts of PbO and SO_2 are expected?

8. Iron ore is converted to iron metal in a reaction with carbon.

$$2\ Fe_2O_3(s) + 3\ C(s) \rightarrow 4\ Fe(s) + 3\ CO_2(g)$$

If 6.2 mol of $Fe_2O_3(s)$ is used, what amount of C(s) is needed, and what amounts of Fe and CO_2 are produced?

9. Chromium metal reacts with oxygen to give chromium(III) oxide, Cr_2O_3.
(a) Write a balanced equation for the reaction.
(b) What mass (in grams) of Cr_2O_3 is produced if 0.175 g of chromium metal is converted completely to the oxide?
(c) What mass of O_2 (in grams) is required for the reaction?

10. Ethane, C_2H_6, burns in oxygen.
(a) What are the products of the reaction?
(b) Write the balanced equation for the reaction.
(c) What mass of O_2, in grams, is required for complete combustion of 13.6 of ethane?
(d) What is the total mass of products expected from the combustion of 13.6 g of ethane?

Limiting Reactants

(See Example 4.2.)

11. Sodium sulfide, Na_2S, is used in the leather industry to remove hair from hides. The Na_2S is made by the reaction

$$Na_2SO_4(s) + 4\ C(s) \rightarrow Na_2S(s) + 4\ CO(g)$$

Suppose you mix 15 g of Na_2SO_4 and 7.5 g of C. Which is the limiting reactant? What mass of Na_2S is produced?

12. Ammonia gas can be prepared by the reaction of a metal oxide such as calcium oxide with ammonium chloride.

$$CaO(s) + 2\ NH_4Cl(s) \rightarrow 2\ NH_3(g) + H_2O(g) + CaCl_2(s)$$

If 112 g of CaO and 224 g of NH_4Cl are mixed, what is the limiting reactant, and what mass of NH_3 can be produced?

13. The compound SF_6 is made by burning sulfur in an atmosphere of fluorine. The balanced equation is

$$S_8(s) + 24\ F_2(g) \rightarrow 8\ SF_6(g)$$

Starting with a mixture of 1.6 mol of sulfur, S_8, and 35 mol of F_2,

(a) Which is the limiting reagent?
(b) What amount of SF_6 is produced?

14. Disulfur dichloride, S_2Cl_2, is used to vulcanize rubber. It can be made by treating molten sulfur with gaseous chlorine:

$$S_8(\ell) + 4\ Cl_2(g) \rightarrow 4\ S_2Cl_2(\ell)$$

Starting with a mixture of 32.0 g of sulfur and 71.0 g of Cl_2,

(a) Which is the limiting reactant?
(b) What is the theoretical yield of S_2Cl_2?
(c) What mass of the excess reactant remains when the reaction is completed?

15. The reaction of methane and water is one way to prepare hydrogen for use as a fuel:

$$CH_4(g) + H_2O(g) \rightarrow CO(g) + 3\ H_2(g)$$

If you begin with 995 g of CH_4 and 2510 g of water,

(a) Which reactant is the limiting reactant?
(b) What is the maximum mass of H_2 that can be prepared?
(c) What mass of the excess reactant remains when the reaction is completed?

16. Aluminum chloride, $AlCl_3$, is made by treating scrap aluminum with chlorine.

$$2\ Al(s) + 3\ Cl_2(g) \rightarrow 2\ AlCl_3(s)$$

If you begin with 2.70 g of Al and 4.05 g of Cl_2,

(a) Which reactant is limiting?
(b) What mass of $AlCl_3$ can be produced?
(c) What mass of the excess reactant remains when the reaction is completed?
(d) Set up an amounts table for this problem.

17. In the thermite reaction, iron(III) oxide is reduced by aluminum to give molten iron.

$$Fe_2O_3(s) + 2\ Al(s) \rightarrow 2\ Fe(\ell) + Al_2O_3(s)$$

If you begin with 10.0 g of Fe_2O_3 and 20.0 g of Al,

(a) Which reactant is limiting?
(b) What mass of Fe can be produced?
(c) What mass of the excess reactant remains after the limiting reactant is consumed?
(d) Set up an amounts table for this problem.

18. Aspirin, $C_6H_4(OCOCH_3)CO_2H$, is produced by the reaction of salicylic acid, $C_6H_4(OH)CO_2H$, and acetic anhydride, $(CH_3CO)_2O$ (page 149).

$$C_6H_4(OH)CO_2H(s) + (CH_3CO)_2O(\ell) \rightarrow C_6H_4(OCOCH_3)CO_2H(s) + CH_3CO_2H(\ell)$$

If you mix 100. g of each of the reactants, what is the maximum mass of aspirin that can be obtained?

Percent Yield

(See Section 4-3.)

19. In Example 4.2, you found that a particular mixture of CO and H_2 could produce 407 g CH_3OH.

$$CO(g) + 2\ H_2(g) \rightarrow CH_3OH(\ell)$$

If only 332 g of CH_3OH is actually produced, what is the percent yield of the compound?

20. Ammonia gas can be prepared by the following reaction:

$$CaO(s) + 2\ NH_4Cl(s) \rightarrow 2\ NH_3(g) + H_2O(g) + CaCl_2(s)$$

If 112 g of CaO and 224 g of NH_4Cl are mixed, the theoretical yield of NH_3 is 68.0 g (Study Question 12). If only 16.3 g of NH_3 is actually obtained, what is its percent yield?

21. The deep blue compound $Cu(NH_3)_4SO_4$ is made by the reaction of copper(II) sulfate and ammonia.

$$CuSO_4(aq) + 4\ NH_3(aq) \rightarrow Cu(NH_3)_4SO_4(aq)$$

(a) If you use 10.0 g of $CuSO_4$ and excess NH_3, what is the theoretical yield of $Cu(NH_3)_4SO_4$?
(b) If you isolate 12.6 g of $Cu(NH_3)_4SO_4$, what is the percent yield of $Cu(NH_3)_4SO_4$?

22. Black smokers are found in the depths of the oceans (page 96). Thinking that the conditions in these smokers might be conducive to the formation of organic compounds, two chemists in Germany found the following reaction could occur in similar conditions.

$$2\ CH_3SH + CO \rightarrow CH_3COSCH_3 + H_2S$$

If you begin with 10.0 g of CH_3SH and excess CO,

(a) What is the theoretical yield of CH_3COSCH_3?
(b) If 8.65 g of CH_3COSCH_3 is isolated, what is its percent yield?

23. The reaction of methane and water is one way to prepare hydrogen for use as a fuel:

$$CH_4(g) + H_2O(g) \rightarrow CO(g) + 3\ H_2(g)$$

Under certain conditions, what mass of CH_4 is required to produce 15 g of H_2 if this reaction has a 37% yield?

24. Methanol, CH_3OH, can be made from the reaction of carbon monoxide and hydrogen.

$$CO(g) + 2\ H_2(g) \rightarrow CH_3OH(\ell)$$

What mass of hydrogen is required to produce 1.0 L of CH_3OH (d = 0.791 g/mL) if this reaction has a 74% yield under certain conditions?

Analysis of Mixtures

(See Example 4.3.)

25. A mixture of $CuSO_4$ and $CuSO_4 \cdot 5\ H_2O$ has a mass of 1.245 g. After heating to drive off all the water, the mass is only 0.832 g. What is the mass percent of $CuSO_4 \cdot 5\ H_2O$ in the mixture? (See page 89.)

26. A 2.634-g sample containing impure $CuCl_2 \cdot 2\ H_2O$ was heated. The sample mass after heating to drive off the water was 2.125 g. What was the mass percent of $CuCl_2 \cdot 2\ H_2O$ in the original sample?

27. A sample of limestone and other soil materials was heated, and the limestone decomposed to give calcium oxide and carbon dioxide.

$$CaCO_3(s) \rightarrow CaO(s) + CO_2(g)$$

A 1.506-g sample of limestone-containing material gave 0.558 g of CO_2, in addition to CaO, after being heated at a high temperature. What was the mass percent of $CaCO_3$ in the original sample?

28. At higher temperatures, $NaHCO_3$ is converted quantitatively to Na_2CO_3.

$$2\ NaHCO_3(s) \rightarrow Na_2CO_3(s) + CO_2(g) + H_2O(g)$$

Heating a 1.7184-g sample of impure $NaHCO_3$ gives 0.196 g of CO_2. What was the mass percent of $NaHCO_3$ in the original 1.7184-g sample?

29. Nickel(II) sulfide, NiS, occurs naturally as the relatively rare mineral millerite. One of its occurrences is in meteorites. To analyze a mineral sample for the quantity of NiS, the sample is dissolved in nitric acid to form a solution of $Ni(NO_3)_2$.

$$NiS(s) + 4\ HNO_3(aq) \rightarrow Ni(NO_3)_2(aq) + 2\ NO_2(g) + 2\ H_2O(\ell) + S(s)$$

The aqueous solution of $Ni(NO_3)_2$ is then reacted with the organic compound dimethylglyoxime ($C_4H_8N_2O_2$) to give the red solid $Ni(C_4H_7N_2O_2)_2$.

$$Ni(NO_3)_2(aq) + 2\ C_4H_8N_2O_2(aq) \rightarrow Ni(C_4H_7N_2O_2)_2(s) + 2\ HNO_3(aq)$$

Suppose a 0.468-g sample containing millerite produces 0.206 g of red, solid $Ni(C_4H_7N_2O_2)_2$. What is the mass percent of NiS in the sample?

A precipitate of nickel with dimethylglyoxime

30. ▲ The aluminum in a 0.764-g sample of an unknown material was precipitated as aluminum hydroxide, $Al(OH)_3$, which was then converted to Al_2O_3 by heating strongly. If 0.127 g of Al_2O_3 is obtained from the 0.764-g sample, what is the mass percent of aluminum in the sample?

Using Stoichiometry to Determine Empirical and Molecular Formulas

(See Examples 4.4 and 4.5.)

31. Styrene, the building block of polystyrene, consists of only C and H. If 0.438 g of styrene is burned in oxygen and produces 1.481 g of CO_2 and 0.303 g of H_2O, what is the empirical formula of styrene?

32. Mesitylene is a liquid hydrocarbon. Burning 0.115 g of the compound in oxygen gives 0.379 g of CO_2 and 0.1035 g of H_2O. What is the empirical formula of mesitylene?

33. Naphthalene is a hydrocarbon that once was used in mothballs. If 0.3093 g of the compound is burned in oxygen, 1.0620 g of CO_2 and 0.1739 g of H_2O are isolated.

(a) What is the empirical formula of naphthalene?
(b) If a separate experiment gave 128.2 g/mol as the molar mass of the compound, what is its molecular formula?

34. Azulene is a beautiful blue hydrocarbon. If 0.106 g of the compound is burned in oxygen, 0.364 g of CO_2 and 0.0596 g of H_2O are isolated.

(a) What is the empirical formula of azulene?
(b) If a separate experiment gave 128.2 g/mol as the molar mass of the compound, what is its molecular formula?

35. An unknown compound has the formula $C_xH_yO_z$. You burn 0.0956 g of the compound and isolate 0.1356 g of CO_2 and 0.0833 g of H_2O. What is the empirical formula of the compound? If the molar mass is 62.1 g/mol, what is the molecular formula?

36. An unknown compound has the formula $C_xH_yO_z$. You burn 0.1523 g of the compound and isolate 0.3718 g of CO_2 and 0.1522 g of H_2O. What is the empirical formula of the compound? If the molar mass is 72.1 g/mol, what is the molecular formula?

37. Nickel forms a compound with carbon monoxide, $Ni_x(CO)_y$. To determine its formula, you carefully heat a 0.0973-g sample in air to convert the nickel to 0.0426 g of NiO and the CO to 0.100 g of CO_2. What is the empirical formula of $Ni_x(CO)_y$?

38. To find the formula of a compound composed of iron and carbon monoxide, $Fe_x(CO)_y$, the compound is burned in pure oxygen to give Fe_2O_3 and CO_2. If you burn 1.959 g of $Fe_x(CO)_y$ and obtain 0.799 g of Fe_2O_3 and 2.200 g of CO_2, what is the empirical formula of $Fe_x(CO)_y$?

Solution Concentration

(See Examples 4.6 and 4.7.)

39. If 6.73 g of Na_2CO_3 is dissolved in enough water to make 250. mL of solution, what is the molar concentration of the sodium carbonate? What are the molar concentrations of the Na^+ and CO_3^{2-} ions?

40. Some potassium dichromate ($K_2Cr_2O_7$), 2.335 g, is dissolved in enough water to make exactly 500. mL of solution. What is the molar concentration of the potassium dichromate? What are the molar concentrations of the K^+ and $Cr_2O_7^{2-}$ ions?

41. What is the mass of solute, in grams, in 250. mL of a 0.0125 M solution of $KMnO_4$?

42. What is the mass of solute, in grams, in 125 mL of a 1.023×10^{-3} M solution of Na_3PO_4? What is the molar concentration of the Na^+ and PO_4^{3-} ion?

43. What volume of 0.123 M NaOH, in milliliters, contains 25.0 g of NaOH?

44. What volume of 2.06 M $KMnO_4$, in liters, contains 322 g of solute?

45. Identify the ions that exist in each aqueous solution, and specify the concentration of each ion.

(a) 0.25 M $(NH_4)_2SO_4$
(b) 0.123 M Na_2CO_3
(c) 0.056 M HNO_3

46. Identify the ions that exist in each aqueous solution, and specify the concentration of each ion.

(a) 0.12 M $BaCl_2$
(b) 0.0125 M $CuSO_4$
(c) 0.500 M $K_2Cr_2O_7$

Preparing Solutions

(See Examples 4.6 and 4.7.)

47. An experiment in your laboratory requires 500. mL of a 0.0200 M solution of Na_2CO_3. You are given solid Na_2CO_3, distilled water, and a 500.-mL volumetric flask. Describe how to prepare the required solution.

48. What mass of oxalic acid, $H_2C_2O_4$, is required to prepare 250. mL of a solution that has a concentration of 0.15 M $H_2C_2O_4$?

49. If you dilute 25.0 mL of 1.50 M hydrochloric acid to 500. mL, what is the molar concentration of the dilute acid?

50. If 4.00 mL of 0.0250 M $CuSO_4$ is diluted to 10.0 mL with pure water, what is the molar concentration of copper(II) sulfate in the diluted solution?

51. Which of the following methods would you use to prepare 1.00 L of 0.125 M H_2SO_4?

(a) Dilute 20.8 mL of 6.00 M H_2SO_4 to a volume of 1.00 L.
(b) Add 950. mL of water to 50.0 mL of 3.00 M H_2SO_4.

52. Which of the following methods would you use to prepare 300. mL of 0.500 M $K_2Cr_2O_7$?

(a) Add 30.0 mL of 1.50 M $K_2Cr_2O_7$ to 270. mL of water.
(b) Dilute 250. mL of 0.600 M $K_2Cr_2O_7$ to a volume of 300. mL.

Serial Dilutions

(See A Closer Look: Serial Dilutions, page 162.)

53. You have 250. mL of 0.136 M HCl. Using a volumetric pipet, you take 25.00 mL of that solution and dilute it to 100.00 mL in a volumetric flask. Now you take 10.00 mL of that solution, using a volumetric pipet, and dilute it to 100.00 mL in a volumetric flask. What is the concentration of hydrochloric acid in the final solution?

54. ▲ Suppose you have 100.00 mL of a solution of a dye and transfer 2.00 mL of the solution to a 100.00-mL volumetric flask. After adding water to the 100.00 mL mark, you take 5.00 mL of that solution and again dilute to 100.00 mL. If you find the dye concentration in the final diluted sample is 0.000158 M, what was the dye concentration in the original solution?

Calculating and Using pH

(See Example 4.8.)

55. A table wine has a pH of 3.40. What is the hydronium ion concentration of the wine? Is it acidic or basic?

56. A saturated solution of milk of magnesia, $Mg(OH)_2$, has a pH of 10.5. What is the hydronium ion concentration of the solution? Is the solution acidic or basic?

57. What is the hydronium ion concentration of a 0.0013 M solution of HNO_3? What is its pH?

58. What is the hydronium ion concentration of a 1.2×10^{-4} M solution of $HClO_4$? What is its pH?

59. Make the following conversions. In each case, tell whether the solution is acidic or basic.

	pH	$[H_3O^+]$
(a)	1.00	_____
(b)	10.50	_____
(c)	_____	1.3×10^{-5} M
(d)	_____	2.3×10^{-8} M

60. Make the following conversions. In each case, tell whether the solution is acidic or basic.

	pH	$[H_3O^+]$
(a)	_____	6.7×10^{-10} M
(b)	_____	2.2×10^{-6} M
(c)	5.25	_____
(d)	_____	2.5×10^{-2} M

Stoichiometry of Reactions in Solution

(See Example 4.9.)

61. What volume of 0.109 M HNO_3, in milliliters, is required to react completely with 2.50 g of $Ba(OH)_2$?

$$2\ HNO_3(aq) + Ba(OH)_2(s) \rightarrow 2\ H_2O(\ell) + Ba(NO_3)_2(aq)$$

62. What mass of Na_2CO_3, in grams, is required for complete reaction with 50.0 mL of 0.125 M HNO_3?

$$Na_2CO_3(aq) + 2\ HNO_3(aq) \rightarrow 2\ NaNO_3(aq) + CO_2(g) + H_2O(\ell)$$

63. When an electric current is passed through an aqueous solution of NaCl, the valuable industrial chemicals $H_2(g)$, $Cl_2(g)$, and NaOH are produced.

$$2\ NaCl(aq) + 2\ H_2O(\ell) \rightarrow H_2(g) + Cl_2(g) + 2\ NaOH(aq)$$

What mass of NaOH can be formed from 15.0 L of 0.35 M NaCl? What mass of chlorine is obtained?

64. Hydrazine, N_2H_4, a base like ammonia, can react with sulfuric acid.

$$2\ N_2H_4(aq) + H_2SO_4(aq) \rightarrow 2\ N_2H_5^+(aq) + SO_4^{2-}(aq)$$

What mass of hydrazine reacts with 250. mL of 0.146 M H_2SO_4?

65. In the photographic developing process, silver bromide is dissolved by adding sodium thiosulfate.

$$AgBr(s) + 2\ Na_2S_2O_3(aq) \rightarrow Na_3Ag(S_2O_3)_2(aq) + NaBr(aq)$$

If you want to dissolve 0.225 g of AgBr, what volume of 0.0138 M $Na_2S_2O_3$, in milliliters, should be used?

Photos: © Cengage Learning/Charles D. Winters

(a) (b)

Silver chemistry. **(a)** A precipitate of AgBr formed by adding $AgNO_3(aq)$ to KBr(aq). **(b)** On adding $Na_2S_2O_3(aq)$, sodium thiosulfate, the solid AgBr dissolves.

66. You can dissolve an aluminum soft drink can in an aqueous base such as potassium hydroxide.

$$2\ Al(s) + 2\ KOH(aq) + 6\ H_2O(\ell) \rightarrow 2\ KAl(OH)_4(aq) + 3\ H_2(g)$$

If you place 2.05 g of aluminum in a beaker with 185 mL of 1.35 M KOH, will any aluminum remain? What mass of $KAl(OH)_4$ is produced?

67. What volume of 0.750 M $Pb(NO_3)_2$, in milliliters, is required to react completely with 1.00 L of 2.25 M NaCl solution? The balanced equation is

$$Pb(NO_3)_2(aq) + 2\ NaCl(aq) \rightarrow PbCl_2(s) + 2\ NaNO_3(aq)$$

68. What volume of 0.125 M oxalic acid, $H_2C_2O_4$, is required to react with 35.2 mL of 0.546 M NaOH?

$$H_2C_2O_4(aq) + 2\ NaOH(aq) \rightarrow Na_2C_2O_4(aq) + 2\ H_2O(\ell)$$

Titrations

(See Examples 4.10–4.13.)

69. What volume of 0.812 M HCl, in milliliters, is required to titrate 1.45 g of NaOH to the equivalence point?

$$NaOH(aq) + HCl(aq) \rightarrow H_2O(\ell) + NaCl(aq)$$

70. What volume of 0.955 M HCl, in milliliters, is required to titrate 2.152 g of Na_2CO_3 to the equivalence point?

$$Na_2CO_3(aq) + 2\ HCl(aq) \rightarrow H_2O(\ell) + CO_2(g) + 2\ NaCl(aq)$$

71. If 38.55 mL of HCl is required to titrate 2.150 g of Na_2CO_3 according to the following equation, what is the concentration (mol/L) of the HCl solution?

$$Na_2CO_3(aq) + 2\ HCl(aq) \rightarrow 2\ NaCl(aq) + CO_2(g) + H_2O(\ell)$$

72. Potassium hydrogen phthalate, $KHC_8H_4O_4$, is used to standardize solutions of bases. The acidic anion reacts with strong bases according to the following net ionic equation:

$$HC_8H_4O_4^-(aq) + OH^-(aq) \rightarrow C_8H_4O_4^{2-}(aq) + H_2O(\ell)$$

If a 0.902-g sample of potassium hydrogen phthalate is dissolved in water and titrated to the equivalence point with 26.45 mL of NaOH(aq), what is the molar concentration of the NaOH?

73. You have 0.954 g of an unknown acid, H_2A, which reacts with NaOH according to the balanced equation

$$H_2A(aq) + 2\ NaOH(aq) \rightarrow Na_2A(aq) + 2\ H_2O(\ell)$$

If 36.04 mL of 0.509 M NaOH is required to titrate the acid to the second equivalence point, what is the molar mass of the acid?

74. An unknown solid acid is either citric acid or tartaric acid. To determine which acid you have, you titrate a sample of the solid with aqueous NaOH and from this determine the molar mass of the unknown acid. The appropriate equations are as follows:

Citric acid:

$$H_3C_6H_5O_7(aq) + 3\ NaOH(aq) \rightarrow 3\ H_2O(\ell) + Na_3C_6H_5O_7(aq)$$

Tartaric acid:

$$H_2C_4H_4O_6(aq) + 2\ NaOH(aq) \rightarrow 2\ H_2O(\ell) + Na_2C_4H_4O_6(aq)$$

A 0.956-g sample requires 29.1 mL of 0.513 M NaOH to consume the acid completely. What is the unknown acid?

75. To analyze an iron-containing compound, you convert all the iron to Fe^{2+} in aqueous solution and then titrate the solution with standardized $KMnO_4$. The balanced, net ionic equation is

$$MnO_4^-(aq) + 5\ Fe^{2+}(aq) + 8\ H_3O^+(aq) \rightarrow Mn^{2+}(aq) + 5\ Fe^{3+}(aq) + 12\ H_2O(\ell)$$

A 0.598-g sample of the iron-containing compound requires 22.25 mL of 0.0123 M $KMnO_4$ for titration to the equivalence point. What is the mass percent of iron in the sample?

76. Vitamin C has the formula $C_6H_8O_6$. Besides being an acid, it is a reducing agent. One method for determining the amount of vitamin C in a sample is to titrate it with a solution of bromine, Br_2, an oxidizing agent.

$$C_6H_8O_6(aq) + Br_2(aq) \rightarrow 2\ HBr(aq) + C_6H_6O_6(aq)$$

A 1.00-g "chewable" vitamin C tablet requires 27.85 mL of 0.102 M Br_2 for titration to the equivalence point. What is the mass of vitamin C in the tablet?

Spectrophotometry

(See Section 4-8 and Example 4.14. The problems below are adapted from Fundamentals of Analytical Chemistry, *8th ed., by D. A. Skoog, D. M. West, F. J. Holler, and S. R. Crouch, Thomson/Brooks-Cole, Belmont, CA 2004.)*

77. A solution of a dye was analyzed by spectrophotometry, and the following calibration data were collected.

Dye Concentration	Absorbance (*A*) at 475 nm
0.50×10^{-6} M	0.24
1.5×10^{-6} M	0.36
2.5×10^{-6} M	0.44
3.5×10^{-6} M	0.59
4.5×10^{-6} M	0.70

(a) Construct a calibration plot, and determine the slope and intercept.
(b) What is the dye concentration in a solution with $A = 0.52$?

78. The nitrite ion is involved in the biochemical nitrogen cycle. You can determine the nitrite ion content of a sample using spectrophotometry by first using several organic compounds to form a colored compound from the ion. The following data were collected.

NO_2^- Ion Concentration	Absorbance of Solution at 550 nm
2.00×10^{-6} M	0.065
6.00×10^{-6} M	0.205
10.00×10^{-6} M	0.338
14.00×10^{-6} M	0.474
18.00×10^{-6} M	0.598
Unknown solution	0.402

(a) Construct a calibration plot, and determine the slope and intercept.
(b) What is the nitrite ion concentration in the unknown solution?

General Questions

These questions are not designated as to type or location in the chapter. They may combine several concepts.

79. Suppose 16.04 g of benzene, C_6H_6, is burned in oxygen.
(a) What are the products of the reaction?
(b) Write a balanced equation for the reaction.
(c) What mass of O_2, in grams, is required for complete combustion of benzene?
(d) What is the total mass of products expected from the combustion of 16.04 g of benzene?

80. The metabolic disorder diabetes causes a buildup of acetone, CH_3COCH_3, in the blood. Acetone, a volatile compound, is exhaled, giving the breath of untreated diabetics a distinctive odor. The acetone is produced by a breakdown of fats in a series of reactions. The equation for the last step, the breakdown of acetoacetic acid to give acetone and CO_2, is

$$CH_3COCH_2CO_2H \rightarrow CH_3COCH_3 + CO_2$$

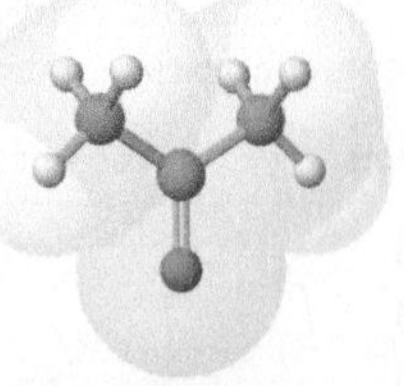

Acetone, CH_3COCH_3

What mass of acetone can be produced from 125 mg of acetoacetic acid?

81. Your body deals with excess nitrogen by excreting it in the form of urea, NH_2CONH_2. The reaction producing it is the combination of arginine ($C_6H_{14}N_4O_2$) with water to give urea and ornithine ($C_5H_{12}N_2O_2$).

$$\underset{\text{arginine}}{C_6H_{14}N_4O_2} + H_2O \rightarrow \underset{\text{urea}}{NH_2CONH_2} + \underset{\text{ornithine}}{C_5H_{12}N_2O_2}$$

If you excrete 95 mg of urea, what mass of arginine must have been used? What mass of ornithine must have been produced?

82. The reaction of iron metal and chlorine gas to give iron(III) chloride is illustrated below.

The reaction of iron and chlorine gas

(a) Write the balanced chemical equation for the reaction.
(b) Beginning with 10.0 g of iron, what mass of Cl_2, in grams, is required for complete reaction? What mass of $FeCl_3$ can be produced?
(c) If only 18.5 g of $FeCl_3$ is obtained from 10.0 g of iron and excess Cl_2, what is the percent yield?
(d) If 10.0 g each of iron and chlorine are combined, what is the theoretical yield of iron(III) chloride?

83. Some metal halides react with water to produce the metal oxide and the appropriate hydrogen halide (see photo). For example,

$$TiCl_4(\ell) + 2\ H_2O(\ell) \rightarrow TiO_2(s) + 4\ HCl(g)$$

The reaction of $TiCl_4$ with the water in moist air

(a) Name the four compounds involved in this reaction.
(b) If you begin with 14.0 mL of $TiCl_4$ (d = 1.73 g/mL), what mass of water, in grams, is required for complete reaction?
(c) What mass of each product is expected?

84. The reaction of 750. g each of NH_3 and O_2 was found to produce 562 g of NO (see pages 144–145).

$$4\ NH_3(g) + 5\ O_2(g) \rightarrow 4\ NO(g) + 6\ H_2O(\ell)$$

(a) What mass of water is produced by this reaction?
(b) What mass of O_2 is required to consume 750. g of NH_3?

85. Sodium azide, an explosive chemical used in automobile airbags, is made by the following reaction:

$$NaNO_3 + 3\ NaNH_2 \rightarrow NaN_3 + 3\ NaOH + NH_3$$

If you combine 15.0 g of $NaNO_3$ with 15.0 g of $NaNH_2$, what mass of NaN_3 is produced?

86. Iodine is made by the following reaction

$$2\ NaIO_3(aq) + 5\ NaHSO_3(aq) \rightarrow 3\ NaHSO_4(aq) + 2\ Na_2SO_4(aq) + H_2O(\ell) + I_2(aq)$$

(a) Name the two reactants.
(b) If you wish to prepare 1.00 kg of I_2, what masses of $NaIO_3$ and $NaHSO_3$ are required?
(c) What is the theoretical yield of I_2 if you mixed 15.0 g of $NaIO_3$ with 125 mL of 0.853 M $NaHSO_3$?

87. Saccharin, an artificial sweetener, has the formula $C_7H_5NO_3S$. Suppose you have a sample of a saccharin-containing sweetener with a mass of 0.2140 g. After decomposition to free the sulfur and convert it to the SO_4^{2-} ion, the sulfate ion is trapped as water-insoluble $BaSO_4$ (Figure 4.4). The quantity of $BaSO_4$ obtained is 0.2070 g. What is the mass percent of saccharin in the sample of sweetener?

88. ▲ Boron forms a series of compounds with hydrogen, all with the general formula B_xH_y.

$$B_xH_y(s) + \text{excess } O_2(g) \rightarrow \frac{x}{2}\ B_2O_3(s) + \frac{y}{2}\ H_2O(g)$$

If 0.148 g of one of these compounds gives 0.422 g of B_2O_3 when burned in excess O_2, what is its empirical formula?

89. ▲ Silicon and hydrogen form a series of compounds with the general formula Si_xH_y. To find the formula of one of them, a 6.22-g sample of the compound is burned in oxygen. All of the Si is converted to 11.64 g of SiO_2, and all of the H is converted to 6.980 g of H_2O. What is the empirical formula of the silicon compound?

90. ▲ Menthol, from oil of mint, has a characteristic odor. The compound contains only C, H, and O. If 95.6 mg of menthol burns completely in O_2, and gives 269 mg of CO_2 and 111 mg of H_2O, what is the empirical formula of menthol?

91. ▲ Benzoquinone, a chemical used in the dye industry and in photography, is an organic compound containing only C, H, and O. What is the empirical formula of the compound if 0.105 g of the compound gives 0.257 g of CO_2 and 0.0350 g of H_2O when burned completely in oxygen?

92. ▲ Aqueous solutions of iron(II) chloride and sodium sulfide react to form iron(II)sulfide and sodium chloride.

(a) Write the balanced equation for the reaction.
(b) If you combine 40. g each of Na_2S and $FeCl_2$, what is the limiting reactant?
(c) What mass of FeS is produced?
(d) What mass of Na_2S or $FeCl_2$ remains after the reaction?
(e) What mass of $FeCl_2$ is required to react completely with 40. g of Na_2S?

93. Sulfuric acid can be prepared starting with the sulfide ore, cuprite (Cu_2S). If each S atom in Cu_2S leads to one molecule of H_2SO_4, what is the theoretical yield of H_2SO_4 from 3.00 kg of Cu_2S?

94. ▲ In an experiment, 1.056 g of a metal carbonate, containing an unknown metal M, is heated to give the metal oxide and 0.376 g CO_2.

$$MCO_3(s) + \text{heat} \rightarrow MO(s) + CO_2(g)$$

What is the identity of the metal M?

(a) M = Ni
(b) M = Cu
(c) M = Zn
(d) M = Ba

95. ▲ An unknown metal reacts with oxygen to give the metal oxide, MO_2. Identify the metal if a 0.356-g sample of the metal produces 0.452 g of the metal oxide.

96. ▲ Titanium(IV) oxide, TiO_2, is heated in hydrogen gas to give water and a new titanium oxide, Ti_xO_y. If 1.598 g of TiO_2 produces 1.438 g of Ti_xO_y, what is the empirical formula of the new oxide?

97. ▲ Potassium perchlorate is prepared by the following sequence of reactions:

$$Cl_2(g) + 2\ KOH(aq) \rightarrow KCl(aq) + KClO(aq) + H_2O(\ell)$$

$$3\ KClO(aq) \rightarrow 2\ KCl(aq) + KClO_3(aq)$$

$$4\ KClO_3(aq) \rightarrow 3\ KClO_4(aq) + KCl(aq)$$

What mass of $Cl_2(g)$ is required to produce 234 kg of $KClO_4$?

98. ▲ Commercial sodium "hydrosulfite" is 90.1% $Na_2S_2O_4$. The sequence of reactions used to prepare the compound is

$$Zn(s) + 2\ SO_2(g) \rightarrow ZnS_2O_4(s)$$

$$ZnS_2O_4(s) + Na_2CO_3(aq) \rightarrow ZnCO_3(s) + Na_2S_2O_4(aq)$$

(a) What mass of pure $Na_2S_2O_4$ can be prepared from 125 kg of Zn, 500. g of SO_2, and an excess of Na_2CO_3?
(b) What mass of the commercial product would contain the $Na_2S_2O_4$ produced using the amounts of reactants in part (a)?

99. What mass of lime, CaO, can be obtained by heating 125 kg of limestone that is 95.0% by mass $CaCO_3$?

$$CaCO_3(s) \rightarrow CaO(s) + CO_2(g)$$

100. ▲ The elements silver, molybdenum, and sulfur combine to form Ag_2MoS_4. What is the maximum mass of Ag_2MoS_4 that can be obtained if 8.63 g of silver, 3.36 g of molybdenum, and 4.81 g of sulfur are combined? (*Hint:* What is the limiting reactant?)

101. ▲ A mixture of butene, C_4H_8, and butane, C_4H_{10}, is burned in air to give CO_2 and water. Suppose you burn 2.86 g of the mixture and obtain 8.80 g of CO_2 and 4.14 g of H_2O. What are the mass percentages of butene and butane in the mixture?

102. ▲ Cloth can be waterproofed by coating it with a silicone layer. This is done by exposing the cloth to $(CH_3)_2SiCl_2$ vapor. The silicon compound reacts with OH groups on the cloth to form a waterproofing film (density = 1.0 g/cm^3) of $[(CH_3)_2SiO]_n$, where n is a large integer number.

$$n\ (CH_3)_2SiCl_2 + 2n\ OH^- \rightarrow 2n\ Cl^- + n\ H_2O + [(CH_3)_2SiO]_n$$

The coating is added layer by layer, with each layer of $[(CH_3)_2SiO]_n$ being 0.60 nm thick. Suppose you want to waterproof a piece of cloth that is 3.00 square meters, and you want 250 layers of waterproofing compound on the cloth. What mass of $(CH_3)_2SiCl_2$ do you need?

103. ▲ Copper metal can be prepared by roasting copper ore, which can contain cuprite (Cu_2S) and copper(II) sulfide.

$$Cu_2S(s) + O_2(g) \rightarrow 2\ Cu(s) + SO_2(g)$$

$$CuS(s) + O_2(g) \rightarrow Cu(s) + SO_2(g)$$

Suppose an ore sample contains 11.0% impurity in addition to a mixture of CuS and Cu_2S. Heating 100.0 g of the mixture produces 75.4 g of copper metal with a purity of 89.5%. What is the weight percent of CuS in the ore? The weight percent of Cu_2S?

104. An Alka-Seltzer tablet contains exactly 100. mg of citric acid, $H_3C_6H_5O_7$, plus some sodium bicarbonate. What mass of sodium bicarbonate is required to consume 100. mg of citric acid by the following reaction?

$$H_3C_6H_5O_7(aq) + 3\ NaHCO_3(aq) \rightarrow 3\ H_2O(\ell) + 3\ CO_2(g) + Na_3C_6H_5O_7(aq)$$

105. ▲ Sodium bicarbonate and acetic acid react according to the equation

$$NaHCO_3(aq) + CH_3CO_2H(aq) \rightarrow NaCH_3CO_2(aq) + CO_2(g) + H_2O(\ell)$$

What mass of sodium acetate can be obtained from mixing 15.0 g of $NaHCO_3$ with 125 mL of 0.15 M acetic acid?

106. A noncarbonated soft drink contains an unknown amount of citric acid, $H_3C_6H_5O_7$. If 100. mL of the soft drink requires 33.51 mL of 0.0102 M NaOH to neutralize the citric acid completely, what mass of citric acid does the soft drink contain per 100. mL? The reaction of citric acid and NaOH is

$$H_3C_6H_5O_7(aq) + 3\ NaOH(aq) \rightarrow Na_3C_6H_5O_7(aq) + 3\ H_2O(\ell)$$

107. Sodium thiosulfate, $Na_2S_2O_3$, is used as a "fixer" in black-and-white photography. Suppose you have a bottle of sodium thiosulfate and want to determine its purity. The thiosulfate ion can be oxidized with I_2 according to the balanced, net ionic equation

$$I_2(aq) + 2\ S_2O_3^{2-}(aq) \rightarrow 2\ I^-(aq) + S_4O_6^{2-}(aq)$$

If you use 40.21 mL of 0.246 M I_2 in a titration, what is the weight percent of $Na_2S_2O_3$ in a 3.232-g sample of impure material?

108. You have a mixture of oxalic acid, $H_2C_2O_4$, and another solid that does not react with sodium hydroxide. If 29.58 mL of 0.550 M NaOH is required to titrate the oxalic acid in the 4.554-g sample to the second equivalence point, what is the mass percent of oxalic acid in the mixture? Oxalic acid and NaOH react according to the equation

$$H_2C_2O_4(aq) + 2\ NaOH(aq) \rightarrow Na_2C_2O_4(aq) + 2\ H_2O(\ell)$$

109. (a) What is the pH of a 0.105 M HCl solution?
(b) What is the hydronium ion concentration in a solution with a pH of 2.56? Is the solution acidic or basic?
(c) A solution has a pH of 9.67. What is the hydronium ion concentration in the solution? Is the solution acidic or basic?
(d) A 10.0-mL sample of 2.56 M HCl is diluted with water to 250. mL. What is the pH of the dilute solution?

110. A solution of hydrochloric acid has a volume of 125 mL and a pH of 2.56. What mass of $NaHCO_3$ must be added to completely consume the HCl?

111. ▲ One half liter (500. mL) of 2.50 M HCl is mixed with 250. mL of 3.75 M HCl. Assuming the total solution volume after mixing is 750. mL, what is the concentration of hydrochloric acid in the resulting solution? What is its pH?

112. A solution of hydrochloric acid has a volume of 250. mL and a pH of 1.92. Exactly 250. mL of 0.0105 M NaOH is added. What is the pH of the resulting solution?

113. ▲ You place 2.56 g of $CaCO_3$ in a beaker containing 250. mL of 0.125 M HCl. When the reaction has ceased, does any calcium carbonate remain? What mass of $CaCl_2$ can be produced?

$$CaCO_3(s) + 2\ HCl(aq) \rightarrow CaCl_2(aq) + CO_2(g) + H_2O(\ell)$$

114. The cancer drug cisplatin, $Pt(NH_3)_2Cl_2$, can be made by reacting $(NH_4)_2PtCl_4$ with ammonia in aqueous solution. Besides cisplatin, the other product is NH_4Cl.
(a) Write a balanced equation for this reaction.
(b) To obtain 12.50 g of cisplatin, what mass of $(NH_4)_2PtCl_4$ is required? What volume of 0.125 M NH_3 is required?
(c) ▲ Cisplatin can react with the organic compound pyridine, C_5H_5N, to form a new compound.

$$Pt(NH_3)_2Cl_2(aq) + x\ C_5H_5N(aq) \rightarrow Pt(NH_3)_2Cl_2(C_5H_5N)_x(s)$$

Suppose you treat 0.150 g of cisplatin with what you believe is an excess of liquid pyridine (1.50 mL; d = 0.979 g/mL). When the reaction is complete, you can find out how much pyridine was not used by titrating the solution with standardized HCl. If 37.0 mL of 0.475 M HCl is required to titrate the excess pyridine,

$$C_5H_5N(aq) + HCl(aq) \rightarrow C_5H_5NH^+(aq) + Cl^-(aq)$$

what is the formula of the unknown compound $Pt(NH_3)_2Cl_2(C_5H_5N)_x$?

115. ▲ You need to know the volume of water in a small swimming pool, but, owing to the pool's irregular shape, it is not a simple matter to determine its dimensions and calculate the volume. To solve the problem, you stir in a solution of a dye (1.0 g of methylene blue, $C_{16}H_{18}ClN_3S$,

in 50.0 mL of water). After the dye has mixed with the water in the pool, you take a sample of the water. Using a spectrophotometer, you determine that the concentration of the dye in the pool is 4.1×10^{-8} M. What is the volume of water in the pool?

116. ▲ Calcium and magnesium carbonates occur together in the mineral dolomite. Suppose you heat a sample of the mineral to obtain the oxides, CaO and MgO, and then treat the oxide sample with hydrochloric acid. If 7.695 g of the oxide sample requires 125 mL of 2.55 M HCl,

$$CaO(s) + 2\ HCl(aq) \rightarrow CaCl_2(aq) + H_2O(\ell)$$

$$MgO(s) + 2\ HCl(aq) \rightarrow MgCl_2(aq) + H_2O(\ell)$$

what is the weight percent of each oxide (CaO and MgO) in the sample?

117. Gold can be dissolved from gold-bearing rock by treating the rock with sodium cyanide in the presence of oxygen.

$$4\ Au(s) + 8\ NaCN(aq) + O_2(g) + 2\ H_2O(\ell) \rightarrow 4\ NaAu(CN)_2(aq) + 4\ NaOH(aq)$$

(a) Name the oxidizing and reducing agents in this reaction. What has been oxidized, and what has been reduced?
(b) If you have exactly one metric ton (1 metric ton = 1000 kg) of gold-bearing rock, what volume of 0.075 M NaCN, in liters, do you need to extract the gold if the rock is 0.019% gold?

118. ▲ You mix 25.0 mL of 0.234 M $FeCl_3$ with 42.5 mL of 0.453 M NaOH.

(a) What mass of $Fe(OH)_3$ (in grams) will precipitate from this reaction mixture?
(b) One of the reactants ($FeCl_3$ or NaOH) is present in a stoichiometric excess. What is the molar concentration of the excess reactant remaining in solution after $Fe(OH)_3$ has been precipitated?

119. ATOM ECONOMY: One type of reaction used in the chemical industry is a substitution, where one atom or group is exchanged for another. In this reaction, an alcohol, 1-butanol, is transformed into 1-bromobutane by substituting Br for the –OH group in the presence of sulfuric acid.

$$CH_3CH_2CH_2CH_2OH + NaBr + H_2SO_4 \rightarrow CH_3CH_2CH_2CH_2Br + NaHSO_4 + H_2O$$

Calculate the % atom economy for the desired product, $CH_3CH_2CH_2CH_2Br$.

120. ATOM ECONOMY: Ethylene oxide, C_2H_4O, is an important industrial chemical [as it is the starting place to make such important chemicals as ethylene glycol (antifreeze) and various polymers]. One way to make the compound is called the "chlorohydrin route."

$$C_2H_4 + Cl_2 + Ca(OH)_2 \rightarrow C_2H_4O + CaCl_2 + H_2O$$

Another route is the modern catalytic reaction.

$$C_2H_4 + 1/2\ O_2 \rightarrow C_2H_4O$$

(a) Calculate the % atom economy for the production of C_2H_4O in each of these reactions. Which is the more efficient method?
(b) What is the percent yield of C_2H_4O if 867 g of C_2H_4 is used to synthesize 762 g of the product by the catalytic reaction?

In the Laboratory

121. Suppose you dilute 25.0 mL of a 0.110 M solution of Na_2CO_3 to exactly 100.0 mL. You then take exactly 10.0 mL of this diluted solution and add it to a 250-mL volumetric flask. After filling the volumetric flask to the mark with distilled water (indicating the volume of the new solution is 250. mL), what is the concentration of the diluted Na_2CO_3 solution?

122. ▲ In some laboratory analyses, the preferred technique is to dissolve a sample in an excess of acid or base and then "back-titrate" the excess with a standard base or acid. This technique is used to assess the purity of a sample of $(NH_4)_2SO_4$. Suppose you dissolve a 0.475-g sample of impure $(NH_4)_2SO_4$ in aqueous KOH.

$$(NH_4)_2SO_4(aq) + 2\ KOH(aq) \rightarrow 2\ NH_3(aq) + K_2SO_4(aq) + 2\ H_2O(\ell)$$

The NH_3 liberated in the reaction is distilled from the solution into a flask containing 50.0 mL of 0.100 M HCl. The ammonia reacts with the acid to produce NH_4Cl, but not all of the HCl is used in this reaction. The amount of excess acid is determined by titrating the solution with standardized NaOH. This titration consumes 11.1 mL of 0.121 M NaOH. What is the weight percent of $(NH_4)_2SO_4$ in the 0.475-g sample?

123. Oyster beds in the oceans require chloride ions for growth. The minimum concentration is 8 mg/L (8 parts per million). To analyze for the amount of chloride ion in a 50.0-mL sample of water, you add a few drops of aqueous potassium chromate and then titrate the sample with 25.60 mL of 0.001036 M silver nitrate. The silver nitrate reacts with chloride ion, and, when the ion is completely removed, the silver nitrate reacts with potassium chromate to give a red precipitate.

(a) Write a balanced net ionic equation for the reaction of silver nitrate with chloride ions.
(b) Write a complete balanced equation and a net ionic equation for the reaction of silver nitrate with potassium chromate, indicating whether each compound is water-soluble or not.
(c) What is the concentration of chloride ions in the sample? Is it sufficient to promote oyster growth?

124. ▲ A compound consisting of yttrium(III) ions, barium(II) ions, both copper(II) and copper(III) ions, and oxide ions is a superconducting material at low temperatures (page 135). It has the formula $YBa_2Cu_3O_{7-x}$ where x is a variable between 1 and 0. To find out the value of x, you dissolve 34.02 mg of the compound in 5 mL of 1.0 M HCl. Bubbles of oxygen gas (O_2) are observed as the following reaction occurs:

$$YBa_2Cu_3O_{7-x}(s) + 13\ H^+(aq) \rightarrow Y^{3+}(aq) + 2\ Ba^{2+}(aq) + 3\ Cu^{2+}(aq) + 1/4(1 - 2x)\ O_2(g) + 13/2\ H_2O(\ell)$$

You then boil the solution, cool it, and add 10 mL of 0.70 M KI under argon. The following reaction occurs:

$$2\ Cu^{2+}(aq) + 5\ I^-(aq) \rightarrow 2\ CuI(s) + I_3^-(aq)$$

When this reaction is complete, a titration of the resulting solution with sodium thiosulfate requires 1.542×10^{-4} mol $S_2O_3^{2-}(aq)$.

$$I_3^-(aq) + 2\ S_2O_3^{2-}(aq) \rightarrow 3\ I^-(aq) + S_4O_6^{2-}(aq)$$

What is the value of x in $YBa_2Cu_3O_{7-x}$?

125. You wish to determine the weight percent of copper in a copper-containing alloy. After dissolving a 0.251-g sample of the alloy in acid, an excess of KI is added, and the Cu^{2+} and I^- ions undergo the reaction

$$2\ Cu^{2+}(aq) + 5\ I^-(aq) \rightarrow 2\ CuI(s) + I_3^-(aq)$$

The liberated I_3^- is titrated with sodium thiosulfate according to the equation

$$I_3^-(aq) + 2\ S_2O_3^{2-}(aq) \rightarrow S_4O_6^{2-}(aq) + 3\ I^-(aq)$$

(a) Designate the oxidizing and reducing agents in the two reactions above.
(b) If 26.32 mL of 0.101 M $Na_2S_2O_3$ is required for titration to the equivalence point, what is the weight percent of Cu in the alloy?

126. ▲ A compound has been isolated that can have either of two possible formulas: (a) $K[Fe(C_2O_4)_2(H_2O)_2]$ or (b) $K_3[Fe(C_2O_4)_3]$. To find which is correct, you dissolve a weighed sample of the compound in acid, forming oxalic acid, $H_2C_2O_4$. You then titrate this acid with potassium permanganate, $KMnO_4$ (the source of the MnO_4^- ion). The balanced, net ionic equation for the titration is

$$5\ H_2C_2O_4(aq) + 2\ MnO_4^-(aq) + 6\ H_3O^+(aq) \rightarrow 2\ Mn^{2+}(aq) + 10\ CO_2(g) + 14\ H_2O(\ell)$$

Titration of 1.356 g of the compound requires 34.50 mL of 0.108 M $KMnO_4$. Which is the correct formula of the iron-containing compound: (a) or (b)?

127. ▲ Chromium(III) chloride forms many compounds with ammonia. To find the formula of one of these compounds, you titrate the NH_3 in the compound with standardized acid.

$$Cr(NH_3)_xCl_3(aq) + x\ HCl(aq) \rightarrow x\ NH_4^+(aq) + Cr^{3+}(aq) + (x + 3)\ Cl^-(aq)$$

Assume that 24.26 mL of 1.500 M HCl is used to titrate 1.580 g of $Cr(NH_3)_xCl_3$. What is the value of x?

128. ▲ Thioridazine, $C_{21}H_{26}N_2S_2$, is a pharmaceutical agent used to regulate dopamine. (Dopamine, a neurotransmitter, affects brain processes that control movement, emotional response, and ability to experience pleasure and pain.) A chemist can analyze a sample of the pharmaceutical for the thioridazine content by decomposing it to convert the sulfur in the compound to sulfate ion. This is then "trapped" as water-insoluble barium sulfate (see Figure 4.4).

$$SO_4^{2-}(\text{aq, from thioridazine}) + BaCl_2(aq) \rightarrow BaSO_4(s) + 2\ Cl^-(aq)$$

Suppose a 12-tablet sample of the drug yielded 0.301 g of $BaSO_4$. What is the thioridazine content, in milligrams, of each tablet?

129. ▲ A herbicide contains 2,4-D (2,4-dichlorophenoxyacetic acid), $C_8H_6Cl_2O_3$. A 1.236-g sample of the herbicide was decomposed to liberate the chlorine as Cl^- ion. This was precipitated as AgCl, with a mass of 0.1840 g. What is the mass percent of 2,4-D in the sample?

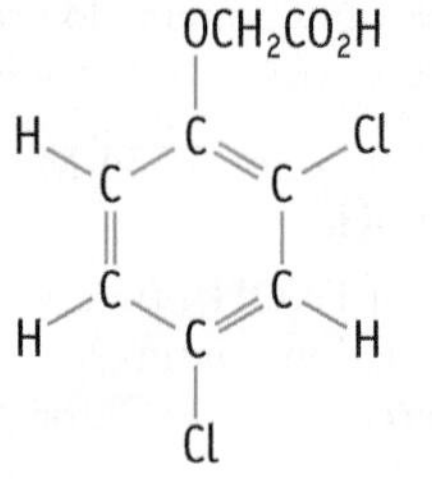

2,4-D (2,4-dichlorophenoxyacetic acid)

130. ▲ Sulfuric acid is listed in a catalog with a concentration of 95–98%. A bottle of the acid in the stockroom states that 1.00 L has a mass of 1.84 kg. To determine the concentration of sulfuric acid in the stockroom bottle, a student dilutes 5.00 mL to 500. mL. She then takes four 10.00-mL samples and titrates each with standardized sodium hydroxide ($c = 0.1760$ M).

Sample	1	2	3	4
Volume NaOH (mL)	20.15	21.30	20.40	20.35

(a) What is the average concentration of the diluted sulfuric acid sample?
(b) What is the mass percent of H_2SO_4 in the original bottle of the acid?

131. ▲ Anhydrous calcium chloride is a good drying agent because it will rapidly pick up water. Suppose you have stored some carefully dried $CaCl_2$ in a desiccator. Unfortunately, someone did not close the top of the desiccator tightly, and the $CaCl_2$ became partially hydrated. A 150-g sample of this partially hydrated material was dissolved in 80 g of hot water. When the solution was cooled to 20 °C, 74.9 g of $CaCl_2 \cdot 6\ H_2O$ precipitated. Knowing the solubility of calcium chloride in water at 20 °C is 74.5 g $CaCl_2$/100 g water, determine the water content of the 150-g sample of partially hydrated calcium chloride (in moles of water per mole of $CaCl_2$).

132. ▲ A 0.5510-g sample consisting of a mixture of iron and iron(III) oxide was dissolved completely in acid to give a solution containing iron(II) and iron(III) ions. A reducing agent was added to convert all of the iron to iron(II) ions, and the solution was then titrated with the standardized $KMnO_4$ (0.04240 M); 37.50 mL of the $KMnO_4$ solution was required. Calculate the mass percent of Fe and Fe_2O_3 in the 0.5510-g sample. (Example 4.13 gives the equation for the reaction of iron(II) ions and $KMnO_4$.)

133. ▲ Phosphate in urine can be determined by spectrophotometry. After removing protein from the sample, it is treated with a molybdenum compound to give, ultimately, a deep blue polymolybdate. The absorbance of the blue polymolybdate can be measured at 650 nm and is directly related to the urine phosphate concentration. A 24-hour urine sample was collected from a patient; the volume of urine was 1122 mL. The phosphate in a 1.00 mL portion of the urine sample was converted to the blue polymolybdate and diluted to 50.00 mL. A calibration curve was prepared using phosphate-containing solutions. (Concentrations are reported in grams of phosphorus (P) per liter of solution.)

Solution (mass P/L)	Absorbance at 650 nm in a 1.0-cm cell
1.00×10^{-6} g	0.230
2.00×10^{-6} g	0.436
3.00×10^{-6} g	0.638
4.00×10^{-6} g	0.848
Urine sample	0.518

(a) What are the slope and intercept of the calibration curve?
(b) What is the mass of phosphorus per liter of urine?
(c) What mass of phosphate did the patient excrete in the one-day period?

134. ▲ A 4.000-g sample containing KCl and $KClO_4$ was dissolved in sufficient water to give 250.00 mL of solution. A 50.00-mL portion of the solution required 41.00 mL of 0.0750 M $AgNO_3$ in a Mohr titration (page 172). Next, a 25.00-mL portion of the original solution was treated with $V_2(SO_4)_3$ to reduce the perchlorate ion to chloride,

$$8\ V^{3+}(aq) + ClO_4^-(aq) + 12\ H_2O(\ell) \rightarrow Cl^-(aq) + 8\ VO^{2+}(aq) + 8\ H_3O^+(aq)$$

and the resulting solution was titrated with $AgNO_3$. This titration required 38.12 mL of 0.0750 M $AgNO_3$. What is the mass percent of KCl and $KClO_4$ in the mixture?

Summary and Conceptual Questions

The following questions may use concepts from this and previous chapters.

135. Two beakers sit on a balance; the total mass is 167.170 g. One beaker contains a solution of KI; the other contains a solution of $Pb(NO_3)_2$. When the solution in one beaker is poured completely into the other, the following reaction occurs:

$$2\ KI(aq) + Pb(NO_3)_2(aq) \rightarrow 2\ KNO_3(aq) + PbI_2(s)$$

Photos: © Cengage Learning/ Charles D. Winters

Solutions of KI and $Pb(NO_3)_2$ before reaction **Solutions after reaction**

What is the total mass of the beakers and solutions after reaction? Explain completely.

136. ▲ A weighed sample of iron (Fe) is added to liquid bromine (Br_2) and allowed to react completely. The reaction produces a single product, which can be isolated and weighed. The experiment was repeated a number of times with different masses of iron but with the same mass of bromine (see graph below).

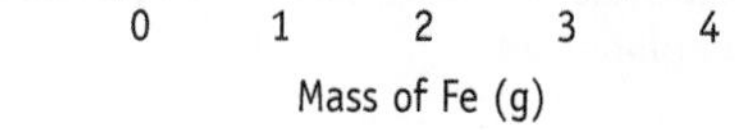

(a) What mass of Br_2 is used when the reaction consumes 2.0 g of Fe?
(b) What is the mole ratio of Br_2 to Fe in the reaction?
(c) What is the empirical formula of the product?
(d) Write the balanced chemical equation for the reaction of iron and bromine.
(e) What is the name of the reaction product?

(f) Which statement or statements best describe the experiments summarized by the graph?
   (i) When 1.00 g of Fe is added to the Br_2, Fe is the limiting reagent.
   (ii) When 3.50 g of Fe is added to the Br_2, there is an excess of Br_2.
   (iii) When 2.50 g of Fe is added to the Br_2, both reactants are used up completely.
   (iv) When 2.00 g of Fe is added to the Br_2, 10.8 g of product is formed. The percent yield must therefore be 20.0%.

137. Let us explore a reaction with a limiting reactant. Here, zinc metal is added to a flask containing aqueous HCl, and H_2 gas is a product.

$$Zn(s) + 2\ HCl(aq) \rightarrow ZnCl_2(aq) + H_2(g)$$

The three flasks each contain 0.100 mol of HCl. Zinc is added to each flask in the following quantities.

Flask 1: 7.00 g Zn **Flask 2:** 3.27 g Zn **Flask 3:** 1.31 g Zn

When the reactants are combined, the H_2 inflates the balloon attached to the flask. The results are as follows:

Flask 1: Balloon inflates completely, but some Zn remains when inflation ceases.
Flask 2: Balloon inflates completely. No Zn remains.
Flask 3: Balloon does not inflate completely. No Zn remains.

Explain these results. Perform calculations that support your explanation.

138. The reaction of aluminum and bromine is pictured below. The white solid on the lip of the beaker at the end of the reaction is Al_2Br_6. In the reaction pictured below, which was the limiting reactant, Al or Br_2?

Before reaction **After reaction**

139. ▲ Two students titrate different samples of the same solution of HCl using 0.100 M NaOH solution and phenolphthalein indicator (Figure 4.12). The first student pipets 20.0 mL of the HCl solution into a flask, adds 20 mL of distilled water and a few drops of phenolphthalein solution, and titrates until a lasting pink color appears. The second student pipets 20.0 mL of the HCl solution into a flask, adds 60 mL of distilled water and a few drops of phenolphthalein solution, and titrates to the first lasting pink color. Each student correctly calculates the molarity of an HCl solution. What will the second student's result be?

(a) four times less than the first student's result
(b) four times greater than the first student's result
(c) two times less than the first student's result
(d) two times greater than the first student's result
(e) the same as the first student's result

140. In most states, a person will receive a "driving while intoxicated" (DWI) ticket if the blood alcohol level (BAL) is 80 mg per deciliter (dL) of blood or higher. Suppose a person is found to have a BAL of 0.033 mol of ethanol (C_2H_5OH) per liter of blood. Will the person receive a DWI ticket?

141. ATOM ECONOMY: Benzene, C_6H_6, is a common compound, and it can be oxidized to give maleic anhydride, $C_4H_2O_3$, which is used in turn to make other important compounds.

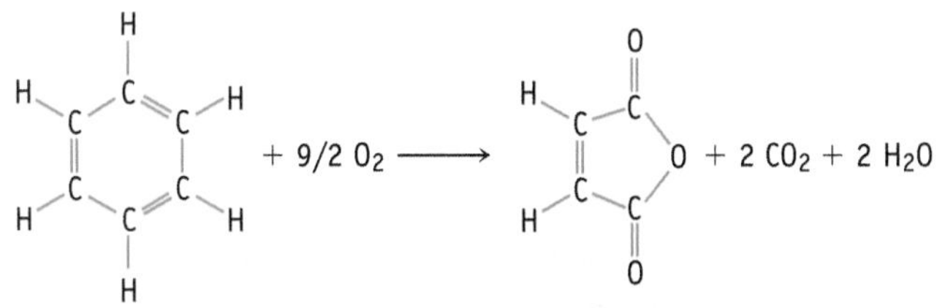

(a) What is the % atom economy for the synthesis of maleic anhydride from benzene by this reaction?

(b) If 972 g of maleic anhydride is produced from exactly 1.00 kg of benzene, what is the percent yield of the anhydride? What mass of the byproduct CO_2 is also produced?

142. ATOM ECONOMY: Maleic anhydride, $C_4H_2O_3$, can be produced by the oxidation of benzene (Study Question 141). It can also be produced from the oxidation of butene.

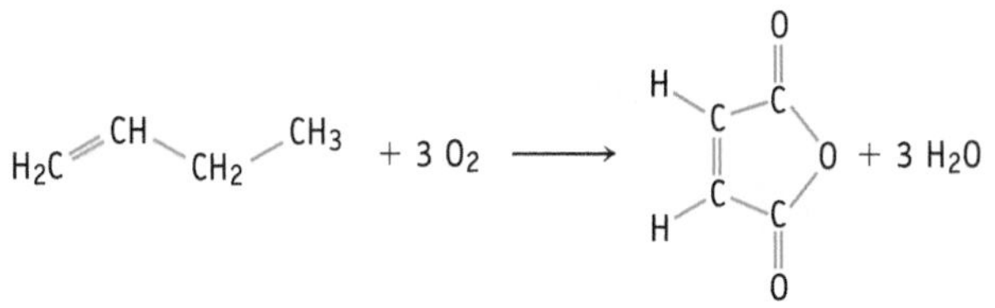

(a) What is the % atom economy for the synthesis of maleic anhydride from butene by this reaction?

(b) If 1.02 kg of maleic anhydride is produced from exactly 1.00 kg of butene, what is the percent yield of the anhydride? What mass of the byproduct H_2O is also produced?

AP Multiple-Choice Review Questions

1. When 78.0 g of aluminum hydroxide, $Al(OH)_3$ (molar mass = 78.0 g/mol), reacts with 49.0 g sulfuric acid, H_2SO_4 (molar mass = 98.1 g/mol), what mass of water is produced? The equation is

$$2Al(OH)_3(s) + 3H_2SO_4(aq) \rightarrow Al_2(SO_4)_3(aq) + 6H_2O(\ell)$$

(A) 18.0 g
(B) 36.0 g
(C) 54.0 g
(D) 127 g

2. What mass of aluminum is required if 40.0 g of iron(III) oxide, Fe_2O_3, is to be completely consumed as shown in the following reaction?

$$Fe_2O_3(s) + 2Al(s) \rightarrow 2Fe(\ell) + Al_2O_3(s)$$

(A) 13.5 g
(B) 27.0 g
(C) 40.0 g
(D) 67.0 g

3. The mineral magnesite contains magnesium carbonate, $MgCO_3$ (molar mass = 84 g/mol), and other impurities. When a 1.26-g sample of magnesite was dissolved in hydrochloric acid, 0.22 g of CO_2 was generated. If the magnesite contained no carbonate other than $MgCO_3$, what was the percent $MgCO_3$ by mass in the magnesite? The equation is

$$MgCO_3(s) + 2HCl(aq) \rightarrow MgCl_2(aq) + H_2O(\ell) + CO_2(g)$$

(A) 25%
(B) 33%
(C) 50.%
(D) 67%

4. Methanol (CH_3OH) can react with oxygen gas to produce formaldehyde (H_2CO) and water. How much formaldehyde can be produced by reacting 4.0 moles of methanol with 4.0 moles of oxygen gas?

(A) 2.0 moles
(B) 4.0 moles
(C) 6.0 moles
(D) 8.0 moles

5. In a Bunsen burner, methane reacts with oxygen to produce carbon dioxide and water, as shown in the balanced equation below:

$$CH_4(g) + 2O_2(g) \rightarrow CO_2(g) + 2H_2O(g)$$

What mass of water can be produced from 16 grams of methane and excess oxygen?

(A) 8.0 g
(B) 16 g
(C) 18 g
(D) 36 g

6. Which of the following reaction mixtures would produce the greatest amount of product, assuming all went to completion? Each involves the reaction symbolized by the equation:

$$N_2(g) + 3H_2(g) \rightarrow 2NH_3(g)$$

(A) 2 mol N_2 and 4 mol H_2
(B) 1 mol N_2 and 5 mol H_2
(C) 4 mol N_2 and 2 mol H_2
(D) 5 mol N_2 and 1 mol H_2

7. If 200. mL of 0.60 *M* $MgCl_2(aq)$ is added to 400. mL of distilled water, what is the concentration of $Mg^{2+}(aq)$ and $Cl^-(aq)$ in the resulting solution? (Assume volumes are additive.)

	$[Mg^{2+}]$ (mol/L)	$[Cl^-]$ (mol/L)
(A)	0.20	0.20
(B)	0.20	0.40
(C)	0.40	0.40
(D)	2.0	2.5

8. Determine the volume of distilled water that should be *added* to 20.0 mL of 12.0 *M* $HCl(aq)$ in order to prepare a 0.500 *M* $HCl(aq)$ solution.

(A) 120. mL
(B) 140. mL
(C) 460. mL
(D) 480. mL

9. What is the molarity of a solution containing $ClO_2^-(aq)$ if 15 mL of the solution is needed to react completely with 20. mL of 0.20 *M* $KMnO_4$ solution? The balanced equation is

$$2H_2O(\ell) + 4MnO_4^-(aq) + 3ClO_2^-(aq) \rightarrow 4MnO_2(s) + 3ClO_4^-(aq) + 4OH^-(aq)$$

(A) 0.10 *M*
(B) 0.20 *M*
(C) 0.30 *M*
(D) 0.40 *M*

10. A sample of 25.0 mL of 0.120 *M* $Ca(OH)_2(aq)$ is titrated with 0.150 *M* $HCl(aq)$. What volume of $HCl(aq)$ is needed to completely neutralize the $Ca(OH)_2(aq)$?

(A) 20.0 mL
(B) 40.0 mL
(C) 60.0 mL
(D) 80.0 mL

11. A 1.0 *M* solution of table salt (NaCl) is considered to be 1.0 *M* Na^+ and 1.0 *M* Cl^-. This means table salt is a

(A) strong electrolyte
(B) weak electrolyte
(C) nonelectrolyte
(D) strong acid

12. Consider 100.0 mL of a 1.00 *M* solution of NaCl in a beaker. After several days, you test the solution and find that it has a concentration of 1.33 *M*. How much water must have evaporated?

(A) 20.0 mL
(B) 25.0 mL
(C) 75.0 mL
(D) 80.0 mL

13. Calculate the concentration of chloride ions when 200.0 mL of 1.00 *M* sodium chloride is mixed with 300.0 mL of 1.00 *M* magnesium chloride.

(A) 1.00 *M*
(B) 1.40 *M*
(C) 1.60 *M*
(D) 2.00 *M*

14. What volume of 0.2000 *M* sulfuric acid is required to neutralize 800.0 mL of 0.1000 *M* potassium hydroxide?

(A) 200.0 mL
(B) 400.0 mL
(C) 800.0 mL
(D) 1600. mL

AP Free Response Review Questions

Question Format: Short

Category of Question: Quantitative

During the 2nd World War, Niels Bohr, a Nobel Prize winner, was given the gold medals of two other winners for safe keeping, as they believed the medals to be safer in Denmark. When Denmark was invaded by Germany, a coworker of Bohr, George de Hevesy, dissolved the medals in aqua regia, a mixture of concentrated hydrochloric and concentrated nitric acids, and then stored the resulting solution. When the Nazis entered the laboratory, they did not find the medals. After the war, the gold solution was reduced back down to solid gold and the Nobel Prize committee recast the gold metals and returned them to their owners.

The reaction of aqua regia on gold is shown below.

$$Au(s) + HNO_3(aq) + 4HCl(aq) \rightarrow HAuCl_4(aq) + NO(g) + 2H_2O(\ell)$$

Questions

(a) Assuming the mass of each medal was 175 g and the medals were 23 carat (96%) pure gold, what mass of pure chloroauric acid, $HAuCl_4$, could be produced when the two medals were dissolved?

(b) Assuming that 200 mL of concentrated nitric acid (16 *M*) and 800 mL of concentrated hydrochloric acid (12 *M*) were used, how many grams of baking soda (pure $NaHCO_3$) would be needed to neutralize the excess acids after the medals were dissolved?

Question Format: Long

Category of Question: Lab 1

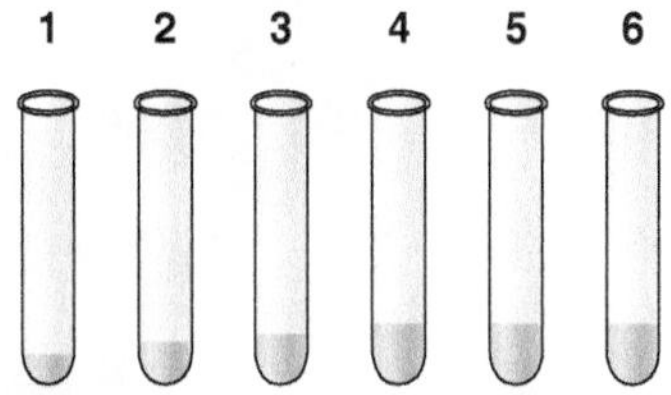

A student is asked to determine the stoichiometric ratios between 0.010 *M* lead(II) nitrate and 0.010 *M* potassium iodide solutions and produces the test tubes pictured above—for clarity, only the precipitate is shown. The following data table was obtained from this investigation.

Test tube	Volume of $Pb(NO_3)_2(aq)$	Volume of $KI(aq)$	Mass of solid product
1	5.00 mL	4.00 mL	0.0182 g
2	5.00 mL	6.00 mL	0.0275 g
3	5.00 mL	8.00 mL	0.0366 g
4	5.00 mL	10.00 mL	0.0459 g
5	5.00 mL	12.00 mL	0.0458 g
6	5.00 mL	14.00 mL	0.0460 g

Questions

(a) Using this table, determine the mole ratio of the reaction between lead(II) nitrate and potassium iodide solutions. Explain how the data in the table supports the mole ratio.

(b) Lead(II) iodide and potassium nitrate are the products of this reaction. Determine which one of the products (or both of the products) is the precipitate **without referring to "solubility rules."** Support your answer with calculations from the data table above.

(c) Assuming that everything else remains constant in the laboratory procedures and setup, how would each of the following changes affect your laboratory results? In each case, explain your reasoning.

(i) The volume of lead(II) nitrate solution was changed to 1.00 mL for each trial.

(ii) The volume of lead(II) nitrate solution was changed to 10.00 mL for each trial.

Another student conducted a similar laboratory investigation with two different reacting 0.10 M solutions. One solution contains substance A and the other solution contains substance B. The student conducts an experiment with six trials and produces the test tubes pictured above—for clarity, only the precipitate is shown.

(d) Briefly list the procedures that would be needed to find the stoichiometric ratios and produce the test tubes shown above.

(e) Create a data table and the data to show that the ratio between A and B was 3 to 2. Explain how this data will show a ratio of 3 to 2.

(f) Assuming that substance B has a molar mass of 156.75 g/mol, what are the correct procedures to make 100.00 mL of a 0.1500 *M* solution of B? Include calculations with your answer.

© Cengage Learning/Charles D. Winters

Principles of Chemical Reactivity: Energy and Chemical Reactions

Chapter Outline

ENERGY AND YOUR DIET Everywhere we turn today the topic of "energy" comes up. On the news we hear about the need to produce more petroleum, to conserve more, or to produce alternative fuels such as ethanol. The energy to run our industrialized society comes primarily from fossil fuels (coal, oil, and natural gas). Unfortunately, the supplies of these fuels are not limitless and the production and consumption of these fuels have environmental consequences. There are those who advocate wind turbines, nuclear power plants, or solar panels. You may favor increased usage of these different sources of energy, but you probably rely on fossil fuels to heat your home or to power your automobile.

If you are like the authors of this text, you also think about the energy in your food. How many Calories did I ingest today or how much energy did I "burn" in the gym? Our bodies derive our energy from the metabolism of carbohydrates, proteins, and fats in foods. As you are aware, the energy content is different for each of these components (see *A Closer Look: Energy and Food* on page 28). For example, 100 g of raw carrots supplies 145 kJ of energy, whereas 100 g of cashew nuts delivers about 2400 kJ, and 100 g of chocolate chip cookies will deliver about 2100 kJ. For comparison, 100 g of ethanol (C_2H_6OH), which can be used to fuel your automobile, delivers 2680 kJ of energy.

Chapter Goals

See Chapter Goals Revisited (page 215) for Study Questions keyed to these goals.

UNDERSTAND

- And apply the first law of thermodynamics.

DO

- Assess the transfer of energy as heat associated with changes in temperature and changes of state.
- Calculate *P–V* work done by a system and use energy as heat (q) and work (w) to calculate changes in internal energy (U).
- Calculate energy and enthalpy changes from data obtained by calorimetry experiments.
- Calculate the energy evolved or required for physical changes and chemical reactions using data in thermodynamic tables.

REMEMBER

- Definitions for terms commonly used: endothermic, exothermic, systems, surroundings, enthalpy, internal energy, reactant-favored, and product-favored.
- Enthalpy and internal energy are state functions.

If you are curious about the energy delivered by the food you ate today, go to the Nutrient Data Laboratory website www.ars.usda.gov/ba/bhnrc/ndl.

Study Questions related to this are: 5.91 and 5.92.

The importance of energy is evident in our daily lives—in heating and cooling our homes, in powering our appliances, and in propelling our vehicles, among other things. Most of the energy we use for these purposes is obtained by carrying out chemical reactions, largely by burning fossil fuels. We use natural gas for heating, coal and natural gas to generate most of our electric power, and fuels derived from petroleum for automobiles and for heat. In addition, energy is required for living: Chemical reactions in our bodies provide the energy for body functions, for movement, and to maintain body temperature.

To scientists, however, energy has a significance that goes well beyond these many practical uses. In this chapter, we will begin a discussion of **thermodynamics**, the science of heat and work. This subject will provide important insights on the following questions:

- How do we measure and calculate the energy changes associated with physical changes and chemical reactions?
- What is the relationship between energy changes, heat, and work?
- How can we determine whether a chemical reaction is product-favored or reactant-favored at equilibrium?
- How can we determine whether a chemical reaction or physical process will occur spontaneously, that is, without outside intervention?

We will concentrate on the first two questions in this chapter and address the other questions in Chapter 18.

World Energy Consumption In 2008, burning fossil fuels provided about 81% of the total energy used by people on our planet. Biomass contributed 10%, nuclear power 6%, and hydroelectric 2%. Less than 1% was provided from solar, wind, and geothermal sources. (Energy resources and consumption are discussed in more detail in Chapter 20: Environmental Chemistry—Earth's Environment, Energy, and Sustainability)

Learning Objectives: LO 5.3

5-1 Energy: Some Basic Principles

In Chapter 1, we defined energy as the capacity to do work and stated that energy could be divided into two basic categories: kinetic energy (the energy associated with motion) and potential energy (the energy that results from an object's position, composition, or state). Let us expand upon those definitions. Chemists often use the term **thermal energy** when referring to the kinetic energy of molecules. As you will soon see, thermal energy is associated with the transfer of heat between a hotter object and a cooler one.

Units of Energy The SI unit for energy (the joule) is discussed on page 27.

One type of potential energy is chemical energy, the energy associated with the forces holding atoms together as molecules or binding atoms and molecules together as solids or liquids. When chemical reactions occur it is the chemical energy that changes.

Also in Chapter 1 you learned that, although energy can be converted from one type into another, the total amount of energy is conserved. This is formally stated in the **law of conservation of energy**: *Energy can neither be created nor destroyed.* Or, stated differently, *the total energy of the universe is constant.* In order to understand the importance of this law, we need to introduce some new terminology and carefully consider the implications of a number of experiments.

This chapter begins the discussion of ways in which the energy of a chemical system can change. We will begin by looking at the transfer of kinetic energy (thermal energy) by heating or cooling. We will also touch on the energy involved in a phase transition, that is, the melting of a solid or the vaporization of a liquid. Finally, we will look at changes in energy in the course of a chemical reaction.

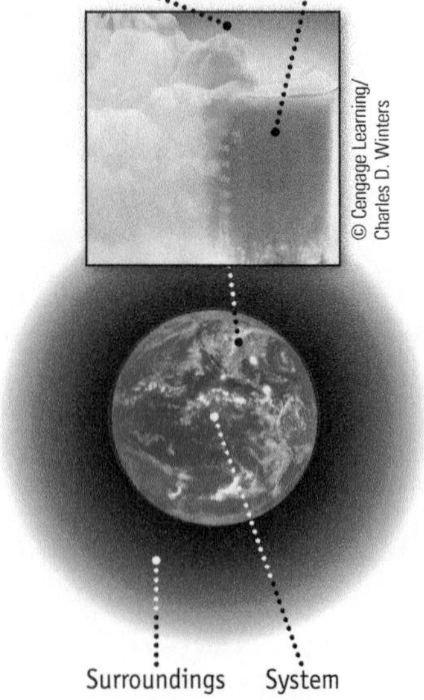

FIGURE 5.1 **Systems and their surroundings.** Earth can be considered a thermodynamic system, with the rest of the universe as its surroundings. A chemical reaction occurring in a laboratory is also a system, with the laboratory its surroundings.

Systems and Surroundings

In thermodynamics, the terms *system and surroundings* have precise and important meanings. A **system** is defined as an object, or collection of objects, being studied (Figure 5.1). The **surroundings** include everything outside the system that can exchange energy and/or matter with the system. In the discussion that follows, we will need to define systems precisely. If we are studying the energy evolved in a chemical reaction carried out in solution, for example, the system might be defined as the reactants, products, and solvent. The surroundings would be the reaction flask and the air in the room and anything else in contact with the flask with which it might exchange energy or matter. At the atomic level, the system could be a single atom or molecule, and the surroundings would be the atoms or molecules in its vicinity. This concept of a system and its surroundings applies to nonchemical situations as well. To study the energy balance on our planet, we might choose to define Earth as the system and outer space as the surroundings. On a cosmic level, the solar system might be defined as the system being studied, and the rest of the galaxy would be the surroundings. How the system and its surroundings for each situation are defined depends on the information we are trying to obtain or convey.

Directionality and Extent of Transfer of Heat: Thermal Equilibrium

Energy can be transferred between a system and its surroundings or between different parts of the system. One way that energy can be transferred is as heat. Energy is transferred as heat if two objects at different temperatures are brought into contact. In Figure 5.2, for example, the beaker of water and the piece of metal being heated in a Bunsen burner flame have different temperatures. When the hot metal is plunged into the cold water, energy is transferred as heat from the metal to the water. The thermal energy (molecular motion) of the water molecules increases, and the thermal energy of the metal atoms decreases. Eventually, the two objects reach the same temperature, and the system has reached **thermal equilibrium**. The distinguishing feature of thermal equilibrium is that, on the macroscopic scale, no further temperature change occurs; both the metal and water are at the same temperature.

Thermal Equilibrium Although no change is evident at the macroscopic level once thermal equilibrium is reached, on the molecular level transfer of energy between individual molecules will continue. A general feature of systems at equilibrium is that there is no change on a macroscopic level but that processes still occur at the particulate level. (See Section 3-3, page 104.)

Photos: © Cengage Learning/Charles D. Winters

FIGURE 5.2 Energy transfer.

Submerging a hot metal bar in water and following the temperature change may seem like a rather simple experiment with an obvious outcome. However, the experiment illustrates two important principles in our discussion:

- Energy transfer as heat will occur spontaneously from an object at a higher temperature to an object at a lower temperature; the object whose temperature increases gains thermal energy and the object whose temperature decreases loses thermal energy.
- Transfer of energy as heat continues until both objects are at the same temperature and thermal equilibrium is achieved.

For the specific case where energy is transferred only as heat within an isolated system (that is, a system that cannot transfer either energy or matter with its surroundings), we can also say that the quantity of energy lost as heat by the hotter object and the quantity of energy gained as heat by the cooler object are numerically equal. This is required by the law of conservation of energy. When energy is

A CLOSER LOOK — What Is Heat?

Two hundred years ago, scientists characterized heat as a real substance called caloric fluid. The caloric hypothesis supposed that when a fuel burned and a pot of water was heated, for example, caloric fluid was transferred from the fuel to the water. Burning the fuel released caloric fluid, and the temperature of the water increased as the caloric fluid was absorbed.

Over the next 50 years, however, the caloric hypothesis lost favor, and we now know it is incorrect. Experiments by James Joule (1818–1889) and Benjamin Thompson (1753–1814) that showed the interrelationship between heat and other forms of energy such as mechanical energy provided the key to dispelling this idea. Even so, some of our everyday language retains the influence of this early theory. For example, we often speak of heat "flowing" as if it were a fluid.

From our discussion so far, we know one thing that "heat" is not—but what is it?

Benjamin Thompson (1753–1814). Thompson, also known as Count Rumford, established his scientific reputation through research on the explosive force of gunpowder. His experience with explosives led to an interest in heat. Rumford designed a classic experiment that showed the relationship between work and heat.

Musee de la Ville de Paris, Musee Carnavalet, Paris, France/Archives Charmet/ The Bridgeman Art Library

Heat is said to be a "process quantity." It is the *process* by which energy is transferred across the boundary of a system owing to a difference in temperature between the two sides of the boundary. In this process, the energy of the object at the lower temperature increases, and the energy of the object at the higher temperature decreases.

Heat is not the only process by which energy can be transferred. Specifically, work is another process that can transfer energy between objects (see page 194).

The idea of energy transfer by the processes of heat and work is embodied in the definition of thermodynamics: the science of heat and work.

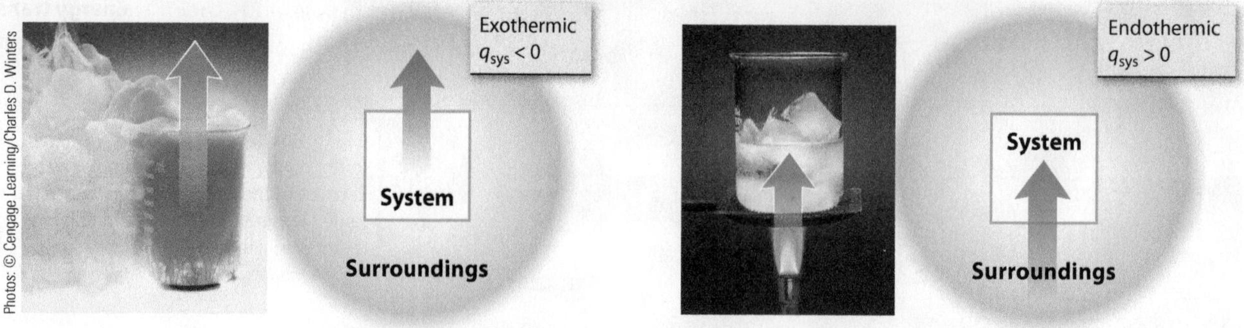

Exothermic: energy transferred from system to surroundings

Endothermic: energy transferred from surroundings to system

FIGURE 5.3 **Exothermic and endothermic processes.** The symbol q represents the energy transferred as heat, and the subscript sys refers to the system.

transferred as heat between a system and its surroundings, we describe the directionality of this transfer as **exothermic** or **endothermic** (Figure 5.3).

- In an **exothermic process**, energy is transferred as heat from a system to its surroundings. The energy of the system decreases and the energy of the surroundings increases. Energy in the form of heat is designated by the symbol q. For an exothermic process, $q_{sys} < 0$.
- An **endothermic process** is the opposite of an exothermic process. Energy is transferred as heat from the surroundings to the system, increasing the energy of the system and decreasing the energy of the surroundings. For an endothermic process, $q_{sys} > 0$.

REVIEW & CHECK FOR SECTION 5-1

1. Which of the following processes is endothermic?

   (a) melting of ice at 0 °C
   (b) the reaction of methane and O_2
   (c) condensation of water vapor at 100 °C
   (d) cooling liquid water from 25 °C to 0 °C

2. Your skin cools as perspiration evaporates. Is the thermal energy change, q, of your body greater than, less than, or equal to zero?

   (a) $q > 0$ (b) $q < 0$ (c) $q = 0$

Learning Objectives: LO 5.3, LO 5.4, LO 5.6

5-2 Specific Heat Capacity: Heating and Cooling

When an object is heated or cooled, the quantity of energy transferred depends on three things:

- the quantity of material
- the magnitude of the temperature change
- the identity, including the phase (g, ℓ, aq, or s), of the material gaining or losing energy

Specific heat capacity (C) is defined as *the energy transferred as heat that is required to raise the temperature of 1 gram of a substance by one kelvin.* It has units of joules per gram per kelvin (J/g · K). A few specific heat capacities are listed in Figure 5.4, and a longer list is given in Appendix D (Table 11).

Heat capacity can also be expressed on a per-mole basis. The amount of energy that is transferred as heat in raising the temperature of one mole of a substance

Specific Heat Capacities of Some Elements, Compounds, and Substances

Substances	Specific Heat Capacity (J/g · K)	Molar Heat Capacity (J/mol · K)
Al, aluminum	0.897	24.2
Fe, iron	0.449	25.1
Cu, copper	0.385	24.5
Au, gold	0.129	25.4
Water (liquid)	4.184	75.4
Water (ice)	2.06	37.1
Water (steam)	1.86	33.6
$HOCH_2CH_2OH(\ell)$, ethylene glycol (antifreeze)	2.39	14.8
Wood	1.8	—
Glass	0.8	—

All metals have molar heat capacities near 25 J/mol · K

FIGURE 5.4 **Specific heat capacity.** Metals have different values of specific heat capacity. However, their molar heat capacities are all near 25 J/mol · K.

by one kelvin is the **molar heat capacity**. For water, the molar heat capacity is 75.4 J/mol · K. The molar heat capacity of metals at room temperature is always near 25 J/mol · K.

The energy gained or lost as heat when a given mass of a substance is warmed or cooled can be calculated using Equation 5.1.

$$q = C \times m \times \Delta T \tag{5.1}$$

Here, q is the energy gained or lost as heat by a given mass of substance (m), C is the specific heat capacity, and ΔT is the change in temperature. The change in temperature, ΔT, is calculated as the final temperature minus the initial temperature.

$$\Delta T = T_{\text{final}} - T_{\text{initial}} \tag{5.2}$$

Calculating a change in temperature using Equation 5.2 will give a result with an algebraic sign that indicates the direction of energy transfer. For example, we can use the specific heat capacity of copper, 0.385 J/g · K, to calculate the energy that must be transferred from the surroundings to a 10.0-g sample of copper if the metal's temperature is raised from 298 K (25 °C) to 598 K (325 °C).

$$q = \left(0.385 \frac{\text{J}}{\text{g} \cdot \text{K}}\right)(10.0\ \text{g})(\underset{\substack{\uparrow \\ T_{\text{final}} \\ \text{Final temp.}}}{598\ \text{K}} - \underset{\substack{\uparrow \\ T_{\text{initial}} \\ \text{Initial temp.}}}{298\ \text{K}}) = +1160\ \text{J}$$

Notice that the answer has a positive sign. This indicates that the energy of the sample of copper has *increased* by 1160 J, which is in accord with energy being transferred as heat to the copper (the system) from the surroundings.

The relationship between energy, mass, and specific heat capacity has numerous implications. The high specific heat capacity of liquid water, 4.184 J/g · K, is a major reason that large bodies of water have a profound influence on climate. In spring, lakes warm up more slowly than the air. In autumn, the energy given off by a large lake as it cools moderates the drop in air temperature. The relevance of specific heat capacity is also illustrated when bread is wrapped in aluminum foil (specific heat capacity 0.897 J/g · K) and heated in an oven. You can remove the foil with your fingers after taking the bread from the oven. The bread and the aluminum foil are very hot, but the small mass of aluminum foil used and its low specific heat capacity result in only a small quantity of energy being transferred to your fingers (which have a larger mass and a higher specific heat capacity) when you touch the hot foil.

A practical example of knowing about specific heat capacity. The filling of the pie from a fast-food restaurant has a higher specific heat capacity (and higher mass) than the crust and the wrapper. Notice the warning label.

EXAMPLE 5.1

Specific Heat Capacity

Problem How much energy must be transferred to raise the temperature of a cup of coffee (250 mL) from 20.5 °C (293.7 K) to 95.6 °C (368.8 K)? Assume that water and coffee have the same density (1.00 g/mL) and specific heat capacity (4.184 J/g · K).

What Do You Know? The energy required to warm a substance is related to its specific heat capacity (C), the mass of the substance, and the temperature change (Equation 5.1). The mass of coffee, initial and final temperatures, and the value for C are given in the problem.

Strategy You can calculate the mass of coffee from the volume and density (mass = volume × density) and the temperature change from the initial and final temperatures ($\Delta T = T_{final} - T_{initial}$). Use Equation 5.1 to solve for q.

Solution

$$\text{Mass of coffee} = (250\text{ mL})(1.00\text{ g/mL}) = 250\text{ g}$$

$$\Delta T = T_{final} - T_{initial} = 368.8\text{ K} - 293.7\text{ K} = 75.1\text{ K}$$

$$q = C \times m \times \Delta T$$

$$q = (4.184\text{ J/g}\cdot\text{K})(250\text{ g})(75.1\text{ K})$$

$$q = 79{,}000\text{ J (or 79 kJ)}$$

Think about Your Answer The positive sign in the answer indicates that energy has been transferred to the coffee. The thermal energy of the coffee is now higher.

Check Your Understanding

In an experiment, it was determined that 59.8 J was required to raise the temperature of 25.0 g of ethylene glycol (a compound used as antifreeze in automobile engines) by 1.00 K. Calculate the specific heat capacity of ethylene glycol from these data.

Strategy Map 5.1

PROBLEM

Calculate the **energy** required to **raise temperature** of liquid.

↓

DATA/INFORMATION

- Specific heat capacity
- Volume of liquid
- Density of liquid
- ΔT

↓ STEP 1. Calculate the **sample mass** and $\boldsymbol{\Delta T}$.

Mass of sample, ΔT, and specific heat capacity

↓ STEP 2. Use **Equation 5.1** to calculate $\boldsymbol{q}$.

Energy required (q) to raise temperature of liquid by ΔT

Quantitative Aspects of Energy Transferred as Heat

Like melting point, boiling point, and density, specific heat capacity is a characteristic intensive property of a pure substance. The specific heat capacity of a substance can be determined experimentally by accurately measuring temperature changes that occur when energy is transferred as heat from the substance to a known quantity of water (whose specific heat capacity is known).

Suppose a 55.0-g piece of metal is heated in boiling water to 99.8 °C and then dropped into cool water in an insulated beaker (Figure 5.5). Assume the beaker contains 225 g of water and its initial temperature (before the metal was dropped in) was 21.0 °C. The final temperature of the metal and water is 23.1 °C. What is the specific heat capacity of the metal? Here are the important aspects of this experiment.

- Let's define the metal and the water as the system and the beaker and environment as the surroundings and assume that energy as heat is transferred only within the system. (This means that energy is not transferred between the system and the surroundings. This assumption is good, but not perfect; for a more accurate result, we would also want to account for any energy transfer to the surroundings.)
- The water and the metal end up at the same temperature. (T_{final} is the same for both.)
- We will also assume energy is transferred *only as heat* within the system.

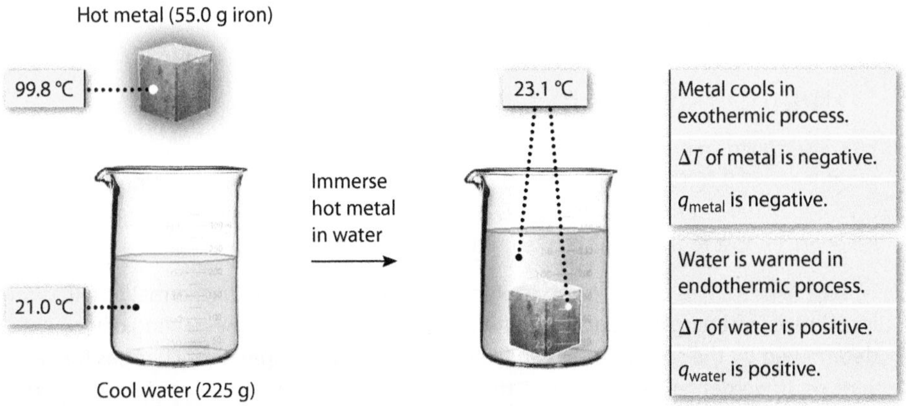

FIGURE 5.5 **Transfer of energy as heat.** When energy is transferred as heat from a hot metal to cool water, the thermal energy of the metal decreases and that of the water increases. The value of q_{metal} is thus negative and the value of q_{water} is positive.

- The energy transferred as heat from the metal to the water, q_{metal}, has a negative value because the temperature of the metal decreases. Conversely, q_{water} has a positive value because its temperature increases.
- The values of q_{water} and q_{metal} are numerically equal but are opposite in sign.

Because of the law of conservation of energy, *in an isolated system the sum of the energy changes within the system must be zero.* If energy is transferred only as heat, then

$$q_1 + q_2 + q_3 + \ldots = 0 \quad (5.3)$$

where the quantities q_1, q_2, and so on represent the energies transferred as heat for the individual parts of the system. For this specific problem, there are thermal energy changes associated with the two components of the system, water and metal, q_{water} and q_{metal}; thus

$$q_{water} + q_{metal} = 0$$

Each of these quantities is related individually to specific heat capacities, masses, and changes of temperature, as defined by Equation 5.1. Thus

$$[C_{water} \times m_{water} \times (T_{final} - T_{initial,\ water})] + [C_{metal} \times m_{metal} \times (T_{final} - T_{initial,\ metal})] = 0$$

The specific heat capacity of the metal, C_{metal}, is the unknown in this problem. Using the specific heat capacity of water (4.184 J/g · K) and converting Celsius to kelvin temperatures gives

$$[(4.184\ J/g \cdot K)(225\ g)(296.3\ K - 294.2\ K)] + [(C_{metal})(55.0\ g)(296.3\ K - 373.0\ K)] = 0$$

$$C_{metal} = 0.47\ J/g \cdot K$$

PROBLEM SOLVING TIP 5.1
Calculating ΔT

Virtually all calculations that involve temperature in chemistry require expressing temperature in kelvins. In calculating ΔT, however, we can use Celsius temperatures because a kelvin and a Celsius degree are the same size. That is, the difference between two temperatures is the same on both scales. For example, the difference between the boiling and freezing points of water is

$$\Delta T\text{, Celsius} = 100\ °C - 0\ °C = 100\ °C$$

$$\Delta T\text{, kelvin} = 373\ K - 273\ K = 100\ K$$

Strategy Map 5.2

PROBLEM

Calculate **final T** when a piece of hot iron is added to **given mass** of cool water.

DATA/INFORMATION

- **Specific heat capacities**
- **Masses** of iron and water
- **Initial T** for iron and water

Use equation $q_{Fe} + q_{water} = 0$. Solve for T_{final}.

T_{final} of water and iron

EXAMPLE 5.2

Using Specific Heat Capacity

Problem In an experiment like that in Figure 5.5, an 88.5-g piece of iron whose temperature is 78.8 °C (352.0 K) is placed in a beaker containing 244 g of water at 18.8 °C (292.0 K). When thermal equilibrium is reached, what is the final temperature? (Assume no energy is lost to warm the beaker and its surroundings.)

What Do You Know? Iron cools and the water warms until thermal equilibrium is reached. The energies associated with the cooling of iron and the heating of water are determined by the specific heat capacities, masses, and temperature changes for each species. If we define the system as the iron and water, the sum of these two energy quantities will be zero. The final temperature is the unknown in this problem. Masses and initial temperatures are given; the specific heat capacities of iron and water can be found in Appendix D or Figure 5.4.

Strategy The sum of the two energy quantities, q_{Fe} and q_{water}, is zero ($q_{Fe} + q_{water} = 0$). Each energy quantity is defined using Equation 5.1; the value of ΔT in each is $T_{final} - T_{initial}$. We can use either kelvin or Celsius temperatures (Problem Solving Tip 5.1). Substitute the given information into Equation 5.3 and solve.

Solution

$$[C_{water} \times m_{water} \times (T_{final} - T_{initial,\ water})] + [C_{Fe} \times m_{Fe} \times (T_{final} - T_{initial,\ Fe})] = 0$$

$$[(4.184\ J/g \cdot K)(244\ g)(T_{final} - 292.0\ K)] + [(0.449\ J/g \cdot K)(88.5\ g)(T_{final} - 352.0\ K)] = 0$$

$$T_{final} = 294\ K\ (21\ °C)$$

Think about Your Answer Be sure to notice that $T_{initial}$ for the metal and $T_{initial}$ for the water in this problem have different values. Also, the low specific heat capacity and smaller quantity of iron result in the temperature of iron being reduced by about 60 degrees; in contrast, the temperature of the water has been raised by only a few degrees. Finally, as expected, T_{final} (294 K) is between $T_{initial,\ Fe}$ and $T_{initial,\ water}$.

Check Your Understanding

A 15.5-g piece of chromium, heated to 100.0 °C, is dropped into 55.5 g of water at 16.5 °C. The final temperature of the metal and the water is 18.9 °C. What is the specific heat capacity of chromium? (Assume no energy is lost to the container or to the surrounding air.)

To summarize this section on specific heat capacity and thermal energy transfer between objects, there are several important ideas to keep in mind.

- As noted earlier in the chapter, the transfer of thermal energy occurs by the transfer of kinetic energy from the hotter body to the cooler one. The amount of energy transferred depends on three variables: the mass of the object (m), its specific heat capacity (C), and the magnitude of the temperature change (ΔT).
- If two objects have the same mass, the object having the larger specific heat capacity will undergo the smaller temperature change for a given amount of energy transferred.
- If two objects have different masses, but the same specific heat capacity, the larger object will undergo a smaller temperature change for a given amount of energy transferred.
- If two objects have different masses and different specific heat capacities (as in Example 5.2), the temperature change must be calculated from the conservation of energy.

REVIEW & CHECK FOR SECTION 5-2

1. Which of the following processes requires the largest input of energy?
   (a) warming 2.0 g of copper by 10 °C (C_{Cu} = 0.385 J/g · K)
   (b) warming 4.0 g of lead by 10 °C (C_{Pb} = 0.127 J/g · K)
   (c) warming 3.0 g of silver by 10 °C (C_{Ag} = 0.236 J/g · K)
2. The samples of water listed below are mixed. After thermal equilibrium is reached, which mixture has the lowest temperature?
   (a) 10 g of water at 20 °C + 10 g of water at 30 °C
   (b) 10 g of water at 20 °C + 20 g of water at 30 °C
   (c) 20 g of water at 20 °C + 10 g of water at 30 °C

5-3 Energy and Changes of State

Learning Objectives: LO 2.3, LO 5.2, LO 5.4, LO 5.6, LO 5.10

A *change of state* is a change, for example, between solid and liquid or between liquid and gas. When a solid melts, its atoms, molecules, or ions move about vigorously enough to break free of the attractive forces holding them in rigid positions in the solid lattice. When a liquid boils, the particles move much farther apart from one another, to distances at which attractive forces are minimal. In both cases, energy must be furnished to overcome attractive forces among the particles.

The energy transferred as heat that is required to convert a substance from a solid at its melting point to a liquid is called the **heat of fusion**. The energy transferred as heat to convert a liquid at its boiling point to a vapor is called the **heat of vaporization**. Heats of fusion and vaporization for many substances are provided along with other physical properties in reference books. Values for a few common substances are given in Appendix D (Table 12).

It is important to recognize that *temperature is constant throughout a change of state* (Figures 5.6). During a change of state, the added energy is used to overcome the forces holding one molecule to another, not to increase the temperature.

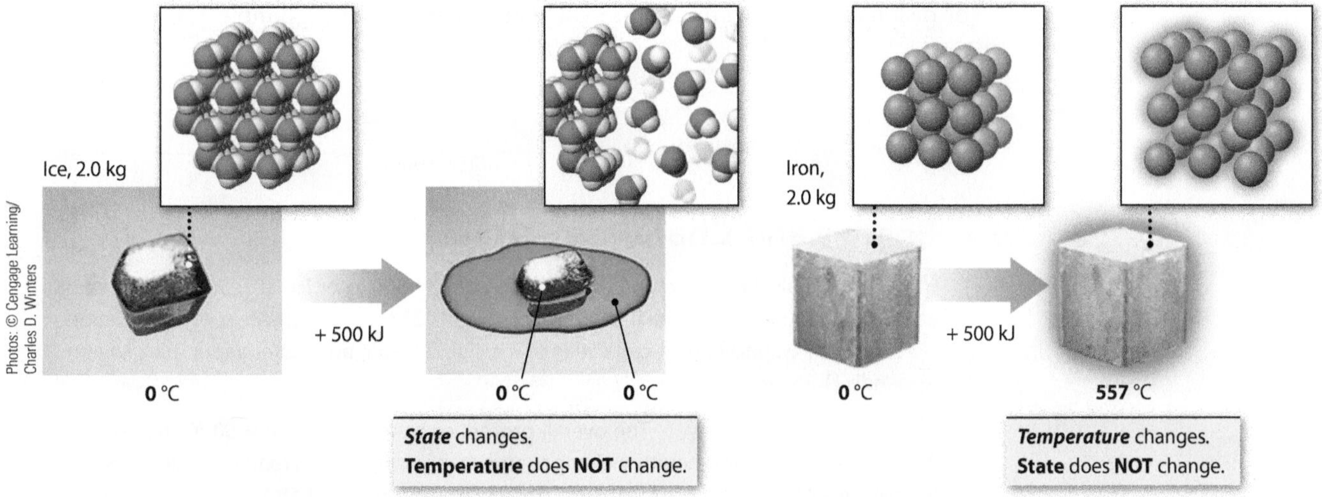

Transferring 500 kJ of energy as heat to 2.0 kg of ice at 0 °C will cause 1.5 kg of ice to melt to water at 0 °C (and 0.5 kg of ice will remain). No temperature change occurs.

In contrast, transferring 500 kJ of energy as heat to 2.0 kg of iron at 0 °C will cause the temperature to increase to 557 °C (and the metal to expand slightly but not melt).

FIGURE 5.6 **Contrast between a change of state and an increase in temperature as a result of adding energy.**

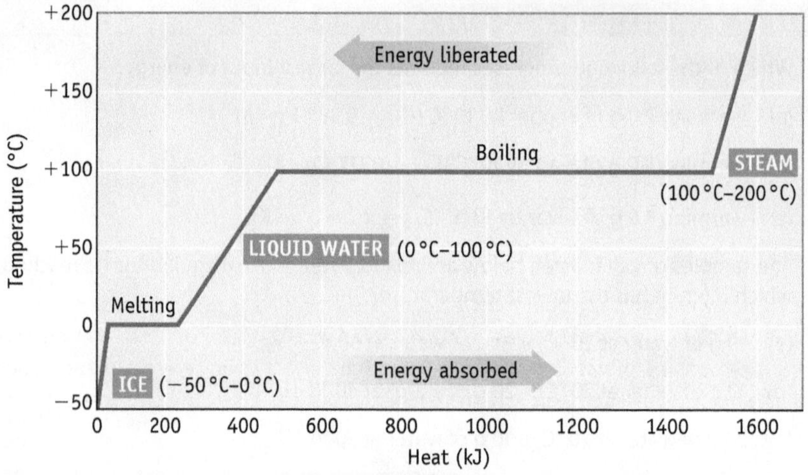

FIGURE 5.7 Energy transfer as heat and the temperature change as 500. g of water warms from −50 °C to 200 °C (at 1 atm).

Temperature Dependence of the Heat of Vaporization The heat of vaporization of a substance is dependent on temperature. For example, the heat of vaporization of water at 25 °C is 2442 J/g. This value is slightly larger than the value at 100 °C (2256 J/g).

For water, the heat of fusion at 0 °C is 333 J/g, and the heat of vaporization at 100 °C is 2256 J/g. These values can be used to calculate the energy required for a given mass of water to melt or evaporate, respectively. For example, the energy required to convert 500. g of water from the liquid to gaseous state at 100 °C is

$$(2256 \text{ J/g})(500. \text{ g}) = 1.13 \times 10^6 \text{ J } (= 1130 \text{ kJ})$$

In contrast, to melt the same mass of ice to form liquid water at 0 °C requires only 167 kJ.

$$(333 \text{ J/g})(500. \text{ g}) = 1.67 \times 10^5 \text{ J } (= 167 \text{ kJ})$$

Figure 5.7 gives a profile of the energy changes occurring as 500. g of ice at −50 °C is converted to water vapor at 200 °C. This involves a series of steps: (1) warming ice to 0 °C, (2) conversion to liquid water at 0 °C, (3) warming liquid water to 100 °C, (4) evaporation at 100 °C, and (5) warming the water vapor to 200 °C. Each step requires the input of additional energy. The energy transferred as heat to raise the temperature of solid, liquid, and vapor can be calculated with Equation 5.1, using the specific heat capacities of ice, liquid water, and water vapor (which are different), and the energies for the changes of state can be calculated using heats of fusion and vaporization. These calculations are done in Example 5.3.

EXAMPLE 5.3

Energy and Changes of State

Problem Calculate the energy needed to convert 500. g of ice at −50.0 °C to steam at 200.0 °C (Figure 5.7). The heat of fusion of water is 333 J/g, and the heat of vaporization is 2256 J/g. The specific heat capacities of ice, liquid water, and water vapor are given in Appendix D.

What Do You Know? The overall process of converting ice at −50 °C to steam at 200 °C involves both temperature changes and changes of state; all require input of energy as heat. Recall that melting occurs at 0 °C and boiling at 100 °C (at 1 atm pressure). You know the mass of the water and will need the specific heat capacities of ice, liquid water, and steam from Appendix D. The heat of fusion of water (333 J/g), and the heat of vaporization (2256 J/g) are given.

Strategy The problem is broken down into a series of steps:

Step 1: Warm the ice from −50 °C to 0 °C.

Step 2: Melt the ice at 0 °C.

Step 3: Raise the temperature of the liquid water from 0 °C to 100 °C.

Step 4: Evaporate the water at 100 °C.

Step 5: Raise the temperature of the steam from 100 °C to 200 °C.

Use Equation 5.1 and the specific heat capacities of solid, liquid, and gaseous water to calculate the energy transferred as heat associated with the temperature changes. Use the heats of fusion and of vaporization to calculate the energy transferred as heat associated with changes of state. The total energy transferred as heat is the sum of the energies of the individual steps.

Strategy Map 5.3

PROBLEM

Calculate **energy required** to heat a mass of water from **−50.0 °C** to steam at **200.0 °C**.

DATA/INFORMATION

- Mass of water
- ΔT
- Heats of fusion and vaporization of water
- Specific heat capacities

Calculate **energy** involved in
STEP 1. warm ice to 0 °C (q_1)
STEP 2. melt ice at 0 °C (q_2)
STEP 3. warm water from 0 °C to 100 °C (q_3)
STEP 4. evaporate water at 100 °C (q_4)
STEP 5. heat steam to 200 °C (q_5)

Values of q_1, q_2, q_3, q_4, and q_5

STEP 6. Sum values of q.

q_{total} for process

Solution

Step 1. (to warm ice from −50.0 °C to 0.0 °C)

$$q_1 = (2.06\ \text{J/g} \cdot \text{K})(500.\ \text{g})(273.2\ \text{K} - 223.2\ \text{K}) = 5.15 \times 10^4\ \text{J}$$

Step 2. (to melt ice at 0.0 °C)

$$q_2 = (500.\ \text{g})(333\ \text{J/g}) = 1.67 \times 10^5\ \text{J}$$

Step 3. (to raise temperature of liquid water from 0.0 °C to 100.0 °C)

$$q_3 = (4.184\ \text{J/g} \cdot \text{K})(500.\ \text{g})(373.2\ \text{K} - 273.2\ \text{K}) = 2.09 \times 10^5\ \text{J}$$

Step 4. (to evaporate water at 100.0 °C)

$$q_4 = (2256\ \text{J/g})(500.\ \text{g}) = 1.13 \times 10^6\ \text{J}$$

Step 5. (to raise temperature of water vapor from 100.0 °C to 200.0 °C)

$$q_5 = (1.86\ \text{J/g} \cdot \text{K})(500.\ \text{g})\ (473.2\ \text{K} - 373.2\ \text{K}) = 9.30 \times 10^4\ \text{J}$$

The total energy transferred as heat is the sum of the energies of the individual steps.

$$q_{\text{total}} = q_1 + q_2 + q_3 + q_4 + q_5$$

$$q_{\text{total}} = 1.65 \times 10^6\ \text{J (or 1650 kJ)}$$

Think about Your Answer The conversion of liquid water to steam is the largest increment of energy by a considerable margin. (You may have noticed that when water is heated at a steady rate on a stove it takes much less time to heat the water to boiling than it takes to boil off the water.)

Check Your Understanding

Calculate the amount of energy necessary to raise the temperature of 1.00 L of ethanol (d = 0.7849 g/cm^3) from 25.0 °C to its boiling point (78.3 °C) and then to vaporize the liquid. (C_{ethanol} = 2.44 J/g · K; heat of vaporization at 78.3 °C = 38.56 kJ/mol.)

EXAMPLE 5.4

Change of State

Problem What is the minimum mass of ice at 0 °C that must be added to the contents of a can of diet cola (340. mL) to cool the cola from 20.5 °C to 0.0 °C? Assume that the specific heat capacity and density of diet cola are the same as for water.

What Do You Know? The final temperature is 0 °C. Melting ice requires energy as heat, and cooling the cola evolves energy as heat. The sum of the energy changes for the two components in the system is zero; that is, the two energy changes (melting ice, cooling cola) will be the same magnitude but opposite in sign. (You also need to assume there is no transfer of energy between the surroundings and the system.) You will need the density and specific heat capacity of water (Appendix D).

Strategy Assuming only energy changes within the system, $q_{cola} + q_{ice} = 0$. The energy evolved as the cola cools, q_{cola}, is calculated using Equation 5.1. The initial temperature is 20.5 °C and the final temperature is 0 °C. The mass of cola is calculated from the volume and density. The energy as heat required to melt the ice, q_{ice}, is determined from the heat of fusion (333 J/g). The mass of ice is the unknown.

Solution The mass of cola is 340. g [(340. mL)(1.00 g/mL) = 340. g], and its temperature changes from 293.7 K to 273.2 K. The heat of fusion of water is 333 J/g, and the mass of ice is the unknown.

$$q_{cola} + q_{ice} = 0$$

$$C_{cola} \times m_{cola} \times (T_{final} - T_{initial}) + (\text{heat of fusion of water})\,(m_{ice}) = 0$$

$$[(4.184\ \text{J/g} \cdot \text{K})(340.\ \text{g})(273.2\ \text{K} - 293.7\ \text{K})] + [(333\ \text{J/g})\,(m_{ice})] = 0$$

$$m_{ice} = 87.6\ \text{g}$$

Think about Your Answer If more than 87.6 g of ice is added, the final temperature will still be 0 °C when thermal equilibrium is reached, but some ice will remain (see problem below). If less than 87.6 g of ice is added, the final temperature will be greater than 0 °C. In this case, all the ice will melt, and the liquid water formed by melting the ice will absorb additional energy to warm up to the final temperature (an example is given in Study Question 79, page 217e).

Check Your Understanding

To make a glass of iced tea, you pour 250 mL of tea, whose temperature is 18.2 °C, into a glass containing five ice cubes. Each cube has a mass of 15 g. What quantity of ice will melt, and how much ice will remain floating in the tea? Assume iced tea has a density of 1.0 g/mL and a specific heat capacity of 4.2 J/g · K, that energy is transferred as heat only within the system, ice is at 0.0 °C, and no energy is transferred between system and surroundings.

REVIEW & CHECK FOR SECTION 5-3

1. Which of the following processes requires the largest input of energy as heat?
   (a) raising the temperature of 100 g of water by 1.0 °C
   (b) vaporization of 0.10 g of water at 100 °C
   (c) melting 1.0 g of ice at 0 °C
   (d) warming 1.0 g of ice from −50 °C to 0 °C (specific heat of ice = 2.06 J/g · K)

2. Ice (5.0 g) at 0 °C is added to 25 g of liquid water at 20 °C. Which statement best describes the system when thermal equilibrium is reached?
   (a) Part of the ice has melted; the remaining ice and water are at 0 °C.
   (b) All of the ice melts; liquid water is at a temperature between 0 °C and 10 °C.
   (c) All of the ice melts; liquid water is at a temperature between 10 °C and 20 °C.
   (d) Part of the ice melts; the ice-water mixture is at a temperature between 0 ° C and 10 °C.

(a) Pieces of dry ice [CO_2(s), −78 °C] are placed in a plastic bag. The dry ice will sublime (change directly from a solid to a gas) upon the input of energy.

(b) Energy is absorbed by CO_2(s) when it sublimes, and the system (the contents of the bag) does work on its surroundings by lifting the book against the force of gravity.

FIGURE 5.8 **Energy changes in a physical process (a phase change as solid CO_2 changes to CO_2 gas).**

5-4 The First Law of Thermodynamics

Learning Objectives: LO 5.6

Recall that *thermodynamics is the science of heat and work.* To this point, we have only considered energy being transferred as heat, but now we need to broaden the discussion to include work. Work done by a system or on a system will also affect the energy in the system. If a system does work on its surroundings, energy must be expended by the system, and the system's energy will decrease. Conversely, if work is done by the surroundings on a system, the energy of the system will increase.

A system doing work on its surroundings is illustrated in Figure 5.8. A small quantity of dry ice, solid CO_2, is sealed inside a plastic bag, and a weight (a book) is placed on top of the bag. When energy is transferred as heat from the surroundings to the dry ice, the dry ice changes directly from solid to gas at −78 °C in a process called **sublimation:**

$$CO_2(s, -78\ °C) \rightarrow CO_2(g, -78\ °C)$$

As sublimation proceeds, gaseous CO_2 expands within the plastic bag, lifting the book against the force of gravity. The system (the CO_2 inside the bag) is expending energy to do this work.

Even if the book had not been on top of the plastic bag, work would have been done by the expanding gas because the gas must push back the atmosphere when it expands. Instead of raising a book, the expanding gas moves a part of the atmosphere.

Now let us restate this example in terms of thermodynamics. First, we must identify the system and the surroundings. The system is the CO_2, initially a solid and later a gas. The surroundings consist of objects that exchange energy with the system. This includes the plastic bag, the book, the table-top, and the surrounding air. Sublimation requires energy, which is transferred as heat to the system (the CO_2) from the surroundings. At the same time, the system does work on the surroundings by lifting the book. An energy balance for the system will include both quantities, energy transferred as heat and energy transferred as work.

This example can be generalized. For any system, we can identify energy transfers both as heat and as work between the system and surroundings. The change in energy for a system is given explicitly by Equation 5.4,

Change in energy content → ΔU; Energy transferred as work to or from the system → w; Energy transferred as heat to or from the system → q

$$\Delta U = q + w \qquad (5.4)$$

which is a mathematical statement of the **first law of thermodynamics**: The energy change for a system (ΔU) is the sum of the energy transferred as heat between the system and its surroundings (q) and the energy transferred as work between the system and its surroundings (w).

The equation defining the first law of thermodynamics is just a restatement of the general principle of conservation of energy. Because energy is conserved, we must be able to account for any change in the energy of the system. All energy transfers between a system and its surroundings occur by the processes of heat and work. Equation 5.4 thus states that the change in the energy of the system is exactly equal to the sum of all of the energy transfers (heat and/or work) from or to the surroundings.

The quantity U in Equation 5.4 has a formal name—**internal energy**—and a precise meaning in thermodynamics. The internal energy in a chemical system is the sum of the potential and kinetic energies inside the system, that is, the energies of the atoms, molecules, or ions in the system. The potential energy here is the energy associated with the attractive and repulsive forces between all the nuclei and electrons in the system. It includes the energy associated with bonds in molecules, forces between ions, and forces between molecules. The kinetic energy is the energy of motion of the atoms, ions, and molecules in the system. Actual values of internal energy are rarely determined or needed. Instead, in most instances, we are interested in the *change* in internal energy, a measurable quantity. In fact, Equation 5.4 tells us how to determine ΔU: *Measure the energy transferred as heat and work to or from the system.*

The sign conventions for Equation 5.4 are important. The following table summarizes how the internal energy of a system is affected by energy transferred as heat and work.

SIGN CONVENTIONS FOR *q* AND *w* OF THE SYSTEM

ENERGY TRANSFERRED AS . . .	SIGN CONVENTION	EFFECT ON U_{system}
Heat to the system (endothermic)	$q > 0\ (+)$	U increases
Heat from the system (exothermic)	$q < 0\ (-)$	U decreases
Work done on system	$w > 0\ (+)$	U increases
Work done by system	$w < 0\ (-)$	U decreases

Heat and Work For an in-depth look at heat and work in thermodynamics, see E. A. Gislason and N. C. Craig, *Journal of Chemical Education*, Vol. 64, No. 8, pp. 660–668, 1987.

The work in the example involving the sublimation of CO_2 (see Figure 5.8) is of a specific type, called P–V (pressure–volume) work. It is the work (w) associated with a change in volume (ΔV) that occurs against a resisting external pressure (P).

A CLOSER LOOK — P–V Work

The example of a gas sealed in a cylinder with a movable piston can be used to understand the work done by a system on its surroundings (or vice versa) when the volume of a system changes. If the gas in the cylinder is heated, it expands, pushing the piston upward until the internal gas pressure equals the (constant) downward external pressure applied by the piston and the atmosphere (see figure). Ideally, the piston moves without friction, so that none of the work done by an expanding gas is lost to heating the cylinder walls.

The work required to move the piston is calculated from a law of physics, $w = F \times d$, or work equals the magnitude of the force (F) applied times the distance (d) over which the force is applied. Pressure is defined as a force divided by the area over which the force is applied: $P = F/A$, where the force is a function of the piston's mass, the external air pressure, and the Earth's gravity. In this example, the force is applied to a piston with an area A. Substituting $P \times A$ for F in the equation for work gives $w = (P \times A) \times d$. The product of $A \times d$ is equivalent to the change in the volume of the gas in the cylinder, and, because $\Delta V = V_{final} - V_{initial}$, this change in volume is positive. Finally, because work done by a system on the surroundings is defined as negative, this means that $w = -P\Delta V$. Expanding the gas and moving the piston upward means we have done work on the surroundings.

In this example, care has been taken to expand the gas against a constant external pressure. Note that for many processes that result in the expansion (or compression) of a gas, the pressure is not constant. Calculating the work for processes where both pressure and volume change is more complicated, though possible.

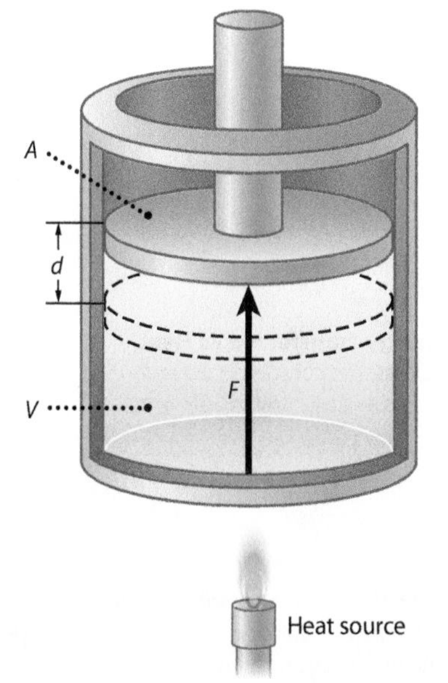

For a system in which the external pressure is constant, the value of P–V work can be calculated using Equation 5.5,

Work (at constant pressure) → w; Change in volume → ΔV; Pressure → P

$$w = -P \times \Delta V \quad (5.5)$$

To calculate this work in units of joules, the pressure is measured in pascals (1 Pa = 1 kg/m · s^2) and the volume change is measured in cubic meters (m^3).

If energy is transferred in a constant-volume process, $\Delta V = 0$. This means the energy transferred as work will also be zero. Thus, the change in internal energy of the system under constant-volume conditions is equal only to the energy transferred as heat (q_v).

Calculating Work Work is calculated using the SI units of pressure and volume. The SI unit of pressure is the pascal (1 Pa = 1 kg/m · s^2), which when multiplied by the volume change in m^3, gives energy in joules (1 J = 1 kg · m^2/s^2).

$$\Delta U = q_V + w_V$$

$$\Delta U = q_V + 0 \text{ when } w_V = 0 \text{ because } \Delta V = 0$$

$$\text{and so } \Delta U = q_V$$

Enthalpy

Most experiments in a chemical laboratory are carried out in beakers or flasks open to the atmosphere, where the external pressure is constant. Similarly, chemical processes that occur in living systems are open to the atmosphere. Because many processes in chemistry and biology are carried out under conditions of constant pressure, it is useful to have a specific measure of the energy transferred as heat under this circumstance.

Under conditions of constant pressure,

$$\Delta U = q_p + w_p$$

where the subscript p indicates conditions of constant pressure. If the only type of work that occurs is P–V work, then

$$\Delta U = q_p - P\Delta V$$

Rearranging this gives

$$q_p = \Delta U + P\Delta V$$

We now introduce a new thermodynamic function called **enthalpy**, H, which is defined as

$$H = U + PV$$

Energy Transferred as Heat
Processes at constant V: $\Delta U = q_v$
Processes at constant P: $\Delta H = q_p$

The *change* in enthalpy for a system at constant pressure would be calculated from the following equation:

$$\Delta H = \Delta U + P\Delta V$$

Thus,

$$\Delta H = q_p$$

Enthalpy and Internal Energy In the AP curriculum internal energy and enthalpy are treated as equivalent.

For a system where the only type of work possible is P–V work, the change in enthalpy, ΔH, is equal to the energy transferred as heat at constant pressure, q_p. The directionality of energy transfer (under conditions of constant pressure) is signified by the sign of ΔH.

- Negative values of ΔH: energy is transferred as heat from the system to the surroundings.
- Positive values of ΔH: energy is transferred as heat from the surroundings to the system.

Enthalpy and Internal Energy Differences The difference between ΔH and ΔU will be quite small unless a large volume change occurs. For example, the difference between ΔH and ΔU for the conversion of ice to liquid water is 0.142 J/mol at 1 atm pressure. For the conversion of liquid water to water vapor at 373 K, the difference is 3100 J/mol.

Under conditions of constant pressure and where the only type of work possible is P–V work, ΔU ($= q_p - P\Delta V$) and ΔH ($= q_p$) differ by $P\Delta V$ (the energy transferred to or from the system as work). We observe that in many processes—such as the melting of ice—the volume change, ΔV, is small, and hence the amount of energy transferred as work is small. Under these circumstances, ΔU and ΔH have almost the same value. The amount of energy transferred as work will be significant, however, when the volume change is large, as when gases are formed or consumed. For example, in the evaporation or condensation of water, the sublimation of CO_2, and chemical reactions in which the number of moles of gas changes, ΔU and ΔH have significantly different values.

EXAMPLE 5.5

Energy and Work

Problem Nitrogen gas (1.50 L) is confined in a cylinder under constant atmospheric pressure (1.01×10^5 pascals). The gas expands to a volume of 2.18 L when 882 J of energy is transferred as heat from the surroundings to the gas. What is the change in internal energy of the gas?

What Do You Know? Energy as heat (882 J) is transferred at constant pressure into the system; thus, $q_p = +882$ J. The system does work on the surroundings when the gas expands from 1.50 L to 2.18 L under a constant pressure of 1.01×10^5 pascals, thereby transferring some energy back to the surroundings.

Strategy Calculate the work done by the system using $w_p = -P(\Delta V)$. The unit of work is joules, provided that SI units are used for pressure and volume. The pressure is given in SI units (pascals, Pa, where 1 Pa = 1 kg/(m · s^2)). To calculate work, the volume must be converted from L to m^3. The change in internal energy of the gas is the sum of the enthalpy change of the gas and the work done by the gas on the surroundings ($\Delta U = q_p + w_p$).

Solution The change in volume of the gas is

$$(2.18\ \text{L} - 1.50\ \text{L N}_2\ \text{gas})(1\ \text{m}^3/1000\ \text{L}) = 6.8 \times 10^{-4}\ \text{m}^3$$

The work done by the system is

$$w_p = -(1.01 \times 10^5\ \text{kg/m} \cdot \text{s}^2)(6.8 \times 10^{-4}\ \text{m}^3) = -68.7\ \text{kg} \cdot \text{m}^2/\text{s}^2 = -68.7\ \text{J}$$

Finally, the change in internal energy is calculated.

$$\Delta U = q_p + w_p = 882\ \text{J} + (-68.7\ \text{J}) = 813\ \text{J}$$

Think about Your Answer The internal energy of a gas increases upon heating. However, the gas does work on the surroundings as it expands against pressure, giving some of its energy to the surroundings.

Check Your Understanding

Nitrogen gas (2.75 L) is confined in a cylinder under constant atmospheric pressure (1.01×10^5 pascals). The volume of gas decreases to 2.10 L when 485 J of energy is transferred as heat to the surroundings. What is the change in internal energy of the gas?

State Functions

Internal energy and enthalpy share a significant characteristic—namely, changes in these quantities depend only on the initial and final states. They do not depend on the path taken on going from the initial state to the final state. No matter how you go from reactants to products in a reaction the values of ΔH and ΔU are always the same. A quantity that has this property is called a **state function**.

Many commonly measured quantities, such as the pressure of a gas, the volume of a gas or liquid, and the temperature of a substance are state functions. For example, if the final temperature of a substance is 75 °C and its initial temperature is 25 °C, the change in temperature, ΔT, is calculated as $T_{\text{final}} - T_{\text{initial}} = 75$ °C $- 25$ °C $= 50$ °C. It does not matter if the substance was heated directly from 25 °C to 75 °C or if the substance was heated from 25 °C to 95 °C and then cooled to 75 °C; the overall change in temperature is still the same, 50 °C.

Not all quantities are state functions; some depend on the pathway taken to get from the initial condition to the final condition. For instance, distance traveled is not a state function (Figure 5.9). The travel distance from New York City to Denver depends on the route taken. Nor is the elapsed time of travel between these two locations a state function. In contrast, a change in altitude is a state function; in going from New York City (at sea level) to Denver (1600 m above sea level), there is an altitude change of 1600 m, regardless of the route followed.

©My Good Images/Shutterstock.com

FIGURE 5.9 **State functions.** There are many ways to climb a mountain, but the change in altitude from the base of the mountain to its summit is the same. The change in altitude is a state function. The distance traveled to reach the summit is not.

Significantly, in the expansion of a gas, neither the energy transferred as heat nor the energy transferred as work individually is a state function. However, their sum, the change in internal energy, ΔU, is. The value of ΔU is fixed by U_{initial} and U_{final}. A transition between the initial and final states can be accomplished by different routes having different values of q and w, but the sum of q and w for each path must always give the same ΔU.

To better understand how the sum of two path-dependent functions can result in a state function, consider the size of your bank account. This is a state function. Let us assume that there are two path-dependent ways to transfer money into or out of your account: either as cash or as an electronic payment. You could have arrived at a current bank balance of \$25 by having deposited \$25 in cash or you could have deposited \$100 in cash and then made a \$75 electronic payment, or you could have deposited \$100 in cash, made an electronic payment of \$50 and withdrawn \$25 in cash. In each of these cases, the change in your bank balance is determined by taking the final balance (\$25) and subtracting the initial balance (\$0), giving a value for $\Delta\$$ of +\$25, but the pathway to get from \$0 to \$25 is different. In addition, the quantity of money transferred as cash and the quantity of money transferred by electronic payment are path-dependent with different values in each case, but by taking into account all of the transfers as cash and all of the transfers as electronic payments, we end up with the overall balance, a state function.

REVIEW & CHECK FOR SECTION 5-4

1. Which of the following processes will lead to a decrease in the internal energy of a system? (1) Energy is transferred as heat to the system; (2) energy is transferred as heat from the system; (3) energy is transferred as work done on the system; or (4) energy is transferred as work done by the system.

   (a) 1 and 3 (b) 2 and 4 (c) 1 and 4 (d) 2 and 3

2. In which of the following reactions is there a significant transfer of energy as work from the system to the surroundings? This occurs if there is a change in the number of moles of gases.

   (a) $C(s) + O_2(g) \rightarrow CO_2(g)$

   (b) $CH_4(g) + 2\,O_2(g) \rightarrow CO_2(g) + 2\,H_2O(g)$

   (c) $2\,C(s) + O_2(g) \rightarrow 2\,CO(g)$

   (d) $2\,Mg(s) + O_2(g) \rightarrow 2\,MgO(s)$

5-5 Enthalpy Changes for Chemical Reactions

Learning Objectives: LO 1.17, LO 1.18, LO 5.6, LO 5.8, LO 5.10

Enthalpy changes accompany chemical reactions. For example, the **standard reaction enthalpy,** $\Delta_r H°$, for the decomposition of water vapor to hydrogen and oxygen at 25 °C is +241.8 kJ/mol-rxn.

$$H_2O(g) \rightarrow H_2(g) + \tfrac{1}{2}\,O_2(g) \qquad \Delta_r H° = +241.8 \text{ kJ/mol-rxn}$$

The positive sign of $\Delta_r H°$ indicates that the decomposition is an endothermic process.

There are several important things to know about $\Delta_r H°$.

- The designation of $\Delta_r H°$ as a "standard enthalpy change" (where the superscript ° indicates standard conditions) means that the pure, unmixed reactants in their standard states have formed pure, unmixed products in their standard states. The **standard state** of an element or a compound is defined as the most stable form of the substance in the physical state that exists at a pressure of 1 bar and at a specified temperature. [Most sources report standard reaction enthalpies at 25 °C (298 K).]
- The "per mol-rxn" designation in the units for $\Delta_r H°$ means this is the enthalpy change for a "mole of reaction" (where *rxn* is an abbreviation for reaction). One mole of reaction is said to have occurred when a chemical reaction occurs exactly in the amounts specified by the coefficients of the balanced chemical equation. For example, for the reaction $H_2O(g) \rightarrow H_2(g) + 1/2\,O_2(g)$, a mole of reaction has occurred when 1 mol of water vapor has been converted completely to 1 mol of H_2 and 1/2 mol of O_2 gas.

Notation for Thermodynamic Parameters NIST and IUPAC (International Union of Pure and Applied Chemistry) specify that descriptors of functions such as ΔH should be written as a subscript, between the Δ and the thermodynamic function. Among the subscripts you will see are a lower case r for "reaction," f for "formation," c for "combustion," fus for "fusion," and vap for "vaporization."

Moles of Reaction, Mol-rxn This concept was also described in one of the methods shown for solving limiting reactant problems on page 148.

Now consider the opposite reaction, the combination of hydrogen and oxygen to form 1 mol of water. The magnitude of the enthalpy change for this reaction is the same as that for the decomposition reaction, but the sign of $\Delta_r H°$ is reversed.

The exothermic formation of 1 mol of water vapor from 1 mol of H_2 and 1/2 mol of O_2 transfers 241.8 kJ to the surroundings (Figure 5.10).

$$H_2(g) + \tfrac{1}{2} O_2(g) \rightarrow H_2O(g) \qquad \Delta_r H° = -241.8 \text{ kJ/mol-rxn}$$

The value of $\Delta_r H°$ depends on the chemical equation used. Let us write the equation for the formation of water again but without a fractional coefficient for O_2.

$$2\, H_2(g) + O_2(g) \rightarrow 2\, H_2O(g) \qquad \Delta_r H° = -483.6 \text{ kJ/mol-rxn}$$

The value of $\Delta_r H°$ for 1 mol of this reaction, the formation of 2 mol of water, is *twice* the value for the formation of 1 mol of water.

It is important to identify the states of reactants and products in a reaction because the magnitude of $\Delta_r H°$ depends on whether they are solids, liquids, or gases. For the formation of 1 mol of *liquid water* from the elements, the enthalpy change is −285.8 kJ.

$$H_2(g) + \tfrac{1}{2} O_2(g) \rightarrow H_2O(\ell) \qquad \Delta_r H° = -285.8 \text{ kJ/mol-rxn}$$

Notice that this value is not the same as $\Delta_r H°$ for the formation of 1 mol of *water vapor* from hydrogen and oxygen. The difference between the two values is equal to the enthalpy change for the condensation of 1 mol of water vapor to 1 mol of liquid water.

These examples illustrate several general features of enthalpy changes for chemical reactions.

- Enthalpy changes are specific to the reaction being carried out. The identities of reactants and products and their states (s, ℓ, g) are important, as are the amounts of reactants and products.
- The enthalpy change depends on the number of moles of reaction, that is, the number of times the reaction *as written* is carried out.

Fractional Stoichiometric Coefficients When writing balanced equations to define thermodynamic quantities, chemists often use fractional stoichiometric coefficients. For example, to define $\Delta_r H$ for the decomposition or formation of 1 mol of H_2O, the coefficient for O_2 must be 1/2.

Changes in Chemical Energy in a Chemical Reaction

- If a reaction is exothermic, the potential energy of the reactants is *greater* than that of the products ($PE_{react} > PE_{prod}$).
- If a reaction is endothermic, the potential energy of the reactants is *less* than that of the products ($PE_{react} < PE_{prod}$).

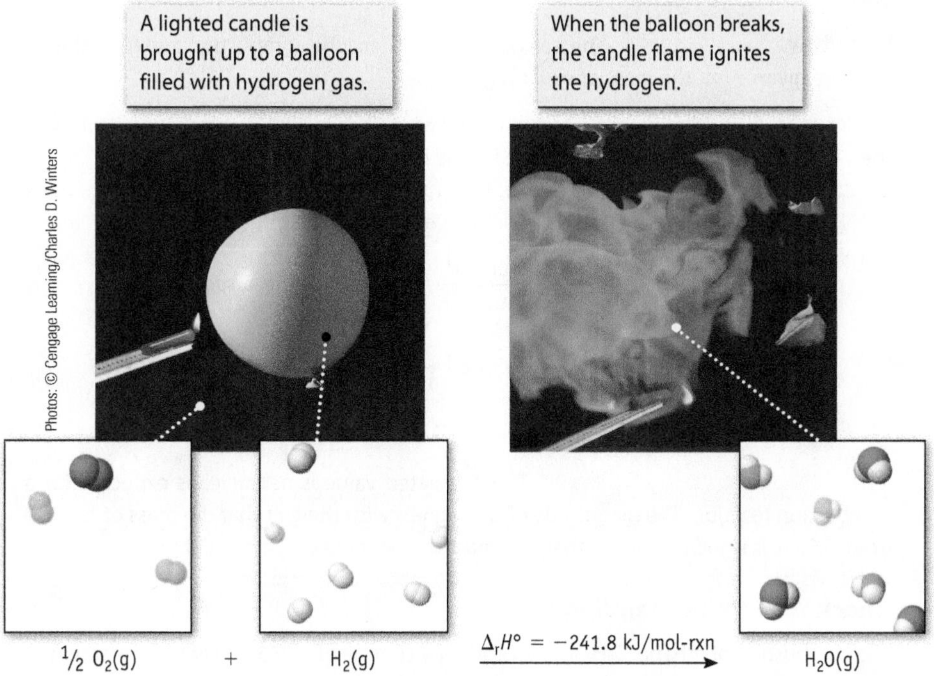

FIGURE 5.10 The exothermic combustion of hydrogen in air. The reaction involves the transfer of energy between the system and surroundings in the form of heat, work, and light.

- $\Delta_r H°$ has a negative value for an exothermic reaction; it has a positive value for an endothermic reaction.
- Values of $\Delta_r H°$ are numerically the same, but opposite in sign, for chemical reactions that are the reverse of each other.

Standard Conditions The superscript ° indicates standard conditions. It is applied to any type of thermodynamic data, such as enthalpy of fusion and vaporization ($\Delta_{fus}H°$ and $\Delta_{vap}H°$) and enthalpy of a reaction ($\Delta_r H°$). Standard conditions refers to reactants and products in their standard states at a pressure of 1 bar. One bar is approximately one atmosphere (1 atm = 1.013 bar; ▶ Chapter 10 and Appendix B).

Standard reaction enthalpies can be used to calculate the energy transferred as heat under conditions of constant pressure for any given mass of a reactant or product. Suppose you want to know the energy transferred to the surroundings as heat if 454 g of propane, C_3H_8, is burned (at constant pressure), given the equation for the exothermic combustion and the enthalpy change for the reaction.

$$C_3H_8(g) + 5\,O_2(g) \rightarrow 3\,CO_2\,(g) + 4\,H_2O(\ell) \qquad \Delta_r H° = -2220 \text{ kJ/mol-rxn}$$

Two steps are needed. First, find the amount of propane present in the sample:

$$454 \text{ g } C_3H_8 \left(\frac{1 \text{ mol } C_3H_8}{44.10 \text{ g } C_3H_8}\right) = 10.3 \text{ mol } C_3H_8$$

Second, use $\Delta_r H°$ to determine $\Delta H°$ for this amount of propane:

$$H° = 10.3 \text{ mol } CH_8 \left(\frac{1 \text{ mol-rxn}}{1 \text{ mol } C_3H_8}\right)\left(\frac{-2220 \text{ kJ}}{1 \text{ mol-rxn}}\right) = -22{,}900 \text{ kJ}$$

Strategy Map 5.6

PROBLEM

Calculate $\Delta H°$ for combustion of **given mass** of sucrose.

↓

DATA/INFORMATION

- **Mass** of sucrose
- **$\Delta_r H°$ per mol** for sucrose combustion

STEP 1. Calculate **amount** of sucrose.

↓

Amount of sucrose

STEP 2. Convert from **mol** of sucrose to **mol-rxn**, then multiply by $\Delta_r H°$.

↓

$\Delta H°$ for combustion of **given mass** of sucrose

EXAMPLE 5.6

Calculating the Enthalpy Change for a Reaction

Problem Sucrose (table sugar, $C_{12}H_{22}O_{11}$) can be oxidized to CO_2 and H_2O, and the enthalpy change for the reaction can be measured.

$$C_{12}H_{22}O_{11}(s) + 12\,O_2(g) \rightarrow 12\,CO_2(g) + 11\,H_2O(\ell) \qquad \Delta_r H° = -5645 \text{ kJ/mol-rxn}$$

What is the enthalpy change when 5.00 g of sugar is burned under conditions of constant pressure?

What Do You Know? The balanced equation for the combustion and the value of $\Delta_r H°$ are given. Also, the mass of sugar is given.

Strategy First determine the amount (mol) of sucrose in 5.00 g, and then use this with the value given for the enthalpy change for the oxidation of 1 mol of sucrose.

Solution

$$5.00 \text{ g sucrose} \times \frac{1 \text{ mol sucrose}}{342.3 \text{ g sucrose}} = 1.46 \times 10^{-2} \text{ mol sucrose}$$

$$\Delta H° = 1.46 \times 10^{-2} \text{ mol sucrose} \left(\frac{1 \text{ mol-rxn}}{1 \text{ mol sucrose}}\right)\left(\frac{-5645 \text{ kJ}}{1 \text{ mol-rxn}}\right)$$

$$\Delta H° = -82.5 \text{ kJ}$$

Think about Your Answer The calculated value is negative, as expected for a combustion reaction. The magnitude of $\Delta H°$ agrees with the fact that the mass of sucrose used, 5.00 g, is significantly less than the mass of one mole of sucrose (342.3 g).

Check Your Understanding

The combustion of ethane, C_2H_6, has an enthalpy change of −2857.3 kJ for the reaction as written below. Calculate $\Delta H°$ for the combustion of 15.0 g of C_2H_6.

$$2\,C_2H_6(g) + 7\,O_2(g) \rightarrow 4\,CO_2(g) + 6\,H_2O(g) \qquad \Delta_r H° = -2857.3 \text{ kJ/mol-rxn}$$

Burning Sugar and Gummi Bears A person on a diet might note that a (level) teaspoonful of sugar (about 3.5 g) supplies about 15 Calories (dietary Calories; the conversion is 4.184 kJ = 1 Cal). As diets go, a single spoonful of sugar doesn't have a large caloric content. But will you use just one level teaspoonful? Or just one Gummi Bear?

REVIEW & CHECK FOR SECTION 5-5

1. For the reaction 2 Hg(ℓ) + O_2(g) → 2 HgO(s), $\Delta_r H° = -181.6$ kJ/mol-rxn. What is the enthalpy change to decompose 1.00 mol of HgO(s) to O_2(g) and Hg(ℓ)?

   (a) 181.6 kJ (b) −90.8 kJ (c) 90.8 kJ (d) 363.3 kJ

2. For the reaction 2 CO(g) + O_2(g) → 2 CO_2(g), $\Delta_r H° = -566$ kJ/mol-rxn. What is the enthalpy change for the oxidation of 42.0 g of CO(g)?

   (a) −283 kJ (b) −425 kJ (c) −566 kJ (d) −393.5 kJ

5-6 Calorimetry

Learning Objectives: LO 5.5, LO 5.7 (see APEC Lab 12 "Analysis by Calorimetry")

The energy evolved or absorbed as heat in a chemical or physical process can be measured by **calorimetry**. The apparatus used in this kind of experiment is a *calorimeter*.

Constant-Pressure Calorimetry, Measuring ΔH

A constant-pressure calorimeter can be used to measure the amount of energy transferred as heat under constant-pressure conditions, that is, the enthalpy change for a chemical reaction.

The constant-pressure calorimeter used in general chemistry laboratories is often a "coffee-cup calorimeter." This inexpensive device consists of two nested Styrofoam coffee cups with a loose-fitting lid and a temperature-measuring device such as a thermometer (Figure 5.11) or thermocouple. Styrofoam, a fairly good insulator, minimizes energy transfer as heat between the system and the surroundings. The reaction is carried out in solution in the cup. If the reaction is exothermic, it releases energy as heat to the solution, and the temperature of the solution rises. If the reaction is endothermic, energy is absorbed as heat from the solution, and a decrease in the temperature of the solution will be seen. The change in temperature of the solution is measured. Knowing the mass and specific heat capacity of the solution and the temperature change, the enthalpy change for the reaction can be calculated.

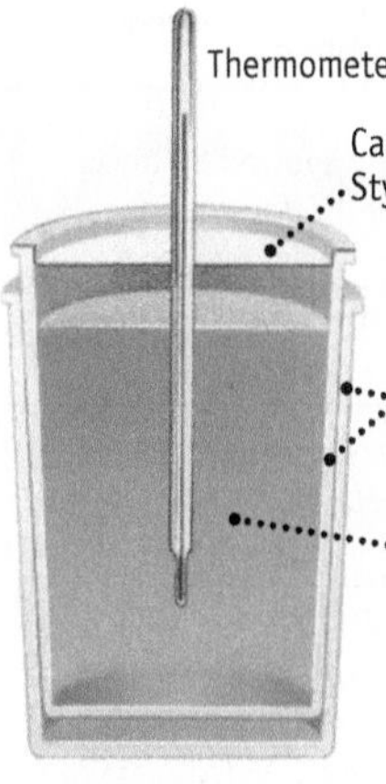

FIGURE 5.11 A coffee-cup calorimeter. A chemical reaction produces a change in temperature of the solution in the calorimeter. The Styrofoam container is fairly effective in preventing the transfer of energy as heat between the solution and its surroundings. Because the cup is open to the atmosphere, this is a constant-pressure measurement.

In this type of calorimetry experiment, it is convenient to define the chemicals and the solution as the system. The surroundings are the cup and everything beyond the cup. As noted above, we assume there is no energy transfer to the cup or beyond and that energy is transferred only as heat within the system. Two energy changes occur within the system. One is the change that takes place as the chemical reaction occurs, either releasing the potential energy stored in the reactants or absorbing energy and converting it to potential energy stored in the products. We label this energy as q_r. The other energy change is the energy gained or lost as heat by the solution ($q_{solution}$). Based on the law of conservation of energy,

$$q_r + q_{solution} = 0$$

The value of $q_{solution}$ can be calculated from the specific heat capacity, mass, and change in temperature of the solution. The quantity of energy evolved or absorbed as heat for the reaction (q_r) is the unknown in the equation.

The accuracy of a calorimetry experiment depends on the accuracy of the measured quantities (temperature, mass, specific heat capacity). In addition, it depends on how closely the assumption is followed that there is no energy transfer beyond the solution. A coffee-cup calorimeter is a simple apparatus, and the results obtained with it are not highly accurate, largely because this assumption is poorly met. In research laboratories, calorimeters are used that more effectively limit the energy transfer between system and surroundings. In addition, it is also possible to correct for the minimal energy transfer that does occur between the system and the surroundings.

Strategy Map 5.7

PROBLEM

Calculate $\Delta_r H$ per mol for reaction of **Mg** with **HCl.**

↓

DATA/INFORMATION

- Mass of Mg and HCl solution
- ΔT
- Specific heat capacity

STEP 1. Calculate amount of **Mg.**

↓

Amount of **Mg**

STEP 2. Use Equation 5.1 to calculate $q_{solution}$.

↓

$q_{solution}$

STEP 3. Use $q_r + q_{solution} = 0$ to calculate q_r.

↓

q_r, the energy evolved by given mass of Mg in HCl(aq)

STEP 4. Divide q_r by amount of **Mg.**

↓

$\Delta_r H$ per mol of Mg

EXAMPLE 5.7

Using a Coffee-Cup Calorimeter

Problem Suppose you place 0.0500 g of magnesium chips in a coffee-cup calorimeter and then add 100.0 mL of 1.00 M HCl. The reaction that occurs is

$$Mg(s) + 2\ HCl(aq) \rightarrow H_2(g) + MgCl_2(aq)$$

The temperature of the solution increases from 22.21 °C (295.36 K) to 24.46 °C (297.61 K). What is the enthalpy change for the reaction per mole of Mg? Assume that the specific heat capacity of the solution is 4.20 J/g · K and the density of the HCl solution is 1.00 g/mL.

What Do You Know? You know that energy is evolved as heat in this reaction because the temperature of the solution rises. Assuming no energy loss to the surroundings, the sum of the energy evolved as heat in the reaction, q_r, and the energy absorbed as heat by the solution, $q_{solution}$, will be zero, that is, $q_r + q_{solution} = 0$. The value of $q_{solution}$ can be calculated from data given; q_r is the unknown.

Strategy Solving the problem has four steps.

Step 1: Calculate the amount of magnesium.

Step 2: Calculate $q_{solution}$ from the values of the mass, specific heat capacity, and ΔT using Equation 5.1.

Step 3: Calculate q_r, assuming no energy transfer as heat occurs beyond the solution, that is, $q_r + q_{solution} = 0$.

Step 4: Use the value of q_r and the amount of Mg to calculate the enthalpy change per mole of Mg.

Solution

Step 1. Calculate the amount of Mg.

$$0.0500\ \text{g Mg} \times \frac{1\ \text{mol Mg}}{24.31\ \text{g Mg}} = 0.00206\ \text{mol Mg}$$

Step 2. Calculate $q_{solution}$. The mass of the solution is the mass of the 100.0 mL of HCl plus the mass of magnesium.

$$q_{solution} = (100.0\ \text{g HCl solution} + 0.0500\ \text{g Mg})(4.20\ \text{J/g} \cdot \text{K})(297.61\ \text{K} - 295.36\ \text{K})$$

$$= 945\ \text{J}$$

Step 3. Calculate q_r.

$$q_r + q_{solution} = 0$$

$$q_r + 945\ \text{J} = 0$$

$$q_r = -945\ \text{J}$$

Step 4. Calculate the value of $\Delta_r H$ per mole of Mg. The value of q_r found in Step 2 resulted from the reaction of 0.00206 mol of Mg. The enthalpy change per mole of Mg is therefore

$$\Delta_r H = (-945\ \text{J}/0.00206\ \text{mol Mg})$$

$$= -4.59 \times 10^5\ \text{J/mol Mg}\ (= -459\ \text{kJ/mol Mg})$$

Think about Your Answer The calculation gives the correct sign of q_r and $\Delta_r H$. The negative sign indicates that this is an exothermic reaction. The balanced equation states that one mole of magnesium is involved in one mole of reaction. The calculated enthalpy change per mole of reaction, $\Delta_r H$, is therefore −459 kJ/mol-rxn.

Check Your Understanding

Assume 200. mL of 0.400 M HCl is mixed with 200. mL of 0.400 M NaOH in a coffee-cup calorimeter. The temperature of the solutions before mixing was 25.10 °C; after mixing and allowing the reaction to occur, the temperature is 27.78 °C. What is the enthalpy change when one mole of acid is neutralized? (Assume that the densities of all solutions are 1.00 g/mL and their specific heat capacities are 4.20 J/g · K.)

Constant-Volume Calorimetry, Measuring ΔU

Constant-volume calorimetry is often used to evaluate the energy released by the combustion of fuels and the caloric value of foods. A weighed sample of a combustible solid or liquid is placed inside a "bomb," often a cylinder about the size of a large fruit juice can with thick steel walls and ends (Figure 5.12). The bomb is placed in a water-filled container with well-insulated walls. After filling the bomb with pure oxygen, the sample is ignited, usually by an electric spark. The heat generated by the combustion reaction warms the bomb and the water around it. The bomb, its contents, and the water are defined as the system. Assessment of energy transfers as heat within the system shows that

$$q_r + q_{bomb} + q_{water} = 0$$

where q_r is the energy released as heat by the reaction, q_{bomb} is the energy involved in heating the calorimeter bomb, and q_{water} is the energy involved in heating the water in the calorimeter. Because the volume does not change in a constant-volume calorimeter, energy transfer as work does not occur. Therefore, the energy transferred as heat at constant volume (q_v) is equal to the change in internal energy, ΔU.

Calorimetry, ΔU, and ΔH The two types of calorimetry (constant volume and constant pressure) highlight the differences between enthalpy and internal energy. The energy transferred as heat at constant pressure, q_p, is, by definition, ΔH, whereas the energy transferred as heat at constant volume, q_v, is ΔU.

Enthalpy and Internal Energy In the AP curriculum internal energy and enthalpy are treated as equivalent.

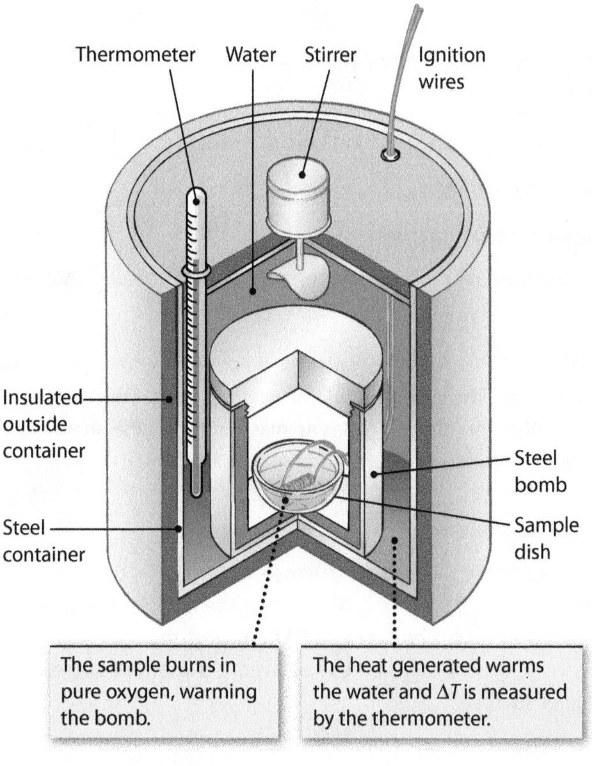

FIGURE 5.12 **Constant-volume calorimeter.** A combustible sample is burned in pure oxygen in a sealed metal container or "bomb." Energy transferred as heat from the reaction warms the bomb and the water surrounding it. By measuring the increase in temperature, the energy transferred as heat in the reaction can be determined.

Strategy Map 5.8

PROBLEM

Calculate ΔU per mol for combustion of octane.

↓

DATA/INFORMATION

- Mass of octane
- Mass of water in calorimeter
- C_{water}
- C_{bomb}
- ΔT

STEP 1. Use Equation 5.1 to calculate q_{water}.

q_{water}

STEP 2. Use C_{bomb} and ΔT to calculate q_{bomb}.

q_{bomb}

STEP 3. Use $q_r + q_{water} + q_{bomb} = 0$ to calculate q_r.

q_r, the energy evolved as heat by given mass of octane (kJ)

STEP 4. Multiply q_r by **molar mass** of octane.

ΔU per mol of octane

EXAMPLE 5.8

Constant-Volume Calorimetry

Problem Octane, C_8H_{18}, a primary constituent of gasoline, burns in air:

$$C_8H_{18}(\ell) + 25/2\ O_2(g) \rightarrow 8\ CO_2(g) + 9\ H_2O(\ell)$$

A 1.00-g sample of octane is burned in a constant-volume calorimeter similar to that shown in Figure 5.12. The calorimeter is in an insulated container with 1.20 kg of water. The temperature of the water and the bomb rises from 25.00 °C (298.15 K) to 33.20 °C (306.35 K). The heat required to raise the bomb's temperature (its heat capacity), C_{bomb}, is 837 J/K. (a) What is the heat of combustion per gram of octane? (b) What is the heat of combustion per mole of octane?

What Do You Know? There are energy changes for the three components of this system: the energy evolved in the reaction, q_r; the energy absorbed by the water, q_{water}; and the energy absorbed by the calorimeter, q_{bomb}. You know the following: the molar mass of octane, masses of the sample and the calorimeter water, $T_{initial}$, T_{final}, C_{bomb}, and C_{water}. You can assume no energy loss to the surroundings.

Strategy

- The sum of all the energies transferred as heat in the system $= q_r + q_{bomb} + q_{water} = 0$. The first term, q_r, is the unknown. The second and third terms in the equation can be calculated from the data given: q_{bomb} is calculated from the bomb's heat capacity and ΔT, and q_{water} is determined from the specific heat capacity, mass, and ΔT for water.
- The value of q_r is the energy evolved in the combustion of 1.00 g of octane. Use this and the molar mass of octane (114.2 g/mol) to calculate the energy evolved as heat per mole of octane.

Solution

(a) $q_{water} = C_{water} \times m_{water} \times \Delta T = (4.184\ J/g \cdot K)(1.20 \times 10^3\ g)(306.35\ K - 298.15\ K) = +41.2 \times 10^3\ J$

$q_{bomb} = (C_{bomb})(\Delta T) = (837\ J/K)(306.35\ K - 298.15\ K) = 6.86 \times 10^3\ J$

$q_r + q_{water} + q_{bomb} = 0$

$q_r + 41.2 \times 10^3\ J + 6.86 \times 10^3\ J = 0$

$q_r = -48.1 \times 10^3\ J$ (or -48.1 kJ)

Heat of combustion per gram $= -48.1$ kJ

(b) Heat of combustion per mole of octane $= (-48.1\ kJ/g)(114.2\ g/mol) = -5.49 \times 10^3\ kJ/mol$

Think about Your Answer Because the volume does not change, no energy transfer in the form of work occurs. The change of internal energy, $\Delta_r U$, for the combustion of $C_8H_{18}(\ell)$ is -5.49×10^3 kJ/mol. Also note that C_{bomb} has no mass units. It is the energy as heat required to warm the particular bomb used in this experiment by 1 kelvin.

Check Your Understanding

A 1.00-g sample of ordinary table sugar (sucrose, $C_{12}H_{22}O_{11}$) is burned in a bomb calorimeter. The temperature of 1.50×10^3 g of water in the calorimeter rises from 25.00 °C to 27.32 °C. The heat capacity of the bomb is 837 J/K, and the specific heat capacity of the water is 4.20 J/g · K. Calculate (a) the heat evolved per gram of sucrose and (b) the heat evolved per mole of sucrose.

REVIEW & CHECK FOR SECTION 5-6

1. A student used a coffee-cup calorimeter to determine the enthalpy of solution for NH_4NO_3. When NH_4NO_3 is added to water, there is a decrease in temperature of the solution. Is the solution process exothermic or endothermic?

   (a) exothermic (b) endothermic

2. If, in the experiment described in the previous question, some energy as heat is transferred from the surroundings to the system, how will this affect the value of $\Delta_{solution}H°$?

   (a) No effect will be seen.

   (b) The calculated value of $\Delta_{solution}H°$ will be too small.

   (c) The calculated value of $\Delta_{solution}H°$ will be too large.

5-7 Enthalpy Calculations

Learning Objectives: LO 3.11

Enthalpy changes for an enormous number of chemical and physical processes are available on the World Wide Web and in reference books. These data have been collected by scientists over a number of years, and this section outlines how to use these data.

Hess's Law

The enthalpy change for a reaction can be measured by calorimetry for many, but not all, chemical processes. Consider, for example, the oxidation of carbon to form carbon monoxide.

$$C(s) + \tfrac{1}{2}\,O_2(g) \rightarrow CO(g)$$

The primary product of the reaction, however, will be CO_2, even if a deficiency of oxygen is used. As soon as CO is formed, it will react with O_2 to form CO_2. It is not possible to measure the change in enthalpy for this reaction by calorimetry because the reaction cannot be carried out in a way that allows CO to be the sole product.

The enthalpy change for the reaction forming CO(g) from C(s) and O_2(g) can be determined indirectly, however, from enthalpy changes for other reactions for which values of $\Delta_rH°$ can be measured. The calculation is based on **Hess's law**, which states that *if a reaction is the sum of two or more other reactions, $\Delta_rH°$ for the overall process is the sum of the $\Delta_rH°$ values of those reactions.*

The oxidation of C(s) to CO(g) can be determined indirectly from thermochemical data obtained from two reactions that can be studied by calorimetry. These reactions are the oxidation of CO(g) and the oxidation of C(s), both of which form CO_2(g) as the sole product.

Equation 1:	$CO(g) + \tfrac{1}{2}\,O_2(g) \rightarrow CO_2(g)$	$\Delta_rH°_1 = -283.0$ kJ/mol-rxn
Equation 2:	$C(s) + O_2(g) \rightarrow CO_2(g)$	$\Delta_rH°_2 = -393.5$ kJ/mol-rxn

The equations above can be manipulated so that when added together they yield the desired net equation. To have CO(g) appear as a product in the net equation, Equation 1 is reversed. The sign of the standard enthalpy change is reversed when the reaction is reversed (Section 5-5). Equation 2 contains C(s) on the correct side of the equation and in the correct stoichiometric amount; it is left unchanged. Adding these two equations gives the equation for the oxidation of C(s) to CO(g).

Equation 1′:	$CO_2(g) \rightarrow CO(g) + \tfrac{1}{2}\,O_2(g)$	$\Delta_rH°_{1'} = +283.0$ kJ/mol-rxn
Equation 2:	$C(s) + O_2(g) \rightarrow CO_2(g)$	$\Delta_rH°_2 = -393.5$ kJ/mol-rxn
Equation 3:	$C(s) + \tfrac{1}{2}\,O_2(g) \rightarrow CO(g)$	$\Delta_rH°_3 = -110.5$ kJ/mol-rxn

Hess's law tells us that the enthalpy change for the overall reaction ($\Delta_r H^\circ_3$) will equal the sum of the enthalpy changes for reactions 1′ and 2 ($\Delta_r H^\circ_{1'} + \Delta_r H^\circ_2$).

$$\Delta_r H^\circ_3 = \Delta_r H^\circ_{1'} + \Delta_r H^\circ_2$$

$$\Delta_r H^\circ_3 = +283.0 \text{ kJ/mol-rxn} + (-393.5 \text{ kJ/mol-rxn})$$

$$\Delta_r H^\circ_3 = -110.5 \text{ kJ/mol-rxn}$$

Hess's law also applies to physical processes. The enthalpy change for the reaction of $H_2(g)$ and $O_2(g)$ to form 1 mol of H_2O vapor is different from the enthalpy change to form 1 mol of liquid H_2O. The difference is the negative of the *enthalpy of vaporization* of water, $\Delta_r H^\circ_2$ ($= -\Delta_{vap}H^\circ$) as shown in the following analysis

Equation 1:	$H_2(g) + \frac{1}{2} O_2(g) \rightarrow H_2O(g)$	$\Delta_r H^\circ_1 = -241.8$ kJ/mol-rxn
Equation 2:	$H_2O(g) \rightarrow H_2O(\ell)$	$\Delta_r H^\circ_2 = -44.0$ kJ/mol-rxn
Equation 3:	$H_2(g) + \frac{1}{2} O_2(g) \rightarrow H_2O(\ell)$	$\Delta_r H^\circ_3 = -285.8$ kJ/mol-rxn

Energy Level Diagrams

When using Hess's law, it is often helpful to represent enthalpy data schematically in an energy level diagram. In such drawings, the various substances being studied—the reactants and products in a chemical reaction, for example—are placed on an arbitrary energy scale. The relative enthalpy of each substance is given by its position on the vertical axis, and numerical differences in enthalpy between them are shown by vertical arrows. Such diagrams provide a visual perspective on the magnitude and direction of enthalpy changes and show how the enthalpies of the substances are related.

Energy level diagrams that summarize the two examples of Hess's law discussed earlier are shown in Figure 5.13. In Figure 5.13a, the elements C(s) and $O_2(g)$ are at the highest enthalpy. The reaction of carbon and oxygen to form $CO_2(g)$ lowers the enthalpy by 393.5 kJ. This can occur either in a single step, shown on the left in Figure 5.13a, or in two steps via initial formation of CO(g), as shown on the right. Similarly, in Figure 5.13b, the mixture of $H_2(g)$ and $O_2(g)$ is at the highest enthalpy.

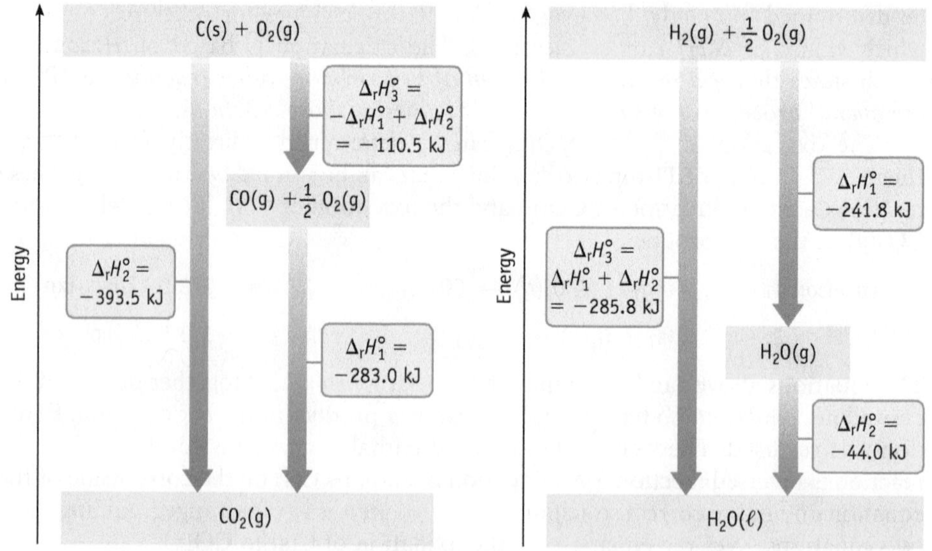

(a) The formation of CO_2 can occur in a single step or in a succession of steps. $\Delta_r H^\circ$ for the overall process is −393.5 kJ, no matter which path is followed.

(b) The formation of $H_2O(\ell)$ can occur in a single step or in a succession of steps. $\Delta_r H^\circ$ for the overall process is −285.8 kJ, no matter which path is followed.

FIGURE 5.13 **Energy level diagrams. (a)** Relating enthalpy changes in the formation of $CO_2(g)$. **(b)** Relating enthalpy changes in the formation of $H_2O(\ell)$. Enthalpy changes associated with changes between energy levels are given alongside the vertical arrows.

Both liquid and gaseous water have lower enthalpies, with the difference between the two being the enthalpy of vaporization.

The enthalpy change for a reaction is a state function; that is, the enthalpy change from reactants to products does not depend on the path taken. Energy diagrams illustrate this point. Chemists often want to know the enthalpy change for one step of a reaction. If we know the overall enthalpy change, and the enthalpy changes for all the steps but one, then the unknown change can be calculated.

EXAMPLE 5.9

Using Hess's Law

Problem Suppose you want to know the enthalpy change for the formation of methane, CH_4, from solid carbon (as graphite) and hydrogen gas:

$$C(s) + 2\ H_2(g) \rightarrow CH_4(g) \qquad \Delta_r H° = ?$$

The enthalpy change for this reaction cannot be measured in the laboratory because the reaction is very slow. We can, however, measure enthalpy changes for the combustion of carbon, hydrogen, and methane.

Equation 1: $C(s) + O_2(g) \rightarrow CO_2(g) \qquad \Delta_r H°_1 = -393.5$ kJ/mol-rxn

Equation 2: $H_2(g) + \frac{1}{2}\ O_2(g) \rightarrow H_2O(\ell) \qquad \Delta_r H°_2 = -285.8$ kJ/mol-rxn

Equation 3: $CH_4(g) + 2\ O_2(g) \rightarrow CO_2(g) + 2\ H_2O(\ell) \qquad \Delta_r H°_3 = -890.3$ kJ/mol-rxn

Use this information to calculate $\Delta_r H°$ for the formation of methane from its elements.

What Do You Know? This is a Hess's law problem. You need to adjust the three equations so they can be added together to give the desired equation, $C(s) + 2\ H_2(g) \rightarrow CH_4(g)$. When an adjustment in an equation is made, you also need to adjust the enthalpy change.

Strategy The three reactions (1, 2, and 3), as written, cannot be added together to obtain the equation for the formation of CH_4 from its elements. Methane, CH_4, is a product in the reaction for which we wish to calculate $\Delta_r H°$, but it is a reactant in Equation 3. Water appears in two of these equations although it is not a component of the reaction forming CH_4 from carbon and hydrogen. To use Hess's law to solve this problem, you first have to

Strategy Map 5.9

PROBLEM
Hess's Law: Calculate $\Delta_r H°$ for **targeted reaction** from $\Delta_r H°$ values for other reactions.

DATA/INFORMATION
Three reactions with known $\Delta_r H°$ values

STEP 1. Manipulate equations with known **$\Delta_r H°$ values** so they sum to the **targeted net equation.**

Targeted **net equation**

STEP 2. Add **$\Delta_r H°$ values** for equations that sum to targeted equation.

$\Delta_r H°$ for targeted reaction

PROBLEM SOLVING TIP 5.2

Using Hess's Law

How did we know how the three equations should be adjusted in Example 5.9? Here is a general strategy for solving this type of problem.

Step 1. Arrange the given equations to get the reactants and products in the equation whose $\Delta_r H°$ you wish to calculate on the correct sides of the equations. You may need to reverse some of the given equations in order to do this. In Example 5.9, the reactants, C(s) and $H_2(g)$, are reactants in Equations 1 and 2, but the product, $CH_4(g)$, is a reactant in Equation 3. Equation 3 was reversed to get CH_4 on the product side.

Step 2. Get the correct amounts of the substances on each side. In Example 5.9, only one adjustment was needed. There is 1 mol of H_2 on the left (reactant side) in Equation 2. We needed 2 mol of H_2 in the overall equation; this required doubling the quantities in Equation 2.

Step 3. Make sure other substances in the equations cancel when the equations are added. In Example 5.9, equal amounts of O_2, H_2O, and CO_2 appeared on the left and right sides in the three equations, and they canceled when the equations are added together.

manipulate the equations and adjust $\Delta_r H°$ values accordingly before adding equations together. Recall, from Section 5-5, that writing an equation in the reverse direction reverses the sign of $\Delta_r H°$ and that doubling the amount of reactants and products doubles the value of $\Delta_r H°$. Adjustments to Equations 2 and 3 will produce new equations that, along with Equation 1, can be combined to give the desired net reaction.

Solution To have CH_4 appear as a product in the overall reaction, reverse Equation 3, which changes the sign of its $\Delta_r H°$.

Equation 3′: $CO_2(g) + 2\ H_2O(\ell) \rightarrow CH_4(g) + 2\ O_2(g)$

$$\Delta_r H°_{3'} = -\Delta_r H°_3 = +890.3 \text{ kJ/mol-rxn}$$

Next, you see that 2 mol of $H_2(g)$ is on the reactant side in our desired equation. Equation 2 is written for only 1 mol of $H_2(g)$ as a reactant. Therefore, multiply the stoichiometric coefficients in Equation 2 by 2 and multiply the value of its $\Delta_r H°$ by 2.

Equation 2′: $2\ H_2(g) + O_2(g) \rightarrow 2\ H_2O(\ell)$

$$\Delta_r H°_{2'} = 2\ \Delta_r H°_2 = 2\ (-285.8 \text{ kJ/mol-rxn}) = -571.6 \text{ kJ/mol-rxn}$$

You now have three equations that, when added together, will give the equation for the formation of methane from carbon and hydrogen. In this summation process, $O_2(g)$, $H_2O(\ell)$, and $CO_2(g)$ all cancel.

Equation 1: $C(s) + O_2(g) \rightarrow CO_2(g)$ $\quad \Delta_r H°_1 = -393.5 \text{ kJ/mol-rxn}$

Equation 2′: $2\ H_2(g) + O_2(g) \rightarrow 2\ H_2O(\ell)$ $\quad \Delta_r H°_{2'} = 2\ \Delta_r H°_2 = -571.6 \text{ kJ/mol-rxn}$

Equation 3′: $CO_2(g) + 2\ H_2O(\ell) \rightarrow CH_4(g) + 2\ O_2\ (g)$ $\quad \Delta_r H°_{3'} = -\Delta_r H°_3 = +890.3 \text{ kJ/mol-rxn}$

Net Equation: $C(s) + 2\ H_2(g) \rightarrow CH_4(g)$ $\quad \Delta_r H°_{net} = \Delta_r H°_1 + \Delta_r H°_{2'} + \Delta_r H°_{3'}$

$$\Delta_r H°_{net} = (-393.5 \text{ kJ/mol-rxn}) + (-571.6 \text{ kJ/mol-rxn}) + (+890.3 \text{ kJ/mol-rxn}) = -74.8 \text{ kJ/mol-rxn}$$

Thus, for the formation of 1 mol of $CH_4(g)$ from the elements, $\Delta_r H° = -74.8$ kJ/mol-rxn.

Think about Your Answer Notice that the enthalpy change for the formation of the compound from its elements is exothermic, as it is for the great majority of compounds.

Check Your Understanding

Use Hess's law to calculate the enthalpy change for the formation of $CS_2(\ell)$ from C(s) and S(s) [$C(s) + 2\ S(s) \rightarrow CS_2(\ell)$] from the following enthalpy values.

$C(s) + O_2(g) \rightarrow CO_2(g)$ $\quad \Delta_r H°_1 = -393.5 \text{ kJ/mol-rxn}$

$S(s) + O_2(g) \rightarrow SO_2(g)$ $\quad \Delta_r H°_2 = -296.8 \text{ kJ/mol-rxn}$

$CS_2(\ell) + 3\ O_2(g) \rightarrow CO_2(g) + 2\ SO_2(g)$ $\quad \Delta_r H°_3 = -1103.9 \text{ kJ/mol-rxn}$

Standard Enthalpies of Formation

Calorimetry and the application of Hess's law have made available a great many $\Delta_r H°$ values for chemical reactions. The table in Appendix L, for example, lists **standard molar enthalpies of formation, $\Delta_f H°$**. *The standard molar enthalpy of formation is the enthalpy change for the formation of 1 mol of a compound directly from its component elements in their standard states.*

Several examples of standard molar enthalpies of formation will be helpful to illustrate this definition.

$\Delta_f H°$ **for NaCl(s):** At 25 °C and a pressure of 1 bar, Na is a solid, and Cl_2 is a gas. The standard enthalpy of formation of NaCl(s) is defined as the enthalpy change that occurs when 1 mol of NaCl(s) is formed from 1 mol of Na(s) and ½ mol of $Cl_2(g)$.

$$\text{Na(s)} + \tfrac{1}{2}\,\text{Cl}_2\text{(g)} \rightarrow \text{NaCl(s)} \qquad \Delta_f H° = -411.12 \text{ kJ/mol}$$

Notice that a fraction is required as the coefficient for the chlorine gas in this equation because the definition of $\Delta_f H°$ specifies the formation of *one* mole of NaCl(s).

$\Delta_f H°$ **for NaCl(aq):** The enthalpy of formation for an aqueous solution of a compound refers to the enthalpy change for the formation of a 1 mol/L solution of the compound starting with the elements making up the compound. It is thus the enthalpy of formation of the compound plus the enthalpy change that occurs when the substance dissolves in water.

$$\text{Na(s)} + \tfrac{1}{2}\,\text{Cl}_2\text{(g)} \rightarrow \text{NaCl(aq)} \qquad \Delta_f H° = -407.27 \text{ kJ/mol}$$

$\Delta_f H°$ **for $C_2H_5OH(\ell)$:** At 25 °C and 1 bar, the standard states of the elements are C(s, graphite), $H_2(g)$, and $O_2(g)$. The standard enthalpy of formation of $C_2H_5OH(\ell)$ is defined as the enthalpy change that occurs when 1 mol of $C_2H_5OH(\ell)$ is formed from 2 mol of C(s), 3 mol of $H_2(g)$, and 1/2 mol of $O_2(g)$.

$$2\ \text{C(s)} + 3\ \text{H}_2\text{(g)} + \tfrac{1}{2}\,\text{O}_2\text{(g)} \rightarrow \text{C}_2\text{H}_5\text{OH}(\ell) \qquad \Delta_f H° = -277.0 \text{ kJ/mol}$$

Notice that the reaction defining the enthalpy of formation for liquid ethanol is not a reaction a chemist can carry out in the laboratory. This illustrates an important point: *The enthalpy of formation of a compound does not necessarily correspond to a reaction that can be carried out.*

Appendix L lists values of $\Delta_f H°$ for some common substances, and a review of these values leads to some important observations.

- *The standard enthalpy of formation for an element in its standard state is zero.*
- Most $\Delta_f H°$ values are negative, indicating that formation of most compounds from the elements is exothermic. Very few values are positive, and these represent compounds that are unstable with respect to decomposition to the elements. (One example is NO(g) with $\Delta_f H° = +90.29$ kJ/mol.)
- Values of $\Delta_f H°$ can often be used to compare the stabilities of related compounds. Consider the values of $\Delta_f H°$ for the hydrogen halides. Hydrogen fluoride is the most stable of these compounds with respect to decomposition to the elements, whereas HI is the least stable (as indicated by $\Delta_f H°$ of HF being the most negative value and that of HI being the most positive).

Enthalpy Change for a Reaction

Using standard molar enthalpies of formation and Equation 5.6, it is possible to calculate the enthalpy change for a reaction under standard conditions.

$$\Delta_r H° = \Sigma n \Delta_f H°(\text{products}) - \Sigma n \Delta_f H°(\text{reactants}) \qquad (5.6)$$

In this equation, the symbol Σ (the Greek capital letter sigma) means "take the sum." To find $\Delta_r H°$, add up the molar enthalpies of formation of the products, each multiplied by its stoichiometric coefficient n, and subtract from this the sum of the molar enthalpies of formation of the reactants, each multiplied by its stoichiometric coefficient. This equation is a logical consequence of the definition of $\Delta_f H°$ and Hess's law (see *A Closer Look: Hess's Law and Equation 5.6*, page 211).

Suppose you want to know how much energy is required to decompose 1 mol of calcium carbonate (limestone) to calcium oxide (lime) and carbon dioxide under standard conditions:

$$\text{CaCO}_3\text{(s)} \rightarrow \text{CaO(s)} + \text{CO}_2\text{(g)} \qquad \Delta_r H° = ?$$

$\Delta_f H°$ Values Consult the National Institute for Standards and Technology website (webbook.nist.gov/chemistry) for an extensive compilation of enthalpies of formation.

Units for Enthalpy of Formation The units for values of $\Delta_f H°$ are usually given simply as kJ/mol rather than as kJ/mol-rxn. However, because an enthalpy of formation is defined as the change in enthalpy for the formation of 1 mol of compound, it is understood that "per mol" also means "per mol-rxn."

$\Delta_f H°$ Values of Hydrogen Halides

Compound	$\Delta_f H°$ (kJ/mol)
HF(g)	−273.3
HCl(g)	−92.31
HBr(g)	−35.29
HI(g)	+25.36

Stoichiometric Coefficients In Equation 5.6 a stoichiometric coefficient, n, is represented as the number of moles of the substance per mole of reaction.

Δ = Final − Initial Equation 5.6 is another example of the convention that a change (Δ) is always calculated by subtracting the value for the initial state (the reactants) from the value for the final state (the products).

You would use the following enthalpies of formation (from Appendix L):

COMPOUND	$\Delta_f H°$ (kJ/mol)
$CaCO_3(s)$	−1207.6
$CaO(s)$	−635.1
$CO_2(g)$	−393.5

and then use Equation 5.6 to find the standard enthalpy change for the reaction, $\Delta_r H°$.

$$\Delta_r H° = \left[\left(\frac{1 \text{ mol CaO}}{1 \text{ mol-rxn}}\right)\left(\frac{-635.1 \text{ kJ}}{\text{mol CaO}}\right) + \left(\frac{1 \text{ mol } CO_2}{1 \text{ mol-rxn}}\right)\left(\frac{-393.5 \text{ kJ}}{1 \text{ mol } CO_2}\right)\right] - \left[\left(\frac{1 \text{ mol } CaCO_3}{1 \text{ mol-rxn}}\right)\left(\frac{-1207.6 \text{ kJ}}{1 \text{ mol } CaCO_3}\right)\right]$$

$$= +179.0 \text{ kJ/mol-rxn}$$

The decomposition of limestone to lime and CO_2 is endothermic. That is, energy (179.0 kJ) must be supplied to decompose 1 mol of $CaCO_3(s)$ to $CaO(s)$ and $CO_2(g)$.

EXAMPLE 5.10

Using Enthalpies of Formation

Problem Nitroglycerin, $C_3H_5(NO_3)_3$, is a powerful explosive that forms four different gases when detonated:

$$2\, C_3H_5(NO_3)_3(\ell) \rightarrow 3\, N_2(g) + \tfrac{1}{2}\, O_2(g) + 6\, CO_2(g) + 5\, H_2O(g)$$

Calculate the enthalpy change that occurs when 10.0 g of nitroglycerin is detonated. The standard enthalpy of formation of nitroglycerin, $\Delta_f H°$, is −364 kJ/mol. Use Appendix L to find other $\Delta_f H°$ values that are needed.

What Do You Know? From Appendix L, $\Delta_f H°[CO_2(g)] = -393.5$ kJ/mol, $\Delta_f H°[H_2O(g)] = -241.8$ kJ/mol, and $\Delta_f H° = 0$ for $N_2(g)$ and $O_2(g)$. The mass and $\Delta_f H°$ for nitroglycerin are also given.

Strategy Substitute the enthalpy of formation values for products and reactants into Equation 5.6 to determine the enthalpy change for 1 mol of reaction. This represents the enthalpy change for detonation of 2 mol of nitroglycerin. Determine the amount (mol) represented by 10.0 g of nitroglycerin, then use this value with $\Delta_r H°$ and the relationship between moles of nitroglycerin and moles of reaction to obtain the answer.

Strategy Map 5.10

PROBLEM
Calculate $\Delta_r H°$ for reaction of a **given mass** of compound.

↓

DATA/INFORMATION
- Mass and $\Delta_f H°$ of compound
- $\Delta_f H°$ values for products
- Balanced equation

STEP 1. Calculate $\Delta_r H°$ for reaction of compound using **$\Delta_f H°$ values** for reactants and products.

↓

$\Delta_r H°$ for reaction of compound

STEP 2. Determine **amount** of compound.

↓

Amount of compound

STEP 3. Convert from **mol** of compound to **mol-rxn** and then multiply by $\Delta_r H°$.

↓

$\Delta_r H°$ for reaction of **given mass** of compound

Solution Using Equation 5.6, we find the enthalpy change for the explosion of 2 mol of nitroglycerin is

$$\Delta_r H° = \left(\frac{6 \text{ mol } CO_2}{1 \text{ mol-rxn}}\right)\Delta_f H°[CO_2(g)] + \left(\frac{5 \text{ mol } H_2O}{1 \text{ mol-rxn}}\right)\Delta_f H°[H_2O(g)] - \left(\frac{2 \text{ mol } C_3H_5(NO_3)_3}{1 \text{ mol-rxn}}\right)\Delta_f H°[C_3H_5(NO_3)_3(\ell)]$$

$$\Delta_r H° = \left(\frac{6 \text{ mol } CO_2}{1 \text{ mol-rxn}}\right)\left(\frac{-393.5 \text{ kJ}}{1 \text{ mol } CO_2}\right) + \left(\frac{5 \text{ mol } H_2O}{1 \text{ mol-rxn}}\right)\left(\frac{-241.8 \text{ kJ}}{1 \text{ mol } H_2O}\right) - \left(\frac{2 \text{ mol } C_3H_5(NO_3)_3}{1 \text{ mol-rxn}}\right)\left(\frac{-364 \text{ kJ}}{1 \text{ mol } C_3H_5(NO_3)_3}\right) = -2842 \text{ kJ/mol-rxn}$$

A CLOSER LOOK — Hess's Law and Equation 5.6

Equation 5.6 is an application of Hess's law. To illustrate this, let us look further at the decomposition of calcium carbonate.

$$CaCO_3(s) \rightarrow CaO(s) + CO_2(g) \qquad \Delta_r H° = ?$$

Because enthalpy is a state function, the change in enthalpy for this reaction is independent of the route from reactants to products (see page 197). We can imagine an alternate route from reactant to products that involves first converting the reactant ($CaCO_3$) to elements in their standard states, then recombining these elements to give the reaction products. Notice that the enthalpy changes for these processes are the enthalpies of formation of the reactants and products in the equation above:

$$CaCO_3(s) \rightarrow Ca(s) + C(s) + 3/2\ O_2(g) \qquad -\Delta_f H°[CaCO_3(s)] = \Delta_r H_1°$$

$$C(s) + O_2(g) \rightarrow CO_2(g) \qquad \Delta_f H°[CO_2(g)] = \Delta_r H_2°$$

$$Ca(s) + \tfrac{1}{2}\ O_2(g) \rightarrow CaO(s) \qquad \Delta_f H°[CaO(s)] = \Delta_r H_3°$$

$$CaCO_3(s) \rightarrow CaO(s) + CO_2(g) \qquad \Delta_r H°_{net}$$

$$\Delta_r H°_{net} = \Delta_r H_1° + \Delta_r H_2° + \Delta_r H_3°$$

$$\Delta_r H° = \Delta_f H°[CaO(s)] + \Delta_f H°[CO_2(g)] - \Delta_f H°[CaCO_3(s)]$$

That is, the change in enthalpy for the reaction is equal to the enthalpies of formation of products (CO_2 and CaO) minus the enthalpy of formation of the reactant ($CaCO_3$), which is, of course, what one does when using Equation 5.6 for this calculation. The relationship among these enthalpy quantities is illustrated in the energy-level diagram.

Energy level diagram for the decomposition of $CaCO_3(s)$

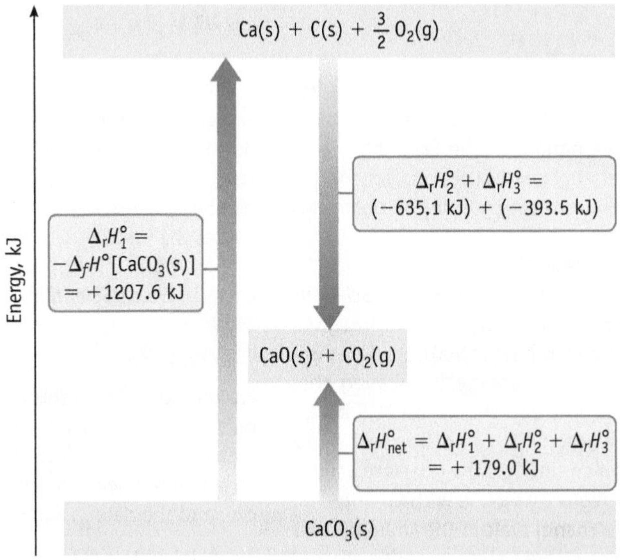

The problem asks for the enthalpy change using 10.0 g of nitroglycerin. You next need to determine the amount of nitroglycerin in 10.0 g.

$$10.0\ \text{g nitroglycerin}\left(\frac{1\ \text{mol nitroglycerin}}{227.1\ \text{g nitroglycerin}}\right) = 0.0440\ \text{mol nitroglycerin}$$

The enthalpy change for the detonation of 0.0440 mol of nitroglycerin is

$$\Delta_r H° = 0.0440\ \text{mol nitroglycerin}\left(\frac{1\ \text{mol-rxn}}{2\ \text{mol nitroglycerin}}\right)\left(\frac{-2842\ \text{kJ}}{1\ \text{mol-rxn}}\right)$$

$$= -62.6\ \text{kJ}$$

Think about Your Answer The large negative value of $\Delta_r H°$ is in accord with the fact that this reaction is highly exothermic.

Check Your Understanding

Calculate the standard enthalpy of combustion for benzene, C_6H_6.

$$C_6H_6(\ell) + 15/2\ O_2(g) \rightarrow 6\ CO_2(g) + 3\ H_2O(\ell) \qquad \Delta_r H° = ?$$

The enthalpy of formation of benzene is known [$\Delta_f H°[C_6H_6(\ell)] = +49.0$ kJ/mol], and other values needed can be found in Appendix L.

REVIEW & CHECK FOR SECTION 5-7

1. The standard enthalpy of formation for $AlCl_3(s)$ is the enthalpy change for what reaction?

   (a) $Al(s) + 3\ Cl_2(g) \longrightarrow AlCl_3(s)$

   (b) $Al(s) + 3\ Cl(g) \longrightarrow AlCl_3(s)$

   (c) $3\ HCl(aq) + Al(OH)_3(s) \longrightarrow AlCl_3(s) + 3\ H_2O(\ell)$

   (d) $Al(s) + 3/2\ Cl_2(g) \longrightarrow AlCl_3(s)$

CASE STUDY: The Fuel Controversy—Alcohol and Gasoline

It is clear that supplies of fossil fuels are declining and their prices are increasing, just as the nations of the Earth have ever greater energy needs. Let's analyze the debate about replacing gasoline with ethanol (C_2H_5OH).

As Matthew Wald said in the article "Is Ethanol in for the Long Haul?" (*Scientific American*, January 2007), "The U.S. has gone on an ethanol binge." In 2007, the U.S. Congress passed an energy bill stating that ethanol production should be 20.5 billion gallons a year by 2015, up from about 4.7 billion gallons in 2007. The goal is to at least partially replace gasoline with ethanol.

Most ethanol fuels in the United States currently used are a mixture of 10% ethanol and 90% gasoline (E10). A 15% mixture (E15) may be available soon and it is expected to be safe to use in most vehicles. A small fraction of fuel is sold as E85—a blend of 85% ethanol and 15% gasoline. This fuel cannot be used in most current vehicles because relatively few vehicles as yet have engines designed for fuels with a high ethanol content (so-called "flexible fuel" engines). The number of these vehicles would need to be increased in order for E85 to have a significant effect on our gasoline usage.

Is a goal of replacing gasoline completely with ethanol reasonable? This is a lofty goal, given that present gasoline consumption in the U.S. is about 140 billion gallons annually. Again, according to Matthew Wald, "Even if 100 percent of the U.S. corn supply was distilled into ethanol, it would supply only a small fraction of the fuel consumed by the nation's vehicles." Wald's thesis in his article, which is supported by numerous scientific studies, is that if ethanol is to be pursued as an alternative to gasoline, more emphasis would have to be placed on deriving ethanol from sources other than corn, such as cellulose from cornstalks and various grasses.

Beyond this, there are other problems associated with ethanol. One is that it cannot be distributed through a pipeline system as gasoline can. Any water in the pipeline is miscible with ethanol, which causes the fuel value to decline.

For more information, see the references in Wald's *Scientific American* article.

Questions:

For the purposes of this analysis, let us use octane (C_8H_{18}) as a substitute for the complex mixture of hydrocarbons in gasoline. Data you will need for this question (in addition to the data in Appendix L) are:

$$\Delta_f H° \ [C_8H_{18}(\ell)] = -250.1 \text{ kJ/mol}$$

$$\text{Density of ethanol} = 0.785 \text{ g/mL}$$

$$\text{Density of octane} = 0.699 \text{ g/mL}$$

1. Calculate $\Delta_r H°$ for the combustion of ethanol and octane, and compare the values per mole and per gram. Which provides more energy per mole? Which provides more energy per gram?
2. Compare the energy produced per liter of the two fuels. Which produces more energy for a given volume (something useful to know when filling your gas tank)?
3. What mass of CO_2, a greenhouse gas, is produced per liter of fuel (assuming complete combustion)?
4. Now compare the fuels on an energy-equivalent basis. What volume of ethanol would have to be burned to get the same energy as 1.00 L of octane? When you burn enough ethanol to have the same energy as a liter of octane, which fuel produces more CO_2?
5. On the basis of this analysis and assuming the same price per liter, which fuel will propel your car further? Which will produce less greenhouse gas?

Answers to these questions are available in Appendix N.

fotog/Getty Images

Ethanol available at a service station. E85 fuel is a blend of 85% ethanol and 15% gasoline. Be aware that you can only use E85 in vehicles designed for the fuel. In an ordinary vehicle, the ethanol leads to deterioration of seals in the engine and fuel system.

2. Acetic acid is made by the reaction $CH_3OH(\ell) + CO(g) \rightarrow CH_3CO_2H(\ell)$. Determine the enthalpy change for this reaction from the enthalpies of the three reactions below.

$$2\ CH_3OH(\ell) + 3\ O_2(g) \rightarrow 2\ CO_2(g) + 4\ H_2O(\ell) \qquad \Delta_rH^\circ_1$$

$$CH_3CO_2H(\ell) + 2\ O_2(g) \rightarrow 2\ CO_2(g) + 2\ H_2O(\ell) \qquad \Delta_rH^\circ_2$$

$$2\ CO(g) + O_2(g) \rightarrow 2\ CO_2(g) \qquad \Delta_rH^\circ_3$$

(a) $\Delta_rH^\circ_1 + \Delta_rH^\circ_2 + \Delta_rH^\circ_3$

(b) $\Delta_rH^\circ_1 - \Delta_rH^\circ_2 + \Delta_rH^\circ_3$

(c) $1/2\ \Delta_rH^\circ_1 - \Delta_rH^\circ_2 + 1/2\ \Delta_rH^\circ_3$

(d) $-1/2\ \Delta_rH^\circ_1 + \Delta_rH^\circ_2 - 1/2\ \Delta_rH^\circ_3$

5-8 Product- or Reactant-Favored Reactions and Thermodynamics

At the beginning of this chapter, we noted that thermodynamics would provide answers to four questions:

- How do we measure and calculate the energy changes associated with physical changes and chemical reactions?
- What is the relationship between energy changes, heat, and work?
- How can we determine whether a chemical reaction is product-favored or reactant-favored at equilibrium?
- How can we determine whether a chemical reaction or physical process will occur spontaneously, that is, without outside intervention?

The first two questions were addressed in this chapter, but the other two important questions still remain. They will be considered in detail in Chapter 18.

We can, however, set the stage for consideration of these issues. In Chapter 3, we learned that chemical reactions proceed toward equilibrium, and spontaneous changes occur in a way that allows a system to approach equilibrium. Reactions in which reactants are largely converted to products when equilibrium is reached are said to be *product-favored at equilibrium.* Reactions in which only small amounts of products are present at equilibrium are called *reactant-favored at equilibrium* (◀ pages 104–105).

Look back at the many chemical reactions that we have seen. For example, all combustion reactions are exothermic, and the oxidation of iron (Figure 5.14) is clearly exothermic.

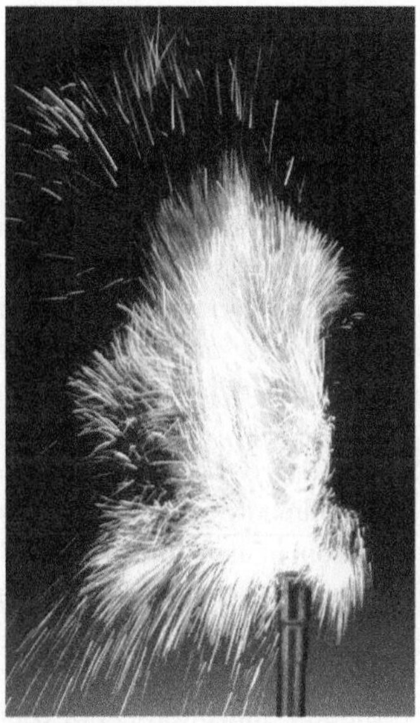

FIGURE 5.14 **The product-favored oxidation of iron.** Iron powder, sprayed into a bunsen burner flame, is rapidly oxidized. The reaction is exothermic and is product-favored.

$$4\ Fe(s) + 3\ O_2(g) \rightarrow 2\ Fe_2O_3(s)$$

$$\Delta_rH^\circ = 2\ \Delta_fH^\circ[Fe_2O_3(s)] = \left(\frac{2\ \text{mol}\ Fe_2O_3}{1\ \text{mol-rxn}}\right)\left(\frac{-825.5\ \text{kJ}}{1\ \text{mol}\ Fe_2O_3}\right) = -1651.0\ \text{kJ/mol-rxn}$$

The reaction has a negative value for Δ_rH°, and it is also product-favored at equilibrium.

Conversely, the decomposition of calcium carbonate is endothermic.

$$CaCO_3(s) \rightarrow CaO(s) + CO_2(g) \qquad \Delta_rH^\circ = +179.0\ \text{kJ/mol-rxn}$$

The decomposition of $CaCO_3$ proceeds to an equilibrium that favors the reactants; that is, it is reactant-favored at equilibrium.

Are all exothermic reactions product-favored at equilibrium and all endothermic reactions reactant-favored at equilibrium? From these examples, we might formulate that idea as a hypothesis that can be tested by experiment and by examination of other examples. You would find that *in most cases, product-favored reactions have negative values of* $\Delta_r H°$, *and reactant-favored reactions have positive values of* $\Delta_r H°$. But this is not *always* true; there are exceptions.

Clearly, a further discussion of thermodynamics must be tied to the concept of equilibrium. This relationship, and the complete discussion of the third and fourth questions, will be presented in Chapter 18.

APPLYING CHEMICAL PRINCIPLES

Gunpowder

Gunpowder has been used in fireworks, explosives, and firearms for over one thousand years. Until the late 1800s, gunpowder was a mixture of saltpeter (KNO_3), charcoal (largely C), and sulfur. Today, this mixture is known as *black powder*. A simplified version of the reaction indicates that the components react to yield both solid and gaseous products.

$$2\ KNO_3(s) + 3\ C(s) + S(s) \rightarrow K_2S(s) + N_2(g) + 3\ CO_2(g)$$

The actual reaction is more complicated because charcoal is not pure carbon. (It also contains some oxygen and hydrogen atoms.) Although black powder was used for hundreds of years, it has some disadvantages as a propellant: it produces a large quantity of white smoke, and the residues from the reaction are corrosive.

Modern firearms use smokeless powders. These powders are primarily composed of nitrocellulose (also known as guncotton) or a mixture of nitrocellulose and nitroglycerin. Nitrocellulose is the product of the reaction of cotton (cellulose, with an empirical formula of $C_6H_{10}O_5$) with nitric acid. The fully nitrated product has the empirical formula $C_6H_7(NO_3)_3O_2$, though guncotton is not usually fully nitrated. Decomposition of nitrocellulose and nitroglycerin releases more energy than the comparable mass of black powder. Just as important, this is a better propellant because all of the products are gaseous.

Black gunpowder. Black gunpowder has been known for over 1000 years. This photo shows one of the disadvantages of black powder: the great amount of smoke produced.

QUESTIONS:

1. The standard enthalpies of formation of $KNO_3(s)$ and $K_2S(s)$ are −494.6 kJ/mol and −376.6 kJ/mol, respectively.
   a. Determine the standard enthalpy change for the reaction of black powder according to the balanced equation above.
   b. Determine the enthalpy change that occurs when 1.00 g of black powder decomposes according to the stoichiometry of the balanced equation above. (Even though black powder is a mixture, assume that we can designate 1 mol of black powder as consisting of exactly 2 mol of KNO_3, 3 mol of C, and 1 mol of S.)
2. The enthalpy of reaction of guncotton depends on the degree of nitration of the cellulose. For a particular sample, when 0.725 g of guncotton is decomposed in a bomb calorimeter, the temperature of the system increases by 1,32 K. Assuming the bomb has a heat capacity of 691 J/K and the calorimeter contains 1.200 kg of water, what is the energy of reaction per gram of guncotton?
3. The decomposition of nitroglycerin ($C_3H_5N_3O_9$) produces carbon dioxide, nitrogen, water, and oxygen gases.
   a. Write a balanced chemical equation for the decomposition of nitroglycerin.
   b. If the decomposition of 1.00 g nitroglycerin releases 6.23 kJ/g of energy in the form of heat, what is the standard molar enthalpy of formation of nitroglycerin?

REFERENCE:

J. Kelly, *Gunpowder, Alchemy, Bombards, and Pyrotechnics: The History of the Explosive That Changed the World,* Basic Books, New York, 2004.

CHAPTER GOALS REVISITED

Now that you have studied this chapter, you should ask whether you have met the chapter goals. In particular, you should be able to

UNDERSTAND

- And apply the first law of thermodynamics.
  - **a.** Understand the basis of the first law of thermodynamics (Section 5-4).
  - **b.** Recognize how energy transferred as heat and work done on or by a system contributes to changes in the internal energy of a system (Section 5-4).

DO

- Assess the transfer of energy as heat associated with changes in temperature and changes of state.
  - **a.** Describe the nature of energy transfers as heat (Section 5-1).
  - **b.** Recognize and use the language of thermodynamics: the system and its surroundings; exothermic and endothermic reactions (Section 5-1). Study Questions: 1, 3, 67.
  - **c.** Use specific heat capacity in calculations of energy transfer as heat and of temperature changes (Section 5-2). Study Questions: 5, 7, 9, 11, 13, 15.
  - **d.** Understand the sign conventions of thermodynamics.
  - **e.** Use enthalpy (heat) of fusion and enthalpy (heat) of vaporization to calculate the energy transferred as heat in changes of state (Section 5-3). Study Questions: 17, 19, 21, 23.
- Calculate P–V work done by a system and use energy as heat (q) and work (w) to calculate changes in internal energy (U).
  - **a.** Calculate the work done by or work done on a system by the expansion or compression of a gas (Section 5-4). Study Questions: 25–28.
  - **b.** Calculate changes in enthalpy and internal energy for reactions that occur under constant pressure (Section 5-4). Study Questions: 29–32, 120.
- Calculate energy and enthalpy changes from data obtained by calorimetry experiments.
  - **a.** Describe how to measure the quantity of energy transferred as heat in a reaction by calorimetry (Section 5-6). Study Questions: 37–48.
- Calculate the energy evolved or required for physical changes and chemical reactions using data in thermodynamic tables.
  - **a.** Apply Hess's law to find the enthalpy change, $\Delta_r H°$, for a reaction (Section 5-7). Study Questions: 49–52, 81, 87.
  - **b.** Know how to draw and interpret energy level diagrams (Section 5-7). Study Questions: 61, 62, 81, 82, 111, 115.
  - **c.** Use standard molar enthalpies of formation, $\Delta_f H°$, to calculate the enthalpy change for a reaction, $\Delta_r H°$ (Section 5-7). Study Questions: 55, 57, 59, 63, 64.

REMEMBER

- Definitions for terms commonly used: endothermic, exothermic, systems, surroundings, enthalpy, internal energy, reactant-favored, and product-favored.
  - **a.** Recognize that when a process is carried out under constant-pressure conditions, the energy transferred as heat is the enthalpy change, ΔH (Section 5-5). Study Questions: 33–36.
- Enthalpy and internal energy are state functions.
  - **a.** Recognize state functions whose values are determined only by the state of the system and not by the pathway by which the state was achieved (Section 5-4).

KEY EQUATIONS

Equation 5.1 (page 185) The energy transferred as heat when the temperature of a substance changes. Calculated from the specific heat capacity (C), mass (m), and change in temperature (ΔT).

$$q(\text{J}) = C(\text{J/g} \cdot \text{K}) \times m(\text{g}) \times \Delta T(\text{K})$$

Equation 5.2 (page 185) Temperature changes are always calculated as final temperature minus initial temperature.

$$\Delta T = T_{\text{final}} - T_{\text{initial}}$$

Equation 5.3 (page 187) If no energy is transferred between a system and its surroundings and if energy is transferred within the system only as heat, the sum of the thermal energy changes within the system equals zero.

$$q_1 + q_2 + q_3 + \ldots = 0$$

Equation 5.4 (page 194) The first law of thermodynamics: The change in internal energy (ΔU) in a system is the sum of the energy transferred as heat (q) and the energy transferred as work (w).

$$\Delta U = q + w$$

Equation 5.5 (page 195) P–V work (w) at constant pressure is the product of pressure (P) and change in volume (ΔV)

$$w = -P \times \Delta V$$

Equation 5.6 (page 209) This equation is used to calculate the standard enthalpy change of a reaction ($\Delta_r H°$) when the enthalpies of formation ($\Delta_f H°$) of all of the reactants and products are known. The parameter n is the stoichiometric coefficient of each product or reactant in the balanced chemical equation.

$$\Delta_r H° = \Sigma n \Delta_f H°(\text{products}) - \Sigma n \Delta_f H°(\text{reactants})$$

STUDY QUESTIONS

▲ denotes challenging questions.

Blue-numbered questions have answers in Appendix N and fully worked solutions in the *Student Solutions Manual.*

Practicing Skills

Energy: Some Basic Principles

(See Section 5-1.)

1. Define the terms *system* and *surroundings*. What does it mean to say that a system and its surroundings are in thermal equilibrium?

2. What determines the directionality of energy transfer as heat?

3. Identify whether the following processes are exothermic or endothermic.
   (a) combustion of methane
   (b) melting of ice
   (c) raising the temperature of water from 25 °C to 100 °C
   (d) heating $CaCO_3(s)$ to form $CaO(s)$ and $CO_2(g)$

4. Identify whether the following processes are exothermic or endothermic.
   (a) the reaction of Na(s) and $Cl_2(g)$
   (b) cooling and condensing gaseous N_2 to form liquid N_2
   (c) cooling a soft drink from 25 °C to 0 °C
   (d) heating HgO(s) to form Hg(ℓ) and $O_2(g)$

Specific Heat Capacity

(See Section 5-2 and Examples 5.1 and 5.2.)

5. The molar heat capacity of mercury is 28.1 J/mol · K. What is the specific heat capacity of this metal in J/g · K?

6. The specific heat capacity of benzene (C_6H_6) is 1.74 J/g · K. What is its molar heat capacity (in J/mol · K)?

7. The specific heat capacity of copper metal is 0.385 J/g · K. How much energy is required to heat 168 g of copper from −12.2 °C to +25.6 °C?

8. How much energy as heat is required to raise the temperature of 50.00 mL of water from 25.52 °C to 28.75 °C? (Density of water at this temperature = 0.997 g/mL.)

9. The initial temperature of a 344-g sample of iron is 18.2 °C. If the sample absorbs 2.25 kJ of energy as heat, what is its final temperature?

10. After absorbing 1.850 kJ of energy as heat, the temperature of a 0.500-kg block of copper is 37 °C. What was its initial temperature?

11. A 45.5-g sample of copper at 99.8 °C is dropped into a beaker containing 152 g of water at 18.5 °C. What is the final temperature when thermal equilibrium is reached?

12. One beaker contains 156 g of water at 22 °C, and a second beaker contains 85.2 g of water at 95 °C. The water in the two beakers is mixed. What is the final water temperature?

13. A 182-g sample of gold at some temperature was added to 22.1 g of water. The initial water temperature was 25.0 °C, and the final temperature was 27.5 °C. If the specific heat capacity of gold is 0.128 J/g · K, what was the initial temperature of the gold sample?

14. When 108 g of water at a temperature of 22.5 °C is mixed with 65.1 g of water at an unknown temperature, the final temperature of the resulting mixture is 47.9 °C. What was the initial temperature of the second sample of water?

15. A 13.8-g piece of zinc is heated to 98.8 °C in boiling water and then dropped into a beaker containing 45.0 g of water at 25.0 °C. When the water and metal come to thermal equilibrium, the temperature is 27.1 °C. What is the specific heat capacity of zinc?

16. A 237-g piece of molybdenum, initially at 100.0 °C, is dropped into 244 g of water at 10.0 °C. When the system comes to thermal equilibrium, the temperature is 15.3 °C. What is the specific heat capacity of molybdenum?

Changes of State

(See Section 5-3 and Examples 5.3 and 5.4.)

17. How much energy is evolved as heat when 1.0 L of water at 0 °C solidifies to ice? (The heat of fusion of water is 333 J/g.)

18. The energy required to melt 1.00 g of ice at 0 °C is 333 J. If one ice cube has a mass of 62.0 g and a tray contains 16 ice cubes, what quantity of energy is required to melt a tray of ice cubes to form liquid water at 0 °C?

19. How much energy is required to vaporize 125 g of benzene, C_6H_6, at its boiling point, 80.1 °C? (The heat of vaporization of benzene is 30.8 kJ/mol.)

20. Chloromethane, CH_3Cl, arises from microbial fermentation and is found throughout the environment. It is also produced industrially, is used in the manufacture of various chemicals, and has been used as a topical anesthetic. How much energy is required to convert 92.5 g of liquid to a vapor at its boiling point, −24.09 °C? (The heat of vaporization of CH_3Cl is 21.40 kJ/mol.)

21. The freezing point of mercury is −38.8 °C. What quantity of energy, in joules, is released to the surroundings if 1.00 mL of mercury is cooled from 23.0 °C to −38.8 °C and then frozen to a solid? (The density of liquid mercury is 13.6 g/cm^3. Its specific heat capacity is 0.140 J/g · K and its heat of fusion is 11.4 J/g.)

22. What quantity of energy, in joules, is required to raise the temperature of 454 g of tin from room temperature, 25.0 °C, to its melting point, 231.9 °C, and then melt the tin at that temperature? (The specific heat capacity of tin is 0.227 J/g · K, and the heat of fusion of this metal is 59.2 J/g.)

23. Ethanol, C_2H_5OH, boils at 78.29 °C. How much energy, in joules, is required to raise the temperature of 1.00 kg of ethanol from 20.0 °C to the boiling point and then to change the liquid to vapor at that temperature? (The specific heat capacity of liquid ethanol is 2.44 J/g · K, and its enthalpy of vaporization is 855 J/g.)

24. A 25.0-mL sample of benzene at 19.9 °C was cooled to its melting point, 5.5 °C, and then frozen. How much energy was given off as heat in this process? (The density of benzene is 0.80 g/mL, its specific heat capacity is 1.74 J/g · K, and its heat of fusion is 127 J/g.)

Heat, Work, and Internal Energy

(See Section 5-4 and Example 5.5.)

25. As a gas cools, it is compressed from 2.50 L to 1.25 L under a constant pressure of 1.01 × 10^5 Pa. Calculate the work (in J) required to compress the gas.

26. A balloon expands from 0.75 L to 1.20 L as it is heated under a constant pressure of 1.01 × 10^5 Pa. Calculate the work (in J) done by the balloon on the environment.

27. A balloon does 324 J of work on the surroundings as it expands under a constant pressure of 7.33 × 10^4 Pa. What is the change in volume (in L) of the balloon?

28. As the gas trapped in a cylinder with a movable piston cools, 1.34 kJ of work is done on the gas by the surroundings. If the gas is at a constant pressure of 1.33 × 10^5 Pa, what is the change of volume (in L) of the gas?

29. When 745 J of energy in the form of heat is transferred from the environment to a gas, the expansion of the gas does 312 J of work on the environment. What is the change in internal energy of the gas?

30. The internal energy of a gas decreases by 1.65 kJ when it transfers 1.87 kJ of energy in the form of heat to the surroundings.

(a) Calculate the work done by the gas on the surroundings.

(b) Does the volume of gas increase or decrease?

31. A volume of 1.50 L of argon gas is confined in a cylinder with a movable piston under a constant pressure of 1.22 × 10^5 Pa. When 1.25 kJ of energy in the form of heat is transferred from the surroundings to the gas, the internal energy of the gas increases by 1.11 kJ. What is the final volume of argon gas in the cylinder?

32. Nitrogen gas is confined in a cylinder with a movable piston under a constant pressure of 9.95 × 10^4 Pa. When 695 J of energy in the form of heat is transferred from the gas to the surroundings, its volume decreases by 1.88 L. What is the change in internal energy of the gas?

Enthalpy Changes

(See Section 5-5 and Example 5.6.)

33. Nitrogen monoxide, a gas recently found to be involved in a wide range of biological processes, reacts with oxygen to give brown NO_2 gas.

$$2\ NO(g) + O_2(g) \rightarrow 2\ NO_2(g) \qquad \Delta_r H° = -114.1 \text{ kJ/mol-rxn}$$

Is this reaction endothermic or exothermic? What is the enthalpy change if 1.25 g of NO is converted completely to NO_2?

34. Calcium carbide, CaC_2, is manufactured by the reaction of CaO with carbon at a high temperature. (Calcium carbide is then used to make acetylene.)

$$CaO(s) + 3\ C(s) \rightarrow CaC_2(s) + CO(g) \qquad \Delta_r H° = +464.8 \text{ kJ/mol-rxn}$$

Is this reaction endothermic or exothermic? What is the enthalpy change if 10.0 g of CaO is allowed to react with an excess of carbon?

35. Isooctane (2,2,4-trimethylpentane), one of the many hydrocarbons that make up gasoline, burns in air to give water and carbon dioxide.

$$2\ C_8H_{18}(\ell) + 25\ O_2(g) \rightarrow 16\ CO_2(g) + 18\ H_2O(\ell)$$
$$\Delta_rH° = -10{,}922\ \text{kJ/mol-rxn}$$

What is the enthalpy change if you burn 1.00 L of isooctane (d = 0.69 g/mL)?

36. Acetic acid, CH_3CO_2H, is made industrially by the reaction of methanol and carbon monoxide.

$$CH_3OH(\ell) + CO(g) \rightarrow CH_3CO_2H(\ell)$$
$$\Delta_rH° = -134.6\ \text{kJ/mol-rxn}$$

What is the enthalpy change for producing 1.00 L of acetic acid (d = 1.044 g/mL) by this reaction?

Calorimetry

(See Section 5-6 and Examples 5.7 and 5.8.)

37. Assume you mix 100.0 mL of 0.200 M CsOH with 50.0 mL of 0.400 M HCl in a coffee-cup calorimeter. The following reaction occurs:

$$CsOH(aq) + HCl(aq) \rightarrow CsCl(aq) + H_2O(\ell)$$

The temperature of both solutions before mixing was 22.50 °C, and it rises to 24.28 °C after the acid–base reaction. What is the enthalpy change for the reaction per mole of CsOH? Assume the densities of the solutions are all 1.00 g/mL and the specific heat capacities of the solutions are 4.2 J/g · K.

38. You mix 125 mL of 0.250 M CsOH with 50.0 mL of 0.625 M HF in a coffee-cup calorimeter, and the temperature of both solutions rises from 21.50 °C before mixing to 24.40 °C after the reaction.

$$CsOH(aq) + HF(aq) \rightarrow CsF(aq) + H_2O(\ell)$$

What is the enthalpy of reaction per mole of CsOH? Assume the densities of the solutions are all 1.00 g/mL, and the specific heat capacities of the solutions are 4.2 J/g · K.

39. A piece of titanium metal with a mass of 20.8 g is heated in boiling water to 99.5 °C and then dropped into a coffee-cup calorimeter containing 75.0 g of water at 21.7 °C. When thermal equilibrium is reached, the final temperature is 24.3 °C. Calculate the specific heat capacity of titanium.

40. A piece of chromium metal with a mass of 24.26 g is heated in boiling water to 98.3 °C and then dropped into a coffee-cup calorimeter containing 82.3 g of water at 23.3 °C. When thermal equilibrium is reached, the final temperature is 25.6 °C. Calculate the specific heat capacity of chromium.

41. Adding 5.44 g of $NH_4NO_3(s)$ to 150.0 g of water in a coffee-cup calorimeter (with stirring to dissolve the salt) resulted in a decrease in temperature from 18.6 °C to 16.2 °C. Calculate the enthalpy change for dissolving $NH_4NO_3(s)$ in water, in kJ/mol. Assume the solution (whose mass is 155.4 g) has a specific heat capacity of 4.2 J/g · K. (Cold packs take advantage of the fact that dissolving ammonium nitrate in water is an endothermic process.)

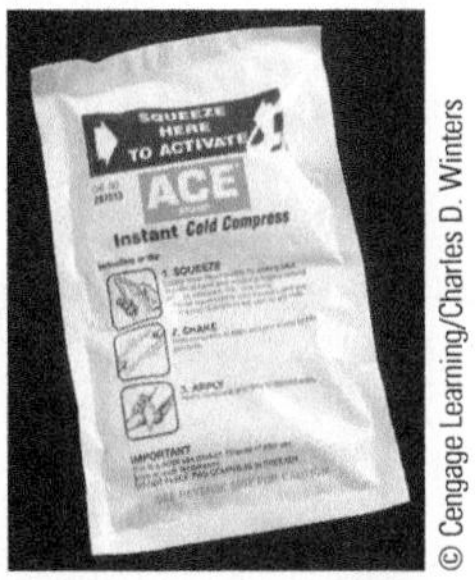

© Cengage Learning/Charles D. Winters

A cold pack uses the endothermic enthalpy of solution of ammonium nitrate.

42. You should use care when dissolving H_2SO_4 in water because the process is highly exothermic. To measure the enthalpy change, 5.2 g of concentrated $H_2SO_4(\ell)$ was added (with stirring) to 135 g of water in a coffee-cup calorimeter. This resulted in an increase in temperature from 20.2 °C to 28.8 °C. Calculate the enthalpy change for the process $H_2SO_4(\ell) \rightarrow H_2SO_4(aq)$, in kJ/mol.

43. Sulfur (2.56 g) was burned in a constant-volume calorimeter with excess $O_2(g)$. The temperature increased from 21.25 °C to 26.72 °C. The bomb has a heat capacity of 923 J/K, and the calorimeter contained 815 g of water. Calculate ΔU per mole of SO_2 formed for the reaction

$$S_8(s) + 8\ O_2(g) \rightarrow 8\ SO_2(g)$$

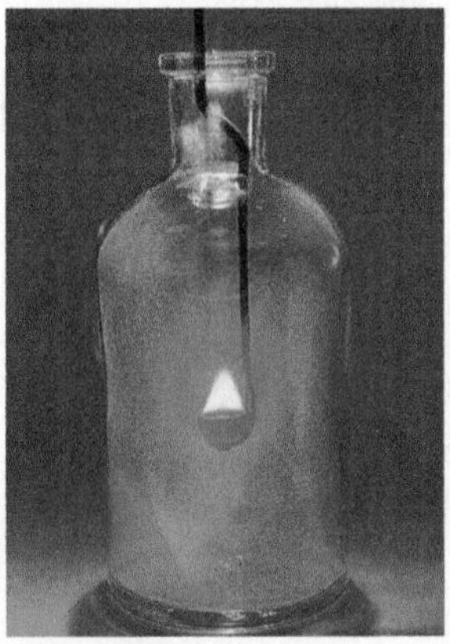

© Cengage Learning/Charles D. Winters

Sulfur burns in oxygen with a bright blue flame to give $SO_2(g)$.

44. Suppose you burned 0.300 g of C(s) in an excess of $O_2(g)$ in a constant-volume calorimeter to give $CO_2(g)$.

$$C(s) + O_2(g) \rightarrow CO_2(g)$$

The temperature of the calorimeter, which contained 775 g of water, increased from 25.00 °C to 27.38 °C. The heat capacity of the bomb is 893 J/K. Calculate ΔU per mole of carbon.

45. Suppose you burned 1.500 g of benzoic acid, $C_6H_5CO_2H$, in a constant-volume calorimeter and found that the temperature increased from 22.50 °C to 31.69 °C. The calorimeter contained 775 g of water, and the bomb had a heat capacity of 893 J/K. Calculate ΔU per mole of benzoic acid.

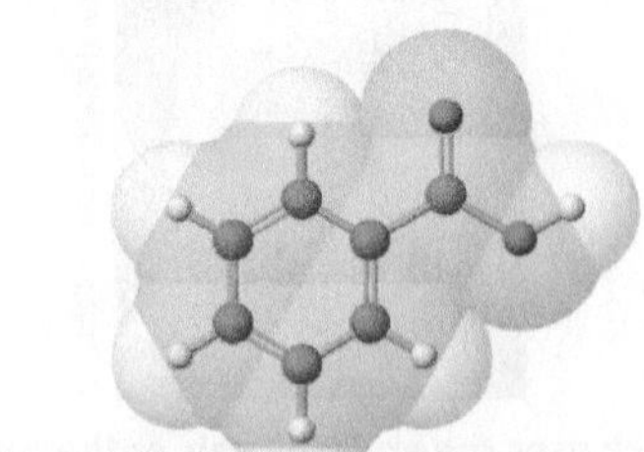

Benzoic acid, $C_6H_5CO_2H$, occurs naturally in many berries. Its heat of combustion is well known, so it is used as a standard to calibrate calorimeters.

46. A 0.692-g sample of glucose, $C_6H_{12}O_6$, was burned in a constant-volume calorimeter. The temperature rose from 21.70 °C to 25.22 °C. The calorimeter contained 575 g of water, and the bomb had a heat capacity of 650 J/K. What is ΔU per mole of glucose?

47. An "ice calorimeter" can be used to determine the specific heat capacity of a metal. A piece of hot metal is dropped onto a weighed quantity of ice. The energy transferred from the metal to the ice can be determined from the amount of ice melted. Suppose you heated a 50.0-g piece of silver to 99.8 °C and then dropped it onto ice. When the metal's temperature had dropped to 0.0 °C, it is found that 3.54 g of ice had melted. What is the specific heat capacity of silver?

48. A 9.36-g piece of platinum was heated to 98.6 °C in a boiling water bath and then dropped onto ice. (See Study Question 47.) When the metal's temperature had dropped to 0.0 °C, it was found that 0.37 g of ice had melted. What is the specific heat capacity of platinum?

Hess's Law

(See Section 5-7 and Example 5.9.)

49. The enthalpy changes for the following reactions can be measured:

$$CH_4(g) + 2\ O_2(g) \rightarrow CO_2(g) + 2\ H_2O(g) \qquad \Delta_rH° = -802.4 \text{ kJ/mol-rxn}$$

$$CH_3OH(g) + \tfrac{3}{2}\ O_2(g) \rightarrow CO_2(g) + 2\ H_2O(g) \qquad \Delta_rH° = -676 \text{ kJ/mol-rxn}$$

(a) Use these values and Hess's law to determine the enthalpy change for the reaction

$$CH_4(g) + \tfrac{1}{2}\ O_2(g) \rightarrow CH_3OH(g)$$

(b) Draw an energy level diagram that shows the relationship between the energy quantities involved in this problem.

50. The enthalpy changes of the following reactions can be measured:

$$C_2H_4(g) + 3\ O_2(g) \rightarrow 2\ CO_2(g) + 2\ H_2O(\ell) \qquad \Delta_rH° = -1411.1 \text{ kJ/mol-rxn}$$

$$C_2H_5OH(\ell) + 3\ O_2(g) \rightarrow 2\ CO_2(g) + 3\ H_2O(\ell) \qquad \Delta_rH° = -1367.5 \text{ kJ/mol-rxn}$$

(a) Use these values and Hess's law to determine the enthalpy change for the reaction

$$C_2H_4(g) + H_2O(\ell) \rightarrow C_2H_5OH(\ell)$$

(b) Draw an energy level diagram that shows the relationship between the energy quantities involved in this problem.

51. Enthalpy changes for the following reactions can be determined experimentally:

$$N_2(g) + 3\ H_2(g) \rightarrow 2\ NH_3(g) \qquad \Delta_rH° = -91.8 \text{ kJ/mol-rxn}$$

$$4\ NH_3(g) + 5\ O_2(g) \rightarrow 4\ NO(g) + 6\ H_2O(g) \qquad \Delta_rH° = -906.2 \text{ kJ/mol-rxn}$$

$$H_2(g) + \tfrac{1}{2}\ O_2(g) \rightarrow H_2O(g) \qquad \Delta_rH° = -241.8 \text{ kJ/mol-rxn}$$

Use these values to determine the enthalpy change for the formation of NO(g) from the elements (an enthalpy change that cannot be measured directly because the reaction is reactant-favored).

$$\tfrac{1}{2}\ N_2(g) + \tfrac{1}{2}\ O_2(g) \rightarrow NO(g) \qquad \Delta_rH° = ?$$

52. You wish to know the enthalpy change for the formation of liquid PCl_3 from the elements.

$$P_4(s) + 6\ Cl_2(g) \rightarrow 4\ PCl_3(\ell) \qquad \Delta_rH° = ?$$

The enthalpy change for the formation of PCl_5 from the elements can be determined experimentally, as can the enthalpy change for the reaction of $PCl_3(\ell)$ with more chlorine to give $PCl_5(s)$:

$$P_4(s) + 10\ Cl_2(g) \rightarrow 4\ PCl_5(s) \qquad \Delta_rH° = -1774.0 \text{ kJ/mol-rxn}$$

$$PCl_3(\ell) + Cl_2(g) \rightarrow PCl_5(s) \qquad \Delta_rH° = -123.8 \text{ kJ/mol-rxn}$$

Use these data to calculate the enthalpy change for the formation of 1.00 mol of $PCl_3(\ell)$ from phosphorus and chlorine.

Standard Enthalpies of Formation

(See Section 5-7 and Example 5.10.)

53. Write a balanced chemical equation for the formation of $CH_3OH(\ell)$ from the elements in their standard states. Find the value for $\Delta_fH°$ for $CH_3OH(\ell)$ in Appendix L.

54. Write a balanced chemical equation for the formation of $CaCO_3(s)$ from the elements in their standard states. Find the value for $\Delta_fH°$ for $CaCO_3(s)$ in Appendix L.

55. (a) Write a balanced chemical equation for the formation of 1 mol of $Cr_2O_3(s)$ from Cr and O_2 in their standard states. (Find the value for $\Delta_f H°$ for $Cr_2O_3(s)$ in Appendix L.)
(b) What is the standard enthalpy change if 2.4 g of chromium is oxidized to $Cr_2O_3(s)$?

56. (a) Write a balanced chemical equation for the formation of 1 mol of MgO(s) from the elements in their standard states. (Find the value for $\Delta_f H°$ for MgO(s) in Appendix L.)
(b) What is the standard enthalpy change for the reaction of 2.5 mol of Mg with oxygen?

57. Use standard enthalpies of formation in Appendix L to calculate enthalpy changes for the following:
(a) 1.0 g of white phosphorus burns, forming $P_4O_{10}(s)$
(b) 0.20 mol of NO(g) decomposes to $N_2(g)$ and $O_2(g)$
(c) 2.40 g of NaCl(s) is formed from Na(s) and excess $Cl_2(g)$
(d) 250 g of iron is oxidized with oxygen to $Fe_2O_3(s)$

58. Use standard enthalpies of formation in Appendix L to calculate enthalpy changes for the following:
(a) 0.054 g of sulfur burns, forming $SO_2(g)$
(b) 0.20 mol of HgO(s) decomposes to Hg(ℓ) and $O_2(g)$
(c) 2.40 g of $NH_3(g)$ is formed from $N_2(g)$ and excess $H_2(g)$
(d) 1.05×10^{-2} mol of carbon is oxidized to $CO_2(g)$

59. The first step in the production of nitric acid from ammonia involves the oxidation of NH_3.

$$4\ NH_3(g) + 5\ O_2(g) \rightarrow 4\ NO(g) + 6\ H_2O(g)$$

(a) Use standard enthalpies of formation to calculate the standard enthalpy change for this reaction.
(b) How much energy is evolved or absorbed as heat in the oxidation of 10.0 g of NH_3?

60. The Romans used calcium oxide, CaO, to produce a strong mortar to build stone structures. Calcium oxide was mixed with water to give $Ca(OH)_2$, which reacted slowly with CO_2 in the air to give $CaCO_3$.

$$Ca(OH)_2(s) + CO_2(g) \rightarrow CaCO_3(s) + H_2O(g)$$

(a) Calculate the standard enthalpy change for this reaction.
(b) How much energy is evolved or absorbed as heat if 1.00 kg of $Ca(OH)_2$ reacts with a stoichiometric amount of CO_2?

61. The standard enthalpy of formation of solid barium oxide, BaO, is −553.5 kJ/mol, and the standard enthalpy of formation of barium peroxide, BaO_2, is −634.3 kJ/mol.
(a) Calculate the standard enthalpy change for the following reaction. Is the reaction exothermic or endothermic?

$$2\ BaO_2(s) \rightarrow 2\ BaO(s) + O_2(g)$$

(b) Draw an energy level diagram that shows the relationship between the enthalpy change of the decomposition of BaO_2 to BaO and O_2 and the enthalpies of formation of BaO(s) and $BaO_2(s)$.

62. An important step in the production of sulfuric acid is the oxidation of SO_2 to SO_3.

$$SO_2(g) + \tfrac{1}{2}\ O_2(g) \rightarrow SO_3(g)$$

Formation of SO_3 from the air pollutant SO_2 is also a key step in the formation of acid rain.
(a) Use standard enthalpies of formation to calculate the enthalpy change for the reaction. Is the reaction exothermic or endothermic?
(b) Draw an energy level diagram that shows the relationship between the enthalpy change for the oxidation of SO_2 to SO_3 and the enthalpies of formation of $SO_2(g)$ and $SO_3(g)$.

63. The enthalpy change for the oxidation of naphthalene, $C_{10}H_8$, is measured by calorimetry.

$$C_{10}H_8(s) + 12\ O_2(g) \rightarrow 10\ CO_2(g) + 4\ H_2O(\ell) \quad \Delta_r H° = -5156.1 \text{ kJ/mol-rxn}$$

Use this value, along with the standard enthalpies of formation of $CO_2(g)$ and $H_2O(\ell)$, to calculate the enthalpy of formation of naphthalene, in kJ/mol.

64. The enthalpy change for the oxidation of styrene, C_8H_8, is measured by calorimetry.

$$C_8H_8(\ell) + 10\ O_2(g) \rightarrow 8\ CO_2(g) + 4\ H_2O(\ell) \quad \Delta_r H° = -4395.0 \text{ kJ/mol-rxn}$$

Use this value, along with the standard enthalpies of formation of $CO_2(g)$ and $H_2O(\ell)$, to calculate the enthalpy of formation of styrene, in kJ/mol.

General Questions

These questions are not designated as to type or location in the chapter. They may combine several concepts.

65. The following terms are used extensively in thermodynamics. Define each and give an example.
(a) exothermic and endothermic
(b) system and surroundings
(c) specific heat capacity
(d) state function
(e) standard state
(f) enthalpy change, ΔH
(g) standard enthalpy of formation

66. For each of the following, tell whether the process is exothermic or endothermic. (No calculations are required.)
(a) $H_2O(\ell) \rightarrow H_2O(s)$
(b) $2\ H_2(g) + O_2(g) \rightarrow 2\ H_2O(g)$
(c) $H_2O(\ell, 25\ °C) \rightarrow H_2O(\ell, 15\ °C)$
(d) $H_2O(\ell) \rightarrow H_2O(g)$

67. For each of the following, define a system and its surroundings, and give the direction of energy transfer between system and surroundings.
   (a) Methane burns in a gas furnace in your home.
   (b) Water drops, sitting on your skin after a swim, evaporate.
   (c) Water, at 25 °C, is placed in the freezing compartment of a refrigerator, where it cools and eventually solidifies.
   (d) Aluminum and $Fe_2O_3(s)$ are mixed in a flask sitting on a laboratory bench. A reaction occurs, and a large quantity of energy is evolved as heat.

68. What does the term *standard state* mean? What are the standard states of the following substances at 298 K: H_2O, NaCl, Hg, CH_4?

69. Use Appendix L to find the standard enthalpies of formation of oxygen atoms, oxygen molecules (O_2), and ozone (O_3). What is the standard state of oxygen? Is the formation of oxygen atoms from O_2 exothermic? What is the enthalpy change for the formation of 1 mol of O_3 from O_2?

70. You have a large balloon containing 1.0 mol of gaseous water vapor at 80 °C. How will each step affect the internal energy of the system?
   (a) The temperature of the system is raised to 90 °C.
   (b) The vapor is condensed to a liquid, at 40 °C.

71. Determine whether energy as heat is evolved or required, and whether work was done on the system or whether the system does work on the surroundings, in the following processes at constant pressure:
   (a) Liquid water at 100 °C is converted to steam at 100 °C.
   (b) Dry ice, $CO_2(s)$, sublimes to give $CO_2(g)$.

72. Determine whether energy as heat is evolved or required, and whether work was done on the system or whether the system does work on the surroundings, in the following processes at constant pressure:
   (a) Ozone, O_3, decomposes to form O_2.
   (b) Methane burns:
   $CH_4(g) + 2\ O_2(g) \rightarrow CO_2(g) + 2\ H_2O(\ell)$

73. Use standard enthalpies of formation to calculate the enthalpy change that occurs when 1.00 g of $SnCl_4(\ell)$ reacts with excess $H_2O(\ell)$ to form $SnO_2(s)$ and HCl(aq).

74. Which evolves more energy on cooling from 50 °C to 10 °C: 50.0 g of water or 100. g of ethanol ($C_{ethanol}$ = 2.46 J/g · K)?

75. You determine that 187 J of energy as heat is required to raise the temperature of 93.45 g of silver from 18.5 °C to 27.0 °C. What is the specific heat capacity of silver?

76. Calculate the quantity of energy required to convert 60.1 g of $H_2O(s)$ at 0.0 °C to $H_2O(g)$ at 100.0 °C. The enthalpy of fusion of ice at 0 °C is 333 J/g; the enthalpy of vaporization of liquid water at 100 °C is 2256 J/g.

77. You add 100.0 g of water at 60.0 °C to 100.0 g of ice at 0.00 °C. Some of the ice melts and cools the water to 0.00 °C. When the ice and water mixture reaches thermal equilibrium at 0 °C, how much ice has melted?

78. ▲ Three 45-g ice cubes at 0 °C are dropped into 5.00×10^2 mL of tea to make iced tea. The tea was initially at 20.0 °C; when thermal equilibrium was reached, the final temperature was 0 °C. How much of the ice melted, and how much remained floating in the beverage? Assume the specific heat capacity of tea is the same as that of pure water.

79. ▲ Suppose that only two 45-g ice cubes had been added to your glass containing 5.00×10^2 mL of tea (see Study Question 78). When thermal equilibrium is reached, all of the ice will have melted, and the temperature of the mixture will be somewhere between 20.0 °C and 0 °C. Calculate the final temperature of the beverage. (*Note:* The 90 g of water formed when the ice melts must be warmed from 0 °C to the final temperature.)

80. You take a diet cola from the refrigerator and pour 240 mL of it into a glass. The temperature of the beverage is 10.5 °C. You then add one ice cube (45 g) at 0 °C. Which of the following describes the system when thermal equilibrium is reached?
   (a) The temperature is 0 °C, and some ice remains.
   (b) The temperature is 0 °C, and no ice remains.
   (c) The temperature is higher than 0 °C, and no ice remains.

   Determine the final temperature and the amount of ice remaining, if any.

81. ▲ The standard molar enthalpy of formation of diborane, $B_2H_6(g)$, cannot be determined directly because the compound cannot be prepared by the reaction of boron and hydrogen. It can be calculated from other enthalpy changes, however. The following enthalpy changes can be measured.

   $4\ B(s) + 3\ O_2(g) \rightarrow 2\ B_2O_3(s)$
   $\Delta_r H° = -2543.8$ kJ/mol-rxn

   $H_2(g) + \frac{1}{2}\ O_2(g) \rightarrow H_2O(g)$
   $\Delta_r H° = -241.8$ kJ/mol-rxn

   $B_2H_6(g) + 3\ O_2(g) \rightarrow B_2O_3(s) + 3\ H_2O(g)$
   $\Delta_r H° = -2032.9$ kJ/mol-rxn

   (a) Show how these equations can be added together to give the equation for the formation of $B_2H_6(g)$ from B(s) and $H_2(g)$ in their standard states. Assign enthalpy changes to each reaction.
   (b) Calculate $\Delta_f H°$ for $B_2H_6(g)$.
   (c) Draw an energy level diagram that shows how the various enthalpies in this problem are related.
   (d) Is the formation of $B_2H_6(g)$ from its elements exo- or endothermic?

82. Chloromethane, CH_3Cl, a compound found throughout the environment, is formed in the reaction of chlorine atoms with methane.

   $CH_4(g) + 2\ Cl(g) \rightarrow CH_3Cl(g) + HCl(g)$

(a) Calculate the enthalpy change for the reaction of $CH_4(g)$ and Cl atoms to give $CH_3Cl(g)$ and HCl(g). Is the reaction exo- or endothermic?
(b) Draw an energy level diagram that shows how the various enthalpies in this problem are related.

83. When heated to a high temperature, coke (mainly carbon, obtained by heating coal in the absence of air) and steam produce a mixture called *water gas*, which can be used as a fuel or as a starting place for other reactions. The equation for the production of water gas is

$$C(s) + H_2O(g) \rightarrow CO(g) + H_2(g)$$

(a) Use standard enthalpies of formation to determine the enthalpy change for this reaction.
(b) Is the reaction exo- or endothermic?
(c) What is the enthalpy change if 1000.0 kg (1 metric ton) of carbon is converted to water gas?

84. Camping stoves are fueled by propane (C_3H_8), butane [$C_4H_{10}(g)$, $\Delta_f H° = -127.1$ kJ/mol], gasoline, or ethanol (C_2H_5OH). Calculate the enthalpy of combustion per gram of each of these fuels. [Assume that gasoline is represented by isooctane, $C_8H_{18}(\ell)$, with $\Delta_f H° = -259.3$ kJ/mol.] Do you notice any great differences among these fuels? How are these differences related to their composition?

© Cengage Learning/Charles D. Winters

A camping stove that uses butane as a fuel.

85. Methanol, CH_3OH, a compound that can be made relatively inexpensively from coal, is a promising substitute for gasoline. The alcohol has a smaller energy content than gasoline, but, with its higher octane rating, it burns more efficiently than gasoline in combustion engines. (It has the added advantage of contributing to a lesser degree to some air pollutants.) Compare the enthalpy of combustion per gram of CH_3OH and C_8H_{18} (isooctane), the latter being representative of the compounds in gasoline. ($\Delta_f H° = -259.3$ kJ/mol for isooctane.)

86. Hydrazine and 1,1-dimethylhydrazine both react spontaneously with O_2 and can be used as rocket fuels.

$$\underset{\text{hydrazine}}{N_2H_4(\ell)} + O_2(g) \rightarrow N_2(g) + 2\ H_2O(g)$$

$$\underset{\text{1,1-dimethylhydrazine}}{N_2H_2(CH_3)_2(\ell)} + 4\ O_2(g) \rightarrow 2\ CO_2(g) + 4\ H_2O(g) + N_2(g)$$

The molar enthalpy of formation of $N_2H_4(\ell)$ is +50.6 kJ/mol, and that of $N_2H_2(CH_3)_2(\ell)$ is +48.9 kJ/mol. Use these values, with other $\Delta_f H°$ values, to decide whether the reaction of hydrazine or 1,1-dimethylhydrazine with oxygen provides more energy per gram.

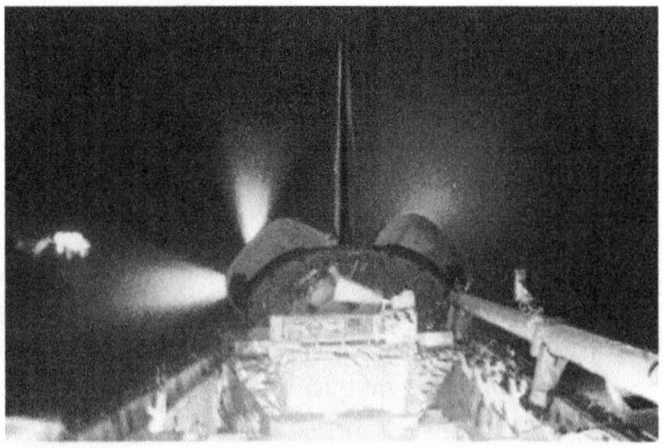
NASA

Space vehicles, such as the Space Shuttle when it was still flying, use hydrazine as a fuel in control rockets.

87. (a) Calculate the enthalpy change, $\Delta_r H°$, for the formation of 1.00 mol of strontium carbonate (the material that gives the red color in fireworks) from its elements.

$$Sr(s) + C(s) + \tfrac{3}{2}\ O_2(g) \rightarrow SrCO_3(s)$$

The experimental information available is

$$Sr(s) + \tfrac{1}{2}\ O_2(g) \rightarrow SrO(s) \qquad \Delta_f H° = -592 \text{ kJ/mol-rxn}$$

$$SrO(s) + CO_2(g) \rightarrow SrCO_3(s) \qquad \Delta_r H° = -234 \text{ kJ/mol-rxn}$$

$$C(graphite) + O_2(g) \rightarrow CO_2(g) \qquad \Delta_f H° = -394 \text{ kJ/mol-rxn}$$

(b) Draw an energy level diagram relating the energy quantities in this problem.

88. You drink 350 mL of diet soda that is at a temperature of 5 °C.

(a) How much energy will your body expend to raise the temperature of this liquid to body temperature (37 °C)? Assume that the density and specific heat capacity of diet soda are the same as for water.
(b) Compare the value in part (a) with the caloric content of the beverage. (The label says that it has a caloric content of 1 Calorie.) What is the net energy change in your body resulting from drinking this beverage? (1 Calorie = 1000 kcal = 4184 J.)
(c) Carry out a comparison similar to that in part (b) for a nondiet beverage whose label indicates a caloric content of 240 Calories.

89. ▲ Chloroform, $CHCl_3$, is formed from methane and chlorine in the following reaction.

$$CH_4(g) + 3\ Cl_2(g) \rightarrow 3\ HCl(g) + CHCl_3(g)$$

Calculate $\Delta_r H°$, the enthalpy change for this reaction, using the enthalpies of formation of $CO_2(g)$, $H_2O(\ell)$, and $CHCl_3(g)$ ($\Delta_f H° = -103.1$ kJ/mol), and the enthalpy changes for the following reactions:

$$CH_4(g) + 2\ O_2(g) \rightarrow 2\ H_2O(\ell) + CO_2(g) \qquad \Delta_r H° = -890.4 \text{ kJ/mol-rxn}$$

$$2\ HCl(g) \rightarrow H_2(g) + Cl_2(g) \qquad \Delta_r H° = +184.6 \text{ kJ/mol-rxn}$$

90. Water gas, a mixture of carbon monoxide and hydrogen, is produced by treating carbon (in the form of coke or coal) with steam at high temperatures. (See Study Question 83.)

$$C(s) + H_2O(g) \rightarrow CO(g) + H_2(g)$$

Not all of the carbon available is converted to water gas since some is burned to provide the heat for the endothermic reaction of carbon and water. What mass of carbon must be burned (to CO_2 gas) to provide the energy to convert 1.00 kg of carbon to water gas?

91. In the opening story to this chapter (page 180), the energy content of ethanol is compared to the energy content of some common foods. Using standard enthalpies of formation, verify that 2680 kJ of energy is released in combustion of 100.0 g of ethanol.

$$C_2H_5OH(\ell) + 3\ O_2(g) \rightarrow 2\ CO_2(g) + 3\ H_2O(g)$$

92. According to the Nutrient Data Laboratory website (www.ars.usda.gov/ba/bhnrc/ndl), corn oil contains 3766 kJ of energy per 100. g serving.

(a) What is the energy content of 100. g of corn oil in units of nutritional calories (Cal)?

(b) How many tablespoons of corn oil have an energy content equivalent to 1500 nutritional calories? (1.0 Tbsp = 14 g of corn oil)

(c) What mass of water can be heated from 25.0 °C to its boiling point of 100.0 °C using the energy of combustion of 1.00 Tbsp of corn oil?

In the Laboratory

93. A piece of lead with a mass of 27.3 g was heated to 98.90 °C and then dropped into 15.0 g of water at 22.50 °C. The final temperature was 26.32 °C. Calculate the specific heat capacity of lead from these data.

94. A 192-g piece of copper is heated to 100.0 °C in a boiling water bath and then dropped into a beaker containing 751 g of water (density = 1.00 g/cm^3) at 4.0 °C. What was the final temperature of the copper and water after thermal equilibrium was reached? (C_{Cu} = 0.385 J/g · K.)

95. Insoluble AgCl(s) precipitates when solutions of $AgNO_3(aq)$ and NaCl(aq) are mixed.

$$AgNO_3(aq) + NaCl(aq) \rightarrow AgCl(s) + NaNO_3(aq) \qquad \Delta_r H° = ?$$

To measure the energy evolved in this reaction, 250. mL of 0.16 M $AgNO_3(aq)$ and 125 mL of 0.32 M NaCl(aq) are mixed in a coffee-cup calorimeter. The temperature of the mixture rises from 21.15 °C to 22.90 °C. Calculate the enthalpy change for the precipitation of AgCl(s), in kJ/mol. (Assume the density of the solution is 1.0 g/mL and its specific heat capacity is 4.2 J/g · K.)

96. Insoluble $PbBr_2(s)$ precipitates when solutions of $Pb(NO_3)_2(aq)$ and NaBr(aq) are mixed.

$$Pb(NO_3)_2(aq) + 2\ NaBr(aq) \rightarrow PbBr_2(s) + 2\ NaNO_3(aq) \qquad \Delta_r H° = ?$$

To measure the enthalpy change, 200. mL of 0.75 M $Pb(NO_3)_2(aq)$ and 200. mL of 1.5 M NaBr(aq) are mixed in a coffee-cup calorimeter. The temperature of the mixture rises by 2.44 °C. Calculate the enthalpy change for the precipitation of $PbBr_2(s)$, in kJ/mol. (Assume the density of the solution is 1.0 g/mL, and its specific heat capacity is 4.2 J/g · K.)

97. The value of ΔU for the decomposition of 7.647 g of ammonium nitrate can be measured in a bomb calorimeter. The reaction that occurs is

$$NH_4NO_3(s) \rightarrow N_2O(g) + 2\ H_2O(g)$$

The temperature of the calorimeter, which contains 415 g of water, increases from 18.90 °C to 20.72 °C. The heat capacity of the bomb is 155 J/K. What is the value of ΔU for this reaction, in kJ/mol?

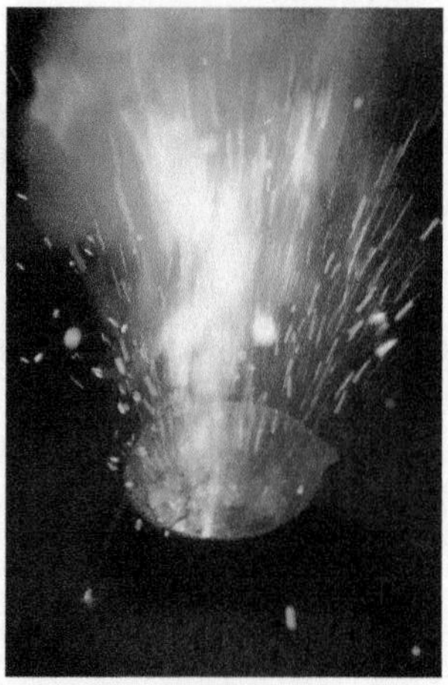
© Cengage Learning/Charles D. Winters

The decomposition of ammonium nitrate is clearly exothermic.

98. A bomb calorimetric experiment was run to determine the enthalpy of combustion of ethanol. The reaction is

$$C_2H_5OH(\ell) + 3\ O_2(g) \rightarrow 2\ CO_2(g) + 3\ H_2O(\ell)$$

The bomb had a heat capacity of 550 J/K, and the calorimeter contained 650 g of water. Burning 4.20 g of ethanol, $C_2H_5OH(\ell)$ resulted in a rise in temperature from 18.5 °C to 22.3 °C. Calculate ΔU for the combustion of ethanol, in kJ/mol.

99. The meals-ready-to-eat (MREs) in the military can be heated on a flameless heater. You can purchase a similar product called "Heater Meals." Just pour water into the heater unit, wait a few minutes, and you have a hot meal. The source of energy in the heater is

$$Mg(s) + 2\ H_2O(\ell) \rightarrow Mg(OH)_2(s) + H_2(g)$$

The "heater meal" uses the reaction of magnesium with water as a source of energy as heat.

Calculate the enthalpy change under standard conditions, in joules, for this reaction. What quantity of magnesium is needed to supply the energy required to warm 25 mL of water (d = 1.00 g/mL) from 25 °C to 85 °C? (See W. Jensen: *Journal of Chemical Education*, Vol. 77, pp. 713–717, 2000.)

100. On a cold day, you can warm your hands with a "heat pad," a device that uses the oxidation of iron to produce energy as heat.

$$4\ Fe(s) + 3\ O_2(g) \rightarrow 2\ Fe_2O_3(s)$$

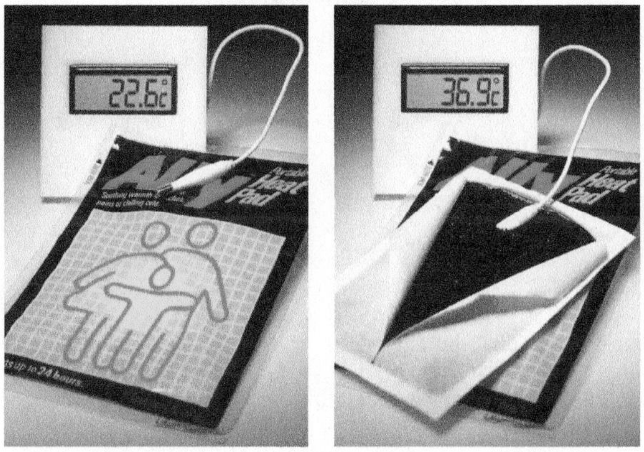

A hand warmer uses the oxidation of iron as a source of thermal energy.

What mass of iron is needed to supply the energy required to warm 15 mL of water (d = 1.00 g/mL) from 23 °C to 37 °C?

Summary and Conceptual Questions

The following questions may use concepts from this and previous chapters.

101. Without doing calculations, decide whether each of the following is exo- or endothermic.
   (a) the combustion of natural gas
   (b) the decomposition of glucose, $C_6H_{12}O_6$, to carbon and water

102. Which of the following are state functions?
   (a) the volume of a balloon
   (b) the time it takes to drive from your home to your college or university
   (c) the temperature of the water in a coffee cup
   (d) the potential energy of a ball held in your hand

103. ▲ You want to determine the value for the enthalpy of formation of $CaSO_4(s)$, but the reaction cannot be done directly.

$$Ca(s) + S(s) + 2\ O_2(g) \rightarrow CaSO_4(s)$$

You know, however, that (a) both calcium and sulfur react with oxygen to produce oxides in reactions that can be studied calorimetrically, and (b) the basic oxide CaO reacts with the acidic oxide $SO_3(g)$ to produce $CaSO_4(s)$ with $\Delta_r H°$ = −402.7 kJ. Outline a method for determining $\Delta_f H°$ for $CaSO_4(s)$, and identify the information that must be collected by experiment. Using information in Appendix L, confirm that $\Delta_f H°$ for $CaSO_4(s)$ = −1433.5 kJ/mol.

104. Prepare a graph of specific heat capacities for metals versus their atomic weights. Combine the data in Figure 5.4 and the values in the following table. What is the relationship between specific heat capacity and atomic weight? Use this relationship to predict the specific heat capacity of platinum. The specific heat capacity for platinum is given in the literature as 0.133 J/g · K. How good is the agreement between the predicted and actual values?

Metal	Specific Heat Capacity (J/g · K)
Chromium	0.450
Lead	0.127
Silver	0.236
Tin	0.227
Titanium	0.522

105. Observe the molar heat capacity values for the metals in Figure 5.4. What observation can you make about these values—specifically, are they widely different or very similar? Using this information, estimate the specific heat capacity for silver. Compare this estimate with the correct value for silver, 0.236 J/g · K.

106. ▲ You are attending summer school and living in a very old dormitory. The day is oppressively hot, there is no air conditioner, and you can't open the windows of your room. There is a refrigerator in the room, however. In a stroke of genius, you open the door of the refrigerator, and cool air cascades out. The relief does not last long, though. Soon the refrigerator motor and condenser begin to run, and not long thereafter the room is hotter than it was before. Why did the room warm up?

107. You want to heat the air in your house with natural gas (CH_4). Assume your house has 275 m^2 (about 2800 ft^2) of floor area and that the ceilings are 2.50 m from the floors. The air in the house has a molar heat capacity of 29.1 J/mol · K. (The number of moles of air in the house can be found by assuming that the average molar mass of air is 28.9 g/mol and that the density of air at these temperatures is 1.22 g/L.) What mass of methane do you have to burn to heat the air from 15.0 °C to 22.0 °C?

108. Water can be decomposed to its elements, H_2 and O_2, using electrical energy or in a series of chemical reactions. The following sequence of reactions is one possibility:

$$CaBr_2(s) + H_2O(g) \rightarrow CaO(s) + 2\ HBr(g)$$

$$Hg(\ell) + 2\ HBr(g) \rightarrow HgBr_2(s) + H_2(g)$$

$$HgBr_2(s) + CaO(s) \rightarrow HgO(s) + CaBr_2(s)$$

$$HgO(s) \rightarrow Hg(\ell) + \tfrac{1}{2}\ O_2(g)$$

(a) Show that the net result of this series of reactions is the decomposition of water to its elements.
(b) If you use 1000. kg of water, what mass of H_2 can be produced?
(c) Calculate the value of $\Delta_r H°$ for each step in the series. Are the reactions predicted to be exo- or endothermic?

$$\Delta_f H°\ [CaBr_2(s)] = -683.2\ kJ/mol$$

$$\Delta_f H°\ [HgBr_2(s)] = -169.5\ kJ/mol$$

(d) Comment on the commercial feasibility of using this series of reactions to produce $H_2(g)$ from water.

109. Suppose that an inch (2.54 cm) of rain falls over a square mile of ground ($2.59 \times 10^6\ m^2$). (Density of water is 1.0 g/cm^3.) The enthalpy of vaporization of water at 25 °C is 44.0 kJ/mol. How much energy is transferred as heat to the surroundings from the condensation of water vapor in forming this quantity of liquid water? (The huge number tells you how much energy is "stored" in water vapor and why we think of storms as such great forces of energy in nature. It is interesting to compare this result with the energy given off, 4.2×10^6 kJ, when a ton of dynamite explodes.)

110. ▲ Peanuts and peanut oil are organic materials and burn in air. How many burning peanuts does it take to provide the energy to boil a cup of water (250 mL of water)? To solve this problem, we assume each peanut, with an average mass of 0.73 g, is 49% peanut oil and 21% starch; the remainder is noncombustible. We further assume peanut oil is palmitic acid, $C_{16}H_{32}O_2$, with an enthalpy of formation of −848.4 kJ/mol. Starch is a long chain of $C_6H_{10}O_5$ units, each unit having an enthalpy of formation of −960 kJ.

© Cengage Learning/Charles D. Winters

How many burning peanuts are required to provide the energy to boil 250 mL of water?

111. ▲ Isomers are molecules with the same elemental composition but a different atomic arrangement. Three isomers with the formula C_4H_8 are shown in the models below. The enthalpy of combustion ($\Delta_c H°$) of each isomer, determined using a calorimeter, is as follows:

Compound	$\Delta_c H°$ (kJ/mol butene)
cis-2-butene	−2709.8
trans-2-butene	−2706.6
1-butene	−2716.8

(a) Draw an energy level diagram relating the energy content of the three isomers to the energy content of the combustion products, $CO_2(g)$ and $H_2O(\ell)$.
(b) Use the $\Delta_c H°$ data in part (a), along with the enthalpies of formation of $CO_2(g)$ and $H_2O(\ell)$ from Appendix L, to calculate the enthalpy of formation for each of the isomers.
(c) Draw an energy level diagram that relates the enthalpies of formation of the three isomers to the energy of the elements in their standard states.
(d) What is the enthalpy change for the conversion of *cis*-2-butene to *trans*-2-butene?

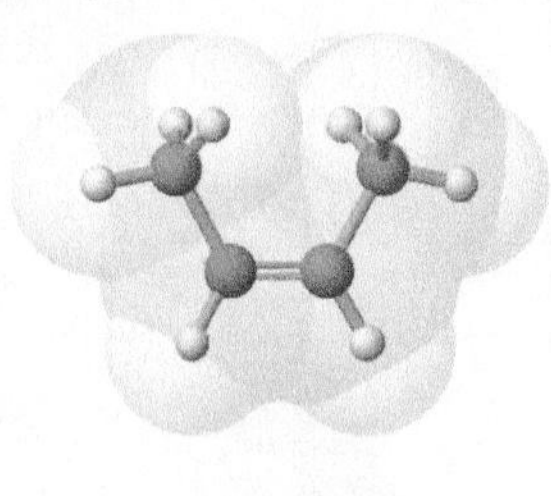

***Cis*-2-butene**

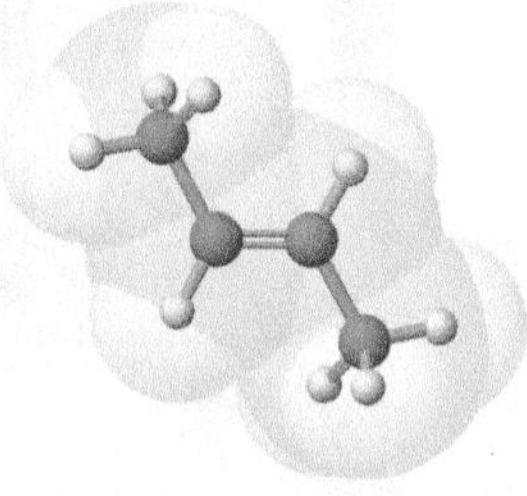

***Trans*-2-butene**

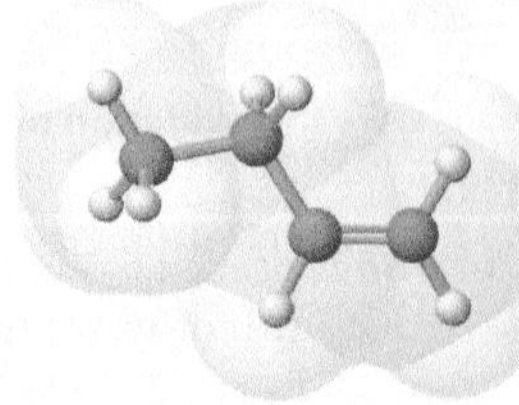

1-butene

112. Several standard enthalpies of formation (from Appendix L) are given below. Use these data to calculate

(a) the standard enthalpy of vaporization of bromine.
(b) the energy required for the reaction $Br_2(g) \rightarrow 2\ Br(g)$. (This is the Br—Br bond dissociation enthalpy.)

Species	$\Delta_f H°$ (kJ/mol)
$Br(g)$	111.9
$Br_2(\ell)$	0
$Br_2(g)$	30.9

113. When 0.850 g of Mg was burned in oxygen in a constant-volume calorimeter, 25.4 kJ of energy as heat was evolved. The calorimeter was in an insulated container with 750. g of water at an initial temperature of 18.6 °C. The heat capacity of the bomb in the calorimeter is 820. J/K.

(a) Calculate ΔU for the oxidation of Mg (in kJ/mol Mg).
(b) What will be the final temperature of the water and the bomb calorimeter in this experiment?

114. ▲ A piece of gold (10.0 g, C_{Au} = 0.129 J/g · K) is heated to 100.0 °C. A piece of copper (also 10.0 g, C_{Cu} = 0.385 J/g · K) is chilled in an ice bath to 0 °C. Both pieces of metal are placed in a beaker containing 150. g H_2O at 20 °C. Will the temperature of the water be greater than or less than 20 °C when thermal equilibrium is reached? Calculate the final temperature.

115. Methane, CH_4, can be converted to methanol, which, like ethanol, can be used as a fuel. The energy level diagram shown here presents relationships between energies of the fuels and their oxidation products. Use the information in the diagram to answer the following questions. (The energy terms are per mol-rxn.)

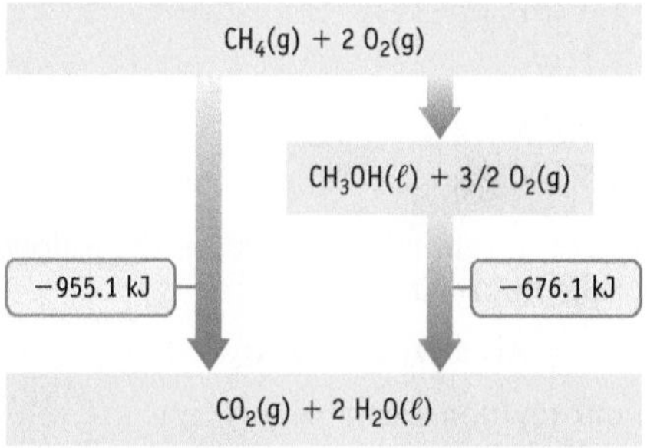

(a) Which fuel, methanol or methane, yields the most energy per mole when burned?
(b) Which fuel yields the most energy per gram when burned?
(c) What is the enthalpy change for the conversion of methane to methanol by reaction with $O_2(g)$?
(d) Each arrow on the diagram represents a chemical reaction. Write the equation for the reaction that converts methane to methanol.

116. Calculate $\Delta_r H°$ for the reaction

$$2\ C(s) + 3\ H_2(g) + \tfrac{1}{2}\ O_2(g) \rightarrow C_2H_5OH(\ell)$$

given the information below.

$$C(s) + O_2(g) \rightarrow CO_2(g) \quad \Delta_r H° = -393.5 \text{ kJ/mol-rxn}$$

$$2\ H_2(g) + O_2(g) \rightarrow 2\ H_2O(\ell) \quad \Delta_r H° = -571.6 \text{ kJ/mol-rxn}$$

$$C_2H_5OH(\ell) + 3\ O_2(g) \rightarrow 2\ CO_2(g) + 3\ H_2O(\ell) \quad \Delta_r H° = -1367.5 \text{ kJ/mol-rxn}$$

117. ▲ You have the six pieces of metal listed below, plus a beaker of water containing 3.00×10^2 g of water. The water temperature is 21.00 °C.

Metals	Specific Heat (J/g K)	Mass (g)
1. Al	0.9002	100.0
2. Al	0.9002	50.0
3. Au	0.1289	100.0
4. Au	0.1289	50.0
5. Zn	0.3860	100.0
6. Zn	0.3860	50.0

(a) In your first experiment you select one piece of metal and heat it to 100 °C, and then select a second piece of metal and cool it to −10 °C. Both pieces of metal are then placed in the beaker of water and the temperatures equilibrated. You want to select two pieces of metal to use, such that the final temperature of the water is as high as possible. What piece of metal will you heat? What piece of metal will you cool? What is the final temperature of the water?
(b) The second experiment is done in the same way as the first. However, your goal now is to cause the temperature to change the least, that is, the final temperature should be as near to 21.00 °C as possible. What piece of metal will you heat? What piece of metal will you cool? What is the final temperature of the water?

118. In the lab, you plan to carry out a calorimetry experiment to determine $\Delta_r H$ for the exothermic reaction of $Ca(OH)_2(s)$ and HCl(aq). Predict how each of the following will affect the calculated value of $\Delta_r H$. (The value calculated for $\Delta_r H$ for this reaction is a negative value so choose your answer from the following: $\Delta_r H$ will be too low [that is, a larger negative value], $\Delta_r H$ will be unaffected, $\Delta_r H$ will be too high [that is, a smaller negative value.])

(a) You spill a little bit of the $Ca(OH)_2$ on the benchtop before adding it to the calorimeter.
(b) Because of a miscalculation, you add an excess of HCl to the measured amount of $Ca(OH)_2$ in the calorimeter.
(c) $Ca(OH)_2$ readily absorbs water from the air. The $Ca(OH)_2$ sample you weighed had been exposed to the air prior to weighing and had absorbed some water.
(d) After weighing out $Ca(OH)_2$, the sample sat in an open beaker and absorbed water.
(e) You delay too long in recording the final temperature.
(f) The insulation in your coffee-cup calorimeter was poor, so some energy as heat was lost to the surroundings during the experiment.
(g) You have ignored the fact that energy as heat also raised the temperature of the stirrer and the thermometer in your system.

119. Sublimation of 1.0 g of dry ice, $CO_2(s)$, forms 0.36 L of $CO_2(g)$ (at −78 °C and 1.01×10^5 Pa). The expanding gas can do work on the surroundings (Figure 5.8). Calculate the amount of work done on the surroundings.

120. In the reaction of two moles of gaseous hydrogen and one mole of gaseous oxygen to form two moles of gaseous water vapor, two moles of products are formed from 3 moles of reactants. If this reaction is done at 1.01×10^5 Pa (and at 0 °C), the volume is reduced by 22.4 L.

(a) In this reaction, how much work is done on the system (H_2, O_2, H_2O) by the surroundings?
(b) The enthalpy change for this reaction is −483.6 kJ. Use this value, along with the answer to (a), to calculate $\Delta_r U$, the change in internal energy in the system.

AP Multiple-Choice Review Questions

1. Given the following data,

Substance	ΔH_f° (kJ/mol)
$CO_2(g)$	−393.5
$H_2O(g)$	−285.8
$C_4H_{10}(g)$	−124.7

calculate the ΔH°_{rxn} for the following reaction.

$$2C_4H_{10}(g) + 13O_2(g) \rightarrow 8CO_2(g) + 10H_2O(g)$$

(A) −6255.4 kJ
(B) −5756.6 kJ
(C) −40.6 kJ
(D) 539.4 kJ

2. Consider the reaction shown below:

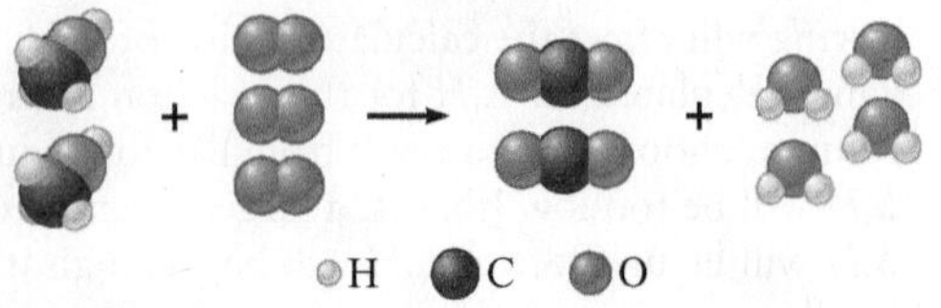

Given the following information, calculate ΔH°_{rxn} for the reaction represented above, where each molecule represents 1 mole of that substance. Assume that all states are those that are listed below.

Substance	ΔH_f° (kJ/mol)
$CO_2(g)$	−393.5
$H_2O(g)$	−285.8
$CH_3OH(g)$	−201.0

(A) −2332.2 kJ
(B) −1528.2 kJ
(C) −478.3 kJ
(D) 45.8 kJ

3. One cup of ice has a mass of approximately 250 g. The ice is at 0.0 °C. How much heat is required to melt the ice and then warm the resulting water to 25.0 °C? A table of useful information is provided.

Heat of fusion of $H_2O(s)$	332 kJ/kg
Specific heat of $H_2O(\ell)$	4.18 J/°C · g

(A) 25 kJ
(B) 58 kJ
(C) 83 kJ
(D) 110 kJ

4. A 20.-g sample of metal at 110. °C is placed into 30. g of kerosene at 35 °C. The final temperature of both the kerosene and the metal is 60. °C. If the specific heat of kerosene is 2.0 J/°C · g, what is the specific heat of the metal?

(A) 1.0 J/°C · g
(B) 1.5 J/°C · g
(C) 2.0 J/°C · g
(D) 2.5 J/°C · g

5. Calculate the enthalpy change for the following reaction given the information below.

$$Al_2(CO_3)_3(s) \rightarrow Al_2O_3(s) + 3CO_2(g)$$

The information available to you is:

$C(\textit{graphite}) + O_2(g) \rightarrow CO_2(g)$	ΔH = W kJ
$4Al(s) + 3O_2(g) \rightarrow 2Al_2O_3(s)$	ΔH = X kJ
$2Al(s) + \frac{9}{2}O_2(g) + 3C(\textit{graphite}) \rightarrow Al_2(CO_3)_3(s)$	ΔH = Y kJ

(A) W + X − Y
(B) 3W + X − Y
(C) $3W + \frac{1}{2}X + Y$
(D) $3W + \frac{1}{2}X - Y$

$3C + 3O_2 \rightarrow 3CO_2$ $\Delta H = 3W$
~~2Al~~ $+ \frac{3}{2}O_2 \rightarrow Al_2O_3$ $\Delta H = \frac{1}{2}X$
$Al_2(CO_3)_3 \rightarrow$ ~~2Al~~ $+ \frac{9}{2}O_2$ $\Delta H = -Y$

$\frac{1}{2}X + 3W - (-Y)$

$\frac{1}{2}X + 3W + Y$

6. In which of the following isothermal expansions of an ideal gas is the work done by the system the largest? Assume the temperature is the same for all choices.
(A) from 1 to 5 L against an opposing pressure of $\frac{1}{2}$ atm
(B) from 1 to 5 L against an opposing pressure of 1 atm
(C) from 1 to 5 L against an opposing pressure of 3 atm
(D) from 1 to 10 L against an opposing pressure of 2 atm

7. Consider four 100.0-g samples of water, each in a separate beaker at 25.0 °C. Into each beaker you drop 10.0 g of a different metal that has been heated to 95.0 °C. Assuming no heat loss to the surroundings, which water sample will have the lowest final temperature?
(A) the water to which you have added aluminum (s = 0.89 J/°C · g)
(B) the water to which you have added iron (s = 0.45 J/°C · g)
(C) the water to which you have added copper (s = 0.20 J/°C · g)
(D) the water to which you have added lead (s = 0.14 J/°C · g)

8. A student performs a neutralization reaction involving an acid and a base in an open polystyrene coffee-cup calorimeter. How would the calculated value of ΔH differ from the actual value if there was significant heat loss to the surroundings?
(A) ΔH_{calc} would be negative, but more negative than the actual value.
(B) ΔH_{calc} would be negative, but less negative than the actual value.
(C) ΔH_{calc} would be positive, but more positive than the actual value.
(D) ΔH_{calc} would be positive, but less positive than the actual value.

9. Which of the following is endothermic?
(A) Water freezes to form ice.
(B) Steam condenses on a bathroom mirror.
(C) Ice cream melts.
(D) Coffee cools as it sits.

10. At 25 °C, the following heats of reaction are known:

$2C_2H_2(g) + 5O_2(g) \rightarrow 4CO_2(g) + 2H_2O(\ell)$ $\Delta H = -2600.0$ kJ
$C(graphite) + O_2(g) \rightarrow CO_2(g)$ $\Delta H = -394$ kJ
$2H_2(g) + O_2(g) \rightarrow 2H_2O(\ell)$ $\Delta H = -574$ kJ

At the same temperature, calculate ΔH for the reaction $2C(graphite) + H_2(\ell) \rightarrow C_2H_2(g)$.
(A) −2422 kJ
(B) −225 kJ
(C) 225 kJ
(D) 2422 kJ

11. Using Hess's law and the equations below find $\Delta H°$ at 25 °C for the oxidation of $C_2H_5OH(\ell)$.

$$C_2H_5OH(\ell) + 3O_2(g) \rightarrow 3H_2O(\ell) + 2CO_2(g)$$

$C_2H_4(g) + 3O_2(g) \rightarrow 2CO_2(g) + 2\,H_2O(\ell)$ $\Delta H° = W$ kJ
$2C(graphite) + 3H_2(g) + \frac{1}{2}O_2(g) \rightarrow C_2H_5OH(\ell)$ $\Delta H° = X$ kJ
$C_2H_4(g) + H_2O(\ell) \rightarrow C_2H_5OH(\ell)$ $\Delta H° = Y$ kJ

(A) W − Y
(B) X − 2Y
(C) X + 2W + Y
(D) 2X − W + Y

12. A popular chemistry demonstration is to drop a piece of sodium metal into water. The products are sodium hydroxide and hydrogen gas. Determine ΔH_{rxn} for this reaction for 1.00 mole of hydrogen gas being produced, given

$\Delta H_f°[H_2O(\ell)] = -286$ kJ/mol
$\Delta H_f°[NaOH(aq)] = -470$ kJ/mol

(A) −368 kJ
(B) −184 kJ
(C) 184 kJ
(D) 368 kJ

AP Free Response Review Questions

Question Format: Short

Category of Question: Representation 2

The reaction when propane is burned in oxygen can be represented several different ways.

Questions:

(a) Write the balanced chemical equation for the complete combustion for propane.

(b) Complete the balanced equation below by drawing the graphical representations of the products. You may indicate the different atoms involved by using a circle with the first letter of the color inside the circle, as shown below:

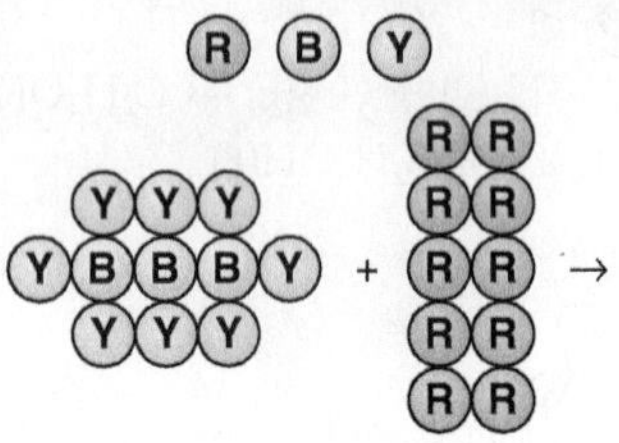

(c) Given the following table of bond energies, calculate the value of $\Delta H_{combustion}$ for this reaction.

Type of Bond	Bond Energy (kJ/mol)
(R)(R)	495
(R)(B)	799
(R)(Y)	467
(B)(Y)	413
(B)(B)	346

(d) Is this reaction exothermic or endothermic? Explain your reasoning.

(e) Give one environmental disadvantage of the combustion of hydrocarbon fuels, such as propane.

Question Format: Long

Category of Question: Lab 1

A student is given an unknown sample of a metal and told to identify it using laboratory investigations. The unknown sample is one of five metals (chromium, cobalt, nickel, copper and zinc). The student is given the following known values for each element.

Element	Atomic number	Atomic mass	Oxidation states	Specific heat (J/gK)	Density (g/cm³)
Chromium	24	52.00	+2, +3	0.448	7.19
Cobalt	27	58.93	+2, +3	0.421	8.9
Nickel	28	58.71	+2, +3	0.445	8.9
Copper	29	63.55	+1, +2	0.384	8.96
Zinc	30	65.38	+2, +3	0.388	7.13

Only the properties listed in the table can be used to identify the element. The student decides to conduct two different tests. A copy of the student's data table for each test is shown below.

Test One – Data Table

Mass of weighing boat	24.972 g
Mass of weighing boat with metal sample	93.762 g
Mass of metal sample	
Volume of water in container before metal is added	12.2 mL
Volume of water in container after metal is added	21.8 mL
Volume of metal	

Test Two – Data Table

Mass of polystyrene cup	24.753 g
Mass of polystyrene cup and water	80.381 g
Mass of water	
Mass of weighing boat	24.972 g
Mass of weighing boat with metal sample	93.762 g
Mass of metal sample	
Initial temperature of metal sample in boiling water bath	100.8 °C
Initial temperature of water in polystyrene cup	23.2 °C
Final temperature of water with metal sample	32.3 °C
Final temperature of metal sample	
	9.1 °C
	−68.5 °C

Questions

(a) Complete the data tables, by filling in data description or the values, including units where appropriate.

(b) For Test One, list the equipment needed to carry out the experiment to produce the results in the table.

(c) For Test Two, briefly list the procedures needed to carry out the experiment to produce the results in the table.

Each of the tests was conducted to produce a result that would eliminate at least one possible choice for the identity of the unknown.

(d) For Test One,

(i) analyze the data to calculate the value of the desired property.

(ii) identify which unknown sample or samples this test eliminates.

(e) For Test Two,

(i) analyze the data to calculate the value of the desired property.

(ii) identify which unknown sample or samples this test eliminates.

(f) Is there enough information to determine the identity of the unknown sample? Explain your reasoning.

© Cengage Learning/Charles D. Winters

The Structure of Atoms

Chapter Outline

SMILE! Ever since the invention of permanent-image photography in the 1800s, people around the world have loved to take pictures. One major change that has occurred in recent years is the replacement of film cameras with digital cameras for many uses. Digital cameras are available as stand-alone devices or as parts of our computers and cellular telephones. In traditional photography, light was focused through a lens onto a piece of film; in many digital cameras, it is focused onto a "charge coupled device" (CCD). The CCD is an integrated circuit made of millions of pixels, each consisting of a light-sensitive material in an electrical device called a capacitor. Each pixel determines a region in the resulting image. In general, the more pixels present per unit area, the greater the resolution of the resulting image.

When light hits one of these pixels, the atoms of the light-sensitive material transfer electrons into the capacitor in a process similar to the photoelectric effect (page 223). Based on the amount of charge that accumulates in the capacitor, a computer can determine the brightness to be used in the resulting image. In order to obtain a color image, some cameras have an array of red,

Chapter Goals

See Chapter Goals Revisited (page 244) for Study Questions keyed to these goals.

UNDERSTAND

- The characteristics of electromagnetic radiation (wavelength, frequency, speed, nodes, and energy).
- The origin of light emitted by excited atoms and its relationship to atomic structure.
- The experimental evidence for particle–wave duality.
- The basic principles of quantum mechanics, such as quantization and wavefunctions.

DO

- Relate wavelength (λ), frequency (ν), speed (c), and energy (E) per photon of electromagnetic radiation.
- Calculate the energy of an electron in a hydrogen atom using Bohr's model.
- Use the four quantum numbers (n, ℓ, m_ℓ, and m_s) to describe the electronic structure of an atom.

REMEMBER

- The order of the different types of electromagnetic radiation by wavelength, frequency, and energy.
- The rules for determining the values for the four quantum numbers (n, ℓ, m_ℓ, and m_s).
- The shapes of atomic orbitals.

blue, and green filters over the CCD. Each pixel thus receives information about only one of these colors. Based on the intensities of these three colors in each region, the computer in the camera can determine the actual color to use in that region of the image.

In order to better understand the processes occurring in a CCD, you will need to understand better the properties of light as well as the arrangement of electrons in atoms. These are the major topics discussed in this chapter.

The picture that many people have of the atom is that of a tiny nucleus, consisting of neutrons and protons, with nearly massless electrons orbiting the nucleus like planets around a star. This simple picture, however, is only partly correct. The nucleus is indeed tiny and composed of neutrons and protons, and electrons are located in the space outside the nucleus, but, as you shall see, a more accurate picture describes the electrons as matter waves, and we can only define regions of space in which it is likely to find an electron.

This chapter lays out the experimental and theoretical background to our current understanding of atomic structure and describes the modern view of the atom. With this knowledge of electronic structure we can predict many of the properties of atoms and better understand the underlying structure of the periodic table.

Much of our understanding of atomic structure comes from a knowledge of how atoms interact with electromagnetic radiation (visible light is one type of electromagnetic radiation) and how atoms that have absorbed energy emit electromagnetic radiation. The first three sections of this chapter describe electromagnetic radiation and its relation to our modern view of the atom.

6-1 Electromagnetic Radiation

In 1864, James Clerk Maxwell (1831–1879) developed a mathematical theory to describe light and other forms of radiation in terms of oscillating, or wave-like, electric and magnetic fields (Figure 6.1). Thus, visible light, microwaves, television and radio signals, x-rays, and other forms of radiation are now called **electromagnetic radiation.**

Electromagnetic radiation is characterized by its wavelength and frequency.

- **Wavelength,** symbolized by the Greek letter *lambda* (λ), is defined as the distance between a given point on a wave and the corresponding point in the next cycle of the wave; it is often measured as the distance between successive crests or high points of a wave (or between successive troughs or low points).
- **Frequency,** symbolized by the Greek letter *nu* (ν), refers to the number of waves that pass a given point in some unit of time, usually per second. The unit for frequency, written either as s^{-1} or 1/s and standing for 1 oscillation per second, is called a **hertz.**

Wavelength and frequency are related to the speed *(c)* at which the wave is propagated (Equation 6.1).

$$c\ (\text{m/s}) = \lambda\ (\text{m}) \times \nu\ (1/\text{s}) \tag{6.1}$$

The speed of visible light and all other forms of electromagnetic radiation in a vacuum is a constant: $c = 2.99792458 \times 10^8$ m/s (approximately 186,000 miles/s or 1.079×10^9 km/h).

Electromagnetic radiation consists of oscillating electric and magnetic disturbances. For this reason electrons in atoms and molecules can interact with these electric and magnetic fields, and those interactions allow scientists to probe matter at the atomic and molecular level.

As illustrated in Figure 6.2, visible light is only a tiny portion of the total spectrum of electromagnetic radiation. Ultraviolet (UV) radiation, the radiation that can lead to sunburn, has wavelengths shorter than those of visible light. X-rays and γ-rays, the latter emitted in the process of the radioactive disintegration of some atoms, have even shorter wavelengths. At wavelengths longer than those of visible light, we first encounter infrared radiation (IR). The wavelengths of the radiation used in microwave ovens, in television and radio transmissions, in MRI instruments, and for cell phones are longer still.

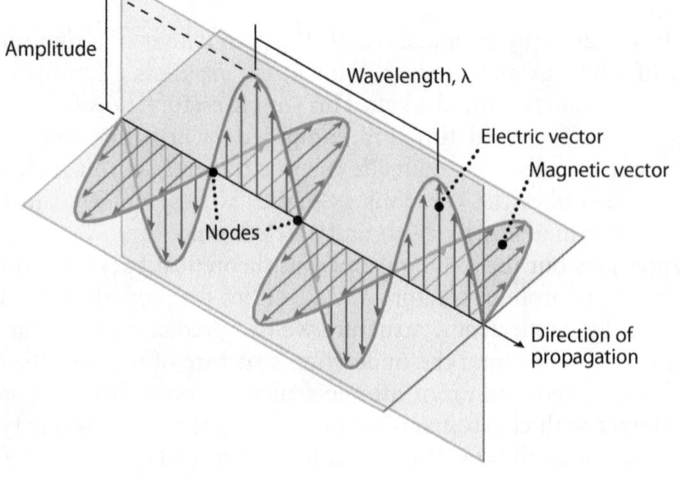

FIGURE 6.1 Electromagnetic radiation is characterized by its wavelength and frequency. All forms of electromagnetic radiation are propagated through space as vibrating electric and magnetic fields at right angles to one another. Each field is described mathematically by a sine wave. Such oscillating fields emanate from vibrating charges in sources such as lightbulbs or your cell phone.

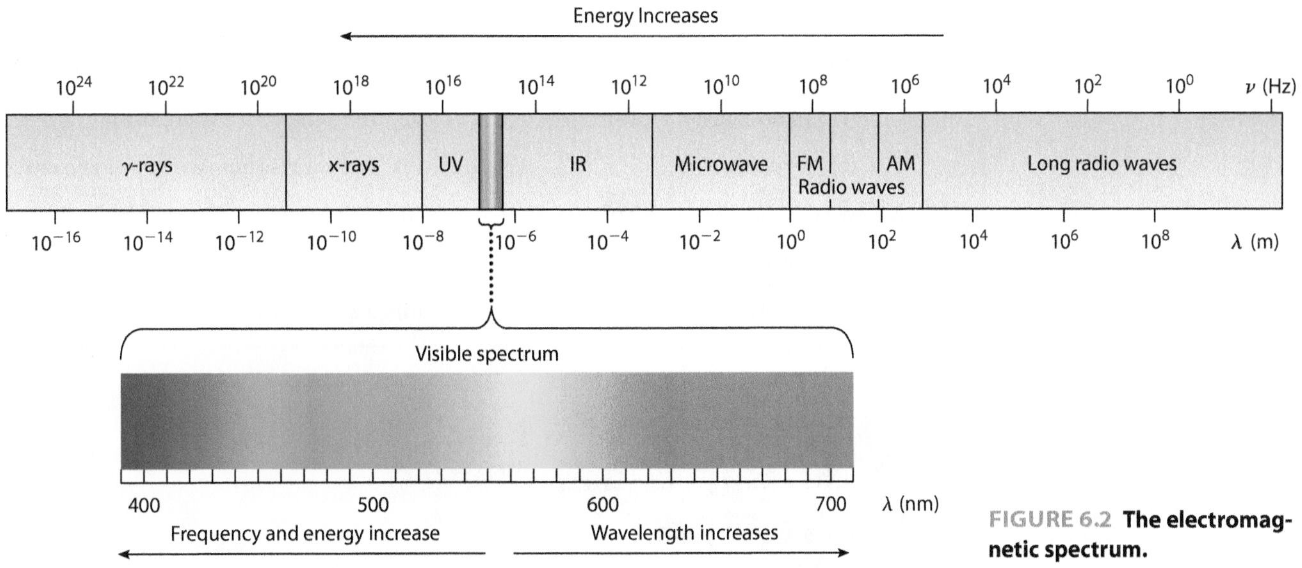

FIGURE 6.2 The electromagnetic spectrum.

EXAMPLE 6.1

Wavelength-Frequency Conversions

Problem The frequency of the radiation used in cell phones covers a range from about 800 MHz to 2 GHz. (MHz stands for "megahertz," where 1 MHz = 10^6 1/s; GHz stands for "gigahertz," where 1 GHz = 10^9 1/s.) What is the wavelength (in meters) of a cell phone signal operating at 1.12 GHz?

What Do You Know? You are given a frequency of radiation, in GHz, and a factor to convert frequency from GHz to Hz (1/s). To calculate the wavelength of this radiation using Equation 6.1, you will need the value of the speed of light, $c = 2.998 \times 10^8$ m/s.

Strategy Rearrange Equation 6.1 to solve for λ. Substitute the values for the speed of light and the frequency (first convert ν to the units 1/s) into the equation and solve.

Solution

$$\lambda = \frac{c}{\nu} = \frac{2.998 \times 10^8 \text{ m/s}}{1.12 \times 10^9 \text{ 1/s}} = 0.268 \text{ m}$$

Think about Your Answer A wavelength of 0.268 m falls in the microwave region of the electromagnetic spectrum (Figure 6.2). Make sure you pay attention to units when solving this problem. Note that by choosing frequency in 1/s and the speed of light in m/s the calculated wavelength will be in meters (m).

Check Your Understanding

(a) Which color in the visible spectrum has the highest frequency? Which has the lowest frequency?

(b) Is the wavelength of the radiation used in a microwave oven (2.45 GHz) longer or shorter than that from your favorite FM radio station (for example, 91.7 MHz)?

(c) Are the wavelengths of x-rays longer or shorter than those of ultraviolet light?

(d) Calculate the frequency of green light with a wavelength of 510. nm.

REVIEW & CHECK FOR SECTION 6-1

1. Which of the following types of electromagnetic radiation has the longest wavelength?
   (a) ultraviolet light
   (b) x-rays
   (c) red light from a laser pointer
   (d) microwaves from a microwave oven
2. What is the wavelength of an FM radio signal that has a frequency of 91.7 MHz?
   (a) 306 nm
   (b) 306 mm
   (c) 3.27 m
   (d) 3.27×10^6 m

6-2 Quantization: Planck, Einstein, Energy, and Photons

Planck's Equation

If a piece of metal is heated to a high temperature, electromagnetic radiation is emitted with wavelengths that depend on temperature (Figure 6.3). At lower temperatures, the color is a dull red. As the temperature increases, the red color brightens, and at even higher temperatures a brilliant white light is emitted. Your eyes detect the emitted radiation in the visible region of the electromagnetic spectrum. Although not seen, both ultraviolet and infrared radiation are also given off by the hot metal (Figure 6.3). The wavelength of the most intense radiation is related to temperature: As the temperature of the metal is raised, the maximum intensity shifts toward shorter wavelengths, that is, toward the ultraviolet. This corresponds to the change in color observed as the temperature is raised.

The light emanating from the spaces between burning briquets approximates blackbody radiation.

© Cengage Learning/Charles D. Winters

Blackbody radiation. In physics a blackbody is something that absorbs all radiation that falls on it. However, it will emit energy with a temperature-dependent wavelength. The color of the emitted light depends on the temperature.

At the end of the 19th century, scientists were not able to explain the relationship between the intensity and the wavelength for radiation given off by a heated object (often called *blackbody radiation*). Theories available at the time predicted that the intensity should increase continuously with decreasing wavelength, instead of reaching a maximum and then declining as is actually observed. This perplexing situation became known as the *ultraviolet catastrophe* because predictions failed in the ultraviolet region.

In 1900, a German physicist, Max Planck (1858–1947), offered an explanation for the ultraviolet catastrophe: The electromagnetic radiation emitted originated in vibrating atoms (called *oscillators*) in the heated object. He proposed that each oscillator had a fundamental frequency (ν) of oscillation and that these oscillators could only oscillate at either this frequency or whole-number multiples of it ($n\nu$). Because of this, the emitted radiation could have only certain energies, given by the equation

$$E = nh\nu$$

where n must be a positive integer. That is, Planck proposed that the energy is *quantized*. **Quantization** means that only certain energies are allowed. The proportionality constant h in the equation is now called **Planck's constant,** and its experimental value is $6.6260693 \times 10^{-34}$ J · s. The unit of frequency is 1/s, so the energy calculated using this equation is in joules (J). If an oscillator changes from a higher energy to a lower one, energy is emitted as electromagnetic radiation, where the difference in energy between the higher and lower energy states is

Night Vision Goggles Even at ambient temperatures objects emit radiation. Some night vision goggles operate by detecting differences in the amount of infrared radiation emitted by different objects. Warmer human bodies, for example, emit more infrared radiation than do cooler objects.

$$\Delta E = E_{\text{higher } n} - E_{\text{lower } n} = \Delta nh\nu$$

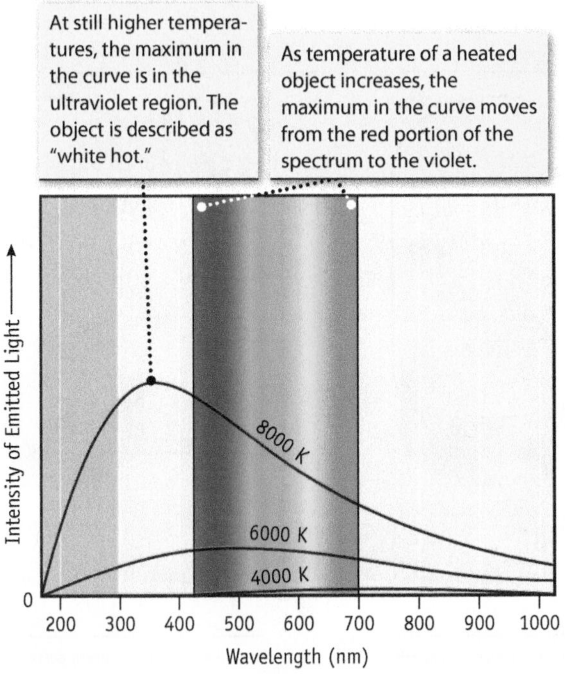

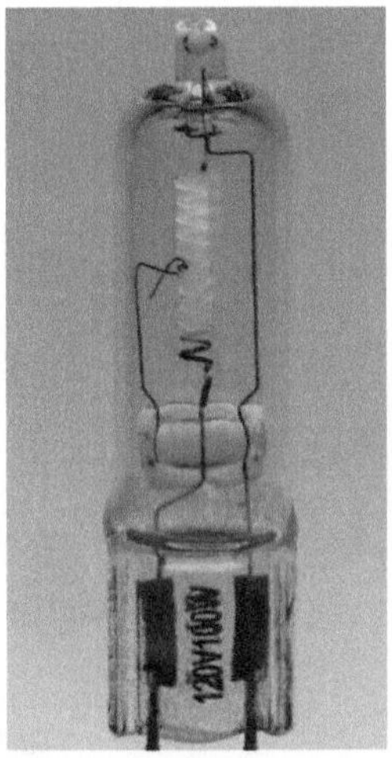

FIGURE 6.3 **The radiation given off by a heated body.** When an object is heated, it emits radiation covering a spectrum of wavelengths. For a given temperature, some of the radiation is emitted at long wavelengths and some at short wavelengths. Most, however, is emitted at some intermediate wavelength, the maximum in the curve.

If the value of Δn is 1, which corresponds to changing from one energy level to the next lower one for that oscillator, then the energy change for the oscillator and the electromagnetic radiation emitted would have an energy equal to

$$E = h\nu \quad (6.2)$$

This equation is called **Planck's equation.**

Now, assume as Planck did that there must be a *distribution* of oscillators in an object—some are vibrating at a high frequency, some are vibrating at a low frequency, but most have some intermediate frequency. The few oscillators with high-frequency vibrations are responsible for some of the light, say in the ultraviolet region, and those few with low-frequency vibrations for energies in the infrared region. However, most of the light must come from the majority of the oscillators that have intermediate vibrational frequencies. That is, a spectrum of light is emitted with a maximum intensity at some intermediate wavelength, in accord with experiment. The intensity should not become greater and greater on approaching the ultraviolet region. With this realization, the ultraviolet catastrophe was solved.

The key aspects of Planck's theory for general chemistry are that Planck introduced the idea of quantized energies and the equation $E = h\nu$, an equation that was to have an important impact on the work of Albert Einstein in explaining another puzzling phenomenon.

The relationship of energy, wavelength, and frequency

As frequency (ν) increases, energy (E) increases

$$E = h\nu = \frac{hc}{\lambda}$$

As wavelength (λ) decreases, energy (E) increases

Einstein and the Photoelectric Effect

A few years after Planck's work, Albert Einstein (1879–1955) incorporated Planck's ideas into an explanation of the *photoelectric effect* and in doing so changed the description of electromagnetic radiation.

In the photoelectric effect, electrons are ejected when light strikes the surface of a metal (Figure 6.4), but only if the frequency of the light is high enough. If light with a lower frequency is used, no electrons are ejected, regardless of the light's intensity (its brightness). If the frequency is at or above a minimum, critical frequency, increasing the light intensity causes more electrons to be ejected.

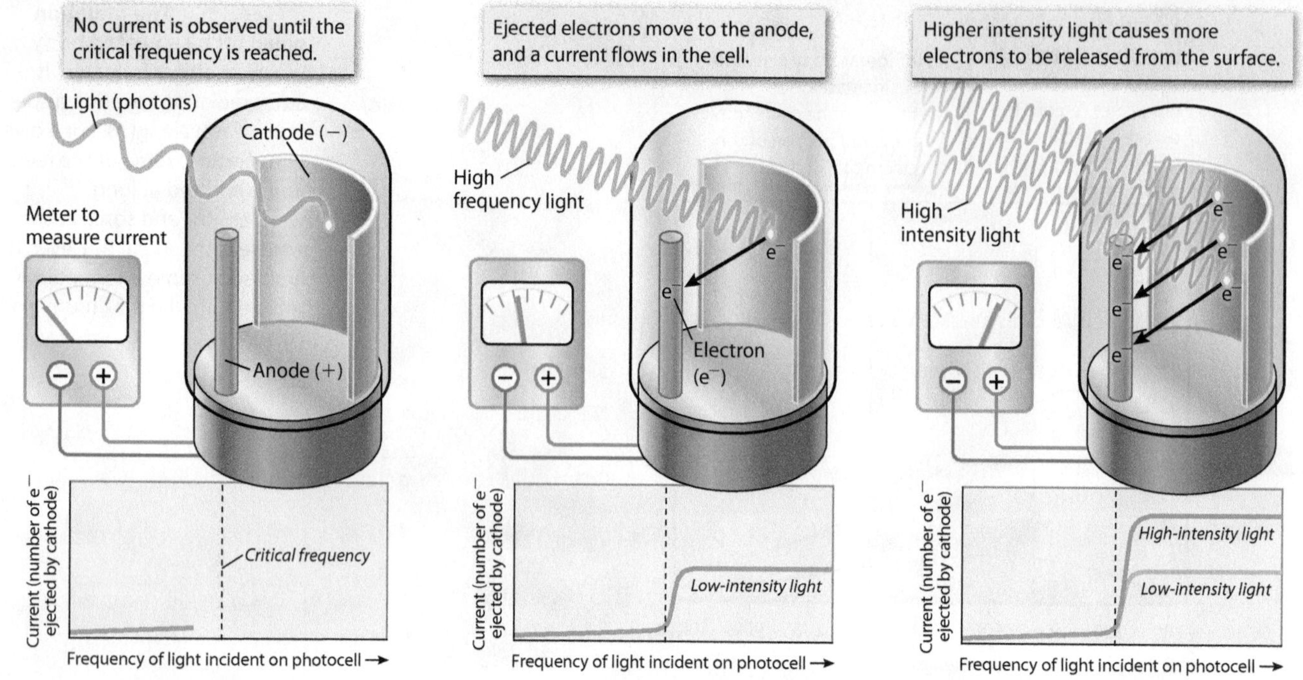

(a) A photocell operates by the photoelectric effect. The main part of the cell is a light-sensitive cathode. This is a material, usually a metal, that ejects electrons if struck by photons of light of sufficient energy.

(b) When light of higher frequency than the minimum is used, the excess energy of the photon allows the electron to escape the atom with greater velocity. Such a device can be used as a switch in electric circuits.

(c) If higher intensity light is used, the only effect is to cause more electrons to be released from the surface. The onset of current is observed at the same frequency as with lower intensity light, but more current flows.

FIGURE 6.4 **A photoelectric cell.**

Einstein decided the experimental observations could be explained by combining Planck's equation ($E = h\nu$) with a new idea, that light has particle-like properties. Einstein characterized these massless particles, now called **photons,** as packets of energy, and stated that the energy of each photon is proportional to the frequency of the radiation as defined by Planck's equation. In the photoelectric effect, photons striking atoms on a metal surface will cause electrons to be ejected only if the photons have high enough energy. The greater the number of photons that strike the surface at or above the threshold energy, the greater the number of electrons dislodged. The metal atoms will not lose electrons, however, if no individual photon has enough energy to dislodge an electron from an atom.

Strategy Map 6.2

PROBLEM

Calculate energy of **red light photons.**

↓

KNOWN DATA/INFORMATION

Wavelength of red light (640 nm)

STEP 1. Convert **wavelength** to **frequency.** (Equation 6.1)

↓

Frequency in *cycles per second*

STEP 2. Calculate **energy** using *Planck's equation.* (Equation 6.2)

↓

Obtain energy in **J/photon.**

STEP 3. Use **Avogadro's number** to convert **J/atom** to **J/mol.**

↓

Obtain energy in **J/mol.**

EXAMPLE 6.2

Energy and Chemistry: Using Planck's Equation

Problem DVD players use lasers that emit red light with a wavelength of 640 nm. What is the energy of one photon of this light? What is the energy of 1.0 mol of photons of red light?

What Do You Know? You are given a wavelength of electromagnetic radiation, in nm. You also know the relationship between wavelength and frequency (Equation 6.1) and also between the energy per photon and frequency (Equation 6.2). Finally, you know that one mole of photons corresponds to 6.022×10^{23} photons.

Strategy

- Convert the wavelength from units of nanometers to units of meters.
- Use Equation 6.1 to determine the frequency of the light.

- Use Equation 6.2 to determine the energy per photon.
- Use the energy per photon and Avogadro's number to calculate the energy per mole of photons.

Solution The wavelength (640 nm) expressed in meters is 6.4×10^{-7} m. The frequency is determined using Equation 6.1

$$\nu = \frac{c}{\lambda} = \frac{2.998 \times 10^{8}\ \text{m/s}}{6.4 \times 10^{-7}\ \text{m}} = 4.7 \times 10^{14}\ 1/\text{s}$$

and then the frequency is used to calculate the energy per photon.

$$E \text{ per photon} = h\nu = (6.626 \times 10^{-34}\ \text{J} \cdot \text{s/photon}) \times (4.7 \times 10^{14}\ 1/\text{s})$$
$$= 3.1 \times 10^{-19}\ \text{J/photon}$$

Finally, the energy of a mole of photons is calculated by multiplying the energy per photon by Avogadro's number:

$$E \text{ per mole} = (3.1 \times 10^{-19}\ \text{J/photon}) \times (6.022 \times 10^{23}\ \text{photons/mol})$$
$$= 1.9 \times 10^{5}\ \text{J/mol (or 190 kJ/mol)}$$

Think about Your Answer Keep in mind that wavelength and frequency are inversely proportional whereas energy per photon and frequency are directly proportional. Red light is at the long wavelength end of the visible spectrum, so the frequency and energy per photon are lower than those of the other colors.

Check Your Understanding

Calculate the energy per mole of photons for the laser used in Blu-ray players ($\lambda = 405$ nm).

A CLOSER LOOK — Sunburn, Sunscreens, and Ultraviolet Radiation

Have you ever had a sunburn? The primary cause is ultraviolet (UV) radiation from the Sun with wavelengths between 200 and 400 nm (Figure 6.2). In addition to causing sunburns, exposure to ultraviolet radiation is a risk factor for developing various types of skin cancer.

Why is exposure to UV light so much more dangerous than even long exposures to visible light? Having a wavelength shorter than that of visible light, UV light has a frequency that is higher and thus the energy delivered per photon is greater. The high energy of ultraviolet photons is sufficient to cause chemical bonds to break in molecules in our bodies, such as in proteins and DNA. This is the underlying cause of sunburns and also of the damage to cells that can lead to skin cancer.

UV radiation can be classified into three main categories based on wavelength: UV-A (315–400 nm), UV-B (280–315 nm), and UV-C (200–280 nm). Based upon their energies you would think you would need to be most worried about exposure to UV-C, and this would indeed be the case were it not for the atmosphere of the Earth. Oxygen and ozone in the atmosphere absorb all of the UV-C coming to Earth from the Sun, so this most dangerous ultraviolet radiation is not a worry for us. Ozone in the atmosphere also absorbs most, but not all, of the UV-B reaching the Earth. In fact, sunburn is caused primarily by UV-B, whereas both UV-A and UV-B exposure are risk factors for skin cancer.

What can you do to avoid the dangers of UV radiation? Clearly, the best solution is to avoid exposure by remaining indoors or wearing protective clothing when sunlight is most intense. If, however, this is not possible, then you can use a sunscreen. Sunscreens contain molecules that absorb UV radiation. The sun protection factor (SPF) rating of a sunscreen indicates the amount of UV required to get a sunburn when the sunscreen has been applied compared to the amount of UV required without the sunscreen. Because sunburn is caused primarily by UV-B, the higher the SPF factor, the better the protection against UV-B. Even with a high SPF, however, a sunscreen might not protect against UV-A, which can also cause skin cancer. In 2011, new U.S. Food and Drug Administration (FDA) guidelines were approved requiring sunscreen makers to label if their products protect against both UV-B and UV-A. If they do, the product can be labeled "Broad Spectrum." In choosing a sunscreen the FDA now recommends that you choose one with an SPF of 15 or higher and that it be labeled "Broad Spectrum."

©iStockphoto.com/markokg

Sunscreens and damage from radiation. Sunscreens contain organic compounds that absorb UV radiation, preventing it from reaching your skin.

We know that electromagnetic radiation has wave properties, but we have also seen that there are experiments, such as the photoelectric effect, for which it is best to model it as particles called photons. But, how can electromagnetic radiation be both a particle and a wave? In part, we are facing limitations in language; the words *particle* and *wave* accurately describe things encountered on a macroscopic scale, but we are using them to model something—electromagnetic radiation—that transcends either of these terms. In addition, no single experiment has yet been done to show electromagnetic radiation behaving *simultaneously* as a wave and a particle. Scientists now accept this **wave-particle duality**—that is, the idea that electromagnetic radiation has the properties of both a wave and a particle (see Section 6-4).

REVIEW & CHECK FOR SECTION 6-2

Various manufacturers have developed mixtures of compounds that protect skin from UV-A (400–315 nm) and UV-B (315–280 nm) radiation. These sunscreens are given "sun protection factor" (SPF) labels that indicate how long the user can stay in the Sun without burning.

1. Calculate the energy of a mole of photons of UV-B light with a wavelength of 310 nm.

   (a) 3.9×10^5 J/mol (b) 1.2×10^5 J/mol (c) 0.00039 J/mol

2. Which has the greater energy per photon, UV-B light at 310 nm or microwave radiation having a frequency of 2.45 GHz (1 GHz = 10^9 s^{-1})?

   (a) UVB (b) microwave

Learning Objectives: LO 1.15 (see APEC Lab 1 "Energy Levels and Electron Transitions"), LO 1.16 (see APEC Lab 2 "The Percentage of Copper in Brass")

6-3 Atomic Line Spectra and Niels Bohr

If a high voltage is applied to atoms of an element in the gas phase at low pressure, the atoms absorb energy and are said to be "excited." The excited atoms can then emit light. A familiar example is the colored light from "neon" advertising signs.

The light from excited atoms is composed of only a few different wavelengths of light. We can demonstrate this by passing a beam of light from excited neon or hydrogen atoms through a prism (Figure 6.5); only a few colored lines are seen. The spectrum obtained in this manner is called a **line emission spectrum.** This is in contrast to the light falling on Earth from the Sun, or the light emitted by a very

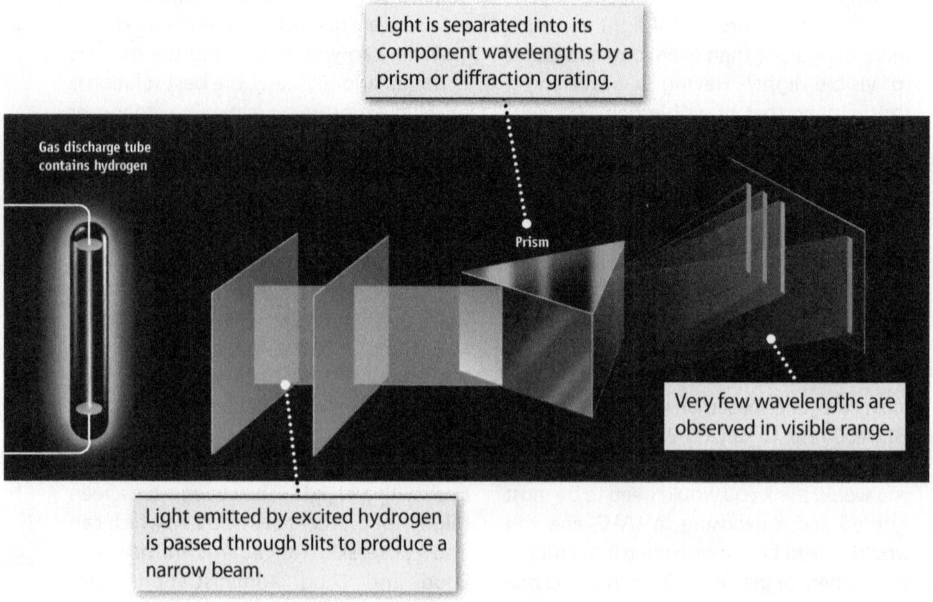

FIGURE 6.5 **The visible emission spectrum of hydrogen.** Based on the appearance, the name *line spectrum* is used for the light emitted by a glowing gas.

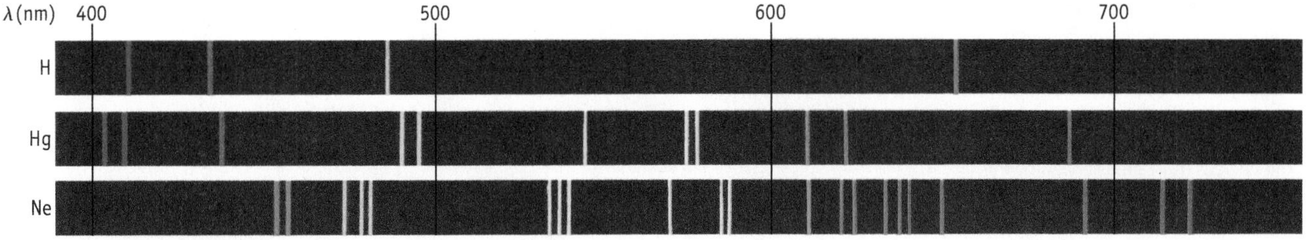

FIGURE 6.6 **Line emission spectra of hydrogen, mercury, and neon.** Excited gaseous elements produce characteristic spectra that can be used to identify the elements and to determine how much of each element is present in a sample.

hot object, which consists of a continuous spectrum of wavelengths (Figures 6.2 and 6.3).

Every element has a unique emission spectrum, as exemplified by the spectra for hydrogen, mercury, and neon in Figure 6.6. Indeed, the characteristic lines in the emission spectrum of an element can be used in chemical analysis, both to identify the element and to determine how much of it is present in a mixture.

A goal of scientists in the late 19th century was to explain why excited gaseous atoms emit light of only certain frequencies. One approach was to look for a mathematical relationship among the observed wavelengths because a regular pattern of information implies a logical explanation. The first steps in this direction were taken by Johann Balmer (1825–1898) and later by Johannes Rydberg (1854–1919). From their studies, an equation—now called the **Balmer equation** (Equation 6.3)—was found that could be used to calculate the wavelength of the red, green, and blue lines in the visible emission spectrum of hydrogen (Figure 6.6).

$$\frac{1}{\lambda} = R\left(\frac{1}{2^2} - \frac{1}{n^2}\right) \text{ when } n > 2 \qquad \textbf{(6.3)}$$

In this equation n is an integer, and R, now called the **Rydberg constant,** has the value $1.0974 \times 10^7\ m^{-1}$. If $n = 3$, for example, the wavelength of the red line in the hydrogen spectrum is obtained (6.563×10^{-7} m, or 656.3 nm). If $n = 4$, the wavelength for the green line is calculated. Using $n = 5$ and $n = 6$ in the equation gives the wavelengths of the blue lines. The four visible lines in the spectrum of hydrogen atoms are now known as the **Balmer series.**

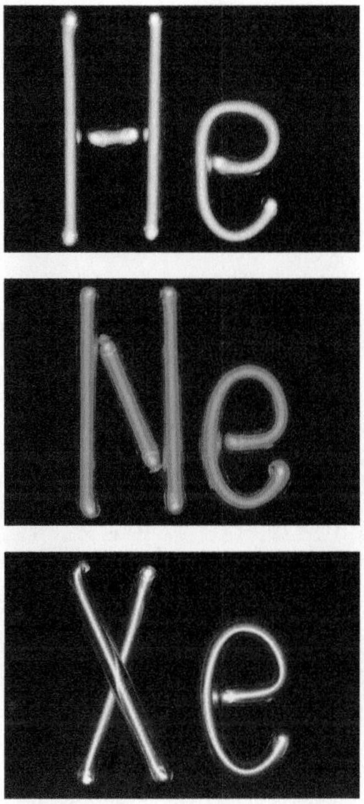

Photos: Phillip Slawinski

"Neon" signs. Not all lighted signs contain neon. Other gases can emit light in the visible spectrum when excited. Alternatively, the glass tubes containing the gases are coated inside with light-emitting phosphors (as in fluorescent lights).

The Bohr Model of the Hydrogen Atom

Early in the 20th century, the Danish physicist Niels Bohr (1885–1962) proposed a model for the electronic structure of atoms and with it an explanation for the emission spectra of excited atoms. Bohr proposed a planetary structure for the hydrogen atom in which the electron moved in a circular orbit around the nucleus, similar to a planet revolving about the Sun. In proposing this model, however, he had to contradict the laws of classical physics. According to classical theories, a charged electron moving in the positive electric field of the nucleus should lose energy; a consequence of the loss of energy is that the electron would eventually crash into the nucleus. This is clearly not the case; if it were, matter would eventually self-destruct. To solve this contradiction, Bohr postulated that there are certain orbits corresponding to particular energy levels where this would not occur. As long as an electron is in one of these energy levels, the system is stable. That is, Bohr introduced *quantization* into the description of electronic structure. By combining this quantization postulate with Coulomb's law and the laws of motion from classical physics, Bohr derived Equation 6.4 for the total energy possessed by the single electron in the nth orbit (energy level) of the H atom.

Equation 6.4 and Coulomb's Law Bohr's derivation of Equation 6.4 began with the postulate that the stability of the electron in an orbit requires that the Coulombic force of attraction between the electron and the nucleus must be balanced by the centrifugal force due to the electron's circular motion: $e^2/r^2 = mv^2/r$ (where e is the electron charge, r is the electron-nucleus separation, m is the electron mass, and v is the electron velocity).

$$\text{Total energy of electron in the } n\text{th level} = E_n = -\frac{Rhc}{n^2} \tag{6.4}$$

(Rydberg constant = R; Planck's constant = h; Speed of light = c; Principal quantum number = n)

Here, E_n is the energy of the electron (in J/atom); and R, h, and c are constants [the Rydberg constant, Planck's constant, and the speed of light, respectively]. The symbol n is a positive, unitless integer called the **principal quantum number**. It can have integral values of 1, 2, 3, and so on.

Figure 6.7 illustrates how Equation 6.4 applies to the electron of the hydrogen atom.

- The quantum number n defines the energies of the allowed orbits in the H atom.
- The energy of an electron in an orbit has a negative value because the electron in the atom has a lower energy than when it is free. The zero of energy occurs when $n = \infty$, that is, when the electron is infinitely separated from the nucleus.
- An atom with its electrons in the lowest possible energy levels is said to be in its **ground state**; for the hydrogen atom, this is the level defined by the quantum number $n = 1$. The energy of this state is $-Rhc/1^2$, meaning that it has an amount of energy equal to Rhc *below* the energy of the infinitely separated electron and nucleus.
- States for the H atom with higher energies (and $n > 1$) are called **excited states.**

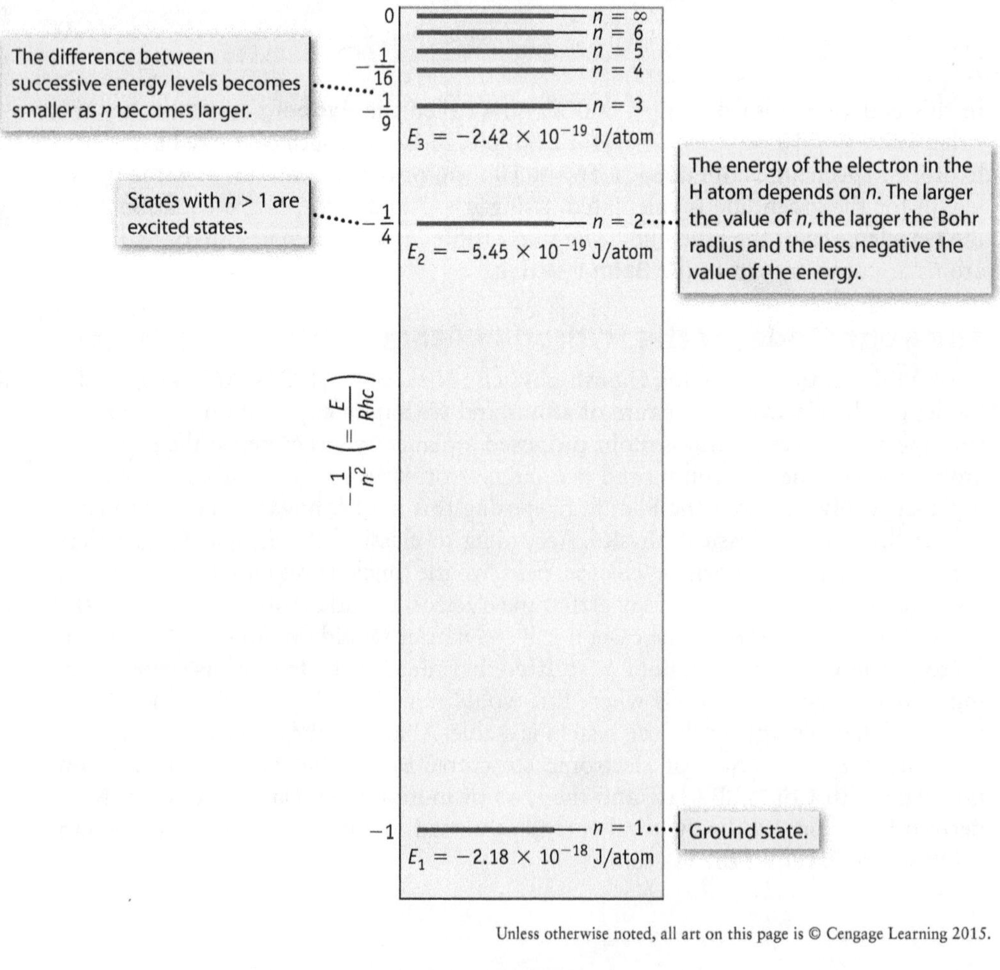

FIGURE 6.7 Energy levels for the H atom in the Bohr model.

- Because the energy is dependent on $1/n^2$, the energy levels are progressively closer together as n increases.
- An electron in the $n = 1$ orbit is closest to the nucleus and has the lowest (most negative) energy. As the value of n increases, the distance of the electron from the nucleus increases, and the energy of the electron becomes higher (less negative).

EXAMPLE 6.3

Energies of the Ground and Excited States of the H Atom

Problem Calculate the energies of the $n = 1$ and $n = 2$ states of the hydrogen atom in joules per atom and in kilojoules per mole. What is the difference in energy of these two states in kJ/mol?

What Do You Know? The $n = 1$ and $n = 2$ states are the first and second states (lowest and next to lowest energy state) in the Bohr description of the hydrogen atom. Use Equation 6.4 to calculate the energy of each state. For the calculations you will need the following constants: R (Rydberg constant) $= 1.097 \times 10^7\ \text{m}^{-1}$; h (Planck's constant) $= 6.626 \times 10^{-34}\ \text{J} \cdot \text{s}$; c (speed of light) $= 2.998 \times 10^8$ m/s; and N_A (Avogadro's number) $= 6.022 \times 10^{23}$ atoms/mol.

Strategy For each energy level, substituting the appropriate values into Equation 6.4 and solving gives the energy in J/atom. Multiply this value by N_A to find the energy in J/mol. Subtract the energy for the $n = 1$ level from the energy of the $n = 2$ level to obtain the energy difference.

Solution When $n = 1$, the energy of an electron in a single H atom is

$$E_1 = -Rhc$$

$$E_1 = -(1.097 \times 10^7\ \text{m}^{-1})(6.626 \times 10^{-34}\ \text{J} \cdot \text{s})(2.998 \times 10^8\ \text{m/s})$$

$$= -2.179 \times 10^{-18}\ \text{J/atom}$$

In units of kJ/mol,

$$E_1 = \frac{-2.179 \times 10^{-18}\ \text{J}}{\text{atom}} \times \frac{6.022 \times 10^{23}\ \text{atoms}}{\text{mol}} \times \frac{1\ \text{kJ}}{1000\ \text{J}} = -1312\ \text{kJ/mol}$$

When $n = 2$, the energy is

$$E_2 = -\frac{Rhc}{2^2} = -\frac{E_1}{4} = -\frac{2.179 \times 10^{-18}\ \text{J/atom}}{4} = -5.448 \times 10^{-19}\ \text{J/atom}$$

In units of kJ/mol,

$$E_1 = \frac{-5.448 \times 10^{-19}\ \text{J}}{\text{atom}} \times \frac{6.022 \times 10^{23}\ \text{atoms}}{\text{mol}} \times \frac{1\ \text{kJ}}{1000\ \text{J}} = -328.1\ \text{kJ/mol}$$

The difference in energy, ΔE, between the first two energy states of the H atom is

$$\Delta E = E_2 - E_1 = (-328.1\ \text{kJ/mol}) - (-1312\ \text{kJ/mol}) = 984\ \text{kJ/mol}$$

Think about Your Answer The calculated energies are negative, with E_1 more negative than E_2. The $n = 2$ state is higher in energy than the $n = 1$ state by 984 kJ/mol. Also, be sure to notice that 1312 kJ/mol is the value of Rhc multiplied by Avogadro's number N_A (that is, N_ARhc). *This value, 1312 kJ/mol, will be useful in future calculations.*

Check Your Understanding

Calculate the energy of the $n = 3$ state of the H atom in (a) joules per atom and (b) kilojoules per mole.

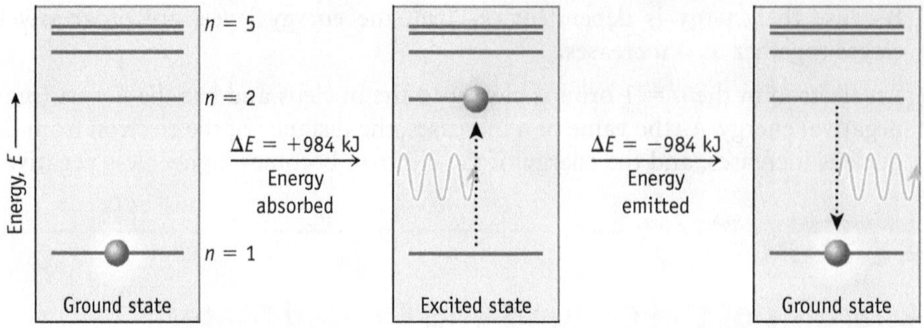

FIGURE 6.8 Absorption of energy by the atom as the electron moves to an excited state. Energy is absorbed when an electron moves from the $n = 1$ state to the $n = 2$ state ($\Delta E > 0$). When the electron returns to the $n = 1$ state from $n = 2$, energy is evolved ($\Delta E < 0$). The energy emitted is 984 kJ/mol, as calculated in Example 6.3.

The Bohr Theory and the Spectra of Excited Atoms

Bohr's theory describes electrons as having only specific orbits and energies. If an electron moves from one energy level to another, then energy must be absorbed or evolved. This idea allowed Bohr to relate energies of electrons and the emission spectrum of hydrogen atoms.

To move an electron from the $n = 1$ state to an excited state, energy must be transferred to the atom (from the surroundings). When E_{final} has $n = 2$ and $E_{initial}$ has $n = 1$, then $0.75Rhc = 1.63 \times 10^{-18}$ J/atom (or 984 kJ/mol) of energy must be transferred (Figure 6.8 and Example 6.3), no more and no less. If $0.7Rhc$ or $0.8Rhc$ is provided, no transition between states is possible. Requiring a specific and precise amount of energy is a consequence of quantization.

The opposite process, in which an electron "falls" from a level of higher n to one of lower n, leads to emission of energy, a transfer of energy, usually as radiation, from the atom to its surroundings. For example, for a transition from the $n = 2$ level to $n = 1$ level,

$$\Delta E = E_{final} - E_{initial} = -1.63 \times 10^{-18} \text{ J/atom } (= -984 \text{ kJ/mol})$$

The negative sign indicates 1.63×10^{-18} J/atom (or 984 kJ/mol) is *emitted.*

Now we can visualize the mechanism by which the characteristic line emission spectrum of hydrogen originates according to the Bohr model. Energy is provided to the atoms from an electric discharge or by heating. Depending on how much energy is added, some atoms have their electrons excited from the $n = 1$ state to the $n = 2$, 3, or even higher states. After absorbing energy, these electrons can return to any lower level (either directly or in a series of steps), releasing energy (Figure 6.9). We observe this released energy as photons of electromagnetic radiation, and,

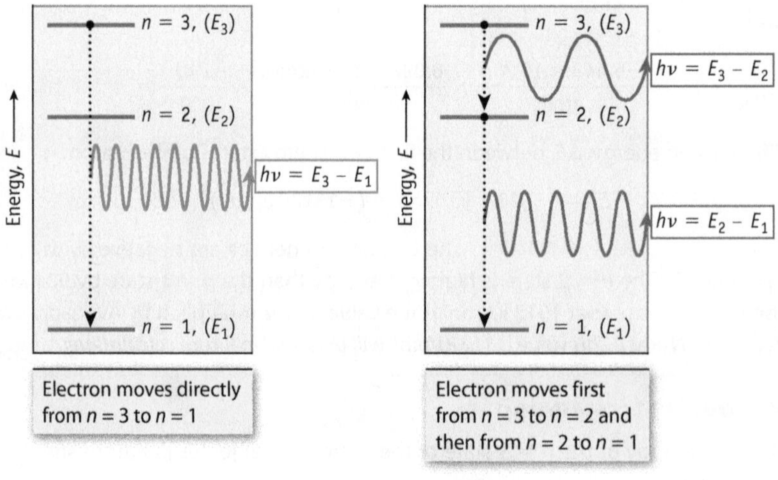

FIGURE 6.9 Radiation emitted on changes in energy levels. An electron excited to $n = 3$ can return directly to $n = 1$, or it can drop to $n = 2$ and then to $n = 1$. These three possible transitions are observed as three different wavelengths of emitted radiation. The energies and frequencies are in the order $(E_3 - E_1) > (E_2 - E_1) > (E_3 - E_2)$.

because only certain energy levels are possible, only photons with particular energies and wavelengths are emitted.

The energy of any emission line (in J/atom) for excited hydrogen atoms can be calculated using Equation 6.5.

$$\Delta E = E_{\text{final}} - E_{\text{initial}} = -Rhc\left(\frac{1}{n^2_{\text{final}}} - \frac{1}{n^2_{\text{initial}}}\right) \quad (6.5)$$

Equation 6.5 and the Balmer Equation Equation 6.5 has the same form as the Balmer Equation (Equation 6.3) where $n^2_{\text{final}} = 2$.

The value of ΔE in J/atom can be related to the wavelength or frequency of radiation using Planck's equation ($\Delta E = h\nu$).

For hydrogen, a series of emission lines having energies in the ultraviolet region (called the **Lyman series**; Figure 6.10) arises from electrons moving from states with $n > 1$ to the $n = 1$ state. The series of lines that have energies in the visible region—the **Balmer series**—arises from electrons moving from states with $n > 2$ to the $n = 2$ state. There are also series of lines in the infrared spectral region, arising from transitions from higher levels to the $n = 3$, 4, or 5 levels.

Bohr's model, introducing quantization into a description of the atom, tied the unseen (the structure of the atom) to the seen (the observable lines in the hydrogen spectrum). This is important because agreement between theory and experiment is taken as evidence that the theoretical model is valid. Nonetheless, the theory was imperfect. This model of the atom explained only the spectrum of hydrogen atoms and of other systems having one electron (such as He^+), but it failed for all other systems. A better model of electronic structure was needed.

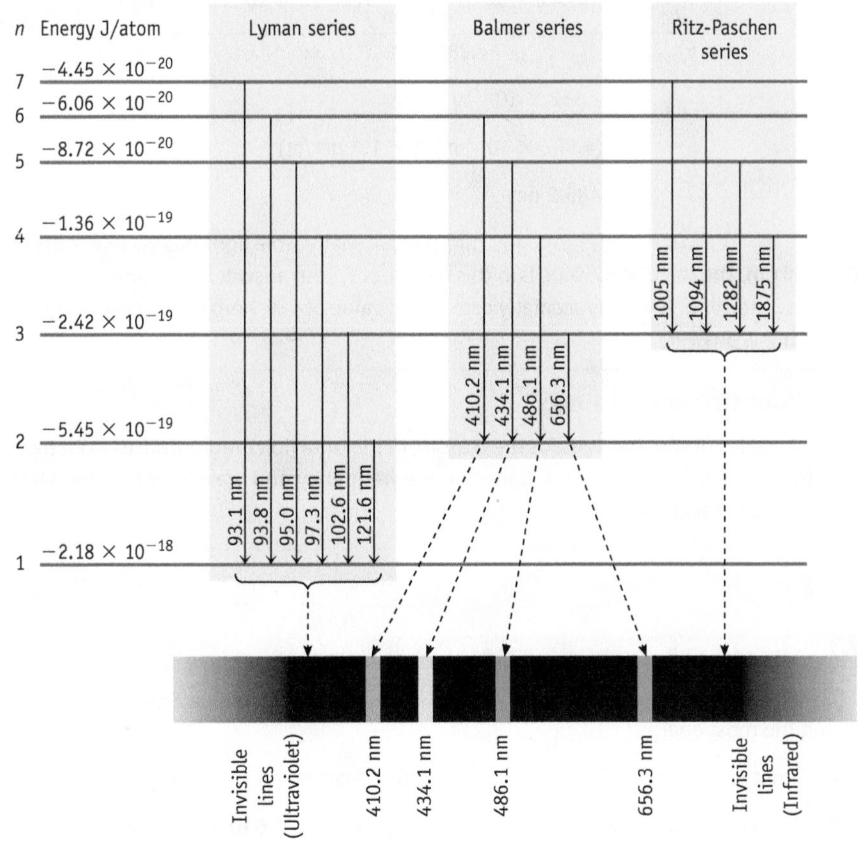

FIGURE 6.10 **Some of the electronic transitions that can occur in an excited H atom.**

- **Lyman** series: ultraviolet region, transitions to the $n = 1$ level.
- **Balmer** series: visible region, transitions from levels with values of $n > 2$ to $n = 2$.
- **Ritz-Paschen** series: infrared region, transitions from levels with $n > 3$ to the $n = 3$ level.
- Transitions from $n = 8$ and higher levels to lower levels occur but are not shown in this figure.

Strategy Map 6.4

PROBLEM

Calculate energy of *green line* in **H spectrum.**

KNOWN DATA/INFORMATION

- Green line involves transition from $n = 4$ to $n = 2$

STEP 1. Use Equation 6.5 to calculate ΔE for $n_{initial} = 4$ and $n_{final} = 2$.

Obtain $\Delta E = E_{final} - E_{initial}$

STEP 2. Determine $E_{photon} = |\Delta E|$

Obtain E_{photon}

STEP 3. Use Planck's equation to convert E_{photon} to wavelength.

Obtain photon **wavelength**

EXAMPLE 6.4

Energies of Emission Lines for Excited Atoms

Problem Calculate the wavelength of the green line in the visible spectrum of excited H atoms.

What Do You Know? The green line in the spectrum of hydrogen arises from the electron transition from the $n = 4$ state ($n_{initial}$) to the $n = 2$ state (n_{final}) (Figure 6.10).

Strategy

- Calculate the difference in energy between the states using Equation 6.5. You can simplify this calculation by using the value of Rhc from Example 6.3 ($= 2.179 \times 10^{-18}$ J).
- Relate the difference in energy to the wavelength of light using the equation $E = hc/\lambda$. (This equation is derived by combining Equations 6.1 and 6.2.)

Solution Calculate ΔE.

$$\Delta E = E_{final} - E_{initial} = \left(-\frac{Rhc}{2^2}\right) - \left(-\frac{Rhc}{4^2}\right)$$

$$\Delta E = -Rhc\left(\frac{1}{4} - \frac{1}{16}\right) = -Rhc(0.1875)$$

$$\Delta E = -(2.179 \times 10^{-18}\ \text{J})(0.1875) = -4.086 \times 10^{-19}\ \text{J/photon}$$

Recognize that, while the change in energy has a sign indicating the "direction" of energy transfer, the energy of the photon emitted, E_{photon}, does not have a sign, $E_{photon} = |\Delta E| = 4.086 \times 10^{-19}$ J/photon, that is, the absolute value of the energy found above. Now apply Planck's equation to calculate the wavelength ($E_{photon} = h\nu = hc/\lambda$, and so $\lambda = hc/E_{photon}$).

$$\lambda = \frac{hc}{E_{photon}} = \frac{\left(6.626 \times 10^{-34}\ \frac{\text{J} \cdot \text{s}}{\text{photon}}\right)(2.998 \times 10^{8}\ \text{m} \cdot \text{s}^{-1})}{4.086 \times 10^{-19}\ \text{J/photon}}$$

$$= 4.862 \times 10^{-7}\ \text{m}$$

$$= (4.862 \times 10^{-7}\ \text{m})(1 \times 10^{9}\ \text{nm/m})$$

$$= 486.2\ \text{nm}$$

Think about Your Answer You might recall that visible light has wavelengths of 400 to 700 nm. The calculated value is in this region, and your answer has a value appropriate for the green line. The experimentally determined value of 486.1 nm is in excellent agreement with this answer.

Check Your Understanding

The Lyman series of spectral lines for the H atom, in the ultraviolet region, arises from transitions from higher levels to $n = 1$. Calculate the frequency and wavelength of the least energetic line in this series.

REVIEW & CHECK FOR SECTION 6-3

1. Based on Bohr's theory, which of the following transitions for the hydrogen atom will emit the most energy?

   (a) from $n = 3$ to $n = 2$
   (b) from $n = 4$ to $n = 2$
   (c) from $n = 5$ to $n = 2$
   (d) from $n = 6$ to $n = 2$

CASE STUDY What Makes the Colors in Fireworks?

Fireworks involve lots of chemistry! For example, there must be an oxidizer and something to oxidize. Today, the oxidizer is usually a perchlorate, chlorate, or nitrate salt, and they are almost always potassium salts. The reason for using potassium and not sodium salts is that sodium salts have two important drawbacks. They are hygroscopic—they absorb water from the air—and so do not remain dry on storage. Also, when heated, sodium salts give off an intense, yellow light that is so bright it can mask other colors.

The parts of any fireworks display we remember best are the vivid colors and brilliant flashes. White light can be produced by oxidizing magnesium or aluminum metal at high temperatures. The flashes you see at rock concerts, for example, are typically $Mg/KClO_4$ mixtures.

Yellow light is easiest to produce because sodium salts give an intense light with a wavelength of 589 nm. Fireworks mixtures usually contain sodium in the form of nonhygroscopic compounds such as cryolite, Na_3AlF_6. Strontium salts are most often used to produce a red light, and green is produced by barium salts such as $Ba(NO_3)_2$.

The next time you see a fireworks display, watch for the ones that are blue. Blue has always been the most difficult color to produce. Recently, however, fireworks designers have found that a really good blue is obtained using copper(I) chloride (CuCl) mixed with $KClO_4$, copper powder, and the organic chlorine-containing compound hexachloroethane, C_2Cl_6.

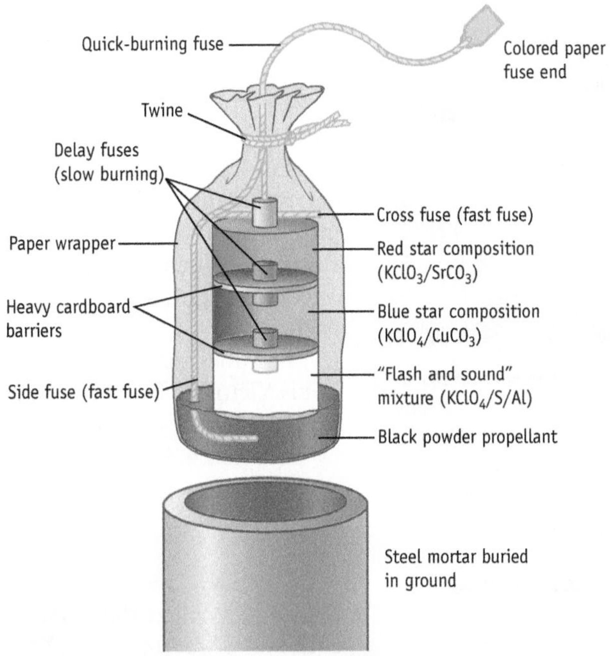

FIGURE B **The design of an aerial rocket for a fireworks display.** When the fuse is ignited, it burns quickly to the delay fuses at the top of the red star mixture as well as to the black powder propellant at the bottom. The propellant ignites, sending the shell into the air. Meanwhile, the delay fuses burn. If the timing is correct, the shell bursts high in the sky into a red star. This is followed by a blue burst and then a flash and sound.

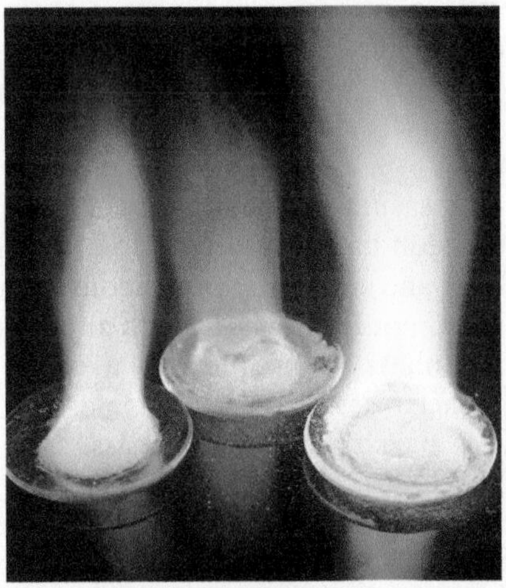

© Cengage Learning/Charles D. Winters

FIGURE A **Emission of light by excited atoms.** Flame tests are often used to identify elements in a chemical sample. Shown here are the colors produced in a flame (burning methanol) by NaCl (yellow), $SrCl_2$ (red), and boric acid (green).

Questions:

1. The main lines in the emission spectrum of sodium are at wavelengths (nm) of 313.5, 589, 590, 818, and 819. Which one or ones are most responsible for the characteristic yellow color of excited sodium atoms?
2. Does the main emission line for $SrCl_2$ (in Figure A) have a longer or shorter wavelength than that of the yellow line from NaCl?
3. Mg is oxidized by $KClO_4$ to make white flashes. One product of the reaction is KCl. Write a balanced equation for the reaction.

Answers to these questions are available in Appendix N.

2. Based on Bohr's theory, which of the following transitions for the hydrogen atom will occur with emission of visible light?

(a) from $n = 3$ to $n = 1$ (c) from $n = 5$ to $n = 3$

(b) from $n = 4$ to $n = 2$ (d) from $n = 6$ to $n = 4$

Learning Objectives: LO 1.12

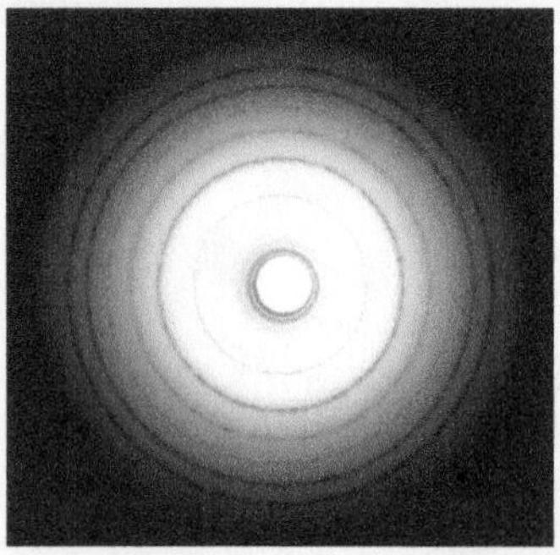

R. K. Bohn, Department of Chemistry, University of Connecticut

Diffraction and the wave nature of electrons. A beam of electrons was passed through a thin film of MgO. The atoms in the MgO lattice diffracted the electron beam, producing this pattern. Diffraction is best explained by assuming electrons have wave properties.

6-4 Particle–Wave Duality: Prelude to Quantum Mechanics

The photoelectric effect demonstrated that light, usually considered to be a wave, can also have the properties of particles, albeit without mass. That is, there is a wave-particle duality associated with light. Is there anything else that exhibits wave-particle duality? The particle properties of matter, electrons for example, are well known. Cathode ray tubes, such as were used by J. J. Thomson in his experiment to determine the charge-to-mass ratio of an electron (page 54) and which were found in television sets before the advent of LCD and plasma TVs, generate a beam of electrons. When the electrons impact the screen, the beam gives rise to tiny flashes of colored light. Such phenomena are best explained if we picture electrons as being particles.

But does matter also exhibit wave properties? This question was pondered by Louis Victor de Broglie (1892–1987), who, in 1925, proposed that a free electron of mass m moving with a velocity v should have an associated wavelength λ, calculated by Equation 6.6.

$$\lambda = \frac{h}{mv} \quad (6.6)$$

De Broglie called the wave corresponding to the wavelength calculated from this equation a "matter wave."

De Broglie's revolutionary idea linked the particle properties of the electron (mass and velocity) with a wave property (wavelength). Experimental proof was soon produced. In 1927, C. J. Davisson (1881–1958) and L. H. Germer (1896–1971) found that diffraction, a property of waves, was observed when a beam of electrons was directed at a thin sheet of metal foil. Furthermore, assuming the electron beam to be a matter wave, de Broglie's relation was followed quantitatively. This was taken as evidence that in certain experiments electrons can be described as having wave properties.

For the wavelength of a matter wave to be measurable, the product of m and v must be very small because h is so small. A 46-g golf ball, traveling at 150 mph, for example, has a large mv product (3.1 kg · m/s) and therefore an incredibly small wavelength, 2.1×10^{-34} m! Such a small value cannot be measured with any instrument now available, nor is such a value meaningful. As a consequence, wave properties are never assigned to a golf ball or any other massive object. It is possible to observe wave-like properties only for particles of extremely small mass, such as protons, electrons, and neutrons.

Like electromagnetic radiation, matter thus exhibits a wave-particle duality. In some experiments, electrons behave as if they are made of particles; in others, they behave as if they are waves. This wave-particle duality is central to an understanding of the modern model of the atom.

New Experiments on Wave-Particle Duality. A Fundamental Idea Discarded? In November 2012 *Science* magazine published two accounts of "delayed-choice" experiments. The authors of these studies stated that the experiments showed that "the photon must simultaneously behave both as a particle and a wave." (*Science*, Volume 238, pages 634–640.)

EXAMPLE 6.5

Using de Broglie's Equation

Problem Calculate the wavelength associated with an electron of mass $m = 9.109 \times 10^{-28}$ g that travels at 40.0% of the speed of light.

What Do You Know? The equation proposed by de Broglie, $\lambda = h/mv$, relates wavelength to the mass and velocity of a moving particle. Here you are given the mass of the electron and its velocity; you will need Planck's constant, $h = 6.626 \times 10^{-34}$ J · s. Note also that 1 J = 1 kg · m^2/s^2 (◀ page 27).

Strategy

- So that the units in the problem are consistent, first express the electron mass in kg and electron velocity in m/s.
- Substitute values of m (in kg), v (in m/s), and h in the de Broglie equation and solve for λ.

Solution

Electron mass $= 9.109 \times 10^{-31}$ kg

Electron speed (40.0% of light speed) $= (0.400)(2.998 \times 10^8\ \text{m/s}) = 1.20 \times 10^8\ \text{m/s}$

Substituting these values into de Broglie's equation, we have

$$\lambda = \frac{h}{mv} = \frac{6.626 \times 10^{-34}\ (\text{kg} \cdot \text{m}^2/\text{s}^2)(\text{s})}{(9.109 \times 10^{-31}\ \text{kg})(1.20 \times 10^8\ \text{m/s})} = 6.07 \times 10^{-12}\ \text{m}$$

In nanometers, the wavelength is

$$\lambda = (6.07 \times 10^{-12}\ \text{m})(1.00 \times 10^9\ \text{nm/m}) = 6.07 \times 10^{-3}\ \text{nm}$$

Think about Your Answer This wavelength is measureable and is about 1/12 of the diameter of the H atom. Also notice the care taken to monitor units in this problem.

Check Your Understanding

Calculate the wavelength associated with a neutron having a mass of 1.675×10^{-24} g and a kinetic energy of 6.21×10^{-21} J. (The kinetic energy of a moving particle is $E = \frac{1}{2}mv^2$.)

REVIEW & CHECK FOR SECTION 6-4

1. The wavelength associated with an electron moving at 40% of the speed of light is 6.07×10^{-3} nm (see Example 6.5). How will the wavelength be changed if the velocity increased to 80% of the speed of light?

   (a) Wavelength will be longer.

   (b) Wavelength will be shorter.

   (c) Wavelength will not change.

6-5 The Modern View of Electronic Structure: Wave or Quantum Mechanics

Learning Objectives: LO 1.12

How does wave–particle duality affect our model of the arrangement of electrons in atoms? Following World War I, German scientists Erwin Schrödinger (1887–1961), Max Born (1882–1970), and Werner Heisenberg (1901–1976) provided the answer.

Erwin Schrödinger received the Nobel Prize in physics in 1933 for a comprehensive theory of the behavior of electrons in atoms. Starting with de Broglie's hypothesis that *an electron could be described as a matter wave*, Schrödinger developed a model for electrons in atoms that has come to be called **quantum mechanics** or **wave mechanics.** Unlike Bohr's model, Schrödinger's model can be difficult to visualize, and the mathematical equations are complex. Nonetheless, understanding its implications is essential to understanding the modern view of the atom.

Let us start by describing the behavior of an electron in the atom as a **standing wave.** If you tie down a string at both ends, as you would the string of a guitar, and then pluck it, the string vibrates as a standing wave (Figure 6.11), and you could show that there are only certain vibrations allowed for these standing waves. That is, the vibrations are quantized. Similarly, as Schrödinger showed, only certain matter waves are possible for an electron in an atom.

FIGURE 6.11 Standing waves. Only certain vibrations are possible.

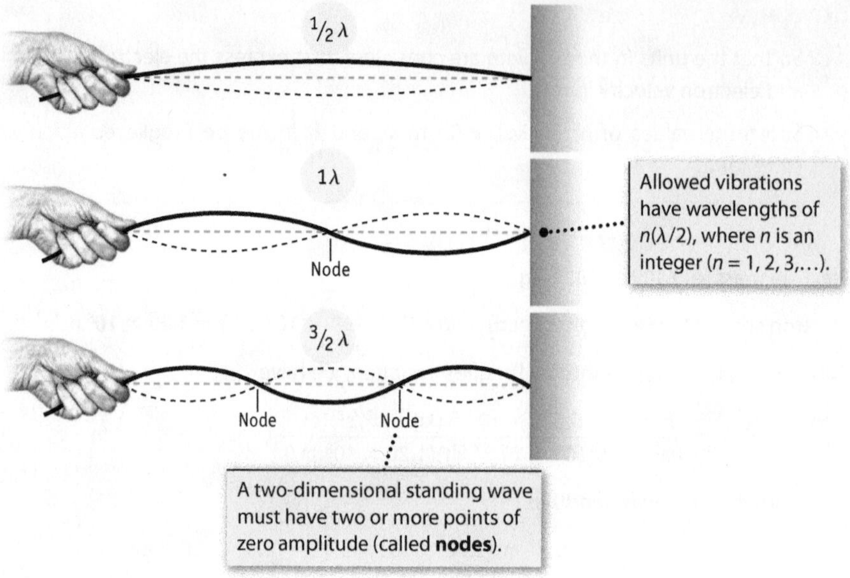

To describe these matter waves, physicists defined a series of mathematical equations called **wavefunctions**, designated by the Greek letter ψ (psi). When these equations are solved for energy, we find the following important outcomes:

- Only certain wavefunctions are found to be acceptable, and each is associated with an allowed energy value. That is, *the energy of the electron in the atom is quantized.*
- The solutions to Schrödinger's equation for an electron in three-dimensional space depend on three integers, n, ℓ, and m_ℓ, which are called **quantum numbers.** Only certain combinations of their values are possible, as we shall outline below.

Wavefunctions and Energy In Bohr's theory, the electron energy for the H atom is given by $E_n = -Rhc/n^2$. Schrödinger's electron wave model gives the same result.

The next step in understanding the quantum mechanical view is to explore the physical significance of the wavefunction, ψ (psi). Here we owe much to Max Born's interpretation. He said that

- the value of the wavefunction ψ at a given point in space (x, y, z) is the amplitude (height) of the electron matter wave. This value has both a magnitude and a sign that can be either positive or negative. (Visualize a vibrating string [see Figure 6.11]. Points of positive amplitude are above the axis of the wave, and points of negative amplitude are below it.)
- the square of the value of the wavefunction (ψ^2) is related to the *probability* of finding an electron in a tiny region of space. Scientists refer to ψ^2 as a **probability density.** Just as we can calculate the mass of an object from the product of its density and volume, we can calculate the *probability* of finding an electron in a tiny volume from the product of ψ^2 and the volume. Born's interpretation is that the probability of finding the electron in a given volume is proportional to ψ^2; for a given volume, whenever ψ^2 is large, the probability of finding the electron is larger than when ψ^2 is small.

There is one more important concept to touch on as we try to understand the modern quantum mechanical model. In Bohr's model of the atom, both the energy and location (the orbit) for the electron in the hydrogen atom can be described accurately. However, Werner Heisenberg postulated that, for a tiny object such as an electron in an atom, it is impossible to determine accurately *both* its position and its energy. That is, any attempt to determine accurately either the location or the energy will leave the other uncertain. This is now known as **Heisenberg's uncertainty principle:** *If we choose to know the energy of an electron in an atom with* *only a small uncertainty, then we must accept a correspondingly large uncertainty in its position.* The importance of this idea is that we can assess only the likelihood, or probability, of finding an electron with a given energy within a given region of space. Because electron energy is the key to understanding the chemistry of an atom, chemists accept the notion of knowing only the approximate location of the electron.

Quantum Numbers and Orbitals

The wavefunction for an electron in an atom describes an **atomic orbital**. We know the energy of this electron, but we only know the region of space within which it is most probably located. When an electron has a particular wavefunction, it is said to "occupy" a particular orbital with a given energy.

Each orbital is described by three quantum numbers: n, ℓ, and m_ℓ. Let us first describe the quantum numbers and the information they provide and then discuss the connection between quantum numbers and the energies and shapes of atomic orbitals.

Orbits and Orbitals In Bohr's model of the H atom, the electron is confined to a prescribed path around the nucleus, its *orbit*, so we should be able to define its position and energy at a given moment in time. In the modern view, the term *orbital* is used. We know the energy of the electron but only the region of space within which it is probably located.

n, the Principal Quantum Number ($n = 1, 2, 3, \ldots$)

The principal quantum number n can have any integer value from 1 to infinity. The value of n is the primary factor in determining the *energy* of an orbital. It also defines the *size* of an orbital: for a given atom, the greater the value of n, the greater the size of the orbital.

In atoms having more than one electron, two or more electrons may have the same n value. These electrons are then said to be in the same **electron shell.**

ℓ, the Orbital Angular Momentum Quantum Number ($\ell = 0, 1, 2, 3, \ldots, n - 1$)

Orbitals of a given electron shell can be grouped into **subshells**, where each subshell is characterized by a different value of the quantum number ℓ. The quantum number ℓ, referred to as the "orbital angular momentum" quantum number, can have any integer value from 0 to a maximum of $n - 1$. This quantum number defines the *characteristic shape of an orbital*; different ℓ values correspond to different orbital shapes.

The value of n limits the number of subshells possible for each shell. The number of possible subshells increases as n increases. For the shell with $n = 1$, ℓ must equal 0; thus, only one subshell is possible. When $n = 2$, ℓ can be either 0 or 1. Two values of ℓ are now possible, and it follows that there are two subshells in the $n = 2$ electron shell.

Electron Energy and Quantum Numbers The electron energy in the H atom depends only on the value of n. In atoms with more electrons, the energy depends on both n and ℓ.

Subshells are usually identified by letters. For example, an $\ell = 1$ subshell is called a "p subshell," and an orbital in that subshell is called a "p orbital."

VALUE OF ℓ	SUBSHELL LABEL
0	*s*
1	*p*
2	*d*
3	*f*

m_ℓ, the Magnetic Quantum Number ($m_\ell = 0, \pm1, \pm2, \pm3, \ldots, \pm\ell$)

The magnetic quantum number, m_ℓ, is related to the *orientation in space of the orbitals within a subshell*. Orbitals in a given subshell differ in their orientation in space, not in their energy.

The value of m_ℓ can range from $+\ell$ to $-\ell$, with 0 included. For example, when $\ell = 2$, m_ℓ can have five values: -2, -1, 0, $+1$, and $+2$. The number of values of m_ℓ for a given subshell ($= 2\ell + 1$) specifies the number of orbitals in the subshell.

Shells, Subshells, and Orbitals—A Summary Electrons in atoms are arranged in shells. Within each shell, there can be one or more electron subshells, each composed of one or more orbitals.

	Quantum Number
Shell	n
Subshell	ℓ
Orbital	m_ℓ

Shells and Subshells

Allowed values of the three quantum numbers are summarized in Table 6.1. By analyzing the sets of quantum numbers in this table, you will discover the following:

- n = the number of subshells in a shell
- $2\ell + 1$ = the number of orbitals in a subshell = the number of values of m_ℓ
- n^2 = the number of orbitals in a shell

The First Electron Shell, $n = 1$

When $n = 1$, the value of ℓ can only be 0, so m_ℓ must also have a value of 0. This means that, in the shell closest to the nucleus, only one subshell exists, and that subshell consists of only a single orbital, the 1*s* orbital.

The Second Electron Shell, $n = 2$

When $n = 2$, ℓ can have two values (0 and 1), so there are two subshells in the second shell. One of these is the 2*s subshell* ($n = 2$ and $\ell = 0$), and the other is the 2*p* subshell ($n = 2$ and $\ell = 1$). The values of m_ℓ can be -1, 0, and $+1$ when $\ell = 1$; three 2*p* orbitals exist. All three orbitals have the same shape. However, each has a different m_ℓ value, that is, the three orbitals differ in their orientation in space.

The Third Electron Shell, $n = 3$

When $n = 3$, three subshells are possible for an electron; there are three values of ℓ: 0, 1, and 2. The first two subshells within the $n = 3$ shell are the 3*s* ($\ell = 0$, one orbital) and 3*p* ($\ell = 1$, three orbitals) subshells. The third subshell is labeled 3*d* ($n = 3$, $\ell = 2$). Because m_ℓ can have five values (-2, -1, 0, $+1$, and $+2$) for $\ell = 2$, there are five *d* orbitals in this *d* subshell.

The Fourth Electron Shell, $n = 4$

There are four subshells in the $n = 4$ shell. In addition to 4*s*, 4*p*, and 4*d* subshells, there is the 4*f* subshell for which $\ell = 3$. Seven such orbitals exist because there are seven values of m_ℓ when $\ell = 3$ (-3, -2, -1, 0, $+1$, $+2$, and $+3$).

Table 6.1 Summary of the Quantum Numbers, Their Interrelationships, and the Orbital Information Conveyed

PRINCIPAL QUANTUM NUMBER SYMBOL = n VALUES = 1, 2, 3, . . .	ANGULAR MOMENTUM QUANTUM NUMBER SYMBOL = ℓ VALUES = 0 . . . $n - 1$	MAGNETIC QUANTUM NUMBER SYMBOL = m_ℓ VALUES = $-\ell$ . . . 0 . . . $+\ell$	NUMBER AND TYPE OF ORBITALS IN THE SUBSHELL n = NUMBER OF SUBSHELLS NUMBER OF ORBITALS IN SHELL = n^2 AND NUMBER OF ORBITALS IN SUBSHELL = $2\ell + 1$
1	0	0	one 1*s* orbital (one orbital of one type in the $n = 1$ shell)
2	0 1	0 $-1, 0, +1$	one 2*s* orbital three 2*p* orbitals (four orbitals of two types in the $n = 2$ shell)
3	0 1 2	0 $-1, 0, +1$ $-2, -1, 0, +1, +2$	one 3*s* orbital three 3*p* orbitals five 3*d* orbitals (nine orbitals of three types in the $n = 3$ shell)
4	0 1 2 3	0 $-1, 0, +1$ $-2, -1, 0, +1, +2$ $-3, -2, -1, 0, +1, +2, +3$	one 4*s* orbital three 4*p* orbitals five 4*d* orbitals seven 4*f* orbitals (16 orbitals of four types in the $n = 4$ shell)

REVIEW & CHECK FOR SECTION 6-5

1. What label is given to an orbital with quantum numbers $n = 4$ and $\ell = 1$?

   (a) 4*s* (b) 4*p* (c) 4*d* (d) 4*f*

2. How many orbitals are in the $n = 4$ shell?

   (a) 1 (b) 4 (c) 9 (d) 16

3. Which quantum number, or combination of quantum numbers, is needed to specify a given subshell in an atom?

   (a) n (b) ℓ (c) n and ℓ

6-6 The Shapes of Atomic Orbitals

We often say the electron is assigned to, or "occupies," an orbital. But what does this mean? What is an orbital? What does it look like? To answer these questions, we have to look at the wavefunctions for the orbitals. (To answer the question of *why* the quantum numbers—small, whole numbers—can be related to orbital shape and energy, see *A Closer Look: More about H Atom Orbital Shapes and Wavefunctions* on page 242.)

s Orbitals

A 1*s* orbital is associated with the quantum numbers $n = 1$ and $\ell = 0$. If we could photograph a 1*s* electron at one-second intervals for a few thousand seconds, the composite picture would look like the drawing in Figure 6.12a. This resembles a cloud of dots, and chemists often refer to such representations as *electron cloud pictures.* In Figure 6.12a, the density of dots is greater close to the nucleus, that is, the electron cloud is denser close to the nucleus. This indicates that the 1*s* electron is most likely to be found near the nucleus. The density of dots declines on moving away from the nucleus and so, therefore, does the probability of finding the electron.

The thinning of the electron cloud at increasing distance is illustrated in a different way in Figure 6.12b. Here we have plotted the square of the wavefunction for

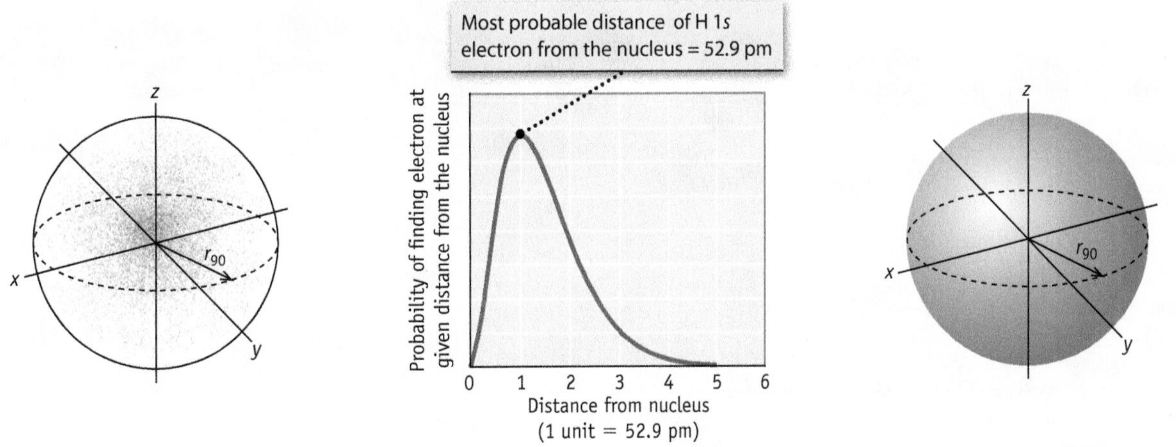

(a) Dot picture of an electron in a 1*s* orbital. Each dot represents the position of the electron at a different instant in time. Note that the dots cluster closest to the nucleus. r_{90} is the radius of a sphere within which the electron is found 90% of the time.

(b) A plot of the surface density ($4\pi r^2\psi^2$) as a function of distance for a hydrogen atom 1*s* orbital. This gives the probability of finding the electron at a given distance from the nucleus.

(c) The surface of the sphere within which the electron is found 90% of the time for a 1*s* orbital. This surface is often called a "boundary surface." (A 90% surface was chosen arbitrarily. If the choice was the surface within which the electron is found 50% of the time, the sphere would be considerably smaller.)

FIGURE 6.12 **Different views of a 1*s* ($n = 1$, $\ell = 0$) orbital.** In panel **(b)** the horizontal axis is marked in units called "Bohr radii," where 1 Bohr radius = 52.9 pm. This is common practice when plotting wavefunctions.

the electron in a 1*s* orbital (ψ^2), times 4π and the distance squared (r^2), as a function of the distance of the electron from the nucleus. This plot represents the probability of finding the electron in a thin spherical shell at a distance *r* from the nucleus. Chemists refer to the plot of $4\pi r^2\psi^2$ vs. *r* as a **surface density plot** or **radial distribution plot.** For the 1*s* orbital, $4\pi r^2\psi^2$ is zero at the nucleus—there is no probability the electron will be exactly at the nucleus (where $r = 0$)—but the probability rises rapidly on moving away from the nucleus, reaches a maximum a short distance from the nucleus (at 52.9 pm), and then decreases rapidly as the distance from the nucleus increases. Notice that the probability of finding the electron approaches but never quite reaches zero, even at very large distances.

Surface Density Plot for 1*s* The maximum value of the radial distribution plot for a 1*s* electron in a hydrogen atom occurs at 52.9 pm. It is interesting to note that this maximum is at exactly the same distance from the nucleus that Niels Bohr calculated for the radius of the orbit occupied by the $n = 1$ electron.

Figure 6.12a shows that, for the 1*s* orbital, the probability of finding an electron is the same at a given distance from the nucleus, no matter in which direction you proceed from the nucleus. Consequently, the *1s orbital is spherical in shape.*

Because the probability of finding the electron approaches but never quite reaches zero, there is no sharp boundary beyond which the electron is never found (although the probability is very small at large distances). Nonetheless, the *s* orbital (and other types of orbitals as well) is often depicted as having a **boundary surface** (Figure 6.12c), largely because it is easier to draw such pictures. To create Figure 6.12c, we drew a sphere centered on the nucleus in such a way that there is a 90% probability of finding the electron somewhere inside the sphere. The choice of 90% is arbitrary—we could have chosen a different value—and if we do, the shape would be the same, but the size of the sphere would be different.

All *s* orbitals (1*s*, 2*s*, 3*s* . . .) are spherical in shape. However, for any atom, the size of *s* orbitals increases as *n* increases (Figure 6.13). For a given atom, the 1*s* orbital is more compact than the 2*s* orbital, which is in turn more compact than the 3*s* orbital.

It is important to recognize several features of this description.

- There is not an impenetrable surface within which the electron is "contained."
- The probability of finding the electron is not the same throughout the volume enclosed by the surface in Figure 6.12c. (An electron in the 1*s* orbital of an H atom has a greater probability of being 52.9 pm from the nucleus than of being closer or farther away.)

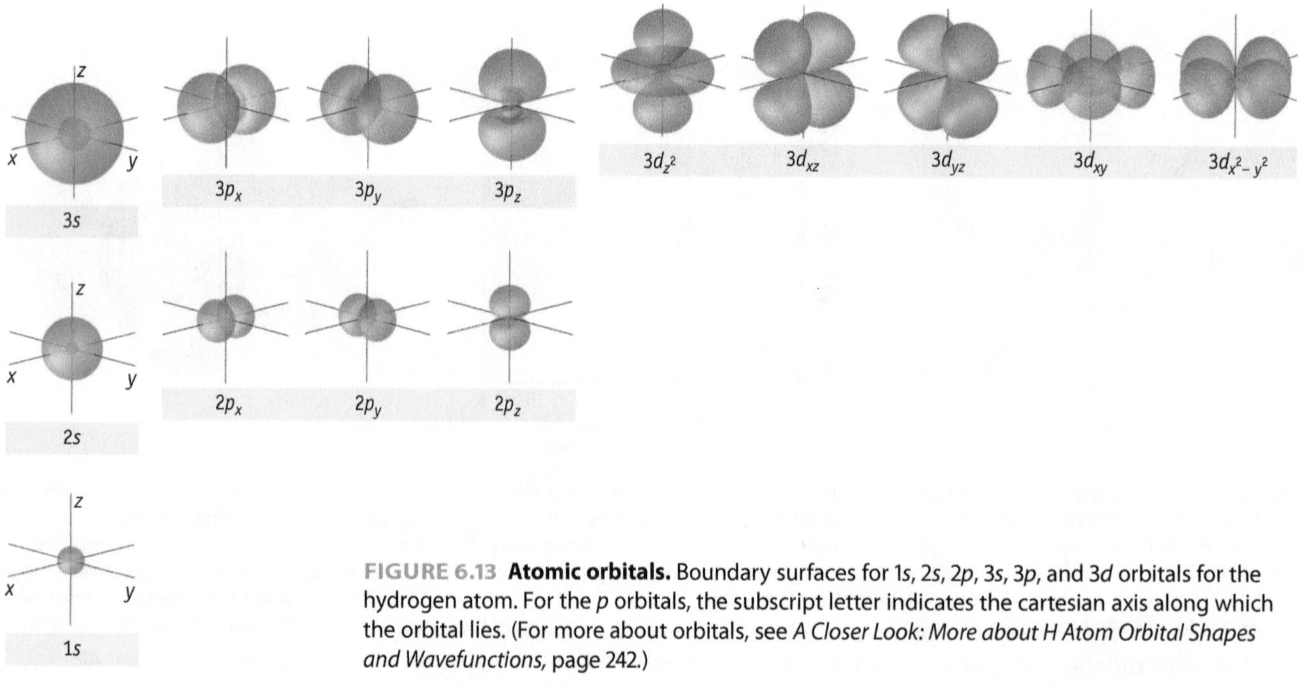

FIGURE 6.13 **Atomic orbitals.** Boundary surfaces for 1*s*, 2*s*, 2*p*, 3*s*, 3*p*, and 3*d* orbitals for the hydrogen atom. For the *p* orbitals, the subscript letter indicates the cartesian axis along which the orbital lies. (For more about orbitals, see *A Closer Look: More about H Atom Orbital Shapes and Wavefunctions,* page 242.)

- The terms "electron cloud" and "electron distribution" imply that the electron is a particle, but the basic premise in quantum mechanics is that the electron is treated as a wave, not a particle.

p Orbitals

All atomic orbitals for which $\ell = 1$ (p orbitals) have the same basic shape. If you enclose 90% of the electron density in a p orbital within a surface, the electron cloud is often described as having a shape like a weight lifter's "dumbbell," and chemists describe p orbitals as having dumbbell shapes (Figures 6.13 and 6.14). A p orbital has a **nodal surface**—a surface on which the probability of finding the electron is zero—that passes through the nucleus. (The nodal surface is a consequence of the wavefunction for p orbitals, which has a value of zero at all points on this surface, including at the nucleus itself. See *A Closer Look: More about H Atom Orbital Shapes and Wavefunctions,* page 242.)

There are three p orbitals in a subshell, and all have the same basic shape with one nodal plane through the nucleus. Usually, p orbitals are drawn along the x-, y-, and z-axes and labeled according to the axis along which they lie (p_x, p_y, or p_z).

ℓ and Nodal Surfaces The number of nodal surfaces passing through the nucleus for an orbital = ℓ.

Orbital	ℓ	Number of Nodal Surfaces through the Nucleus
s	0	0
p	1	1
d	2	2
f	3	3

d Orbitals

Orbitals with $\ell = 0$, s orbitals, have no nodal surfaces through the nucleus, and p orbitals, for which $\ell = 1$, have one nodal surface through the nucleus. *The value of ℓ is equal to the number of nodal surfaces slicing through the nucleus.* It follows that the five d orbitals, for which $\ell = 2$, have two nodal surfaces through the nucleus, resulting in four regions of electron density. The d_{xy} orbital, for example, lies in the xy-plane, and the two nodal surfaces are the xz- and yz-planes (see Figure 6.14). Two other orbitals, d_{xz} and d_{yz}, lie in planes defined by the xz- *and* yz-axes, respectively; they also have two, mutually perpendicular nodal surfaces (see Figure 6.13).

Of the two remaining d orbitals, the $d_{x^2-y^2}$ orbital is easier to visualize. In the $d_{x^2-y^2}$ orbital, the nodal planes bisect the x- and y-axes, so the regions of electron density lie along the x- and y-axes. The d_{z^2} orbital has two main regions of electron density along the z-axis, and a "doughnut" of electron density also occurs in the xy-plane. This orbital has two cone-shaped nodal surfaces.

Nodal Surfaces Nodal surfaces that cut through the nucleus occur for all *p*, *d*, and *f* orbitals. These surfaces are usually flat, so they are often referred to as *nodal planes*. In some cases (for example, d_{z^2}), however, the "plane" is not flat and so is better referred to as a *nodal surface*.

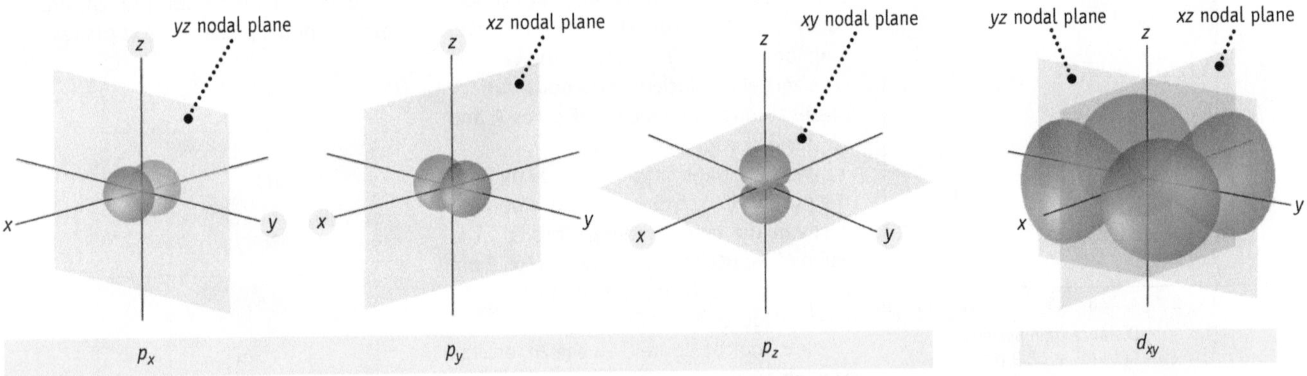

(a) The three p orbitals each have one nodal plane ($\ell = 1$) that is perpendicular to the axis along which the orbital lies.

(b) The d_{xy} orbital. All five d orbitals have two nodal surfaces ($\ell = 2$) passing through the nucleus. Here, the nodal surfaces are the xz- and yz-planes, so the regions of electron density lie between the x- and y-axes in the xy-plane.

FIGURE 6.14 **Nodal surfaces of *p* and *d* orbitals.** A nodal surface is a surface on which the probability of finding the electron is zero.

A CLOSER LOOK | More about H Atom Orbital Shapes and Wavefunctions

How do quantum numbers, which are small, integer numbers, relate to the shape of atomic orbitals? The answer lies in the orbital wavefunctions (ψ), which are mathematical equations. These equations are the product of two functions: the *radial function* and the *angular function*. You need to look at each type to get a picture of an orbital.

Let's first consider the *radial function*, which depends on *n* and ℓ. This tells us how the value of ψ depends on the distance from the nucleus. The radial functions for the hydrogen atom 1*s* ($n = 1$ and $\ell = 0$), 2*s* ($n = 2$ and $\ell = 0$) orbitals, and 2*p* orbitals ($n = 2$ and $\ell = 1$) are plotted in Figure A. (The horizontal axis has units of a_o, where a_o is a constant equal to 52.9 pm.)

Waves have crests, troughs, and nodes, and plots of the wavefunctions show this. For the 1*s* orbital of the H atom, the radial wavefunction ψ_{1s} approaches a maximum at the nucleus (Figure A), but the wave's amplitude declines rapidly at points farther removed from the nucleus. The sign of ψ_{1s} is positive at all points in space.

For a 2*s* orbital, there is a different profile: the sign of ψ_{2s} is positive near the nucleus, drops to zero (there is a node at $r = 2a_o = 2 \times 52.9$ pm), and then becomes negative with increasing *r* before approaching zero at greater distances.

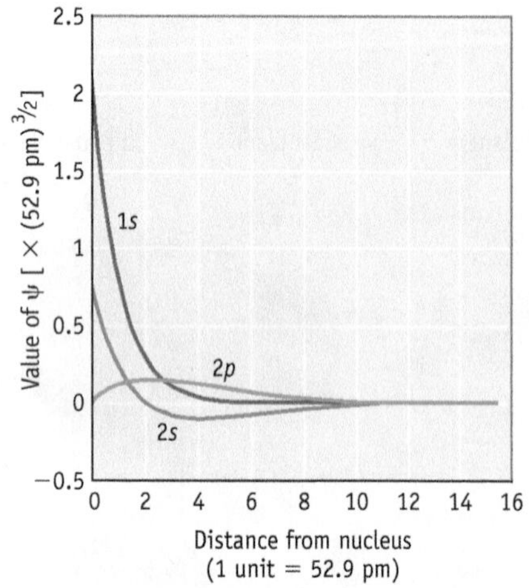

FIGURE A Plot of the wavefunctions for 1*s*, 2*s*, and 2*p* orbitals for an H atom versus distance from the nucleus. As in other plots of wavefunctions, the horizontal axis is marked in units called "Bohr radii," where 1 Bohr radius = 52.9 pm.

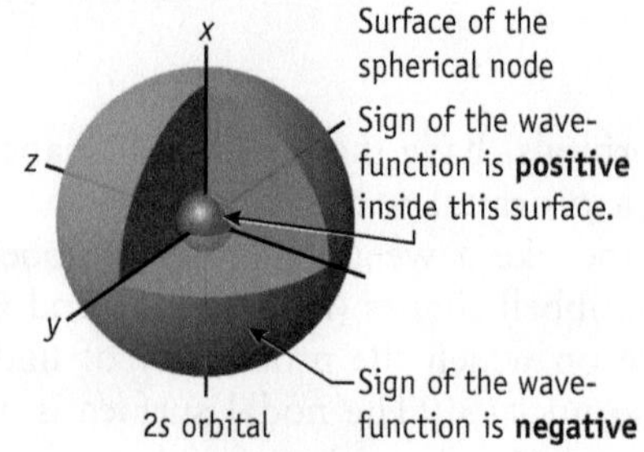

FIGURE B Wavefunction for a 2*s* orbital. A 2*s* orbital for the H atom showing the spherical node (at $2a_o$ = 105.8 pm) around the nucleus.

Now to the *angular portion* of the wavefunction: this reflects changes that occur when you travel outward from the nucleus in different directions. It is a function of the quantum numbers ℓ and m_ℓ.

As illustrated in Figure 6.12 the value of ψ_{1s} is the same in every direction. This is a reflection of the fact that, while the radial portion of the wavefunction for *s* orbitals changes with *r*, the angular portion for all *s* orbitals is a constant. As a consequence, all *s* orbital are spherical.

For the 2*s* orbital, you see a node in Figure A at 105.8 pm (= $2a_o$) when plotting the radial portion of the wavefunction. However, because the angular part of ψ_{2s} has the same value in all directions, this means there is a node—a *spherical nodal surface*—at the same distance in every direction (as illustrated in Figure B). For any orbital, the number of spherical nodes is $n - \ell - 1$.

Now let's look at a *p* orbital, first the radial portion and then the angular portion. For a *p* orbital the radial portion of the wavefunction is 0 when $r = 0$. Thus, the value of ψ_{2p} is zero at the nucleus and a nodal surface passes through the nucleus (Figures A and C). This is true for all *p* orbitals.

What happens as you move away from the nucleus in one direction, say along the *x*-axis in the case of the $2p_x$ orbital? The value of ψ_{2p} rise to a maximum at 105.9 pm (= $2a_o$) before falling off at greater distances (Figures A and C).

Next, look at Figure C for the $2p_x$ orbital. Moving away along the $-x$ direction, the value of ψ_{2p} is the same but opposite in sign to the value in the $+x$ direction. The 2*p* electron is a wave with a node at the nucleus. (In drawing orbitals, we indicate this with + or − signs or with two different colors as in Figure 6.13.)

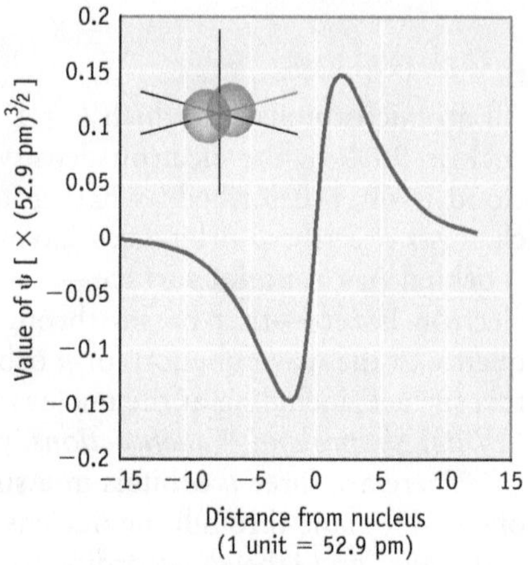

FIGURE C Wavefunctions for a 2*p* orbital for an H atom. The sign of ψ for a 2*p* orbital is positive on one side of the nucleus and negative on the other (but it has a 0 value at the nucleus). A nodal plane separates the two lobes of this "dumbbell-shaped" orbital. (The vertical axis is the value of ψ, and the horizontal axis is the distance from the nucleus, where 1 unit = 52.9 pm.)

What about the *angular portion* of the wavefunction for $2p_x$? The angular portion for all three *p* orbitals has the same general form: $c(x/r)$ for the p_x orbital, $c(y/r)$ for the p_y orbital, and $c(z/r)$ for the p_z orbital (where c is a constant). Consider a $2p_x$ orbital in Figure D. As long as *x* has a nonzero value, the wavefunction has a nonzero value. But when $x = 0$ (in the *yz* plane), then ψ is zero. This is the nodal plane for the *x* orbital. Similarly, the angular portion of the wavefunction for the $2p_y$ orbital means its nodal plane is the *xz* plane.

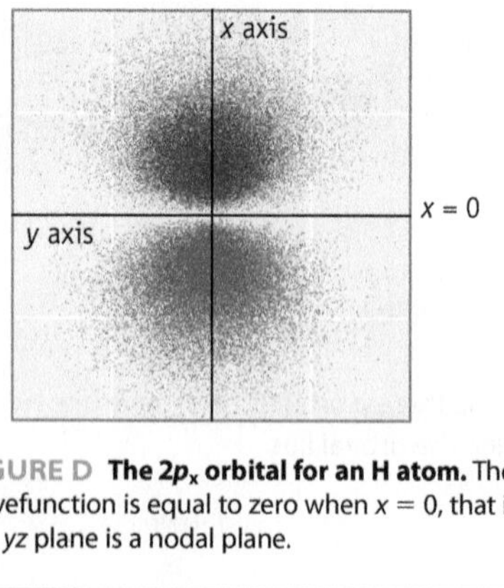

FIGURE D The $2p_x$ orbital for an H atom. The wavefunction is equal to zero when $x = 0$, that is, the *yz* plane is a nodal plane.

f Orbitals

Seven *f* orbitals arise with $\ell = 3$. Three nodal surfaces through the nucleus cause the electron density to lie in up to eight regions of space. One of the *f* orbitals is illustrated in Figure 6.15.

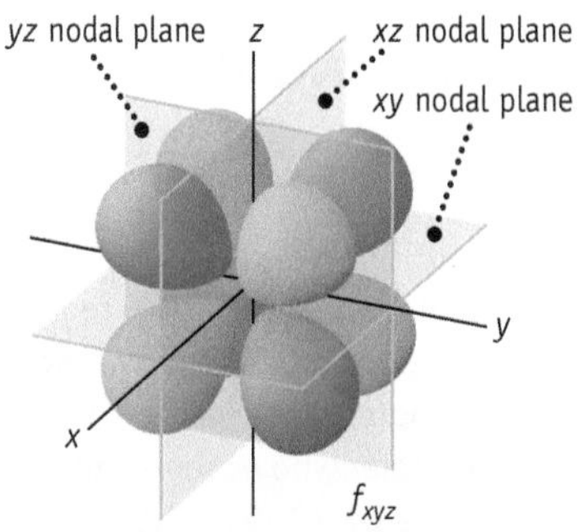

FIGURE 6.15 One of the seven possible *f* orbitals. Notice the presence of three nodal planes as required by an orbital with $\ell = 3$.

REVIEW & CHECK FOR SECTION 6-6

1. Which of the following is not a correct representation of an orbital?

   (a) 3*s* (b) 3*p* (c) 3*d* (d) 3*f*

2. Which of the following sets of quantum numbers correctly represents a 4*p* orbital?

   (a) $n = 4, \ell = 0, m_\ell = -1$ (c) $n = 4, \ell = 2, m_\ell = 1$

   (b) $n = 4, \ell = 1, m_\ell = 0$ (d) $n = 4, \ell = 1, m_\ell = 2$

3. How many nodal planes exist for a 5*d* orbital?

   (a) 0 (b) 1 (c) 2 (d) 3

6-7 One More Electron Property: Electron Spin

There is one more property of the electron that plays an important role in the arrangement of electrons in atoms: electron spin. In 1921 Otto Stern and Walther Gerlach performed an experiment that probed the magnetic behavior of atoms by passing a beam of silver atoms in the gas phase through a magnetic field. Although the results were complex, they were best interpreted by *imagining* the electron has a spin and behaves as a tiny magnet that can be attracted or repelled by another magnet. If atoms with a single unpaired electron are placed in a magnetic field, the Stern-Gerlach experiment showed there are two orientations for the atoms: with the electron spin aligned with the field or opposed to the field. That is, *the electron spin is quantized.* This fact is accounted for by introducing a fourth quantum number, the **electron spin quantum number,** m_s. One orientation is associated with a value of m_s of $+\frac{1}{2}$ and the other with m_s of $-\frac{1}{2}$.

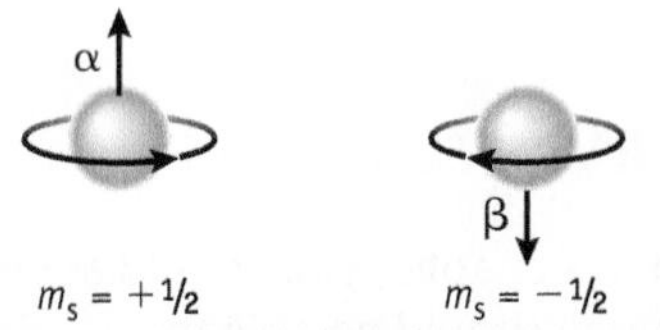

When it was recognized that electron spin is quantized, scientists realized that a complete description of an electron in any atom requires four quantum numbers, n, ℓ, m_ℓ, and m_s. The important consequences of this fact are explored in Chapter 7.

REVIEW & CHECK FOR SECTION 6-7

1. Which of the following is a valid set of quantum numbers for an electron in a hydrogen atom?

   (a) $n = 1, \ell = 0, m_\ell = 0, m_s = 1$ (c) $n = 1, \ell = 0, m_\ell = 1, m_s = +1/2$

   (b) $n = 1, \ell = 1, m_\ell = 0, m_s = -1/2$ (d) $n = 1, \ell = 0, m_\ell = 0, m_s = -1/2$

APPLYING CHEMICAL PRINCIPLES

Chemistry of the Sun

An optical spectrum of our Sun reveals a continuous emission of radiation in the visible region with sharp, darkened lines at hundreds of different wavelengths. These lines are named Fraunhofer lines, after the German physicist Joseph von Fraunhofer who observed them in 1814. Fraunhofer was able to observe over 570 of these lines, but over one thousand dark lines may be observed with modern instrumentation. In 1859, Gustav Robert Kirchhoff and Robert Bunsen deduced that the dark lines are the result of absorption of sunlight by elements in the outer layers of the Sun.

The fact that atoms of a particular element absorb or emit light of only a few wavelengths may be used to identify elements (page 227). Most stars are rich in hydrogen, so the Balmer series (page 231) is commonly observed in their spectra. The discovery and naming of helium is credited to Sir Joseph Norman Lockyer (1836–1920), who observed its yellow spectral line during a total solar eclipse in 1868. Helium is common in stars, but less common on Earth.

QUESTIONS:

1. Helium absorbs light at 587.6 nm. What is the frequency of this light?
2. Iron atoms absorb light at a frequency of 5.688×10^{14} s^{-1}. What is the wavelength of this light (in nm)?
3. Sodium atoms are responsible for a closely spaced pair of lines in the yellow region of the Sun's visible spectrum at 589.00 nm and 589.59 nm. Determine the energy (in joules) of a photon at each of these wavelengths. Determine the difference in energy between the two photons.
4. Hydrogen has an absorption line at 434.1 nm. What is the energy (in kilojoules per mole) of photons with this wavelength?
5. What are the final and initial electronic states (n) for the hydrogen line (in the Balmer series) labeled F in the figure?

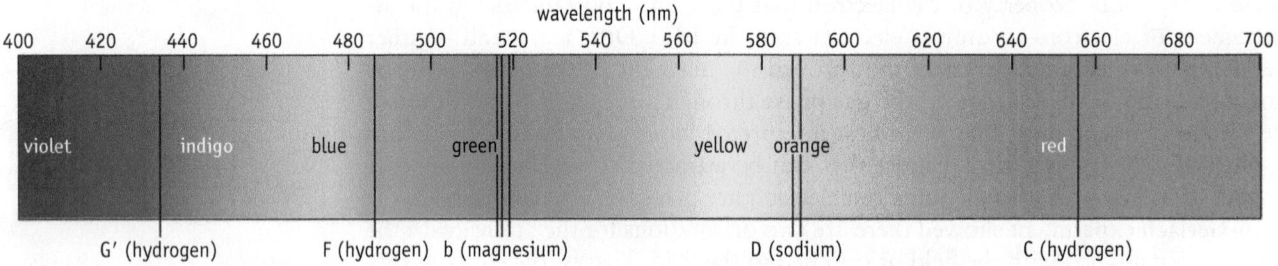

The spectrum of sunlight with Fraunhofer lines. The German physicist Joseph von Fraunhofer (1787–1826) discovered the dark lines in the spectrum of sunlight and carefully mapped and measured them. He designated the principal lines with letters A through K and less prominent lines with lowercase letters.

CHAPTER GOALS REVISITED

Now that you have studied this chapter, you should ask whether you have met the chapter goals. In particular, you should be able to:

UNDERSTAND

- The characteristics of electromagnetic radiation (wavelength, frequency, speed, nodes, and energy).
  - **a.** Use the terms wavelength, frequency, amplitude, and node (Section 6-1). Study Question: 3.
  - **b.** Understand how Einstein explained the photoelectric effect by assuming that light consists of massless particles called photons (Section 6-2).

- The origin of light emitted by excited atoms and its relationship to atomic structure.
  - **a.** Describe the Bohr model of the atom, its ability to account for the emission line spectra of excited hydrogen atoms, and the limitations of the model (Section 6-3). Study Question: 74.
  - **b.** Understand that, in the Bohr model of the H atom, the electron can occupy only certain energy states, each with an energy proportional to $1/n^2$ ($E_n = -Rhc/n^2$), where n is the principal quantum number (Equation 6.4, Section 6-3). If an electron moves from one energy state to another, the amount of energy absorbed or emitted in the process is equal to the difference in energy between the two states (Equation 6.5, Section 6-3). Study Questions: 16, 18, 19, 21, 22, 60.
- The experimental evidence for particle–wave duality.
  - **a.** Understand that electromagnetic radiation and, in the modern view of the atom, electrons can be described either as particles or as waves (Section 6-4). The wavelength of an electron or any subatomic particle is given by de Broglie's equation (Equation 6.6). Study Questions: 23–26, 82.
- The basic principles of quantum mechanics, such as quantization and wavefunctions.
  - **a.** Understand that the quantum mechanical model for an atom is based on the assumption that the electron behaves as a wave.
  - **b.** Recognize the significance of quantum mechanics in describing atomic structure (Section 6-5).
  - **c.** Understand that an orbital for an electron in an atom corresponds to the allowed energy of that electron.
  - **d.** Understand that the position of the electron is not known with certainty; only the probability of the electron being at a given point of space can be calculated. This is a consequence of the Heisenberg uncertainty principle.

DO

- Relate wavelength (λ), frequency (ν), speed (c), and energy (E) per photon of electromagnetic radiation.
  - **a.** Use Equation 6.1 ($c = \lambda\nu$), relating wavelength (λ) and frequency (ν) of electromagnetic radiation and the speed of light (c). Study Question: 3.
  - **b.** Understand that the energy of a photon is proportional to its frequency (Planck's equation, Equation 6.2) (Section 6-2). Study Questions: 5, 7–9, 12, 14, 56–58, 63, 64, 66, 72, 73, 83.
- Calculate the energy of an electron in a hydrogen atom using Bohr's model.
  - **a.** Calculate the energy of the electron in a particular energy level in a hydrogen atom (Section 6-3).
  - **b.** Calculate the energy of a photon absorbed or emitted when the electron in a hydrogen atom moves from one energy level to another (Section 6-3).

- Use the four quantum numbers (n, ℓ, m_ℓ, and m_s) to describe the electronic structure of an atom.
  - **a.** Describe orbitals in an atom using three quantum numbers n, ℓ, and m_ℓ (Section 6-5). Study Questions: 27–34, 36–41, 43, 44, 80, 83.
  - **b.** Describe shapes of the orbitals (Section 6-6). Study Questions: 46, 53, 67f, 68e.
  - **c.** Recognize the spin quantum number, m_s, which has values of $\pm\frac{1}{2}$ (Section 6-7). Study Questions: 68h.

REMEMBER

- The order of the different types of electromagnetic radiation by wavelength, frequency, and energy (Figure 6.2).
- The rules for determining the values for the four quantum numbers (n, ℓ, m_ℓ, and m_s) (Sections 6-5–6-7).
- The shapes of atomic orbitals (Section 6-6).

KEY EQUATIONS

Equation 6.1 (page 220) The product of the wavelength (λ) and frequency (ν) of electromagnetic radiation is equal to the speed of light (c).

$$c = \lambda \times \nu$$

Equation 6.2 (page 223) Planck's equation: The energy of a photon, a massless particle of radiation, is proportional to its frequency (ν). The proportionality constant, h, is called Planck's constant (6.626×10^{-34} J · s).

$$E = h\nu$$

Equation 6.3 (page 227) The Rydberg equation can be used to calculate the wavelengths of the lines in the Balmer series of the hydrogen spectrum. The Rydberg constant, R, is 1.0974×10^7 m^{-1}, and n is 3 or larger.

$$\frac{1}{\lambda} = R\left(\frac{1}{2^2} - \frac{1}{n^2}\right) \text{ when } n > 2$$

Equation 6.4 (page 228) In Bohr's theory, the energy of the electron, E_n, in the nth quantum level of the H atom is proportional to $1/n^2$, where n is a positive integer (the principal quantum number) and $Rhc = 2.179 \times 10^{-18}$ J/atom or $N_ARhc = 1312$ kJ/mol.

$$E_n = -\frac{Rhc}{n^2}$$

Equation 6.5 (page 231) The energy change for an electron moving between two quantum levels (n_{final} and $n_{initial}$) in the H atom.

$$\Delta E = E_{final} - E_{initial} = -Rhc\left(\frac{1}{n_{final}^2} - \frac{1}{n_{initial}^2}\right)$$

Equation 6.6 (page 234) De Broglie's equation: The wavelength of a particle (λ) is related to its mass (m) and speed (v) and to Planck's constant (h).

$$\lambda = \frac{h}{mv}$$

© Cengage Learning/Charles D. Winters

STUDY QUESTIONS

▲ denotes challenging questions.

Blue-numbered questions have answers in Appendix N and fully worked solutions in the *Student Solutions Manual.*

Practicing Skills

Electromagnetic Radiation

(See Example 6.1 and Figure 6.2.)

1. Answer the following questions based on Figure 6.2:
   (a) Which type of radiation involves less energy, x-rays or microwaves?
   (b) Which radiation has the higher frequency, radar or red light?
   (c) Which radiation has the longer wavelength, ultraviolet or infrared light?

2. Consider the colors of the visible spectrum.
   (a) Which colors of light involve less energy than green light?
   (b) Which color of light has photons of greater energy, yellow or blue?
   (c) Which color of light has the higher frequency, blue or green?

3. Traffic signals are often now made of LEDs (light-emitting diodes). Amber and green ones are pictured here.
   (a) The light from an amber signal has a wavelength of 595 nm, and that from a green signal has a wavelength of 500 nm. Which has the higher frequency?
   (b) Calculate the frequency of amber light.

(a) (b)

Photos: Mike Condren/UW/MRSEC

4. Suppose you are standing 225 m from a radio transmitter. What is your distance from the transmitter in terms of the number of wavelengths if
   (a) the station is broadcasting at 1150 kHz (on the AM radio band)? (1 kHz = 1×10^3 Hz)
   (b) the station is broadcasting at 98.1 MHz (on the FM radio band)? (1 MHz $\times$ 10^6 Hz)

Electromagnetic Radiation and Planck's Equation

(See Example 6.2.)

5. Green light has a wavelength of 5.0×10^2 nm. What is the energy, in joules, of one photon of green light? What is the energy, in joules, of 1.0 mol of photons of green light?

6. Violet light has a wavelength of about 410 nm. What is its frequency? Calculate the energy of one photon of violet light. What is the energy of 1.0 mol of violet photons? Compare the energy of photons of violet light with those of red light. Which is more energetic?

7. The most prominent line in the emission spectrum of aluminum is at 396.15 nm. What is the frequency of this line? What is the energy of one photon with this wavelength? Of 1.00 mol of these photons?

8. The most prominent line in the emission spectrum of magnesium is 285.2 nm. Other lines are found at 383.8 and 518.4 nm. In what region of the electromagnetic spectrum are these lines found? Which is the most energetic line? What is the energy of 1.00 mol of photons with the wavelength of the most energetic line?

9. Place the following types of radiation in order of increasing energy per photon:
   (a) yellow light from a sodium lamp
   (b) x-rays from an instrument in a dentist's office
   (c) microwaves in a microwave oven
   (d) your favorite FM music station at 91.7 MHz

10. Place the following types of radiation in order of increasing energy per photon:
   (a) radiation within a microwave oven
   (b) your favorite radio station
   (c) gamma rays from a nuclear reaction
   (d) red light from a neon sign
   (e) ultraviolet radiation from a sun lamp

Photoelectric Effect

(See page 223 and Figure 6.4.)

11. An energy of 3.3×10^{-19} J/atom is required to cause a cesium atom on a metal surface to lose an electron. Calculate the longest possible wavelength of light that can ionize a cesium atom. In what region of the electromagnetic spectrum is this radiation found?

12. You are an engineer designing a switch that works by the photoelectric effect. The metal you wish to use in your device requires 6.7×10^{-19} J/atom to remove an electron. Will the switch work if the light falling on the metal has a wavelength of 540 nm or greater? Why or why not?

Atomic Spectra and the Bohr Atom

(See Examples 6.3 and 6.4 and Figures 6.5–6.10.)

13. The most prominent line in the spectrum of mercury is at 253.652 nm. Other lines are located at 365.015 nm, 404.656 nm, 435.833 nm, and 1013.975 nm.
   (a) Which of these lines represents the most energetic light?
   (b) What is the frequency of the most prominent line? What is the energy of one photon with this wavelength?
   (c) Are any of these lines found in the spectrum of mercury shown in Figure 6.6? What color or colors are these lines?

14. The most prominent line in the spectrum of neon is found at 865.438 nm. Other lines are located at 837.761 nm, 878.062 nm, 878.375 nm, and 885.387 nm.
   (a) In what region of the electromagnetic spectrum are these lines found?
   (b) Are any of these lines found in the spectrum of neon shown in Figure 6.6?
   (c) Which of these lines represents the most energetic radiation?
   (d) What is the frequency of the most prominent line? What is the energy of one photon with this wavelength?

15. A line in the Balmer series of emission lines of excited H atoms has a wavelength of 410.2 nm (Figure 6.10). What color is the light emitted in this transition? What quantum levels are involved in this emission line? That is, what are the values of n_{initial} and n_{final}?

16. What are the wavelength and frequency of the radiation involved in the least energetic emission line in the Lyman series? What are the values of n_{initial} and n_{final}?

17. Consider only transitions involving the $n = 1$ through $n = 5$ energy levels for the H atom (see Figures 6.7 and 6.10).
   (a) How many emission lines are possible, considering only the five quantum levels?
   (b) Photons of the highest frequency are emitted in a transition from the level with $n =$ ________ to a level with $n =$ ________.
   (c) The emission line having the longest wavelength corresponds to a transition from the level with $n =$ ________ to the level with $n =$ ________.

18. Consider only transitions involving the $n = 1$ through $n = 4$ energy levels for the hydrogen atom (see Figures 6.7 and 6.10).
   (a) How many emission lines are possible, considering only the four quantum levels?
   (b) Photons of the lowest energy are emitted in a transition from the level with $n =$ ________ to a level with $n =$ ________.
   (c) The emission line having the shortest wavelength corresponds to a transition from the level with $n =$ ________ to the level with $n =$ ________.

19. The energy emitted when an electron moves from a higher energy state to a lower energy state in any atom can be observed as electromagnetic radiation.
   (a) Which involves the emission of less energy in the H atom, an electron moving from $n = 4$ to $n = 2$ or an electron moving from $n = 3$ to $n = 2$?
   (b) Which involves the emission of more energy in the H atom, an electron moving from $n = 4$ to $n = 1$ or an electron moving from $n = 5$ to $n = 2$? Explain fully.

20. If energy is absorbed by a hydrogen atom in its ground state, the atom is excited to a higher energy state. For example, the excitation of an electron from $n = 1$ to $n = 3$ requires radiation with a wavelength of 102.6 nm. Which of the following transitions would require radiation of *longer wavelength* than this?
(a) $n = 2$ to $n = 4$
(b) $n = 1$ to $n = 4$
(c) $n = 1$ to $n = 5$
(d) $n = 3$ to $n = 5$

21. Calculate the wavelength and frequency of light emitted when an electron changes from $n = 3$ to $n = 1$ in the H atom. In what region of the spectrum is this radiation found?

22. Calculate the wavelength and frequency of light emitted when an electron changes from $n = 4$ to $n = 3$ in the H atom. In what region of the spectrum is this radiation found?

De Broglie and Matter Waves

(See Example 6.5.)

23. An electron moves with a velocity of 2.5×10^8 cm/s. What is its wavelength?

24. A beam of electrons ($m = 9.11 \times 10^{-31}$ kg/electron) has an average speed of 1.3×10^8 m/s. What is the wavelength of electrons having this average speed?

25. Calculate the wavelength, in nanometers, associated with a 46-g golf ball moving at 30. m/s (about 67 mph). At what speed must the ball travel to have a wavelength of 5.6×10^{-3} nm?

26. A rifle bullet (mass = 1.50 g) has a velocity of 7.00×10^2 mph (miles per hour). What is the wavelength associated with this bullet?

Quantum Mechanics

(See Sections 6-5–6-7.)

27. (a) When $n = 4$, what are the possible values of ℓ?
(b) When ℓ is 2, what are the possible values of m_ℓ?
(c) For a 4*s* orbital, what are the possible values of n, ℓ, and m_ℓ?
(d) For a 4*f* orbital, what are the possible values of n, ℓ, and m_ℓ?

28. (a) When $n = 4$, $\ell = 2$, and $m_\ell = -1$, to what orbital type does this refer? (Give the orbital label, such as 1*s*.)
(b) How many orbitals occur in the $n = 5$ electron shell? How many subshells? What are the letter labels of the subshells?
(c) How many orbitals occur in an *f* subshell? What are the values of m_ℓ?

29. A possible excited state of the H atom has the electron in a 4*p* orbital. List all possible sets of quantum numbers n, ℓ, and m_ℓ for this electron.

30. A possible excited state for the H atom has an electron in a 5*d* orbital. List all possible sets of quantum numbers n, ℓ, and m_ℓ for this electron.

31. How many subshells occur in the electron shell with the principal quantum number $n = 4$?

32. How many subshells occur in the electron shell with the principal quantum number $n = 5$?

33. Explain briefly why each of the following is *not* a possible set of quantum numbers for an electron in an atom.
(a) $n = 2, \ell = 2, m_\ell = 0$
(b) $n = 3, \ell = 0, m_\ell = -2$
(c) $n = 6, \ell = 0, m_\ell = 1$

34. Which of the following represent valid sets of quantum numbers? For a set that is invalid, explain briefly why it is not correct.
(a) $n = 3, \ell = 3, m_\ell = 0$
(b) $n = 2, \ell = 1, m_\ell = 0$
(c) $n = 6, \ell = 5, m_\ell = -1$
(d) $n = 4, \ell = 3, m_\ell = -4$

35. What is the maximum number of orbitals that can be identified by each of the following sets of quantum numbers? When "none" is the correct answer, explain your reasoning.
(a) $n = 3, \ell = 0, m_\ell = +1$
(b) $n = 5, \ell = 1$
(c) $n = 7, \ell = 5$
(d) $n = 4, \ell = 2, m_\ell = -2$

36. What is the maximum number of orbitals that can be identified by each of the following sets of quantum numbers? When "none" is the correct answer, explain your reasoning.
(a) $n = 4, \ell = 3$
(b) $n = 5$
(c) $n = 2, \ell = 2$
(d) $n = 3, \ell = 1, m_\ell = -1$

37. Explain briefly why each of the following is not a possible set of quantum numbers for an electron in an atom. In each case, change the incorrect value (or values) to make the set valid.
(a) $n = 4, \ell = 2, m_\ell = 0, m_s = 0$
(b) $n = 3, \ell = 1, m_\ell = -3, m_s = -\frac{1}{2}$
(c) $n = 3, \ell = 3, m_\ell = -1, m_s = +\frac{1}{2}$

38. Explain briefly why each of the following is not a possible set of quantum numbers for an electron in an atom. In each case, change the incorrect value (or values) to make the set valid.
(a) $n = 2, \ell = 2, m_\ell = 0, m_s = +\frac{1}{2}$
(b) $n = 2, \ell = 1, m_\ell = -1, m_s = 0$
(c) $n = 3, \ell = 1, m_\ell = -2, m_s = +\frac{1}{2}$

39. State which of the following orbitals cannot exist according to the quantum theory: 2*s*, 2*d*, 3*p*, 3*f*, 4*f*, and 5*s*. Briefly explain your answers.

40. State which of the following orbitals cannot exist according to the quantum theory: 3*p*, 4*s*, 2*f*, and 1*p*. Briefly explain your answers.

41. Write a complete set of quantum numbers (n, ℓ, and m_ℓ) that quantum theory allows for each of the following orbitals: (a) 2*p*, (b) 3*d*, and (c) 4*f*.

42. Write a complete set of quantum numbers (n, ℓ, and m_ℓ) for each of the following orbitals: (a) 5*f*, (b) 4*d*, and (c) 2*s*.

43. A particular orbital has $n = 4$ and $\ell = 2$. What must this orbital be: (a) 3*p*, (b) 4*p*, (c) 5*d*, or (d) 4*d*?

44. A given orbital has a magnetic quantum number of $m_\ell = -1$. This could *not* be a(n)

(a) *f* orbital (c) *p* orbital
(b) *d* orbital (d) *s* orbital

45. How many nodal surfaces through the nucleus (planar nodes) are associated with each of the following orbitals?

(a) 2*s* (b) 5*d* (c) 5*f*

46. How many nodal surfaces through the nucleus (planar nodes) are associated with each of the following atomic orbitals?

(a) 4*f* (b) 2*p* (c) 6*s*

General Questions on Atomic Structure

These questions are not designated as to type or location in the chapter. They may combine several concepts.

47. Which of the following are applicable when explaining the photoelectric effect? Correct any statements that are wrong.

(a) Light is electromagnetic radiation.
(b) The intensity of a light beam is related to its frequency.
(c) Light can be thought of as consisting of massless particles whose energy is given by Planck's equation, $E = h\nu$.

48. In what region of the electromagnetic spectrum for hydrogen is the Lyman series of lines found? The Balmer series?

49. Give the number of nodal surfaces through the nucleus (planar nodes) for each orbital type: *s*, *p*, *d*, and *f*.

50. What is the maximum number of *s* orbitals found in a given electron shell? The maximum number of *p* orbitals? Of *d* orbitals? Of *f* orbitals?

51. Match the values of ℓ shown in the table with orbital type (*s*, *p*, *d*, or *f*).

ℓ Value	Orbital Type
3	________
0	________
1	________
2	________

52. Sketch a picture of the 90% boundary surface of an *s* orbital and the p_x orbital. Be sure the latter drawing shows why the *p* orbital is labeled p_x and not p_y, for example.

53. Complete the following table.

Orbital Type	Number of Orbitals in a Given Subshell	Number of Nodal Surfaces through the Nucleus
s	________	________
p	________	________
d	________	________
f	________	________

54. Excited H atoms have many emission lines. One series of lines, called the *Pfund series,* occurs in the infrared region. It results when an electron changes from higher energy levels to a level with $n = 5$. Calculate the wavelength and frequency of the lowest energy line of this series.

55. An advertising sign gives off red light and green light.

(a) Which light has higher-energy photons?
(b) One of the colors has a wavelength of 680 nm, and the other has a wavelength of 500 nm. Which color has which wavelength?
(c) Which light has the higher frequency?

56. Radiation in the ultraviolet region of the electromagnetic spectrum is quite energetic. It is this radiation that causes dyes to fade and your skin to develop a sunburn. If you are bombarded with 1.00 mol of photons with a wavelength of 375 nm, what amount of energy, in kilojoules per mole of photons, are you being subjected to?

57. A cell phone sends signals at about 850 MHz (where 1 MHz = 1×10^6 Hz or cycles per second).

(a) What is the wavelength of this radiation?
(b) What is the energy of 1.0 mol of photons with a frequency of 850 MHz?
(c) Compare the energy in part (b) with the energy of a mole of photons of violet light (420 nm).
(d) Comment on the difference in energy between 850 MHz radiation and violet light.

58. Assume your eyes receive a signal consisting of blue light, $\lambda = 470$ nm. The energy of the signal is 2.50×10^{-14} J. How many photons reach your eyes?

59. If sufficient energy is absorbed by an atom, an electron can be lost by the atom and a positive ion formed. The amount of energy required is called the ionization energy. In the H atom, the ionization energy is that required to change the electron from $n = 1$ to n = infinity. Calculate the ionization energy for the He^+ ion. Is the ionization energy of the He^+ more or less than that of H? (Bohr's theory applies to He^+ because it, like the H atom, has a single electron. The electron energy, however, is now given by $E = -Z^2Rhc/n^2$, where *Z* is the atomic number of helium.)

60. Suppose hydrogen atoms absorb energy so that electrons are excited to the $n = 7$ energy level. Electrons then undergo these transitions, among others: (a) $n = 7 \rightarrow n = 1$; (b) $n = 7 \rightarrow n = 6$; and (c) $n = 2 \rightarrow n = 1$. Which of these transitions produces a photon with (i) the smallest energy, (ii) the highest frequency, and (iii) the shortest wavelength?

61. Rank the following orbitals in the H atom in order of increasing energy: 3*s*, 2*s*, 2*p*, 4*s*, 3*p*, 1*s*, and 3*d*.

62. How many orbitals correspond to each of the following designations?

(a) 3*p* (d) 6*d* (g) $n = 5$
(b) 4*p* (e) 5*d* (h) 7*s*
(c) $4p_x$ (f) 5*f*

63. Cobalt-60 is a radioactive isotope used in medicine for the treatment of certain cancers. It produces β particles and γ rays, the latter having energies of 1.173 and 1.332 MeV. (1 MeV = 10^6 electron-volts and 1 eV = 1.6022×10^{-19} J.) What are the wavelength and frequency of a γ-ray photon with an energy of 1.173 MeV?

64. ▲ Exposure to high doses of microwaves can cause tissue damage. Estimate how many photons, with $\lambda = 12$ cm, must be absorbed to raise the temperature of your eye by 3.0 °C. Assume the mass of an eye is 11 g and its specific heat capacity is 4.0 J/g · K.

65. When the Sojourner spacecraft landed on Mars in 1997, the planet was approximately 7.8×10^7 km from Earth. How long did it take for the television picture signal to reach Earth from Mars?

66. The most prominent line in the emission spectrum of chromium is found at 425.4 nm. Other lines in the chromium spectrum are found at 357.9 nm, 359.3 nm, 360.5 nm, 427.5 nm, 429.0 nm, and 520.8 nm.

(a) Which of these lines represents the most energetic light?
(b) What color is light of wavelength 425.4 nm?

67. Answer the following questions as a summary quiz on the chapter.

(a) The quantum number n describes the ______ of an atomic orbital.
(b) The shape of an atomic orbital is given by the quantum number ______.
(c) A photon of green light has ______ (less or more) energy than a photon of orange light.
(d) The maximum number of orbitals that may be associated with the set of quantum numbers $n = 4$ and $\ell = 3$ is ______.
(e) The maximum number of orbitals that may be associated with the quantum number set $n = 3$, $\ell = 2$, and $m_\ell = -2$ is ______.
(f) Label each of the following orbital pictures with the appropriate letter:

(g) When $n = 5$, the possible values of ℓ are ______.
(h) The number of orbitals in the $n = 4$ shell is ______.

68. Answer the following questions as a summary quiz on this chapter.

(a) The quantum number n describes the ______ of an atomic orbital, and the quantum number ℓ describes its ______.
(b) When $n = 3$, the possible values of ℓ are ______.
(c) What type of orbital corresponds to $\ell = 3$? ______
(d) For a $4d$ orbital, the value of n is ______, the value of ℓ is ______, and a possible value of m_ℓ is ______.
(e) Each of the following drawings represents a type of atomic orbital. Give the letter designation for the orbital, give its value of ℓ, and specify the number of planar nodes.

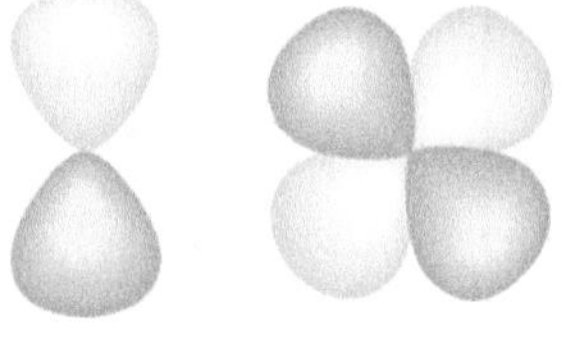

Letter = ______ ______
ℓ value = ______ ______
Planar nodes = ______ ______

(f) An atomic orbital with three planar nodes through the nucleus is a(n) ______ orbital.
(g) Which of the following orbitals cannot exist according to modern quantum theory: $2s$, $3p$, $2d$, $3f$, $5p$, $6p$?
(h) Which of the following is not a valid set of quantum numbers?

n	ℓ	m_ℓ	m_s
3	2	1	$-\frac{1}{2}$
2	1	2	$+\frac{1}{2}$
4	3	0	0

(i) What is the maximum number of orbitals that can be associated with each of the following sets of quantum numbers? (One possible answer is "none.")
(i) $n = 2$ and $\ell = 1$
(ii) $n = 3$
(iii) $n = 3$ and $\ell = 3$
(iv) $n = 2$, $\ell = 1$, and $m_\ell = 0$

69. For an electron in a hydrogen atom, calculate the energy of the photon emitted when an electron falls in energy from the $n = 5$ level to the $n = 2$ state. What are the frequency and wavelength of this electromagnetic radiation?

In the Laboratory

70. A solution of $KMnO_4$ absorbs light at 540 nm (page 175). What is the frequency of the light absorbed? What is the energy of one mole of photons with $\lambda = 540$ nm?

71. A large pickle is attached to two electrodes, which are then attached to a 110-V power supply. As the voltage is increased across the pickle, it begins to glow with a yellow color. Knowing that pickles are made by soaking the vegetable in a concentrated salt solution, describe why the pickle might emit light when electrical energy is added.

The "electric pickle"

72. The spectrum shown here is for aspirin. The vertical axis is the amount of light absorbed, and the horizontal axis is the wavelength of incident light (in nm). (For more on spectrophotometry, see pages 172–177.)

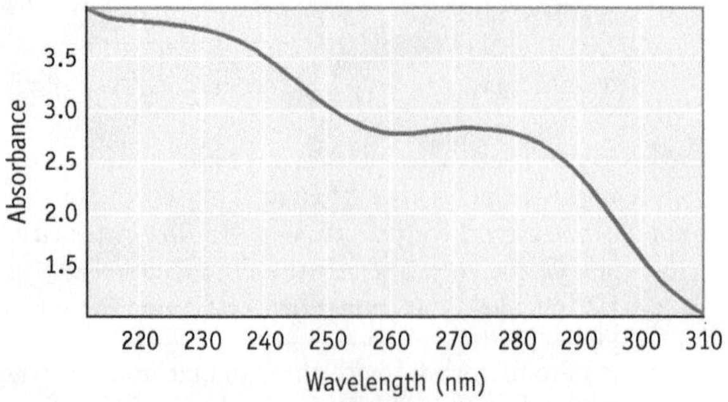

What is the frequency of light with a wavelength of 278 nm? What is the energy of one mole of photons with $\lambda = 278$ nm? What region of the electromagnetic spectrum is covered by the spectrum above? Knowing that aspirin only absorbs light in the region depicted by this spectrum, what is the color of aspirin?

73. The infrared spectrum for methanol, CH_3OH, is illustrated below. It shows the amount of light in the infrared region that methanol transmits as a function of wavelength. The vertical axis is the amount of light transmitted. At points near the top of the graph, most of the incident light is being transmitted by the sample (or, conversely, little light is absorbed.) Therefore, the "peaks" or "bands" that descend from the top indicate light absorbed; the longer the band, the more light is being absorbed. The horizontal scale is in units of "wavenumbers," abbreviated cm^{-1}. The energy of light is given by Planck's law as $E = hc/\lambda$; that is, E is proportional to $1/\lambda$. Therefore, the horizontal scale is in units of $1/\lambda$ and reflects the energy of the light incident on the sample.

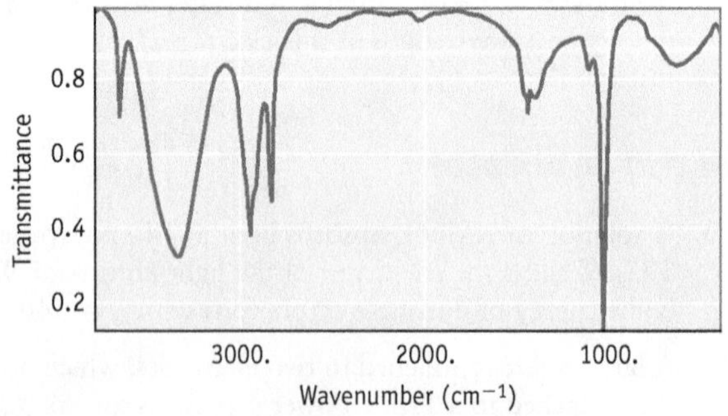

(a) One point on the horizontal axis is marked as 2000 cm^{-1}. What is the wavelength of light at this point?
(b) Which is the low energy end of this spectrum (left or right), and which is the high energy end?
(c) The broad absorption at about 3300–3400 cm^{-1} indicates that infrared radiation is interacting with the OH group of the methanol molecule. The narrower absorptions around 2800–3000 cm^{-1} are for interactions with C—H bonds. Which interaction requires more energy, with O—H or with C—H?

Summary and Conceptual Questions

The following questions may use concepts from this and previous chapters.

74. Bohr pictured the electrons of the atom as being located in definite orbits about the nucleus, just as the planets orbit the Sun. Criticize this model.

75. Light is given off by a sodium- or mercury-containing streetlight when the atoms are excited. The light you see arises for which of the following reasons?
(a) Electrons are moving from a given energy level to one of higher energy.
(b) Electrons are being removed from the atom, thereby creating a metal cation.
(c) Electrons are moving from a given energy level to one of lower energy.

76. How do we interpret the physical meaning of the square of the wavefunction? What are the units of $4\pi r^2\psi^2$?

77. What does "wave–particle duality" mean? What are its implications in our modern view of atomic structure?

78. Which of these are observable?
(a) position of an electron in an H atom
(b) frequency of radiation emitted by H atoms
(c) path of an electron in an H atom
(d) wave motion of electrons
(e) diffraction patterns produced by electrons
(f) diffraction patterns produced by light
(g) energy required to remove electrons from H atoms
(h) an atom
(i) a molecule
(j) a water wave

79. In principle, which of the following can be determined?
(a) the energy of an electron in the H atom with high precision and accuracy
(b) the position of a high-speed electron with high precision and accuracy
(c) at the same time, both the position and the energy of a high-speed electron with high precision and accuracy

80. ▲ Suppose you live in a different universe where a different set of quantum numbers is required to describe the atoms of that universe. These quantum numbers have the following rules:

N, principal $1, 2, 3, \ldots, \infty$
L, orbital $= N$
M, magnetic $-1, 0, +1$

How many orbitals are there altogether in the first three electron shells?

81. A photon with a wavelength of 93.8 nm strikes a hydrogen atom, and light is emitted by the atom. How many emission lines would be observed? At what wavelengths? Explain briefly (see Figure 6.10).

82. Explain why you could or could not measure the wavelength of a golf ball in flight.

83. The radioactive element technetium is not found naturally on Earth; it must be synthesized in the laboratory. It is a valuable element, however, because it has medical uses. For example, the element in the form of sodium pertechnetate ($NaTcO_4$) is used in imaging studies of the brain, thyroid, and salivary glands and in renal blood flow studies, among other things.

(a) In what group and period of the periodic table is the element found?

(b) The valence electrons of technetium are found in the $5s$ and $4d$ subshells. What is a set of quantum numbers (n, ℓ, and m_ℓ) for one of the electrons of the $5s$ subshell?

(c) Technetium emits a γ-ray with an energy of 0.141 MeV. (1 MeV = 10^6 electron-volts, where 1 eV = 1.6022×10^{-19} J.) What are the wavelength and frequency of a γ-ray photon with an energy of 0.141 MeV?

(d) To make $NaTcO_4$, the metal is dissolved in nitric acid.

$$7\ HNO_3(aq) + Tc(s) \rightarrow HTcO_4(aq) + 7\ NO_2(g) + 3\ H_2O(\ell)$$

and the product, $HTcO_4$, is treated with NaOH to make $NaTcO_4$.

(i) Write a balanced equation for the reaction of $HTcO_4$ with NaOH.

(ii) If you begin with 4.5 mg of Tc metal, what mass of $NaTcO_4$ can be made? What mass of NaOH, in grams, is required to convert all of the $HTcO_4$ into $NaTcO_4$?

(e) If you synthesize 1.5 micromoles of $NaTcO_4$, what mass of compound do you have? If the compound is dissolved in 10.0 mL of solution, what is the concentration?

84. ▲ Figure 6.12b shows the probability of finding a hydrogen $1s$ electron at various distances from the nucleus. To create the graph in this figure, the electron cloud is first divided into a series of thin concentric shells about the nucleus and then the probability of finding the electron in each shell is evaluated. The volume of each shell is given by the equation $V = 4\pi r^2(d)$, where d is the thickness of the shell and r is the distance of the shell from the nucleus. The probability of finding the electron in each shell is

$$\text{Probability} = 4\pi r^2 \psi^2 (d)$$

where ψ is the $1s$ wavefunction for hydrogen (a_o in this equation is 52.9 pm).

$$\psi = \frac{1}{(\pi a_0^3)^{1/2}} e^{-r/a_0}$$

(a) The most probable distance for a 1s electron in the hydrogen atom is at 52.9 pm. Evaluate the probability of finding the electron in a concentric shell 1.0 pm thick at this distance from the nucleus.

(b) Calculate the probability of finding the electron in a shell 1.0 pm thick at distances from the nucleus of 0.50 a_o and 4 a_o. Compare the results with the probabilities at a_o. Are these probabilities in accord with the surface density plot shown in Figure 6.12b?

Rubies. Red rubies and deep blue sapphires are both aluminum oxide but with different impurities.

The Structure of Atoms and Periodic Trends

Chapter Outline

RUBIES AND SAPPHIRES People have been fascinated by, and have coveted, precious stones such as rubies and sapphires for hundreds of years.

To a chemist both of these gemstones are just aluminum oxide with traces of impurities. But it is the impurities that turn simple aluminum oxide into a beautiful gemstone.

Rubies come in a variety of colors. Most are red, but they can have tints of brown, purple, and pink due to different amounts and identities of trace elements present. The red color comes from the substitution of a few of the Al^{3+} ions in Al_2O_3 by Cr^{3+} ions. The price of a ruby usually depends on its color and its clarity, the most valuable being deep red, said to resemble "pigeon blood," and being as transparent as possible. Rubies often have inclusions of tiny needles of titanium dioxide (rutile), which makes them a little cloudy. In fact, if a ruby is not slightly cloudy, it may be a synthetic stone with much less value.

Chapter Goals

See Chapter Goals Revisited (page 280) for Study Questions keyed to these goals.

UNDERSTAND

- The relationship of the four quantum numbers (n, ℓ, m_ℓ, and m_s) to atomic structure.
- Effective nuclear charge, Z^*, and its implications for subshell energies and properties of atoms.

DO

- Write the electron configuration for atoms and monatomic ions.

REMEMBER

- Electrons are assigned to the subshells of an atom in order of increasing energy.
- Trends in atom and ion sizes, ionization energy, and electron attachment enthalpy.

Most rubies come from southeast and central Asia and east Africa, but there are a few deposits in the United States. Interestingly, as glaciers have receded in Greenland, large ruby deposits have been discovered.

Synthetic rubies were first made in the 19th century, the best known process being that developed by Auguste Verneuil in 1902. In this process, aluminum oxide and barium fluoride are fused with a chromium(III) compound. The synthetic materials produced in this way are now used in commercial lasers such as those in DVD players.

Sapphires are also based on aluminum oxide. Their usual blue color results from traces of elements such as iron, titanium, and vanadium. When iron and titanium are present as Fe^{2+} and Ti^{4+}, the result is the deep blue color for which sapphires are famous. Like rubies, sapphires can also be synthesized, and synthetic sapphires are used in some jewelry.

Study Questions related to this story are: 7.37 and 7.38.

The wave mechanical model of the atom developed in Chapter 6 describes electrons as matter waves and introduces four quantum numbers that are used to describe these matter waves. The electrons are assigned to orbitals that are arranged in subshells that are in turn part of electron shells. One objective of this chapter is to use this model to describe the electronic structure of all the elements.

A second objective is to explore some of the properties of elements, among them the energy changes that occur when atoms lose or gain electrons to form ions and the sizes of atoms and ions. These properties are directly related to the electronic structure of the atoms, that is, to the arrangement of electrons in atoms.

7-1 The Pauli Exclusion Principle

To make the quantum theory consistent with experiment, the Austrian physicist Wolfgang Pauli (1900–1958) stated in 1925 his **exclusion principle:** *No more than two electrons can be assigned to the same orbital, and, if there are two electrons in the same orbital, they must have opposite spins.* This leads to the general statement that *no two electrons in an atom can have the same set of four quantum numbers* (n, ℓ, m_ℓ, and m_s).

An electron assigned to the 1*s* orbital of the H atom may have the set of quantum numbers $n = 1$, $\ell = 0$, $m_\ell = 0$, and $m_s = +\frac{1}{2}$. If we represent an orbital by a box and the electron spin by an arrow (↑ or ↓), a representation of the hydrogen atom is then:

Electron in 1*s* orbital: [↑] Quantum number set
1*s* $n = 1, \ell = 0, m_\ell = 0, m_s = +\frac{1}{2}$

The choice of m_s (either $+\frac{1}{2}$ or $-\frac{1}{2}$) and the direction of the electron spin arrow are arbitrary; that is, we could choose either value, and the arrow may point in either direction. Diagrams such as these are called **orbital box diagrams.**

Orbitals Are Not Boxes Orbitals are not boxes in which electrons are placed. Thus, it is not conceptually correct to talk about electrons being in orbitals or occupying orbitals, although this is commonly done for the sake of simplicity.

A helium atom has two electrons. In the lowest energy (ground state) electronic configuration both electrons are assigned to the 1*s* orbital. The Pauli exclusion principle requires that each electron must have a different set of quantum numbers, so the orbital box diagram now is:

Two electrons in 1*s* orbital: 1*s* [↑↓]
← This electron has $n = 1, \ell = 0, m_\ell = 0, m_s = -\frac{1}{2}$
← This electron has $n = 1, \ell = 0, m_\ell = 0, m_s = +\frac{1}{2}$

By having opposite or "paired" spins, the two electrons in the 1*s* orbital of an He atom have different sets of the four quantum numbers. Our understanding of orbitals and the knowledge that an orbital can accommodate no more than two electrons tell us the maximum number of electrons that can occupy each electron shell or subshell. For example, because two electrons can be assigned to each of the three orbitals in a *p* subshell, these subshells can hold a maximum of six electrons. By the same reasoning, the five orbitals of a *d* subshell can accommodate a total of 10 electrons, and the seven *f* orbitals can accommodate 14 electrons. Recall that there are n subshells in the nth shell, and that there are n^2 orbitals in that shell (◀ Table 6.1). Thus, *the maximum number of electrons in any shell is* $2n^2$. The relationship among the quantum numbers and the numbers of electrons is shown in Table 7.1.

REVIEW & CHECK FOR SECTION 7-1

1. How many electrons can be accommodated in the $n = 7$ shell?

   (a) 18 (b) 36 (c) 72 (d) 98

2. If one electron in an orbital has quantum numbers $n = 3$, $\ell = 2$, $m_\ell = -1$, and $m_s = +1/2$, what are the quantum numbers for the other electron in that orbital?

   (a) $n = 3, \ell = 2, m_\ell = -1, m_s = +1/2$
   (b) $n = 3, \ell = 2, m_\ell = -1, m_s = -1/2$
   (c) $n = 3, \ell = 2, m_\ell = 0, m_s = -1/2$
   (d) $n = 3, \ell = 1, m_\ell = -1, m_s = +1/2$

Table 7.1 Number of Electrons Accommodated in Electron Shells and Subshells with $n = 1$ to 6

Electron Shell (n)	Subshells Available	Orbitals Available ($2\ell + 1$)	Number of Electrons Possible in Subshell [$2(2\ell + 1)$]	Maximum Electrons Possible for nth Shell ($2n^2$)
1	*s*	1	2	2
2	*s*	1	2	8
	p	3	6	
3	*s*	1	2	18
	p	3	6	
	d	5	10	
4	*s*	1	2	32
	p	3	6	
	d	5	10	
	f	7	14	
5	*s*	1	2	50
	p	3	6	
	d	5	10	
	f	7	14	
	*g**	9	18	
6	*s*	1	2	72
	p	3	6	
	d	5	10	
	*f**	7	14	
	*g**	9	18	
	*h**	11	22	

*These orbitals are not occupied in the ground state of any known element.

7-2 Atomic Subshell Energies and Electron Assignments

Our goal in this section is to understand and predict the distribution of electrons in atoms with many electrons. The procedure by which electrons are assigned to orbitals is known as the *Aufbau principle* (the German word *Aufbau* means "building up"). Electrons in an atom are assigned to shells (defined by the quantum number n) and subshells (defined by the quantum numbers n and ℓ) in order of increasingly higher energy. In this way, the total energy of the atom is as low as possible.

Order of Subshell Energies and Assignments

Quantum theory and the Bohr model state that the energy of the H atom, with a single electron, depends only on the value of n (Equation 6.4, $E_n = -Rhc/n^2$). For atoms with more than one electron, however, the situation is more complex. The order of subshell energies for $n = 1$, 2, and 3 in **Figure 7.1a** shows that subshell energies in multielectron atoms depend on *both n and ℓ*.

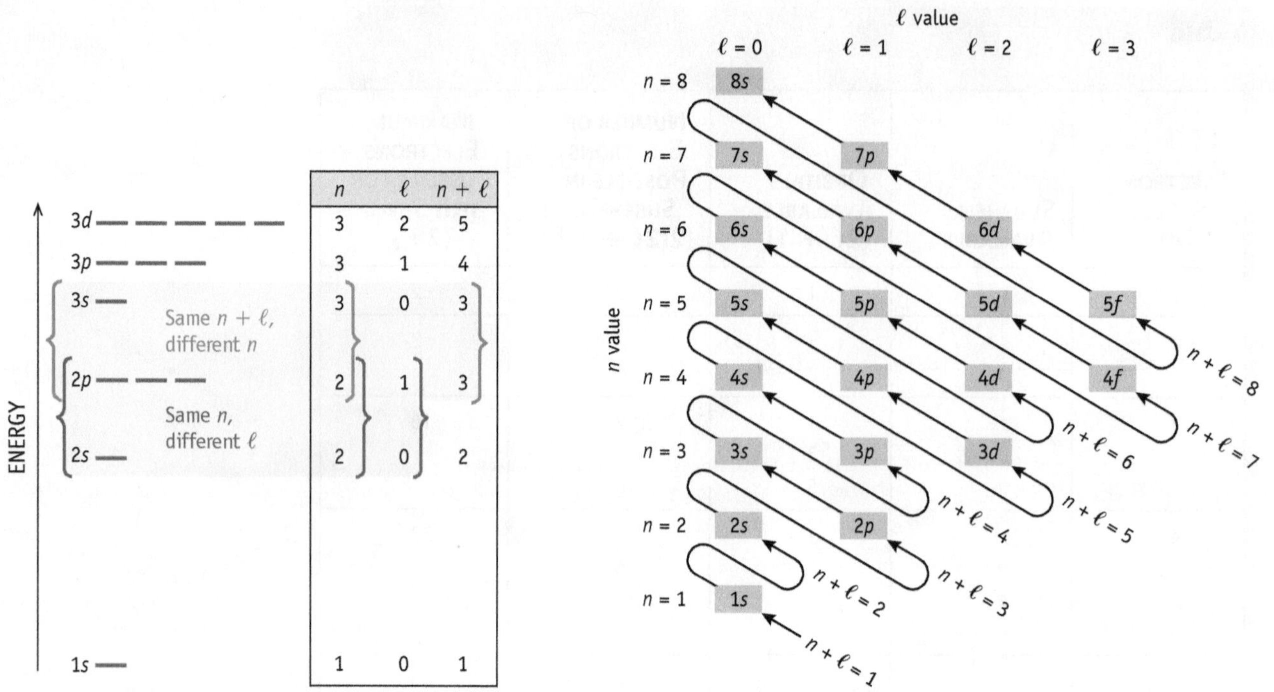

(a) Order of subshell energies in a multielectron atom. Energies of electron shells increase with increasing n, and, within a shell, subshell energies increase with increasing ℓ. (The energy axis is not to scale. The energy gaps between subshells of a given shell become smaller as n increases.)

(b) Subshell filling order. Subshells in atoms are filled in order of increasing $n + \ell$. When two subshells have the same $n + \ell$ value, the subshell of lower n is filled first. To use the diagram, begin at 1s and follow the arrows of increasing $n + \ell$. (Thus, the order of filling is $1s \Rightarrow 2s \Rightarrow 2p \Rightarrow 3s \Rightarrow 3p \Rightarrow 4s \Rightarrow 3d$ and so on.)

FIGURE 7.1 **Subshell energies and filling order in a multielectron atom.**

Based on theoretical and experimental studies of electron distributions in atoms, chemists have found there are two general rules that help predict these arrangements:

1. Electrons are assigned to subshells in order of increasing "$n + \ell$" value.
2. For two subshells with the same value of "$n + \ell$," electrons are assigned first to the subshell of lower n.

The following are examples of these rules:

- Electrons are assigned to the 2s subshell ($n + \ell = 2 + 0 = 2$) before the 2p subshell ($n + \ell = 2 + 1 = 3$).
- Electrons are assigned to 2p orbitals ($n + \ell = 2 + 1 = 3$) before the 3s subshell ($n + \ell = 3 + 0 = 3$) because n for the 2p electrons is less than n for the 3s electrons.
- Electrons are assigned to the 4s subshell ($n + \ell = 4 + 0 = 4$) before the 3d subshell ($n + \ell = 3 + 2 = 5$) because $n + \ell$ is less for 4s than for 3d.

Figure 7.1b summarizes the assignment of electrons according to increasing $n + \ell$ values. The discussion that follows explores the basis for this assignment of electron configurations.

Effective Nuclear Charge, Z^*

The order in which electrons are assigned to subshells in an atom, and many atomic properties, can be rationalized by introducing the concept of **effective nuclear charge (Z^*)**. This is the *net charge experienced by a particular electron in a multielectron atom resulting from a balance of the attractive force of the nucleus and the repulsive forces of other electrons.*

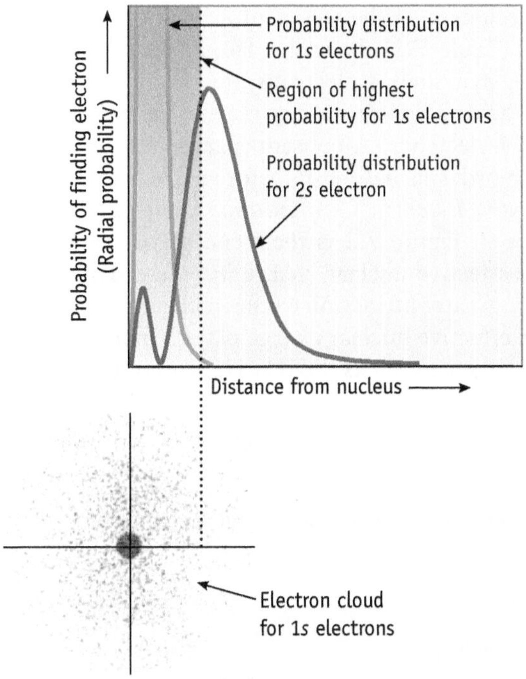

(left) The two 1s electrons of lithium have their highest probability in the shaded region, but this region is penetrated by the 2s electron (whose approximate surface density plot is shown here). As the 2s electron penetrates the 1s region, however, the 2s electron experiences a larger and larger positive charge, to a maximum of +3. On average, the 2s electron experiences a charge, called the effective nuclear charge (*Z**), which is smaller than +3 but greater than +1.

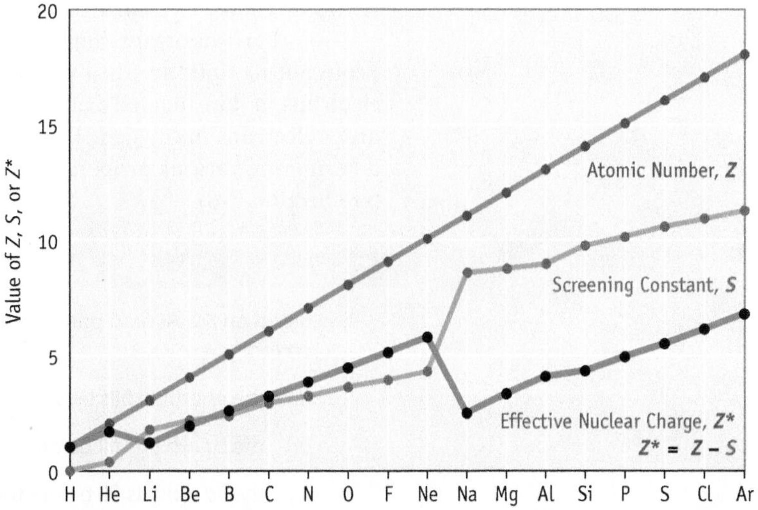

(right) The value of *Z* for the highest occupied orbital* is given by ($Z - S$), where Z is the atomic number and S is the screening constant. (S reflects how much the inner electrons shield or screen the outermost electron from the nucleus.) Notice that S increases greatly on going from Ne in the second period to Na in the third period.

FIGURE 7.2 **Effective nuclear charge, *Z**.**

The surface density plot ($4\pi r^2\psi^2$) for a 2*s* electron for a lithium atom is given in **Figure 7.2.** (Lithium has three protons in the nucleus, two 1*s* electrons in the first shell, and a 2*s* electron in the second shell.) The probability of finding the 2*s* electron (recorded on the vertical axis) changes as one moves away from the nucleus (horizontal axis). The region in which the two 1*s* electrons have their highest probability is shaded in Figure 7.2. Notice that the 2*s* electron wave occurs partly within the region of space occupied by 1*s* electrons. Chemists say that the 2*s* orbital *penetrates* the region defining the 1*s* orbital.

At a large distance from the nucleus, the third electron in lithium will experience a +1 charge, the net effect of the two 1*s* electrons (total charge = −2) and the nucleus (+3 charge). The 1*s* electrons *screen* the electron from experiencing the full nuclear charge. However, as the 2*s* electron wave penetrates the 1*s* electron region, it experiences the attraction of an increasingly higher net positive charge. When the 2*s* electron is close to the nucleus, it is poorly screened from the nucleus by the 1*s* electrons, and the 2*s* electron experiences a charge close to +3. Figure 7.2 shows that a 2*s* electron has some probability of being inside and outside the region occupied by the 1*s* electrons. Thus, on average, a 2*s* electron experiences a positive charge greater than +1 but much smaller than +3. The *average* or *effective* charge, Z^*, experienced by the 2*s* electron in Li is 1.28 (Table 7.2).

In the hydrogen atom, with only one electron, the 2*s* and 2*p* subshells have the same energy. However, in atoms with two or more electrons, the energies of the 2*s* and 2*p* subshells are different. Why should this be true? The relative extent to which an outer electron penetrates inner orbitals occurs in the order $s > p > d > f$. Thus, the effective nuclear charge experienced by electrons in a multielectron atom is in

Table 7.2 Effective Nuclear Charges, Z^*, for $n = 2$ Elements

Atom	$Z^*(2s)$	$Z^*(2p)$
Li	1.28	
B	2.58	2.42
C	3.22	3.14
N	3.85	3.83
O	4.49	4.45
F	5.13	5.10

the order $ns > np > nd > nf$. This is reflected in the values of Z^* for s and p electrons for the second-period elements (Table 7.2). In each case, Z^* is greater for s electrons than for p electrons. In a given shell, s electrons always have a lower energy than p electrons; p electrons have a lower energy than d electrons, and d electrons have a lower energy than f electrons. A consequence is that subshells within an electron shell are filled in the order ns before np before nd before nf. (See *A Closer Look: Orbital Energies, Z^*, and Electron Configurations*, page 262.)

Another important thing to notice in Figure 7.2 is the trend across a period. From left to right across a period, the effective nuclear charge *increases*. The outer electrons in fluorine, for example, feel a greater attraction to the nucleus than do the outer electrons in oxygen. This greater effective nuclear charge plays a major role in determining various properties of the elements such as the relative sizes of the atoms (see Section 7-6).

REVIEW & CHECK FOR SECTION 7-2

1. Based on the Aufbau principle and the $n + \ell$ rule, which of following statements is correct?

   (a) the 4*s* orbital fills before the 4*p* orbitals

   (b) the 5*d* orbitals fill before the 6*s* orbital

   (c) the 3*d* orbitals fill before the 3*p* orbitals

   (d) the 4*f* orbitals fill before the 5*p* orbitals

Learning Objectives: LO 1.5, LO 1.6, LO 1.7, LO 1.8, LO 1.10, LO 1.13

7-3 Electron Configurations of Atoms

Arrangements of electrons in the elements up to 109—their **electron configurations**—are given in Table 7.3. Specifically, these are the *ground state electron configurations*, where electrons are found in the shells, subshells, and orbitals that result in the lowest energy for an isolated atom of the element in the gaseous state. In general, electrons are assigned to orbitals in order of increasing $n + \ell$. The emphasis here, however, will be to connect the configurations of the elements with their positions in the periodic table (Figure 7.3).

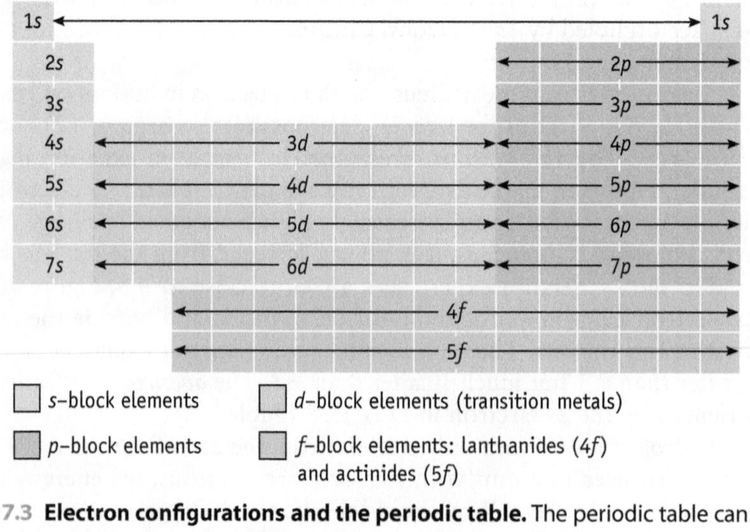

FIGURE 7.3 **Electron configurations and the periodic table.** The periodic table can serve as a guide in determining the order of filling of atomic orbitals (see Table 7.3).

Table 7.3 Ground State Electron Configurations

Z	Element	Configuration	Z	Element	Configuration	Z	Element	Configuration
1	H	$1s^1$	37	Rb	$[Kr]5s^1$	74	W	$[Xe]4f^{14}5d^4 6s^2$
2	He	$1s^2$	38	Sr	$[Kr]5s^2$	75	Re	$[Xe]4f^{14}5d^5 6s^2$
3	Li	$[He]2s^1$	39	Y	$[Kr]4d^1 5s^2$	76	Os	$[Xe]4f^{14}5d^6 6s^2$
4	Be	$[He]2s^2$	40	Zr	$[Kr]4d^2 5s^2$	77	Ir	$[Xe]4f^{14}5d^7 6s^2$
5	B	$[He]2s^2 2p^1$	41	Nb	$[Kr]4d^4 5s^1$	78	Pt	$[Xe]4f^{14}5d^9 6s^1$
6	C	$[He]2s^2 2p^2$	42	Mo	$[Kr]4d^5 5s^1$	79	Au	$[Xe]4f^{14}5d^{10}6s^1$
7	N	$[He]2s^2 2p^3$	43	Tc	$[Kr]4d^5 5s^2$	80	Hg	$[Xe]4f^{14}5d^{10}6s^2$
8	O	$[He]2s^2 2p^4$	44	Ru	$[Kr]4d^7 5s^1$	81	Tl	$[Xe]4f^{14}5d^{10}6s^2 6p^1$
9	F	$[He]2s^2 2p^5$	45	Rh	$[Kr]4d^8 5s^1$	82	Pb	$[Xe]4f^{14}5d^{10}6s^2 6p^2$
10	Ne	$[He]2s^2 2p^6$	46	Pd	$[Kr]4d^{10}$	83	Bi	$[Xe]4f^{14}5d^{10}6s^2 6p^3$
11	Na	$[Ne]3s^1$	47	Ag	$[Kr]4d^{10}5s^1$	84	Po	$[Xe]4f^{14}5d^{10}6s^2 6p^4$
12	Mg	$[Ne]3s^2$	48	Cd	$[Kr]4d^{10}5s^2$	85	At	$[Xe]4f^{14}5d^{10}6s^2 6p^5$
13	Al	$[Ne]3s^2 3p^1$	49	In	$[Kr]4d^{10}5s^2 5p^1$	86	Rn	$[Xe]4f^{14}5d^{10}6s^2 6p^6$
14	Si	$[Ne]3s^2 3p^2$	50	Sn	$[Kr]4d^{10}5s^2 5p^2$	87	Fr	$[Rn]7s^1$
15	P	$[Ne]3s^2 3p^3$	51	Sb	$[Kr]4d^{10}5s^2 5p^3$	88	Ra	$[Rn]7s^2$
16	S	$[Ne]3s^2 3p^4$	52	Te	$[Kr]4d^{10}5s^2 5p^4$	89	Ac	$[Rn]6d^1 7s^2$
17	Cl	$[Ne]3s^2 3p^5$	53	I	$[Kr]4d^{10}5s^2 5p^5$	90	Th	$[Rn]6d^2 7s^2$
18	Ar	$[Ne]3s^2 3p^6$	54	Xe	$[Kr]4d^{10}5s^2 5p^6$	91	Pa	$[Rn]5f^2 6d^1 7s^2$
19	K	$[Ar]4s^1$	55	Cs	$[Xe]6s^1$	92	U	$[Rn]5f^3 6d^1 7s^2$
20	Ca	$[Ar]4s^2$	56	Ba	$[Xe]6s^2$	93	Np	$[Rn]5f^4 6d^1 7s^2$
21	Sc	$[Ar]3d^1 4s^2$	57	La	$[Xe]5d^1 6s^2$	94	Pu	$[Rn]5f^6 7s^2$
22	Ti	$[Ar]3d^2 4s^2$	58	Ce	$[Xe]4f^1 5d^1 6s^2$	95	Am	$[Rn]5f^7 7s^2$
23	V	$[Ar]3d^3 4s^2$	59	Pr	$[Xe]4f^3 6s^2$	96	Cm	$[Rn]5f^7 6d^1 7s^2$
24	Cr	$[Ar]3d^5 4s^1$	60	Nd	$[Xe]4f^4 6s^2$	97	Bk	$[Rn]5f^9 7s^2$
25	Mn	$[Ar]3d^5 4s^2$	61	Pm	$[Xe]4f^5 6s^2$	98	Cf	$[Rn]5f^{10}7s^2$
26	Fe	$[Ar]3d^6 4s^2$	62	Sm	$[Xe]4f^6 6s^2$	99	Es	$[Rn]5f^{11}7s^2$
27	Co	$[Ar]3d^7 4s^2$	63	Eu	$[Xe]4f^7 6s^2$	100	Fm	$[Rn]5f^{12}7s^2$
28	Ni	$[Ar]3d^8 4s^2$	64	Gd	$[Xe]4f^7 5d^1 6s^2$	101	Md	$[Rn]5f^{13}7s^2$
29	Cu	$[Ar]3d^{10}4s^1$	65	Tb	$[Xe]4f^9 6s^2$	102	No	$[Rn]5f^{14}7s^2$
30	Zn	$[Ar]3d^{10}4s^2$	66	Dy	$[Xe]4f^{10}6s^2$	103	Lr	$[Rn]5f^{14}6d^1 7s^2$
31	Ga	$[Ar]3d^{10}4s^2 4p^1$	67	Ho	$[Xe]4f^{11}6s^2$	104	Rf	$[Rn]5f^{14}6d^2 7s^2$
32	Ge	$[Ar]3d^{10}4s^2 4p^2$	68	Er	$[Xe]4f^{12}6s^2$	105	Db	$[Rn]5f^{14}6d^3 7s^2$
33	As	$[Ar]3d^{10}4s^2 4p^3$	69	Tm	$[Xe]4f^{13}6s^2$	106	Sg	$[Rn]5f^{14}6d^4 7s^2$
34	Se	$[Ar]3d^{10}4s^2 4p^4$	70	Yb	$[Xe]4f^{14}6s^2$	107	Bh	$[Rn]5f^{14}6d^5 7s^2$
35	Br	$[Ar]3d^{10}4s^2 4p^5$	71	Lu	$[Xe]4f^{14}5d^1 6s^2$	108	Hs	$[Rn]5f^{14}6d^6 7s^2$
36	Kr	$[Ar]3d^{10}4s^2 4p^6$	72	Hf	$[Xe]4f^{14}5d^2 6s^2$	109	Mt	$[Rn]5f^{14}6d^7 7s^2$
			73	Ta	$[Xe]4f^{14}5d^3 6s^2$			

*This table follows the general convention of writing the orbitals in order of increasing n when writing electron configurations. For a given n, the subshells are listed in order of increasing ℓ.

Electron Configurations of the Main Group Elements

Hydrogen, the first element in the periodic table, has one electron in a 1*s* orbital. One way to depict its electron configuration is with the orbital box diagram used earlier, but an alternative and more frequently used method is the *spdf* notation. Using this method, the electron configuration of H is $1s^1$, read "one *s* one." This indicates that there is one electron (indicated by the superscript) in the 1*s* orbital.

Hydrogen electron configuration: [↑] 1*s* or $1s^1$

number of electrons assigned to designated orbital (points to superscript 1)

orbital type (ℓ) (points to *s*)

electron shell (*n*) (points to 1)

Orbital Box Notation — *spdf* Notation

Helium, the second element on the periodic table, has two electrons. The electron configuration is $1s^2$, with both electrons in the 1*s* orbital but having opposite spins, as dictated by the Pauli exclusion principle. With helium, the first energy level is complete.

Helium: *spdf* notation $1s^2$

Box notation [↑↓] 1*s* [ ] 2*s* [ ][ ][ ] 2*p*

Lithium (Li) and Other Elements of Group 1A

Lithium, with three electrons, is the first element in the second period of the periodic table. In an atom of lithium, the first two electrons are in the 1*s* subshell, and the third electron is in the *s* subshell of the $n = 2$ shell. The *spdf* notation, $1s^22s^1$, is read "one *s* two, two *s* one."

Lithium: *spdf* notation $1s^22s^1$

Box notation [↑↓] 1*s* [↑] 2*s* [ ][ ][ ] 2*p*

© Cengage Learning/Charles D. Winters

Lithium. Lithium-ion batteries are increasingly used in consumer products. All Group 1A elements such as lithium have an outer electron configuration of ns^1.

Electron configurations are often written in abbreviated form by writing in brackets the symbol for the noble gas preceding the element (called the **noble gas notation**) and then indicating any electrons beyond those in the noble gas by using *spdf* or orbital box notation. In lithium, the arrangement preceding the 2*s* electron is the electron configuration of the noble gas helium. Instead of writing out $1s^22s^1$ for lithium's configuration, it can be written as [He]$2s^1$.

The electrons included in the noble gas notation are often referred to as the **core electrons** of the atom. The core electrons can generally be ignored when considering the chemistry of an element. The electrons beyond the core electrons—the $2s^1$ electron in the case of lithium—are called **valence electrons**; these are the electrons that determine the chemical properties of an element.

All the elements of Group 1A have one electron assigned to an *s* orbital of the *n*th shell, for which *n* is the number of the period in which the element is found (**Figure 7.3**). For example, potassium is the first element in the $n = 4$ row (the fourth period), so potassium has the electron configuration of the element preceding it in the table (Ar) plus a single electron assigned to the 4*s* orbital: [Ar]$4s^1$.

Image Courtesy of New Southern Resistance Welding

Beryllium. Beryllium is one of the components of beryllium-copper alloy, which is used in the oil and gas industry and in electronics. All Group 2A elements like beryllium have an outer electron configuration of ns^2.

Beryllium (Be) and Other Elements of Group 2A

All elements of Group 2A have electron configurations of [electrons of preceding noble gas]ns^2, where *n* is the period in which the element is found in the periodic table. An atom of beryllium, for example, has two electrons in the 1*s* orbital plus two additional electrons.

Beryllium: *spdf* notation $1s^2 2s^2$ or $[He]2s^2$

Box notation [↑↓] [↑↓] [| |]
1s 2s 2p

Because all the elements of Group 1A have the valence electron configuration ns^1, and those in Group 2A have ns^2, these elements are called **s-block elements.**

Boron (B) and Other Elements of Group 3A

Boron (Group 3A) is the first element in the block of elements on the right side of the periodic table. Because the 1*s* and 2*s* orbitals are filled in a boron atom, the fifth electron must be assigned to a 2*p* orbital.

Boron: *spdf* notation $1s^2 2s^2 2p^1$ or $[He]2s^2 2p^1$

Box notation [↑↓] [↑↓] [↑| |]
1s 2s 2p

Verco Materials, LLC

Boron. Boron carbide, B_4C, is used in body armor. All Group 3A elements such as boron have an outer electron configuration of ns^2np^1.

Elements from Group 3A through Group 8A are often called the **p-block elements.** All have the outer shell configuration ns^2np^x, where x varies from 1 to 6. The elements in Group 3A, for example, are in the first column of the *p*-block and have two *s* electrons and one *p* electron (ns^2np^1) in their outer shells.

Carbon (C) and Other Elements of Group 4A

Carbon (Group 4A) is in the second column of the *p*-block and thus an atom of carbon has two electrons assigned to the 2*p* orbitals. You can write the electron configuration of carbon by referring to the periodic table: Starting at H and moving from left to right across the successive periods, you write $1s^2$ to reach the end of period 1 and then $2s^2$ and finally $2p^2$ to bring the electron count to six. For carbon to be in its lowest energy (ground) state, these electrons must be assigned to different *p* orbitals, and both will have the same spin direction.

Carbon: *spdf* notation $1s^2 2s^2 2p^2$ or $[He]2s^2 2p^2$

Box notation [↑↓] [↑↓] [↑|↑|]
1s 2s 2p

Hund's Rule and Exchange Energy The reason a configuration with the maximum number of unpaired electrons is more stable is due to the *exchange energy,* a concept that comes out of quantum mechanics and goes beyond the level of general chemistry. Due to the exchange interaction, electrons with parallel spins result in a lower overall energy. The first of the configurations below is more stable than the second by an amount of energy equal to the *exchange energy.*

[↑|↑|↑]

[↑|↑|↓]

When assigning electrons to *p*, *d*, or *f* orbitals, each successive electron is assigned to a different orbital of the subshell, and each electron has the same spin as the previous one, until the subshell is half full. Additional electrons must then be assigned to half-filled orbitals. This procedure follows **Hund's rule,** which states that *the most stable arrangement of electrons in a subshell is that with the maximum number of unpaired electrons, all with the same spin direction.*

All elements in Group 4A have similar outer shell configurations, ns^2np^2, where n is the period in which the element is located in the periodic table.

Nitrogen (N) and Oxygen (O) and Elements of Groups 5A and 6A

An atom of nitrogen (Group 5A) has five valence electrons. Besides the two 2*s* electrons, it has three electrons, all with the same spin, in three different 2*p* orbitals.

Nitrogen: *spdf* notation $1s^2 2s^2 2p^3$ or $[He]2s^2 2p^3$

Box notation [↑↓] [↑↓] [↑|↑|↑]
1s 2s 2p

An atom of oxygen (Group 6A) has six valence electrons. Two of these six electrons are assigned to the 2*s* orbital, and the other four electrons are assigned to 2*p* orbitals.

Oxygen: *spdf* notation $1s^2 2s^2 2p^4$ or $[He]2s^2 2p^4$

Box notation [↑↓] [↑↓] [↑↓|↑|↑]
1*s* 2*s* 2*p*

The fourth 2*p* electron must pair up with one already present. It makes no difference to which orbital this electron is assigned (the 2*p* orbitals all have the same energy), but it must have a spin opposite to the other electron already assigned to that orbital so that each electron has a different set of quantum numbers (the Pauli principle).

All elements in Group 5A have an outer shell configuration of ns^2np^3, and all elements in Group 6A have an outer shell configuration of ns^2np^4, where n is the period in which the element is located in the periodic table.

Fluorine (F) and Neon (Ne) and Elements of Groups 7A and 8A

An atom of fluorine (Group 7A) has seven electrons in the $n = 2$ shell. Two of these electrons occupy the 2*s* subshell, and the remaining five electrons occupy the 2*p* subshell.

© Cengage Learning/Charles D. Winters

Fluorine. Fluorine is found as the fluoride ion in the mineral fluorite (CaF_2), sometimes called *fluorspar*. The mineral, which is the state mineral of Illinois, comes in many colors. All Group 7A elements have an outer electron configuration of ns^2np^5.

Fluorine: *spdf* notation $1s^2 2s^2 2p^5$ or $[He]2s^2 2p^5$

Box notation [↑↓] [↑↓] [↑↓|↑↓|↑]
1*s* 2*s* 2*p*

All halogen atoms have similar outer shell configurations, ns^2np^5, where n is the period in which the element is located.

Like all the elements in Group 8A, neon is a noble gas. Atoms of Group 8A elements (except helium) have eight electrons in the shell of highest n value, so all have the outer shell configuration ns^2np^6, where n is the period in which the element is found. That is, all the noble gases have filled *ns* and *np* subshells. The nearly complete chemical inertness of the noble gases is associated with this electron configuration.

Neon: *spdf* notation $1s^2 2s^2 2p^6$ or $[He]2s^2 2p^6$

Box notation [↑↓] [↑↓] [↑↓|↑↓|↑↓]
1*s* 2*s* 2*p*

Elements of Period 3

© Cengage Learning/Charles D. Winters

Silicon. Si is the fourth element in the third period. The Earth's crust is largely composed of silicon-containing minerals. This photo shows some elemental silicon and a thin wafer of silicon on which electronic circuits are etched.

The elements of the third period have valence electron configurations similar to those of the second period, except that the preceding noble gas is neon and the valence shell is the third energy level. For example, silicon has four electrons and a neon core. Because it is the second element in the *p* block, it has two electrons in 3*p* orbitals. Thus, its electron configuration is

Silicon: *spdf* notation $1s^2 2s^2 2p^6 3s^2 3p^2$ or $[Ne]3s^2 3p^2$

Box notation [↑↓] [↑↓] [↑↓|↑↓|↑↓] [↑↓] [↑|↑|]
1*s* 2*s* 2*p* 3*s* 3*p*

EXAMPLE 7.1

Electron Configurations

Problem Give the electron configuration of sulfur, using the *spdf*, *spdf* with noble gas, and orbital box with noble gas notations.

What Do You Know? From the periodic table: sulfur, atomic number 16, is the sixth element in the third period ($n = 3$) and is in the fourth column of the *p*-block. You need to know the order of filling (Figure 7.1).

Strategy

- For the *spdf* and orbital box notations: assign the 16 electrons for sulfur to orbitals based on the order of filling.
- For the noble gas notation: The first 10 electrons are identified by the symbol of the previous noble gas, Ne. The remaining 6 electrons are assigned to the 3*s* and 3*p* subshells. Make sure Hund's rule is followed in the box notation.

Solution Sulfur, atomic number 16, is the sixth element in the third period ($n = 3$) and is in the *p*-block. The last six electrons assigned to the atom, therefore, have the configuration $3s^2 3p^4$. These are preceded by the completed shells $n = 1$ and $n = 2$, the electron arrangement for Ne.

Complete *spdf* notation:	$1s^2 2s^2 2p^6 3s^2 3p^4$
spdf with noble gas notation:	$[Ne]3s^2 3p^4$
Orbital box notation:	[Ne] [↑↓] (3*s*) [↑↓][↑][↑] (3*p*)

Think about Your Answer The orbital box notation conveys information not found in the *spdf* notation, namely the number of unpaired electrons.

Check Your Understanding

(a) What element has the configuration $1s^2 2s^2 2p^6 3s^2 3p^5$?

(b) Using *spdf* notation and an orbital box diagram, show the electron configuration of phosphorus.

Sulfur. Sulfur is widely distributed on Earth. Like all Group 6A elements, it has the outer electron configuration ns^2np^4.

EXAMPLE 7.2

Electron Configurations and Quantum Numbers

Problem Write the electron configuration for Al using the *spdf* and orbital box notations with the noble gas notation, and give a set of quantum numbers for each of the electrons with $n = 3$ (the valence electrons).

What Do You Know? The periodic table informs you that Al (atomic number 13) is the third element after the noble gas neon.

Strategy Because aluminum is the third element in the third period, it has three electrons with $n = 3$. Two of the electrons are assigned to 3*s*, and the remaining electron is assigned to 3*p*.

Solution The element is preceded by the noble gas neon, so the electron configuration is [Ne]$3s^2 3p^1$. Using the box notation, the configuration is

Aluminum configuration: [Ne] [↑↓] (3s) [↑][ ][ ] (3p)

The possible sets of quantum numbers for the two 3s electrons are

	n	ℓ	m_ℓ	m_s
For ↑	3	0	0	$+\frac{1}{2}$
For ↓	3	0	0	$-\frac{1}{2}$

For the single 3p electron, one of six possible sets is $n = 3$, $\ell = 1$, $m_\ell = +1$, and $m_s = +\frac{1}{2}$.

Think about Your Answer Each set of four quantum numbers identifies a unique electron in an atom's electron configuration. No two sets of four quantum numbers can be the same.

Check Your Understanding

Write one possible set of quantum numbers for the valence electrons of calcium.

Electron Configurations of the Transition Elements

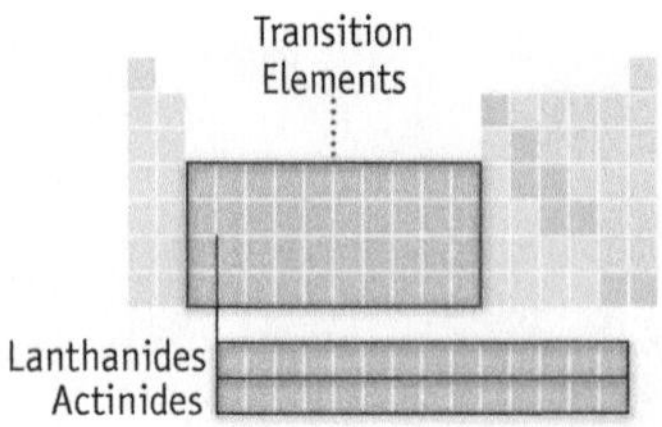

The elements of the fourth through the seventh periods use *d* and *f* subshells, in addition to *s* and *p* subshells, to accommodate electrons (see Figure 7.3 and Tables 7.3 and 7.4). Elements whose atoms have partially filled *d* subshells are called **transition elements.** Those elements for which atoms are filling *f* subshells are sometimes called the **inner transition elements** or, more often, the **lanthanides** (filling 4*f* orbitals, Ce through Lu) and **actinides** (filling 5*f* orbitals, Th through Lr).

In a given period in the periodic table, the transition elements are always preceded by two *s*-block elements. After filling the *ns* orbital in the period, we begin filling the $(n - 1)d$ orbitals. Scandium, the first transition element, has the configuration [Ar]$3d^1 4s^2$, and titanium follows with [Ar]$3d^2 4s^2$ (Table 7.4).

The general procedure for assigning electrons would suggest that the configuration of a chromium atom should be [Ar]$3d^4 4s^2$. The actual configuration, however, has one electron assigned to each of the six available 3*d* and 4*s* orbitals: [Ar]$3d^5 4s^1$. This configuration has a lower total energy (due to maximizing the number of unpaired electron spins) than the alternative configuration.

Following chromium, atoms of manganese, iron, and nickel have the configurations that would be expected from the order of orbital filling in Figure 7.1. Copper ([Ar]$3d^{10} 4s^1$) is the second "exception" in this series; it has a single electron in the 4*s* orbital, and the remaining 10 electrons beyond the argon core are assigned to the 3*d* orbitals. Zinc, with the configuration [Ar]$3d^{10} 4s^2$, ends the first transition series.

The fifth period transition elements follow the pattern of the fourth period but have more exceptions to the general rules of orbital filling.

Writing Configurations for Transition Metals We follow the convention of writing configurations with shells listed in order of increasing *n* and, within a given shell, writing subshells in order of increasing ℓ. However, some chemists reverse the order of the *ns* and $(n - 1)d$ orbitals to reflect the order of orbital filling.

Lanthanides and Actinides

The sixth period includes the lanthanide series. As the first element in the *d*-block, lanthanum has the configuration [Xe]$5d^1 6s^2$. The next element, cerium (Ce), is set out in a separate row at the bottom of the periodic table, and it is with the elements in this row (Ce through Lu) that electrons are first assigned to *f* orbitals. Thus, the configuration of cerium is [Xe]$4f^1 5d^1 6s^2$. Moving across the lanthanide series, the pattern continues (although with occasional variations in occupancy of the 5*d* and

Table 7.4 Orbital Box Diagrams for the Elements Ca Through Zn

		3d	4s
Ca	$[Ar]4s^2$	[ ][ ][ ][ ][ ]	[↑↓]
Sc	$[Ar]3d^14s^2$	[↑][ ][ ][ ][ ]	[↑↓]
Ti	$[Ar]3d^24s^2$	[↑][↑][ ][ ][ ]	[↑↓]
V	$[Ar]3d^34s^2$	[↑][↑][↑][ ][ ]	[↑↓]
Cr*	$[Ar]3d^54s^1$	[↑][↑][↑][↑][↑]	[↑]
Mn	$[Ar]3d^54s^2$	[↑][↑][↑][↑][↑]	[↑↓]
Fe	$[Ar]3d^64s^2$	[↑↓][↑][↑][↑][↑]	[↑↓]
Co	$[Ar]3d^74s^2$	[↑↓][↑↓][↑][↑][↑]	[↑↓]
Ni	$[Ar]3d^84s^2$	[↑↓][↑↓][↑↓][↑][↑]	[↑↓]
Cu*	$[Ar]3d^{10}4s^1$	[↑↓][↑↓][↑↓][↑↓][↑↓]	[↑]
Zn	$[Ar]3d^{10}4s^2$	[↑↓][↑↓][↑↓][↑↓][↑↓]	[↑↓]

*See *A Closer Look: Questions about Transition Element Electron Configurations*, page 263.

4*f* orbitals). The lanthanide series ends with 14 electrons being assigned to the seven 4*f* orbitals in the last element, lutetium (Lu, $[Xe]4f^{14}5d^16s^2$) (see Table 7.3).

The seventh period also includes an extended series of elements utilizing *f* orbitals, the actinides. Actinium has the configuration (Ac, $[Rn]6d^17s^2$). The next element is thorium (Th), which is followed by protactinium (Pa) and uranium (U). The electron configuration of uranium is $[Rn]5f^36d^17s^2$.

Lanthanides. These elements have many uses. Pictured are samples of lanthanide metal oxides.

EXAMPLE 7.3

Electron Configurations of the Transition Elements

Problem Using the *spdf* notation with the noble gas notation, give electron configurations for (a) technetium, Tc, and (b) osmium, Os.

What Do You Know? Base your answer on the positions of the elements in the periodic table. Technetium is the seventh element in period 5 and osmium is the 22nd element in the 6th period.

Strategy For each element, find the preceding noble gas, and then note the number of *s*, *p*, *d*, and *f* electrons that lead from the noble gas to the element.

Solution

(a) Technetium, Tc: The noble gas that precedes Tc is krypton, Kr, at the end of the $n = 4$ row. After 36 electrons are assigned to the core as [Kr], seven electrons remain. Two of these electrons are in the 5*s* orbital, and the remaining five are in 4*d* orbitals. Therefore, the technetium configuration is $[Kr]4d^55s^2$.

A CLOSER LOOK

Orbital Energies, Z^*, and Electron Configurations

The graph below shows how the energies of different atomic orbitals change on going from one element to the next in the periodic table. Here are some significant observations drawn from the graph.

(1) Generally, as one moves from left to right in any period, the energies of the atomic orbitals decrease. This trend correlates with the changes in Z^*, the effective charge experienced by an electron in a given orbital (Figure 7.2). As noted, Z^* is a parameter related to the nuclear charge and the shielding effect of all the other electrons. When moving from one element to the next across each period, the attractive effect of an additional proton in the nucleus outweighs the repulsive effect of an additional electron.

(2) Electrons are classified as either valence electrons or core electrons. We can now see from this graph the obvious distinction in these groups. Valence electrons are found in orbitals that have higher (less negative) energies. In contrast, the core electrons are in orbitals that have very low energy, because they experience a much higher Z^*. Furthermore, as one moves from one period to the next period (for example from Ar in period 3 to K in period 4) the energies of core orbitals plummet. The very low energy of electrons in these orbitals rules out the ability of these electrons to be involved in chemical reactions.

(3) Notice also the orbital energies of the first transition series. Each step going across the transition series involves adding a proton to the nucleus and a 3*d* electron to an inner shell. The 4*s* energy level decreases only slightly in this series of elements, reflecting the fact that the additional 3*d* electrons effectively shield a 4*s* electron from the higher charge resulting from addition of a proton. The additional nuclear charge has a greater effect on the 3*d* orbitals, and their energies decrease to a greater extent across the transition series. When the end of the transition series is reached the 3*d* electrons become part of the core and their energies plummet.

(4) Finally, note the exceptional behavior of Cr and Cu in this sequence. These elements have unexpected electron configurations (page 261), arising because another factor, exchange energy (page 257), is a contributor to overall energy in the system.

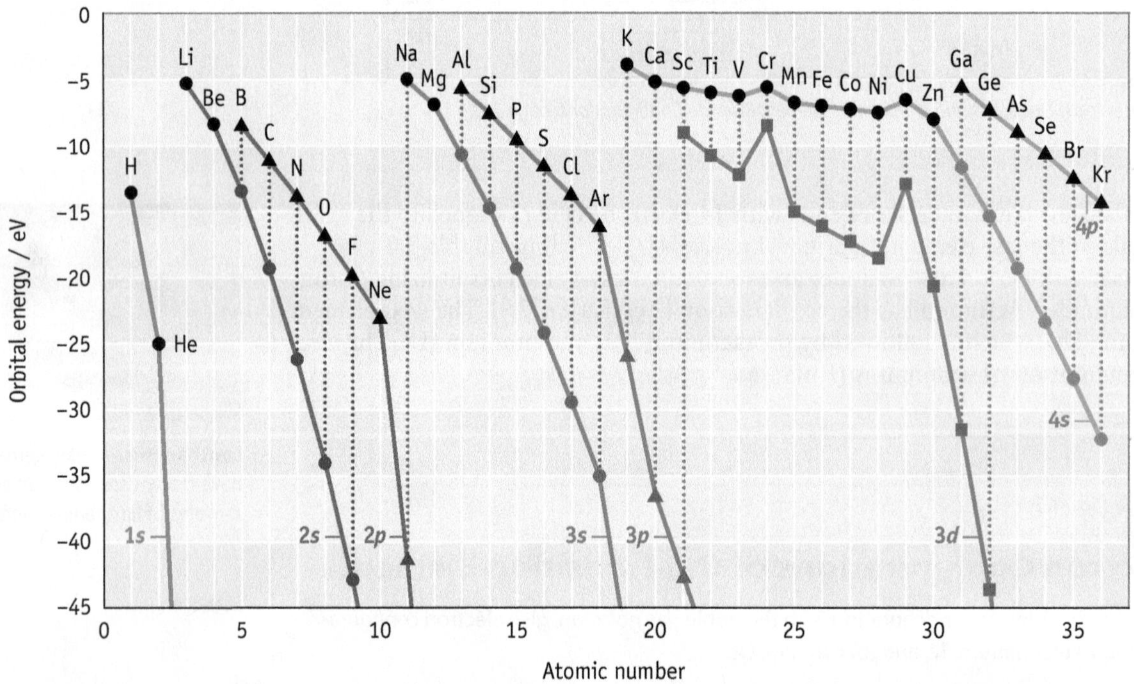

Variation in orbital energies (derived from photoelectron spectroscopy data, ▶ page 272) with atomic number. The energies are in electron-volts (eV) where 1 eV = 1.602×10^{-19} J. (Figure redrawn from *Chemical Structure and Reactivity*, J. Keeler and P. Wothers, Oxford, 2008; used with permission.)

(b) Osmium, Os: Osmium is a sixth-period element. Of the 22 electrons to be added after the Xe core, two are assigned to the 6*s* orbital and 14 to 4*f* orbitals. The remaining six are assigned to 5*d* orbitals. Thus, the osmium configuration is $[Xe]4f^{14}5d^66s^2$.

Think about Your Answer The periodic table is a useful guide when determining electron configurations. Keep in mind, however, that some exceptions exist, particularly in the heavier transition elements and the lanthanides and actinides.

A CLOSER LOOK Questions about Transition Element Electron Configurations

Why don't all of the $n = 3$ subshells fill before beginning to fill the $n = 4$ subshells? Why is scandium's configuration [Ar]$3d^14s^2$ and not [Ar]$3d^3$? Why is chromium's configuration [Ar]$3d^54s^1$ and not [Ar]$3d^44s^2$? As we search for explanations keep in mind that the most stable configuration will be that with the lowest *total* energy.

From scandium to zinc the energies of the 3*d* orbitals are always lower than the energy of the 4*s* orbital, so for scandium the configuration [Ar]$3d^3$ would seem to be preferred. One way to understand why it is not is to consider the effect of electron–electron repulsion in 3*d* and 4*s* orbitals. The most stable configuration will be the one that most effectively minimizes electron–electron repulsions.

Plots of 3*d* and 4*s* orbitals (as was done for 1*s* and 2*s* in Figure 7.2) show the most probable distance of a 3*d* electron from the nucleus is less than that for a 4*s* electron. Being closer to the nucleus, the 3*d* orbitals are more compact than the 4*s* orbital. This means the 3*d* electrons are closer together, and so two 3*d* electrons would repel each other more strongly than two 4*s* electrons, for example. A consequence is that placing electrons in the slightly higher energy 4*s* orbital lessens the effect of electron–electron repulsions and lowers the overall energy of the atom.

For chromium the 4*s* and 3*d* orbital energies are closer together than other 4th period transition elements. Again, thinking in terms of total energy, it is the effect of exchange energy (page 257) that tips the balance and causes the configuration [Ar]$3d^54s^1$, in which all electron spins are the same, to be most stable.

For more on these questions, see the following papers in the *Journal of Chemical Education,* and Chapter 9 of the book *The Periodic Table* by E. Scerri.

- E. Scerri, *The Periodic Table*, Oxford, 2007.
- F. L. Pilar, "4*s* is Always Above 3*d*," *Journal of Chemical Education*, Vol. 55, pp. 1–6, 1978.
- E. R. Scerri, "Transition Metal Configurations and Limitations of the Orbital Approximation," *Journal of Chemical Education*, Vol. 66, pp. 481–483, 1989.
- L. G. Vanquickenborne, K. Pierloot, and D. Devoghel, "Transition Metals and the Aufbau Principle," *Journal of Chemical Education*, Vol. 71, pp. 469–471, 1994.
- M. P. Melrose and E. R. Scerri, "Why the 4*s* Orbital is Occupied before the 3*d*," *Journal of Chemical Education*, Vol. 73, pp. 498–503, 1996.
- W. H. E. Schwarz, "The Full Story of the Electron Configurations of the Transition Elements," *Journal of Chemical Education*, Vol. 87, pp. 444-448, 2010.

Check Your Understanding

Using the periodic table and without looking at Table 7.3, write electron configurations for the following elements:

(a) P (c) Zr (e) Pb

(b) Zn (d) In (f) U

Use the *spdf* and noble gas notations. When you have finished, check your answers with Table 7.3.

REVIEW & CHECK FOR SECTION 7-3

1. What is the electron configuration of selenium beyond its noble gas core?

   (a) $4p^4$ (b) $4s^24p^4$ (c) $3d^{10}4s^24p^4$ (d) [Ar]

2. Based on electron configurations, which of the following atoms has the smallest number of unpaired electrons?

   (a) Cr (b) Fe (c) Ni (d) Mn

7-4 Electron Configurations of Ions

Learning Objectives: LO 1.5, LO 1.6, LO 1.10, LO 1.11, LO 1.13

Chemistry often involves ions, so we need to understand ion electron configurations and their relation to the properties of substances and their reactions.

Anions and Cations

To form a monatomic anion, one or more electrons is added to the valence shell of a nonmetal atom so that the electron configuration of the ion is the same as the electron configuration of the next noble gas in the periodic table. Thus, a fluorine atom gains one electron and becomes a fluoride ion with the same electron configuration as the noble gas neon.

$$F\ [1s^2 2s^2 2p^5] + e^- \rightarrow F^-\ [1s^2 2s^2 2p^6]$$

Similarly, a sulfur atom gains two electrons to become the sulfide ion with the same electron configuration as the noble gas argon.

$$S\ [1s^2 2s^2 2p^6 3s^2 3p^4] + 2\ e^- \rightarrow S^{2-}\ [1s^2 2s^2 2p^6 3s^2 3p^6]$$

To form a cation from a neutral atom, one or more of the valence electrons is removed. *Electrons are always removed first from the electron shell of highest n. If several subshells are present within the nth shell, the electron or electrons of maximum ℓ are removed.* Thus, a sodium ion is formed by removing the $3s^1$ electron from the Na atom,

$$Na\ [1s^2 2s^2 2p^6 3s^1] \rightarrow Na^+\ [1s^2 2s^2 2p^6] + e^-$$

and Ge^{2+} is formed by removing two $4p$ electrons from a germanium atom,

$$Ge\ [Ar]3d^{10}4s^2 4p^2 \rightarrow Ge^{2+}\ [Ar]3d^{10}4s^2 + 2\ e^-$$

The same general rule applies to transition metal atoms. This means, for example, that the titanium(II) cation has the configuration $[Ar]3d^2$

$$Ti\ [Ar]3d^2 4s^2 \rightarrow Ti^{2+}\ [Ar]3d^2 + 2\ e^-$$

Iron(II) and iron(III) cations have the configurations $[Ar]3d^6$ and $[Ar]3d^5$, respectively:

$$Fe\ [Ar]3d^6 4s^2 \rightarrow Fe^{2+}\ [Ar]3d^6 + 2\ e^-$$

$$Fe^{2+}\ [Ar]3d^6 \rightarrow Fe^{3+}\ [Ar]3d^5 + e^-$$

Note that in the ionization of transition metals the ns electrons are always lost before the $(n - 1)d$ electrons. All transition metals lose their ns electrons first, and the cations formed all have electron configurations of the general type [noble gas core]$(n - 1)d^x$. How do we know this is true? One important source of evidence is the study of the magnetic properties of matter.

Diamagnetism and Paramagnetism

If a hydrogen atom is placed in a magnetic field, the single electron will interact with the external field like the needle of a compass aligns with the magnetic lines of force on the Earth. As a result the hydrogen atom is attracted by the magnet.

In contrast, helium atoms, each with two electrons, are not attracted to a magnet. In fact, they are slightly repelled by the magnet. To account for this observation, we assume, in line with the Pauli exclusion principle, that the two electrons of helium have different values of m_s, that is, they have *opposite* spin orientations. We say their spins are *paired*, and the result is that the magnetic field of one electron is canceled out by the magnetic field of the second electron with opposite spin.

Elements and compounds that have unpaired electrons are attracted to a magnet. Such species are said to be **paramagnetic.** Substances in which all electrons are paired (with the two electrons of each pair having opposite spins) experience a slight repulsion when subjected to a magnetic field; they are said to be **diamagnetic**. The magnetism of a substance can be determined by placing it in a magnetic field and observing the extent of attraction or repulsion (Figure 7.4).

By determining the magnetic behavior of a substance we can gain information about the electronic structure. For example, the Fe^{3+} ion is paramagnetic (Figure 7.4) to the extent of five unpaired electrons. This is consistent with two $4s$ electrons and one $3d$ electron being removed from an iron atom to form a Fe^{3+} ion, leaving behind five unpaired $3d$ electrons. If, instead, three $3d$ electrons had been removed, the Fe^{3+} ion would still be paramagnetic but only to the extent of three unpaired electrons.

Laboratory measurement of paramagnetism

The paramagnetism of a sample can be measured by suspending a small sample between the poles of a magnet.

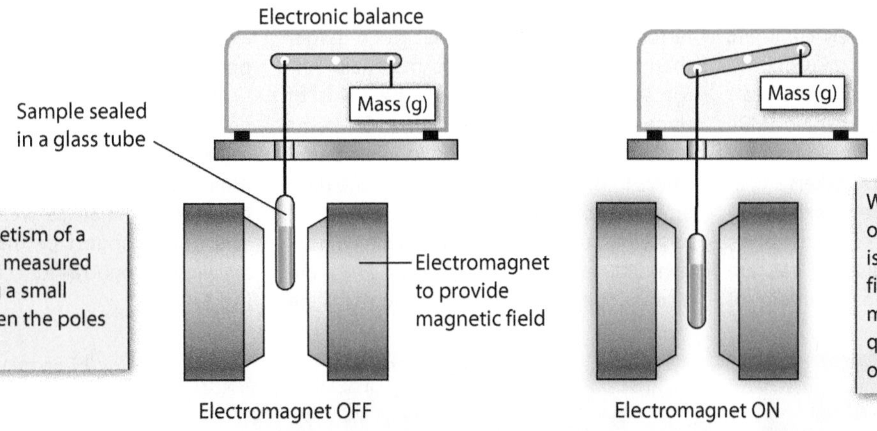

When the magnet is turned on, the paramagnetic sample is drawn into the magnetic field. The change in apparent mass can be related quantitatively to the degree of paramagnetism.

Observing the paramagnetism of iron(III) oxide.

To demonstrate paramagnetism, a sample of iron(III) oxide is packed into a plastic tube and suspended from a thin nylon filament.

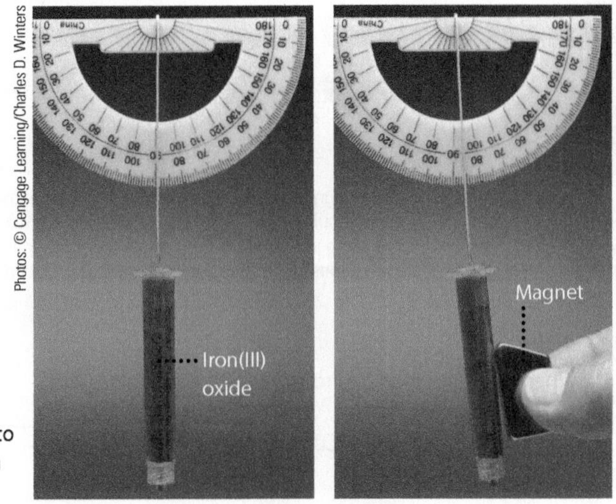

When a powerful magnet is brought near the sample, the paramagnetic iron(III) ions in Fe_2O_3 cause the sample to be attracted to the magnet.

The magnet is made of neodymium, iron, and boron [$Nd_2Fe_{14}B$]. These powerful magnets are used in acoustic speakers.

FIGURE 7.4 **Measuring and observing paramagnetism of compounds.**

EXAMPLE 7.4

Configurations of Transition Metal Ions

Problem Give the electron configurations for Cu, Cu^+, and Cu^{2+}. Are any of these species paramagnetic? How many unpaired electrons does each have?

What Do You Know? You know the electron configuration of copper, which has one 4*s* electron and ten 3*d* electrons. When forming a transition metal ion, the outermost *ns* electrons are lost first, followed by the $(n-1)d$ electrons.

Strategy Start with the electron configuration of copper (Table 7.4). It is always observed that the *ns* electron or electrons are ionized first followed by one or more $(n-1)d$ electrons.

Solution Copper has only one electron in the 4*s* orbital and ten electrons in 3*d* orbitals:

Cu [Ar]$3d^{10}4s^1$ [↑↓][↑↓][↑↓][↑↓][↑↓] (3*d*) [↑] (4*s*)

A CLOSER LOOK: Paramagnetism and Ferromagnetism

Magnetic materials are relatively common, and many are important in our economy. For example, a large magnet is at the heart of the magnetic resonance imaging (MRI) instruments used in medicine, and tiny magnets are found in stereo speakers and in telephone handsets. Magnetic oxides are used in recording tapes and computer disks.

The magnetic materials we use are **ferromagnetic**. The magnetic effect of ferromagnetic materials is much larger than that of paramagnetic materials. Ferromagnetism occurs when the spins of unpaired electrons in a cluster of atoms (called a *domain*) in the solid align themselves in the same direction. Only the metals of the iron, cobalt, and nickel subgroups, as well as a few other metals such as neodymium, exhibit this property. They are also unique in that, once the domains are aligned in a magnetic field, the metal is permanently magnetized.

Many alloys exhibit greater ferromagnetism than do the pure metals themselves. One example of such a material is Alnico, which is composed of aluminum, nickel, and cobalt as well as copper and iron. The strongest permanent magnet is an alloy of neodymium, iron, and boron ($Nd_2Fe_{14}B$).

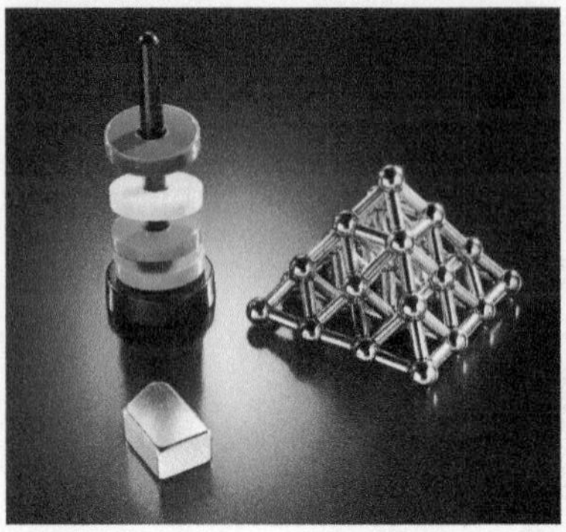

Magnets. Many common consumer products such as loudspeakers contain permanent magnets.

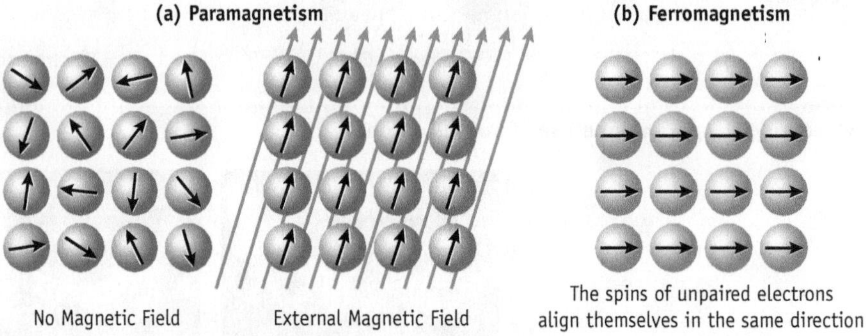

Magnetism. (a) Paramagnetism: In the absence of an external magnetic field, the unpaired electrons in the atoms or ions of the substance are randomly oriented. If a magnetic field is imposed, however, these spins will tend to become aligned with the field. **(b)** Ferromagnetism: The spins of the unpaired electrons in a cluster of atoms or ions align themselves in the same direction even in the absence of a magnetic field.

When copper is oxidized to Cu^+, the 4*s* electron is lost.

Cu^+ $[Ar]3d^{10}$ [↑↓][↑↓][↑↓][↑↓][↑↓] (3*d*) [ ] (4*s*)

The copper(II) ion is formed from copper(I) by removal of one of the 3*d* electrons.

Cu^{2+} $[Ar]3d^9$ [↑↓][↑↓][↑↓][↑↓][↑] (3*d*) [ ] (4*s*)

A copper atom and a copper(II) ion (Cu^{2+}) have one unpaired electron, so they are paramagnetic. In contrast, Cu^+ is diamagnetic.

Think about Your Answer Be sure to recall that the electron configuration for Cu is $[Ar]3d^{10}4s^1$ and not $[Ar]3d^94s^2$. Copper is one of two exceptions in the first transition series in the order of filling (Cr is the other).

Check Your Understanding

Depict the electron configurations for V^{2+}, V^{3+}, and Co^{3+}. Use orbital box diagrams and the noble gas notation. Are any of the ions paramagnetic? If so, give the number of unpaired electrons.

REVIEW & CHECK FOR SECTION 7-4

1. Three of the four ions shown below have the same electron configuration but the fourth does not. Identify the one that does not match.

   (a) Fe^{3+} (b) Cr^+ (c) Mn^{2+} (d) Fe^{2+}

2. Which of the following ions has the largest number of unpaired electrons?

   (a) Cr^{3+} (b) Cu^{2+} (c) Co^{3+} (d) Ni^{2+}

3. Which of the following species is most paramagnetic?

   (a) Cr (b) Cr^{3+} (c) Mn (d) Mn^{2+}

7-5 Atomic Properties and Periodic Trends

Learning Objectives: LO 1.6, LO 1.7, LO 1.8, LO 1.11, LO 1.13

Once electron configurations were understood, chemists realized that *similarities in properties of the elements are the result of similar valence shell electron configurations*. An objective of this section is to describe how atomic electron configurations are related to some of the physical and chemical properties of the elements and why those properties change in a predictable manner when moving down groups and across periods.

Atomic Size

The sizes of atoms (Figure 7.5) influence many aspects of their properties and reactivity. Size can determine the number of atoms that may surround and be bound to a central atom and can be a determining factor in the shape of a molecule. As you will see in the next chapter in particular, the shapes of molecules are important in determining their properties.

Atom size is also geochemically and technologically important. For example, one atom may take the place of a similarly sized atom in an *alloy*, a solid solution

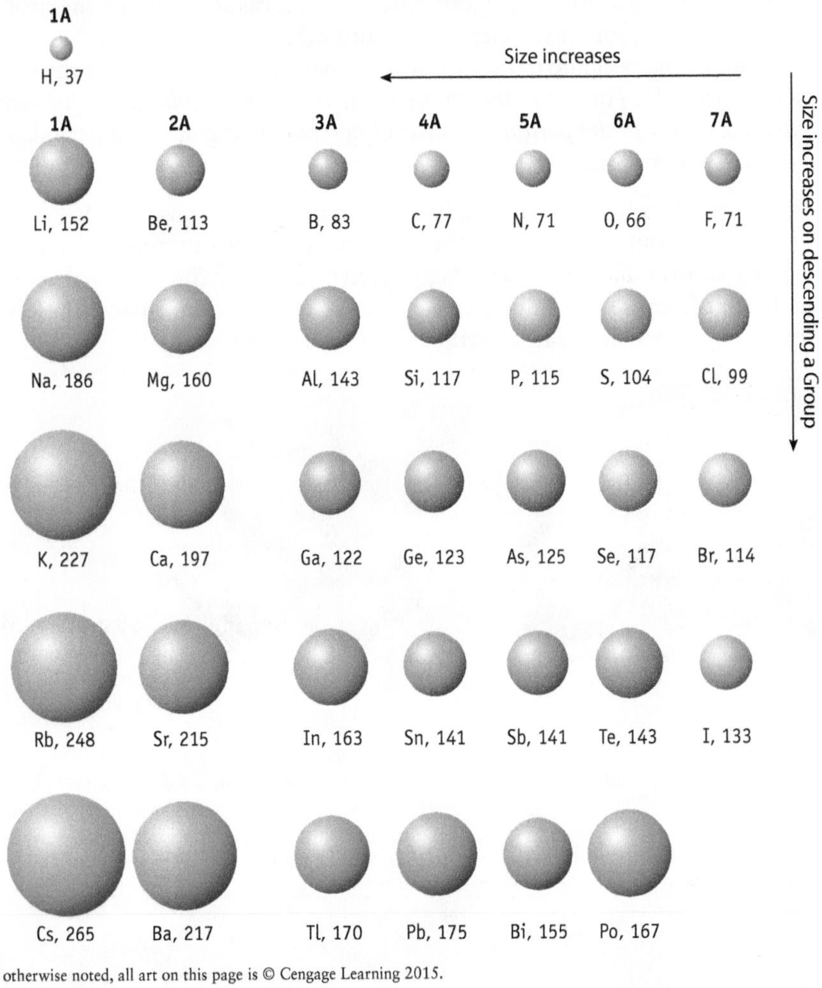

FIGURE 7.5 **Atomic radii in picometers for main group elements.** 1 pm = 1×10^{-12} m = 1×10^{-3} nm. *(Data taken from J. Emsley:* The Elements, *Clarendon Press, Oxford, 1998, 3rd ed.)*

FIGURE 7.6 The Willamette iron meteorite. This 14150-kg meteorite is composed of 92.38% Fe and 7.62% Ni (with traces of Ga, Ge, and Ir). Iron and nickel atoms have nearly identical radii (124 pm and 125 pm, respectively), so one can substitute for the other in the solid. (The meteorite was discovered in Oregon in 1902, and it is now on display at the American Museum of Natural History.)

of various elements in a metallic matrix (▶ Section 12-5). Our technology-based industrial society depends on these materials. Substituting one element for another of similar size can often lead to alloys with different properties. But this is nothing new: humans made implements from iron meteorites (Figure 7.6) over 5000 years ago. Iron meteorites are an alloy composed of about 90% iron and 10% nickel, two elements of very similar size.

We know an orbital has no sharp boundary (◀ Figure 6.12a), so how can we define the size of an atom? There are actually several ways, and they can give slightly different results.

One of the simplest and most useful ways to define atomic size is to relate it to the distance between atoms in a sample of the element. Let us consider a diatomic molecule such as Cl_2 (Figure 7.7a). The radius of a Cl atom is assumed to be half the experimentally determined distance between the centers of the two atoms (198 pm), so the radius of one Cl atom is 99 pm. Similarly, the C—C distance in diamond is 154 pm, so a radius of 77 pm can be assigned to carbon. To test these estimates, we can add them together to estimate the C—Cl distance in CCl_4. The predicted distance of 176 pm agrees with the experimentally measured C—Cl distance of 176 pm. (Radii determined this way are often called *covalent radii.*)

This approach to determining atomic radii applies only if molecular compounds of the element exist (and so it is largely limited to nonmetals and metalloids). For metals, atomic radii are sometimes estimated from measurements of the atom-to-atom distance in a crystal of the element (Figure 7.7b).

Some interesting periodic trends are seen immediately on looking at the table of radii (see Figure 7.5). *For the main group elements, atomic radii generally increase going down a group in the periodic table and decrease going across a period.* These trends reflect two important effects:

- The size of an atom is determined by the outermost electrons. In going from the top to the bottom of a group in the periodic table, the outermost electrons are assigned to orbitals with increasingly higher values of the principal quantum number, *n*. Because the underlying electrons require some space, these outer shell electrons are necessarily farther from the nucleus.

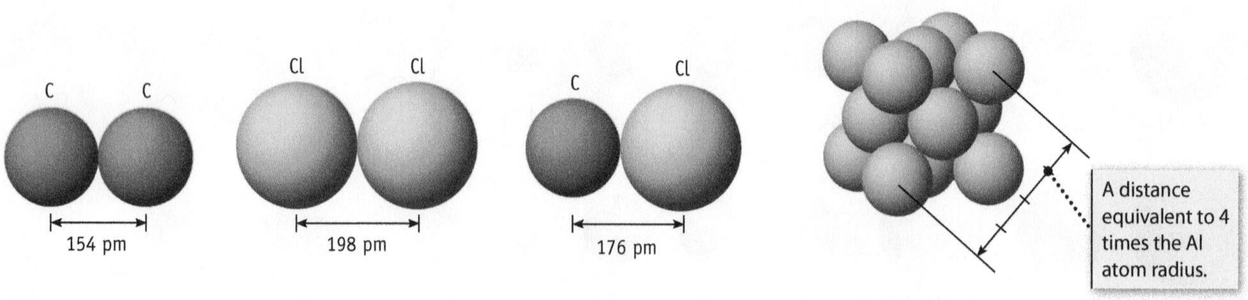

(a) The sum of the atomic radii of C and Cl provides a good estimate of the C-Cl distance in a molecule having such a bond.

(b) Pictured here is a tiny piece of an aluminum crystal. Each sphere represents an aluminum atom. Measuring the distance shown allows a scientist to estimate the radius of an aluminum atom.

FIGURE 7.7 Determining atomic radii.

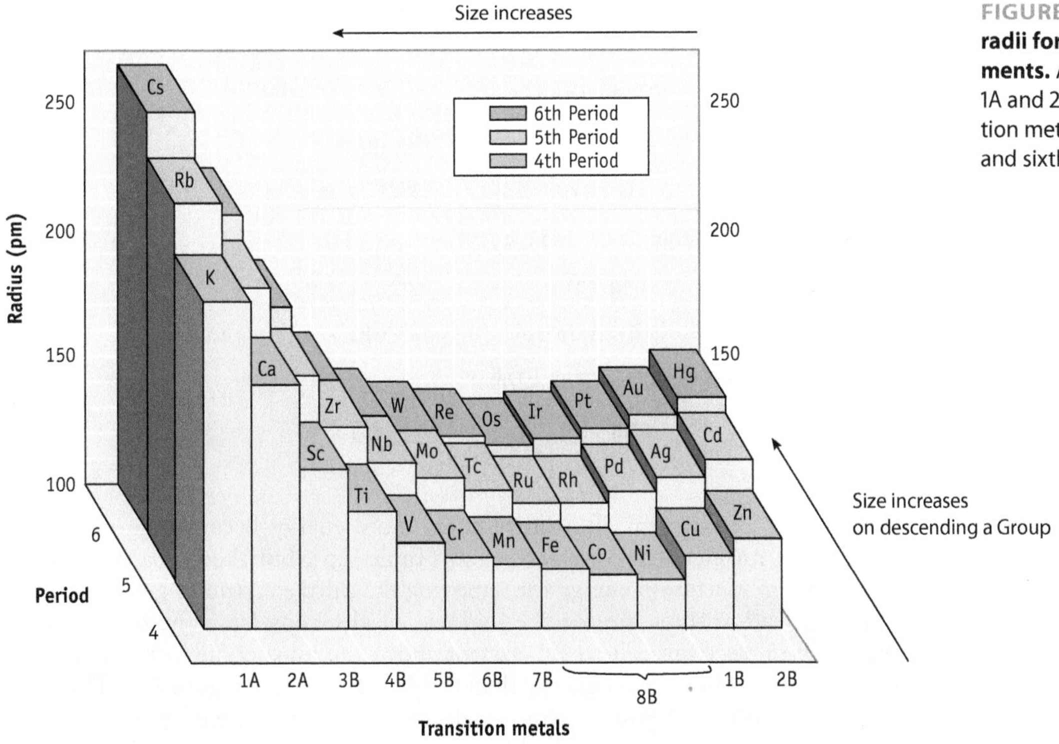

FIGURE 7.8 Trends in atomic radii for the transition elements. Atomic radii of the Group 1A and 2A metals and the transition metals of the fourth, fifth, and sixth periods.

- For main group elements of a given period, the principal quantum number, n, of the valence electron orbitals is the same. In going from one element to the next across a period, the effective nuclear charge (Z^*) increases (see Figure 7.2). This results in an increased Coulombic force of attraction between the nucleus and the valence electrons, and the atomic radius decreases.

Atomic Radii—Caution Numerous tabulations of atomic and covalent radii exist, and the values quoted in them often differ somewhat. The variation comes about because several methods are used to determine the radii of atoms.

The periodic trend in the atomic radii of transition metal atoms (Figure 7.8) across a period is somewhat different from that for main group elements. Going from left to right in a given period, the radii initially decrease. However, the sizes of the elements in the middle of a transition series change very little, and a small increase in size occurs at the end of the series. The size of transition metal atoms is determined largely by electrons in the outermost shell—that is, by the electrons of the ns subshell—but electrons are being added to the $(n-1)d$ orbitals across the series. The increased nuclear charge on the atoms as one moves from left to right should cause the radius to decrease. This effect, however, is mostly canceled out by increased electron–electron repulsion. On reaching the Group 1B and 2B elements at the end of the series, the size increases slightly because the d subshell is filled and electron–electron repulsions dominate.

Ionization Energy

Ionization energy *(IE)* is the energy required to remove an electron from an atom in the gas phase.

$$\text{Atom in ground state(g)} \longrightarrow \text{Atom}^+\text{(g)} + e^-$$

$$\Delta U \equiv \text{ionization energy, } IE$$

As predicted by Coulomb's law, energy must be supplied to overcome the attraction between an electron and the nucleus and to separate the electron from the atom. Thus, ionization energies always have positive values. An electron farther from the nucleus generally has a smaller ionization energy, and an electron closer to the nucleus has a larger ionization energy.

Measuring Ionization Energy
Ionization energy values can be measured to a high level of accuracy. In contrast, atomic radii are approximate values.

Atoms other than hydrogen have a series of ionization energies as electrons are removed sequentially. For example, the first three ionization energies of magnesium are

First ionization energy, IE_1 = 738 kJ/mol

$$Mg(g) \rightarrow Mg^+(g) + e^-$$
$$1s^22s^22p^63s^2 \quad\quad 1s^22s^22p^63s^1$$

Second ionization energy, IE_2 = 1451 kJ/mol

$$Mg^+(g) \rightarrow Mg^{2+}(g) + e^-$$
$$1s^22s^22p^63s^1 \quad\quad 1s^22s^22p^6$$

Third ionization energy, IE_3 = 7732 kJ/mol

$$Mg^{2+}(g) \rightarrow Mg^{3+}(g) + e^-$$
$$1s^22s^22p^6 \quad\quad 1s^22s^22p^5$$

Removing each subsequent electron requires more energy because the electron is removed from an increasingly positive ion (Table 7.5), but there is a particularly large increase in ionization energy for removing the third electron to give Mg^{3+}. The first two ionization steps are for the removal of electrons from the outermost or valence shell of electrons. The third electron, however, must come from the 2*p* subshell, which has a much lower energy than the 3*s* subshell (see Figure 7.1). This large increase is experimental evidence for the electron shell structure of atoms.

For main group (*s*- and *p*-block) elements, *first ionization energies generally increase across a period and decrease down a group* (Figure 7.9, Table 7.5, and Appendix F). The trend across a period corresponds to the increase in effective nuclear charge, Z^*, with increasing atomic number (see Figure 7.2). As predicted by Coulomb's law, as Z^* increases across a period, the energy required to remove an electron increases. Going down a group, the ionization energy decreases. The electron removed is increasingly farther from the nucleus and thus is held less strongly.

Valence and Core Electrons
Removal of core electrons requires much more energy than removal of a valence electron. Core electrons are not lost in chemical reactions. (See the plot of orbital energies on page 262.)

Notice that the trends in atomic radius and ionization energy for a given period are both linked to Z^* although they are inversely related. *Owing to an increase in*

Table 7.5 First, Second, and Third Ionization Energies for the Main Group Elements in Periods 2–4 (kJ/mol)

2ND PERIOD	Li	Be	B	C	N	O	F	Ne
1st	513	899	801	1086	1402	1314	1681	2080
2nd	7298	1757	2427	2352	2856	3388	3374	3952
3rd	11815	14848	3660	4620	4578	5300	6050	6122
3RD PERIOD	**Na**	**Mg**	**Al**	**Si**	**P**	**S**	**Cl**	**Ar**
1st	496	738	577	787	1012	1000	1251	1520
2nd	4562	1451	1817	1577	1903	2251	2297	2665
3rd	6912	7732	2745	3231	2912	3361	3826	3928
4TH PERIOD	**K**	**Ca**	**Ga**	**Ge**	**As**	**Se**	**Br**	**Kr**
1st	419	590	579	762	947	941	1140	1351
2nd	3051	1145	1979	1537	1798	2044	2104	2350
3rd	4411	4910	2963	3302	2735	2974	3500	3565

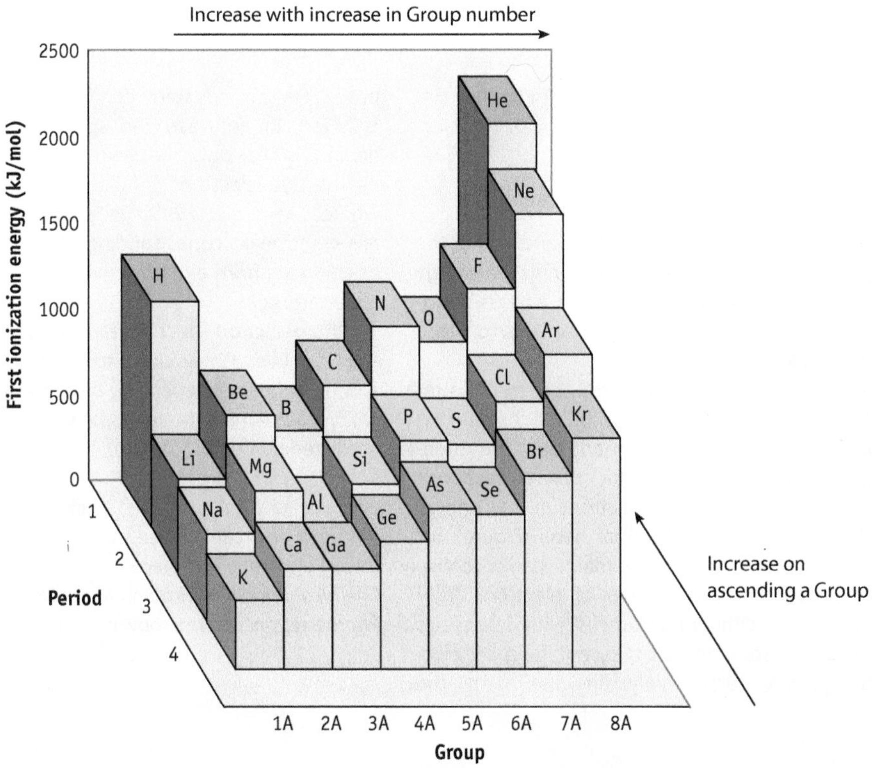

FIGURE 7.9 First ionization energies of the main group elements in the first four periods. (For specific values of the ionization energies for these elements see Table 7.5 and Appendix F.)

effective nuclear charge across a period, the atomic radius generally decreases and the ionization energy increases.

A closer look at ionization energies reveals variations to the general trend in a period. One variation occurs on going from *s*-block to *p*-block elements—from beryllium to boron, for example. The 2*p* electrons are slightly higher in energy than the 2*s* electrons so the ionization energy for boron is slightly less than that for beryllium. Another dip to lower ionization energy occurs on going from nitrogen to oxygen. No change occurs in either *n* or *ℓ*, but electron–electron repulsions increase for the following reason. In Groups 3A–5A, electrons are assigned to separate *p* orbitals (p_x, p_y, and p_z). Beginning in Group 6A, however, two electrons must be assigned to the same *p* orbital. The fourth *p* electron shares an orbital with another electron and thus experiences greater repulsion than it would if it had been assigned to an orbital of its own.

$$\text{O (oxygen atom)} \xrightarrow{+1314 \text{ kJ/mol}} \text{O}^+ \text{ (oxygen cation)} + e^-$$

The greater repulsion experienced by the fourth 2*p* electron makes it easier to remove. The usual trend resumes on going from oxygen to fluorine to neon, reflecting the increase in Z^*.

Electron Attachment Enthalpy and Electron Affinity

The **electron attachment enthalpy**, $\Delta_{EA}H$, is defined as the enthalpy change occurring when a gaseous atom adds an electron, forming a gaseous anion.

$$A(g) + e^- \rightarrow A^-(g) \qquad \text{Electron attachment enthalpy} = \Delta_{EA}H$$

As illustrated in Figure 7.10, the value of $\Delta_{EA}H$ for many elements is negative, indicating that this process is exothermic and that energy is evolved. For example, $\Delta_{EA}H$

A CLOSER LOOK Photoelectron Spectroscopy

Photoelectron spectroscopy (PES) is an experimental technique that provides information about the energies of electrons in atoms and molecules and yields evidence in favor of our modern orbital model of electrons in atoms. In this technique, sample atoms are bombarded with high-energy electromagnetic radiation. If a photon has sufficient energy, it can cause an electron in the sample to be ejected. In order to eject valence electrons, the energy required often corresponds to radiation in the ultraviolet region; to remove core electrons, however, higher-energy radiation, such as that in the x-ray region, is required.

The key to understanding PES is that all of the ejected electrons result from bombarding the atom with photons of the same energy ($h\nu$). Some of this energy goes into ejecting the electron from the atom, corresponding to the *ionization energy* (*IE*) of the electron, with the remainder going into kinetic energy of the electron [*KE*(electron)].

$$h\nu = IE + KE(\text{electron})$$

By analyzing the kinetic energies of the electrons emitted and knowing the energy of the original photons, it is possible to determine the ionization energy of each electron ejected.

Each peak in the PES spectrum corresponds to the energy of a subshell that contains electrons. In addition, the intensity of a peak in the spectrum corresponds to the number of electrons in that energy level. The spectrum of neon (Figure), for example, has three major peaks, corresponding to ejection of electrons from three different subshells with intensities corresponding to two, two, and six electrons, respectively, in line with the predicted ground state configuration of $1s^22s^22p^6$. In contrast, the spectrum for helium ($1s^2$) has only one peak, corresponding to two electrons in the 1s subshell, whereas krypton ($1s^22s^22p^63s^23p^63d^{10}4s^24p^6$) has eight peaks corresponding to ejection of electrons from eight subshells of different energies.

Photoelectron spectra clearly show that electrons in subshells closer to the nucleus, and thus those experiencing higher values of Z^*, require more energy to be ejected (as predicted by Coulomb's law).

Just as PES provides evidence for the energies (and thus orbitals) of electrons in atoms, it also can be used to probe energies of electrons in molecules. See *Applying Chemical Principles, Probing Molecules with Photoelectron Spectroscopy*, p. 367).

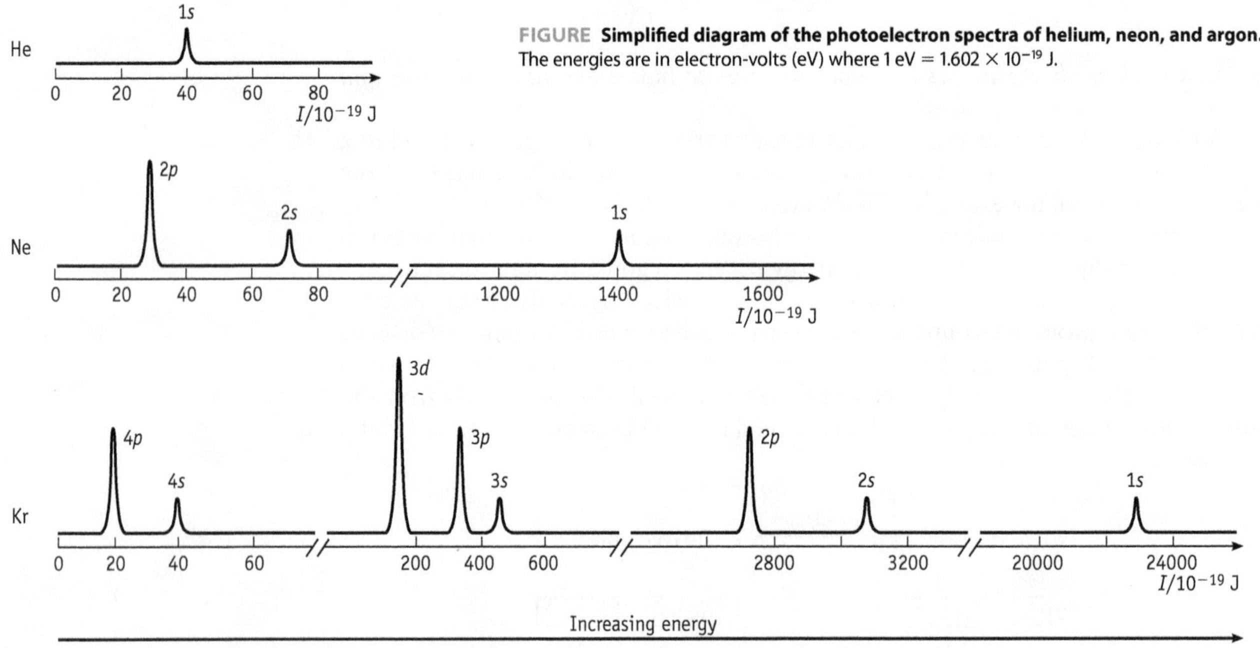

FIGURE **Simplified diagram of the photoelectron spectra of helium, neon, and argon.** The energies are in electron-volts (eV) where 1 eV = 1.602×10^{-19} J.

for fluorine is quite exothermic (−328 kJ/mol), whereas boron has a much less negative value of −26.7 kJ/mol. Values of $\Delta_{EA}H$ for a number of elements are given in Appendix F.

The **electron affinity**, EA, of an atom is closely related to $\Delta_{EA}H$. Electron affinity is equal in magnitude but opposite in sign to the internal energy change associated with a gaseous atom adding an electron.

$$A(g) + e^- \rightarrow A^-(g) \qquad \text{Electron affinity, } EA = -\Delta U$$

We expect EA and $\Delta_{EA}H$ to have nearly identical numerical values; however, current convention gives the two values opposite signs.

Because electron attachment enthalpy and ionization energy represent the energy involved in the gain or loss of an electron by an atom, respectively, it makes sense that periodic trends in these properties are also related. The increase in effective nuclear charge of atoms across a period (see Figure 7.2) makes it more difficult to ionize the atom, and it also increases the attraction of the atom for an additional electron. Thus, an element with a high ionization energy generally has a more negative value for its electron attachment enthalpy.

As seen in Figure 7.10, the values of $\Delta_{EA}H$ generally become more negative on moving across a period, but the trend is not smooth. The elements in Group 2A and 5A appear as variations to the general trend, corresponding to cases where the added electron would start a *p* subshell or would be paired with another electron in the *p* subshell, respectively.

The value of electron attachment enthalpy usually becomes less negative on descending a group of the periodic table. Electrons are added increasingly farther from the nucleus, so the attractive force between the nucleus and electrons decreases. This general trend does not apply to second period elements, however. For example, the value of the electron attachment enthalpy of fluorine is less negative than the value for chlorine. The same phenomenon is observed in Groups 3A through 6A. One explanation is that significant electron–electron repulsions occur in small anions such as F^-. That is, adding an electron to the seven electrons already present in the $n = 2$ shell of the small F atom leads to considerable repulsion between electrons. Chlorine has a larger atomic volume than fluorine, so adding an electron leads to a lesser degree of electron–electron repulsions.

A few elements, such as nitrogen and the Group 2A elements, have no affinity for electrons and are listed as having a $\Delta_{EA}H$ value of zero. The noble gases are generally not listed in tables of $\Delta_{EA}H$ values. They have no affinity for electrons, because any additional electron must be added to the next higher electron shell with a considerably higher energy.

No atom has a negative $\Delta_{EA}H$ value for a second electron. So what accounts for the existence of ions such as O^{2-} that occur in many compounds? The answer is that

Electron Affinity, Electron Attachment Enthalpy, and Sign Conventions Changes in sign conventions for electron affinities over the years have caused confusion. For a useful discussion of electron affinity, see J. C. Wheeler: "Electron affinities of the alkaline earth metals and the sign convention for electron affinity," *Journal of Chemical Education*, Vol. 74, pp. 123–127, 1997. In this paper the electron affinity is taken as equivalent to the ionization energy of the anion (which is in fact the way electron affinities can be measured experimentally).

Electron Attachment Enthalpy for the Halogens

Element	$\Delta_{EA}H$ (kJ/mol)	Atomic Radius (pm)
F	−328.0	71
Cl	−349.0	99
Br	−324.7	114
I	−295.2	133

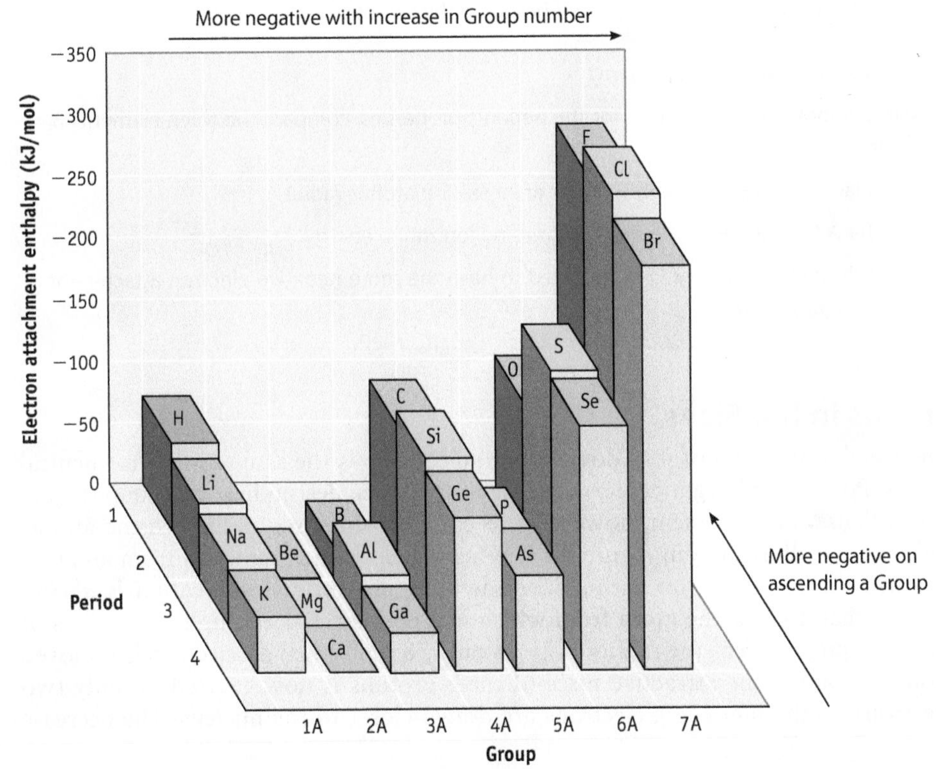

FIGURE 7.10 **Electron attachment enthalpy.** The greater the affinity of an atom for an electron, the more negative the value for $\Delta_{EA}H$. For numerical values, see Appendix F. (Data were taken from H. Hotop and W. C. Lineberger: "Binding energies of atomic negative ions," *Journal of Physical Chemistry*, Reference Data, Vol. 14, p. 731, 1985.)

doubly charged anions can be stabilized in crystalline environments by electrostatic attraction to neighboring positive ions (▶ Chapters 8 and 12).

EXAMPLE 7.5

Periodic Trends

Problem Compare the three elements C, O, and Si.

(a) Place them in order of increasing atomic radius.

(b) Which has the largest ionization energy?

(c) Which has the more negative electron attachment enthalpy, O or C?

What Do You Know? Carbon and silicon are the first and second elements in Group 4A and oxygen is the first element in Group 6A. You also know the trends in the periodic properties across periods and down groups.

Strategy Use the trends in atomic properties in Figure 7.5, Figures 7.8–7.10, Table 7.5, and Appendix F.

Solution

(a) *Atomic size:* Atomic radii decrease on moving across a period, so oxygen has a smaller radius than carbon. However, the radius increases on moving down a periodic group. Because C and Si are in the same group (Group 4A), silicon must be larger than carbon. The trend is O < C < Si.

(b) *Ionization energy:* Ionization energies generally increase across a period and decrease down a group. Thus, the trend in ionization energies is Si (787 kJ/mol) < C (1086 kJ/mol) < O (1314 kJ/mol).

(c) *Electron attachment enthalpy:* Values generally become less negative down a group (except for the second period elements) and more negative across a period. Therefore, O (= −141.0 kJ/mol) has a more negative $\Delta_{EA}H$ than C (= −121.9 kJ/mol).

Think about Your Answer Notice the trends in atom size and ionization energy are in the opposite order as expected based on the values of Z^*.

Check Your Understanding

Without looking at the figures for the periodic properties, compare the three elements B, Al, and C.

(a) Place the three elements in order of increasing atomic radius.

(b) Rank the elements in order of increasing ionization energy.

(c) Which element, B or C, is expected to have the more negative electron attachment enthalpy value?

Trends in Ion Sizes

The trend in the sizes of ions down a periodic group is the same as that for neutral atoms: Positive and negative ions increase in size when descending the group (Figure 7.11). Pause for a moment, however, and compare the ionic radii with the atomic radii, as also illustrated in Figure 7.11. When an electron is removed from an atom to form a cation, the size shrinks considerably. The radius of a cation is *always* smaller than that of the atom from which it is derived. For example, the radius of Li is 152 pm, whereas the radius of Li^+ is only 78 pm. When an electron is removed from a Li atom, the attractive force of three protons is now exerted on only two electrons, so the remaining electrons are drawn closer to the nucleus. The decrease

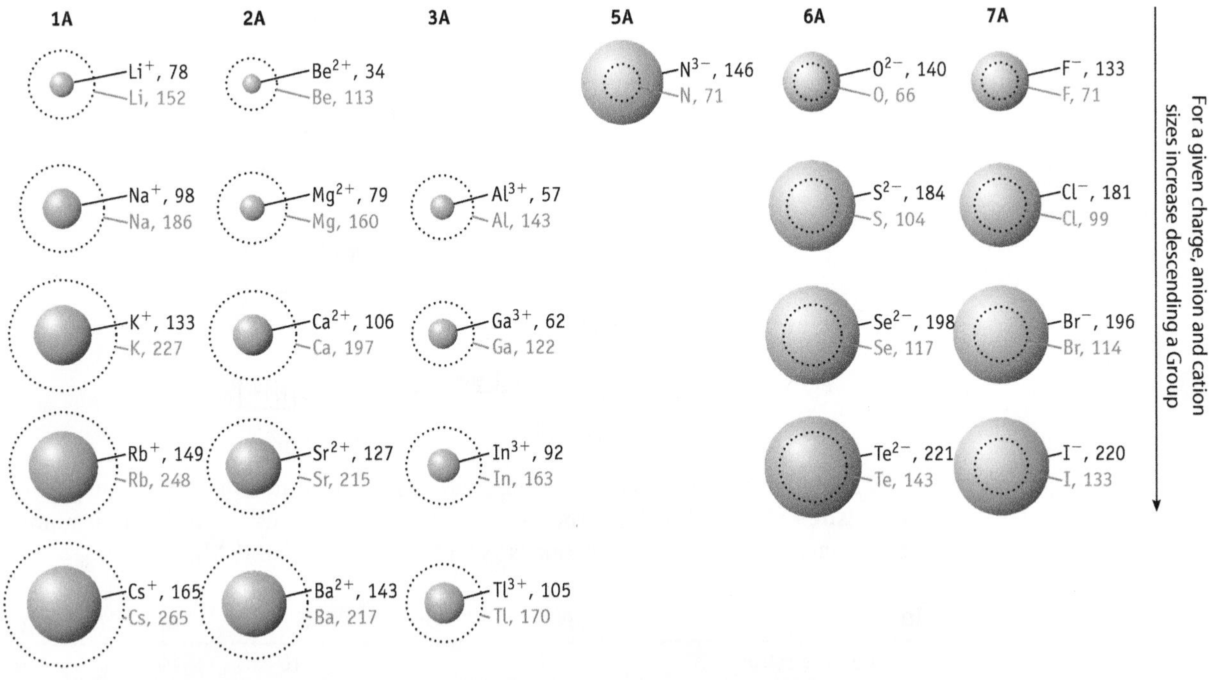

FIGURE 7.11 **Relative sizes of some common ions.** Radii are given in picometers (1 pm = 1×10^{-12} m). (Data taken from J. Emsley, *The Elements*, Clarendon Press, Oxford, 1998, 3rd edition.)

in ion size is especially great when the last electron of a particular shell is removed, as is the case for Li. The loss of the 2*s* electron from Li leaves Li^+ with no electrons in the $n = 2$ shell.

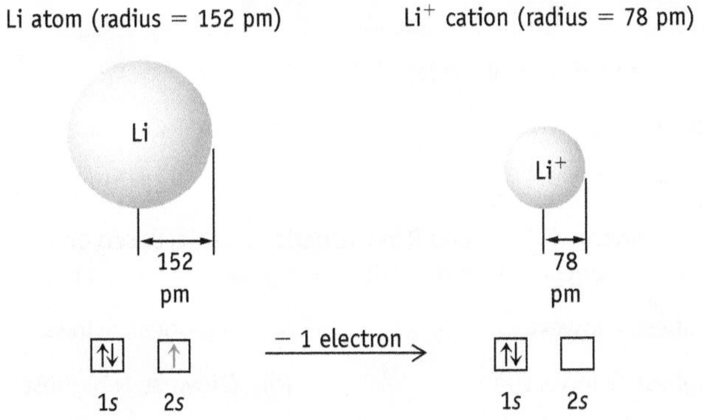

A large decrease in size is also expected if two or more electrons are removed from an atom. For example, an aluminum ion, Al^{3+}, has a radius of 57 pm, whereas the radius of an aluminum atom is 143 pm.

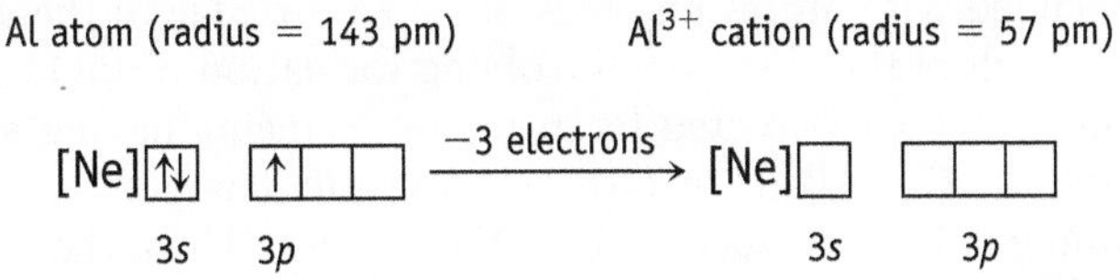

You can also see in Figure 7.11 that anions are *always* larger than the atoms from which they are derived. Here, the argument is the opposite of that used to explain positive ion radii. The F atom, for example, has nine protons and nine electrons. On forming the anion, the nuclear charge is still +9, but the anion has ten electrons. The F^- ion is larger than the F atom because of increased electron–electron repulsions.

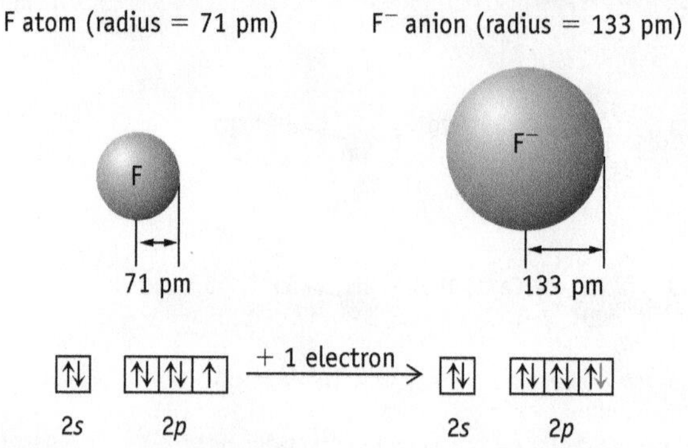

Finally, it is useful to compare the sizes of isoelectronic ions across the periodic table. **Isoelectronic** ions have the same number of electrons but a different number of protons. One such series of ions is N^{3-}, O^{2-}, F^-, Na^+, and Mg^{2+}:

Ion	N^{3-}	O^{2-}	F^-	Na^+	Mg^{2+}
Number of electrons	10	10	10	10	10
Number of nuclear protons	7	8	9	11	12
Ionic radius (pm)	146	140	133	98	79

All these ions have 10 electrons but they differ in the number of protons. As the number of protons increases in a series of isoelectronic ions, the balance between electron–proton attraction and electron–electron repulsion shifts in favor of attraction, and the radius decreases.

REVIEW & CHECK FOR SECTION 7-5

1. What is the trend in sizes of the ions K^+, S^{2-}, and Cl^-?

   (a) $K^+ > S^{2-} > Cl^-$ (c) $S^{2-} < Cl^- < K^+$

   (b) $K^+ < S^{2-} < Cl^-$ (d) $S^{2-} > Cl^- > K^+$

2. Locate the elements C, N, Si, and P in the periodic table. Based on general trends, identify the elements in this group with the highest and lowest ionization energy.

   (a) C highest, P lowest (c) N highest, Si lowest

   (b) C highest, Si lowest (d) C lowest, N highest

Learning Objectives: LO 1.6, LO 1.10, LO 1.11, LO 1.13

7-6 Periodic Trends and Chemical Properties

Atomic and ionic radii, ionization energies, and electron attachment enthalpies are properties associated with atoms and their ions. Knowledge of these properties will be useful as we explore the chemistry involving formation of ionic compounds.

The periodic table was created by grouping elements having similar chemical properties (Figure 7.12). Alkali metals, for example, characteristically form compounds containing a 1+ ion, such as Li^+, Na^+, or K^+. Thus, the reaction between sodium and chlorine gives the ionic compound, NaCl (composed of $Na^+$and Cl^- ions) (see Figure 1.2), and potassium and water react to form an aqueous solution of KOH, a solution containing the hydrated ions $K^+(aq)$ and $OH^-(aq)$.

$$2\ Na(s) + Cl_2(g) \rightarrow 2\ NaCl(s)$$

$$2\ K(s) + 2\ H_2O(\ell) \rightarrow 2\ K^+(aq) + 2\ OH^-(aq) + H_2(g)$$

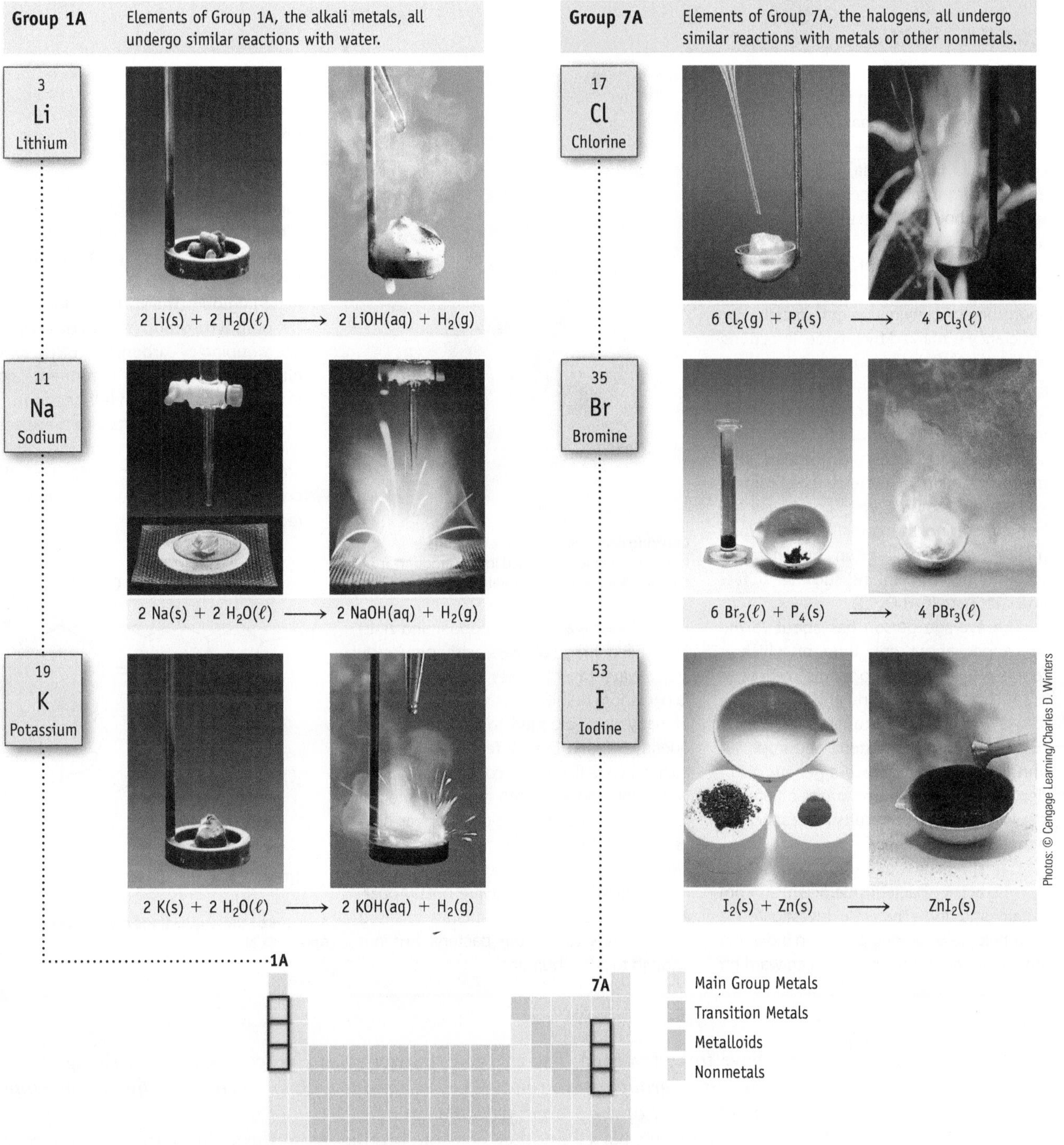

FIGURE 7.12 **Examples of the periodicity of Group 1A and Group 7A elements.** Dmitri Mendeleev developed the first periodic table by listing elements in order of increasing atomic weight. Every so often, an element had properties similar to those of a lighter element, and these were placed in vertical columns or groups. We now recognize that the elements should be listed in order of increasing atomic number and that the periodic occurrence of similar properties is related to the electron configurations of the elements.

The low ionization energies of alkali metals is the primary reason why Na^+ and K^+ are readily formed in chemical reactions.

Ionization energies also account for the fact that these reactions of sodium and potassium do not produce compounds such as $NaCl_2$ or $K(OH)_2$. The formation of an Na^{2+} or K^{2+} ion would be a very unfavorable process. Removing a second electron from these metals requires a great deal of energy because a core electron would

CASE STUDY Metals in Biochemistry and Medicine

Many main group and transition metals play an important role in biochemistry and in medicine. Your body has low levels of the following metals in the form of various compounds: Ca, 1.5%; Na, 0.1%; Mg, 0.05%, as well as iron, cobalt, zinc, and copper, all less than about 0.05%. (Levels are percentages by mass.)

Much of the 3–4 g of iron in your body is found in hemoglobin, the substance responsible for carrying oxygen to cells. Iron deficiency is marked by fatigue, infections, and mouth inflammations.

Iron in your diet can come from eggs and brewer's yeast, which has a very high iron content. In addition, foods such as some breakfast cereals are "fortified" with metallic iron. (In an interesting experiment you can do at home, you can remove the iron by stirring the cereal with a strong magnet.) Vitamin pills often contain iron(II) compounds with anions such as sulfate and succinate ($C_4H_4O_4^{2-}$).

The average person has about 75 mg of copper, about one third of which is found in the muscles. Copper is involved in many biological functions, and a deficiency shows up in many ways: anemia, degeneration of the nervous system, and impaired immunity. Wilson's disease, a genetic disorder, leads to the over-accumulation of copper in the body and results in hepatic and neurological damage.

Like silver ions (page 132), copper ions can also act as a bacteriocide. Scientists from Britain and India recently investigated a long-held belief among people in India that storing water in brass pitchers can ward off illness. (Brass is an alloy of copper and zinc.) They filled brass pitchers with previously sterile water to which they had added *E. coli* (a bacterium that lives in the lower intestine of many warm-blooded animals and consequently is found in their feces). Other brass pitchers were filled with contaminated river water from India. In both cases, they found fecal bacteria counts dropped from as high as 1,000,000 bacteria per milliliter to zero in two days. In contrast, bacteria levels stayed high in plastic or earthenware pots. Apparently, just enough copper ions are released by the brass to kill the bacteria but not enough to affect humans.

Carrying drinking water in brass jugs in India. Copper ions released in tiny amounts from the brass kill bacteria in contaminated water.

Questions:

1. Give the electron configurations for iron and the iron(II) and iron(III) ions.
2. In hemoglobin, iron can be in the iron(II) or iron(III) state. Are either of these iron ions paramagnetic?
3. Why are copper atoms (radius = 128 pm) slightly larger than iron atoms (radius = 124 pm)?
4. In hemoglobin, the iron is enclosed by the porphyrin group (shown below), a flat grouping of carbon, hydrogen, and nitrogen atoms. (This is in turn encased in a protein.) When iron is in the form of the Fe^{3+} ion, it just fits into the space within the four N atoms, and the arrangement is flat. Speculate on what occurs to the structure when iron is reduced to the Fe^{2+} ion.

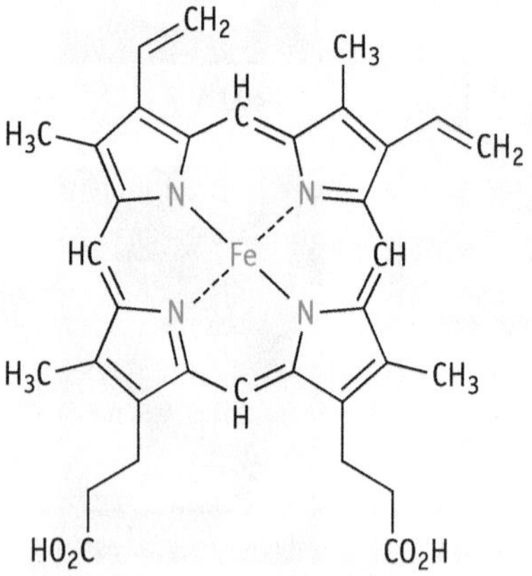

Answers to these questions are available in Appendix N.

have to be removed. The energetic barrier to this process is the underlying reason that *main group metals generally form cations with an electron configuration equivalent to that of the preceding noble gas.*

Why isn't Na_2Cl another possible product from the sodium and chlorine reaction? This formula would imply that the compound contains Na^+ and Cl^{2-} ions. Adding two electrons per atom to Cl means that the second electron must enter the next higher shell at much higher energy. Thus, anions such as Cl^{2-} are not known. This example also leads to a general statement: *nonmetals generally acquire enough electrons to form an anion with the electron configuration of the next noble gas.*

We can use similar logic to rationalize other observations. Ionization energies increase on going from left to right across a period. We have seen that elements from Groups 1A and 2A form ionic compounds, an observation directly related to the low ionization energies for these elements. Ionization energies for elements toward the right side of a period, however, are sufficiently large that cation formation is unfavorable. On the right side of the second period, oxygen and fluorine much prefer taking on electrons to giving them up; these elements have high ionization energies and relatively large, negative electron attachment enthalpies. Thus, oxygen and fluorine form anions and not cations when they react.

Finally, let us think for a moment about carbon, the basis of thousands of chemical compounds. Its ionization energy is not favorable for cation formation, and it also does not generally form anions. Thus, we do not find many binary ionic compounds containing carbon; instead, we find carbon sharing electrons with other elements in compounds such as CO_2 and CCl_4. We will study those kinds of compounds in the next two chapters.

REVIEW & CHECK FOR SECTION 7-6

1. Which of the following is an incorrect formula?

   (a) MgCl (b) $CaCl_2$ (c) $AlCl_3$ (d) RbCl

2. Which of the following is not the formula for a common ion?

   (a) Cl^- (b) K^+ (c) O^{2-} (d) S^{3-}

APPLYING CHEMICAL PRINCIPLES

The Not-So-Rare Earths

Lanthanum and the block of 14 elements stretching from cerium (element 58) through lutetium (element 71) are referred to as the lanthanides or, often, as the rare earth elements. The "rare earth" name is perhaps a misnomer because the elements are in fact not all that rare. With the exception of promethium, which is not found naturally, these elements are more abundant than gold. Cerium, for example, is the 26th most abundant element in the Earth's crust. Unfortunately, high concentrations of rare earth elements are rarely found in ore deposits. Furthermore, these elements are often mixed in the same deposits and their separation is difficult due to their similar chemical properties.

The rare earth elements possess electronic and optical properties that make them valuable in the production of electronics, lasers, magnets, superconductors, lighting devices, and even jewelry. Ferromagnetism is common among the rare earth elements, with neodymium and samarium used extensively in strong, permanent magnets (page 266). These magnets are commonly used in computer hard drives and electric motors. Neodymium is also used in high-powered scientific and industrial lasers, and yttrium is used in high-temperature superconductors. Europium and terbium are used to produce fluorescent phosphors for television displays and mercury-vapor lamps.

© Cengage Learning/Charles D. Winters

(a) Mixtures of lanthanides shoot showers of sparks when struck by iron.

© Cengage Learning/Charles D. Winters

(b) Most compact fluorescent bulbs use europium phosphors to produce a pleasing spectrum of light.

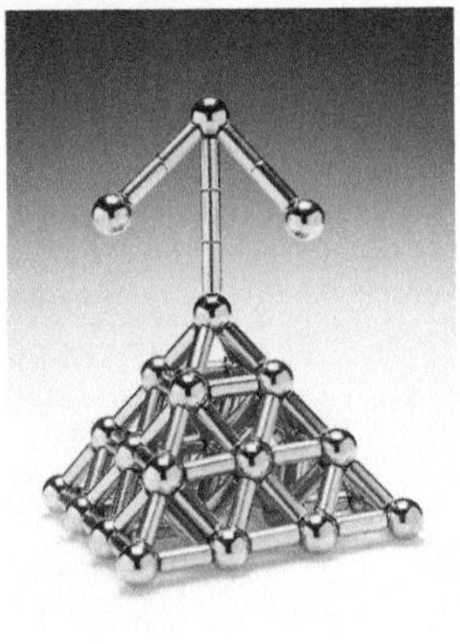

© Cengage Learning/Charles D. Winters

(c) Neodymium-iron-boron magnets.

Uses of lanthanides.

QUESTIONS:

1. The most common oxidation state of a rare earth element is +3.
   a. What is the ground state electron configuration of Sm^{3+}?
   b. Write a balanced chemical equation for the reaction of Sm(s) and O_2(g).
2. This textbook places lanthanum directly below yttrium in the periodic table. However, there is a minor controversy about this in the scientific community, and other periodic tables locate lanthanum at the front of the lanthanide series and place lutetium directly below yttrium. Does the electronic configuration argue for the placement of La or Lu below Y? Explain.

3. Gadolinium has eight unpaired electrons, the greatest number of any lanthanide element.
   a. Draw an orbital box diagram depicting the ground state electron configuration of Gd based upon its number of unpaired electrons.
   b. Predict the most common oxidation state for Gd. What is the ground state electron configuration of the most common oxidation state?
4. Use the atomic radii of scandium, yttrium, lanthanum, and lutetium to answer the questions below.

Element	**Radii (pm)**
Sc	160
Y	180
La	195
Lu	175

   a. Explain why lutetium has a smaller atomic radius than lanthanum, even though it has a greater number of electrons.
   b. Do the atomic radii argue for the placement of La or Lu below Y in the periodic table? Explain.
5. Europium oxide (Eu_2O_3) is used in the production of red phosphors for television displays. If the europium compound emits light with a wavelength of 612 nm, what is the frequency (s^{-1}) and energy (J/photon) of the light?
6. Neodymium is commonly used in magnets, usually as $Nd_2Fe_{14}B$. (Neodymium is combined with other elements to protect it from air oxidation.) Determine the mass percentage of neodymium in $Nd_2Fe_{14}B$.

CHAPTER GOALS REVISITED

Now that you have studied this chapter, you should ask whether you have met the chapter goals. In particular, you should be able to:

UNDERSTAND

- The relationship of the four quantum numbers (n, ℓ, m_ℓ, and m_s) to atomic structure.
  - **a.** Recognize that each electron in an atom has a different set of the four quantum numbers, n, ℓ, m_ℓ, and m_s (Sections 6-5–6-7, 7-1, and 7-3). Study Questions: 11, 13, 41, 43, 58.
  - **b.** Understand that the Pauli exclusion principle leads to the conclusion that no atomic orbital can be assigned more than two electrons and that the two electrons in an orbital must have opposite spins (different values of m_s) (Section 7-1).
- Effective nuclear charge, Z^*, and its implications for subshell energies and properties of atoms.
  - **a.** Understand effective nuclear charge, Z^*, and its ability to explain why different subshells in the same shell of multielectron atoms have different energies. Also, understand the role of Z^* in determining the properties of atoms (Section 7-2).

DO

- Write the electron configuration for atoms and monatomic ions.
  - **a.** Using the periodic table as a guide, depict electron configurations of neutral atoms (Section 7-3) and monatomic ions (Section 7-4) using the orbital box or *spdf* notation. In both cases, configurations can be abbreviated with the noble gas notation. Study Questions: 1, 3, 5–10, 13, 15, 18, 20, 21, 39–42, 45, 79.
  - **b.** When assigning electrons to atomic orbitals, apply the Pauli exclusion principle and Hund's rule (Sections 7-3 and 7-4). Study Question: 67.
  - **c.** Understand the role magnetism plays in revealing atomic structure (Section 7-4). Study Questions: 19–21, 39, 45, 58.

REMEMBER

- Electrons are assigned to the subshells of an atom in order of increasing energy.
  - **a.** In the H atom, the subshell energies increase with increasing n, but, in a many-electron atom, the energies depend on both n and ℓ (see Figure 7.1).

- Trends in atom and ion sizes, ionization energy, and electron attachment enthalpy.
  - **a.** Predict how properties of atoms—size, ionization energy *(IE)*, and electron attachment enthalpy ($\Delta_{EA}H$)—change on moving down a group or across a period of the periodic table (Section 7-5). The general periodic trends for these properties are as follows: Study Questions: 24, 26, 28, 30, 32, 46–49, 52–55, 66, 72.
    - (i) Atomic size decreases across a period and increases down a group.
    - (ii) *IE* increases across a period and decreases down a group.
    - (iii) The value of $\Delta_{EA}H$ becomes more negative across a period and becomes less negative down a group.
  - **b.** Recognize the role that ionization energy and electron attachment enthalpy play in forming ionic compounds (Section 7-6). Study Questions: 51, 80.

STUDY QUESTIONS

▲ denotes challenging questions.

Blue-numbered questions have answers in Appendix N and fully worked solutions in the *Student Solutions Manual.*

Practicing Skills

Writing Electron Configurations of Atoms

(See Section 7-3, Examples 7.1–7.3; Tables 7.1, 7.3, and 7.4.)

1. Write the electron configurations for P and Cl using both *spdf* notation and orbital box diagrams. Describe the relationship between each atom's electron configuration and its position in the periodic table.

2. Write the electron configurations for Mg and Ar using both *spdf* notation and orbital box diagrams. Describe the relationship of the atom's electron configuration to its position in the periodic table.

3. Using *spdf* notation, write the electron configurations for atoms of chromium and iron, two of the major components of stainless steel.

4. Using *spdf* notation, give the electron configuration of vanadium, V, an element found in some brown and red algae and some toadstools.

5. Depict the electron configuration for each of the following atoms using *spdf* and noble gas notations.
   (a) Arsenic, As. A deficiency of As can impair growth in animals, and larger amounts are poisonous.
   (b) Krypton, Kr. It ranks seventh in abundance of the gases in Earth's atmosphere.

6. Using *spdf* and noble gas notations, write electron configurations for atoms of the following elements. (Try to do this by looking at the periodic table but not at Table 7.3.)
   (a) Strontium, Sr. This element is named for a town in Scotland.
   (b) Zirconium, Zr. The metal is exceptionally resistant to corrosion and so has important industrial applications. Moon rocks show a surprisingly high zirconium content compared with rocks on Earth.
   (c) Rhodium, Rh. This metal is used in jewelry and in catalysts in industry.
   (d) Tin, Sn. The metal was used in the ancient world. Alloys of tin (solder, bronze, and pewter) are important.

7. Use noble gas and *spdf* notations to depict electron configurations for the following metals of the third transition series.
   (a) Tantalum, Ta. The metal and its alloys resist corrosion and are often used in surgical and dental tools.
   (b) Platinum, Pt. This metal was used by pre-Columbian Indians in jewelry. Now it is still used in jewelry but it is also the basis for anticancer drugs and catalysts (such as those in automobile exhaust systems).

8. The lanthanides, once called the rare earth elements, are really only "medium rare." Using noble gas and *spdf* notations, depict reasonable electron configurations for the following elements.

(a) Samarium, Sm. This lanthanide is used in magnetic materials.
(b) Ytterbium, Yb. This element was named for the village of Ytterby in Sweden, where a mineral source of the element was found.

9. Americium, Am, is a radioactive element isolated from spent fuel in nuclear reactors and used in home smoke detectors. Depict its electron configuration using noble gas and *spdf* notations.

10. Predict electron configurations for the following elements of the actinide series of elements. Use noble gas and *spdf* notations.

(a) Plutonium, Pu. The element is best known as a byproduct of nuclear power plant operations.
(b) Curium, Cm. This actinide was named for Marie Curie (page 54).

Quantum Numbers and Electron Configurations

(See Section 7-3 and Example 7.2.)

11. What is the maximum number of electrons that can be identified with each of the following sets of quantum numbers? In some cases, the answer may be "none." In such cases, explain why "none" is the correct answer.

(a) $n = 4, \ell = 3, m_\ell = 1$
(b) $n = 6, \ell = 1, m_\ell = -1, m_s = -\frac{1}{2}$
(c) $n = 3, \ell = 3, m_\ell = -3$

12. What is the maximum number of electrons that can be identified with each of the following sets of quantum numbers? In some cases, the answer may be "none." In such cases, explain why "none" is the correct answer.

(a) $n = 3$
(b) $n = 3$ and $\ell = 2$
(c) $n = 4, \ell = 1, m_\ell = -1$, and $m_s = +\frac{1}{2}$
(d) $n = 5, \ell = 0, m_\ell = -1, m_s = +\frac{1}{2}$

13. Depict the electron configuration for magnesium using an orbital box diagram and noble gas notation. Give a complete set of four quantum numbers for each of the electrons beyond those of the preceding noble gas.

14. Depict the electron configuration for phosphorus using an orbital box diagram and noble gas notation. Give one possible set of four quantum numbers for each of the electrons beyond those of the preceding noble gas.

15. Using an orbital box diagram and noble gas notation, show the electron configuration of gallium, Ga. Give a set of quantum numbers for the highest-energy electron.

16. Using an orbital box diagram and noble gas notation, show the electron configuration of titanium. Give one possible set of four quantum numbers for each of the electrons beyond those of the preceding noble gas.

Electron Configurations of Atoms and Ions and Magnetic Behavior

(See Section 7-4 and Example 7.4.)

17. Using orbital box diagrams, depict an electron configuration for each of the following ions: (a) Mg^{2+}, (b) K^+, (c) Cl^-, and (d) O^{2-}.

18. Using orbital box diagrams, depict an electron configuration for each of the following ions: (a) Na^+, (b) Al^{3+}, (c) Ge^{2+}, and (d) F^-.

19. Using orbital box diagrams and noble gas notation, depict the electron configurations of (a) V, (b) V^{2+}, and (c) V^{5+}. Is the element or any of the ions paramagnetic?

20. Using orbital box diagrams and noble gas notation, depict the electron configurations of (a) Ti, (b) Ti^{2+}, and (c) Ti^{4+}. Is the element or any of the ions paramagnetic?

21. Manganese is found as MnO_2 in deep ocean deposits.

(a) Depict the electron configuration of this element using the noble gas notation and an orbital box diagram.
(b) Using an orbital box diagram, show the electrons beyond those of the preceding noble gas for Mn^{4+}.
(c) Is Mn^{4+} paramagnetic?
(d) How many unpaired electrons does the Mn^{4+} ion have?

22. One compound found in alkaline batteries is NiOOH, a compound containing Ni^{3+} ions. When the battery is discharged, the Ni^{3+} is reduced to Ni^{2+} ions [as in $Ni(OH)_2$]. Using orbital box diagrams and the noble gas notation, show electron configurations of these ions. Are either of these ions paramagnetic?

Periodic Properties

(See Section 7-5 and Example 7.5.)

23. Arrange the following elements in order of increasing size: Al, B, C, K, and Na. (Try doing it without looking at Figure 7.5; then check yourself by looking up the necessary atomic radii.)

24. Arrange the following elements in order of increasing size: Ca, Rb, P, Ge, and Sr. (Try doing it without looking at Figure 7.5; then check yourself by looking up the necessary atomic radii.)

25. Select the atom or ion in each pair that has the larger radius.

(a) Cl or Cl^- (b) Al or O (c) In or I

26. Select the atom or ion in each pair that has the larger radius.

(a) Cs or Rb (b) O^{2-} or O (c) Br or As

27. Which of the following groups of elements is arranged correctly in order of increasing ionization energy?

(a) C < Si < Li < Ne
(b) Ne < Si < C < Li
(c) Li < Si < C < Ne
(d) Ne < C < Si < Li

28. Arrange the following atoms in order of increasing ionization energy: Li, K, C, and N.

29. Compare the elements Na, Mg, O, and P.

(a) Which has the largest atomic radius?
(b) Which has the most negative electron attachment enthalpy?
(c) Place the elements in order of increasing ionization energy.

30. Compare the elements B, Al, C, and Si.

(a) Which has the most metallic character?
(b) Which has the largest atomic radius?

(c) Which has the most negative electron attachment enthalpy?
(d) Place the three elements B, Al, and C in order of increasing first ionization energy.

31. Explain each answer briefly.
(a) Place the following elements in order of increasing ionization energy: F, O, and S.
(b) Which has the largest ionization energy: O, S, or Se?
(c) Which has the most negative electron attachment enthalpy: Se, Cl, or Br?
(d) Which has the largest radius: O^{2-}, F^-, or F?

32. Explain each answer briefly.
(a) Rank the following in order of increasing atomic radius: O, S, and F.
(b) Which has the largest ionization energy: P, Si, S, or Se?
(c) Place the following in order of increasing radius: O^{2-}, N^{3-}, and F^-.
(d) Place the following in order of increasing ionization energy: Cs, Sr, and Ba.

33. Identify the element that corresponds to each of the simplified photoelectron spectral data given below. (Energy data taken from D. A. Shirley, R. L. Martin, S. P. Kowalczyk, F. R. McFeely, and L. Ley: "Core-electron binding energies of the first thirty elements," *Physical Review B*, Vol. 15, pp. 544–552, 1977.)
(a) There are peaks at energies of 64.8 and 5.4 eV, corresponding to 2 and 1 electrons, respectively.
(b) There are peaks at energies of 3614, 384, 301, 40.9, 24.7, and 4.34 eV, corresponding to 2, 2, 6, 2, 6, and 1 electrons, respectively.
(c) There are peaks at energies of 4494, 503, 404, 56.4, 33.6, 8.01, and 6.65 eV, corresponding to 2, 2, 6, 2, 6, 1, and 2 electrons, respectively.

34. Identify the element that corresponds to each of the simplified photoelectron spectral data given below. (Energy data taken from D. A. Shirley, R. L. Martin, S. P. Kowalczyk, F. R. McFeely, and L. Ley: "Core-electron binding energies of the first thirty elements," *Physical Review B*, Vol. 15, pp. 544–552, 1977.)
(a) There are peaks at energies corresponding to 1079, 70.8, 38.0, 5.14 eV, corresponding to 2, 2, 6, and 1 electrons, respectively.
(b) There are peaks at energies corresponding to 4043, 443, 351, 48.4, 30.1, and 6.11 eV, corresponding to 2, 2, 6, 2, 6, and 2 electrons, respectively.
(c) There are peaks at energies corresponding to 5475, 638, 524, 77, 47, 12, and 7.3 eV, corresponding to 2, 2, 6, 2, 6, 3, and 2 electrons, respectively.

35. Explain why the photoelectron spectra of hydrogen and helium each has one peak whereas that for lithium has two peaks. What would be the relative intensity of each of the peaks in these spectra?

36. Sketch the major features (number of peaks and relative intensities for the peaks) of the expected photoelectron spectrum for atoms of nitrogen.

General Questions

These questions are not designated as to type or location in the chapter. They may combine several concepts.

37. The red color of rubies is the result of the substitution of some Cr^{3+} ions for Al^{3+} ions in solid Al_2O_3.
(a) Using *spdf* notation with the noble gas notation, write the electron configuration for the Cr atom and for the Cr^{3+} ion?
(b) Is Cr^{2+} paramagnetic? Is Cr^{3+}?
(c) The radius of the Cr^{3+} ion is 64 pm. How does this compare with the radius of the Al^{3+} ion?

38. The deep blue color of sapphires comes from the presence of Fe^{2+} and Ti^{4+} in solid Al_2O_3. Using *spdf* notation with the noble gas notation, write the electron configuration for each of these ions.

39. Using an orbital box diagram and noble gas notation, show the electron configurations of uranium and of the uranium(IV) ion. Is either of these paramagnetic?

40. The rare earth elements, or lanthanides, commonly exist as 3+ ions. Using an orbital box diagram and noble gas notation, show the electron configurations of the following elements and ions.
(a) Ce and Ce^{3+} (cerium) (b) Ho and Ho^{3+} (holmium)

41. A neutral atom has two electrons with $n = 1$, eight electrons with $n = 2$, eight electrons with $n = 3$, and two electrons with $n = 4$. Assuming this element is in its ground state, supply the following information:
(a) atomic number
(b) total number of *s* electrons
(c) total number of *p* electrons
(d) total number of *d* electrons
(e) Is the element a metal, metalloid, or nonmetal?

42. Element 109, now named meitnerium (in honor of the Austrian–Swedish physicist, Lise Meitner [1878–1968]), was produced in August 1982 by a team at Germany's Institute for Heavy Ion Research. Depict its electron configuration using *spdf* and noble gas notations. Name another element found in the same group as meitnerium.

Lise Meitner (1878–1968) and Otto Hahn (1879–1968). Element 109 (Mt) was named after Meitner. She earned her Ph.D. in physics under Ludwig Boltzmann at the University of Vienna, and she was the first woman to earn a Ph.D. at that university.

43. Which of the following is *not* an allowable set of quantum numbers? Explain your answer briefly. For those sets that are valid, identify an element in which an outermost valence electron could have that set of quantum numbers.

	n	ℓ	m_ℓ	m_s
(a)	2	0	0	$-\frac{1}{2}$
(b)	1	1	0	$+\frac{1}{2}$
(c)	2	1	-1	$-\frac{1}{2}$
(d)	4	2	$+2$	$-\frac{1}{2}$

44. A possible excited state for the H atom has an electron in a 4*p* orbital. List all possible sets of quantum numbers (n, ℓ, m_ℓ, m_s) for this electron.

45. The magnet in the photo is made from neodymium, iron, and boron.

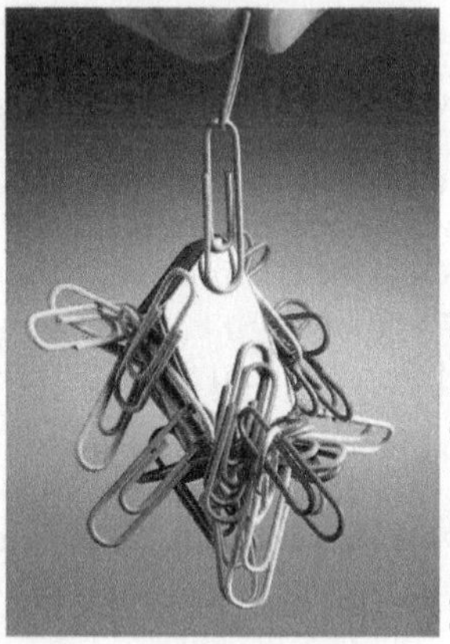

A magnet made of an alloy containing the elements Nd, Fe, and B.

(a) Write the electron configuration of each of these elements using an orbital box diagram and noble gas notation.
(b) Are these elements paramagnetic or diamagnetic?
(c) Write the electron configurations of Nd^{3+} and Fe^{3+} using orbital box diagrams and noble gas notation. Are these ions paramagnetic or diamagnetic?

46. Name the element corresponding to each characteristic below.

(a) the element with the electron configuration $1s^22s^22p^63s^23p^3$
(b) the alkaline earth element with the smallest atomic radius
(c) the element with the largest ionization energy in Group 5A
(d) the element whose 2+ ion has the configuration $[Kr]4d^5$
(e) the element with the most negative electron attachment enthalpy in Group 7A
(f) the element whose electron configuration is $[Ar]3d^{10}4s^2$

47. Arrange the following atoms in order of increasing ionization energy: Si, K, P, and Ca.

48. Rank the following in order of increasing ionization energy: Cl, Ca^{2+}, and Cl^-. Briefly explain your answer.

49. Answer the questions below about the elements A and B, which have the electron configurations shown.

A = $[Kr]5s^1$ B = $[Ar]3d^{10}4s^24p^4$

(a) Is element A a metal, nonmetal, or metalloid?
(b) Which element has the greater ionization energy?
(c) Which element has the less negative electron attachment enthalpy?
(d) Which element has the larger atomic radius?
(e) What is the formula for a compound formed between A and B?

50. Answer the following questions about the elements with the electron configurations shown here:

A = $[Ar]4s^2$ B = $[Ar]3d^{10}4s^24p^5$

(a) Is element A a metal, metalloid, or nonmetal?
(b) Is element B a metal, metalloid, or nonmetal?
(c) Which element is expected to have the larger ionization energy?
(d) Which element has the smaller atomic radius?

51. Which of the following ions are unlikely to be found in a chemical compound: Cs^+, In^{4+}, Fe^{6+}, Te^{2-}, Sn^{5+}, and I^-? Explain briefly.

52. Place the following ions in order of decreasing size: K^+, Cl^-, S^{2-}, and Ca^{2+}.

53. Answer each of the following questions:

(a) Of the elements S, Se, and Cl, which has the largest atomic radius?
(b) Which has the larger radius, Br or Br^-?
(c) Which should have the largest difference between the first and second ionization energy: Si, Na, P, or Mg?
(d) Which has the largest ionization energy: N, P, or As?
(e) Which of the following has the largest radius: O^{2-}, N^{3-}, or F^-?

54. ▲ The following are isoelectronic species: Cl^-, K^+, and Ca^{2+}. Rank them in order of increasing (a) size, (b) ionization energy, and (c) electron attachment enthalpy.

55. Compare the elements Na, B, Al, and C with regard to the following properties:

(a) Which has the largest atomic radius?
(b) Which has the most negative electron attachment enthalpy?
(c) Place the elements in order of increasing ionization energy.

56. ▲ Two elements in the second transition series (Y through Cd) have four unpaired electrons in their 3+ ions. What elements fit this description?

57. The configuration for an element is given here.

[Ar] [↑↓][↑↓][↑][↑][↑] (3*d*) [↑↓] (4*s*)

(a) What is the identity of the element with this configuration?
(b) Is a sample of the element paramagnetic or diamagnetic?
(c) How many unpaired electrons does a 3+ ion of this element have?

58. The configuration of an element is given here.

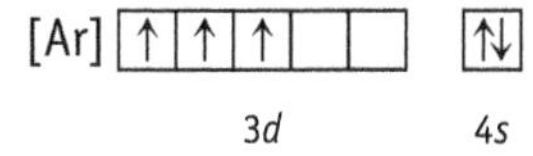

(a) What is the identity of the element?
(b) In what group and period is the element found?
(c) Is the element a nonmetal, a main group element, a transition metal, a lanthanide, or an actinide?
(d) Is the element diamagnetic or paramagnetic? If paramagnetic, how many unpaired electrons are there?
(e) Write a complete set of quantum numbers (n, ℓ, m_ℓ, m_s) for each of the valence electrons.
(f) What is the configuration of the 2+ ion formed from this element? Is the ion diamagnetic or paramagnetic?

59. Answer the questions below about the elements A and B, which have the ground state electron configurations shown.

A = $[Kr]5s^2$ B = $[Kr]4d^{10}5s^25p^5$

(a) Is element A a metal, nonmetal, or metalloid?
(b) Which element has the greater ionization energy?
(c) Which element has a larger atomic radius?
(d) Which element has the more negative electron attachment enthalpy?
(e) Which is more likely to form a cation?
(f) What is a likely formula for a compound formed between A and B?

60. Answer the questions below concerning ground state electron configurations.

(a) What element has the electron configuration $[Ar]3d^64s^2$?
(b) What element has a 2+ ion with the configuration $[Ar]3d^5$? Is the ion paramagnetic or diamagnetic?
(c) How many unpaired electrons are in a Ni^{2+} ion?
(d) The configuration for an element is given here.

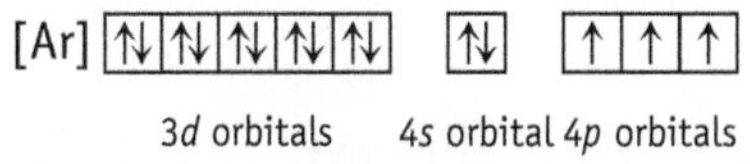

What is the identity of the element? Is a sample of the element paramagnetic or diamagnetic? How many unpaired electrons does a 3− ion of this element have?

(e) What element has the following electron configuration?
Write a complete set of quantum numbers for electrons 1-3.

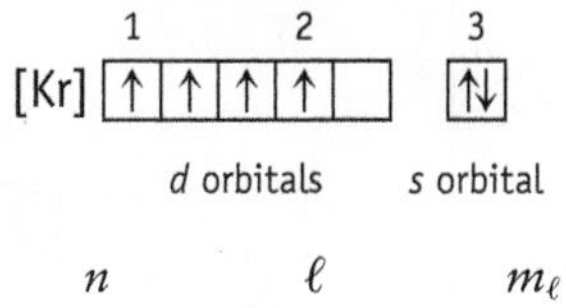

Electron	n	ℓ	m_ℓ	m_s
1	____	____	____	____
2	____	____	____	____
3	____	____	____	____

In the Laboratory

61. Nickel(II) formate $[Ni(HCO_2)_2]$ is widely used as a catalyst precursor and to make metallic nickel. It can be prepared in the general chemistry laboratory by treating nickel(II) acetate with formic acid (HCO_2H).

$$Ni(CH_3CO_2)_2(aq) + 2\ HCO_2H(aq) \rightarrow Ni(HCO_2)_2(aq) + 2\ CH_3CO_2H(aq)$$

Green crystalline $Ni(HCO_2)_2$ is precipitated after adding ethanol to the solution.

(a) What is the theoretical yield of nickel(II) formate from 0.500 g of nickel(II) acetate and excess formic acid?
(b) Is nickel(II) formate paramagnetic or diamagnetic? If it is paramagnetic, how many unpaired electrons would you expect?
(c) If nickel(II) formate is heated to 300 °C in the absence of air for 30 minutes, the salt decomposes to form pure nickel powder. What mass of nickel powder should be produced by heating 253 mg of nickel(II) formate? Are nickel atoms paramagnetic?

62. ▲ Spinels are solids with the general formula $M^{2+}(M'^{3+})_2O_4$ (where M^{2+} and M'^{3+} are metal cations of the same or different metals). The best-known example is common magnetite, Fe_3O_4 [which you can formulate as $(Fe^{2+})(Fe^{3+})_2O_4$].

A crystal of a spinel

(a) Given its name, it is evident that magnetite is ferromagnetic. How many unpaired electrons are in iron(II) and in iron(III) ions?
(b) Two other spinels are $CoAl_2O_4$ and $SnCo_2O_4$. What metal ions are involved in each? What are their electron configurations? Are the metal ions paramagnetic, and if so, how many unpaired electrons are involved?

Summary and Conceptual Questions

The following questions use concepts from this and previous chapters.

63. Why is the radius of Li^+ so much smaller than the radius of Li? Why is the radius of F^- so much larger than the radius of F?

64. Which ions in the following list are not likely to be found in chemical compounds: K^{2+}, Cs^+, Al^{4+}, F^{2-}, and Se^{2-}? Explain briefly.

65. Answer the following questions about first ionization energies.

(a) Generally ionization energies increase on proceeding across a period, but this is not true for magnesium (738 kJ/mol) and aluminum (578 kJ/mol). Explain this observation.

(b) Explain why the ionization energy of phosphorus (1012 kJ/mol) is greater than that of sulfur (1000 kJ/mol) when the general trend in ionization energies in a period would predict the opposite.

66. ▲ The ionization of the hydrogen atom can be calculated from Bohr's equation for the electron energy.

$$E = -(N_ARhc)(Z^2/n^2)$$

where $N_ARhc = 1312$ kJ/mol and Z is the atomic number. Let us use this approach to calculate a possible ionization energy for helium. First, assume the electrons of the He experience the full 2+ nuclear charge. This gives us the upper limit for the ionization energy. Next, assume one electron of He completely screens the nuclear charge from the other electrons, so $Z = 1$. This gives us a lower limit to the ionization energy. Compare these calculated values for the upper and lower limits to the experimental value of 2372.3 kJ/mol. What does this tell us about the ability of one electron to screen the nuclear charge?

67. Compare the configurations below with two electrons located in *p* orbitals. Which would be the most stable (have the lowest energy)? Which would be the least stable? Explain your answers.

(a) 

(b) 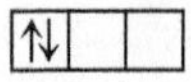

(c) 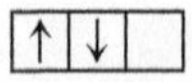

(d) 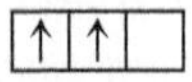

68. The bond lengths in Cl_2, Br_2, and I_2 are 200, 228, and 266 pm, respectively. Knowing that the tin radius is 141 pm, estimate the bond distances in Sn—Cl, Sn—Br, and Sn—I. Compare the estimated values with the experimental values of 233, 250, and 270 pm, respectively.

69. Write electron configurations to show the first two ionization processes for potassium. Explain why the second ionization energy is much greater than the first.

70. What is the trend in ionization energy when proceeding down a group in the periodic table. Rationalize this trend.

71. (a) Explain why the sizes of atoms change when proceeding across a period of the periodic table.
(b) Explain why the sizes of transition metal atoms change very little across a period.

72. Which of the following elements has the greatest difference between its first and second ionization energies: C, Li, N, Be? Explain your answer.

73. ▲ What arguments would you use to convince another student in general chemistry that MgO consists of the ions Mg^{2+} and O^{2-} and not the ions Mg^{+} and O^{-}? What experiments could be done to provide some evidence that the correct formulation of magnesium oxide is $Mg^{2+}O^{2-}$?

74. Explain why the first ionization energy of Ca is greater than that of K, whereas the second ionization energy of Ca is lower than the second ionization energy of K.

75. The energies of the orbitals in many elements have been determined. For the first two periods they have the following values:

Element	1*s* (kJ/mol)	2*s* (kJ/mol)	2*p* (kJ/mol)
H	−1313		
He	−2373		
Li		−520.0	
Be		−899.3	
B		−1356	−800.8
C		−1875	−1029
N		−2466	−1272
O		−3124	−1526
F		−3876	−1799
Ne		−4677	−2083

(a) ▲ Why do the orbital energies generally become more negative on proceeding across the second period?
(b) How are these values related to the ionization energy and electron attachment enthalpy of the elements?
(c) Use these energy values to explain the observation that the ionization energies of the first four second-period elements are in the order Li < Be > B < C.

(Data from J. B. Mann, T. L. Meek, and L. C. Allen: *Journal of the American Chemical Society*, Vol. 122, p. 2780, 2000.)

76. ▲ The ionization energies for the removal of the first electron in Si, P, S, and Cl are as listed in the table below. Briefly rationalize this trend.

Element	First Ionization Energy (kJ/mol)
Si	787
P	1012
S	1000
Cl	1251

77. Using your knowledge of the trends in element sizes on going across the periodic table, explain briefly why the density of the elements increases from K through V.

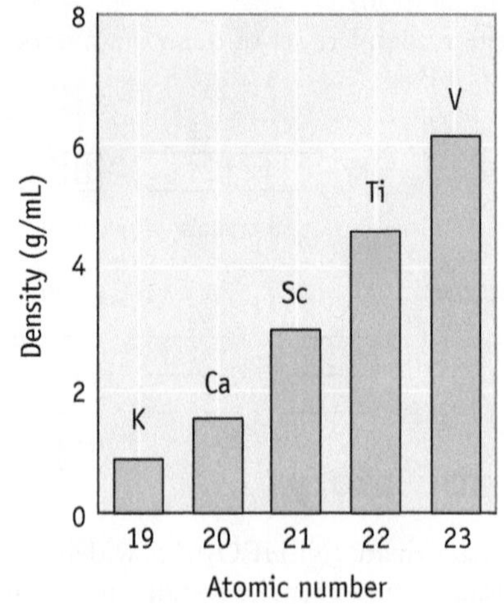

78. The densities (in g/cm^3) of elements in Groups 6B, 8B, and 1B are given in the table below.

Period 4	Cr, 7.19	Co, 8.90	Cu, 8.96
Period 5	Mo, 10.22	Rh, 12.41	Ag, 10.50
Period 6	W, 19.30	Ir, 22.56	Au, 19.32

Transition metals in the sixth period all have much greater densities than the elements in the same groups in the fourth and fifth periods. Refer to Figure 7.8, and explain this observation.

79. The discovery of two new elements (atomic numbers 113 and 115) was announced in February 2004.

(a) Use *spdf* and noble gas notations to give the electron configurations of these two elements.
(b) For each of these elements, name another element in the same periodic group.
(c) Element 113 was made by firing the nucleus of a light atom at a heavy americium atom. The two nuclei combine to give a nucleus with 113 protons. What light atom was used as a projectile?

80. Explain why the reaction of calcium and fluorine does not form CaF_3.

81. ▲ Thionyl chloride, $SOCl_2$, is an important chlorinating and oxidizing agent in organic chemistry. It is prepared industrially by oxygen atom transfer from SO_3 to SCl_2.

$$SO_3(g) + SCl_2(g) \rightarrow SO_2(g) + SOCl_2(g)$$

(a) Give the electron configuration for an atom of sulfur using an orbital box diagram. Do not use the noble gas notation.
(b) Using the configuration given in part (a), write a set of quantum numbers for the highest-energy electron in a sulfur atom.
(c) What element involved in this reaction (O, S, Cl) should have the smallest ionization energy? The smallest radius?
(d) Which should be smaller: the sulfide ion, S^{2-}, or a sulfur atom, S?
(e) If you want to make 675 g of $SOCl_2$, what mass of SCl_2 is required?
(f) If you use 10.0 g of SO_3 and 10.0 g of SCl_2, what is the theoretical yield of $SOCl_2$?
(g) $\Delta_rH°$ for the reaction of SO_3 and SCl_2 is −96.0 kJ/mol $SOCl_2$ produced. Using data in Appendix L, calculate the standard molar enthalpy of formation of SCl_2.

82. Sodium metal reacts readily with chlorine gas to give sodium chloride.

$$Na(s) + \tfrac{1}{2} Cl_2(g) \rightarrow NaCl(s)$$

(a) What is the reducing agent in this reaction? What property of the element contributes to its ability to act as a reducing agent?
(b) What is the oxidizing agent in this reaction? What property of the element contributes to its ability to act as an oxidizing agent?
(c) Why does the reaction produce NaCl and not a compound such as Na_2Cl or $NaCl_2$?

83. ▲ Slater's rules are a simple way to estimate the effective nuclear charge experienced by an electron. In this approach, the "shielding constant," *S*, is calculated. The effective nuclear charge is then the difference between *S* and the atomic number, *Z*. (Note that the results in Table 7.2 and Figure 7.2 were calculated in a slightly different way.)

$$Z^* = Z - S$$

The shielding constant, *S*, is calculated using the following rules:

1. The electrons of an atom are grouped as follows: (1*s*) (2*s*, 2*p*) (3*s*, 3*p*) (3*d*) (4*s*, 4*p*) (4*d*), and so on.
2. Electrons in higher groups (to the right) do not shield those in the lower groups.
3. For *ns* and *np* valence electrons
   a) Electrons in the same *ns*, *np* group contribute 0.35 (for 1*s* 0.30 works better).
   b) Electrons in $n - 1$ groups contribute 0.85.
   c) Electrons in $n - 2$ groups (and lower) contribute 1.00.
4. For *nd* and *nf* electrons, electrons in the same *nd* or *nf* group contribute 0.35, and those in groups to the left contribute 1.00.

   As an example, let us calculate Z^* for the outermost electron of oxygen:

$$S = (2 \times 0.85) + (5 \times 0.35) = 3.45$$
$$Z^* = 8 - 3.45 = 4.55$$

Here is a calculation for a *d* electron in Ni:

$$Z^* = 28 - [18 \times 1.00] - [7 \times 0.35] = 7.55$$

and for an *s* electron in Ni:

$$Z^* = 28 - [10 \times 1.00] - [16 \times 0.85] - [1 \times 0.35] = 4.05$$

(Here 3*s*, 3*p*, and 3*d* electrons are in the $(n - 1)$ groups.)

(a) Calculate Z^* for F and Ne. Relate the Z^* values for O, F, and Ne to their relative atomic radii and ionization energies.
(b) Calculate Z^* for one of the 3*d* electrons of Mn, and compare this with Z^* for one of the 4*s* electrons of the element. Do the Z^* values give us some insight into the ionization of Mn to give the cation?

AP Multiple-Choice Review Questions

1. The first ionization energy of magnesium is 738 kJ/mol. A good estimate for the second ionization energy of magnesium is

(A) 370 kJ/mol
(B) 735 kJ/mol
(C) 1450 kJ/mol
(D) 6900 kJ/mol

Use the following graph to answer questions 2–4.

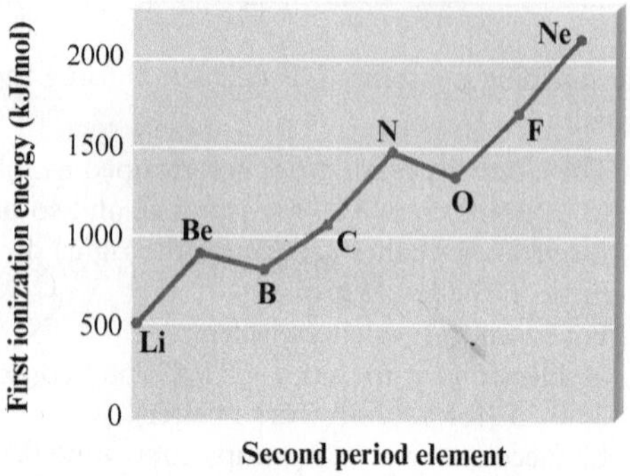

2. Which of the following is the *reason* that ionization energy generally increases from left to right across the first period of the periodic table?

(A) As the atomic number increases, the electrons are harder to remove.
(B) Ionization energy increases as the atomic number increases in a period.
(C) As the atomic number increases, more electrons are added to the atoms, thus increasing the electron–electron repulsions.
(D) As the atomic number increases, more protons in the nucleus cause an increase in the effective nuclear charge, making it harder to remove the electrons.

3. What is the best explanation for the decrease in first ionization energy moving from Be to B?

(A) Moving from Be to B, more electrons are added to the atoms, thus increasing the electron–electron repulsions.
(B) Moving from Be to B, more protons in the nucleus attract the valence electrons, making it harder to remove the electrons.
(C) The electrons in Be are being removed from a full subshell, which is more stable than the half-filled subshell in B.
(D) The electrons in Be are located in the 2*s* subshell, which is closer to the nucleus and thus harder to remove than the 2*p* electrons in B.

4. What is the best explanation for the decrease in first ionization energy moving from N to O?

(A) The oxygen atom is smaller, thus making it easier to remove the electrons compared with N.
(B) The electrons in N are being removed from a half-full subshell, which is more stable than the partially filled subshell in O.
(C) The electrons in N occupy the 2*p* orbitals singularly, whereas the electrons in one of the 2*p* orbitals of O are paired, thus increasing the electron–electron repulsions.
(D) Moving from N to O, there are more protons in the nucleus, thus increasing the effective nuclear charge (Z_{eff}), causing a greater amount of attraction for the valence electrons and making it harder to remove the electrons.

5. The table shows the first ionization energies of element X in kJ/mol.

First ionization energy	Second ionization energy	Third ionization energy
738	1450	7730

What is the most likely formula of the compound between element X and Y, where Y is a halogen?

(A) XY
(B) XY_2
(C) XY_3
(D) X_3Y

6. Which diagram shows an excited state?

(A) 1*s*
[↑]

(B) 1*s* 2*s*
[↑] [↑]

(C) 1*s* 2*s* 2*p*
[⇅] [⇅] [↑][↑][ ]

(D) 1*s* 2*s* 2*p*
[⇅] [⇅] [⇅][⇅][⇅]

7. What is the electron configuration for Zn^{2+}?

(A) $1s^22s^22p^63s^23p^63d^8$
(B) $1s^22s^22p^63s^23p^63d^{10}$
(C) $1s^22s^22p^63s^23p^63d^84s^2$
(D) $1s^22s^22p^63s^23p^63d^{10}4s^2$

8. Which of the following electron configurations shows the ground state of an ion of a halogen?

(A) $1s^22s^22p^53s^23p^5$
(B) $1s^22s^22p^63s^23p^6$
(C) $1s^22s^22p^63s^23p^63d^5$
(D) $1s^22s^22p^62d^{10}3s^23p^6$

9. When placed in order of increasing atomic radius, what is the correct order for the elements Al, Ca, and Mg?

(A) Al, Mg, Ca
(B) Mg, Al, Ca
(C) Ca, Al, Mg
(D) Ca, Mg, Al

10. Which of the following electron configurations shows a violation of Hund's rule?

(A) $1s$
[↑]

(B) $1s$ $2s$
[↑↓] [↑]

(C) $1s$ $2s$ $2p$
[↑↓] [↑↓] [↑↓] [ ] [ ]

(D) $1s$ $2s$ $2p$
[↑↓] [↑↓] [↑↓] [↑↓] [↑↓]

11. The reactivity of the alkali metals increases going down the group. Which is the correct explanation for this trend?

(A) The ionization energy decreases as you move down the group, thus it requires less energy to remove the valence electron and results in greater reactivity.
(B) The greater nuclear charge as you move down the group results in a greater ability to attract electrons to the atom, thus making them more reactive.
(C) As you move down the group, the nucleus's stability decreases, thus causing an increase in the number of radioactive isotopes, hence an increase in the reactivity of the alkali metals.
(D) The greater mass as you move down the group causes an increase in the kinetic energy for any given molecular velocity. The increase in kinetic energy accounts for the increase in reactivity.

12. In which of the following electron transitions for a hydrogen atom does the light emitted have the longest wavelength?

(A) $n = 5$ to $n = 2$
(B) $n = 4$ to $n = 3$
(C) $n = 3$ to $n = 1$
(D) $n = 2$ to $n = 1$

13. An element X has the ground-state valence electron configuration of ns^2np^5. The formula for the compound composed of element X and nitrogen is most likely

(A) NX
(B) NX_2
(C) NX_3
(D) NX_5

14. When placed in order of increasing ionization energy, what is the correct order for the species O, O^+, and O^-?

(A) O, O^+, O^-
(B) O, O^-, O^+
(C) O^+, O, O^-
(D) O^-, O, O^+

15. The table below shows the first eight ionization energies for four random elements from the second and third periods of the periodic table. Based on these data, which elements would most likely have similar chemical properties?

Ionization Energy (kJ/mol)	Elements W	X	Y	Z
First	1,314	1,000	578	496
Second	3,388	2,252	1,817	4,562
Third	5,301	3,357	2,745	6,910
Fourth	7,469	4,556	11,577	9,543
Fifth	10,990	7,004	14,842	13,354
Sixth	13,327	8,496	18,379	16,613
Seventh	71,330	27,107	23,326	20,117
Eighth	84,078	31,719	27,465	25,496

(A) W and X
(B) W and Y
(C) X and Z
(D) Y and Z

16. Of the most common ions of the third period elements Mg, Al, P, and S, which is the largest?

(A) Mg
(B) Al
(C) P
(D) S

17. Which of the following correctly ranks the following species from smallest to largest ionic radius?

(A) Cl^-, S^{2-}, K^+, Ca^{2+}
(B) K^+, Ca^{2+}, Cl^-, S^{2-}
(C) S^{2-}, Cl^-, K^+, Ca^{2+}
(D) Ca^{2+}, K^+, Cl^-, S^{2-}

18. The expected electron configuration for copper should be [Ar]$4s^2 3d^9$. However, copper's electron configuration is [Ar]$4s^1 3d^{10}$. Which of the following would provide experimental evidence of copper's exception to the normal electron configuration?

(A) The mass spectrum of copper shows the different isotopes of copper.
(B) Copper ions in solution have color, which indicates that there are unpaired *d* orbital electrons.
(C) The photoelectron spectroscopy spectrum for copper shows the relative number of electrons in each orbit.
(D) Copper has the ability to form cations of plus one and plus two, whereas the other transition elements generally form cations of plus two and plus three.

19. Identify the element whose photoelectron spectrum is shown below.

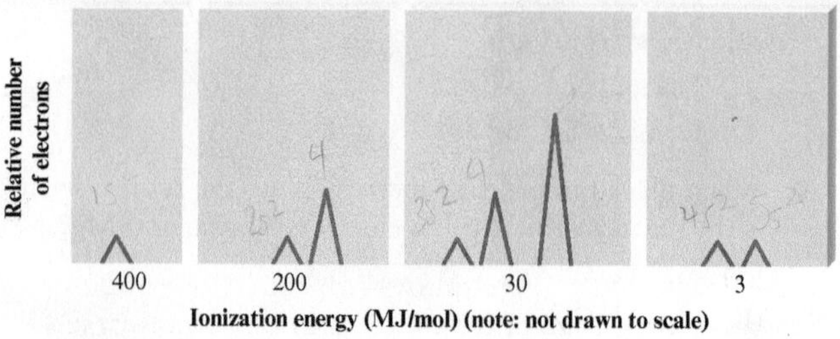

(A) O
(B) Ca
(C) Ti
(D) Ge

20. Identify the element whose photoelectron spectrum is shown below.

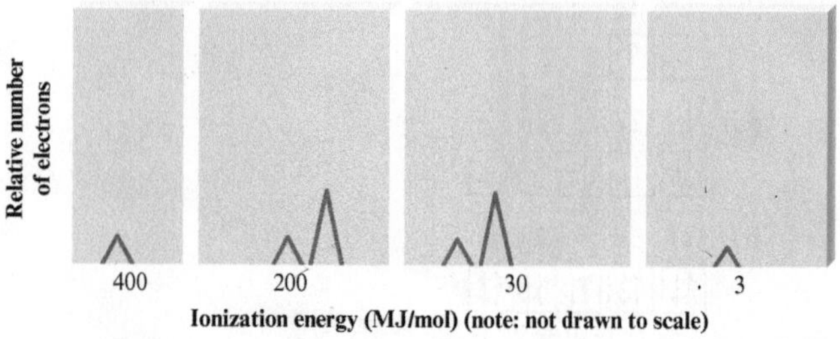

(A) N
(B) K
(C) Ca
(D) Sc

AP Free Response Review Questions

Question Format: Short

Category of Question: Quantitative or Lab 2

Fireworks produce dramatic color effects by the use of metallic salts and highly exothermic reactions. Barium salts are often responsible for the green color seen in fireworks, while calcium compounds produce the orange color. The green colored light has a wavelength of approximately 589 nm while the orange is approximately 628 nm. The exothermic reaction causes some of the electrons in the respective metal to become excited and move to higher energy levels. As these excited electrons lose some or all of their extra energy, the energy is released in the form of visible light.

Questions

(a) Which color of light, green or orange, has a higher frequency?

(b) Calculate the energy of a photon of green light.

(c) Write the complete electron configurations for a neutral calcium atom and the shorthand electron configuration (noble gas configuration) for a neutral barium atom.

(d) Considering their electron configurations, explain why calcium and barium produce different flame colors.

Question Format: Long

Category of Question: Lab 2 (or Representation 1)

There are period trends and there are group trends on the periodic table. Answer the following questions about these trends.

Alkali Metals		Halogens	
Element	**Melting points (°C)**	**Element**	**Melting points (°C)**
Li	181	F_2	−119
Na	98	Cl_2	−101
K	63	Br_2	−7
Rb	39	I_2	+104
Cs	29		

Questions

(a) Provide an explanation for the group trend in the melting points of the alkali metals.

(b) Provide an explanation for the group trend in the melting points of the halogens.

The graphs below show the first ionization energy for the elements in the second period and the sixth period of the periodic table.

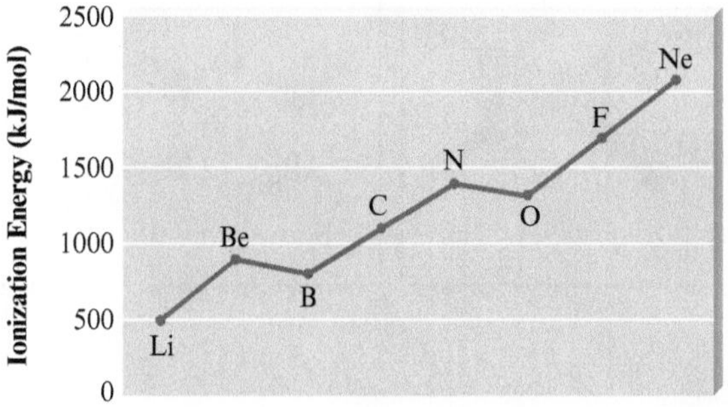

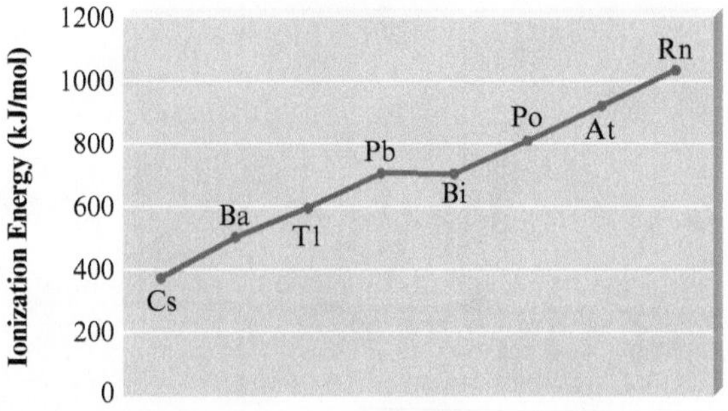

(c) There is a clear drop in the first ionization energy between Be and B.

(i) Explain why there is a drop in the first ionization energy between Be and B.

(ii) Explain why there is not a corresponding drop between Ba and Tl in the sixth period, even though they are in the same groups as Be and B.

(d) There is a clear drop in the first ionization energy between N and O.

(i) Explain why there is a drop in the first ionization energy between N and O.

(ii) Explain why there is not a corresponding drop between Bi and Po in the sixth period, even though they are in the same groups as N and O.

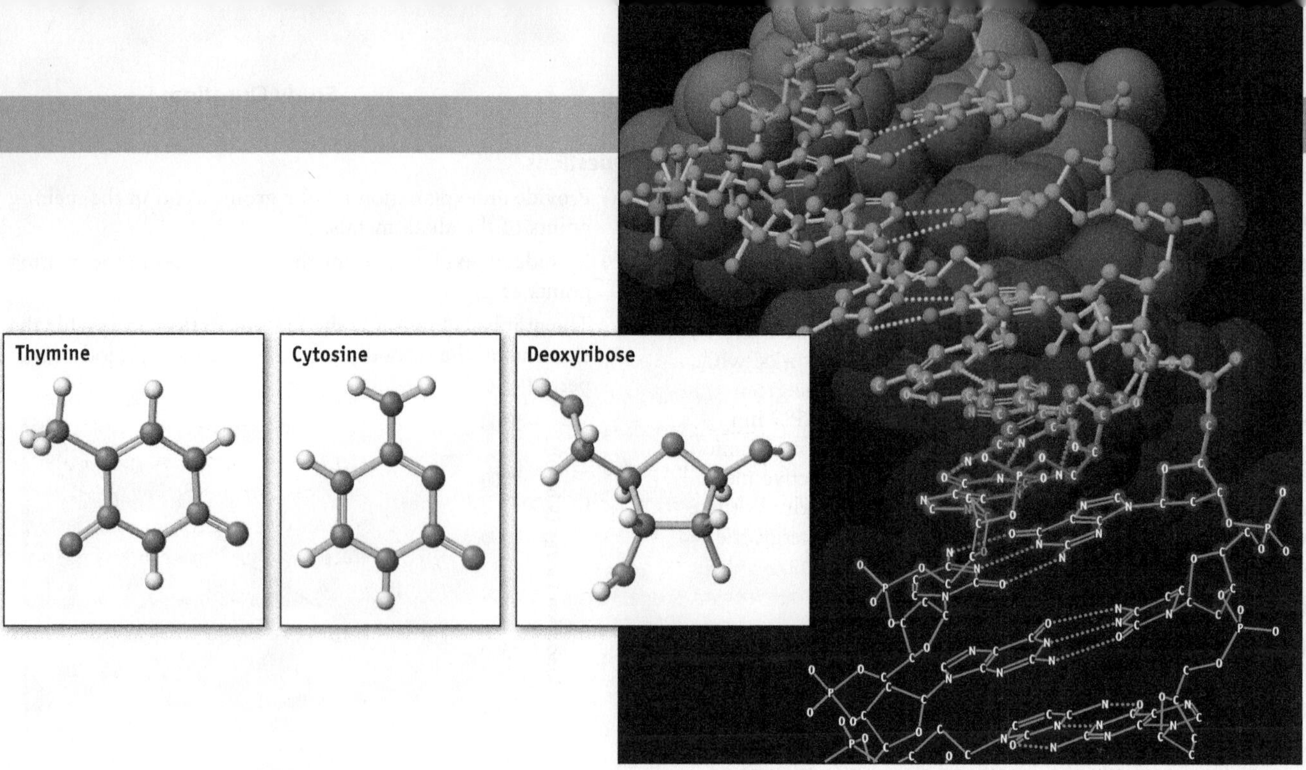

The structure of a segment of DNA.

Bonding and Molecular Structure

Chapter Outline

CHEMICAL BONDING IN DNA The theme of this chapter and the next is molecular bonding and structure, subjects well illustrated by the figure showing a portion of a DNA molecule. DNA consists of a helical coil of two chains of tetrahedral phosphate groups (PO_4) and deoxyribose groups. Organic bases (such as thymine and cytosine) on one chain interact with complementary bases on the other chain.

As you look carefully at this structure, there are a number of questions that may occur to you. Why are there four bonds to carbon and phosphorus atoms in the backbone of the helix? Why are these atoms in the backbone surrounded by bonded atoms at an angle of 109°? Why are the six-member rings in the bases thymine and cytosine flat? Why do certain H atoms attached to a base in one chain interact with N and O atoms on bases in the neighboring chain? All of these questions, and many others, can be answered by an understanding of chemical bonding and molecular structure.

Study Questions related to this story are: 8.25, 8.30, 8.79, and 8.88.

CHAPTER 8

Chapter Goals

See Chapter Goals Revisited (page 335) for Study Questions keyed to these goals.

UNDERSTAND

- The basic assumptions about ionic and covalent bonds.
- The relationship of Lewis electron dot structures and molecular structures.
- The relationship between bond order, bond length, and bond energy.

DO

- Draw Lewis electron dot structures for small molecules and polyatomic ions.
- Use the valence shell electron pair repulsion (VSEPR) theory to predict the shapes of small molecules and ions and to understand the structures of more complex molecules.
- Use electronegativity and formal charge to predict the charge distribution in molecules and ions, to define the polarity of bonds, and to predict the polarity of molecules.
- Use bond enthalpies to estimate enthalpy changes for chemical reactions.

REMEMBER

- There are common electron distributions (as indicated by Lewis structures) and molecular structures shared by molecules and ions. Knowing these patterns allows you to predict properties of unfamiliar molecules and ions.
- The Lewis symbols of atoms.
- The common electron-pair geometries and their associated bond angles.

Scientists have long known that the key to interpreting the properties of a chemical substance is first to recognize and understand its structure and bonding. **Structure** refers to the way atoms are arranged in space, and **bonding** describes the forces that hold adjacent atoms together.

Our discussion of structure and bonding begins with small molecules and polyatomic ions and then progresses to larger molecules. From compound to compound, atoms of the same element participate in bonding and structure in predictable ways. This consistency allows us to develop principles that apply to many different chemical compounds, from a simple molecule like water to such complex molecules as DNA.

8-1 Chemical Bond Formation

Learning Objectives: LO 2.1, LO 2.17, LO 2.19

When a chemical reaction occurs between two atoms, some of their electrons are reorganized, resulting in a net attractive force—a **chemical bond**—between the atoms. Chemists generally think of bonds as falling into three broad categories—metallic, covalent, and ionic—but, as illustrated in *A Closer Look: A Triangular View of Chemical Bonding* (page 284), the boundaries between them can be indistinct. This chapter is largely devoted to covalent bonds, whereas ionic and metallic bonds are described in Chapter 12.

Covalent bonding *involves a sharing of electrons from each atom's outermost shell* (valence electrons) *between atoms.* Two chlorine atoms, for example, share a pair of electrons, one electron from each atom, to form a covalent bond.

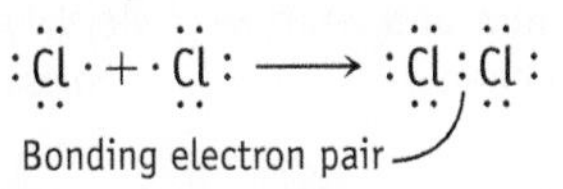

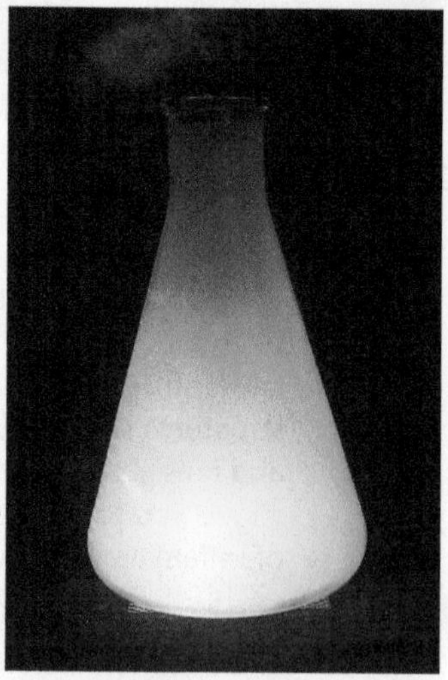

Formation of an ionic compound. The reaction of Na and Cl_2 is quite exothermic. $\Delta_f H°$ [NaCl(s)] = −411.12 kJ/mol.

An ionic bond forms when *one or more electrons from an atom's outermost shell is transferred from one atom to another*, creating positive and negative ions. When sodium and chlorine gas (Cl_2) react, we might imagine the reaction occurs by the transfer of an electron from a sodium atom to a chlorine atom to form Na^+ and Cl^- ions.

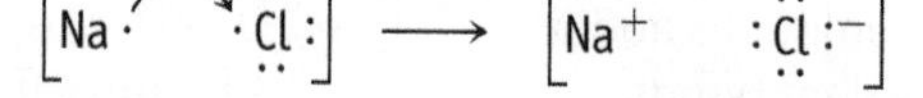

Sodium [$1s^2 2s^2 2p^6 3s^1$] has a low ionization energy and so readily loses an electron to form Na^+ [$1s^2 2s^2 2p^6$]. Chlorine [$1s^2 2s^2 2p^6 3s^2 3p^5$], on the other hand, has a high electron affinity and so readily gains an electron to form Cl^- [$1s^2 2s^2 2p^6 3s^2 3p^6$]. The resulting Na^+ and Cl^- ions are attracted to each other due to their electrostatic charges, and it is this electrostatic attraction between oppositely charged ions that constitutes the **ionic bond.** The resulting ions arrange themselves into a crystal lattice in which the attractions between the oppositely charged ions are maximized and the repulsions between ions of the same charge are minimized.

As we describe bonding in greater detail, you will discover that these two types of bonding between two atoms—equal sharing of electrons or complete electron transfer—are extreme cases. *In most chemical compounds, electrons are shared unequally between atoms, with the extent of sharing varying widely from very little sharing (mostly ionic) to considerable sharing (mostly covalent).*

A CLOSER LOOK

A Triangular View of Chemical Bonding

In chemistry we think in terms of three "limiting" forms of bonding: pure covalent (equal sharing of electrons between two atoms), pure ionic (complete transfer of electrons from one atom to another), and metallic. The Figure here, a van Arkel-Ketelaar diagram, has those limiting cases at the corners of a triangle. Depending on the atoms involved, the bonding can be described as ionic (CsF), covalent (F_2), or metallic (Cs). Others are a blend of these forms. For example, the bonding in CO_2 is more covalent than ionic whereas NaCl is largely ionic. A semiconductor like AlAs tends toward metallic bonding with some properties of ionic and covalent bonding. And bonding in solid Si is partially metallic and partially covalent.

This chapter and the next are concerned with covalent bonding. Chapter 12 will take up ionic and metallic bonding. Although we have "compartmentalized" these topics, *do not lose sight of the fact that, as the Figure shows, bonding in virtually all materials is a blend of the three limiting forms.*

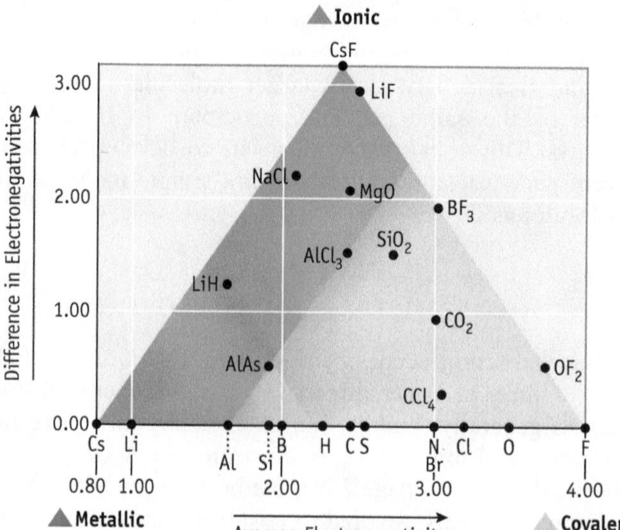

FIGURE **A van Arkel–Ketelaar diagram.** The four regions of this triangle represent the locations of metallic (blue), semiconducting (green), ionic (red), and covalent (orange) compounds

The powerful concept of "electronegativity " is used in the Figure and is introduced on page 314 of this chapter.

For more on this view of bonding see *Applying Chemical Principles: van Arkel Triangles and Bonding,* Chapter 21.

8-2 Covalent Bonding and Lewis Structures

Learning Objectives: LO 2.21

There are many examples of compounds having covalent bonds, including the gases in our atmosphere (O_2, N_2, H_2O, and CO_2), common fuels (CH_4), and most of the compounds in your body. Covalent bonds are also responsible for the atom-to-atom connections in polyatomic ions such as CO_3^{2-}, CN^-, NH_4^+, NO_3^-, and PO_4^{3-}. We will develop the basic principles of structure and bonding using these and other small molecules and ions, but the same principles apply to larger molecules from aspirin to proteins and DNA with many thousands of atoms.

The molecules and ions just mentioned are composed entirely of *nonmetal* atoms. A point that needs special emphasis is that, *in molecules or polyatomic ions made up only of nonmetal atoms, the atoms are attached by covalent bonds.* Conversely, the presence of a metal in a formula is a signal that the compound is likely to be ionic.

Valence Electrons and Lewis Symbols for Atoms

The electrons in an atom may be categorized as either **valence electrons** or **core electrons.** Chemical reactions result in the loss, gain, or rearrangement of valence electrons. The core electrons are not involved in bonding or in chemical reactions.

For main group elements (elements of the A groups in the periodic table), the valence electrons are the *s* and *p* electrons in the outermost shell (Table 8.1). All electrons in inner shells are core electrons. For example,

Na, Group 1A Core electrons $= 1s^2 2s^2 2p^6 =$ [Ne] Valence electrons $= 3s^1$

As, Group 5A Core electrons $= 1s^2 2s^2 2p^6 3s^2 3p^6 3d^{10} = [Ar]3d^{10}$ Valence electrons $= 4s^2 4p^3$

For *main group elements the number of valence electrons is equal to the group number*. The fact that all elements in a periodic group have the same number of valence electrons accounts for the similarity of chemical properties among members of the group.

Valence electrons for transition elements include the electrons in the ns and $(n-1)d$ orbitals. The remaining electrons are core electrons. As with main group elements, the valence electrons for transition metals determine the chemical properties of these elements.

Ti, Group 4B Core electrons $= 1s^2 2s^2 2p^6 3s^2 3p^6 =$ [Ar] Valence electrons $= 3d^2 4s^2$

Oesper Collection in the History of Chemistry/University of Cincinnati

Gilbert Newton Lewis (1875–1946) Lewis introduced the theory of shared electron-pair chemical bonds in a paper published in the *Journal of the American Chemical Society* in 1916. Lewis also made major contributions in acid–base chemistry, thermodynamics, and the interaction of light with substances.

Lewis was born in Massachusetts but raised in Nebraska. After earning his B.A. and Ph.D. at Harvard, he began his career in 1912 at the University of California at Berkeley. He was not only a productive researcher but was also an influential teacher. Among his ideas was the use of problem sets in teaching, a practice still in use today.

The American chemist Gilbert Newton Lewis (1875–1946) introduced a useful way to represent electrons in the valence shell of an atom. The element's symbol represents the atomic nucleus together with the core electrons. Up to four valence electrons, represented by dots, are placed one at a time around the symbol; then, if any valence electrons remain, they are paired with ones already there. Chemists now refer to these pictures as **Lewis electron dot symbols.** Lewis dot symbols for main group elements of the second and third periods are shown in Table 8.1.

Arranging the valence electrons of a main group element around an atom in four groups is meant to convey the idea that the valence shell can accommodate four pairs of electrons. Because this represents eight electrons in all, this is referred to as

Table 8.1 Lewis Electron Dot Symbols for Main Group Atoms

1A ns^1	2A ns^2	3A ns^2np^1	4A ns^2np^2	5A ns^2np^3	6A ns^2np^4	7A ns^2np^5	8A ns^2np^6
Li·	·Be·	·B·	·C·	·N·	:O·	:F·	:Ne:
Na·	·Mg·	·Al·	·Si·	·P·	:S·	:Cl·	:Ar:

an **octet** of electrons. The noble gases, with the exception of helium, already have an octet of valence electrons and demonstrate a notable lack of reactivity. (Helium and neon do not undergo any chemical reactions, and the other noble gases have very limited chemical reactivity.) Because chemical reactions involve changes in the valence electron shell, the limited reactivity of the noble gases is taken as evidence of the stability of their noble gas (ns^2np^6) electron configuration. Many elements gain, lose, or share electrons to achieve an octet of valence electrons, a noble gas configuration. This is sometimes referred to as the **octet rule**. Hydrogen, which in its compounds has two electrons in its valence shell, obeys the spirit of this rule by matching the electron configuration of the helium atom.

Lewis Electron Dot Structures and the Octet Rule

In a simple description of covalent bonding, a bond results when one or more electron pairs are shared between two atoms.

The electron pair bond between the two atoms of an H_2 molecule is represented by a pair of dots or, alternatively, a line.

The representation of a molecule in this fashion is called a **Lewis electron dot structure** or just a **Lewis structure**.

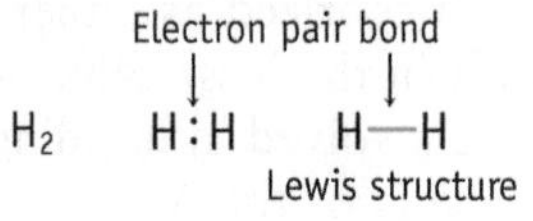

Simple Lewis structures, such as that for F_2, can be drawn starting with Lewis dot symbols for atoms and arranging the valence electrons to form bonds. Fluorine, an element in Group 7A, has seven valence electrons. The Lewis symbol shows that an F atom has a single unpaired electron along with three electron pairs. In F_2, the single electrons, one on each F atom, pair up in the covalent bond.

In the Lewis structure for F_2 the pair of electrons in the F—F bond is the bonding pair, or **bond pair.** The other six pairs reside on single atoms and are called **lone pairs.** Because they are not involved in bonding, they are also called **nonbonding electrons.**

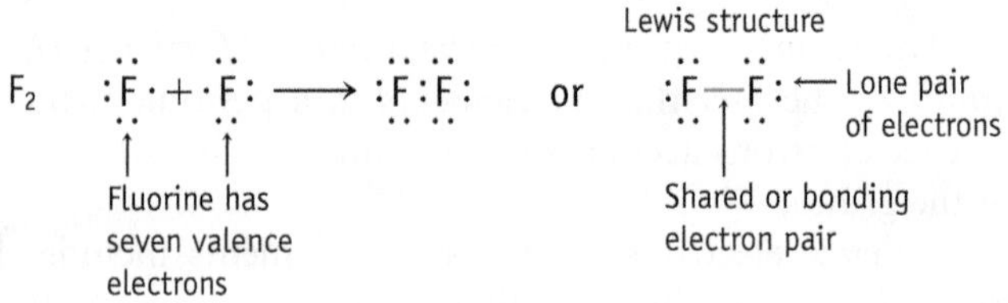

Carbon dioxide, CO_2, and dinitrogen, N_2, are examples of molecules in which two atoms share more than one electron pair.

In carbon dioxide, the carbon atom shares two pairs of electrons with each oxygen and so is linked to each O atom by a **double bond**. The valence shell of each oxygen atom in CO_2 has two bonding pairs and two lone pairs.

In dinitrogen, the two nitrogen atoms share three pairs of electrons, so they are linked by a **triple bond**. In addition, each N atom has a single lone pair.

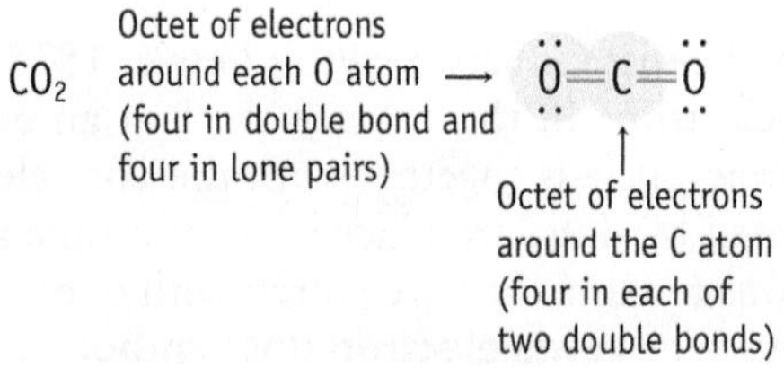

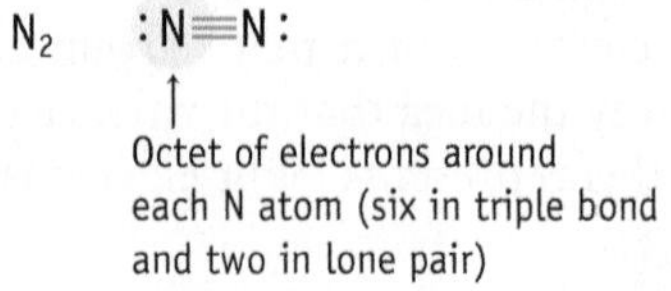

Importance of Lone Pairs Lone pairs can be important in a structure. Because they are in the same valence electron shell as the bonding electrons, they can influence molecular shape (see Section 8-6).

An important observation can be made about the molecules you have seen so far: Each atom has a share in four pairs of electrons, so each has achieved a *noble gas configuration. Each atom is surrounded by an octet of eight electrons.* (The exception is hydrogen, which typically forms a bond to only one other atom, resulting in two electrons in its valence shell.) *The tendency of molecules and polyatomic ions to have structures in which eight electrons surround each atom is the basis for the octet rule.* As an example, given the number of valence electrons available on nitrogen, a triple bond is necessary in N_2 in order to have an octet around each nitrogen atom. The carbon atom and both oxygen atoms in CO_2 achieve the octet configuration by forming double bonds.

The octet rule is extremely useful, but keep in mind that it is more a *guideline* than a rule. Particularly for the second period elements C, N, O, and F, a Lewis structure in which each atom achieves an octet is likely to be a good representation of the bonding. Although there are a few exceptions, if you find a Lewis structure does not follow the octet rule, you should question the structure's validity. If a structure obeying the octet rule cannot be written, then it is possible an incorrect formula has been assigned to the compound or the atoms have been assembled in an incorrect way.

Exceptions to the Octet Rule
Although the octet rule is widely applicable, there are exceptions. Fortunately, many will be obvious, such as when there are more than four bonds to an element or when an odd number of electrons occurs (see Section 8-5).

Drawing Lewis Electron Dot Structures

A systematic approach to constructing Lewis structures is illustrated with chloroform, $CHCl_3$, a compound once used as an anesthetic.

STEP 1 *Determine the arrangement of atoms within a molecule.* The central atom is *usually* the one with the lowest affinity for electrons (least negative electron attachment enthalpy, Section 7-5).

$CHCl_3$
↑
Central atom

STEP 2 *Determine the total number of valence electrons in the molecule or ion.* In a neutral molecule, this number will be the sum of the valence electrons for each atom. The number of valence electron *pairs* will be half the total number of valence electrons.

$CHCl_3$ valence electrons
C = 4
H = 1
Cl = 3 × 7 = 21
Total = 26 electrons or 13 pairs

STEP 3 *Place one pair of electrons between each pair of bonded atoms to form a single bond.* Here, four electron pairs are used to make four single bonds (which are represented by single lines). Nine pairs of electrons, of the original 13, remain to be used.

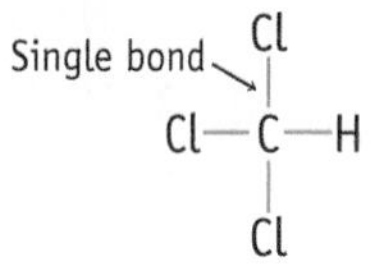

PROBLEM SOLVING TIP 8.1

Choosing the Central Atom in a Dot Structure

The first step in building a Lewis electron dot structure is to choose the central atom.

1. Generally the central atom is the one of lowest electronegativity. Electronegativity is discussed in Section 8-7.
2. For simple compounds and ions, the first atom in a formula is often the central atom (e.g., SO_2, NH_4^+, NO_3^-). This is not always a reliable predictor, however. Notable exceptions include water (H_2O) and most common acids (HNO_3, H_2SO_4), in which the acidic hydrogen is usually written first but where another atom (such as N or S) is the central atom.
3. You will come to recognize that certain elements often appear as the central atom, among them C, N, P, and S.
4. Halogens are often terminal atoms forming a single bond to one other atom, but they can be the central atom when combined with O in oxoacids (such as in $HClO_4$).
5. Oxygen is the central atom in water, but in combination with nitrogen, phosphorus, and the halogens it is usually a terminal atom.
6. With rare exceptions, hydrogen is a terminal atom because it typically bonds to only one other atom.

STEP 4 *Use remaining pairs as lone pairs around each terminal atom (except H) so that each terminal atom is surrounded by eight electrons.* If, after this is done, there are electrons left over, assign them to the central atom. All 13 pairs have now been assigned in $CHCl_3$. The H atom has a share in two electrons, as it normally does, and all other atoms have a share in an octet of electrons. The Lewis structure for $CHCl_3$ is complete.

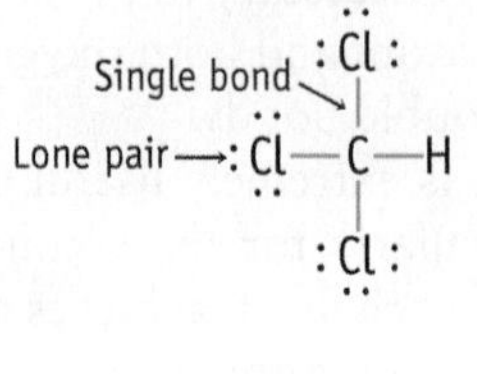

STEP 5 *If no valence electron pairs remain after forming single bonds and completing the octets of terminal atoms, and the central atom does not have an octet of electrons, then multiple bonds can be created by sharing one or more pairs of electrons between terminal atoms and the central atom.* (See the case of CH_2O on page 289).

This step is not required for $CHCl_3$.

EXAMPLE 8.1

Drawing Lewis Electron Dot Structures

Problem Draw the Lewis electron dot structures for chloramine, NH_2Cl (a disinfectant) and thionyl chloride, $SOCl_2$, a reagent widely used in organic chemistry.

What Do You Know? The formula of each compound is given so you can determine the number of valence electrons. Further, you can expect that each atom (except H) will achieve an octet configuration.

Strategy Follow the steps outlined for $CHCl_3$ in the preceding text.

Solution for NH_2Cl

1. N is the central atom, and the H and Cl atoms are terminal atoms.
2. Valence electrons = 14 (7 pairs) = 5 (for N) + 2 × 1 (1 for each H) + 7 (for Cl)
3. Three electron pairs form single bonds from N to the H and Cl terminal atoms.

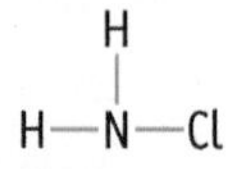

4. Distribute three lone pairs on the terminal Cl atom to complete the octet of electrons around this atom.

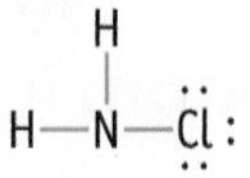

5. One pair of electrons remains, and it is placed on the central N atom to complete its octet.

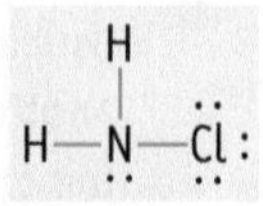

The N and Cl atoms now have a share in four pairs of electrons, and the H atoms share two electrons. The Lewis structure is complete.

Solution for $SOCl_2$

1. Sulfur is the central atom. The electron affinity of sulfur is lower than that of both oxygen and chlorine. (The electron attachment enthalpy of S is less negative than that of O or Cl.)

2. Valence electrons = 26 (13 pairs) = 6 (for S) + 6 (for O) + 2 × 7 (for each Cl)
3. Three electron pairs form single bonds from the sulfur to oxygen and chlorine:

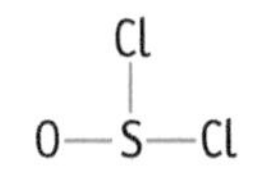

4. Distribute nine pairs of electrons around the O and Cl terminal atoms.

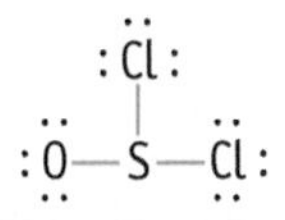

5. One pair of electrons remains. The central S atom as yet has only three electron pairs surrounding it, so the last of the pairs is placed there. Each atom now has a share in four electron pairs.

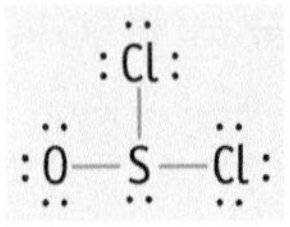

Think about Your Answer In both of these molecules a pair of electrons remained after forming bonds and completing the octet around the terminal atoms. This electron pair was then placed on the central atom.

Check Your Understanding

Draw Lewis electron dot structures for CH_3Cl (methyl chloride, a topical anesthetic), H_2O, H_2O_2 (hydrogen peroxide, with an O—O bond), NH_3, and NH_2OH (with an N—O bond).

There are many molecules that have two or even three bonds between a pair of atoms, and a simple example of this is the formaldehyde molecule, CH_2O. Here carbon is the central atom, and there is a total of 12 valence electrons.

Valence electrons for CH_2O = 12 electrons (or 6 electron pairs)

= 4 (for C) + 2 × 1 (for two H atoms) + 6 (for O)

As usual, we place one pair of electrons between each pair of bonded atoms to form a single bond.

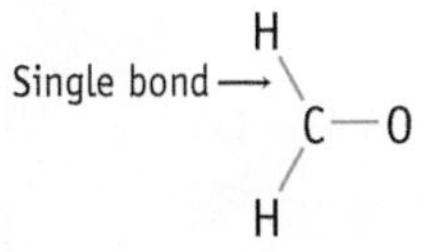

and then we place the three remaining pairs as lone pairs around the terminal O atom.

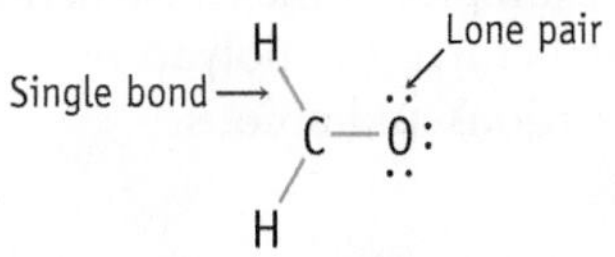

Now all six pairs have been assigned, but the C atom still has a share in only three pairs. *If the central atom has fewer than eight electrons at this point, change one or more of the lone pairs on a terminal atom into a bonding pair between the central and terminal atom to form a multiple bond.*

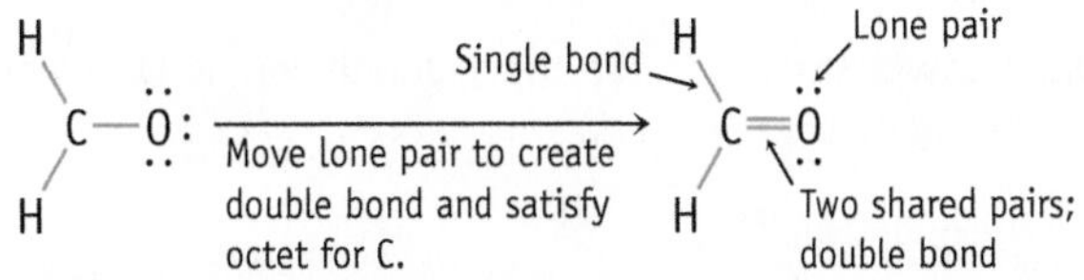

As a general rule, double or triple bonds are most often encountered when *both* atoms are C, N, or O. That is, bonds such as C=C, C=N, and C=O will be observed frequently.

EXAMPLE 8.2

Drawing Lewis Electron Dot Structures with a Multiple Bond

Problem Draw the Lewis electron dot structure for CO_2, carbon dioxide.

What Do You Know? The formula is given so you can determine the number of valence electrons. Further, you can expect that each atom will achieve an octet configuration.

Strategy Follow the steps outlined for CH_2O in the preceding text.

Solution

1. Designate C as the central atom.
2. Valence electrons = 16 (8 pairs) = 4 (for C) + 2 × 6 (for O)
3. Two electron pairs form single bonds between C and O.

   O—C—O

4. Distribute three lone pairs on the terminal O atoms to complete their octets.

   :Ö—C—Ö:

5. None of the original 8 electron pairs remain to be used, but the C atom does not yet have an octet of electrons. Therefore, we use lone pairs of electrons on the O atoms to form additional CO bonds, one on each side of the molecule.

   Ö=C=Ö

Think about Your Answer Why do we not take two lone pairs from one side and none from the other (to give a CO triple bond and a CO single bond, respectively)? We shall discuss that possibility after describing charge distribution in molecules and ions (Section 8-7).

Check Your Understanding

Draw the Lewis electron dot structure for CO.

To complete our initial examples of the construction of Lewis electron dot structures, let's look at Lewis structures for polyatomic ions. You encounter many of these in chemistry, as both cations and anions.

EXAMPLE 8.3

Drawing Lewis Electron Dot Structures for Polyatomic Ions

Problem Draw Lewis structures for the chlorate ion (ClO_3^-) and the nitronium ion (NO_2^+).

What Do You Know? The formula of each ion is given so you can determine the number of valence electrons. Further, you can expect that each atom will achieve an octet configuration.

Strategy Follow the steps outlined in the preceding examples with the added step of accounting for the ion charge.

- For an *anion, add* the number of electrons equal to the negative charge.
- For a *cation, subtract* the number of electrons equal to the ion charge.

Solution for chlorate ion, ClO_3^-

1. Cl is the central atom, and the O atoms are terminal atoms.
2. Valence electrons = 26 (13 pairs)
   = 7 (for Cl) + 18 (six for each O) + 1 (for the negative charge)
3. Three electron pairs form single bonds from Cl to the O terminal atoms.

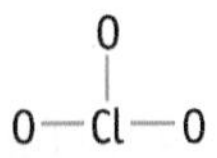

4. Distribute three lone pairs on each of the terminal O atoms to complete the octet of electrons around each of these atoms.

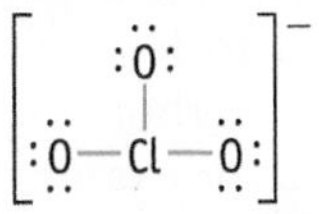

5. One pair of electrons remains, and it is placed on the central Cl atom to complete its octet.

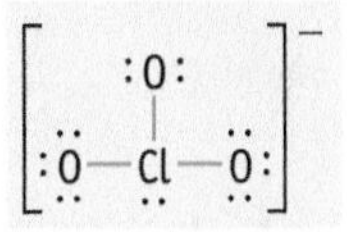

Each atom now has a share in four pairs of electrons, and the Lewis structure is complete.

Solution for nitronium ion, NO_2^+

1. Nitrogen is the central atom.
2. Valence electrons = 16 (8 pairs)
   = 5 (for N) + 12 (six for each O) − 1 (for the positive charge)
3. Two electron pairs form single bonds from the nitrogen to each oxygen:

O—N—O

4. Distribute the remaining six pairs of electrons on the terminal O atoms:

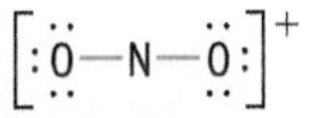

5. The central nitrogen atom is two electron pairs short of an octet. As in CO_2, a lone pair of electrons on each oxygen atom is converted to a bonding electron pair to give two N=O double bonds. Each atom in the ion now has four electron pairs. Nitrogen has four bonding pairs, and each oxygen atom has two lone pairs and shares two bond pairs.

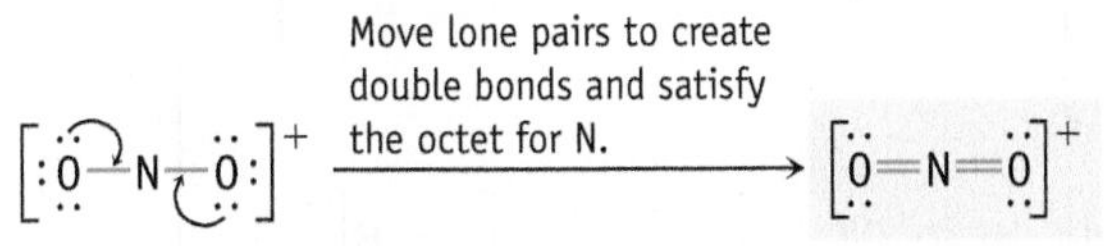

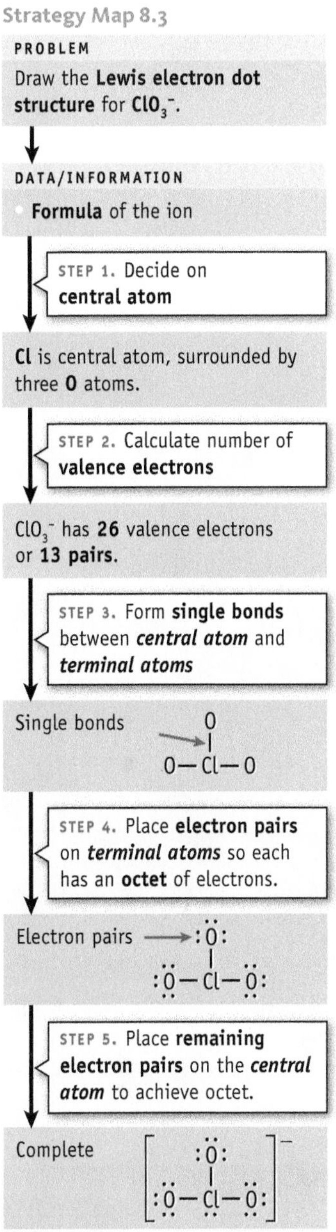

Think about Your Answer Notice that the dot structure of ClO_3^- and NO_2^+ resemble those of $SOCl_2$ (Example 8.1) and CO_2 (Example 8.2), respectively. Both ClO_3^- and $SOCl_2$ have the same number of valence electron pairs, the same number of bond and lone pairs, and both have a lone pair on the central atom. Similarly, CO_2 and NO_2^+ have the same number of valence electrons, and both have two double bonds. You will find it very helpful to observe common features of electron dot structures.

Check Your Understanding

Draw Lewis structures for NH_4^+, NO^+, and SO_4^{2-}.

Predicting Lewis Structures

The guidelines for drawing Lewis structures are helpful, but you will find you can also rely on patterns of bonding in related molecules.

Hydrogen Compounds

The Lewis symbol for an element is a useful guide in determining the number of bonds formed by the element. For example, nitrogen has five valence electrons. Two electrons occur as a lone pair; the other three occur as unpaired electrons. To reach an octet, it is necessary to pair each of the unpaired electrons with an electron from another atom. Thus, N is predicted to form three bonds in *uncharged* molecules. Similarly, for *uncharged* compounds, carbon is expected to form four bonds, oxygen two, and fluorine one. See Table 8.2 for examples of common hydrogen-containing molecules and ions based on C, N, O, and F.

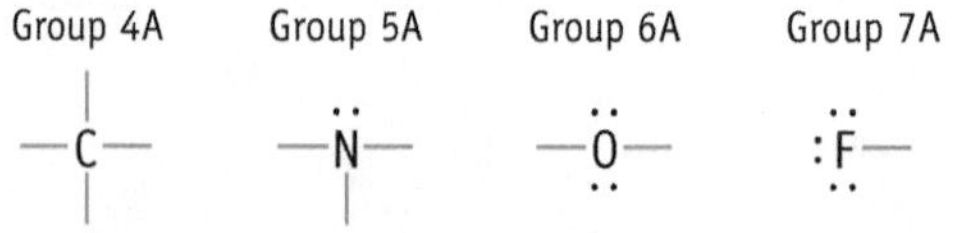

The elements C, N, and O are the basis for common polyatomic ions, for example the ammonium and hydronium ions. Here we could think of NH_4^+ as based on N^+, a cation formed by taking away one electron from N. The N^+ ion has four

Table 8.2 Lewis Structures of Common Hydrogen-Containing Molecules and Ions of Second-Period Elements

Group 4A	Group 5A	Group 6A	Group 7A
CH_4 methane 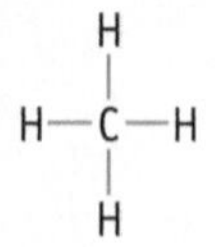	NH_3 ammonia 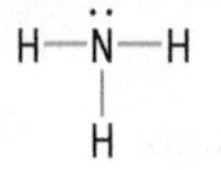	H_2O water 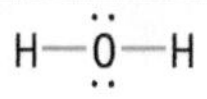	HF hydrogen fluoride 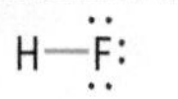
C_2H_6 ethane 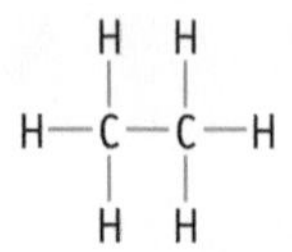	N_2H_4 hydrazine 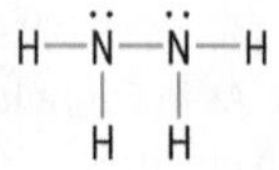	H_2O_2 hydrogen peroxide 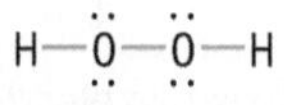	
C_2H_4 ethylene 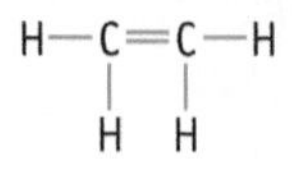	NH_4^+ ammonium ion 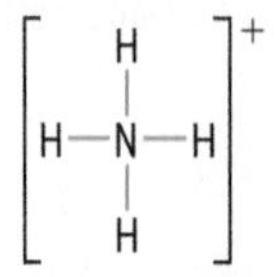	H_3O^+ hydronium ion 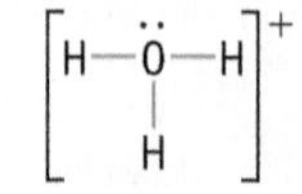	
C_2H_2 acetylene 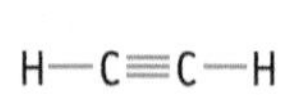	NH_2^- amide ion 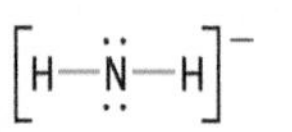	OH^- hydroxide ion 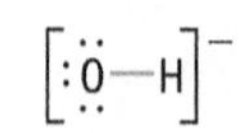	

unpaired valence electrons (analogous to C) and so is capable of forming four single bonds to hydrogen atoms. The amide anion, NH_2^-, can be broken down similarly. In this anion N^- has 6 electrons, two pairs of electrons and two unpaired electrons (analogous to O) and is capable of forming two single bonds.

EXAMPLE 8.4

Predicting Lewis Electron Dot Structures

Problem Draw Lewis electron dot structures for CCl_4 and NF_3.

What Do You Know? Carbon tetrachloride (CCl_4) and NF_3 have stoichiometries similar to CH_4 and NH_3 (Table 8.2), so you might reasonably expect similar Lewis structures.

Strategy Recall that carbon is expected to form four bonds and nitrogen three bonds to achieve an octet of electrons. In addition, halogen atoms have seven valence electrons, so both Cl and F can attain an octet by forming one covalent bond.

Solution

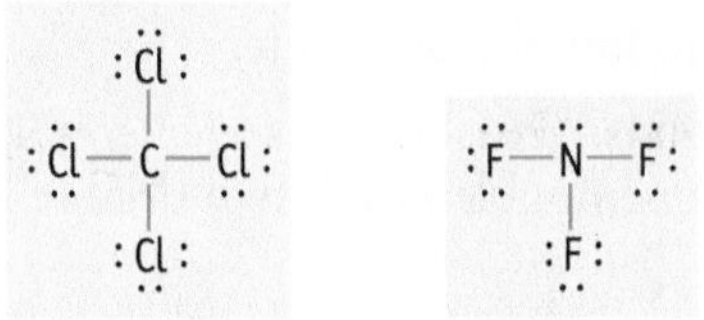

carbon tetrachloride nitrogen trifluoride

Think about Your Answer As a check, count the number of valence electrons for each molecule, and verify that all are shown in the Lewis structure.

CCl_4: Valence electrons = 4 (for C) + 4 × 7 (for Cl) = 32 electrons (16 pairs)

The Lewis structure for CCl_4 shows 8 electrons in single bonds and 24 electrons as lone pair electrons, for a total of 32 electrons. The structure is correct.

NF_3: Valence electrons = 5 (for N) + 3 × 7 (for F) = 26 electrons (13 pairs)

The Lewis structure for NF_3 shows 6 electrons in single bonds and 20 electrons as lone pair electrons, for a total of 26 electrons. The structure is correct.

Check Your Understanding

Predict Lewis structures for methanol, CH_3OH, and hydroxylamine, H_2NOH. (In each molecule the central C or N atom is bonded to H atoms and one O atom.)

Oxoacids and Their Anions

Oxoacids such as HNO_3, H_2SO_4, H_3PO_4, and $HClO_4$ are covalently bonded molecular compounds, a conclusion that we should draw because all elements in the formula are nonmetals. In aqueous solution oxoacids ionize to give a hydronium ion and the appropriate anion. A Lewis structure for the nitrate ion, for example, can be created using the guidelines in the preceding examples, and the result is a structure with two N—O single bonds and one N=O double bond. To form nitric acid from the nitrate ion, a hydrogen ion is attached utilizing a lone pair on one of the O atoms.

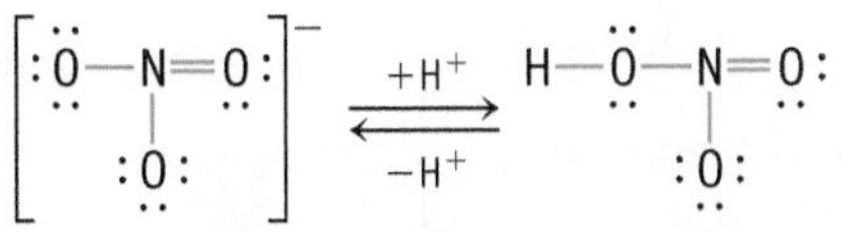

nitrate ion nitric acid

Isoelectronic Species

The species NO^+, N_2, CO, and CN^- are similar in that they each have two atoms and the same total number of valence electrons, 10, which leads to a similar Lewis structure for each molecule or ion. The two atoms in each are linked with a triple bond. With three bonding pairs and one lone pair, each atom thus has an octet of electrons.

$[:N{\equiv}O:]^+$ $:N{\equiv}N:$ $:C{\equiv}O:$ $[:C{\equiv}N:]^-$

Isoelectronic Structures There are similarities and important differences in chemical properties of isoelectronic species. For example, both carbon monoxide, CO, and cyanide ion, CN^-, are very toxic, which results from the fact that they can bind to the iron of hemoglobin in blood and block the uptake of oxygen. They are different, though, in their acid–base chemistry. In aqueous solution, cyanide ion readily adds H^+ to form hydrogen cyanide, whereas CO is not protonated.

Molecules and ions having the *same number of valence electrons and similar Lewis structures* are said to be **isoelectronic** (Table 8.3). As you saw in Examples 8.1–8.4, it is helpful to recognize isoelectronic molecules and ions because these species have similar electronic (Lewis) structures.

Carbon-Based Organic Compounds

The vast majority of the molecules in our world and within our bodies are carbon-based organic molecules that consist of C and H with N, O, and, occasionally, other elements such as S and P. You can often draw Lewis structures of organic molecules quickly by following a few guidelines.

- All organic molecules follow the octet rule.
- Carbon forms four bonds. (Possible arrangements include four single bonds; two single bonds and one double bond; two double bonds; or one single bond and one triple bond.)
- In uncharged species, nitrogen forms three bonds and oxygen forms two bonds.
- Hydrogen forms only one bond to another atom.
- When multiple bonds are formed, both atoms involved are usually one of the following: C, N, and O. Oxygen has the ability to form multiple bonds with a variety of elements. Carbon forms many compounds having multiple bonds to another carbon or to N or O.
- Always account for single bonds and lone pairs before determining whether multiple bonds are present.

Let us take the hydrocarbon C_3H_6 (with 18 valence electrons) as an example. There are only two ways to arrange three C atoms: in a triangle or in line. If we draw a bond between the C atoms in those structures, we have:

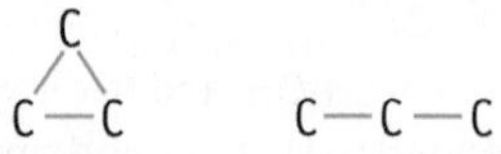

Table 8.3 Some Common Isoelectronic Molecules and Ions

Formulas	Representative Lewis Structure	Formulas	Representative Lewis Structure
BH_4^-, CH_4, NH_4^+	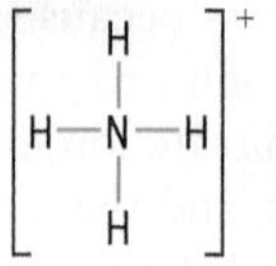	CO_3^{2-}, NO_3^-	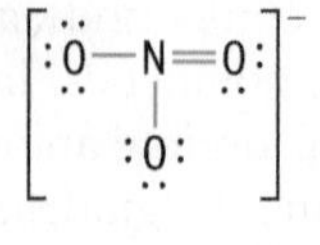
NH_3, H_3O^+	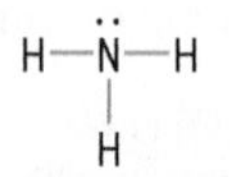	PO_4^{3-}, SO_4^{2-}, ClO_4^-	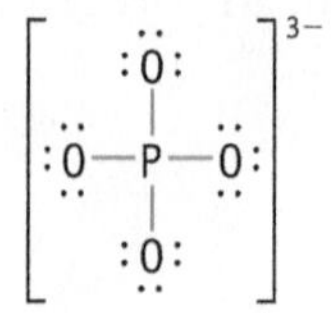
CO_2, OCN^-, SCN^-, N_2O, NO_2^+, OCS, CS_2	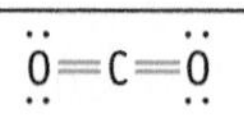		

Table 8.4 Lewis Structures for Simple Organic Molecules Based on C, H, N, and O

CH_4O	14 valence electrons	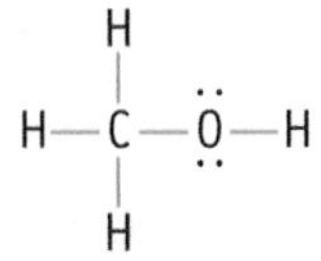	methyl alcohol
CH_5N	14 valence electrons	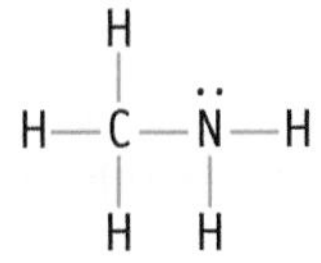	methyl amine
CH_2O_2	18 valence electrons	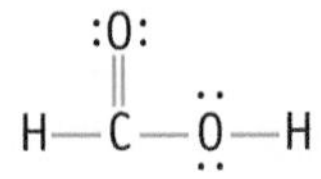	formic acid (methanoic acid)
$C_2H_5NO_2$	20 valence electrons	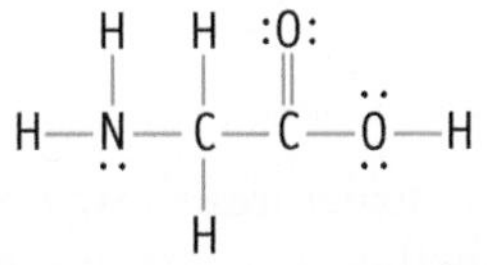	glycine

Next, attach H atoms to the C atoms. In the C_3 triangle arrangement each C atom can accommodate two H atoms. Each C atom has an octet of electrons, and the structure is complete.

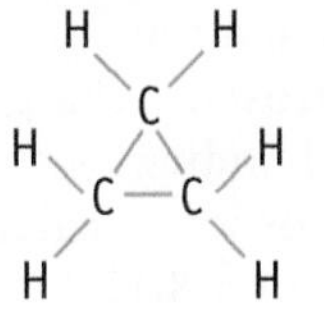

The situation is different for the "linear" structure. Each C atom must have four bonds. If the C atoms are connected by single bonds and each C atom has H atoms attached, we would need eight H atoms. As the molecule has only six H atoms, the structure can only be that below, a structure with one C=C double bond.

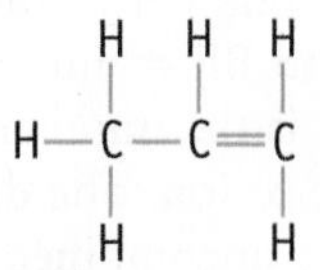

You have already seen another example of the Lewis structure of a simple organic molecule (CH_2O, page 289). See Table 8.4 for several more examples of Lewis structures of common organic molecules.

REVIEW & CHECK FOR SECTION 8-2

1. Which of the following describes the sulfur atom in the Lewis structure of the sulfite ion, SO_3^{2-}?

   (a) Sulfur has three single bonds to oxygen and a lone pair.

   (b) Sulfur bonds to two oxygen atoms with single bonds and one oxygen atom with a double bond.

   (c) Sulfur forms double bonds to three oxygen atoms.

   (d) Sulfur forms three single bonds to oxygen and has no lone pairs.

2. Which one of the species in the list below is NOT isoelectronic with N_3^-?

   (a) N_2O (b) NO_2^+ (c) O_3 (d) CO_2

3. Identify the species in the list below that is NOT isoelectronic with the others.

   (a) O_3 (b) OCN^- (c) NO_2^- (d) SO_2

4. Which of the following is NOT a possible structure for a molecule with the formula C_2H_6O?

   (a) 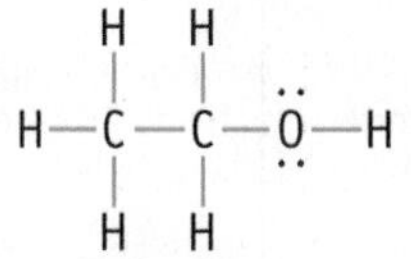 (b) 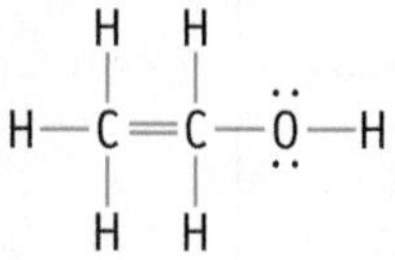 (c) 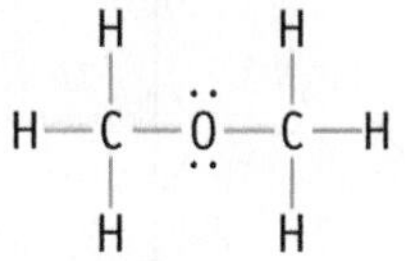

Learning Objectives: LO 2.21

8-3 Atom Formal Charges in Covalent Molecules and Ions

You have seen that Lewis structures show how electron pairs are placed in a covalently bonded species, whether it is a neutral molecule or a polyatomic ion. Now we turn to one of the consequences of the placement of electron pairs in this way: Individual atoms can be negatively or positively charged or have no electric charge. The location of a positive or negative charge in a molecule or ion will influence, among other things, the atom at which a reaction occurs. For example, does a positive H^+ ion attach itself to the Cl or the O of ClO^-? It is reasonable to expect H^+ to attach to the more negatively charged atom, and we can predict this by evaluating atom formal charges in molecules and ions.

The **formal charge** is the electrostatic charge that would reside on an atom in a molecule or polyatomic ion if all bonding electrons are shared equally. The formal charge for an atom in a molecule or ion is calculated based on the Lewis structure of the molecule or ion, using Equation 8.1,

$$\text{Formal charge of an atom in a molecule or ion} = \text{NVE} - [\text{LPE} + \tfrac{1}{2}(\text{BE})] \quad \textbf{(8.1)}$$

where NVE = number of valence electrons in the uncombined atom (and, for main group elements, equal to its group number in the periodic table), LPE = number of lone pair electrons on an atom, and BE = number of bonding electrons around an atom. The term in square brackets is the number of electrons assigned by the Lewis structure to an atom in a molecule or ion. The difference between this term and the number of valence electrons on the uncombined atom is the formal charge. A positive formal charge means that an atom in a molecule or ion "contributed" more electrons to bonding than it "got back." The atom's formal charge will be negative if the reverse is true.

There are two important assumptions in Equation 8.1. First, lone pairs are assumed to "belong" to the atom on which they reside in the Lewis structure. Second, bond pairs are assumed to be divided *equally* between the bonded atoms (and is the reason BE is multiplied by ½).

The sum of the formal charges on the atoms in a molecule must be zero, whereas the sum for atoms in an ion equals the charge on the ion. Consider the hypochlorite ion, ClO^-. Oxygen is in Group 6A and so has six valence electrons. However, the oxygen atom in OCl^- can lay claim to seven electrons (six lone pair electrons and one bonding electron), so the atom has a formal charge of −1. The O atom has formally gained an electron by bonding to chlorine.

A CLOSER LOOK — Comparing Oxidation Number and Formal Charge

In Section 3-8 you learned to calculate the oxidation number of an atom as a way to tell if a reaction involves oxidation and reduction. Are an atom's oxidation number and its formal charge related? To answer this question, let us look at the hydroxide ion. The formal charges are −1 on the O atom and 0 on the H atom. Recall that these formal charges are calculated assuming the O—H bond electrons are shared equally in an O—H covalent bond.

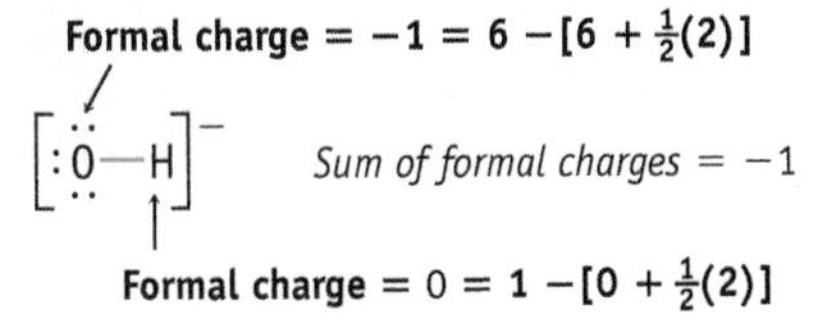

In contrast, in Chapter 3 (page 128), you learned that O has an oxidation number of −2 and H has an oxidation number of +1. *Oxidation numbers are determined by assuming that the bond between a pair of atoms is ionic,* not covalent. For OH^- this means the pair of electrons between O and H is located *fully* on O. Thus, the O atom now has eight valence electrons instead of six and a charge of −2. The H atom now has no valence electrons and a charge of +1.

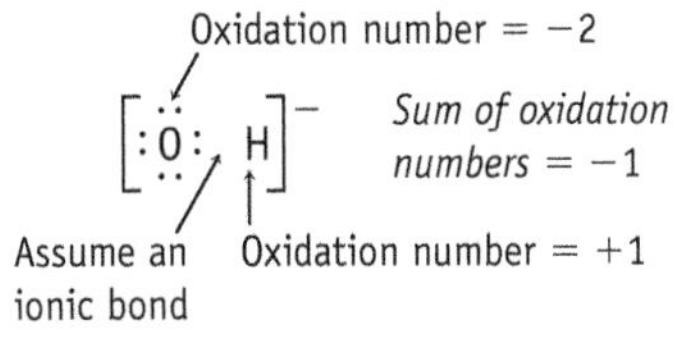

Formal charges and oxidation numbers are calculated for different purposes. Oxidation numbers allow us to follow changes in redox reactions. Formal charges provide insight into the distribution of charges in molecules and polyatomic ions.

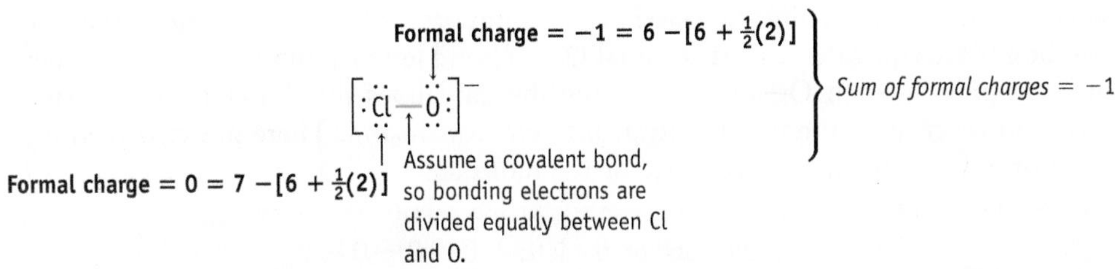

The formal charge on the Cl atom in ClO^- is zero. So we have −1 for oxygen and 0 for chlorine, and the sum of these equals the net charge of −1 for the ion. An important conclusion we can draw from the formal charges in ClO^- is that, if an H^+ ion approaches the ion, it should attach itself to the negatively charged O atom to give hypochlorous acid, HOCl.

EXAMPLE 8.5

Calculating Formal Charges

Problem Calculate formal charges for the atoms of the ClO_3^- ion.

What Do You Know? You know the Lewis structure of ClO_3^-, which was developed in Example 8.3.

Strategy The first step is always to write the Lewis structure for the molecule or ion. Then Equation 8.1 can be used to calculate the formal charges.

Solution

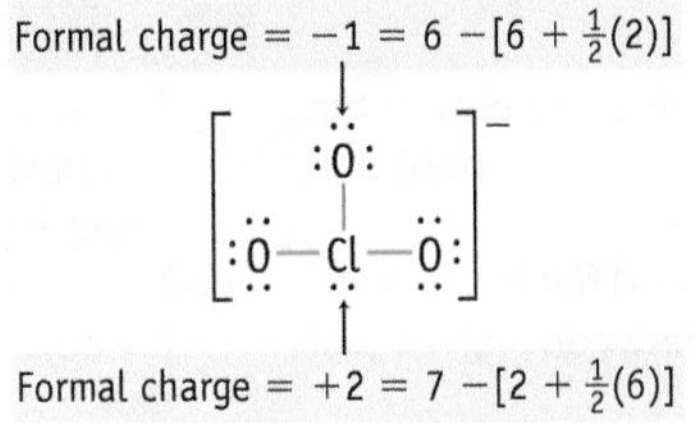

The formal charge on each O atom is −1, whereas for the Cl atom it is +2.

Think about Your Answer Notice that the sum of the formal charges on all the atoms equals the charge on the ion.

Check Your Understanding

Calculate formal charges on each atom in (a) CN^- and (b) SO_3^{2-}.

REVIEW & CHECK FOR SECTION 8-3

1. What is the formal charge of the P atom in the anion $H_2PO_4^-$? (The dihydrogen phosphate ion is the anion derived from H_3PO_4 by loss of H^+.)

(a) +3 (b) 0 (c) +1 (d) +5

Learning Objectives: LO 2.21

8-4 Resonance

Ozone, O_3, an unstable, blue, diamagnetic gas with a characteristic pungent odor, protects Earth and its inhabitants from intense ultraviolet radiation from the Sun. An important feature of its structure is that the two oxygen–oxygen bonds are the same length. This experimental observation is important because it suggests that the two bonds are equivalent. That is, equal O—O bond lengths imply an equal number of bond pairs in each O—O bond. Using the guidelines for drawing Lewis structures, however, you might come to a different conclusion. There are two possible ways of writing the Lewis structure for the molecule:

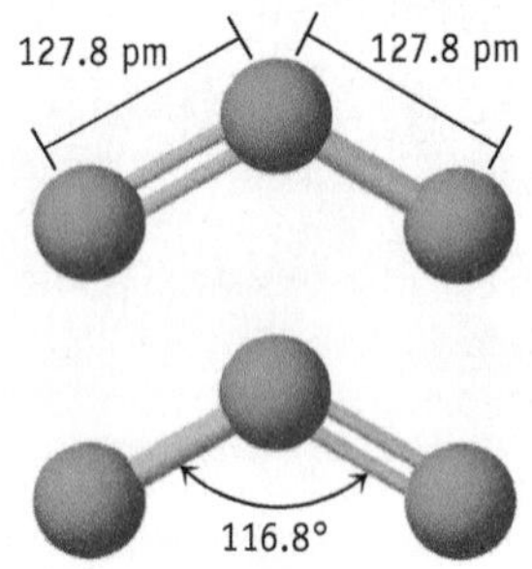

Ozone, O_3, is a bent molecule with oxygen–oxygen bonds of the same length.

Double bond on the left: O=O—O

Double bond on the right: O—O=O

These structures are equivalent in that each has a double bond on one side of the central oxygen atom and a single bond on the other side. If either were the actual structure of ozone, one bond (O=O) should be shorter than the other (O—O). The actual structure of ozone shows this is not the case. The inescapable conclusion is that neither Lewis structure correctly represents the bonding in ozone.

Linus Pauling (1901–1994) proposed the concept of **resonance** to solve the problem. *Resonance structures are used to represent bonding in a molecule or ion when a single Lewis structure fails to describe accurately the actual electronic structure.* The alternative structures shown for ozone are called **resonance structures.** They have identical patterns of bonding and equal energy. The actual structure of this molecule is a *composite*, or **hybrid,** of the equivalent resonance structures. In this resonance hybrid, the bonds between the oxygens are between a single bond and

A CLOSER LOOK Resonance

- Resonance is a means of representing the bonding in a molecule or polyatomic ion when a single Lewis structure fails to give an accurate picture.
- The atoms must have the same arrangement in each resonance structure. Do not attach the atoms in a different fashion as this creates a different compound.
- Resonance structures differ only in the assignment of electron-pair positions, never atom positions.
- Resonance structures differ in the number of bond pairs between a given pair of atoms.
- Resonance is not meant to indicate the motion of electrons.
- The actual structure of a molecule is a composite or hybrid of the resonance structures.
- There will always be at least one multiple bond (double or triple) in each resonance structure.

a double bond in length, in this case corresponding to one and a half bonds. This is a reasonable conclusion because we see that the O—O bonds in ozone both have a length of 127.8 pm, intermediate between the average length of an O═O double bond (121 pm) and an O—O single bond (132 pm). Because a single Lewis structure cannot represent fractions of a bond, chemists draw the resonance structures and connect them with double-headed arrows (⟷) to indicate that the true structure is a composite of these extreme structures.

Benzene, C_6H_6, is the classic example of the use of resonance to describe a structure. The benzene molecule is a six-member ring of carbon atoms with six equivalent carbon–carbon bonds (and a hydrogen atom attached to each carbon atom). The carbon–carbon bonds are 139 pm long, intermediate between the average length of a C═C double bond (134 pm) and a C—C single bond (154 pm). Two resonance structures that differ only in double bond placement can be written for the molecule. A hybrid of these two structures, however, will lead to a molecule with six equivalent carbon–carbon bonds.

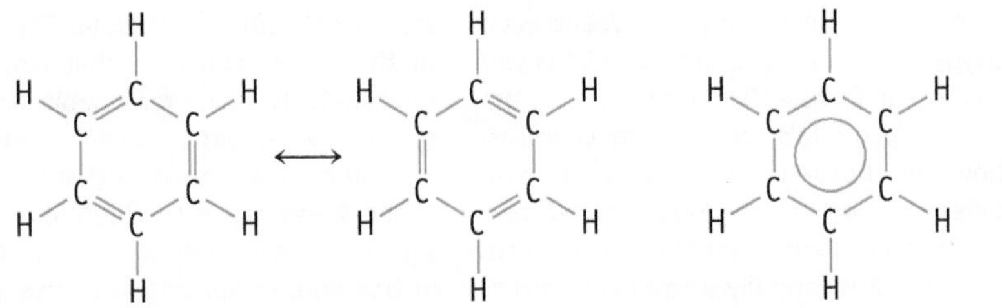

resonance structures of benzene, C_6H_6

abbreviated representation of resonance structures

Let us use resonance to describe bonding in the carbonate ion, CO_3^{2-}, an anion with 24 valence electrons (12 pairs).

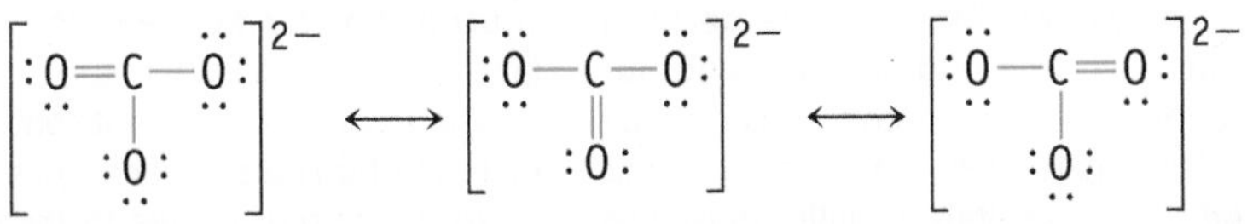

Three equivalent structures can be drawn for this ion, differing only in the location of the C═O double bond, but no single structure correctly describes this ion. Instead, the actual structure is a composite of the three structures, in good agreement with experimental results. In the CO_3^{2-} ion, all three carbon–oxygen bond lengths are 129 pm, intermediate between the lengths of C—O single bonds (143 pm) and C═O double bonds (122 pm).

Formal charges can be calculated for each atom in the resonance structure for a molecule or ion. For example, using one of the resonance structures for the nitrate ion, we find that the central N atom has a formal charge of +1, and the singly bonded O atoms are both −1. The doubly bonded O atom has no charge. The net charge for the ion is thus −1.

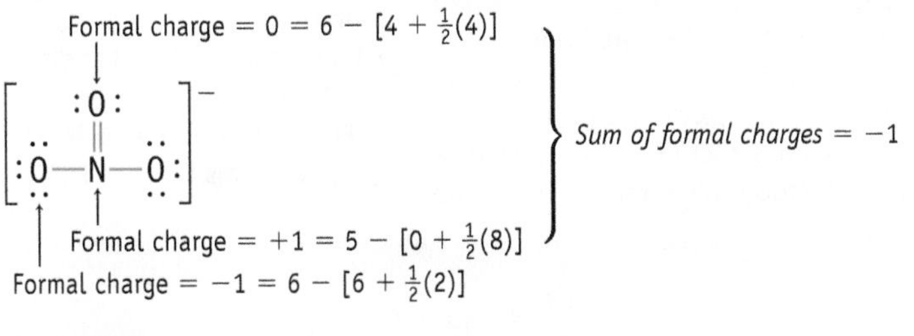

Depicting Resonance Structures The use of an arrow (⟷) as a symbol to link resonance structures and the term *resonance* are somewhat unfortunate. An arrow might seem to imply that a change is occurring, and the term *resonance* has the connotation of vibrating or alternating back and forth between different forms. Neither view is correct. Electron pairs are not actually moving from one atom to another.

Ted Streshinsky/Corbis

Linus Pauling (1901–1994). Linus Pauling was born in Portland, Oregon. He earned a B.Sc. degree in chemical engineering from Oregon State College in 1922 and a Ph.D. in chemistry at the California Institute of Technology in 1925. He is well known for his book *The Nature of the Chemical Bond,* a seminal work in chemistry. In the words of Francis Crick, Pauling was also "one of the founders of molecular biology." It was this and his study of chemical bonding that were cited in the award of the Nobel Prize in Chemistry in 1954. Finally, he also received the Nobel Peace Prize in 1962 for the role he and his wife played in advocating for the nuclear test ban treaty.

Is this a reasonable charge distribution for the nitrate ion? The answer is no. The actual structure of the nitrate ion is a resonance hybrid of three equivalent resonance structures. Because the three oxygen atoms in NO_3^- are equivalent, the charge on one oxygen atom should not be different from the other two. This can be resolved if the formal charges are averaged to give a formal charge of $-2/3$ on the oxygen atoms. Summing the charges on the three oxygen atoms and the $+1$ charge on the nitrogen atom then gives -1, the charge on the ion.

In the resonance structures for O_3, CO_3^{2-}, and NO_3^- all the possible resonance structures are equally likely; they are "equivalent" structures. Therefore, the molecule or ion has a symmetrical distribution of electrons over all the atoms involved—that is, its electronic structure consists of an equal mixture or "hybrid" of the resonance structures. However, there are also many examples in which reasonable

A CLOSER LOOK

A Scientific Controversy—Resonance, Formal Charges, and the Question of Double Bonds in Sulfate and Phosphate Ions

Now that we have introduced Lewis structures, resonance, and formal charge, we want to discuss a current scientific controversy: the disagreement among chemists about drawing Lewis structures for such simple species as sulfate ion and phosphate ion. For example, two different Lewis structures have been proposed for the sulfate ion:

1

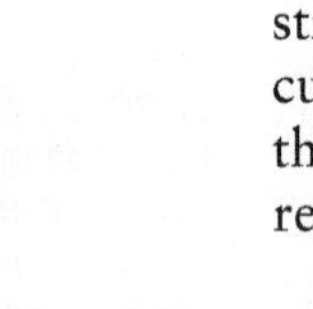

2

When drawing Lewis structures, *the most important step is first to satisfy the octet rule for each atom in a molecule or ion*. If a single Lewis structure does not accurately represent a species, resonance can be introduced. [If two resonance structures are different (as with ions such as SCN^- or a compound like N_2O), a decision can be made among the possible choices by giving preference to structures that minimize formal charges and place negative charges on the most electronegative atoms (page 317).] In the large majority of cases, Lewis structures created by this approach can then be used to determine molecular structure and provide a qualitative picture of bonding.

In this book, we choose to represent the sulfate ion with Lewis structure 1 in which all of the atoms achieve an octet of electrons. The S—O bond order is 1, the sulfur atom has a formal charge of +2, and each oxygen has a formal charge of −1. (As you shall see in Chapter 9, these bonds use the 3*s* and 3*p* orbitals for S.) Some chemists, however, choose to represent sulfate by a different Lewis structure (structure 2, one of six equivalent resonance structures). Structure 2 is formally a resonance structure of 1, and the average sulfur–oxygen bond order is 1.5. This structure is attractive because it minimizes formal charges: sulfur has a formal charge of 0, two of the oxygen atoms have a formal charge of zero, and the other two have formal charges of −1. However, as described in more detail in Chapter 9, for sulfur to form six bonds requires that S have six valence orbitals available. This implies that, in addition to 3*s* and 3*p* orbitals, 3*d* orbitals on sulfur must also be involved when describing bonding.

A similar situation is encountered with the phosphate ion and a number of other related species. Several resonance structures can be drawn with double bonds.

The question is which is the better representation of bonding in SO_4^{2-}, 1 or 2? Here we find a controversy. A paper in the *Journal of Chemical Education*[1] presents arguments supporting the description of sulfate by structure 2. Among data offered to support multiple bonding between sulfur and oxygen is the observation that the sulfate ion has shorter SO bonds (149 pm) than the known S—O single bond length (about 170 pm) but longer than the double bond in sulfur monoxide (128 pm).

Support for structure 1 comes from a theoretical study also reported in the *Journal of Chemical Education*.[2] The authors of this paper conclude that structure 1 for sulfate is more reasonable and that structure 2 "should be given no weight at all." The basic argument is that the energy of the 3*d* orbitals is too high to allow any significant involvement of these orbitals in bonding. In keeping with this the authors determined that ". . . the calculated *d*-orbital occupancies . . . are quite small . . . and inconsistent with any significant valence shell expansion."

We give more credence to the theoretical study in reference 2 and believe that structure 1 better represents the sulfate ion (and related species) than 2.

There are two important conclusions:

- In this book we shall *always show Lewis structures that adhere to the octet rule even if this leads occasionally to larger formal charges.*
- Finally, you should recognize that *Lewis structures represent only an approximation when representing structure and bonding.*

References:

1. R. F. See, *J. Chem. Ed.*, 2009, *86*, 1241–1247.
2. L. Suidan, J. K. Badenhoop, E. D. Glendening, and F. Weinhold, *J. Chem. Ed.*, 1995, *72*, 583–586.

Additional comments on this matter are found in:

F. Weinhold and C. R. Landis, *Science*, 2007, *316*, 61.

G. Frenking, R. Tanner, F. Weinhold, and C. R. Landis, *Science*, 2007, *318*, 746a.

resonance structures can be drawn that are not equivalent. For example there are three possible resonance structures for the thiocyanate ion, SCN^-.

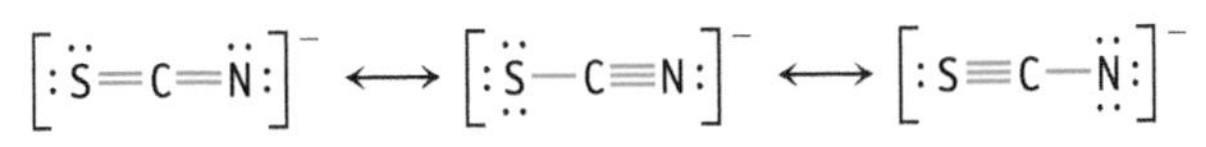

All obey the octet rule, and the electronic structure of this ion can be described as a hybrid of these structures. However, because the structures are not equivalent, there will be unequal mixing in the resonance hybrid, and the actual electronic structure will resemble one of these structures more than the other two. We will discuss this later in this chapter (Section 8-7) and describe the use of formal charge to decide which resonance structure is more important than another.

EXAMPLE 8.6

Drawing Resonance Structures

Problem Draw resonance structures for the nitrite ion, NO_2^-. Are the N—O bonds single, double, or intermediate in value? What are the formal charges on the N and O atoms?

What Do You Know? The N atom is the central atom, bonded to two terminal oxygen atoms. You need to determine whether two or more equivalent Lewis structures can be written for this ion.

Strategy

- Using the guidelines for drawing Lewis structures, determine whether there is more than one way to achieve an octet of electrons around each atom.
- Use one of the Lewis structures to determine the formal charges on the atoms.
- If the formal charges on the two oxygen atoms are different, then the formal charge on oxygen will be an average of the two values.

Solution Nitrogen is the central atom in the nitrite ion, which has a total of 18 valence electrons.

Valence electrons = 5 (for the N atom) + 12 (6 for each O atom) + 1 (for negative charge)

After forming N—O single bonds and distributing lone pairs on the terminal O atoms, one electron pair remains, which is placed on the central N atom.

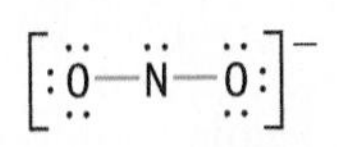

To complete the octet of electrons about the N atom, form a N=O double bond. Because there are two ways to do this, two equivalent structures can be drawn, and the actual structure must be a composite or resonance hybrid of these two structures. The nitrogen–oxygen bonds are neither single nor double bonds but have an intermediate value.

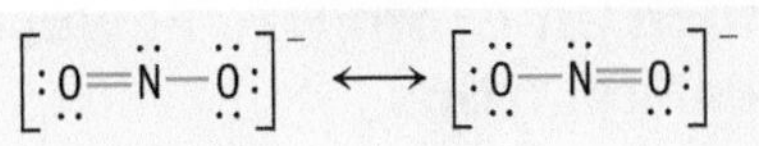

Taking one of the resonance structures, you should find the formal charge for the N atom is 0. The charge on one O atom is 0 and −1 for the other O atom. Because the two resonance structures are of equal importance, however, the net formal charge on each O atom is −1/2.

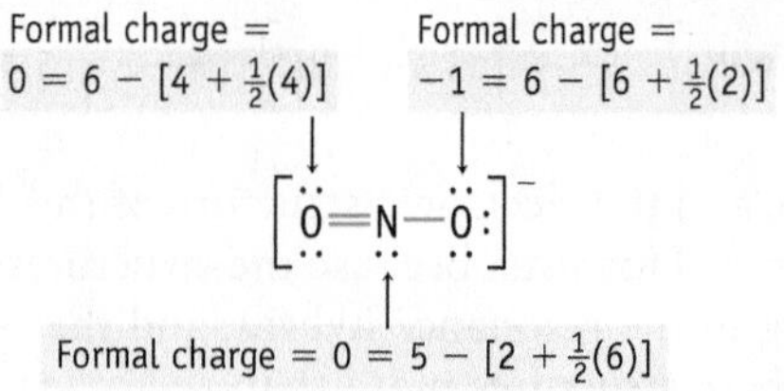

Think about Your Answer The NO bonds in NO_2^- are equivalent, each being intermediate in length between a single N—O bond and a double N═O bond.

Check Your Understanding

Draw resonance structures for the bicarbonate ion, HCO_3^-.

(a) Does HCO_3^- have the same number of resonance structures as the CO_3^{2-} ion?

(b) What are the formal charges on the O and C atoms in HCO_3^-? What is the average formal charge on the O atoms? Compare this with the O atoms in CO_3^{2-}.

(c) Protonation of HCO_3^- gives H_2CO_3. How do formal charges predict where the H^+ ion will be attached?

REVIEW & CHECK FOR SECTION 8-4

1. For which of the following species, SO_3^{2-}, NO^+, or NO_2^+, is the bonding described by two or more resonance structures?

   (a) SO_3^{2-} and NO^+ (b) NO^+ and NO_2^+ (c) NO_2^+ (d) SO_3^{2-}

2. What are the formal charges on nitrogen and oxygen in NO_2^+?

   (a) Formal charges on N and O are 0.

   (b) Formal charge on N is +1; formal charge on oxygen is 0.

   (c) Formal charge on N is 0; formal charge on oxygen is +1.

   (d) Formal charge on N is −1, formal charge on oxygen is +2.

Learning Objectives: LO 2.21

8-5 Exceptions to the Octet Rule

Although the vast majority of molecular compounds and ions obey the octet rule, there are exceptions. These include molecules and ions that have fewer than four pairs of electrons on a central atom, those that have more than four pairs, and those that have an odd number of electrons.

Compounds in Which an Atom Has Fewer Than Eight Valence Electrons

Boron, a metalloid in Group 3A, has three valence electrons and so is expected to form three covalent bonds with other nonmetallic elements. This results in a valence shell for boron in its compounds with only six electrons, two short of an octet. Many boron compounds of this type are known, including such common compounds as boric acid ($B(OH)_3$), borax ($Na_2B_4O_5(OH)_4 \cdot 8\ H_2O$) (Figure 8.1), and the boron trihalides (BF_3, BCl_3, BBr_3, and BI_3).

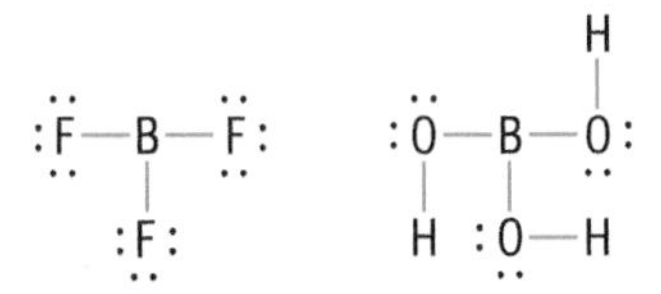

boron trifluoride boric acid

Boron compounds such as BF_3 that are two electrons short of an octet are quite reactive. The boron atom can accommodate a fourth electron pair when that pair is provided by another atom, and molecules or ions with lone pairs can fulfill this role. Ammonia, for example, reacts with BF_3 to form $H_3N{\rightarrow}BF_3$.

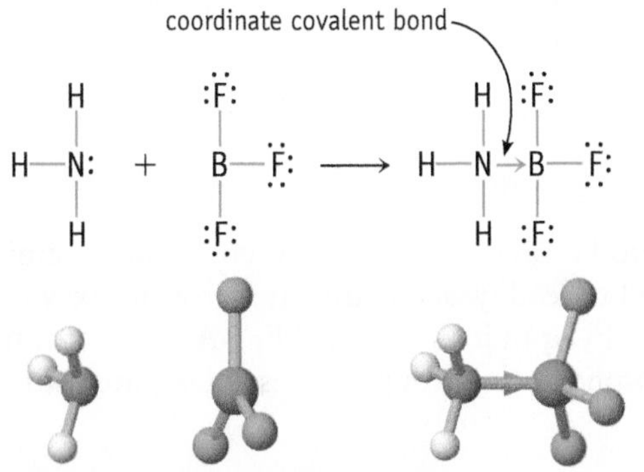

If a bonding pair of electrons originates on one of the bonded atoms, the bond is called a **coordinate covalent bond.** In Lewis structures, a coordinate covalent bond is often symbolized by an arrow that points away from the atom donating the electron pair.

© Cengage Learning/Charles D. Winters

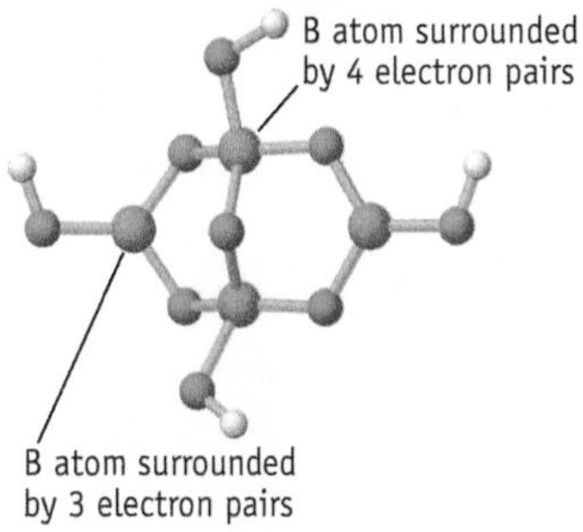

FIGURE 8.1 **The anion in borax.** Borax is a common mineral that is used in soaps and contains an interesting anion, $B_4O_5(OH)_4^{2-}$. The anion has two B atoms surrounded by four electron pairs, and two B atoms surrounded by only three pairs.

Compounds in Which an Atom Has More Than Eight Valence Electrons

Elements in the third or higher periods form compounds and ions in which the central element can be surrounded by more than four valence electron pairs. (Some examples are illustrated in Table 8.5.) Such compounds are often referred to as **hypervalent**, and in most cases the central atom is bonded to fluorine, chlorine, or oxygen.

It is often obvious from the formula of a compound that an octet around an atom has been exceeded. As an example, consider sulfur hexafluoride, SF_6, a gas formed by the reaction of sulfur and excess fluorine. Sulfur is the central atom in this compound, and fluorine typically bonds to only one other atom with a single electron pair bond (as in HF and CF_4). Six S—F bonds are required in SF_6, meaning there will be six electron pairs in the valence shell of the sulfur atom.

More than four groups bonded to a central atom is a reliable signal that there are more than eight electrons around a central atom. But be careful—the central atom octet can also be exceeded with four or fewer atoms bonded to the central atom. Consider three examples from Table 8.5: The central atom in SF_4, ClF_3, and XeF_2 has five electron pairs in its valence shell.

A useful observation is that *only elements of the third and higher periods in the periodic table form compounds and ions in which an octet is exceeded.* Second-period elements (B, C, N, O, F) are restricted to a maximum of eight electrons in their compounds. For example, nitrogen forms compounds and ions such as NH_3, NH_4^+, and NF_3, but NF_5 is unknown. Phosphorus, the third-period element just below

Table 8.5 Lewis Structures for Hypervalent Compounds in Which the Central Atom Exceeds an Octet

Group 4A	Group 5A	Group 6A	Group 7A	Group 8
SiF_5^- 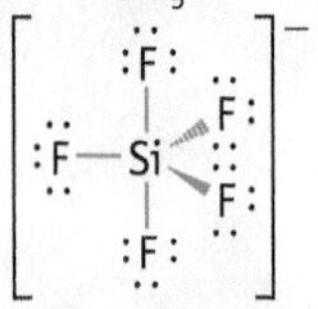	PF_5 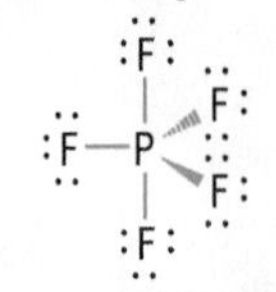	SF_4 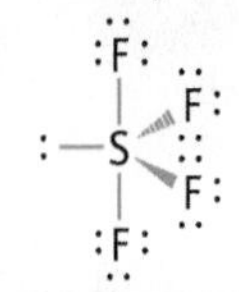	ClF_3 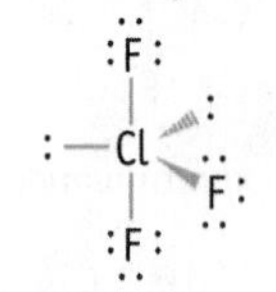	XeF_2 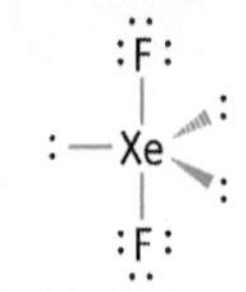
SiF_6^{2-} 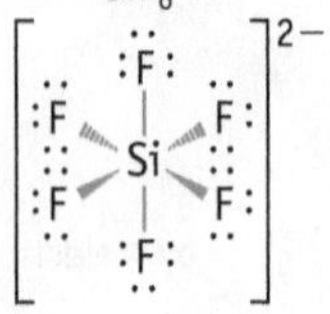	PF_6^- 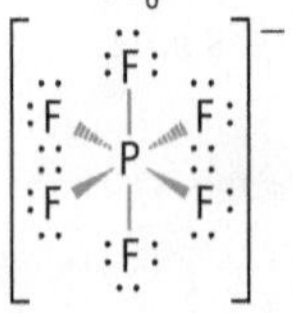	SF_6 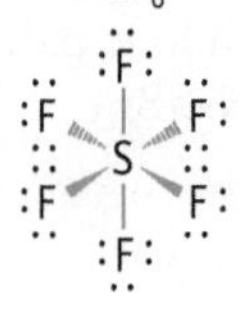	BrF_5 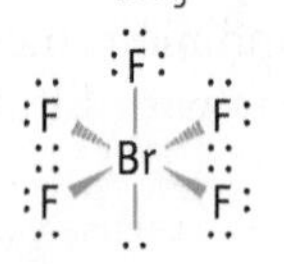	XeF_4 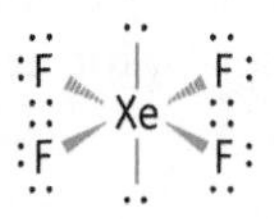

nitrogen in the periodic table, forms many compounds similar to nitrogen (PH_3, PH_4^+, PF_3), but it also readily accommodates five or six valence electron pairs in compounds such as PF_5 or in ions such as PF_6^-. Arsenic, antimony, and bismuth, the elements below phosphorus in Group 5A, resemble phosphorus in their behavior.

Xenon Compounds—More Than 8 Valence Electrons Compounds of xenon are among the more interesting entries in Table 8.5 because noble gas compounds were not discovered until the early 1960s. One of the more intriguing compounds is XeF_2, in part because of the simplicity of its synthesis: XeF_2 can be made by placing a flask containing xenon gas and fluorine gas in the sunlight. After several weeks, crystals of colorless XeF_2 are found in the flask (▶ see page 338).

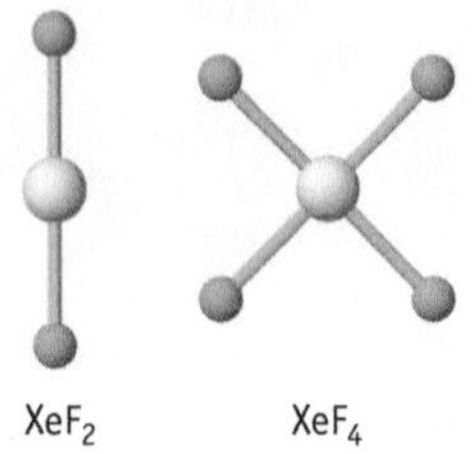

XeF_2 XeF_4

EXAMPLE 8.7

Lewis Structures in Which the Central Atom Has More Than Eight Electrons

Problem Sketch the Lewis structure of the $[ClF_4]^-$ ion.

What Do You Know? Chlorine is the central atom, bonded to four fluorine atoms. The ion has 36 valence electrons (18 pairs) [7 (for Cl) + 4 × 7 (for F) + 1 (for ion charge) = 36].

Strategy Use the guidelines in Example 8.3 to complete the structure.

Solution Draw the ion with four single covalent Cl—F bonds.

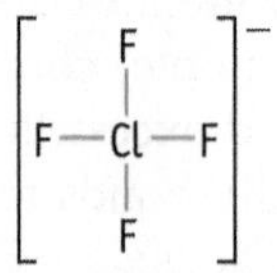

Place lone pairs on the terminal atoms. Because two electron pairs remain after placing lone pairs on the four F atoms and because we know that Cl can accommodate more than four pairs, these two pairs are placed on the central Cl atom.

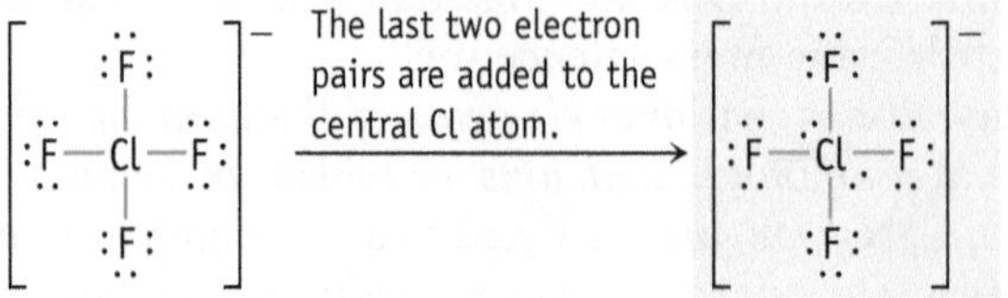

A CLOSER LOOK — Chemical Bonding Using *d* Orbitals

The usual explanation for the contrasting behavior of second- and third-period elements centers on the number of orbitals in the valence shell of an atom. Second-period elements have four valence orbitals (one 2*s* and three 2*p* orbitals). Two electrons per orbital means a total of eight electrons can be accommodated around an atom. For elements in the third and higher periods, the *d* orbitals in the outer shell are traditionally included among valence orbitals for the elements. Thus, for phosphorus, the 3*d* orbitals are included with the 3*s* and 3*p* orbitals as valence orbitals. The extra orbitals provide the element with an opportunity to accommodate up to 12 electrons and thus form six bonds. More recent research, however, has shown that involving *d* orbitals is not necessary. Bonding in species such as SF_4, XeF_2, and SiF_6^{2-} can be adequately explained using only *s* and *p* orbitals. See page 364.

Think about Your Answer The central atom, chlorine, has more than 8 electrons (4 bond pairs and 2 lone pairs). Because chlorine is in the third period of the periodic table, this is not unreasonable.

Check Your Understanding

Sketch the Lewis structures for $[ClF_2]^+$ and $[ClF_2]^-$. How many lone pairs and bond pairs surround the Cl atom in each ion?

Molecules with an Odd Number of Electrons

Two nitrogen oxides—NO, with 11 valence electrons, and NO_2, with 17 valence electrons—are among a very small group of stable molecules with an odd number of electrons. Because they have an odd number of electrons, it is impossible to draw a structure obeying the octet rule; at least one electron must be unpaired.

Even though NO_2 does not obey the octet rule, an electron dot structure can be written that approximates the bonding in the molecule. This Lewis structure places the unpaired electron on nitrogen, and two resonance structures show that the nitrogen-oxygen bonds are expected to be equivalent, as is observed.

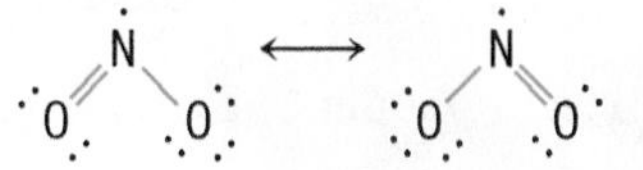

Bonding in NO_2—A Comment Evidence for the NO_2 structure in the text includes the fact that the N—O bond length is intermediate between a single and a double bond as well as the observation that two NO_2 molecules come together to give N_2O_4 with an N—N bond.

Experimental evidence for NO indicates that the bonding between N and O is intermediate between a double and a triple bond. It is not possible to write a Lewis structure for NO that reflects the properties of this substance, so a different theory is needed to understand bonding in this molecule. We shall return to compounds of this type when molecular orbital theory is introduced in Section 9-3.

The two nitrogen oxides, NO and NO_2, are members of a class of chemical substances called free radicals. A **free radical** is a chemical species with an unpaired electron, and this makes them generally quite reactive. Atoms such as H and Cl, for example, are free radicals and readily combine with each other to give molecules such as H_2, Cl_2, and HCl.

Free radicals are involved in many reactions in the environment. For example, small amounts of NO are released from vehicle exhausts. The NO rapidly forms NO_2, which is even more harmful to human health and to plants. Exposure to NO_2 at concentrations of 50–100 parts per million can lead to significant inflammation of lung tissue. Nitrogen dioxide is also generated by natural processes. For example, when hay, corn, or silage, which have a high level of nitrates, is stored in silos on farms, NO_2 can be generated as the organic material ferments, and there have been

FIGURE 8.2 Free radical chemistry. When cooled, the concentration of the brown gas NO_2 drops dramatically. Nitrogen dioxide is a free radical, and two NO_2 molecules couple to form colorless N_2O_4, a molecule with an N—N single bond. (N_2O_4 has a boiling point of about 21 °C, so it is liquid at 0 °C. This photo shows some NO_2 remains at this temperature.)

reports of farm workers dying from exposure to this gas in the silo (because NO_2 reacts with water in the lungs to produce nitric acid).

The two nitrogen oxides, NO and NO_2, are unique in that they can be isolated, and neither has the extreme reactivity of most free radicals. When cooled, however, two NO_2 molecules join or "dimerize" to form colorless N_2O_4; the unpaired electrons combine to form an N—N bond in N_2O_4 (Figure 8.2).

CASE STUDY Free Radicals, Atmospheric Chemistry, and Hair Dyes

Free radical is a term chemists use for molecules containing an unpaired electron. Such molecules are often highly reactive and are crucially important in environmental chemistry and biochemistry. One example is the hydroxyl radical, •OH. A paper in *Science* magazine called hydroxyl radicals "the 'detergent' of the atmosphere. . . . Hydroxyl radicals are the single most important oxidant in the atmosphere because they are the agent primarily responsible for removing the majority of gases emitted into the atmosphere by natural and anthropogenic activity."

The *Science* paper describes what happens when NO_2, a free radical and a common air pollutant, reacts with water in the presence of sunlight. One product is the hydroxyl radical, •OH.

$$NO_2(g) + H_2O(g) \rightarrow \cdot OH(g) + HONO(g)$$

The other product, HONO, decomposes with sunlight, to also give a hydroxyl radical and another free radical, NO.

$$HONO(g) \rightarrow \cdot OH(g) + \cdot NO(g)$$

The hydroxyl radicals then go on to react with trace gases (such as SO_2, NH_3, CO, and hydrocarbons) in the atmosphere.

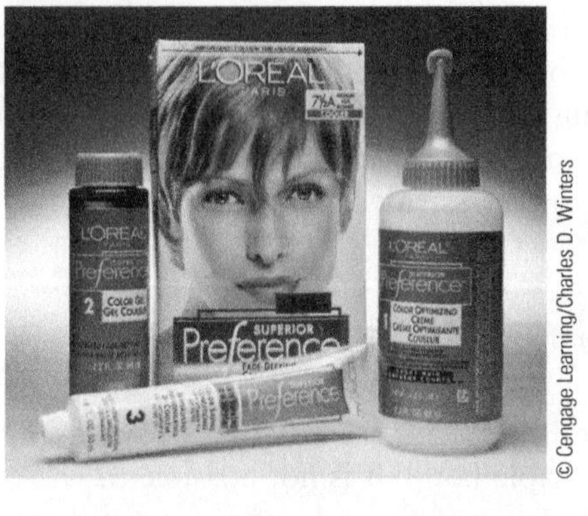

Hydroxyl radicals also play a role in dyeing your hair. Most hair dyes are a mixture of a dye, ammonia, and hydrogen peroxide (H_2O_2). These species react to produce the perhydroxyl anion (HOO^-) and the •OH radical. The HOO^- ion is a base, and the basic solution causes the hair to swell. This helps in allowing the perhydroxyl anion to react with the melamine pigment in the hair and lighten it. The problem with this approach is that the •OH radical damages hair, so chemists came up with a new product. This is a mixture of ammonium carbonate, $(NH_4)_2CO_3$, and H_2O_2 in the presence of sodium glycinate, $Na[H_2NCH_2CO_2]$. The mixture is less basic and produces the peroxymonocarbonate ion (HCO_4^-) and a carbonate radical anion ($CO_3{\cdot}^-$). The HCO_4^- ion functions as the bleach, and the glycinate ion scavenges the carbonate radicals that could otherwise damage the hair.

Questions:

1. Draw a Lewis structure for HONO. Are there any resonance structures? What is the formal charge on each atom?
2. Draw a Lewis structure for the peroxymonocarbonate ion. (One feature of this ion is a C-O-O-H grouping.) Give the formal charge on each atom and draw any resonance structures.

Answers to these questions are available in Appendix N.

References:

S. Li, J. Matthews, and A. Sinha, *Science*, 2008, *319*, 1657. See also L. Jarvis, *Chemical & Engineering News*, February 11, 2008, 32.

FIGURE 8.3 **Balloon models of electron-pair geometries for two to six electron pairs.** If two to six balloons of similar size and shape are tied together, they will naturally assume the arrangements shown. These pictures illustrate the predictions of VSEPR.

REVIEW & CHECK FOR SECTION 8-5

1. In which of the following sulfur species, SF_2, SF_3^+, SF_4, SF_5^+, and SF_6, does S exceed the octet configuration?

   (a) SF_5^+ and SF_6 (c) SF_6 only

   (b) SF_4, SF_5^+, and SF_6 (d) all five species

2. How many lone pairs of electrons are on the central atom Xe in XeF_2?

   (a) 0 (b) 1 (c) 2 (d) 3

8-6 Molecular Shapes

Learning Objectives: LO 2.21

Lewis structures show how atoms are connected in molecules and polyatomic ions. However, they do not show three-dimensional geometry, which is often crucial to molecular function. For that reason we want to take the next step: Use Lewis structures to predict three-dimensional structures.

The **valence shell electron-pair repulsion (VSEPR)** model is a method for predicting the shapes of covalent molecules and polyatomic ions. It is based on the idea that *bond and lone electron pairs in the valence shell of an element repel each other and seek to be as far apart as possible.* The positions assumed by the bond and lone electron pairs thus define the angles between bonds to surrounding atoms. VSEPR is remarkably successful in predicting structures of molecules and polyatomic ions of main group elements, although it is less effective (and seldom used) in predicting structures of compounds containing transition metals.

To have a sense of how valence shell electron pairs determine structure, blow up several balloons to a similar size. Imagine that each balloon represents an electron cloud. When two, three, four, five, or six balloons are tied together at a central point (representing the nucleus and core electrons of a central atom), the balloons naturally form the shapes shown in Figure 8.3. These geometric arrangements minimize interactions between the balloons and are the same as the arrangements of electron pairs observed in molecules.

Central Atoms Surrounded Only by Single-Bond Pairs

Figure 8.4 illustrates the geometries predicted for such molecules or polyatomic ions based on a central atom with two to six bonded atoms. For molecules with two pairs of electrons around the central atom, a linear geometry is expected, with a bond angle of 180°. Three electron pairs around a central atom leads to a trigonal planar geometry with 120° bond angles. Molecules with four electron pairs assume

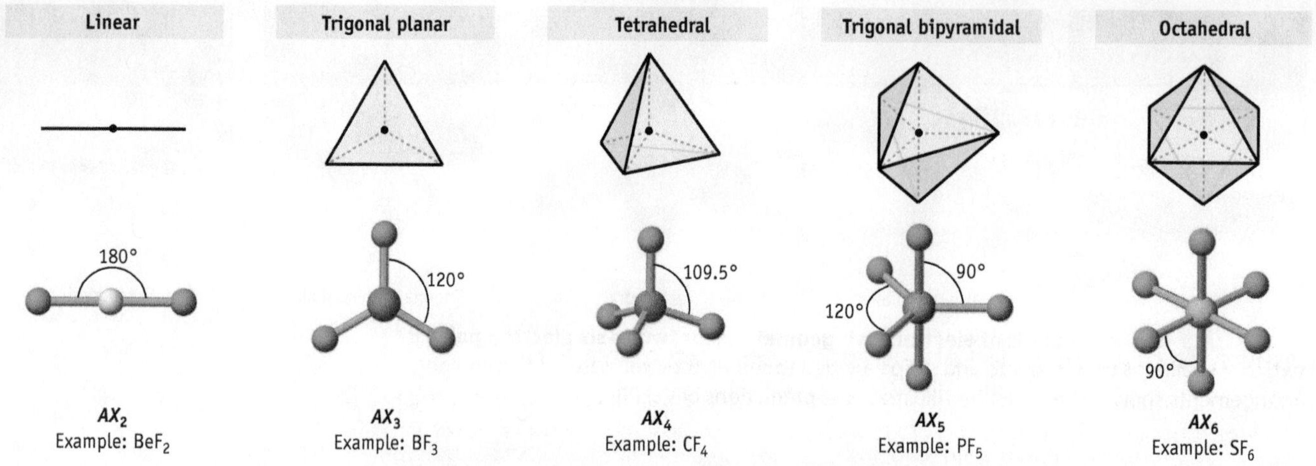

FIGURE 8.4 Geometries predicted by VSEPR. Geometries predicted by VSEPR for molecules of the type AX_n, where A is the central atom and n is the number of X groups covalently bonded to it.

a tetrahedral geometry and bond angles of 109.5°. Pay attention particularly to the three dimensionality of the tetrahedral arrangement; the importance of this geometry will become especially evident when we look at the wide range of carbon-based organic compounds. Molecules with five electron pairs around a central atom assume a trigonal bipyramidal configuration, with angles of 120° or 90°. Octahedral geometry with 90° bond angles is adopted if there are six electron pairs surrounding a central atom.

EXAMPLE 8.8

Predicting Molecular Shapes

Problem Predict the shape of silicon tetrachloride, $SiCl_4$.

What Do You Know? You know the compound's formula and the number of valence electrons. In $SiCl_4$ there are 32 valence electrons or 16 pairs, and Si is the central atom.

Strategy The first step is to draw the Lewis structure. Don't worry about drawing it in any particular way because its purpose is only to describe the number of bonds around an atom and to determine if there are any lone pairs, particularly on the central atom. The shape of the molecule is dictated by the positions of the bond and lone electron pairs on the central atom.

Solution The Lewis structure of $SiCl_4$ has four electron pairs, all of them bond pairs, around the central Si atom. Therefore, a tetrahedral structure is predicted for the $SiCl_4$ molecule, with Cl—Si—Cl bond angles of 109.5°. This agrees with the actual structure for $SiCl_4$.

Lewis structure Molecular geometry

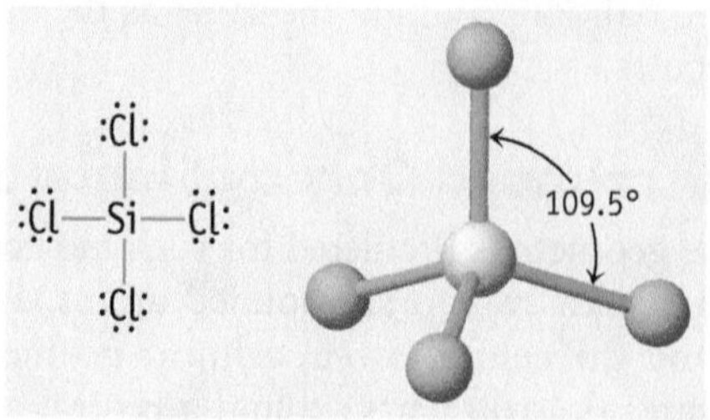

Think about Your Answer Be sure to recognize that all four positions in a tetrahedral geometry are equivalent.

Check Your Understanding

What is the shape of the dichloromethane (CH_2Cl_2) molecule? Predict the Cl—C—Cl bond angle.

Central Atoms with Single-Bond Pairs and Lone Pairs

To see how lone pairs affect the geometry of a molecule or polyatomic ion, return to the balloon models in Figure 8.3. If you assume the balloons represent *all* the electron pairs in the valence shell, the model predicts the "electron-pair geometry" of the molecule or ion. The **electron-pair geometry** is the geometry assumed by *all* the valence electron pairs around a central atom (both bond and lone pairs). This is different than the **molecular geometry**, which describes only the geometry of the central atom and the atoms directly attached to it. It is important to recognize that *lone pairs of electrons on the central atom occupy spatial positions, but their location is not included in the verbal description of the shape of the molecule or ion.*

Let us use the VSEPR model to predict the molecular geometry and bond angles in the NH_3 molecule. On drawing the Lewis structure, we see there are four pairs of electrons surrounding the central nitrogen atom: three bond pairs and one lone pair. Thus, the predicted *electron-pair geometry* is *tetrahedral*. The *molecular geometry*, however, is said to be *trigonal pyramidal* because that describes the location of the atoms. The nitrogen atom is at the apex of the pyramid, and the three hydrogen atoms form the trigonal base.

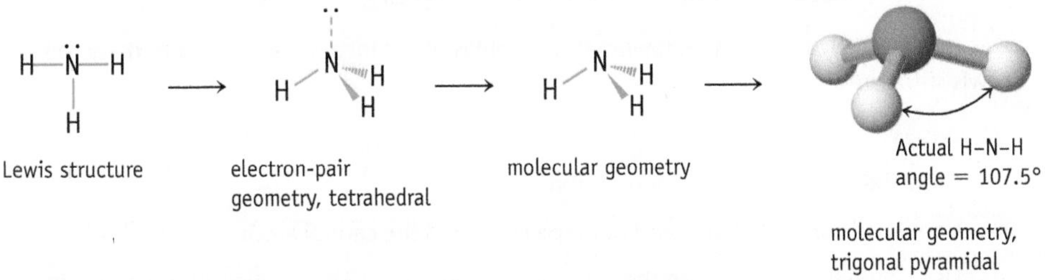

Effect of Lone Pairs on Bond Angles

Because the electron-pair geometry in NH_3 is tetrahedral, we would expect the H—N—H bond angle to be 109.5°. However, the experimentally determined bond angles in NH_3 are 107.5°, and the H—O—H angle in water is smaller still (104.5°) (Figure 8.5). These angles are close to the tetrahedral angle but not exactly that value. This highlights the fact that VSEPR theory does not give exact bond angles; it can only predict approximate geometry. Small variations in geometry are quite common and arise because there is a difference between the spatial requirements of lone pairs and bond pairs. Lone pairs of electrons seem to occupy a larger volume than bonding pairs, and the increased volume of lone pairs causes bond pairs to squeeze closer together. In general, the relative strengths of repulsions that determine the overall structure and the bond angles are in the order

$$\text{Lone pair–lone pair} > \text{lone pair–bond pair} > \text{bond pair–bond pair}$$

This is clearly seen in the decrease in bond angles in the series CH_4, NH_3, and H_2O as the number of lone pairs on the central atom increases (Figure 8.5).

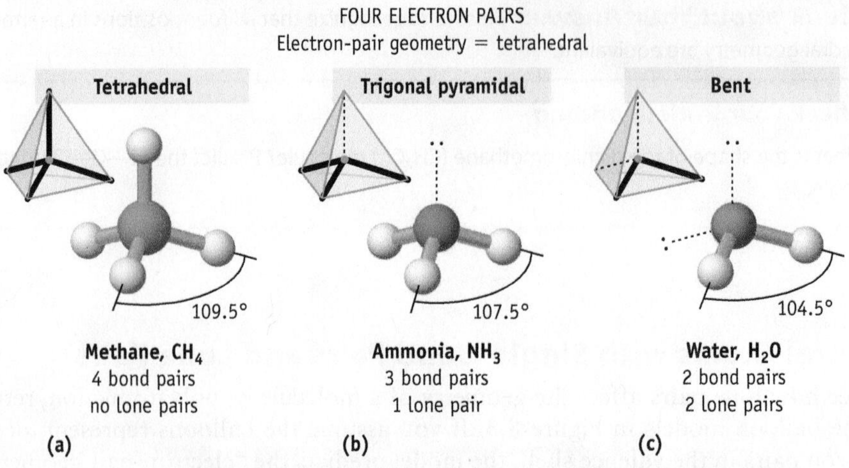

FIGURE 8.5 The molecular geometries of methane, ammonia, and water. All have four electron pairs around the central atom and have a tetrahedral electron-pair geometry. The decrease in bond angles in the series can be explained by the fact that the lone pairs have a larger spatial requirement than the bond pairs. **(a)** Methane has four bond pairs, so it has a tetrahedral molecular shape. **(b)** Ammonia has three bond pairs and one lone pair, so it has a trigonal-pyramidal molecular shape. **(c)** Water has two bond pairs and two lone pairs, so it has a bent, or angular, molecular shape.

Strategy Map 8.9

PROBLEM

Determine the **molecular geometry** of H_3O^+.

DATA/INFORMATION

- **Formula** of the ion (H_3O^+).

STEP 1. Draw the **Lewis electron dot structure.**

Lewis structure

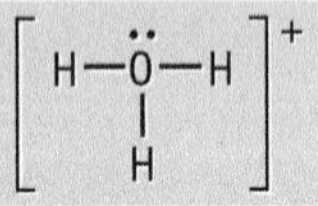

STEP 2. Count the number of **bond** and **lone pairs** on the *central atom.*

In this ion there are ***three* bond pairs** and ***one* lone pair.**

STEP 3. Decide on the **electron-pair geometry.**

Four pairs = **tetrahedral** electron-pair geometry

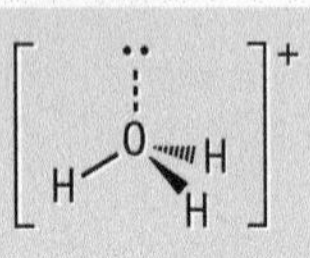

STEP 4. Decide on the **molecular geometry.**

The molecular geometry is **trigonal pyramidal.**

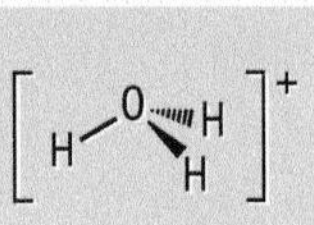

EXAMPLE 8.9

Predicting the Shapes of Molecules and Polyatomic Ions

Problem What are the shapes of the ions H_3O^+ and ClF_2^+?

What Do You Know? Knowing the formulas of the ions will allow you to draw the Lewis structures.

Strategy

- Draw the Lewis structures for each ion.
- Count the number of lone and bond pairs around the central atom.
- Use Figure 8.4 to decide on the electron-pair geometry. The location of the atoms in the ion gives the molecular geometry of the ion.

Solution

(a) The Lewis structure for H_3O^+ shows the oxygen atom is surrounded by four electron pairs, so the electron-pair geometry is tetrahedral. Because three of the four pairs are used to bond terminal atoms, the central O atom and the three H atoms form a trigonal-pyramidal molecular shape like that of NH_3.

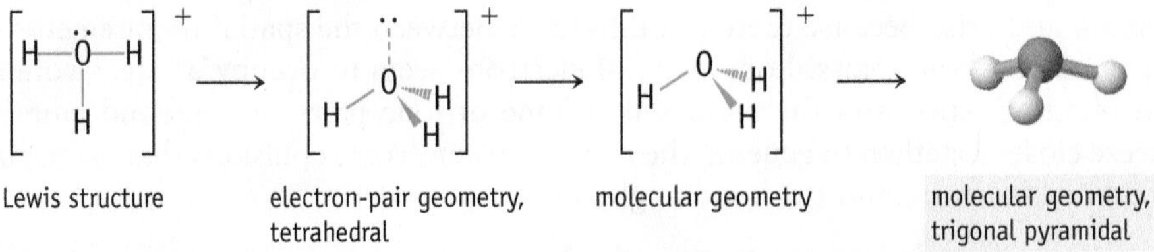

(b) Chlorine, the central atom in ClF_2^+ is surrounded by four electron pairs, so the electron-pair geometry around chlorine is tetrahedral. Because only two of the four pairs are bonding pairs, the ion has a bent geometry.

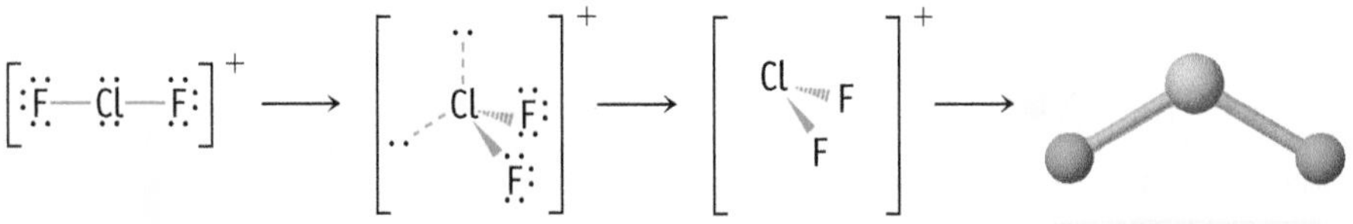

Think about Your Answer In each of these ions the occurrence of lone pairs on the central atom influences the molecular geometry. In both ions the angle (H–O–H or F–Cl–F) is likely to be slightly less than 109.5°.

Check Your Understanding

Give the electron-pair geometry and molecular shape for BF_3 and BF_4^-. What is the effect on the molecular geometry of adding an F^- ion to BF_3 to give BF_4^-?

Central Atoms with More Than Four Valence Electron Pairs

What structures are observed if the central atom has five or six electron pairs, some of which are lone pairs? A trigonal-bipyramidal structure (Figures 8.4 and 8.6) has two sets of positions that are not equivalent. The positions in the trigonal plane lie in the equator of an imaginary sphere around the central atom and are called *equatorial* positions. The north and south poles in this representation are called *axial* positions. Each equatorial atom has two neighboring groups (the axial atoms) at 90°, and each axial atom has three groups (the equatorial atoms) at 90°. If lone pairs are present in the valence shell, they require more space than bonding pairs and so prefer to occupy equatorial positions rather than axial positions.

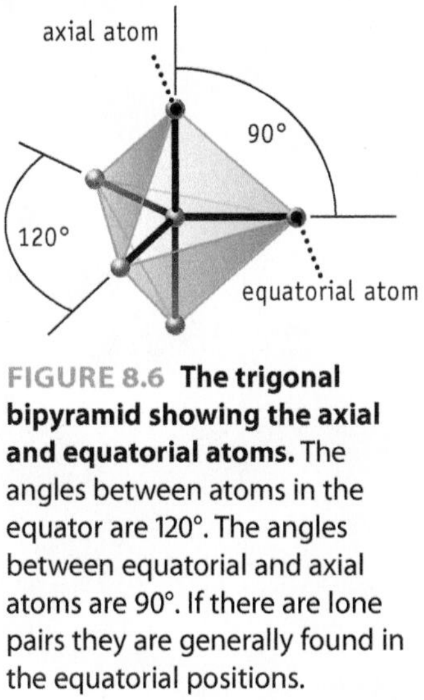

FIGURE 8.6 **The trigonal bipyramid showing the axial and equatorial atoms.** The angles between atoms in the equator are 120°. The angles between equatorial and axial atoms are 90°. If there are lone pairs they are generally found in the equatorial positions.

The entries in the top row of Figure 8.7 show species having a total of five valence electron pairs, with zero, one, two, and three lone pairs. In SF_4, with one lone pair, the molecule assumes a "*seesaw*" shape with the lone pair in one of the equatorial positions. The ClF_3 molecule has three bond pairs and two lone pairs. The two lone pairs in ClF_3 are in equatorial positions; two bond pairs are axial, and the third is in the equatorial plane, so the molecular geometry is *T-shaped*. The third molecule shown is XeF_2. Here, all three equatorial positions are occupied by lone pairs, so the molecular geometry is *linear*.

The geometry assumed by six electron pairs is *octahedral* (Figure 8.7), and all the angles at adjacent positions are 90°. Unlike the trigonal bipyramid, all positions in the octahedron are the same. Therefore, if the molecule has one lone pair, as in BrF_5, it makes no difference which position it occupies. The lone pair is often drawn in the top or bottom position to make it easier to visualize the molecular geometry, which in this case is *square pyramidal*. If two pairs of electrons in an octahedral arrangement are lone pairs, they seek to be as far apart as possible. The result is a *square planar* molecule, as illustrated by XeF_4.

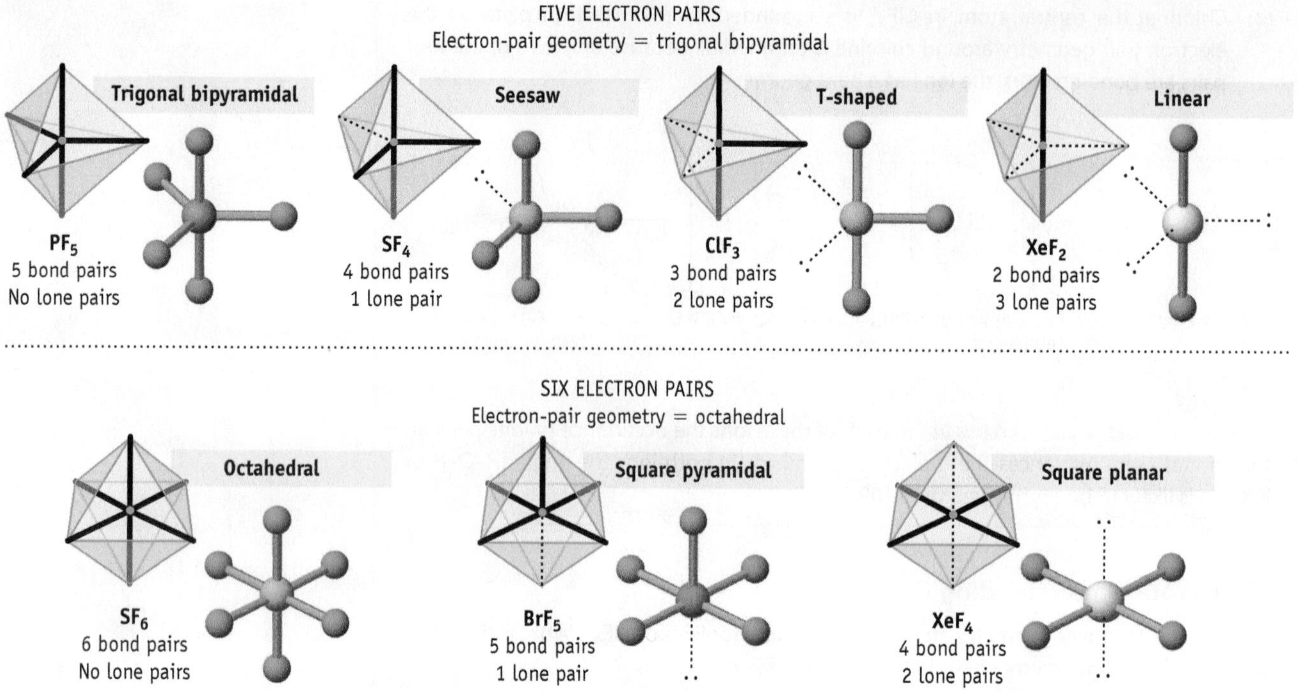

FIGURE 8.7 Electron-pair and molecular geometries for molecules and ions with five or six electron pairs around the central atom.

EXAMPLE 8.10

Predicting Molecular Shape

Problem What is the shape of the ICl_4^- ion?

What Do You Know? You know the number of valence electrons, so you can draw the Lewis electron dot structure.

Strategy Draw the Lewis structure, and then decide on the electron-pair geometry. The position of the atoms gives the molecular geometry of the ion (see Example 8.7 and Figure 8.7).

Solution A Lewis structure for the ICl_4^- ion shows that the central iodine atom has six electron pairs in its valence shell. Two of these are lone pairs. Placing the lone pairs on opposite sides leaves the four chlorine atoms in a square-planar geometry.

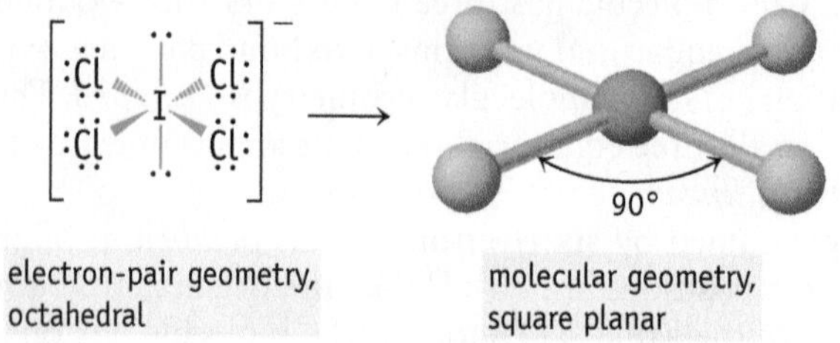

Think about Your Answer Square-planar geometry allows the two lone pairs on the central atom to be as far apart as possible.

Check Your Understanding

Draw the Lewis structure for ICl_2^-, and then decide on the geometry of the ion.

Multiple Bonds and Molecular Geometry

Double and triple bonds involve more electron pairs than single bonds, but this has little effect on the overall molecular shape. *All the electron pairs in a multiple bond are shared between the same two nuclei and occupy the same region of space.* Therefore, all electron pairs in a multiple bond count as one bonding group and affect the molecular geometry the same as a single bond does. For example, the carbon atom in CO_2 has no lone pairs and participates in two double bonds. Each double bond is a region of electron density and effectively counts as one bond for the purpose of predicting geometry; the structure of CO_2 is *linear.*

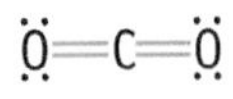

Lewis structure, electron-pair geometry = linear

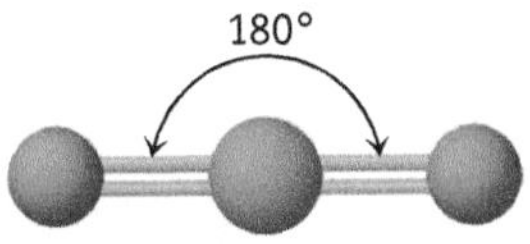

molecular structure, linear

When resonance structures are possible, the geometry can be predicted from any of the Lewis resonance structures or from the resonance hybrid structure. For example, the geometry of the CO_3^{2-} ion is predicted to be *trigonal planar* because the carbon atom has three sets of bonds and no lone pairs.

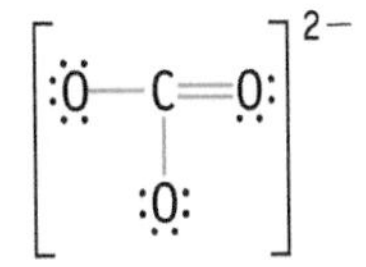

Lewis structure, one resonance structure, electron-pair geometry = trigonal planar

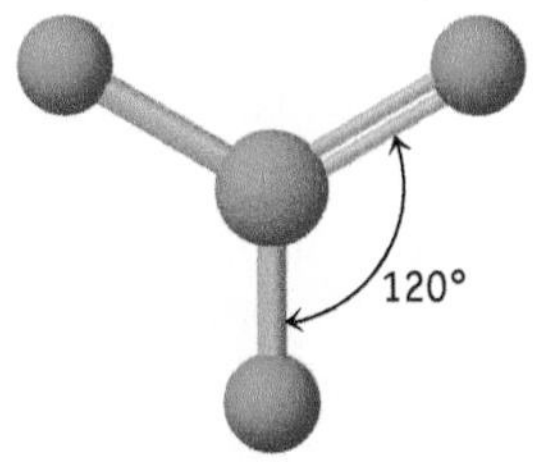

molecular structure, trigonal planar

The NO_2^- ion also has a trigonal-planar electron-pair geometry. Because there is a lone pair on the central nitrogen atom, and bonds in the other two positions, the geometry of the ion is *angular or bent.*

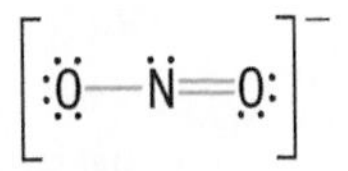

Lewis structure, one resonance structure, electron-pair geometry = trigonal planar

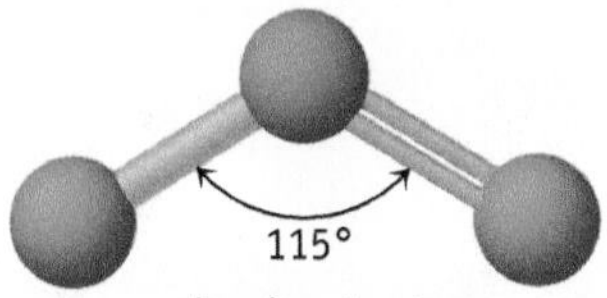

molecular structure, angular or bent

The techniques just outlined can be used to find the geometries around the atoms in more complicated molecules. Consider, for example, cysteine, one of the natural amino acids. Four pairs of electrons occur around the S, N, C_2, and C_3 atoms, and around the oxygen attached to the hydrogen, so the electron-pair geometry around each is tetrahedral. Thus, all of the angles in the molecule are predicted to be approximately 109° except for the angles around C_1, which are 120° because the electron-pair geometry around C_1 is trigonal planar.

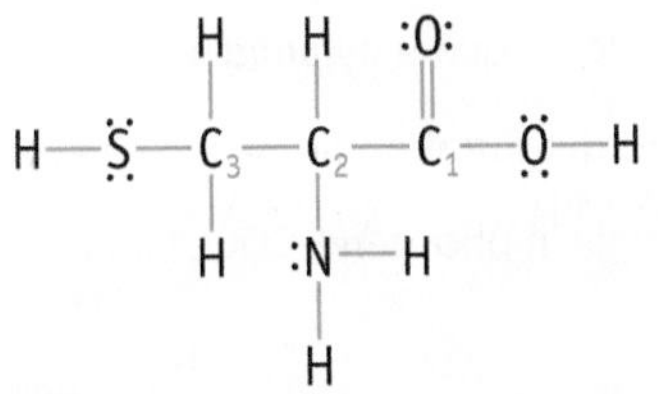

Cysteine, $HSCH_2CH(NH_2)CO_2H$

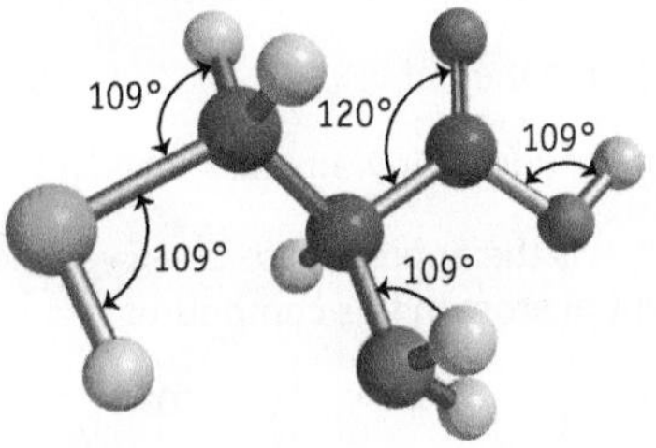

EXAMPLE 8.11

Finding the Shapes of Molecules and Polyatomic Ions

Problem What is the shape of the nitrate ion, NO_3^-? And of the molecule $XeOF_4$?

What Do You Know? You know the number of valence electrons in each species. Also, note in the discussion above that multiple bonds are treated as one bonding group in determining geometry.

Strategy Questions on molecular structure can be answered using the following roadmap: Formula → Lewis structure → electron-pair geometry → molecular geometry.

Solution

(a) The NO_3^- and CO_3^{2-} ions are isoelectronic (both having 32 electrons). Thus, like the carbonate ion described in the text above, the electron-pair geometry and molecular shape of NO_3^- are trigonal planar.

(b) The $XeOF_4$ molecule has a Lewis structure with a total of six electron pairs about the central Xe atom, one of which is a lone pair. It has a square-pyramidal molecular structure.

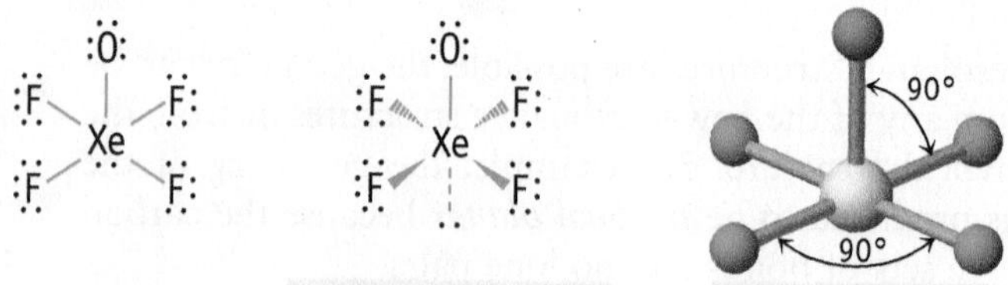

Lewis structure | electron-pair geometry, octahedral | molecular geometry, square pyramidal

Think about Your Answer Two structures are possible for $XeOF_4$ based on the position occupied by the oxygen atom, but there is no way to predict which is correct. The actual structure is the one shown, with the oxygen in the apex of the square pyramid.

Check Your Understanding

Use Lewis structures and the VSEPR model to determine the electron-pair and molecular geometries for (a) the phosphate ion, PO_4^{3-}; (b) the sulfite ion, SO_3^{2-}; and (c) IF_5.

REVIEW & CHECK FOR SECTION 8-6

1. Which of the following species has trigonal-pyramidal geometry?

   (a) PCl_3 (b) BCl_3 (c) SO_3 (d) ClF_3

2. What is the molecular geometry of the SbF_5^{2-} ion?

   (a) octahedral (c) square pyramidal
   (b) trigonal bipyramidal (d) tetrahedral

3. What is the approximate Cl—C—Cl bond angle in phosgene, $COCl_2$? (Carbon is the central atom in this compound.)

   (a) 90° (b) 109.5° (c) 120° (d) 180°

4. What is the molecular geometry of N_2O (where the atoms are connected in the order NNO)?

   (a) linear, 180° angle (c) bent, 90° angle
   (b) bent, 109.5° angle (d) bent, 120° angle

Learning Objectives: LO 2.17, LO 2.18, LO 2.21

8-7 Bond Polarity and Electronegativity

"Pure" covalent bonding, in which atoms share an electron pair *equally*, occurs *only* when two identical atoms are bonded. When two dissimilar atoms form a covalent bond, the electron pair will be unequally shared. The result is a **polar covalent bond,** a bond in which the two atoms have partial electrostatic charges (Figure 8.8).

Bonds are polar because not all atoms hold onto their valence electrons with the same force or take on additional electrons with equal ease. Recall from the discussion of atom properties that different elements have different values of ionization energy and electron affinity (electron attachment enthalpy) (Section 7-5). These differences in behavior for free atoms carry over to atoms in molecules.

If a bond pair is not equally shared between atoms, the bonding electrons are on average nearer to one of the atoms. The atom toward which the pair is displaced has a larger share of the electron pair and so has a partial negative charge. At the same time, the atom at the other end of the bond is depleted in electrons and has a partial positive charge. The bond between the two atoms is **polar**; that is, it has a positive end and a negative end.

In ionic compounds, displacement of the bonding pair to one of the two atoms is complete, and + and − symbols are written alongside the atom symbols in the Lewis drawings. For a polar covalent bond, the polarity is indicated by writing the symbols δ^+ and δ^- alongside the atom symbols, where δ (the Greek lowercase letter "delta") stands for a *partial* charge. With so many atoms to use in covalent bond formation, it is not surprising that bonds between atoms can fall anywhere in a continuum from completely covalent to completely ionic (Figure 8.9 and *A Closer Look: A Triangular View of Chemical Bonding*, page 284).

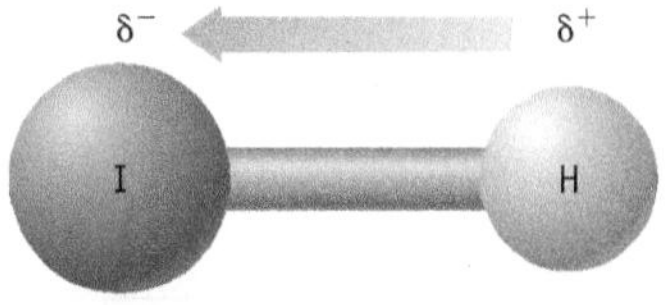

FIGURE 8.8 **A polar covalent bond.** Iodine has a larger share of the bonding electrons, and hydrogen has a smaller share. The result is that I has a partial negative charge (δ^-), and H has an equal partial positive charge (δ^+). Sometimes bond polarity is shown by an arrow pointing from + to −.

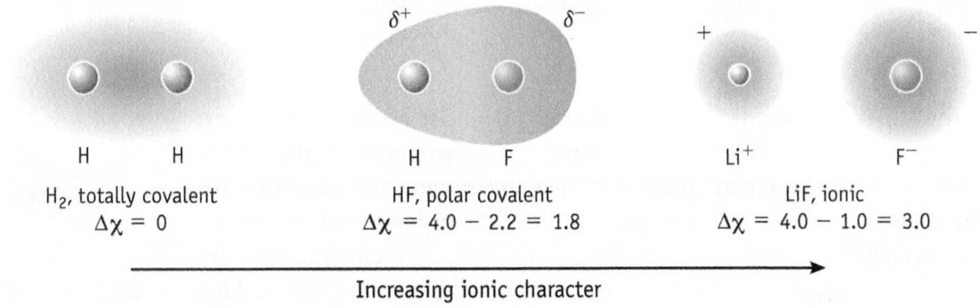

FIGURE 8.9 **Covalent to ionic bonding.** As the electronegativity difference increases between the atoms of a bond, the bond becomes increasingly ionic.

In the 1930s, Linus Pauling proposed a parameter called *atom electronegativity* that allows us to decide if a bond is polar, which atom of the bond is partially negative and which is partially positive, and if one bond is more polar than another. The **electronegativity,** χ, of an atom is defined as a measure of *the ability of an atom in a molecule to attract electrons to itself.*

Looking at the values of electronegativity in Figure 8.10 you will notice several important features:

- Fluorine has the largest value of electronegativity; it is assigned a value of χ = 4.0. The element with the smallest value is the alkali metal cesium.
- Electronegativities generally increase from left to right across a period and decrease down a group. This is the opposite of the trend observed for metallic character.
- Metals typically have low values of electronegativity, ranging from slightly less than 1 to about 2.
- Electronegativity values for the metalloids are around 2, whereas nonmetals have values greater than 2.

Notice that there is a large *difference* in electronegativity for atoms from the left and right sides of the periodic table. For cesium fluoride, for example, the difference in electronegativity values, $\Delta\chi$, is 3.2 [= 4.0 (for F) − 0.8 (for Cs)]. Bonding in CsF is decidedly ionic, with Cs the cation (Cs^+) and F the anion (F^-). In contrast, the electronegativity difference between H and F in HF is only 1.8 [= 4.0 (for F) − 2.2

Metals have low values

Metalloids have intermediate values

Increasing electronegativity →

H 2.2

1A	2A	3B	4B	5B	6B	7B	8B	8B	8B	1B	2B	3A	4A	5A	6A	7A
Li 1.0	Be 1.6											B 2.0	C 2.5	N 3.0	O 3.5	F 4.0
Na 0.9	Mg 1.3											Al 1.6	Si 1.9	P 2.2	S 2.6	Cl 3.2
K 0.8	Ca 1.0	Sc 1.4	Ti 1.5	V 1.6	Cr 1.7	Mn 1.5	Fe 1.8	Co 1.9	Ni 1.9	Cu 1.9	Zn 1.6	Ga 1.8	Ge 2.0	As 2.2	Se 2.6	Br 3.0
Rb 0.8	Sr 1.0	Y 1.2	Zr 1.3	Nb 1.6	Mo 2.2	Tc 1.9	Ru 2.2	Rh 2.3	Pd 2.2	Ag 1.9	Cd 1.7	In 1.8	Sn 2.0	Sb 1.9	Te 2.1	I 2.7
Cs 0.8	Ba 0.9	La 1.1	Hf 1.3	Ta 1.5	W 2.4	Re 1.9	Os 2.2	Ir 2.2	Pt 2.3	Au 2.5	Hg 2.0	Tl 1.6	Pb 2.3	Bi 2.0	Po 2.0	At 2.2

Increasing electronegativity ↑

Nonmetals have high values

<1.0 | 1.0–1.4 | 1.5–1.9 | 2.0–2.4 | 2.5–2.9 | 3.0–4.0

FIGURE 8.10 Pauling electronegativity values for the elements. (Values are also available for the noble gases and the lanthanides and actinides. The values in this table are from J. Emsley, *The Elements*, 3rd ed., Clarendon Press, Oxford, 1998.)

(for H)]. We conclude that bonding in HF must be more covalent, as expected for a compound formed from two nonmetals. However, because the electronegativities of hydrogen and fluorine are different, the H—F bond is quite polar. In a polar bond, the more electronegative atom takes on the partial negative charge, and the less electronegative atom takes on the partial positive charge. Thus, hydrogen is the positive end of this molecule and fluorine is the negative end ($H^{\delta+}$—$F^{\delta-}$).

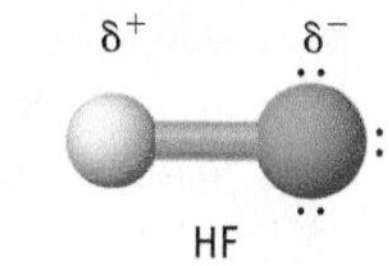

HF

EXAMPLE 8.12

Estimating Bond Polarities

Problem For each of the following bond pairs, decide which bond is more polar and indicate the negative and positive poles.

(a) B—F and B—Cl (b) Si—O and P—P

What Do You Know? You know the general trends in electronegativity and can look up the actual values in Figure 8.10.

Strategy Locate the elements in the periodic table and try to answer the questions based on general trends in electronegativity. Recall that electronegativity generally increases across a period and up a group.

Solution

(a) B and F lie relatively far apart in the periodic table. B is a metalloid, and F is a nonmetal. Here, χ for B = 2.0, and χ for F = 4.0. Similarly, B and Cl are relatively far apart in the periodic table, but Cl is below F in the periodic table (χ for Cl = 3.2) and is therefore less electronegative than F. The difference in electronegativity for B—F is 2.0, and for B—Cl it is 1.2. Both B—F and B—Cl bonds are expected to be polar, with B positive and the halide atom negative, but a B—F bond is more polar than a B—Cl bond.

(b) The P—P bond is nonpolar because the bond is between two atoms of the same kind. In the case of Si—O, the O atom has a greater electronegativity (3.5) than Si (1.9), and the bond is highly polar ($\Delta\chi = 1.6$), with O the more negative atom.

Think about Your Answer When F is one of the bonded atoms, a highly polar bond usually results. Bonds involving identical elements, as in the P—P bond in this example, will be nonpolar.

Check Your Understanding

For each of the following pairs of bonds, decide which is more polar. For each polar bond, indicate the positive and negative poles. After making your prediction from the relative atom positions in the periodic table, check your prediction by calculating $\Delta\chi$ from electronegativity values in Figure 8.10.

(a) H—F and H—I (b) B—C and B—F (c) C—Si and C—S

Charge Distribution: Combining Formal Charge and Electronegativity

The way electrons are distributed in a molecule or ion is called its **charge distribution.** Charge distribution can profoundly affect the properties of a molecule. Examples include physical properties such as melting and boiling points, and chemical properties such as susceptibility to attack by an anion or cation or whether the molecule is an acid or a base.

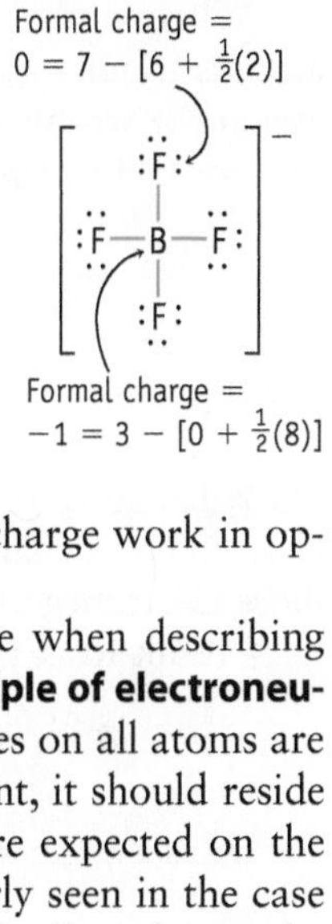

The site of a charge in a molecule or an ion can often be learned from a formal charge calculation (◀ page 296). However, it is possible to get a meaningless result from this determination because formal charge calculations assume there is equal sharing of electrons in all bonds. The BF_4^- ion illustrates this point. Boron has a formal charge of -1 in this ion, and the formal charge calculated for the fluorine atoms is 0. Based on the electronegativity difference between fluorine and boron ($\Delta\chi = 2.0$), the B—F bonds are expected to be polar with the fluorine atom the negative end of the bond ($B^{\delta+}$—$F^{\delta-}$). So, in this instance, predictions based on electronegativity and formal charge work in opposite directions.

According to Linus Pauling, there are two guidelines to use when describing charge distributions in molecules and ions. The first is the **principle of electroneutrality:** Electrons will be distributed in such a way that the charges on all atoms are as close to zero as possible. Second, if a negative charge is present, it should reside on the most electronegative atoms. Similarly, positive charges are expected on the least electronegative atoms. The effect of these principles is clearly seen in the case of BF_4^-, where it turns out that the negative charge is indeed distributed over the four fluorine atoms, as predicted by the atoms' electronegativities, rather than residing on boron, as would be predicted by formal charge calculations.

Considering the concepts of electronegativity and formal charge together can help to decide which of several resonance structures is the more important. For example, Lewis structure A for CO_2 is the logical one to draw. But what is wrong with B, in which each atom also has an octet of electrons?

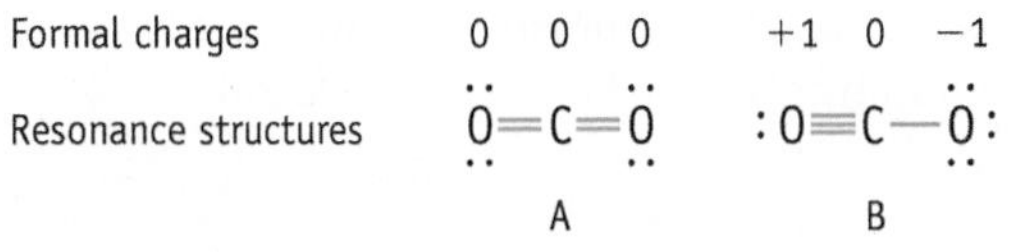

For structure A, each atom has a formal charge of 0, a favorable situation. In B, however, one oxygen atom has a formal charge of +1, and the other has −1. This is contrary to the principle of electroneutrality. In addition, B places a positive charge on an O atom, which is also unsatisfactory. Because carbon is less electronegative than oxygen, any positive charge in this molecule should be on carbon. The best description for CO_2 is structure A. At the same time, because the electronegativity of O is greater than C, the bond is polar ($C^{\delta+}—O^{\delta-}$).

Now use the same logic to decide which of the three possible resonance structures for the OCN^- ion is the most reasonable. Formal charges for each atom are given above each element's symbol.

Formal charges

Resonance structures

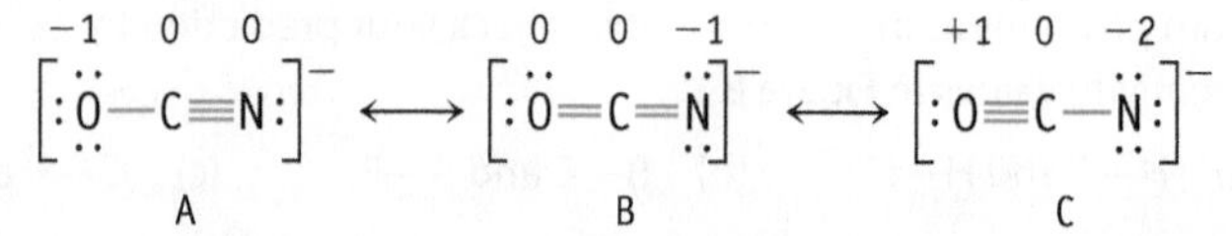

Structure C is not expected to contribute significantly to the overall electronic structure of the ion. It has a −2 formal charge on the N atom and a +1 formal charge on the O atom. Not only is the charge on the N atom high, but O is more electronegative than N and would be expected to take on a more negative charge than N. Structure A is more significant than structure B because the negative charge in A is placed on the most electronegative atom (O). We predict, therefore, that the resonance hybrid will reflect most strongly structure A and that the carbon–nitrogen bond will most resemble a triple bond. The result for OCN^- also allows us to predict that protonation of the ion will lead to HOCN and not HNCO. That is, an H^+ ion will add to the more negative oxygen atom.

When we began to discuss drawing Lewis structures we said that the central atom is usually the atom of lowest electronegativity. Let's look at a case where we assign the wrong atom as the central atom. For example, suppose the Lewis structure for CH_2O has the more electronegative O atom as the central atom.

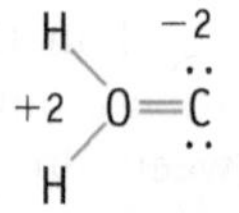

On calculating the formal charge, you would find that the very electronegative O atom has a charge of +2, and the C atom has a charge of −2. Not only does the more electronegative atom have a positive formal charge, but large formal charges (±2) result from the requirement of having an octet around carbon and oxygen.

EXAMPLE 8.13

Calculating and Using Formal Charges

Problem Boron-containing compounds often have a boron atom with only three bonds (and no lone pairs). Why not form a double bond with a terminal atom to complete the boron octet? To answer this, consider possible resonance structures of BF_3, and calculate the formal charges of the B and F atoms. Are the bonds polar in BF_3? If so, which is the more negative atom?

What Do You Know? Boron trihalides are good examples of compounds that do not obey the octet rule. The most common Lewis structure given for BF_3, for example, shows the boron atom with only three bond pairs of electrons.

Strategy

- Draw the commonly used Lewis structure for BF_3. Then draw a resonance structure (one of three possible) in which boron achieves an octet structure, using one of the electron pairs for fluorine to create a double bond between boron and fluorine.
- Determine the formal charges on each atom in the two structures.
- Decide the importance of the different resonance structures based on the positions of charges in the molecule.

Solution The two possible structures for BF_3 are illustrated here with the calculated formal charges on the B and F atoms.

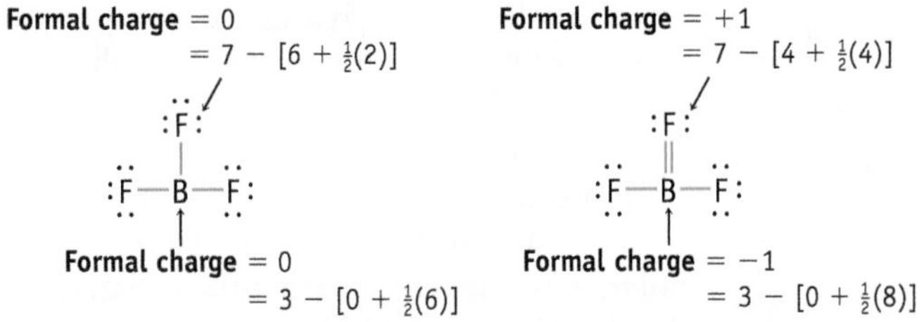

The structure on the left is strongly preferred because all atoms have a zero formal charge and the very electronegative F atom does not have a charge of +1. F ($\chi = 4.0$) is much more electronegative than B ($\chi = 2.0$), so the B—F bond is highly polar, the F atom being partially negative and the B atom partially positive.

Think about Your Answer We can clearly say that the BF_3 structure with three single bonds is strongly preferred. However, there is experimental evidence that the B—F bonds in BF_3 do have a slight amount of double bond character in spite of an unfavorable charge distribution.

Check Your Understanding

Draw the resonance structures for SCN^-. What are the formal charges on each atom in each resonance structure? What are the bond polarities? Do they agree with the formal charges?

REVIEW & CHECK FOR SECTION 8-7

1. Which bond among those listed below is the most polar?

   (a) C—Cl (b) Si—Cl (c) B—Cl (d) Al—Cl

2. Which of the following best describes the bonding in the compound ICl?

   (a) The I—Cl bond is not polar.

   (b) The I—Cl bond is polar with I being the negative end.

   (c) The I—Cl bond is polar with I being the positive end.

3. Three resonance forms can be drawn for the molecule N_2O. Which resonance form is likely to more closely resemble the structure of this molecule?

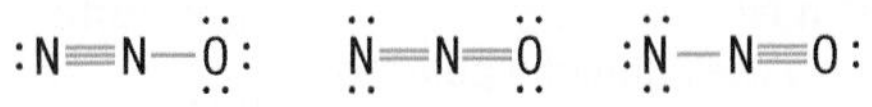

(a) (b) (c)

Learning Objectives: LO 2.21

8-8 Bond and Molecular Polarity

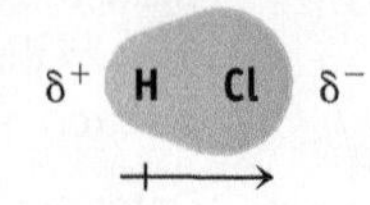

The term "polar" describes a bond in which one atom has a partial positive charge and the other a partial negative charge. Because most molecules have polar bonds, molecules as a whole can also be polar. In a polar molecule, electron density accumulates toward one side of the molecule, giving that side a partial negative charge (δ^-), and leaving the other side with an equal but positive partial charge (δ^+).

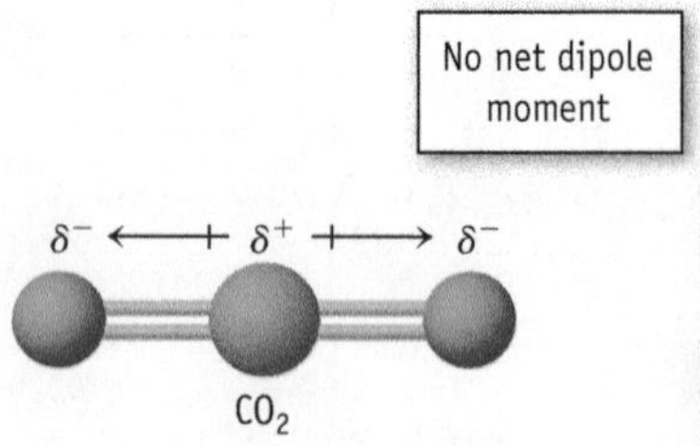

For CO_2, the CO bonds are polar, but the electron density is distributed symmetrically over the molecule, and the charges of δ− lie 180° apart. The molecule has no net dipole.

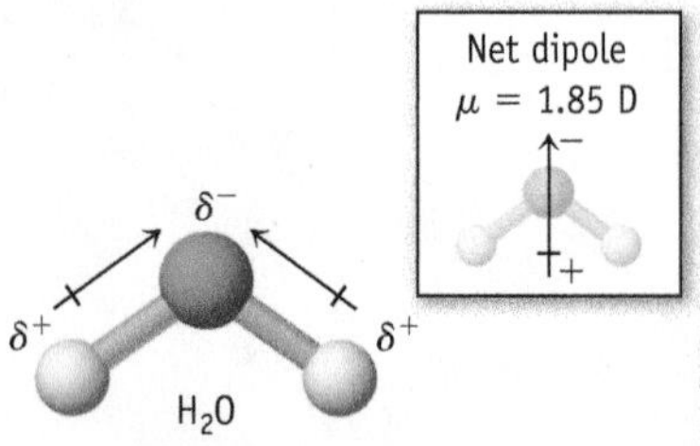

In a water molecule, the O atom is negative, and the H atoms are positive. However, the positively charged H atoms lie on one side of the molecule, and the negatively charged O atom is on the other side. The molecule is polar.

To predict if a molecule is polar, we need to consider how the atoms are positioned relative to one another. The polarity of the bonds is a secondary consideration.

Diatomic molecules composed of two atoms with different electronegativities are always polar (Table 8.6); there is one bond, and the molecule has a positive and a negative end.

But what happens with a molecule composed of three or more atoms? Consider a linear triatomic molecule such as carbon dioxide, CO_2. Here, each C═O bond is polar, with the oxygen atom the negative end of the bond dipole. The terminal O atoms are at the same distance from the C atom, they both have the same δ^- charge, and they are symmetrically arranged around the central C atom. Therefore, CO_2 has no molecular dipole, even though each bond is polar. This is analogous to a tug-of-war in which the people at opposite ends of the rope are pulling with equal force.

In contrast, water is a bent triatomic molecule. Because O has a larger electronegativity ($\chi = 3.5$) than H ($\chi = 2.2$), each of the O—H bonds is polar, with the

A CLOSER LOOK Polar Molecules in an Electric Field

Let us look at the experimental measurement of the polarity of a molecule. When placed in an electric field created by a pair of oppositely charged plates, polar molecules experience a force that tends to align them with the field. The positive end of each molecule is attracted to the negative plate, and the negative end is attracted to the positive plate. The orientation of the polar molecule affects the electrical capacitance of the plates (their ability to hold a charge), and this provides a way to measure experimentally the magnitude of the dipole moment.

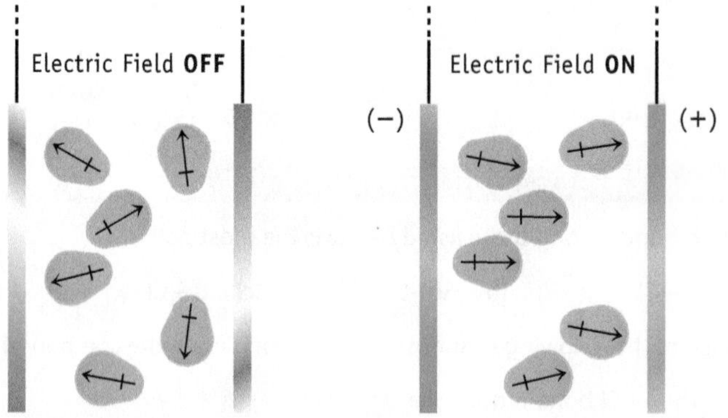

Polar molecules in an electric field.

The extent to which the molecules line up with the field depends on their **dipole moment,** μ. In a molecule with partial charges equal to $+q$ and $-q$ and in which these charges are separated by a distance, d, in the molecule, the magnitude of the dipole moment is given by the equation $\mu = q \times d$. The SI unit of the dipole moment is the coulomb-meter, but dipole moments have traditionally been given using a derived unit called the *debye* (D; $1\text{ D} = 3.34 \times 10^{-30}\text{ C}\cdot\text{m}$). Experimental values of some dipole moments are listed in Table 8.6.

The commonly used unit of dipole moments is named in honor of Peter Debye (1884–1966). Debye was born in the Netherlands and educated in Germany. He received the Nobel Prize in Chemistry in 1936 and was later a professor at Cornell University.

Table 8.6 Dipole Moments (μ) of Selected Molecules (in debye units)

Molecule (*AX*)	Moment (μ, D)	Geometry	Molecule (*AX*$_2$)	Moment (μ, D)	Geometry
HF	1.78	Linear	H_2O	1.85	Bent
HCl	1.07	Linear	H_2S	0.95	Bent
HBr	0.79	Linear	SO_2	1.62	Bent
HI	0.38	Linear	CO_2	0	Linear
H_2	0	Linear			
Molecule (*AX*$_3$)	**Moment (μ, D)**	**Geometry**	**Molecule (*AX*$_4$)**	**Moment (μ, D)**	**Geometry**
NH_3	1.47	Trigonal pyramidal	CH_4	0	Tetrahedral
NF_3	0.23	Trigonal pyramidal	CH_3Cl	1.92	Tetrahedral
BF_3	0	Trigonal planar	CH_2Cl_2	1.60	Tetrahedral
			$CHCl_3$	1.04	Tetrahedral
			CCl_4	0	Tetrahedral

H atoms having the same δ^+ charge and oxygen having a negative charge (δ^-). Electron density accumulates on the O side of the molecule, making the molecule electrically "lopsided" and therefore polar ($\mu = 1.85$ D).

In trigonal-planar BF_3, the B—F bonds are highly polar because F is much more electronegative than B (χ of B = 2.0 and χ of F = 4.0) (Figure 8.11). The molecule

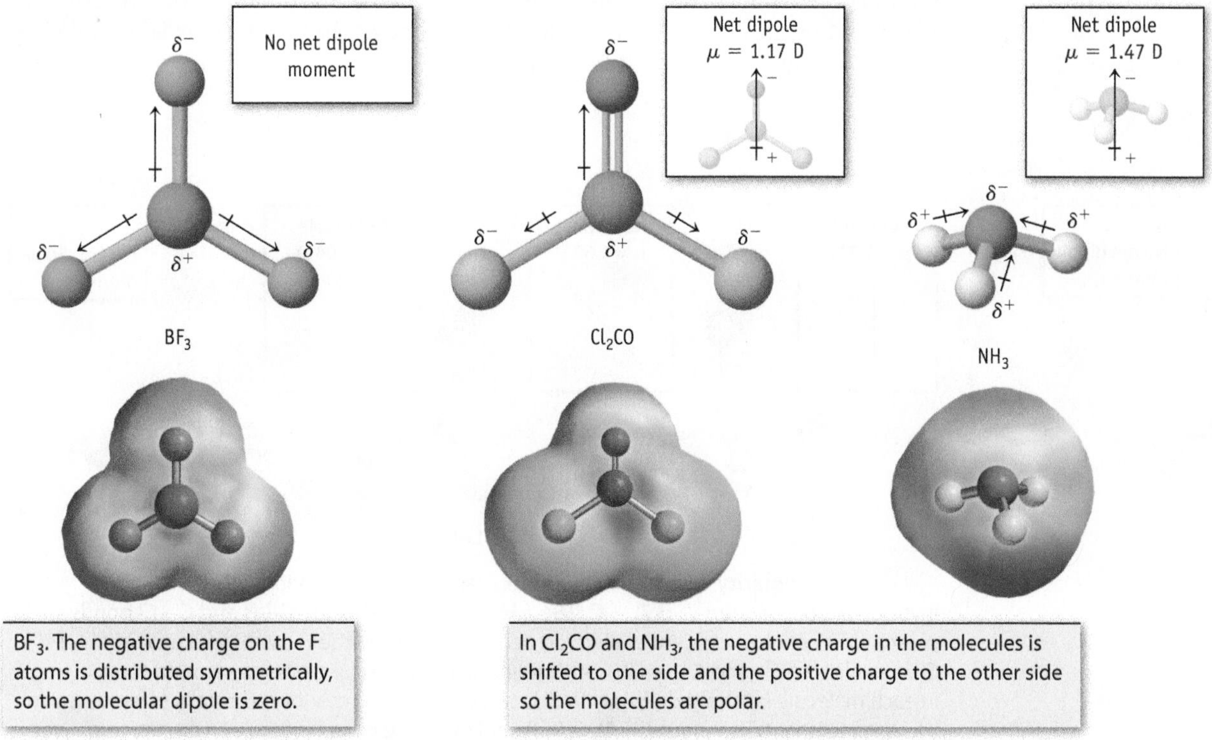

FIGURE 8.11 **Polar and nonpolar molecules of the type AX$_3$.** Charge distributions are reflected in the electrostatic potential surfaces (where a red color indicates a negative charge and blue a positive charge). (See *A Closer Look: Visualizing Charge Distributions and Molecular Polarity—Electrostatic Potential Surfaces and Partial Charge,* page 324.)

Ozone, a Surprisingly Polar Molecule Ozone, O_3, has a dipole moment of 0.53 D. In spite of having chemical bonds between identical elements, the bent structure (see page 298) results in the molecule being polar. The central O atom has a positive formal charge, whereas the two terminal O atoms have negative formal charges.

is nonpolar, however, because the three terminal F atoms have the same δ^- charge, are the same distance from the boron atom, and are arranged symmetrically around the central boron atom. In contrast, the trigonal-planar molecule phosgene is polar (Cl_2CO, μ = 1.17 D) (Figure 8.11). Here, the angles are all about 120°, so the O and Cl atoms are symmetrically arranged around the C atom. The electronegativities of the three types of atoms in the molecule differ, however: $\chi(O) > \chi(Cl) > \chi(C)$. There is therefore a net displacement of electron density away from the center of the molecule, more toward the O atom than the Cl atoms.

Ammonia, like BF_3, has AX_3 stoichiometry and polar bonds. In contrast to BF_3, however, NH_3 is a trigonal-pyramidal molecule. The positive H atoms are located in the base of the pyramid, and the negative N atom is on the apex of the pyramid. As a consequence, NH_3 is polar (Figure 8.11). Indeed, trigonal-pyramidal molecules are generally polar.

Molecules like carbon tetrachloride, CCl_4, and methane, CH_4, are nonpolar, owing to their symmetrical, tetrahedral structures. The four atoms bonded to C have the same partial charge and are the same distance from the C atom. Tetrahedral molecules with both Cl and H atoms ($CHCl_3$, CH_2Cl_2, and CH_3Cl) are polar, however (Figure 8.12). The electronegativity for H atoms (2.2) is less than that of Cl atoms (3.2), and the carbon–hydrogen distance is different from the carbon–chlorine distances. Because Cl is more electronegative than H, the Cl atoms are on the more negative side of the molecule. This means the positive end of the molecular dipole is toward the H atom.

To summarize this discussion of molecular polarity, look again at Figure 8.4 (page 308). These are sketches of molecules of the type AX_n where A is the central atom and X is a terminal atom. You can predict that a molecule AX_n will not be polar, regardless of whether the A—X bonds are polar, if

- all the terminal atoms (or groups), X, are identical, and
- all the X atoms (or groups) are arranged symmetrically around the central atom, A.

On the other hand, if one of the X atoms (or groups) is different in the structures in Figure 8.4 (as in Figures 8.11 and 8.12), or if one of the X positions is occupied by a lone pair, the molecule will be polar.

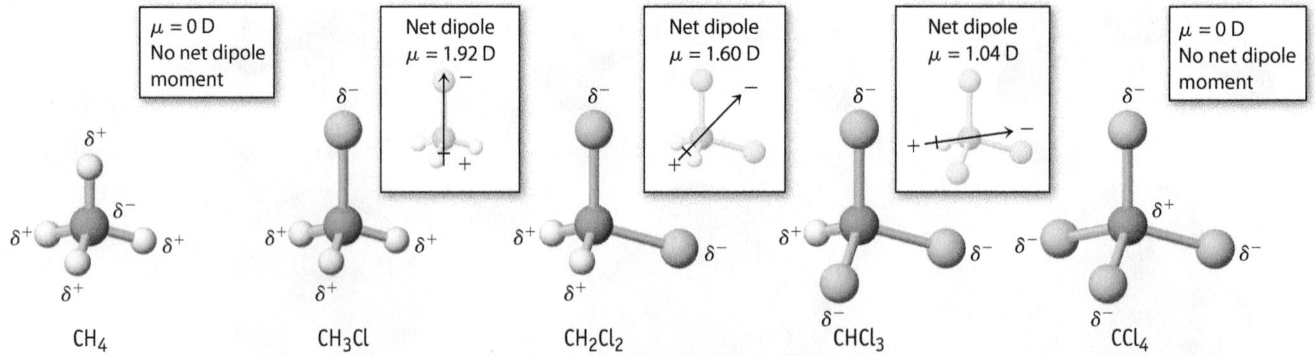

FIGURE 8.12 **Polarity of tetrahedral molecules.** The electronegativities of the atoms involved are in the order Cl (3.2) > C (2.5) > H (2.2). This means the C—H and C—Cl bonds are polar with a net displacement of electron density away from the H atoms and toward the Cl atoms [$H^{\delta+}$—$C^{\delta-}$ and $C^{\delta+}$—$Cl^{\delta-}$]. Although the electron-pair geometry around the C atom in each molecule is tetrahedral, only in CH_4 and CCl_4 are the polar bonds totally symmetrical in their arrangement. Therefore, CH_3Cl, CH_2Cl_2, and $CHCl_3$ are polar molecules, with the negative end toward the Cl atoms and the positive end toward the H atoms.

EXAMPLE 8.14

Molecular Polarity

Problem Are sulfur tetrafluoride (SF_4) and nitrogen trifluoride (NF_3) polar or nonpolar? If polar, indicate the negative and positive sides of the molecule.

What Do You Know? Based on the discussion in this chapter, you know how to derive the molecular geometry of molecules and how to decide which bonds are polar. Based on this information you can decide if the molecule is polar.

Strategy Draw the Lewis structure, decide on the electron-pair geometry, and determine the molecular geometry. Determine if the molecule is completely symmetrical. If it is, then it is nonpolar; if it is not, the molecule is polar.

Solution

(a) The S—F bonds in sulfur tetrafluoride, SF_4, are polar, the bond dipole having F as the negative end (χ for S is 2.6 and χ for F is 4.0). The molecule has a trigonal bipyramidal electron-pair geometry (Figure 8.7). Because the lone pair occupies one of the positions, the S—F bonds are not arranged symmetrically. The axial S—F bond dipoles cancel each other because they point in opposite directions. The equatorial S—F bonds, however, both point to one side of the molecule, so SF_4 is polar.

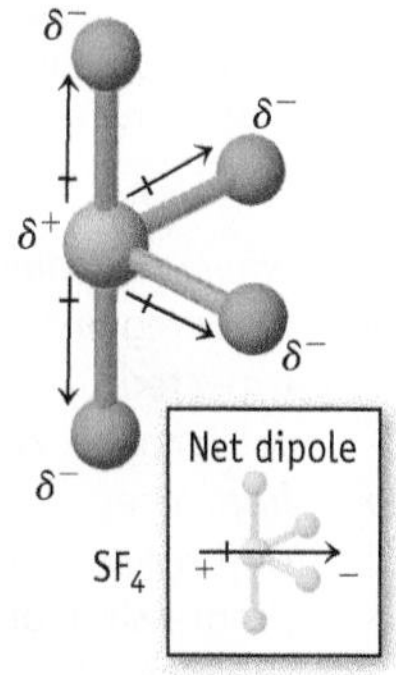

SF_4

(b) NF_3 has the same trigonal-pyramidal structure as NH_3. Because F is more electronegative than N, each bond is polar, the more negative end being the F atom. Because this molecule contains polar bonds and because the geometry is not symmetrical (three positions of the tetrahedron occupied by bonding groups and one by a lone pair), the NF_3 molecule as a whole is expected to be polar.

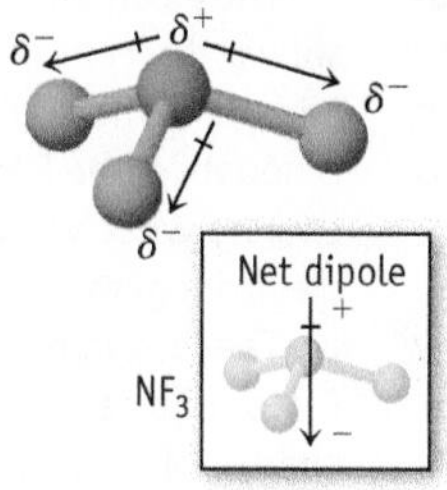

NF_3

Think about Your Answer It is interesting that the dipole moment for NF_3 is quite small (0.23 D, Table 8.6), much smaller than the dipole moment of NH_3. This illustrates *the effect of lone pairs on molecular polarity*. For NH_3, the bond polarity is $N^{\delta-}$—$H^{\delta+}$, and the dipole created by these bonds is reinforced by the negatively charged lone pair on the N atom. In contrast, the polarity of the bonds in NF_3 is $N^{\delta+}$—$F^{\delta-}$. This is counterbalanced by the lone pair, and the overall dipole is diminished. These effects are illustrated by the electrostatic potential surfaces for these two molecules.

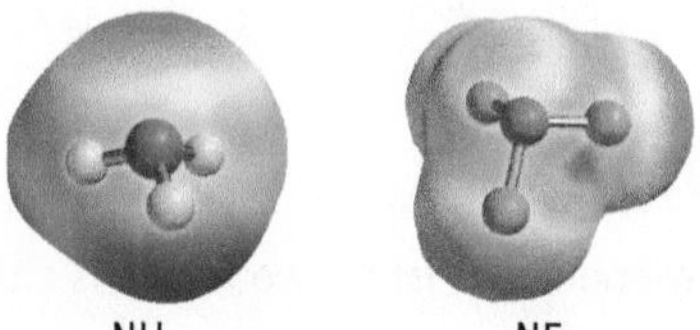

NH_3 NF_3

Ammonia, $\mu = 1.47$ D Nitrogen trifluoride, $\mu = 0.23$ D

Check Your Understanding

For each of the following molecules, decide whether the molecule is polar and which side is positive and which negative: $BFCl_2$, NH_2Cl, and SCl_2.

Strategy Map 8.14

PROBLEM

Is a molecule **polar?**

DATA/INFORMATION

Formula of the molecule (SF_4)

STEP 1. Draw the **Lewis electron dot structure.**

Lewis structure

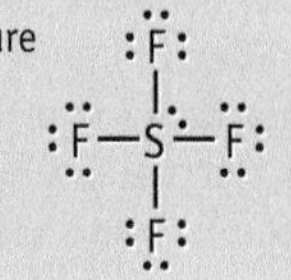

STEP 2. Decide on the **electron-pair geometry.**

Trigonal bipyramidal

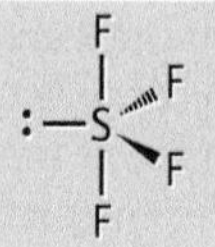

STEP 3. Decide on the **molecular geometry.**

"Seesaw"

STEP 4. Decide if the molecule is **symmetrical.**

Yes → **Not** polar

No → SF_4 is **polar**

A CLOSER LOOK — Visualizing Charge Distributions and Molecular Polarity—Electrostatic Potential Surfaces and Partial Charge

In Chapter 6, you learned about atomic orbitals. The boundary surface of these orbitals was created in such a way that the electron wave amplitude at all points of the surface was the same value. When we use advanced molecular modeling software, we can generate the same type of pictures for molecules, and in Figure A you see a surface defining the electron density in the HF molecule. The electron density surface, calculated using software from Wavefunction, is made up of all of the points in space around the HF molecule where the electron density is 0.002 $e^-/Å^3$ (where 1 Å = 0.1 nm). You can see that the surface bulges toward the F end of the molecule, an indication of the larger size of the F atom. The larger size of the F atom here is mainly related to the fact that it has more valence electrons than H, and to a lesser extent to the fact that the H—F bond is polar and electron density in that bond is shifted toward the F atom.

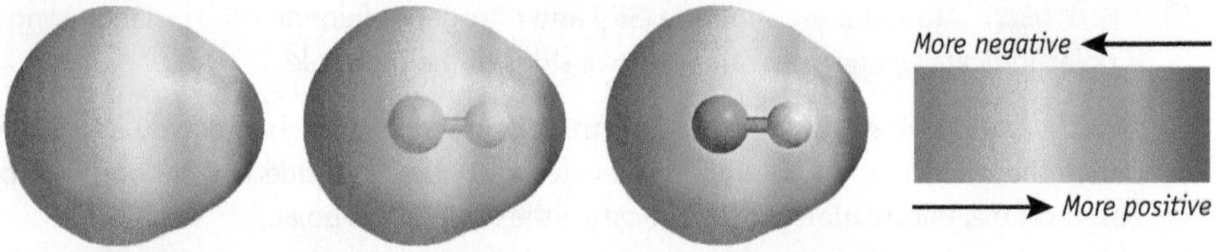

FIGURE A **Three views of the electrostatic potential surface for HF.** (*left*) The electron density surface around HF. The F atom is at the left. The surface is made up of all of the points in space around the HF molecule where the electron density is 0.002 $e^-/Å^3$ (where 1 Å = 0.1 nm). (*middle*) The surface is made more transparent, so you can see the HF atom nuclei inside the surface. (*right*) The front of the electron density surface has been "peeled away" for a view of the HF molecule inside. **Color scheme:** The colors on the electron density surface reflect the charge in the different regions of the molecule. Colors toward the blue end of the spectrum indicate a positive charge, whereas colors to the red end of the spectrum indicate a negative charge.

We can add another layer of information to our picture. The electron density surface can be colored according to the *electrostatic potential.* (Hence, this figure is called an *electrostatic potential surface.*) The computer program calculates the electrostatic potential that would be observed by a proton (H^+) at every point on the surface. This is the sum of the attractive and repulsive forces on that proton due to the nuclei and the electrons in the molecule. Regions of the molecule in which there is an attractive potential are colored red. That is, this is a region of negative charge on the molecule. Repulsive potentials occur in regions where the molecule is positively charged; these regions are colored blue. As might be expected, the net electrostatic potential will change continuously as one moves from a negative portion of a molecule to a positive portion, and this is indicated by a progression of colors from red to blue (from negative to positive).

The electrostatic potential surface for HF shows the H atom is positive (the H atom end of the molecule is blue), and the F atom is negative (the F atom end is red). This is, of course, what we would predict based on electronegativity.

The program also calculated that the F atom has a charge of −0.3 and H has a charge of +0.3. Finally, the calculated dipole moment for the molecule is about 1.7 D, in good agreement with the experimental value in Table 8.6.

Other examples of electrostatic potential surfaces illustrate the polarity of water and methylamine, CH_3NH_2.

The surface for water shows the O atom of the molecule bears a partial negative charge and the H atoms are positive. The surface for the amine shows the molecule is polar and that the region around the N atom is negative. Indeed, we know from experiment that an H^+ ion will attack the N atom to give the cation $CH_3NH_3^+$.

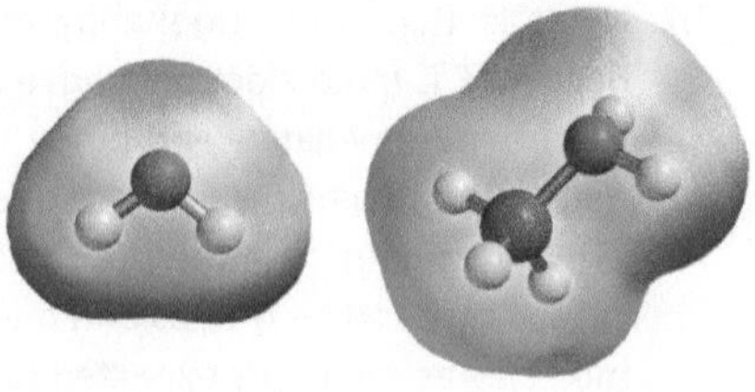

water — methylamine, CH_3NH_2

You will see many examples in this book in which electrostatic potential diagrams are used to illustrate important features of other molecules.

EXAMPLE 8.15

Molecular Polarity

Problem 1,2-Dichloroethylene can exist in two forms. Is either of these planar molecules polar?

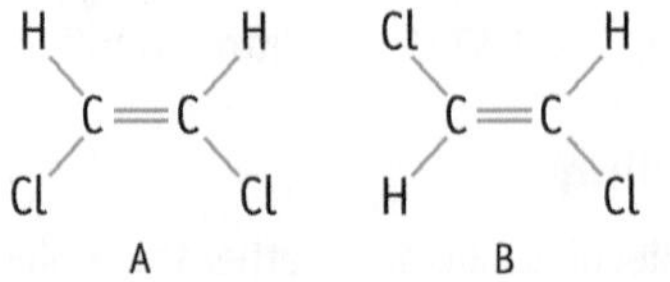

A B

What Do You Know? The structures for the two molecules are given. Note that these are planar molecules.

Strategy

- Use electronegativity values to decide on the bond polarity.
- Decide if the electron density in the bonds is distributed symmetrically or if it is shifted to one side of the molecule.

Solution Here, the H and Cl atoms are arranged around the C=C double bonds with all bond angles 120° (and all the atoms lie in one plane). The electronegativities of the atoms involved are in the order Cl (3.2) > C (2.5) > H (2.2). This means the C—H and C—Cl bonds are polar with a net displacement of electron density away from the H atoms and toward the Cl atoms [$H^{\delta+}$—$C^{\delta-}$ and $C^{\delta+}$—$Cl^{\delta-}$]. In structure A, the Cl atoms are located on one side of the molecule, so electrons in the H—C and C—Cl bonds are displaced toward the side of the molecule with Cl atoms and away from the side with the H atoms. Molecule A is polar. In molecule B, the displacement of electron density toward the Cl atom on one end of the molecule is counterbalanced by an opposing displacement on the other end. Molecule B is not polar.

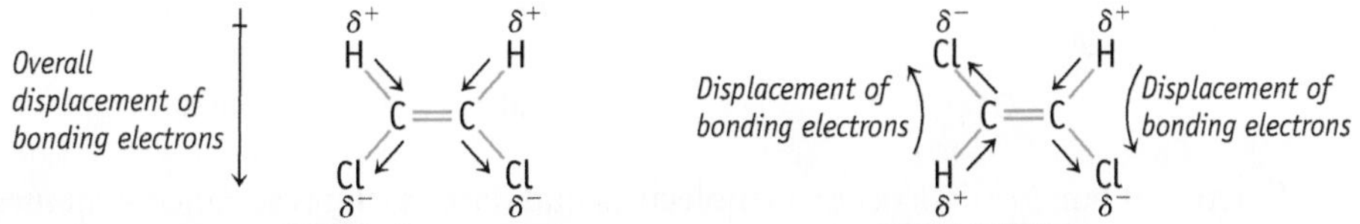

A, polar, displacement of bonding electrons to one side of the molecule

B, not polar, no net displacement of bonding electrons to one side of the molecule

Think about Your Answer The electrostatic potential surfaces reflect the fact that molecule A is polar because the electron density is shifted to one side of the molecule. Molecule B is not polar because the electron density is distributed symmetrically.

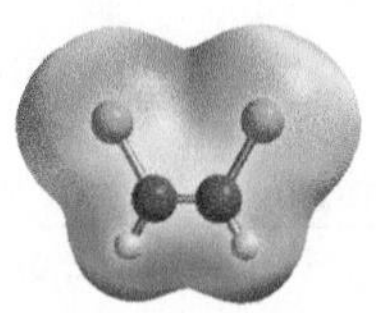

A = *cis*-1,2-dichloroethylene

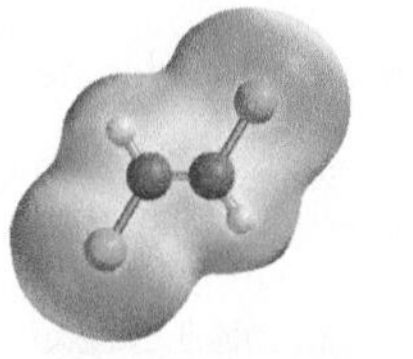

B = *trans*-1,2-dichloroethylene

Check Your Understanding

The electrostatic potential surface for $OSCl_2$ is pictured here.

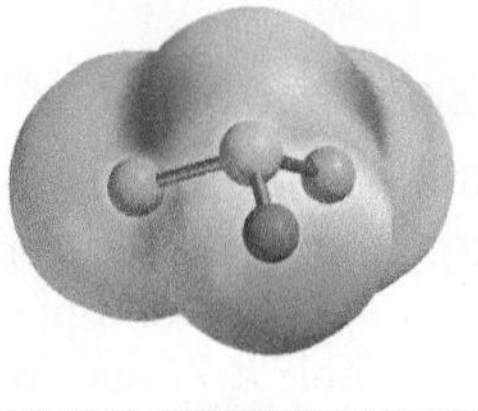

(a) Draw a Lewis electron dot picture for the molecule, and give the formal charge of each atom.

(b) What is the molecular geometry of $OSCl_2$? Is it polar?

REVIEW & CHECK FOR SECTION 8-8

1. Which of the hydrogen halides is the most polar?

   (a) HF (b) HCl (c) HBr (d) HI

2. Which of the molecules listed below is nonpolar?

   (a) BCl_3 (b) PCl_3 (c) $POCl_3$ (d) SO_2Cl_2

Learning Objectives: LO 2.21, LO 5.8

8-9 Bond Properties: Order, Length, and Energy

Bond Order

The **order of a bond** is the number of bonding electron pairs shared by two atoms in a molecule. You will encounter bond orders of 1, 2, and 3, as well as fractional bond orders.

When the bond order is 1, there is only a single covalent bond between a pair of atoms. Examples are the bonds in molecules such as H_2, NH_3, and CH_4. The bond order is 2 when two electron pairs are shared between atoms, such as the C=O bonds in CO_2 and the C=C bond in ethylene, $H_2C{=}CH_2$. The bond order is 3 when two atoms are connected by three bonds. Examples include the carbon–oxygen bond in carbon monoxide, CO, and the nitrogen–nitrogen bond in N_2.

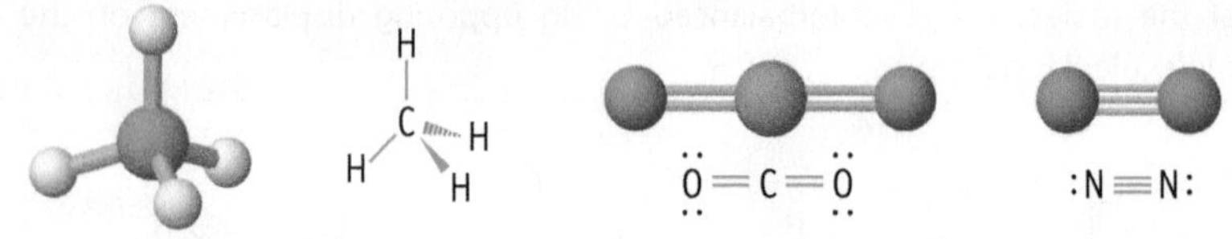

B.O. for CH = 1 B.O. for CO = 2 B.O. for NN = 3

Fractional bond orders occur in molecules and ions having resonance structures. For example, what is the bond order for each oxygen–oxygen bond in O_3? Each resonance structure of O_3 has one O—O single bond and one O=O double bond, for a total of three shared bonding pairs accounting for two oxygen–oxygen links.

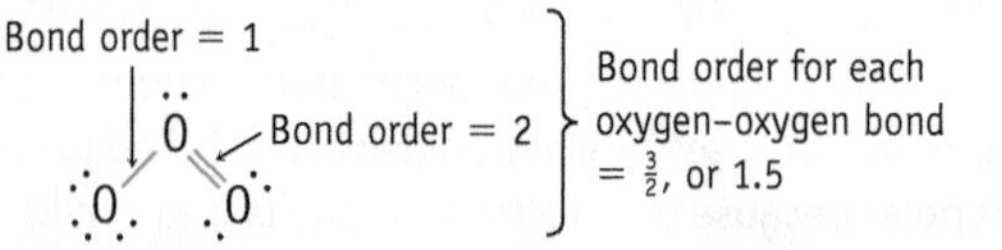

One resonance structure

We can define the bond order between any bonded pair of atoms X and Y as

$$\text{Bond order} = \frac{\text{number of shared pairs in all X—Y bonds}}{\text{number of X—Y links in the molecule or ion}} \qquad \textbf{(8.2)}$$

For ozone, there are three bond pairs involved in two oxygen–oxygen links, so the bond order for each oxygen–oxygen bond is $3/2$, or 1.5.

Bond Length

Bond length, the distance between the nuclei of two bonded atoms, is clearly related to the sizes of the atoms (see Section 7-5). In addition, for a given pair of atoms, the order of the bond plays a role.

Table 8.7 lists average bond lengths for a number of common chemical bonds. It is important to recognize that these are *average* values. Neighboring parts of a molecule can affect the length of a particular bond, so there can be a range of values for a particular bond type. For example, Table 8.7 gives the average C—H bond as 110 pm. However, in methane, CH_4, the measured bond length is 109.4 pm, whereas the C—H bond is only 105.9 pm long in acetylene, H—C≡C—H. Variations as great as 10% from the average values listed in Table 8.7 are possible.

Because atom sizes vary in a regular fashion with the position of the element in the periodic table (see Figure 7.5), we can predict trends in bond lengths. For example, the H—X distance in the hydrogen halides increases in the order predicted by the relative sizes of the halogens: H—F < H—Cl < H—Br < H—I. Likewise, bonds between carbon and another element in a given period decrease going from left to right, in a predictable fashion; for example, C—C > C—N > C—O. Trends

Table 8.7 Some Average Single- and Multiple-Bond Lengths in Picometers (pm)*

SINGLE BOND LENGTHS

	H	C	N	O	F	Si	P	S	Cl	Br	I
Group	**1A**	**4A**	**5A**	**6A**	**7A**	**4A**	**5A**	**6A**	**7A**	**7A**	**7A**
H	74	110	98	94	92	145	138	132	127	142	161
C		154	147	143	141	194	187	181	176	191	210
N			140	136	134	187	180	174	169	184	203
O				132	130	183	176	170	165	180	199
F					128	181	174	168	163	178	197
Si						234	227	221	216	231	250
P							220	214	209	224	243
S								208	203	218	237
Cl									200	213	232
Br										228	247
I											266

MULTIPLE BOND LENGTHS

C=C	134	C≡C	121
C=N	127	C≡N	115
C=O	122	C≡O	113
N=O	115	N≡O	108

*1 pm = 10^{-12} m.

for multiple bonds are similar. A C=O bond is shorter than a C=S bond, and a C=N bond is shorter than a C=C bond.

The effect of bond order is evident when bonds between the same two atoms are compared. For example, the bonds become shorter as the bond order increases in the series C—O, C=O, and C≡O:

Bond	**C—O**	**C=O**	**C≡O**
Bond order	1	2	3
Average bond length (pm)	143	122	113

The carbonate ion, CO_3^{2-}, has three equivalent resonance structures. Each CO bond has a bond order of 1.33 (or 4/3) because four electron pairs are used to form three carbon–oxygen links. The CO bond distance (129 pm) is intermediate between a C—O single bond (143 pm) and a C=O double bond (122 pm).

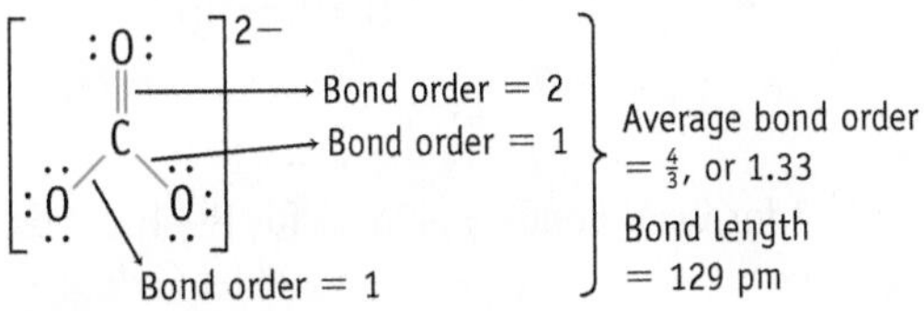

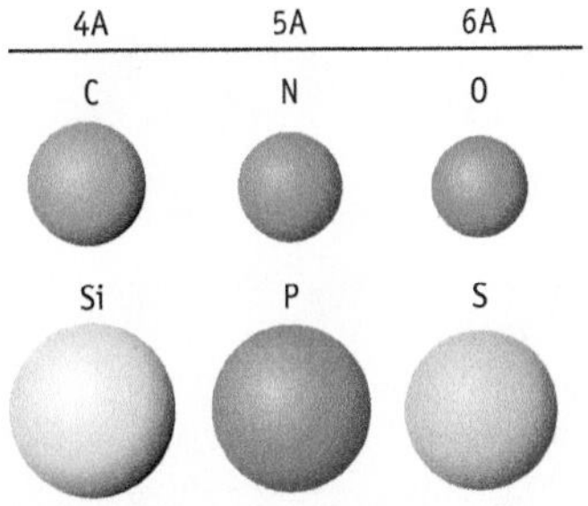

Relative sizes of some atoms of Groups 4A, 5A, and 6A.

Bond lengths are related to atom sizes.

C—H	**N—H**	**O—H**
110	98	94 pm
Si—H	**P—H**	**S—H**
145	138	132 pm

Bond Dissociation Enthalpy

The **bond dissociation enthalpy** is the enthalpy change for breaking a bond in a molecule with the reactants and products *in the gas phase. The process of breaking bonds in a molecule is always endothermic,* so $\Delta_r H$ for bond breaking is always positive.

$$\text{Molecule (g)} \underset{\text{Energy released, } \Delta H < 0}{\overset{\text{Energy supplied, } \Delta H > 0}{\rightleftharpoons}} \text{Molecular fragments (g)}$$

Suppose you wish to break the carbon–carbon bonds in ethane ($H_3C—CH_3$), ethylene ($H_2C═CH_2$), and acetylene ($HC≡CH$). The carbon–carbon bond orders in these molecules are 1, 2, and 3, respectively, and these bond orders are reflected in the bond dissociation enthalpies. Breaking the single C—C bond in ethane requires the least energy in this group, whereas breaking the C—C triple bond in acetylene requires the most energy.

$$H_3C{-}CH_3(g) \rightarrow H_3C\cdot(g) + \cdot CH_3(g) \qquad \Delta_r H = +368 \text{ kJ/mol-rxn}$$

$$H_2C{=}CH_2(g) \rightarrow H_2C\cdot(g) + \cdot CH_2(g) \qquad \Delta_r H = +682 \text{ kJ/mol-rxn}$$

$$HC{\equiv}CH(g) \rightarrow HC\cdot(g) + \cdot CH(g) \qquad \Delta_r H = +962 \text{ kJ/mol-rxn}$$

The energy supplied to break carbon–carbon bonds must be the same as the energy released when the same bonds form. *The formation of bonds from atoms or radicals in the gas phase is always exothermic.* This means, for example, that $\Delta_r H$ for the formation of $H_3C—CH_3$ from two $\cdot CH_3(g)$ radicals is −368 kJ/mol-rxn.

$$H_3C\cdot\,(g) + \cdot CH_3(g) \rightarrow H_3C{-}CH_3(g) \qquad \Delta_r H = -368 \text{ kJ/mol-rxn}$$

Generally, the bond energy for a given type of bond (a C—C bond, for example) varies somewhat, depending on the compound, just as bond lengths vary from one molecule to another. Thus, data provided in tables are *average bond dissociation enthalpies* (Table 8.8). The values in such tables may be used to *estimate* the enthalpy change for a reaction, as described below.

In reactions between molecules, bonds in reactants are broken, and new bonds are formed as products form. If the total energy released when new bonds form exceeds the energy required to break the original bonds, the overall reaction is predicted to be exothermic. If the opposite is true, then the overall reaction is endothermic.

Let us use bond dissociation enthalpies to estimate the enthalpy change for the hydrogenation of propene to propane:

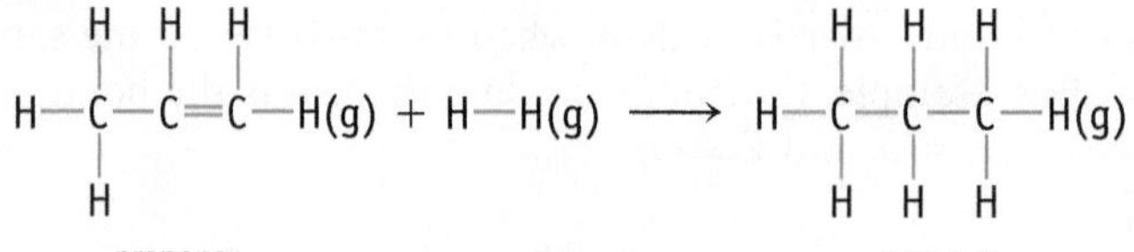

The first step is to identify which bonds are broken and which bonds are formed. In this case, the C═C bond in propene and the H—H bond in hydrogen are broken. One C—C bond and two C—H bonds are formed.

Bonds broken: 1 mol of C═C bonds and 1 mol of H—H bonds

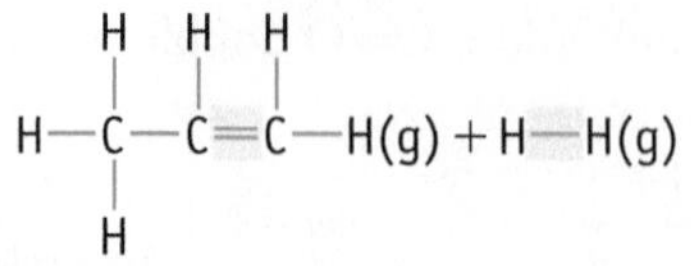

Energy required = 610 kJ for C═C bonds + 436 kJ for H—H bonds = 1046 kJ/mol-rxn

Table 8.8 Some Average Bond Dissociation Enthalpies (kJ/mol)*

SINGLE BONDS

	H	C	N	O	F	Si	P	S	Cl	Br	I
H	436	413	391	463	565	328	322	347	432	366	299
C		346	305	358	485	—	—	272	339	285	213
N			163	201	283	—	—	—	192	—	—
O				146	—	452	335	—	218	201	201
F					155	565	490	284	253	249	278
Si						222	—	293	381	310	234
P							201	—	326	—	184
S								226	255	—	—
Cl									242	216	208
Br										193	175
I											151

MULTIPLE BONDS

N=N	418	C=C	610
N≡N	945	C≡C	835
C=N	615	C=O	745
C≡N	887	C=O (in CO_2)	803
O=O (in O_2)	498	C≡O	1046

*Sources of dissociation enthalpies: I. Klotz and R. M. Rosenberg, *Chemical Thermodynamics*, 4th Ed., p. 55, New York, John Wiley, 1994; and J. E. Huheey, E. A. Keiter, and R. L. Keiter, *Inorganic Chemistry* 4th Ed., Table E. 1, New York, HarperCollins, 1993. See also Lange's *Handbook of Chemistry*, J. A. Dean (ed.), McGraw-Hill Inc., New York.

Bonds formed: 1 mol of C—C bonds and 2 mol of C—H bonds

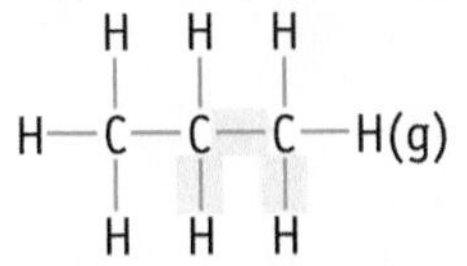

Energy evolved = 346 kJ for C—C bonds + 2 mol × 413 kJ/mol for C—H bonds = 1172 kJ/mol-rxn

By combining the enthalpy changes for breaking bonds and for making bonds, we can estimate $\Delta_r H$ for the hydrogenation of propene and predict that the reaction is exothermic.

$$\Delta_r H = 1046 \text{ kJ/mol-rxn} - 1172 \text{ kJ/mol-rxn} = -126 \text{ kJ/mol-rxn}$$

In general, the enthalpy change for any reaction can be estimated using the equation

$$\Delta_r H = \Sigma\Delta H(\text{bonds broken}) - \Sigma\Delta H(\text{bonds formed}) \quad (8.3)$$

Such calculations can give acceptable results in many cases.

Variability in Bond Dissociation Enthalpies The values of $\Delta_r H$ for ethane, ethylene, and acetylene shown in the text are for the reactions of those molecules in particular. The bond dissociation enthalpies in Table 8.8 are average values for a range of molecules containing the indicated bond.

$\Delta_r H$ from Enthalpies of Formation Using $\Delta_f H°$ values for propane and propene, we calculate $\Delta_r H° = -125.1$ kJ/mol–rxn. The bond dissociation enthalpy calculation is in excellent agreement with that from enthalpies of formation in this case.

EXAMPLE 8.16

Using Bond Dissociation Enthalpies

Problem Acetone, a common industrial solvent, can be converted to 2-propanol (rubbing alcohol) by hydrogenation. Calculate the enthalpy change for this reaction using bond enthalpies.

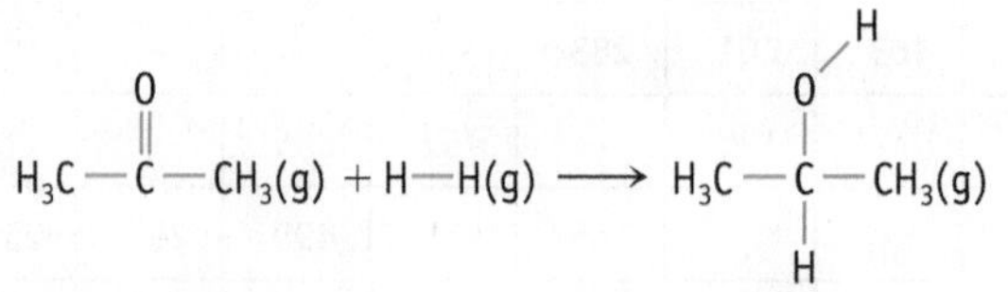

acetone 2-propanol

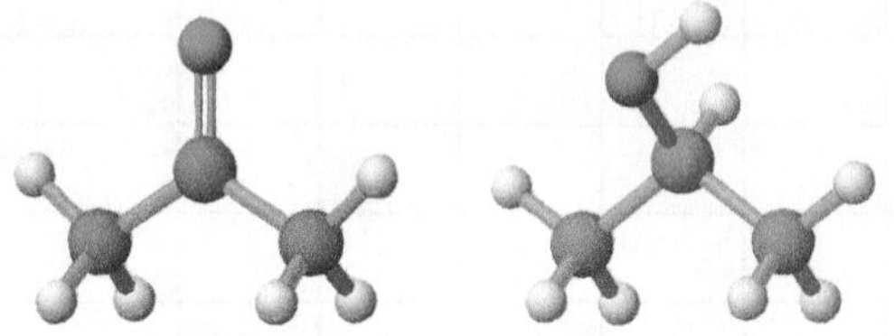

What Do You Know? You know the molecular structures of the reactants and the products as well as relevant bond dissociation enthalpies.

Strategy Determine which bonds are broken and which are formed. Add up the enthalpy changes for breaking bonds in the reactants and for forming bonds in the product. The difference in the sums of bond dissociation enthalpies can be used as an estimate of the enthalpy change of the reaction (Equation 8.3).

Solution

Bonds broken: 1 mol of C═O bonds and 1 mol of H—H bonds

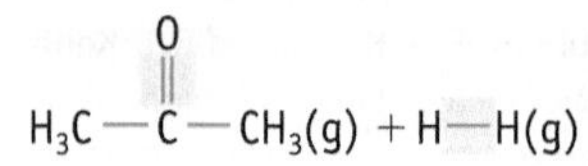

$\Sigma\Delta H$(bonds broken) = 745 kJ for C═O bonds + 436 kJ for H—H bonds = 1181 kJ/mol-rxn

Bonds formed: 1 mol of C—H bonds, 1 mol of C—O bonds, and 1 mol of O—H bonds

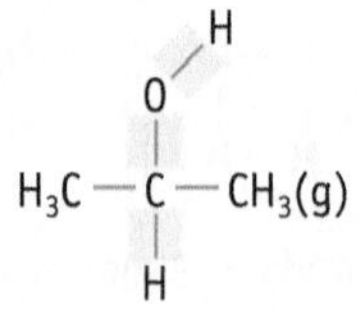

$\Sigma\Delta H$(bonds formed) = 413 kJ for C—H + 358 kJ for C—O + 463 kJ for O—H = 1234 kJ/mol-rxn

$\Delta_r H = \Sigma\Delta H(\text{bonds broken}) - \Sigma\Delta H(\text{bonds formed})$

$\Delta_r H = 1181\ \text{kJ} - 1234\ \text{kJ} = -53\ \text{kJ/mol-rxn}$

Think about Your Answer The overall reaction is predicted to be exothermic by 53 kJ per mol of product formed. This is in good agreement with the value calculated from $\Delta_f H°$ values (−55.8 kJ/mol-rxn).

CASE STUDY
Ibuprofen, a Study in Green Chemistry

Ibuprofen, $C_{13}H_{18}O_2$, is now one of the world's most common, over-the-counter drugs. It is an effective anti-inflammatory drug and is used to treat arthritis and similar conditions. Unlike aspirin it does not decompose in solution, so ibuprofen can be applied to the skin as a topical gel, thus avoiding the gastrointestinal problems sometimes associated with aspirin.

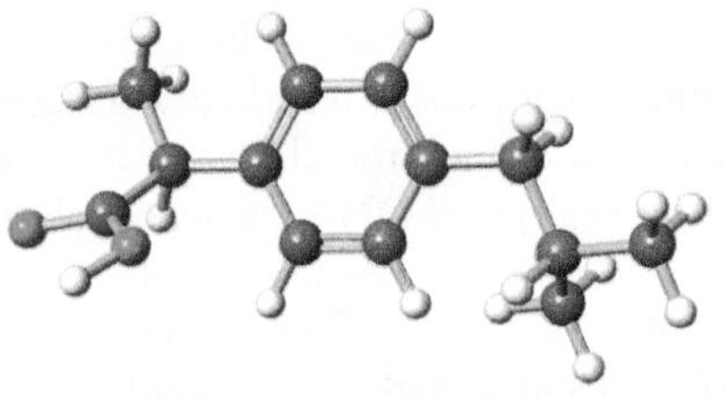

FIGURE A **Ibuprofen, $C_{13}H_{18}O_2$**

Ibuprofen was first synthesized in the 1960s by the Boots Company in England, and millions of kilograms are now sold every year.

Unfortunately, the original method of making ibuprofen took six steps, wasted chemicals, and produced by-products that required disposal. Many of the atoms of the reagents used to make the drug did not end up in the drug itself, that is, the method had a very poor atom economy (page 150). Recognizing this, chemists looked for new approaches for the synthesis of ibuprofen. A method was soon found that uses only three steps, severely reduces waste, and uses reagents that can be recovered and reused. A plant in Texas now makes more than 3 million kilograms of ibuprofen annually by the new method, enough to make over 6 billion tablets.

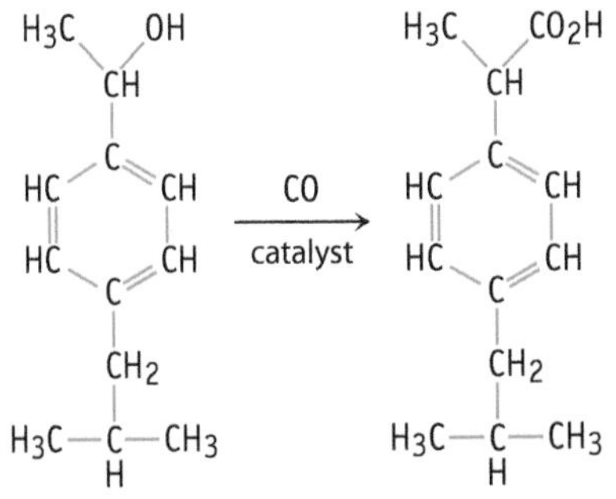

FIGURE B **The final step in the synthesis of ibuprofen.**

Questions:

1. The third and final step in the synthesis involves the transformation of an OH group with CO to a carboxylic acid group ($-CO_2H$) (Figure B). Using bond enthalpy data, is this an endothermic or exothermic step?
2. Do any of the atoms in an ibuprofen molecule have a nonzero formal charge?
3. What is the most polar bond in the molecule?
4. Is the molecule polar?
5. What is the shortest bond in the molecule?
6. What bond or bonds have the highest bond order?
7. Are there any 120° bond angles in ibuprofen? Any 180° angles?
8. If you were to titrate 200. mg of ibuprofen to the equivalence point with 0.0259 M NaOH, what volume of NaOH would be required?

Answers to these questions are available in Appendix N.

Check Your Understanding

Using the bond dissociation enthalpies in Table 8.8, estimate the enthalpy of combustion of gaseous methane, CH_4, to give water vapor and carbon dioxide gas.

REVIEW & CHECK FOR SECTION 8-9

1. Which of the following species has the longest N—O bond?

   (a) NO_3^- (b) NO^+ (c) NO_2^- (d) H_2NOH

2. Which of the following species has the largest C—N bond order?

   (a) CN^- (b) OCN^- (c) CH_3NH_2 (d) $N(CH_3)_3$

3. Use bond dissociation enthalpies to estimate the enthalpy change for the decomposition of hydrogen peroxide.

$$2\ H_2O_2(g) \rightarrow 2\ H_2O(g) + O_2(g)$$

   (a) +352 kJ/mol-rxn (c) +1037 kJ/mol-rxn

   (b) −206 kJ/mol-rxn (d) −2204 kJ/mol-rxn

8-10 DNA, Revisited

This chapter opened with some questions about the structure of DNA, one of the key molecules in all biological organisms. Now that you have studied this chapter, let's look at the structure of this important molecule and ask why it looks the way it does.

As shown in Figure 8.13, each strand of the double-stranded DNA molecule consists of three repeating parts: a phosphate, a deoxyribose molecule (a sugar molecule with a five-member ring), and a nitrogen-containing base. (The bases in DNA can be one of four molecules: adenine, guanine, cytosine, and thymine; in Figure 8.13, the base is adenine.) Two units of the backbone (without the adenine on the deoxyribose ring) are also illustrated in Figure 8.13a.

One important point here is that the repeating unit in the backbone of DNA consists of the atoms O—P—O—C—C—C. Each atom has a tetrahedral electron-pair geometry. Therefore, the chain cannot be linear. In fact, the chain twists as one moves along the backbone, and it is this twisting that gives DNA its helical shape.

Why are there two strands in DNA with the O—P—O—C—C—C backbone on the outside and the nitrogen-containing bases on the inside? This structure arises from the polarity of the bonds in the base molecules attached to the backbone. For example, the N–H bonds in the adenine molecule are very polar, which leads to a special type of intermolecular force—hydrogen bonding—binding the adenine to

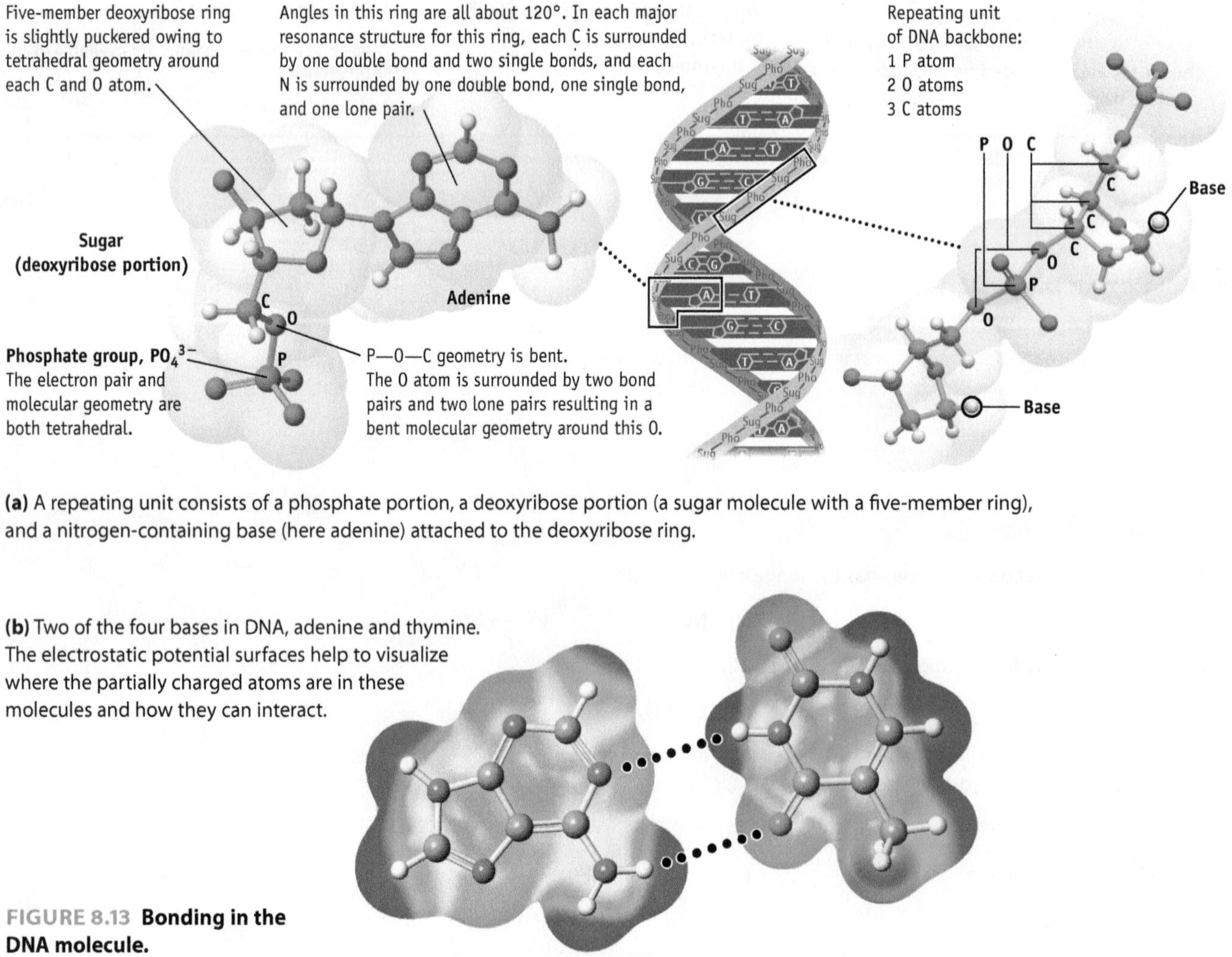

(a) A repeating unit consists of a phosphate portion, a deoxyribose portion (a sugar molecule with a five-member ring), and a nitrogen-containing base (here adenine) attached to the deoxyribose ring.

(b) Two of the four bases in DNA, adenine and thymine. The electrostatic potential surfaces help to visualize where the partially charged atoms are in these molecules and how they can interact.

FIGURE 8.13 **Bonding in the DNA molecule.**

A CLOSER LOOK DNA—Watson, Crick, and Franklin

DNA is the substance in every plant and animal that carries the exact blueprint of that plant or animal. The structure of this molecule, the cornerstone of life, was uncovered in 1953, and James D. Watson, Francis Crick, and Maurice Wilkins shared the 1962 Nobel Prize in Medicine and Physiology for the work. It was one of the most important scientific discoveries of the 20th century, and the story has been told by Watson in his book *The Double Helix*.

A. Barrington Brown/Science Source

James D. Watson (1928–) and Francis Crick (1918–2004). Watson *(left)* and Crick *(right)* stand by their model of the DNA double helix (at The University of Cambridge, England in 1953). Together with Maurice Wilkins, Watson and Crick received the Nobel Prize in Medicine and Physiology in 1962.

When Watson was a graduate student at Indiana University, he had an interest in the gene and said he hoped that its biological role might be solved "without my learning any chemistry." Later, however, he and Crick found out just how useful chemistry can be when they began to unravel the structure of DNA.

Watson went to Cambridge in 1951. There he met Crick, who, Watson said, talked louder and faster than anyone else. Crick shared Watson's belief in the fundamental importance of DNA, and the pair soon learned that Maurice Wilkins and Rosalind Franklin at King's College in London were using a technique called *x-ray crystallography* to learn more about DNA's structure. Watson and Crick believed that understanding this structure was crucial to understanding genetics. To solve the structural problem, however, they needed experimental data of the type that could come from the experiments at King's College.

The King's College group was initially reluctant to share their data, and, what is more, they did not seem to share Watson and Crick's sense of urgency. There was also an ethical dilemma: Could Watson and Crick work on a problem that others had claimed as theirs? "The English sense of fair

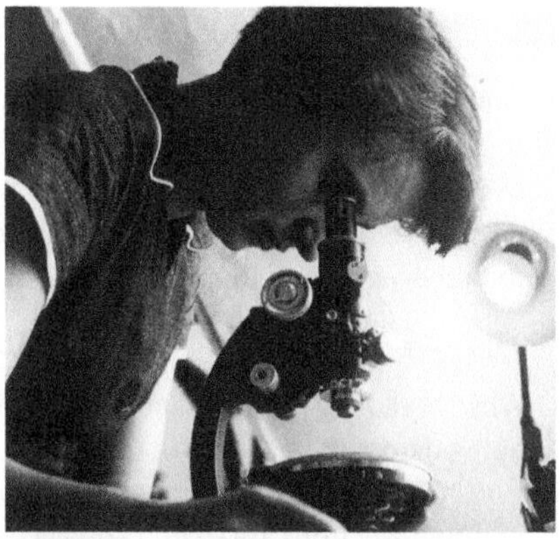

Henry Grant Collection/Museum of London

Rosalind Franklin (1920–1958). King's College, London. She died at the age of 37. Because Nobel Prizes are never awarded posthumously, she did not share in this honor with Watson, Crick, and Wilkins. See *Rosalind Franklin: The Dark Lady of DNA*, by Brenda Maddox.

play would not allow Francis to move in on Maurice's problem," said Watson.

Watson and Crick approached the problem through a technique chemists now use frequently—model building. They built models of the pieces of the DNA chain, and they tried various chemically reasonable ways of fitting them together. Finally, they discovered that one arrangement was "too pretty not to be true." Ultimately, the experimental evidence of Wilkins and Franklin confirmed the "pretty structure" to be the real DNA structure.

thymine in the neighboring chain (Figure 8.13b). You will learn more about this in Chapter 11 when we explore intermolecular forces and also in Chapter 25, *The Chemistry of Life: Biochemistry*.

The rings in the nitrogen-containing bases are all flat with trigonal-planar electron-pair geometry around each atom in the rings. For example, look at the electron-pair geometries in one of the bases, adenine. There are two major resonance structures for this ring system. In these, each carbon atom is surrounded by one double bond and two single bonds, leading to a trigonal-planar electron-pair geometry. Each nitrogen atom in the rings, except the one attached to the sugar, is surrounded by a double bond, a single bond, and a lone pair, likewise leading to trigonal-planar electron-pair geometries around these atoms. The nitrogen attached to the sugar, however, is different from what we would normally predict. It is surrounded by three single bonds and one lone pair. We would normally expect it to have a tetrahedral electron-pair geometry (and trigonal-pyramidal molecular geometry), but it does not. Instead, the bonding groups assume a trigonal-planar geometry, and the lone pair is in a plane perpendicular to the bonds. After studying Chapter 9, you will understand how this allows the electrons in this lone pair to interact with the electrons in the rings' double bonds in a favorable way.

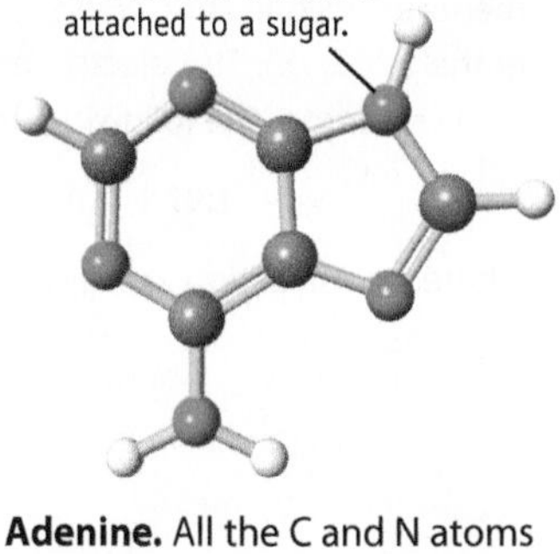

Adenine. All the C and N atoms of the five- and six-member rings have trigonal-planar electron pair geometry. The indicated N atom of the five-member ring is attached to a sugar in DNA.

APPLYING CHEMICAL PRINCIPLES

Linus Pauling and Electronegativity

Linus Pauling noticed that, when he compared the bond dissociation enthalpies ($\Delta_{diss}H$) between identical atoms, say A—A or B—B, with the bond dissociation enthalpies for different atoms, A—B, the energy for the A—B bond was always larger than the average of the A—A and B—B energies.

$$\Delta_{diss}H(\text{A—B}) > 1/2\ [\Delta_{diss}H(\text{A—A}) + \Delta_{diss}H(\text{B—B})]$$

Why should this be true, and what useful information can be derived from it?

When a bond forms between two identical atoms, the bonding electrons are shared equally between the two atoms. In a bond between dissimilar atoms, the atoms do not share the electrons equally. When this is the case, one atom incurs a slightly positive charge and the other a slightly negative one. A coulombic attraction between the oppositely charged atoms increases the strength of the bond. Pauling said that this difference in energy is related to the electronegativities of the atoms involved and defined electronegativity (χ) as "the ability of an atom in a molecule to attract electrons to itself." More specifically, he said the difference he observed is mathematically related to the difference in electronegativities by

$$\chi_A - \chi_B = 0.102\sqrt{\Delta_{diss}H(AB) - \frac{\Delta_{diss}H(AA) + \Delta_{diss}H(BB)}{2}}$$

Using bond dissociation enthalpies, Pauling created absolute electronegativity values by assigning fluorine a value of 4.0. Because they are so useful, Pauling's values have been continually refined since Pauling's 1932 publication, but Pauling's calculated electronegativity values are close to those computed today.

A variety of methods for quantifying electronegativity values have been developed since Pauling's initial work. One notable method, developed by Robert Mulliken (1896–1986) in 1934, calculates electronegativity values for individual elements using ionization energy (IE) and the electron attachment enthalpy ($\Delta_{EA}H$). The electronegativity of an element may be calculated from the following equation,

$$\chi_A = 1.97 \times 10^{-3}\ (\text{IE} - \Delta_{EA}H) + 0.19$$

where the ionization energy and $\Delta_{EA}H$ have units of kJ/mol.

Joe McNally/Getty Images

Linus Pauling (1901–1994)

QUESTIONS:

1. Calculate the difference in electronegativity between hydrogen and chlorine ($\chi_{Cl} - \chi_H$) in hydrogen chloride using average bond dissociation enthalpy values (Table 8.8). Compare your results with those calculated using electronegativity values from Figure 8.10.
2. Predict the bond dissociation enthalpy for a nitrogen-iodine bond in NI_3 using bond dissociation enthalpy values (Table 8.8) and electronegativity values (Figure 8.10).
3. Calculate the electronegativity of sulfur atoms using ionization energy and electron attachment enthalpy values (Appendix F). Compare the value with the one in Figure 8.10.

REFERENCES:

Pauling, L., *Journal of the American Chemical Society,* Vol. 54, p. 3570, 1932.

Mulliken, R. S., *Journal of Chemical Physics,* Vol. 2, p. 782, 1934.

CHAPTER GOALS REVISITED

Now that you have studied this chapter, you should ask whether you have met the chapter goals. In particular, you should be able to:

UNDERSTAND

- The basic assumptions about ionic and covalent bonds (Section 8-1).
- The relationship of Lewis electron dot structures and molecular structures (Sections 8-2–8-8).
- The relationship between bond order, bond length, and bond energy (Section 8-9).

DO

- Draw Lewis electron dot structures for small molecules and polyatomic ions.
  - **a.** Draw Lewis structures for molecular compounds and ions (Section 8-2). Study Questions: 5–12.
  - **b.** Understand and apply the octet rule; recognize exceptions to the octet rule (Sections 8-2–8-5). Study Questions: 5–12, 59, 60.
  - **c.** Write resonance structures, understand what resonance means, and know how and when to use this means of representing bonding (Section 8-4). Study Questions: 9, 10, 33, 37, 64, 66.
- Use the valence shell electron pair repulsion (VSEPR) theory to predict the shapes of small molecules and ions and to understand the structures of more complex molecules.
  - **a.** Determine the shape or geometry of molecules and ions of main group elements using VSEPR theory (Section 8-6). Table 8.9 is a summary of the relation between valence electron pairs, electron-pair and molecular geometry, and molecular polarity. Study Questions: 17–24, 76.
- Use electronegativity and formal charge to predict the charge distribution in molecules and ions, to define the polarity of bonds, and to predict the polarity of molecules.
  - **a.** Calculate formal charges for atoms in a molecule based on the Lewis structure (Section 8-3). Study Questions: 13–16, 38.
  - **b.** Define electronegativity and understand how it is used to describe the unequal sharing of electrons between atoms in a bond (Section 8-7).
  - **c.** Combine formal charge and electronegativity to gain a perspective on the charge distribution in covalent molecules and ions (Section 8-7). Study Questions: 27–38, 78, 79.
  - **d.** Understand why some molecules are polar whereas others are nonpolar (Section 8-8). (See Table 8.6.)
  - **e.** Predict the polarity of a molecule (Section 8-8). Study Questions: 39–42, 82, 83, 85, 90.

Table 8.9 Summary of Molecular Shapes and Molecular Polarity

Pairs of Valence Electrons	Electron-Pair Geometry	Number of Bond Pairs	Number of Lone Pairs	Molecular Geometry	Molecular Dipole?*	Examples
2	Linear	2	0	Linear	No	$BeCl_2$
3	Trigonal planar	3	0	Trigonal planar	No	BF_3, BCl_3
		2	1	Bent	Yes	$SnCl_2$(g)
4	Tetrahedral	4	0	Tetrahedral	No	CH_4, BF_4^-
		3	1	Trigonal pyramidal	Yes	NH_3, PF_3
		2	2	Bent	Yes	H_2O, SCl_2
5	Trigonal bipyramidal	5	0	Trigonal bipyramidal	No	PF_5
		4	1	Seesaw	Yes	SF_4
		3	2	T-shaped	Yes	ClF_3
		2	3	Linear	No	XeF_2, I_3^-
6	Octahedral	6	0	Octahedral	No	SF_6, PF_6^-
		5	1	Square pyramidal	Yes	ClF_5
		4	2	Square planar	No	XeF_4

*For molecules of AX_n, where the X atoms are identical.

- Use bond enthalpies to estimate enthalpy changes for chemical reactions.
  - **a.** Define and predict trends in bond order, bond length, and bond dissociation enthalpy (Section 8-9). Study Questions: 43–50, 62, 85.
  - **b.** Use bond dissociation enthalpies in calculations (Section 8-9 and Example 8.16). Study Questions: 51–56, 73.

REMEMBER

- There are common electron distributions (as indicated by Lewis structures) and molecular structures shared by molecules and ions. Knowing these patterns allows you to predict properties of unfamiliar molecules and ions (Sections 8-2–8-6, Tables 8.2–8.5 and 8.9, and Figures 8.4, 8.5, and 8.7).
- The Lewis symbols of atoms (Table 8.1).
- The common electron-pair geometries and their associated bond angles (Section 8-6 and Figure 8.4).

KEY EQUATIONS

Equation 8.1 (page 296) Used to calculate the formal charge on an atom in a molecule.

$$\text{Formal charge of an atom in a molecule or ion} = \text{NVE} - [\text{LPE} + \tfrac{1}{2}(\text{BE})]$$

Equation 8.2 (page 326) Used to calculate bond order.

$$\text{Bond order} = \frac{\text{number of shared pairs in all X—Y bonds}}{\text{number of X—Y links in the molecule or ion}}$$

Equation 8.3 (page 329) Used to estimate the enthalpy change for a reaction using bond dissociation enthalpies.

$$\Delta_r H = \Sigma\Delta H(\text{bonds broken}) - \Sigma\Delta H(\text{bonds formed})$$

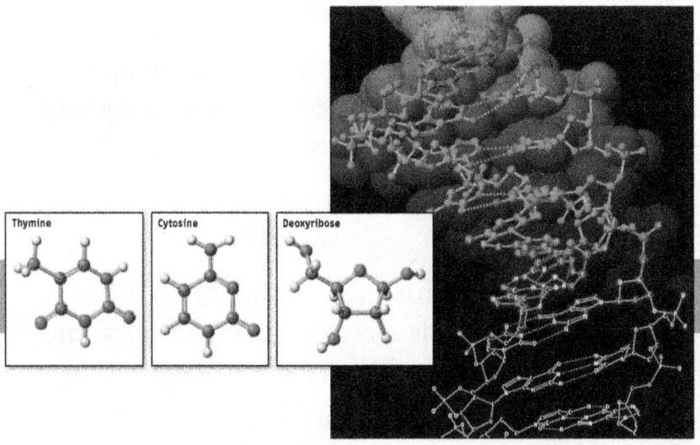

STUDY QUESTIONS

▲ denotes challenging questions.

Blue-numbered questions have answers in Appendix N and fully worked solutions in the *Student Solutions Manual.*

Practicing Skills

Valence Electrons and the Octet Rule

(See Section 8-1.)

1. Give the periodic group number and number of valence electrons for each of the following atoms.

   (a) O (b) B (c) Na (d) Mg (e) F (f) S

2. Give the periodic group number and number of valence electrons for each of the following atoms.

   (a) C (b) Cl (c) Ne (d) Si (e) Se (f) Al

3. For elements in Groups 4A–7A of the periodic table, give the number of bonds an element is expected to form (in an uncharged molecule) if it obeys the octet rule.

4. Which of the following elements are capable of forming hypervalent compounds?

   (a) C (b) P (c) O (d) F (e) Cl (f) B (g) Se (h) Sn

Lewis Electron Dot Structures

(See Sections 8-2, 8-4, and 8-5; Examples 8.1–8.4 and 8.6–8.7.)

5. Draw a Lewis structure for each of the following molecules or ions.

   (a) NF_3
   (b) ClO_3^-
   (c) HOBr
   (d) SO_3^{2-}

6. Draw a Lewis structure for each of the following molecules or ions:

   (a) CS_2
   (b) BF_4^-
   (c) HNO_2 (where the arrangement of atoms is HONO)
   (d) $OSCl_2$ (where S is the central atom)

7. Draw a Lewis structure for each of the following molecules:

   (a) chlorodifluoromethane, $CHClF_2$
   (b) propanoic acid, $C_2H_5CO_2H$ (basic structure pictured below)

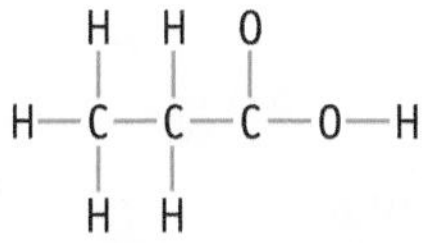

   (c) acetonitrile, CH_3CN (the framework is $H_3C—C—N$)
   (d) allene, H_2CCCH_2

8. Draw a Lewis structure for each of the following molecules:

   (a) methanol, CH_3OH
   (b) vinyl chloride, $H_2C{=}CHCl$, the molecule from which PVC plastics are made
   (c) acrylonitrile, $H_2C{=}CHCN$, the molecule from which materials such as Orlon are made

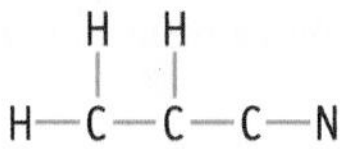

9. Show all possible resonance structures for each of the following molecules:

   (a) sulfur dioxide, SO_2
   (b) nitrous acid, HNO_2
   (c) thiocyanic acid, HSCN

10. Show all possible resonance structures for each of the following molecules or ions:

(a) nitrate ion, NO_3^-
(b) nitric acid, HNO_3
(c) dinitrogen monoxide (nitrous oxide, laughing gas), N_2O (where the bonding is in the order N—N—O)

11. Draw a Lewis structure for each of the following molecules or ions:

(a) BrF_3 (c) XeO_2F_2
(b) I_3^- (d) XeF_3^+

12. Draw a Lewis structure for each of the following molecules or ions:

(a) BrF_5 (c) IBr_2^-
(b) IF_3 (d) BrF_2^+

Formal Charge

(See Section 8-3 and Example 8.5.)

13. Determine the formal charge on each atom in the following molecules or ions:

(a) N_2H_4 (c) BH_4^-
(b) PO_4^{3-} (d) NH_2OH

14. Determine the formal charge on each atom in the following molecules or ions:

(a) SCO
(b) HCO_2^- (formate ion)
(c) CO_3^{2-}
(d) HCO_2H (formic acid)

15. Determine the formal charge on each atom in the following molecules and ions:

(a) NO_2^+ (c) NF_3
(b) NO_2^- (d) HNO_3

16. Determine the formal charge on each atom in the following molecules and ions:

(a) SO_2 (c) O_2SCl_2
(b) $OSCl_2$ (d) FSO_3^-

Molecular Geometry

(See Section 8-6 and Examples 8.8–8.11.)

17. Draw a Lewis structure for each of the following molecules or ions. Describe the electron-pair geometry and molecular geometry around the central atom.

(a) NH_2Cl
(b) Cl_2O (O is the central atom)
(c) SCN^-
(d) HOF

18. Draw a Lewis structure for each of the following molecules or ions. Describe the electron-pair geometry and molecular geometry around the central atom.

(a) ClF_2^+ (c) PO_4^{3-}
(b) $SnCl_3^-$ (d) CS_2

19. The following molecules or ions all have two oxygen atoms attached to a central atom. Draw a Lewis structure for each one, and then describe the electron-pair geometry and molecular geometry around the central atom. Comment on similarities and differences in the series.

(a) CO_2 (c) O_3
(b) NO_2^- (d) ClO_2^-

20. The following molecules or ions all have three oxygen atoms attached to a central atom. Draw a Lewis structure for each one, and then describe the electron-pair geometry and molecular geometry around the central atom. Comment on similarities and differences in the series.

(a) CO_3^{2-} (c) SO_3^{2-}
(b) NO_3^- (d) ClO_3^-

21. Draw a Lewis structure for each of the following molecules or ions. Describe the electron-pair geometry and molecular geometry around the central atom.

(a) ClF_2^- (c) ClF_4^-
(b) ClF_3 (d) ClF_5

22. Draw a Lewis structure for each of the following molecules or ions. Describe the electron-pair geometry and molecular geometry around the central atom.

(a) SiF_6^{2-} (c) SF_4
(b) PF_5 (d) XeF_4

23. Give approximate values for the indicated bond angles.

(a) O—S—O in SO_2
(b) F—B—F angle in BF_3
(c) Cl—C—Cl angle in Cl_2CO
(d) H—C—H (angle 1) and C—C≡N (angle 2) in acetonitrile

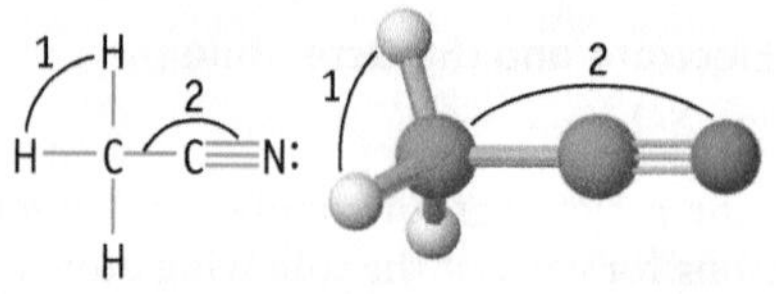

Acetonitrile

24. Give approximate values for the indicated bond angles:

(a) Cl—S—Cl in SCl_2
(b) N—N—O in N_2O
(c) Bond angles 1, 2, and 3 in vinyl alcohol (a component of polymers and a molecule found in outer space)

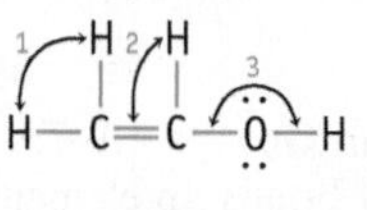

25. Phenylalanine is one of the natural amino acids and is a "breakdown" product of the artificial sweetener aspartame. Estimate the values of the indicated angles in the amino acid. Explain why the —CH_2—CH(NH_2)—CO_2H chain is not linear.

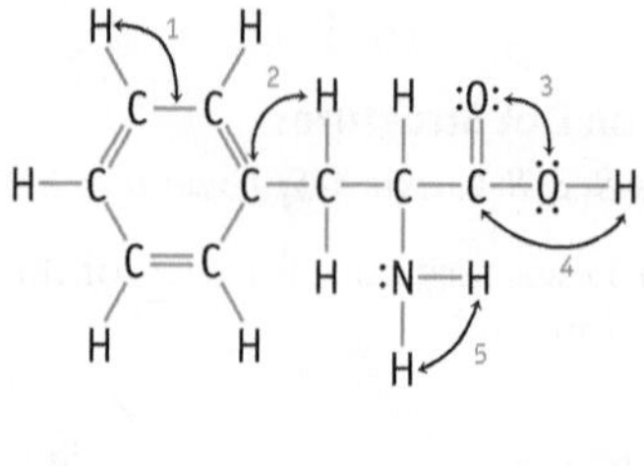

26. Acetylacetone has the structure shown here. Estimate the values of the indicated angles.

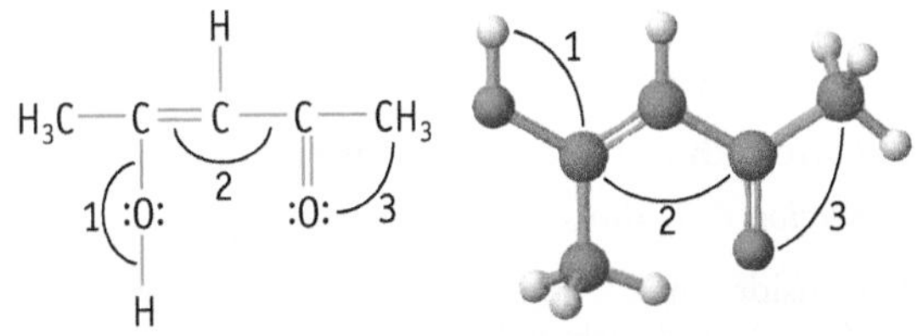

Acetylacetone

Bond Polarity, Electronegativity, and Formal Charge

(See Sections 8-7 and 8-8 and Examples 8.12 and 8.13.)

27. For each pair of bonds, indicate the more polar bond, and use an arrow to show the direction of polarity in each bond.

(a) C—O and C—N
(b) P—Br and P—Cl
(c) B—O and B—S
(d) B—F and B—I

28. For each of the bonds listed below, tell which atom is the more negatively charged.

(a) C—N
(b) C—H
(c) C—Br
(d) S—O

29. Acrolein, C_3H_4O, is the starting material for certain plastics.

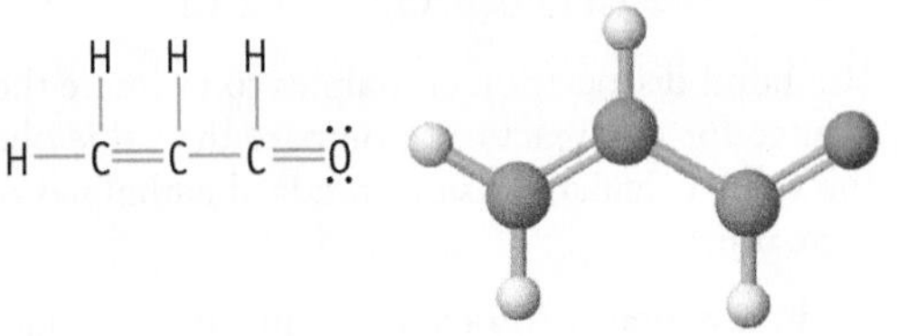

Acrolein

(a) Which bonds in the molecule are polar, and which are nonpolar?
(b) Which is the most polar bond in the molecule? Which is the more negative atom of this bond?

30. Urea, $(NH_2)_2CO$, is used in plastics and fertilizers. It is also the primary nitrogen-containing substance excreted by humans.

(a) Which bonds in the molecule are polar, and which are nonpolar?
(b) Which is the most polar bond in the molecule? Which atom is the negative end of the bond dipole?

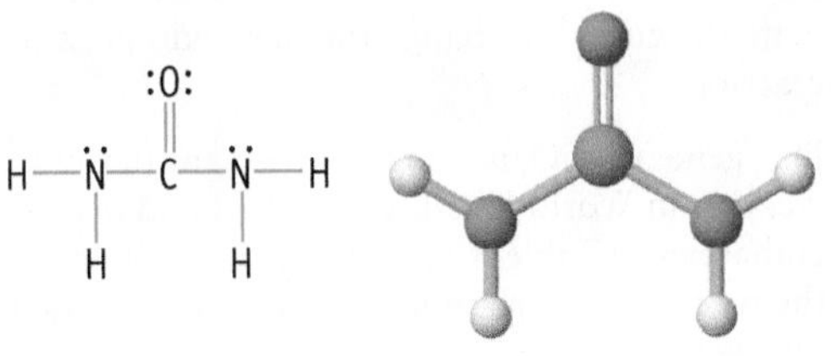

Urea

31. Considering both formal charges and bond polarities, predict on which atom or atoms the negative charge resides in the following anions:

(a) OH^-
(b) BH_4^-
(c) $CH_3CO_2^-$

32. Considering both formal charge and bond polarities, predict on which atom or atoms the positive charge resides in the following cations:

(a) H_3O^+
(b) NH_4^+
(c) NO_2^+
(d) NF_4^+

33. Three resonance structures are possible for dinitrogen monoxide, N_2O.

(a) Draw the three resonance structures.
(b) Calculate the formal charge on each atom in each resonance structure.
(c) Based on formal charges and electronegativity, predict which resonance structure is the most reasonable.

34. Three resonance structures are possible for the thiocyanate ion, SCN^-.

(a) Draw the three resonance structures.
(b) Calculate the formal charge on each atom in each resonance structure.
(c) Based on formal charges and electronegativity, predict which resonance structure most closely approximates the bonding in this ion?
(d) What are the similarities and differences of bonding in SCN^- compared to the bonding in OCN^- (page 318).

35. Compare the electron dot structures of the hydrogen carbonate ion and nitric acid.

(a) Are these species isoelectronic?
(b) How many resonance structures does each species have?
(c) What are the formal charges of each atom in these species?
(d) Compare the two species with respect to their acid-base behavior. (Can either or both species behave as a base and form a bond to H^+?)

36. Compare the electron dot structures of the carbonate (CO_3^{2-}) and borate (BO_3^{3-}) ions.

(a) Are these ions isoelectronic?
(b) How many resonance structures does each ion have?
(c) What are the formal charges of each atom in these ions?
(d) If an H^+ ion attaches to CO_3^{2-} to form the bicarbonate ion, HCO_3^-, does it attach to an O atom or to the C atom?

37. The chemistry of the nitrite ion and HNO_2:

(a) Two resonance structures are possible for NO_2^-. Draw these structures, and then find the formal charge on each atom in each resonance structure.
(b) In forming the acid HNO_2 an H^+ ion attaches to the O atom and not the N atom of NO_2^-. Explain why you would predict this result.
(c) Two resonance structures are possible for HNO_2. Draw these structures, and then find the formal charge on each atom in each resonance structure. Is either of these structures strongly preferred over the other?

38. Draw the resonance structures for the formate ion, HCO_2^-, and find the formal charge on each atom. If an H^+ ion is attached to HCO_2^- (to form formic acid), does it attach to C or O?

Molecular Polarity

(See Section 8-8 and Examples 8.14 and 8.15.)

39. Consider the following molecules:

(a) H_2O (b) NH_3 (c) CO_2 (d) ClF (e) CCl_4

(i) In which compound are the bonds most polar?
(ii) Which compounds in the list are *not* polar?
(iii) Which atom in ClF is more negatively charged?

40. Consider the following molecules:

(a) CH_4 (b) NH_2Cl (c) BF_3 (d) CS_2

(i) In which compound are the bonds most polar?
(ii) Which compounds are *not* polar?
(iii) Are the H atoms in NH_2Cl negative or positive?

41. Which of the following molecules is(are) polar? For each polar molecule, indicate the direction of polarity—that is, which is the negative end, and which is the positive end of the molecule.

(a) $BeCl_2$ (b) HBF_2 (c) CH_3Cl (d) SO_3

42. Which of the following molecules is(are) not polar? For each polar molecule, indicate the direction of polarity—that is, which is the negative end and which is the positive end.

(a) CO (b) BCl_3 (c) CF_4 (d) PCl_3 (e) GeH_4

Bond Order and Bond Length

(See Section 8-9.)

43. Give the bond order for each bond in the following molecules or ions:

(a) CH_2O (b) SO_3^{2-} (c) NO_2^+ (d) NOCl

44. Give the bond order for each bond in the following molecules or ions:

(a) CN^- (b) CH_3CN (c) SO_3 (d) $CH_3CH{=}CH_2$

45. In each pair of bonds, predict which is shorter.

(a) B—Cl or Ga—Cl (b) Sn—O or C—O (c) P—S or P—O (d) C=O or C=N

46. In each pair of bonds, predict which is shorter.

(a) Si—N or Si—O
(b) Si—O or C—O
(c) C—F or C—Br
(d) The C—N bond or the C≡N bond in $H_2NCH_2C{\equiv}N$

47. Consider the nitrogen–oxygen bond lengths in NO_2^+, NO_2^-, and NO_3^-. In which ion is the bond predicted to be longest? In which is it predicted to be the shortest? Explain briefly.

48. Compare the carbon–oxygen bond lengths in the formate ion (HCO_2^-), in methanol (CH_3OH), and in the carbonate ion (CO_3^{2-}). In which species is the carbon–oxygen bond predicted to be longest? In which is it predicted to be shortest? Explain briefly.

Bond Strength and Bond Dissociation Enthalpy

(See Section 8-9, Table 8.8, and Example 8.16.)

49. Consider the carbon–oxygen bond in formaldehyde (CH_2O) and carbon monoxide (CO). In which molecule is the CO bond shorter? In which molecule is the CO bond stronger?

50. Compare the nitrogen–nitrogen bond in hydrazine, H_2NNH_2, with that in "laughing gas," N_2O. In which molecule is the nitrogen–nitrogen bond shorter? In which is the bond stronger?

51. Ethanol can be made by the reaction of ethylene and water:

$$H_2C{=}CH_2(g) + H_2O(g) \rightarrow CH_3CH_2OH(g)$$

Use bond dissociation enthalpies to estimate the enthalpy change in this reaction. Compare the value obtained to the value calculated from enthalpies of formation.

52. Methanol can be made by partial oxidation of methane using O_2 in the presence of a catalyst:

$$2\ CH_4(g) + O_2(g) \rightarrow 2\ CH_3OH(\ell)$$

Use bond dissociation enthalpies to estimate the enthalpy change for this reaction. Compare the value obtained to the value calculated using standard enthalpies of formation.

53. Hydrogenation reactions, which involve the addition of H_2 to a molecule, are widely used in industry to transform one compound into another. For example, 1-butene (C_4H_8) is converted to butane (C_4H_{10}) by addition of H_2.

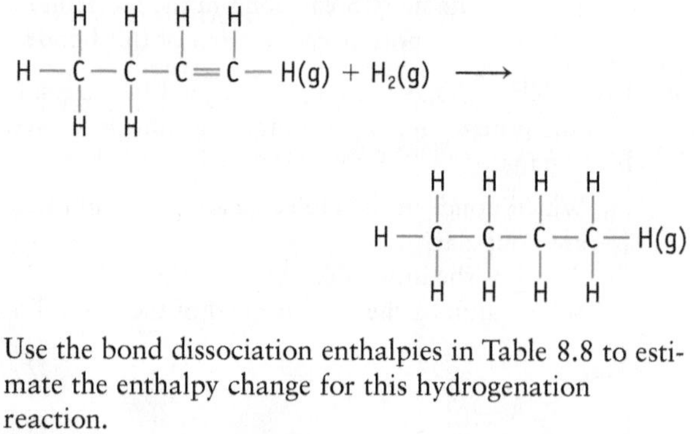

Use the bond dissociation enthalpies in Table 8.8 to estimate the enthalpy change for this hydrogenation reaction.

54. Phosgene, Cl_2CO, is a highly toxic gas that was used as a weapon in World War I. Using the bond dissociation enthalpies in Table 8.8, estimate the enthalpy change for the reaction of carbon monoxide and chlorine to produce phosgene.

$$CO(g) + Cl_2(g) \rightarrow Cl_2CO(g)$$

55. The compound oxygen difluoride is quite reactive, giving oxygen and HF when treated with water:

$$OF_2(g) + H_2O(g) \rightarrow O_2(g) + 2\ HF(g)$$

$$\Delta_r H° = -318\ \text{kJ/mol-rxn}$$

Using bond dissociation enthalpies, calculate the bond dissociation enthalpy of the O—F bond in OF_2.

56. Oxygen atoms can combine with ozone to form oxygen:

$$O_3(g) + O(g) \rightarrow 2\ O_2(g)$$

$$\Delta_r H° = -392\ \text{kJ/mol-rxn}$$

Using $\Delta_r H°$ and the bond dissociation enthalpy data in Table 8.8, estimate the bond dissociation enthalpy for the oxygen–oxygen bond in ozone, O_3. How does your estimate compare with the energies of an O—O single bond and an O═O double bond? Does the oxygen–oxygen bond dissociation enthalpy in ozone correlate with its bond order?

General Questions

These questions are not designated as to type or location in the chapter. They may combine several concepts.

57. Specify the number of valence electrons for Li, Ti, Zn, Si, and Cl.

58. In boron compounds, the B atom often is not surrounded by four valence electron pairs. Illustrate this with BCl_3. Show how the molecule can achieve an octet configuration by forming a coordinate covalent bond with ammonia (NH_3).

59. Which of the following compounds or ions do *not* have an octet of electrons surrounding the central atom: BF_4^-, SiF_4, SeF_4, BrF_4^-, XeF_4?

60. In which of the following does the central atom obey the octet rule: NO_2, SF_4, NH_3, SO_3, ClO_2, and ClO_2^-? Are any of these species odd-electron molecules or ions?

61. Draw resonance structures for the formate ion, HCO_2^- and then determine the C—O bond order in the ion.

62. Consider a series of molecules in which carbon is attached by single covalent bonds to atoms of second-period elements: C—O, C—F, C—N, C—C, and C—B. Place these bonds in order of increasing bond length.

63. To estimate the enthalpy change for the reaction

$$O_2(g) + 2\ H_2(g) \rightarrow 2\ H_2O(g)$$

what bond dissociation enthalpies do you need? Outline the calculation, being careful to show correct algebraic signs.

64. What is the principle of electroneutrality? Use this rule to exclude a possible resonance structure of CO_2.

65. Draw Lewis structures (and resonance structures where appropriate) for the following molecules and ions. What similarities and differences are there in this series?

(a) CO_2 (b) N_3^- (c) OCN^-

66. Draw resonance structures for the SO_2 molecule, and determine the formal charges on the S and O atoms. Are the S—O bonds polar, and is the molecule as a whole polar? If so, what is the direction of the net dipole in SO_2? Is your prediction confirmed by the electrostatic potential surface? Explain briefly.

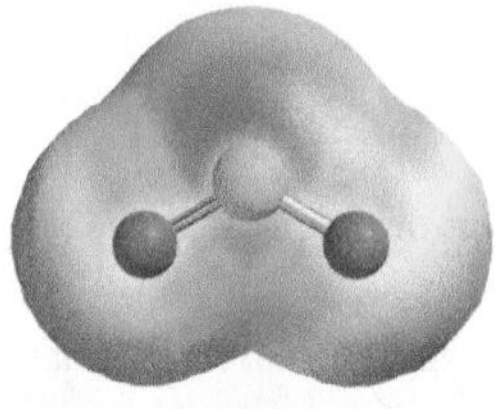

Electrostatic potential surface for sulfur dioxide

67. What are the orders of the N—O bonds in NO_2^- and NO_2^+? The nitrogen–oxygen bond length in one of these ions is 110 pm and 124 pm in the other. Which bond length corresponds to which ion? Explain briefly.

68. Which has the greater O—N—O bond angle, NO_2^- or NO_2^+? Explain briefly.

69. Compare the F—Cl—F angles in ClF_2^+ and ClF_2^-. Using Lewis structures, determine the approximate bond angle in each ion. Which ion has the greater bond angle?

70. Draw an electron dot structure for the cyanide ion, CN^-. In aqueous solution, this ion interacts with H^+ to form the acid. Should the acid formula be written as HCN or CNH?

71. Draw the electron dot structure for the sulfite ion, SO_3^{2-}. In aqueous solution, the ion interacts with H^+. Predict whether a H^+ ion will attach to the S atom or the O atom of SO_3^{2-}.

72. Dinitrogen monoxide, N_2O, can decompose to nitrogen and oxygen gas:

$$2\ N_2O(g) \rightarrow 2\ N_2(g) + O_2(g)$$

Use bond dissociation enthalpies to estimate the enthalpy change for this reaction.

73. ▲ The equation for the combustion of gaseous methanol is

$$2\ CH_3OH(g) + 3\ O_2(g) \rightarrow 2\ CO_2(g) + 4\ H_2O(g)$$

(a) Using the bond dissociation enthalpies in Table 8.8, estimate the enthalpy change for this reaction. What is the enthalpy of combustion of one mole of gaseous methanol?

(b) Compare your answer in part (a) with the value of $\Delta_r H°$ calculated using enthalpies of formation data.

74. ▲ Acrylonitrile, C_3H_3N, is the building block of the synthetic fiber Orlon.

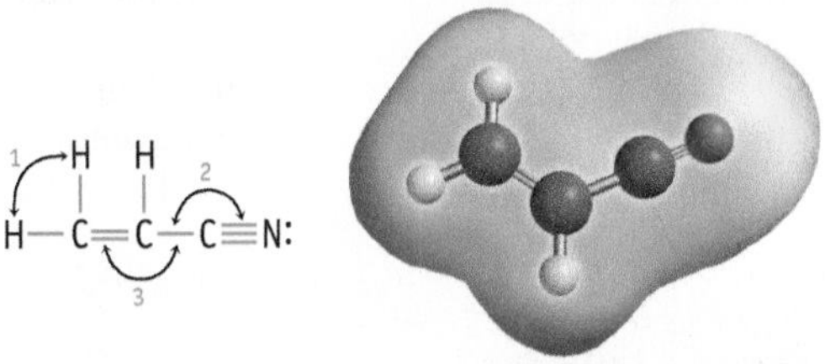

Electrostatic potential surface for acrylonitrile

(a) Give the approximate values of angles 1, 2, and 3.
(b) Which is the shorter carbon–carbon bond?
(c) Which is the stronger carbon–carbon bond?
(d) Based on the electrostatic potential surface, where are the positive and negative charges located in the molecule?
(e) Which is the most polar bond?
(f) Is the molecule polar?

75. ▲ The cyanate ion, OCN^-, has the least electronegative atom, C, in the center. The unstable fulminate ion, CNO^-, has the same molecular formula, but the N atom is in the center.

(a) Draw the three possible resonance structures of CNO^-.
(b) On the basis of formal charges, decide on the resonance structure with the most reasonable distribution of charge.
(c) Mercury fulminate is so unstable it is used in blasting caps for dynamite. Can you offer an explanation for this instability? (*Hint:* Are the formal charges in any resonance structure reasonable in view of the relative electronegativities of the atoms?)

76. Vanillin is the flavoring agent in vanilla extract and in vanilla ice cream. Its structure is shown here:

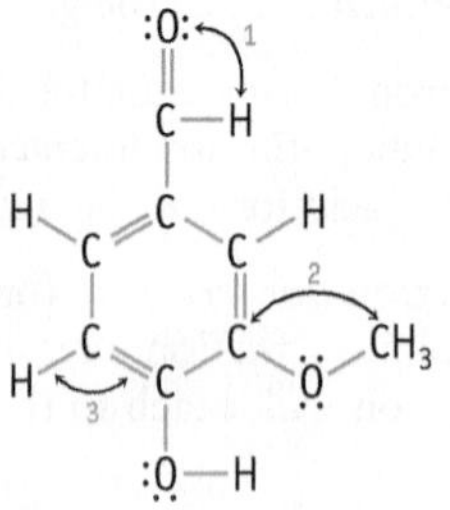

(a) Give values for the three bond angles indicated.
(b) Indicate the shortest carbon–oxygen bond in the molecule.
(c) Indicate the most polar bond in the molecule.

77. ▲ Explain why

(a) XeF_2 has a linear molecular structure and not a bent one.
(b) ClF_3 has a T-shaped structure and not a trigonal-planar one.

78. The formula for nitryl chloride is $ClNO_2$ (in which N is the central atom).

(a) Draw the Lewis structure for the molecule, including all resonance structures.
(b) What is the N—O bond order?
(c) Describe the electron-pair and molecular geometries, and give values for all bond angles.
(d) What is the most polar bond in the molecule? Is the molecule polar?
(e) ▲ The computer program used to calculate electrostatic potential surfaces gave the following charges on atoms in the molecule: A = −0.03, B = −0.26, and C = +0.56. Identify the atoms A, B, and C. Are these calculated charges in accord with your predictions?

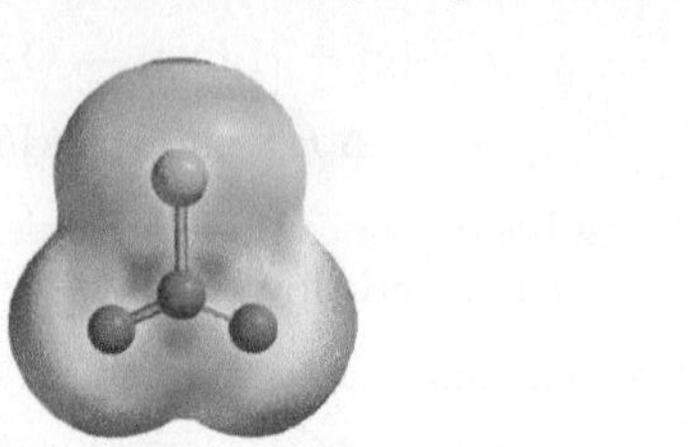

Electrostatic potential surface for $ClNO_2$

79. Hydroxyproline is a less-common amino acid.

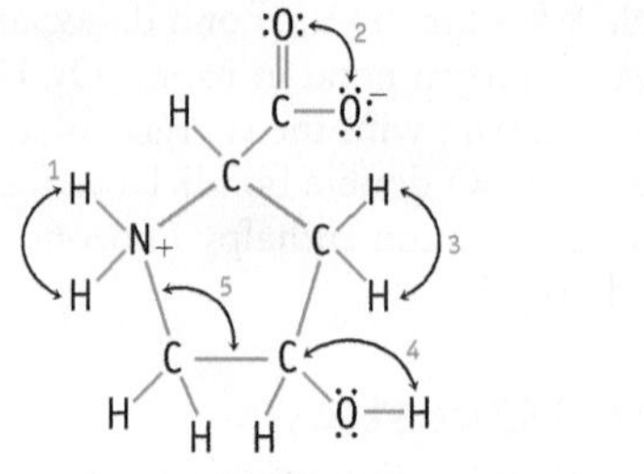

(a) Give approximate values for the indicated bond angles.
(b) Which are the most polar bonds in the molecule?

80. Amides are an important class of organic molecules. They are usually drawn as sketched here, but another resonance structure is possible.

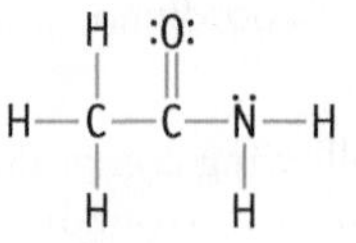

(a) Draw a second resonance structure of the structure above. Do you think that this should be a significant contributor to the bonding? Explain your answer.
(b) The H—N—H angle is close to 120° in this molecule. Does this fact influence your thoughts on the importance of this structure?

81. Use the bond dissociation enthalpies in Table 8.8 to estimate the enthalpy change for the decomposition of urea (See Study Question 30) to hydrazine, $H_2N—NH_2$, and carbon monoxide. (Assume all compounds are in the gas phase.)

82. The molecule shown here, 2-furylmethanethiol, is responsible for the aroma of coffee:

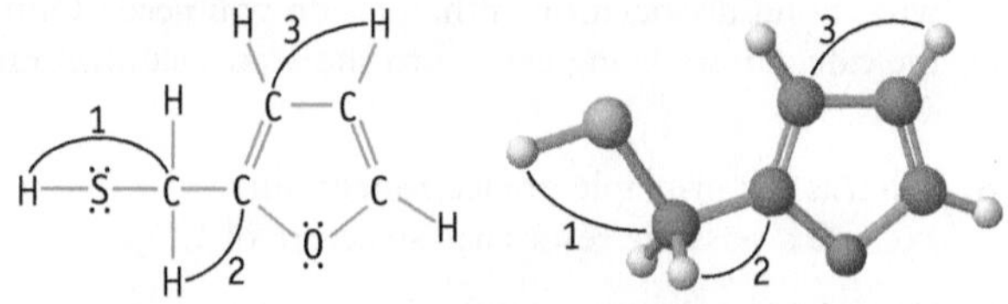

2-Furylmethanethiol

(a) What are the formal charges on the S and O atoms?
(b) Give approximate values of angles 1, 2, and 3.
(c) Which are the shorter carbon–carbon bonds in the molecule?

(d) Which bond in this molecule is the most polar?
(e) Is the molecule polar or nonpolar?
(f) The four C atoms of the ring are all in a plane. Is the O atom in that same plane (making the five-member ring planar), or is the O atom bent above or below the plane?

83. ▲ Dihydroxyacetone is a component of quick-tanning lotions. (It reacts with the amino acids in the upper layer of skin and colors them brown in a reaction similar to that occurring when food is browned as it cooks.)

(a) Use bond dissociation enthalpies to estimate the enthalpy change for the following reaction. Is the reaction exothermic or endothermic?

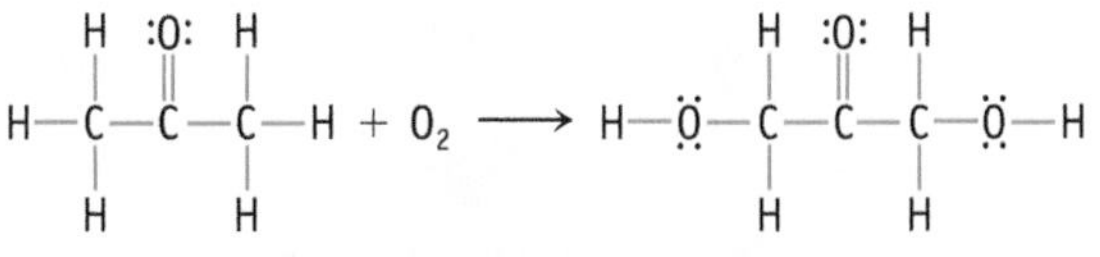

Acetone   Dihydroxyacetone

(b) Are dihydroxyacetone and acetone polar molecules?
(c) A proton (H^+) can be removed from a molecule of dihydroxyacetone with strong bases (which is in part what happens in the tanning reaction). Which H atoms are the most positive in dihydroxyacetone?

84. It is possible to draw three resonance structures for HNO_3, one of which contributes much less to the resonance hybrid than the other two. Sketch the three resonance structures, and assign a formal charge to each atom. Which one of your structures is the least important?

85. ▲ Acrolein is used to make plastics. Suppose this compound can be prepared by inserting a carbon monoxide molecule into the C—H bond of ethylene.

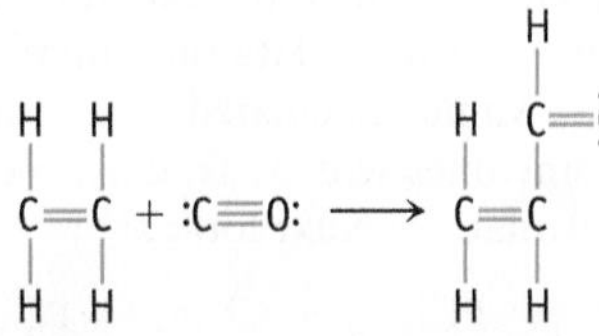

Ethylene   Acrolein

(a) Which is the stronger carbon–carbon bond in acrolein?
(b) Which is the longer carbon–carbon bond in acrolein?
(c) Is ethylene or acrolein polar?
(d) Use bond dissociation enthalpies to predict whether the reaction of CO with C_2H_4 to give acrolein is endothermic or exothermic?

86. Molecules in space:

(a) In addition to molecules such as CO, HCl, H_2O, and NH_3, glycolaldehyde has been detected in outer space. Is the molecule polar?

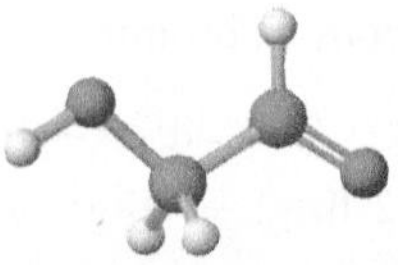

$HOCH_2CHO$, glycolaldehyde

(b) Where do the positive and negative charges lie in the molecule?
(c) One molecule found in the 1995 Hale-Bopp comet is HC_3N. Suggest a structure for this molecule.

87. 1,2-Dichloroethylene can be synthesized by adding Cl_2 to the carbon–carbon triple bond of acetylene.

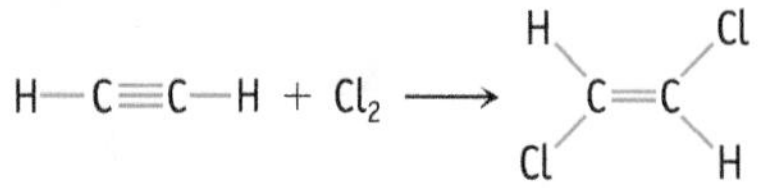

Using bond dissociation enthalpies, estimate the enthalpy change for this reaction in the gas phase.

88. The molecule pictured below is epinephrine, a compound used as a bronchodilator and antiglaucoma agent.

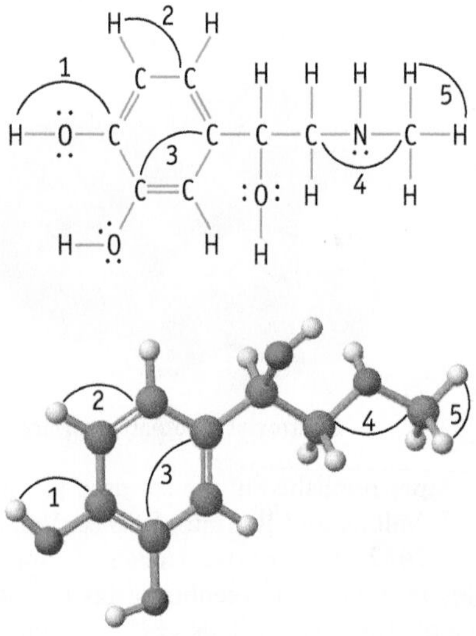

Epinephrine

(a) Give a value for each of the indicated bond angles.
(b) What are the most polar bonds in the molecule?

In the Laboratory

89. You are doing an experiment in the laboratory and want to prepare a solution in a polar solvent. Which solvent would you choose, methanol (CH_3OH) or toluene ($C_6H_5CH_3$)? Explain your choice.

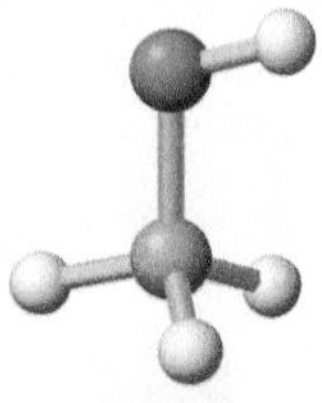

Methanol

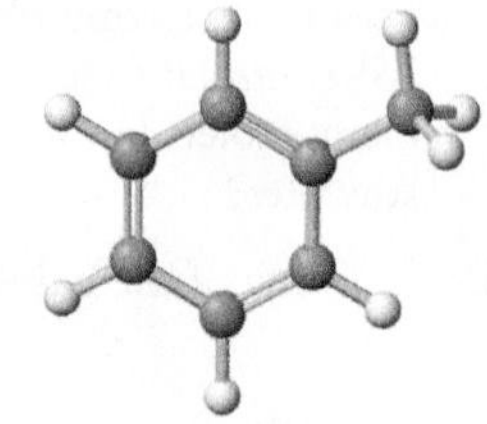

Toluene

90. Methylacetamide, $CH_3CONHCH_3$, is a small molecule with an amide link (CO—NH), the group that binds one amino acid to another in proteins.

(a) Is this molecule polar?
(b) Where do you expect the positive and negative charges to lie in this molecule? Does the electrostatic potential surface confirm your predictions?

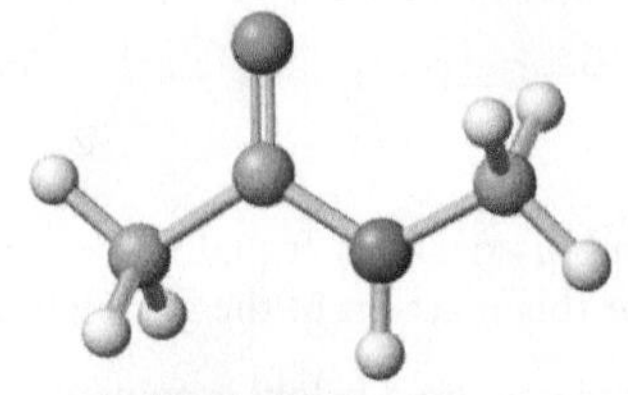

Methylacetamide
Ball-and-stick model

Electrostatic potential surface

91. ▲ A paper published in the research journal *Science* in 2007 (S. Vallina and R. Simo, *Science*, Vol. 315, p. 506, January 26, 2007) reported studies of dimethylsulfide (DMS), an important greenhouse gas that is released by marine phytoplankton. This gas "represents the largest natural source of atmospheric sulfur and a major precursor of hygroscopic (i.e., cloud-forming) particles in clean air over the remote oceans, thereby acting to reduce the amount of solar radiation that crosses the atmosphere and is absorbed by the ocean."

(a) Sketch the Lewis structure of dimethylsulfide, CH_3SCH_3, and list the bond angles in the molecule.
(b) Use electronegativities to decide where the positive and negative charges lie in the molecule. Is the molecule polar?
(c) The mean seawater concentration of DMS in the ocean in the region between 15° north latitude and 15° south latitude is 2.7 nM (nanomolar). How many molecules of DMS are present in 1.0 m^3 of seawater?

92. Uracil is one of the bases in RNA.

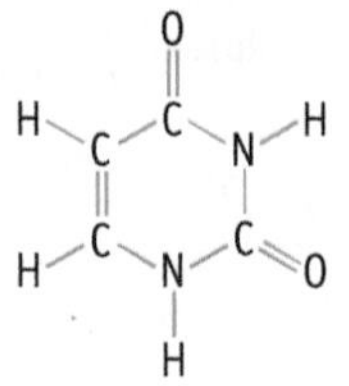

Uracil, $C_4H_4N_2O_2$

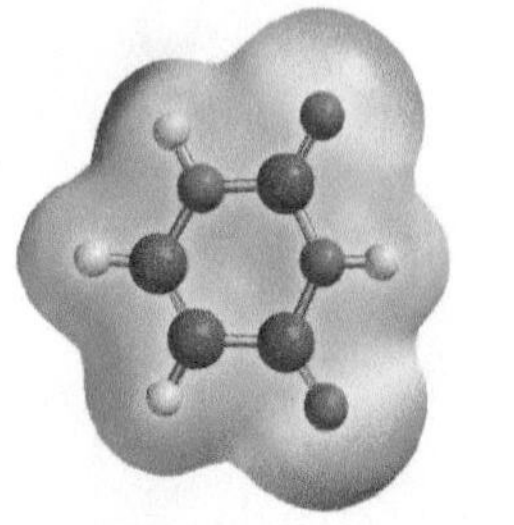

Electrostatic potential surface for uracil

(a) What are the values of the O—C—N and C—N—H angles?
(b) There are two carbon–carbon bonds in the molecule. Which is predicted to be shorter?
(c) If a proton attacks the molecule, decide on the basis of the electrostatic potential surface to which atom or atoms it could be attached.

Summary and Conceptual Questions

The following questions may use concepts from this and previous chapters.

93. White phosphorus exists as P_4 molecules with phosphorus atoms at the corners of a tetrahedron.

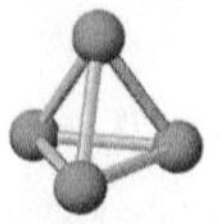

White phosphorus, P_4

(a) Elemental phosphorus reacts with Cl_2 to form PCl_3. Write a balanced chemical equation for this reaction.
(b) The standard enthalpy of formation ($\Delta_f H°$) of $P_4(g)$ is +58.9 kJ/mol; for $PCl_3(g)$ it is −287.0 kJ/mol. Use these numbers to calculate the enthalpy change for the reaction of $P_4(g)$ and $Cl_2(g)$ to give $PCl_3(g)$.
(c) Based on the equation in (a), determine what bonds are broken and what bonds are formed. Then, use this information along with the value of $\Delta_r H°$ calculated in (b) and the bond dissociation enthalpies for the P—P and Cl—Cl bonds from Table 8.8 to estimate the bond dissociation enthalpy for the P—Cl bonds. How does your estimate compare with the value in Table 8.8?

94. The answer in Study Question 93 does not exactly match the value for the bond dissociation enthalpy of P—Cl in Table 8.8. The reason is that the numbers in the table are averages, derived from data on a number of different compounds. Values calculated from different compounds do vary, sometimes widely. To illustrate this, let's do another calculation. Next look at the following reaction:

$$PCl_3(g) + Cl_2(g) \rightarrow PCl_5(g)$$

The enthalpy of formation of $PCl_5(g)$ is −374.9 kJ/mol. Use this and $\Delta_f H°$ of $PCl_3(g)$ to determine the enthalpy change for this reaction. Then, use that value of $\Delta_r H°$, along with the bond dissociation enthalpy of Cl_2, to calculate the enthalpy change for the formation of a P—Cl bond in this reaction.

95. Bromine-containing species play a role in environmental chemistry. For example, they are evolved in volcanic eruptions.

(a) The following molecules are important in bromine environmental chemistry: HBr, BrO, and HOBr. Which is an odd-electron molecule?
(b) Use bond dissociation enthalpies to estimate $\Delta_r H$ for three reactions of bromine:

$$Br_2(g) \rightarrow 2\ Br(g)$$

$$2\ Br(g) + O_2(g) \rightarrow 2\ BrO(g)$$

$$BrO(g) + H_2O(g) \rightarrow HOBr(g) + OH(g)$$

(c) Using bond dissociation enthalpies, estimate the standard enthalpy of formation of $HOBr(g)$ from $H_2(g)$, $O_2(g)$, and $Br_2(g)$.
(d) Are the reactions in parts (b) and (c) exothermic or endothermic?

96. Acrylamide, $H_2C{=}CHCONH_2$, is a known neurotoxin and possible carcinogen. It was a shock to all consumers of potato chips and french fries a few years ago when it was found to occur in those products.

(a) Sketch the molecular structure of acrylamide and identify all bond angles.
(b) Indicate which carbon–carbon bond is the stronger of the two.
(c) Is the molecule polar or nonpolar?
(d) The amount of acrylamide found in potato chips is 1.7 mg/kg. If a serving of potato chips is 28 g, how many moles of acrylamide are you consuming?

AP Multiple-Choice Review Questions

1. Consider the reaction shown below:

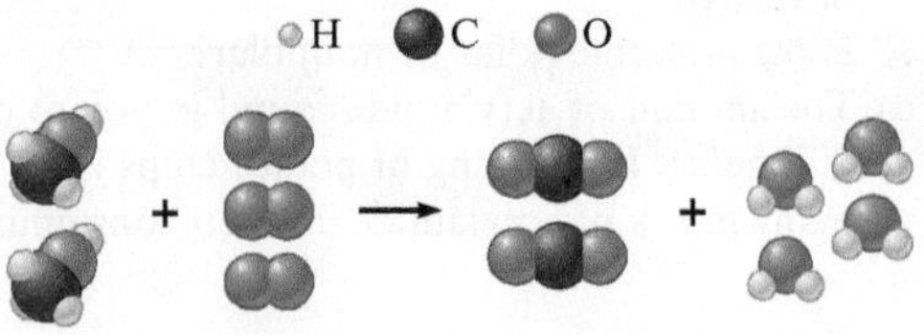

Type of Bond	Bond Energy (kJ/mol)
	500
	800
	475
	400

Determine ΔH for the reaction represented above, where each molecule represents 1 mole of that substance.

(A) −2150 kJ
(B) −550 kJ
(C) 100 kJ
(D) 2175 kJ

2. Which of the following has a bent molecular geometry with a bond angle of approximately 120°?

(A) 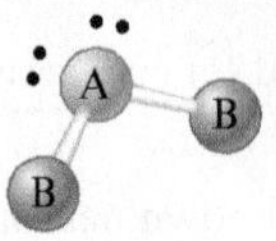
(B) 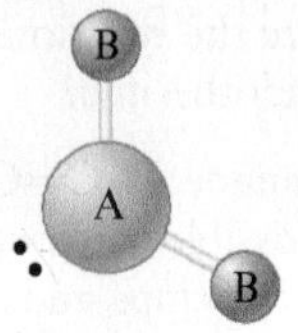
(C) 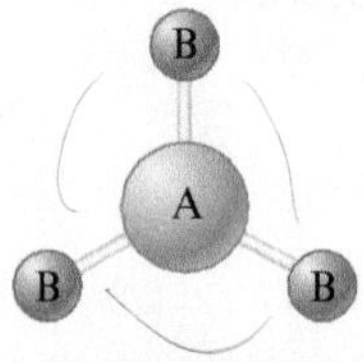
(D) 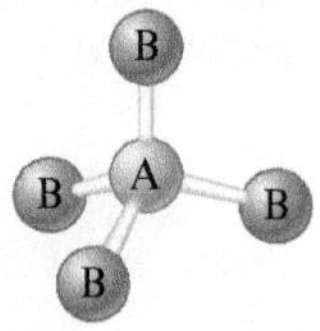

3. Which of the following is nonpolar?

(A) 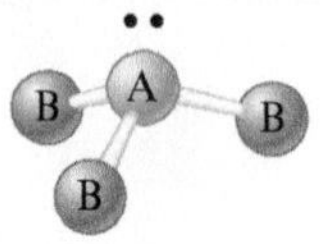
(B) 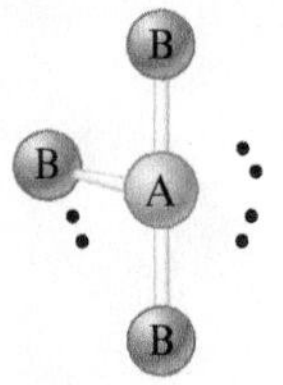
(C) 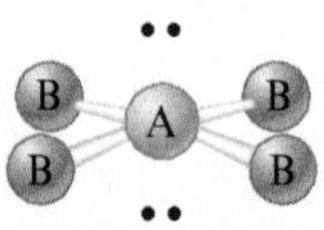
(D) 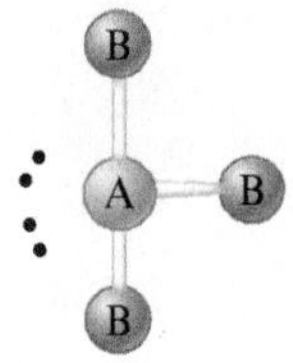

4. Which diagram best represents the shape of the SF_5^- ion?

(A) 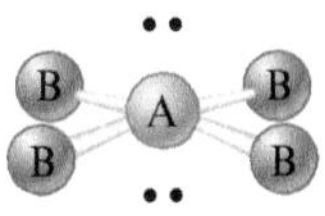

(B) 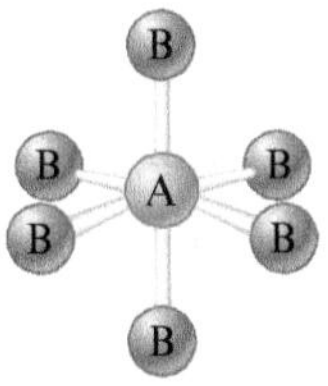

(C) 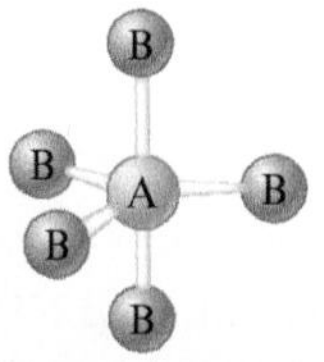

(D) 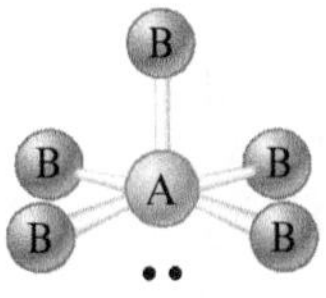

5. Which pair of elements is likely to produce a highly polar covalent bond?

(A) Mg and O
(B) Li and F
(C) O and F
(D) C and F

6. Which pair of elements is likely to produce a nearly non-polar covalent bond?

(A) Li and Rb
(B) Mg and O
(C) N and F
(D) Te and I

7. Which pair of elements is likely to produce an ionic bond?

(A) O and F
(B) S and N
(C) Li and Cl
(D) Ca and Ba

8. Which molecule is likely to have a measurable dipole moment?

(A) 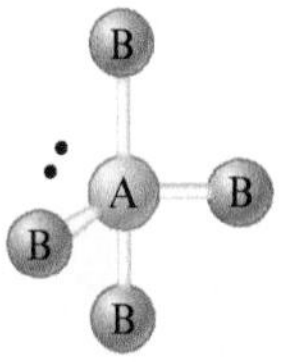

(B) 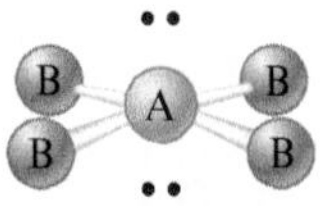

(C) 

(D) 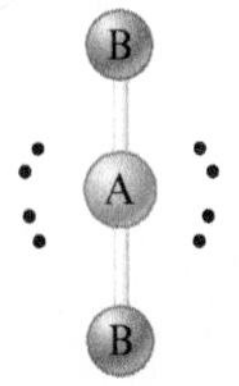

9. The cyanate ion has three possible Lewis structures. Based on formal charges, which Lewis structure is the dominant structure, that is, the structure that best represents the cyanate ion?

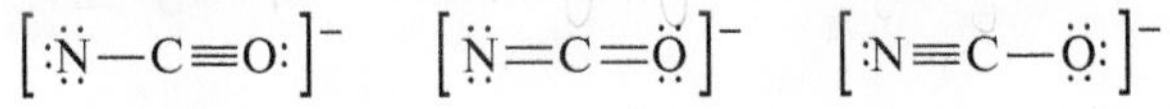

A B C

(A) Diagram A best represents the cyanate ion.
(B) Diagram B best represents the cyanate ion.
(C) Diagram C best represents the cyanate ion.
(D) Due to resonance, all three diagrams best represent the cyanate ion.

10. Determine ΔH for the reaction of methane with oxygen.

$$CH_4(g) + 2O_2(g) \rightarrow 3H_2O(\ell) + 2CO_2(g)$$

Bond	Bond Energy (kJ/mol)
C—H	400.
O═O	500.
C═O	800.
O—H	470.

(A) −3420 kJ
(B) −880 kJ
(C) −430 kJ
(D) −370 kJ

11. Use the following information to calculate the H—Cl bond energy.

Reaction	$\Delta H°$ (kJ)
$H_2(g) + Cl_2(g) \rightarrow 2HCl(g)$	−180
$H_2(g) \rightarrow 2H(g)$	430
$Cl_2(g) \rightarrow 2Cl(g)$	240

(A) 325 kJ
(B) 425 kJ
(C) 490 kJ
(D) 950 kJ

12. Which of the following best describes BF_3 and NF_3? (*Note: Geometry* refers to the electron pair arrangement, and *shape* refers to the atom arrangement.)
(A) They have the same geometry and different shapes.
(B) They have the same geometry and the same shape.
(C) They have different geometry and different shapes.
(D) They have different geometry and the same shape.

AP Free Response Review Questions

Question Format: Short

Category of Question: Representation 2

Sulfur can be found in many different forms in nature. Three formulas that illustrate this are S_8, SO_2, and Na_2S.

Questions

(a) Draw diagrams that demonstrate the bonding found within each of these species, showing resonance structures where appropriate.

(b) Briefly describe the type of bonding present in each species.

Question Format: Long

Category of Question: Representation 1

Hydrazine, N_2H_4, has several commercial uses, one of which is as rocket fuel.

Bond	Bond Energy (kJ/mol)
N—H	391
N—N	160
N=N	418
N≡N	941
O—O	146
O=O	495
N—O	201
N=O	607
O—H	467

Questions

(a) Write a balanced chemical equation for the combustion of hydrazine to produce nitrogen dioxide and water.

(b) Draw Lewis electron dot structures for each reactant and product in the reaction in part (a) above.

(c) Given the bond energies in the table, determine the $\Delta H°_{rxn}$. Justify the sign of the $\Delta H°_{rxn}$, using principles of bond breakage and formation.

(d) Experimental evidence shows that the bond angle in NO_2 is approximately 134°. Explain.

(e) Experimental evidence shows that the two nitrogen-oxygen bond lengths in NO_2 are identical. Explain.

(f) Which type of nitrogen-nitrogen bond (N—N, N=N, or N≡N) is the shortest?

Explain your reasoning.

Crystals of XeF_2 formed from Xe(g) and F_2(g) in sunlight.

Bonding and Molecular Structure: Orbital Hybridization and Molecular Orbitals

Chapter Outline

THE NOBLE GASES: NOT SO INERT

Generations of chemistry professors once taught that the noble gases were chemically inert. However, in 1962 chemists learned this was not so. Xenon at the very least was found to form compounds! The first was an ionic compound, now known to be $XeF^+Pt_2F_{11}^-$. However, this was followed shortly thereafter with the discovery of a large number of covalently bonded compounds, including XeF_4, XeF_6, $XeOF_4$, and XeO_3. And, since 1962, the field of noble gas chemistry has expanded with the discovery of such interesting molecules as FXeOXeF.

Initially, xenon compounds were thought to form only under the most severe conditions. Therefore, it was again a surprise when it was found that putting a mixture of xenon and fluorine gases in sunlight at room temperature gave crystals of XeF_2 (as seen in the photo).

Chapter Goals

See Chapter Goals Revisited (page 368) for Study Questions keyed to these goals.

UNDERSTAND

- Orbital overlap is the basis for covalent bonding.
- The theory of orbital hybridization.
- The differences between valence bond theory and molecular orbital theory and how each theory is applied.

DO

- Identify the hybridization of an atom in a molecule or poly–atomic ion.
- Describe the bonding in a molecule or polyatomic ion using valence bond theory.
- Write the molecular orbital configurations for simple diatomic molecules or ions, determine the bond order of each species, and predict its magnetic behavior.

REMEMBER

- Chemical bonding may be described using different theories, each having its advantages and disadvantages.
- The types of hybrid orbital sets and their orientations in space.
- The terms sigma and pi and their meaning in terms of orbital overlap and bond shape.

Two of the authors of this text were graduate students at the time of this discovery. Everyone discussed it, and among important questions were the structures of the molecules and nature of their bonding. The structures have since been determined experimentally, and, now based on the concepts in a general chemistry book, a student can predict the structures using VSEPR theory (a theory not yet developed when these molecules were discovered). Ideas on bonding, though, have continued to evolve. For example, in recent years researchers have questioned how, or whether, *d* orbitals might be involved in bonding in molecules such as XeF_4 and XeF_2.

There is an important observation to be made here: the structure of a molecule is a fact. Bonding descriptions, however, are theories, constructed to rationalize facts that we learn from experiment and can change as we acquire more information.

How can we account for the bonding in molecules, especially given the range of possible molecular shapes? For instance, millions of organic compounds are based on carbon atoms surrounded tetrahedrally by other atoms. How can a carbon atom be bonded to atoms at the corners of a tetrahedron when carbon's atomic orbitals don't point in those directions? How can a dye molecule absorb light? Why is oxygen paramagnetic, and how is this property connected with bonding in the molecule? These are just a few of the fundamental and interesting questions that are raised in this chapter and that require us to take a more advanced look at bonding.

9-1 Orbitals and Theories of Chemical Bonding

From Chapter 6, you know that the electronic structure of the atom is described by an orbital model. Therefore, it seems reasonable that a similar orbital model could be used to describe electrons in molecules.

Two common approaches to rationalizing chemical bonding based on orbitals are **valence bond (VB) theory** and **molecular orbital (MO) theory**. The former was developed largely by Linus Pauling (page 299) and the latter by another American scientist, Robert S. Mulliken (1896–1986). The valence bond approach is closely tied to Lewis's idea that there are electron pairs between bonded atoms and lone pairs of electrons localized on a particular atom. In contrast, Mulliken's approach was to derive molecular orbitals that are "spread out," or *delocalized*, over the molecule. One way to do this is to combine atomic orbitals to form a set of orbitals that are the property of the molecule and then to distribute the electrons of the molecule within those orbitals.

Bonds Are a "Figment of Our Own Imagination" C. A. Coulson, a prominent theoretical chemist at the University of Oxford, England, has said that "Sometimes it seems to me that a bond between atoms has become so real, so tangible, so friendly, that I can almost see it. Then I awake with a little shock, for a chemical bond is not a real thing. It does not exist. No one has ever seen one. No one ever can. It is a figment of our own imagination" (*Chemical and Engineering News,* January 29, 2007, page 37). Nonetheless, bonds are a useful figment, and this chapter presents some of these ideas.

Both valence bond theory and molecular orbital theory give good descriptions of the bonding in molecules and polyatomic ions, but they are most useful in different situations. Valence bond theory is generally the method of choice to provide a qualitative, visual picture of molecular structure and bonding. This theory is particularly useful for molecules made up of many atoms. In contrast, molecular orbital theory is used when a more quantitative picture of bonding is needed. Valence bond theory provides a good description of bonding for molecules in their ground or lowest energy state. Molecular orbital theory is essential if we want to describe molecules in higher-energy, excited states. Among other things, this is important in explaining the colors of compounds. Finally, for a few molecules such as NO and O_2, MO theory is the only one of the two theories that can describe their bonding accurately.

Learning Objectives: LO 5.1

9-2 Valence Bond Theory

The Orbital Overlap Model of Bonding

What happens if two hydrogen atoms at an infinite distance apart are brought together to form a bond? Widely separated, the two atoms do not interact. If the atoms move closer together, however, the electron on one atom is attracted to the positive charge of the nucleus of the other atom. As illustrated in Figure 9.1, this distorts the electron clouds of the two atoms, drawing the electrons toward the region of space between the atoms where the two orbitals overlap. Because of the attractive forces between the nuclei and electrons, the potential energy of the system decreases. At a distance of 74 pm between the H atoms, the potential energy reaches a minimum. Decreasing the distance between the H atoms further, however, results in a rapid increase in the potential energy due to repulsions between the nuclei of the two atoms and between the electrons of the atoms.

A system is stable when the potential energy is lowest. Based on the analysis described here, this is predicted to occur when the two hydrogen atoms are 74 pm apart. Significantly, 74 pm also corresponds to the experimentally measured bond distance in the H_2 molecule.

In the H_2 molecule, the two electrons, one from each atom and with opposite spins, pair up to form the bond. There is a net stabilization, representing the extent to which the energies of the two electrons are lowered from their value in the free atoms. The calculated net stabilization matches the experimentally determined bond energy, and this agreement between theory and experiment on both bond distance and energy is evidence that this theoretical approach has merit.

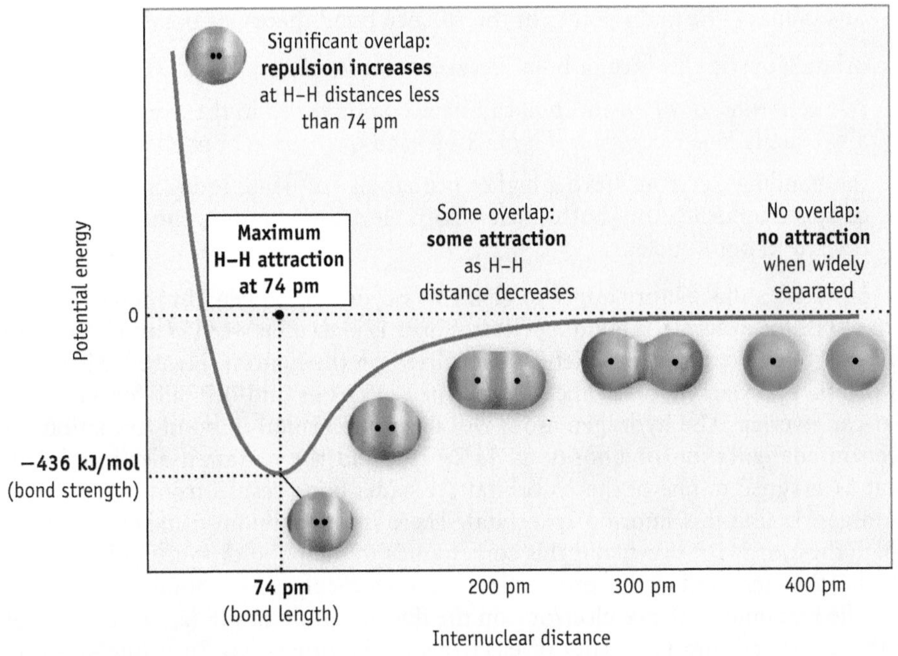

FIGURE 9.1 **Potential energy change during H—H bond formation from isolated hydrogen atoms.** The red color in the orbital pictures reflects the increase in electron density between the H atoms as the distance decreases.

The idea that bonds are formed by the overlap of atomic orbitals is the basis for valence bond theory. This is usually illustrated as in Figures 9.1 and 9.2, where the electron clouds on the two atoms are seen to interpenetrate or overlap. This orbital overlap increases the probability of finding the bonding electrons in the region of space between the two nuclei.

The covalent bond in H_2 that arises from the overlap of two *s* orbitals, one from each of two H atoms, is called a **sigma (σ) bond**. *A sigma bond is a bond in which electron density is greatest along the axis of the bond.*

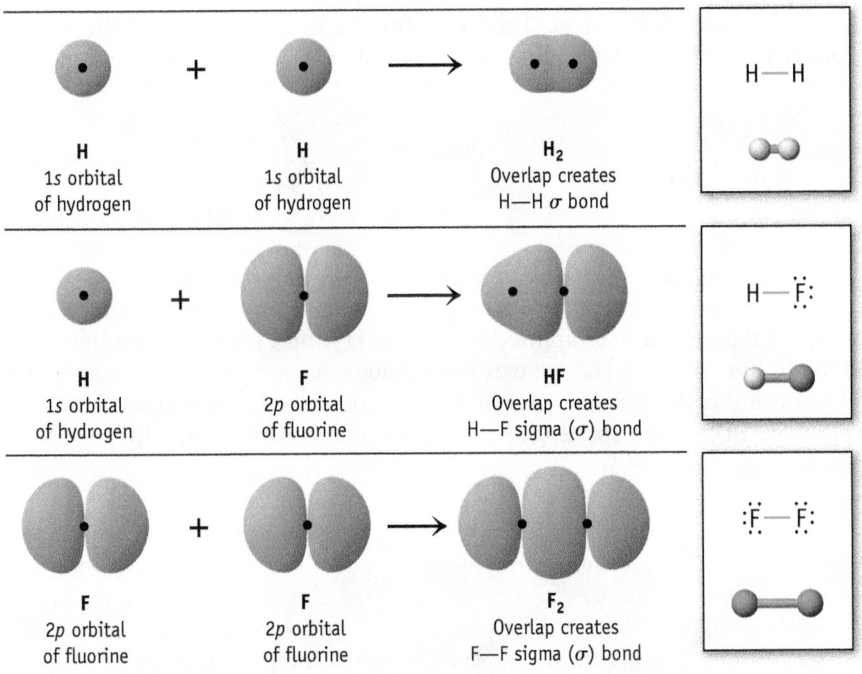

(a) Overlap of hydrogen 1*s* orbitals to form the H—H sigma (σ) bond.

(b) Overlap of hydrogen 1*s* and fluorine 2*p* orbitals to form the sigma (σ) bond in HF.

(c) Overlap of 2*p* orbitals on two fluorine atoms forming the sigma (σ) bond in F_2.

FIGURE 9.2 **Covalent (sigma) bond formation in H_2, HF, and F_2.**

In summary, the main points of the valence bond theory of bonding are that

- orbitals overlap to form a bond between two atoms.
- two electrons, *of opposite spin*, can be accommodated in the overlapping orbitals. Usually, one electron is supplied by each of the two bonded atoms.
- the bonding electrons have a higher probability of being found within a region of space influenced by both nuclei. Both electrons are thus simultaneously attracted to both nuclei.

How does this picture apply to elements beyond hydrogen? In the Lewis structure of HF, for example, a bonding electron pair is placed between H and F, and three lone pairs of electrons are depicted as localized on the F atom (Figure 9.2b). To use an orbital approach, look at the valence shell electrons and orbitals for each atom that can overlap. The hydrogen atom will use its 1*s* orbital in bond formation. The electron configuration of fluorine is $1s^22s^22p^5$, and the unpaired electron for this atom is assigned to one of the 2*p* orbitals. A sigma bond results from overlap of the hydrogen 1*s* and this fluorine 2*p* orbital. There is an optimum distance (92 pm) at which the energy is lowest, and this corresponds to the bond distance in HF. The net stabilization achieved in this process is the energy for the H—F bond.

The remaining valence electrons on the fluorine atom in HF (a pair of electrons in the 2*s* orbital and two pairs of electrons in the other two 2*p* orbitals) are not involved in bonding. They are nonbonding electrons, the lone pairs associated with this element in the Lewis structure.

This model can be extended to a description of bonding in F_2. The 2*p* orbitals on the two atoms overlap, and the single electron from each atom is paired in the resulting σ bond (Figure 9.2c). The 2*s* and the 2*p* electrons not involved in the bond are the lone pairs on each atom.

Hybridization Using *s* and *p* Atomic Orbitals

The simple picture using orbital overlap to describe bonding in H_2, HF, and F_2 works well, but we run into difficulty when molecules with more atoms are considered. For example, a Lewis dot structure of methane, CH_4, shows four C—H covalent bonds. VSEPR theory predicts, and experiments confirm, that the electron-pair geometry of the C atom in CH_4 is tetrahedral, with an angle of 109.5° between the bond pairs. The hydrogen atoms are identical in this structure. This means that four equivalent bonding electron pairs occur around the C atom. An orbital picture of the bonds should convey both the geometry and the fact that all C—H bonds are the same.

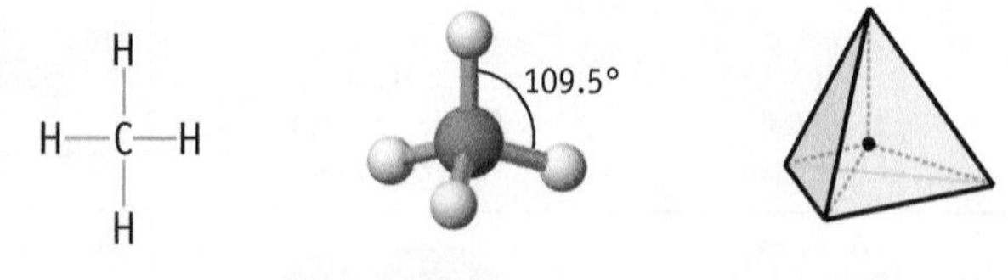

Lewis structure | molecular model | electron-pair geometry

If we apply the orbital overlap model used for H_2 and F_2 without modification to describe the bonding in CH_4, we can immediately see a problem. Although the spherical 2*s* orbital could form a bond in any direction, the three *p*-orbitals for the valence electrons of carbon ($2p_x$, $2p_y$, $2p_z$) are at right angles (90°) and do not match the tetrahedral angle of 109.5°.

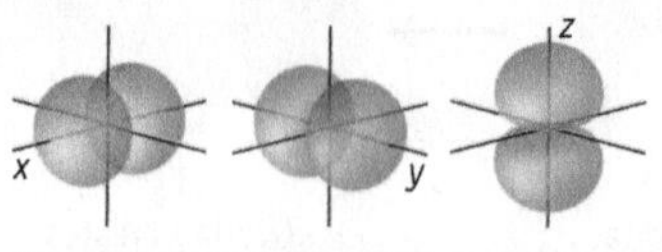

$2p_x$ $2p_y$ $2p_z$

Furthermore, a carbon atom in its ground state ($1s^22s^22p^2$) has only two unpaired electrons (in the $2p$ orbitals), not the four that are needed to allow formation of four bonds.

To describe the bonding in methane and other molecules, Linus Pauling proposed the theory of **orbital hybridization**. He suggested that a new set of orbitals, called **hybrid orbitals**, could be created by mixing the *s* and *p* orbitals on an atom (Figure 9.3). There are three principles that govern the outcome.

- The number of hybrid orbitals on an atom is always equal to the number of atomic orbitals that are mixed to create the hybrid orbital set.
- Hybrid orbital sets are always built by combining an *s* orbital with as many *p* orbitals as needed to have enough hybrid orbitals to accommodate the sigma bonding and lone electron pairs on the central atom.
- The hybrid orbitals are directed toward the terminal atoms, leading to better orbital overlap and a stronger bond between the central and terminal atoms.

Hybridization and Geometry
Hybridization reconciles the electron-pair geometry with the orbital overlap criterion of bonding. A statement such as "the atom is tetrahedral because it is sp^3 hybridized" is backward. That the electron-pair geometry around the atom is tetrahedral is a fact. Hybridization is one way to describe the bonding that can occur in this geometry.

The sets of hybrid orbitals that arise from mixing *s* and *p* atomic orbitals are illustrated in Figure 9.3. *The hybrid orbitals required by an atom in a molecule or ion are chosen to match the electron-pair geometry of the atom* because a hybrid

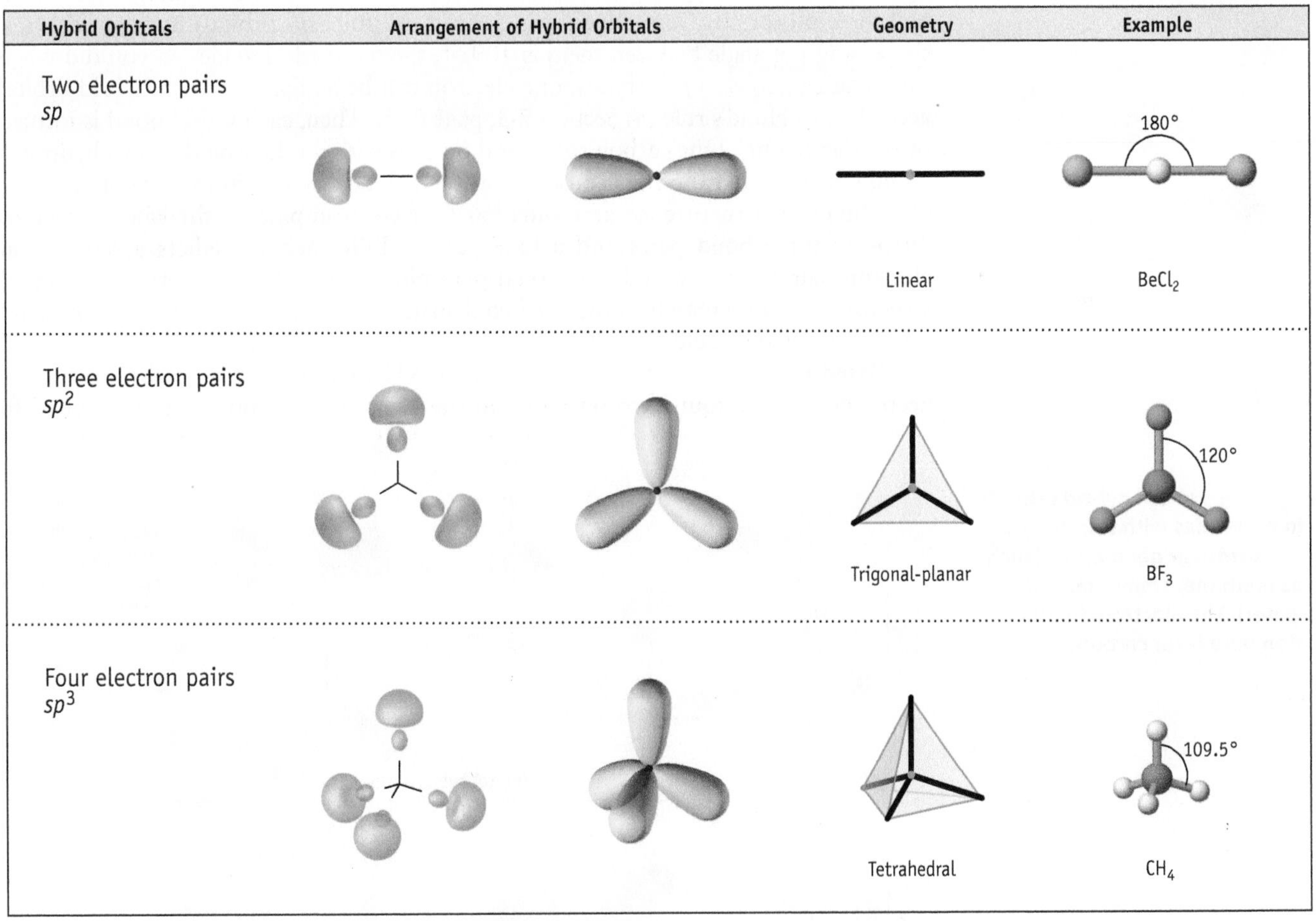

FIGURE 9.3 **Hybrid orbitals for two to four electron pairs.** The geometry of the hybrid orbital sets for two to four valence shell electron pairs is given in the right column. In forming a hybrid orbital set, the *s* orbital is always used, plus as many *p* orbitals as are required to give the necessary number of σ-bonding and lone-pair orbitals.

orbital is required for each sigma bond electron pair and each lone pair. The following types of hybridization are important:

- ***sp***: If the valence shell *s* orbital on the central atom in a molecule or ion is mixed with a valence shell *p* orbital on that same atom, two *sp* hybrid orbitals are created. They are separated by 180°.
- ***sp*²**: If an *s* orbital is combined with two *p* orbitals, all in the same valence shell, three sp^2 hybrid orbitals are created. They are in the same plane and are separated by 120°.
- ***sp*³**: When the *s* orbital is combined with three *p* orbitals in the same valence shell, the result is four hybrid orbitals, each labeled sp^3. The hybrid orbitals are separated by 109.5°, the tetrahedral angle.

Hybrid Orbitals for Molecules and Ions with Tetrahedral Electron-Pair Geometries

Methane, ammonia, and water all have tetrahedral electron-pair geometries and are examples of molecules in which valence bond theory assigns sp^3 hybridization to the central atom (Figures 9.4 and 9.5).

In methane, four orbitals directed to the corners of a tetrahedron are needed to match the electron-pair geometry on the central carbon atom. By combining the four valence shell orbitals, the 2*s* and all three of the 2*p* orbitals on carbon, a new set of four hybrid orbitals is created that has tetrahedral geometry (Figure 9.4). Each of the four hybrid orbitals is labeled sp^3 to indicate the atomic orbital combination (an *s* orbital and three *p* orbitals) from which it is derived. All four sp^3 orbitals have an identical shape, and the angle between them is 109.5°, the tetrahedral angle. As you did when assigning electrons to *p*- orbitals, one electron can be assigned to each hybrid orbital according to Hund's rule (◀ Section 7-3, page 257). Then, each C—H bond is formed by overlap of one of the carbon sp^3 hybrid orbitals with the 1*s* orbital from a hydrogen atom; one electron from the C atom is paired with an electron from an H atom.

The Lewis structure for ammonia has four electron pairs in the valence shell of nitrogen: three bond pairs and a lone pair. VSEPR theory predicts a tetrahedral electron-pair geometry and a trigonal-pyramidal molecular geometry. The actual structure is a close match to the predicted structure; the H—N—H bond angles are 107.5° in this molecule.

Based on the electron-pair geometry of NH_3, we predict sp^3 hybridization to accommodate the four electron pairs on the N atom. The lone pair is assigned to

FIGURE 9.4 *sp*³ hybrid orbitals in molecules with tetrahedral electron-pair geometries (such as methane, ammonia, and water). The electron distribution here is for carbon.

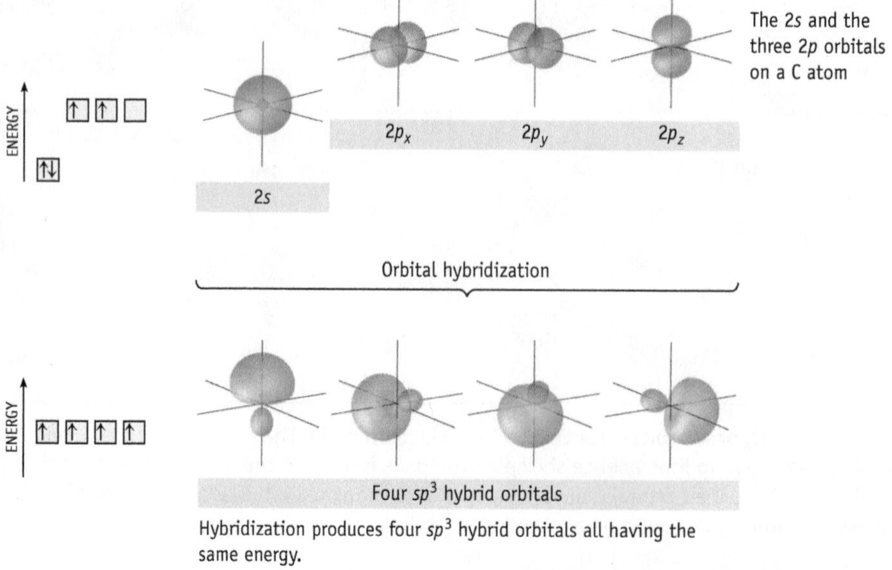

Hybridization produces four sp^3 hybrid orbitals all having the same energy.

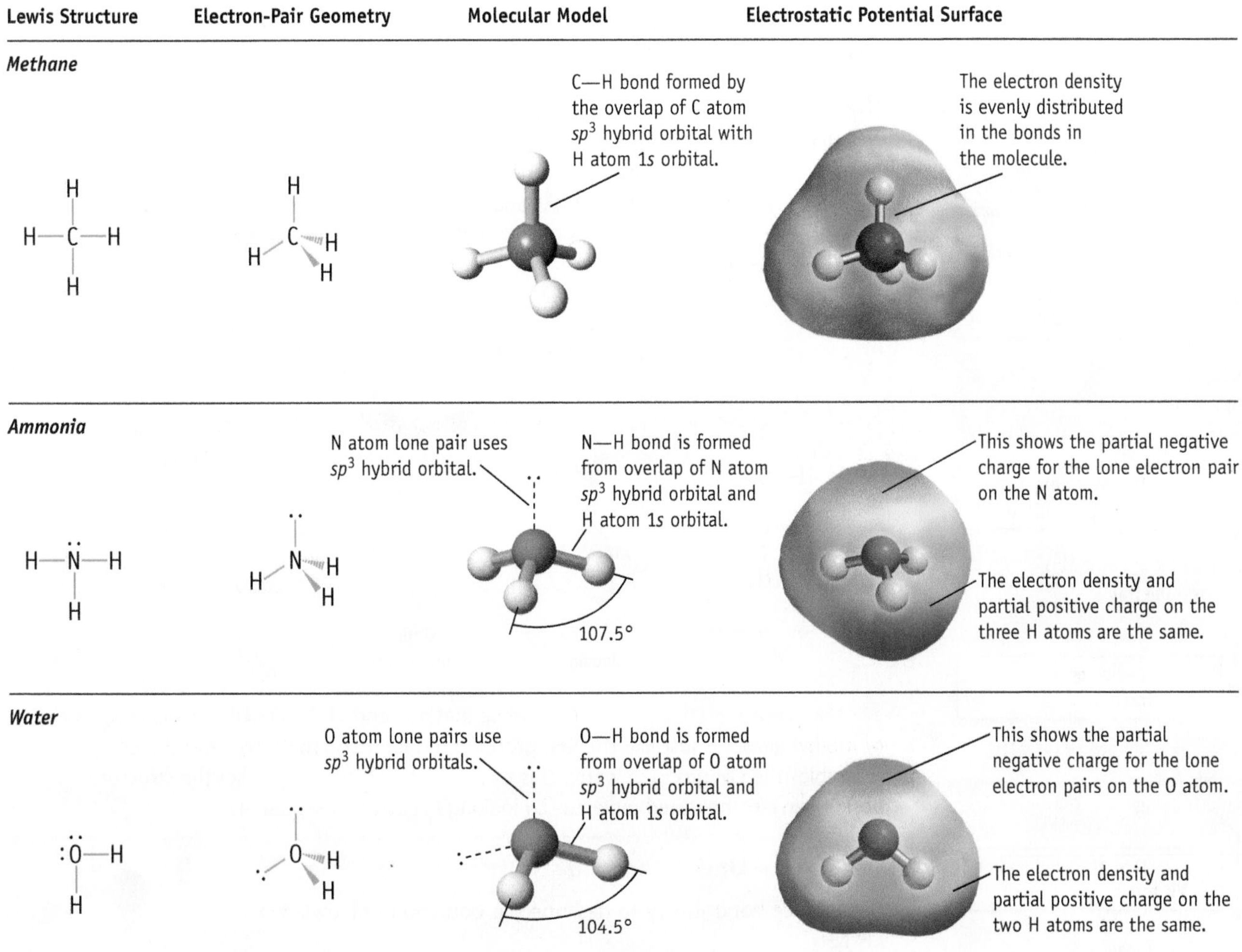

FIGURE 9.5 **Bonding in molecules with tetrahedral electron-pair geometry.**

one of the hybrid orbitals, and each of the other three hybrid orbitals is occupied by a single electron. Overlap of each of the singly occupied, sp^3 hybrid orbitals with a 1*s* orbital from a hydrogen atom, and pairing of the electrons in these orbitals, create the N—H bonds.

The oxygen atom of water has two bonding pairs and two lone pairs in its valence shell, and the H—O—H angle is 104.5°. Four sp^3 hybrid orbitals are created from the 2*s* and 2*p* atomic orbitals of oxygen. Two of these sp^3 orbitals are occupied by unpaired electrons and are used to form O—H bonds. Lone pairs occupy the other two hybrid orbitals.

Now, let us examine the use of hybrid orbitals in more complex molecules.

EXAMPLE 9.1

Valence Bond Description of Bonding in Methanol

Problem Describe the bonding in the methanol molecule, CH_3OH, using valence bond theory.

What Do You Know? The formula, CH_3OH, helps to define how atoms are linked together. Three hydrogen atoms are linked to carbon. The fourth bond from carbon is to oxygen, and oxygen is attached to the remaining hydrogen.

Strategy Map 9.1

PROBLEM

Describe the bonding in CH_3OH.

DATA/INFORMATION

- The **formula** of the molecule and thus the ***number of valence electrons***

STEP 1. Draw the **Lewis electron dot structure.**

Lewis structure 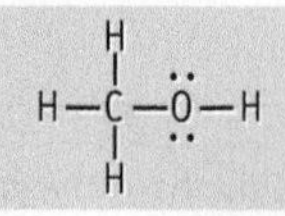

STEP 2. Decide on **electron-pair geometry** at each atom.

The C and O atoms have **tetrahedral** geometry. 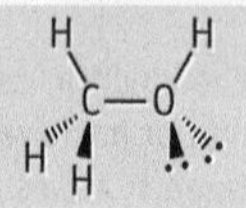

STEP 3. Decide on **atom hybridization.**

sp^3 hybrid orbitals for the **C** and **O** atoms 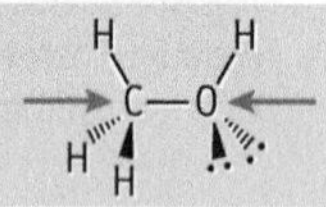

STEP 4. Describe the bonding in **VB** terms.

C—O bond formed by overlap of C and O sp^3 orbitals. C—H and O—H bonds formed by overlap of C and O atom sp^3 orbitals with H atom 1*s* orbital.

Strategy First, construct the Lewis structure for the molecule. The electron-pair geometry around each atom determines the hybrid orbital set used by that atom.

Solution The electron-pair geometry around both the C and O atoms in CH_3OH is tetrahedral. Thus, we assign sp^3 hybridization to each atom, and the C—O bond is formed by overlap of sp^3 orbitals on these atoms. Each C—H bond is formed by overlap of a carbon sp^3 orbital with a hydrogen 1*s* orbital, and the O—H bond is formed by overlap of an oxygen sp^3 orbital with the hydrogen 1*s* orbital. Two lone pairs on oxygen occupy the remaining sp^3 orbitals on the atom.

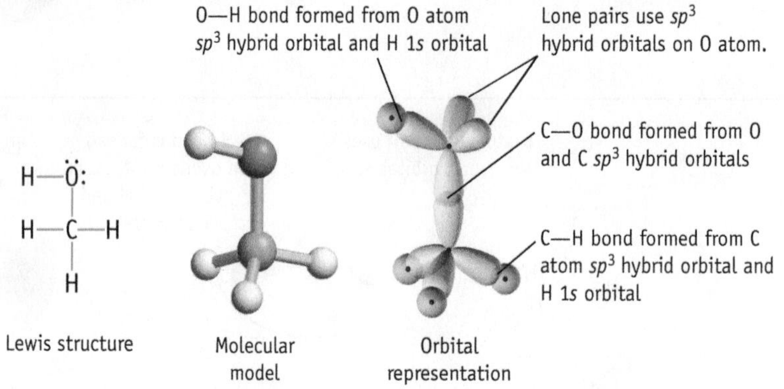

Think about Your Answer Notice that one end of the CH_3OH molecule (the CH_3 or methyl group) is just like the CH_3 group in the methane molecule, and the OH group resembles the OH group in water. This example shows how to predict the structure and bonding in a complicated molecule by looking at each part separately.

Check Your Understanding

Use valence bond theory to describe the bonding in methylamine, CH_3NH_2.

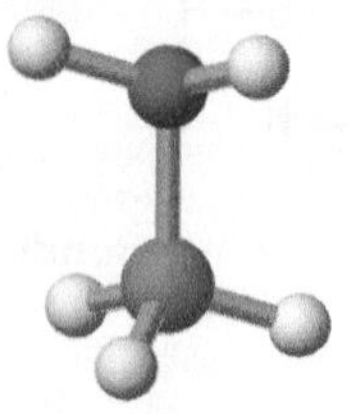

methylamine, CH_3NH_2

Hybrid Orbitals for Molecules and Ions with Trigonal-Planar and Linear Electron-Pair Geometries

The central atoms in species such as BF_3, O_3, NO_3^-, and CO_3^{2-} all have a trigonal-planar electron-pair geometry, which requires a central atom with three hybrid orbitals in a plane, 120° apart. Three hybrid orbitals mean three atomic orbitals must be combined, and the combination of an *s* orbital with two *p* orbitals is appropriate. Assuming the p_x and p_y orbitals are used in hybrid orbital formation, the three hybrid sp^2 orbitals will lie in the *xy*-plane. The p_z orbital not used to form these hybrid orbitals is perpendicular to the plane containing the three sp^2 orbitals.

Boron trifluoride has a trigonal-planar electron-pair and molecular geometry (Figure 9.6). Each boron–fluorine bond in this compound results from overlap of an sp^2 orbital on boron with a *p* orbital on fluorine. Notice that one *p* orbital on boron, which is not used to form the sp^2 hybrid orbitals, is not occupied by electrons.

For molecules in which the central atom has a linear electron-pair geometry, two hybrid orbitals, 180° apart, are required. One *s* and one *p* orbital can be hybridized to form two *sp* hybrid orbitals (Figure 9.7). If the p_z orbital is used in hybrid orbital formation, then the *sp* orbitals are oriented along the *z*-axis. The p_x and p_y orbitals are perpendicular to this axis.

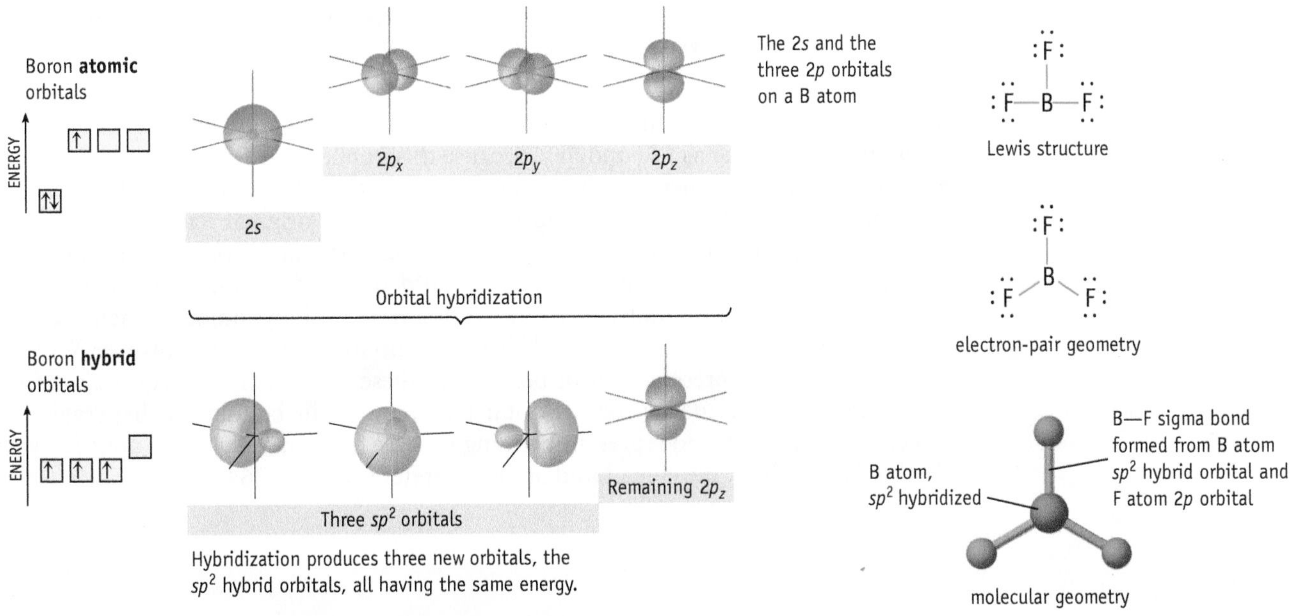

FIGURE 9.6 Bonding in BF_3, a trigonal-planar molecule.

Beryllium dichloride, $BeCl_2$, is a solid under ordinary conditions. When it is heated to over 520 °C, however, it vaporizes to give $BeCl_2$ vapor. In the gas phase, $BeCl_2$ is a linear molecule, so *sp* hybridization for the beryllium atom is appropriate. Combining beryllium's 2*s* and $2p_z$ orbitals gives the two *sp* hybrid orbitals that lie along the *z*-axis. Each Be—Cl bond arises by overlap of an *sp* hybrid orbital on beryllium with a 3*p* orbital on chlorine. In this molecule, there are only two electron pairs around the beryllium atom, so the p_x and p_y orbitals (perpendicular to the Cl—Be—Cl axis) are not occupied (Figure 9.7).

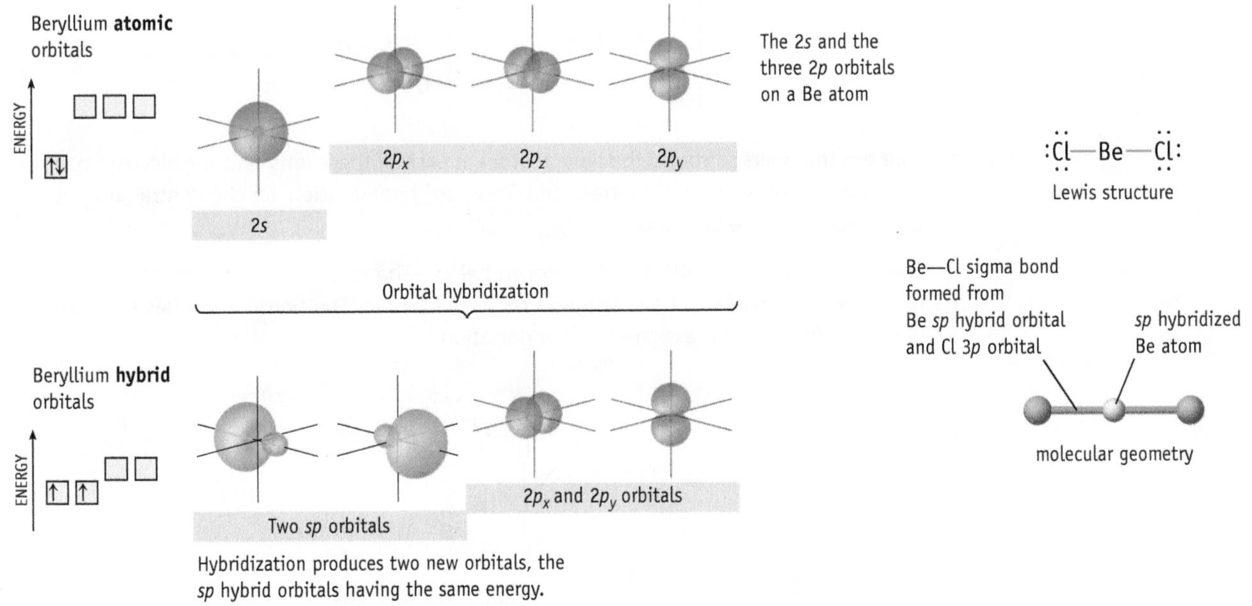

FIGURE 9.7 Bonding in a linear molecule. Because only one *p* orbital is incorporated in the hybrid orbital, two *p* orbitals remain unhybridized. These orbitals are perpendicular to each other and to the axis along which the two *sp* hybrid orbitals lie.

Hybrid Orbitals for Molecules and Ions with Trigonal-Bipyramidal or Octahedral Electron-Pair Geometries: Possible *d*-Orbital Participation

In Chapter 8 you learned that elements beyond the second period could form *hypervalent* molecules such as PF_5 and SF_6. Because this implies there are five or six bonds around the central element, chemists might assume the element must utilize five or six atomic orbitals to form a hybrid orbital set. In the original Pauling theory of hybridization, one or two *d* orbitals were combined with *s* and *p* orbitals in the same valence shell to create the hybrid orbital sets sp^3d and sp^3d^2. These could be utilized by the central atom of a molecule or ion with a trigonal-bipyramidal or octahedral electron-pair geometry, respectively. This view is no longer in favor, however. While it is a convenient representation of bonding in these species, current research indicate there is little evidence for *d* orbital participation in bonding in hypervalent molecules. Other ways to represent bonding in these compounds that do not involve *d* orbitals have been developed and are now preferred (page 364).

EXAMPLE 9.2

Recognizing Hybridization

Problem Identify the hybridization of each underlined atom in the following compounds and ions:

(a) $\underline{S}F_3^+$ (b) $\underline{S}O_4^{2-}$ (c) $H_3\underline{C}B(\underline{O}H)_2$

What Do You Know? To determine hybridization, you need to know the electron-pair geometry.

Strategy The strategy map here is the same as in Example 9.1: Formula ⟶ Lewis structure ⟶ electron-pair geometry ⟶ hybridization.

Solution The structures for SF_3^+, and SO_4^{2-} are written as follows:

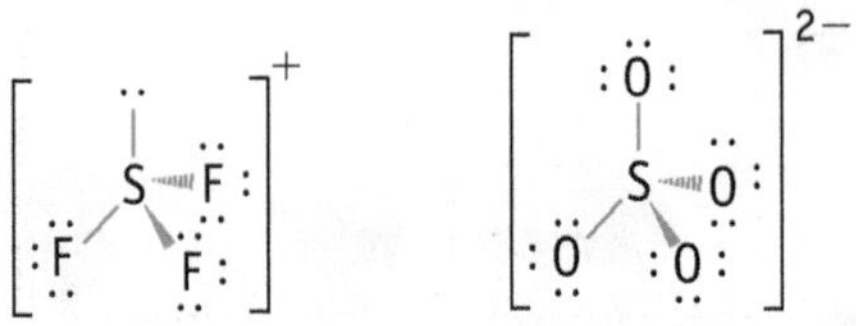

Four electron pairs surround the central atom in each of these ions, and the electron-pair geometry for these atoms is tetrahedral. Thus, sp^3 hybridization for the central atom is used to describe the bonding.

The Lewis structure for $CH_3B(OH)_2$ is drawn below. The carbon and oxygen atoms have tetrahedral geometry and are assigned sp^3 hybridization. The boron atom has trigonal-planar geometry and is assigned sp^2 hybridization.

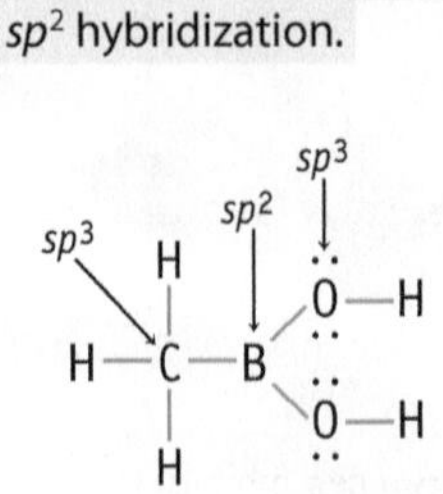

Think about Your Answer You can describe the bonding in molecules like $CH_3B(OH)_2$ by thinking in terms of small pieces of the molecule. There is a CH_3— group like the one in CH_3OH. The two —OH groups are like the ones in CH_3OH or in water, and the central B is planar trigonal like the B atom in BF_3.

Check Your Understanding

Identify the hybridization of each underlined atom in the following compounds and ions:

(a) $\underline{B}H_4^-$ (b) $H_2\underline{C}{=}\underline{C}H{-}\underline{C}H_3$ (c) $\underline{B}Cl_3$

Valence Bond Theory and Multiple Bonds

Many molecules have double or triple bonds, that is, there are two or three bonds, respectively, between pairs of atoms. According to valence bond theory, bond formation requires that two orbitals on adjacent atoms overlap, so a double bond requires *two* sets of overlapping orbitals and *two* electron pairs. For a triple bond, *three* sets of atomic orbitals are required, each set accommodating a pair of electrons.

Double Bonds

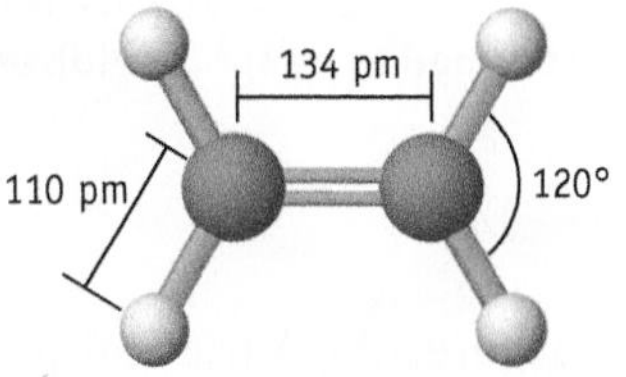

ethylene, C_2H_4

Consider ethylene, $H_2C{=}CH_2$, a common molecule with a double bond. The molecular structure of ethylene places all six atoms in a plane, with H—C—H and H—C—C angles of approximately 120°. Each carbon atom has trigonal-planar geometry, so sp^2 hybridization is assumed for these atoms.

The valence bond description of bonding in ethylene starts with each carbon atom having three sp^2 hybrid orbitals in the molecular plane and an unhybridized p orbital perpendicular to that plane. Because each carbon atom is involved in four bonds, a single unpaired electron is placed in each of these orbitals.

[↑] Unhybridized p orbital perpendicular to molecular plane. Used for π bonding in C_2H_4.

[↑][↑][↑] Three sp^2 hybrid orbitals in molecular plane. Used for C—H and C—C σ bonding in C_2H_4.

The C—H bonds of C_2H_4 arise from overlap of sp^2 orbitals on carbon with hydrogen 1s orbitals. After accounting for these bonds, one sp^2 orbital on each carbon atom remains. These hybrid orbitals point toward each other and overlap to form one of the bonds linking the carbon atoms (Figure 9.8). This leaves one other orbital unaccounted for on each carbon, an unhybridized p orbital, and these orbitals are used to create the second bond between carbon atoms in C_2H_4. If they are aligned correctly, the unhybridized p orbitals on the two carbons can overlap, allowing the electrons in these orbitals to be paired. The overlap does not occur directly along the C—C axis, however. Instead, the arrangement compels these orbitals to overlap sideways, and the electron pair occupies an orbital with electron density above and below the plane containing the six atoms.

This description results in two types of bonds in C_2H_4. The C—H and C—C σ bonds arise from the overlap of atomic orbitals that lie along the bond axes. The other is the bond formed by sideways overlap of p atomic orbitals, called a **pi (π) bond.** In a π bond, the overlap region is above and below the internuclear axis, and the electron density of the π bond is above and below the bond axis.

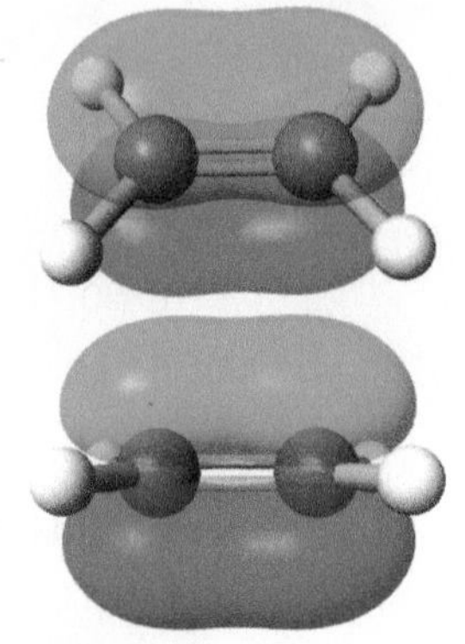
Two views of a computer-generated representation of the π bond in ethylene, C_2H_4

A π bond can form *only* if (a) there are unhybridized p orbitals on adjacent atoms and (b) the p orbitals are perpendicular to the plane of the molecule and parallel to one another. This happens only if the sp^2 orbitals of both carbon atoms are in the same plane.

Double bonds between carbon and oxygen, sulfur, or nitrogen are quite common. Consider formaldehyde, CH_2O, in which a carbon–oxygen π bond occurs

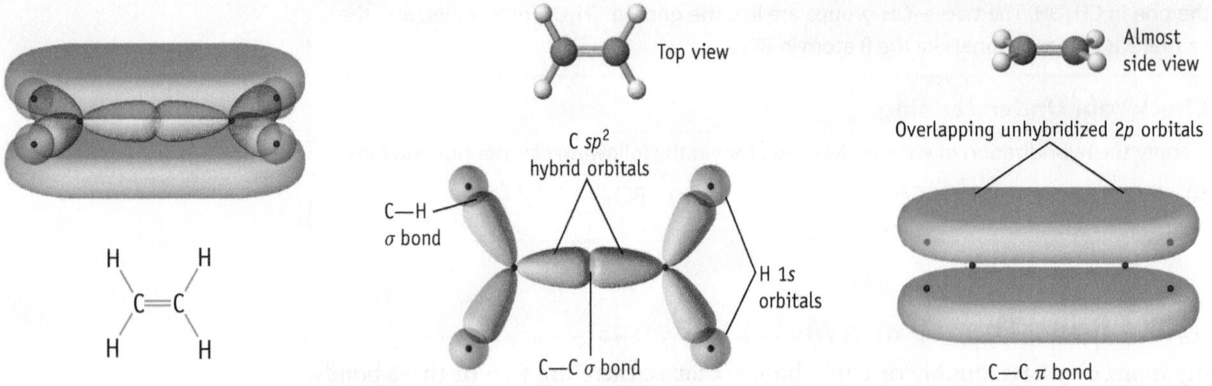

(a) Lewis structure and bonding of ethylene, C_2H_4.

(b) The C—H σ bonds are formed by overlap of C atom sp^2 hybrid orbitals with H atom 1s orbitals. The σ bond between C atoms arises from overlap of sp^2 orbitals.

(c) The carbon–carbon π bond is formed by overlap of an unhybridized 2p orbital on each atom. Note the lack of electron density along the C—C bond axis from this bond.

FIGURE 9.8 The valence bond model of bonding in ethylene, C_2H_4. Each C atom is assumed to be sp^2 hybridized.

(Figure 9.9). A trigonal-planar electron-pair geometry indicates sp^2 hybridization for the C atom. The σ bonds from carbon to the O atom and the two H atoms form by overlap of sp^2 hybrid orbitals with half-filled orbitals from the oxygen and two hydrogen atoms. An unhybridized *p* orbital on carbon is oriented perpendicular to the molecular plane (just as for the carbon atoms of C_2H_4). This *p* orbital is available for π bonding, this time with an oxygen orbital.

What orbitals on oxygen are used in this model? The approach in Figure 9.9 assumes sp^2 hybridization for oxygen. This uses one O atom sp^2 orbital in σ bond formation, leaving two sp^2 orbitals to accommodate lone pairs. The remaining *p* orbital on the O atom participates in the π bond.

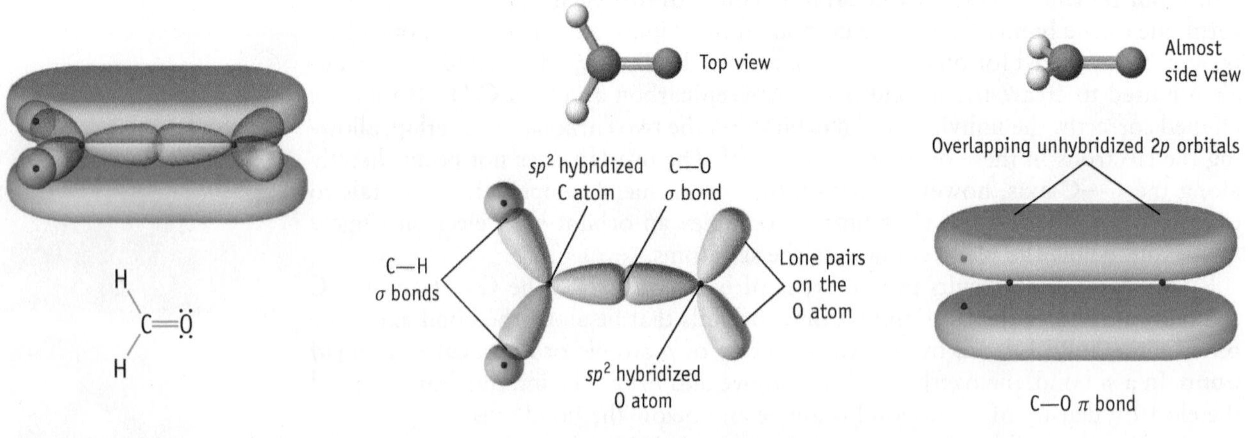

(a) Lewis structure and bonding of formaldehyde, CH_2O.

(b) The C—H σ bonds are formed by overlap of C atom sp^2 hybrid orbitals with H atom 1s orbitals. The σ bond between C and O atoms arises from overlap of sp^2 orbitals.

(c) The C—O π bond comes from the side-by-side overlap of *p* orbitals on the two atoms.

FIGURE 9.9 Valence bond description of bonding in formaldehyde, CH_2O.

EXAMPLE 9.3

Bonding in Acetic Acid

Problem Using valence bond theory, describe the bonding in acetic acid, CH_3CO_2H, the important ingredient in vinegar.

What Do You Know? Acetic acid is an organic acid and so contains the CO_2H group in which both oxygen atoms are attached to the carbon. A CH_3— group is also part of the molecule.

Strategy Write a Lewis electron dot structure, and determine the geometry around each atom using VSEPR theory. Use this geometry to decide what hybrid orbitals are used in σ bonding. If unhybridized *p* orbitals are available on adjacent C and O or C and C atoms, then π bonding can occur.

Solution

The carbon atom of the CH_3 group has tetrahedral electron-pair geometry and so is assumed to be sp^3 hybridized. Three sp^3 orbitals are used to form the C—H bonds. The fourth sp^3 orbital is used to bond to the carbon atom of the CO_2H group.

The C atom of the CO_2H group has a trigonal-planar electron-pair geometry; it must be sp^2 hybridized. A bond to the —CH_3 group is formed using one of these hybrid orbitals, and the other two sp^2 orbitals are used to form the σ bonds to the two oxygen atoms.

The oxygen of the O—H group has four electron pairs; it must be tetrahedral and sp^3 hybridized. Thus, this O atom uses two sp^3 orbitals to bond to the adjacent carbon and the hydrogen atoms, and two sp^3 orbitals accommodate the two lone pairs.

The carbon–oxygen double bond can be described by assuming the C and O atoms are both sp^2 hybridized (like the C—O π bond in formaldehyde, Figure 9.9). The unhybridized *p* orbital remaining on each atom is used to form the carbon–oxygen π bond, and the lone pairs on the O atom are accommodated in sp^2 hybrid orbitals.

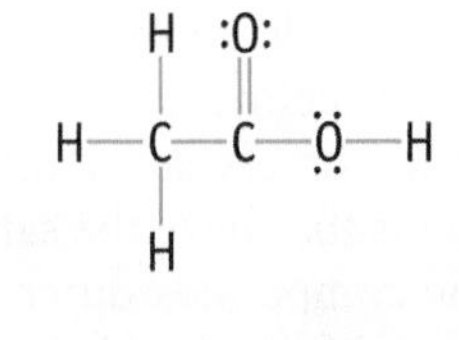

Lewis dot structure

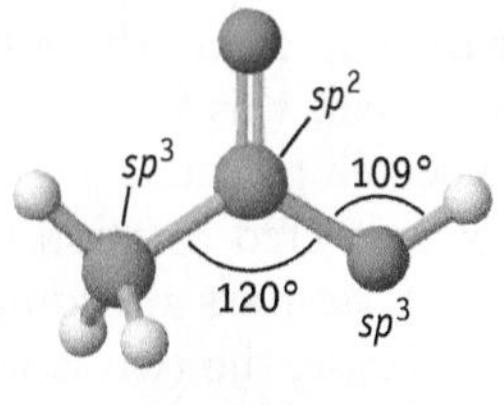

molecular model

Think about Your Answer Notice that the hybridization for each atom is determined by considering its electron-pair geometry.

Check Your Understanding

Use valence bond theory to describe the bonding in acetone, CH_3COCH_3.

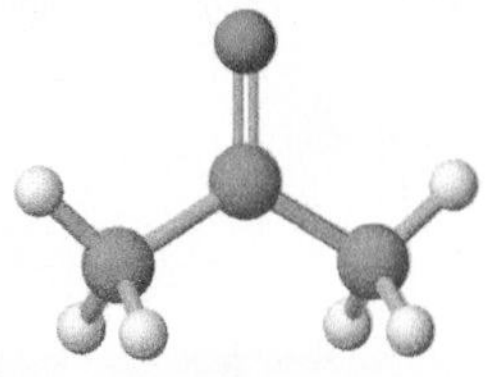

acetone

Triple Bonds

Acetylene, H—C≡C—H, is an example of a molecule with a triple bond. VSEPR theory predicts that the four atoms lie in a straight line with H—C—C angles of 180°. This implies that the carbon atom is *sp* hybridized (Figure 9.10). For each carbon atom, there are two *sp* orbitals, one directed toward hydrogen and used to create the C—H σ bond and the second directed toward the other carbon and used

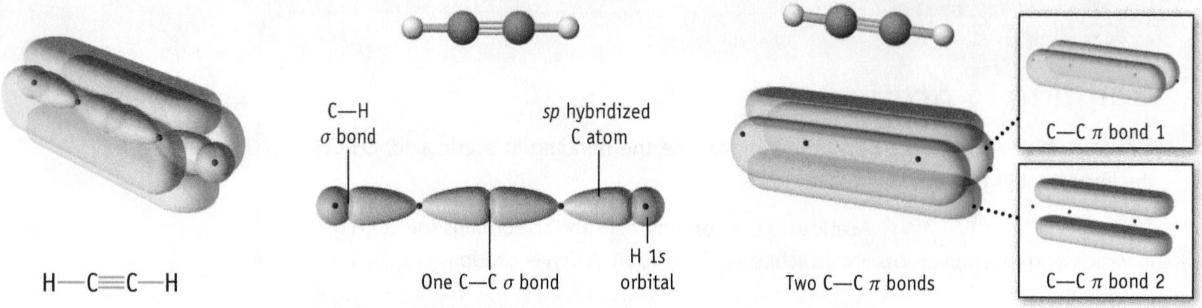

FIGURE 9.10 **A valence bond description of bonding in acetylene.**

to create a σ bond between the two carbon atoms. Two unhybridized p orbitals remain on each carbon, and they are oriented so that it is possible to form *two* π bonds in HC≡CH.

[↑|↑] Two unhybridized p orbitals. Used for π bonding in C_2H_2.

[↑|↑] Two sp hybrid orbitals. Used for C—H and C—C σ bonding in C_2H_2.

These π bonds are perpendicular to the molecular axis and perpendicular to each other. Three electrons on each carbon atom are used to form the triple bond consisting of a σ bond and two π bonds (Figure 9.10).

Cis-Trans Isomerism: A Consequence of π Bonding

Ethylene, C_2H_4, is a planar molecule, a geometry that allows the unhybridized p orbitals on the two carbon atoms to line up and form a π bond (see Figure 9.8). But what would happen if one end of the ethylene molecule were twisted relative to the other end (Figure 9.11)? This would distort the molecule away from planarity, and the p orbitals would rotate out of alignment. Rotation would diminish the extent of overlap of these orbitals, and, if a twist of 90° were achieved, the two p orbitals would no longer overlap at all; the π bond would be broken. However, so much energy is required to break this bond (about 260 kJ/mol) that rotation around a C=C bond is not expected to occur at room temperature.

A consequence of restricted rotation is that isomers occur for many compounds containing a C=C bond. **Isomers** are compounds that have the same formula but different structures. In this case, the two isomeric compounds differ with respect to the orientation of the groups attached to the carbons of the double bond. Two isomers of $C_2H_2Cl_2$ are *cis*- and *trans*-1,2-dichloroethylene. Their structures resemble ethylene, except that two hydrogen atoms have been replaced by chlorine atoms. Because a large amount of energy is required to break the π bond, the *cis* compound cannot rearrange

PROBLEM SOLVING TIP 9.1
Multiple Bond Formation

Let us summarize several important points regarding double and triple bond formation:

- In valence bond theory a double bond *always* consists of a σ bond and a π bond, and a triple bond *always* consists of a σ bond and two π bonds.
- A π bond may form *only* if unhybridized p orbitals remain on the bonded atoms.
- If a Lewis structure shows multiple bonds, the atoms involved must be either sp^2 or sp hybridized. With these hybridizations, unhybridized p orbitals will be available to form one or two π bonds, respectively.

FIGURE 9.11 Rotation around bonds.

(a) In ethane nearly free rotation can occur around the axis of a single (σ) bond.

(b) Rotation is severely restricted around the double bond in ethylene because doing so would break the π bond, a process requiring a great deal of energy.

to the *trans* compound under ordinary conditions. Each compound can be obtained separately, and each has unique physical properties. [*Cis*-1,2-dichloroethylene boils at 60.3 °C, whereas *trans*-1,2-dichloroethylene boils at 47.5 °C.]

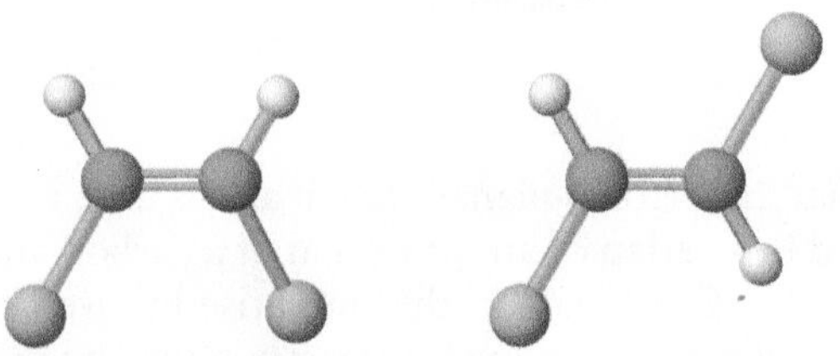

cis-1,2-dichloroethylene *trans*-1,2-dichloroethylene

Although *cis* and *trans* isomers do not interconvert at ordinary temperatures, they will do so at higher temperatures. If the temperature is sufficiently high, the molecular motions can become sufficiently energetic that rotation around the C=C bond can occur. Interconversion of isomers may also occur under other special conditions, such as when the molecule absorbs light energy.

Benzene: A Special Case of π Bonding

Benzene, C_6H_6, is the simplest member of a large group of substances known as *aromatic* compounds, a historical reference to their odor. The compound occupies a pivotal place in the history and practice of chemistry.

To 19th-century chemists, benzene was a perplexing substance with an unknown structure. Based on its chemical reactions, however, August Kekulé (1829–1896) suggested that the molecule has a planar, symmetrical ring structure. We know now he was correct. The ring is flat, and all the carbon–carbon bonds are the same length, 139 pm, a distance intermediate between the average single bond (154 pm) and double bond (134 pm) lengths. Assuming the molecule has two resonance structures with alternating double bonds, the observed structure is rationalized. The C—C bond order in C_6H_6 (1.5) is the average of a single and a double bond.

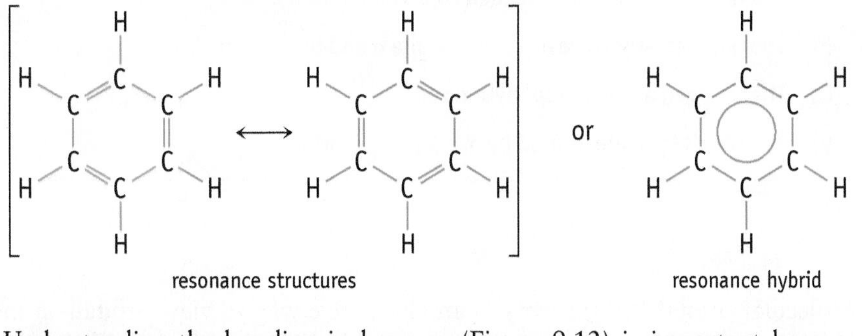

resonance structures resonance hybrid

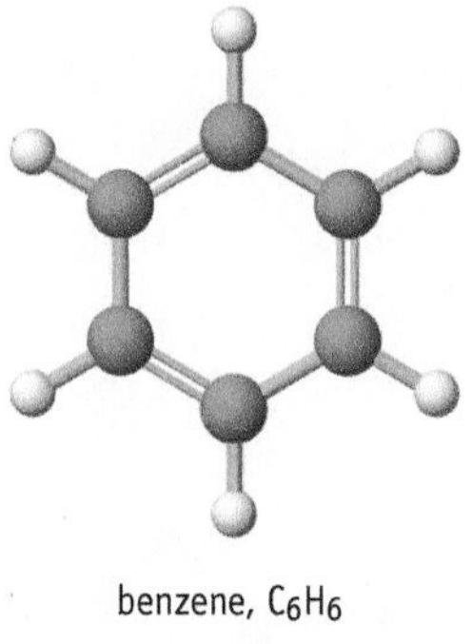

benzene, C_6H_6

Understanding the bonding in benzene (Figure 9.12) is important because the benzene ring structure occurs in an enormous number of chemical compounds. We

FIGURE 9.12 Bonding in benzene, C_6H_6.

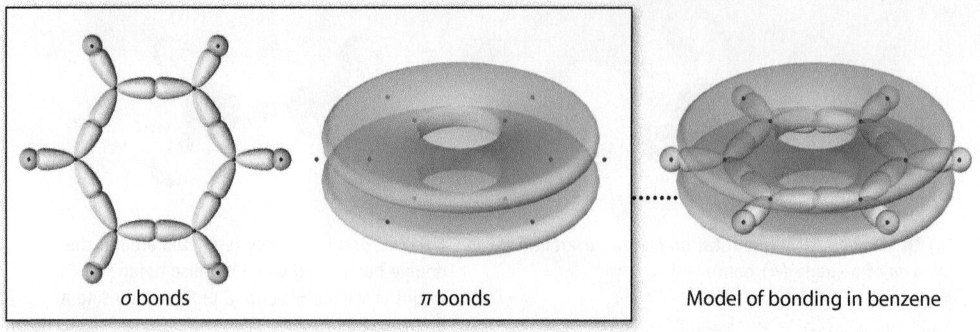

The C atoms of the ring are bonded to each other through σ bonds using C atom sp^2 hybrid orbitals. The C—H bonds also use C atom sp^2 hybrid orbitals.

The π framework of the molecule arises from overlap of C atom *p* orbitals not used in hybrid orbital formation. Because these orbitals are perpendicular to the ring, π electron density is above and below the plane of the ring.

A composite of σ and π bonding in benzene.

begin by assuming that the trigonal-planar carbon atoms have sp^2 hybridization. Each C—H bond is formed by overlap of an sp^2 orbital of a carbon atom with a 1*s* orbital of hydrogen, and the C—C σ bonds in the ring arise by overlap of sp^2 orbitals on adjacent carbon atoms. After accounting for the σ bonding, an unhybridized *p* orbital remains on each C atom, and each is occupied by a single electron. These six orbitals and six electrons form three π bonds. Because all carbon–carbon bond lengths are the same, each *p* orbital overlaps equally well with the *p* orbitals of both adjacent carbons, and the π interaction is unbroken around the six-member ring.

REVIEW & CHECK FOR SECTION 9-2

1. What is the hybridization of the S atom (the central atom) in OSF_2?

   (a) *sp* (b) sp^2 (c) sp^3

2. Which of the following is incorrect?

   (a) The hybridization of N in NH_4^+ is sp^3.
   (b) The hybridization of S in SO_4^{2-} is sp^3.
   (c) The hybridization of N in NO_2^- is sp^3.
   (d) The hybridization of O in H_3O^+ is sp^3.

3. π bonds between two atoms are formed by overlap of what orbitals?

   (a) sp^3 on atom A with sp^3 on atom B
   (b) sp^2 on atom A with sp^2 on atom B
   (c) *sp* on atom A with *sp* on atom B
   (d) *p* on atom A with *p* on atom B

4. Which description of the bond between nitrogen atoms in N_2 is correct?

   (a) The nitrogen atoms are attached by a single σ bond.
   (b) The nitrogen atoms are attached by one σ and two π bonds.
   (c) The nitrogen atoms are sp^3 hybridized.
   (d) The bonds in N_2 are formed by overlap of sp^2 orbitals.

9-3 Molecular Orbital Theory

Molecular orbital (MO) theory is an alternative way to view orbitals in molecules. According to MO theory, pure atomic orbitals of the atoms in the molecule are combined to produce **molecular orbitals** that are spread out, or delocalized, over some or all the atoms in the molecule.

(a) Liquid oxygen (boiling point, −183 °C) is a pale blue liquid.

(b) Because O_2 molecules have two unpaired electrons, oxygen in the liquid state is paramagnetic and clings to a relatively strong neodymium-based magnet.

FIGURE 9.13 **The paramagnetism of liquid oxygen.**

One reason for learning about the MO concept is that it correctly predicts the electronic structures of molecules such as O_2 that do not follow the electron-pairing assumptions of the Lewis approach. The rules of Section 8-2 would guide you to draw the electron dot structure of O_2 with all the electrons paired, which fails to explain its paramagnetism (Figure 9.13). The molecular orbital approach can account for this property, but valence bond theory cannot. To see how MO theory can be used to describe the bonding in O_2 and other diatomic molecules, let us first describe four principles of the theory.

Principles of Molecular Orbital Theory

In MO theory, we begin with a given arrangement of atoms in the molecule at the known bond distances and then determine the *sets* of molecular orbitals. One way to do this is to combine available orbitals on all the constituent atoms. These molecular orbitals more or less encompass all the atoms of the molecule, and the valence electrons for all the atoms in the molecule occupy the molecular orbitals. Just as with orbitals in atoms, electrons are assigned in order of increasing orbital energy and according to the Pauli principle and Hund's rule (see Sections 7-1 and 7-3).

The **first principle of molecular orbital theory** is that *the total number of molecular orbitals is always equal to the total number of atomic orbitals contributed by the combining atoms.* To illustrate this orbital conservation principle, let us consider the H_2 molecule.

Molecular Orbitals for H_2

Molecular orbital theory specifies that when the 1*s* orbitals of two hydrogen atoms overlap, *two* molecular orbitals result. One molecular orbital results from the *addition* of the 1*s* atomic orbital wave functions, leading to an increased probability that electrons will reside in the bond region between the two nuclei (Figures 9.14 and 9.15). This is called a **bonding molecular orbital**. It is also a σ orbital because the region of electron probability lies directly along the bond axis. This molecular orbital is labeled σ_{1s}, the subscript 1*s* indicating that 1*s* atomic orbitals were used to create the molecular orbital.

Combining Atomic Orbitals
MOs are created by combining atomic orbitals. If the orbitals have the same sign of the wave function, the effect is additive. If they have opposite signs, the effect is subtractive. See Figure 9.14, and recall page 242 where we introduced the fact that wave functions have an algebraic sign.

The other molecular orbital is constructed by *subtracting* one atomic orbital wave function from the other (Figures 9.14 and 9.15). When this happens, the probability of finding an electron between the nuclei in the molecular orbital is reduced, and the probability of finding the electron in other regions is higher. Without significant electron density between the nuclei, they repel one another. This an **antibonding molecular orbital.** Because it is also a σ orbital, derived from 1*s* atomic orbitals, it is labeled $\sigma^*{}_{1s}$ (the * denotes it as antibonding) and is referred to as a "sigma-star" orbital. *Antibonding orbitals have no counterpart in valence bond theory.*

A **second principle of molecular orbital theory** is that *the bonding molecular orbital is lower in energy than the parent orbitals, and the antibonding orbital is higher in energy* (Figure 9.15). This means that the energy of a group of atoms is

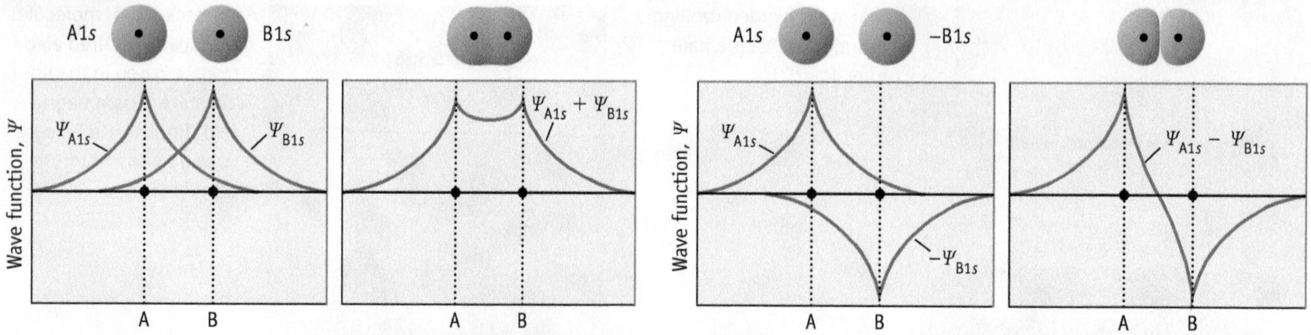

Uncombined 1s atomic orbitals with the same wave function signs.

Bonding molecular orbital (σ_{1s}). The MO is created by adding the two 1s wave functions; this results in an enhancement of the wave and an increased probability of finding the electrons between the nuclei.

Uncombined 1s atomic orbitals with opposite wave function signs.

Antibonding molecular orbital (σ^*_{1s}). This MO created by combining two 1s orbitals of opposite sign. There is now a node between the nuclei.

FIGURE 9.14 **Molecular orbitals in H_2.** The matter waves for the 1s electrons overlap along the bond axis to create bonding and antibonding molecular orbitals. The interference can be constructive, giving a bonding MO, or destructive, giving an antibonding MO.

lower than the energy of the separated atoms when electrons occupy bonding molecular orbitals. Chemists say the system is "stabilized" by chemical bond formation. Conversely, the system is "destabilized" when electrons occupy antibonding orbitals because the energy of the system is higher than that of the atoms themselves.

A **third principle of molecular orbital theory** is that the *electrons of the molecule are assigned to orbitals of successively higher energy*, just as they are in atoms and according to the Pauli exclusion principle and Hund's rule. Thus, electrons occupy the lowest energy orbitals available, and, when two electrons are assigned to an orbital, their spins must be paired.

Energy level diagrams are commonly used in describing bonding using MO theory. These diagrams show the relative energies of the atomic orbitals for the individual atoms and the derived molecular orbitals. In the energy level diagram for H_2 (Figure 9.15) you see the energy of the electrons in the bonding orbital is lower than the energy of either parent 1s electron. The antibonding orbital has a higher energy. In the H_2 molecule, the two electrons are assigned to the bonding orbital. We write the molecular electron configuration of H_2 as $(\sigma_{1s})^2$.

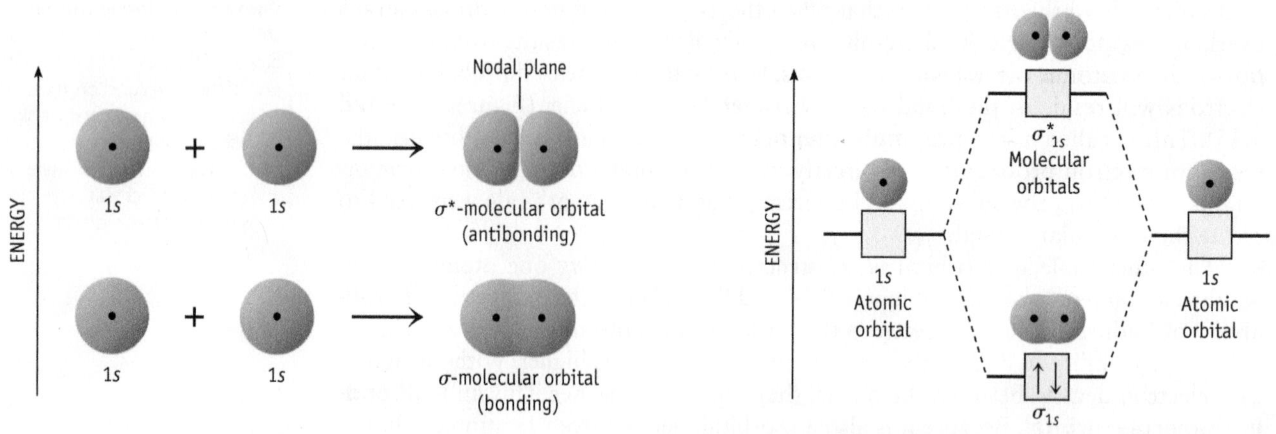

(a) Bonding and antibonding σ-molecular orbitals are formed from two 1s atomic orbitals on adjacent atoms. Notice the presence of a node between the nuclei in the antibonding orbital. (The node is a plane on which there is zero probability of finding an electron.)

(b) A molecular orbital diagram for H_2. The two electrons are placed in the σ_{1s} orbital. This bonding molecular orbital is lower in energy than the parent 1s orbitals.

FIGURE 9.15 **Molecular orbitals for H_2.**

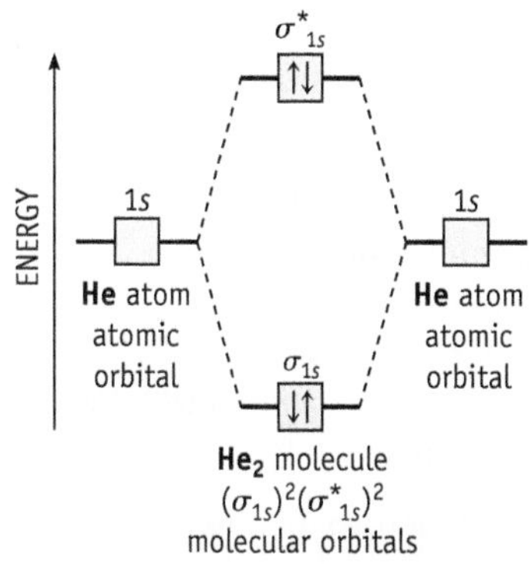

(a) Dihelium molecule, He_2. This diagram provides a rationalization for the nonexistence of the molecule. In He_2, both the bonding (σ_{1s}) and antibonding orbitals (σ^*_{1s}) would be fully occupied.

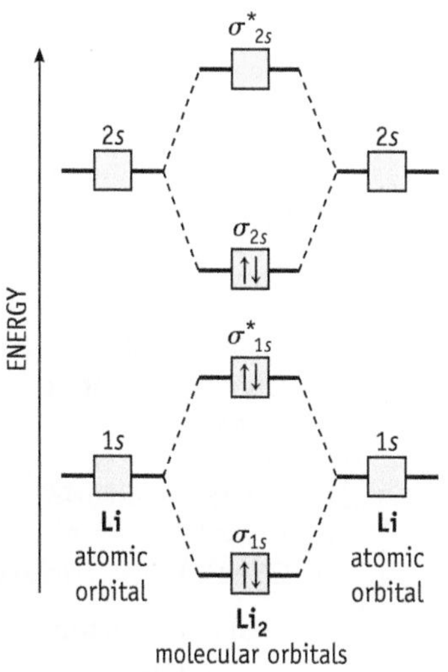

(b) Dilithium molecule, Li_2. The molecular orbitals are created by combining orbitals of similar energies (1*s* on one Li with 1*s* on the other Li and 2*s* on one Li with 2*s* on the other Li).

FIGURE 9.16 **Molecular orbital diagrams for atoms with 1*s* and 2*s* orbitals.**

What would happen if we tried to combine two helium atoms to form dihelium, He_2? Both He atoms have a 1*s* valence orbital that can produce the same kind of molecular orbitals as in H_2. However, four electrons now need to be assigned to these orbitals (Figure 9.16a). The pair of electrons in the σ_{1s} orbital stabilizes He_2 whereas the two electrons in σ^*_{1s} destabilize the molecule. The energy decrease from the electrons in the σ_{1s} bonding molecular orbital is fully offset by the energy increase due to the electrons in the σ^*_{1s} antibonding molecular orbital. Thus, molecular orbital theory predicts that He_2 has no net stability; that is, two He atoms should have no tendency to combine. This confirms what we already know, that elemental helium exists in the form of single atoms and not as a diatomic molecule.

Bond Order

Bond order was defined in Section 8-9 as the net number of bonding electron pairs linking a pair of atoms. This same concept can be applied directly to molecular orbital theory, but now bond order is defined as

$$\text{Bond order} = 1/2\,(\text{number of electrons in bonding MOs} - \text{number of electrons in antibonding MOs}) \quad (9.1)$$

In the H_2 molecule, there are two electrons in a bonding orbital and none in an antibonding orbital, so H_2 has a bond order of 1 [½(2 − 0) = 1]. In contrast, in the hypothetical molecule He_2 the stabilizing effect of the σ_{1s} pair would be canceled by the destabilizing effect of the σ^*_{1s} pair, and so the bond order would be 0.

Fractional bond orders are possible. Consider the ion He_2^+. Its molecular orbital electron configuration is $(\sigma_{1s})^2(\sigma^*_{1s})^1$. In this ion, there are two electrons in a bonding molecular orbital, but only one in an antibonding orbital. MO theory predicts that He_2^+ should have a bond order of 0.5; that is, a weak bond should exist between helium atoms in the ion. Interestingly, this ion has been identified in the gas phase using special experimental techniques.

EXAMPLE 9.4

Molecular Orbitals and Bond Order

Problem Write the electron configuration of the H_2^- ion in molecular orbital terms. What is the bond order of the ion?

What Do You Know? Combining the 1*s* orbitals on the two hydrogen atoms will give two molecular orbitals (Figure 9.15). One is a bonding orbital (σ_{1s}) and the second is an antibonding orbital (σ^*_{1s}).

Strategy Count the number of valence electrons in the ion, and then place those electrons in the MO diagram for the H_2 molecule. Find the bond order using Equation 9.1.

Solution This ion has three electrons (one each from the H atoms plus one for the negative charge). Therefore, its electronic configuration is $(\sigma_{1s})^2(\sigma^*_{1s})^1$, identical with the configuration for He_2^+. This means H_2^- has a net bond order of 0.5.

Think about Your Answer There is a weak bond in this ion, so it is predicted to exist only under special circumstances.

Check Your Understanding

What is the electron configuration of the H_2^+ ion? Compare the bond order of this ion with He_2^+ and H_2^-. Do you expect H_2^+ to exist?

Molecular Orbitals of Li_2 and Be_2

A **fourth principle of molecular orbital theory** is that *atomic orbitals combine to form molecular orbitals most effectively when the atomic orbitals are of similar energy.* This principle becomes important when we move past He_2 to Li_2, dilithium, and heavier molecules such as O_2 and N_2.

A lithium atom has electrons in two orbitals of the *s* type (1*s* and 2*s*), so a 1*s* ± 2*s* combination is theoretically possible. Because the 1*s* and 2*s* orbitals are quite different in energy, however, this interaction can be disregarded. Thus, the molecular orbitals come only from 1*s* ± 1*s* and 2*s* ± 2*s* combinations (Figure 9.16b). This means the molecular orbital electron configuration of dilithium, Li_2, is

$$Li_2 \text{ MO Configuration:} \quad (\sigma_{1s})^2(\sigma^*_{1s})^2(\sigma_{2s})^2$$

Diatomic Molecules Molecules such as H_2, Li_2, and N_2, in which two identical atoms are bonded, are examples of *homonuclear* diatomic molecules.

The bonding effect of the σ_{1s} electrons is canceled by the antibonding effect of the σ^*_{1s} electrons, so these pairs make no net contribution to bonding in Li_2. Bonding in Li_2 is due to the electron pair assigned to the σ_{2s} orbital, and the bond order is 1.

The fact that the σ_{1s} and σ^*_{1s} electron pairs of Li_2 make no net contribution to bonding makes sense. In the valence bond description of bonding in this molecule, these electrons are core electrons. In MO theory, just as in valence bond theory, the bond between lithium atoms arises by overlap of valence orbitals and sharing of valence electrons; core electrons can be ignored.

EXAMPLE 9.5

Molecular Orbitals in Homonuclear Diatomic Molecules

Problem Should the Be_2 molecule or Be_2^+ ion exist? Describe their electron configurations in molecular orbital terms, and give the net bond order of each.

What Do You Know? The MO diagram in Figure 9.16b applies to this question because we are dealing only with 1*s* and 2*s* orbitals in the original atoms.

Strategy Count the number of electrons in the molecule or ion, and place them in the MO diagram in Figure 9.16b. Write the electron configuration, and calculate the bond order from Equation 9.1.

Solution The Be_2 molecule has eight electrons, of which four are core electrons. (The four core electrons are assigned to σ_{1s} and σ^*_{1s} molecular orbitals.) The remaining four electrons are assigned to the σ_{2s} and σ^*_{2s} molecular orbitals, so the MO electron configuration for Be_2 is [core electrons]$(\sigma_{2s})^2(\sigma^*_{2s})^2$. This leads to a net bond order of 0, so the Be_2 molecule does not exist.

The Be_2^+ ion has only seven electrons, of which four are core electrons. The remaining three electrons are assigned to the σ_{2s} and σ^*_{2s} molecular orbitals, so the MO electron configuration of Be_2^+ is [core electrons]$(\sigma_{2s})^2(\sigma^*_{2s})^1$. This means the net bond order is 0.5.

Think about Your Answer Be_2^+ is predicted to exist under special circumstances. Scientists might search for such species in gas discharge experiments (gaseous atoms subjected to a strong electrical potential) and use spectroscopy to confirm their existence.

Check Your Understanding

Could the anion Li_2^- exist? What is the ion's bond order?

Molecular Orbitals from Atomic *p* Orbitals

With the principles of molecular orbital theory in place, we are ready to account for bonding in such important homonuclear diatomic molecules as N_2, O_2, and F_2. To describe the bonding in these molecules, we will have to use both *s* and *p* valence orbitals in forming molecular orbitals.

For *p*-block elements, sigma-bonding and antibonding molecular orbitals are formed by their *s* orbitals interacting as in Figure 9.16b. Similarly, it is possible for a *p* orbital on one atom to interact with a *p* orbital on the other atom to produce a pair of σ-bonding and σ^*-antibonding molecular orbitals (Figure 9.17a).

In addition, each *p*-block atom has *two p* orbitals in planes perpendicular to the σ bond connecting the two atoms. These *p* orbitals can interact in a side-by-side fashion to give *two* π-bonding molecular orbitals (π_{2p}) and *two* π-antibonding molecular orbitals (π^*_{2p}) (Figure 9.17b).

Phases of Atomic Orbitals and Molecular Orbitals Recall that electron wave functions have positive and negative phases (Chapter 6). For this reason, the atomic orbitals in Figures 9.15 and 9.17 are drawn with two different colors. Looking at the *p* orbitals in Figure 9.17, you see that a bonding MO is formed when *p* orbitals with the same wave function sign overlap (+ with +). An antibonding orbital arises if they overlap out of phase (+ with −). See Figure 9.14.

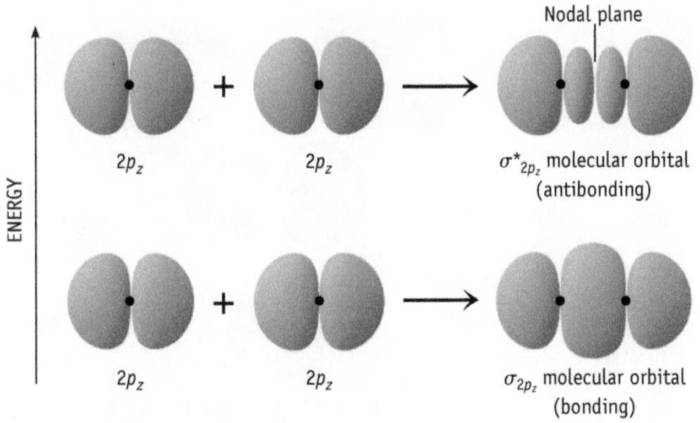

(a) Sigma (σ) molecular orbitals from *p* atomic orbitals. Sigma-bonding (σ_{2p}) and antibonding (σ^*_{2p}) molecular orbitals arise from overlap of 2*p* orbitals. Each orbital can accommodate two electrons.

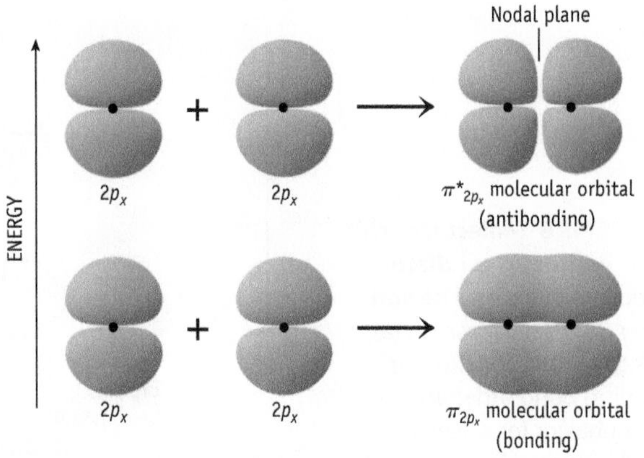

(b) Pi (π) molecular orbitals. Sideways overlap of atomic 2*p* orbitals that lie in the same direction in space gives rise to pi-bonding (π_{2p}) and pi-antibonding (π^*_{2p}) molecular orbitals.

FIGURE 9.17 **Combinations of *p* atomic orbitals to yield σ and π molecular orbitals.** The *p* orbitals in electron shells of higher *n* give σ and π molecular orbitals of the same basic shape.

Electron Configurations for Homonuclear Molecules for Boron Through Fluorine

Orbital interactions in a second-period, homonuclear, diatomic molecule lead to the energy level diagram in Figure 9.18. Electron assignments can be made using this diagram, and the results for the diatomic molecules B_2 through F_2 are summarized in Table 9.1, which has two noteworthy features.

First, notice the correlation between the electron configurations and the bond orders, bond lengths, and bond energies at the bottom of Table 9.1. As the bond order between a pair of atoms increases, the energy required to break the bond increases, and the bond length decreases. Dinitrogen, N_2, with a bond order of 3, has the largest bond energy and shortest bond length in this group of five homonuclear diatomic molecules.

Second, notice the configuration for dioxygen, O_2. Dioxygen has 12 valence electrons (six from each atom), so it has the molecular orbital configuration

O_2 *MO Configuration:* [core electrons]$(\sigma_{2s})^2(\sigma^*_{2s})^2(\sigma_{2p})^2(\pi_{2p})^4(\pi^*_{2p})^2$

This configuration leads to a bond order of 2 in agreement with experiment and also specifies two unpaired electrons (in π^*_{2p} molecular orbitals), thus predicting that dioxygen should be paramagnetic. This is in contrast to a Lewis dot (valence bond) model, which predicts incorrectly that dioxygen should be diamagnetic. Molecular orbital theory succeeds where valence bond theory fails. MO theory explains both the observed bond order and, as illustrated in Figure 9.11, the paramagnetic behavior of O_2.

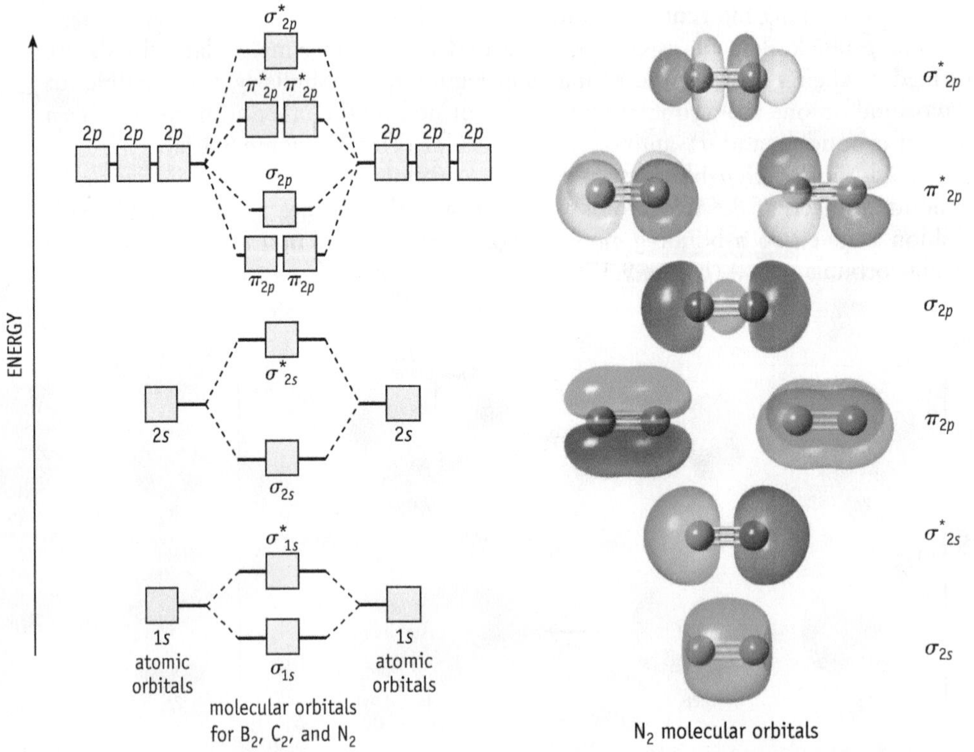

(a) Energy level diagram for B_2, C_2, and N_2.

(b) Computer-generated molecular orbitals for N_2. Color scheme: occupied MOs are blue/green. Unoccupied MOs are red/yellow. The different colors in a given orbital reflect the different phases [positive or negative signs] of the wave functions.

FIGURE 9.18 **Molecular orbitals for homonuclear diatomic molecules of second period elements.** The diagram in (a) leads to correct conclusions regarding bond order and magnetic behavior for all second period homonuclear diatomic molecules, but the energy ordering of the MOs in this figure is correct only for B_2, C_2, and N_2. For O_2 and F_2, the σ_{2p} MO is lower in energy than the π_{2p} MOs. See *A Closer Look,* page 361.

Table 9.1 Molecular Orbital Occupations and Physical Data for Homonuclear Diatomic Molecules of Second-Period Elements*

	B_2	C_2	N_2		O_2	F_2
σ^*_{2p}	[ ]	[ ]	[ ]	σ^*_{2p}	[ ]	[ ]
π^*_{2p}	[ ][ ]	[ ][ ]	[ ][ ]	π^*_{2p}	[↑][↑]	[↑↓][↑↓]
σ_{2p}	[ ]	[ ]	[↑↓]	π_{2p}	[↑↓][↑↓]	[↑↓][↑↓]
π_{2p}	[↑][↑]	[↑↓][↑↓]	[↑↓][↑↓]	σ_{2p}	[↑↓]	[↑↓]
σ^*_{2s}	[↑↓]	[↑↓]	[↑↓]	σ^*_{2s}	[↑↓]	[↑↓]
σ_{2s}	[↑↓]	[↑↓]	[↑↓]	σ_{2s}	[↑↓]	[↑↓]
Bond order	One	Two	Three		Two	One
Bond-dissociation energy (kJ/mol)	290	620	945		498	155
Bond distance (pm)	159	131	110		121	143
Observed magnetic behavior (paramagnetic or diamagnetic)	Para	Dia	Dia		Para	Dia

*The π_{2p} and σ_{2p} orbitals are inverted in energy on going to elements later in the second period. See *A Closer Look* on this page.

HOMO and LUMO Chemists often refer to the highest energy MO that contains electrons as the HOMO (for "highest occupied molecular orbital"). For O_2, this is the π^*_{2p} orbital. We also use the term LUMO for the "lowest unoccupied molecular orbital." For O_2, this would be σ^*_{2p}.

EXAMPLE 9.6

Electron Configuration for a Homonuclear Diatomic Ion

Problem Potassium superoxide, KO_2, one of the products from the reaction of K and O_2, contains the superoxide ion, O_2^-. Write the molecular orbital electron configuration for the ion, and predict its bond order and magnetic behavior.

What Do You Know? The 2*s* and 2*p* orbitals on the two oxygen atoms can be combined to give the series of molecular orbitals shown in Table 9.1. The O_2^- ion has 13 valence electrons.

A CLOSER LOOK Molecular Orbitals for Molecules Formed from *p*-Block Elements

Several features of the molecular orbital energy level diagram in Figure 9.18 should be described in more detail.

(a) The bonding and antibonding σ orbitals from 2*s* interactions are lower in energy than the σ and π MOs from 2*p* interactions. The reason is that 2*s* orbitals have a lower energy than 2*p* orbitals in the separated atoms.

(b) The energy separation of the bonding and antibonding orbitals is greater for σ_{2p} than for π_{2p}. This happens because *p* orbitals overlap to a greater extent when they are oriented head to head (to give σ_{2p} MOs) than when they are side by side (to give π_{2p} MOs). The greater the orbital overlap, the greater the stabilization of the bonding MO and the greater the destabilization of the antibonding MO.

(c) You may have been surprised that Figure 9.18 shows the π_{2p} orbitals lower in energy than the σ_{2p} orbital. Why would the π_{2p} orbitals be lower? A more sophisticated approach to construct MOs takes into account the "mixing" of *s* and *p* atomic orbitals, which have similar energies. This causes the σ_{2s} and σ^*_{2s} molecular orbitals to be lower in energy than otherwise expected, and the σ_{2p} and σ^*_{2p} orbitals to be higher in energy.

(d) The mixing of *s* and *p* orbitals is important for B_2, C_2, and N_2, so Figure 9.18 applies strictly only to these molecules. For O_2 and F_2 mixing is less important, so σ_{2p} is lower in energy than π_{2p} (as shown in Table 9.1).

Strategy Use the energy level diagram for O_2 in Table 9.1 to generate the electron configuration of the ion, and use Equation 9.1 to determine the bond order. The magnetism is determined by whether there are unpaired electrons.

Solution The MO configuration for O_2^-, an ion with 13 valence electrons, is

O_2^- MO Configuration: $[\text{core electrons}](\sigma_{2s})^2(\sigma^*_{2s})^2(\sigma_{2p})^2(\pi_{2p})^4(\pi^*_{2p})^3$

The ion is predicted to be paramagnetic to the extent of one unpaired electron, a prediction confirmed by experiment. The bond order is 1.5, because there are eight bonding electrons and five antibonding electrons. The bond order for O_2^- is lower than for O_2 so we predict the O—O bond in O_2^- should be longer than the oxygen–oxygen bond in O_2. The superoxide ion in fact has an O—O bond length of 134 pm, whereas the bond length in O_2 is 121 pm.

Think about Your Answer The superoxide ion contains an odd number of electrons. This is another diatomic species (in addition to NO and O_2) for which it is not possible to write a Lewis structure that accurately represents the bonding.

Check Your Understanding

The cations O_2^+ and N_2^+ are formed when molecules of O_2 and N_2 are subjected to intense, high-energy solar radiation in Earth's upper atmosphere. Write the electron configuration for O_2^+. Predict its bond order and magnetic behavior.

Electron Configurations for Heteronuclear Diatomic Molecules

Molecules such as CO, NO, and ClF, which contain two different elements, are examples of *heteronuclear* diatomic molecules. Molecular orbital descriptions for heteronuclear diatomic molecules resemble those for homonuclear diatomic molecules, but there can be significant differences.

Carbon monoxide is an important molecule, so it is worth looking at its bonding. The 2*s* and 2*p* orbitals of O are at a lower relative energy than the 2*s* and 2*p* orbitals of C (◀ page 262). These atoms and their orbitals can nonetheless be combined in the same way as in homonuclear diatomic molecules to give an ordering of molecular orbitals that is similar to N_2. The 10 valence electrons of CO are added to the available molecular orbitals from lowest to highest energy, and the molecular orbital electron configuration for CO is

CO MO Configuration: $[\text{core electrons}](\sigma_{2s})^2(\sigma^*_{2s})^2(\pi_{2p})^4(\sigma_{2p})^2$

This shows that CO has a bond order of 3 (two π bonds and one σ bond), as expected from the Lewis electron dot structure.

Resonance and MO Theory

Ozone, O_3, is a simple triatomic molecule with equal oxygen–oxygen bond lengths. Equal X—O bond lengths are also observed in other molecules and ions, such as SO_2, NO_2^-, and HCO_2^-. Valence bond theory introduced resonance to represent the equivalent bonding to the oxygen atoms in these structures, but MO theory also provides a useful view of bonding in these molecules and ions.

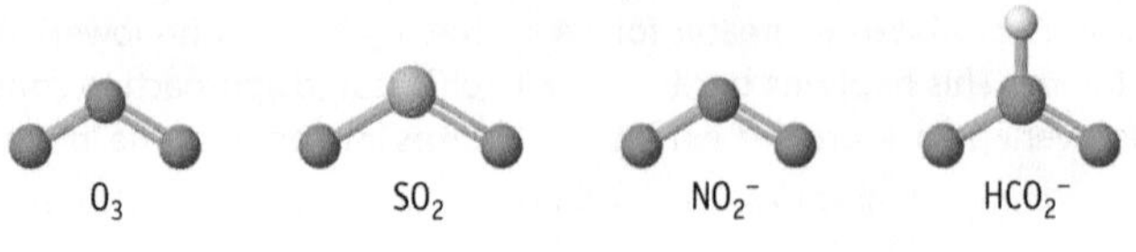

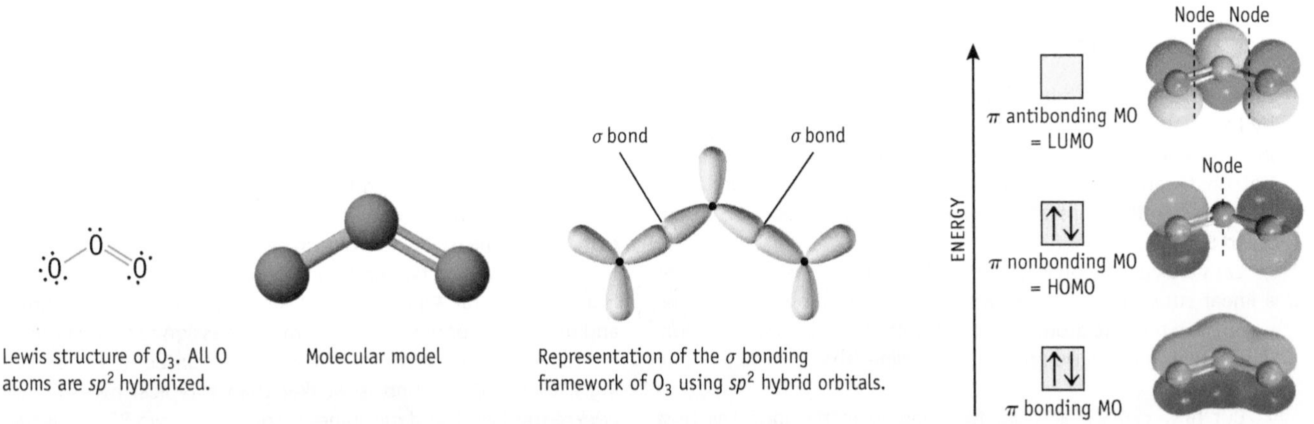

(a) Ozone, O_3, has equal-length oxygen–oxygen bonds, which, in valence bond theory, would be rationalized by resonance structures.

The σ bonding framework of O_3 is formed by utilizing sp^2 hybrid orbitals on each O atom. These accommodate two σ bonds and five lone pairs.

(b) The π molecular orbital diagram for ozone. Notice that, as in the other MO diagrams illustrated (especially Figure 9.18), the energy of the molecular orbitals increases as the number of nodes increases.

FIGURE 9.19. **A bonding model for ozone, O_3.**

To understand the bonding in ozone, let's begin by looking at the valence bond picture. First, assume that all three O atoms are sp^2 hybridized. The central atom uses its sp^2 hybrid orbitals to form two σ bonds and to accommodate a lone pair. The terminal atoms use their sp^2 hybrid orbitals to form one σ bond and to accommodate two lone pairs. Thus, seven of the nine valence electron pairs in O_3 are either lone pairs or bonding pairs in the σ framework of O_3 (Figure 9.19a). The π bond in ozone arises from the two remaining pairs (Figure 9.19b). Because we have assumed that each oxygen atom in O_3 is sp^2 hybridized, an unhybridized p orbital perpendicular to the O_3 plane remains on each of the three oxygen atoms. These orbitals are in the correct orientation to form a π bond.

To simplify matters, let's now apply MO theory only to these three p orbitals that can be involved in π bonding in ozone. We begin by remembering a principle of MO theory: the number of molecular orbitals must equal the number of combining atomic orbitals. Thus, the three $2p$ atomic orbitals must be combined in a way that forms three molecular orbitals.

One π_p MO for ozone is a bonding orbital because the three p orbitals are "in phase" across the molecule (Figure 9.19b). Another π_p MO is an antibonding orbital because the atomic orbital on the central atom is "out of phase" with the terminal atom p orbitals. The third π_p MO is a *nonbonding* orbital because the middle p orbital does not participate in the MO. (Electrons in this molecular orbital would reside on the two terminal atoms only; they do not overlap, and thus they neither help nor hinder the bonding in the molecule.)

One of the two pairs of π_p electrons of O_3 occupies the lowest energy or π_p-bonding MO, which is delocalized, or "spread over," the molecule (just as the resonance hybrid of valence bond theory implies). The π_p-nonbonding orbital is also occupied, but the electrons in this orbital are concentrated near the two terminal oxygens. Thus, there is a net of only one pair of π_p-bonding electrons for two O—O bonds, giving a π bond order for O_3 of 0.5 for each O—O bond. Because the σ bond order is 1.0 and the π bond order is 0.5 for each O—O linkage, each oxygen–oxygen bond order is 1.5—the same value given by valence bond theory.

The observation that the π molecular orbitals for ozone extend over three atoms illustrates an important point regarding molecular orbital theory: *Molecular orbitals can extend beyond two atoms.* In valence bond theory, in contrast, all representations for bonding are based on being able to localize pairs of electrons in

A CLOSER LOOK

Three-Center Bonds in HF_2^-, B_2H_6, and SF_6

Although a large majority of known compounds can be described by Lewis electron dot pictures, nature (and chemistry) has a surprise now and then. You have already seen several examples (most notably O_2 and NO) where it is not possible to draw simple dot structures. In these instances we turned to MO theory to understand the bonding.

Let's look at the ion HF_2^-, formed from F^- and HF. This ion has a linear structure (F—H—F) with a hydrogen atom midway between two fluorine atoms. Of the 16 valence electrons in the ion, there are 4 that can be utilized in bonding (the other 12 are lone pairs on F).

But how can we account for bonding in the ion? The best way is to use MO theory. We begin with three atomic orbitals, the $2p_z$ orbitals on each fluorine atom and the 1s orbital on hydrogen.

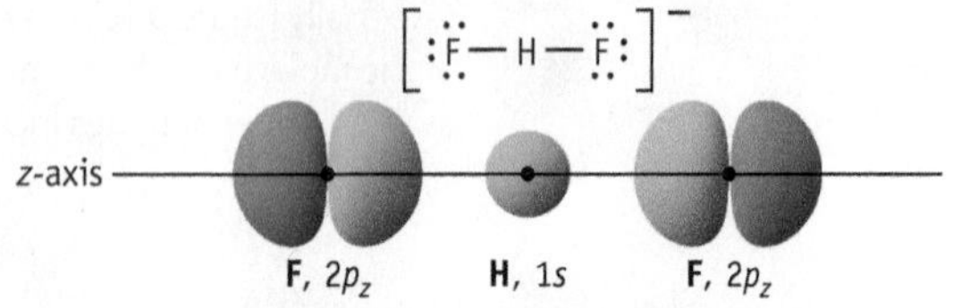

valence orbitals available in F—H—F⁻

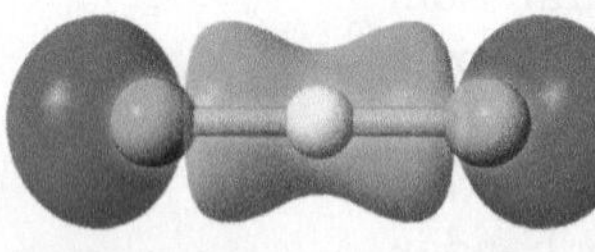

The bonding MO of the FHF⁻ ion extends across the ion. Each H—F bond has a bond order of ½.

As in the model used for π bonding in ozone (Figure 9.19) three orbitals (here, the 1s for H and the $2p_z$ orbitals for each F) combine to form three molecular orbitals, one bonding, one nonbonding, and one antibonding. One pair of valence electrons is placed in the bonding MO and one in the nonbonding MO, to give a net of one bond. This result, which nicely accounts for the bonding, is often referred to as a *three-center/four-electron bond* model.

Diborane, B_2H_6, is another molecule for which an acceptable Lewis dot structure cannot be drawn. As the structure below shows, each boron atom has distorted tetrahedral geometry.

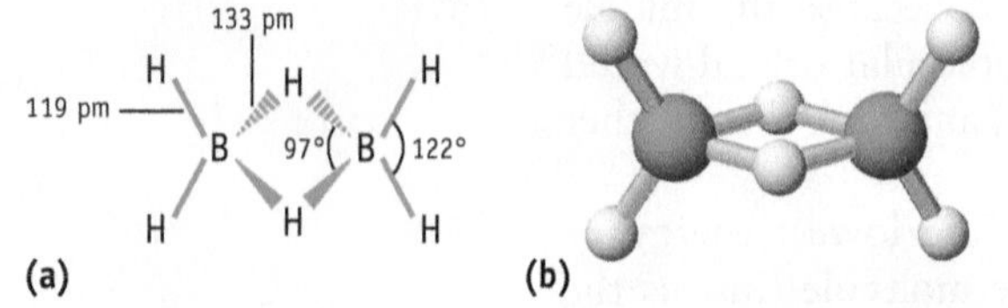

The structure of diborane, B_2H_6, a molecule involving three-center, two-electron B—H—B bonds

The molecule has two terminal hydrogen atoms bonded to each boron atom, and two hydrogen atoms bridge the two boron atoms. Chemists refer to diborane as "electron deficient" because two B atoms and six H atoms do not contribute enough electrons for eight, two-electron bonds.

We can again account for the bonding in this molecule using MO theory with three-center bonds, each involving the two boron atoms and an H atom. Let's begin by assuming that each B atom is sp^3 hybridized. The four terminal H atoms bond to the B atoms with two-electron bonds using 8 of the 12 electrons and two of the sp^3 hybrid orbitals on each B atom. The 4 remaining electrons account for the two B—H—B bridges. Three molecular orbitals encompassing the B—H—B atoms in each bridge can be constructed from the remaining two sp^3 hybrid orbitals on each B atom and an H atom 1s orbital. Again, one MO is bonding, one is nonbonding, and one is antibonding. Two electrons are assigned to the bonding orbital, resulting in a *three-center/two-electron* bond. Not surprisingly, this kind of bond is weaker than a typical two-electron/two-center bond, and diborane dissociates to two BH_3 molecules at fairly low temperatures.

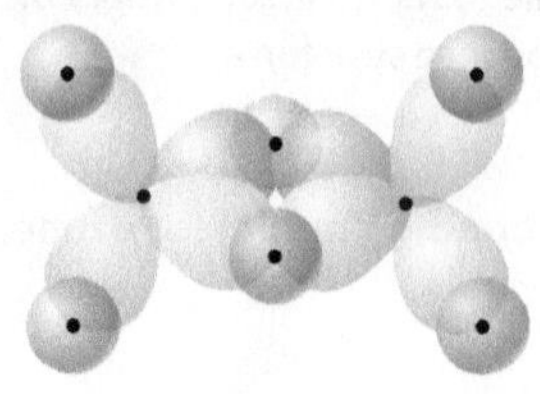

An overlap of sp^3 orbitals, one from each B atom, and an H 1s creates two, three-center/two-electron bonds.

And finally we return to an issue introduced earlier: *whether d orbitals are involved in bonding in some main group element compounds.* Theory suggests that *d* orbitals are not significantly involved in bonding in ions such as SO_4^{2-} and PO_4^{3-} (page 300). If we accept the idea that *d* orbitals are too high in energy to be used in bonding in main group element compounds, how can we use hybrid orbitals that involve *d* orbitals to describe bonding in PF_5 and SF_6, for example? Another bonding model is needed, and molecular orbital theory provides the alternative without the use of *d* orbitals.

Consider SF_6 with an octahedral electron-pair geometry. The molecule has a total of 24 valence electron pairs. Of these, 18 are involved as lone pairs on the F atoms, so 6 electron pairs remain to account for 6 S-F bonds. Let's look specifically at the bonding between sulfur and two fluorine atoms across from each other along each of the three axes.

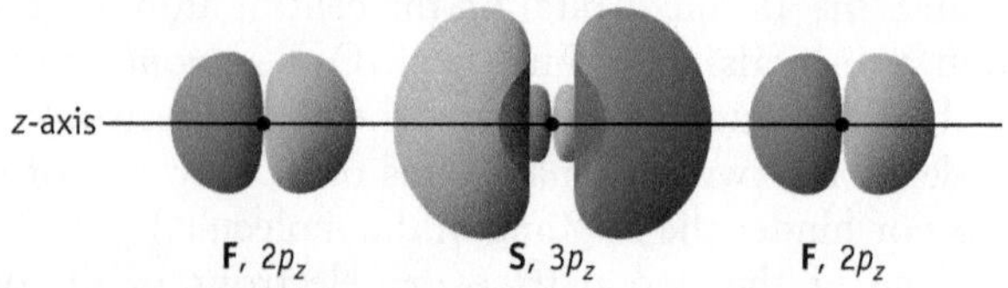

Three-center, four-electron F—S—F bonding in SF_6

Along the *z*-axis, for example, bonding, nonbonding, and antibonding orbitals can be constructed from combinations of the $3p_z$ orbital on sulfur and the two $2p_z$ orbitals on fluorine. Four electrons are placed in the bonding and nonbonding orbitals. This description is repeated on the *x*- and *y*-axis, which means that two electron pairs are involved in the F—S—F group along each axis. That is, each of the three F—S—F "groups" is bonded with a three-center/four-electron bond, thus accounting nicely for the bonding in SF_6 without using *d* orbitals.

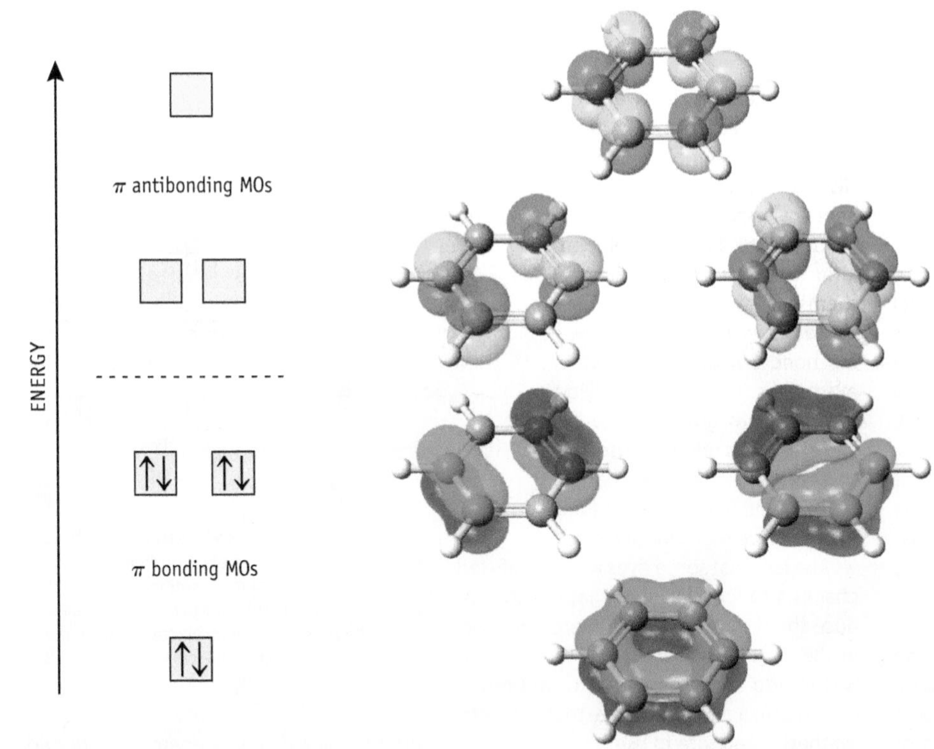

FIGURE 9.20 **Molecular orbital energy level diagram for benzene.** Because there are six unhybridized *p* orbitals (one on each C atom), six π molecular orbitals can be formed—three bonding and three antibonding. The three bonding molecular orbitals accommodate the six π electrons.

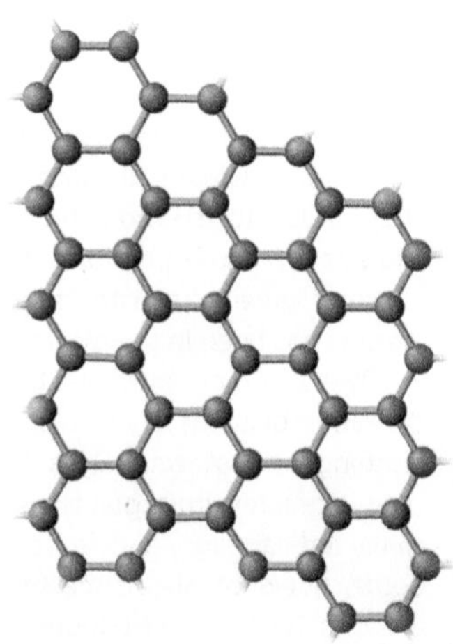

π Bonds, electrical conductivity, and graphene. Graphene, a recently discovered and important new material, consists of a sheet of six-member rings of carbon atoms. In graphene, electrons in π orbitals are delocalized, not just over one ring but over the sheet. As a result, these electrons can be influenced by an electric field, and graphene is an excellent electrical conductor. (See Study Question 9.72 and Chapter 12.)

bonds between two atoms. To further illustrate the MO approach, look again at benzene (Figure 9.20). On page 354, we noted that the π electrons in this molecule were spread out over all six carbon atoms. You can now see how the same case can be made with MO theory. Six *p* orbitals contribute to the π system. Because the number of molecular orbitals must equal the number of atomic orbitals, there must be six π molecular orbitals in benzene. An energy level diagram for benzene shows that the six π electrons reside in the three lowest-energy (bonding) molecular orbitals.

REVIEW & CHECK FOR SECTION 9-3

1. What is the N—O bond order in nitrogen monoxide, NO?

   (a) 2 (b) 2.5 (c) 3.0 (d) 1

2. What is the HOMO in the peroxide ion, O_2^{2-}?

   (a) π_{2p} (b) π^*_{2p} (c) σ^*_{2p} (d) σ^*_{2s}

3. Which of the following species is diamagnetic?

   (a) O_2 (b) B_2 (c) C_2 (d) N_2^+

4. Among the known dioxygen species (O_2^+, O_2, O_2^-, and O_2^{2-}), which is expected to have the shortest bond length?

   (a) O_2^+ (b) O_2 (c) O_2^- (d) O_2^{2-}

CASE STUDY Green Chemistry, Safe Dyes, and Molecular Orbitals

Chemists are obligated not only to search for useful new materials but also to ensure they are safe to use and to produce them in the safest manner possible. This is the essence of "green chemistry," and one recent success has been in the dye industry.

Dyes and pigments have been used for centuries because humans want colorful clothing and objects. Dyes have always been extracted from plants such as onion skins, red cabbage, and fruits and berries. Some, however, also came from animals, and one, Tyrian purple (Figure A), was especially prized. This dye, known to the ancient Greeks, can be extracted from a marine snail, *Murex brandaris*. The problem is that it takes over 12,000 tiny snails to produce enough dye to color a small portion of one garment. Fortunately, it was later discovered that a similar dye (with the same structure except for the Br atoms) could be obtained from the indigo plant, and indigo plantations were established in parts of colonial America.

The first synthetic dye was produced by accident in 1856. William Perkin, then 18, was searching for an antimalarial drug, but the route he chose to make it led instead to the dye mauveine. Because dyes were so highly prized, his discovery led to the synthesis of many more dyes. Indeed, some say Perkin's discovery led to the modern chemical industry.

Chemists have developed large numbers of dyes, among them azo dyes, so named because they contain a N═N double bond (an azo group). One example is "butter yellow" (Figure B). It was given this name because it was originally used to give butter a more appealing yellow color. The problem is that the molecule is carcinogenic.

The fact that some dyes were unsafe led chemists to look for ones that would produce the desired color but were not toxic. In the case of butter yellow, the solution was to add an $—NO_2$ group to the molecule to give a new yellow dye that is easy to synthesize and safe to use.

The structure of indigo is typical of many dyes: It has alternating double bonds (C═C and C═O) extending across the molecule. Azo dyes similarly have extended frameworks of alternating double bonds. Indeed, all organic dye molecules have extended π bonding networks, and it is this that leads to their color. The extended π bonds give rise to low-energy π antibonding molecular orbitals. When visible light strikes such a molecule, an electron can be excited from a bonding or nonbonding molecular orbital to an antibonding molecular orbital, and light is absorbed (Figure C). Your eye sees the wavelengths of light not absorbed by the molecule, so it has the color of the remaining wavelengths of light. For example, on page 174 you see a case where a substance absorbs wavelengths of light in the blue region of the spectrum, so you see red light.

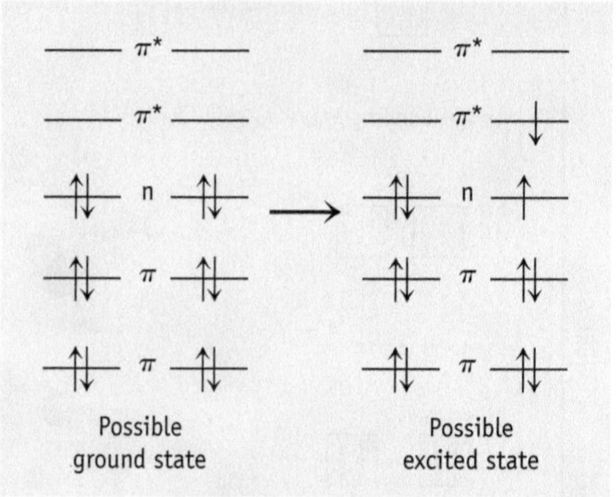

FIGURE C Light is absorbed by a dye molecule by the promotion of an electron from a nonbonding molecular orbital to an antibonding π molecular orbital. (Light absorption by all molecules occurs by promotion of an electron from a low-lying to a higher-lying molecular orbital.)

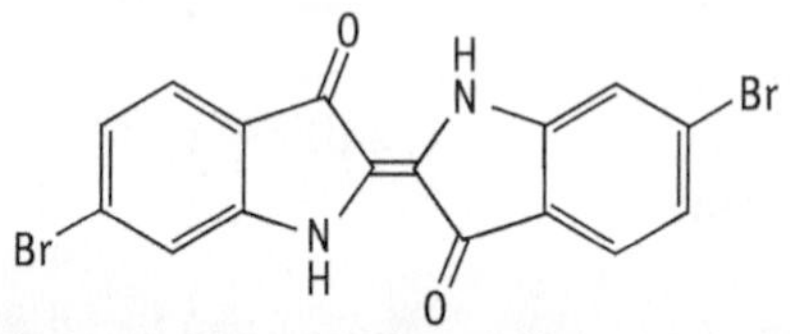

John C. Kotz

FIGURE A **Indigo.** (above) Tyrian purple or 6,6′-dibromoindigo ($C_{16}H_8N_2O_2Br_2$). (below) Indigo plant.

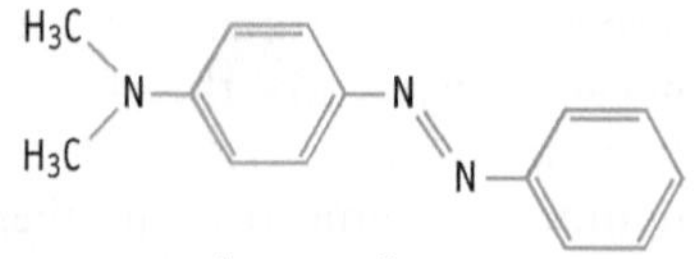

butter yellow

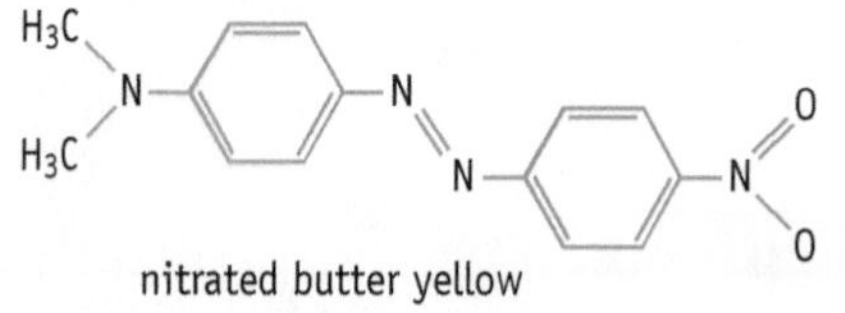

nitrated butter yellow

FIGURE B **The structure of "butter yellow" and "nitrated butter yellow."** The first is a synthetic dye originally used to color butter. It is in the class of azo dyes, all characterized by an N═N double bond. The nitrated version is safe for human consumption.

Questions:

1. What is the empirical formula of Tyrian purple?
2. Butter yellow absorbs light with a wavelength of 408 nm, whereas the nitrated form absorbs at 478 nm. Which absorbs the higher energy light?
3. How many alternating double bonds are there in Tyrian purple? In nitrated butter yellow?

Answers to these questions are available in Appendix N.

APPLYING CHEMICAL PRINCIPLES

Probing Molecules with Photoelectron Spectroscopy

Photoelectron spectroscopy is an instrumental technique that enables the measurement of orbital energies in atoms and molecules. (See page 272 for an introduction to the technique.) In this technique gas phase atoms or molecules are ionized by high-energy radiation. For a molecule (M), the process is as follows:

$$M + h\nu \rightarrow M^+ + e^-$$

A photon with sufficient energy ($h\nu$) can cause an electron to be ejected from the atom or molecule. If the photon has energy that is above the threshold required for ionization, the excess energy is imparted as kinetic energy to the ejected electron. The ionization energy, the energy of the absorbed photon, and the kinetic energy of the ejected electron are related by the equation.

$$IE = h\nu - KE(\text{electron})$$

Photoelectron spectroscopy may be used to study orbital energies of either core or valence electrons. Ionization of a core electron requires x-ray radiation, whereas ionization of valence electrons (which are responsible for bonding in molecules) requires lower energy ultraviolet (UV) radiation.

Helium gas is the most common UV radiation source used for the photoelectron spectroscopy of molecules. When electronically excited, He atoms emit nearly monochromatic (single wavelength) radiation at a wavelength of 58.4 nm. The energy of these photons is above the threshold required to eject electrons from many valence shell molecular orbitals.

The figure shows the valence shell photoelectron spectrum for N_2 molecules. The molecular orbital diagram (Figure 9.18 and Table 9.1) indicates that N_2 has four types of filled orbitals: σ_{2s}, σ^*_{2s}, π_{2p}, and σ_{2p}. The photoelectron spectrum detects three groupings of ejected electrons with average ionization energies of 15.6 eV, 16.7 eV, and 18.6 eV (where 1 electron volt = 1.60218×10^{-19} J). These electrons are ejected from the σ^*_{2s}, π_{2p}, and σ_{2p} orbitals, respectively. A fourth peak is not seen because the energy required to remove an electron from the σ_{2s} orbital is higher than that of the photons emitted by the excited helium atoms.

The extra peaks, most obvious around 17–18 eV, are associated with ionization from the π orbital. They result from coupling of the ionization energy and the energy resulting from molecular vibrations.

QUESTIONS:

1. Photoelectron spectroscopy is similar to the photoelectric effect (Section 6-2). However, in the photoelectric effect, electrons are ejected when light strikes the surface of a(n) ________.
2. What is the energy of a photon with a wavelength of 58.4 nm in kilojoules/mole?
3. Using the accompanying figure, state which molecular orbital (σ^*_{2s}, π_{2p}, or σ_{2p}) has an ionization energy of 15.6 eV.
4. The kinetic energy of an electron ejected from the σ^*_{2s} molecular orbital of N_2 using 58.4 nm radiation is 4.23×10^{-19} J. What is the ionization energy, in both kJ/mol and eV, of an electron from this orbital?
5. The N_2^+ ions that are formed when electrons with ionization energies of 15.6 eV and 16.7 eV are ejected have longer bond lengths than the ion when an electron with an ionization energy of 18.6 eV is created. Why?

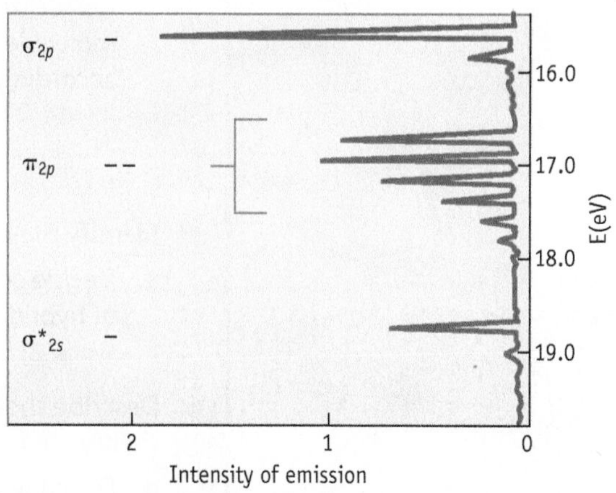

The photoelectron spectrum of N_2 gas. (Adapted from G. L. Miessler and D. A. Tarr, *Inorganic Chemistry*, Pearson, 3rd edition, 2004, page 131.)

CHAPTER GOALS REVISITED

Now that you have studied this chapter, you should ask whether you have met the chapter goals.

UNDERSTAND

- Orbital overlap is the basis for covalent bonding.
  - **a.** Recognize that the premise for valence bond theory is that bonding results from the overlap of atomic orbitals. By virtue of the overlap of orbitals, electrons are concentrated (or localized) between two atoms (Section 9-2).
  - **b.** The molecular orbital model of bonding also depends on orbital overlap but atoms in the entire molecule can be involved (Section 9-3).
  - **c.** Distinguish how sigma (σ) and pi (π) bonds arise through orbital overlap. For σ bonding, orbitals overlap in a head-to-head fashion, concentrating electrons along the bond axis. Sideways overlap of *p* atomic orbitals results in π bond formation, with electron density above and below the molecular plane (Section 9-2).
- The theory of orbital hybridization.
  - **a.** Understand that the rationale for orbital hybridization is to have a set of central atom orbitals that can form effective bonds by orbital overlap (Section 9-2).
- The differences between valence bond theory and molecular orbital theory and how each theory is applied.
  - **a.** In molecular orbital theory (Section 9-3) atomic orbitals combine to form bonding orbitals, nonbonding orbitals, or antibonding orbitals that are delocalized over several atoms. In this description, the electrons of the molecule or ion are assigned to the orbitals in order of increasing energy, according to the Pauli exclusion principle and Hund's rule. Study Questions: 43, 64, 71.

DO

- **Identify the hybridization of an atom in a molecule or polyatomic ion.**
  - **a.** Decide on the hybridization used by atoms in a molecule and use the concept of hybridization to rationalize molecular structure (Section 9-2). Study Questions: 3, 5, 15, 16, 31–33, 37, 48, 49, 54, 55, 68.
- Describe the bonding in a molecule or polyatomic ion using valence bond theory.
  - **a.** Describe bonds between atoms, specifying the atomic and/or hybrid orbitals that overlap to form the bond. Study Questions: 1–6, 15, 16, 55, 58.
- Write the molecular orbital configurations for simple diatomic molecules or ions, determine the bond order of each species, and predict its magnetic behavior.
  - **a.** Use molecular orbital theory to explain the properties of O_2 and other diatomic molecules. Study Questions: 21–28, 42, 45–47, 57.

REMEMBER

- Chemical bonding may be described using different theories, each having its advantages and disadvantages.

- The types of hybrid orbital sets and their orientations in space.

Hybrid Orbitals	Atomic Orbitals Used	Number of Hybrid Orbitals	Electron-Pair Geometry
sp	$s + p$	2	Linear
sp^2	$s + p + p$	3	Trigonal-planar
sp^3	$s + p + p + p$	4	Tetrahedral

- The terms sigma and pi and their meaning in terms of orbital overlap and bond shape.

KEY EQUATION

Equation 9.1 (page 357) Used to calculate the order of a bond from the molecular orbital electron configuration.

Bond order = 1/2 (number of electrons in bonding MOs − number of electrons in antibonding MOs)

© Gary J. Schrobilgen

STUDY QUESTIONS

▲ denotes challenging questions.

Blue-numbered questions have answers in Appendix N and fully worked solutions in the *Student Solutions Manual.*

Practicing Skills

Valence Bond Theory

(See Examples 9.1–9.3.)

1. Draw the Lewis structure for chloroform, $CHCl_3$. What are its electron-pair and molecular geometries? What orbitals on C, H, and Cl overlap to form bonds involving these elements?

2. Draw the Lewis structure for NF_3. What are its electron-pair and molecular geometries? What is the hybridization of the nitrogen atom? What orbitals on N and F overlap to form bonds between these elements?

3. Draw the Lewis structure for hydroxylamine, H_2NOH. What is the hybridization for nitrogen and oxygen in this molecule? What orbitals overlap to form the bond between nitrogen and oxygen?

4. Draw the Lewis structure for 1,1-dimethylhydrazine [$(CH_3)_2NNH_2$, a compound used as a rocket fuel]. What is the hybridization for the two nitrogen atoms in this molecule? What orbitals overlap to form the bond between the nitrogen atoms?

5. Draw the Lewis structure for carbonyl fluoride, COF_2. What are the electron-pair geometry and molecular geometry around the central atom? What is the hybridization of the carbon atom? What orbitals overlap to form the σ and π bonds between carbon and oxygen?

6. Draw the Lewis structure for acetamide, CH_3CONH_2. What are the electron-pair geometry and molecular geometry around the two C atoms? What is the hybridization of each of the C atoms? What orbitals overlap to form the σ and π bonds between carbon and oxygen?

7. Specify the electron-pair and molecular geometry for each underlined atom in the following list. Describe the hybrid orbital set used by this atom in each molecule or ion.
   (a) $\underline{B}Br_3$ (b) $\underline{C}O_2$ (c) $\underline{C}H_2Cl_2$ (d) $\underline{C}O_3^{2-}$

8. Specify the electron-pair and molecular geometry for each underlined atom in the following list. Describe the hybrid orbital set used by this atom in each molecule or ion.

(a) $\underline{C}Se_2$ (b) $\underline{S}O_2$ (c) $\underline{C}H_2O$ (d) $\underline{N}H_4^+$

9. What hybrid orbital set is used by each of the indicated atoms in the molecules below?

(a) the carbon atoms and the oxygen atom in dimethyl ether, CH_3OCH_3

(b) each carbon atom in propene

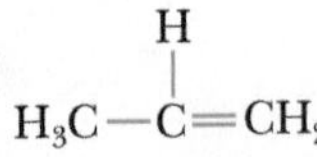

(c) the two carbon atoms and the nitrogen atom in the amino acid glycine

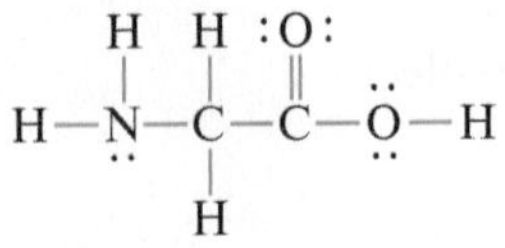

10. What is the hybrid orbital set used by each of the underlined atoms in the following molecules?

(a) 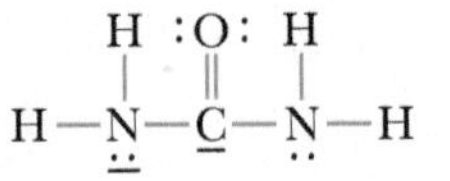 (c) 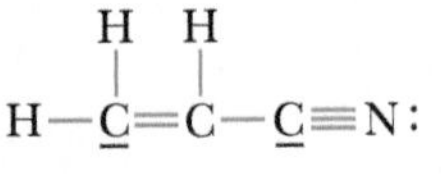

(b) 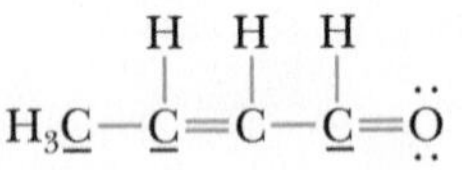

11. Draw the Lewis structures of the acid HPO_2F_2 and its anion $PO_2F_2^-$. What is the molecular geometry and hybridization for the phosphorus atom in each species? (H is bonded to an O atom in the acid.)

12. Draw the Lewis structures of the acid HSO_3F and its anion SO_3F^-. What is the molecular geometry and hybridization for the sulfur atom in each species? (H is bonded to an O atom in the acid.)

13. What is the hybridization of the carbon atom in phosgene, Cl_2CO? Give a complete description of the σ and π bonding in this molecule.

14. What is the hybridization of the carbon atoms in benzene, C_6H_6? Describe the σ and π bonding in this compound.

15. What is the electron-pair and molecular geometry around the central S atom in thionyl chloride, $SOCl_2$? What is the hybridization of sulfur in this compound?

16. What is the electron-pair and molecular geometry around the central S atom in sulfuryl chloride, SO_2Cl_2? What is the hybridization of sulfur in this compound?

17. The arrangement of groups attached to the C atoms involved in a C=C double bond leads to *cis* and *trans* isomers. For each compound below, draw the other isomer.

(a) 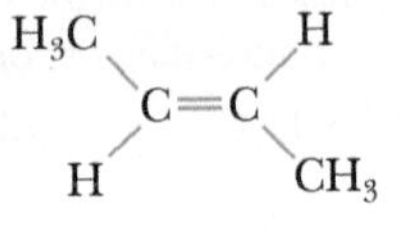 (b) 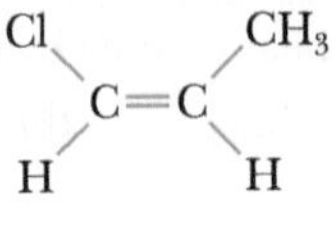

18. For each compound below, decide whether *cis* and *trans* isomers are possible. If isomerism is possible, draw the other isomer.

(a) 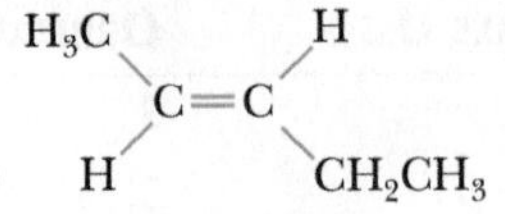

(b) 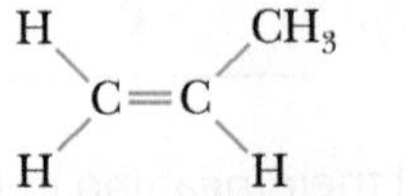 (c) 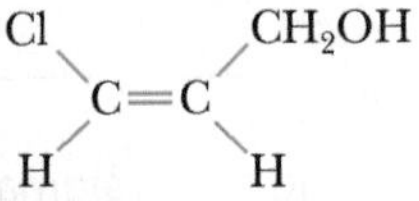

Molecular Orbital Theory

(See Examples 9.4–9.6.)

19. The hydrogen molecular ion, H_2^+, can be detected spectroscopically. Write the electron configuration of the ion in molecular orbital terms. What is the bond order of the ion? Is the hydrogen–hydrogen bond stronger or weaker in H_2^+ than in H_2?

20. Give the electron configurations for the ions Li_2^+ and Li_2^- in molecular orbital terms. Compare the Li—Li bond order in these ions with the bond order in Li_2.

21. Calcium carbide, CaC_2, contains the acetylide ion, C_2^{2-}. Sketch the molecular orbital energy level diagram for the ion. How many net σ and π bonds does the ion have? What is the carbon–carbon bond order? How has the bond order changed on adding electrons to C_2 to obtain C_2^{2-}? Is the C_2^{2-} ion paramagnetic?

22. Platinum hexafluoride is an extremely strong oxidizing agent. It can even oxidize oxygen, its reaction with O_2 giving $O_2^+PtF_6^-$. Sketch the molecular orbital energy level diagram for the O_2^+ ion. How many net σ and π bonds does the ion have? What is the oxygen–oxygen bond order? How has the bond order changed on taking away electrons from O_2 to obtain O_2^+? Is the O_2^+ ion paramagnetic?

23. When sodium and oxygen react, one of the products obtained is sodium peroxide, Na_2O_2. The anion in this compound is the peroxide ion, O_2^{2-}. Write the electron configuration for this ion in molecular orbital terms, and then compare it with the electron configuration of the O_2 molecule with respect to the following criteria:

(a) magnetic character
(b) net number of σ and π bonds
(c) bond order
(d) oxygen–oxygen bond length

24. When potassium and oxygen react, one of the products obtained is potassium superoxide, KO_2. The anion in this compound is the superoxide ion, O_2^-. Write the electron configuration for this ion in molecular orbital terms, and then compare it with the electron configuration of the O_2 molecule with respect to the following criteria:

(a) magnetic character
(b) net number of σ and π bonds
(c) bond order
(d) oxygen–oxygen bond length

Courtesy of the Mine Safety Appliances Company

A closed-circuit breathing apparatus that generates its own oxygen. One source of oxygen is potassium superoxide (KO_2). Both carbon dioxide and moisture exhaled by the wearer into the breathing tube react with the KO_2 to generate oxygen.

25. Among the following, which has the shortest bond and which has the longest: Li_2, B_2, C_2, N_2, O_2?

26. Consider the following list of small molecules and ions: C_2, O_2^-, CN^-, O_2, CO, NO, NO^+, C_2^{2-}, OF^-. Identify
   (a) all species that have a bond order of 3
   (b) all species that are paramagnetic
   (c) species that have a fractional bond order

27. Assume the energy level diagram shown in Figure 9.18 can be applied to the heteronuclear molecule ClO.
   (a) Write the electron configuration for chlorine monoxide, ClO.
   (b) What is the highest-energy, occupied molecular orbital (the HOMO)?
   (c) Is the molecule diamagnetic or paramagnetic?
   (d) What is the net number of σ and π bonds? What is the ClO bond order?

28. The nitrosyl ion, NO^+, has an interesting chemistry.
   (a) Is NO^+ diamagnetic or paramagnetic? If paramagnetic, how many unpaired electrons does it have?
   (b) Assume the molecular orbital diagram shown in Figure 9.18 applies to NO^+. What is the highest-energy molecular orbital (HOMO) occupied by electrons?
   (c) What is the nitrogen–oxygen bond order?
   (d) Is the N—O bond in NO^+ stronger or weaker than the bond in NO?

General Questions

These questions are not designated as to type or location in the chapter. They may combine several concepts.

29. Draw the Lewis structure for AlF_4^-. What are its electron-pair and molecular geometries? What orbitals on Al and F overlap to form bonds between these elements? What are the formal charges on the atoms? Is this a reasonable charge distribution?

30. What is the O—S—O angle and the hybrid orbital set used by sulfur in each of the following molecules or ions?

(a) SO_2 (b) SO_3 (c) SO_3^{2-} (d) SO_4^{2-}

Do all have the same value for the O—S—O angle? Does the S atom in all these species use the same hybrid orbitals?

31. Sketch the resonance structures for the nitrite ion, NO_2^-. Describe the electron-pair and molecular geometries of the ion. From these geometries, decide on the O—N—O bond angle, the average NO bond order, and the N atom hybridization.

32. Sketch the resonance structures for the nitrate ion, NO_3^-. Is the hybridization of the N atom the same or different in each structure? Describe the orbitals involved in bond formation by the central N atom.

33. Sketch the resonance structures for the N_2O molecule. Is the hybridization of the N atoms the same or different in each structure? Describe the orbitals involved in bond formation by the central N atom.

34. Compare the structure and bonding in CO_2 and CO_3^{2-} with regard to the O—C—O bond angles, the CO bond order, and the C atom hybridization.

35. Numerous molecules are detected in deep space. Three of them are illustrated here.

Ethylene oxide

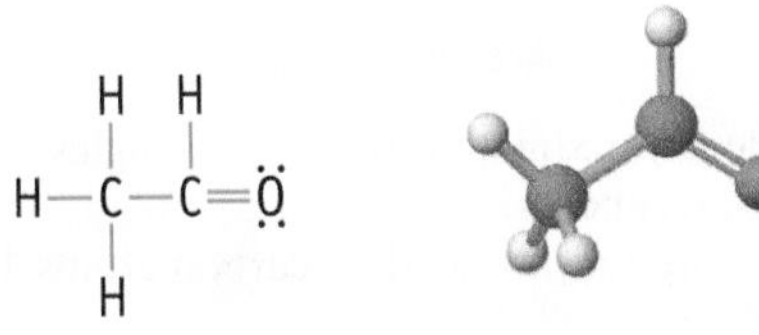

Acetaldehyde

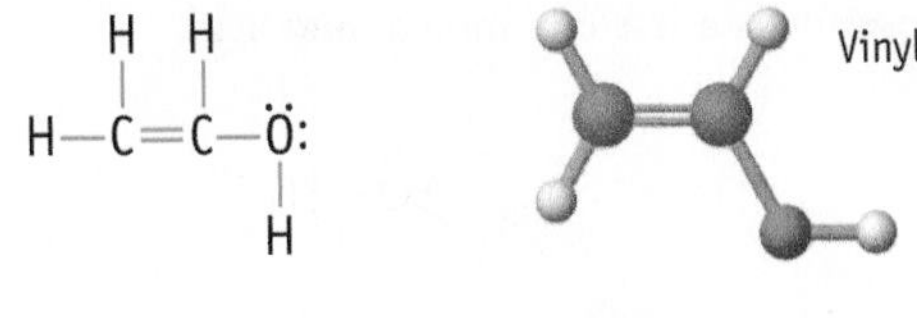

Vinyl alcohol

   (a) Are these compounds isomers?
   (b) Indicate the hybridization of each C atom in each molecule.
   (c) What is the value of the H—C—H angle in each of the three molecules?
   (d) Which of these molecules is/are polar?
   (e) Which molecule should have the strongest carbon–carbon bond? The strongest carbon–oxygen bond?

36. Acrolein, a component of photochemical smog, has a pungent odor and irritates eyes and mucous membranes.

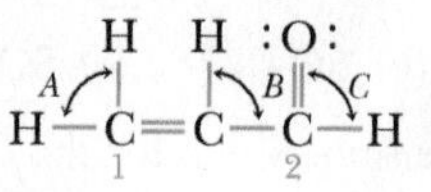

(a) What are the hybridizations of carbon atoms 1 and 2?

(b) What are the approximate values of angles *A*, *B*, and *C*?

(c) Is *cis-trans* isomerism possible here?

37. The organic compound below is a member of a class known as oximes.

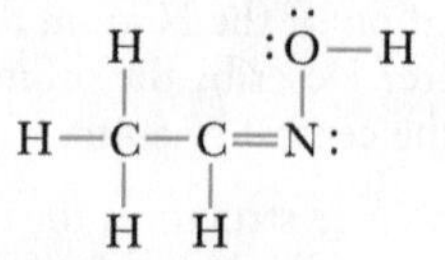

(a) What are the hybridizations of the two C atoms and of the N atom?

(b) What is the approximate C—N—O angle?

38. The compound sketched below is acetylsalicylic acid, commonly known as aspirin.

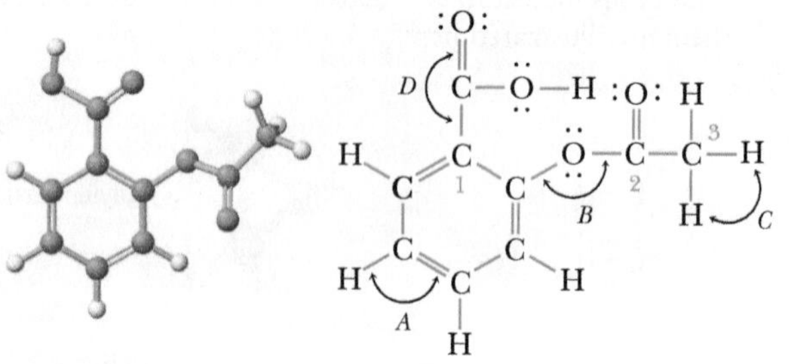

Aspirin

(a) What are the approximate values of the angles marked *A*, *B*, *C*, and *D*?

(b) What hybrid orbitals are used by carbon atoms 1, 2, and 3?

39. Phosphoserine is a less-common amino acid.

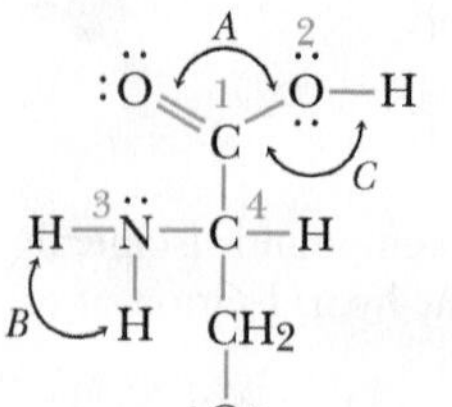

Phosphoserine

(a) Identify the hybridizations of atoms 1 through 5.

(b) What are the approximate values of the bond angles *A*, *B*, *C*, and *D*?

(c) What are the most polar bonds in the molecule?

40. Lactic acid is a natural compound found in sour milk.

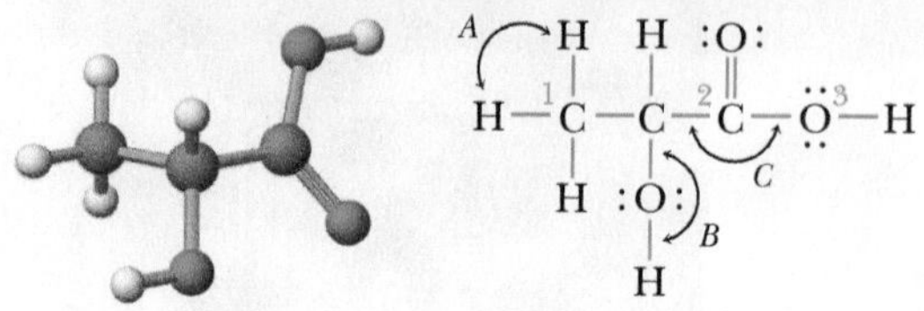

Lactic acid

(a) How many π bonds occur in lactic acid? How many σ bonds?

(b) What is the hybridization of atoms 1, 2, and 3?

(c) Which CO bond is the shortest in the molecule? Which CO bond is the strongest?

(d) What are the approximate values of the bond angles *A*, *B*, and *C*?

41. Cinnamaldehyde occurs naturally in cinnamon oil.

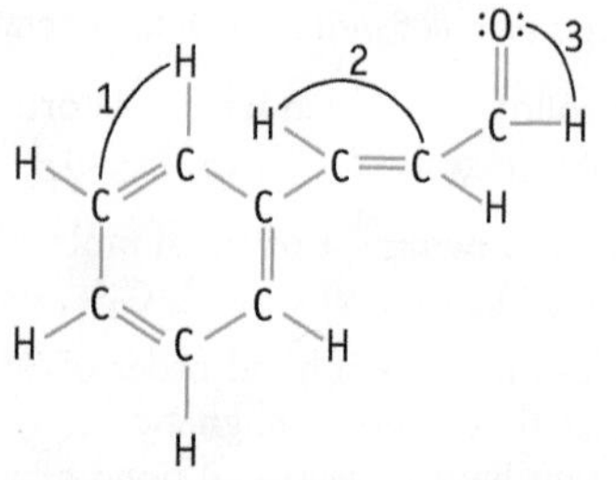

Cinnamaldehyde

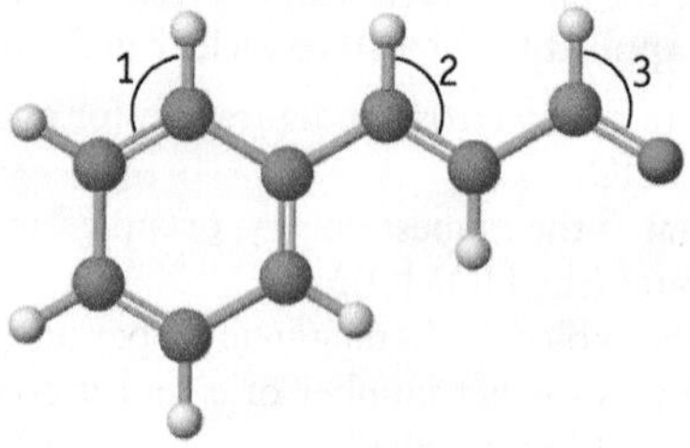

(a) What is the most polar bond in the molecule?

(b) How many σ bonds and how many π bonds are there?

(c) Is *cis-trans* isomerism possible? If so, draw the isomers of the molecule.

(d) Give the hybridization of the C atoms in the molecule.

(e) What are the values of the bond angles *1*, *2*, and *3*?

42. The ion Si_2^- was reported in a laboratory experiment in 1996.

(a) Using molecular orbital theory, predict the bond order for the ion.

(b) Is the ion paramagnetic or diamagnetic?

(c) What is the highest energy molecular orbital that contains one or more electrons?

43. The simple valence bond picture of O_2 does not agree with the molecular orbital view. Compare these two theories with regard to the peroxide ion, O_2^{2-}.

(a) Draw an electron dot structure for O_2^{2-}. What is the bond order of the ion?

(b) Write the molecular orbital electron configuration for O_2^{2-}. What is the bond order based on this approach?
(c) Do the two theories of bonding lead to the same magnetic character and bond order for O_2^{2-}?

44. Nitrogen, N_2, can ionize to form N_2^+ or add an electron to give N_2^-. Using molecular orbital theory, compare these species with regard to (a) their magnetic character, (b) net number of π bonds, (c) bond order, (d) bond length, and (e) bond strength.

45. Which of the homonuclear, diatomic molecules of the second-period elements (from Li_2 to Ne_2) are paramagnetic? Which have a bond order of 1? Which have a bond order of 2? Which diatomic molecule has the highest bond order?

46. Which of the following molecules or ions are paramagnetic? What is the highest occupied molecular orbital (HOMO) in each one? Assume the molecular orbital diagram in Figure 9.18 applies to all of them.

(a) NO
(b) OF^-
(c) O_2^{2-}
(d) Ne_2^+

47. The CN molecule has been found in interstellar space. Assuming the electronic structure of the molecule can be described using the molecular orbital energy level diagram in Figure 9.18, answer the following questions.

(a) What is the highest energy occupied molecular orbital (HOMO) to which an electron (or electrons) is (are) assigned?
(b) What is the bond order of the molecule?
(c) How many net σ bonds are there? How many net π bonds?
(d) Is the molecule paramagnetic or diamagnetic?

48. The structure of amphetamine, a stimulant, is shown below. (Replacing one H atom on the NH_2, or amino, group with CH_3 gives methamphetamine, a particularly dangerous drug commonly known as "speed.")

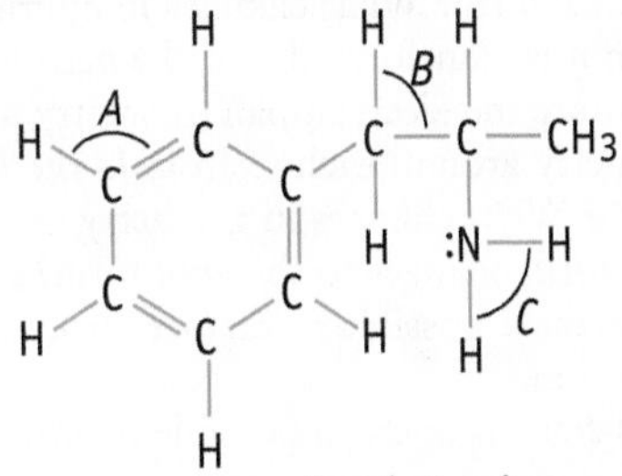

Amphetamine

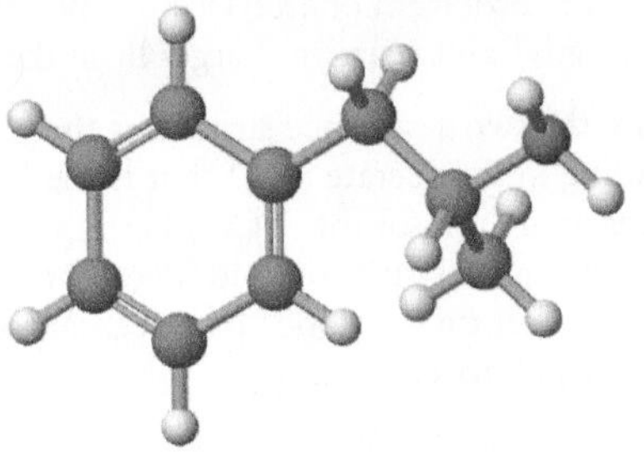

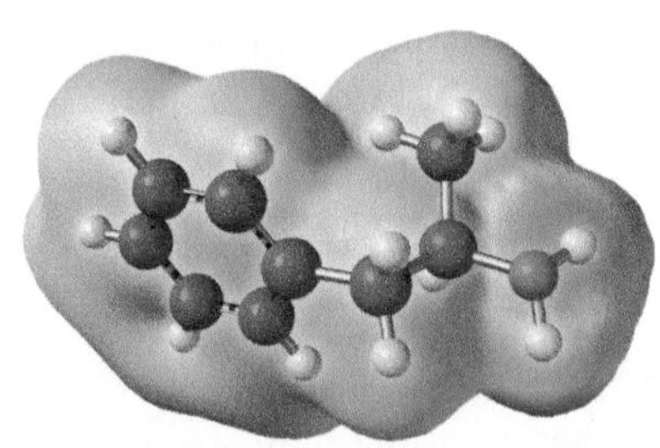

(a) What are the hybrid orbitals used by the C atoms of the C_6 ring, by the C atoms of the side chain, and by the N atom?
(b) Give approximate values for the bond angles *A*, *B*, and *C*.
(c) How many σ bonds and π bonds are in the molecule?
(d) Is the molecule polar or nonpolar?
(e) Amphetamine reacts readily with a proton (H^+) in aqueous solution. Where does this proton attach to the molecule? Explain how the electrostatic potential map predicts this site of protonation.

49. Menthol is used in soaps, perfumes, and foods. It is present in the common herb mint, and it can be prepared from turpentine.

(a) What are the hybridizations used by the C atoms in the molecule?
(b) What is the approximate C—O—H bond angle?
(c) Is the molecule polar or nonpolar?
(d) Is the six-member carbon ring planar or nonplanar? Explain why or why not.

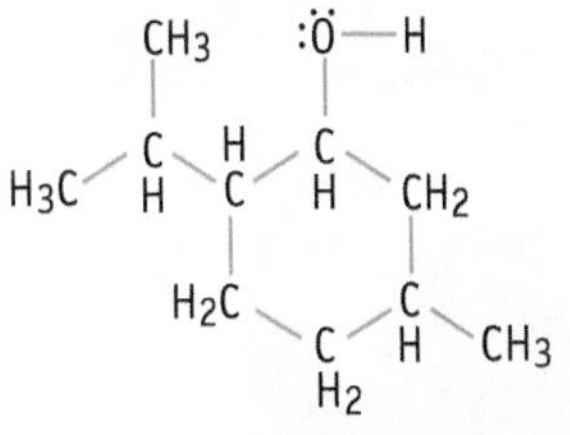

Menthol

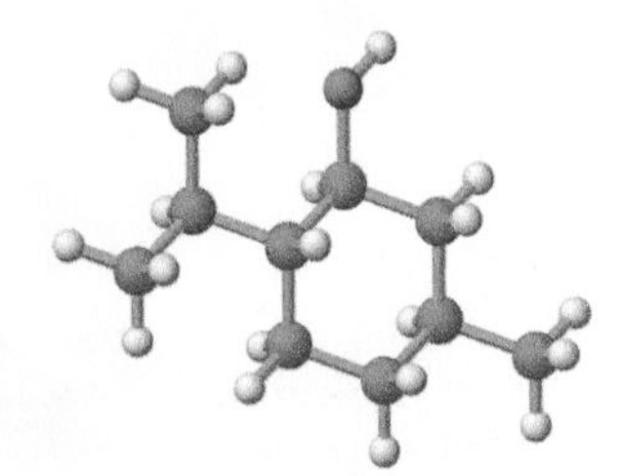

50. The elements of the second period from boron to oxygen form compounds of the type $X_nE—EX_n$, where X can be H or a halogen. Sketch possible Lewis structures for B_2F_4, C_2H_4, N_2H_4, and O_2H_2. Give the hybridizations of E in each molecule and specify approximate X—E—E bond angles.

In the Laboratory

51. Suppose you carry out the following reaction of ammonia and boron trifluoride in the laboratory.

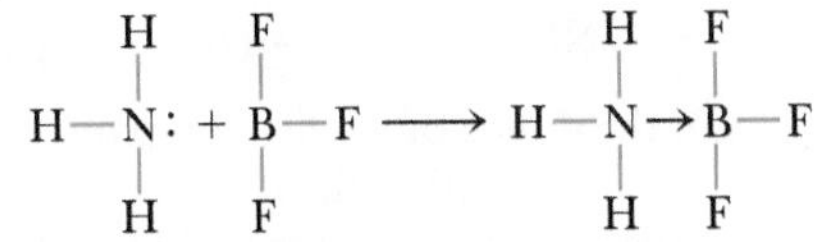

(a) What is the geometry of the boron atom in BF_3? In $H_3N{\rightarrow}BF_3$?
(b) What is the hybridization of the boron atom in the two compounds?
(c) Considering the structures and bonding of NH_3 and BF_3, why do you expect the nitrogen on NH_3 to donate an electron pair to the B atom of BF_3?
(d) BF_3 also reacts readily with water. Based on the ammonia reaction above, speculate on how water can interact with BF_3.

52. ▲ Ethylene oxide is an intermediate in the manufacture of ethylene glycol (antifreeze) and polyester polymers. More than 4 million tons are produced annually in the United States. The molecule has a three-member ring of two C atoms and an O atom.

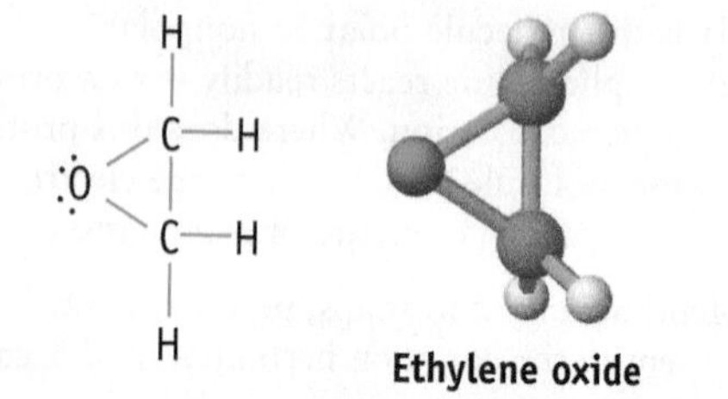

Ethylene oxide

(a) What are the bond angles in the ring? Comment on the relation between the bond angles expected based on hybridization and the bond angles expected for a three-member ring.
(b) Is the molecule polar? Based on the electrostatic potential map shown below, where do the negative and positive charges lie in the molecule?

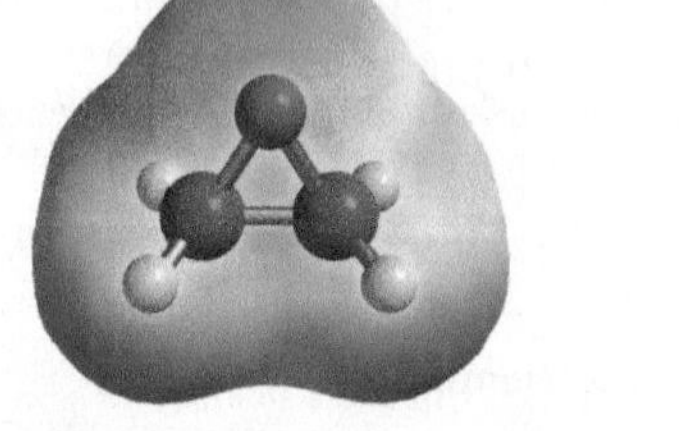

Electrostatic potential map for ethylene oxide

53. The sulfamate ion, $H_2NSO_3^-$, can be thought of as having been formed from the amide ion, NH_2^-, and sulfur trioxide, SO_3.
(a) What are the electron-pair and molecular geometries of the amide ion and of SO_3? What are the hybridizations of the N and S atoms, respectively?
(b) Sketch a structure for the sulfamate ion, and estimate the bond angles.
(c) What changes in hybridization do you expect for N and S in the course of the reaction

$$NH_2^- + SO_3 \rightarrow H_2N{-}SO_3^-?$$

(d) Is SO_3 the donor of an electron pair or the acceptor of an electron pair in the reaction with amide ion? Does the electrostatic potential map shown above confirm your prediction?

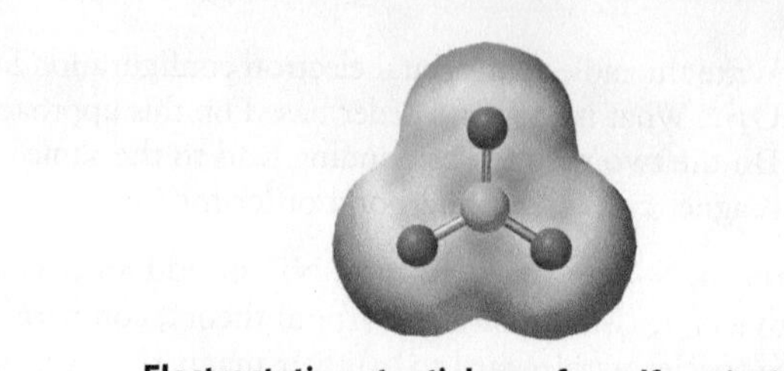

Electrostatic potential map for sulfur trioxide

54. ▲ The compound whose structure is shown here is acetylacetone. It exists in two forms: the *enol* form and the *keto* form.

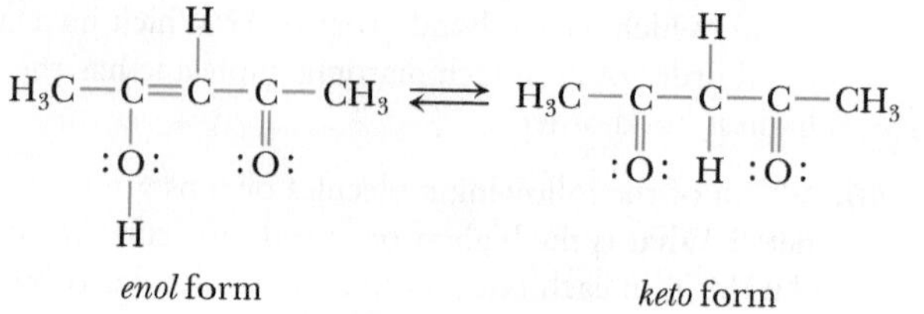

Acetylacetone

The molecule reacts with OH^- to form an anion, $[CH_3COCHCOCH_3]^-$ (often abbreviated acac$^-$ for acetylacetonate ion). One of the most interesting aspects of this anion is that one or more of them can react with transition metal cations to give stable, highly colored compounds.

Acetylacetonate complexes $(CH_3COCHCOCH_3)_3M$ where M = Co, Cr, and Fe

(a) Are the *keto* and *enol* forms of acetylacetone resonance forms? Explain your answer.
(b) What is the hybridization of each atom (except H) in the *enol* form? What changes in hybridization occur when it is transformed into the *keto* form?
(c) What are the electron-pair geometry and molecular geometry around each C atom in the *keto* and *enol* forms? What changes in geometry occur when the *keto* form changes to the *enol* form?
(d) Draw three possible resonance structures for the acac$^-$ ion.
(e) Is *cis-trans* isomerism possible in either the *enol* or the *keto* form of acetylacetone?
(f) Is the *enol* form of acetylacetone polar? Where do the positive and negative charges lie in the molecule?

55. Draw the two resonance structures that describe the bonding in the acetate ion. What is the hybridization of the carbon atom of the $—CO_2^-$ group? Select one of the two resonance structures and identify the orbitals that overlap to form the bonds between carbon and the three elements attached to it.

56. Carbon dioxide (CO_2), dinitrogen monoxide (N_2O), the azide ion (N_3^-), and the cyanate ion (OCN^-) have the same geometry and the same number of valence shell electrons. However, there are significant differences in their electronic structures.

(a) What hybridization is assigned to the central atom in each species? Which orbitals overlap to form the bonds between atoms in each structure.

(b) Evaluate the resonance structures of these four species. Which most closely describe the bonding in these species? Comment on the differences in bond lengths and bond orders that you expect to see based on the resonance structures.

57. Draw the two resonance structures that describe the bonding in SO_2. Then describe the bonding in this compound using MO theory. How does MO theory rationalize the bond order of 1.5 for the two S—O bonds in this compound?

58. Draw a Lewis structure for diimide, H—N=N—H. Then, using valence bond theory, describe the bonding in this compound. What orbitals overlap to form the bond between nitrogen atoms in this compound?

Summary and Conceptual Questions

The following questions may use concepts from this and previous chapters.

59. What is the maximum number of hybrid orbitals that a carbon atom may form? What is the minimum number? Explain briefly.

60. Consider the three fluorides BF_4^-, SiF_4, and SF_4.

(a) Identify a molecule that is isoelectronic with BF_4^-.

(b) Are SiF_4 and SF_4 isoelectronic?

(c) What is the hybridization of the central atom in BF_4^- and SiF_4?

61. ▲ When two amino acids react with each other, they form a linkage called an *amide group*, or a peptide link. (If more linkages are added, a protein or polypeptide is formed.)

(a) What are the hybridizations of the C and N atoms in the peptide linkage?

(b) Is the structure illustrated the only resonance structure possible for the peptide linkage? If another resonance structure is possible, compare it with the one shown. Decide which is the more important structure.

(c) The computer-generated structure shown here, which contains a peptide linkage, shows that this linkage is flat. This is an important feature of proteins. Speculate on reasons that the CO—NH linkage is planar. What are the sites of positive and negative charge in this dipeptide?

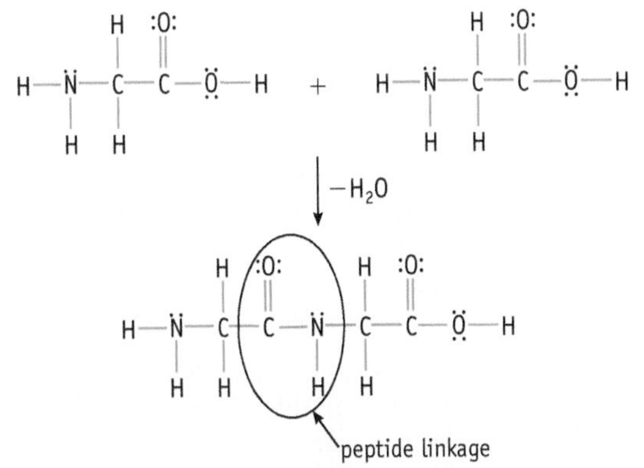

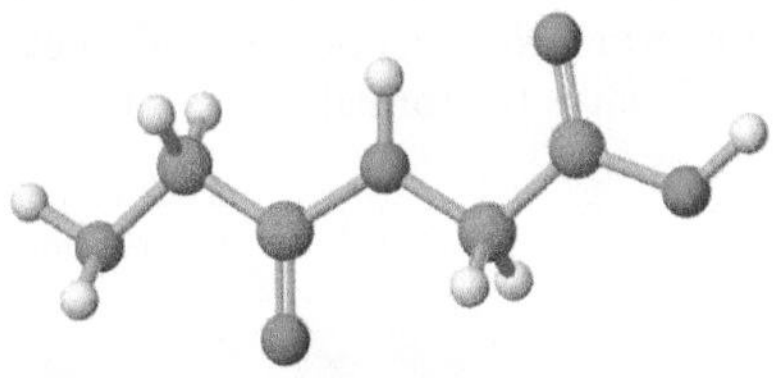

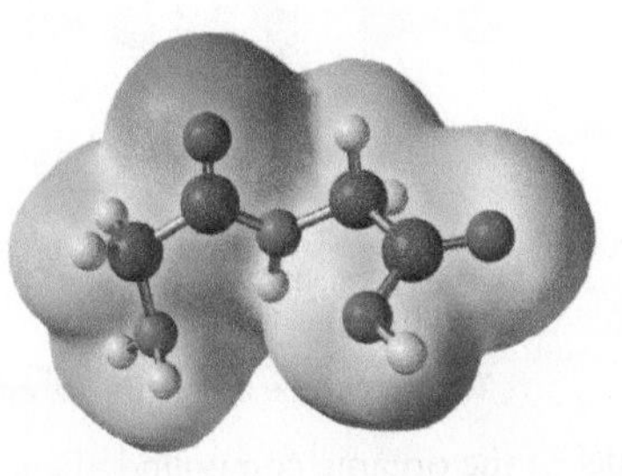

Electrostatic potential map for a peptide

62. What is the connection between bond order, bond length, and bond energy? Use ethane (C_2H_6), ethylene (C_2H_4), and acetylene (C_2H_2) as examples.

63. When is it desirable to use MO theory rather than valence bond theory?

64. Show how valence bond theory and molecular orbital theory rationalize the O—O bond order of 1.5 in ozone.

65. Three of the four π molecular orbitals for cyclobutadiene are pictured here. Place them in order of increasing energy. (As shown in Figures 9.15, 9.17, and 9.18 orbitals increase in energy in order of an increasing number of nodes. If a pair of orbitals have the same number of nodes, they have the same energy.)

Orbital A

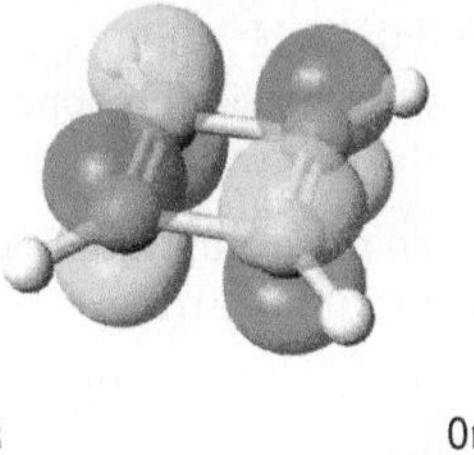

Orbital B

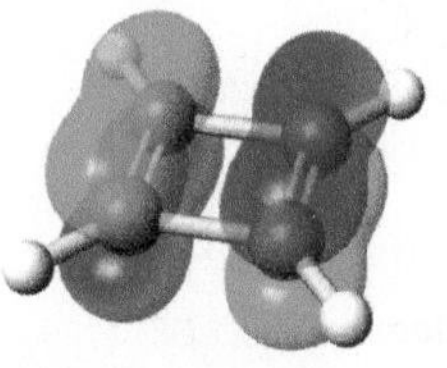

Orbital C

66. Let's look more closely at the process of hybridization.
(a) What is the relationship between the number of hybrid orbitals produced and the number of atomic orbitals used to create them?
(b) Do hybrid atomic orbitals form between different *p* orbitals without involving *s* orbitals?
(c) What is the relationship between the energy of hybrid atomic orbitals and the atomic orbitals from which they are formed?

67. Borax has the molecular formula $Na_2B_4O_5(OH)_4$. The structure of the anion in this compound is shown below. What is the electron pair geometry and molecular geometry surrounding each of the boron atoms in this anion? What hybridization can be assigned to each of the boron atoms? What is the formal charge of each boron atom?

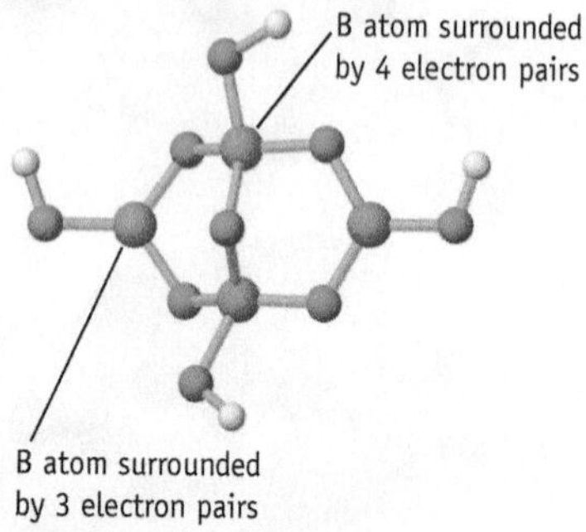

The structure of the borax anion

68. A model of the organic compound allene is shown below.

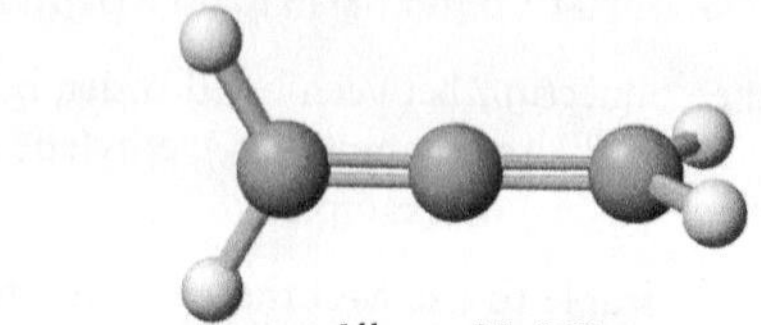

Allene, CH_2CCH_2

(a) Explain why the allene molecule is not flat. That is, explain why the CH_2 groups at opposite ends do not lie in the same plane.
(b) What is the hybridization of each of the carbon atoms in allene?
(c) What orbitals overlap to form the bonds between carbon atoms in allene?

69. Should the energy required to break one of the H—F bonds in HF_2^- ($HF_2^- \rightarrow HF + F^-$) be greater than, less than, or the same as the energy required to break the bond in HF ($HF \rightarrow H + F$). Explain your answer, considering the 3-center-4-electron bond model for HF_2^- described in the *Closer Look* box on page 364.

70. Melamine is an important industrial chemical, used to make fertilizers and plastics.

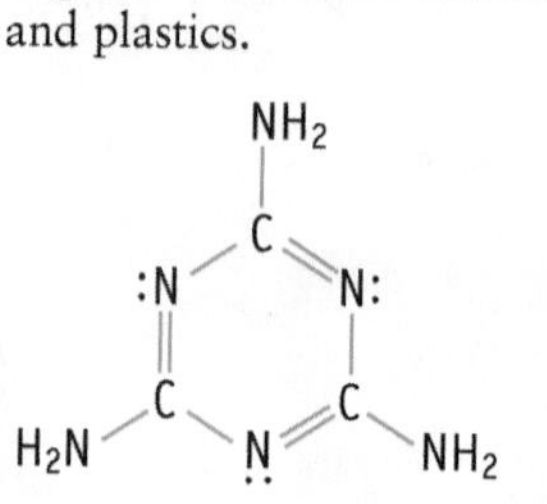

Melamine

(a) The carbon-nitrogen bond lengths in the ring are all the same length (about 140 pm). Explain.
(b) Melamine is made by the decomposition of urea, $(H_2N)_2CO$.

$$6\ (H_2N)_2CO(s) \rightarrow C_3H_6N_6(s) + 6\ NH_3(g) + 3\ CO_2(g)$$

Calculate the enthalpy change for this reaction. Is it endo- or exothermic? [$\Delta_f H°$ for melamine(s) = -66.1 kJ/mol and for urea(s) = -333.1 kJ/mol]

71. Bromine forms a number of oxides of varying stability.
(a) One oxide has 90.90% Br and 9.10% O. Assuming its empirical and molecular formulas are the same, draw a Lewis structure of the molecule and specify the hybridization of the central atom (O).
(b) Another oxide is unstable BrO. Assuming the molecular orbital diagram in Figure 9.18 applies to BrO, write its electron configuration (where Br uses 4*s* and 4*p* orbitals). What is the highest occupied molecular orbital (HOMO) for the molecule?

72. The following problem is taken from the Theoretical Examination of the 44th annual International Chemistry Olympiad in 2012, a competition attended by four secondary school students from each of about 70 countries. (Used with permission.)

Graphene is a sheet of carbon atoms arranged in a two-dimensional honeycomb pattern. It can be considered as an extreme case of a polyaromatic hydrocarbon with essentially infinite length in two dimensions. Graphene has remarkable strength, flexibility, and electrical properties. The Nobel Prize for Physics was awarded in 2010 to Andre Geim and Konstantin Novoselov for groundbreaking experiments on graphene. A section of the graphene sheet is shown below.

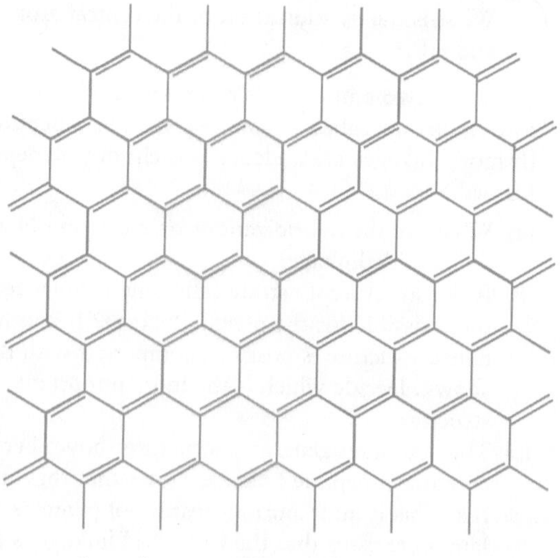

The area of one hexagonal 6-carbon unit is ~52400 pm^2. Calculate the number of π electrons in a tiny 25 nm × 25 nm sheet of graphene. For this problem you can ignore edge electrons (i.e., those outside the full hexagons in the picture).

73. Urea reacts with malonic acid to produce barbituric acid, a member of the class of compounds called phenobarbitals, which are widely prescribed as sedatives.

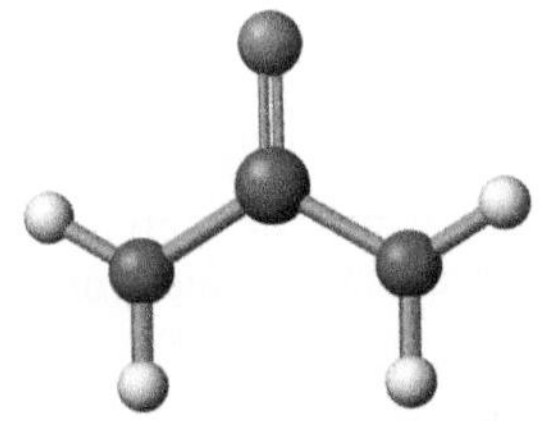

Urea

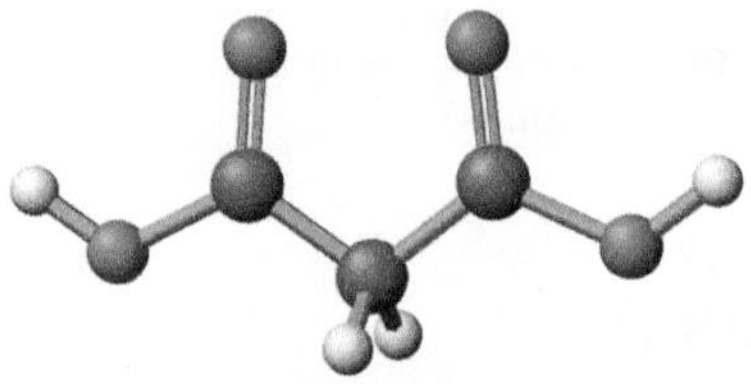

Malonic acid

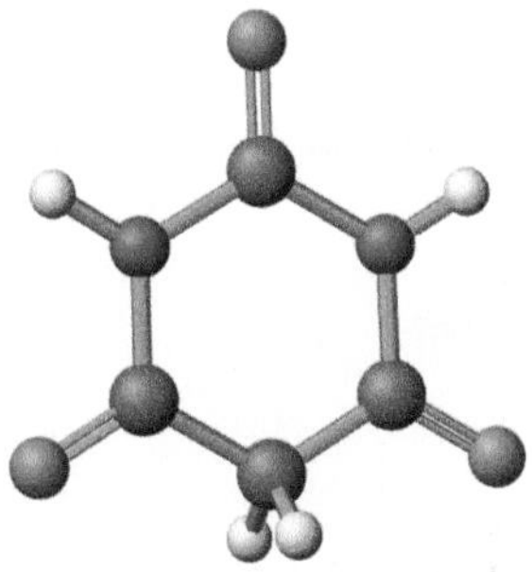

Barbituric acid

(a) What bonds are broken and what bonds are made when malonic acid and urea combine to make barbituric acid? Is the reaction predicted to be exo- or endothermic?
(b) Write a balanced equation for the reaction.
(c) Specify the bond angles in barbituric acid.
(d) Give the hybridization of the C atoms in barbituric acid.
(e) What is(are) the most polar bond(s) in barbituric acid?
(f) Is the molecule polar?

AP Multiple-Choice Review Questions

1. Which of the following has sp^3 hybridization and is bent?

(A)

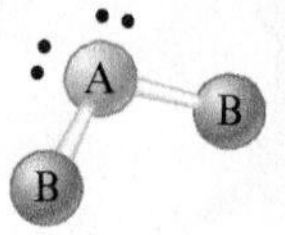

(B)

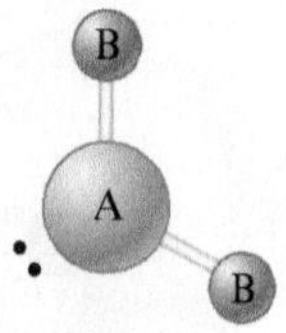

(C)

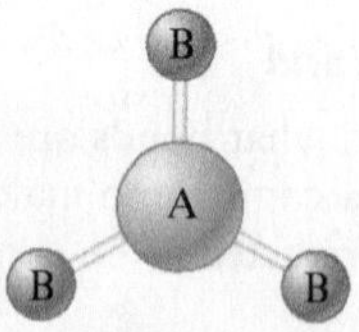

(D)

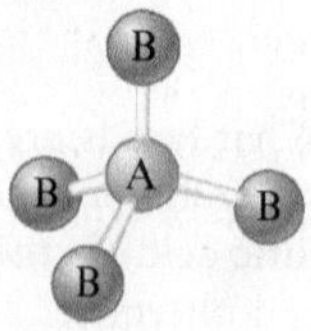

2. In a molecule in which the central atom exhibits sp^3 hybrid orbitals, the electron pairs are directed toward the corners of a

(A) tetrahedron
(B) trigonal pyramid
(C) trigonal bipyramid
(D) square-based pyramid

3. Of HCO_3^-, CO_3^{2-}, CO_2, and CO, which one has the shortest C—O bond length?

(A) HCO_3^-
(B) CO_3^{2-}
(C) CO_2
(D) CO

4. Which ion listed has no resonance structures and exactly two pi (π) bonds?

(A) CN^-
(B) O_3^-
(C) OH^-
(D) CO_3^{2-}

5. In a molecule in which the central atom exhibits sp^2 hybrid orbitals, the arrangement of electron pairs is

(A) linear
(B) tetrahedral
(C) trigonal planar
(D) trigonal bipyramidal

6. Which of the following is ionic and contains both sigma (σ) and pi (π) bonds?

(A) NO_2
(B) KCN
(C) C_2H_4
(D) NaOH

7. How many of the following molecules have two pi (π) bonds?

HCN, C_2H_2, CO_2, OCl_2

(A) 0
(B) 1
(C) 2
(D) 3

AP Free Response Review Questions

Question Format: Short

Category of Question: Representation 2

Many different molecules have the same chemical formula of JQ_3, but will have very different molecular geometries.

Questions

In the boxes, draw a Lewis Electron Dot diagram for a molecular compound that matches the given hybridization and answer the questions that follow. Use the actual formula for a compound, rather than JQ_3 in your diagram.

Hybridization of central atom:	***sp*²**
Chemical formula:	
Molecular geometry:	
Bond angles:	

Hybridization of central atom:	***sp*³**
Chemical formula:	
Molecular geometry:	
Bond angles:	

Question Format: Long

Category of Question: Representation 1

The molecular shape of hypothetical molecule ZX_2 is not readily apparent from its formula because we don't know how many valence electrons elements Z and X have.

Questions

(a) Draw three different Lewis structures that could be possible for ZX_2, assuming that Z is the central atom and that X is not hydrogen. Both Z and X obey the octet rule. Give molecular shapes and bond angles for each. In each case, use Valence Shell Electron Pair Repulsion theory to explain why the molecular shape is possible.

(b) Give the hybridization of Z in each of the different structures.

(c) Assume that the electronegativity values of Z = 2.5 and X = 3.5. Draw space-filling structures for each of the Lewis structures drawn in part a) indicating the polarity of the molecule, if it is polar. If it is nonpolar, label it as such.

(d) Another hypothetical molecule, QR_3, is found to have 106.7° bond angles. In which group of the periodic table is Q likely to be found? Explain.

(e) A hypothetical ion, T_2^+, has 3 bonding electrons and 2 antibonding electrons in its molecular orbital configuration. What is its bond order? Is it more stable or less stable than a molecule with a bond order of 2?

Courtesy Ciprian Popoviciu

Climbing very high mountains often requires the use of supplemental oxygen.

Gases and Their Properties

Chapter Outline

THE ATMOSPHERE AND ALTITUDE SICKNESS Some of you may have dreamed of climbing to the summits of the world's tallest mountains, or you may be an avid skier and visit high-mountain ski areas. In either case, "acute mountain sickness" (AMS) is a possibility. AMS is common at higher altitudes and is characterized by a headache, nausea, insomnia, dizziness, lassitude, and fatigue. It can be prevented by a slow ascent, and its symptoms can be relieved by a mild pain reliever.

AMS and more serious forms of high-altitude sickness are generally due to oxygen deprivation, also called *hypoxia*. The oxygen concentration in Earth's atmosphere is 21%. As you go higher into the atmosphere, the concentration remains 21%, but the atmospheric pressure drops. When you reach 3000 m (the altitude of some ski resorts), the barometric pressure is about 70% of that at sea level. At 5000 m, barometric pressure is only 50% of sea level, and on the summit of Mount Everest (altitude = 8848 m),

Chapter Goals

See Chapter Goals Revisited (page 402) for Study Questions keyed to these goals.

UNDERSTAND

- The experimental basis of Boyle's law, Charles's law, Avogadro's hypothesis, and Dalton's law of partial pressures.
- Kinetic-molecular theory as it is applied to gases, especially the distribution of molecular speeds (energies).
- Why real gases do not behave like ideal gases under some conditions.

DO

- Describe how changing one property of a gas (*P*, *V*, *T*, or *n*) changes the others.
- Apply the gas laws to stoichiometric calculations.
- Use the principles of the kinetic-molecular theory to describe the behavior of gases.
- Determine the relative rates of effusion of gases.
- Use the ideal gas law and the van der Waals equation.

REMEMBER

- The various units of pressure.
- The effects of temperature and molar mass on the rates of effusion and diffusion.
- How properties of gases are explained by the kinetic-molecular theory.

it is only 29% of the sea level pressure. At sea level, where the partial pressure of oxygen is 160 mm Hg, your blood is nearly saturated with oxygen, but as the partial pressure of oxygen [$P(O_2)$] drops, the percent saturation drops as well. At $P(O_2)$ of 50 mm Hg, hemoglobin in the red blood cells is about 80% saturated. Other saturation levels are given in the table (for a pH of 7.4).

$P(O_2)$ (mm Hg)	Approximate Percent Saturation
90	95%
80	92%
70	90%
60	85%
50	80%
40	72%

For more information on the atmosphere, see page 392.

In this chapter, we will evaluate the properties of gases on the macroscopic level, and explain these properties by looking at the behavior of gaseous molecules at the particulate level.

Study Questions related to this story are: 10.57 and 10.88.

FIGURE 10.1 **Automobile air bags.** Automobiles are now equipped with air bags to protect the driver and passengers in the event of a head-on or side crash. Such bags are inflated with nitrogen gas, which is generated by the explosive decomposition of sodium azide (in the presence of KNO_3 and silica):

$$2\ NaN_3(s) \rightarrow 2\ Na(s) + 3\ N_2(g)$$

The air bag is fully inflated in about 0.050 s. This is important because the typical automobile collision lasts about 0.125 s.

Hot air balloons, SCUBA diving tanks, and automobile air bags (Figure 10.1) depend on the properties of gases. Aside from understanding how these work, there are other reasons for studying gases. First, some common elements and compounds (such as oxygen, nitrogen, and methane) exist in the gaseous state under normal conditions of pressure and temperature. Second, atmospheric gases provide one means of transferring energy and material throughout the globe, and they are a source of life-sustaining chemicals. In addition, the issue of "climate change" is one of the major debates of our time, and gases such as carbon dioxide and methane play a role in this debate (see Chapter 20).

But there is yet another reason for studying gases. Of the three states of matter, the behavior of gases is reasonably simple when viewed at the molecular level and, as a result, it is well understood. It is possible to describe the properties of gases qualitatively in terms of the behavior of the molecules that make up the gas. Even more impressive, it is possible to describe the properties of gases quantitatively using simple mathematical models. One objective of scientists is to develop precise mathematical and conceptual models of natural phenomena, and a study of gas behavior will introduce you to this approach. As you will see, a remarkably accurate description of most gases requires knowing only four quantities: the pressure (P), volume (V), temperature (T, kelvins), and amount (n, mol) of the gas.

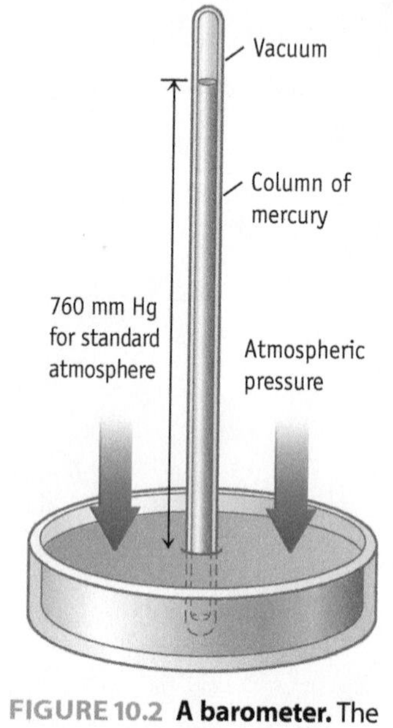

FIGURE 10.2 **A barometer.** The pressure of the atmosphere on the surface of the mercury in the dish is balanced by the downward pressure exerted by the column of mercury. The barometer was invented in 1643 by Evangelista Torricelli (1608–1647). A unit of pressure called the *torr* in his honor is equivalent to 1 mm Hg.

10-1 Gas Pressure

Pressure is the force exerted on an object divided by the area over which it is exerted, and the atmospheric pressure can be measured with a barometer. A barometer can be made by filling a tube with a liquid, often mercury, and inverting the tube in a dish containing the same liquid (Figure 10.2). If the air has been removed completely from the vertical tube, the liquid in the tube assumes a level such that the pressure exerted by the mass of the column of liquid in the tube is balanced by the pressure of the atmosphere pressing down on the surface of the liquid in the dish.

Pressure is often reported in units of **millimeters of mercury (mm Hg)**, the height (in mm) of the mercury column in a mercury barometer above the surface of the mercury in the dish. At sea level, this height is about 760 mm. Pressures are also reported as **standard atmospheres (atm)**, a unit defined as follows:

$$1 \text{ standard atmosphere (1 atm)} = 760 \text{ mm Hg (exactly)}$$

The SI unit of pressure is the **pascal (Pa)**.

$$1 \text{ pascal (Pa)} = 1 \text{ newton/meter}^2$$

(The newton is the SI unit of force.) Because the pascal is a very small unit compared with ordinary pressures, the unit kilopascal (kPa) is more often used. Another unit used for gas pressures is the **bar**, where 1 bar = 100,000 Pa = 100 kPa.

A CLOSER LOOK Measuring Gas Pressure

Pressure is the force exerted on an object divided by the area over which the force is exerted:

$$Pressure = force/area$$

This book, for example, weighs more than 4 lb and has an area of 96 in^2, so it exerts a pressure of about 0.04 lb/in^2 when it lies flat on a surface. (In metric units, the pressure is about 300 Pa.)

Now consider the pressure that the column of mercury exerts on the mercury in the dish in the barometer shown in Figure 10.2. This pressure exactly balances the pressure of the atmosphere. Thus, the pressure of the atmosphere (or of any other gas) is equal to the height of the column of mercury (or any other liquid) the gas can support.

Mercury is the liquid of choice for barometers because of its high density. A barometer filled with water would be over 10 m in height. [The water column is about 13.6 times as high as a column of mercury because mercury's density (13.53 g/cm^3) is 13.6 times that of water (density = 0.997 g/cm^3, at 25 °C).]

In the laboratory, we often use a U-tube manometer, which is a mercury-filled, U-shaped glass tube. The closed side of the tube has been evacuated so that no gas remains to exert pressure on the mercury on that side. The other side is open to the gas whose pressure we want to measure. When the gas presses on the mercury in the open side, the gas pressure is read directly (in mm Hg) as the difference in mercury levels on the closed and open sides.

You may have used a tire gauge to check the pressure in your car or bike tires. In the United States, such gauges usually indicate the pressure in pounds per square inch (psi) where 1 atm = 14.7 psi. Some newer gauges give the pressure in kilopascals as well. Be sure to recognize that the reading on the scale refers to the pressure *in excess of atmospheric pressure.* (A flat tire is not a vacuum; it contains air at atmospheric pressure.) For example, if the gauge reads 35 psi (2.4 atm), the pressure in the tire is actually about 50 psi or 3.4 atm.

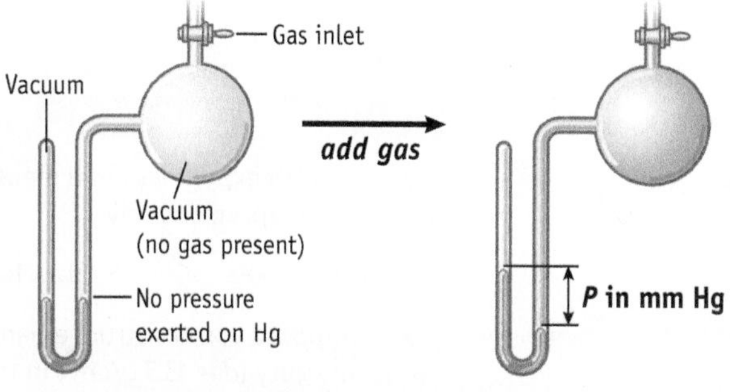

Using a manometer to measure pressure.

To summarize, the units used in science for pressure are

$$1 \text{ atm} = 760 \text{ mm Hg (exactly)} = 101.325 \text{ kilopascals (kPa)} = 1.01325 \text{ bar}$$

or

$$1 \text{ bar} = 1 \times 10^5 \text{ Pa (exactly)} = 1 \times 10^2 \text{ kPa} = 0.98692 \text{ atm}$$

EXAMPLE 10.1

Pressure Unit Conversions

Problem Convert a pressure of 635 mm Hg into its corresponding value in units of atmospheres (atm), bars, and kilopascals (kPa).

What Do You Know? You will need the following conversion factors:

$$1 \text{ atm} = 760 \text{ mm Hg} = 1.013 \text{ bar} \qquad 760 \text{ mm Hg} = 101.3 \text{ kPa}$$

Strategy Use the relationships between millimeters of Hg, atmospheres, bars, and pascals described in the text. (The use of dimensional analysis, page 38, is highly recommended.)

Solution

(a) Convert pressure in units of mm Hg to units of atm.

$$635 \text{ mm Hg} \times \frac{1 \text{ atm}}{760 \text{ mm Hg}} = 0.836 \text{ atm}$$

(b) Convert pressure in units of mm Hg to units of bar.

$$635 \text{ mm Hg} \times \frac{1.013 \text{ bar}}{760 \text{ mm Hg}} = 0.846 \text{ bar}$$

(c) Convert pressure in units of mm Hg to units of kilopascals.

$$635 \text{ mm Hg} \times \frac{101.3 \text{ kPa}}{760 \text{ mm Hg}} = 84.6 \text{ kPa}$$

Think about Your Answer The original pressure, 635 mm Hg, is less than 1 atm, so the pressure is also less than 1 bar and less than 100 kPa.

Check Your Understanding

At the summit of Mount Everest (altitude = 8848 m), atmospheric pressure is 0.29 atm (or 29% of the pressure at sea level). Convert the pressure into its corresponding value in units of mm Hg, bars, and kilopascals.

REVIEW & CHECK FOR SECTION 10-1

1. In a lab experiment you measure a gas pressure of 120 mm Hg. This pressure in units of kPa is approximately

   (a) 12 kPa (b) 16 kPa (c) 900 kPa

2. Suppose you construct a barometer filled with an oil (d = 1.25 g/cm^3) instead of mercury (d = 13.5 g/cm^3) in the vertical tube. If the atmosphere has a pressure of 0.95 atm, what is the approximate height of the oil in the tube?

   (a) 7.2 m (b) 7.8 m (c) 8.3 m

Learning Objectives: LO 2.5, LO 2.6

10-2 Gas Laws: The Experimental Basis

Boyle's Law: The Compressibility of Gases

When you add air to the tires of your bicycle, you use a bicycle pump to force air into the tire. The pump compresses a volume of air into the smaller volume of the tire. It was the Englishman Robert Boyle (1627–1691) (page 381) who first studied the compressibility of gases and observed that the volume of a fixed amount of gas at a given temperature is inversely proportional to the pressure exerted by the gas. All gases behave in this manner, and we now refer to this relationship as **Boyle's law.**

Boyle's law can be demonstrated in many ways. In Figure 10.3, a hypodermic syringe was filled with air (n moles) and sealed. When pressure was applied to the movable plunger of the syringe, the air inside was compressed. As the pressure (P) increased on the syringe, the gas volume in the syringe (V) decreased. When $1/V$ of the gas in the syringe is plotted as a function of P (as measured by mass of lead), a straight line results. This type of plot demonstrates that the pressure and volume of the gas are inversely proportional; that is, they change in opposite directions.

Mathematically, we can write Boyle's law as:

$$P \propto \frac{1}{V} \quad \text{when } n \text{ (amount of gas) and } T \text{ (temperature) are constant}$$

where the symbol $\propto$ means "proportional to."

When two quantities are proportional to each other, they can be equated if a *proportionality constant*, here called C_B, is introduced.

$$P = C_B \times \frac{1}{V} \quad \text{or} \quad PV = C_B \text{ at constant } n \text{ and } T$$

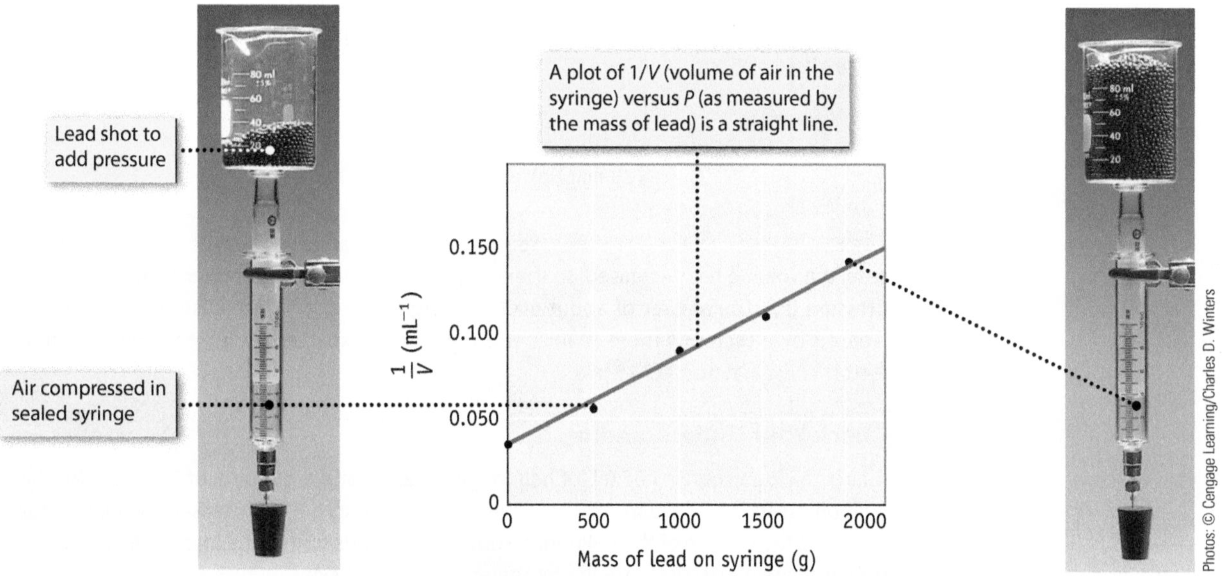

FIGURE 10.3 **An experiment to demonstrate Boyle's law.** A syringe filled with air was sealed. Pressure was applied by adding lead shot to the beaker on top of the syringe. As the mass of lead increased, the pressure on the air in the sealed syringe increased, and the gas was compressed.

This form of Boyle's law expresses the fact that *the product of the pressure and volume of a gas sample is a constant at a given temperature*, where the constant C_B is determined by the amount of gas (in moles) and its temperature (in kelvins). Because the PV product is always equal to C_B [assuming no change in the number of moles of gas (n) and the temperature (T)], it follows that, if PV is known for a gas sample under one set of conditions (P_1 and V_1), then it is known for another set of conditions (P_2 and V_2).

$$P_1V_1 = P_2V_2 \text{ at constant } n \text{ and } T \qquad (10.1)$$

This form of **Boyle's law** is useful when we want to know, for example, what happens to the volume of a given amount of gas when the pressure changes at a constant temperature.

EXAMPLE 10.2

Boyle's Law

Problem A bicycle pump has a volume of 1400 cm^3. If a sample of air in the pump has a pressure of 730 mm Hg, what is the pressure when the volume is reduced to 170 cm^3?

What Do You Know? This is a Boyle's law problem because you are dealing with changes in pressure and/or volume of a given amount of gas at constant temperature. Here the original pressure and volume of gas (P_1 and V_1) and the new volume (V_2) are known, but the final pressure (P_2) is not known. Both volumes are in the same unit so no unit changes are necessary.

Initial Conditions	**Final Conditions**
P_1 = 730 mm Hg	P_2 = ?
V_1 = 1400 cm^3	V_2 = 170 cm^3

Strategy Use Boyle's law, Equation 10.1.

Strategy Map 10.2

PROBLEM

Calculate the **pressure** when the *volume of a gas* is **reduced.**

DATA/INFORMATION

- *Initial* pressure
- *Initial* volume
- *Final* volume

Rearrange **Boyle's law** (Equation 10.1) to calculate **final pressure** (P_2).

Pressure (P_2) after reducing the volume

Solution You can solve this problem by substituting data into a rearranged version of Boyle's law.

$$P_2 = P_1\ (V_1/V_2)$$

$$P_2 = (730\ \text{mm Hg}) \times \frac{1400\ \text{cm}^3}{170\ \text{cm}^3} = 6.0 \times 10^3\ \text{mm Hg}$$

Think about Your Answer You know *P* and *V* change in opposite directions. In this case, the volume has decreased, so the new pressure (P_2) must be greater than the original pressure (P_1). The answer of about 6000 mm Hg is reasonable; because the volume decreased by a factor of more than 8, the pressure is expected to increase by the same factor.

Check Your Understanding

A large balloon contains 65.0 L of helium gas at 25 °C and a pressure of 745 mm Hg. The balloon ascends to 3000 m, at which the external pressure has decreased by 30.%. What would be the volume of the balloon, assuming it expands so that the internal and external pressures are equal? (Assume the temperature is still 25 °C.)

The Effect of Temperature on Gas Volume: Charles's Law

In 1787, the French scientist Jacques Charles (1746–1823) discovered that the volume of a fixed quantity of gas at constant pressure decreases with decreasing temperature. The demonstration in Figure 10.4 shows a dramatic decrease in volume with temperature, and the graph shown in Figure 10.5 illustrates more quantitatively how the volumes of two different gas samples change with temperature (at a constant pressure). When the plots of volume versus temperature are extrapolated to lower temperatures, they all reach zero volume at the same temperature, −273.15 °C. (Of course, gases will not actually reach zero volume; they liquefy or solidify above that temperature.) This temperature is significant, however. William Thomson (1824–1907), also known as Lord Kelvin, proposed a temperature scale—now known as the Kelvin scale—for which the zero point is −273.15 °C (◀ page 25). It is important to recognize that the Kelvin scale places an absolute limit (0 K) on the lowest attainable temperature.

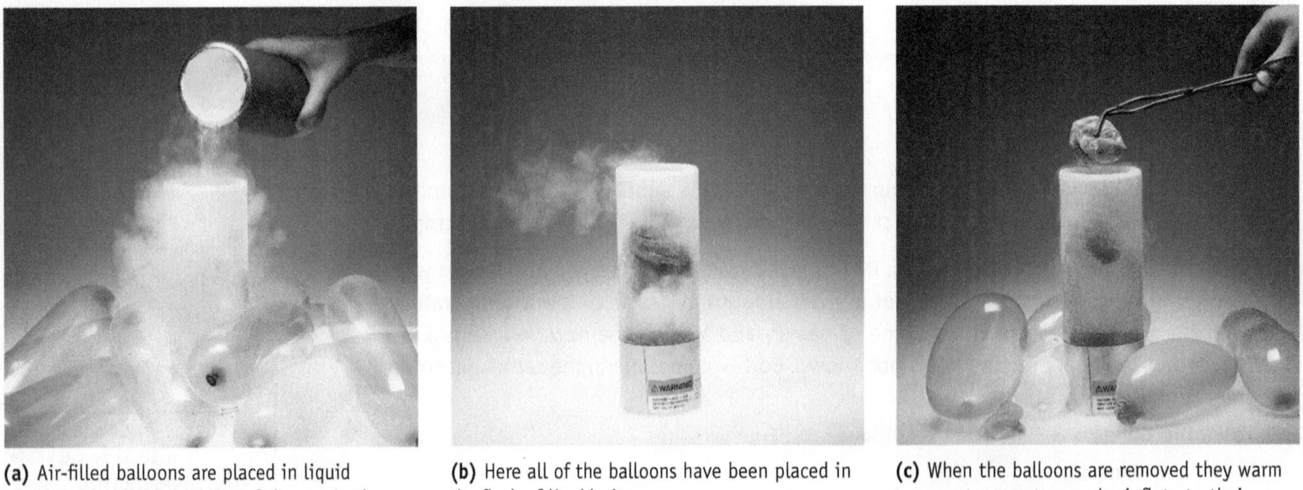

Photos: © Cengage Learning/Charles D. Winters

(a) Air-filled balloons are placed in liquid nitrogen (77 K). The volume of the gas in the balloons is dramatically reduced at this temperature.

(b) Here all of the balloons have been placed in the flask of liquid nitrogen.

(c) When the balloons are removed they warm to room temperature and reinflate to their original volume.

FIGURE 10.4 A dramatic illustration of Charles's law.

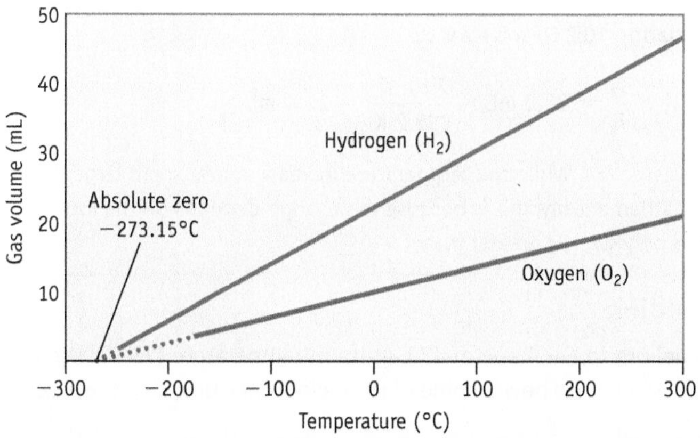

T (°C)	T (K)	Vol. H_2 (mL)	Vol. O_2 (mL)
300	573	47.0	21.1
200	473	38.8	17.5
100	373	30.6	13.8
0	273	22.4	10.1
−100	173	14.2	6.39
−200	73	6.00	—

FIGURE 10.5 **Charles's law.** The solid lines represent the volumes of samples of hydrogen (0.00100 mol) and oxygen (0.000450 mol) at a pressure of 1.00 atm but at different temperatures. The volumes decrease as the temperature is lowered (at constant pressure). These lines, if extended, intersect the temperature axis at approximately −273 °C.

When Kelvin temperatures are used with volume measurements, the volume–temperature relationship is

$$V = C_c \times T$$

where C_c is a proportionality constant (which depends on the amount of gas and its pressure). This is **Charles's law**, which states that *if a given amount of gas is held at a constant pressure, its volume is directly proportional to the Kelvin temperature.*

Writing Charles's law another way, we have $V/T = C_c$; that is, the volume of a gas divided by the temperature of the gas (in kelvins) is constant for a given sample of gas at a specified pressure. Therefore, if we know the volume and temperature of a given quantity of gas (V_1 and T_1), we can find the volume, V_2, at some other temperature, T_2, using the equation

$$\frac{V_1}{T_1} = \frac{V_2}{T_2} \quad \text{at constant } n \text{ and } P \qquad (10.2)$$

A calculation using Charles's law is illustrated by the following example. Be sure to notice that the temperature T *must always be expressed in kelvins.*

EXAMPLE 10.3

Charles's Law

Problem A sample of CO_2 in a gas-tight syringe (as in Figure 10.3) has a volume of 25.0 mL at room temperature (20.0 °C). What is the final volume of the gas if you hold the syringe in your hand to raise its temperature to 37 °C (and hold the pressure constant)?

What Do You Know? This is a Charles's law problem: There is a change in volume of a gas sample with temperature at constant pressure. You know the original volume and temperature, and you want to know the volume at a new temperature. Recall that, to use Charles's law, the temperature must be expressed in kelvins.

Initial Conditions	**Final Conditions**
$V_1 = 25.0$ mL	$V_2 = ?$
$T_1 = 20.0 + 273.2 = 293.2$ K	$T_2 = 37 + 273 = 310.$ K

Strategy Use Charles's Law, Equation 10.2.

Solution Rearrange Equation 10.2 to solve for V_2:

$$V_2 = V_1 \times \frac{T_2}{T_1} = 25.0 \text{ mL} \times \frac{310.\text{ K}}{293.2 \text{ K}} = 26.4 \text{ mL}$$

Think about Your Answer While the temperature increase might seem large, the change in volume is small. Mathematically, this is because the change depends on the *ratio* of Kelvin temperatures, which is only slightly greater than 1.

Check Your Understanding

A balloon is inflated with helium to a volume of 45 L at room temperature (25 °C). If the balloon is cooled to −10 °C, what is the new volume of the balloon? Assume that the pressure does not change.

Combining Boyle's and Charles's Laws: The General Gas Law

You now know that the volume of a given amount of gas is inversely proportional to its pressure at constant temperature (Boyle's law) and directly proportional to the Kelvin temperature at constant pressure (Charles's law). But what if you need to know what happens to the gas when two of the three parameters (*P*, *V*, and *T*) change? For example, what would happen to the pressure of a sample of nitrogen in an automobile air bag if the same amount of gas were placed in a smaller bag and heated to a higher temperature? You can deal with this situation by combining the two equations that express Boyle's and Charles's laws.

$$\frac{P_1V_1}{T_1} = \frac{P_2V_2}{T_2} \text{ for a given amount of gas, } n \quad (10.3)$$

This equation is sometimes called the **general gas law** or **combined gas law**. It applies specifically to situations in which the *amount of gas does not change.*

© David R. Frazier Photolibrary, Inc./Alamy

A weather balloon is filled with helium. As it ascends into the troposphere, does the volume increase or decrease?

EXAMPLE 10.4

General Gas Law

Problem Helium-filled balloons are used to carry scientific instruments high into the atmosphere. Suppose a balloon is launched when the temperature is 22.5 °C and the barometric pressure is 754 mm Hg. If the balloon's volume is 4.19×10^3 L (and no helium escapes from the balloon), what will the volume be at a height of 20 miles, where the pressure is 76.0 mm Hg and the temperature is −33.0 °C?

What Do You Know? Here you know the initial volume, temperature, and pressure of the gas. You want to know the volume of the same amount of gas at a new pressure and temperature.

Initial Conditions	Final Conditions
$V_1 = 4.19 \times 10^3$ L	$V_2 = ?$ L
$P_1 = 754$ mm Hg	$P_2 = 76.0$ mm Hg
$T_1 = 22.5$ °C (295.7 K)	$T_2 = -33.0$ °C (240.2 K)

Strategy It is most convenient to use Equation 10.3, the general gas law.

Solution You can rearrange the general gas law to calculate the new volume V_2:

$$V_2 = \left(\frac{T_2}{P_2}\right) \times \left(\frac{P_1V_1}{T_1}\right) = V_1 \times \frac{P_1}{P_2} \times \frac{T_2}{T_1}$$

$$= 4.19 \times 10^3 \text{ L} \times \left(\frac{754 \text{ mm Hg}}{76.0 \text{ mm Hg}}\right) \times \left(\frac{240.2 \text{ K}}{295.7 \text{ K}}\right) = 3.38 \times 10^4 \text{ L}$$

Think about Your Answer The pressure decreased by almost a factor of 10, which should lead to about a ten-fold volume increase. This increase is partly offset by a drop in temperature that leads to a volume decrease. On balance, the volume increases because the pressure has dropped so substantially.

Check Your Understanding

You have a 22-L cylinder of helium at a pressure of 150 atm (above atmospheric pressure) and at 31 °C. How many balloons can you fill, each with a volume of 5.0 L, on a day when the atmospheric pressure is 755 mm Hg and the temperature is 22 °C?

Strategy Map 10.4

PROBLEM

Calculate the **volume** of a gas sample after it undergoes a change in ***T*** and ***P***.

DATA/INFORMATION

- *Initial* pressure, volume, and temperature
- *Final* pressure and temperature

Rearrange the **general gas law** (Equation 10.3) to calculate **final volume** (V_2).

Volume (V_2) after change in T and P

The general gas law leads to other, useful predictions of gas behavior. For example, if a given amount of gas is held in a closed container, that is, n and V are constant, the pressure of the gas will increase with increasing temperature.

$$\frac{P_1}{T_1} = \frac{P_2}{T_2} \text{ when } V_1 = V_2\text{, so } P_2 = P_1 \times \frac{T_2}{T_1}$$

That is, when T_2 is greater than T_1, P_2 will be greater than P_1. In fact, this is the reason tire manufacturers recommend checking tire pressures when the tires are cold. After driving for some distance, friction warms a tire and increases the internal pressure. Filling a warm tire to the recommended pressure may lead to an underinflated tire.

Avogadro's Hypothesis

Front and side air bags are now common in automobiles. In the event of an accident, a bag is rapidly inflated with nitrogen gas generated by a chemical reaction. The air bag unit has a sensor that is sensitive to sudden deceleration of the vehicle and will send an electrical signal that will trigger the reaction (Figures 10.1 and 10.6). In many types of air bags, the explosion of sodium azide generates nitrogen gas.

$$2 \text{ NaN}_3\text{(s)} \rightarrow 2 \text{ Na(s)} + 3 \text{ N}_2\text{(g)}$$

Photos: Autoliv/ASP

When a car decelerates in a collision, an electrical contact is made in the sensor unit. The propellant (green solid) detonates, releasing nitrogen gas, and the folded nylon bag explodes out of the plastic housing.

Driver-side air bags inflate with 35–70 L of N_2 gas, whereas passenger air bags hold 60–160 L.

The bag deflates within 0.2 second, the gas escaping through holes in the bottom of the bag.

FIGURE 10.6 Automobile air bags.

(The sodium produced in the reaction is converted to harmless salts by adding KNO_3 and silica to the mixture.) Driver-side air bags inflate to a volume of 35–70 L, and passenger air bags inflate to 60–160 L. The final volume of the bag will depend on the amount of nitrogen gas generated.

The relationship between volume and amount of gas was first noted by Amedeo Avogadro (1776–1856). In 1811, he used work on gases by the chemist (and early experimenter with hot air balloons) Joseph Gay-Lussac (1778–1850) to propose that *equal volumes of gases under the same conditions of temperature and pressure have equal numbers of particles* (either molecules or atoms, depending on the composition of the gas). This idea is now called **Avogadro's hypothesis**. Stated another way, the volume of a gas at a given temperature and pressure is directly proportional to the amount of gas in moles:

$$V \propto n \quad \text{at constant } T \text{ and } P$$

EXAMPLE 10.5

Avogadro's Hypothesis

Problem Dinitrogen monoxide, commonly known as laughing gas, is used in dental procedures as an anesthetic. At elevated temperatures and with the proper catalyst, dinitrogen monoxide can be produced from the reaction of ammonia and oxygen:

$$2\ NH_3(g) + 2\ O_2(g) \rightarrow N_2O(g) + 3\ H_2O(g)$$

If you begin with 15.0 L of $NH_3(g)$, what volume of $O_2(g)$ is required for complete reaction (both gases being at the same *T* and *P*)? What is the theoretical yield of N_2O, in liters, under the same conditions?

What Do You Know? From Avogadro's hypothesis, you know that gas volume is proportional to the amount of gas. You know the volume of ammonia, and, from the balanced equation, you know the stoichiometric factors that relate the known amount of NH_3 to the unknown amounts of O_2 and N_2O.

Strategy This is a stoichiometry problem where you can substitute gas volumes for moles. That is, you can calculate the volumes of O_2 required and N_2O produced (here in liters) by multiplying the volume of NH_3 available by a stoichiometric factor obtained from the balanced chemical equation.

Solution

$$V\ (O_2 \text{ required}) = (15.0\ \text{L}\ \cancel{NH_3 \text{ available}})\left(\frac{2\ \text{L}\ O_2 \text{ required}}{2\ \text{L}\ \cancel{NH_3 \text{ available}}}\right) = 15.0\ \text{L}\ O_2 \text{ required}$$

$$V\ (N_2O \text{ produced}) = (15.0\ \text{L}\ \cancel{NH_3 \text{ available}})\left(\frac{1\ \text{L}\ N_2O \text{ produced}}{2\ \text{L}\ \cancel{NH_3 \text{ available}}}\right) = 7.50\ \text{L}\ N_2O \text{ produced}$$

Think about Your Answer The balanced equation informs you that the amount of O_2 required is equal to the amount of NH_3 present, and the amount of N_2O produced is 1/2 of the amount of NH_3.

Check Your Understanding

Methane burns in oxygen to give CO_2 and H_2O, according to the balanced equation

$$CH_4(g) + 2\ O_2(g) \rightarrow CO_2(g) + 2\ H_2O(g)$$

If 22.4 L of gaseous CH_4 is burned, what volume of O_2 is required for complete combustion? What volumes of CO_2 and H_2O are produced? Assume all gases have the same temperature and pressure.

A CLOSER LOOK Studies on Gases—Robert Boyle and Jacques Charles

Robert Boyle (1627–1691) was born in Ireland as the 14th and last child of the first Earl of Cork. In his book *Uncle Tungsten*, Oliver Sacks tells us that "Chemistry as a true science made its first emergence with the work of Robert Boyle in the middle of the seventeenth century. Twenty years [Isaac] Newton's senior, Boyle was born at a time when the practice of alchemy still held sway, and he maintained a variety of alchemical beliefs and practices, side by side with his scientific ones. He believed gold could be created, and that he had succeeded in creating it (Newton, also an alchemist, advised him to keep silent about this)."

Boyle examined crystals, explored color, devised an acid–base indicator from the syrup of violets, and provided the first modern definition of an element. He was also a physiologist and was the first to show that the healthy human body has a constant temperature. Today, Boyle is best known for his studies of gases, which were described in his book *The Sceptical Chymist*, published in 1680.

The French chemist and inventor Jacques Alexandre César Charles began his career as a clerk in the French finance ministry, but his real interest was science. He developed several inventions and was best known in his lifetime for inventing the hydrogen balloon. In August 1783, Charles exploited his recent studies on hydrogen gas by inflating a balloon with this gas. Because hydrogen would escape easily from a paper bag, he made a silk bag coated with rubber. Inflating the bag took several days and required nearly 225 kg of sulfuric acid and 450 kg of iron to produce the H_2 gas. The balloon stayed aloft for almost 45 minutes and traveled about 15 miles. When it landed in a village, however, the people were so terrified they tore it to shreds. Several months later, Charles and a passenger flew a new hydrogen-filled balloon some distance across the French countryside and ascended to the then-incredible altitude of 2 miles.

See K. R. Williams, "Robert Boyle: Founder of Modern Chemistry," *Journal of Chemical Education*, Vol. 86, page 148, 2009.

Oesper Collection in the History of Chemistry, University of Cincinnati

Robert Boyle (1627–1691).

Image Courtesy of the Library of Congress

Jacques Alexandre César Charles (1746–1823).

Smithsonian National Air & Space Museum

Jacques Charles and Nicolas-Louis Robert ascended over Paris on December 1, 1783, in a hydrogen-filled balloon.

REVIEW & CHECK FOR SECTION 10-2

1. A sample of a gas has a volume of 222 mL at 695 mm Hg and 0 °C. What is the volume of this same sample of gas if it is measured at 333 mm Hg and 0 °C?

   (a) 894 mL (b) 463 mL (c) 657 mL (d) 359 mL

2. The volume of a gas sample is 235 mL at a temperature of 25 °C. At what temperature would that same gas sample have a volume of 310. mL, if the pressure of the gas sample is held constant?

   (a) −47.0 °C (b) 69.4 °C (c) 33.1 °C (d) 120. °C

3. A gas at 25 °C in a 10.0-L tank has a pressure of 1.00 atm. The gas is transferred to a 20.0-L tank at 0 °C. Which statement is true?

   (a) The pressure of the gas is halved.
   (b) The pressure in the tank is doubled.
   (c) The gas pressure is 1.00 atm.
   (d) None of the above.

10-3 The Ideal Gas Law

Learning Objectives: LO 2.5, LO 2.6

Four interrelated quantities can be used to describe a gas: pressure, volume, temperature, and amount (moles). We know from experiments that the following gas laws can be used to describe the relationship of these properties (see Section 10-2).

Boyle's Law	Charles's Law	Avogadro's Hypothesis
$V \propto (1/P)$	$V \propto T$	$V \propto n$
(constant T, n)	(constant P, n)	(constant T, P)

If all three laws are combined, the result is

$$V \propto \frac{nT}{P}$$

This can be made into a mathematical equation by introducing a proportionality constant, now labeled ***R***. This constant, called the **gas constant**, is a *universal constant*, a number you can use to interrelate the properties of any gas:

$$V = R\left(\frac{nT}{P}\right)$$

or

$$PV = nRT \quad \textbf{(10.4)}$$

Properties of an Ideal Gas For ideal gases, it is assumed that there are no forces of attraction between molecules and that the molecules themselves occupy no volume.

The equation $PV = nRT$ is called the **ideal gas law**. It describes the behavior of a so-called ideal gas. Unfortunately, there is no such thing as an ideal gas, but real gases at pressures around one atmosphere and room temperature usually behave close enough to the ideal that $PV = nRT$ adequately describes their behavior (see Section 10-8).

To use the equation $PV = nRT$, we need a value for R. This is readily determined experimentally. By carefully measuring P, V, n, and T for a sample of gas, we can calculate the value of R from these values using the ideal gas law equation. For example, under conditions of **standard temperature and pressure (STP)** (a gas temperature of 0 °C or 273.15 K and a pressure of 1 atm), 1 mol of an ideal gas occupies 22.414 L, a quantity called the **standard molar volume**. Substituting these values into the ideal gas law gives a value for R:

STP—What Is It? STP stands for standard temperature and pressure, defined as 0 °C (or 273.15 K) and 1 atm. Under these conditions, exactly 1 mol of an ideal gas occupies 22.414 L.

$$R = \frac{PV}{nT} = \frac{(1.0000\ \text{atm})(22.414\ \text{L})}{(1.0000\ \text{mol})(273.15\ \text{K})} = 0.082057\ \frac{\text{L} \cdot \text{atm}}{\text{K} \cdot \text{mol}}$$

With a value for R, we can now use the ideal gas law in calculations.

Strategy Map 10.6

PROBLEM

Calculate the amount of a gas using the **ideal gas law.**

↓

DATA/INFORMATION

- **Pressure** of the gas
- **Volume** of the gas
- **Temperature** of the gas

Rearrange the **ideal gas law** (Equation 10.4) to calculate the **amount** (n).

↓

Amount of gas, n

EXAMPLE 10.6

Ideal Gas Law

Problem The nitrogen gas in an automobile air bag, with a volume of 65 L, exerts a pressure of 829 mm Hg at 25 °C. What amount of N_2 gas (in moles) is in the air bag?

What Do You Know? You are given P, V, and T for a gas sample and want to calculate the amount of gas (n). P = 829 mm Hg, V = 65 L, T = 25 °C, n = ? You also know R = 0.082057 L · atm/K · mol.

Strategy Use the ideal gas law, Equation 10.4.

Solution To use the ideal gas law with R having units of L · atm/K · mol, the pressure must be expressed in atmospheres and the temperature in kelvins. Therefore, you should first convert the pressure and temperature to values with these units.

$$P = 829\ \text{mm Hg}\left(\frac{1\ \text{atm}}{760\ \text{mm Hg}}\right) = 1.09\ \text{atm}$$

$$T = 25 + 273 = 298\ \text{K}$$

Now substitute the values of *P*, *V*, *T*, and *R* into the ideal gas law, and solve for the amount of gas, *n*:

$$n = \frac{PV}{RT} = \frac{(1.09\ \text{atm})(65\ \text{L})}{(0.082057\ \text{L} \cdot \text{atm/K} \cdot \text{mol})(298\ \text{K})} = 2.9\ \text{mol}$$

Notice that units of atmospheres, liters, and kelvins cancel to leave the answer in units of moles.

Think about Your Answer You know that 1 mol of an ideal gas at STP occupies about 22.4 L, so it is reasonable to guess that 65 L of gas (under only slightly different conditions) would be about three times this amount, or 3 mol.

Check Your Understanding

The balloon used by Jacques Charles in his historic balloon flight in 1783 (see page 381) was filled with about 1300 mol of H_2. If the temperature of the gas was 23 °C and the gas pressure was 750 mm Hg, what was the volume of the balloon?

The Density of Gases

The density of a gas at a given temperature and pressure is a useful quantity (Figure 10.7). Because the amount (*n*, mol) of any compound is given by its mass *(m)* divided by its molar mass *(M)*, we can substitute *m*/*M* for *n* in the ideal gas equation.

$$PV = \left(\frac{m}{M}\right)RT$$

Density *(d)* is defined as mass divided by volume *(m*/*V)*. We can rearrange the form of the gas law above to give the following equation, which has the term *(m*/*V)* on the left. This is the density of the gas expressed in units of g/L.

$$d = \frac{m}{V} = \frac{PM}{RT} \quad (10.5)$$

FIGURE 10.7 Gas density.

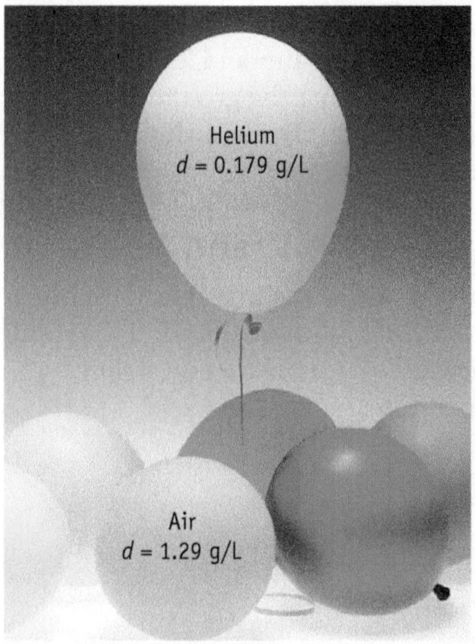

©KENNY TONG/Shutterstock.com

The balloons are filled with nearly equal amounts of gas at the same temperature and pressure. One yellow balloon contains helium, a low-density gas. The other balloons contain air.

©KENNY TONG/Shutterstock.com

The heated air in a "hot air balloon" has a lower density than the surrounding air and allows the balloon to rise.

Gas density is directly proportional to the pressure and molar mass and inversely proportional to the temperature. Equation 10.5 is useful because gas density can be calculated from the molar mass, or the molar mass can be found from a measurement of gas density at a given pressure and temperature.

EXAMPLE 10.7

Density and Molar Mass

Problem Calculate the density of CO_2 at STP. Is CO_2 more or less dense than air (whose density is 1.29 g/L at STP)?

What Do You Know? The known quantities are molar mass of CO_2 (M = 44.0 g/mol), gas pressure (P) = 1.00 atm, temperature (T) = 273.15 K, and the gas constant (R). The density of CO_2 gas (d) is unknown.

Strategy Use Equation 10.5, the equation relating gas density and molar mass.

Solution The known values are substituted into Equation 10.5, which is then solved for density (d):

$$d = \frac{PM}{RT} = \frac{(1.00\ \text{atm})(44.0\ \text{g/mol})}{(0.082057\ \text{L} \cdot \text{atm/K} \cdot \text{mol})(273\ \text{K})} = 1.96\ \text{g/L}$$

Think about Your Answer The density of CO_2 is considerably greater than that of dry air at STP (1.29 g/L). (See Figure 10.8.)

Check Your Understanding

At 1.00 atm and 25 °C, the density of dry air is 1.18 g/L. If the air is heated to 55 °C at constant pressure, what is its density?

© Cengage Learning/Charles D. Winters

FIGURE 10.8 Gas density. Because carbon dioxide from fire extinguishers is denser than air, it settles on top of a fire and smothers it. (When CO_2 gas is released from the tank, it expands and cools significantly. The white cloud is condensed moisture from the air.)

Gas density has practical implications. From the equation $d = PM/RT$, you recognize that the density of a gas is directly proportional to its molar mass. Dry air, which has an average molar mass of about 29 g/mol, has a density of about 1.18 g/L at 1 atm and 25 °C. Gases or vapors with molar masses greater than 29 g/mol have densities larger than 1.2 g/L under these same conditions (1 atm and 25 °C). Therefore, gases such as CO_2, SO_2, and gasoline vapor settle along the ground if released into the atmosphere (Figure 10.8). Conversely, gases such as H_2, He, CO, CH_4 (methane), and NH_3 rise if released into the atmosphere.

Calculating the Molar Mass of a Gas from *P*, *V*, and *T* Data

When a new compound is isolated in the laboratory, one of the first things we often do is determine its molar mass. If the compound is easily volatilized, a classical method of determining the molar mass is to measure the pressure and volume exerted by a given mass of the gas at a given temperature.

EXAMPLE 10.8

Calculating the Molar Mass of a Gas from *P*, *V*, and *T* Data

Problem You are trying to determine, by experiment, the formula of a gaseous compound you made to replace chlorofluorocarbons in air conditioners. You have determined the empirical formula is CHF_2, but to determine the molecular formula you need to know the molar mass. You find that a 0.100-g sample of the compound exerts a pressure of 70.5 mm Hg in a 256-mL container at 22.3 °C. What is the molar mass of the compound? What is its molecular formula?

What Do You Know? You know the mass of a gas in a given volume at a known pressure and temperature. The molar mass of the gas, *M*, is unknown.

m = mass of gas = 0.100 g P = 70.5 mm Hg, or 0.0928 atm

V = 256 mL, or 0.256 L T = 22.3 °C, or 295.5 K

Strategy Dividing the mass of the gas by its volume gives its density, which is related to the molar mass through Equation 10.5. Alternatively, the *P*, *V*, and *T* data can be used to calculate the amount of gas (moles). The molar mass is then the quotient of the mass of gas and its amount.

Solution The density of the gas is the mass of the gas divided by the volume.

$$d = \frac{0.100\text{ g}}{0.256\text{ L}} = 0.391\text{ g/L}$$

Use this value of density along with the values of pressure and temperature in Equation 10.5 ($d = PM/RT$), and solve for the molar mass (M).

$$M = \frac{dRT}{P} = \frac{(0.391\text{ g/L})(0.082057\text{ L}\cdot\text{atm/K}\cdot\text{mol})(295.5\text{ K})}{0.0928\text{ atm}} = 102\text{ g/mol}$$

With this result, you can compare the experimentally determined molar mass with the mass of a mole of gas having the empirical formula CHF_2.

$$\frac{\text{Experimental molar mass}}{\text{Mass of 1 mol CHF}_2} = \frac{102\text{ g/mol}}{51.0\text{ g/formula unit}} = 2\text{ formula units of CHF}_2\text{ per mole}$$

Therefore, the formula of the compound is $C_2H_2F_4$.

In the alternative approach, you use the ideal gas law to calculate the amount of gas, *n*.

$$n = \frac{PV}{RT} = \frac{(0.0928\text{ atm})(0.256\text{ L})}{(0.082057\text{ L}\cdot\text{atm/K}\cdot\text{mol})(295.5\text{ K})} = 9.80 \times 10^{-4}\text{ mol}$$

You now know that 0.100 g of gas is equivalent to 9.80×10^{-4} mol. Therefore,

$$\text{Molar mass} = \frac{0.100\text{ g}}{9.80 \times 10^{-4}\text{ mol}} = 102\text{ g/mol}$$

Think about Your Answer If the calculated molar mass is not the same as that for the empirical formula or a simple multiple of that value, then you can assume that there is an error somewhere.

Check Your Understanding

A 0.105-g sample of a gaseous compound has a pressure of 561 mm Hg in a volume of 125 mL at 23.0 °C. What is its molar mass?

Strategy Map 10.8

PROBLEM

Calculate the molar mass of a gas using the **ideal gas law.**

DATA/INFORMATION

- **Pressure** of the gas
- **Volume** of the gas
- **Temperature** of the gas

STEP 1. Rearrange the **ideal gas law** (Equation 10.4) to calculate the **amount** (*n*).

Amount of gas, *n*

STEP 2. Divide the **mass** of gas by its **amount** (*n*).

Molar mass of gas

REVIEW & CHECK FOR SECTION 10-3

1. Which gas has the greatest density at 25 °C and 1.00 atm pressure?

   (a) O_2 (b) N_2 (c) H_2 (d) CO_2 (e) Xe

2. Gas A is in a 2-L flask with a pressure of 1 atm at 298 K. Gas B is in a 4-L flask with a pressure of 0.5 atm at 273 K. Which gas is present in greater amount?

   (a) A (b) B (c) Neither. The amounts are the same.

3. Measured at a pressure of 1.0 atm and 298 K, gas C has a density of 2.0 g/L. The density of gas D, measured at a pressure of 0.5 atm and 298 K, is 1.3 g/L. Which gas has the larger molar mass?

(a) C (b) D (c) Neither. The molar masses are the same.

Learning Objectives: LO 3.4

10-4 Gas Laws and Chemical Reactions

Many industrially important reactions involve gases. Two examples are the combination of nitrogen and hydrogen to produce ammonia,

$$N_2(g) + 3\ H_2(g) \rightarrow 2\ NH_3(g)$$

and the electrolysis of aqueous NaCl to produce hydrogen and chlorine,

$$2\ NaCl(aq) + 2\ H_2O(\ell) \rightarrow 2\ NaOH(aq) + H_2(g) + Cl_2(g)$$

If we want to understand the quantitative aspects of such reactions, we need to carry out stoichiometry calculations. The scheme in Figure 10.9 connects these calculations for gas reactions with the stoichiometry calculations in Chapter 4.

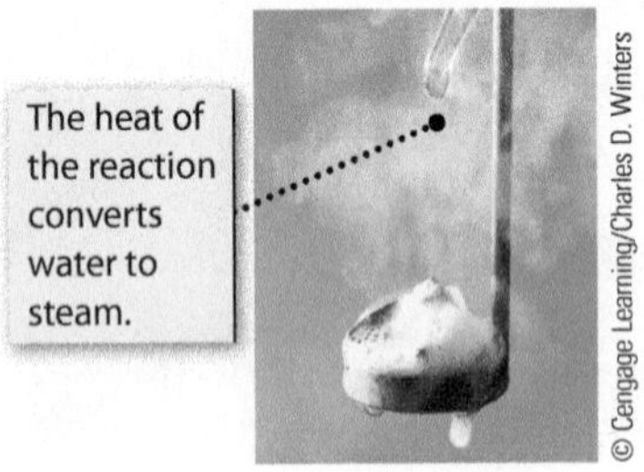

Lithium and water produce H_2 gas and LiOH.

EXAMPLE 10.9

Gas Laws and Stoichiometry

Problem Hydrogen gas is produced from the reaction of lithium and water. What mass of lithium is required to produce 23.5 L of $H_2(g)$ at 17.0 °C and a pressure of 743 mm Hg? The gas-producing reaction is

$$2\ Li(s) + 2\ H_2O(aq) \rightarrow 2\ LiOH(aq) + H_2(g)$$

What Do You Know? You know the pressure, volume, and temperature of the H_2 gas to be produced, and you know the balanced equation that relates the amounts of the reactant, Li, to the product, H_2.

$$P = 743\text{ mm Hg }(1\text{ atm}/760\text{ mm Hg}) = 0.978\text{ atm}$$

$$V = 23.5\text{ L}$$

$$T = 17.0\ °C\text{, or }290.2\text{ K}$$

You want to know the mass of Li required to produce a given amount of H_2. This will require knowing the molar mass of Li.

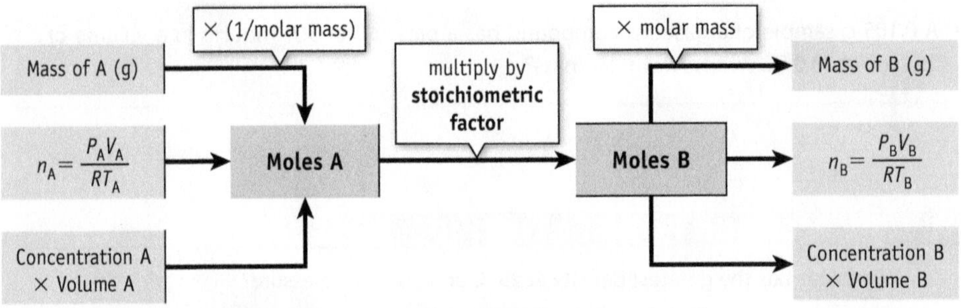

FIGURE 10.9 **A scheme for stoichiometry calculations.** Here, A and B may be either reactants or products. The amount of A (mol) can be calculated from its mass in grams and its molar mass, from the concentration and volume of a solution, or from *P*, *V*, and *T* data by using the ideal gas law. Once the amount of B is determined, this value can be converted to a mass or solution concentration or volume, or to a property of a gas.

Strategy The general logic to be used here follows a pathway in Figure 10.9 and in Strategy Map 10.9. First, use $PV = nRT$ with gas data to calculate the amount of H_2 produced. Then use that amount with a stoichiometric factor and the molar mass of Li to calculate the mass of Li required.

Solution

Step 1: Find the amount (mol) of gas produced.

$$n = H_2 \text{ produced (mol)} = \frac{PV}{RT}$$

$$n = \frac{(0.978 \text{ atm})(23.5 \text{ L})}{(0.082057 \text{ L} \cdot \text{atm/K} \cdot \text{mol})(290.2 \text{ K})} = 0.965 \text{ mol } H_2$$

Step 2: Calculate the quantity of lithium that will produce 0.965 mol of H_2 gas.

$$\text{Mass of Li} = 0.965 \text{ mol } H_2 \left(\frac{2 \text{ mol Li}}{1 \text{ mol } H_2}\right)\left(\frac{6.941 \text{ g}}{1 \text{ mol Li}}\right) = 13.4 \text{ g Li}$$

Think about Your Answer You know that at STP, 1 mol of an ideal gas has a volume of 22.4 L. While not at STP exactly, the conditions here are close to it, so a volume of 23.5 L should correspond to about 1 mol of H_2. Based on the stoichiometry of the reaction, you will need twice this amount of Li, or about 2 mol. Based on the molar mass of Li (6.941 g/mol) this will be about 14 g.

Check Your Understanding

If 15.0 g of sodium reacts with water, what volume of hydrogen gas is produced at 25.0 °C and a pressure of 1.10 atm?

Strategy Map 10.9

PROBLEM

Calculate the **mass of reactant** needed to produce a gas at a known ***P***, ***V***, and ***T***.

DATA/INFORMATION

- **Pressure** of the gas
- **Volume** of the gas
- **Temperature** of the gas
- Balanced equation

STEP 1. Calculate the *amount of gas* (*n*) using the **ideal gas law.**

Amount of gas, *n*

STEP 2. Use **stoichiometric factor** to relate *amount of gas* (*n*) to *amount of reactant* required.

Amount of reactant

STEP 3. Calculate **mass of reactant** from its amount.

Mass of reactant

REVIEW & CHECK FOR SECTION 10-4

Diborane reacts with O_2 to give boric oxide and water vapor.

$$B_2H_6(g) + 3\ O_2(g) \rightarrow B_2O_3(s) + 3\ H_2O(g)$$

1. What mass of O_2 gas is required to react completely with 1.5 L of B_2H_6 at 25 °C and 0.15 atm?

   (a) 0.29 g (b) 0.59 g (c) 0.44 g (d) 0.88 g

2. If you mix 1.5 L of B_2H_6 with 4.0 L of O_2, each at 0 °C and a pressure of 1.0 atm, what amount of water is produced?

   (a) 0.18 mol (b) 0.067 ml (c) 0.060 mol (d) 0.25 mol

10-5 Gas Mixtures and Partial Pressures

The air you breathe is a mixture of nitrogen, oxygen, argon, carbon dioxide, water vapor, and small amounts of other gases (Table 10.1). Each of these gases exerts its own pressure, and atmospheric pressure is the sum of the pressures exerted by each gas. The pressure of each gas in the mixture is called its **partial pressure**.

John Dalton (1766–1844) was the first to observe that the pressure of a mixture of ideal gases is the sum of the partial pressures of the different gases in the mixture. This observation is now known as **Dalton's law of partial pressures** (Figure 10.10). Mathematically, we can write Dalton's law of partial pressures as

$$P_{total} = P_1 + P_2 + P_3 \ldots \quad (10.6)$$

Table 10.1 Major Components of Atmospheric Dry Air

CONSTITUENT	MOLAR MASS*	MOLE PERCENT	PARTIAL PRESSURE AT STP (ATM)
N_2	28.01	78.08	0.7808
O_2	32.00	20.95	0.2095
Ar	39.95	0.934	0.00934
CO_2	44.01	0.0393	0.000393

*The average molar mass of dry air = 28.960 g/mol.

where P_1, P_2, and P_3 are the pressures of the different gases in a mixture, and P_{total} is the total pressure.

In a mixture of gases, each gas behaves independently of all others. Therefore, we can consider the behavior of each gas in a mixture separately. As an example, take a mixture of three ideal gases, labeled A, B, and C. There are n_A moles of A, n_B moles of B, and n_C moles of C. Assume that the mixture ($n_{total} = n_A + n_B + n_C$) is contained in a given volume (V) at a given temperature (T). We can calculate the pressure exerted by each gas from the ideal gas law equation:

$$P_AV = n_ART \qquad P_BV = n_BRT \qquad P_CV = n_CRT$$

According to Dalton's law, the total pressure exerted by the mixture is the sum of the pressures exerted by each component:

$$P_{total} = P_A + P_B + P_C = n_A\left(\frac{RT}{V}\right) + n_B\left(\frac{RT}{V}\right) + n_C\left(\frac{RT}{V}\right)$$

$$P_{total} = (n_A + n_B + n_C)\left(\frac{RT}{V}\right)$$

$$P_{total} = (n_{total})\left(\frac{RT}{V}\right) \qquad \textbf{(10.7)}$$

For mixtures of gases, it is convenient to introduce a quantity called the **mole fraction, *X***, which is defined as the number of moles of a particular substance in a

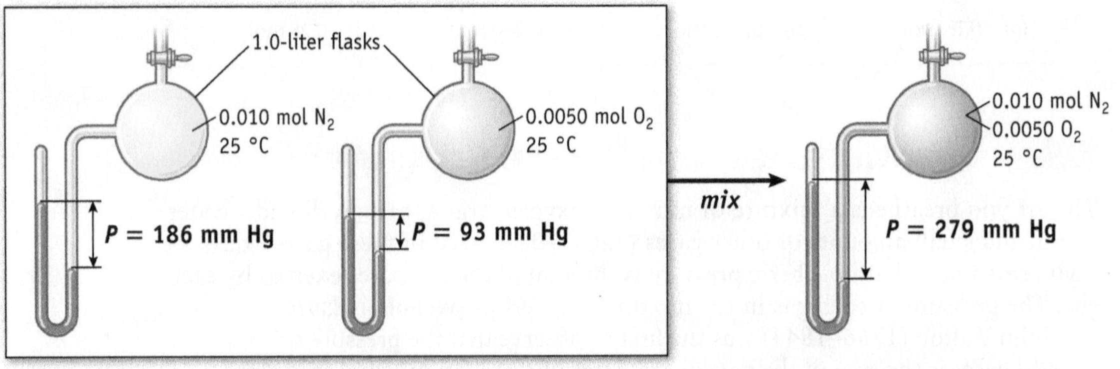

In a 1.0-L flask at 25 °C, 0.010 mol of N_2 exerts a pressure of 186 mm Hg, and 0.0050 mol of O_2 in a 1.0-L flask at 25 °C exerts a pressure of 93 mm Hg.

The N_2 and O_2 samples are both placed in a 1.0-L flask at 25 °C. The total pressure, 279 mm Hg, is the sum of the pressures that each gas alone exerts in the flask.

FIGURE 10.10 **Dalton's law.**

mixture divided by the total number of moles of all substances present. Mathematically, the mole fraction of a substance A in a mixture with B and C is expressed as

$$X_A = \frac{n_A}{n_A + n_B + n_C} = \frac{n_A}{n_{total}}$$

Now we can combine this equation (written as $n_{total} = n_A/X_A$) with the equations for P_A and P_{total}, and derive the equation

$$P_A = X_A P_{total} \qquad (10.8)$$

This equation tells us that *the pressure of a gas in a mixture of gases is the product of its mole fraction and the total pressure of the mixture.* In other words, the partial pressure of a gas is directly related to the fraction of particles of that gas in the mixture. For example, the mole fraction of N_2 in air is 0.78, so, at STP, its partial pressure is 0.78 atm or 590 mm Hg.

EXAMPLE 10.10

Partial Pressures of Gases

Problem Halothane, $C_2HBrClF_3$, is a nonflammable, nonexplosive, and nonirritating gas that was widely used as an inhalation anesthetic. The total pressure of a mixture of 15.0 g of halothane vapor and 23.5 g of oxygen gas is 855 mm Hg. What is the partial pressure of each gas?

What Do You Know? You know the identity and mass of each gas, so you can calculate the amount of each. You also know the total pressure of the gas mixture.

Strategy Because you can calculate the amount of each gas, you can determine the total amount (moles) of gas and thus the mole fraction of each. The partial pressure of a gas is given by the total pressure of the mixture multiplied by the mole fraction of the gas (Equation 10.8).

Solution

Step 1. Calculate mole fractions.

$$\text{Amount of } C_2HBrClF_3 = 15.0\ g\left(\frac{1\ mol}{197.4\ g}\right) = 0.0760\ mol$$

$$\text{Amount of } O_2 = 23.5\ g\left(\frac{1\ mol}{32.00\ g}\right) = 0.734\ mol$$

$$\text{Total amount of gas} = 0.0760\ mol\ C_2HBrClF_3 + 0.734\ mol\ O_2 = 0.810\ mol$$

$$\text{Mole fraction of } C_2HBrClF_3 = \frac{0.0760\ mol\ C_2HBrClF_3}{0.810\ total\ moles} = 0.0938$$

Because the sum of the mole fraction of halothane and of O_2 must equal 1.0000, this means that the mole fraction of oxygen is 0.906.

$$X_{halothane} + X_{oxygen} = 1.0000$$

$$0.0938 + X_{oxygen} = 1.0000$$

$$X_{oxygen} = 0.906$$

Strategy Map 10.10

PROBLEM
Calculate the **partial pressure** of two gases in a mixture.

DATA/INFORMATION
- **Mass** of each gas
- **Total pressure**

STEP 1. Calculate *amount* (*n*) of each gas from its **mass**.

Amount of each gas, *n*

STEP 2. Calculate **mole fraction** of each gas, ***X***.

Mole fraction of each gas, ***X***

STEP 3. Calculate **partial pressure** of gases using Equation 10.8.

Partial pressure of each gas

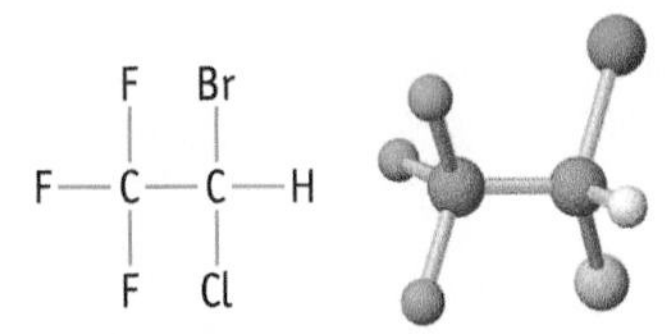

1,1,1-trifluorobromochloroethane, halothane

Step 2. Calculate partial pressures.

$$\text{Partial pressure of halothane} = P_{halothane} = X_{halothane} \times P_{total}$$

$$P_{halothane} = 0.0938 \times P_{total} = 0.0938\ (855\ \text{mm Hg})$$

$$P_{halothane} = 80.2\ \text{mm Hg}$$

The total pressure of the mixture is the sum of the partial pressures of the gases in the mixture.

$$P_{halothane} + P_{oxygen} = 855\ \text{mm Hg}$$

and so

$$P_{oxygen} = 855\ \text{mm Hg} - P_{halothane}$$

$$P_{oxygen} = 855\ \text{mm Hg} - 80.2\ \text{mm Hg} = 775\ \text{mm Hg}$$

Think about Your Answer The amount of halothane is about 1/10th of the amount of oxygen so we would expect the ratio of partial pressures of the two gases to be in a similar ratio.

Check Your Understanding

The halothane–oxygen mixture described in this Example is placed in a 5.00-L tank at 25.0 °C. What is the total pressure (in mm Hg) of the gas mixture in the tank? What are the partial pressures (in mm Hg) of the gases?

© Cengage Learning/Charles D. Winters

FIGURE 10.11 **A molecular view of gases and liquids.** The fact that a large volume of N_2 gas can be condensed to a small volume of liquid indicates that the distance between molecules in the gas phase is very large as compared with the distances between molecules in liquids.

REVIEW & CHECK FOR SECTION 10-5

1. Acetylene reacts with O_2 to give carbon dioxide and water vapor.

$$2\ C_2H_2(g) + 5\ O_2(g) \rightarrow 4\ CO_2(g) + 2\ H_2O(g)$$

If you mix C_2H_2 and O_2 in the correct stoichiometric ratio, and if the total pressure of the mixture is 140. mm Hg, what are the partial pressures of the gases before the reaction occurs?

(a) 100. mm Hg C_2H_2 and 40. mm Hg O_2
(b) 140. mm Hg C_2H_2 and 700. mm Hg O_2
(c) 40. mm Hg C_2H_2 and 100. mm Hg O_2
(d) 140. mm Hg C_2H_2 and 56.0 mm Hg O_2

Learning Objectives: LO 2.4, LO 5.2

10-6 The Kinetic-Molecular Theory of Gases

So far, we have discussed the macroscopic properties of gases, properties such as pressure and volume that result from the behavior of a system with a large number of particles. Now we turn to a description of the behavior of matter at the molecular or atomic level using kinetic-molecular theory (◀ page 16). Hundreds of experimental observations have led to the following postulates regarding the behavior of gases.

- Gases consist of particles (molecules or atoms) whose separation is much greater than the size of the particles themselves (Figure 10.11).
- The particles of a gas are in continual, random, and rapid motion. As they move, they collide with one another and with the walls of the container, but they do so in a way in which the total energy is unchanged.
- The average kinetic energy of gas particles is proportional to the gas temperature. *All gases, regardless of their molecular mass, have the same average kinetic energy at the same temperature.*

Let us discuss the behavior of gases from this point of view.

Molecular Speed and Kinetic Energy

Suppose your friend walks into your room carrying a large, flat box. How could you know there is a pizza in the box? You could tell by the odors coming from the box, because we know that the odor-causing molecules of food enter the gas phase and drift through space until they reach the cells of your body that react to odors. The same thing happens in the laboratory when dishes of aqueous ammonia (NH_3) and hydrochloric acid (HCl) sit side by side (Figure 10.12). Molecules of the two compounds enter the gas phase and drift along until they encounter one another, at which time they react and form a cloud of tiny particles of solid ammonium chloride (NH_4Cl).

If you lower the temperature of the environment of the containers in Figure 10.12 and measure the time needed for the cloud of ammonium chloride to form, you would find the time would be longer. The reason for this is that the speed at which molecules move depends on the temperature.

Let us expand on our experimental observations with pizza and ammonia. First, it is important to understand that the molecules in a gas sample do not all move at the same speed. Rather, as illustrated in Figure 10.13 for O_2 molecules, there is a distribution of speeds and the distribution depends on temperature. There are several important observations we can make.

- At a given temperature some molecules in a sample have high speeds and others have low speeds.
- Most of the molecules in the sample have some intermediate speed, and their most probable speed corresponds to the maximum in the curve. For oxygen gas at 25 °C, for example, most molecules have speeds in the range from 200 m/s to 700 m/s, and their most probable speed is about 400 m/s. (These are very high speeds, indeed. A speed of 400 m/s corresponds to about 900 miles per hour!)
- When you compare the distribution curves for O_2 molecules at 25 °C and 1000 °C, you see that, as the temperature increases the most probable speed increases and the number of molecules traveling at very high speeds increases greatly.

The kinetic energy of a single molecule of mass m (in kg) in a gas sample is given by the equation

$$KE = \frac{1}{2}(mass)(speed)^2 = \frac{1}{2}\,mu^2$$

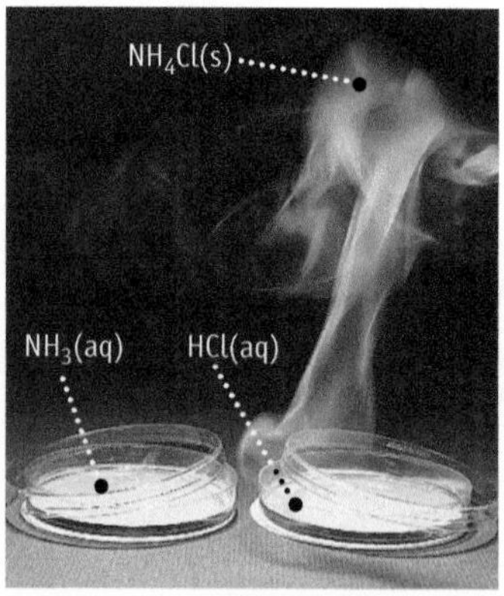

FIGURE 10.12 The movement of gas molecules. Open dishes of aqueous ammonia and hydrochloric acid are placed side by side. When molecules of NH_3 and HCl escape from solution to the atmosphere and encounter one another, a cloud of solid ammonium chloride, NH_4Cl, is observed.

Maxwell-Boltzmann Curves Plots such as those in Figures 10.13 and 10.14 are often referred to as Maxwell-Boltzmann curves. They are named for two scientists who studied the physical properties of gases: James Clerk Maxwell (1831–1879) and Ludwig Boltzmann (1844–1906).

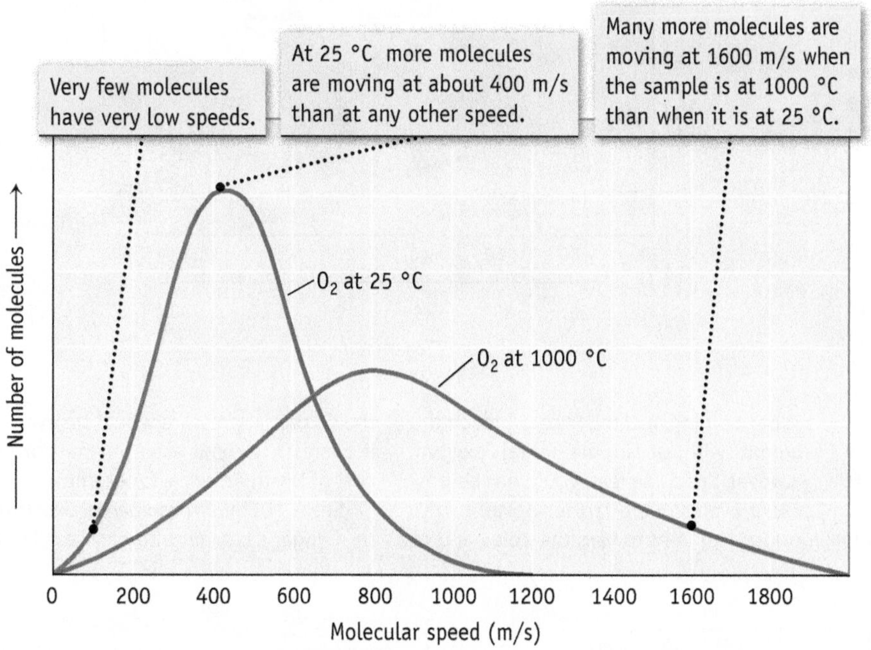

FIGURE 10.13 The distribution of molecular speeds. The figure depicts how the distribution of molecular speeds in a gas sample changes with temperature. The areas under the curves are the same because the number of molecules in the sample is fixed.

where u is the speed of that molecule (in m/s). We can calculate the kinetic energy of a single gas molecule from this equation but not of a collection of molecules because, as you see in Figure 10.13, not all of the molecules in a gas sample are moving at the same speed. However, we can calculate the *average* kinetic energy of a collection of molecules by relating it to other averaged quantities of the system. In particular, the average kinetic energy of a mole of molecules in a gas sample is related to the average speed:

$$\overline{KE} = \frac{1}{2} N_A m\overline{u^2}$$

A CLOSER LOOK

The Earth's Atmosphere

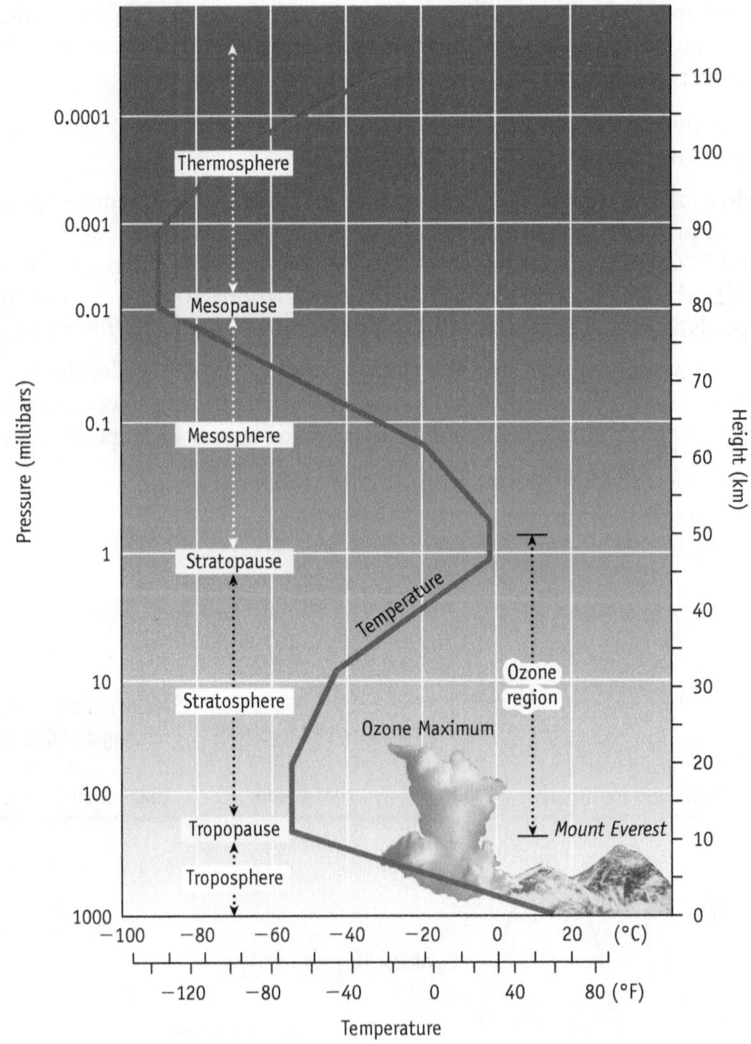

Earth's atmosphere is a fascinating mixture of gases in more or less distinct layers with widely differing temperatures.

Up through the troposphere, there is a gradual decline in temperature (and pressure) with altitude. The temperature climbs again in the stratosphere due to the absorption of energy from the Sun by stratospheric ozone, O_3.

Above the stratosphere, the pressure declines because there are fewer molecules present. At still higher altitudes, we observe a dramatic increase in temperature in the thermosphere. This is an illustration of the difference between *temperature* and *thermal energy*. The temperature of a gas reflects the average kinetic energy of the molecules of the gas, whereas the thermal energy present in an object is the *total* kinetic energy of the molecules. In the thermosphere, the molecules present have a very high temperature, but the thermal energy is exceedingly small because there are so few molecules.

Gases within the troposphere are well mixed by convection. Pollutants that are evolved on Earth's surface can rise to the stratosphere, but the stratosphere acts as a "thermal lid" on the troposphere and prevents significant mixing of polluting gases into the stratosphere and beyond. Nonetheless, small amounts of pollutants such as chlorofluorocarbons do enter the stratosphere and contribute to destruction of ozone (see Section 20-1).

The pressure of the atmosphere declines with altitude, and so the partial pressure of O_2 declines. The figure shows why climbers have a hard time breathing on Mount Everest, where the altitude is 29,028 ft (8848 m) and the O_2 partial pressure is only 29% of the sea level partial pressure. With proper training, a climber could reach the summit without supplemental oxygen. However, this same feat would not be possible if Everest were farther north. Earth's atmosphere thins toward the poles, and so the O_2 partial pressure would be even less if Everest's summit were in the northern part of North America, for example.

See G. N. Eby, *Environmental Geochemistry,* Cengage Learning/Brooks/Cole, 2004.

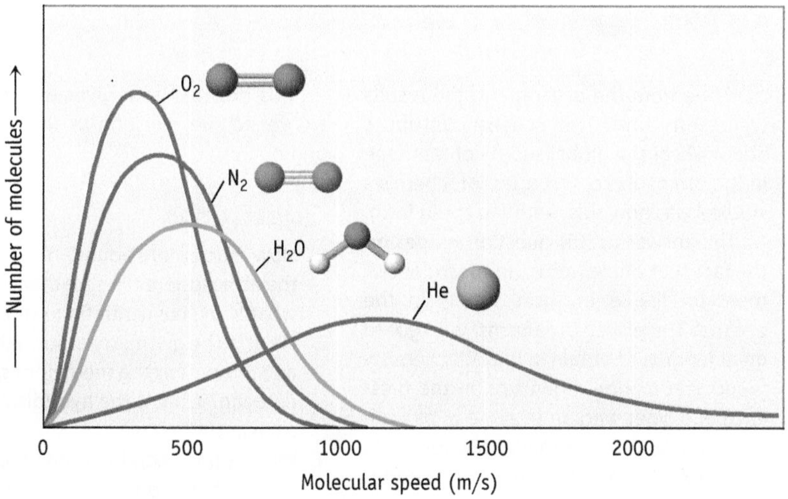

FIGURE 10.14 The effect of molecular mass on the distribution of speeds. At a given temperature, molecules with higher masses have lower speeds.

where N_A is Avogadro's number. (The horizontal bar over the symbols $\overline{KE}$ and $\overline{u}$ indicates an average value.) The product of the mass per molecule and Avogadro's constant is the molar mass (in units of kg/mol), so we can write

$$\overline{KE} = \frac{1}{2}M\overline{u^2}$$

This equation states that the average kinetic energy of the molecules in a gas sample, $\overline{KE}$, is related to $\overline{u^2}$, the average of the squares of their speeds (called the "mean square speed").

Experiments also show that the average kinetic energy, $\overline{KE}$, of a mole of gas molecules is directly proportional to temperature with a proportionality constant of $\frac{3}{2}R$,

$$\overline{KE} = \frac{3}{2}RT$$

where R is the gas constant expressed in SI units (8.314472 J/K · mol).

The two kinetic energy equations can be combined to yield an equation that relates mass, average speed, and temperature (Equation 10.9).

$$\sqrt{\overline{u^2}} = \sqrt{\frac{3RT}{M}} \qquad \textbf{(10.9)}$$

Here, the square root of the mean square speed ($\sqrt{\overline{u^2}}$, called the **root-mean-square speed**, or **rms speed**), the temperature (T, in kelvins), and the molar mass (M) are related. This equation shows that the speeds of gas molecules are indeed related to the temperature (Figure 10.13). The rms speed is a useful quantity because of its relationship to the average kinetic energy and because it is very close to the true average speed for a sample. (The average speed is 92% of the rms speed.)

All gases have the same average kinetic energy at the same temperature. However, if you compare a sample of one gas with another, say compare O_2 and N_2, this does not mean the molecules have the same rms speed (Figure 10.14). Instead, Equation 10.9 shows that the smaller the molar mass of the gas the greater the rms speed.

CASE STUDY The Methane Mystery

Carbon dioxide, methane, nitrous oxide, and even water are "greenhouse gases." One role they play in the atmosphere is to moderate the temperature of the planet. However, there is concern that increases in the atmospheric concentrations of these gases are leading to a warming of the Earth and to climate change. (This issue is described in Chapter 20.)

Courtesy John Kotz

Among greenhouse gases of concern, methane is second only to carbon dioxide in its atmospheric concentration. The current value for CO_2 is over 390 ppm (parts per million) and for methane it is 177.4 ppb (parts per billion). The CO_2 concentration has been rising for years and is continuing to rise. The level of methane in the atmosphere is also rising. Indeed, according to the fourth report from the Intergovernmental Panel on Climate Change (IPCC) the current level of methane in the atmosphere is the highest it has been in at least 650,000 years.

Where does methane come from? Again according to the IPCC report, "Methane has increased as a result of human activities related to agriculture, natural gas distribution and landfills. Methane is also released from natural processes that occur, for example, in wetlands." One natural source that was recently studied is methane from the oceans, and the results were surprising. The oceans contribute about 4% of the global supply of methane in the atmosphere. The question chemists studied was how this methane could form.

The answer to this question hinges on the fact that phosphorus, an essential element for life, is in short supply in the oceans. Therefore, organisms will go to great lengths to obtain it. In 2008 chemists found that marine organisms, in the presence of oxygen and an enzyme (a biological catalyst), can use methylphosphonate ion ($CH_3PO_3H^-$) as a source of phosphorus. Methane is a byproduct.

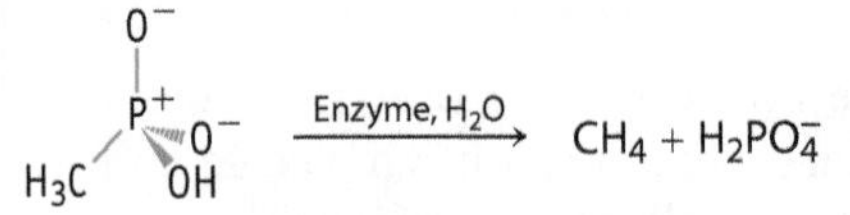

It was known that phosphonates are a significant source of phosphorus for some marine microorganisms, so the methylphosphonate route to methane seemed attractive. Unfortunately, methylphosphonate had never been detected in marine environments nor was it a known natural product.

The question then was how, or if, methylphosphonate ion can be produced in the ocean. Even more recent research (2012) has found the answer: An iron-dependent enzyme converts a phosphonate derivative known to be present in the ocean, 2-hydroxyethylphosphonate ion, to the methylphosphonate ion

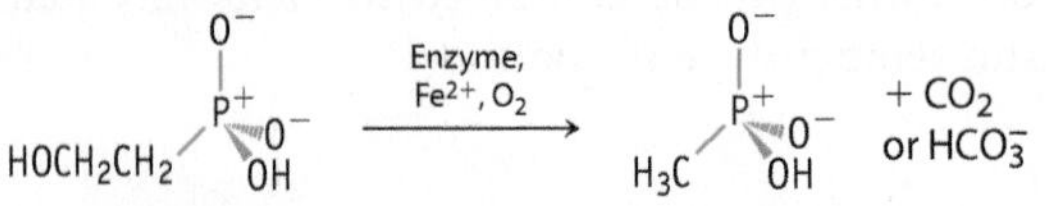

This new research gives us a plausible answer to the question of the methane's origin.

Questions:

1. How much more abundant is CO_2 in the atmosphere than methane? That is, what is the concentration ratio?
2. What is the geometry around the C and P atoms in the methylphosphonate ion? What is the hybridization of each atom?
3. What is the oxidation number of the phosphorus atom in the methylphosphonate ion?
4. Suppose you examine the methane in 1.00 cubic kilometer of the atmosphere at sea level. (Assume that the atmosphere is dry, has a molar mass of 28.96 g/mol, and the pressure is 1.00 atm at 25.0 °C.)
   (a) How many molecules of methane are present in 1.00 km^3 under these conditions?
   (b) What mass of methylphosphonate ion is required to produce the methane in 1.00 km^3 of atmosphere?

References:

1. W. W. Metcalf, et al. *Science*, Vol 337, page 1104. August 31, 2012.
2. *Chemical & Engineering News*, page 11, September 3, 2012.

EXAMPLE 10.11

Molecular Speed

Problem Calculate the rms speed of oxygen molecules at 25 °C.

What Do You Know? You know the molar mass of O_2 and the temperature, the main determinants of speed.

Strategy Use Equation 10.9 with M in units of kg/mol. The reason for this is that R is in units of J/K · mol, and 1 J = 1 kg · m^2/s^2.

Solution The molar mass of O_2 is 32.0×10^{-3} kg/mol.

$$\sqrt{\overline{u^2}} = \sqrt{\frac{3(8.3145\ \text{J/K} \cdot \text{mol})(298\ \text{K})}{32.0 \times 10^{-3}\ \text{kg/mol}}} = \sqrt{2.32 \times 10^5\ \text{J/kg}}$$

To obtain the answer in meters per second, use the relation 1 J = 1 kg · m²/s². This means you have

$$\sqrt{\overline{u^2}} = \sqrt{2.32 \times 10^5\ \text{kg} \cdot \text{m}^2/(\text{kg} \cdot \text{s}^2)} = \sqrt{2.32 \times 10^5\ \text{m}^2/\text{s}^2} = 482\ \text{m/s}$$

Think about Your Answer The calculated rms speed is equivalent to about 1100 miles per hour! This is greater than the speed of sound in air, 343 m/s.

Check Your Understanding

Calculate the rms speeds of helium atoms and N_2 molecules at 25 °C.

Kinetic-Molecular Theory and the Gas Laws

The gas laws, which come from experiment, can be explained by the kinetic-molecular theory. The starting place is to describe how pressure arises from collisions of gas molecules with the walls of the container holding the gas (Figure 10.15). Remember that pressure is related to the force of the collisions (see Section 10-1).

$$\text{Gas pressure} = \frac{\text{force of collisions}}{\text{area}}$$

The force exerted by the collisions depends on the number of collisions and the average force per collision. When the temperature of a gas is increased, we know the average kinetic energy of the molecules increases. This causes the average force of the collisions with the walls to increase as well. Also, because the speed of gas molecules increases with temperature, more collisions occur per second. Thus, the collective force per square centimeter is greater, and the pressure increases. Mathematically, this is related to the direct proportionality between P and T when n and V are fixed, that is, $P = (nR/V)T$.

Increasing the number of molecules of a gas at a fixed temperature and volume does not change the average collision force, but it does increase the number of collisions occurring per second. Thus, the pressure increases, and we can say that P is proportional to n when V and T are constant, that is, $P = n(RT/V)$.

If the pressure is to remain constant when either the number of molecules of gas or the temperature is increased, then the volume of the container (and the area over which the collisions occur) must increase. This is expressed by stating that V is proportional to nT when P is constant [$V = nT(R/P)$], a statement that is a *combination of Avogadro's hypothesis and Charles's law*.

Finally, if the temperature is constant, the average impact force of molecules of a given mass with the container walls must be constant. If n is kept constant while the volume of the container is made smaller, the number of collisions with the container walls per second must increase. This means the pressure increases, and so P is proportional to $1/V$ when n and T are constant, as stated by *Boyle's law*, that is, $P = (1/V)(nRT)$.

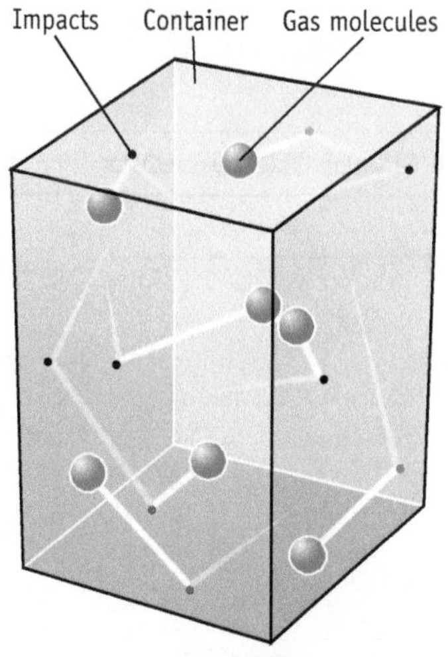

FIGURE 10.15 **Gas pressure.** According to the kinetic-molecular theory, gas pressure is caused by gas molecules bombarding the container walls.

REVIEW & CHECK FOR SECTION 10-6

1. What is the rms speed of chlorine molecules at 35.0 °C?

   (a) 10.4 m/s (b) 32.7 m/s (c) 111 m/s (d) 329 m/s

2. The species identified with each curve in the Maxwell-Boltzmann plot below are: (Assume all gases are at the same temperature.)

   (a) A = Xe, B = O_2, C = Ne, and D = He
   (b) A = Xe, B = He, C = Ne, and D = O_2
   (c) A = He, B = Ne, C = O_2, and D = Xe
   (d) A = He, B = O_2, C = Ne, and D = Xe

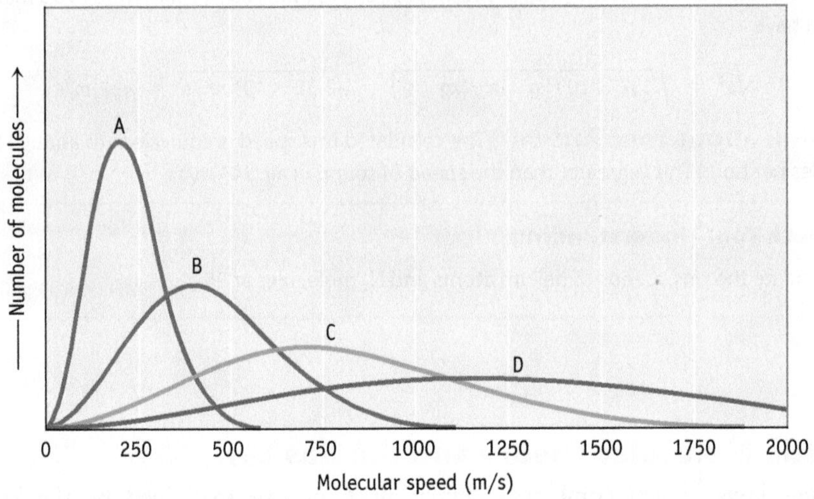

Learning Objectives: LO 2.4

10-7 Diffusion and Effusion

When a warm pizza is brought into a room, the volatile aroma-causing molecules vaporize into the atmosphere, where they mix with the oxygen, nitrogen, carbon dioxide, water vapor, and other gases present. Even if there were no movement of the air in the room caused by fans or people moving about, the odor would eventually reach everywhere in the room. This mixing of molecules of two or more gases due to their random molecular motions is the result of **diffusion**. Given time, the molecules of one component in a gas mixture will thoroughly and completely mix with all other components of the mixture (Figure 10.16).

Diffusion is also illustrated by the experiment in Figure 10.17. Here, we placed cotton moistened with hydrochloric acid at one end of a glass U-tube and cotton moistened with aqueous ammonia at the other end. Molecules of HCl and NH_3 diffused into the tube, and, when they met, they produced white, solid NH_4Cl.

$$HCl(g) + NH_3(g) \rightarrow NH_4Cl(s)$$

FIGURE 10.16 **Gaseous diffusion.** Here bromine diffuses out of a flask and mixes with air in the bottle over time.

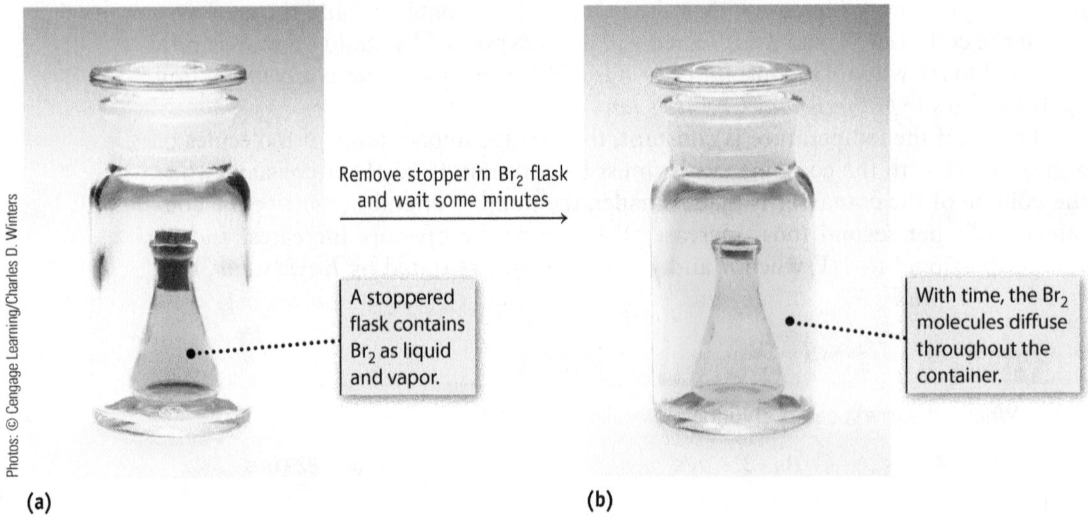

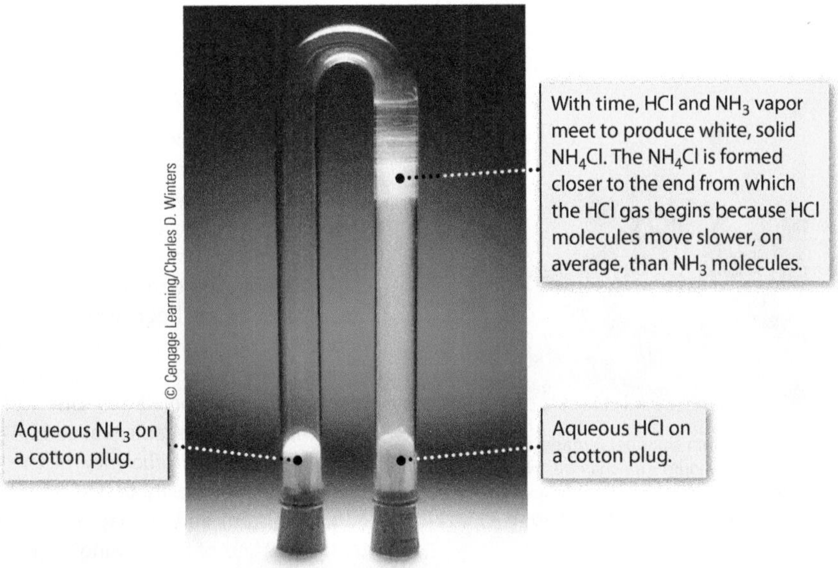

FIGURE 10.17 **Gaseous diffusion.** Here, HCl gas (from hydrochloric acid) and ammonia gas (from aqueous ammonia) diffuse from opposite ends of a glass U-tube.

We found that the gases did not meet in the middle. Rather, because the heavier HCl molecules diffuse less rapidly than the lighter NH_3 molecules, the molecules met closer to the HCl end of the U-tube.

Closely related to diffusion is **effusion**, which is the movement of gas through a tiny opening in a container into another container where the pressure is very low (Figure 10.18). Thomas Graham (1805–1869), a Scottish chemist, studied the effusion of gases and found that the rate of effusion of a gas—the amount of gas moving from one place to another in a given amount of time—is inversely proportional to the square root of its molar mass. Based on these experimental results, the rates of effusion of two gases can be compared:

$$\frac{\text{Rate of effusion of gas 1}}{\text{Rate of effusion of gas 2}} = \sqrt{\frac{\text{molar mass of gas 2}}{\text{molar mass of gas 1}}} \tag{10.10}$$

The relationship in Equation 10.10—now known as **Graham's law**—is derived from Equation 10.9 by recognizing that the rate of effusion depends on the speed of the molecules. The ratio of the rms speeds is the same as the ratio of the effusion rates:

$$\frac{\text{Rate of effusion of gas 1}}{\text{Rate of effusion of gas 2}} = \frac{\sqrt{\overline{u^2} \text{ of gas 1}}}{\sqrt{\overline{u^2} \text{ of gas 2}}} = \frac{\sqrt{3RT/(M \text{ of gas 1})}}{\sqrt{3RT/(M \text{ of gas 2})}}$$

Canceling out like terms gives the expression in Equation 10.10.

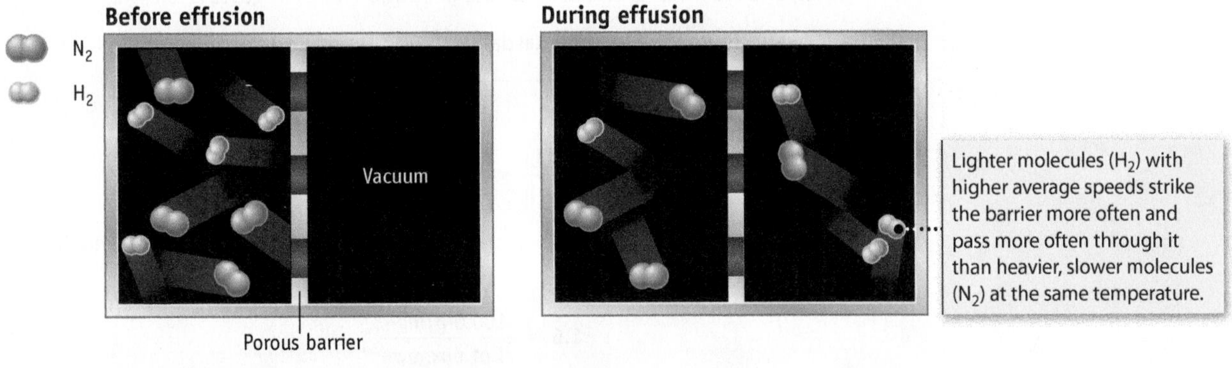

FIGURE 10.18 **Gaseous effusion.** H_2 and N_2 gas molecules effuse through the pores of a porous barrier. According to Graham's law, H_2 molecules effuse 3.72 times faster than N_2 molecules at the same temperature.

A CLOSER LOOK | Surface Science and the Need for Ultrahigh Vacuum Systems

Surface science is the study of processes that occur at interfaces between phases. The interface between a solid and a gas is particularly important in areas such as catalysis and microelectronics. An automobile's catalytic converter facilitates the decomposition of hazardous molecules in an automobile's exhaust. In the electronics industry, as the size of semiconductor devices is decreased, surface atoms play an increasingly important role in their behavior. Understanding and controlling the chemical and physical processes that occur at these surfaces is important.

In order to study surface phenomena, surface scientists often need to have a clean surface, but obtaining one is a challenge. When real gases collide with a clean surface they often stick to the surface, quickly forming a monolayer—approximately 10^{15} molecules/cm^2—of adsorbed molecules on the surface. To avoid this contamination, surface scientists conduct studies in vacuum chambers, where contact between gas phase molecules and surfaces may be minimized. But, how good a vacuum is needed to keep a surface clean of adsorbed molecules?

© Cultura Creative/Alamy

A high vacuum chamber is made of polished steel or aluminum. The chamber often has multiple portals where vacuum pumps, instruments, or windows into the chamber may be attached.

The term "high vacuum" describes a system where gas pressure is less than 10^{-6} mm Hg. The ideal gas law can be used to show that at 10^{-6} mm Hg and room temperature over 3×10^{13} gas particles occupy each liter of space. Even at this pressure, over 10^{14} collisions/cm^2 per second occur between gas molecules and a surface. In only a few seconds a clean surface will be completely covered with adsorbed molecules.

To maintain a clean surface, ultrahigh vacuum (10^{-9} mm Hg or better) conditions are required. Reducing the number of gas phase molecules by a factor of one thousand also reduces the rate of gas-surface collisions by the same factor. Under ultrahigh vacuum conditions, a surface will stay clean for over an hour, which is usually enough time for an analysis of the surface.

Is it possible to remove all gas particles in a vacuum chamber? No, a variety of factors limit an achievable vacuum. These factors include the efficiency of the vacuum pumps, the ability to avoid any leaks into the system, and, perhaps most importantly, the rate of "outgassing" in the system. Outgassing is a process in which molecules desorb from the surfaces within the system. Prior to pumping out a vacuum chamber, the inner surfaces are saturated with adsorbed molecules. As these molecules desorb, they increase the pressure in the vacuum system. Under ideal conditions, pressures might be reduced below 10^{-10} mm Hg, at which point the rate at which gas is pumped out of the system equals the rate of outgassing.

EXAMPLE 10.12

Using Graham's Law of Effusion to Calculate a Molar Mass

Problem Tetrafluoroethylene, C_2F_4, effuses through a barrier at a rate of 4.6×10^{-6} mol/h. An unknown gas, consisting only of boron and hydrogen, effuses at the rate of 5.8×10^{-6} mol/h under the same conditions. What is the molar mass of the unknown gas?

What Do You Know? You have two gases, one with a known molar mass (C_2F_4, 100.0 g/mol) and the other unknown. The rate of effusion for both gases is known.

Strategy Substitute the experimental data into Graham's law equation (Equation 10.10).

Solution

$$\frac{5.8 \times 10^{-6}\ \text{mol/h}}{4.6 \times 10^{-6}\ \text{mol/h}} = 1.3 = \sqrt{\frac{100.0\ \text{g/mol}}{M \text{ of unknown}}}$$

To solve for the unknown molar mass, square both sides of the equation and rearrange to find M for the unknown.

$$1.6 = \frac{100.0\ \text{g/mol}}{M \text{ of unknown}}$$

$$M = 63\ \text{g/mol}$$

Think about Your Answer From Graham's law, we know that a light molecule will effuse more rapidly than a heavier one. Because the unknown gas effuses more rapidly than C_2F_4 (M = 100.0 g/mol), the unknown must have a molar mass less than 100 g/mol. A boron–hydrogen compound corresponding to this molar mass is B_5H_9, called *pentaborane.*

Check Your Understanding

A sample of methane, CH_4, is found to effuse through a porous barrier in 1.50 minutes. Under the same conditions, an equal number of molecules of an unknown gas effuses through the barrier in 4.73 minutes. What is the molar mass of the unknown gas?

REVIEW & CHECK FOR SECTION 10-7

1. In Figure 10.17, ammonia gas and hydrogen chloride are introduced from opposite ends of a glass U-tube. The gases react to produce white, solid NH_4Cl. What are the relative root mean square speeds of HCl and NH_3?

   (a) rms for HCl/rms for NH_3 = 2.2
   (b) rms for HCl/rms for NH_3 = 1.5
   (c) rms for HCl/rms for NH_3 = 0.68
   (d) rms for HCl/rms for NH_3 = 0.46

10-8 Nonideal Behavior of Gases

Learning Objectives: LO 2.12

If you are working with a gas at approximately room temperature and a pressure of 1 atm or less, the ideal gas law is remarkably successful in relating the amount of gas and its pressure, volume, and temperature. At higher pressures or lower temperatures, however, deviations from the ideal gas law occur. The origin of these deviations is explained by the breakdown of the assumptions used when describing ideal gases, specifically the assumptions that the particles have no size and that there are no forces between them.

At standard temperature and pressure (STP), the volume occupied by a single molecule is *very* small relative to its share of the total gas volume. Relatively speaking, a helium atom with a radius of 31 pm has about the same space to move about as a pea has inside a basketball. Now suppose the pressure is increased significantly, to 1000 atm. The volume available to each molecule is a sphere with a radius of only about 200 pm, which means the situation is now like that of a pea inside a sphere a bit larger than a Ping-Pong ball.

How Much Space Does a Molecule Take Up? The volume of a methane (CH_4) molecule is 3.31×10^{-23} cm^3. Suppose you have 1.00 mol of CH_4 gas in a 1.00-L flask at 273 K. The pressure would be high, 22.4 atm, and 19.9 cm^3 of the space in the flask would be occupied by CH_4 molecules. This is about 2% of the flask volume.

The kinetic-molecular theory and the ideal gas law are concerned with the volume available to the molecules to move about, not the total volume of the container. For example, suppose you have a flask marked with a volume of 500 mL. The volume available to molecules is less than 500 mL because the molecules themselves occupy some of the volume. At low pressures, the volume occupied by the gas molecules in the container is so small in comparison to the space available that neglecting to subtract it from the total volume does not introduce significant error. At higher pressures, however, the volume occupied by gas molecules is not negligible.

Another assumption of the kinetic-molecular theory is that the atoms or molecules of the gas never stick to one another. This is clearly not true. All gases can be liquefied—although some gases require a very low temperature—and the only way this can happen is if there are forces of attraction between the molecules. Attractive forces slow the speed of molecules, causing them to hit the walls of their container with less force than in the absence of these forces. Thus, because collisions between molecules in a real gas and the wall are softer, the observed gas pressure is less than that predicted by the ideal gas law. Additionally, because the attractive forces pull the gas molecules closer together, the volume occupied by a real gas is often less than the volume calculated using the ideal gas laws. These effects on pressure and volume are particularly pronounced when the temperature is near the condensation temperature of a gas.

The y-axis is actually $V_{real}/(RT/P)$, where RT/P is the ideal volume of 1 mol of gas. Thus, the y-axis is the ratio of the volume of a real gas to the volume of an ideal gas.

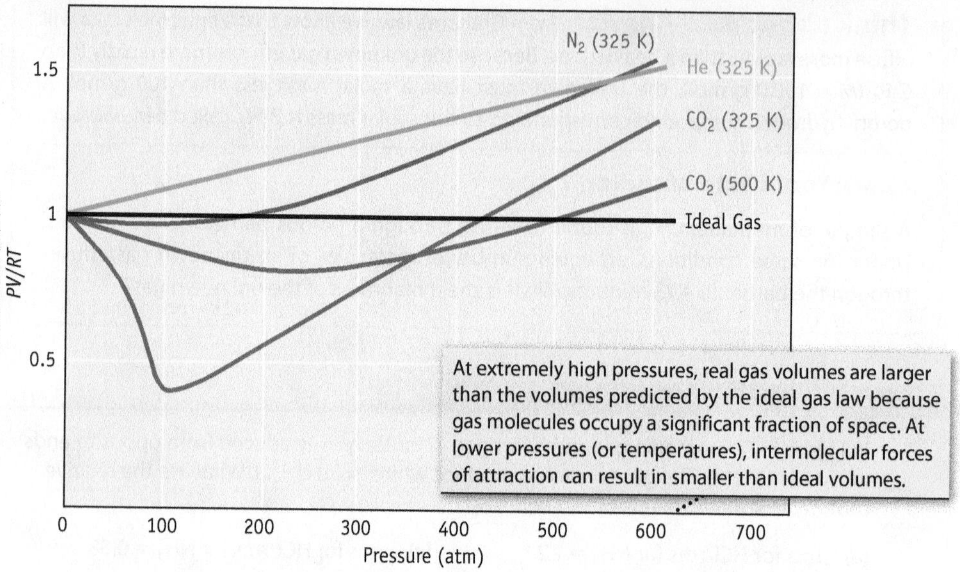

FIGURE 10.19 Real gas deviations from ideal behavior. Here, PV/RT for 1 mol of N_2, He, and CO_2 gases are plotted versus P. For 1 mol of an ideal gas $PV/RT = 1$ at all pressures.

Gases with weak intermolecular forces, such as helium, generally have observed volumes that are greater than predicted by the ideal gas law (Figure 10.19). Intermolecular forces, which reduce the volume of a gas, are small for helium and have little effect on its volume or pressure (except at very low temperatures). The deviation occurs because helium atoms occupy a fraction of the space within a container. Gases such as carbon dioxide often have smaller volumes than predicted by the ideal gas law at high pressures. Here, intermolecular forces of attraction have the effect of reducing the volume of a gas. However, even carbon dioxide eventually deviates toward higher than ideal volumes as the pressure increases and the molecules occupy an increasing fraction of space within a container.

The Dutch physicist Johannes van der Waals (1837–1923) studied the breakdown of the ideal gas law equation and developed an equation to correct for some of the errors arising from nonideality. This equation is known as the **van der Waals equation**:

observed pressure — container V

$$\left(P + a\left[\frac{n}{V}\right]^2\right)(V - bn) = nRT \qquad \textbf{(10.11)}$$

correction for intermolecular forces — correction for molecular volume

Table 10.2 van der Waals Constants

Gas	a Values (atm·L²/mol²)	b Values (L/mol)
He	0.034	0.0237
Ar	1.34	0.0322
H_2	0.244	0.0266
N_2	1.39	0.0391
O_2	1.36	0.0318
CO_2	3.59	0.0427
Cl_2	6.49	0.0562
H_2O	5.46	0.0305

where a and b are experimentally determined constants (Table 10.2). Although Equation 10.11 might seem complicated at first glance, the terms in parentheses are those of the ideal gas law, each corrected for the effects discussed previously. The pressure correction term, $a(n/V)^2$, accounts for intermolecular forces. Owing to intermolecular forces, the observed gas pressure is lower than the ideal pressure ($P_{observed} < P_{ideal}$ where P_{ideal} is calculated using the equation $PV = nRT$). Therefore, the term $a(n/V)^2$ is *added* to the observed pressure. The constant a typically has values in the range 0.01 to 10 atm · L²/mol².

The actual volume available to the molecules is smaller than the volume of the container because the molecules themselves take up space. Therefore, an amount is *subtracted* from the container volume ($= bn$) to take this into account. Here, n is the number of moles of gas, and b is an experimental quantity that corrects for the molecular volume. Typical values of b range from 0.01 to 0.1 L/mol, roughly increasing with increasing molecular size.

Pressure and volume are not the only factors that influence nonideal behavior in gases. As the temperature of a gas decreases, the attractive intermolecular forces slow the speed of the gas molecules and soften their collisions with container walls. Comparison of the behavior of carbon dioxide at two temperatures, 325 K and 500 K, shows a substantially greater negative deviation from ideality at the lower temperature (Figure 10.19).

As an example of the importance of these corrections, consider a sample of 4.00 mol of chlorine gas, Cl_2, in a 4.00-L tank at 100.0 °C. The ideal gas law would lead you to expect a pressure of 30.6 atm. A better estimate of the pressure, obtained from the van der Waals equation, is 26.0 atm, about 4.6 atm less than the ideal pressure!

© Cengage Learning/Charles D. Winters

A flask of helium gas for filling party balloons. The tank holds about 15 cubic feet (about 425 L) of helium. (*Note:* These tanks are not designed to be reused! Dispose of them properly. Also, use helium sparingly. The supply of the gas on the planet is not limitless.)

REVIEW & CHECK FOR SECTION 10-8

1. You can purchase tanks of helium at a party store to fill balloons. Such a tank may hold 343 mol of He in a volume of 473 L. Use the van der Waals equation to calculate the pressure in the tank at 25 °C.

   (a) 18.0 atm (b) 17.7 atm (c) 17.3 atm

APPLYING CHEMICAL PRINCIPLES

The Goodyear Blimp

Goodyear blimps are a familiar sight at sporting events. They hover at altitudes between 1000–3000 feet, providing a stable platform for television cameras. The outer surface, or envelope, of a Goodyear blimp is constructed of polyester fabric impregnated with neoprene rubber. The envelope contains the lighter-than-air gas helium. Within the fore and aft sections of the envelope are two air-filled structures called ballonets, which serve two purposes. As the blimp changes altitude, the ballonets are inflated or deflated with air to maintain a helium pressure within the envelope that is similar to the external air pressure. The ballonets also are used to keep the craft level. The pilot and passengers ride in the gondola, which is attached to the bottom of the envelope.

One of the Goodyear blimps has a gross weight of 12,840 lbs (5820 kg), and the volume of the inner envelope is 202,700 ft^3 (5740 m^3). The ballonets, when both fully inflated with air, occupy a total of 18,000 ft^3 (510 m^3) of the envelope. Helium is neither added nor removed from the envelope during operation. Loss of helium through the rubber impregnated polyester fabric is slow, at approximately 10,000 ft^3 (280 m^3) per month.

Diamond Images/Getty Images

Goodyear blimp. Here the blimp flies over a packed stadium at Ohio State University.

QUESTIONS:

1. At sea level, atmospheric pressure is 1.00 atm. Calculate the density (in g/L) of helium at this pressure and 25 °C.
2. Use the data provided in Table 10.1 to calculate the density of dry air at 1.00 atm and 25 °C.
3. To stay aloft, a blimp must achieve neutral buoyancy; that is, its density must equal that of the surrounding air. The density of the blimp is its total weight (blimp, helium and air, passengers, and ballast) divided by its volume. Assume that the gross weight of the blimp includes the blimp's structure and the helium, but does not include the air in the ballonets or the weights of the passengers and ballast. If the ballonets are filled with 12,000 ft^3 (340 m^3) of air at 1.00 atm and 25 °C, what additional weight (of passengers and ballast) is required for neutral buoyancy?

CHAPTER GOALS REVISITED

Now that you have studied this chapter, you should ask whether you have met the chapter goals. In particular, you should be able to:

UNDERSTAND

- The experimental basis of Boyle's law, Charles's law, Avogadro's hypothesis, and Dalton's law of partial pressures.
  - **a.** Describe how pressure measurements are made and the units of pressure, especially atmospheres (atm) and millimeters of mercury (mm Hg) (Section 10-1). Study Questions: 1, 3.
  - **b.** Understand the basis of the gas laws and how to apply these laws (Section 10-2). Study Questions: 6, 8, 10, 12, 14–16.
- Kinetic-molecular theory as it is applied to gases, especially the distribution of molecular speeds (energies).
  - **a.** Apply the kinetic-molecular theory of gas behavior at the molecular level (Section 10-6). Study Questions: 41–46, 107.
- Why real gases do not behave like ideal gases under some conditions.
  - **a.** Appreciate the fact that real gases can deviate from ideal behavior, especially at high pressure and low temperature (Section 10-8). Study Questions: 51, 52.

DO

- Describe how changing one property of a gas (*P*, *V*, *T*, or *n*) changes the others.
  - **a.** Apply Boyle's law, Charles's law, and Avogadro's hypothesis to the study of gases (Section 10-2). Study Questions: 5–10, 15.
- Apply the gas laws to stoichiometric calculations.
  - **a.** Apply the gas laws to a study of the stoichiometry of reactions (Section 10-4). Study Questions: 31–36, 65.
  - **b.** Use Dalton's law of partial pressures (Section 10-5). Study Questions: 39, 40.
- Use the principles of the kinetic-molecular theory to describe the behavior of gases.
  - **a.** Relate the average kinetic energies and the root mean velocities of gas molecules to temperature (Section 10-5). Study Questions: 41, 43, 44, 107.
- Determine the relative rates of effusion of gases.
  - **a.** Understand the phenomena of diffusion and effusion and use Graham's law (Section 10-7). Study Questions: 47–50.
- Use the ideal gas law and the van der Waals equation.
  - **a.** Understand the origin of the ideal gas law and how to use the ideal gas equation (Section 10-3). Study Questions: 17–24, 63, 85, 102.
  - **b.** Calculate the molar mass of a compound from a knowledge of the pressure of a known quantity of a gas in a given volume at a known temperature (Section 10-3). Study Questions: 25–30.

REMEMBER

- The various units of pressure.
- The effects of temperature and molar mass on the rates of effusion and diffusion.
- How properties of gases are explained by the kinetic-molecular theory.

KEY EQUATIONS

Equation 10.1 (page 375) Boyle's law (where P is the pressure and V is the volume).

$$P_1V_1 = P_2V_2 \text{ at constant } n \text{ and } T$$

Equation 10.2 (page 377) Charles's law (where T is the Kelvin temperature).

$$\frac{V_1}{T_1} = \frac{V_2}{T_2} \text{ at constant } n \text{ and } P$$

Equation 10.3 (page 378) General gas law (combined gas law).

$$\frac{P_1V_1}{T_1} = \frac{P_2V_2}{T_2} \text{ for a given amount of gas, } n$$

Equation 10.4 (page 382) Ideal gas law (where n is the amount of gas in moles and R is the universal gas constant, 0.082057 L · atm/K · mol).

$$PV = nRT$$

Equation 10.5 (page 383) Density of gases (where d is the gas density in g/L and M is the molar mass of the gas).

$$d = \frac{m}{V} = \frac{PM}{RT}$$

Equation 10.6 (page 387) Dalton's law of partial pressures. The total pressure of a gas mixture is the sum of the partial pressures of the component gases (P_n).

$$P_{\text{total}} = P_1 + P_2 + P_3 + \ldots$$

Equation 10.7 (page 388) The total pressure of a gas mixture is equal to the total number of moles of gases multiplied by (RT/V).

$$P_{\text{total}} = (n_{\text{total}})\left(\frac{RT}{V}\right)$$

Equation 10.8 (page 389) The pressure of a gas (A) in a mixture is the product of its mole fraction (X_A) and the total pressure of the mixture.

$$P_A = X_AP_{\text{total}}$$

Equation 10.9 (page 393) The rms speed ($\sqrt{\overline{u^2}}$) depends on the molar mass of a gas (M) and its temperature (T).

$$\sqrt{\overline{u^2}} = \sqrt{\frac{3RT}{M}}$$

Equation 10.10 (page 397) Graham's law. The rate of effusion of a gas is inversely proportional to the square root of its molar mass.

$$\frac{\text{Rate of effusion of gas 1}}{\text{Rate of effusion of gas 2}} = \sqrt{\frac{\text{molar mass of gas 2}}{\text{molar mass of gas 1}}}$$

Equation 10.11 (page 400) The van der Waals equation, which relates pressure, volume, temperature, and amount of gas for a nonideal gas.

observed pressure (points to P); container V (points to V)

$$\left(P + a\left[\frac{n}{V}\right]^2\right)(V - bn) = nRT$$

correction for intermolecular forces (points to $a[n/V]^2$); correction for molecular volume (points to bn)

Courtesy Ciprian Popoviciu

STUDY QUESTIONS

▲ denotes challenging questions.

Blue-numbered questions have answers in Appendix N and fully worked solutions in the *Student Solutions Manual.*

Practicing Skills

Pressure

(See Section 10-1 and Example 10.1.)

1. The pressure of a gas is 440 mm Hg. Express this pressure in units of (a) atmospheres, (b) bars, and (c) kilopascals.

2. The average barometric pressure at an altitude of 10 km is 210 mm Hg. Express this pressure in atmospheres, bars, and kilopascals.

3. Indicate which represents the higher pressure in each of the following pairs:
   (a) 534 mm Hg or 0.754 bar
   (b) 534 mm Hg or 650 kPa
   (c) 1.34 bar or 934 kPa

4. Put the following in order of increasing pressure: 363 mm Hg, 363 kPa, 0.256 atm, and 0.523 bar.

Boyle's Law and Charles's Law

(See Section 10-2 and Examples 10.2 and 10.3.)

5. A sample of nitrogen gas has a pressure of 67.5 mm Hg in a 500.-mL flask. What is the pressure of this gas sample when it is transferred to a 125-mL flask at the same temperature?

6. A sample of CO_2 gas has a pressure of 56.5 mm Hg in a 125-mL flask. The sample is transferred to a new flask, where it has a pressure of 62.3 mm Hg at the same temperature. What is the volume of the new flask?

7. You have 3.5 L of NO at a temperature of 22.0 °C. What volume would the NO occupy at 37 °C? (Assume the pressure is constant.)

8. A 5.0-mL sample of CO_2 gas is enclosed in a gas-tight syringe (Figure 10.3) at 22 °C. If the syringe is immersed in an ice bath (0 °C), what is the new gas volume, assuming that the pressure is held constant?

The General Gas Law

(See Section 10-2 and Example 10.4.)

9. You have 3.6 L of H_2 gas at 380 mm Hg and 25 °C. What is the pressure of this gas if it is transferred to a 5.0-L flask at 0.0 °C?

10. You have a sample of CO_2 in flask A with a volume of 25.0 mL. At 20.5 °C, the pressure of the gas is 436.5 mm Hg. To find the volume of another flask, B, you move the CO_2 to that flask and find that its pressure is now 94.3 mm Hg at 24.5 °C. What is the volume of flask B?

11. You have a sample of gas in a flask with a volume of 250 mL. At 25.5 °C, the pressure of the gas is 360 mm Hg. If you decrease the temperature to −5.0 °C, what is the gas pressure at the lower temperature?

12. A sample of gas occupies 135 mL at 22.5 °C; the pressure is 165 mm Hg. What is the pressure of the gas sample when it is placed in a 252-mL flask at a temperature of 0.0 °C?

13. One of the cylinders of an automobile engine has a volume of 400. cm^3. The engine takes in air at a pressure of 1.00 atm and a temperature of 15 °C and compresses the air to a volume of 50.0 cm^3 at 77 °C. What is the final pressure of the gas in the cylinder? (The ratio of before and after volumes—in this case, 400:50 or 8:1—is called the *compression ratio*.)

14. A helium-filled balloon of the type used in long-distance flying contains 420,000 ft^3 (1.2×10^7 L) of helium. Suppose you fill the balloon with helium on the ground, where the pressure is 737 mm Hg and the temperature is 16.0 °C. When the balloon ascends to a height of 2 miles, where the pressure is only 600. mm Hg and the temperature is −33 °C, what volume is occupied by the helium gas? Assume the pressure inside the balloon matches the external pressure.

Avogadro's Hypothesis

(See Section 10-2 and Example 10.5.)

15. Nitrogen monoxide reacts with oxygen to give nitrogen dioxide.

$$2\ NO(g) + O_2(g) \rightarrow 2\ NO_2(g)$$

(a) You wish to react NO and O_2 in the correct stoichiometric ratio. The sample of NO has a volume of 150 mL. What volume of O_2 is required (at the same pressure and temperature)?
(b) What volume of NO_2 (at the same pressure and temperature) is formed in this reaction?

16. Ethane burns in air to give H_2O and CO_2.

$$2\ C_2H_6(g) + 7\ O_2(g) \rightarrow 4\ CO_2(g) + 6\ H_2O(g)$$

What volume of O_2 (L) is required for complete reaction with 5.2 L of C_2H_6? What volume of H_2O vapor (L) is produced? Assume all gases are measured at the same temperature and pressure.

Ideal Gas Law

(See Section 10-3 and Example 10.6.)

17. A 1.25-g sample of CO_2 is contained in a 750.-mL flask at 22.5 °C. What is the pressure of the gas?

18. A balloon holds 30.0 kg of helium. What is the volume of the balloon if its pressure is 1.20 atm and the temperature is 22 °C?

19. A flask is first evacuated so that it contains no gas at all. Then, 2.2 g of CO_2 is introduced into the flask. On warming to 22 °C, the gas exerts a pressure of 318 mm Hg. What is the volume of the flask?

20. A steel cylinder holds 1.50 g of ethanol, C_2H_5OH. What is the pressure of the ethanol vapor if the cylinder has a volume of 251 cm^3 and the temperature is 250 °C? (Assume all of the ethanol is in the vapor phase at this temperature.)

21. A balloon for long-distance flying contains 1.2×10^7 L of helium. If the helium pressure is 737 mm Hg at 25 °C, what mass of helium (in grams) does the balloon contain?

22. What mass of helium, in grams, is required to fill a 5.0-L balloon to a pressure of 1.1 atm at 25 °C?

Gas Density and Molar Mass

(See Section 10-3 and Examples and 10.7 and 10.8.)

23. Forty miles above Earth's surface, the temperature is 250 K, and the pressure is only 0.20 mm Hg. What is the density of air (in grams per liter) at this altitude? (Assume the molar mass of air is 28.96 g/mol.)

24. Diethyl ether, $(C_2H_5)_2O$, vaporizes easily at room temperature. If the vapor exerts a pressure of 233 mm Hg in a flask at 25 °C, what is the density of the vapor?

25. A gaseous organofluorine compound has a density of 0.355 g/L at 17 °C and 189 mm Hg. What is the molar mass of the compound?

26. Chloroform is a common liquid used in the laboratory. It vaporizes readily. If the pressure of chloroform vapor in a flask is 195 mm Hg at 25.0 °C and the density of the vapor is 1.25 g/L, what is the molar mass of chloroform?

27. A 1.007-g sample of an unknown gas exerts a pressure of 715 mm Hg in a 452-mL container at 23 °C. What is the molar mass of the gas?

28. A 0.0130-g sample of a gas with an empirical formula of C_4H_5 is placed in a 165-mL flask. It has a pressure of 13.7 mm Hg at 22.5 °C. What is the molecular formula of the compound?

29. A new boron hydride, B_xH_y, has been isolated. To find its molar mass, you measure the pressure of the gas in a known volume at a known temperature. The following experimental data are collected:

Mass of gas = 12.5 mg	Pressure of gas = 24.8 mm Hg
Temperature = 25 °C	Volume of flask = 125 mL

Which formula corresponds to the calculated molar mass?

(a) B_2H_6
(b) B_4H_{10}
(c) B_5H_9
(d) B_6H_{10}
(e) $B_{10}H_{14}$

30. Acetaldehyde is a common liquid compound that vaporizes readily. Determine the molar mass of acetaldehyde from the following data:

Sample mass = 0.107 g	Volume of gas = 125 mL
Temperature = 0.0 °C	Pressure = 331 mm Hg

Gas Laws and Chemical Reactions

(See Section 10-4 and Example 10.9.)

31. Iron reacts with hydrochloric acid to produce iron(II) chloride and hydrogen gas:

$$Fe(s) + 2\ HCl(aq) \rightarrow FeCl_2(aq) + H_2(g)$$

The H_2 gas from the reaction of 2.2 g of iron with excess acid is collected in a 10.0-L flask at 25 °C. What is the pressure of the H_2 gas in this flask?

32. Silane, SiH_4, reacts with O_2 to give silicon dioxide and water:

$$SiH_4(g) + 2\ O_2(g) \rightarrow SiO_2(s) + 2\ H_2O(\ell)$$

A 5.20-L sample of SiH_4 gas at 356 mm Hg pressure and 25 °C is allowed to react with O_2 gas. What volume of O_2 gas, in liters, is required for complete reaction if the oxygen has a pressure of 425 mm Hg at 25 °C?

33. Sodium azide, the explosive compound in automobile air bags, decomposes according to the following equation:

$$2\ NaN_3(s) \rightarrow 2\ Na(s) + 3\ N_2(g)$$

What mass of sodium azide is required to provide the nitrogen needed to inflate a 75.0-L bag to a pressure of 1.3 atm at 25 °C?

34. The hydrocarbon octane (C_8H_{18}) burns to give CO_2 and water vapor:

$$2\ C_8H_{18}(g) + 25\ O_2(g) \rightarrow 16\ CO_2(g) + 18\ H_2O(g)$$

If a 0.048-g sample of octane burns completely in O_2, what will be the pressure of water vapor in a 4.75-L flask at 30.0 °C? If the O_2 gas needed for complete combustion was contained in a 4.75-L flask at 22 °C, what would its pressure be?

35. Hydrazine reacts with O_2 according to the following equation:

$$N_2H_4(g) + O_2(g) \rightarrow N_2(g) + 2\ H_2O(\ell)$$

Assume the O_2 needed for the reaction is in a 450-L tank at 23 °C. What must the oxygen pressure be in the tank to have enough oxygen to consume 1.00 kg of hydrazine completely?

36. A self-contained underwater breathing apparatus (SCUBA) uses canisters containing potassium superoxide. The superoxide consumes the CO_2 exhaled by a person and replaces it with oxygen.

$$4\ KO_2(s) + 2\ CO_2(g) \rightarrow 2\ K_2CO_3(s) + 3\ O_2(g)$$

What mass of KO_2, in grams, is required to react with 8.90 L of CO_2 at 22.0 °C and 767 mm Hg?

Gas Mixtures and Dalton's Law

(See Section 10-5 and Example 10.10.)

37. What is the total pressure in atmospheres of a gas mixture that contains 1.0 g of H_2 and 8.0 g of Ar in a 3.0-L container at 27 °C? What are the partial pressures of the two gases?

38. A cylinder of compressed gas is labeled "Composition (mole %): 4.5% H_2S, 3.0% CO_2, balance N_2." The pressure gauge attached to the cylinder reads 46 atm. Calculate the partial pressure of each gas, in atmospheres, in the cylinder.

39. A halothane–oxygen mixture ($C_2HBrClF_3 + O_2$) can be used as an anesthetic. A tank containing such a mixture has the following partial pressures: P (halothane) = 170 mm Hg and P (O_2) = 570 mm Hg.

(a) What is the ratio of the number of moles of halothane to the number of moles of O_2?
(b) If the tank contains 160 g of O_2, what mass of $C_2HBrClF_3$ is present?

40. A collapsed balloon is filled with He to a volume of 12.5 L at a pressure of 1.00 atm. Oxygen, O_2, is then added so that the final volume of the balloon is 26 L with a total pressure of 1.00 atm. The temperature, which remains constant throughout, is 21.5 °C.

(a) What mass of He does the balloon contain?
(b) What is the final partial pressure of He in the balloon?
(c) What is the partial pressure of O_2 in the balloon?
(d) What is the mole fraction of each gas?

Kinetic-Molecular Theory

(See Section 10-6 and Example 10.11.)

41. You have two flasks of equal volume. Flask A contains H_2 at 0 °C and 1 atm pressure. Flask B contains CO_2 gas at 25 °C and 2 atm pressure. Compare these two gases with respect to each of the following:

(a) average kinetic energy per molecule
(b) root mean square speed
(c) number of molecules
(d) mass of gas

42. Equal masses of gaseous N_2 and Ar are placed in separate flasks of equal volume at the same temperature. Tell whether each of the following statements is true or false. Briefly explain your answer in each case.

(a) There are more molecules of N_2 present than atoms of Ar.
(b) The pressure is greater in the Ar flask.
(c) The Ar atoms have a greater rms speed than the N_2 molecules.
(d) The N_2 molecules collide more frequently with the walls of the flask than do the Ar atoms.

43. If the rms speed of an oxygen molecule is 4.28×10^4 cm/s at a given temperature, what is the rms speed of a CO_2 molecule at the same temperature?

44. Calculate the rms speed for CO molecules at 25 °C. What is the ratio of this speed to that of Ar atoms at the same temperature?

45. Place the following gases in order of increasing rms speed at 25 °C: Ar, CH_4, N_2, CH_2F_2.

46. The reaction of SO_2 with Cl_2 gives dichlorine oxide, which is used to bleach wood pulp and to treat wastewater:

$$SO_2(g) + 2\ Cl_2(g) \rightarrow SOCl_2(g) + Cl_2O(g)$$

Assume all of the compounds involved in the reaction are gases. List them in order of increasing rms speed.

Diffusion and Effusion

(See Section 10-7 and Example 10.12.)

47. In each pair of gases below, tell which will effuse faster:

(a) CO_2 or F_2
(b) O_2 or N_2
(c) C_2H_4 or C_2H_6
(d) two chlorofluorocarbons: $CFCl_3$ or $C_2Cl_2F_4$

48. Argon gas is 10 times denser than helium gas at the same temperature and pressure. Which gas is predicted to effuse faster? How much faster?

49. A gas whose molar mass you wish to know effuses through an opening at a rate one third as fast as that of helium gas. What is the molar mass of the unknown gas?

50. ▲ A sample of uranium fluoride is found to effuse at the rate of 17.7 mg/h. Under comparable conditions, gaseous I_2 effuses at the rate of 15.0 mg/h. What is the molar mass of the uranium fluoride? (*Hint:* Rates must be converted to units of moles per time.)

Nonideal Gases

(See Section 10-8.)

51. Under which set of conditions will CO_2 deviate most from ideal gas behavior?

(a) 1 atm, 0 °C
(b) 0.1 atm, 100 °C
(c) 10 atm, 0 °C
(d) 1 atm, 100 °C

52. Under which set of conditions will Cl_2 deviate least from ideal gas behavior?

(a) 1 atm, 0 °C
(b) 0.1 atm, 100 °C
(c) 10 atm, 0 °C
(d) 1 atm, 100 °C

53. In the text, it is stated that the pressure of 4.00 mol of Cl_2 in a 4.00-L tank at 100.0 °C should be 26.0 atm if calculated using the van der Waals equation. Verify this result, and compare it with the pressure predicted by the ideal gas law.

54. You want to store 165 g of CO_2 gas in a 12.5-L tank at room temperature (25 °C). Calculate the pressure the gas would have using (a) the ideal gas law and (b) the van der Waals equation. (For CO_2, $a = 3.59$ atm · L^2/mol^2 and $b = 0.0427$ L/mol.)

55. Consider a 5.00-L tank containing 325 g of H_2O at a temperature of 275 °C.

(a) Calculate the pressure in the tank using both the ideal gas law and the van der Waals equation.
(b) Which correction term, $a(n/V)^2$ or bn, has the greatest influence on the pressure of this system?

56. Consider a 5.00-L tank containing 375 g of Ar at a temperature of 25 °C.

(a) Calculate the pressure in the tank using both the ideal gas law and the van der Waals equation.
(b) Which correction term, $a(n/V)^2$ or bn, has the greatest influence on the pressure of this system?

General Questions

These questions are not designated as to type or location in the chapter. They may combine several concepts.

57. Complete the following table:

	atm	mm Hg	kPa	bar
Standard atmosphere	___	___	___	___
Partial pressure of N_2 in the atmosphere	___	593	___	___
Tank of compressed H_2	___	___	___	133
Atmospheric pressure at the top of Mount Everest	___	___	33.7	___

58. On combustion, 1.0 L of a gaseous compound of hydrogen, carbon, and nitrogen gives 2.0 L of CO_2, 3.5 L of H_2O vapor, and 0.50 L of N_2 at STP. What is the empirical formula of the compound?

59. ▲ You have a sample of helium gas at −33 °C, and you want to increase the rms speed of helium atoms by 10.0%. To what temperature should the gas be heated to accomplish this?

60. If 12.0 g of O_2 is required to inflate a balloon to a certain size at 27 °C, what mass of O_2 is required to inflate it to the same size (and pressure) at 5.0 °C?

61. Butyl mercaptan, C_4H_9SH, has a very bad odor and is among the compounds added to natural gas to help detect a leak of otherwise odorless natural gas. In an experiment, you burn 95.0 mg of C_4H_9SH and collect the product gases (SO_2, CO_2, and H_2O) in a 5.25-L flask at 25 °C. What is the total gas pressure in the flask, and what is the partial pressure of each of the product gases?

62. A bicycle tire has an internal volume of 1.52 L and contains 0.406 mol of air. The tire will burst if its internal pressure reaches 7.25 atm. To what temperature, in degrees Celsius, does the air in the tire need to be heated to cause a blowout?

63. The temperature of the atmosphere on Mars can be as high as 27 °C at the equator at noon, and the atmospheric pressure is about 8 mm Hg. If a spacecraft could collect 10. m^3 of this atmosphere, compress it to a small volume, and send it back to Earth, how many moles would the sample contain?

64. If you place 2.25 g of solid silicon in a 6.56-L flask that contains CH_3Cl with a pressure of 585 mm Hg at 25 °C, what mass of dimethyldichlorosilane, $(CH_3)_2SiCl_2$, can be formed?

$$Si(s) + 2\ CH_3Cl(g) \rightarrow (CH_3)_2SiCl_2(g)$$

What pressure of $(CH_3)_2SiCl_2(g)$ would you expect in this same flask at 95 °C on completion of the reaction? (Dimethyldichlorosilane is one starting material used to make silicones, polymeric substances used as lubricants, antistick agents, and water-proofing caulk.)

65. What volume (in liters) of O_2, measured at standard temperature and pressure, is required to oxidize 0.400 mol of phosphorus (P_4)?

$$P_4(s) + 5\ O_2(g) \rightarrow P_4O_{10}(s)$$

66. Nitroglycerin decomposes into four different gases when detonated:

$$4\ C_3H_5(NO_3)_3(\ell) \rightarrow 6\ N_2(g) + O_2(g) + 12\ CO_2(g) + 10\ H_2O(g)$$

The detonation of a small quantity of nitroglycerin produces a total pressure of 4.2 atm at a temperature of 450 °C.

(a) What is the partial pressure of N_2?
(b) If the gases occupy a volume of 1.5 L, what mass of nitroglycerin was detonated?

67. $Ni(CO)_4$ can be made by reacting finely divided nickel with gaseous CO. If you have CO in a 1.50-L flask at a pressure of 418 mm Hg at 25.0 °C, along with 0.450 g of Ni powder, what is the theoretical yield of $Ni(CO)_4$?

68. Ethane burns in air to give H_2O and CO_2.

$$2\ C_2H_6(g) + 7\ O_2(g) \rightarrow 4\ CO_2(g) + 6\ H_2O(g)$$

(a) Four gases are involved in this reaction. Place them in order of increasing rms speed. (Assume all are at the same temperature.)
(b) A 3.26-L flask contains C_2H_6 at a pressure of 256 mm Hg and a temperature of 25 °C. Suppose O_2 gas is added to the flask until C_2H_6 and O_2 are in the correct stoichiometric ratio for the combustion reaction. At this point, what is the partial pressure of O_2 and what is the total pressure in the flask?

69. You have four gas samples:

1. 1.0 L of H_2 at STP
2. 1.0 L of Ar at STP
3. 1.0 L of H_2 at 27 °C and 760 mm Hg
4. 1.0 L of He at 0 °C and 900 mm Hg

(a) Which sample has the largest number of gas particles (atoms or molecules)?
(b) Which sample contains the smallest number of particles?
(c) Which sample represents the largest mass?

70. Propane reacts with oxygen to give carbon dioxide and water vapor.

$$C_3H_8(g) + 5\ O_2(g) \rightarrow 3\ CO_2(g) + 4\ H_2O(g)$$

If you mix C_3H_8 and O_2 in the correct stoichiometric ratio, and if the total pressure of the mixture is 288 mm Hg, what are the partial pressures of C_3H_8 and O_2? If the temperature and volume do not change, what is the pressure of the water vapor after reaction?

71. Iron carbonyl can be made by the direct reaction of iron metal and carbon monoxide.

$$Fe(s) + 5\ CO(g) \rightarrow Fe(CO)_5(\ell)$$

What is the theoretical yield of $Fe(CO)_5$ if 3.52 g of iron is treated with CO gas having a pressure of 732 mm Hg in a 5.50-L flask at 23 °C?

72. Analysis of a gaseous chlorofluorocarbon, CCl_xF_y, shows that it contains 11.79% C and 69.57% Cl. In another experiment, you find that 0.107 g of the compound fills a 458-mL flask at 25 °C with a pressure of 21.3 mm Hg. What is the molecular formula of the compound?

73. There are five compounds in the family of sulfur–fluorine compounds with the general formula S_xF_y. One of these compounds is 25.23% S. If you place 0.0955 g of the compound in a 89-mL flask at 45 °C, the pressure of the gas is 83.8 mm Hg. What is the molecular formula of S_xF_y?

74. A miniature volcano can be made in the laboratory with ammonium dichromate. When ignited, it decomposes in a fiery display.

$$(NH_4)_2Cr_2O_7(s) \rightarrow N_2(g) + 4\ H_2O(g) + Cr_2O_3(s)$$

If 0.95 g of ammonium dichromate is used and the gases from this reaction are trapped in a 15.0-L flask at 23 °C, what is the total pressure of the gas in the flask? What are the partial pressures of N_2 and H_2O?

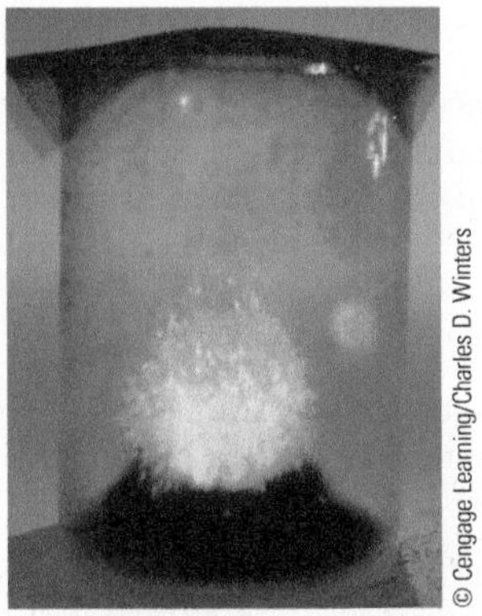

Thermal decomposition of $(NH_4)_2Cr_2O_7$

75. The density of air 20 km above Earth's surface is 92 g/m^3. The pressure of the atmosphere is 42 mm Hg, and the temperature is −63 °C.
   (a) What is the average molar mass of the atmosphere at this altitude?
   (b) If the atmosphere at this altitude consists of only O_2 and N_2, what is the mole fraction of each gas?

76. A 3.0-L bulb containing He at 145 mm Hg is connected by a valve to a 2.0-L bulb containing Ar at 355 mm Hg (see figure below). Calculate the partial pressure of each gas and the total pressure after the valve between the flasks is opened.

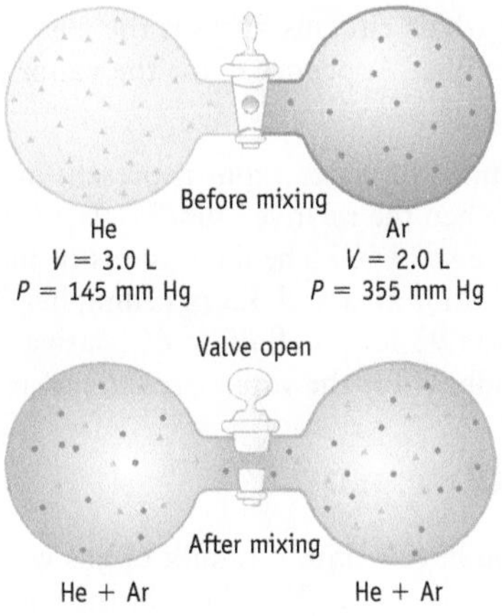

77. Chlorine dioxide, ClO_2, reacts with fluorine to give a new gas that contains Cl, O, and F. In an experiment, you find that 0.150 g of this new gas has a pressure of 17.2 mm Hg in a 1850-mL flask at 21 °C. What is the identity of the unknown gas?

78. A xenon fluoride can be prepared by heating a mixture of Xe and F_2 gases to a high temperature in a pressure-proof container. Assume that xenon gas was added to a 0.25-L container until its pressure reached 0.12 atm at 0.0 °C. Fluorine gas was then added until the total pressure reached 0.72 atm at 0.0 °C. After the reaction was complete, the xenon was consumed completely, and the pressure of the F_2 remaining in the container was 0.36 atm at 0.0 °C. What is the empirical formula of the xenon fluoride?

79. Several small molecules (besides water) are important in biochemical systems: O_2, CO, CO_2, and NO. You have isolated one of these and to identify it you determine its molar mass. You release 0.37 g of the gas into a flask with a volume of 732 mL at 21 °C. The gas pressure in the flask is 209 mm Hg. What is the unknown gas?

80. Consider the following gases: He, SO_2, CO_2, and Cl_2.
   (a) Which has the largest density (assuming that all gases are at the same T and P)?
   (b) Which gas will effuse fastest through a porous plate?

81. Which of the following is *not* correct?
   (a) Diffusion of gases occurs more rapidly at higher temperatures.
   (b) Effusion of H_2 is faster than effusion of He (assume similar conditions and a rate expressed in units of mol/h).
   (c) Diffusion will occur faster at low pressure than at high pressure.
   (d) The rate of effusion of a gas (mol/h) is directly proportional to molar mass.

82. The ideal gas law is least accurate under conditions of high pressure and low temperature. In those situations, using the van der Waals equation is advisable.
   (a) Calculate the pressure exerted by 12.0 g of CO_2 in a 500-mL vessel at 298 K, using the ideal gas equation. Then, recalculate the pressure using the van der Waals equation. Assuming the pressure calculated from van der Waals equation is correct, what is the percent error in the answer when using the ideal gas equation?
   (b) Next, cool this sample to −70 °C. Then perform the same calculation for the pressure exerted by CO_2 at this new temperature, using both the ideal gas law and the van der Waals equation. Again, what is the percent error when using the ideal gas equation?

83. Carbon dioxide, CO_2, was shown to effuse through a porous plate at the rate of 0.033 mol/min. The same quantity of an unknown gas, 0.033 moles, is found to effuse through the same porous barrier in 104 seconds. Calculate the molar mass of the unknown gas.

84. In an experiment, you have determined that 0.66 moles of CF_4 effuse through a porous barrier over a 4.8 minute period. How long will it take for 0.66 moles of CH_4 to effuse through the same barrier?

85. A balloon is filled with helium gas to a gauge pressure of 22 mm Hg at 25 °C. The volume of the gas is 305 mL, and the barometric pressure is 755 mm Hg. What amount of helium is in the balloon? (Remember that gauge pressure = total pressure − barometric pressure. See page 373.)

86. If you have a sample of water in a closed container, some of the water will evaporate until the pressure of the water vapor, at 25 °C, is 23.8 mm Hg. How many molecules of water per cubic centimeter exist in the vapor phase?

87. You are given 1.56 g of a mixture of $KClO_3$ and KCl. When heated, the $KClO_3$ decomposes to KCl and O_2,

$$2\ KClO_3(s) \rightarrow 2\ KCl(s) + 3\ O_2(g)$$

and 327 mL of O_2 with a pressure of 735 mm Hg is collected at 19 °C. What is the weight percentage of $KClO_3$ in the sample?

88. A study of climbers who reached the summit of Mount Everest without supplemental oxygen showed that the partial pressures of O_2 and CO_2 in their lungs were 35 mm Hg and 7.5 mm Hg, respectively. The barometric pressure at the summit was 253 mm Hg. Assume the lung gases are saturated with moisture at a body temperature of 37 °C [which means the partial pressure of water vapor in the lungs is $P(H_2O) = 47.1$ mm Hg]. If you assume the lung gases consist of only O_2, N_2, CO_2, and H_2O, what is the partial pressure of N_2?

89. Nitrogen monoxide reacts with oxygen to give nitrogen dioxide:

$$2\ NO(g) + O_2(g) \rightarrow 2\ NO_2(g)$$

(a) Place the three gases in order of increasing rms speed at 298 K.
(b) If you mix NO and O_2 in the correct stoichiometric ratio and NO has a partial pressure of 150 mm Hg, what is the partial pressure of O_2?
(c) After reaction between NO and O_2 is complete, what is the pressure of NO_2 if the NO originally had a pressure of 150 mm Hg and O_2 was added in the correct stoichiometric amount?

90. ▲ Ammonia gas is synthesized by combining hydrogen and nitrogen:

$$3\ H_2(g) + N_2(g) \rightarrow 2\ NH_3(g)$$

(a) If you want to produce 562 g of NH_3, what volume of H_2 gas, at 56 °C and 745 mm Hg, is required?
(b) Nitrogen for this reaction will be obtained from air. What volume of air, measured at 29 °C and 745 mm Hg pressure, will be required to provide the nitrogen needed to produce 562 g of NH_3? Assume the sample of air contains 78.1 mole % N_2.

91. Nitrogen trifluoride is prepared by the reaction of ammonia and fluorine.

$$4\ NH_3(g) + 3\ F_2(g) \rightarrow 3\ NH_4F(s) + NF_3(g)$$

If you mix NH_3 with F_2 in the correct stoichiometric ratio, and if the total pressure of the mixture is 120 mm Hg, what are the partial pressures of NH_3 and F_2? When the reactants have been completely consumed, what is the total pressure in the flask? (Assume *T* is constant.)

92. Chlorine trifluoride, ClF_3, is a valuable reagent because it can be used to convert metal oxides to metal fluorides:

$$6\ NiO(s) + 4\ ClF_3(g) \rightarrow 6\ NiF_2(s) + 2\ Cl_2(g) + 3\ O_2(g)$$

(a) What mass of NiO will react with ClF_3 gas if the gas has a pressure of 250 mm Hg at 20 °C in a 2.5-L flask?
(b) If the ClF_3 described in part (a) is completely consumed, what are the partial pressures of Cl_2 and of O_2 in the 2.5-L flask at 20 °C (in mm Hg)? What is the total pressure in the flask?

93. ▲ Relative humidity is the ratio of the partial pressure of water in air at a given temperature to the vapor pressure of water at that temperature. Calculate the mass of water per liter of air under the following conditions:

(a) at 20 °C and 45% relative humidity
(b) at 0 °C and 95% relative humidity

Under which circumstances is the mass of H_2O per liter greater? (See Appendix G for the vapor pressure of water.)

94. What mass of water vapor is present in a dormitory room when the relative humidity is 55% and the temperature is 23 °C? The dimensions of the room are 4.5 m^2 floor area and 3.5 m ceiling height. (See Study Question 93 for a definition of relative humidity and Appendix G for the vapor pressure of water.)

In the Laboratory

95. ▲ You have a 550.-mL tank of gas with a pressure of 1.56 atm at 24 °C. You thought the gas was pure carbon monoxide gas, CO, but you later found it was contaminated by small quantities of gaseous CO_2 and O_2. Analysis shows that the tank pressure is 1.34 atm (at 24 °C) if the CO_2 is removed. Another experiment shows that 0.0870 g of O_2 can be removed chemically. What are the masses of CO and CO_2 in the tank, and what is the partial pressure of each of the three gases at 25 °C?

96. ▲ Methane is burned in a laboratory Bunsen burner to give CO_2 and water vapor. Methane gas is supplied to the burner at the rate of 5.0 L/min (at a temperature of 28 °C and a pressure of 773 mm Hg). At what rate must oxygen be supplied to the burner (at a pressure of 742 mm Hg and a temperature of 26 °C)?

97. ▲ Iron forms a series of compounds of the type $Fe_x(CO)_y$. In air, these compounds are oxidized to Fe_2O_3 and CO_2 gas. After heating a 0.142-g sample of $Fe_x(CO)_y$ in air, you isolate the CO_2 in a 1.50-L flask at 25 °C. The pressure of the gas is 44.9 mm Hg. What is the empirical formula of $Fe_x(CO)_y$?

98. ▲ Group 2A metal carbonates are decomposed to the metal oxide and CO_2 on heating:

$$MCO_3(s) \rightarrow MO(s) + CO_2(g)$$

You heat 0.158 g of a white, solid carbonate of a Group 2A metal (M) and find that the evolved CO_2 has a pressure of 69.8 mm Hg in a 285-mL flask at 25 °C. Identify M.

99. One way to synthesize diborane, B_2H_6, is the reaction

$$2\ NaBH_4(s) + 2\ H_3PO_4(\ell) \rightarrow B_2H_6(g) + 2\ NaH_2PO_4(s) + 2\ H_2(g)$$

(a) If you have 0.136 g of $NaBH_4$ and excess H_3PO_4, and you collect the resulting B_2H_6 in a 2.75-L flask at 25 °C, what is the pressure of the B_2H_6 in the flask?

(b) A by-product of the reaction is H_2 gas. If both B_2H_6 and H_2 gas come from this reaction, what is the *total* pressure in the 2.75-L flask (after reaction of 0.136 g of $NaBH_4$ with excess H_3PO_4) at 25 °C?

100. You are given a solid mixture of $NaNO_2$ and NaCl and are asked to analyze it for the amount of $NaNO_2$ present. To do so, you allow the mixture to react with sulfamic acid, HSO_3NH_2, in water according to the equation

$$NaNO_2(aq) + HSO_3NH_2(aq) \rightarrow NaHSO_4(aq) + H_2O(\ell) + N_2(g)$$

What is the weight percentage of $NaNO_2$ in 1.232 g of the solid mixture if reaction with sulfamic acid produces 295 mL of dry N_2 gas with a pressure of 713 mm Hg at 21.0 °C?

101. ▲ You have 1.249 g of a mixture of $NaHCO_3$ and Na_2CO_3. You find that 12.0 mL of 1.50 M HCl is required to convert the sample completely to NaCl, H_2O, and CO_2.

$$NaHCO_3(aq) + HCl(aq) \rightarrow NaCl(aq) + H_2O(\ell) + CO_2(g)$$

$$Na_2CO_3(aq) + 2\ HCl(aq) \rightarrow 2\ NaCl(aq) + H_2O(\ell) + CO_2(g)$$

What volume of CO_2 is evolved at 745 mm Hg and 25 °C?

102. ▲ A mixture of $NaHCO_3$ and Na_2CO_3 has a mass of 2.50 g. When treated with HCl(aq), 665 mL of CO_2 gas is liberated with a pressure of 735 mm Hg at 25 °C. What is the weight percent of $NaHCO_3$ and Na_2CO_3 in the mixture? (See Study Question 101 for the reactions that occur.)

103. ▲ Many nitrate salts can be decomposed by heating. For example, blue, anhydrous copper(II) nitrate produces the gases nitrogen dioxide and oxygen when heated. In the laboratory, you find that a sample of this salt produced a 0.195-g mixture of gaseous NO_2 and O_2 with a total pressure of 725 mm Hg at 35 °C in a 125-mL flask (and black, solid CuO was left as a residue). What is the average molar mass of the gas mixture? What are the mole fractions of NO_2 and O_2 in the mixture? What amount of each gas is in the mixture? Do these amounts reflect the relative amounts of NO_2 and O_2 expected based on the balanced equation? Is it possible that the fact that some NO_2 molecules combine to give N_2O_4 plays a role?

Heating copper(II) nitrate produces nitrogen dioxide and oxygen gas and leaves a residue of copper(II) oxide.

104. ▲ A compound containing C, H, N, and O is burned in excess oxygen. The gases produced by burning 0.1152 g are first treated to convert the nitrogen-containing product gases into N_2, and then the resulting mixture of CO_2, H_2O, N_2, and excess O_2 is passed through a bed of $CaCl_2$ to absorb the water. The $CaCl_2$ increases in mass by 0.09912 g. The remaining gases are bubbled into water to form H_2CO_3, and this solution is titrated with 0.3283 M NaOH; 28.81 mL is required to achieve the second equivalence point. The excess O_2 gas is removed by reaction with copper metal (to give CuO). Finally, the N_2 gas is collected in a 225.0-mL flask, where it has a pressure of 65.12 mm Hg at 25 °C. In a separate experiment, the unknown compound is found to have a molar mass of 150 g/mol. What are the empirical and molecular formulas of the unknown compound?

105. You have a gas, one of the three known phosphorus–fluorine compounds (PF_3, PF_5, and P_2F_4). To find out which, you have decided to measure its molar mass.

(a) First, you determine that the density of the gas is 5.60 g/L at a pressure of 0.971 atm and a temperature of 18.2 °C. Calculate the molar mass and identify the compound.
(b) To check the results from part (a), you decide to measure the molar mass based on the relative rates of effusion of the unknown gas and CO_2. You find that CO_2 effuses at a rate of 0.050 mol/min, whereas the unknown phosphorus fluoride effuses at a rate of 0.028 mol/min. Calculate the molar mass of the unknown gas based on these results.

106. A 1.50 L constant-volume calorimeter (Figure 5.12) contains $C_3H_8(g)$ and $O_2(g)$. The partial pressure of C_3H_8 is 0.10 atm and the partial pressure of O_2 is 5.0 atm. The temperature is 20.0 °C. A reaction occurs between the two compounds, forming $CO_2(g)$ and $H_2O(\ell)$. The heat from the reaction causes the temperature to rise to 23.2 °C.

(a) Write a balanced chemical equation for the reaction.
(b) How many moles of $C_3H_8(g)$ are present in the flask initially?
(c) What is the mole fraction of $C_3H_8(g)$ in the flask before reaction?
(d) After the reaction, the flask contains excess oxygen and the products of the reaction, $CO_2(g)$ and $H_2O(\ell)$. What amount of unreacted $O_2(g)$ remains?
(e) After the reaction, what is the partial pressure exerted by the $CO_2(g)$ in this system?
(f) What is the partial pressure exerted by the excess oxygen remaining after the reaction?

Summary and Conceptual Questions

The following questions may use concepts from this and previous chapters.

107. A 1.0-L flask contains 10.0 g each of O_2 and CO_2 at 25 °C.

(a) Which gas has the greater partial pressure, O_2 or CO_2, or are they the same?
(b) Which molecules have the greater rms speed, or are they the same?
(c) Which molecules have the greater average kinetic energy, or are they the same?

108. If equal masses of O_2 and N_2 are placed in separate containers of equal volume at the same temperature, which of the following statements is true? If false, explain why it is false.

(a) The pressure in the flask containing N_2 is greater than that in the flask containing O_2.
(b) There are more molecules in the flask containing O_2 than in the flask containing N_2.

109. You have two pressure-proof steel cylinders of equal volume, one containing 1.0 kg of CO and the other containing 1.0 kg of acetylene, C_2H_2.

(a) In which cylinder is the pressure greater at 25 °C?
(b) Which cylinder contains the greater number of molecules?

110. Two flasks, each with a volume of 1.00 L, contain O_2 gas with a pressure of 380 mm Hg. Flask A is at 25 °C, and flask B is at 0 °C. Which flask contains the greater number of O_2 molecules?

111. ▲ State whether each of the following samples of matter is a gas. If there is not enough information for you to decide, write "insufficient information."

(a) A material is in a steel tank at 100 atm pressure. When the tank is opened to the atmosphere, the material suddenly expands, increasing its volume by 1%.
(b) A 1.0-mL sample of material weighs 8.2 g.
(c) The material is transparent and pale green in color.
(d) One cubic meter of material contains as many molecules as 1.0 m^3 of air at the same temperature and pressure.

112. Each of four flasks is filled with a different gas. Each flask has the same volume, and each is filled to the same pressure, 3.0 atm, at 25 °C. Flask A contains 116 g of air, flask B has 80.7 g of neon, flask C has 16.0 g of helium, and flask C has 160. g of an unknown gas.

(a) Do all four flasks contain the same number of gas molecules? If not, which one has the greatest number of molecules?
(b) How many times heavier is a molecule of the unknown gas than an atom of helium?
(c) In which flask do the molecules have the largest kinetic energy? The highest rms speed?

113. You have two gas-filled balloons, one containing He and the other containing H_2. The H_2 balloon is twice the volume of the He balloon. The pressure of gas in the H_2 balloon is 1 atm, and that in the He balloon is 2 atm. The H_2 balloon is outside in the snow (−5 °C), and the He balloon is inside a warm building (23 °C).

(a) Which balloon contains the greater number of molecules?
(b) Which balloon contains the greater mass of gas?

114. The sodium azide required for automobile air bags is made by the reaction of sodium metal with dinitrogen monoxide in liquid ammonia:

$$3\ N_2O(g) + 4\ Na(s) + NH_3(\ell) \rightarrow NaN_3(s) + 3\ NaOH(s) + 2\ N_2(g)$$

(a) You have 65.0 g of sodium, a 35.0-L flask containing N_2O gas with a pressure of 2.12 atm at 23 °C, and excess ammonia. What is the theoretical yield (in grams) of NaN_3?
(b) Draw a Lewis structure for the azide ion. Include all possible resonance structures. Which resonance structure is most likely?
(c) What is the shape of the azide ion?

115. If the absolute temperature of a gas doubles, by how much does the rms speed of the gaseous molecules increase?

116. ▲ Chlorine gas (Cl_2) is used as a disinfectant in municipal water supplies, although chlorine dioxide (ClO_2) and ozone are becoming more widely used. ClO_2 is a better choice than Cl_2 in this application because it leads to fewer chlorinated by-products, which are themselves pollutants.

(a) How many valence electrons are in ClO_2?

(b) The chlorite ion, ClO_2^-, is obtained by reducing ClO_2. Draw a possible electron dot structure for ClO_2^-. (Cl is the central atom.)

(c) What is the hybridization of the central Cl atom in ClO_2^-? What is the shape of the ion?

(d) Which species has the larger bond angle, O_3 or ClO_2^-? Explain briefly.

(e) Chlorine dioxide, ClO_2, a yellow-green gas, can be made by the reaction of chlorine with sodium chlorite:

$$2\ NaClO_2(s) + Cl_2(g) \rightarrow 2\ NaCl(s) + 2\ ClO_2(g)$$

Assume you react 15.6 g of $NaClO_2$ with chlorine gas, which has a pressure of 1050 mm Hg in a 1.45-L flask at 22 °C. What mass of ClO_2 can be produced?

AP Multiple-Choice Review Questions

1. On a cold day near the ocean, it was found that 8 g of an unknown gas occupies a volume that is a little less than 6 L. Based on this information, what is the most likely identity of the unknown gas?
(A) CO_2
(B) Ne
(C) O_2
(D) CH_4

2. Which of the following gases is expected to behave most ideally at a given temperature and pressure?
(A) H_2O
(B) NH_3
(C) Xe
(D) He

The following information is used to answer questions 3 and 4.

Nitroglycerine, $C_3H_5N_3O_9$, explodes with tremendous force due to the numerous gaseous products. The equation for the explosion of nitroglycerine is:

$$4C_3H_5N_3O_9(\ell) \rightarrow 12CO_2(g) + O_2(g) + 6N_2(g) + 10H_2O(g)$$

A scientist conducts an experiment to characterize a bomb containing nitroglycerine. She uses a steel, rigid container for the test.

Volume of rigid steel container	1.00 L
Molar mass of nitroglycerine	227 g/mol
Temperature	300. K
Amount of nitroglycerine tested	227 g
Value for ideal gas constant, *R*	$0.0821 \frac{\text{L atm}}{\text{mol K}}$

3. What is the total pressure produced in this explosion?
(A) 25.0 atm
(B) 52.0 atm
(C) 179 atm
(D) 435 atm

4. In a second experiment, the total pressure is observed to be 58 atm. What is the partial pressure of the water vapor produced?
(A) 10. atm
(B) 20. atm
(C) 30. atm
(D) 40. atm

5. There are two equations of state commonly used for gas law problems in chemistry: the ideal gas law and the van der Waals equation, both shown in the table below. A sample of 6.00 moles of chlorine gas has a volume of 2.00 L at 273 K. A student is asked to determine the pressure using these two equations.

	Ideal Gas Law	van der Waals Equation
Equation	$PV = nRT$	$\left(P + \frac{n^2a}{V^2}\right)(V - nb) = nRT$
Calculated pressure	67.2 atm	22.5 atm

What is the major factor that accounts for most of the difference in the two values?
(A) chlorine is a halogen
(B) diatomic nature of chlorine
(C) volume of the chlorine particles
(D) forces of attraction between chlorine molecules

6. A sample of gas is heated from 35 °C to 70. °C. Which statement correctly describes what happens to the volume?
(A) The volume increases by a factor of less than 2.
(B) The volume increases by a factor of 2.
(C) The volume decreases by a factor of less than 2.
(D) The volume decreases by a factor of 2.

7. The Maxwell-Boltzmann distribution for unknown gas is shown. At which point on the graph is the average temperature of the gas most directly related to its translational kinetic energy?

Maxwell-Boltzmann distribution for an unknown gas

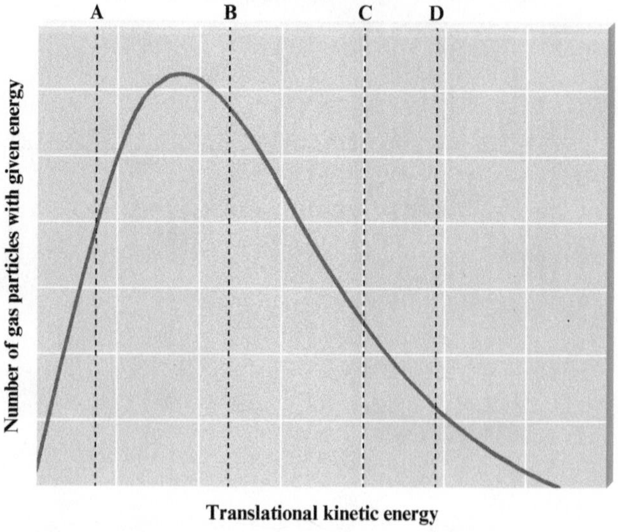

(A) A
(B) B
(C) C
(D) D

8. Two gases are removed from their original container and placed into a third container, where they react with each other. All three containers have identical volumes, and all gasses are at the same temperature.

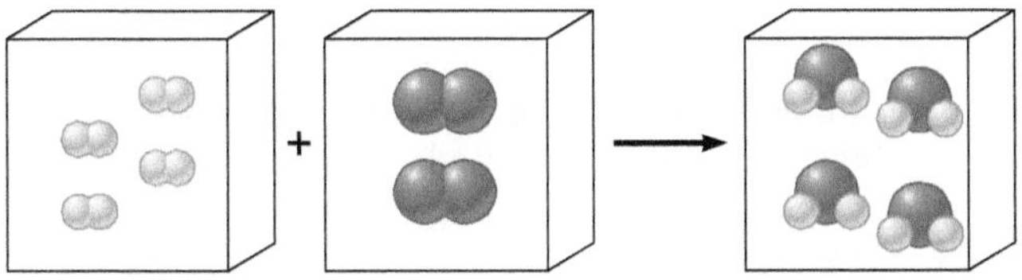

A B C

Which container has the lowest pressure?

(A) container A before the reaction
(B) container B before the reaction
(C) container C after the reaction
(D) they all have the same pressure

9. A sample of neon gas is contained in the left-hand bulb and a sample of helium gas is contained in the right-hand bulb of a two-bulb container connected by a valve, as shown in the diagram. Initially the valve is closed.

The left-hand bulb has a volume of 9.00 L, and the Ne gas is at a pressure of 2.00 atm. The right-hand bulb has a volume of 3.00 L, and the He gas is at a pressure of 4.00 atm. After the valve is opened, what is true about the relative partial pressures of helium and neon? Assume constant temperature.

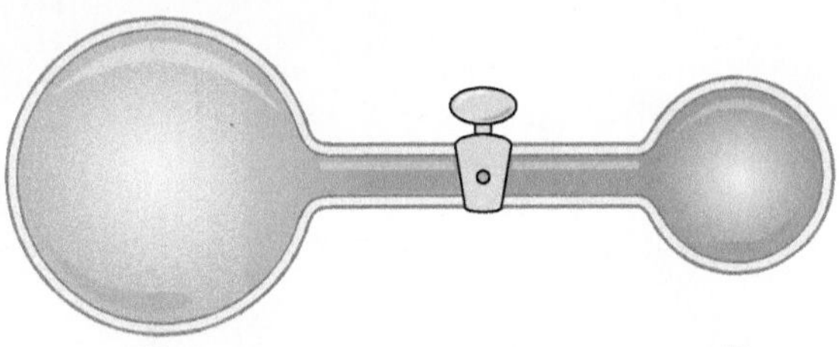

(A) The partial pressure of helium is 1.50 times as great as the partial pressure of neon.
(B) The partial pressure of neon is 2.00 times as great as the partial pressure of helium.
(C) The partial pressure of neon is 1.50 times as great as the partial pressure of helium.
(D) The partial pressure of helium is 2.00 times as great as the partial pressure of neon.

10. Which of the following is a reasonable estimate for the volume of a balloon that has been filled with 300 g of oxygen gas at STP?

(A) 1 L
(B) 10 L
(C) 50 L
(D) 200 L

11. Which of the following most closely estimates the density of air at 1.0 atm and 25 °C to one significant figure?

(A) 0.1 g/L
(B) 1 g/L
(C) 10 g/L
(D) 100 g/L

12. A certain mass of neon gas is contained in a rigid steel container. The same mass of helium gas is added to this container. Which of the following best describes what happens? Assume the temperature is constant.

(A) The pressure in the container doubles.
(B) The pressure in the container increases but does not double.
(C) The pressure in the container more than doubles.
(D) The pressure in the container does not change.

13. Which of the following statements is true concerning real gases?

(A) The observed pressure will be less than the ideal pressure, and the volume available for the gas particles is less than the volume of the container.
(B) The observed pressure will be less than the ideal pressure, and the volume available for the gas particles is greater than the volume of the container.
(C) The observed pressure will be greater than the ideal pressure, and the volume available for the gas particles is greater than the volume of the container.
(D) The observed pressure will be greater than the ideal pressure, and the volume available for the gas particles is less than the volume of the container.

Use the following information to answer questions 14–16.

(A) (B) (C) (D)

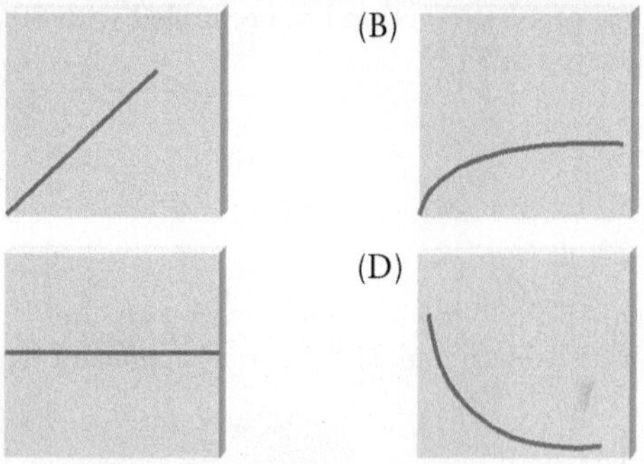

14. Indicate which of the above graphs represents *PV* (y) vs. *V* (x) for 1.0 mole of an ideal gas at constant *T*.

15. Indicate which of the above graphs represents *PV* (y) vs. *n* (x) for an ideal gas at constant *T*.

16. Indicate which of the above graphs represents gas density (y) vs. *T* (x) for 1.0 mole of an ideal gas at constant *P*.

Use the following information to answer questions 17 and 18. Aluminum reacts with hydrochloric acid according to the following equation:

$$2Al(s) + 6HCl(aq) \rightarrow 2AlCl_3(aq) + 3H_2(g)$$

17. If a sample of 27.0 g of aluminum metal is added to 333 mL of 3.0 *M* hydrochloric acid, the volume of hydrogen gas produced at standard temperature and pressure is

(A) 2.80 L.

(B) 5.60 L.

(C) 11.2 L.

(D) 22.4 L.

18. What is the approximate density of the hydrogen gas produced at STP?

(A) 0.1 g/L

(B) 0.2 g/L

(C) 0.3 g/L

(D) 0.4 g/L

AP Free Response Review Questions

Question Format: Short

Category of Question: Representation 1

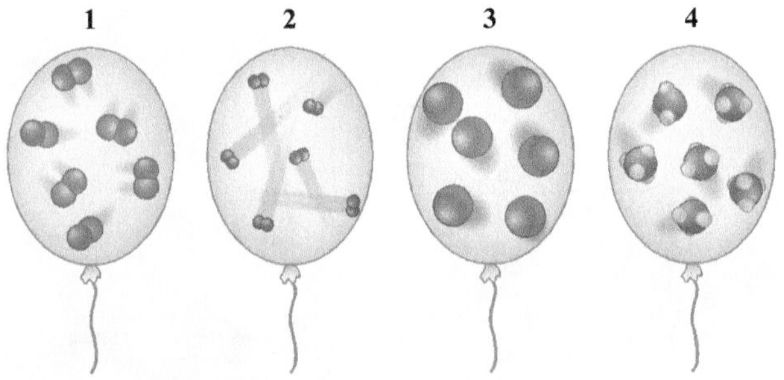

Questions

All four balloons above are at the same volume, pressure, and temperature.

(a) Which balloon contains the gas with the lightest molar mass? Explain your reasoning.

(b) Which balloon contains the gas with the heaviest molar mass?

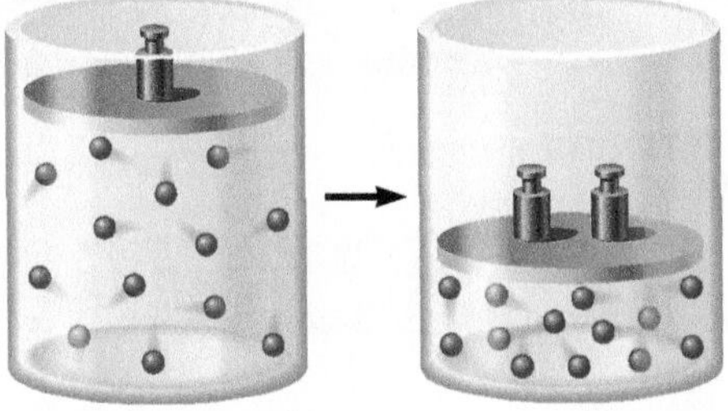

Diagram 1

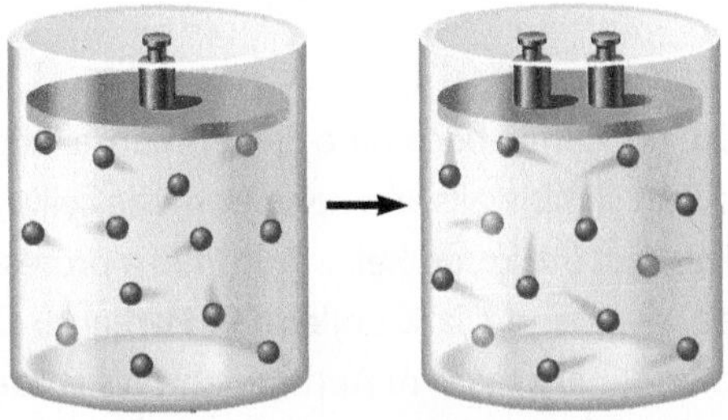

Diagram 2

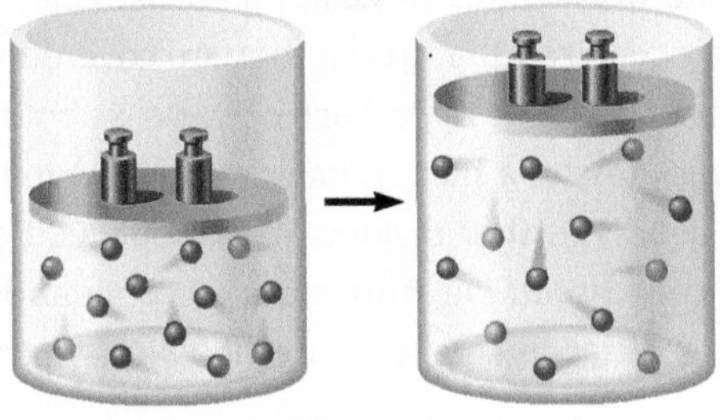

Diagram 3

(c) Which of the three diagrams supports the direct relationship between the temperature of a gas and its pressure? Explain your reasoning.

Question Format: Long

Category of Question: Lab 2

A student was given a 10 mL sample of a clear, colorless liquid. She was assigned the task of identifying the unknown liquid and was told that the sample could be methanol (CH_3OH), acetone (C_3H_6O), or ethanol (C_2H_5OH). She decided to attempt to determine the molar mass of the liquid by the vapor density method, which involves completely vaporizing a small sample of the liquid, cooling it, and determining the mass of the condensed vapor. She also collects the volume of the container, temperature, and pressure when the liquid is vaporized.

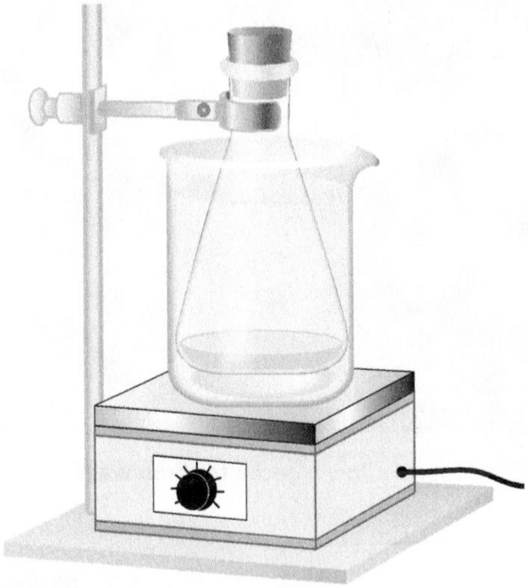

The following data were collected:

	Trial #1	Trial #2
Mass of empty flask + foil cap	125.194 g	125.194 g
Mass of flask, cap, condensed vapor	125.470 g	125.592 g
Mass of condensed vapor		
Temperature of boiling water bath (°C)	99.8 °C	99.6 °C
Temperature of boiling water bath (K)		
Atmospheric pressure (mm Hg)	752 mm Hg	756 mm Hg
Atmospheric pressure (atm)		
Volume of flask (mL)	288 mL	288 mL
Volume of flask (L)	0.288 L	0.288 L

Questions

(a) Fill in the missing data in the data table.

(b) What could account for the difference in the masses in the two trials?

(c) Determine the molar masses for each trial, showing all calculations.

(d) The student reported that the unknown liquid was definitely methanol. Do you agree with her conclusion? Why or why not?

(e) The formulas used in the calculations assume that the gas behaves ideally. State one factor that could cause the vapor to deviate from ideal behavior. State whether the factor would cause the experimental molar mass to be too high, too low, or remain the same.

© Picade LLC/Alamy

Van der Waals forces allow a gecko to climb walls.

Intermolecular Forces and Liquids

Chapter Outline

GECKOS CAN CLIMB UP DER WAALS

Just like the comic-book hero Spider-Man, a little lizard, the gecko, can climb walls and hang from the ceiling.

This fact intrigued Kellar Autumn, a professor of biology at Lewis and Clark College in Portland, Oregon. An interdisciplinary team of Autumn and his students, along with scientists and engineers from Stanford University and the Universities of California at Berkeley and Santa Barbara, realized that gecko toes are covered with an array of stiff hair-like *setae*. Each of these is about as long as the thickness of a human hair or about 0.1 mm long. But each seta is further divided into about 1000 even tinier pads called *spatulae*. And these are only about 200 nm wide, a distance smaller than the wavelength of visible light!

The design of gecko feet is the secret to their wall-crawling abilities. Autumn said, "We discovered that the seta is 10 times more adhesive than predicted from prior measurements on whole animals. In fact, the adhesive is

Chapter Goals

See Chapter Goals Revisited (page 433) for Study Questions keyed to these goals.

UNDERSTAND

- The nature of the various types of intermolecular forces.
- The origin and importance of hydrogen bonding.
- The relationship between the properties of liquids and intermolecular forces.
- The nature of critical temperature and pressure and supercritical fluids.

DO

- Identify the intermolecular forces between simple molecules.
- Calculate enthalpy changes for changes of state.
- Represent the connection between vapor pressure and temperature graphically.
- Use the Clausius–Clapeyron equation to relate vapor pressure and enthalpy of vaporization.

REMEMBER

- The various intermolecular forces and how they arise.

so strong that a single seta can lift the weight of an ant. A million setae, which could easily fit onto the area of a dime, could lift a 45-pound child. Our discovery explains why the gecko can support its entire body weight with only a single finger."

"When the gecko attaches itself to a surface, it uncurls its toes like a party favor that uncurls when you blow into it," Autumn says. "But," he adds, "getting yourself to stick isn't really that difficult. It's getting off the surface that is the major problem. When a gecko runs, it has to attach and detach its feet 15 times a second."

But what is the "adhesive effect" that allows a gecko to climb a wall? It is an intermolecular force, called a *van der Waals force*. This is ordinarily a weak force that operates only over a very short distance. However, each *spatula* of the millions in each toe experiences an attractive van der Waals force with the surface.

Van der Waals forces are one of the important topics in this chapter. As you learn about this, think about the possibilities of using the design of gecko feet to make even more useful adhesives.

References:

1. http://kellarautumn.com
2. http://geckolab.lclark.edu/Welcome.html

Study Questions related to this story are: 11.1, 11.29, and 11.43.

In the last chapter, we studied gases, one of the states of matter. Most of the time we were able to ignore the forces of attraction between the molecules. However, at the end of that chapter we pointed out that at high pressures and/or low temperatures we had to consider intermolecular forces when accounting for the nonideal behavior of gases. In the other two states of matter, the liquid and solid states, intermolecular forces play a major role. In order to describe these states of matter, we will first need to explore the different types of intermolecular forces.

The primary objectives of this chapter are (1) to examine the forces that are responsible for the attraction of molecules to each other—*intermolecular forces*—and (2) to look at liquids, a state of matter that results from these interactions. You will find this a useful chapter because it explains, among other things, why your body is cooled when you sweat and why ice floats on liquid water, a property shared by very few other substances.

Learning Objectives: LO 2.12

11-1 States of Matter and Intermolecular Forces

The kinetic-molecular theory of gases (◀ Section 10-6) assumes that gas molecules or atoms are widely separated and can be considered to be independent of one another. Consequently, we can relate the properties of gases under most conditions by the ideal gas law equation, $PV = nRT$ (◀ Equation 10.4). In real gases, however, there are forces between molecules, that is, *inter*molecular forces. If these forces are strong enough, the gas can condense to a liquid and eventually form a solid.

How different are the states of matter at the particulate level? We can get a sense of this by comparing the volumes occupied by equal numbers of molecules of a material in different states. Figure 11.1*(left)* shows a flask containing about 300 mL of liquid nitrogen. If all of the liquid were allowed to evaporate, the gaseous nitrogen, at 1 atm and room temperature, would fill a 200-L balloon, more than a 600-fold increase in volume. A great amount of space exists between molecules in a gas, whereas in liquids the molecules are much closer together.

The increase in volume when converting liquids to gases is strikingly large. In contrast, no dramatic change in volume occurs when a solid is converted to a liquid. Figure 11.1*(right)* shows the same amount of liquid and solid benzene, C_6H_6, side by side. They are not appreciably different in volume. To explain this observation, we imagine that the molecules are packed together about as tightly in the liquid phase as in the solid phase and that they are packed relatively tightly in both. We also assume there are intermolecular forces of some kind that allow them to cling together. It is these forces that are the focus of this chapter.

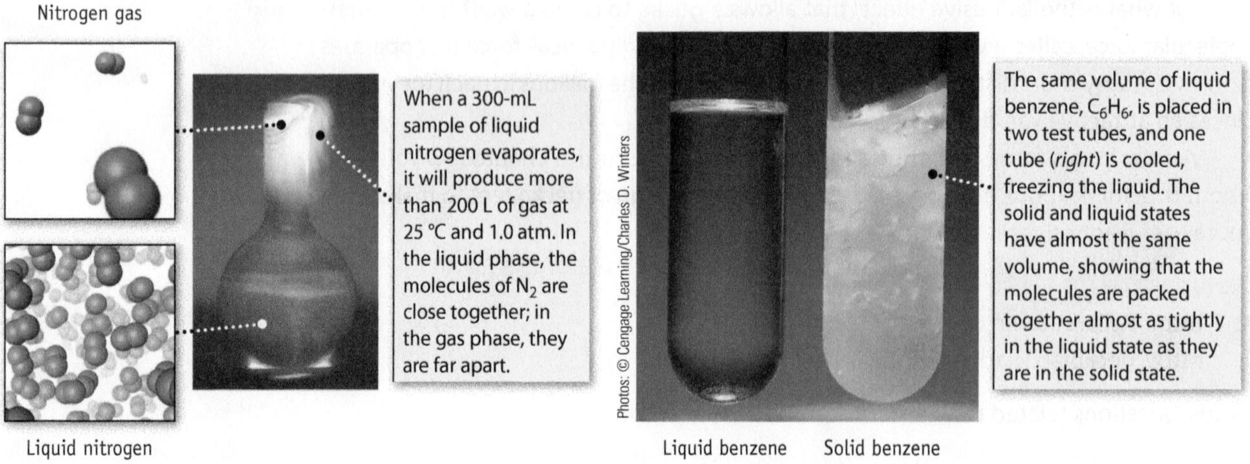

FIGURE 11.1 Contrasting gases, liquids, and solids.

We first want to focus on the nature of intermolecular forces. As we described in Chapter 2 (and will take up again in Chapter 12), bonding in ionic compounds depends on the electrostatic forces of attraction between oppositely charged ions. Intermolecular forces are similarly electrostatic.

Collectively, intermolecular forces are called **van der Waals forces**; they include the attractive and repulsive forces between

- molecules with permanent dipoles (*dipole-dipole forces,* Section 11-3)
- polar molecules and nonpolar ones (*dipole-induced dipole forces,* sometimes called *Debye* forces, Section 11-4)
- nonpolar molecules (*induced dipole-induced dipole forces,* Section 11-4)

Our second major focus is the influence of intermolecular forces on the properties of substances. Even though these forces are generally less than about 15% of covalent bond energies, intermolecular forces can have a profound effect on molecular properties. Among other things, intermolecular forces are

- directly related to melting point, boiling point, and the energy needed to convert a solid to a liquid or a liquid to a vapor.
- important in determining the solubility of gases, liquids, and solids in various solvents.
- crucial in determining the structures of biologically important molecules such as DNA and proteins.

11-2 Interactions between Ions and Molecules with a Permanent Dipole

Learning Objectives: LO 2.14, LO 5.9

Many molecules are polar, a result of the polarity of individual bonds and their geometry (see Section 8-7). Conceptually, we can view polar molecules as having positive and negative ends. When a polar molecule such as water encounters an ionic compound, the negative end of the dipole is attracted to the positive cation and the positive end of the dipole is attracted to the negative anion. Forces of attraction between a positive or negative ion and polar molecules—ion–dipole forces—are less than those for ion–ion attractions, but they are greater than other types of forces between molecules.

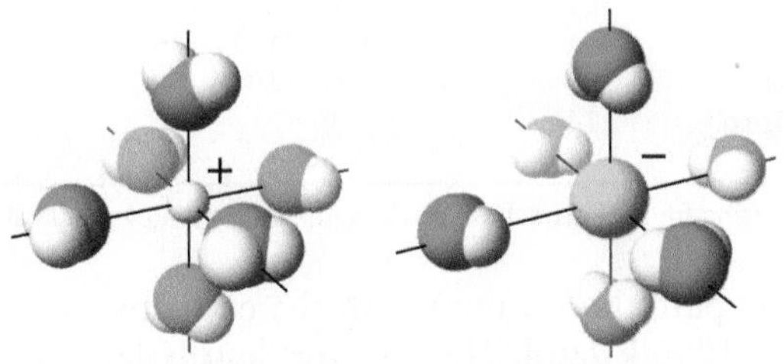

water surrounding a cation   water surrounding an anion

Ion–dipole attractions can be evaluated using Coulomb's law, which tells us that the force of attraction between two charged objects depends on the product of their charges divided by the square of the distance between them (see Section 2-7). Therefore, when a polar molecule encounters an ion, the attractive forces depend on three factors:

- The distance between the ion and the dipole. The closer they are, the stronger the attraction.
- The charge on the ion. The higher the ion charge, the stronger the attraction.
- The magnitude of the dipole. The greater the magnitude of the dipole, the stronger the attraction.

Coulomb's Law The force of attraction between oppositely charged particles depends directly on the product of their charges and inversely on the square of the distance (d) between the ions ($1/d^2$) (◀ Equation 2.3, page 73). The energy of the attraction is also proportional to the charge product, but it is inversely proportional to the distance between them ($1/d$).

Table 11.1 Radii and Enthalpies of Hydration of Alkali Metal Ions

CATION	ION RADIUS (pm)	ENTHALPY OF HYDRATION (kJ/mol)
Li^+	78	−515
Na^+	98	−405
K^+	133	−321
Rb^+	149	−296
Cs^+	165	−263

The formation of hydrated ions in aqueous solution is one of the most important examples of the interaction between an ion (such as Na^+ or Cl^-) and a polar molecule (water, for example). The enthalpy change associated with the hydration of ions—which is generally called the *enthalpy of solvation* or, for ions in water, the *enthalpy of hydration*—is substantial. The enthalpy of solvation for an individual ion cannot be measured directly, but values can be estimated. For example, the hydration of sodium ions is described by the following reaction:

$$Na^+(g) + \text{water} \rightarrow Na^+(aq) \qquad \Delta_{hydration}H° = -405 \text{ kJ/mol}$$

The enthalpy of hydration depends on the charge of the ion and on $1/d$, where d is the distance between the center of the ion and the oppositely charged "pole" of the water dipole.

The effect of ion radius is illustrated by comparing the enthalpies of hydration of the alkali metal cations in Table 11.1, and the effects of radius *and* charge by comparing $\Delta_{hydration}H°$ for Mg^{2+}, Li^+, and K^+.

Enthalpy of Hydration The energy evolved when an ion is hydrated depends on the dipole moment of water, the ion charge, and the distance d between centers of the ion and the polar water molecule. The distance d increases as ion size increases.

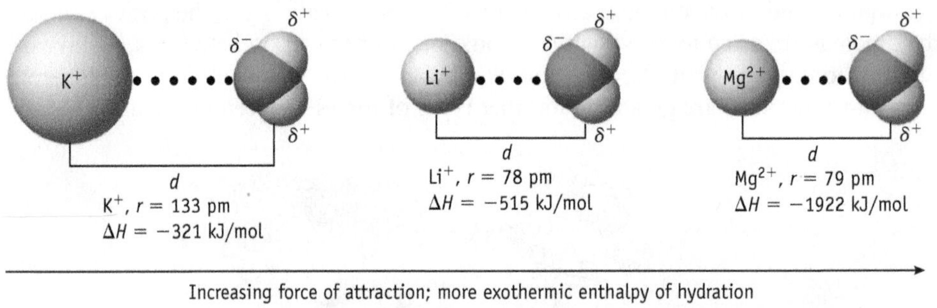

It is interesting to compare these values with the enthalpy of hydration of the H^+ ion, estimated to be −1090 kJ/mol. This extraordinarily large value for a 1+ ion is due to the tiny size of the H^+ ion.

EXAMPLE 11.1

Hydration Energy

Problem Explain why the enthalpy of hydration of Na^+ (−405 kJ/mol) is more negative than that of Cs^+ (−263 kJ/mol), whereas that of Mg^{2+} is much more negative (−1922 kJ/mol) than that of either Na^+ or Cs^+.

What Do You Know? You know the ion charges and the trend in their sizes. (From Figure 7.11 we have: Na^+ = 98 pm, Cs^+ = 165 pm, and Mg^{2+} = 79 pm.)

Strategy The energy associated with ion–dipole attractions depends directly on the size of the ion charge and the magnitude of the dipole, and inversely on the distance between them. Here the water dipole is a constant factor, so the answer depends only on ion size and charge.

Solution From the ion sizes, we can predict that the distances between the center of the positive charge of the ion and the water dipole will vary in this order: $Mg^{2+} < Na^{+} < Cs^{+}$. The hydration energy varies in the reverse order (with the hydration energy of Mg^{2+} being the most negative value). Notice also that Mg^{2+} has a 2+ charge, whereas the other ions are 1+. The greater charge on Mg^{2+} leads to a much greater force of ion–dipole attraction than for the other two ions, which have only a 1+ charge. As a result, the hydration energy for Mg^{2+} is much more negative than for the other two ions.

Thinking about Your Answer The charge difference between Mg^{2+} and the other ions has a much greater effect than the size difference.

Check Your Understanding

Which should have the more negative hydration energy, F^- or Cl^-? Explain briefly.

REVIEW & CHECK FOR SECTION 11-2

1. Which should have the more negative enthalpy of hydration?

   (a) $MgCl_2$ (b) $AlCl_3$

11-3 Interactions between Molecules with a Permanent Dipole

Learning Objectives: LO 2.13, LO 2.15, LO 2.16, LO 2.31, LO 2.32, LO 5.1, LO 5.9

Dipole–Dipole Forces

When a polar molecule encounters another polar molecule, of the same or a different kind, the positive end of one molecule is attracted to the negative end of the other polar molecule. This is called a **dipole–dipole interaction**.

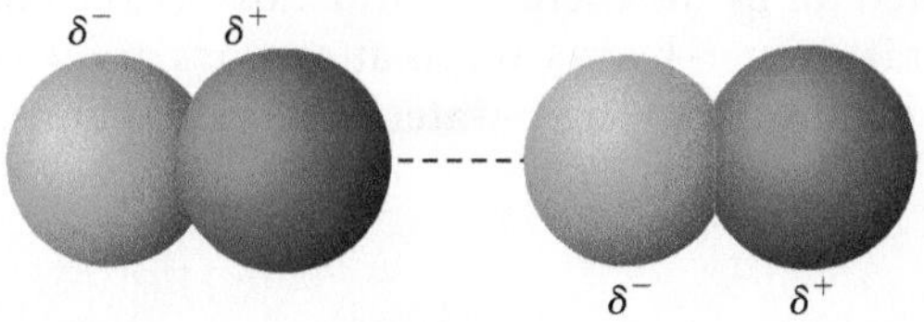

For polar molecules, dipole–dipole attractions influence, among other things, the evaporation of a liquid and the condensation of a gas (Figure 11.2). An energy change occurs in both processes. Evaporation requires the input of energy, specifically the enthalpy of vaporization ($\Delta_{vap}H°$) (see Sections 5-3 and 11-6). The value for the enthalpy of vaporization has a positive sign, indicating that evaporation is an endothermic process. The enthalpy change for the condensation process—the reverse of evaporation—has a negative value.

The greater the forces of attraction between molecules in a liquid, the greater the energy that must be supplied to separate them. Thus, we expect polar compounds to have a higher value for their enthalpy of vaporization than nonpolar compounds with similar molar masses. For example, notice in Table 11.2 that $\Delta_{vap}H°$ for polar molecules is greater than for nonpolar molecules of approximately the same size and mass.

The boiling point of a liquid also depends on intermolecular forces of attraction. As the temperature of a substance is raised, its molecules gain kinetic energy.

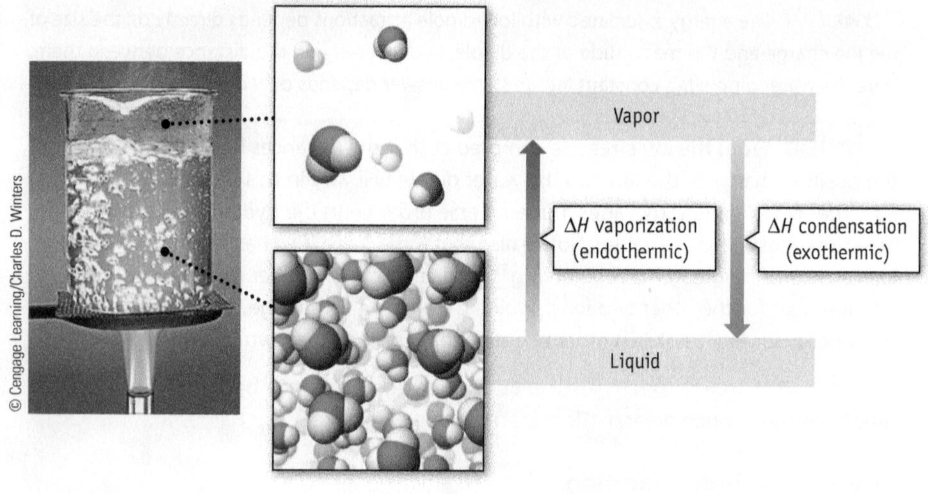

FIGURE 11.2 Evaporation at the molecular level. Energy must be supplied to separate molecules in the liquid state against intermolecular forces of attraction.

Eventually, when the boiling point is reached, the molecules have sufficient kinetic energy to escape the forces of attraction with their neighbors. For molecules of similar molar mass, the greater the polarity, the higher the temperature required for the liquid to boil. In Table 11.2, you see, for example, that the boiling point for polar ICl is greater than that for nonpolar Br_2, a molecule of almost identical mass.

Intermolecular forces also influence solubility. A qualitative observation you have perhaps made yourself is that *like dissolves like*. That is, polar molecules are likely to dissolve in a polar solvent, and nonpolar molecules are likely to dissolve in a nonpolar solvent (Figure 11.3). The converse is also true; that is, it is unlikely that polar molecules will dissolve in nonpolar solvents or that nonpolar molecules will dissolve in polar solvents.

For example, water and polar ethanol (C_2H_5OH) can be mixed in any ratio to give a homogeneous mixture. In contrast, water does not dissolve in gasoline to an appreciable extent. The difference in these two situations is that ethanol and water are polar molecules, whereas the hydrocarbon molecules in gasoline (such as octane, C_8H_{18}) are nonpolar. The water–ethanol interactions are strong enough that the energy expended in pushing water molecules apart to make room for ethanol molecules is compensated for by the energy of attraction between the two kinds of polar molecules. In contrast, water–hydrocarbon attractions are weak. The hydrocarbon molecules cannot disrupt the stronger water–water attractions.

Table 11.2 Molar Masses, Boiling Points, and $\Delta_{vap}H°$ of Nonpolar and Polar Substances

NONPOLAR				POLAR			
	M (g/mol)	BP (°C)	$\Delta_{vap}H°$ (kJ/mol)		M (g/mol)	BP (°C)	$\Delta_{vap}H°$ (kJ/mol)
N_2	28	−196	5.57	CO	28	−192	6.04
SiH_4	32	−112	12.10	PH_3	34	−88	14.06
GeH_4	77	−90	14.06	AsH_3	78	−62	16.69
Br_2	160	59	29.96	ICl	162	97	—

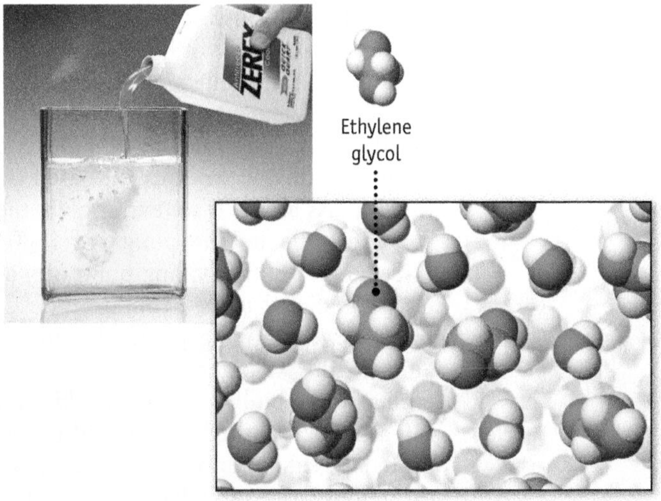

(a) Ethylene glycol ($HOCH_2CH_2OH$), a polar compound used as antifreeze in automobiles, dissolves in water.

(b) Nonpolar motor oil (a hydrocarbon) dissolves in nonpolar solvents such as gasoline or CCl_4. It will not dissolve in a polar solvent such as water, however. Commercial spot removers use nonpolar solvents to dissolve oil and grease from fabrics.

FIGURE 11.3 **"Like dissolves like."**

Hydrogen Bonding

Hydrogen fluoride, water, ammonia, and many other compounds with O—H and N—H bonds have exceptional properties. Notable examples are the boiling points for hydrogen compounds of elements in Groups 4A through 7A (Figure 11.4). Generally, the boiling points of related compounds increase with molar mass, and this trend is seen in the boiling points of the hydrogen compounds of Group 4A elements. The

A CLOSER LOOK

Hydrated Salts: A Result of Ion–Dipole Bonding

Solid salts with waters of hydration are common. The formulas of these compounds are given by appending a specific number of water molecules to the end of the formula, as in $BaCl_2 \cdot 2\,H_2O$. Sometimes, the water molecules simply fill in empty spaces in a crystalline lattice, but often the cation in these salts is directly bound to water molecules. For example, the compound $CrCl_3 \cdot 6\,H_2O$ is better written as $[Cr(H_2O)_4Cl_2]Cl \cdot 2\,H_2O$. Four of the six water molecules are bound to the Cr^{3+} ion by ion–dipole attractive forces; the remaining two water molecules are in the lattice. Common examples of hydrated salts are listed in the table.

Compound	Common Name	Uses
$Na_2CO_3 \cdot 10\,H_2O$	Washing soda	Water softener
$Na_2S_2O_3 \cdot 5\,H_2O$	Hypo	Photography
$MgSO_4 \cdot 7\,H_2O$	Epsom salt	Cathartic, dyeing and tanning
$CaSO_4 \cdot 2\,H_2O$	Gypsum	Wallboard
$CuSO_4 \cdot 5\,H_2O$	Blue vitriol	Biocide

Hydrated cobalt(II) chloride, $CoCl_2 \cdot 6\,H_2O$. In the solid state, the compound is best described by the formula $[Co(H_2O)_4Cl_2] \cdot 2\,H_2O$. The cobalt(II) ion is surrounded by four water molecules and two chloride ions in an octahedral arrangement. In water, the ion is completely hydrated, now being surrounded by six water molecules. Cobalt(II) ions and water molecules interact by ion–dipole forces. This is an example of a coordination compound, a class of compounds discussed in detail in Chapter 22.

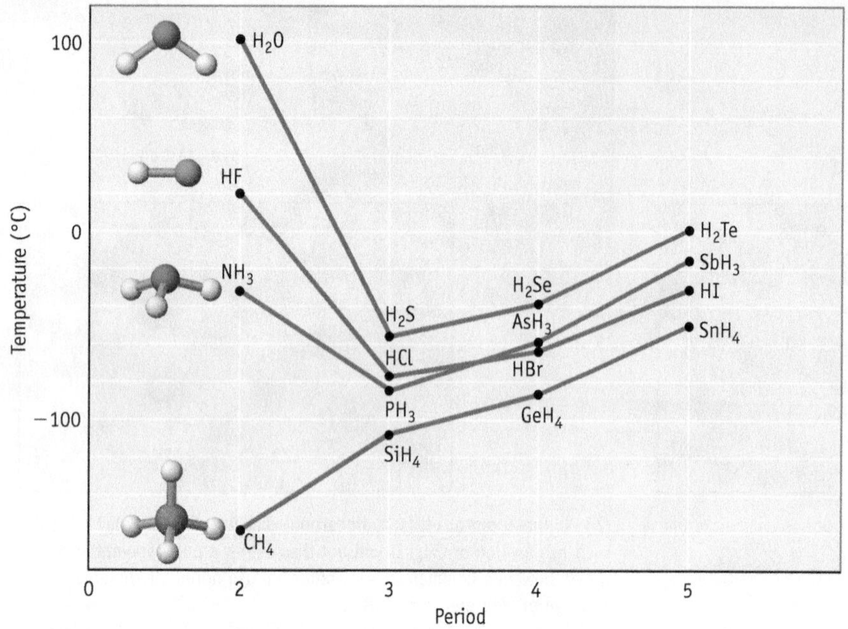

FIGURE 11.4 The boiling points of some simple hydrogen compounds. The effect of hydrogen bonding is apparent in the unusually high boiling points of H_2O, HF, and NH_3. (Also, notice that the boiling point of HCl is somewhat higher than expected based on the data for HBr and HI. It is apparent that some degree of hydrogen bonding also occurs in liquid HCl.)

same effect is also observed for the heavier molecules of the hydrogen-containing compounds of Group 5A, 6A, and 7A elements. The boiling points of NH_3, H_2O, and HF, however, deviate from what might be expected based on molar mass alone. If we extrapolate the curve for the boiling points of H_2Te, H_2Se, and H_2S, the boiling point of water is predicted to be around −90 °C. However, the boiling point of water is almost 200 °C higher than this value! Similarly, the boiling points of NH_3 and HF are much higher than would be expected based on molar mass. Because the temperature at which a substance boils depends on the attractive forces between molecules, the high boiling points of H_2O, HF, and NH_3 indicate strong intermolecular attractions.

Why should H_2O, NH_3, and HF have such strong intermolecular forces? The classical explanation is based on dipole–dipole interactions. The electronegativities of N (3.0), O (3.5), and F (4.0) are among the highest of all the elements, whereas the electronegativity of hydrogen is much lower (2.2). This large difference in electronegativity means that N—H, O—H, and F—H bonds are very polar. In bonds between H and N, O, or F, the more electronegative element takes on a significant negative charge (◀ Figure 8.10), and the hydrogen atom acquires a significant positive charge. Because the H atom bonded to N, O, or F (designated X) can be so highly positively charged, it can interact electrostatically with another electronegative atom (Y) in the same or different molecule to form a **hydrogen bond**, X—H - - - Y—.

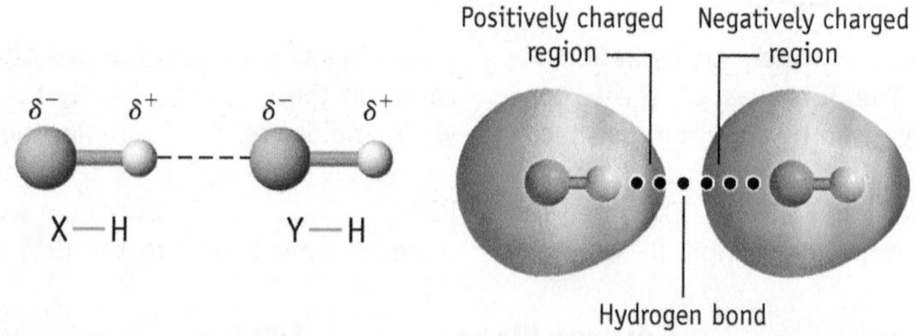

Hydrogen bonding between HF molecules. The partially negative F atom of one HF molecule interacts through hydrogen bonding with a neighboring HF molecule. (Red regions of the molecule are negatively charged, whereas blue regions are positively charged. For more on electrostatic potential surfaces, ◀ page 324.)

Redefinition of Hydrogen Bonding In 2011 the International Union of Pure and Applied Chemistry (IUPAC) redefined hydrogen bonding: "The hydrogen bond is an attractive interaction between a hydrogen atom from a molecule or molecular fragment X—H in which X is more electronegative than H, and an atom or group of atoms in the same or different molecule, in which there is evidence of bond formation." E. Arunan, *et al., Pure and Applied Chemistry*, Vol. 83, page 1637, 2011.

The hydrogen atom becomes a bridge between the two electronegative atoms X and Y, and the dashed line in the figure represents the hydrogen bond. The most pronounced effects of hydrogen bonding occur where both X and Y are N, O, or F. Energies associated with most hydrogen bonds involving these elements are in the range of 5 to 30 kJ/mol.

Pauling suggested an alternative hydrogen bonding model involving resonance structures and partial covalent bonding rather than just intermolecular electrostatic interactions. Recent theoretical work has led to renewed interest in this approach.

Specifically, the recent work suggests viewing a hydrogen bond using two resonance structures:

$$X—H \cdots\cdot :Y \longleftrightarrow X:^- \cdots H—Y^+$$

If X and Y are identical (as in HF_2^-), then the two resonance structures are equally weighted and the bond order is 0.5. If X and Y are different, then one resonance form is more important than the other.

Hydrogen bonding has important implications for any property of a compound that is influenced by intermolecular forces of attraction. It is responsible for the unique properties of water (described below) and plays a central role in biochemistry (see *A Closer Look: Hydrogen Bonding in Biochemistry,* page 414).

The Importance of H Atom Charge Density in Hydrogen Bonding The H atom has an extraordinarily small radius. This means that the partial charge on the H atom in a hydrogen bond is concentrated in a small volume; that is, it has a high charge density (charge density = charge/volume). The result is that it is strongly attractive to the negative charge on a neighboring molecule.

EXAMPLE 11.2

The Effect of Hydrogen Bonding

Problem Ethanol, CH_3CH_2OH, and dimethyl ether, CH_3OCH_3, have the same molecular formula but a different arrangement of atoms. Predict which of these compounds has the higher boiling point.

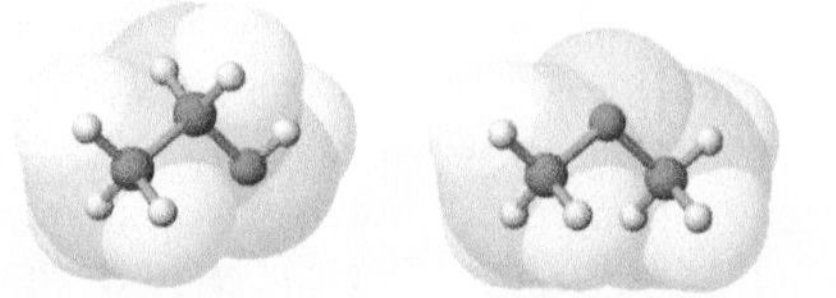

ethanol, CH_3CH_2OH dimethyl ether, CH_3OCH_3

What Do You Know? You know these compounds have the same molar mass and that, when comparing compounds of the same mass, the compound with the stronger intermolecular forces will have the higher boiling point.

Strategy Inspect the structure of each molecule to decide whether each is polar and, if polar, whether hydrogen bonding is possible.

Solution Ethanol has a polar O—H group and so can participate in hydrogen bonding. Dimethyl ether is polar, and the O atom has a partial negative charge. However, no H atom is attached to the O atom. Thus, there is no opportunity for hydrogen bonding in dimethyl ether. We can predict, therefore, that intermolecular forces will be stronger in ethanol than in dimethyl ether and that ethanol will have the higher boiling point.

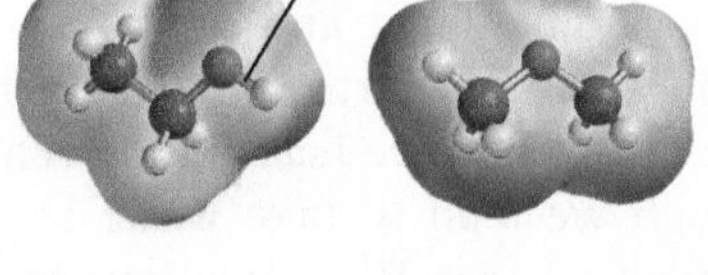

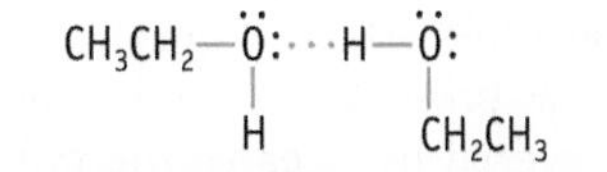

hydrogen bonding in ethanol, CH_3CH_2OH

Think about Your Answer Ethanol boils at 78.3 °C, whereas dimethyl ether has a boiling point of −24.8 °C, more than 100 °C lower. At room temperature and 1 atm pressure, dimethyl ether is a gas, whereas ethanol is a liquid.

Check Your Understanding

Using structural formulas, describe the hydrogen bonding between methanol (CH_3OH) molecules. What physical properties of methanol are affected by hydrogen bonding?

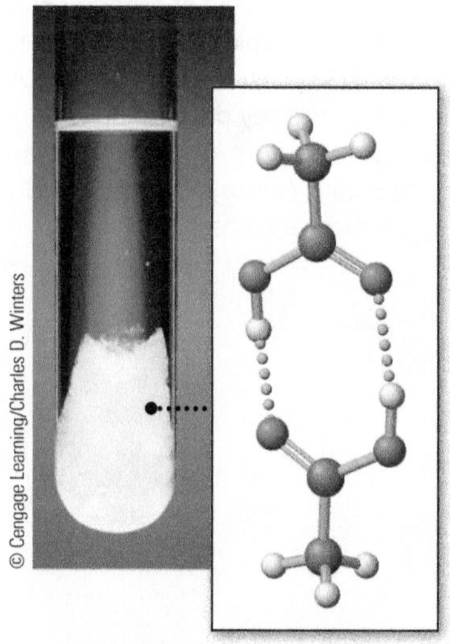

Hydrogen Bonding in Acetic Acid, CH_3CO_2H. Two acetic acid molecules can interact through hydrogen bonds. This photo shows partly solid glacial acetic acid. Notice that the solid is denser than the liquid, a property shared by virtually all substances, the notable exception being water.

A CLOSER LOOK Hydrogen Bonding in Biochemistry

It is arguable that life on Earth as we know it is what it is because of hydrogen bonding in water and in biochemical systems. Perhaps the most important occurrence is in DNA and RNA where the organic bases adenine, cytosine, guanine, and thymine (in DNA) or uracil (in RNA) are attached to sugar-phosphate chains (Figure A). The chains in DNA are joined by the pairing of bases, adenine with thymine and guanine with cytosine.

Figure B illustrates the hydrogen bonding between adenine and thymine. These models show that the molecules naturally fit together to form a six-sided ring, where two of the six sides involve hydrogen bonds. One side consists of a N • • • H—N grouping, and the other side is N—H • • • O. Here, the electrostatic potential surfaces show that the N atoms of adenine and the O atoms of thymine bear partial negative charges, and the H atoms of the N—H groups bear a positive charge. These charges and the geometry of the bases lead to these very specific interactions.

The fact that base pairing through hydrogen bonding leads to the joining of the sugar-phosphate chains of DNA, and to the double helical form of DNA, was first recognized by James Watson and Francis Crick on the basis of experimental work by Rosalind Franklin and Maurice Wilkins in the 1950s. Determination of the DNA structure was a key development in the molecular biology revolution in the last part of the 20th century. (See page 333 for more on these scientists.)

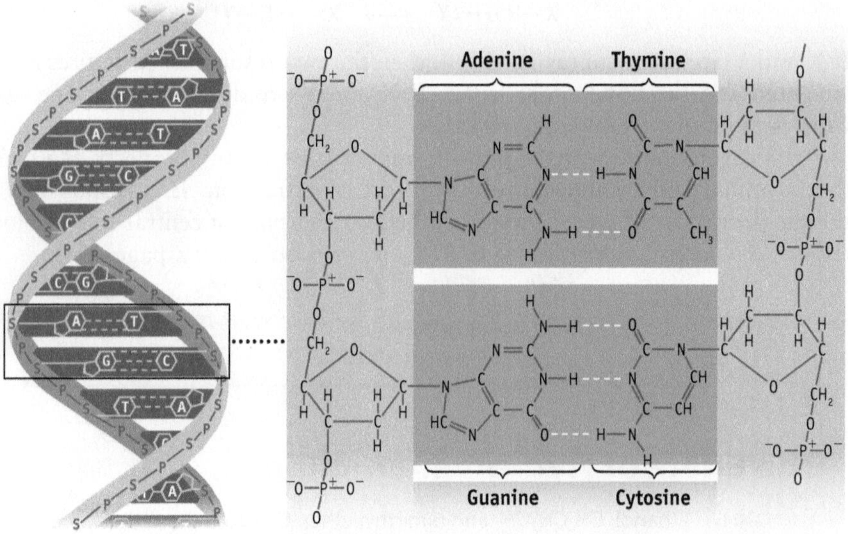

FIGURE A **Hydrogen bonding in DNA.** With the four bases in DNA, the usual pairings are adenine with thymine and guanine with cytosine. This pairing is promoted by hydrogen bonding.

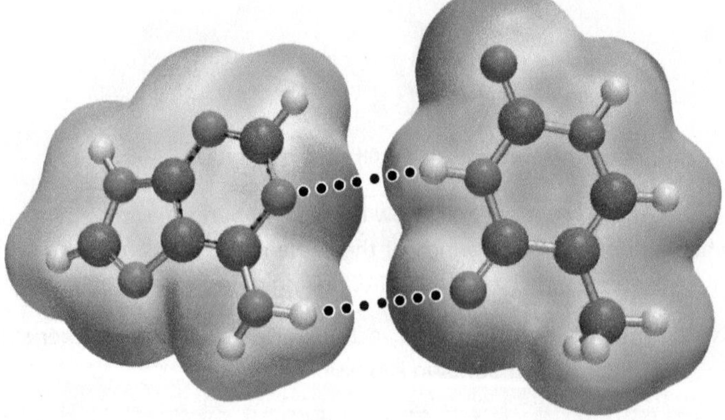

FIGURE B **Hydrogen bonding between adenine and thymine.** Electrostatic potential surfaces depict the hydrogen bonding interactions between adenine and thymine. The polar N—H bond on one molecule can hydrogen bond to an electronegative N or O atom in a neighboring molecule.

Hydrogen Bonding and the Unusual Properties of Water

One of the most striking differences between our planet and others in our solar system is the presence of large amounts of water on Earth. Three fourths of the planet is covered by oceans; the polar regions are vast ice fields; and even soil and rocks hold large amounts of water. Although we tend to take water for granted, almost no other substance behaves in a similar manner. Water's unique features are a consequence of the ability of H_2O molecules to cling tenaciously to one another by hydrogen bonding.

The unusually great intermolecular forces of attraction between water molecules are a result of the fact that each water molecule can participate in *four* hydrogen bonds. An individual water molecule has two polar O—H bonds and two lone pairs. Both hydrogen atoms are available to hydrogen-bond to oxygen atoms in adjacent water molecules. In addition, the oxygen lone pairs can participate in hydrogen bonding to the hydrogen atoms in two other water molecules (Figure 11.5). The result, seen particularly in ice, is a tetrahedral arrangement for the hydrogen

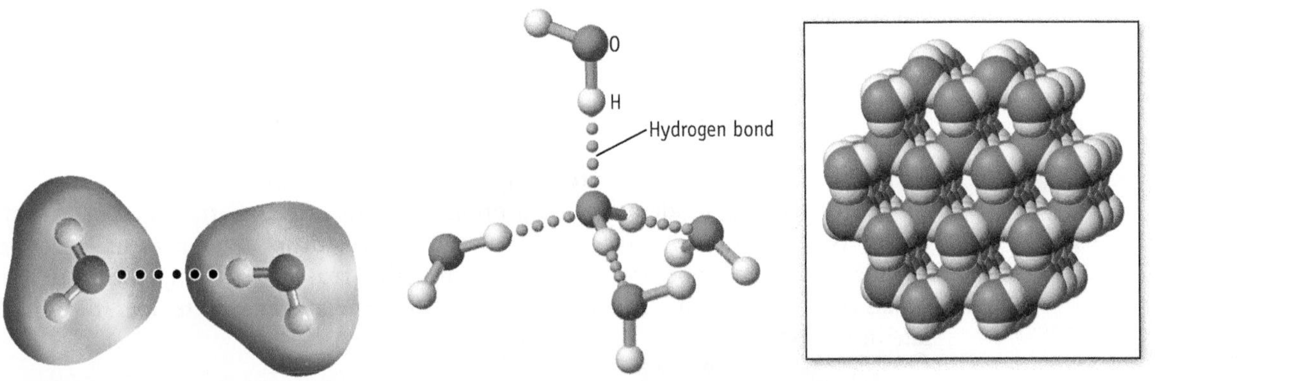

(a) Electrostatic potential surfaces for two water molecules.

(b) The oxygen atom of a water molecule attaches itself to two other water molecules by hydrogen bonds. Each O atom is covalently bonded to two H atoms and hydrogen bonded to H atoms from two other molecules. The hydrogen bonds are longer than the covalent bonds.

(c) In ice, the structural unit shown in part (b) is repeated in the crystalline lattice. This computer-generated structure shows a small portion of the extensive lattice. Notice the six-member, hexagonal rings. The vertices of each hexagon are O atoms, and each side is composed of two oxygen atoms with a hydrogen atom in between. One of the oxygen atoms is covalently bonded to the hydrogen atom, and the other is attracted to it by a hydrogen bond.

FIGURE 11.5 **Hydrogen bonding in water and the structure of ice.**

atoms around each oxygen, involving two covalently bonded hydrogen atoms and two hydrogen-bonded hydrogen atoms.

As a consequence of the regular arrangement of water molecules linked by hydrogen bonding, ice has an open-cage structure with lots of empty space (Figure 11.5c). The result is that ice has a density about 10% less than that of liquid water, which explains why ice floats. (In contrast, virtually all other solids sink in their liquid phase.) We can also see in this structure that the oxygen atoms are arranged at the corners of puckered, hexagonal rings. Snowflakes are always based on six-sided figures (◀ page 64), a reflection of this internal molecular structure of ice.

When ice melts at 0 °C, the regular structure imposed on the solid state by hydrogen bonding breaks down, and a relatively large increase in density occurs (Figure 11.6). Another surprising thing occurs when the temperature of liquid water is raised from 0 °C to 4 °C: The density of water increases. For almost every other substance known, density decreases as the temperature is raised. Once again, hydrogen bonding is the reason for water's seemingly odd behavior. At a temperature just above the melting point, some of the water molecules continue to cluster in ice-like arrangements, which require extra space. As the temperature is raised from 0 °C to 4 °C, the final vestiges of the ice structure disappear, and the volume contracts further, giving rise to the increase in density. Water's density reaches a maximum at about 4 °C. From this point, the density declines with increasing temperature as observed for most substances.

Because of the way that water's density changes as the temperature approaches the freezing point, lakes do not freeze from the bottom up in the winter. When lake water cools with the approach of winter, its density increases, the cooler water sinks, and the warmer water rises. This "turn over" process continues until all the water reaches 4 °C, the maximum density. (This is the way oxygen-rich water moves to the lake bottom to restore the oxygen used during the summer and nutrients are brought to the top layers of the lake.) As the temperature decreases further, the colder water stays on the top of the lake, because water cooler than 4 °C is less dense than water at 4 °C. With further heat loss, ice can then begin to form on the surface, floating there and protecting the underlying water and aquatic life from further heat loss.

Extensive hydrogen bonding is also the origin of the extraordinarily high heat capacity of water. Although liquid water does not have the regular structure of ice,

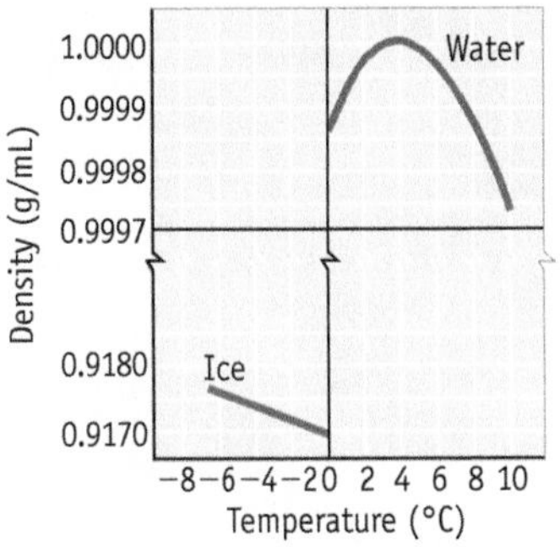

FIGURE 11.6 **The temperature dependence of the densities of ice and water.**

hydrogen bonding still occurs. When the temperature is raised, there must be a significant input of energy to disrupt the intermolecular forces and to raise the temperature even a small amount.

The high specific heat capacity of water is, in large part, why oceans and lakes have such an enormous effect on weather. In autumn, when the temperature of the air is lower than the temperature of the ocean or lake, water transfers energy as heat to the atmosphere, moderating the drop in air temperature. Furthermore, so much energy is available to be transferred for each degree drop in temperature that the decline in water temperature is gradual. For this reason, the temperature of the ocean or of a large lake is generally higher than the average air temperature until late in the autumn.

REVIEW & CHECK FOR SECTION 11-3

1. In which of the following substances would hydrogen bonding be expected?

   (a) CH_4 (b) CH_3OH (c) H_3COCH_3 (d) $H_2C{=}CH_2$

2. Which compound has the strongest intermolecular forces?

   (a) H_2O (b) H_2S (c) H_2Se (d) H_2Te

Learning Objectives: LO 2.1, LO 2.2, LO 2.11, LO 2.12, LO 2.15, LO 2.16, LO 5.9, LO 5.11

11-4 Intermolecular Forces Involving Nonpolar Molecules

Many important molecules such as O_2, N_2, and the halogens are not polar. Why, then, does O_2 dissolve in polar water? Why can the N_2 of the atmosphere be liquefied? Some intermolecular forces must be acting between O_2 and water and between N_2 molecules, but what is their nature?

Dipole-Induced Dipole Forces

Polar molecules such as water can induce, or create, a dipole in molecules that do not have a permanent dipole. To see how this can happen, picture a polar water molecule approaching a nonpolar molecule such as O_2.

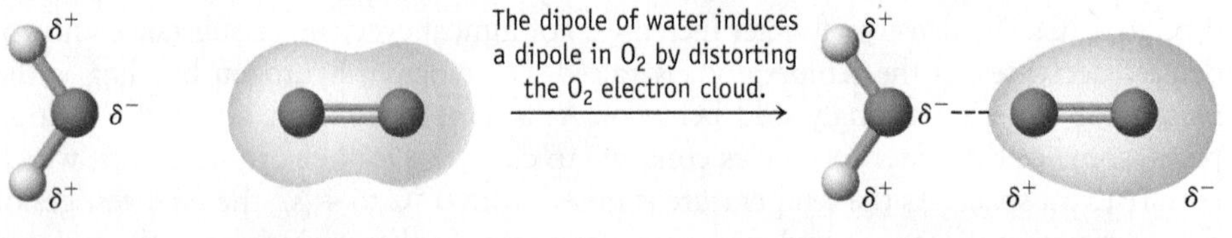

The electron cloud of an isolated (gaseous) O_2 molecule is symmetrically distributed between the two oxygen atoms. As the negative end of the polar H_2O molecule approaches, however, the O_2 electron cloud becomes distorted. In this process, the O_2 molecule itself becomes polar; that is, a dipole is *induced* in the otherwise nonpolar O_2 molecule. The result is that H_2O and O_2 molecules are now attracted to one another, albeit only weakly. Oxygen can dissolve in water because a force of attraction exists between water's permanent dipole and the induced dipole in O_2. Chemists refer to such interactions as **dipole-induced dipole interactions.**

The process of inducing a dipole is called **polarization**, and the degree to which the electron cloud of an atom or a molecule can be distorted depends on the **polarizability** of that atom or molecule. The electron cloud of an atom or molecule with a large, extended electron cloud such as I_2 can be polarized more readily than the electron cloud in a much smaller atom or molecule, such as He or H_2, in which the valence electrons are close to the nucleus and more tightly held. Here you see

Table 11.3 The Solubility of Some Gases in Water*

	Molar Mass (g/mol)	Solubility at 20 °C (g gas/100 g water)†
H_2	2.01	0.000160
N_2	28.0	0.00190
O_2	32.0	0.00434

*Data taken from J. Dean: *Lange's Handbook of Chemistry*. 14th Ed., pp. 5.3–5.8, New York, McGraw-Hill, 1992.
†Measured under conditions where pressure of gas + pressure of water vapor = 760 mm Hg.

Table 11.4 Enthalpies of Vaporization and Boiling Points of Some Nonpolar Substances

	$\Delta_{vap}H°$ (kJ/mol)	Element/Compound BP (°C)
N_2	5.57	−196
O_2	6.82	−183
CH_4 (methane)	8.2	−161.5
Br_2	29.96	+58.8
C_6H_6 (benzene)	30.7	+80.1
I_2	41.95	+185

that polar ethanol (C_2H_5OH) can interact with I_2, and iodine dissolves readily in ethanol.

In general, for an analogous series of substances, say the halogens or alkanes (such as CH_4, C_2H_6, C_3H_8, and so on), the higher the molar mass, the greater the polarizability of the molecule. Indeed, the solubilities of common gases in water illustrate the effect of interactions between a dipole and an induced dipole. As the molar mass of the gas increases, polarizability of the electron cloud increases, the strength of the dipole-induced dipole interaction increases, and solubility in a polar solvent increases (Table 11.3).

London Dispersion Forces: Induced Dipole-Induced Dipole Forces

Nonpolar compounds can be liquids or solids if the intermolecular forces are sufficient to bind the molecules together. Iodine, I_2, is a solid and not a gas around room temperature and pressure for this reason.

The enthalpy of vaporization of a substance at its boiling point is a good indicator of the magnitude of intermolecular forces. The data in Table 11.4 suggest that forces between nonpolar molecules can range from very weak (N_2, O_2, and CH_4 with low enthalpies of vaporization and very low boiling points) to more substantial (I_2 and benzene).

To understand how two nonpolar molecules can attract each other, recall that the electron cloud surrounding atoms or molecules can be distorted. Thus, when two atoms or nonpolar molecules approach each other, attractions or repulsions between their electrons and nuclei can lead to distortions in their electron clouds (Figure 11.7). That is, dipoles can be induced momentarily in neighboring atoms or molecules, and

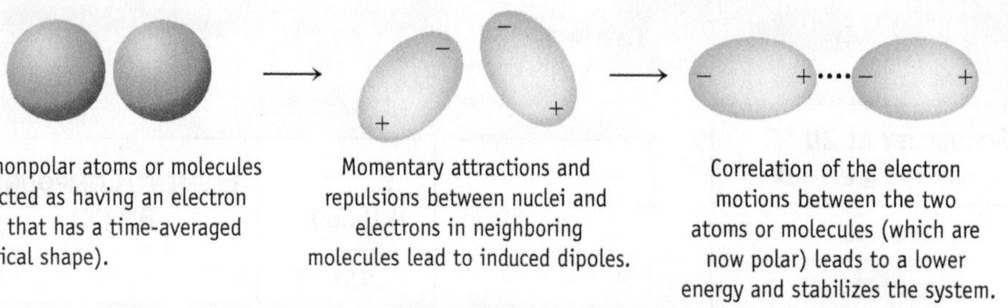

FIGURE 11.7 **Induced dipole-induced dipole interactions or London dispersion forces.** Momentary attractions and repulsions between nuclei and electrons create induced dipoles and lead to a net stabilization due to attractive forces. Nonpolar Br_2 and I_2 both exemplify such forces. They are a liquid and a solid, respectively, indicating that there are forces between the molecules sufficient to cause them to be in a condensed phase.

these *induced* dipoles lead to intermolecular attractions. The intermolecular force of attraction in gases, liquids, and solids composed of nonpolar molecules is an **induced dipole-induced dipole force**. Chemists often call them **London dispersion forces**, and we should make three important points regarding these forces.

The Balance of Intermolecular Forces For water, for example, it is estimated that the net intermolecular force consists of 85% dipole–dipole (including H-bonding), 5% dipole-induced dipole, and 10% dispersion force.

- London dispersion forces occur between all molecules, both nonpolar and polar, but dispersion forces are the only intermolecular forces between nonpolar molecules (Figure 11.8).
- London dispersion forces can account for a major part of the net intermolecular force, even for polar molecules (Figure 11.8).
- London dispersion forces increase with molar mass in a related series of compounds (such as the series CH_4 ... SnH_4 in Figure 11.4).

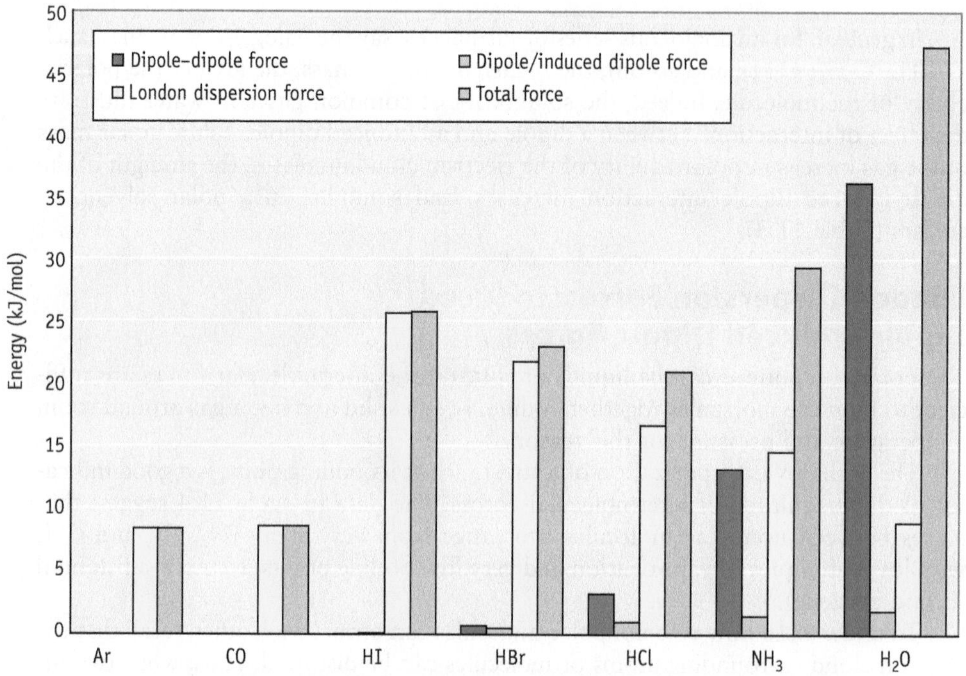

FIGURE 11.8 **Energies associated with intermolecular forces in several common molecules.**

EXAMPLE 11.3

Intermolecular Forces

Problem Suppose you have a mixture of solid iodine, I_2, and the liquids water and carbon tetrachloride (CCl_4). What intermolecular forces exist between each possible pair of compounds?

What Do You Know? Iodine, I_2, is a nonpolar molecule composed of large iodine atoms. It has an extensive electron cloud and is polarizable. CCl_4 is a symmetrical tetrahedral molecule and is not polar (◀ Figure 8.12). Polar H_2O could be involved in hydrogen bonding with other water molecules or with other molecules with highly polar groups.

Strategy You know whether each substance is polar or nonpolar so you need only to determine the types of intermolecular forces that can exist between the different pairs.

Solution Nonpolar iodine, I_2, is easily polarized, and iodine can interact with polar water molecules by dipole-induced dipole and dispersion forces. Nonpolar carbon tetrachloride can interact with nonpolar iodine only by dispersion forces. Water and CCl_4 could interact by dipole-induced dipole and dispersion forces.

Think about Your Answer The photos here show the result of mixing these three compounds. Iodine does dissolve to a small extent in water to give a brown solution. When this brown solution is added to a test tube containing CCl_4, the liquid layers do not mix. (Polar water does not dissolve in nonpolar CCl_4.) (Notice the more dense CCl_4 layer [$d = 1.58$ g/mL] is underneath the less dense water layer.) When the test tube is shaken, nonpolar I_2 is extracted into nonpolar CCl_4, as evidenced by the disappearance of the color of I_2 in the water layer (top) and the appearance of the purple I_2 color in the CCl_4 layer (bottom).

Check Your Understanding

You mix water, CCl_4, and hexane ($CH_3CH_2CH_2CH_2CH_2CH_3$). What type of intermolecular forces can exist between each pair of these compounds?

REVIEW & CHECK FOR SECTION 11-4

1. In which of the following solids are the component particles attracted to each other only by induced dipole-induced dipole (dispersion) forces?

   (a) ice
   (b) solid NH_3 at low temperature
   (c) NaCl
   (d) I_2

2. Which of the following compounds has the largest intermolecular forces?
   (a) pentane, C_5H_{11}
   (b) hexane, C_6H_{14}
   (c) heptane, C_7H_{16}
   (d) octane, C_8H_{18}

Learning Objectives: LO 2.16, LO 5.9

11-5 A Summary of van der Waals Intermolecular Forces

Van der Waals intermolecular forces involve molecules that are polar or those in which polarity can be induced (Table 11.5). It is important to recognize that

- several types of intermolecular forces may contribute to the overall ability of a molecule to interact with another of the same or different kind (Figure 11.8).
- induced dipole-induced dipole (London dispersion) forces can be quite substantial, even in a polar molecule like HCl (Figure 11.8).
- among the various types of van der Waals forces, hydrogen bonding can be a particularly important factor that influences molecular properties.

EXAMPLE 11.4

Intermolecular Forces

Problem Decide which are the most important intermolecular forces between each of the following: (a) between molecules in liquid methane, CH_4; (b) between molecules of water and methanol (CH_3OH); and (c) between molecules of bromine and water.

What Do You Know? Methane, CH_4, is a symmetrical, tetrahedral molecule and so is not polar. Both water and methanol are polar, and both have —OH groups that can be involved in hydrogen bonding. Bromine, Br_2, is nonpolar, but it is a large molecule and has an extensive, polarizable electron cloud.

Strategy Determine the type of interaction possible between pairs of molecules based on the structure and characteristics of each species.

Solution

(a) Methane is not polar. Therefore, the only way methane molecules can interact with one another is through induced dipole-induced dipole forces (dispersion forces).

Table 11.5 Summary of Intermolecular Forces

Type of Interaction	Factors Responsible for Interaction	Example
Hydrogen bonding, X—H · · · :Y	Very polar X—H bond and atom Y with lone pair of electrons (where X and Y are often F, N, O).	$H_2O \cdots H_2O$
Dipole–dipole	Dipole moment (depends on electronegativities and molecular structure).	$(CH_3)_2O \cdots (CH_3)_2O$
Dipole-induced dipole	Dipole moment of polar molecule and polarizability of nonpolar molecule.	$H_2O \cdots I_2$
Induced dipole-induced dipole (London dispersion forces)	Polarizability (depends on molar mass)	$I_2 \cdots I_2$

(b) Both water and methanol are polar, and both have an O—H bond. They therefore interact through the special dipole–dipole force called hydrogen bonding as well as dispersion forces.

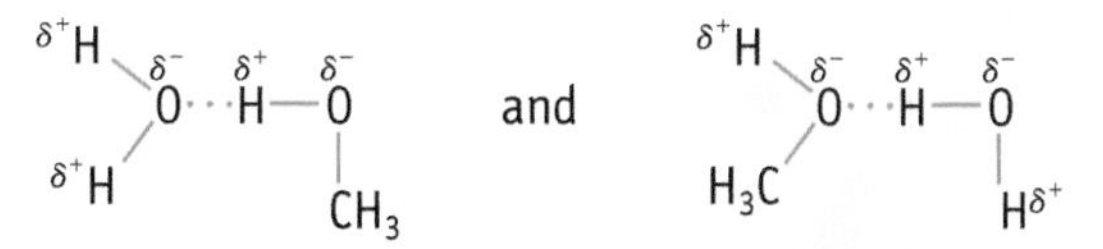

(c) Nonpolar molecules of bromine, Br_2, and polar water molecules interact through dipole-induced dipole forces (and dispersion forces). (This is similar to the I_2–ethanol interaction on page 417.)

Think about Your Answer The fact that CH_4 is a liquid only at very low temperatures suggests it has weak attractive forces. We would expect significant forces of attraction to be those involving hydrogen bonding, and we observe that water is readily soluble in methanol. Finally, bromine is poorly soluble in water, so there are relatively weak intermolecular forces.

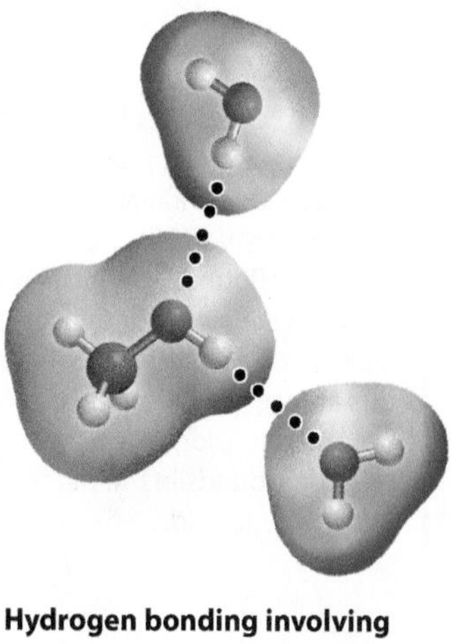

Hydrogen bonding involving methanol (CH_3OH) and water.

Check Your Understanding

Decide which type of intermolecular force is involved in (a) liquid O_2; (b) liquid CH_3OH; and (c) N_2 dissolved in H_2O.

REVIEW & CHECK FOR SECTION 11-5

1. What type of intermolecular forces is likely to be most important between molecules of CH_3CH_2OH and CCl_4?

   (a) dispersion only
   (b) hydrogen bonding
   (c) dipole–dipole
   (d) dipole-induced dipole

11-6 Properties of Liquids

Learning Objectives: LO 2.3, LO 2.7, LO 2.10 (see APEC Lab 5 "Thin-Layer Chromatography"), LO 2.16

Of the three states of matter, liquids are the most difficult to describe precisely. The molecules in a gas under normal conditions are far apart and may be considered more or less independent of one another. The structures of solids can be described readily because the particles that make up solids are usually in an orderly arrangement. The particles of a liquid interact with their neighbors, like the particles in a solid, but, unlike solids, there is little long-range order.

In spite of the fact that liquids do not have a simple or regular structure, we can still explain qualitatively many properties of liquids by viewing them at the particulate level. Here we want to look further at the process of vaporization, at the vapor pressure of liquids, at their boiling points and critical properties, and at surface tension, capillary action, and viscosity.

Vaporization and Condensation

Vaporization or evaporation is the process in which a substance in the liquid state becomes a gas. In this process, molecules escape from the liquid surface and enter the gaseous state.

To understand evaporation, we have to look at molecular energies. Molecules in a liquid have a range of energies (Figure 11.9) that resembles the distribution of energies for molecules of a gas (◀ Figure 10.14). As with gases, the average energy for molecules in a liquid depends only on temperature: The higher the temperature, the higher the average energy and the greater the relative number of molecules with

CASE STUDY
A Pet Food Catastrophe

In early 2007 pet owners all over the United States reported pets becoming seriously ill or dying. Dogs and cats developed symptoms of kidney failure, which included loss of appetite, vomiting, extreme thirst, and lethargy. Round, greenish-brown kidney stones were also found to be clogging the kidneys of stricken pets. This was mysterious at first, but, within two months, chemists and toxicologists traced the ailments to two compounds in the pet food: melamine and cyanuric acid.

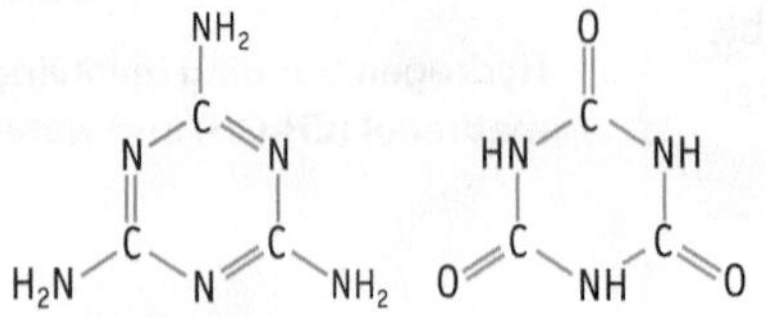

Melamine Cyanuric acid

Melamine is used to make plastics and fertilizers. It is not approved for food use. Cyanuric acid is used to stabilize chlorine in swimming pools and to sanitize food processing equipment. The acid is sometimes formed as a by-product in the manufacture of melamine, so melamine samples can be contaminated with cyanuric acid.

But why was melamine in pet food in the first place? A U.S. manufacturer of pet food, which also supplied other companies that in turn distributed the food under their brand names, had purchased wheat gluten from a supplier in China. Wheat gluten is a concentrated vegetable protein used as a thickener and binder in pet food. The speculation is that the Chinese supplier had added melamine to the wheat gluten to raise the apparent nitrogen content. When products are tested for protein content, any nitrogen found is assumed to come from protein. Adding melamine is an inexpensive way to deceive the buyer into thinking that the product contains a higher percentage of protein.

©Eric Isselee/Shutterstock.com

Melamine and cyanuric acid by themselves are not toxic, but when the compounds are present together they are. The reason is hydrogen bonding! Mixing melamine and cyanuric acid in water produces insoluble crystals of melamine cyanurate.

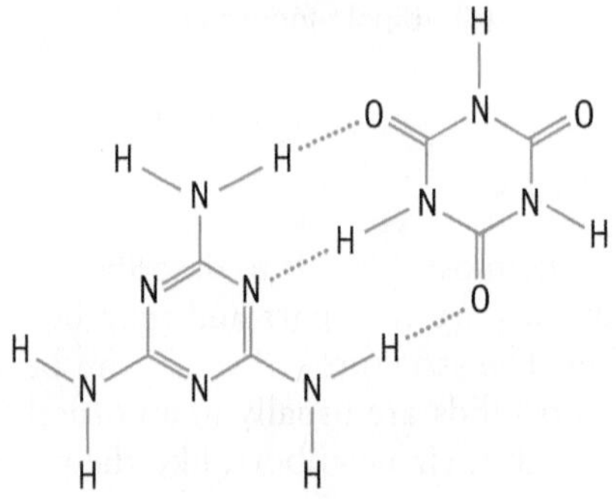

The structure shows only the hydrogen bonding between two molecules. However, additional hydrogen bonding to other molecules is possible, and the result is further aggregation of cyanuric acid and melamine to form an insoluble material.

The behavior of the hydrogen-bonded complex depends on pH. In the stomach, a very acidic medium with a low pH, hydrogen bonding does not occur between these compounds, and the compounds are soluble. The body seeks to get rid of these chemicals through the kidneys, however, and there the compounds encounter a near neutral pH. Hydrogen bonding can then occur, and the molecules aggregate to form solid melamine cyanurate.

In 2008 melamine was also found in milk products, including infant formula, in China. Several thousand babies became ill, having suffered acute kidney failure after being fed a formula contaminated with melamine.

Questions:

1. Calculate the weight percent of nitrogen in melamine and cyanuric acid and compare this value to the average percent of nitrogen in protein (14%).
2. An infant formula was found to have 0.14 ppm melamine. (The abbreviation ppm stands for parts per million. This means, for example, there is 1 g of a substance per million grams of the product.) What mass of melamine is there in a package of infant formula with a mass of 454 g (one pound)?

Answers to these questions are available in Appendix N.

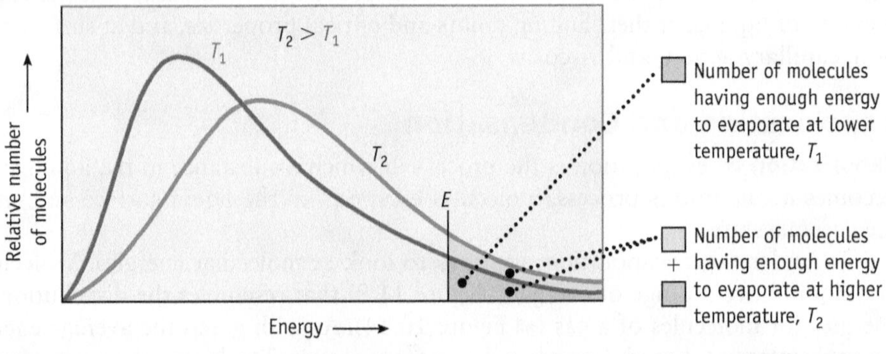

FIGURE 11.9 **The distribution of energy among molecules in a liquid sample.** T_2 **is a higher temperature than** T_1**, and at the higher temperature, there are more molecules with an energy greater than E.**

high kinetic energy. In a sample of a liquid, at least a few molecules have more kinetic energy than the potential energy arising from the intermolecular attractive forces holding the liquid molecules to one another. If these high-energy molecules are at the surface of the liquid and if they are moving in the right direction, they can break free of their neighbors and enter the gas phase.

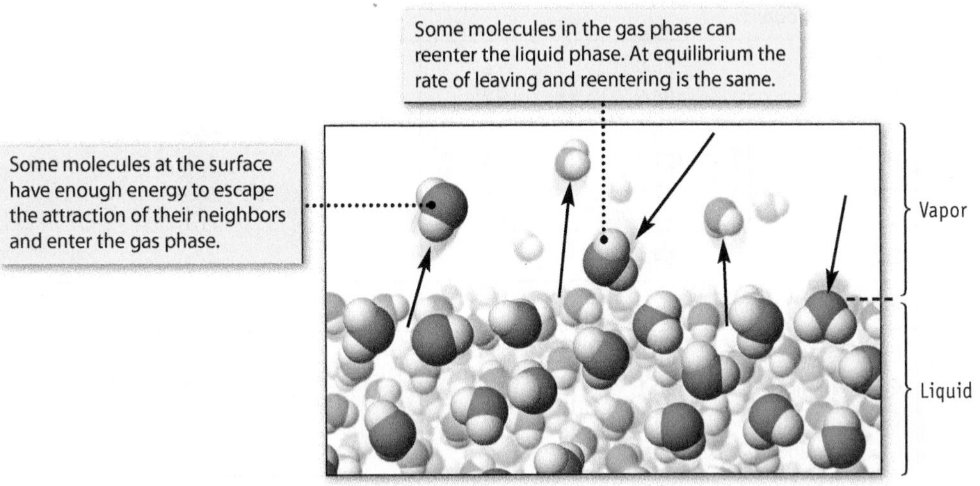

Vaporization is an endothermic process because energy is required to overcome the intermolecular forces of attraction holding the molecules together. The energy required to vaporize a sample is often given as the standard **molar enthalpy of vaporization, $\Delta_{vap}H°$** (in units of kilojoules per mole; see Tables 11.4 and 11.6).

$$\text{liquid} \xrightarrow[\text{energy absorbed by liquid}]{\text{vaporization}} \text{vapor} \qquad \Delta_{vap}H° = \text{molar enthalpy of vaporization}$$

A molecule in the gas phase can transfer some of its kinetic energy by colliding with slower gaseous molecules and solid objects. If this molecule loses sufficient energy and comes in contact with the surface of the liquid, it can reenter the liquid phase in the process called **condensation**.

$$\text{vapor} \xrightarrow[\text{energy released by vapor}]{\text{condensation}} \text{liquid} \qquad -\Delta_{vap}H° = \text{molar enthalpy of condensation}$$

Condensation is the reverse of vaporization and so is an exothermic process. Energy is transferred to the surroundings. *The enthalpy change for condensation is equal but opposite in sign to the enthalpy of vaporization.*

As illustrated by the data in Table 11.6, there is a relationship between the $\Delta_{vap}H°$ values for various substances and the temperatures at which they boil. Both properties reflect the attractive forces between particles in the liquid. The boiling points of nonpolar liquids (such as the hydrocarbons, atmospheric gases, and the halogens) increase with increasing atomic or molecular mass, a reflection of increased intermolecular dispersion forces. The alkanes listed in Table 11.6 (methane, ethane, propane, and butane) show this trend clearly. Similarly, the boiling points and enthalpies of vaporization of the heavier hydrogen halides (HCl, HBr, HI) increase with increasing molecular mass. For these molecules, dispersion forces and ordinary dipole–dipole forces account for their intermolecular attractions (see Figure 11.8). Because dispersion forces become increasingly important with increasing mass, the enthalpies of vaporization and the boiling points are in the order HCl < HBr < HI. Among the hydrogen halides HF is the exception; the high enthalpy of vaporization and boiling point are a direct result of extensive hydrogen bonding.

Table 11.6 Molar Enthalpies of Vaporization and Boiling Points for Common Substances*

Compound	Molar Mass (g/mol)	$\Delta_{vap}H°$ (kJ/mol)†	Boiling Point (°C) (Vapor Pressure = 760 mm Hg)
Polar Compounds			
HF	20.0	25.2	19.7
HCl	36.5	16.2	−84.8
HBr	80.9	19.3	−66.4
HI	127.9	19.8	−35.6
NH_3	17.0	23.3	−33.3
H_2O	18.0	40.7	100.0
SO_2	64.1	24.9	−10.0
Nonpolar Compounds			
CH_4 (methane)	16.0	8.2	−161.5
C_2H_6 (ethane)	30.1	14.7	−88.6
C_3H_8 (propane)	44.1	19.0	−42.1
C_4H_{10} (butane)	58.1	22.4	−0.5
Monatomic Elements			
He	4.0	0.08	−268.9
Ne	20.2	1.7	−246.1
Ar	39.9	6.4	−185.9
Xe	131.3	12.6	−108.0
Diatomic Elements			
H_2	2.0	0.90	−252.9
N_2	28.0	5.6	−195.8
O_2	32.0	6.8	−183.0
F_2	38.0	6.6	−188.1
Cl_2	70.9	20.4	−34.0
Br_2	159.8	30.0	58.8

*Data taken from D. R. Lide: *Basic Laboratory and Industrial Chemicals,* Boca Raton, FL, CRC Press, 1993.
†$\Delta_{vap}H°$ is measured at the normal boiling point of the liquid.

EXAMPLE 11.5

Enthalpy of Vaporization

Problem You put 925 mL of water (about 4 cupfuls) in a pan at 100 °C, and the water slowly evaporates. How much energy is transferred as heat to vaporize all the water? (Density of water at 100 °C = 0.958 g/cm³.)

What Do You Know? You know the volume of water and wish to know the energy required for evaporation. Two additional pieces of information are needed to solve this problem:

1. $\Delta_{vap}H°$ for water = +40.7 kJ/mol at 100 °C (from Table 11.6).
2. Molar mass of water = 18.02 g/mol.

Strategy $\Delta_{vap}H°$ has units of kilojoules per mole, so you first must find the mass of water and then the amount. Finally, use the enthalpy of vaporization (in kJ/mol) to calculate the energy required as heat.

Solution Using the density of water at this temperature, we find that 925 mL of water is equivalent to 886 g, and this mass is in turn equivalent to 49.2 mol of water.

$$925 \text{ mL}\left(\frac{0.958 \text{ g}}{1 \text{ mL}}\right)\left(\frac{1 \text{ mol}}{18.02 \text{ g}}\right) = 49.2 \text{ mol } H_2O$$

Therefore, the amount of energy required is

$$49.2 \text{ mol } H_2O\left(\frac{40.7 \text{ kJ}}{\text{mol}}\right) = 2.00 \times 10^3 \text{ kJ}$$

Think about Your Answer 2000 kJ is equivalent to the energy obtained by burning about 60 g of carbon.

Check Your Understanding

The molar enthalpy of vaporization of methanol, CH_3OH, is 35.2 kJ/mol at 64.6 °C. How much energy is required to evaporate 1.00 kg of methanol at 64.6 °C?

Strategy Map 11.5

PROBLEM

Calculate the **energy** required to **evaporate** water sample.

DATA/INFORMATION

- Enthalpy of vaporization at boiling point
- Volume of water

STEP 1. Use **density** and **molar mass** to convert ***volume*** of water to ***amount*** (mol).

Amount of sample

STEP 2. Multiply **amount** of sample by **molar enthalpy**.

Energy required (kJ) to evaporate sample at boiling point

Liquid water is an exceptional substance. Among its unique properties, an enormous amount of energy is required to convert liquid water to water vapor, and this fact is important to your own physical well-being. When you exercise vigorously, your body responds by sweating. Energy from your body is transferred to sweat in the process of evaporation, and your body is cooled.

Enthalpies of vaporization and condensation of water also play a role in weather (Figure 11.10). For example, if enough water condenses from the air to fall as an inch of rain on an acre of ground, the energy released exceeds 2.0×10^8 kJ! This is equivalent to the energy released by a small bomb.

James Cowlin

FIGURE 11.10 Rainstorms release an enormous quantity of energy. When water vapor condenses, energy is transferred to the surroundings. The enthalpy of condensation of water is large, so a large quantity of energy is released in a rainstorm.

Vapor Pressure

If you put some water in an open beaker, it will eventually evaporate completely. Air movement and gas diffusion remove the water vapor from the vicinity of the liquid surface, so many water molecules are not able to return to the liquid.

If you put water in a sealed flask (Figure 11.11), however, the water vapor cannot escape, and some will recondense to form liquid water. Eventually, the masses of liquid and vapor in the flask will remain constant, another example of a **dynamic equilibrium** (◀ page 104).

$$\text{liquid} + \text{energy} \rightleftharpoons \text{vapor}$$

At equilibrium, molecules still move continuously from the liquid phase to the vapor phase and from the vapor phase back to the liquid phase (page 423). Importantly, the rate at which molecules move from liquid to vapor is the same as the rate at which they move from vapor to liquid; thus, there is no net change in the masses of the two phases.

When a liquid–vapor equilibrium has been established, the equilibrium vapor pressure (often just called the vapor pressure) can be measured. The **equilibrium vapor pressure** of a substance is the pressure exerted by the vapor in equilibrium with the liquid phase. Conceptually, the vapor pressure of a liquid is a measure of the tendency of its molecules to escape from the liquid phase and enter the vapor phase at a given temperature. This tendency is referred to qualitatively as the

FIGURE 11.11 Vapor pressure.

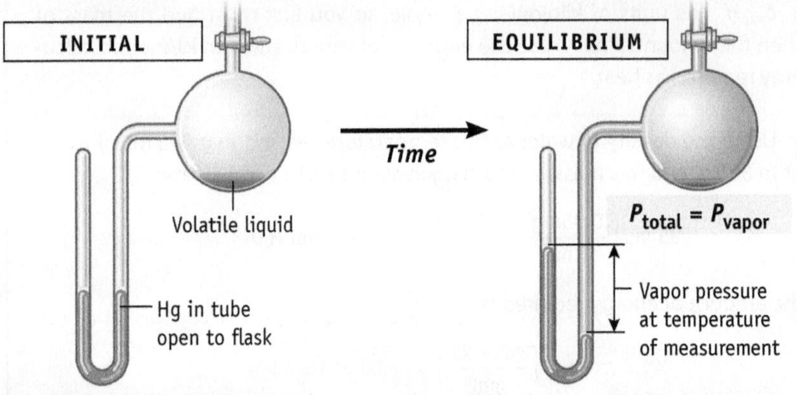

A volatile liquid is placed in an evacuated flask. At the beginning, no molecules of the liquid are in the vapor phase.

After a short time some liquid evaporates, and the molecules now in the vapor phase exert a pressure. The pressure of the vapor measured when the liquid and the vapor are in equilibrium is called the *equilibrium vapor pressure.*

volatility of the compound. The higher the equilibrium vapor pressure at a given temperature, the more volatile the substance.

As described previously (see Figure 11.9), the distribution of molecular energies in the liquid phase is a function of temperature. At a higher temperature, more molecules have sufficient energy to escape the surface of the liquid. The equilibrium vapor pressure must, therefore, increase with temperature.

Plots of vapor pressure as a function of temperature can give us a great deal of information (Figure 11.12). *All points along the vapor pressure versus temperature curves represent conditions of pressure and temperature at which liquid and vapor are in equilibrium.* For example, at 60 °C the vapor pressure of water is 149 mm Hg. If water is placed in an evacuated flask that is maintained at 60 °C, liquid water will evaporate until the pressure exerted by the water vapor is 149 mm Hg (assuming enough water is in the flask so that some liquid remains when equilibrium is reached).

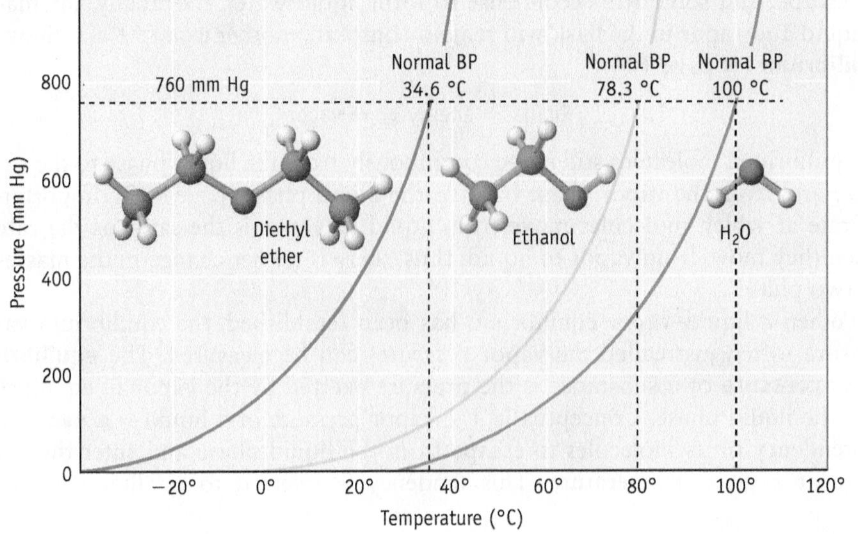

FIGURE 11.12 Vapor pressure curves for diethyl ether [$(C_2H_5)_2O$], ethanol (C_2H_5OH), and water. Each curve represents conditions of *T* and *P* at which the two phases, liquid and vapor, are in equilibrium. These compounds exist as liquids for temperatures and pressures to the left of the curve and as gases under conditions to the right of the curve. (Vapor pressures for a number of liquids are given in Appendix G.)

EXAMPLE 11.6

Using Vapor Pressure

Problem You place 2.00 L of water in an open container in your dormitory room; the room has a volume of 4.25×10^4 L. You seal the room and wait for the water to evaporate. Will all of the water evaporate at 25 °C? Although it is not realistic, assume for simplicity there is zero humidity to start. (At 25 °C the density of water is 0.997 g/mL, and its vapor pressure is 23.8 mm Hg.)

What Do You Know? You know the volume of water, the density of the water, the volume of the room, and the vapor pressure of the water at 25 °C.

Strategy One approach to solving this problem is to use the ideal gas law to calculate the amount of liquid water that must evaporate for the vapor produced to exert a pressure of 23.8 mm Hg in a volume of 4.25×10^4 L at 25 °C. Next, determine the volume of liquid water from the amount and compare the answer to the 2.00 L of water available.

Solution

$$P = 23.8 \text{ mm Hg}\left(\frac{1 \text{ atm}}{760 \text{ mm Hg}}\right) = 0.0313 \text{ atm}$$

$$n = \frac{PV}{RT} = \frac{(0.0313 \text{ atm})(4.25 \times 10^4 \text{ L})}{\left(0.082057 \frac{\text{L} \cdot \text{atm}}{\text{K} \cdot \text{mol}}\right)(298 \text{ K})} = 54.4 \text{ mol}$$

$$54.4 \text{ mol } H_2O\left(\frac{18.02 \text{ g}}{1 \text{ mol } H_2O}\right) = 980. \text{ g } H_2O$$

$$980. \text{ g } H_2O\left(\frac{1 \text{ mL}}{0.997 \text{ g } H_2O}\right) = 983 \text{ mL}$$

Only about half of the available water needs to evaporate to achieve the equilibrium water vapor pressure of 23.8 mm Hg at 25 °C.

Think about Your Answer Another approach to the problem is to calculate the pressure exerted if all of the water had evaporated. The answer would be 48.4 mm Hg. This is about twice the equilibrium vapor pressure at 25 °C, so only about half of the water needs to evaporate, as you found in the other approach.

Check Your Understanding

Examine the vapor pressure curve for ethanol in Figure 11.12.

(a) What is the approximate vapor pressure of ethanol at 40 °C?

(b) Are liquid and vapor in equilibrium when the temperature is 60 °C and the pressure is 600 mm Hg? If not, does the liquid evaporate to form more vapor, or does vapor condense to form more liquid?

Strategy Map 11.6

PROBLEM

Will a sample of water **evaporate completely** in a given volume at known ***T***?

DATA/INFORMATION

- Volume of water
- Density of water
- Vapor pressure at *T*

STEP 1. Use **ideal gas law** to calculate *amount of water vapor* needed to have a ***P*** equal to vapor pressure in *given volume*.

Amount of water (mol) in the vapor phase to achieve ***P*** equal to the vapor pressure at given ***T***.

STEP 2. Convert **amount of water** to a **volume of liquid water** using ***molar mass*** and ***density***.

Volume of water that evaporated to achieve the ***vapor pressure*** at given ***T***.

STEP 3. **Compare** *volume of water evaporated to volume available before evaporation.*

Volume of water that evaporated is ***less*** than that available.
Some liquid water remains.

Vapor Pressure, Enthalpy of Vaporization, and the Clausius–Clapeyron Equation

As Figure 11.12 illustrates, plotting the vapor pressure for a liquid as a function of temperature results in a curved line. However, we see a linear relationship if the reciprocal of the Kelvin temperature ($1/T$) is plotted as a function of the logarithm of the vapor pressure ($\ln P$) (Figure 11.13), and the equation for the line is

$$\ln P = -(\Delta_{vap}H°/RT) + C \qquad (11.1)$$

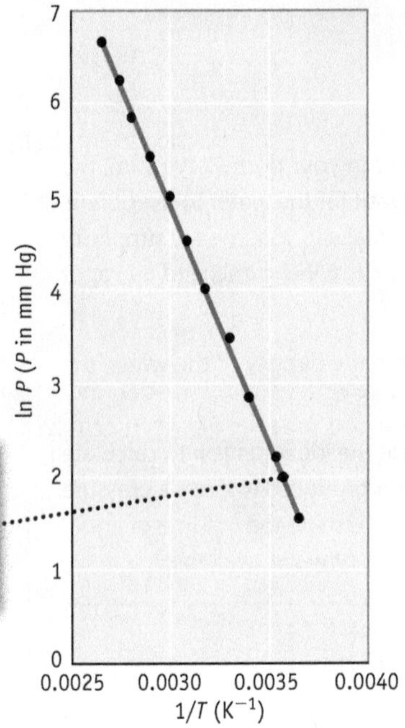

FIGURE 11.13 **Clausius–Clapeyron equation.** This equation is named after the German physicist R. Clausius (1822–1888) and the Frenchman B. P. E. Clapeyron (1799–1864). Values of T and P for water for this plot are from Appendix G.

When the natural logarithm of the vapor pressure (ln P) of water at various temperatures (T) is plotted against $1/T$, the slope of the straight line is $-\Delta_{vap}H°/R$.

The value of this relationship—called the Clausius–Clapeyron equation—is that you can calculate the enthalpy of vaporization of a liquid, $\Delta_{vap}H°$, from experimental measurements of vapor pressure and temperature. (In this equation R is the ideal gas constant (0.008314462 kJ/K · mol), and C is a constant characteristic of the liquid in question.)

The equilibrium vapor pressure of a liquid can be measured at several different temperatures, and, if the logarithm of these pressures is plotted versus $1/T$, the result is a straight line with a slope of $-\Delta_{vap}H°/R$. For example, plotting data for water (Figure 11.13), we find the slope of the line is -4.90×10^3 K, which gives $\Delta_{vap}H° = 40.7$ kJ/mol.

As an alternative to plotting ln P versus $1/T$, we can use the following equation (derived from Equation 11.1) that allows us to calculate $\Delta_{vap}H°$ if we know the vapor pressure of a liquid at two different temperatures.

$$\ln \frac{P_2}{P_1} = -\frac{\Delta_{vap}H°}{R}\left[\frac{1}{T_2} - \frac{1}{T_1}\right] \qquad \textbf{(11.2)}$$

Let us use Equation 11.2 to calculate the enthalpy of vaporization of ethylene glycol, a common ingredient in antifreeze. Suppose we do experiments where we find the liquid has a vapor pressure of 14.9 mm Hg (P_1) at 373 K (T_1), and a vapor pressure of 49.1 mm Hg (P_2) at 398 K (T_2). This gives $\Delta_{vap}H°$ of 59.0 kJ/mol.

$$\ln\left(\frac{49.1 \text{ mm Hg}}{14.9 \text{ mm Hg}}\right) = -\frac{\Delta_{vap}H°}{0.0083145 \text{ kJ/K} \cdot \text{mol}}\left[\frac{1}{398 \text{ K}} - \frac{1}{373 \text{ K}}\right]$$

$$1.192 = -\frac{\Delta_{vap}H°}{0.0083145 \text{ kJ/K} \cdot \text{mol}}\left(-\frac{0.000168}{K}\right)$$

$$\Delta_{vap}H° = 59.0 \text{ kJ/mol}$$

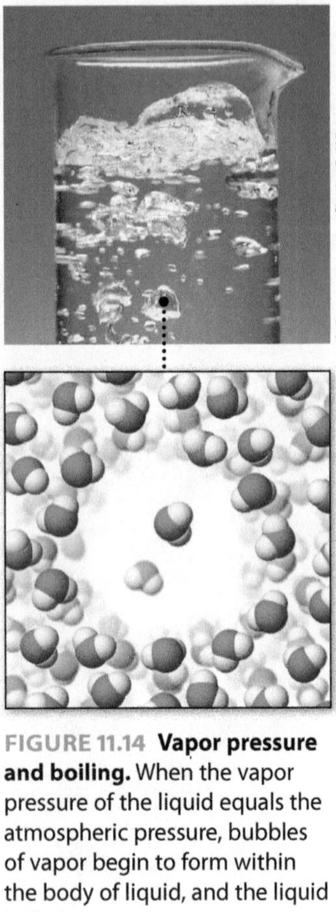

© Cengage Learning/Charles D. Winters

FIGURE 11.14 **Vapor pressure and boiling.** When the vapor pressure of the liquid equals the atmospheric pressure, bubbles of vapor begin to form within the body of liquid, and the liquid boils.

Boiling Point

If you have a beaker of water open to the atmosphere, the atmosphere presses down on the surface. If enough energy is added, a temperature is eventually reached when the vapor pressure of the liquid equals the atmospheric pressure. At this temperature, bubbles of the liquid's vapor will not be crushed by the atmospheric pressure. Instead, bubbles can rise to the surface, and the liquid boils (Figure 11.14).

The boiling point of a liquid is the temperature at which its vapor pressure is equal to the external pressure. If the external pressure is 760 mm Hg, this temperature is called the **normal boiling point.** This point is highlighted on the vapor pressure curves for the substances in Figure 11.12.

The normal boiling point of water is 100 °C, and in a great many places in the United States, water boils at or near this temperature. If you live at higher altitudes, however, such as in Salt Lake City, Utah, where the barometric pressure is about 650 mm Hg, water will boil at a noticeably lower temperature. The curve in Figure 11.12 shows that a pressure of 650 mm Hg corresponds to a boiling temperature of about 95 °C. Food, therefore, has to be cooked a little longer in Salt Lake City to achieve the same result as in New York City at sea level.

Critical Temperature and Pressure

On first thought, it might seem that vapor pressure–temperature curves (such as shown in Figure 11.12) should continue upward without limit, but this is not so. Instead, when a high enough temperature and pressure are reached, the interface between the liquid and the vapor disappears at the **critical point**. The temperature at which this occurs is the **critical temperature, T_c**, and the corresponding pressure is the **critical pressure, P_c** (Figure 11.15). The substance that exists under these conditions is called a **supercritical fluid**. It is like a gas under such a high pressure that its density resembles that of a liquid, while its viscosity (resistance to flow) remains close to that of a gas.

Consider what the substance looks like at the molecular level under these conditions. The molecules have been forced almost as close together as they are in the liquid state, but, unlike the situation in liquids, each molecule in the supercritical fluid has enough kinetic energy to exceed the forces holding the molecules together.

For most substances, the critical point is at a very high temperature and pressure (Table 11.7). Water, for instance, has a critical temperature of 374 °C and a critical pressure of 217.7 atm.

Supercritical fluids can have beneficial uses, such as the ability to extract caffeine from coffee beans. As described in *A Closer Look: Supercritical CO_2 and Green Chemistry* (page 430), this property can also be useful in our movement to "green chemistry."

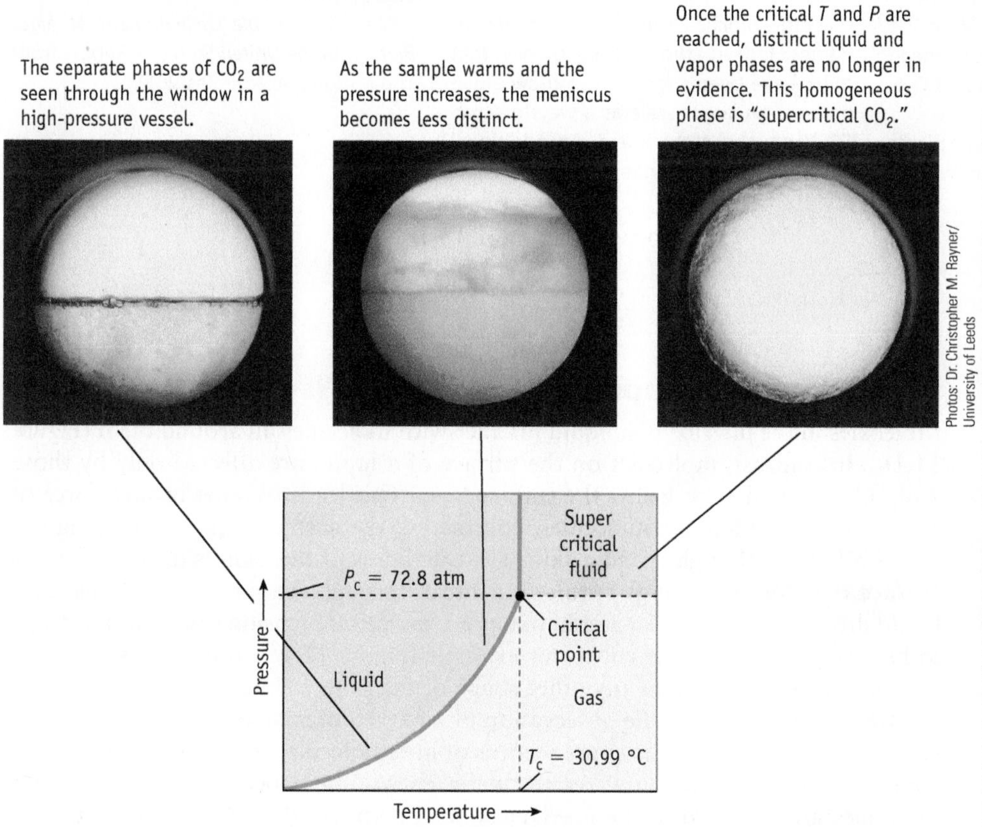

FIGURE 11.15 **Critical temperature and pressure for CO_2.** The pressure versus temperature curve representing equilibrium conditions for liquid and gaseous carbon dioxide ends at the critical point; above that temperature and pressure, water becomes a supercritical fluid.

TABLE 11.7 Critical Temperatures and Pressures for Common Compounds*

COMPOUND	T_c (°C)	P_c (atm)
CH_4 (methane)	−82.6	45.4
C_2H_6 (ethane)	32.3	49.1
C_3H_8 (propane)	96.7	41.9
C_4H_{10} (butane)	152.0	37.3
CCl_2F_2 (CFC-12)	111.8	40.9
NH_3	132.4	112.0
H_2O	374.0	217.7
CO_2	30.99	72.8
SO_2	157.7	77.8

*Data taken from D. R. Lide: *Basic Laboratory and Industrial Chemicals*, Boca Raton, FL, CRC Press, 1993.

A CLOSER LOOK Supercritical CO_2 and Green Chemistry

Much has been written recently about CO_2, particularly its role as a greenhouse gas. But it is also a useful compound, in particular as a solvent in the form of a supercritical fluid (SCF).

Carbon dioxide is widely available, essentially nontoxic, nonflammable, and inexpensive. Importantly, it is relatively easy to reach its critical temperature of 30.99 °C and critical pressure of 72.8 atm. In the supercritical state, the molecules are in close proximity, so the substance behaves as a liquid. However, because the kinetic energy of CO_2 molecules is greater than the energy associated with the forces of attraction between molecules, supercritical CO_2 has some properties of a gas. A result is that the supercritical fluid has the density of a liquid but the low viscosity of a gas.

One use of supercritical CO_2 is to extract caffeine from coffee. Coffee beans are treated with steam to bring the caffeine to the surface. The beans are then immersed in supercritical CO_2, which selectively dissolves the caffeine but leaves intact the compounds that give flavor to coffee. (Decaffeinated coffee contains less than 3% of the original caffeine.) The solution of caffeine in supercritical CO_2 is poured off, and the CO_2 is evaporated, trapped, and reused.

Algae are a large group of simple plants that appear in many different forms and that grow prolifically under a variety of conditions. Indeed, they are so prolific that there have been proposals to grow algae on an even larger scale as a way to scrub CO_2 from the atmosphere. An additional advantage is that algae produce organic compounds such as fatty acids, which can be extracted from the algae and then converted to biodiesel fuel. (This conversion is described in Chapters 20 and 23.) Indeed, it was recently reported that SCFs such as CO_2 can be used for the extraction with very high efficiency.

John C. Kotz

Algae growing on a fresh-water pond. Fatty acids can be extracted from algae using supercritical CO_2 and then converted to biodiesel fuel.

Yet another recently discovered use of supercritical CO_2 is in the process of dyeing polyester fabrics. The Dutch company that developed the process said, "On average, an estimated 100–150 L of water is needed to process 1 kg of textile material, with some 28 billion kilograms of textiles being dyed annually. Water is used as a solvent in many pretreatment and finishing processes .... Hence, the elimination of process-water and chemicals would be a real breakthrough for the textile dyeing industry .... Supercritical fluid CO_2 ... causes the polymer fiber to swell, allowing the dye to diffuse and penetrate the pore and capillary structure of the fibers. The viscosity of the dye solution is lower, making the circulation of the dye solutions easier and less energy intensive."

See *Sustainable Development of Algal Biofuels in the United States*, A Report from The National Academies, 2012.

Surface Tension, Capillary Action, and Viscosity

Molecules in the interior of a liquid interact with molecules all around them (Figure 11.16). In contrast, molecules on the surface of a liquid are affected only by those molecules located at or below the surface layer. This leads to a net inward force of attraction on the surface molecules, contracting the surface area and making the liquid behave as though it had a skin. The toughness of this skin is measured by its **surface tension**—the energy required to break through the surface or to disrupt a liquid drop and spread the material out as a film. Surface tension causes water drops to be spheres and not little cubes, for example (Figure 11.16), because a sphere has a smaller surface area than any other shape of the same volume.

Capillary action and the observation of a curved **meniscus** when liquids are in various containers are other consequences of intermolecular forces. When a piece of paper is partly immersed in water, the water rises in the paper because polar water molecules are attracted to the C—OH bonds present in the cellulose molecules in the paper (Figure 11.17, *left*).

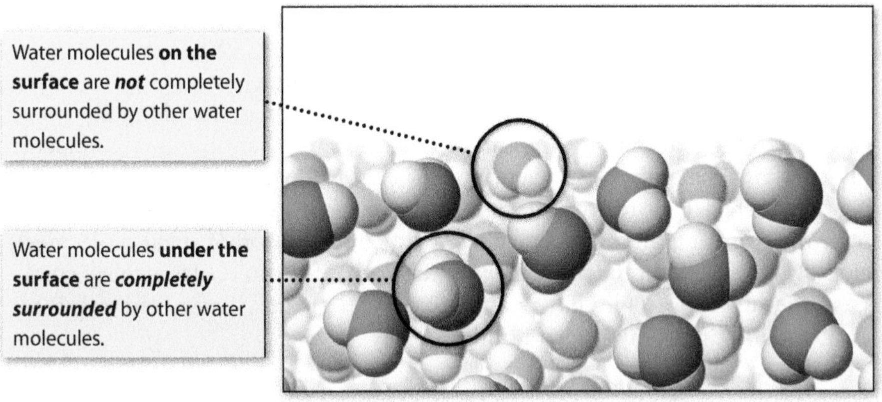

FIGURE 11.16 **Intermolecular forces in a liquid and surface tension.**

Spherical water droplets. Forces acting on molecules at the surface of a liquid are different than those acting on a molecule in the interior of a liquid. This causes water droplets to be spheres and not little cubes.

In Figure 11.17 (*right*) we observe the different behavior of water and mercury in glass tubes. Polar water molecules are attracted to the Si—OH bonds on the surface of glass by **adhesive forces.** These forces are strong enough that they can compete with the **cohesive forces** between the water molecules themselves. Thus, some water molecules can adhere to the walls; other water molecules are attracted to them by cohesive forces and build a "bridge" back into the liquid. The adhesive forces between the water and the glass are great enough that the water level rises along the edges. The rise will continue until the attractive forces—adhesion between water and glass, cohesion between water molecules—are balanced by the force of gravity pulling down on the water column. These forces lead to the characteristic concave, or downward-curving, **meniscus** seen with water in a glass tube (Figure 11.17).

In some liquids, cohesive forces (high surface tension) are greater than adhesive forces with glass. Mercury is one example. Mercury does not climb the walls of a glass capillary. In fact, when it is in a glass tube, mercury will form a convex, or upward-curving, meniscus (Figure 11.17).

Capillary Action
A piece of paper is partly immersed in water. Polar water molecules are attracted to the C–OH groups in the cellulose of the paper and water moves up the paper.

Meniscus
Water in glass tubes (*right*) is attracted to the polar –OH groups on the surface of glass and so water forms a downward facing or concave meniscus. Mercury, however, is not attracted to the glass surface, and so forms a convex meniscus (*left*).

FIGURE 11.17 **Intermolecular forces: capillary action (left) and the formation of a meniscus (right).**

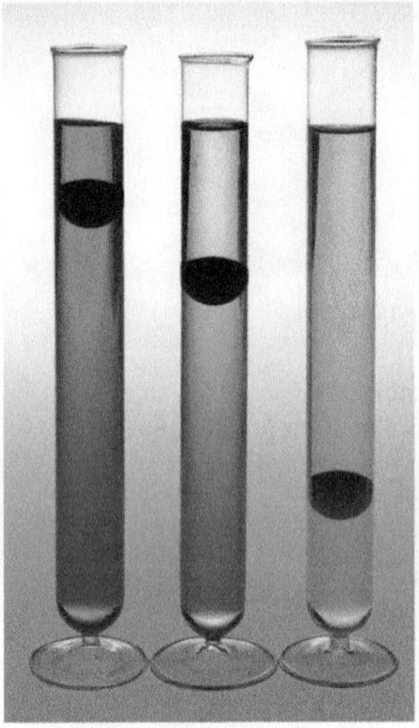
© Cengage Learning/Charles D. Winters

FIGURE 11.18 **Viscosity.** One way to measure viscosity is to compare the rate at which a heavy object drops in a liquid. Here you see the difference in viscosity of various motor oils. The oils become less viscous from left to right.

One other important property of liquids in which intermolecular forces play a role is **viscosity**, the resistance of liquids to flow (Figure 11.18). When you turn over a glassful of water, it empties quickly. In contrast, it takes much more time to empty a glassful of olive oil or honey. Olive oil consists of molecules with long chains of carbon atoms, and it is about 70 times more viscous than ethanol, a small molecule with only two carbons and one oxygen. Longer chains have greater intermolecular forces because there are more atoms to attract one another, with each atom contributing to the total force. Honey (a concentrated aqueous solution of sugar molecules), however, is also a viscous liquid, even though the size of the molecules is fairly small. In this case, the sugar molecules have numerous —OH groups. These lead to greater forces of attraction due to hydrogen bonding.

REVIEW & CHECK FOR SECTION 11-6

1. *Vapor pressure:* Suppose 0.50 g of pure water is sealed in an evacuated 5.0-L flask and the whole assembly is heated to 60 °C. Will any liquid water be left in the flask or does all of the water evaporate?

   (a) liquid is left (b) all the water evaporates

2. *Using the Clausius–Clapeyron equation:* Calculate the enthalpy of vaporization of diethyl ether, $(C_2H_5)_2O$ (Figure 11.12). This compound has vapor pressures of 57.0 mm Hg and 534 mm Hg at −22.8 °C and 25.0 °C, respectively.

   (a) 29.0 kJ/mol (b) 112 kJ/mol (c) 2.44 kJ/mol

3. At higher atmospheric pressures, to cook a hard-boiled egg, you should boil the egg for a ________ time because the water is boiling at a ________ temperature.

   (a) longer, lower

   (b) longer, higher

   (c) shorter, lower

   (d) shorter, higher

APPLYING CHEMICAL PRINCIPLES

Chromatography

Separation of mixtures into pure components is important in both the synthesis and the analysis of chemical compounds. A variety of methods are used for separations, including distillation, precipitation, and filtration. However, the most common means of separation of mixtures is chromatography, and the photo here shows a forensic chemist using an instrument called a high performance liquid chromatograph.

Chromatography is a general term for a collection of related separation methods. It entails using a mobile phase (commonly a liquid or gas) to move a sample (that is, the components in a mixture) through an immiscible stationary phase (usually a liquid or solid). The mobile and stationary phases are chosen so that the components in the mixture distribute themselves to varying degrees between the two phases. The rate at which components in a mixture move through the stationary phase depends on their intermolecular interactions with the mobile and stationary phases. Components that interact weakly with the stationary phase move more quickly through the stationary phase than the components that interact more strongly with that phase.

In one common form of chromatography, called partition chromatography, both the mobile and stationary phases are liquids. For example, a polar mobile phase (such as a mixture of methanol and water) is passed through a very thin column containing a nonpolar stationary phase. A common stationary phase is nonpolar octadecane ($C_{18}H_{38}$). The linear, 18-carbon chain (referred to as C-18) is usually bonded to a solid support, such as small silica particles, to immobilize it inside the column. As the mixture passes through the C-18 column, the components continuously move back and forth between the two liquid phases, with the less polar components spending more time in the nonpolar phase than the more polar components. In an ideal separation, the components that emerge from the column (that is, the eluents) are completed separated.

QUESTIONS:

1. Assume that a mixture of the three molecules below are separated on a C-18 column using a methanol/water mixture as the mobile phase.
   a. Which of the three molecules is most attracted to the mobile phase? What are the forces that attract the molecule to the water/methanol phase?
   b. Which molecule is most attracted to the stationary phase? What are the forces that attract the molecule to the nonpolar phase?
   c. In what order will the three molecules exit (or "elute from") the column?

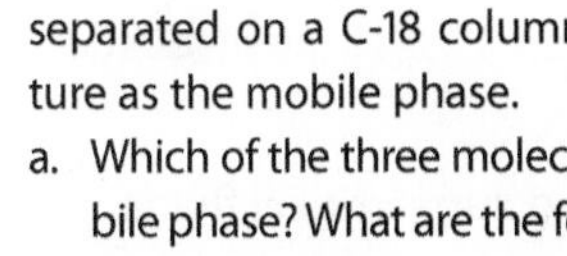

1-pentanol

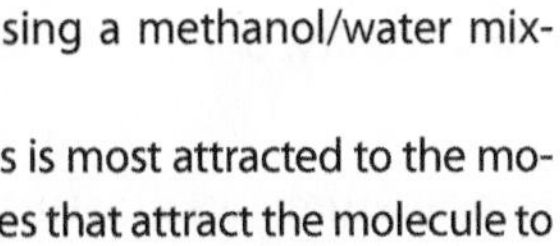

propyl ethyl ether

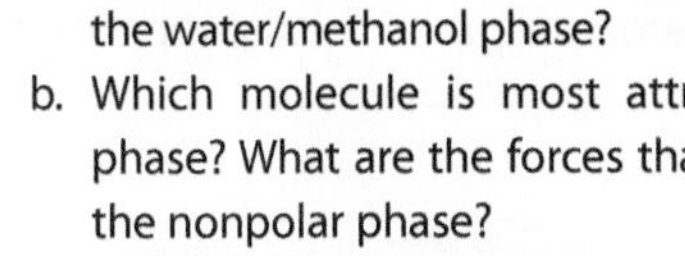

1,5-pentanediol

Caitlin Kilcoin

A forensic chemist uses a high performance liquid chromatograph (HPLC) for an analysis.

2. In gas chromatography the mobile phase is an inert gas such as N_2 or He. A mixture's components must be volatile if they are to move in the mobile phase. As with liquid chromatography, the separation is based upon forces of attraction of the various sample components with the mobile and the stationary phases; greater attractive forces between a compound and the column will result in a longer elution time. Assume that you want to separate a group of hydrocarbons, such as pentane (C_5H_{12}), hexane (C_6H_{14}), heptane (C_7H_{16}), and octane (C_8H_{18}) using a column with a nonpolar stationary phase. Predict the order of elution of these species from the column and explain your answer.

CHAPTER GOALS REVISITED

Now that you have studied this chapter, you should ask whether you have met the chapter goals. In particular, you should be able to:

UNDERSTAND

- The nature of the various types of intermolecular forces.
  a. Describe the various intermolecular forces found in liquids and solids (Sections 11-3 and 11-4). Study Questions: 1–10, 29–32, 43.

b. Decide when two molecules can interact through a dipole–dipole attraction and when hydrogen bonding may occur. (Section 11-3). Study Questions: 1–8.
c. Identify instances in which molecules interact by induced dipoles (London dispersion forces) (Section 11-4). Study Questions: 1–8.

- The origin and importance of hydrogen bonding.
  a. Explain how hydrogen bonding affects the properties of water (Section 11-3). Study Questions: 1–8.
- The relationship between the properties of liquids and intermolecular forces.
  a. Define the equilibrium vapor pressure of a liquid, and explain the relationship between the vapor pressure and boiling point of a liquid (Section 11-6). Study Questions: 13, 15, 17, 19, 20, 33.
  b. Describe how intermolecular interactions affect the cohesive forces between identical liquid molecules, the energy necessary to break through the surface of a liquid (surface tension), capillary action, and the resistance to flow, or viscosity, of liquids (Section 11-6). Study Questions: 25–28, 45, 46.
- The nature of critical temperature and pressure and supercritical fluids.
  a. Describe the phenomena of the critical temperature, T_c, and critical pressure, P_c, of a substance (Section 11-6). Study Questions: 23, 24, 53.

DO

- Identify the intermolecular forces between simple molecules. Study Questions: 1–8.
- Calculate enthalpy changes for changes of state (Section 11-6). Study Questions: 11, 12.
- Represent the connection between vapor pressure and temperature graphically (Section 11-6). Study Questions: 13, 19, 33, 39.
- Use the Clausius–Clapeyron equation to relate vapor pressure and enthalpy of vaporization (Section 11-6). Study Questions: 21, 22, 38, 39.

REMEMBER

- The various intermolecular forces and how they arise (Sections 11-2–11-5). Study Questions: 1–8.

KEY EQUATIONS

Equation 11.1 (page 427) The Clausius–Clapeyron equation relates the equilibrium vapor pressure, P, of a volatile liquid to the molar enthalpy of vaporization ($\Delta_{vap}H°$) at a given temperature, T. (R is the universal constant, 8.314472 J/K · mol.)

$$\ln P = -(\Delta_{vap}H°/RT) + C$$

Equation 11.2 (page 428) This modification of the Clausius–Clapeyron equation allows you to calculate $\Delta_{vap}H°$ if you know the vapor pressures at two different temperatures.

$$\ln\frac{P_2}{P_1} = -\frac{\Delta_{vap}H°}{R}\left[\frac{1}{T_2} - \frac{1}{T_1}\right]$$

© Picade LLC/Alamy

STUDY QUESTIONS

▲ denotes challenging questions.

Blue-numbered questions have answers in Appendix N and fully worked solutions in the *Student Solutions Manual.*

Practicing Skills

Intermolecular Forces

(See Sections 11-1–11-5 and Examples 11.1–11.4.)

1. What intermolecular force(s) must be overcome to perform the following?
   (a) melt ice
   (b) sublime solid I_2
   (c) convert liquid NH_3 to NH_3 vapor
2. Intermolecular forces: What type of forces must be overcome between I_2 molecules when solid I_2 dissolves in methanol, CH_3OH? What type of forces must be disrupted between CH_3OH molecules when I_2 dissolves? What type of forces exist between I_2 and CH_3OH molecules in solution?
3. What type of intermolecular forces must be overcome in converting each of the following from a liquid to a gas?
   (a) liquid O_2
   (b) mercury
   (c) CH_3I (methyl iodide)
   (d) CH_3CH_2OH (ethanol)
4. What type of intermolecular forces must be overcome in converting each of the following from a liquid to a gas?
   (a) CO_2
   (b) NH_3
   (c) $CHCl_3$
   (d) CCl_4
5. Considering intermolecular forces in the pure substance, which of these substances exists as a gas at 25 °C and 1 atm?
   (a) Ne
   (b) CH_4
   (c) CO
   (d) CCl_4
6. Considering intermolecular forces in the pure substance, which of these substances exists as a gas at 25 °C and 1 atm?
   (a) $CH_3CH_2CH_2CH_3$ (butane)
   (b) CH_3OH (methanol)
   (c) Ar
7. Which of the following compounds would be expected to form intermolecular hydrogen bonds in the liquid state?
   (a) CH_3OCH_3 (dimethyl ether)
   (b) CH_4
   (c) HF
   (d) CH_3CO_2H (acetic acid)

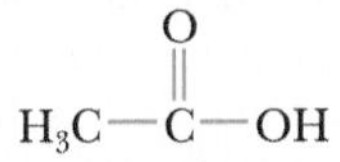

acetic acid

   (e) Br_2
   (f) CH_3OH (methanol)
8. Which of the following compounds would be expected to form intermolecular hydrogen bonds in the liquid state?
   (a) H_2Se
   (b) HCO_2H (formic acid)

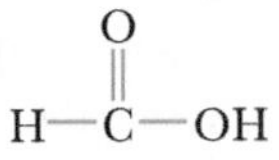

formic acid

   (c) HI
   (d) acetone, $(CH_3)_2CO$

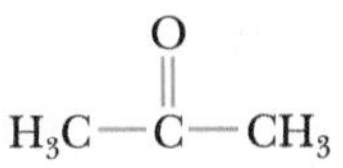

acetone

9. In each pair of ionic compounds, which is more likely to have the more negative enthalpy of hydration? Briefly explain your reasoning in each case.
   (a) LiCl or CsCl
   (b) $NaNO_3$ or $Mg(NO_3)_2$
   (c) RbCl or $NiCl_2$

10. When salts of Mg^{2+}, Na^+, and Cs^+ are placed in water, the ions are hydrated. Which of these three cations is most strongly hydrated? Which one is least strongly hydrated?

Liquids

(See Section 11-6 and Examples 11.5 and 11.6.)

11. Ethanol, CH_3CH_2OH, has a vapor pressure of 59 mm Hg at 25 °C. What quantity of energy as heat is required to evaporate 125 mL of the alcohol at 25 °C? The enthalpy of vaporization of the alcohol at 25 °C is 42.32 kJ/mol. The density of the liquid is 0.7849 g/mL.

12. The enthalpy of vaporization of liquid mercury is 59.11 kJ/mol. What quantity of energy as heat is required to vaporize 0.500 mL of mercury at 357 °C, its normal boiling point? The density of mercury is 13.6 g/mL.

13. Answer the following questions using Figure 11.12:
   (a) What is the approximate equilibrium vapor pressure of water at 60 °C? Compare your answer with the data in Appendix G.
   (b) At what temperature does water have an equilibrium vapor pressure of 600 mm Hg?
   (c) Compare the equilibrium vapor pressures of water and ethanol at 70 °C. Which is higher?

14. Answer the following questions using Figure 11.12:
   (a) What is the equilibrium vapor pressure of diethyl ether at room temperature (approximately 20 °C)?
   (b) Place the three compounds in Figure 11.12 in order of increasing intermolecular forces.
   (c) If the pressure in a flask is 400 mm Hg and if the temperature is 40 °C, which of the three compounds (diethyl ether, ethanol, and water) are liquids, and which are gases?

15. Assume you seal 1.0 g of diethyl ether (Figure 11.12) in an evacuated 100.-mL flask. If the flask is held at 30 °C, what is the approximate gas pressure in the flask? If the flask is placed in an ice bath, does additional liquid ether evaporate, or does some ether condense to a liquid?

16. Refer to Figure 11.12 to answer these questions:
   (a) You heat some water to 60 °C in a lightweight plastic bottle and seal the top very tightly so gas cannot enter or leave the carton. What happens when the water cools?
   (b) If you put a few drops of liquid diethyl ether on your hand, does it evaporate completely or remain a liquid?

17. Which member of each of the following pairs of compounds has the higher boiling point?
   (a) O_2 or N_2
   (b) SO_2 or CO_2
   (c) HF or HI
   (d) SiH_4 or GeH_4

18. Place the following four compounds in order of increasing boiling point:
   (a) C_5H_{12}
   (b) CCl_4
   (c) C_2H_6
   (d) Ne

19. Vapor pressure curves for CS_2 (carbon disulfide) and CH_3NO_2 (nitromethane) are drawn here.
   (a) What are the approximate vapor pressures of CS_2 and CH_3NO_2 at 40 °C?
   (b) What type(s) of intermolecular forces exist in the liquid phase of each compound?
   (c) What is the normal boiling point of CS_2? Of CH_3NO_2?
   (d) At what temperature does CS_2 have a vapor pressure of 600 mm Hg?
   (e) At what temperature does CH_3NO_2 have a vapor pressure of 600 mm Hg?

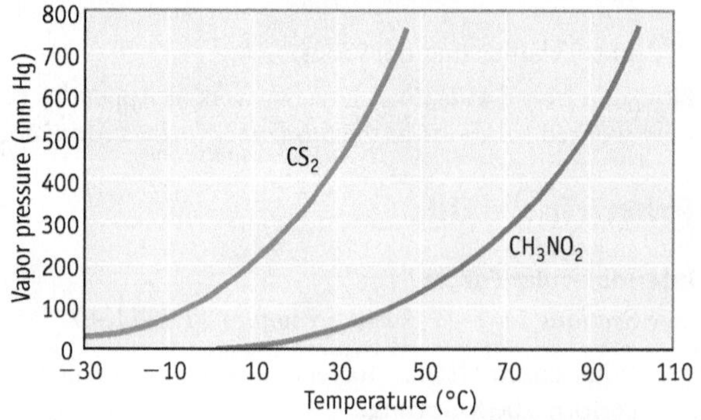

20. You are comparing three different substances, A, B, and C, all liquids and having similar molar masses. The vapor pressure at 25 °C for substance A is less than the vapor pressure for B at this temperature. Substance C has the highest boiling point of the three substances. List the three substances A, B, or C in order of the strength of intermolecular forces, from least to greatest.

21. Equilibrium vapor pressures of benzene, C_6H_6, at various temperatures are given in the table.

Temperature (°C)	Vapor Pressure (mm Hg)
7.6	40.
26.1	100.
60.6	400.
80.1	760.

   (a) What is the normal boiling point of benzene?
   (b) Plot these data so that you have a graph resembling the one in Figure 11.12. At what temperature does the liquid have an equilibrium vapor pressure of 250 mm Hg? At what temperature is the vapor pressure 650 mm Hg?
   (c) Calculate the molar enthalpy of vaporization for benzene using the Clausius–Clapeyron equation.

22. Vapor pressure data are given here for octane, C_8H_{18}.

Temperature (°C)	Vapor Pressure (mm Hg)
25	13.6
50.	45.3
75	127.2
100.	310.8

Use the Clausius–Clapeyron equation to calculate the molar enthalpy of vaporization of octane and its normal boiling point.

23. Can carbon monoxide (T_c = 132.9 K; P_c = 34.5 atm) be liquefied at or above room temperature? Explain briefly.

24. Methane (CH_4) cannot be liquefied at room temperature, no matter how high the pressure. Propane (C_3H_8), another simple hydrocarbon, has a critical pressure of 42 atm and a critical temperature of 96.7 °C. Can this compound be liquefied at room temperature?

25. What is surface tension? Give an example illustrating the phenomenon of surface tension. Explain why surface tension is the consequence of intermolecular forces.

26. What factors affect the viscosity of a substance? Which of the following substances, water (H_2O), ethanol (CH_3CH_2OH), ethylene glycol ($HOCH_2CH_2OH$), and glycerol ($HOCH_2CH(OH)CH_2OH$), is expected to have the highest viscosity? Should viscosity of a substance be affected by temperature? Explain your answers.

27. If a piece of filter paper (an absorbent paper used in laboratories) is suspended above a beaker of water and just touching the surface, water will slowly move up the paper. What is the name given to this phenomenon, and how is this behavior explained?

28. When water is placed in a buret it forms a concave meniscus at the surface. In contrast, mercury (in a manometer for example) forms a convex meniscus (Figure 11.17). Explain why this phenomenon occurs, and why the two liquids give different results. Predict the meniscus shape if the buret is filled with ethylene glycol ($HOCH_2CH_2OH$).

General Questions

These questions are not designated as to type or location in the chapter. They may combine several concepts.

29. What types of intermolecular forces are important in the liquid phase of (a) CCl_4, (b) CH_3Cl, and (c) CH_3CO_2H (acetic acid)?

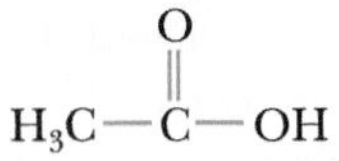

acetic acid

30. What types of intermolecular forces are important in the liquid phase of (a) C_2H_6 and (b) $(CH_3)_2CHOH$?

31. Which of the following salts, Li_2SO_4 or Cs_2SO_4, is expected to have the more exothermic enthalpy of hydration?

32. Select the substance in each of the following pairs that should have the higher boiling point:

(a) Br_2 or ICl
(b) neon or krypton
(c) CH_3CH_2OH (ethanol) or C_2H_4O (ethylene oxide, structure below)

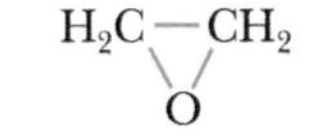

ethylene oxide

33. Use the vapor pressure curves illustrated here to answer the questions that follow.

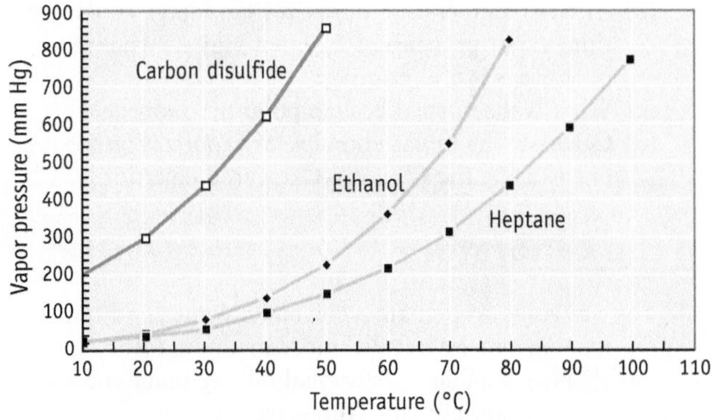

(a) What is the vapor pressure of ethanol, C_2H_5OH, at 60 °C?
(b) Considering only carbon disulfide (CS_2) and ethanol, which has the stronger intermolecular forces in the liquid state?
(c) At what temperature does heptane (C_7H_{16}) have a vapor pressure of 500 mm Hg?
(d) What are the approximate normal boiling points of each of the three substances?
(e) At a pressure of 400 mm Hg and a temperature of 70 °C, is each substance a liquid, a gas, or a mixture of liquid and gas?

34. Which of the following ionic compounds will have the most negative enthalpy of hydration?

(a) $Fe(NO_3)_2$
(b) $CoCl_2$
(c) NaCl
(d) $Al(NO_3)_3$

35. Rank the following compounds in order of increasing molar enthalpy of vaporization: CH_3OH, C_2H_6, HCl.

36. Rank the following molecules in order of increasing boiling point: $CH_3CH_2CH_2CH_2CH_3$, CH_3F, CH_3Cl.

37. Mercury and many of its compounds are dangerous poisons if breathed, swallowed, or even absorbed through the skin. The liquid metal has a vapor pressure of 0.00169 mm Hg at 24 °C. If the air in a small room is saturated with mercury vapor, how many atoms of mercury vapor occur per cubic meter?

38. ▲ The following data are the equilibrium vapor pressure of limonene, $C_{10}H_{16}$, at various temperatures. (Limonene is used as a scent in commercial products.)

Temperature (°C)	Vapor Pressure (mm Hg)
14.0	1.0
53.8	10.
84.3	40.
108.3	100.
151.4	400.

(a) Plot these data as ln P versus $1/T$ so that you have a graph resembling the one in Figure 11.13.
(b) At what temperature does the liquid have an equilibrium vapor pressure of 250 mm Hg? At what temperature is it 650 mm Hg?
(c) What is the normal boiling point of limonene?
(d) Calculate the molar enthalpy of vaporization for limonene using the Clausius–Clapeyron equation.

In the Laboratory

39. You are going to prepare a silicone polymer, and one of the starting materials is dichlorodimethylsilane, $SiCl_2(CH_3)_2$. You need its normal boiling point and to measure equilibrium vapor pressures at various temperatures.

Temperature (°C)	Vapor Pressure (mm Hg)
−0.4	40.
+17.5	100.
51.9	400.
70.3	760.

(a) What is the normal boiling point of dichlorodimethylsilane?
(b) Plot these data as ln P versus $1/T$ so that you have a plot resembling the one in Figure 11.13. At what temperature does the liquid have an equilibrium vapor pressure of 250 mm Hg? At what temperature is it 650 mm Hg?
(c) Calculate the molar enthalpy of vaporization for dichlorodimethylsilane using the Clausius–Clapeyron equation.

40. A "hand boiler" can be purchased in toy stores or at science supply companies. If you cup your hand around the bottom bulb, the volatile liquid in the boiler boils, and the liquid moves to the upper chamber.

(a) Using your knowledge of kinetic molecular theory and intermolecular forces, explain how the hand boiler works.

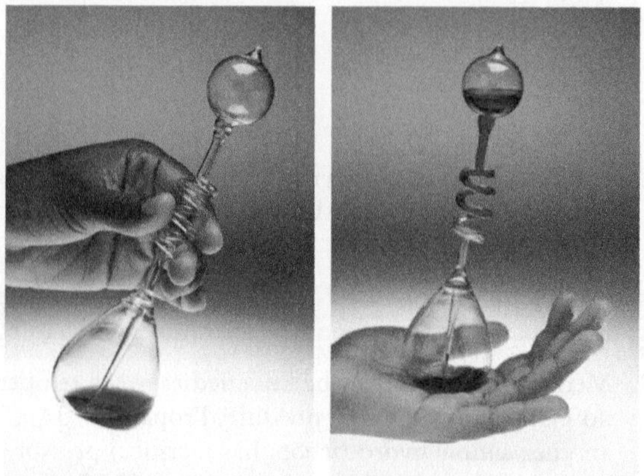

Photos: © Cengage Learning/Charles D. Winters

(b) Which of the following liquids would be best to use in the hand boiler? Explain.

Compound	Normal Boiling Point
Ethanol	78.4 °C
Chloroform	61.3 °C
CCl_3F	23.7 °C

41. ▲ The photos below illustrate an experiment you can do yourself. Place 10 mL of water in an empty soda can, and heat the water to boiling. Using tongs or pliers, turn the can over in a pan of cold water, making sure the opening in the can is below the water level in the pan.

Photos: © Cengage Learning/Charles D. Winters

(a) **(b)**

(a) Describe what happens, and explain it in terms of the subject of this chapter.
(b) Prepare a molecular level sketch of the situation inside the can before heating and after heating (but prior to inverting the can).

42. If you place 1.0 L of ethanol (C_2H_5OH) in a small laboratory that is 3.0 m long, 2.5 m wide, and 2.5 m high, will all the alcohol evaporate? If some liquid remains, how much will there be? The vapor pressure of ethanol at 25 °C is 59 mm Hg, and the density of the liquid at this temperature is 0.785 g/cm³.

Summary and Conceptual Questions

The following questions may use concepts from this and previous chapters.

43. Acetone, CH_3COCH_3, is a common laboratory solvent. It is usually contaminated with water, however. Why does acetone absorb water so readily? Draw molecular structures showing how water and acetone can interact. What intermolecular force(s) is(are) involved in the interaction?

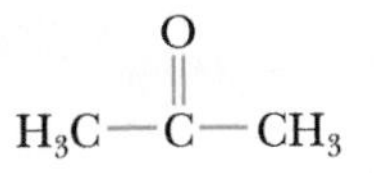

44. Cooking oil floats on top of water. From this observation, what conclusions can you draw regarding the polarity or hydrogen-bonding ability of molecules found in cooking oil?

45. Liquid ethylene glycol, $HOCH_2CH_2OH$, is one of the main ingredients in commercial antifreeze. Would you predict its viscosity to be greater or less than that of ethanol, CH_3CH_2OH?

46. Liquid methanol, CH_3OH, is placed in a glass tube. Is the meniscus of the liquid concave or convex? Explain briefly.

47. Account for these facts:
   (a) Although ethanol (C_2H_5OH) (bp, 80 °C) has a higher molar mass than water (bp, 100 °C), the alcohol has a lower boiling point.
   (b) Mixing 50 mL of ethanol with 50 mL of water produces a solution with a volume slightly less than 100 mL.

48. Rationalize the observation that $CH_3CH_2CH_2OH$, 1-propanol, has a boiling point of 97.2 °C, whereas a compound with the same empirical formula, methyl ethyl ether ($CH_3CH_2OCH_3$), boils at 7.4 °C.

49. Cite two pieces of evidence to support the statement that water molecules in the liquid state exert considerable attractive force on one another.

50. During thunderstorms in the Midwest, very large hailstones can fall from the sky. (Some are the size of golf balls!) To preserve some of these stones, we put them in the freezer compartment of a frost-free refrigerator. Our friend, who is a chemistry student, tells us to use an older model that is not frost-free. Why?

51. Refer to Figure 11.8 to answer the following questions:
   (a) Of the three hydrogen halides (HX), which has the largest total intermolecular force?
   (b) Why are the dispersion forces greater for HI than for HCl?
   (c) Why are the dipole–dipole forces greater for HCl than for HI?
   (d) Of the seven molecules in Figure 11.8, which involves the largest dispersion forces? Explain why this is reasonable.

52. At the Fred Hutchison Cancer Research Center in Seattle it was discovered that mice can be put into a state of suspended animation by applying a low dose of hydrogen sulfide, H_2S. The breathing rate of the mice fell from 120 to 10 breaths per minute and their temperature fell to just 2 °C above ambient temperature. Six hours later the mice were revived and seemed to show no negative effects.
   (a) Hydrogen sulfide is a gas at room temperature and normal atmospheric pressure whereas water is a liquid with a low vapor pressure under the same conditions. Explain this observation.
   (b) The H_2S gas delivered to the mice had a concentration of 80 ppm. (A concentration of 1 ppm is 1 part per million, or one molecule in every 1 million molecules.) If you deliver 1.0 L of gas (a mixture of O_2, N_2, and H_2S) at a total pressure of 725 mm Hg at a temperature of 22 °C, what is the partial pressure of the H_2S gas?
   (c) Hydrogen sulfide can be converted to sulfuric acid. If 5.2 L of H_2S gas at 130 mm Hg pressure and 25 °C is allowed to react with O_2 gas, how many liters of O_2 gas, also at 130 mm Hg pressure and 25 °C, are required for complete reaction? Assume the following reaction occurs.

$$H_2S(g) + 2\,O_2(g) \rightarrow H_2SO_4(\ell)$$

53. A fluorocarbon, CF_4, has a critical temperature of −45.7 °C and a critical pressure of 37 atm. Are there any conditions under which this compound can be a liquid at room temperature? Explain briefly.

54. ▲ The figure below is a plot of vapor pressure versus temperature for dichlorodifluoromethane, CCl_2F_2. The enthalpy of vaporization of the liquid is 165 kJ/g, and the specific heat capacity of the liquid is about 1.0 J/g · K.

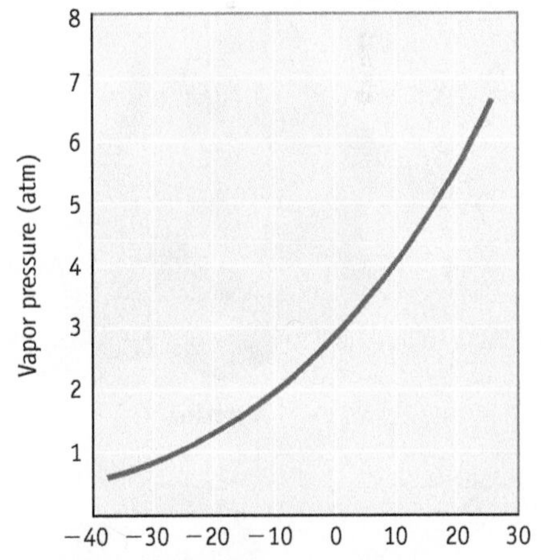

   (a) What is the approximate normal boiling point of CCl_2F_2?
   (b) A steel cylinder containing 25 kg of CCl_2F_2 in the form of liquid and vapor is set outdoors on a warm day (25 °C). What is the approximate pressure of the vapor in the cylinder?
   (c) The cylinder valve is opened, and CCl_2F_2 vapor gushes out of the cylinder in a rapid flow. Soon, however, the flow becomes much slower, and the outside of the cylinder is coated with ice frost. When the valve is closed and the cylinder is reweighed, it is found that 20 kg of CCl_2F_2 is still in the cylinder.

Why is the flow fast at first? Why does it slow down long before the cylinder is empty? Why does the outside become icy?

(d) Which of the following procedures would be effective in emptying the cylinder rapidly (and safely)? (1) Turn the cylinder upside down, and open the valve. (2) Cool the cylinder to −78 °C in dry ice, and open the valve. (3) Knock off the top of the cylinder, valve and all, with a hammer.

55. Acetaminophen is used in analgesics. A model of the molecule is shown here with its electrostatic potential surface. Where are the most likely sites for hydrogen bonding?

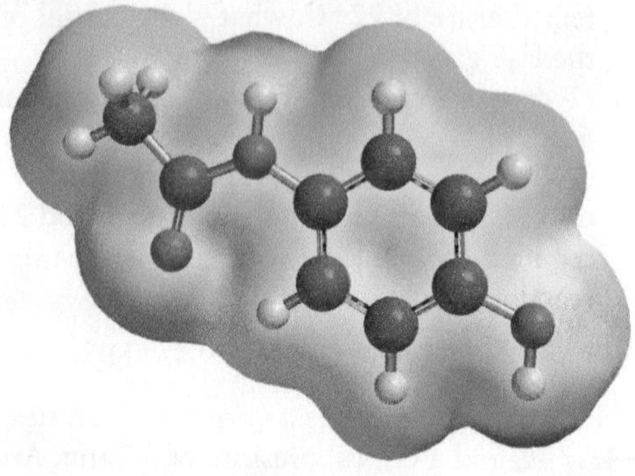

Acetaminophen

56. Shown here are models of two bases in DNA with the electrostatic potential surfaces: cytosine and guanine. What sites in these molecules are involved in hydrogen bonding with each other? Draw molecular structures showing how cytosine can hydrogen-bond with guanine.

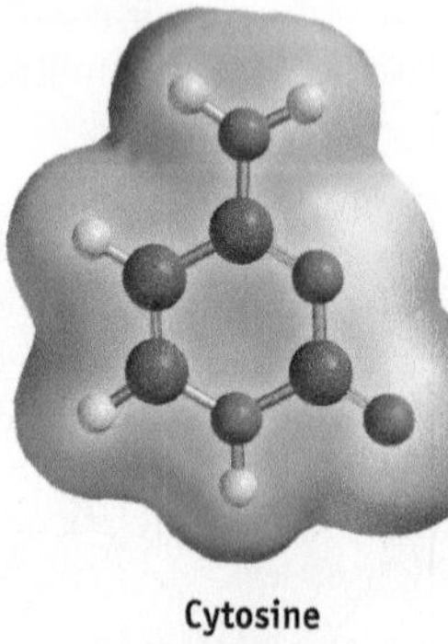

Cytosine

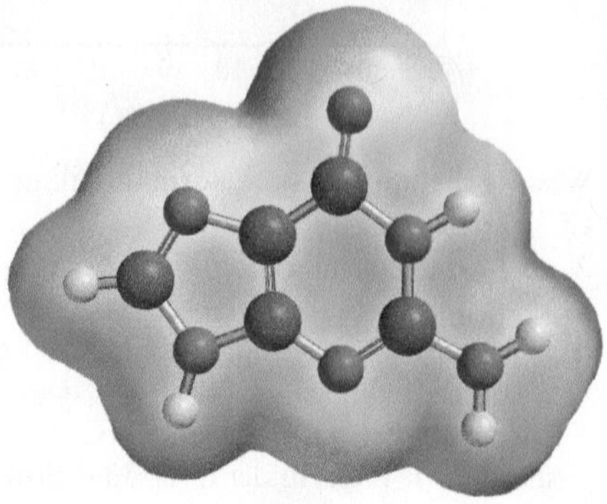

Guanine

57. List four properties of liquids that are directly determined by intermolecular forces.

58. List the following ions in order of hydration energies: Na^+, K^+, Mg^{2+}, Ca^{2+}. Explain how you determined this order.

59. Compare the boiling points of the various isomeric hydrocarbons shown in the table below. Notice the relationship between boiling point and structure; branched-chain hydrocarbons have lower boiling points than the unbranched isomer. Speculate on possible reasons for this trend. Why might the intermolecular forces be slightly different in these compounds?

Compound	Boiling Point (°C)
Hexane	68.9
3-Methylpentane	63.2
2-Methylpentane	60.3
2,3-Dimethylbutane	58.0
2,2-Dimethylbutane	49.7

60. An 8.82 g sample of Br_2 is placed in an evacuated 1.00 L flask and heated to 58.8 °C, the normal boiling point of bromine. Describe the contents of the flask under these conditions.

61. Polarizability is defined as the extent to which the electron cloud surrounding an atom or molecule can be distorted by an external charge. Rank the halogens (F_2, Cl_2, Br_2, I_2) and the noble gases (He, Ne, Ar, Kr, Xe) in order of polarizability (from least polarizable to most polarizable). What characteristics of these substances could be used to determine this ranked order?

62. In which of the following organic molecules might we expect hydrogen bonding to occur?

(a) methyl acetate, $CH_3CO_2CH_3$

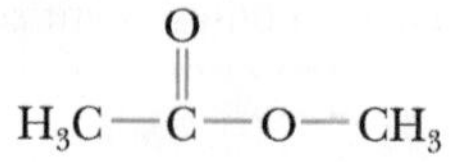

(b) acetaldehyde (ethanal), CH_3CHO

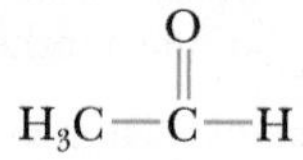

(c) acetone (2-propanone) (see Question 8)

(d) benzoic acid ($C_6H_5CO_2H$)

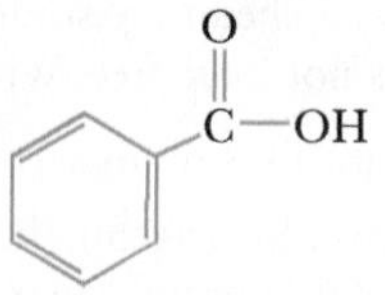

(e) acetamide (CH_3CONH_2 an amide formed from acetic acid and ammonia)

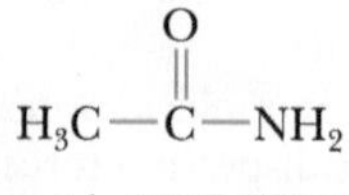

(f) N,N-dimethylacetamide [$CH_3CON(CH_3)_2$, an amide formed from acetic acid and dimethylamine]

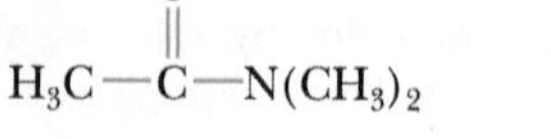

63. A pressure cooker (a kitchen appliance) is a pot on which the top seals tightly, allowing pressure to build up inside. You put water in the pot and heat it to boiling. At the higher pressure, water boils at a higher temperature, and this allows food to cook at a faster rate. Most pressure cookers have a setting of 15 psi, which means that the pressure in the pot is 15 psi above atmospheric pressure (1 atm = 14.70 psi). Use the Clausius–Clapeyron equation to calculate the temperature at which water boils in the pressure cooker.

64. Vapor pressures of $NH_3(\ell)$ at several temperatures are given in the table below. Use this information to calculate the enthalpy of vaporization of ammonia.

Temperature (°C)	Vapor Pressure (atm)
−68.4	0.132
−45.4	0.526
−33.6	1.000
−18.7	2.00
4.7	5.00
25.7	10.00
50.1	20.00

65. Chemists sometimes carry out reactions in liquid ammonia as a solvent. With adequate safety protection these reactions can be done at temperatures above ammonia's boiling point in a sealed, thick-walled glass tube. If the reaction is being carried out at 20 °C, what is the pressure of ammonia inside the tube? (Use data from the previous question to answer this question.)

66. The data in the following table were used to create the graph shown below (P = vapor pressure of ethanol (CH_3CH_2OH) expressed in mm Hg, T = kelvin temperature).

ln *P*	1/*T* (K^{-1})
2.30	0.00369
3.69	0.00342
4.61	0.00325
5.99	0.00297
6.63	0.00285

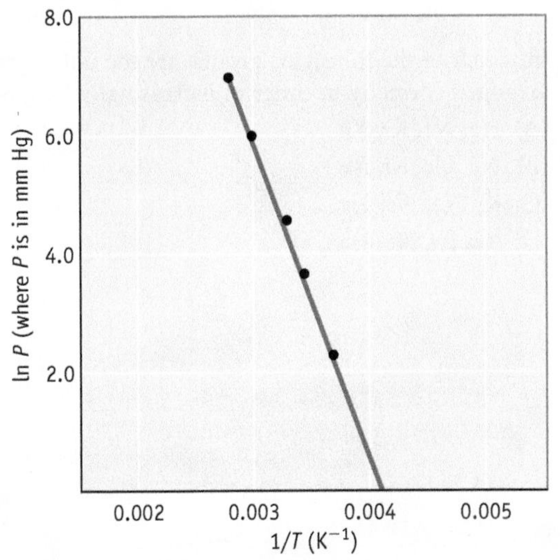

(a) Derive an equation for the straight line in this graph.
(b) Describe in words how to use the graph to determine the enthalpy of vaporization of ethanol.
(c) Calculate the vapor pressure of ethanol at 0.00 °C and at 100 °C.

67. Water (10.0 g) is placed in a thick-walled glass tube whose internal volume is 50.0 cm^3. Then all the air is removed, the tube is sealed, and then the tube and contents are heated to 100 °C.

(a) Describe the appearance of the system at 100 °C.
(b) What is the pressure inside the tube?
(c) At this temperature, liquid water has a density of 0.958 g/cm^3. Calculate the volume of liquid water in the tube.
(d) Some of the water is in the vapor state. Determine the mass of water in the gaseous state.

68. Acetone is a common solvent. (See Study Question 8 for the structure of acetone.)

(a) Allyl alcohol, $CH_2{=}CH{-}CH_2OH$, is an isomer of acetone. Acetone has a vapor pressure of 100 mm Hg at +7.7 °C. Predict whether the vapor pressure of allyl alcohol is higher or lower than 100 mm Hg at this temperature? Explain.
(b) Use the Clausius–Clapeyron equation to calculate the enthalpy of vaporization of acetone from the following data.

Temperature (°C)	Vapor Pressure (mm Hg)
−9.4	40.
+7.7	100.
39.5	400.
56.5	760.

(c) Fluorination of acetone, C_3H_6O (substitution of fluorine for H) produces a gaseous compound with the formula $C_3H_{6-x}F_xO$. To identify this compound its molar mass was determined by measuring the gas density. The following data were obtained: Mass of gas, 1.53 g; volume of flask = 264 mL; pressure exerted by gas, 722 mm Hg; temperature, 22 °C. Calculate the molar mass from this information, then identify the molecular formula.

AP Multiple-Choice Review Questions

1. The boiling points of hydrogen chloride and hydrogen bromide are given in the table below. Based on periodicity and intermolecular forces, which of the other two hydrogen halides would have a boiling point that is higher than that of HBr?

Compound	HCl	HBr	HI	HF
Boiling Point	−85 °C	−66 °C	?	?

(A) HI only
(B) HF only
(C) HI and HF
(D) Neither HI nor HF

2. Which statement correctly describes the changes occurring in the two equations shown below?

Equation I: $H_2O(s) \rightarrow H_2O(\ell)$
Equation II: $2H_2O(\ell) \rightarrow 2H_2(g) + O_2(g)$

(A) Equation I represents a physical change because only intermolecular bonds are broken, whereas Equation II represents a chemical change because intramolecular bonds are broken.
(B) Equation I represents a physical change because only intramolecular bonds are broken, whereas Equation II represents a chemical change because intermolecular bonds are broken.
(C) Equation I represents a chemical change because only intermolecular bonds are broken, whereas Equation II represents a physical change because intramolecular bonds are broken.
(D) Equation I represents a chemical change because only intramolecular bonds are broken, whereas Equation II represents a physical change because intermolecular bonds are broken.

3. Based on molecular structure and intermolecular forces, which of these substances would you predict to have the greatest viscosity?

(A)
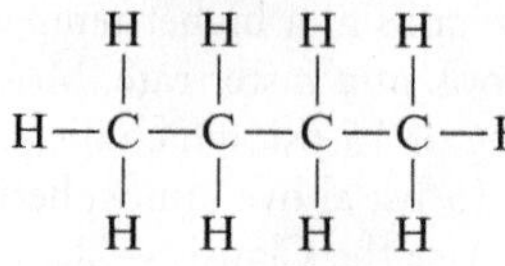

(B)
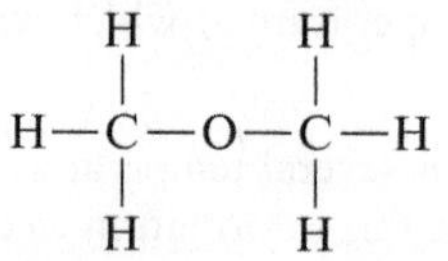

(C)
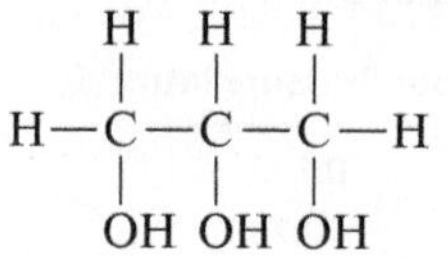

(D)
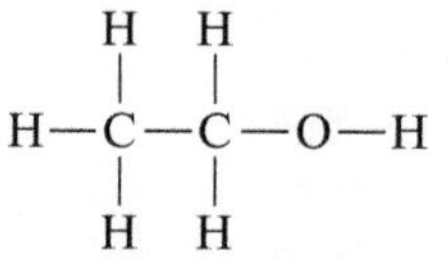

4. The physical properties of four unknown pure substances were determined in a laboratory. Based on the information given in the table below, which correctly identifies the type of element or compound?

Unknown	**Physical State at 25 °C**	**Conductivity at 25 °C**	**Solubility in Water**	**Vapor Pressure**	**Melting Point**
W	Solid	No	Soluble	Low	High
X	Solid	No	Insoluble	Low	Very high
Y	Liquid	No	Soluble	High	Low
Z	Solid	Yes	Insoluble	Low	High

(A) W = covalent network; X = metallic; Y = molecular; Z = ionic
(B) W = molecular; X = covalent network; Y = ionic; Z = metallic
(C) W = metallic; X = ionic; Y = covalent network; Z = molecular
(D) W = ionic; X = covalent network; Y = molecular; Z = metallic

5. In which of the following groups are the noble gases arranged correctly in order of increasing boiling point?

(A) He, Ne, Kr, Xe
(B) Ne, He, Kr, Xe
(C) Kr, Xe, Ne, He
(D) Xe, Kr, Ne, He

6. Which of these would best show the structure of solid carbon dioxide (dry ice)?

(A)

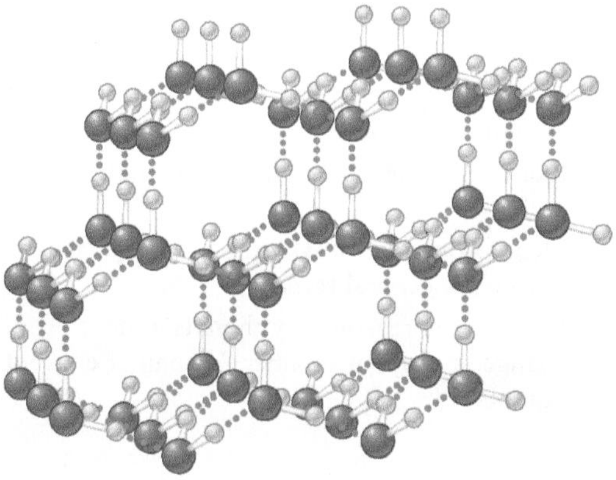

(B)

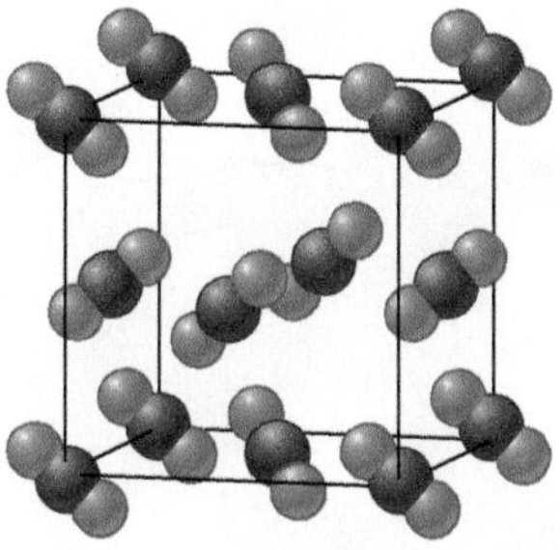

(C)

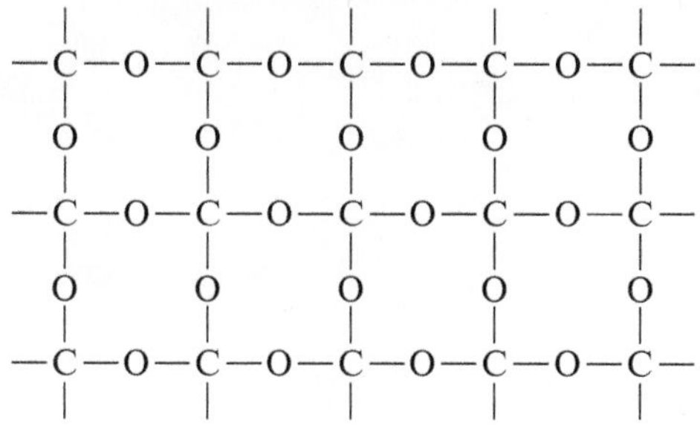

(D)

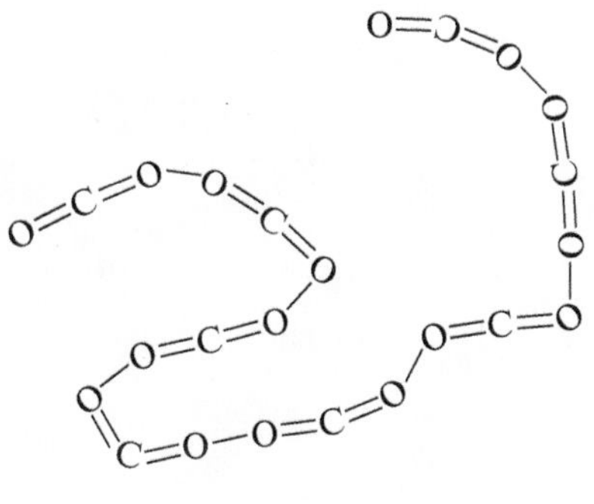

7. Silicon dioxide, SiO_2, is a covalent network solid with each silicon atom bonded to four oxygen atoms, forming a large network of SiO_4 tetrahedra of great strength. Which of these other compounds would you predict to have similar properties?

(A) MgO
(B) CO_2
(C) SO_2
(D) GeO_2

AP Free Response Review Questions

Question Format: Short

Category of Question: Lab 2

Below is a graph relating the specific heat of the elements to their atomic number.

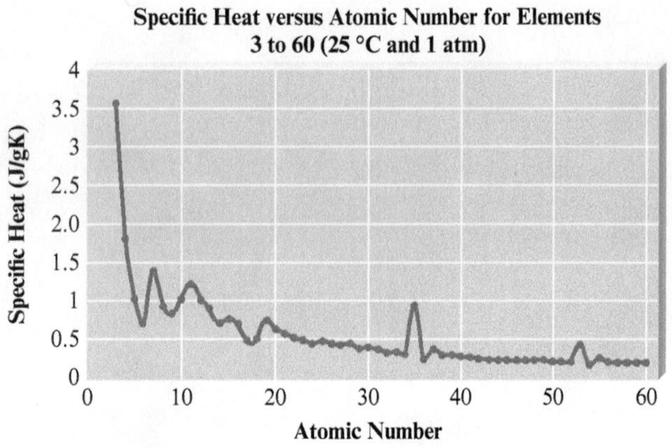

Questions

(a) What is the general trend as the atomic number of the elements is increased?

(b) From atomic number 20 to atomic number 60, although there is an observable trend, the trend is not followed at atomic numbers 35 and 53.

(i) Identify the elements with atomic numbers 35 and 53.

(ii) Identify one reason why those two elements do not follow the general trend.

(iii) Provide one reason why there is a more pronounced change at element number 35 than at element number 53.

Question Format: Short

Category of Question: Rep 1 or 2

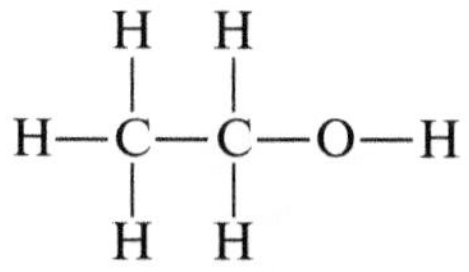

Ethanol

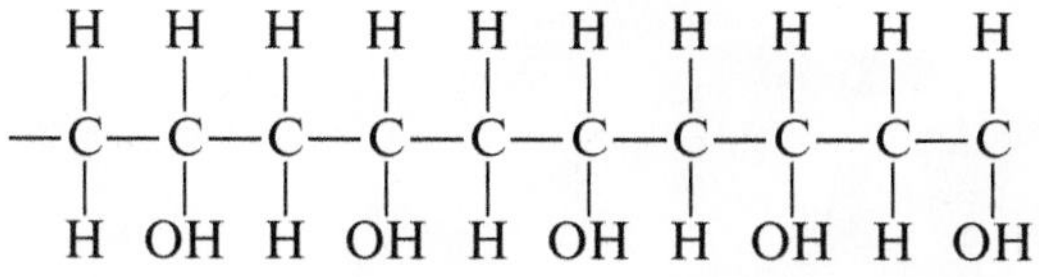

Polyvinyl alcohol (only part of molecule is shown)

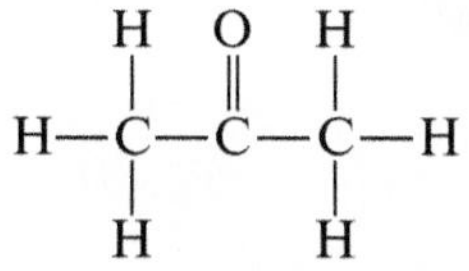

Acetone

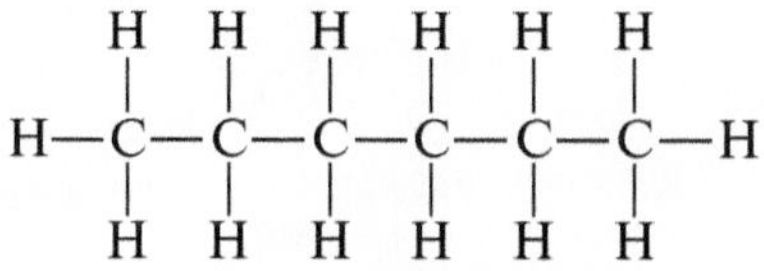

Hexane

Questions

(a) Polyvinyl alcohol exhibits hydrogen bonding within a single molecule.

(i) Draw a diagram that illustrates this concept.

(ii) How does this affect the viscosity of an aqueous solution of polyvinyl alcohol?

(b) Do all of these compounds exhibit hydrogen bonding with other molecules of their own species? If not, explain why not.

(c) A solution is made between acetone and hexane. Describe the interactions in the solution between

(i) acetone and acetone

(ii) hexane and hexane

(iii) acetone and hexane

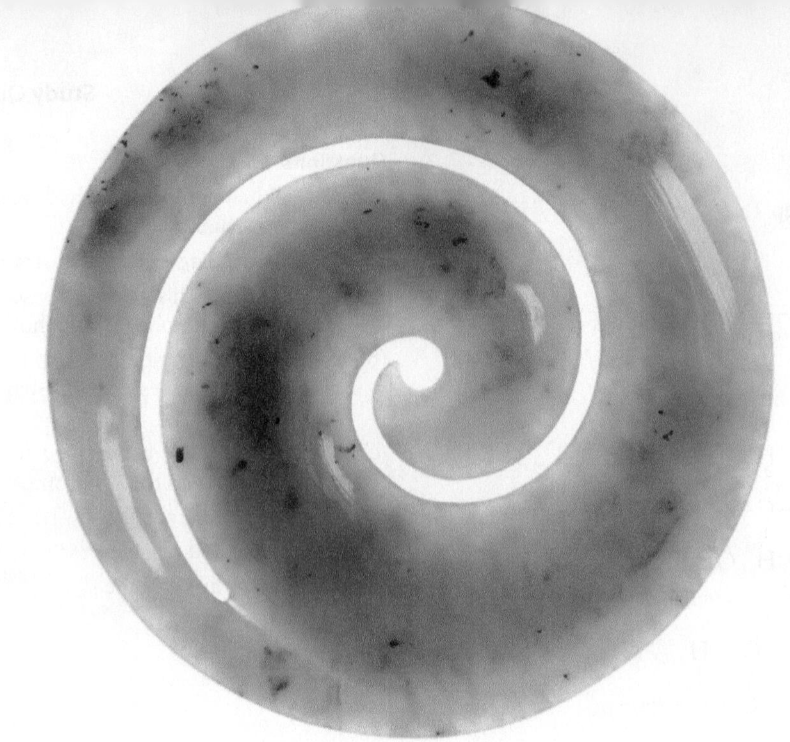
Steven Hyatt

New Zealand jade carved to resemble the opening of a leaf of a fern.

The Solid State

Chapter Outline

JADE, A BEAUTIFUL SOLID The beautiful green stone on the cover of this book is a piece of jade carved in New Zealand. Jade is found in many parts of the world. Because of its beauty it has been used for centuries for decorative and religious items, and because it is hard and withstands high temperatures, it has been used for tools such as axe blades. In China in the period from 200 BC to 200 AD members of royalty were buried in suits made of jade panels sewn with gold thread. In New Zealand the stone is called "pounamu," the name given by the indigenous people of that country, the Maori. To the Maori pounamu has immense spiritual and material value; objects made of jade are among their most prized possessions.

The name "jade" comes from the Spanish *piedra de ijada,* which means "loin stone," a name given it because it was thought to cure kidney diseases.

There are actually two different minerals called jade, jadeite and nephrite. Both are silicates that consist of a network of chains or sheets of linked $[SiO_4]^{4-}$ tetrahedra along with other structural elements.

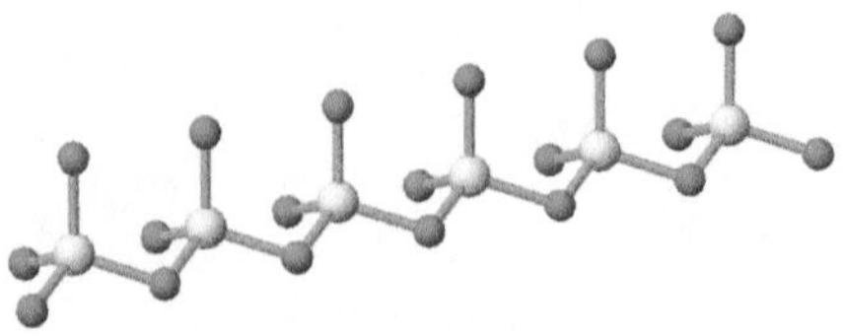

Chapter Goals

See Chapter Goals Revisited (page 465) for Study Questions keyed to these goals.

UNDERSTAND

- The concept of a unit cell for a solid and the varieties of cubic unit cells in particular.
- The importance of lattice energy and how it is calculated.
- The band model for bonding in metals and semiconductors and how this relates to their properties.
- The features of phase diagrams.

DO

- Relate unit cells for ionic compounds to their formulas.
- Relate unit cell dimensions, ionic or metallic radii, and solid density.
- Use lattice energy in calculations.
- Construct a phase diagram from information on the substance.
- Relate the processes of melting and sublimation and the associated enthalpy changes.

REMEMBER

- The three types of cubic unit cells.
- The physical properties of ionic, metallic, molecular, and network solids and examples of each.
- The unique features of the water phase diagram and their basis in molecular properties.

Jadeite is much rarer and a bit harder than nephrite. The two are difficult to tell apart visually, but nephrite has a "silkier" feel in the hand than jadeite, a feature that arises from differences in their underlying silicate structure.

The jade on the book cover and above is nephrite with the formula $Ca_2(Mg, Fe)_5(Si_4O_{11})_2(OH)_2$. The formula is written to emphasize that there can be varying amounts of Mg^{2+} and Fe^{2+} ions in the solid. The green color of nephrite in particular comes from iron(II) ions, a feature that makes the stone weakly paramagnetic. As the amount of iron(II) ions can vary from stone to stone, the color can vary from white (low iron content) to deep green (higher iron content).

A Study Question related to this story is: 12.66.

Many kinds of solids exist in the world around us. Among them are beautiful gems and minerals, such as the jade on the cover of this book. Research in solid state chemistry is one of the booming areas of science, especially because it relates to the development of interesting new materials. As we describe various kinds of solids, we hope to provide an insight into reasons why this area is exciting.

12-1 Crystal Lattices and Unit Cells

Learning Objectives: LO 2.22 (see APEC Lab 6 "Intermolecular Forces")

In both gases and liquids, molecules move continually and randomly, and they rotate and vibrate as well. Because of this movement, an orderly arrangement of molecules in the gaseous or liquid state is not possible. In solids, however, the molecules, atoms, or ions cannot change their relative positions (although they vibrate and occasionally rotate). Thus, a regular, repeating pattern of atoms or molecules within the structure—a long-range order—is a characteristic of most solids. The beautiful,

FIGURE 12.1 **Common salt, NaCl.**

external (macroscopic) regularity of many crystalline compounds (such as those of salt, Figure 12.1) is a consequence of this internal order.

Structures of solids can be described as three-dimensional lattices of atoms, ions, or molecules. For a crystalline solid, we can identify the **unit cell**, the smallest repeating unit that has all of the symmetry characteristic of the arrangement of atoms, ions, or molecules in the solid.

To understand unit cells, consider first a two-dimensional lattice model, the repeating pattern of circles in Figure 12.2. The yellow square at the left is a unit cell because the overall pattern can be created from a group of these cells by joining them edge to edge. It is also a requirement that unit cells reflect the stoichiometry of the solid. Here, the square unit cell at the left contains one smaller circle and one fourth of each of the four larger circles, giving a total of one small and one large circle per two-dimensional unit cell.

You may recognize that it is possible to draw other unit cells for this two-dimensional lattice. One option is the square in the middle of Figure 12.2 that fully encloses a single large circle and parts of small circles that add up to one net small circle. Yet another possible unit cell is the parallelogram at the right. Other unit cells can be drawn, but it is conventional to draw unit cells in which atoms or ions are placed at the **lattice points**; that is, at the corners of the cube or other geometric object that constitutes the unit cell.

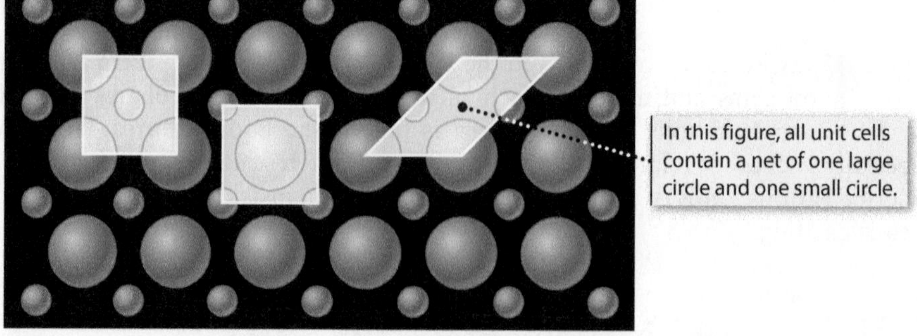

FIGURE 12.2 **Unit cells for a flat, two-dimensional solid made from circular "atoms."** A lattice can be represented as being built from repeating unit cells. This two-dimensional lattice can be built by translating the unit cells throughout the plane of the figure. Each unit cell must move by the length of one side of the cell. Be sure to notice that several unit cells are possible, with two of the most obvious being squares.

Types of cells. There are seven basic unit cells. All except the hexagonal unit cell are parallelepipeds (a solid with six faces, each of which is a parallelogram). In a cube, all angles (*a-o-c*, *a-o-b*, and *c-o-b*; where *o* is the origin) are 90°, and all sides are equal. In other cells, the angles and sides may be the same or different.

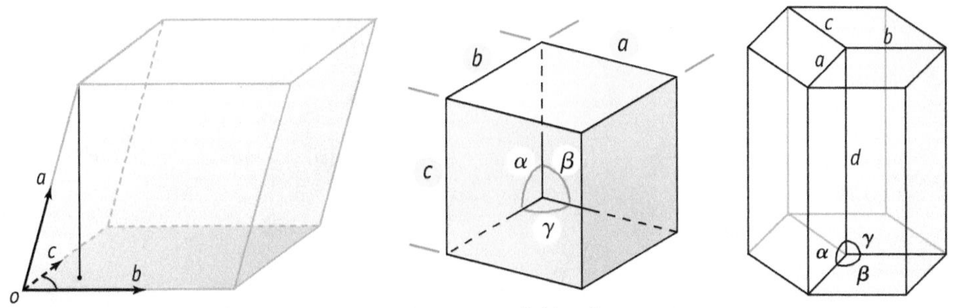

Unit cells are generally defined by three dimensions (*a*, *b*, and *c*) and a set of angles (*a-o-b*, *a-o-c*, *b-o-c*).

Cubic cell
$a = b = c$
$\alpha = \beta = \gamma = 90°$

Hexagonal unit cell
$a = b = c \neq d$
$\alpha = \gamma = 90°$
$\beta = 120°$

FIGURE 12.3 **Unit cells.**

The three-dimensional lattices of solids can be built by assembling three-dimensional unit cells much like building blocks. The assemblage of these three-dimensional unit cells defines the **crystal lattice.**

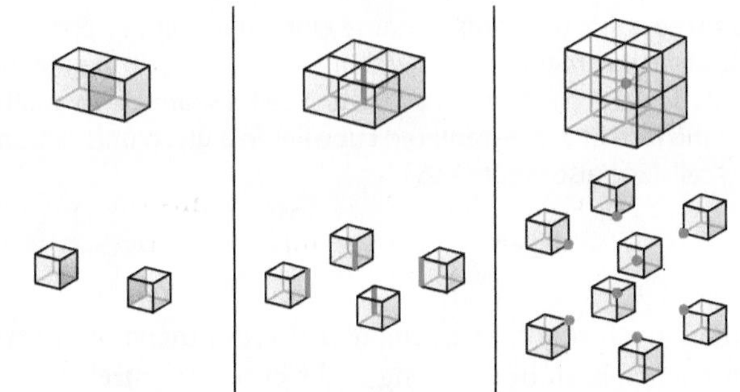

Assembling a crystal lattice from cubic unit cells

To construct crystal lattices, nature can use any of seven three-dimensional unit cells (Figure 12.3). They differ from one another in that their sides have different relative lengths and their edges meet at different angles. The simplest of the seven crystal lattices is the **cubic unit cell**, a cell with edges of equal length that meet at 90° angles. We shall look in detail at only this structure because cubic unit cells are the simplest unit cells to understand and because they are commonly encountered.

Cubic Unit Cells

Within the cubic class, three cell symmetries occur: **primitive cubic (pc), body-centered cubic (bcc)**, and **face-centered cubic (fcc)** (Figure 12.4). All three have identical atoms, molecules, or ions at the corners of the cubic unit cell. The bcc and fcc arrangements, however, differ from the primitive cube in that they have additional particles at other locations. The bcc structure is called *body-centered* because it has an additional particle, of the same type as those at the corners, at the center of the cube. The fcc arrangement is called *face-centered* because it has a particle, of the same type as the corner atoms, in the center of each of the six faces of the cube. Examples of each structure are found among the crystal lattices of the metals (Figure 12.5). The alkali metals, for example, are body-centered cubic, whereas nickel, copper, and aluminum are face-centered cubic. Notice that only one metal, polonium, has a primitive cubic lattice.

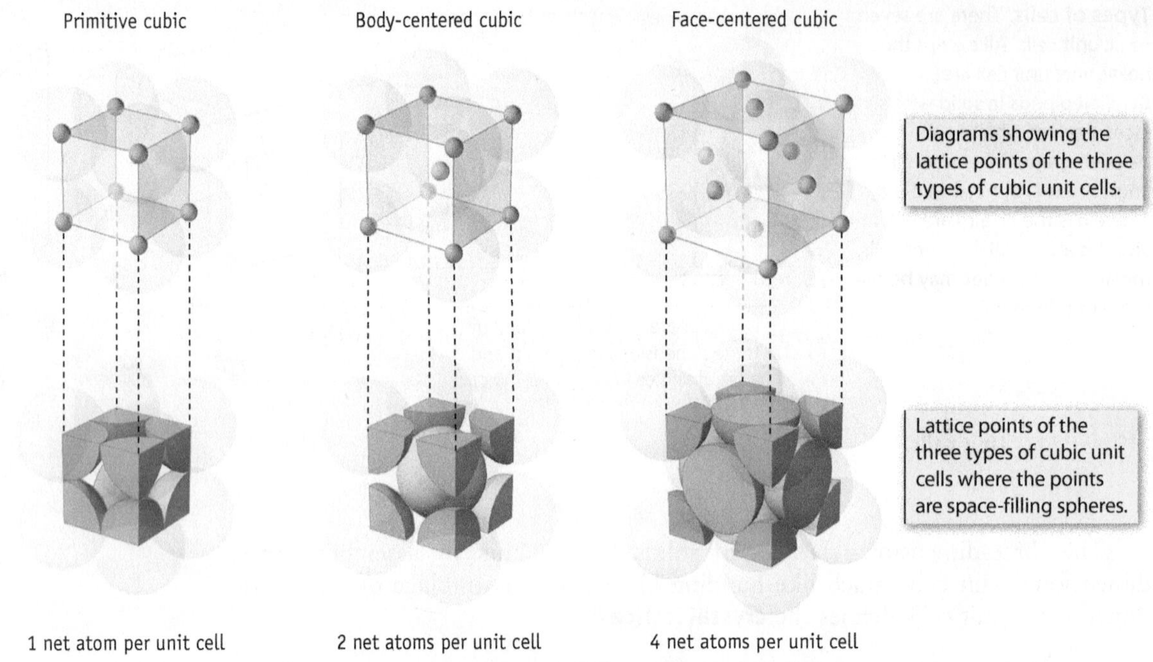

FIGURE 12.4 The three cubic unit cells. Because eight unit cells in a crystal lattice share a corner atom, only ⅛ of each corner atom lies within a given unit cell; the remaining ⅞ lies in seven other unit cells. Because each face of an fcc unit cell is shared with another unit cell, one half of each atom in the face of a face-centered cube lies in a given unit cell, and the other half lies in the adjoining cell. (See also Figure 12.6.)

When the cubes pack together to make a three-dimensional crystal of a metal, the atom at each corner is shared among eight cubes (Figures 12.4 and 12.6, *left*). Because of this, only one eighth of each corner atom is actually within a given unit cell. Furthermore, because a cube has eight corners, and because one eighth of the atom at each corner "belongs to" a particular unit cell, the corner atoms contribute

FIGURE 12.5 Metals use four different unit cells. Three are based on the cube, and the fourth is the hexagonal unit cell (see *A Closer Look: Packing Oranges, Marbles, and Atoms,* page 442). (Many metals can crystallize in more than one structure. Mn, for example, can be bcc or fcc.)

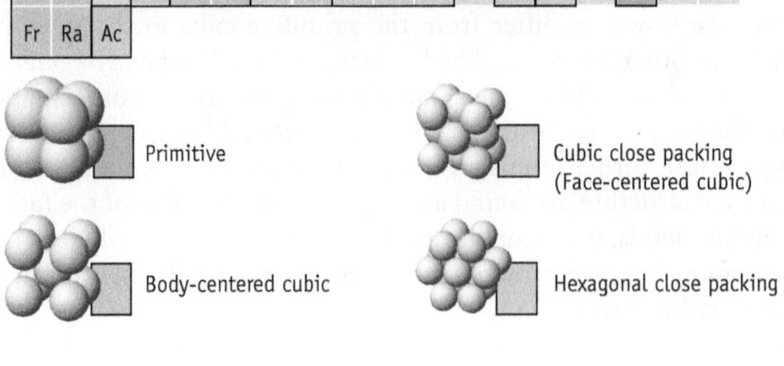

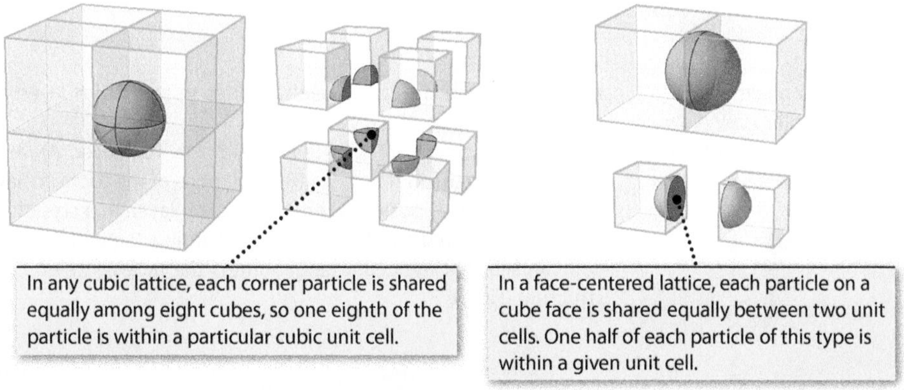

FIGURE 12.6 **Atom sharing at cube corners and faces.**

a net of one atom to a given unit cell. Thus, *the primitive cubic arrangement has one net atom within the unit cell.*

(8 corners of a cube)($^1/_8$ of each corner atom within a unit cell) =
1 net atom per unit cell for the primitive cubic unit cell

In contrast to the primitive cubic lattice, a body-centered cube has an additional atom wholly within the unit cell at the cube's center. The center particle is present in addition to those at the cube corners, so *the body-centered cubic arrangement has a net of two atoms within the unit cell.*

In a face-centered cubic arrangement, there is an atom on each of the six faces of the cube in addition to those at the cube corners. One half of each atom on a face belongs to a given unit cell (Figure 12.6, *right*). Three net particles are therefore contributed by the particles on the faces of the cube:

(6 faces of a cube)($^1/_2$ of an atom within a unit cell) =
3 net face-centered atoms within a face-centered cubic unit cell

Thus, *the face-centered cubic arrangement has a net of four atoms within the unit cell,* one contributed by the corner atoms and another three contributed by the atoms centered in the six faces.

An experimental technique, x-ray crystallography, can be used to determine the structure of a crystalline substance (Figure 12.7). Once the structure is known, the information can be combined with other experimental information to calculate such useful parameters as the radius of an atom (Example 12.1).

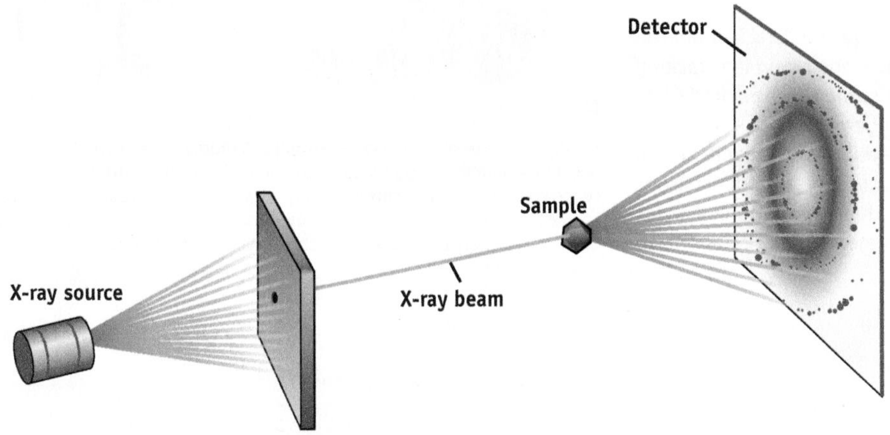

FIGURE 12.7 **X-ray crystallography.** In the x-ray diffraction experiment, a beam of x-rays is directed at a crystalline solid. The photons of the x-ray beam are scattered by the atoms of the solid. The pattern of scattered x-rays is recorded and related to the locations of the atoms or ions in the crystal.

A CLOSER LOOK | Packing Oranges, Marbles, and Atoms

Have you ever tried to stack some oranges into a pile that doesn't fall over and that takes up as little space as possible? How did you do it? Clearly, the pyramid arrangement below on the right works, whereas the cubic one on the left is much less efficient.

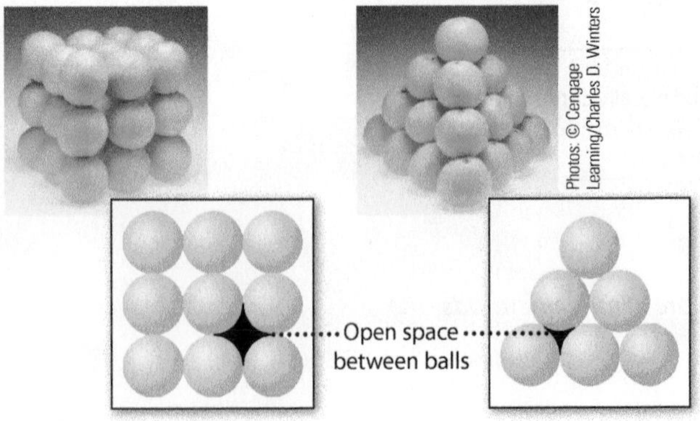

If you could look inside the pile, you would find that less open space occurs in the pyramid stacking than in the cube stacking. Only 52% of the space is filled in the cubic packing arrangement. (If you could stack oranges as a body-centered cube, that would be slightly better; 68% of the space is used.) However, the best method is the pyramid stack, which is really a face-centered cubic arrangement. Oranges, marbles, or atoms packed this way occupy 74% of the available space.

To fill three-dimensional space, the most efficient way to pack spherical objects like atoms or ions is to begin with a hexagonal arrangement of spheres, as in this arrangement of marbles.

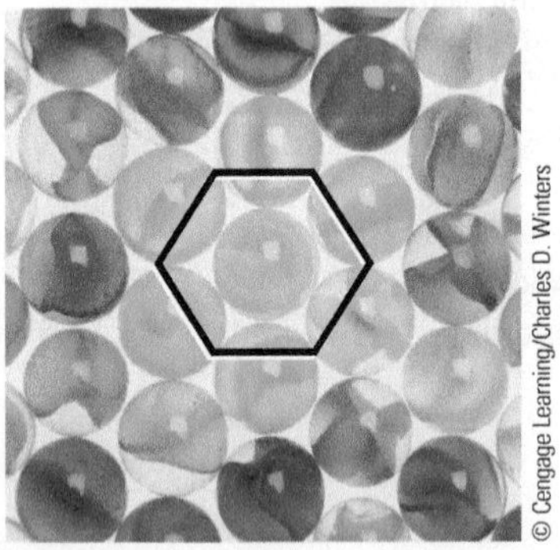

Succeeding layers of atoms (or ions) are then stacked one on top of the other in two different ways. Depending on the stacking pattern (Figure A), you will get either a **cubic close-packed (ccp)** or **hexagonal close-packed (hcp)** arrangement.

In the hcp arrangement, additional layers of particles are placed above and below a given layer, fitting into the same depressions on either side of the middle layer. In a three-dimensional crystal, the layers repeat their pattern in the manner ABABAB. . . . Atoms in each A layer are directly above the ones in another A layer; the same holds true for the B layers.

In the ccp arrangement, the atoms of the "top" layer (A) rest in depressions in the middle layer (B), and those of the "bottom" layer (C) are oriented opposite to those in the top layer. In a crystal, the pattern is repeated ABCABCABC. . . . By turning the whole crystal, you can see that the ccp arrangement is the face-centered cubic structure (Figure B).

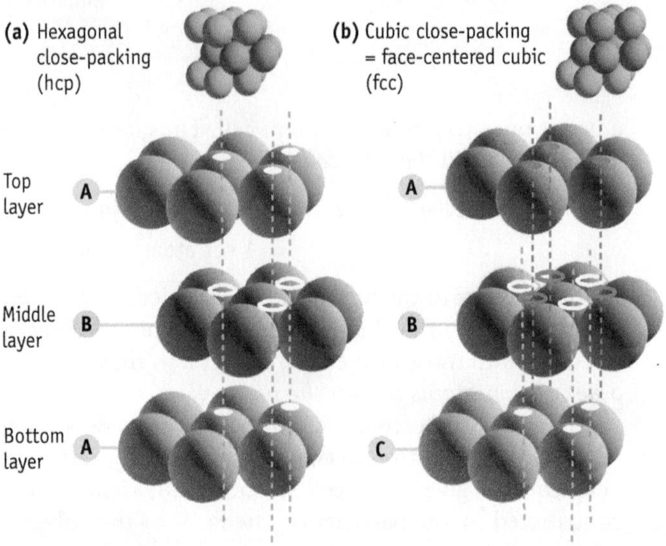

FIGURE A **Efficient packing.** The most efficient ways to pack atoms (or ions) in crystalline materials are hexagonal close-packing (hcp) and cubic close packing (ccp).

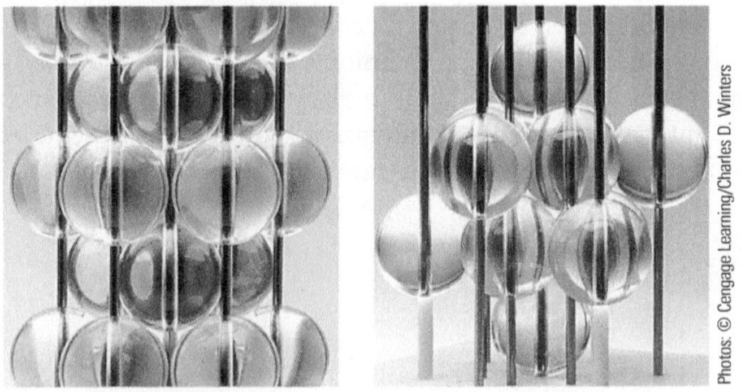

(a) (b)

FIGURE B **Models of close packing.** **(a)** A model of hexagonal close-packing, where the layers repeat in the order ABABAB. . . . **(b)** A face-centered unit cell (cubic close-packing), where the layers repeat in the order ABCABC. . . . (A kit from which these models can be built is available from the Institute for Chemical Education at the University of Wisconsin at Madison.)

EXAMPLE 12.1

Determining an Atom Radius from Lattice Dimensions

Problem Aluminum has a density of 2.699 g/cm^3, and the atoms are packed in a face-centered cubic crystal lattice. What is the radius of an aluminum atom (in picometers)?

What Do You Know? You know aluminum atoms are packed in a face-centered cubic unit cell. It is important to recognize the atoms in a face-centered cube do not touch along the cell edges but do so in the faces (as illustrated just below).

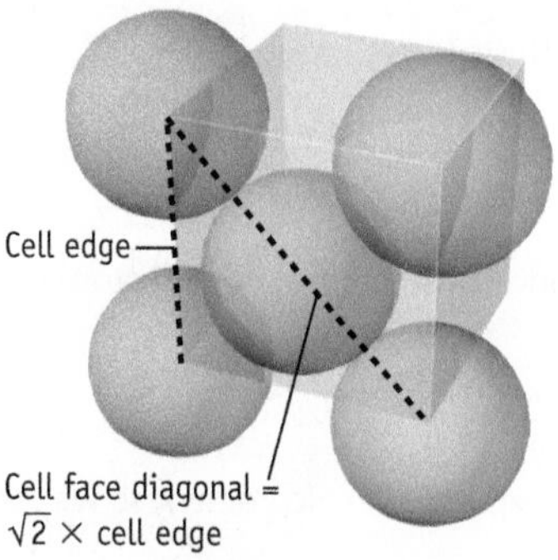

One face of a face-centered cubic unit cell.

The figure shows that the atoms touch along the cell face diagonal, so the length of the diagonal is four times the radius of the atoms. A geometric calculation indicates that this distance is equal to the square root of 2 times the length of the cell edge.

Strategy If you know the cell edge length, you can calculate the diagonal distance across a face, and the illustration above shows the atom radius is one fourth of this distance. So, the problem comes down to finding the length of the cell edge. This dimension is the cube root of the cell volume, and you can find the volume from the density and mass of the unit cell. The density is given, and the mass of the cell is 4 times the mass of an atom. As described in Chapter 2, the mass of an Al atom can be found from its atomic mass and Avogadro's number. Therefore, you should proceed as follows:

1. Find the mass of a unit cell from the knowledge that it is face-centered cubic.
2. Determine the volume of the unit cell using the cell mass and the density of aluminum.
3. Find the length of a side of the unit cell from its volume.
4. Calculate the atom radius from the edge dimension.

Solution

1. *Calculate the mass of the unit cell.*

$$\text{Mass of 1 Al atom} = \left(\frac{26.98\text{ g}}{1\text{ mol}}\right)\left(\frac{1\text{ mol}}{6.022 \times 10^{23}\text{ atoms}}\right) = 4.480 \times 10^{-23}\text{ g/atom}$$

$$\text{Mass of unit cell} = \left(\frac{4.480 \times 10^{-23}\text{ g}}{1\text{ Al atom}}\right)\left(\frac{4\text{ Al atoms}}{1\text{ unit cell}}\right) = 1.792 \times 10^{-22}\text{ g/unit cell}$$

2. *Calculate the volume of the unit cell from the unit cell mass and density.*

$$\text{Volume of unit cell} = \left(\frac{1.792 \times 10^{-22}\text{ g}}{\text{unit cell}}\right)\left(\frac{1\text{ cm}^3}{2.699\text{ g}}\right) = 6.640 \times 10^{-23}\text{ cm}^3\text{/unit cell}$$

Strategy Map 12.1

PROBLEM
What is the **radius** of **Al** in solid Al?

DATA/INFORMATION
- Al unit cell is **FCC** with d = 2.699 g/cm^3
- Need Al ***atomic weight***
- Need ***Avogadro's number***

STEP 1. Calculate **mass** of unit cell (= 4 Al atoms).

Mass of Al atom, **mass** of unit cell

STEP 2. Calculate **volume** of unit cell from mass and density.

Volume of unit cell

STEP 3. Calculate **length** of unit cell ***edge*** from cell volume.

Length of unit cell edge

STEP 4. Relate **atom radius** to **unit cell edge length.**

Radius of atom

3. *Calculate the length of a unit cell edge.* The length of the unit cell edge is the cube root of the cell volume.

$$\text{Length of unit cell edge} = \sqrt[3]{6.640 \times 10^{-23}\ \text{cm}^3} = 4.049 \times 10^{-8}\ \text{cm}$$

4. *Calculate the atom radius.* As illustrated in the model above, the diagonal distance across the face of the cell is equal to four times the Al atom radius.

$$\text{Cell face diagonal} = 4 \times (\text{Al atom radius})$$

The cell diagonal is the hypotenuse of a right isosceles triangle, so, using the Pythagorean theorem,

$$(\text{Diagonal distance})^2 = 2 \times (\text{edge})^2$$

Taking the square root of both sides, we have

$$\text{Diagonal distance} = \sqrt{2} \times (\text{cell edge})$$
$$= \sqrt{2} \times (4.049 \times 10^{-8}\ \text{cm}) = 5.727 \times 10^{-8}\ \text{cm}$$

We divide the diagonal distance by 4 to obtain the Al atom radius in cm.

$$\text{Al atom radius} = \frac{5.727 \times 10^{-8}\ \text{cm}}{4} = 1.432 \times 10^{-8}\ \text{cm}$$

Atomic dimensions are often expressed in picometers, so we convert the radius to that unit.

$$1.432 \times 10^{-8}\ \text{cm}\left(\frac{1\ \text{m}}{100\ \text{cm}}\right)\left(\frac{1\ \text{pm}}{1 \times 10^{-12}\ \text{m}}\right) = 143.2\ \text{pm}$$

Think about Your Answer This calculation illustrates one method by which the atomic radii of metals (given in Figure 7.8) were determined.

Check Your Understanding

(a) *Determining an Atom Radius from Lattice Dimensions:* Gold has a face-centered unit cell, and its density is 19.32 g/cm^3. Calculate the radius of a gold atom.

(b) *The Structure of Solid Iron:* Iron has a density of 7.8740 g/cm^3, and the radius of an iron atom is 126 pm. Verify that solid iron has a body-centered cubic unit cell. (Be sure to note that the atoms in a body-centered cubic unit cell touch along the diagonal across the cell. They do not touch along the edges of the cell.) (*Hint:* The diagonal distance across the unit cell = edge × $\sqrt{3}$.)

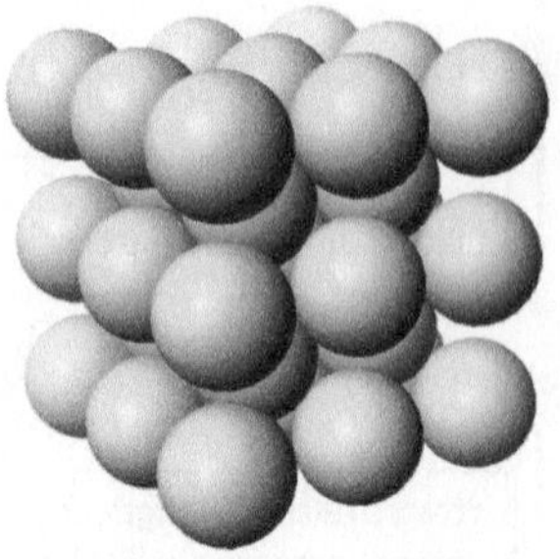

A portion of the solid state structure of potassium.

REVIEW & CHECK FOR SECTION 12-1

1. A portion of the crystalline lattice for potassium is illustrated in the margin. In what type of unit cell are the K atoms arranged?

   (a) primitive cubic (b) body-centered cubic (c) face-centered cubic

2. If one edge of the potassium unit cell is 533 pm, what is the density of potassium?

   (a) 0.858 g/cm^3 (b) 1.17 g/cm^3 (c) 0.428 g/cm^3

Learning Objectives: LO 2.22 (see APEC Lab 6 "Intermolecular Forces")

12-2 Structures and Formulas of Ionic Solids

The lattices of many ionic compounds are built by taking a primitive cubic or face-centered cubic lattice of ions of one type and placing ions of opposite charge in the holes within the lattice. This produces a three-dimensional lattice of regularly placed

CASE STUDY Lithium and "Green Cars"

You are well aware of the use of metals in our economy: copper in electric wiring; aluminum in airplanes and soft drink cans; lead and zinc in batteries; and iron in cars, buses, and bridges. You may be less aware of metals such as the platinum group metals (platinum, palladium, rhodium, iridium, and ruthenium) in the catalytic converter in your car and lanthanides used in ultrastrong magnets in audio headsets. And that lithium is used in the batteries in your laptop.

Much of the world's lithium comes from northern Chile and southern Bolivia. There, groundwater with high concentrations of Group 1A salts is pumped into ponds. The solution slowly evaporates in the intense Sun of the high Andes plateau, and, after about a year, the highly concentrated solution is finally taken to a chemical plant where it is evaporated to give white, powdered lithium carbonate. It is estimated that Bolivia alone has a reserve of about 73 million metric tons of Li_2CO_3. To produce lithium metal, the carbonate is converted to LiCl, which is then electrolyzed to produce the metal.

Fortunately lithium is quite abundant on the Earth. We say "fortunately" because lithium compounds have a wide range of uses: in ceramics and glass, in reagents for the production of pharmaceuticals, and in lubricating greases. However, there is one emerging use of lithium that may exceed all the others in the future: batteries for electric and hybrid cars and for aircraft.

As this book was being prepared, lithium batteries were much in the news. A new passenger aircraft, the Boeing 787, was successfully launched. However, after some months problems with overheating in the lithium batteries prompted a delay in further use of the planes. Lithium batteries are powerful and light-weight, but there are engineering problems to overcome.

As we gradually rely more and more on automobiles using battery power instead of gasoline-fueled engines, lithium will become ever more important. And, consequently, the availability of lithium will be critical.

© nick baylis/Alamy

Lithium and lithium salts. The high plateau in Bolivia where ground water contains high concentrations of Group 1A salts, among them lithium carbonate. The water is left in the Sun to deposit the salts by evaporation.

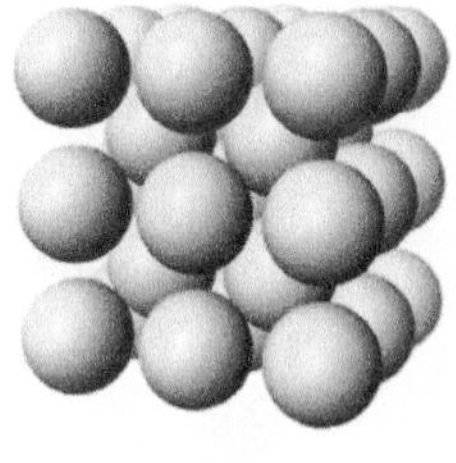

A view of the solid state structure of lithium.

Questions:

1. What mass of lithium can be obtained from 73 million metric tons of lithium carbonate? (1 metric ton = 1000 kg.)
2. Describe the unit cell of lithium (see Figure).
3. The lithium unit cell is a cube with sides of 351 pm. Use this information, and a knowledge of unit cells, to calculate the density of lithium metal.
4. In the process of making lithium metal, Li_2CO_3 is converted to LiCl. Suggest a way to do this.

Answers to these questions are available in Appendix N.

ions. The smallest repeating unit in these structures is, by definition, the unit cell for the ionic compound.

The choice of the lattice and the number and location of the holes in the lattice that are filled are the keys to understanding the relationship between the lattice structure and the formula of a salt.

Generally, ionic lattices are assembled by placing the larger ions at the lattice points and placing the smaller ions in the holes in the lattice. Consider, for example, the ionic compound cesium chloride, CsCl (Figure 12.8). The structure of CsCl has a primitive cubic unit cell of chloride ions, and a cesium ion fits into a hole in the center of the cube. Most importantly, this arrangement leads to a ratio of one Cl^- ion to one Cs^+ ion. In a lattice of primitive cubic unit cells of Cl^- ions there in a net of one Cl^- ion "inside" a given unit cell (as illustrated in Figure 12.6). Given that there is a Cs^+ ion in the hole in the unit cell, this leads to a formula of CsCl.

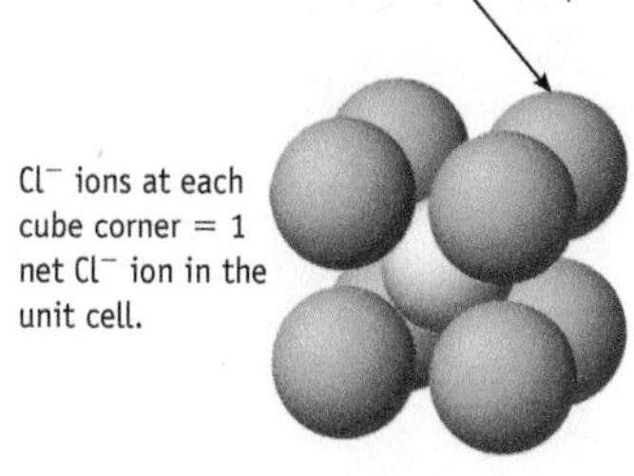

FIGURE 12.8 Cesium chloride (CsCl) unit cell. The unit cell of CsCl is a primitive cubic unit cell of Cl^- ions with a Cs^+ ion in the center of the unit cell.

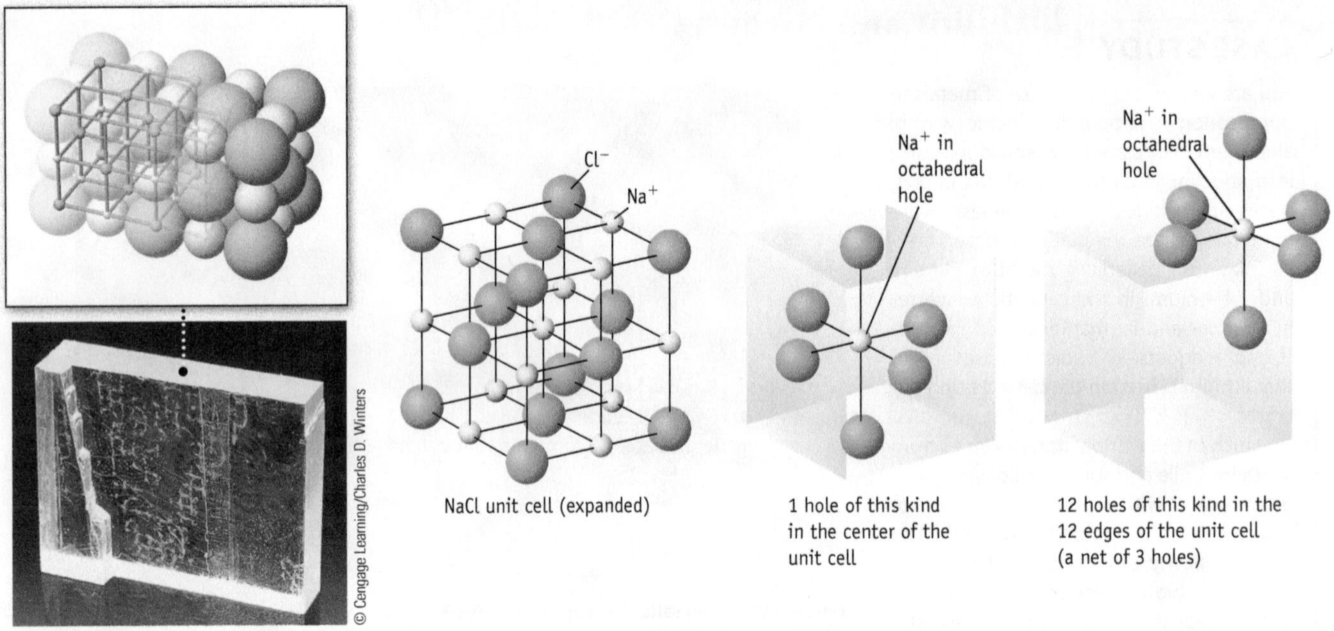

(a) Cubic NaCl. The solid is based on a face-centered cubic unit cell of Na$^+$ and Cl$^-$ ions.

(b) Expanded view of the NaCl lattice. (The lines are not bonds; they are there to help visualize the lattice.) The smaller Na$^+$ ions (silver) are packed into a face-centered cubic lattice of larger Cl$^-$ ions (yellow).

(c) Octahedral holes. A view showing the octahedral holes in the lattice.

FIGURE 12.9 **Sodium chloride.**

Next, consider the structure for NaCl. An extended view of the lattice and one unit cell are illustrated in Figures 12.9a and 12.9b, respectively. The Cl$^-$ ions are arranged in a face-centered cubic unit cell, and the Na$^+$ ions are arranged in a regular manner between these ions. Notice that each Na$^+$ ion is surrounded by six Cl$^-$ ions in an octahedral geometry. Thus, the Na$^+$ ions are said to be in **octahedral holes** (Figure 12.9c).

The formula of an ionic compound must reflect the composition of its unit cell; therefore, the formula can always be derived from the unit cell structure. The formula for NaCl can be obtained by counting the number of cations and anions contained in one unit cell. A face-centered cubic lattice of Cl$^-$ ions has a net of four Cl$^-$ ions within the unit cell. There is one Na$^+$ ion in the center of the unit cell, contained totally within the unit cell. In addition, there are 12 Na$^+$ ions along the edges of the unit cell. Each of these Na$^+$ ions is shared among four unit cells, so each contributes one fourth of an Na$^+$ ion to the unit cell, giving three additional Na$^+$ ions within the unit cell.

$$(1 \text{ Na}^+ \text{ ion in the center of the unit cell}) + (\tfrac{1}{4} \text{ of a Na}^+ \text{ ion in each edge} \times 12 \text{ edges})$$
$$= \text{net of 4 Na}^+ \text{ ions in NaCl unit cell}$$

This accounts for all of the ions contained in the unit cell: four Cl$^-$ and four Na$^+$ ions. Thus, a unit cell of NaCl has a 1:1 ratio of Na$^+$ and Cl$^-$ ions, as the formula requires.

Another common unit cell has a different placement of ions. Again, there are ions of one type in a face-centered cubic unit cell. Ions of the other type are located in **tetrahedral holes**, wherein each ion is surrounded by four oppositely charged ions. As illustrated in Figure 12.10a, there are eight tetrahedral holes in a face-centered cubic unit cell. In ZnS (zinc blende), the sulfide ions (S^{2-}) form a face-centered cubic unit cell. The zinc ions (Zn^{2+}) occupy one half of the tetrahedral holes, and each Zn^{2+}

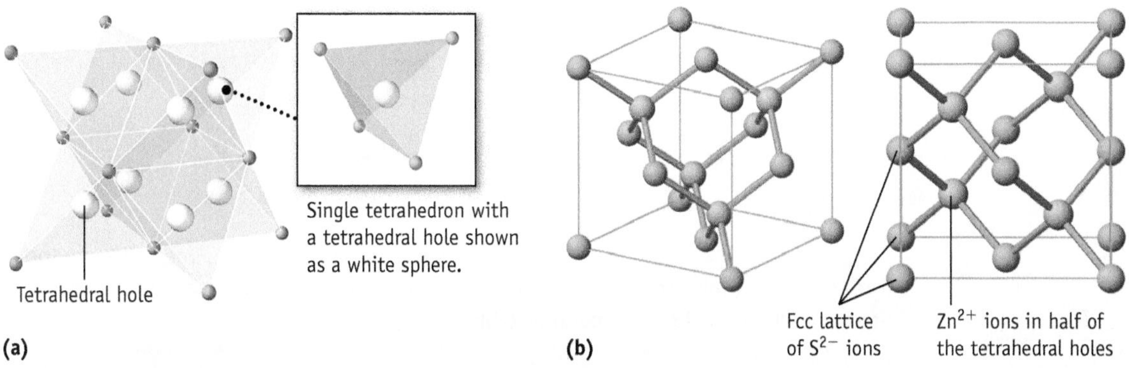

FIGURE 12.10 **Tetrahedral holes and two views of the ZnS (zinc blende) unit cell.** **(a)** The tetrahedral holes in a face-centered cubic lattice. **(b)** This unit cell is an example of a face-centered cubic lattice of ions of one type with ions of the opposite type in one half of the tetrahedral holes.

ion is surrounded by four S^{2-} ions. The unit cell has four S^{2-} ions (making up the fcc lattice) and four Zn^{2+} ions contained wholly within the unit cell (in tetrahedral holes). This 1 : 1 ratio of ions matches the ratio in the formula.

In summary, compounds with the formula MX commonly form one of three possible crystal structures:

1. M^{n+} ions occupying the cubic hole in a primitive cubic X^{n-} lattice. Example: CsCl.
2. M^{n+} ions in all the octahedral holes in a face-centered cubic X^{n-} lattice. Example: NaCl.
3. M^{n+} ions occupying half of the tetrahedral holes in a face-centered cubic lattice of X^{n-} ions. Example: ZnS.

Chemists and geologists in particular have observed that the sodium chloride or "rock salt" structure is adopted by many ionic compounds, most especially by all the alkali metal halides (except CsCl, CsBr, and CsI), all the oxides and sulfides of the alkaline earth metals, and all the oxides of formula MO of the transition metals of the fourth period.

EXAMPLE 12.2

Ionic Structure and Formula of Perovskite

Problem One unit cell of the common mineral perovskite is illustrated in the margin. This compound is composed of calcium and titanium cations and oxide anions. Based on the unit cell, what is the formula of perovskite?

What Do You Know? The cell is composed of the ions Ca^{2+}, Ti^{4+}, and O^{2-}. The Ca^{2+} ion is wholly within the cell, the Ti^{4+} ions are at the corners of the cell, and the O^{2-} ions are in the cell edges.

Strategy Based on the locations of the ions, decide on the net number of ions of each kind within the cell.

Solution

Number of Ti^{4+} ions:

(8 Ti^{4+} ions at cube corners) × (1/8 of each ion inside unit cell) = 1 net Ti^{4+} ion

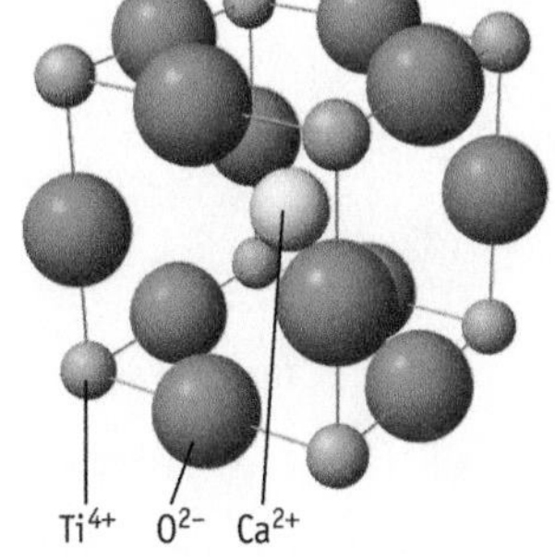

The unit cell of the mineral perovskite.

Number of Ca^{2+} ions:

One ion is in the cube center = 1 net Ca^{2+} ion

Number of O^{2-} ions:

(12 O^{2-} ions in cube edges) × (¼ of each ion inside unit cell) = 3 net O^{2-} ions

Thus, the formula of perovskite is $CaTiO_3$.

Think about Your Answer $CaTiO_3$ is a reasonable formula. One Ca^{2+} ion and three O^{2-} ions would require a titanium ion with a 4+ charge, a reasonable value because titanium is in Group 4B of the periodic table.

Check Your Understanding

If an ionic solid has an fcc lattice of anions (X) and all of the tetrahedral holes are occupied by metal cations (M), is the formula of the compound MX, MX_2, or M_2X?

EXAMPLE 12.3

The Relation of the Density of an Ionic Compound and Its Unit Cell Dimensions

Problem Magnesium oxide has a face-centered cubic unit cell of oxide ions with magnesium ions in octahedral holes. If the radius of Mg^{2+} is 79 pm and the density of MgO is 3.56 g/cm³, what is the radius of an oxide ion?

What Do You Know? This is similar to Example 12.1 in that you wish to know the size of one ion or atom in the cell. You are given the density of the compound and the fact that the unit cell is face-centered cubic. In addition, you know the radius of a Mg^{2+} ion.

Strategy Our strategy can be outlined as follows:

1. Calculate the mass of a unit cell:
   a) Use the atomic masses of Mg and O and Avogadro's number to calculate the mass of one formula unit of MgO.
   b) The unit cell is face-centered cubic. Because the lattice points are O^{2-} ions, this tells you there are 4 O^{2-} ions within the cell. There are Mg^{2+} ions in the octahedral holes, so you know there are also 4 Mg^{2+} ions within the cell. The unit cell thus contains 4 MgO units.
2. Calculate the volume of the unit cell from the unit cell mass and known density of MgO.
3. Calculate the length of one edge from the cell volume (Length = volume$^{1/3}$).
4. Calculate the radius of the oxide ion.

Solution

1. *Calculate the mass of the unit cell.* An ionic compound of formula MX (here MgO) and based on a face-centered cubic lattice of X^- ions with M^+ ions in the octahedral holes has 4 MX units per unit cell.

$$\text{Unit cell mass} = \left(\frac{40.304\text{ g}}{1\text{ mol MgO}}\right)\left(\frac{1\text{ mol MgO}}{6.022 \times 10^{23}\text{ units of MgO}}\right)\left(\frac{4\text{ MgO units}}{1\text{ unit cell}}\right)$$

$$= 2.677 \times 10^{-22}\text{ g/unit cell}$$

2. *Calculate the volume of the unit cell from the unit cell mass and density.*

$$\text{Unit cell volume} = \left(\frac{2.667 \times 10^{-22}\ \text{g}}{\text{unit cell}}\right)\left(\frac{1\ \text{cm}^3}{3.56\ \text{g}}\right) = 7.52 \times 10^{-23}\ \text{cm}^3/\text{unit cell}$$

3. *Calculate the edge dimension of the unit cell in pm.*

$$\text{Unit cell edge} = (7.52 \times 10^{-23}\ \text{cm}^3)^{1/3} = 4.22 \times 10^{-8}\ \text{cm}$$

$$\text{Unit cell edge} = 4.22 \times 10^{-8}\ \text{cm}\left(\frac{1\ \text{m}}{100\ \text{cm}}\right)\left(\frac{1 \times 10^{12}\ \text{pm}}{1\ \text{m}}\right) = 422\ \text{pm}$$

4. *Calculate the oxide ion radius.*

One face of the MgO unit cell is shown in the margin. The O^{2-} ions define the lattice, and the Mg^{2+} and O^{2-} ions along the cell edge just touch one another. This means that one edge of the cell is equal to one O^{2-} radius (*x*) plus twice the Mg^{2+} radius plus one more O^{2-} radius.

$$\text{MgO unit cell edge} = x\ \text{pm} + 2(79\ \text{pm}) + x\ \text{pm} = 422\ \text{pm}$$

$$x = \text{oxide ion radius} = 132\ \text{pm}$$

Think about Your Answer Chemists often check the chemical literature to judge the reasonableness of an answer. The calculated result here is very close to the value in Figure 7.11 (140 pm).

Check Your Understanding

Potassium chloride has the same unit cell as NaCl. Using the ion sizes in Figure 7.11, calculate the density of KCl.

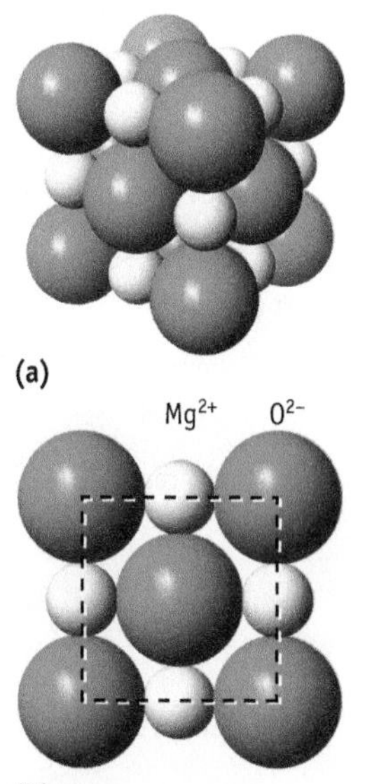

Magnesium oxide. (a) A unit cell of MgO showing oxide ions in a face-centered cubic lattice with Mg^{2+} ions in the octahedral holes. **(b)** One face of the cell.

REVIEW & CHECK FOR SECTION 12-2

1. The unit cell of silicon carbide, SiC, is illustrated in the margin. In what type of unit cell are the (dark gray) C atoms arranged?

   (a) primitive cubic (b) body-centered cubic (c) face-centered cubic

2. If one edge of the silicon carbide unit cell is 436.0 pm, what is the calculated density of this compound?

   (a) 0.803 g/cm³ (b) 0.311 g/cm³ (c) 3.21 g/cm³

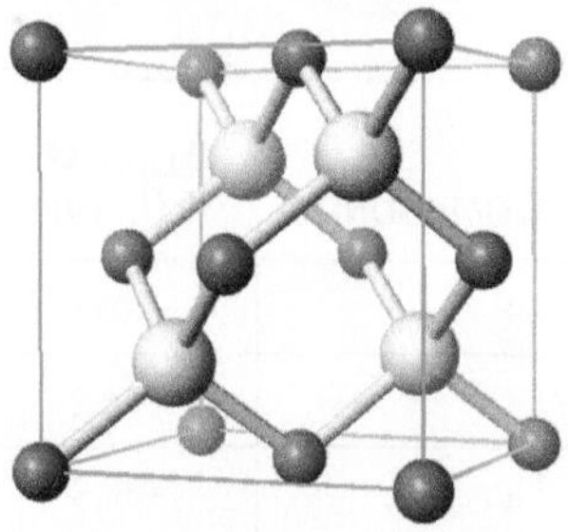

Unit cell of silicon carbide, SiC.

12-3 Bonding in Ionic Compounds: Lattice Energy

Learning Objectives: LO 2.19, LO 2.22 (see APEC Lab 6 "Intermolecular Forces"), LO 2.23, LO 2.24

Ionic compounds typically have high melting points, an indication of the strength of the bonding in the ionic crystal lattice. A measure of that is the lattice energy, the main topic of this section.

Ionic compounds have positive and negative ions arranged in a three-dimensional lattice in which there are extensive attractions between ions of opposite charge and repulsions between ions of like charge. Each of these interactions is governed by an equation related to Coulomb's law (◀ Equation 2.3). For example, $U_{\text{ion pair}}$, the energy of attractive interactions between a pair of ions, is given by

$$U_{\text{ion pair}} = C \times \frac{(n^+e)(n^-e)}{d}$$

The symbol C represents a constant, d is the distance between the ion centers, and e is the charge on an electron. The term n^+e represents the charge on the cation in the ion pair, and the term n^-e is the charge on the negative ion. The important thing to notice about this equation is that *the energy depends directly on the charges on the ions and inversely on the distance between them.*

Because n^+e and n^-e have different signs, the energy calculated by this equation will have a negative value. That is, the energy of the system is *lowered* based on the attractive forces between the two particles. A similar equation (using n^+e and n^+e, or n^-e and n^-e) can be used to calculate the energy associated with the repulsion of two particles having similar charges. In this case the net energy is *higher* due to the repulsion of the two particles.

We can use information on the charges of the ions and their location in the lattice to calculate the energy of the system. Taking NaCl as an example (see Figure 12.9), focus on a Na^+ ion in the center of the unit cell. We see it is surrounded by, and attracted to, six Cl^- ions. Just a bit farther away from the Na^+ ion, however, there are 12 Na^+ ions along the edges of the cubes, and there is a force of repulsion between the center Na^+ and these ions. And if we still focus on the Na^+ ion in the "center" of the unit cell, we see there are eight more Cl^- ions at the corners of the cube, and these are attracted to the center Na^+ ion. Taking into account *all* of the interactions between the ions in a lattice, we can calculate the **lattice energy, $\Delta_{lattice}U$**, the energy of formation of one mole of a solid crystalline ionic compound when ions in the gas phase combine (Table 12.1). For sodium chloride, this reaction is

$$Na^+(g) + Cl^-(g) \rightarrow NaCl(s)$$

When dealing with ionic compounds chemists often use **lattice enthalpy, $\Delta_{lattice}H$**. The same trends are seen in both lattice energy and enthalpy, and, because we are dealing with a condensed phase, the numerical values are nearly the same.

We shall focus here on the dependence of lattice enthalpy on ion charges and sizes. As given by Coulomb's law, the higher the ion charges, the greater the attraction between oppositely charged ions, so $\Delta_{lattice}H$ has a larger negative value for more highly charged ions. This is illustrated by the lattice enthalpies of MgO and NaF. The value of $\Delta_{lattice}H$ for MgO (−4050 kJ/mol) is about four times more negative than the value for NaF (−926 kJ/mol) because the charges on the Mg^{2+} and O^{2-} ions [(2+) × (2−)] are twice as large as those on Na^+ and F^- ions.

Because the attraction between ions is inversely proportional to the distance between them, the effect of ion size on lattice enthalpy is also predictable: A lattice built from smaller ions generally leads to a more negative value for the lattice enthalpy (Table 12.1 and Figure 12.11). For alkali metal halides, for example, the

Table 12.1 Lattice Energies of Some Ionic Compounds

COMPOUND	$\Delta_{lattice}U$ (kJ/mol)
LiF	−1037
LiCl	−852
LiBr	−815
LiI	−761
NaF	−926
NaCl	−786
NaBr	−752
NaI	−702
KF	−821
KCl	−717
KBr	−689
KI	−649

Source: D. Cubicciotti: Lattice energies of the alkali halides and electron affinities of the halogens. *Journal of Chemical Physics*, Vol. 31, p. 1646, 1959.

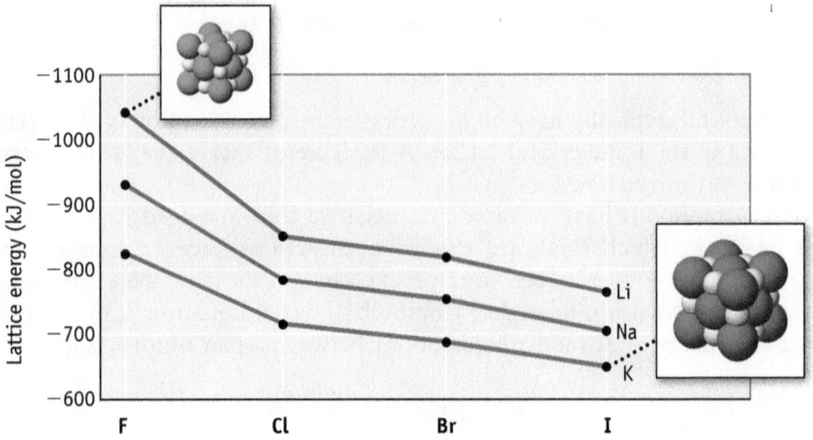

FIGURE 12.11 **Lattice energy.** $\Delta_{lattice}U$ is illustrated for the formation of the alkali metal halides, MX(s), from the ions $M^+(g) + X^-(g)$.

lattice enthalpy for lithium compounds is generally more negative than that for potassium compounds because the Li^+ ion is much smaller than the K^+ cation. Similarly, lattice enthalpies of fluorides are more negative than those for iodides with the same cation.

Calculating a Lattice Enthalpy from Thermodynamic Data

Lattice enthalpies can be calculated using a thermodynamic approach known as a **Born–Haber cycle**, an application of Hess's law described in Section 5-7. The energy level diagram in Figure 12.12 shows the enthalpy terms involved in this calculation. Recall that the enthalpy change involved along one path from reactants to products is the same as the sum of enthalpy changes along another path. Let us use as an example the calculation of the lattice enthalpy for NaCl(s). Here one path is

$$\text{Na(s)} + 1/2\ \text{Cl}_2\text{(g)} \rightarrow \text{NaCl(s)} \qquad \Delta_f H^\circ\ [\text{NaCl(s)}] = -411.12\ \text{kJ/mol}$$

Another pathway illustrated in Figure 12.12 for sodium chloride involves five steps. In Step 1A Cl_2 molecules are converted to Cl atoms, and in Step 2A solid sodium is vaporized to Na atoms in the gas phase. In Step 1B the Cl atoms form Cl^-(g) ions, and in Step 2B the Na atoms form Na^+(g) ions. With the ions having been formed, they combine to form solid NaCl. The enthalpy of each of these steps is known, except for Step 3, $\Delta_{lattice}H$.

Step 1A	$1/2\ Cl_2(g) \rightarrow Cl(g)$	$\Delta H^\circ_{1A} = +121.3$ kJ/mol (Enthalpy of dissociation, Appendix L)
Step 2A	$Na(s) \rightarrow Na(g)$	$\Delta H^\circ_{2A} = +107.3$ kJ/mol (Enthalpy of formation, Appendix L)
Step 1B	$Cl(g) + e^- \rightarrow Cl^-(g)$	$\Delta H^\circ_{1B} = -349$ kJ/mol (Electron attachment enthalpy, Appendix F)
Step 2B	$Na(g) \rightarrow Na^+(g) + e^-$	$\Delta H^\circ_{2B} = +496$ kJ/mol) (Enthalpy of ionization, Appendix F)
Step 3	$Na^+(g) + Cl^-(g) \rightarrow NaCl(s)$	$\Delta_{lattice}H = ?$
	$Na(s) + 1/2\ Cl_2(g) \rightarrow NaCl(s)$	$\Delta_f H^\circ[NaCl(s)] = -411.12$ kJ/mol (Enthalpy of formation, Appendix L)

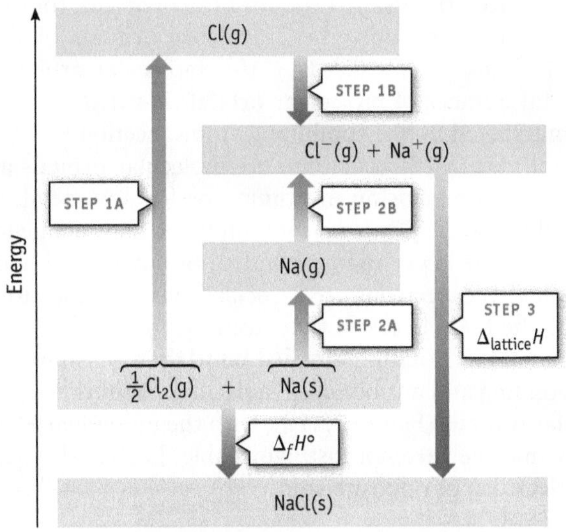

FIGURE 12.12 Born–Haber cycle for the formation of NaCl(s) from the elements. The calculation in the text uses enthalpy values, and the value obtained is the lattice enthalpy, $\Delta_{lattice}H$. The difference between $\Delta_{lattice}U$ and $\Delta_{lattice}H$ is generally small and can be corrected for, if desired. (Note that the energy diagram is not to scale.)

Calculation of lattice energies by this procedure (a Born–Haber cycle) is named for Max Born (1882–1970) and Fritz Haber (1868–1934), German scientists who played prominent roles in thermodynamic research.

Notice that the chemical equations along one pathway—Steps 1A, 1B, 2A, 2B, and 3—add up to the equation for formation of NaCl(s) from the elements, and the enthalpy changes for those steps add up to the enthalpy of formation of NaCl(s).

$$\Delta_f H^\circ\ [\text{NaCl(s)}] = \Delta H_{\text{Step 1A}} + \Delta H_{\text{Step 1B}} + \Delta H_{\text{Step 2A}} + \Delta H_{\text{Step 2B}} + \Delta H_{\text{Step 3}}$$

Because the values for all of these quantities are known except for $\Delta H_{\text{Step 3}}$ ($\Delta_{\text{lattice}}H$), the value for this step can be calculated and is found to be −787 kJ/mol.

REVIEW & CHECK FOR SECTION 12-3

1. Which sodium halide has the most negative lattice enthalpy?

   (a) NaI (b) NaBr (c) NaCl (d) NaF

2. The lattice enthalpy for NaCl is defined as the enthalpy change for which of the following reactions?

   (a) $Na(s) + Cl_2(g) \rightarrow NaCl(s)$
   (b) $Na(g) + Cl(g) \rightarrow NaCl(s)$
   (c) $Na^+(g) + Cl^-(g) \rightarrow NaCl(s)$
   (d) $NaOH(s) + HCl(g) \rightarrow NaCl(s) + H_2O(\ell)$

3. Given that the molar enthalpy of formation, $\Delta_f H^\circ$, of solid sodium iodide is −287 kJ/mol, calculate the lattice enthalpy for NaI(s). The required data can be found in Appendices F and L.

   (a) −796 kJ/mol
   (b) −702 kJ/mol
   (c) −287 kJ/mol
   (d) +222 kJ/mol

12-4 Bonding in Metals and Semiconductors

Learning Objectives: LO 2.20 (see Appendix O-1 "Metals and Alloys"), LO 2.22 (see APEC Lab 6 "Intermolecular Forces"), LO 2.25 (see Appendix O-1 "Metals and Alloys"), LO 2.26 (see Appendix O-1 "Metals and Alloys"), LO 2.27 (see Appendix O-1 "Metals and Alloys"), LO 2.28 (see Appendix O-1 "Metals and Alloys")

Electron Sea Model For more information about the electron sea model of metallic bonding, see Appendix O-1 "Metals and Alloys."

The melting point of most metals is quite high so we know there must be substantial forces holding them together. The classic description of these structures involves a lattice of metal atoms in a sea of delocalized electrons, and one can visualize that coulombic forces of attraction between the electrons and the charged nuclei provide this force. This model readily explains the electrical conductivity of metals which results because the electrons are free to move with little resistance through the lattice under the influence of an electric potential.

An alternative and more detailed view of metallic bonding is the band model. Recall that molecular orbital theory (Chapter 9) was used to rationalize covalent bonding in molecules. MO theory can be applied to bonding in metals by viewing a metal as a kind of "supermolecule" with an enormous number of atoms.

Even a tiny piece of metal contains a very large number of atoms and an even larger number of valence orbitals. In 1 mol of lithium atoms, for example, there are 6×10^{23} atoms. Considering only the 2*s* valence orbitals of lithium, there are 6×10^{23} atomic orbitals, from which 6×10^{23} molecular orbitals can be created. (Recall that the total number of molecular orbitals is equal to the total number of atomic orbitals contributed by the combining atoms; Section 9-3. If *p* and *d* orbitals are brought into the picture, then many more molecular orbitals are created.) The molecular orbitals that we envision in lithium, or for any metal, will span all the atoms in the crystalline solid. A mole of lithium has 1 mol of valence electrons, and these electrons occupy the lower-energy bonding orbitals. The bonding is described as *delocalized* because the electrons are associated with all the atoms in the crystal and not with a specific bond between two atoms.

This theory of metallic bonding is called **band theory**. An energy level diagram would show the bonding and antibonding molecular orbitals blending together into a band of molecular orbitals (Figure 12.13), with the individual MOs being so close together in energy that they are not distinguishable. Each molecular orbital can accommodate two electrons of opposite spin.

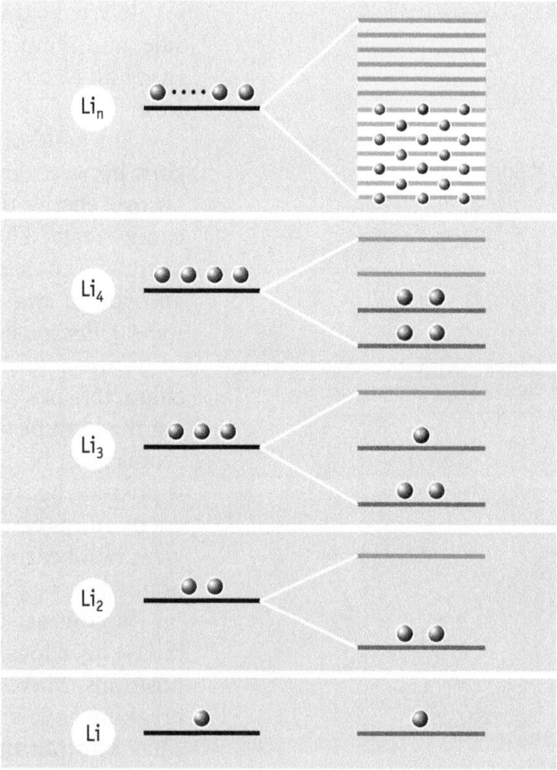

FIGURE 12.13 **Bands of molecular orbitals in a lithium crystal.** Here, the 2*s* valence orbitals of Li atoms are combined to form molecular orbitals. As more and more atoms with the same valence orbitals are added, the number of molecular orbitals grows until the orbitals are so close in energy that they merge into a band of molecular orbitals. If 1 mol of Li atoms, each with its 2*s* valence orbital, is combined, 6×10^{23} molecular orbitals are formed. However, only 1 mol of electrons, or 3×10^{23} electron pairs, is available, so only half of these molecular orbitals are filled. (See Section 9-3 for the discussion of molecular orbital theory.)

In metals, there are not enough electrons to fill all of the molecular orbitals. In 1 mol of Al atoms, for example, 18×10^{23} *s* and *p* electrons, or 9×10^{23} electron pairs, are sufficient to fill only a portion of the 24×10^{23} molecular orbitals created by the *s* and *p* orbitals of the Al atoms. Many more orbitals are available than electron pairs to occupy them.

At 0 K, the electrons in any metal will all be in orbitals with the lowest possible energy, corresponding to the lowest possible energy for the system. The highest filled level at 0 K is called the **Fermi level** (Figure 12.14).

In metals at temperatures above 0 K, thermal energy will cause some electrons to occupy orbitals above the Fermi level. Even a small input of energy (for example, raising the temperature a few degrees above 0 K) will cause electrons to move from filled orbitals to higher-energy orbitals. For each electron promoted, two singly occupied levels result: a negative electron in an orbital above the Fermi level and a positive "hole"—from the absence of an electron—below the Fermi level.

The positive holes and negative electrons in a piece of metal account for its electrical conductivity. Electrical conductivity arises from the movement of electrons and holes in singly occupied states in the presence of an applied electric field. When

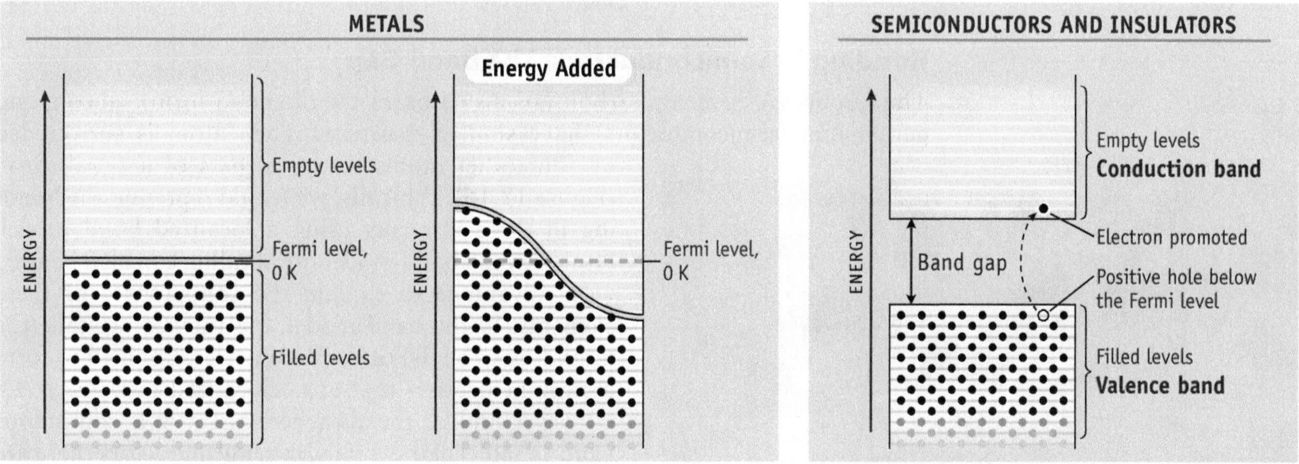

Metals. The highest filled level at 0 K is referred to as the *Fermi level*. As energy is added as the temperature increases, some electrons now occupy levels above the Fermi level, which depletes levels below the Fermi level.

Semiconductors. In contrast to metals, the band of filled levels (the valence band) is separated from the band of empty levels (the conduction band) by a band gap. In insulators, the energy of the band gap is large.

FIGURE 12.14 **Band theory applied to metals, semiconductors, and insulators.** The bonding in metals and semiconductors can be described using molecular orbital theory. Molecular orbitals are constructed from the valence orbitals on each atom and are delocalized over all the atoms.

an electric field is applied to the metal, negative electrons move toward the positive side, and the positive "holes" move to the negative side. (Positive holes "move" because an electron from an adjacent atom can move into the hole, thereby creating a fresh "hole.")

The band of energy levels in a metal is essentially continuous, that is, the energy gaps between levels are extremely small. A consequence of this is that a metal can absorb energy of nearly any wavelength, causing an electron to move to a higher energy state. The now-excited system can immediately emit a photon of the same energy as the electron returns to the original energy level. This rapid and efficient absorption *and* reemission of light make polished metal surfaces be reflective and appear lustrous (shiny).

Alloys For information about alloys, see Appendix O-1 "Metals and Alloys."

This picture for metallic bonding provides an interpretation for other physical characteristics of metals. For example, most metals are malleable and ductile, meaning they can be rolled into sheets and drawn into wires. In these processes, the metal atoms must be able to move fairly freely with respect to their nearest neighbors. This is possible because metallic bonding is delocalized—that is, nondirectional. The layers of atoms can slip past one another relatively easily (as if the delocalized electrons were ball bearings that facilitate this motion), while at the same time the layers are bonded through coulombic attractions between the nuclei and the electrons.

In contrast to metals, rigid network solids such as diamond, silicon, and silica (SiO_2) have localized bonding, which anchors the component atoms or ions in fixed positions. Movement of atoms in these structures relative to their neighbors requires breaking covalent bonds. As a result, such substances are typically hard and brittle. They will not deform under stress as metals do, but instead tend to cleave along crystal planes.

Semiconductors

Semiconducting materials are at the heart of solid-state electronic devices such as computer chips and light-emitting diodes (LEDs) (Figure 12.15). Semiconductors do not conduct electricity easily but can be encouraged to do so by the input of energy. This property allows devices made from semiconductors to essentially have "on" and "off" states, which form the basis of the binary logic used in computers. We can understand how semiconductors function by looking at their electronic structure, following the band theory approach used for metals.

Bonding in Semiconductors: The Band Gap

The Group 4A elements carbon (an insulator, in the diamond form), silicon, and germanium (semiconductors) have similar structures. Each atom is surrounded by four other atoms at the corners of a tetrahedron (Figure 12.16). Typically, we would represent the bonding in these elements using a localized bond model. However, the band model for bonding can also be used with advantage to explain the conductivity of these elements. In the band model, the valence orbitals (the *ns* and *np* orbitals) of each atom are combined to form molecular orbitals that are delocalized over the solid. However, unlike metals where there is a continuous band of molecular orbitals, in semiconductors there are two distinct bands, a lower-energy *valence band* and a higher-energy *conduction band*, separated by a *band gap* [Figure 12.14, *right*, and Figure 12.17]. In the Group 4A elements, the orbitals of the valence band are completely filled and the conduction band is empty. The band gap is an energy barrier to the promotion of electrons from the valence band to the higher-energy conduction band.

© Cengage Learning/Charles D. Winters

FIGURE 12.15 **Electronic devices all made from semiconductors.** (top) Computer chip. (left) LED lights. (right) Transistors.

The band gap in diamond is 580 kJ/mol—so large that electrons are trapped in the filled valence band and cannot make the transition to the conduction band, even at elevated temperatures. Thus, it is not possible to create positive "holes," and diamond is an insulator, a nonconductor.

Silicon and germanium have much smaller band gaps, 106 kJ/mol for silicon and 68 kJ/mol for germanium. As a result they are semiconductors. These elements can conduct a small current because thermal energy is sufficient to promote a few electrons from the valence band across the band gap to the conduction band (Figure 12.17). Conduction then occurs when the electrons in the conduction band migrate in one direction and the positive holes in the valence band migrate in the opposite direction.

Pure silicon and germanium are called **intrinsic semiconductors**, with the name referring to the fact that this is an intrinsic or naturally occurring property of the pure material. In intrinsic semiconductors, the number of electrons in the conduction band is determined by the temperature and the magnitude of the band gap. The smaller the band gap, the smaller the energy required to promote a significant number of electrons. As the temperature increases, more electrons are promoted into the conduction band, and a higher conductivity results.

There are also **extrinsic semiconductors**. The conductivity of these materials is controlled by adding small numbers of different atoms (typically 1 in 10^6 to 1 in 10^8) called *dopants*. That is, the characteristics of semiconductors can be changed by altering their chemical makeup.

Suppose a few silicon atoms in the silicon lattice are replaced by aluminum atoms (or atoms of some other Group 3A element). Aluminum has only three valence electrons, whereas silicon has four. Four Si-Al bonds are created per aluminum atom in the lattice, but these bonds must be deficient in electrons. According to band theory, the Si-Al bonds form a discrete but empty band at an energy level higher than the valence band but lower than the conduction band. This level is referred to as an *acceptor level* because it can accept electrons from the valence band. The gap between the valence band and the acceptor level is usually quite small, so electrons can be promoted readily to the acceptor level. The positive holes created in the valence band are able to move under the influence of an electric potential, so current results from the hole mobility. Because *positive* holes are created in an aluminum-doped semiconductor, this is called a ***p*-type semiconductor** (Figure 12.17b, *left*).

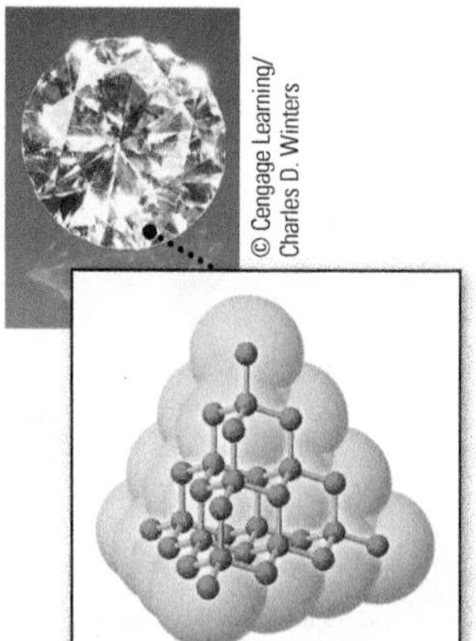

FIGURE 12.16 **The structure of diamond, an insulator.** The structures of silicon and germanium, semiconductors, are similar in that each atom is bound tetrahedrally to four others.

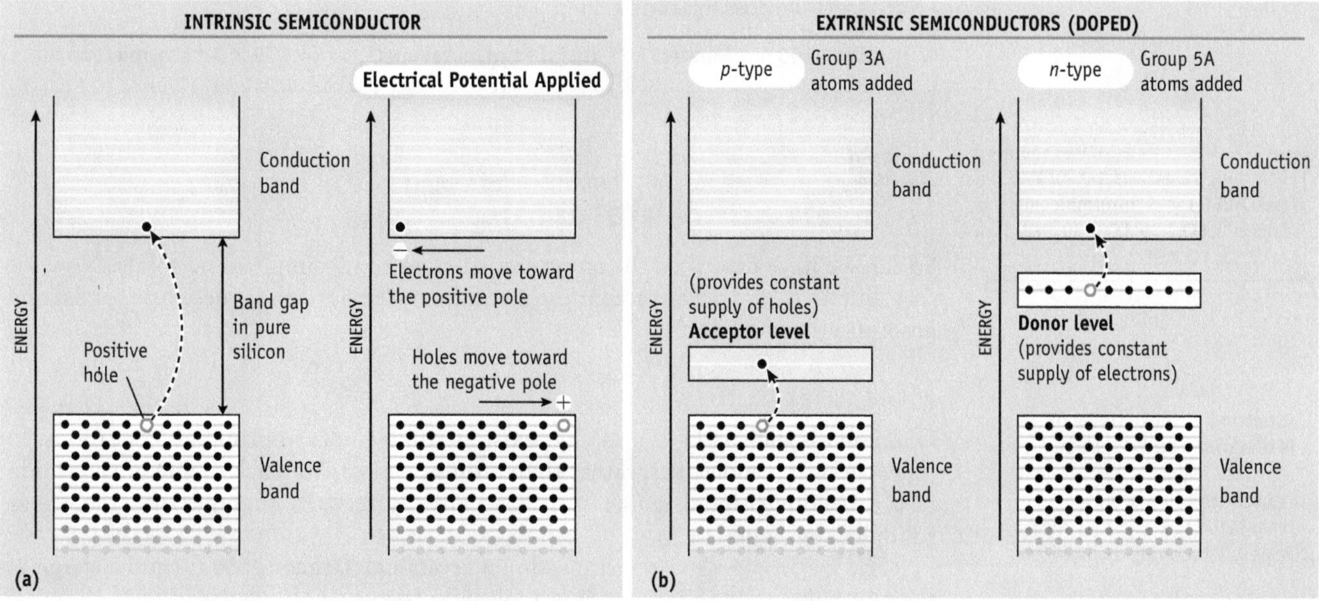

FIGURE 12.17 **Intrinsic (a) and extrinsic (b) semiconductors.**

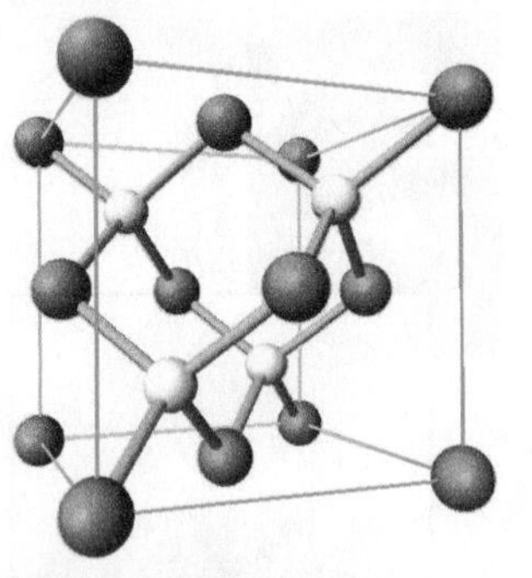

Gallium arsenide, GaAs. The unit cell of GaAs has Ga atoms in an fcc lattice with As atoms in tetrahedral holes. It is an important semiconductor used in infrared emitting diodes, laser diodes, and solar cells.

Now suppose phosphorus atoms (or atoms of some other Group 5A element such as arsenic) are incorporated into the silicon lattice instead of aluminum atoms. This material is also a semiconductor, but it now has extra electrons because each phosphorus atom has one more valence electron than the silicon atom it replaces in the lattice. Semiconductors doped in this manner have a discrete, partially filled donor level that resides just below the conduction band. Electrons can be promoted to the conduction band from this donor band, and electrons in the conduction band carry the charge. Such a material, consisting of *negative* charge carriers, is called an ***n*-type semiconductor** (Figure 12.17b, *right*).

One group of materials that have desirable semiconducting properties is the III-V semiconductors, so called because they are formed by combining elements from Group 3A (such as Ga and In) with elements from Group 5A (such as As or Sb).

Gallium arsenide, GaAs, is a common semiconducting material that has electrical conductivity properties that are sometimes preferable to those of pure silicon or germanium. The crystal structure of GaAs is similar to that of diamond and silicon; each Ga atom is tetrahedrally coordinated to four As atoms, and vice versa.

It is also possible for Group 2B and 6A elements to form semiconducting compounds such as cadmium sulfide, CdS. The farther apart the elements are found in the periodic table, however, the more ionic the bonding becomes. As the ionic character of the bonding increases, the band gap will increase, and the material will become a weaker semiconductor. Thus, the band gap in CdS is 232 kJ/mol, compared to a band gap in GaAs of 140 kJ/mol.

These materials can also be modified by substituting other atoms into the structure. For example, in one widely used semiconductor, aluminum atoms are substituted for gallium atoms in GaAs, giving materials with a range of compositions ($Ga_{1-x}Al_xAs$). The importance of this modification is that the band gap depends on the relative proportions of the elements, so it is possible to control the size of the band gap by adjusting the stoichiometry. As Al atoms are substituted for Ga atoms, for example, the band gap energy increases. This consideration is important for the specific uses of these materials in devices such as LEDs (light-emitting diodes).

REVIEW & CHECK FOR SECTION 12-4

1. Germanium was one of the first materials used as a semiconductor. Given that it has a band gap of 68 kJ/mol, what is the maximum wavelength of light that can excite an electron transition across the band gap of Ge? To what region of the electromagnetic spectrum does this correspond?

   (a) 1800 nm, infrared (b) 29 nm, ultraviolet (c) 15×10^6 nm, microwave

Learning Objectives: LO 2.22 (see APEC Lab 6 "Intermolecular Forces"), LO 2.29, LO 2.30, LO 2.31, LO 2.32

12-5 The Solid State: Other Types of Solid Materials

So far, we have described the structures of metals and simple ionic solids. Now we turn briefly to the other categories of solids: molecular solids, network solids, and amorphous solids (Table 12.2).

Molecular Solids

Electrical Conductivity of Molecular Solids Because molecular solids are made up of discrete neutral particles that are locked in place in the solid and have their valence electrons tied up in either lone pairs or covalent bonding, most molecular solids do not conduct electricity.

Compounds such as H_2O and CO_2 exist as solids under appropriate conditions. In these cases, it is molecules, rather than atoms or ions, that pack in a regular fashion in a three-dimensional lattice. You have already seen an example of a molecular solid: ice (◀ Figure 11.5).

The way molecules are arranged in a crystalline lattice depends on the shape of the molecules and the types of intermolecular forces. Molecules tend to pack in the most efficient manner and to align in ways that maximize intermolecular forces of

Table 12.2 Structures and Properties of Various Types of Solid Substances

Type	Examples	Structural Units	Forces Holding Units Together	Typical Properties
Ionic	NaCl, K_2SO_4, $CaCl_2$, $(NH_4)_3PO_4$	Positive and negative ions; no discrete molecules	Ionic; attractions among charges on positive and negative ions	Hard; brittle; high melting point; poor electric conductivity as solid, good as liquid; often water-soluble
Metallic	Iron, silver, copper, other metals and alloys	Metal atoms (positive metal ions with delocalized electrons)	Metallic; electrostatic attraction among metal ions and electrons	Malleable; ductile; good electric conductivity in solid and liquid; good heat conductivity; wide range of hardness and melting points
Molecular	H_2, O_2, I_2, H_2O, CO_2, CH_4, CH_3OH, CH_3CO_2H	Molecules	Dispersion forces, dipole–dipole forces, hydrogen bonds	Low to moderate melting points and boiling points; soft; poor electric conductivity in solid and liquid
Network	Graphite, diamond, quartz, feldspars, mica	Atoms held in an infinite two- or three-dimensional network	Covalent; directional electron-pair bonds	Wide range of hardness and melting points (three-dimensional bonding > two-dimensional bonding); poor electric conductivity, with some exceptions
Amorphous	Glass, polyethylene, nylon	Covalently bonded networks with no long-range regularity	Covalent; directional electron-pair bonds	Noncrystalline; wide temperature range for melting; poor electric conductivity, with some exceptions

attraction. Thus, the water structure was established to gain the maximum intermolecular attraction through hydrogen bonding.

Most of the information on molecular geometries, bond lengths, and bond angles discussed in Chapter 8 came from studies of the structures of molecular solids.

Network Solids

Network solids are composed entirely of a three-dimensional array of covalently bonded atoms. Common examples include allotropes of carbon: graphite, graphene, and diamond. Elemental silicon is also a network solid with a diamond-like structure.

Graphite consists of carbon atoms bonded together in flat sheets that cling only weakly to one another (Figure 12.18). Within the layers, each carbon atom is

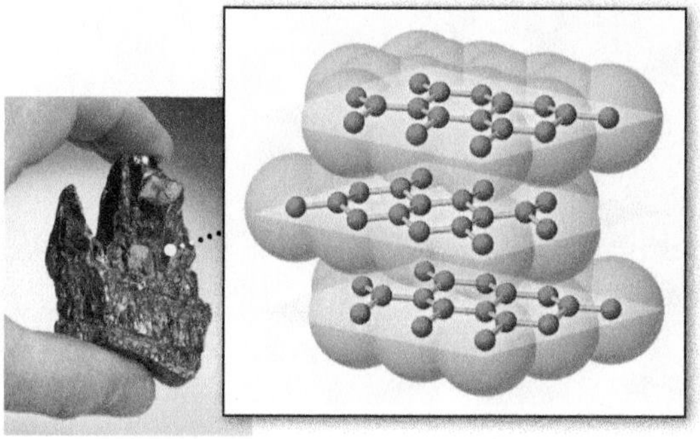

Graphite, layers of six-member rings of carbon atoms.

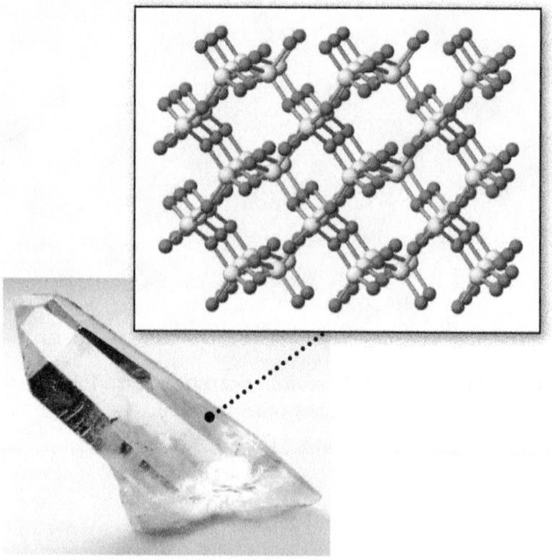

Silicon dioxide, SiO_2. Common quartz is a network of linked SiO_4 tetrahedra.

FIGURE 12.18 **Network solids: graphite and quartz are among many examples.**

CASE STUDY Nanotubes and Graphene—The Hottest New Network Solids

One of the most interesting developments in chemistry in the last 20 years has been the discovery of new forms of carbon. First, there were buckyballs and then carbon nanotubes.

Common graphite, from which your pencil lead is made, consists of six-member rings of carbon atoms connected in sheets, and the sheets stack one on top of another like cards in a deck (Figure 12.18). But if carbon compounds are heated under the right conditions, the carbon atoms assemble into sheets, and the sheets close on themselves to form tubes. These are called **nanotubes** because the tubes are only a nanometer or so in diameter. Sometimes they are single tubes, and other times they are tubes within tubes. Carbon nanotubes are at least 100 times stronger than steel but only one sixth as dense, and they conduct heat and electricity far better than copper. Thus, there has been enormous interest in their commercial applications, but it has also been difficult to make them with consistent properties.

Now there is also **graphene**, a single sheet of six-member carbon atoms. Researchers in England, Andre Geim and Kostya Novoselov, discovered graphene in a simple way: Put a flake of graphite on Scotch tape, fold the tape over, and then pull it apart. The graphite layers come apart, and, if you do it enough times, only one layer—one C atom thick!—is left on the tape. Chemists and physicists soon found that the material is extremely strong and that it is a better conductor of electrons than any other material at room temperature. Several thousand research papers were soon published about graphene, and Geim and Novoselov received the 2010 Nobel Prize in Physics for their discovery.

©Digital Art/Corbis

Carbon nanotube. These tubes are assembled from six-member rings of carbon atoms and are typically about 1 nm in diameter.

The sticky tape method is clearly not suitable for producing large quantities of graphene, so now it is made by high-temperature vapor deposition, in which carbon atoms in the gas phase are deposited on a surface, or by using chemical methods to pry open graphite layers. A commercial product, "graphene nanoplatelets," which are small stacks of graphene sheets, is now available.

Chemical and Engineering News (March 2009) said that although it was "considered a hypothetical curiosity just a few years ago, . . . graphene has stormed the world of scientific research." Research is proceeding worldwide, primarily on its use in electronics.

Vorbeck Materials

Graphene "paper." Graphene nanoplatelets can be used to make electrically conducting ink. One application is to use such inks to print theft- and tamper-resistant packaging. (Vorbeck Materials.)

Questions:

1. Based on a C–C distance of 139 pm, what is the side-to-side dimension of a planar, C_6 ring?
2. If a graphene sheet has a width of 1.0 micrometer, how many C_6 rings are joined across the sheet?
3. Estimate the thickness of a sheet of graphene (in pm). How did you determine this value?

Answers to these questions are available in Appendix N.

©ogwen/Shutterstock.com

Graphene is a single sheet of six-member carbon rings. This latest material in the world of carbon chemistry is a better conductor of electrons than any other material.

surrounded by three other carbon atoms in a trigonal–planar arrangement. The layers can slip easily over one another, which explains why graphite is soft, a good lubricant, and used in pencil lead. (Pencil "lead" is not the element lead but rather a composite of clay and graphite.)

As described in more detail in *Case Study: Nanotubes and Graphene—The Hottest New Network Solids*, the past two decades have seen the discovery of materials such as carbon nanotubes and graphene. Both are under intense development and both have commercial potential.

Diamond, which has a relatively low density (d = 3.51 g/cm^3), is the hardest material and the best conductor of heat known. It is transparent to visible light, as well as to infrared and ultraviolet radiation. In addition to its use in jewelry, diamond is used in abrasives and in diamond-coated cutting tools. In the structure of diamond (see Figure 12.16), each carbon atom is bonded to four other carbon atoms at the corners of a tetrahedron, and this pattern extends throughout the solid.

Silicates, compounds composed of silicon and oxygen, are also network solids and make up an enormous class of chemical compounds. You know them in the form of sand, quartz, talc, and mica, or as a major constituent of rocks such as granite. The jade on the cover of this book, and described at the beginning of this chapter, is based on a network of SiO_4 tetrahedra. Quartz is also a network solid (Figure 12.18) consisting of tetrahedral silicon atoms covalently bonded to oxygen atoms in a giant three-dimensional lattice.

Most network solids are hard and rigid and are characterized by high melting and boiling points. These characteristics reflect the fact that a great deal of energy must be provided to break the covalent bonds in the lattice. For example, silicon dioxide melts at temperatures higher than 1600 °C.

Amorphous Solids

A characteristic property of pure crystalline solids—whether metals, ionic solids, or molecular solids—is that they melt at a specific temperature. For example, water in the form of ice melts at 0 °C, aspirin at 135 °C, lead at 327.5 °C, and NaCl at 801 °C. Because pure solids have specific and reproducible values, their melting points are often used to identify chemical compounds.

Another property of crystalline solids is that they form well-defined crystals, with smooth, flat faces. When a sharp force is applied to a crystal, it will most often cleave to give smaller pieces with smooth, flat faces. The resulting solid particles are smaller versions of the original crystal (Figure 12.19a).

Photos: © Cengage Learning/Charles D. Winters

(a) A salt crystal, a crystalline solid, can be cleaved cleanly into smaller and smaller crystals that are duplicates of the larger crystal.

(b) Glass is an amorphous solid composed of silicon and oxygen atoms. It has, however, no long-range order as in crystalline quartz.

FIGURE 12.19 **Crystalline and amorphous solids.**

Many common solids, including ones that we encounter every day, do not have these properties, however. These are *amorphous solids*, solids that do not have a regular structure. Glass is a good example. When glass is heated, it softens over a wide temperature range, a property useful for artisans and craftsmen who can create beautiful and functional products for our enjoyment and use. Glass also possesses a property that we would rather it not have: When glass breaks, it leaves randomly shaped pieces (Figure 12.19b). Other amorphous solids that behave similarly include common polymers such as polyethylene terephthalate (PET), nylon, and other plastics.

REVIEW & CHECK FOR SECTION 12-5

1. Which of the following allotropes of carbon is not a network solid?

   (a) graphite (b) diamond (c) buckyballs (C_{60}) (d) graphene

2. A soft, white waxy solid melts over a temperature range from 120 °C to 130 °C. It doesn't dissolve in water and it doesn't conduct electricity. These properties are consistent with its identity as

   (a) a network solid (c) an ionic solid

   (b) an amorphous solid (d) a metallic solid

Learning Objectives: LO 2.22 (see APEC Lab 6 "Intermolecular Forces"), LO 5.6

12-6 Phase Changes Involving Solids

Phase changes of materials, and the conditions under which they occur, are of interest to chemists and geologists as well as to physicists and engineers who are developing the latest electronics (see *A Closer Look: New Memory for Your Computer Based on Phase Changes*, page 462).

Melting: Conversion of Solid into Liquid

The melting point of a solid is the temperature at which the lattice collapses and the solid is converted into a liquid. Like any phase change, melting involves an energy change, called the *enthalpy of fusion* (given in kilojoules per mole) (◀ Chapter 5).

Energy absorbed as heat on melting = enthalpy of fusion = $\Delta_{fusion}H$ (kJ/mol)

Energy evolved as heat on freezing = enthalpy of crystallization = $-\Delta_{fusion}H$ (kJ/mol)

© Cengage Learning/Charles D. Winters

Molten ionic compounds conduct electricity. Ionic solids generally have high lattice energies and require energy to disrupt the lattice. However, once molten the ions are mobile, and the liquid will conduct electricity.

Enthalpies of fusion have a very wide range of values (Table 12.3). A low melting temperature will certainly mean a low value for the enthalpy of fusion, whereas high melting points are associated with high enthalpies of fusion. Figure 12.20 shows the enthalpies of fusion for the metals of the fourth through the sixth periods. Here we see that transition metals have high enthalpies of fusion, with many of those in the sixth period being extraordinarily high. Tungsten, which has the second highest melting point of all the known elements (carbon has the highest melting point), also has the highest enthalpy of fusion among the transition metals. This is the reason tungsten is used for the filaments in incandescent lightbulbs; no other material has been found to work better since the invention of the lightbulb in 1908.

Table 12.3 presents some data for several basic types of substances: metals, polar and nonpolar molecules, and ionic solids. In general, nonpolar molecular solids have low melting points. Melting points increase within a series of related molecules, however, as the size and molar mass increase. This happens because London dispersion forces are generally larger when the molar mass is larger. Thus, increasing amounts of energy are required to break down the intermolecular forces in the solid.

The ionic compounds in Table 12.3 have higher melting points and higher enthalpies of fusion than the molecular solids. This property is due to the strong ion–ion forces present in ionic solids, forces that are reflected in large negative lattice energies. Because ion–ion forces depend on ion size (as well as ion charge), there is

Table 12.3 Melting Points and Enthalpies of Fusion of Some Elements and Compounds

Element or Compound	Melting Point (°C)	Enthalpy of Fusion (kJ/mol)	Type of Interparticle Forces
Metals			
Hg	−39	2.29	Metal bonding.
Na	98	2.60	
Al	660	10.7	
Ti	1668	20.9	
W	3422	35.2	
Molecular Solids: Nonpolar Molecules			
O_2	−219	0.440	London dispersion forces (which increase with size and molar mass).
F_2	−220	0.510	
Cl_2	−102	6.41	
Br_2	−7.2	10.8	
Molecular Solids: Polar Molecules			
HCl	−114	1.99	All three HX molecules have dipole–dipole forces as well as London dispersion forces (which increase with size and molar mass).
HBr	−87	2.41	
HI	−51	2.87	
H_2O	0	6.01	Hydrogen bonding, dispersion forces.
Ionic Solids			
NaF	996	33.4	All ionic solids have extended ion–ion interactions. Note the general trend is the same as for lattice energies (see Section 12-3 and Figure 12.11).
NaCl	801	28.2	
NaBr	747	26.1	
NaI	660	23.6	

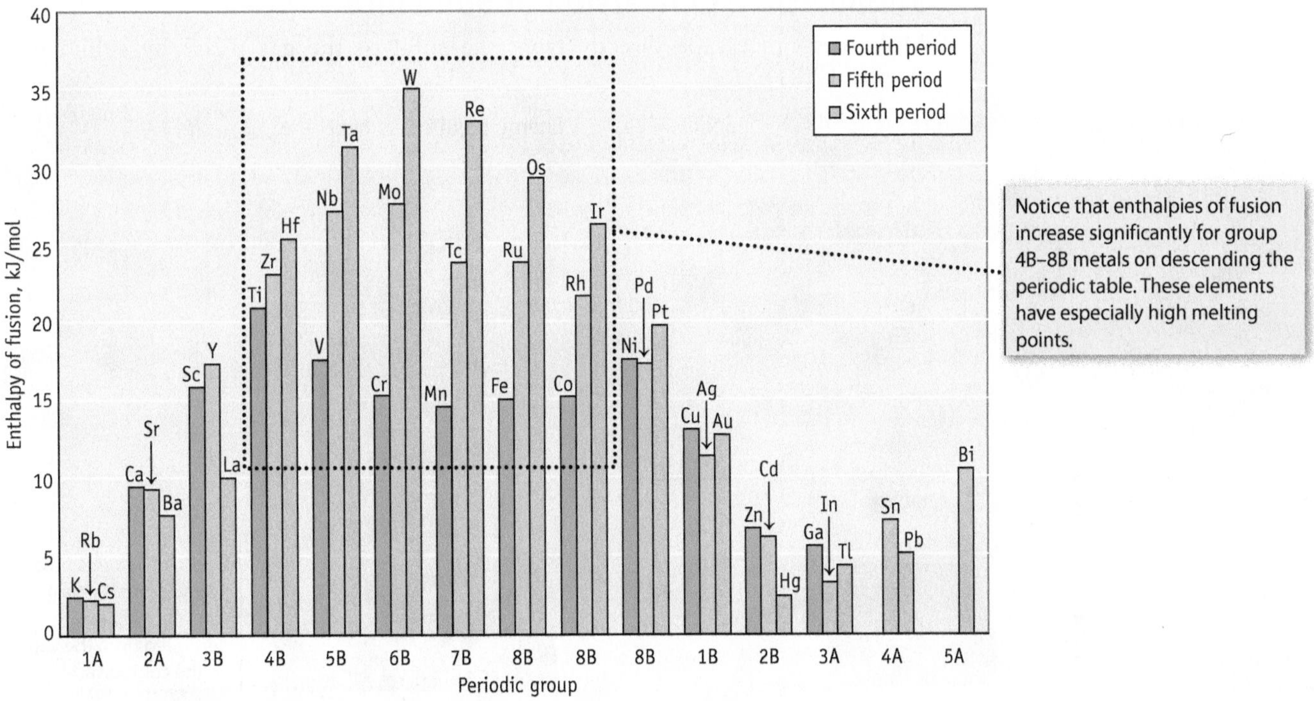

FIGURE 12.20 **Enthalpy of fusion of fourth-, fifth-, and sixth-period metals.** Enthalpies of fusion range from 2–5 kJ/mol for Group 1A elements to 35.2 kJ/mol for tungsten.

A CLOSER LOOK New Memory for Your Computer Based on Phase Changes

You may keep the file for your term paper on a little "thumb drive" or record your photos in your camera on a memory card. These are "flash memory" cards that use electric signals to change the ability of the material to trap or release charge and thus record information. Flash memory materials, however, degrade with time and the time to charge or discharge is long enough that there is a limit to the speed of data transfer. That is why there is much interest now in "phase change random access memory" or PRAM materials.

As the name implies, PRAM materials work by a phase change. As *Computerworld* magazine said in 2007, "These silvery semiconductors, as soft as lead, have the unique property that their physical state can be changed from crystalline to amorphous through the application of heat." To record data, an electric current heats the PRAM at a given spot where the material is crystalline. The material melts, and the atoms take on a random or amorphous arrangement. When the heating ends, the temperature drops quickly, and the atoms are frozen in the amorphous state. To change the material back to a crystalline arrangement, the spot is again heated, but this time it does not melt but instead rearranges into the original crystalline structure.

The reason PRAMs can store information is that there is a difference in electrical resistance in the two states. In the amorphous state the material has a high resistance, whereas the crystalline state has a low resistance. Since digital information is stored by detecting whether a particular state is "on" or "off," the PRAM materials are ideal for data storage.

If you read more about PRAM materials, you will often see the word "chalcogenide." This is because one of the first materials used was $Ge_2Sb_2Te_5$. Tellurium (Te) is in Group 6A, where the elements S, Se, and Te are sometimes referred to as "chalcogenides."

© Cengage Learning/Charles D. Winters

Flash memory cards and a USB drive.

Courtesy: Samsung Electronics

Phase-change memory chip from Samsung.

a good correlation between lattice energy and the position of the metal or halogen in the periodic table. For example, the data in Table 12.3 show a decrease in melting point and enthalpy of fusion for sodium salts as the halide ion increases in size. This parallels the decrease in lattice energy seen with increasing ion size.

Sublimation: Conversion of Solid into Vapor

Molecules can escape directly from the solid to the gas phase by sublimation (Figure 12.21).

$$\text{Solid} \rightarrow \text{gas} \qquad \text{Energy required as heat} = \Delta_{\text{sublimation}}H$$

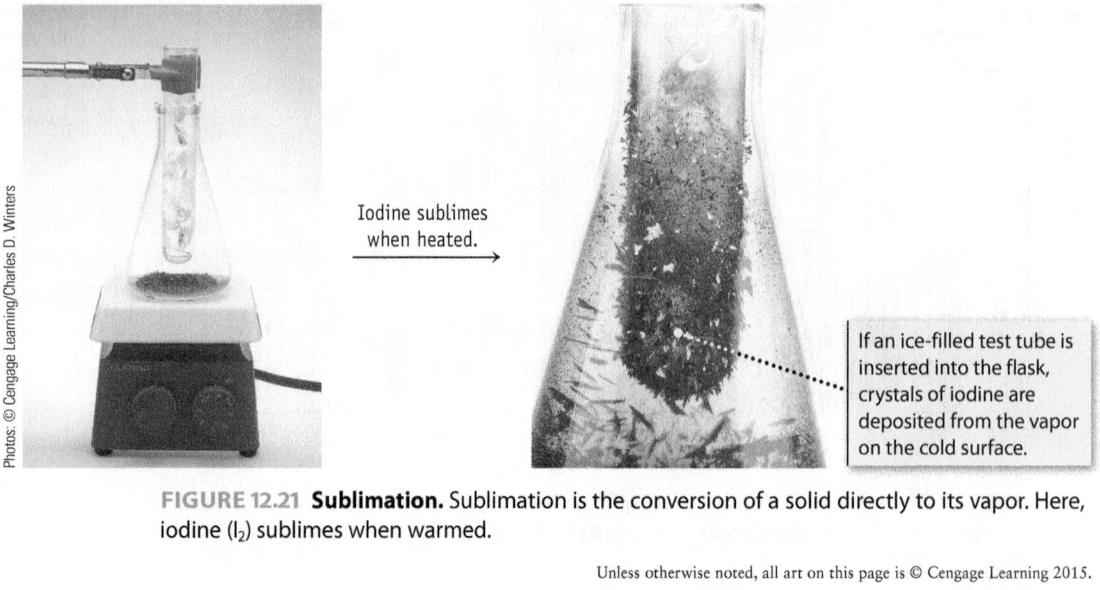

Photos: © Cengage Learning/Charles D. Winters

FIGURE 12.21 **Sublimation.** Sublimation is the conversion of a solid directly to its vapor. Here, iodine (I_2) sublimes when warmed.

Sublimation, like fusion and evaporation, is an endothermic process. The energy required as heat is called the **enthalpy of sublimation**. Water, which has a molar enthalpy of sublimation of 51 kJ/mol, can be converted from solid ice to water vapor quite readily. A good example of this phenomenon is the sublimation of frost from grass and trees as night turns to day on a cold winter morning.

AP: Vapor Pressure of Solids Solids can sublime if they have sufficient vapor pressure at a reasonable temperature. This can be true for covalent solids such as I_2 in which the intermolecular forces are weak. Because of strong coulombic forces between ions, sublimation of ionic compounds can occur only at very high temperatures.

REVIEW & CHECK FOR SECTION 12-6

1. Which of the following Group 1A halides is expected to have the highest enthalpy of fusion?

   (a) NaCl (b) KCl (c) NaBr (d) KBr

2. Suppose you wanted to cool 100. g of water from 20 °C to 0 °C using dry ice, $CO_2(s)$. The enthalpy of sublimation of $CO_2(s)$ is 25.2 kJ/mol. What mass of dry ice should you need?

   (a) 0.33 g (b) 15 g (c) 3.5 g (d) 150 g

12-7 Phase Diagrams

Depending on the conditions of temperature and pressure, a substance can exist as a gas, a liquid, or a solid. In addition, under certain specific conditions, two (or even three) states can coexist in equilibrium. It is possible to summarize this information in the form of a graph called a **phase diagram**. Phase diagrams are used to illustrate the relationship between phases of matter and the pressure and temperature.

Water

Figure 12.22 illustrates the phase diagram for water. The lines in a phase diagram identify the temperatures and pressures under which two phases exist at equilibrium. Conversely, all points that do not fall on the lines in the figure represent conditions under which there is only one stable state. Line *A–B* represents conditions for solid–vapor equilibrium, and line *A–C* for liquid–solid equilibrium. The line from point *A* to point *D*, representing the temperatures and pressures at which the liquid

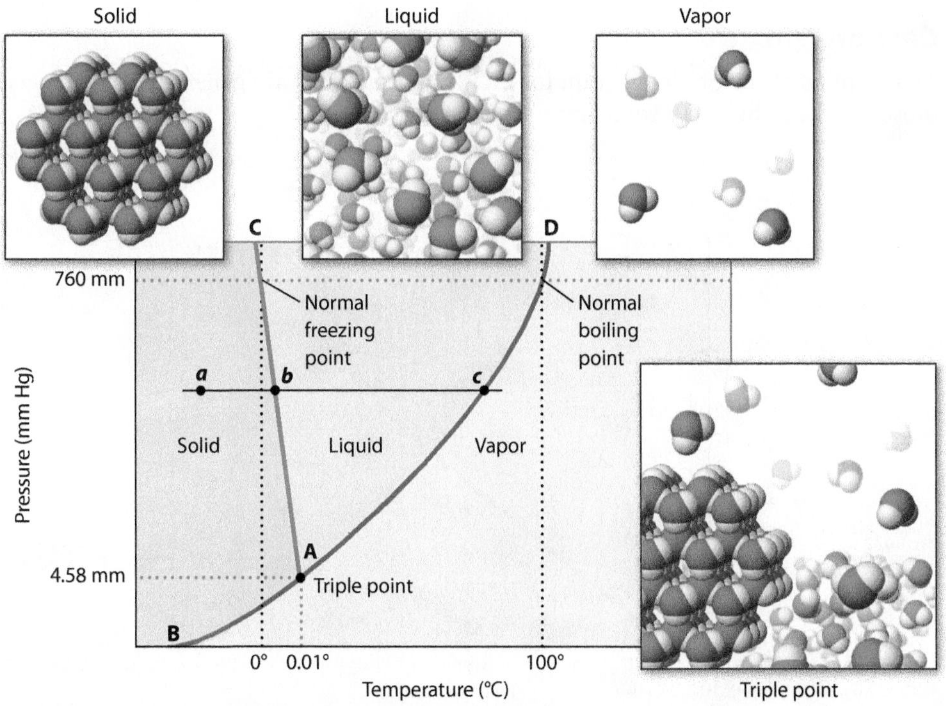

FIGURE 12.22 **Phase diagram for water.** The scale is intentionally exaggerated to be able to show the triple point and the negative slope of the line representing the liquid–solid equilibrium. (Points *a*, *b*, and *c* are discussed in the text.)

and vapor phases are in equilibrium, is the same curve plotted for water vapor pressure in Figure 11.12. Recall that the normal boiling point, 100 °C in the case of water, is the temperature at which the equilibrium vapor pressure is 760 mm Hg.

Point *A*, appropriately called the **triple point**, indicates the conditions under which all three phases coexist in equilibrium. For water, the triple point is at $P =$ 4.6 mm Hg and $T = 0.01$ °C.

The line *A–C* shows the conditions of pressure and temperature at which solid–liquid equilibrium exists. (Because no vapor pressure is involved here, the pressure referred to is the external pressure on the liquid.) For water, this line has a *negative slope* of about −0.01 °C for each one-atmosphere increase in pressure. That is, the higher the external pressure, the lower the melting point.

Perhaps the most interesting feature of the water phase diagram is the negative slope of the solid–liquid equilibrium line. Very few other substances in the universe have this property! The negative slope of this equilibrium line can be explained from our knowledge of the structure of water and ice. When the pressure on an object increases, common sense tells us that the volume of the object will become smaller, giving the substance a higher density. Because ice is less dense than liquid water (due to the open lattice structure of ice, Figure 11.5), ice and water in equilibrium respond to increased pressure (at constant *T*) by melting ice to form more water because the same mass of liquid water requires less volume.

Phase Diagrams and Thermodynamics

Phase Change and Thermodynamics The connection between the phase changes of water and thermodynamics is also illustrated in Figure 5.7.

Let us explore the water phase diagram further by correlating phase changes with thermodynamic data. Suppose we begin with ice at −10 °C and under a pressure of 500 mm Hg (point *a* on Figure 12.22). As ice is heated (at constant *P*), it absorbs about 2.1 J/g · K in warming from −10 °C (point *a*) to a temperature between 0 °C and 0.01 °C (point *b*). At this point, the solid is in equilibrium with liquid water. Solid-liquid equilibrium is maintained until 333 J/g has been transferred to the sample and it has become liquid water at this temperature. If the liquid, still under a pressure of 500 mm Hg, absorbs 4.184 J/g · K, it warms to point *c*. The temperature at point *c* is about 89 °C, and equilibrium is established between liquid water and water vapor. The equilibrium vapor pressure of the liquid water is 500 mm Hg. If about 2300 J/g is transferred to the liquid–vapor sample, the equilibrium vapor pressure remains 500 mm Hg until the liquid is completely converted to vapor at 89 °C.

Carbon Dioxide

The features of the phase diagram for CO_2 (Figure 12.23) are generally the same as those for water but with some important differences.

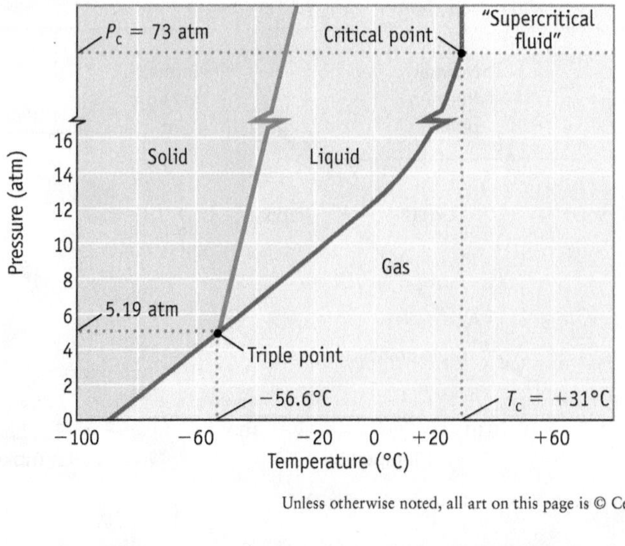

FIGURE 12.23 The phase diagram of CO_2. Notice in particular the positive slope of the solid–liquid equilibrium line. (For more on the critical point, see Section 11-6.)

In contrast to water, the CO_2 solid–liquid equilibrium line has a positive slope. Once again, increasing pressure on the solid in equilibrium with the liquid will shift the equilibrium to the more dense phase, but for CO_2 this will be the solid. Because solid CO_2 is denser than the liquid, the newly formed solid CO_2 sinks to the bottom in a container of liquid CO_2.

Another feature of the CO_2 phase diagram is the triple point that occurs at a pressure of 5.19 atm (3940 mm Hg) and 216.6 K (−56.6 °C). Carbon dioxide cannot be a liquid at pressures less than 5.19 atm.

At pressures around normal atmospheric pressure, CO_2 will be either a solid or a gas, depending on the temperature. At a pressure of 1 atm, solid CO_2 is in equilibrium with the gas at a temperature of 197.5 K (−78.7 °C). As a result, as solid CO_2 warms above this temperature, it sublimes rather than melts. Carbon dioxide is called *dry ice* for this reason; it looks like water ice, but it does not melt.

From the CO_2 phase diagram, we can also learn that CO_2 gas can be converted to a liquid at room temperature (20–25 °C) by exerting a moderate pressure on the gas. In fact, CO_2 is regularly shipped in tanks as a liquid to laboratories and industrial companies.

Finally, the critical pressure and temperature for CO_2 are 73 atm and 31 °C, respectively. Because the critical temperature and pressure are easily attained in the laboratory, it is possible to observe the transformation to supercritical CO_2 (see Figure 11.15).

REVIEW & CHECK FOR SECTION 12-7

1. Refer to the phase diagram for CO_2 in Figure 12.23. Which of the following statements is *not* true?

   (a) Liquid and gaseous CO_2 exist in equilibrium at approximately 0 °C and 12 atm.

   (b) Liquid CO_2 can only exist at a pressure greater than 5.19 atm.

   (c) Increasing the pressure leads to an increase in the melting point of $CO_2(s)$.

   (d) Supercritical CO_2 can be obtained at 25 °C if a high enough pressure is applied.

CHAPTER GOALS REVISITED

Now that you have studied this chapter, you should ask whether you have met the chapter goals. In particular, you should be able to:

UNDERSTAND

- The concept of a unit cell for a solid and the varieties of cubic unit cells in particular (Sections 12-1 and 12-2).
- The importance of lattice energy and how it is calculated (Section 12-3).
- The band model for bonding in metals and semiconductors and how this relates to their properties.
  - **a.** Understand the band theory of bonding in metals and the electrical conductivity of metals (Section 12-4). Study Questions: 17, 18.
  - **b.** Understand the nature of semiconductors (Section 12-4). Study Questions: 21–24, 51–55.
- The features of phase diagrams (Section 12-6).
  - **a.** Identify the different points (triple point, critical point, normal boiling point, freezing point) and regions (solid, liquid, vapor) of a phase diagram, and use the diagram to evaluate the vapor pressure of a liquid and the relative densities of a liquid and a solid (Section 12-7). Study Questions: 33–36.

APPLYING CHEMICAL PRINCIPLES

Tin Disease

Organ pipes in northern European cathedrals have been made of tin for several hundred years. It is believed that the metal improves both the tone and appearance of the pipes. Now organ pipes are made of a tin-lead alloy, in part because many old organ pipes have crumbled over time due to "tin disease." Gray splotches appear on the normally shiny metal, and over time the metal crumbles to a gray powder. Although it could be assumed that the tin reacted with other elements or compounds to form this gray substance, chemical analysis shows the substance is pure tin.

What is the cause of "tin disease"? Two allotropes of tin exist at atmospheric pressure. The metallic form, known as white tin (or β-tin), is stable at temperatures above 13 °C (Figure 1). This metallic form of tin has a tetragonal crystal structure (Figure 2). Below 13 °C, the metal undergoes a phase transition to a cubic crystal structure that is similar to diamond (Figure 12.16). The transition occurs slowly, with a rate that depends on the purity of the tin and the temperature, but the final product is gray tin or α-tin.

The tetragonal structure of white tin has atoms at each corner as well as an atom in four of its six faces and an atom at the center of the lattice. The cubic crystal lattice structure of gray tin has an atom on each of the six faces and four atoms within the unit cell (in addition to atoms at the corners) as in the diamond structure.

The low-temperature transformation of white tin to gray tin has been used to explain some famous disasters in history, one apparently true, the other false.

Early in the 20th century, there was great interest in reaching the South Pole, and many tried. The British explorer Robert Scott mounted a large expedition and reached the Pole in January 1912 with a party of five. It was an enormous accomplishment, but he learned to his great disappointment that the Norwegian Roald Amundsen had beaten him by five weeks. Having reached their goal, the Scott party started the 800-mile journey back across the polar ice to the Ross Sea. Along the journey to the Pole they had left food and fuel for use on their return trip. Both fuel and food were packed in tin cans with tin-soldered joints. Unfortunately, in the extremely low temperature, the tin in the joints turned into gray tin, flaked off, and the fuel leaked out. None was available to use, and all in Scott's party perished.

Another story of tin disease is a myth: the legend of crumbling buttons on the overcoats of French soldiers in 1812. In the winter of 1812, Napoleon's army fought and lost a brutal campaign in Russia. The shiny tin buttons used by the French soldiers are said to have crumbled in the cold Russian climate so they could not keep their clothing around them in the frigid weather. The problem with this story is that the uniform buttons at the time were made of bone.

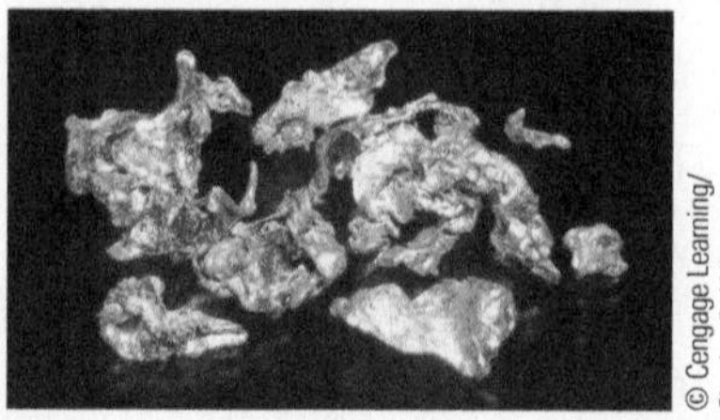
© Cengage Learning/Charles D. Winters

FIGURE 1 **A sample of white tin.** This common element has a density of 7.31 g/cm³ and a melting point of 232 °C.

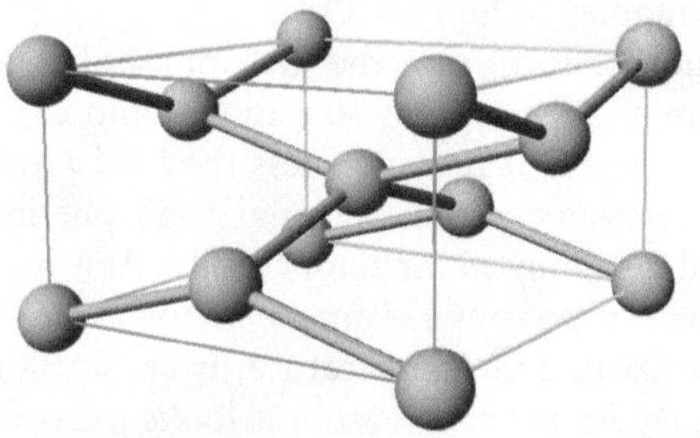

FIGURE 2 **A tetragonal unit cell of white of β-tin.** The tetragonal unit cell has 90° angles at each corner. Two of the three sides are equal in length (583 pm) while the third side is shorter (318 pm). (Note that the lines connecting atoms are not bonds. They are meant only to show the spatial relationship of the atoms.)

QUESTIONS:

1. How many tin atoms are contained in the tetragonal crystal lattice unit cell of β-tin? How many tin atoms are contained in the cubic crystal lattice unit cell of α-tin?
2. Using the dimensions of the unit cell and the molar mass of tin, calculate the density of white tin (in g/cm^3).
3. The density of gray tin is 5.769 g/cm^3. Determine the dimensions (in pm) of the cubic crystal lattice.
4. Determine the percentage of space occupied by tin atoms in both the tetragonal and cubic crystal lattices. The atomic radius of tin is 141 pm.

REFERENCES:

1. J. Emsley, *Nature's Building Blocks, An A–Z Guide to the Elements*, Oxford University Press, 2001.
2. P. LeCouteur and J. Burreson, *Napoleon's Buttons*, Penguin Putnam, New York, 2003.

DO

- Relate unit cells for ionic compounds to their formulas.
  - **a.** Understand the relation of unit cell structure and formula for ionic compounds (Section 12-2). Study Questions: 3–6, 8, 40, 42, 59.
- Relate unit cell dimensions, ionic or metallic radii, and solid density. Study Questions: 7, 8, 10, 38, 41, 44, 46, 59, 61.
- Use lattice energy in calculations.
  - **a.** Calculate the lattice enthalpy for an ionic solid using a Born-Haber cycle (Section 12-3). Study Questions: 15, 16, 50.
- Construct a phase diagram from information on the substance. Study Questions: 33–37.
- Relate the processes of melting and sublimation and the associated enthalpy changes (Sections 12-6 and 12-7). Study Questions: 31, 32.

REMEMBER

- The three types of cubic unit cells (Section 12-1).
- The physical properties of ionic, metallic, molecular, and network solids and examples of each.
  - **a.** Characterize different types of solids: metallic (e.g., copper), ionic (e.g., NaCl and CaF_2), molecular (e.g., water and I_2), network (e.g., diamond), and amorphous (e.g., glass and many synthetic polymers) (Table 12.2). Study Questions: 25–30.
- The unique features of the water phase diagram and their basis in molecular properties.

Steven Hyatt

STUDY QUESTIONS

▲ denotes challenging questions.

Blue-numbered questions have answers in Appendix N and fully worked solutions in the *Student Solutions Manual.*

Practicing Skills

Metallic and Ionic Solids

(See Sections 12-1 and 12-2 and Examples 12.1–12.3.)

1. Outline a two-dimensional unit cell for the pattern shown here. If the black squares are labeled A and the white squares are B, what is the simplest formula for a "compound" based on this pattern?

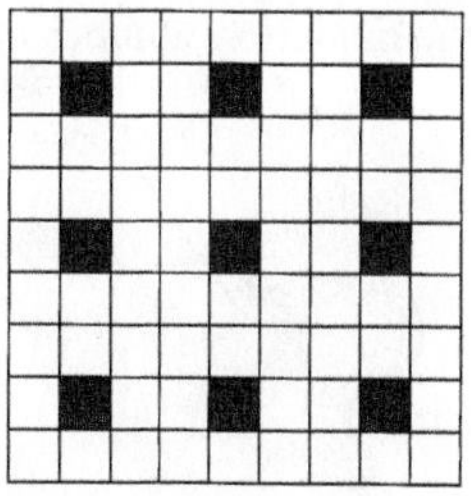

2. Outline a two-dimensional unit cell for the pattern shown here. If the black squares are labeled A and the white squares are B, what is the simplest formula for a "compound" based on this pattern?

3. One way of viewing the unit cell of perovskite was illustrated in Example 12.2. Another way is shown here. Prove that this view also leads to a formula of $CaTiO_3$.

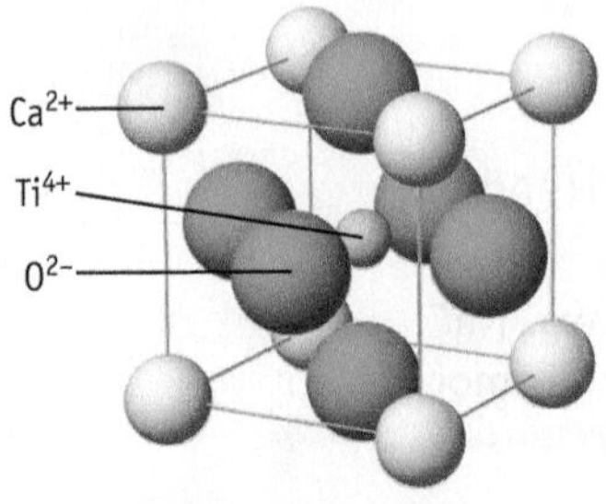

Perovskite unit cell

4. Rutile, TiO_2, crystallizes in a structure characteristic of many other ionic compounds. How many formula units of TiO_2 are in the unit cell illustrated here? (The oxide ions marked by an x are wholly within the cell; the others are in the cell faces.)

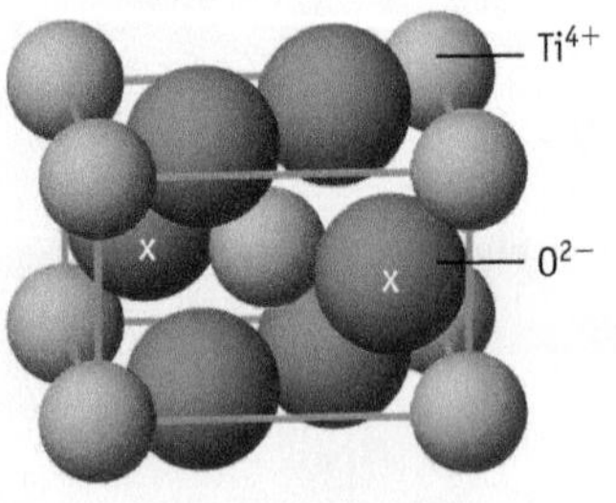

Unit cell for rutile

5. Cuprite is a semiconductor. Oxide ions are at the cube corners and in the cube center. Copper ions are wholly within the unit cell.

(a) What is the formula of cuprite?
(b) What is the oxidation number of copper?

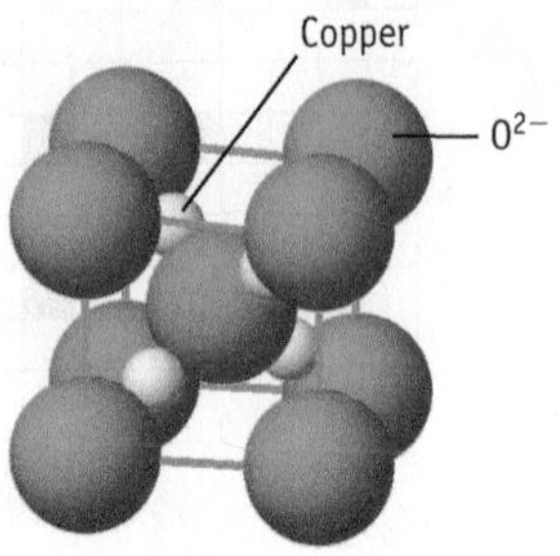

Unit cell for cuprite

6. The mineral fluorite, which is composed of calcium ions and fluoride ions, has the unit cell shown here.

(a) What type of unit cell is described by the Ca^{2+} ions?
(b) Where are the F^- ions located, in octahedral holes or tetrahedral holes?
(c) Based on this unit cell, what is the formula of fluorite?

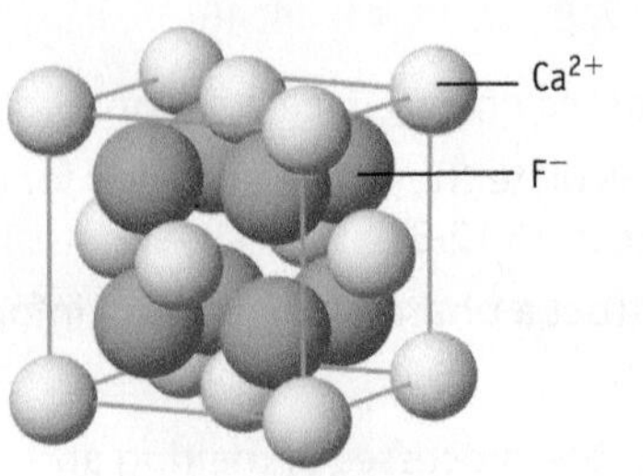

Unit cell of fluorite

7. Calcium metal crystallizes in a face-centered cubic unit cell. The density of the solid is 1.54 g/cm^3. What is the radius of a calcium atom?

8. The density of copper metal is 8.95 g/cm^3. If the radius of a copper atom is 127.8 pm, is the copper unit cell primitive, body-centered cubic, or face-centered cubic?

9. Potassium iodide has a face-centered cubic unit cell of iodide ions with potassium ions in octahedral holes. The density of KI is 3.12 g/cm^3. What is the length of one side of the unit cell? (Ion sizes are found in Figure 7.11.)

10. ▲ A unit cell of cesium chloride is illustrated in Figure 12.8. The density of the solid is 3.99 g/cm^3, and the radius of the Cl^- ion is 181 pm. Calculate the radius of the Cs^+ ion in the center of the cell. (Assume that the Cs^+ ion touches all of the corner Cl^- ions.)

Ionic Bonding and Lattice Energy

(See Section 12-3.)

11. Predict the trend in lattice energy, from least negative to most negative, for the following compounds based on the ion charges and ionic radii: LiI, LiF, CaO, RbI.

12. Examine the trends in lattice energy in Table 12.1. The value of the lattice energy becomes somewhat more negative on going from NaI to NaBr to NaCl, and all are in the range from −700 to −800 kJ/mol. Suggest a reason for the observation that the lattice energy of NaF ($\Delta_{lattice}U$ = −926 kJ/mol) is much more negative than those of the other sodium halides.

13. To melt an ionic solid, energy must be supplied to disrupt the forces between ions so the regular array of ions collapses. Predict (and explain) how the melting point is expected to vary as a function of the distance between cation and anion.

14. Which compound in each of the following pairs should have the higher melting point? Explain briefly.

(a) NaCl or RbCl
(b) BaO or MgO
(c) NaCl or MgS

15. Calculate the molar enthalpy of formation, $\Delta_f H°$, of solid lithium fluoride from the lattice energy (Table 12.1) and other thermochemical data. The enthalpy of formation of Li(g), $\Delta_f H°$ [Li(g)] = 159.37 kJ/mol. Other required data can be found in Appendices F and L.

16. Calculate the lattice enthalpy for RbCl. In addition to data in Appendices F and L, you will need the following information:

$$\Delta_f H° \text{ [Rb(g)]} = 80.9 \text{ kJ/mol}$$
$$\Delta_f H° \text{ [RbCl(s)]} = -435.4 \text{ kJ/mol}$$

Metals and Semiconductors

(See Section 12-4.)

17. Considering only the molecular orbitals formed by combinations of the 2*s* atomic orbitals, how many molecular orbitals can be formed by 1000 Li atoms? In the lowest energy state, how many of these orbitals will be populated by pairs of electrons and how many will be empty?

18. How many molecular orbitals will be formed by combination of the 3*s* and 3*p* atomic orbitals in 1.0 mol of Mg atoms? At 0 K, what fraction of these orbitals will be occupied by electron pairs?

19. Conduction of an electric current is a general property associated with metals. How does the band theory for metallic bonding explain conductivity?

20. Most metals are shiny, that is, they reflect light. How does the band theory for metals explain this characteristic?

21. Elemental silicon and carbon (in the diamond allotropic form) have the same solid-state structure. However, diamond is an insulator and silicon is a semiconductor. Explain why there is a difference.

22. List the Group 4A elements in order of the size of the band gap.

23. Define the terms intrinsic semiconductor and extrinsic semiconductor. Give an example of each.

24. Is aluminum-doped silicon a *p*-type or an *n*-type semiconductor? Explain how conductivity occurs in this semiconductor.

Other Types of Solids

(See Section 12-5.)

25. A diamond unit cell is shown here.

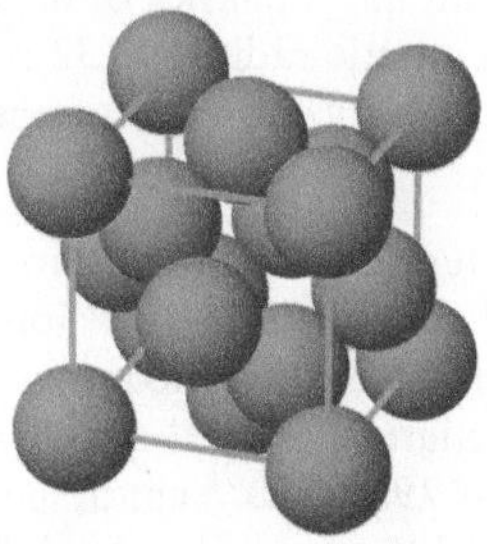

Unit cell of diamond

(a) How many carbon atoms are in one unit cell?
(b) The unit cell can be considered as a cubic unit cell of C atoms with other C atoms in holes in the lattice. What type of unit cell is this (pc, bcc, fcc)? In what holes are other C atoms located, octahedral or tetrahedral holes?

26. The structure of graphite is given in Figure 12.18.
(a) What type of intermolecular forces exist between the layers of six-member carbon rings?
(b) Account for the lubricating ability of graphite. That is, why does graphite feel slippery? Why does pencil lead (which is really graphite in clay) leave black marks on paper?

27. We have identified five types of solids (metallic, ionic, molecular, network, amorphous). What particles make up each of these solids and what are the forces of attraction between these particles?

28. List the general properties of each type of solid.

29. Classify each of the following materials as falling into one of the categories listed in Table 12.2. What particles make up these solids and what are the forces of attraction between particles? Give one physical property of each.
(a) gallium arsenide
(b) polystyrene
(c) silicon carbide
(d) perovskite, $CaTiO_3$

30. Classify each of the following materials as falling into one of the categories listed in Table 12.2. What particles make up these solids, and what are the forces of attraction between particles? Give one physical property of each.
(a) Si doped with P
(b) graphite
(c) benzoic acid, $C_6H_5CO_2H$
(d) Na_2SO_4

Phase Changes for Solids

(See Section 12-6.)

31. Benzene, C_6H_6, is an organic liquid that freezes at 5.5 °C (Figure 11.1) to form beautiful, feather-like crystals. How much energy is evolved as heat when 15.5 g of benzene freezes at 5.5 °C? (The enthalpy of fusion of benzene is 9.95 kJ/mol.) If the 15.5-g sample is remelted, again at 5.5 °C, what quantity of energy is required to convert it to a liquid?

32. The specific heat capacity of silver is 0.235 J/g · K. Its melting point is 962 °C, and its enthalpy of fusion is 11.3 kJ/mol. What quantity of energy, in joules, is required to change 5.00 g of silver from a solid at 25 °C to a liquid at 962 °C?

Phase Diagrams and Phase Changes

(See Section 12-7.)

33. Consider the phase diagram of CO_2 in Figure 12.23.
    (a) Is the density of liquid CO_2 greater or less than that of solid CO_2?
    (b) In what phase do you find CO_2 at 5 atm and 0 °C?
    (c) Can CO_2 be liquefied at 45 °C?

34. Use the phase diagram given here to answer the following questions:

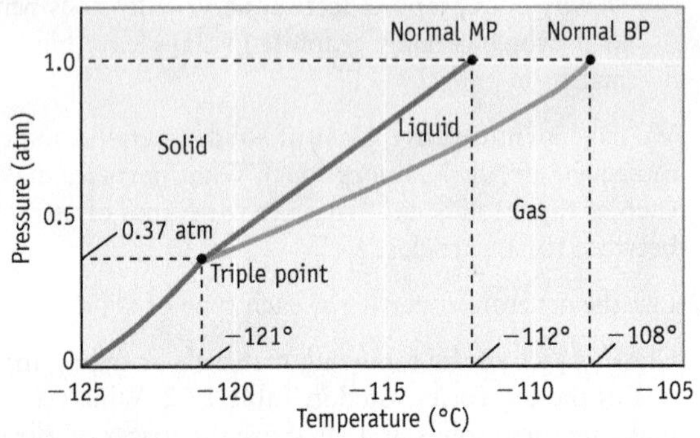

(a) In what phase is the substance found at room temperature and 1.0 atm pressure?
(b) If the pressure exerted on a sample is 0.75 atm and the temperature is −114 °C, in what phase does the substance exist?
(c) If you measure the vapor pressure of a liquid sample and find it to be 380 mm Hg, what is the temperature of the liquid phase?
(d) What is the vapor pressure of the solid at −122 °C?
(e) Which is the denser phase—solid or liquid? Explain briefly.

35. Liquid ammonia, $NH_3(\ell)$, was once used in home refrigerators as the heat transfer fluid. The specific heat capacity of the liquid is 4.7 J/g · K and that of the vapor is 2.2 J/g · K. The enthalpy of vaporization is 23.33 kJ/mol at the boiling point. If you heat 12 kg of liquid ammonia from −50.0 °C to its boiling point of −33.3 °C, allow it to evaporate, and then continue warming to 0.0 °C, how much energy must you supply?

36. If your air conditioner is more than several years old, it may use the chlorofluorocarbon CCl_2F_2 as the heat transfer fluid. The normal boiling point of CCl_2F_2 is −29.8 °C, and the enthalpy of vaporization is 20.11 kJ/mol. The gas and the liquid have molar heat capacities of 117.2 J/mol · K and 72.3 J/mol · K, respectively. How much energy is evolved as heat when 20.0 g of CCl_2F_2 is cooled from +40 °C to −40 °C?

General Questions

These questions are not designated as to type or location in the chapter. They may combine several concepts.

37. Construct a phase diagram for O_2 from the following information: normal boiling point, 90.18 K; normal melting point, 54.8 K; and triple point, 54.34 K at a pressure of 2 mm Hg. Very roughly estimate the vapor pressure of liquid O_2 at −196 °C, the lowest temperature easily reached in the laboratory. Is the density of liquid O_2 greater or less than that of solid O_2?

38. ▲ Tungsten crystallizes in the unit cell shown here.

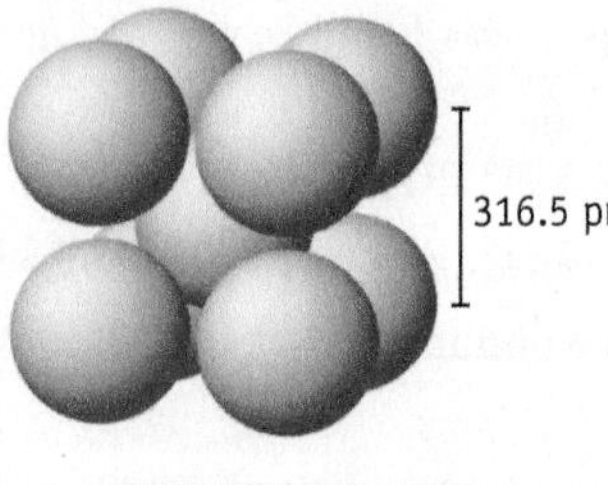

Unit cell for tungsten

(a) What type of unit cell is this?
(b) How many tungsten atoms occur per unit cell?
(c) If the edge of the unit cell is 316.5 pm, what is the radius of a tungsten atom? (*Hint:* The W atoms touch each other along the diagonal line from one corner of the unit cell to the opposite corner of the unit cell.)

39. Silver crystallizes in a face-centered cubic unit cell. Each side of the unit cell has a length of 409 pm. What is the radius of a silver atom?

40. ▲ The unit cell shown here is for calcium carbide. How many calcium atoms and how many carbon atoms are in each unit cell? What is the formula of calcium carbide? (Calcium ions are silver in color and carbon atoms are gray.)

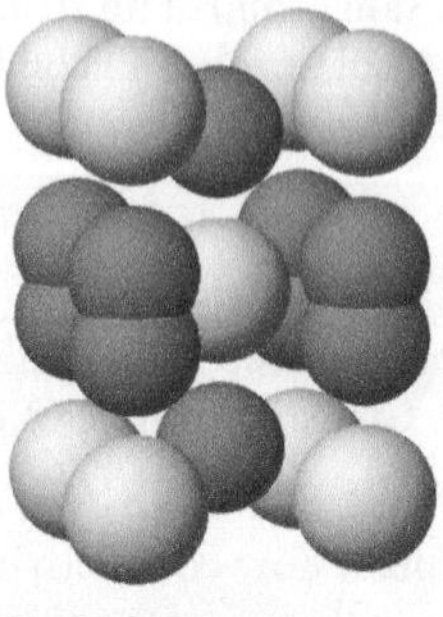

Unit cell for calcium carbide

41. The very dense metal iridium has a face-centered cubic unit cell and a density of 22.56 g/cm³. Use this information to calculate the radius of an atom of the element.

42. Vanadium metal has a density of 6.11 g/cm³. Assuming the vanadium atomic radius is 132 pm, is the vanadium unit cell primitive cubic, body-centered cubic, or face-centered cubic?

43. ▲ Calcium fluoride is the well-known mineral fluorite. Each unit cell contains four Ca^{2+} ions and eight F^- ions. The F^- ions fill all the tetrahedral holes in a face-centered cubic lattice of Ca^{2+} ions. The edge of the CaF_2 unit cell is 5.46295×10^{-8} cm in length. The density of the solid is 3.1805 g/cm³. Use this information to calculate Avogadro's number.

44. ▲ Iron has a body-centered cubic unit cell with a cell dimension of 286.65 pm. The density of iron is 7.874 g/cm^3. Use this information to calculate Avogadro's number.

45. ▲ You can get some idea of how efficiently spherical atoms or ions are packed in a three-dimensional solid by seeing how well circular atoms pack in two dimensions. Using the drawings shown here, prove that B is a more efficient way to pack circular atoms than A. The unit cell of A contains portions of four circles and one hole. In B, packing coverage can be calculated by looking at a triangle that contains portions of three circles and one hole. Show that A fills about 80% of the available space, whereas B fills closer to 90% of the available space.

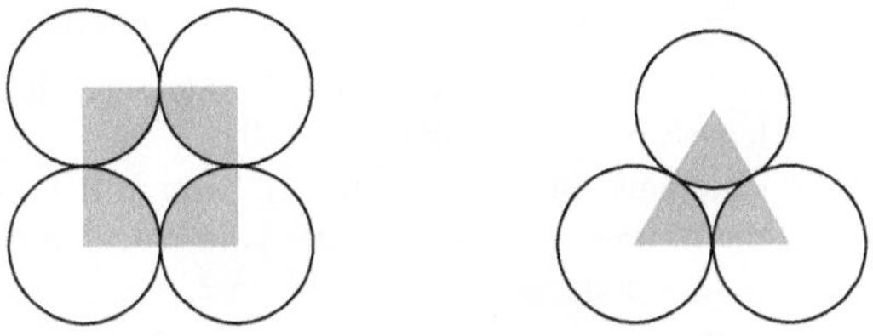

A B

46. Consider the three types of cubic units cells.

(a) ▲ Assuming that the spherical atoms or ions in a primitive cubic unit cell just touch along the cube's edges, calculate the percentage of occupied space within the unit cell. (Recall that the volume of a sphere is $(4/3)\pi r^3$, where r is the radius of the sphere.)

(b) Compare the percentage of occupied space in the primitive cell (pc) with the bcc and fcc unit cells. Based on this, will a metal in these three forms have the same or different densities? If different, in which is it most dense? In which is it least dense?

47. The solid state structure of silicon is shown below.

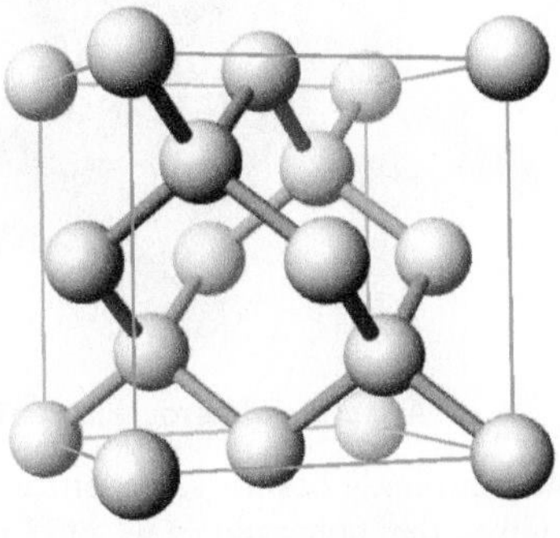

Unit cell for silicon

(a) Describe this crystal as pc, bcc, or fcc.

(b) What type of holes are occupied in the lattice?

(c) How many Si atoms are there per unit cell?

(d) Calculate the density of silicon in g/cm^3 (given that the cube edge has a length of 543.1 pm).

(e) ▲ Estimate the radius of the silicon atom. (*Note:* The Si atoms on the edges do not touch one another.)

48. The solid state structure of silicon carbide is shown below.

(a) How many atoms of each type are contained within the unit cell? What is the formulas of silicon carbide?

(b) ▲ Knowing that the Si—C bond length is 188.8 pm (and the Si—C—Si bond angle is 109.5°), calculate the density of SiC.

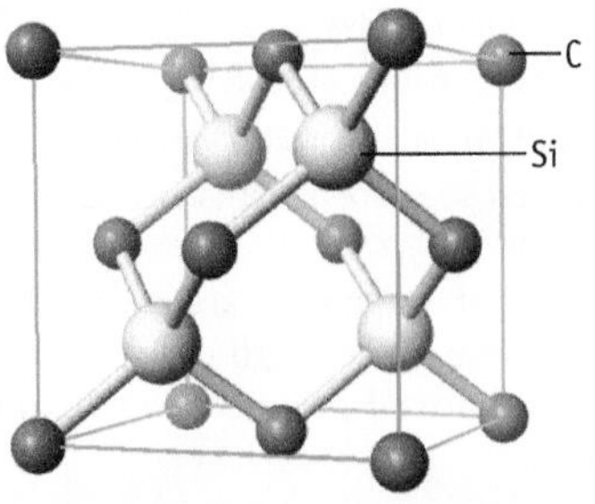

Unit cell of SiC

Sample of silicon carbide

49. Spinels are solids with the general formula AB_2O_4 (where A^{2+} and B^{3+} are metal cations of the same or different metals). The best-known example is common magnetite, Fe_3O_4 [which you can formulate as $(Fe^{2+})(Fe^{3+})_2O_4$]. Another example is the mineral often referred to as *spinel*, $MgAl_2O_4$.

A crystal of the spinel $MgAl_2O_4$

The oxide ions of spinels form a face-centered cubic lattice. In a *normal spinel,* cations occupy ⅛ of the tetrahedral sites and ½ of the octahedral sites.

(a) In $MgAl_2O_4$, in what types of holes are the magnesium and aluminum ions found?

(b) The mineral chromite has the formula $FeCr_2O_4$. What ions are involved, and in what types of holes are they found?

50. Using the thermochemical data below and an estimated value of −2481 kJ/mol for the lattice energy for Na_2O, calculate the value for the *second* electron affinity of oxygen [$O^-(g) + e^- \rightarrow O^{2-}(g)$].

Quantity	Numerical Value (kJ/mol)
Enthalpy of atomization of Na	107.3
Ionization energy of Na	495.9
Enthalpy of formation of solid Na_2O	−418.0
Enthalpy of formation of O(g) from O_2	249.1
First electron attachment enthalpy of O	−141.0

51. The band gap in gallium arsenide is 140 kJ/mol. What is the maximum wavelength of light needed to excite an electron to move from the valence band to the conduction band?

52. The conductivity of an intrinsic semiconductor increases with increasing temperature. How can this be rationalized?

53. Which will show the highest conductivity at 298 K, silicon or germanium?

54. Identify the following as either *p*- or *n*-type semiconductors.

(a) germanium doped with arsenic
(b) silicon doped with phosphorus
(c) germanium doped with indium
(d) germanium doped with antimony

55. Diamond-based semiconductors are currently of enormous interest in the research community. Although diamond itself is an insulator, the addition of a dopant will narrow the band gap. One semiconductor system has diamond with boron as a dopant. Is this a *p*- or an *n*-type semiconductor?

56. Molecular solids, network solids, and amorphous solids all contain atoms that are joined together by covalent bonds. However, these classes of compounds are very different in overall structure, and this leads to different physical properties associated with each group. Describe how the overall structures of these classes of solids differ from each other.

In the Laboratory

57. Like ZnS, lead(II) sulfide, PbS (commonly called *galena*), has a 1:1 empirical formula with a 2+ cation combined with the sulfide anion.

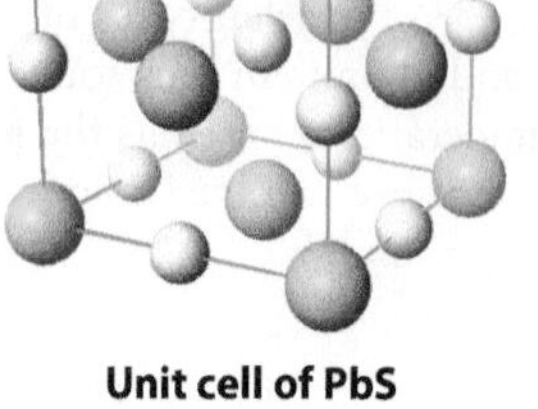

Unit cell of PbS

© Cengage Learning/Charles D. Winters

Sample of galena

Does PbS have the same solid structure as ZnS? If different, how are they different? How is the unit cell of PbS related to its formula?

58. $CaTiO_3$, a perovskite, has the structure below.

(a) If the density of the solid is 4.10 g/cm³, what is the length of a side of the unit cell?
(b) Calculate the radius of the Ti^{4+} ion in the center of the unit cell. How well does your calculation agree with a literature value of 75 pm?

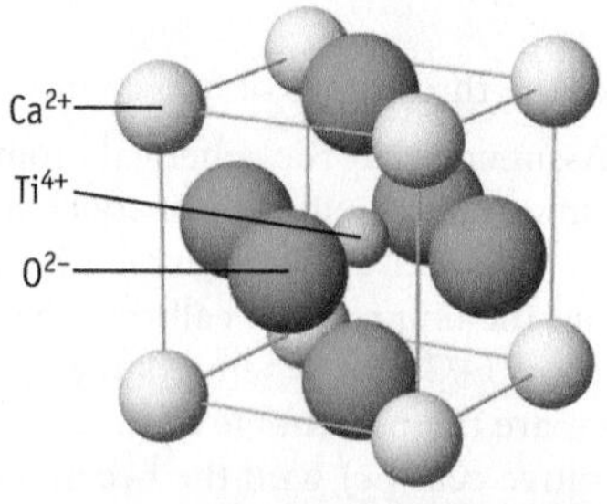

Unit cell of the perovskite $CaTiO_3$

© Cengage Learning/Charles D. Winters

A sample of perovskite, $CaTiO_3$

59. Potassium bromide has the same lattice structure as NaCl. Given the ionic radii of K^+ (133 pm) and Br^- (196 pm), calculate the density of KBr.

60. Calculate the lattice energy of $CaCl_2$ using a Born-Haber cycle and data from Appendices F and L and Table 7.5.

Summary and Conceptual Questions

The following questions may use concepts from this and previous chapters.

61. ▲ Boron phosphide, BP, is a semiconductor and a hard, abrasion-resistant material. It is made by reacting boron tribromide and phosphorus tribromide in a hydrogen atmosphere at high temperature (>750 °C).
   (a) Write a balanced chemical equation for the synthesis of BP. (*Hint:* Hydrogen is a reducing agent.)
   (b) Boron phosphide crystallizes in a zinc-blend structure, formed from boron atoms in a face-centered cubic lattice and phosphorus atoms in tetrahedral holes. How many tetrahedral holes are filled with P atoms in each unit cell?
   (c) The length of a unit cell of BP is 478 pm. What is the density of the solid in g/cm^3?
   (d) Calculate the closest distance between a B and a P atom in the unit cell. (Assume the B atoms do not touch along the cell edge. The B atoms in the faces touch the B atoms at the corners of the unit cell.)

62. ▲ Why is it not possible for a salt with the formula M_3X (Na_3PO_4, for example) to have a face-centered cubic lattice of X anions with M cations in octahedral holes?

63. ▲ Two identical swimming pools are filled with uniform spheres of ice packed as closely as possible. The spheres in the first pool are the size of grains of sand; those in the second pool are the size of oranges. The ice in both pools melts. In which pool, if either, will the water level be higher? (Ignore any differences in filling space at the planes next to the walls and bottom.)

64. Spinels are described in Study Question 49. Consider two normal spinels, $CoAl_2O_4$ and $SnCo_2O_4$. What metal ions are involved in each? What are their electron configurations? Are the metal ions paramagnetic, and if so how many unpaired electrons are involved?

65. Outline a procedure to calculate the percent of space occupied by the atoms in an fcc arrangement.

66. The sample of nephrite jade shown in the introductory story had the formula $Ca_2(Mg, Fe)_5(Si_4O_{11})_2(OH)_2$. (Iron in this formula is in the +2 oxidation state.)
   (a) What is the charge on the $(Si_4O_{11})^n$ ion in this compound?
   (b) What is the oxidation state of Si in this compound?
   (c) What is the percent of iron in a sample of jade that has the formula $Ca_2(Mg_{0.35}Fe_{0.65})_5(Si_4O_{11})_2(OH)_2$?
   (d) The iron ions in the formula for nephrite have the same degree of paramagnetism as seen for Fe^{2+}(g). How many unpaired electrons per iron ion does this represent?

67. Phase diagrams for materials that have allotropes can be more complicated than those shown in the chapter. Use the phase diagram for carbon given here to answer the following questions.

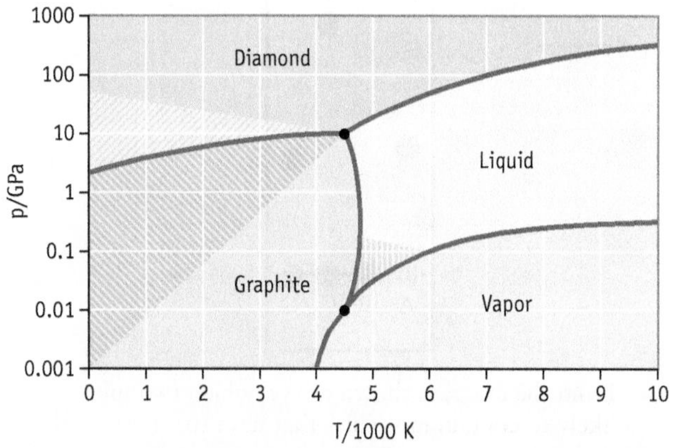

   (a) How many triple points are present and what phases are in equilibrium for each?
   (b) Is there a single point where all four phases are in equilibrium?
   (c) Which is more stable at high pressures, diamond or graphite?
   (d) Which is the stable phase of carbon at room temperature and 1 atmosphere pressure?

68. Prepare a graph of lattice enthalpy for lithium, sodium, and potassium halides (Table 12.2) vs. the sum of the ionic radii for the component ions (Figure 7.11). Evaluate the results and comment on the relationship between these quantities.

AP Multiple-Choice Review Questions

1. Four different kinds of inks are placed on chromatography paper, and a solvent is introduced and allowed to move up the paper.

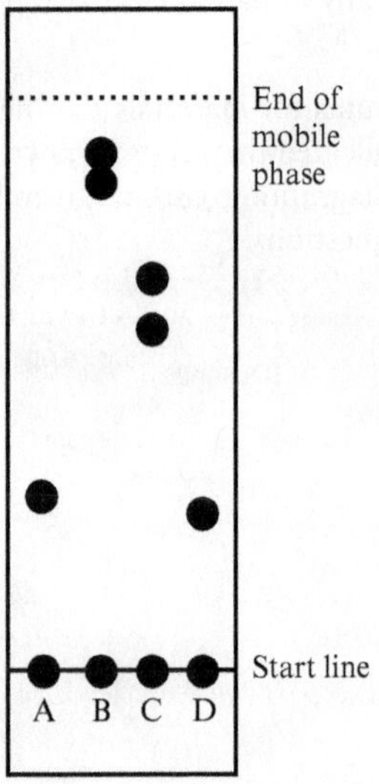

From the diagram shown above, which two inks are likely to contain molecules that have the most similar molecular structures?

(A) A and D
(B) B and D
(C) B and C
(D) A and C

2. Four different inks are placed on chromatography paper, and a solvent is introduced and allowed to move up the paper.

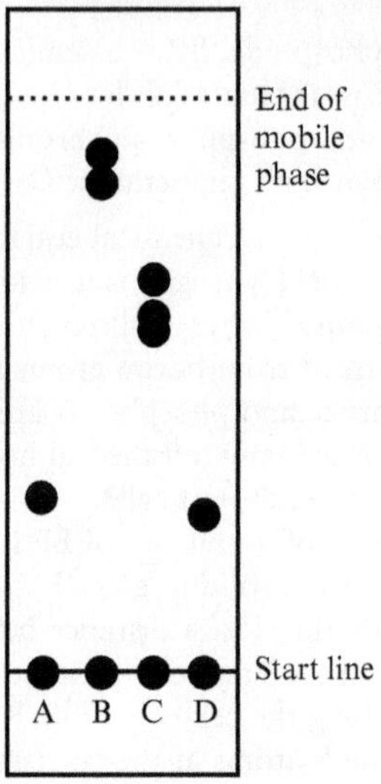

From the diagram shown above, which ink contains a component likely to have a molecular structure most similar to that of the solvent?

(A) A
(B) B
(C) C
(D) D

3. Four substances with the following structures are placed on chromatography paper with water as the mobile phase. The paper is allowed to touch the water. After an hour, which substance will have moved the farthest on the paper? Water consists of H—O—H molecules.

(A) 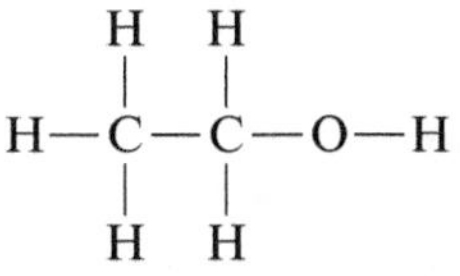

(B) 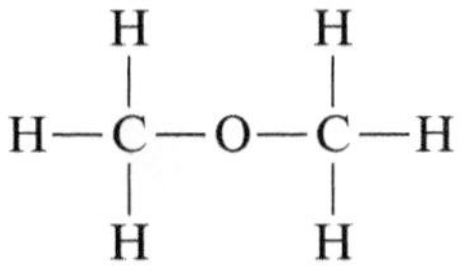

(C) 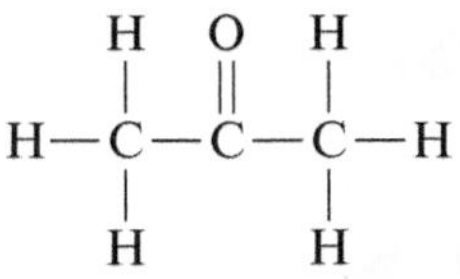

(D) 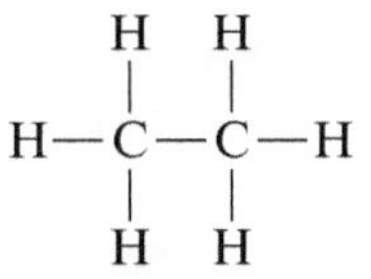

4. Which of the following best explains the difference in the melting points of MgO (2852 °C) and NaF (1819 °C)?

(A) There are greater Coulombic attractions in MgO due to the greater charges on the ions.

(B) Na is above Mg on the activity series of metals.

(C) F is more electronegative than O.

(D) Na is an alkali metal, and Mg is an alkaline earth metal. Alkali metals are more reactive than the alkaline earth metals.

5. The melting points of the compounds LiF, NaCl, KBr, and CsI exhibit the following trend:

Melting point order: LiF > NaCl > KBr > CsI

Which of the following correctly explains this trend?

(A) The increasing molar mass requires more energy to melt the substances.

(B) The greater radii of the larger ions results in smaller lattice energies, leading to lower melting points.

(C) Reactivity increases as you increase the atomic number in the alkali metals. The more reactive, the easier it is to lose electrons, hence a lower melting point.

(D) The melting point is directly proportional to the electronegative value for the halogen ions in the compound; there is more attraction for the electrons in the chemical bonds.

6. A correct representation of an ionic solid could be described as having

(A) mobile valence electrons shared between positive metal ions

(B) positive and negative ions in fixed positions in a framework

(C) electrons and positive metal ions in fixed positions in a framework

(D) metallic and nonmetallic atoms bonded covalently in a three-dimensional pattern

7. Ionic solids are not able to conduct electricity in the solid phase but are able to conduct electricity when dissolved in water. This can best be explained by the fact that the ions

(A) release free electrons when dissolved in water

(B) form molecules that conduct electricity when dissolved in water

(C) are in fixed positions in the solid phase, whereas they are free to move in solution

(D) are not able to conduct electricity themselves, but water molecules can conduct electricity

8. An example of an alloy is shown in the diagram below. Compared with the pure metal X, how would you expect the properties of the alloy to vary?

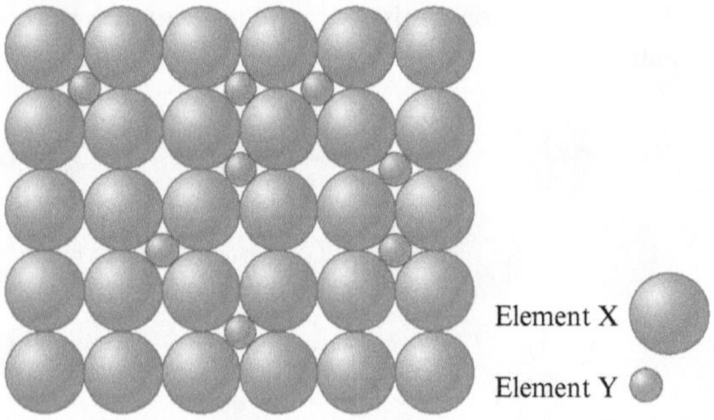

(A) The alloy has higher malleability and higher density.

(B) The alloy has lower malleability and lower density.

(C) The alloy has higher malleability and lower density

(D) The alloy has lower malleability and higher density.

9. Which best explains why an aluminum can may be crushed without it breaking into pieces?

(A) Aluminum has ionic bonds that are not easily broken.

(B) Aluminum has covalent bonds that are not easily broken.

(C) Aluminum has localized valence electrons with directional bonding.

(D) Aluminum has delocalized valence electrons with nondirectional bonding.

10. A sample of an unknown material consists of positive ions surrounded by delocalized valence electrons. Which properties are likely for this material?

(A) poor conductor of electricity, brittle, volatile

(B) good conductor of electricity, easily deformed, nonvolatile

(C) poor conductor of electricity, easily deformed, volatile

(D) good conductor of electricity, brittle, nonvolatile

11. A representation of the bonding in solid silver is shown below.

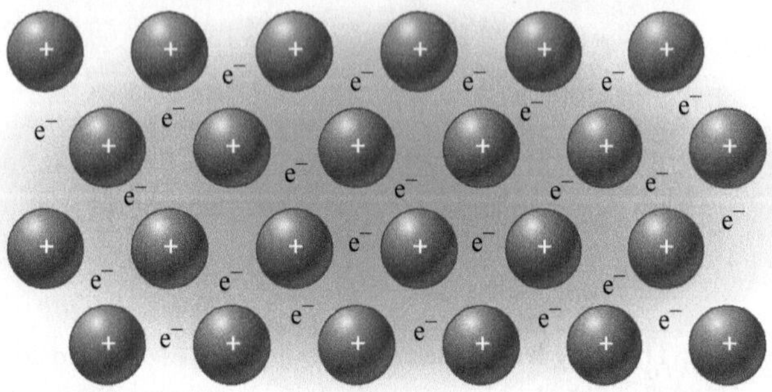

This representation best shows which of the following?

(A) Each silver atom has one valence electron that is tightly bound to the atom, resulting in a rigid, hard material.

(B) Each silver atom has one valence electron that is found in the interstitial holes of the silver crystal structure, making it behave as an alloy.

(C) Each silver atom has one valence electron that is free to move throughout the piece of metal, allowing silver to conduct electricity.

(D) Each silver atom loses an electron to form a silver cation. This makes the silver very soluble.

12. Which best represents the structure and bonding in solid lithium?

(A)

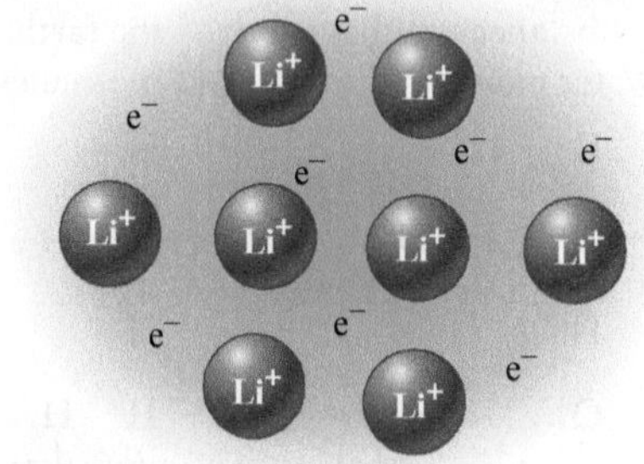

(B)

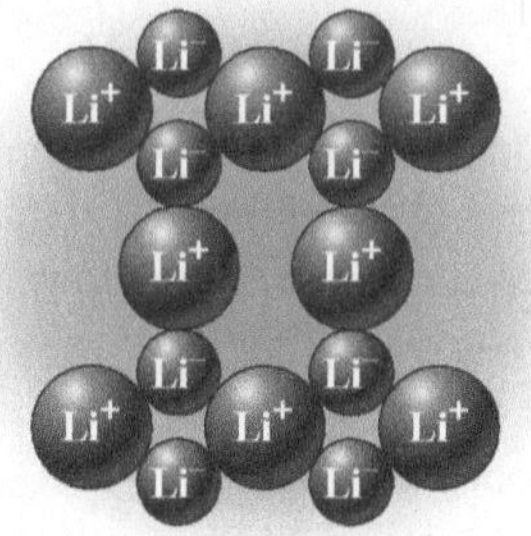

(C)

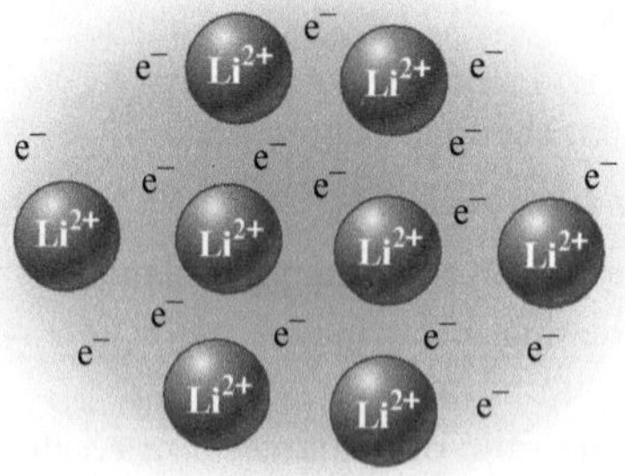

(D)

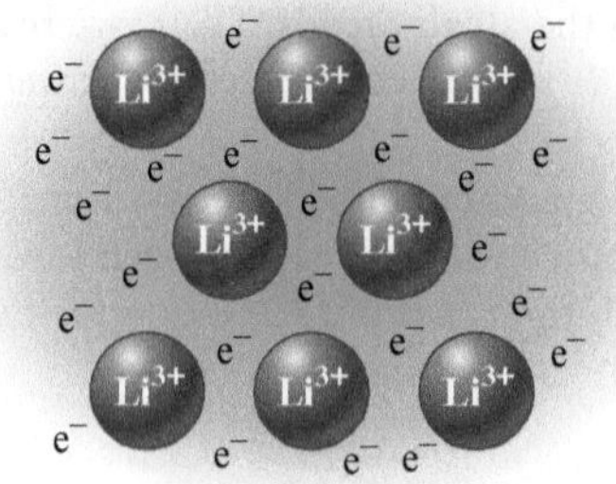

13. Doping of silicon is achieved by the substitution of a different element for some of the silicon atoms. What type of semiconductor is shown below?

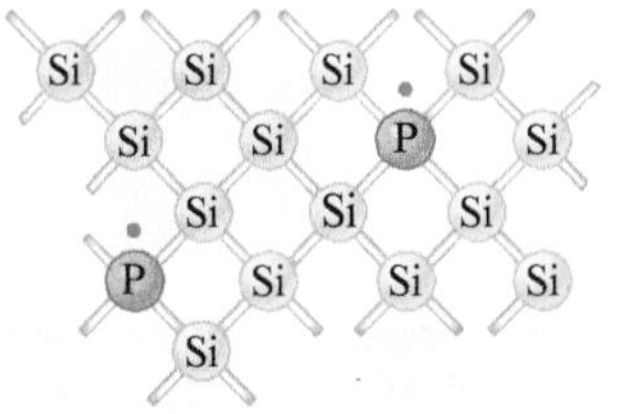

(A) It is a *p*-type semiconductor because the phosphorus atoms have one more electron than the silicon atoms.
(B) It is an *n*-type semiconductor because the phosphorus atoms have one more electron than the silicon atoms.
(C) It is an *n*-type semiconductor because phosphorus is a nonmetal, whereas silicon is a metalloid.
(D) It is a *p*-type semiconductor because phosphorus was substituted for silicon, rather than nitrogen being substituted for silicon.

14. An unknown solid substance was found to have the following properties:

1. Extremely high melting point
2. Conducts electricity in solid form
3. Breaks apart easily

Which of these compounds could be this unknown substance?

(A)

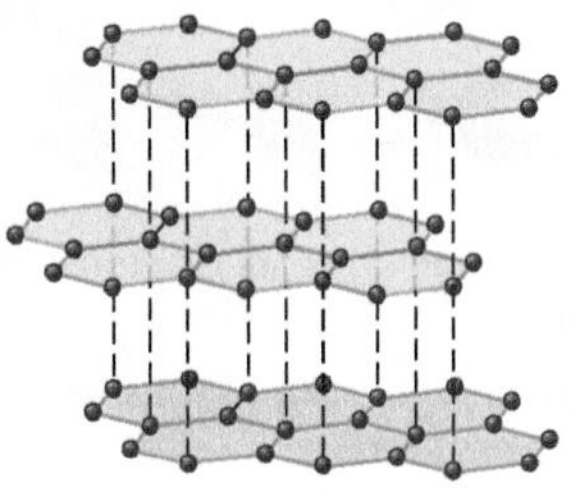

(B)

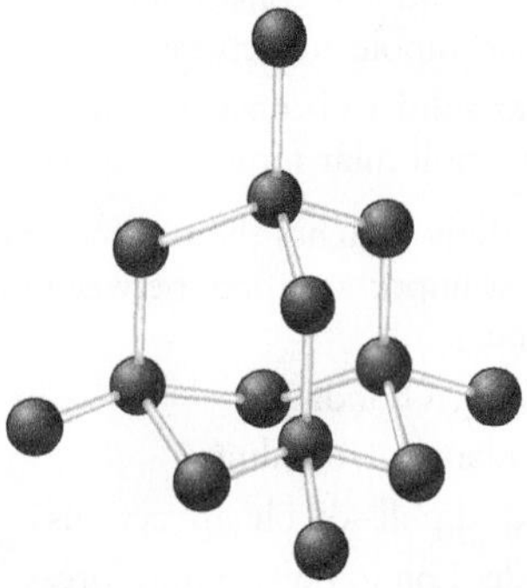

(C)

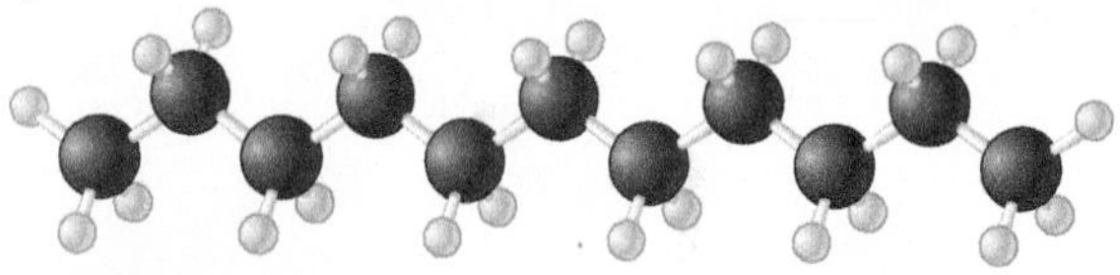

(D)

15. Which of the following is true for a solid with a structure as shown in the diagram below?

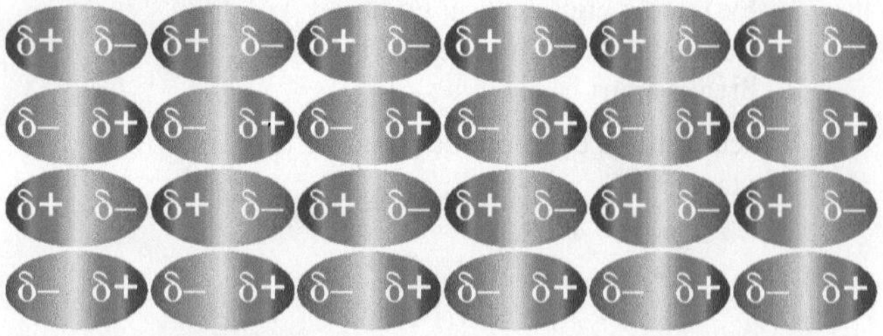

(A) It is an atomic solid and consists of atoms with electrostatic attractions.

(B) It is an ionic solid and consists of ions held together by electrostatic attractions.

(C) It is a molecular solid and consists of polar molecules with dipole–dipole attractions.

(D) It is a molecular solid and consists of nonpolar molecules with intermolecular forces.

16. Which of these correctly matches the molecular compound with the most important force between molecules of the same substance?

(A) ammonia: hydrogen bonding

(B) hydrogen cyanide: ionic bonding

(C) propane (C_3H_8): dipole–dipole attractions

(D) hydrogen sulfide: London dispersion forces

17. What properties would a compound like the one pictured below be likely to have in its pure, solid form?

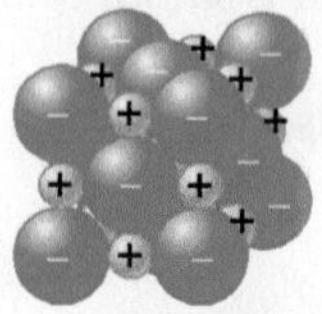

(A) high vapor pressure, low melting point, nonconductor of electricity

(B) high vapor pressure, high melting point, good conductor of electricity

(C) low vapor pressure, high melting point, good conductor of electricity

(D) low vapor pressure, high melting point, nonconductor of electricity

18. Which of these statements provides an accurate comparison of the general properties of solids and liquids?

(A) In a solid, particles are slightly closer together, have greater interparticle attractions, and have lower particle motion compared with a liquid.

(B) In a solid, particles are slightly further apart, have weaker interparticle attractions, and have lower particle motion compared with a liquid.

(C) In a solid, particles are slightly closer together, have weaker interparticle attractions, and have greater particle motion compared with a liquid.

(D) In a solid, particles are slightly further apart, have weaker interparticle attractions, and have greater particle motion compared with a liquid.

AP Free Response Review Questions

Question Format: Long

Category of Question: Representation 2

Three common ores of iron are FeO, Fe_2O_3, and Fe_3O_4. Iron ores are often reduced to elemental iron by heating in the presence of carbon monoxide. These iron ores are all brittle and do not conduct electricity in their solid form.

(a) Identify the oxidation number of the iron atoms in each of the three ores.

(b) Choose one of the iron ores and write a balanced chemical equation to show its reduction reaction with carbon monoxide.

(c) Considering the types of bonding involved, how and why do the properties of the ores differ from those of pure iron?

Carbon steel is an interstitial alloy of iron with a small amount of carbon which has greater strength and density than pure iron but maintains the metallic properties of iron.

(d) Is the combination of iron with carbon to form steel a chemical or physical change? Explain your answer.

(e) In the box, draw a representation of the structure of this alloy.

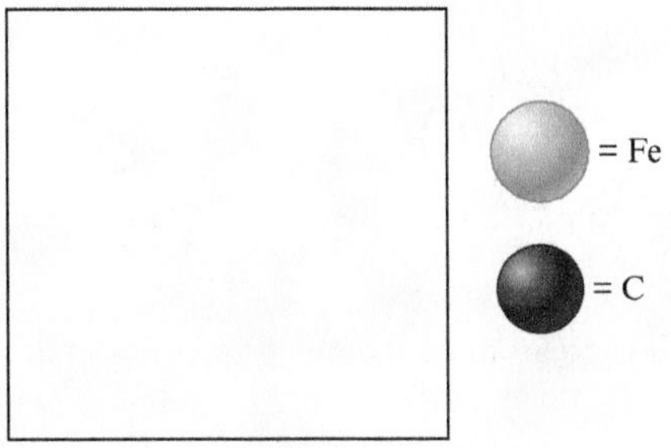

(f) As the percent carbon increases in steel, the ductility of the steel decreases. Explain why this might occur.

Scuba diving: The solubility of gases in your bodily fluids is important to consider when diving.

Solutions and Their Behavior

Chapter Outline

- 13-1 Units of Concentration
- 13-2 The Solution Process
- 13-3 Factors Affecting Solubility: Pressure and Temperature
- 13-4 Colligative Properties
- 13-5 Colloids

NARCOSIS AND THE BENDS If you have ever been scuba diving, you have heard about narcosis, also called "nitrogen narcosis," the "martini effect," or "rapture of the deep." And you probably discussed the "bends" with your diving instructor. Both of these effects are caused by gases dissolving in your blood as you breathe O_2 and N_2 from the scuba tank under pressure.

When you dive, the pressure of the air you breathe must be balanced against the external pressure of the water against your body. The pressure on your body when you are under water is normal atmospheric pressure plus the pressure of water, or about 1 atm for every 10 m of depth. To counter this, modern dive regulators automatically supply the breathing mixture at higher and higher pressures as you descend.

But here is the problem: as the gas pressure increases, the partial pressures of O_2 and N_2 increase, causing more gas to dissolve in your blood. These gases also dissolve in nerve cells in the brain and alter nerve transmission, and they have a narcotic effect. The effect is comparable to drinking a martini on an empty stomach or inhaling laughing gas (nitrous oxide, N_2O) at the

Chapter Goals

See Chapter Goals Revisited (page 503) for Study Questions keyed to these goals.

UNDERSTAND

- The energetics of the solution process.
- The basis of the "like dissolves like" rule.
- How changes in pressure and temperature affect solubility.
- How solutes in solution affect a solvent's vapor pressure, freezing point, and boiling point, and the osmotic pressure of the solution (colligative properties).

DO

- Use the units of solution concentration.
- Calculate the enthalpy of solution from thermodynamic data.
- Use Henry's law.
- Use Le Chatelier's principle to predict qualitatively the effect of stresses on systems at equilibrium.
- Calculate changes in vapor pressure, freezing point, and boiling point as solute is added to a solvent (colligative properties).
- Calculate the osmotic pressure of a solution.
- Use colligative properties to determine the molar mass of a solute.
- Apply the van't Hoff factor in calculations involving ionic solutes.

REMEMBER

- The difference between molarity (M) and molality (*m*).
- Le Chatelier's principle, which predicts how systems at equilibrium respond to stresses.
- Henry's law, the relationship of pressure and gas solubility.
- The effect of solutes on the properties of a solution.
- The importance and properties of colloids.
- The terminology of solutions and their behavior.

dentist; it makes you slightly giddy. In severe cases, it can impair your judgment and even cause you to take the regulator out of your mouth and hand it to a fish! Some people can go as deep as 30–40 m with no problem, but others experience narcosis at shallower depths.

Another problem with breathing air at depths is oxygen toxicity. Our bodies are accustomed to a partial pressure of O_2 of 0.21 atm. At a depth of 30 m, using compressed air, the partial pressure of O_2 is about one atmosphere, which means it is comparable to breathing 100% oxygen at sea level. These higher partial pressures can harm the lungs and cause central nervous system damage.

If you ascend too rapidly from a dive, you can experience the "bends," a painful and potentially lethal condition in which dissolved nitrogen gas bubbles form in the blood as the solubility of nitrogen decreases with decreasing pressure. To diminish the likelihood of getting the "bends," divers can use a gas mixture called "nitrox." This mixture is usually about 32–36% O_2 with correspondingly less N_2. With the lower N_2 pressure, less N_2 is dissolved in the blood. Use of nitrox allows a diver to ascend more rapidly because less time is needed to expel N_2 from the blood. And, because of the higher O_2 content of this gas mixture, nitrox has an added advantage of allowing more extended dive times.

For deep dives (about 100 m) different gas mixtures are used. A common mixture (Trimix) might contain 10% O_2, 70% He, and 20% N_2; other mixtures contain only oxygen and helium (Heliox). The lower percentage of O_2 lowers the danger of O_2 toxicity. Helium is substituted for N_2 because it is less soluble in blood and tissue, but it introduces an interesting side effect. If there is a voice link to the surface, the diver's speech sounds like Donald Duck! Speech is altered because the velocity of sound in helium is different from that in air.

It is clear that diving safely requires an understanding of the solubility of gases in liquids, one of the topics in this chapter.

Study Questions related to this story are: 13.19, 13.69, and 13.83.

We come into contact with solutions every day: aqueous solutions of ionic salts, gasoline with additives to improve its properties, and household cleaners such as ammonia in water. We add sugar, flavoring, and sometimes CO_2 to water to produce a palatable soft drink. Athletes drink commercial beverages with dissolved salts to match salt concentrations in body fluids precisely, thus allowing the fluid to be taken into the body more rapidly. In medicine, saline solutions (aqueous solutions containing NaCl and other soluble salts) are infused into the body to replace lost fluids.

A **solution** is a homogeneous mixture of two or more substances in a single phase. By convention, the component present in largest amount is identified as the **solvent** and the other component(s) as the **solute**(s) (Figure 13.1). Although other types of solutions exist (such as alloys, solid solutions of metals), the objective in this chapter is to develop an understanding of gases, liquids, and solids dissolved in liquid solvents.

Experience tells you that adding a solute to a pure liquid will change the properties of the liquid. Indeed, that is the reason some solutions are made. For instance, adding antifreeze to the water in your car's radiator prevents the coolant from boiling in the summer and freezing in the winter. The changes that occur in the freezing and boiling points when a substance is dissolved in a pure liquid are two observations we want to examine in detail. These properties, as well as the osmotic pressure of a solution and changes in solvent vapor pressure, are examples of colligative properties. **Colligative properties** are properties of solutions that depend only on the number of solute particles per solvent molecule and not on the identity of the solute.

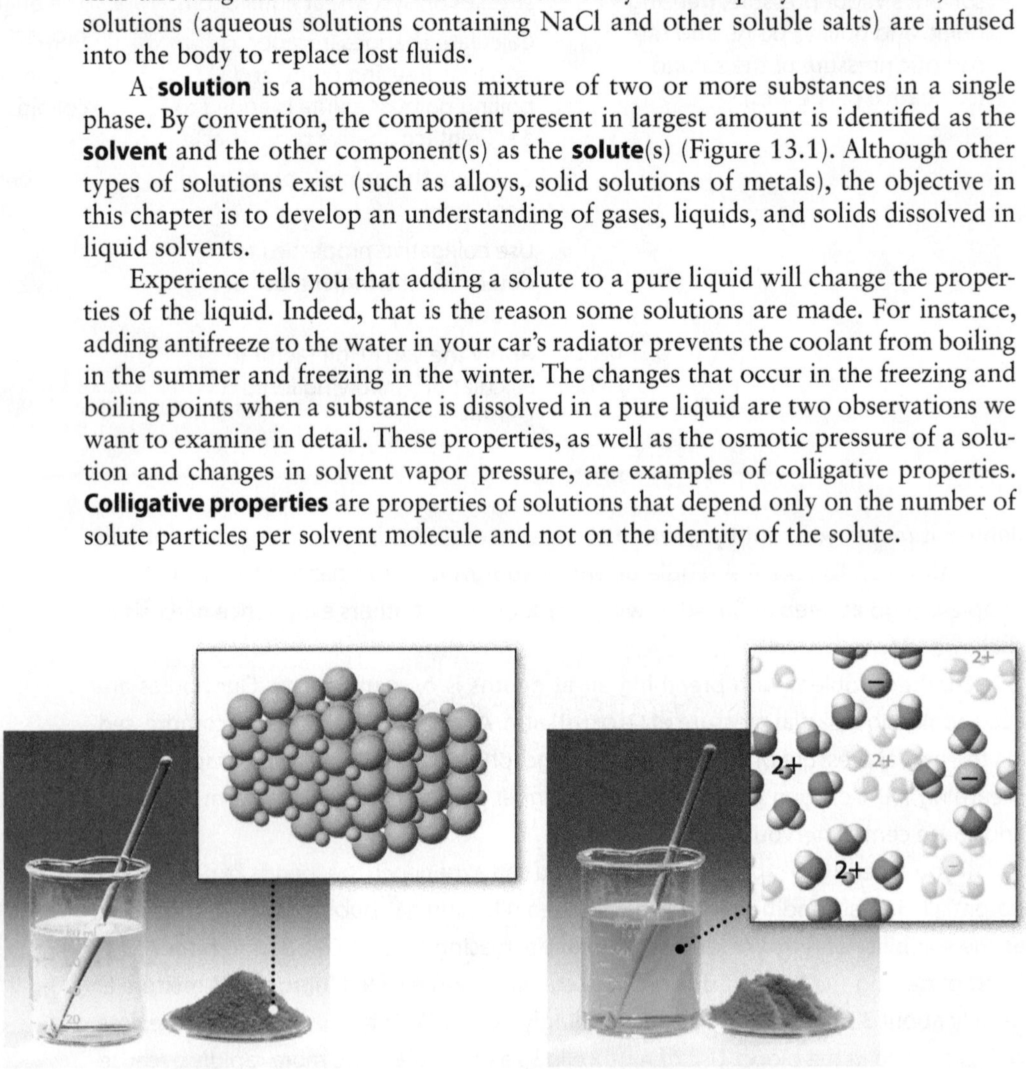

Photos: © Cengage Learning/Charles D. Winters

(a) Copper(II) chloride, the solute, is added to water, the solvent.

(b) Interactions between water molecules and Cu^{2+} and Cl^- ions allow the solid to dissolve. The ions are now sheathed with water molecules.

FIGURE 13.1 **Making a solution of copper(II) chloride (the solute) in water (the solvent).** When ionic compounds dissolve in water, each ion is surrounded by water molecules. The number of water molecules depends on ion size and charge.

13-1 Units of Concentration

To analyze the colligative properties of solutions, we need ways of defining solute concentrations that reflect the number of molecules or ions of solute per molecule of solvent. Four concentration units described here have this characteristic: molality, mole fraction, weight percent, and parts per million (ppm).

The **molality**, *m*, of a solution is defined as the amount of solute (mol) per kilogram of solvent.

$$\text{Concentration } (c, \text{mol/kg}) = \text{molality of solute} = \frac{\text{amount of solute (mol)}}{\text{mass of solvent (kg)}} \quad (13.1)$$

To prepare a 1.00 molal solution, for example, you would add 1.00 mol of solute to 1.00 kg of water.

Molarity is a concentration unit defined earlier and used in stoichiometry calculations (see Section 4-5). This unit is not useful when dealing with most colligative properties because, when preparing a solution of given molarity, the amount of solvent is not known as it would be when making a solution of given molality.

The difference between *molality* (*m*) and *molarity* (M) is illustrated in Figure 13.2. The flask on the right contains a 0.100 M aqueous solution of potassium chromate. It was made by adding enough water to 0.100 mol of K_2CrO_4 to make 1.000 L of solution. If 1.00 L (1.00 kg) of water is added to 0.100 mol of K_2CrO_4 to make a 0.100 molal solution, the volume of solution is greater than 1.000 L, as you see in the left side of the photograph.

The **mole fraction**, *X*, of a solution component is defined as the amount of that component (n_A) divided by the total amount of all of the components of the mixture ($n_A + n_B + n_C + \ldots$). Mathematically it is represented as

Mole Fraction and Gases We previously introduced the use of mole fractions when discussing mixtures of gases in Section 10-5.

$$\text{Mole fraction of A } (X_A) = \frac{n_A}{n_A + n_B + n_C + \ldots} \quad (13.2)$$

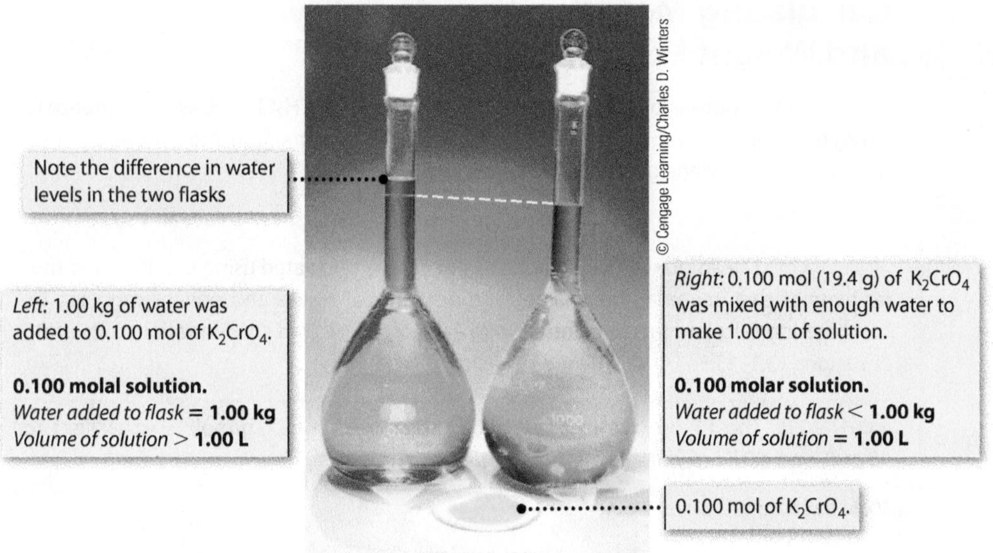

FIGURE 13.2 **Preparing 0.100 molal and 0.100 molar solutions.**

Consider a solution that contains 1.00 mol (46.1 g) of ethanol, C_2H_5OH, in 9.00 mol (162 g) of water. The mole fraction of alcohol is 0.100, and that of water is 0.900.

$$X_{\text{ethanol}} = \frac{1.00\text{ mol ethanol}}{1.00\text{ mol ethanol} + 9.00\text{ mol water}} = 0.100$$

$$X_{\text{water}} = \frac{9.00\text{ mol water}}{1.00\text{ mol ethanol} + 9.00\text{ mol water}} = 0.900$$

Notice that the sum of the mole fractions of the components in the solution equals 1.000, a relationship that must be true, based on how mole fraction is defined.

Weight percent is the mass of one component divided by the total mass of the mixture, multiplied by 100%:

$$\text{Weight \% A} = \frac{\text{mass of A}}{\text{mass of A} + \text{mass of B} + \text{mass of C} + \ldots} \times 100\% \qquad \textbf{(13.3)}$$

The alcohol–water mixture has 46.1 g of ethanol and 162 g of water, so the total mass of solution is 208 g, and the weight % of alcohol is

$$\text{Weight \% ethanol} = \frac{46.1\text{ g ethanol}}{46.1\text{ g ethanol} + 162\text{ g water}} \times 100\% = 22.2\%$$

FIGURE 13.3 **Weight percent.** The composition of many common products is often given in terms of weight percent.

Weight percent is a common unit in consumer products (Figure 13.3). Vinegar, for example, is an aqueous solution containing approximately 5% acetic acid and 95% water. The label on a common household bleach lists its active ingredient as 6.00% sodium hypochlorite (NaOCl) and 94.00% inert ingredients.

The unit **ppm (parts per million)** also refers to relative quantities of solute and solvent by mass; 1.0 ppm represents a solution containing 1.0 g of a substance in a sample with a total mass of 1.0 million g (equivalent to 1 mg in 1000 g). This unit is typically used to identify concentrations of solutes in very dilute solutions. It is useful in chemistry (especially in environmental chemistry) and in disciplines such as biology, geology, and oceanography.

Ppb and ppt The units ppb (parts per billion) and ppt (parts per trillion) are related to ppm. Sophisticated analytic techniques are now available that can detect trace impurities at the ppb and ppt range.

EXAMPLE 13.1

Calculating Mole Fraction, Molality, and Weight Percent

Problem Suppose you add 1.2 kg of ethylene glycol, $HOCH_2CH_2OH$, as an antifreeze to 4.0 kg of water in the radiator of your car. What are the mole fraction, molality, and weight percent of the ethylene glycol?

What Do You Know? You know the identity and masses of solute and solvent.

Strategy The amount of solute and solvent can be calculated using the mass and molar mass of each material. The masses and amounts of solute and solvent can then be combined to calculate the concentration in each of the desired concentration units using Equations 13.1–13.3.

Solution The 1.2 kg of ethylene glycol (molar mass = 62.1 g/mol) is equivalent to 19 mol, and 4.0 kg of water represents 220 mol.

Mole fraction:

$$X_{\text{glycol}} = \frac{19\text{ mol ethylene glycol}}{19\text{ mol ethylene glycol} + 220\text{ mol water}} = 0.080$$

Molality:

$$c_{glycol} = \frac{19 \text{ mol ethylene glycol}}{4.0 \text{ kg water}} = 4.8 \text{ mol/kg} = 4.8\ m$$

Weight percent:

$$\text{Weight \%} = \frac{1.2 \times 10^3 \text{ g ethylene glycol}}{1.2 \times 10^3 \text{g ethylene glycol} + 4.0 \times 10^3 \text{ g water}} \times 100\% = 23\%$$

Think about Your Answer Although the numerical values are very different, the information contained in these values is similar; each relates the relative numbers of solvent and solute particles.

Check Your Understanding

(a) Mole fraction, molality, and weight percent: If you dissolve 10.0 g (about one heaping teaspoonful) of sugar (sucrose, $C_{12}H_{22}O_{11}$) in a cup of water (250. g), what are the mole fraction, molality, and weight percent of sugar?

(b) Parts per million: Seawater has a sodium ion concentration of 1.08×10^4 ppm. If the sodium is present in the form of dissolved sodium chloride, what mass of NaCl is in each liter of seawater? Seawater is denser than pure water because of dissolved salts. Its density is 1.05 g/mL.

© Cengage Learning/Charles D. Winters

Commercial antifreeze. This solution contains ethylene glycol, $HOCH_2CH_2OH$, an organic alcohol that is readily soluble in water. Regulations specify that the weight percent of ethylene glycol in ethylene glycol–based antifreeze must be at least 75%. (The remainder of the solution can be other glycols and water.)

REVIEW & CHECK FOR SECTION 13-1

1. You dissolve 1.0 mol of urea (H_2NCONH_2) in 270 g of water. The mole fraction of urea is

   (a) 3.7×10^{-3} (b) 0.063 (c) 16 (d) 1.0

   and its molality is

   (a) 1.0 (b) 3.7 (c) 0.063 (d) 0.27

2. The concentration of acetic acid, CH_3CO_2H, in a sample of vinegar is 5.0 weight percent. What is the concentration of vinegar expressed as mol/kg solvent (molality)?

   (a) 0.83 mol/kg (b) 0.88 mol/kg (c) 5.2 mol/kg (d) 0.083 mol/kg

13-2 The Solution Process

Learning Objectives: LO 2.15, LO 6.24

If solid $CuCl_2$ is added to a beaker of water, the salt will begin to dissolve (see Figure 13.1). The amount of solid diminishes, and the concentrations of Cu^{2+}(aq) and Cl^-(aq) in the solution increase. If we continue to add $CuCl_2$, however, we will eventually reach a point when no additional $CuCl_2$ seems to dissolve. The concentrations of Cu^{2+}(aq) and Cl^-(aq) will not increase further, and any additional solid $CuCl_2$ added after this point will remain as a solid at the bottom of the beaker. We say that such a solution is **saturated.**

Unsaturated The term unsaturated is used when referring to solutions with solute concentrations that are less than that of a saturated solution.

Although no change is observed on the macroscopic level when a solution is saturated, it is a different matter on the particulate level. The process of dissolving continues, with Cu^{2+} and Cl^- ions leaving the solid state and entering solution. However, at the same time solid $CuCl_2$(s) is being formed from Cu^{2+}(aq) and Cl^-(aq). The rates at which $CuCl_2$ is dissolving and reprecipitating are equal in a saturated solution, so that no net change in the concentration of ions is observed on the macroscopic level.

This process is another example of a dynamic equilibrium (◀ Section 3-3), and we can describe the situation in terms of an equation with substances linked by a set of double arrows ($\rightleftharpoons$):

$$CuCl_2(s) \rightleftharpoons Cu^{2+}(aq) + 2\ Cl^-(aq)$$

A CLOSER LOOK Supersaturated Solutions

Although at first glance it may seem a contradiction, it is possible for a solution to hold more dissolved solute than the amount in a saturated solution. Such solutions are referred to as **supersaturated**. Supersaturated solutions are unstable, and the excess solid eventually crystallizes from the solution until the equilibrium concentration of the solute is reached.

The solubility of substances often decreases if the temperature is lowered. Supersaturated solutions are usually made by preparing a saturated solution at an elevated temperature and then carefully cooling it. If the rate of crystallization is slow, the solid may not precipitate when the solubility is exceeded. The result is a solution that has more solute than the amount defined by equilibrium conditions; it is supersaturated.

When disturbed in some manner, a supersaturated solution moves toward equilibrium by precipitating solute. This change can occur rapidly, often with the evolution of thermal energy. In fact, supersaturated solutions are used in "heat packs" to apply heat to injured muscles. When crystallization of sodium acetate ($NaCH_3CO_2$) from a supersaturated solution in a heat pack is initiated, the temperature of the heat pack rises to about 50 °C and crystals of solid sodium acetate are detected inside the bag.

Supersaturated solutions. When a supersaturated solution is disturbed, the dissolved salt (here sodium acetate, $NaCH_3CO_2$) rapidly crystallizes.

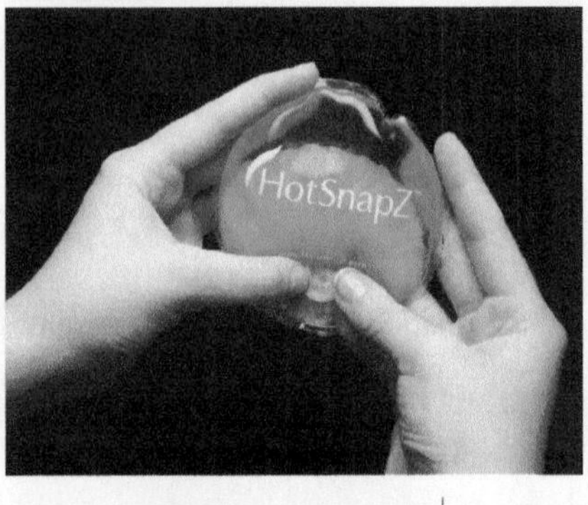

Heat of crystallization. A heat pack relies on the heat evolved by the crystallization of sodium acetate.

A saturated solution gives us a way to define precisely the solubility of a solid in a liquid. **Solubility** is the concentration of solute in a saturated solution in equilibrium with undissolved solute. The solubility of $CuCl_2$, for example, is 70.6 g in 100 mL of water at 0 °C. If we add 100.0 g of $CuCl_2$ to 100 mL of water at 0 °C, we can expect 70.6 g to dissolve, and 29.4 g of solid to remain.

Liquids Dissolving in Liquids

If two liquids can be mixed in any proportion to form a homogeneous mixture they are said to be **miscible**. In contrast, **immiscible** liquids do not fully mix in all proportions; they exist in contact with each other as separate layers (Figure 13.4). Ethanol (C_2H_5OH) and water, both polar compounds, are miscible, as are the nonpolar liquids octane (C_8H_{18}) and carbon tetrachloride (CCl_4). Many similar observations like these have led to a familiar rule of thumb: *Like dissolves like.* Nonpolar liquids frequently are miscible, as are polar liquids.

On the other hand, nonpolar solvents such as C_8H_{18} and CCl_4 are not miscible with polar water. As a general rule, polar solvents are likely not to be miscible with nonpolar solvents.

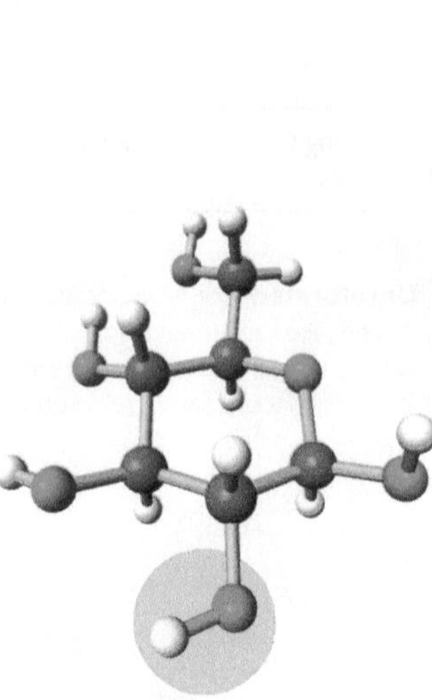

Like dissolves like. Glucose has five —OH groups on each molecule, groups that allow it to form hydrogen bonds with water molecules. As a result, glucose dissolves readily in water.

Solids Dissolving in Liquids

The "like dissolves like" guideline also holds for molecular solids dissolving in liquids. Nonpolar solids such as naphthalene, $C_{10}H_8$, dissolve readily in nonpolar solvents such as benzene, C_6H_6, and hexane, C_6H_{14}. Iodine, I_2, a nonpolar inorganic solid, dissolves in water to some extent, but, given a choice, it dissolves to a larger extent in a nonpolar liquid such as CCl_4 (Figure 13.5). Polar solids are often soluble in polar liquids such as water. Sucrose (sugar), a polar molecular solid with multiple —OH groups, is readily soluble in water, a fact well known because of its use to sweeten beverages.

As was seen with nonpolar liquids, most nonpolar solids are likely to be insoluble or have low solubilities in polar solvents such as water. The reverse is also true;

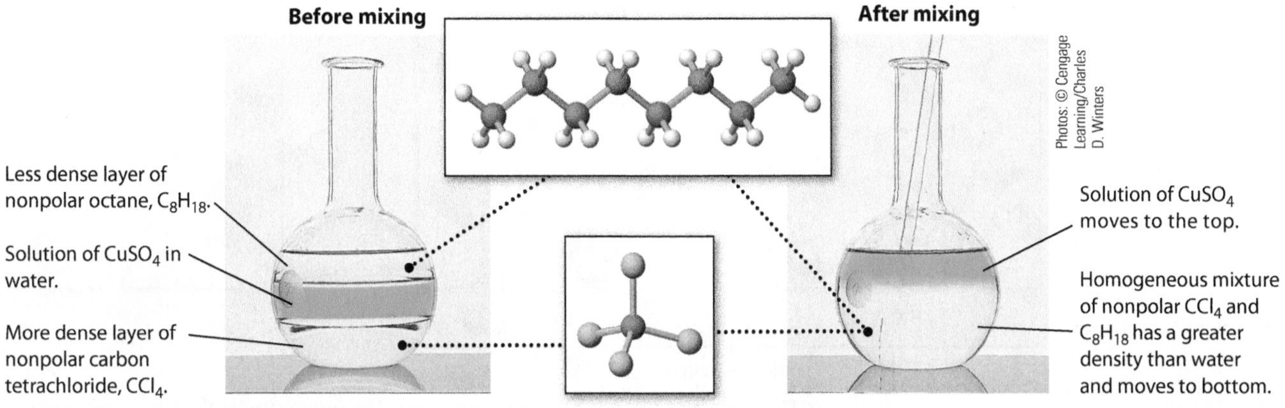

(a) Before mixing. The colorless, denser bottom layer is nonpolar carbon tetrachloride, CCl_4. The blue middle layer is a solution of $CuSO_4$ in water, and the colorless, less dense top layer is nonpolar octane, C_8H_{18}. This mixture was prepared by carefully layering one liquid on top of another, without mixing.

(b) After mixing. After stirring the mixture, the two nonpolar liquids form a homogeneous mixture. This layer of mixed liquids is under the water layer because the mixture of CCl_4 and C_8H_{18} has a greater density than water.

FIGURE 13.4 **Miscibility.**

polar solutes, sugar for example, are likely to have low solubility in nonpolar solvents such as gasoline.

Ionic compounds can be considered extreme examples of polar compounds, and they do not dissolve in nonpolar solvents. Sodium chloride, for example, does not dissolve in liquids such as hexane or CCl_4. However, the solubility of ionic compounds in the polar solvent water is not as easily predicted. Recall the solubility guidelines (◀ Figure 3.10), which predict that some ionic compounds are soluble in water while others are not.

Network solids, including graphite, diamond, and quartz sand (SiO_2), do not dissolve in water. (Where would all the beaches be if sand dissolved in water?) The covalent chemical bonding in network solids is simply too strong to be broken; the lattice remains intact when in contact with water.

Enthalpy of Solution

What is the basis for the "like dissolves like" guideline? First, we recognize there are two factors that determine whether any process will occur. One factor is the enthalpy change for the process, here the *enthalpy of solution*. The second factor is *entropy*, a thermodynamic function that is a measure of the wider dispersal of the

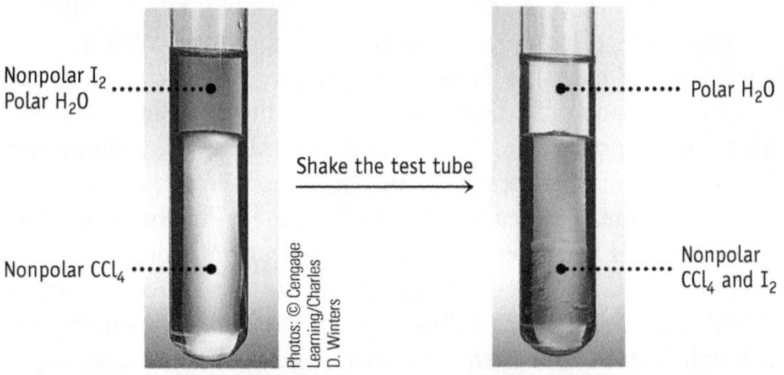

FIGURE 13.5 **Solubility of nonpolar iodine in polar water and nonpolar carbon tetrachloride.** When a solution of nonpolar I_2 in water (the brown layer on top in the left test tube) is shaken with nonpolar CCl_4 (the colorless bottom layer in the left test tube), the I_2 transfers preferentially to the nonpolar solvent. Evidence for this is the purple color of the bottom CCl_4 layer in the test tube on the right.

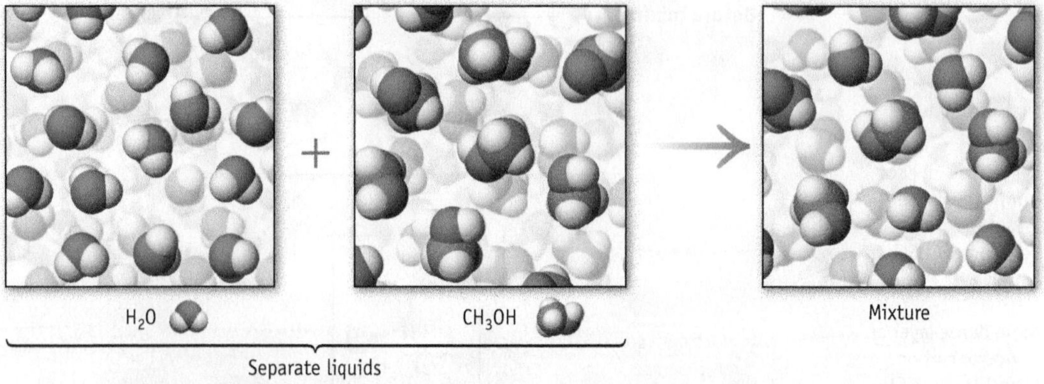

FIGURE 13.6 **Driving the solution process—entropy.** When two similar liquids—here water and methanol—are mixed, the molecules intermingle, and the energy of the system is more dispersed than in the two, separate pure liquids. A measure of this energy dispersal is entropy, a thermodynamic function described in more detail in Chapter 18.

Entropy and the Solution Process It is generally accepted that entropy is a more important contributor to the solution process. (See Chapter 18 and T. P. Silverstein: "The real reason why oil and water don't mix." *Journal of Chemical Education,* Vol. 75, pp. 116–118, 1998.)

energy of the particles in the mixture relative to the pure liquids (Figure 13.6). The greater the energy dispersal, the greater is the entropy, and the more favorable the process. We discuss entropy more fully in Chapter 18, but here we only point out that in evaluating solutions, the entropy effect is often dominant. The enthalpy of solution, which can be interpreted readily based on attractive forces between particles, is an important factor in determining solubility, but less so than entropy.

It is possible to assess the enthalpy change that occurs when a solution forms by evaluating the intermolecular forces between particles. In pure water and pure methanol, the major force between molecules is hydrogen bonding involving —OH groups. When the two liquids are mixed, hydrogen bonding between methanol and water molecules also occurs. Because solute-solvent and solute-solute forces of attraction are of similar magnitude, we can predict that the enthalpy change for the solution process will be small.

Similarly, the enthalpy change when dissolving a nonpolar solute in a nonpolar solvent is expected to be near zero. Molecules of pure octane or pure CCl_4, both of which are nonpolar, are held together in the liquid phase by dispersion forces (◀ Section 11-4). When these nonpolar liquids are mixed, the energy associated with the forces of attraction between solute and solvent are similar to the forces of attraction between octane and CCl_4 molecules in the pure liquids. As with solutions of polar solutes in polar solvents, little or no energy change occurs; the solution process is expected to be nearly energy neutral.

For ionic compounds dissolving in water, a favorable enthalpy change (a negative $\Delta_{soln}H$) generally leads to a compound being soluble. For example, sodium hydroxide is very soluble, dissolving in water with significant heat evolution (Figure 13.7a). An unfavorable enthalpy factor, however, does not guarantee that an ionic compound will not dissolve. Sodium chloride is quite soluble in water despite the fact that the solution process is slightly endothermic. And, ammonium nitrate is quite soluble in water in a process that is also endothermic, evidenced by the fact that the solution becomes noticeably colder (Figure 13.7b.) In these cases, we must conclude that entropy is the driving force in the solution process.

To further understand the energetics of the solution process, we will use the process of dissolving KF in water to illustrate what occurs. The energy level diagram in Figure 13.8 will help us follow the changes. Solid potassium fluoride has an ionic crystal lattice with alternating K^+ and F^- ions held in place by attractive forces due to their opposite charges. In water, these ions are separated from each other and *hydrated*; that is, they are surrounded by water molecules (see Figure 13.1). Ion–dipole forces of attraction bind water molecules strongly to each ion. The energy

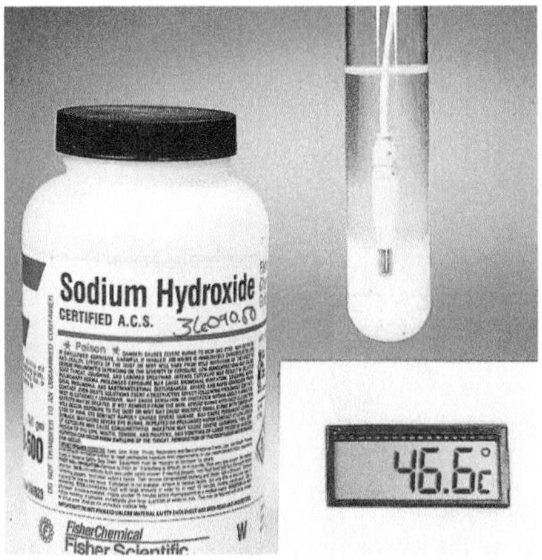

(a) Dissolving NaOH in water is a strongly exothermic process.

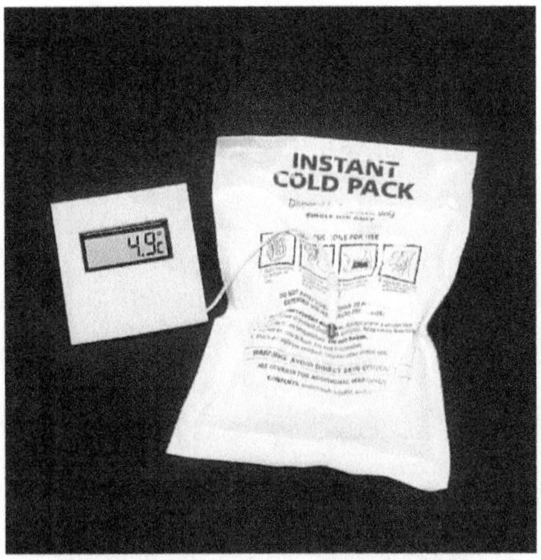

(b) A "cold pack" contains solid ammonium nitrate, NH_4NO_3, and a package of water. When the water and NH_4NO_3 are mixed and the salt dissolves, the temperature of the system drops, owing to the endothermic enthalpy of solution of ammonium nitrate ($\Delta_{soln}H° = +25.7$ kJ/mol).

Photos: © Cengage Learning/Charles D. Winters

FIGURE 13.7 **Dissolving ionic solids and enthalpy of solution.**

change occurring on going from the reactant, KF(s), to the products, K^+(aq) and F^-(aq), is the sum of the energies of two individual steps:

1. Energy must be supplied to separate the ions in the lattice against their attractive forces. This is the reverse of the process defining the lattice enthalpy of an ionic compound (◀ Section 12-3), and its value will be equal to $-\Delta_{lattice}H$. Separating the ions from one another is highly endothermic because the attractive forces between ions are strong.
2. Energy is evolved when the individual ions dissolve in water, where each ion becomes surrounded by water molecules. Again, strong forces of attraction (ion–dipole forces) are involved (◀ Section 11-2). This process, referred to as **hydration** when water is the solvent, is strongly exothermic.

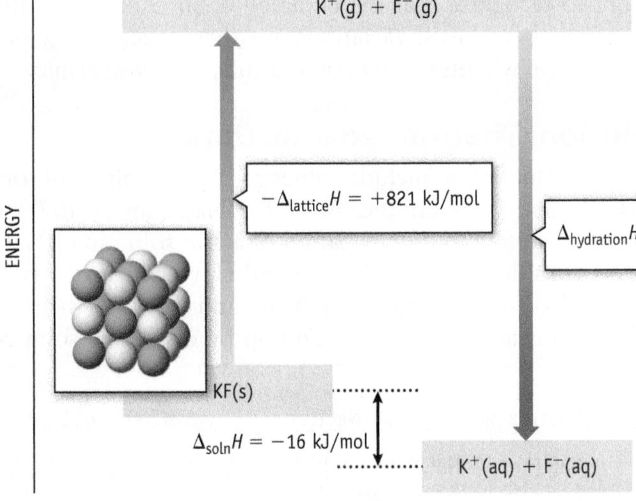

FIGURE 13.8 **Model for energy changes on dissolving KF.** An estimate of the magnitude of the energy change on dissolving an ionic compound in water is achieved by imagining it as occurring in two steps at the particulate level. Here, KF is first separated into cations and anions in the gas phase with an expenditure of 821 kJ per mol of KF. These ions are then hydrated, with $\Delta_{hydration}H$ estimated to be −837 kJ. Thus, the net energy change is −16 kJ, a slightly exothermic enthalpy of solution.

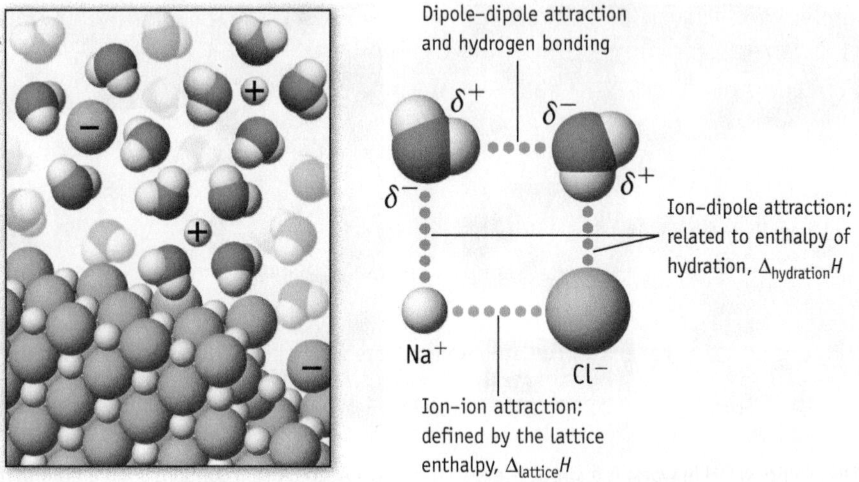

FIGURE 13.9 **Dissolving an ionic solid in water.** This process is a balance of forces. There are intermolecular forces between water molecules, and ion–ion forces are at work in the ionic crystal lattice. To dissolve, the ion–dipole forces between water and the ions (as measured by $\Delta_{hydration}H$) must overcome the ion–ion forces (as measured by $\Delta_{lattice}H$) and the intermolecular forces in water.

We can therefore represent the process of dissolving KF in terms of these chemical equations:

$$\text{Step 1: } KF(s) \longrightarrow K^+(g) + F^-(g) \qquad -\Delta_{lattice}H$$
$$\text{Step 2: } K^+(g) + F^-(g) \longrightarrow K^+(aq) + F^-(aq) \qquad \Delta_{hydration}H$$

The enthalpy of the overall reaction, called the **enthalpy of solution** ($\Delta_{soln}H$), is the sum of the two enthalpy changes.

$$\text{Overall: } KF(s) \longrightarrow K^+(aq) + F^-(aq) \qquad \Delta_{soln}H = -\Delta_{lattice}H + \Delta_{hydration}H$$

We can use this equation to estimate the value of $\Delta_{hydration}H$. From the lattice energy for KF (−821 kJ/mol, calculated using a Born-Haber cycle; see Section 12-3), and the value of $\Delta_{soln}H$ (−16.4 kJ/mol, determined by calorimetry) we can determine $\Delta_{hydration}H$ to be −837 kJ/mol.

As a general rule, to be water-soluble an ionic compound will have an enthalpy of solution that is exothermic or only slightly endothermic (Figure 13.9). In the latter instance, it is assumed that the enthalpy-disfavored solution process will be balanced by a favorable entropy of solution. If the enthalpy of solution is very endothermic (because of a low hydration energy) then the compound is unlikely to be soluble. Similarly, we can conclude that nonpolar solvents would not solvate ions strongly, and that solution process would thus be energetically unfavorable. We therefore predict that an ionic compound, such as copper(II) sulfate, is not very soluble in nonpolar solvents such as carbon tetrachloride and octane (see Figure 13.4).

It is also important to recognize that the enthalpy of solution is the difference between two very large numbers. Small variations in either lattice energy or hydration enthalpies can determine whether dissolution is endo- or exothermic.

Table 13.1 Data for Calculating Enthalpy of Solution

COMPOUND	$\Delta_f H°$(s) (kJ/mol)	$\Delta_f H°$ (aq, 1 *m*) (kJ/mol)
LiF	−616.9	−611.1
NaF	−573.6	−572.8
KF	−568.6	−585.0
RbF	−557.7	−583.8
LiCl	−408.7	−445.6
NaCl	−411.1	−407.3
KCl	−436.7	−419.5
RbCl	−435.4	−418.3
NaOH	−425.9	−469.2
NH_4NO_3	−365.6	−339.9

Enthalpy of Solution: Thermodynamic Data

Tables of thermodynamic values often include values for the enthalpies of formation of aqueous solutions of salts. For example, $\Delta_f H°$ for NaCl(aq) (−407.3 kJ/mol, Table 13.1 and Appendix L) refers to the formation of a 1 *m* solution of NaCl from the elements. It may be considered to involve the enthalpy changes for two steps: (1) the formation of NaCl(s) from the elements Na(s) and Cl_2(g) in their standard states ($\Delta_f H°$), and (2) the formation of a 1 *m* solution by dissolving solid NaCl in water ($\Delta_{soln}H°$):

$$\text{Formation of NaCl(s): } Na(s) + \tfrac{1}{2}\, Cl_2(g) \longrightarrow NaCl(s) \qquad \Delta_f H° = -411.1 \text{ kJ/mol}$$
$$\text{Dissolving NaCl(s): } NaCl(s) \longrightarrow NaCl(aq, 1\ m) \qquad \Delta_{soln}H° = +3.8 \text{ kJ/mol}$$
$$\text{Net process: } Na(s) + \tfrac{1}{2}\, Cl_2(g) \longrightarrow NaCl(aq, 1\ m) \qquad \Delta_f H° = -407.3 \text{ kJ/mol}$$

By combining the enthalpies of formation of a solid and of its aqueous solution, we can calculate the enthalpy of solution, as outlined in Example 13.2.

EXAMPLE 13.2

Calculating an Enthalpy of Solution

Problem Determine the enthalpy of solution for NH_4NO_3, the compound used in cold packs.

What Do You Know? The solution process for NH_4NO_3 is represented by the equation

$$NH_4NO_3(s) \longrightarrow NH_4NO_3(aq)$$

The enthalpies of formation of NH_4NO_3 in the solid state (−365.6 kJ/mol) and in solution (−339.9 kJ/mol) are given in Table 13.1.

Strategy Equation 5.6 (Section 5-7) states that the enthalpy change for a process is the difference between the enthalpy of formation, $\Delta_f H$, of the final state (here the compound in solution) and the initial state (the solid).

Solution The enthalpy change for this process is calculated using Equation 5.6 as follows:

$$\begin{aligned}\Delta_{soln}H^\circ &= \Sigma[n\Delta_f H^\circ(\text{product})] - \Sigma[n\Delta_f H^\circ(\text{reactant})]\\ &= \Delta_f H^\circ[NH_4NO_3(aq)] - \Delta_f H^\circ[NH_4NO_3(s)] \text{ (where } n = 1 \text{ for both)}\\ &= -339.9 \text{ kJ} - (-365.6 \text{ kJ}) = +25.7 \text{ kJ}\end{aligned}$$

Think about Your Answer The process is endothermic, as indicated by the fact that $\Delta_{soln}H^\circ$ has a positive value and as verified by the experiment in Figure 13.7b.

Check Your Understanding

Use the data in Table 13.1 to calculate the enthalpy of solution for NaOH.

REVIEW & CHECK FOR SECTION 13-2

1. Given the enthalpy of formation data below, calculate $\Delta_{soln}H^\circ$ for LiOH.

   $\Delta_f H^\circ$ [LiOH(s)] = −484.93 kJ/mol $\Delta_f H^\circ$ [LiOH(aq)] = −508.48 kJ/mol

   (a) +23.55 kJ/mol   (c) −23.55 kJ/mol

   (b) +993.41 kJ/mol   (d) −993.41 kJ/mol

13-3 Factors Affecting Solubility: Pressure and Temperature

Pressure and temperature are two external factors that influence solubility. Both affect the solubility of gases in liquids, whereas only temperature is a factor in the solubility of solids in liquids.

Dissolving Gases in Liquids: Henry's Law

The solubility of a gas in a liquid is directly proportional to the gas pressure. This is a statement of **Henry's law**,

$$S_g = k_H P_g \quad (13.4)$$

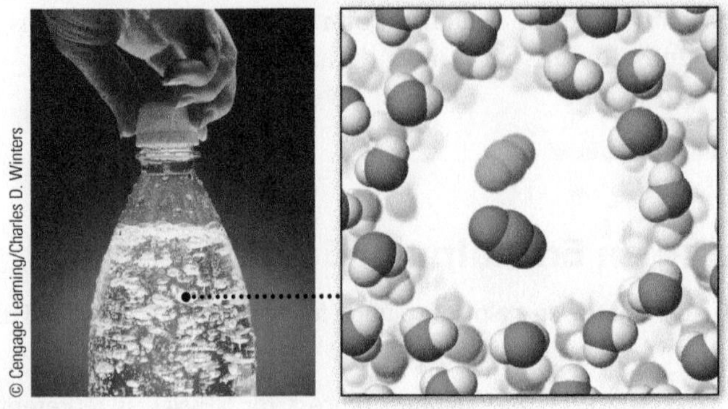

FIGURE 13.10 Gas solubility and pressure. Carbonated beverages are bottled under high CO_2 pressure. When the bottle is opened, the pressure is released, and bubbles of CO_2 form within the liquid and rise to the surface. After some time, an equilibrium between dissolved CO_2 and atmospheric CO_2 is reached. The beverage tastes flat when most of its dissolved CO_2 is lost.

Table 13.2 Henry's Law Constants for Gases in Water (25 °C)*

GAS	k_H (mol/kg·bar)
He	3.8×10^{-4}
H_2	7.8×10^{-4}
N_2	6.0×10^{-4}
O_2	1.3×10^{-3}
CO_2	0.034
CH_4	1.4×10^{-3}
C_2H_6	1.9×10^{-3}

*From http://webbook.nist.gov/chemistry/. *Note:* 1 bar = 0.9869 atm.

Limitations of Henry's Law
Henry's law holds quantitatively only for gases that do not interact chemically with the solvent. It does not accurately predict the solubility of NH_3 in water, for example, because this compound gives small concentrations of NH_4^+ and OH^- in water.

where S_g is the gas solubility (in mol/kg), P_g is the partial pressure of the gaseous solute, and k_H is Henry's law constant (Table 13.2), a constant characteristic of the solute and solvent.

Carbonated soft drinks illustrate how Henry's law works. These beverages are packed under pressure in a chamber filled with carbon dioxide gas, some of which dissolves in the beverage. When the can or bottle is opened, the partial pressure of CO_2 above the solution drops, causing the solubility of CO_2 to drop. Gas bubbles out of the solution (Figure 13.10).

Henry's law has important consequences in scuba diving. As explained in the account of *Narcosis and the Bends* at the beginning of this chapter, when you dive, the pressure of the air you breathe must be balanced against the external pressure of the water. In deeper dives, the pressure of the gases in the scuba gear must be several atmospheres and, as a result, more gas dissolves in the blood. If you ascend from a dive too rapidly, you can experience a painful and potentially lethal condition referred to as the "bends," in which nitrogen gas bubbles form in the blood as the solubility of nitrogen decreases with decreasing pressure. To minimize the possibility of experiencing the bends, divers may use a helium–oxygen mixture (rather than nitrogen–oxygen) because helium is not as soluble in blood as nitrogen.

We can better understand the effect of pressure on solubility by examining the system at the particulate level. The solubility of a gas is defined as the concentration of the dissolved gas in equilibrium with the substance in the gaseous state. At equilibrium, the rate at which solute gas molecules escape the solution and enter the gaseous state equals the rate at which gas molecules reenter the solution. An increase in pressure results in more molecules of gas striking the surface of the liquid and entering solution in a given time. The solution eventually reaches a new equilibrium when the concentration of gas dissolved in the solvent is high enough that the rate of gas molecules escaping the solution again equals the rate of gas molecules entering the solution.

EXAMPLE 13.3

Using Henry's Law

Problem What is the concentration of O_2 in a freshwater stream in equilibrium with air at 25 °C and at a pressure of 1.0 bar? Express the answer in grams of O_2 per kg of water.

What Do You Know? You know the total air pressure and temperature, and you can look up the Henry's law constant at the indicated temperature (1.3×10^{-3} mol/kg · bar). (Note that 1 bar is approximately 1 atm; Section 10-1.)

Strategy You first must find the partial pressure of O_2 from its mole fraction in air (0.21) and the specified atmospheric pressure (1.0 bar). Then use Henry's law to calculate its molar solubility.

Solution

(a) The mole fraction of O_2 in air is 0.21, and, because the total pressure is 1.0 bar, the partial pressure of O_2 is 0.21 bar.

(b) Using the O_2 partial pressure for P_g in Henry's law, we have:

$$\text{Solubility of } O_2 = k_H P_g = \left(\frac{1.3 \times 10^{-3}\ \text{mol}}{\text{kg} \cdot \text{bar}}\right)(0.21\ \text{bar}) = 2.7 \times 10^{-4}\ \text{mol/kg}$$

(c) Calculate the concentration in g/kg from the concentration in mol/kg and the molar mass of O_2:

$$\text{Solubility of } O_2 = \left(\frac{2.7 \times 10^{-4}\ \text{mol}}{\text{kg}}\right)\left(\frac{32.0\ \text{g}}{\text{mol}}\right) = 0.0087\ \text{g/kg}$$

Think about Your Answer The concentration of O_2 is 8.7 ppm (8.7 mg/1000 g). This concentration is quite low, but it is sufficient to provide the oxygen required by aquatic life.

Check Your Understanding

What is the concentration of CO_2 in water at 25 °C when the partial pressure is 0.33 bar? (Although CO_2 reacts with water to give traces of H_3O^+ and HCO_3^-, the reaction occurs to such a small extent that Henry's law is obeyed at low CO_2 partial pressures.)

Temperature Effects on Solubility: Le Chatelier's Principle

The solubility of all gases in water decreases with increasing temperature. You may realize this from everyday observations such as the appearance of bubbles of air as water is heated below the boiling point.

It is possible to predict the effect of temperature on the solubility of a gas from the enthalpy of solution. When gases dissolve in water they usually do so in an exothermic process

$$\text{Gas} + \text{liquid solvent} \xrightleftharpoons{\Delta_{soln}H < 0} \text{saturated solution} + \text{energy}$$

The reverse process, loss of dissolved gas molecules from a solution, requires energy as heat. At equilibrium, the rates of the two processes are the same.

To account for the effect of temperature on solubility, we turn to **Le Chatelier's principle**, which states that a change in any of the factors determining an equilibrium causes the system to adjust by shifting in the direction that reduces or counteracts the effect of the change. If a solution of a gas in a liquid is heated, for example, the equilibrium will shift to absorb some of the added energy. That is, the reaction

$$\text{Gas} + \text{liquid solvent} \xrightleftharpoons[\text{Add energy. Equilibrium shifts left.}]{\text{Exothermic process}\ \Delta_{soln}H \text{ is negative.}} \text{saturated solution} + \text{energy}$$

shifts to the left if the temperature is raised because energy is absorbed in the process that produces free gas molecules and pure solvent. This shift corresponds to less gas dissolved and a lower solubility at higher temperature—the observed result.

CASE STUDY Henry's Law and Exploding Lakes

On Thursday, August 21, 1986, people and animals around Lake Nyos in Cameroon, a small nation on the west coast of Africa, suddenly collapsed and died. More than 1700 people and hundreds of animals were dead, but there was no apparent cause—no fire, no earthquake, no storm. What had brought on this disaster?

Some weeks later, the mystery was solved. Lake Nyos and nearby Lake Monoun are crater lakes, which formed when cooled volcanic craters filled with water. Importantly, Lake Nyos contains an enormous amount of dissolved carbon dioxide, which was generated as a result of volcanic activity deep in the Earth. Under the high pressure at the bottom of the lake, a very large amount of CO_2 dissolved in the water.

But on that evening in 1986, something disturbed the lake. The CO_2-saturated water at the bottom of the lake was carried to the surface, where, under lower pressure, the gas was much less soluble. About one cubic kilometer of carbon dioxide was released into the atmosphere. A geyser of water and CO_2 shot up about 260 feet; then, because this gas is more dense than air, it hugged the ground and began to move with the prevailing breeze at about 45 miles per hour. When it reached villages 12 miles away, vital oxygen was displaced. The result was that both people and animals were asphyxiated.

In most lakes, this situation would not occur because lake water "turns over" as the seasons change. In the autumn, the top layer of water in a lake cools; its density increases; and the water sinks. This process continues, with warmer water coming to the surface and cooler water sinking. Dissolved CO_2 at the bottom of a lake would normally be expelled in this turnover process, but geologists found that the lakes in Cameroon are different. The chemocline, the boundary between deep water, rich in gas and minerals, and the upper layer, full of freshwater, stayed intact. As carbon dioxide continued to enter the lake through vents in the bottom of the lake, the water became supersaturated with this gas. It is presumed that a minor disturbance—perhaps a small earthquake, a strong wind, or an underwater landslide—caused the lake water to turn over and led to the explosive release of CO_2.

Lake Nyos in Cameroon (western Africa), the site of a natural disaster. In 1986, a huge bubble of CO_2 escaped from the lake and asphyxiated more than 1700 people.

The explosive release of CO_2 that occurred in Lake Nyos is much like what occurs when you shake a bottle of carbonated soft drink. Carbonated sodas are bottled under a high pressure of CO_2. Some of the gas dissolves in the soda, but some also remains in the small space above the liquid (called the *headspace*). The pressure of the CO_2 in the headspace is between 2 and 4 atm. When the bottle cap is removed, the CO_2 in the headspace escapes rapidly. Some of the dissolved CO_2 also comes out of solution, and you see bubbles of gas rising to the surface. If the bottle remains open, this continues until equilibrium is established with CO_2 in the atmosphere (where the partial pressure of CO_2 is 3.75×10^{-4} atm),

$$CO_2(\text{solution}) \rightleftharpoons CO_2(g)$$

and the soda goes "flat." If the newly opened soda bottle is undisturbed, however, the loss of CO_2 from solution is rather slow because bubble formation is not rapid, and your soda keeps its fizz.

Questions:

1. If the headspace of a soda is 25 mL and the pressure of CO_2 in the space is 4.0 atm (≈4.0 bar) at 25 °C, what amount of CO_2 is contained in the headspace?
2. If the CO_2 in the headspace escapes into the atmosphere where the partial pressure of CO_2 is 3.7×10^{-4} atm, what volume would the CO_2 occupy (at 25 °C)? By what amount did the CO_2 expand when it was released?
3. What is the solubility of CO_2 in water at 25 °C when the pressure of the gas is 3.7×10^{-4} bar?
4. After opening a 1.0 L soda, what mass of the dissolved CO_2 is released to the atmosphere in order to reach equilibrium? Assume that the CO_2 dissolved in the soda in the sealed bottle was in equilibrium with the CO_2 in the headspace at 4.0 bar pressure.

Answers to these questions are available in Appendix N.

The solubility of solids in water is also affected by temperature, but, unlike the situation involving solutions of gases, no general pattern of behavior is observed. In Figure 13.11, the solubilities of several salts are plotted versus temperature. The solubility of many salts increases with increasing temperature, but there are notable exceptions. Predictions based on whether the enthalpy of solution is positive or negative work most of the time, but exceptions do occur.

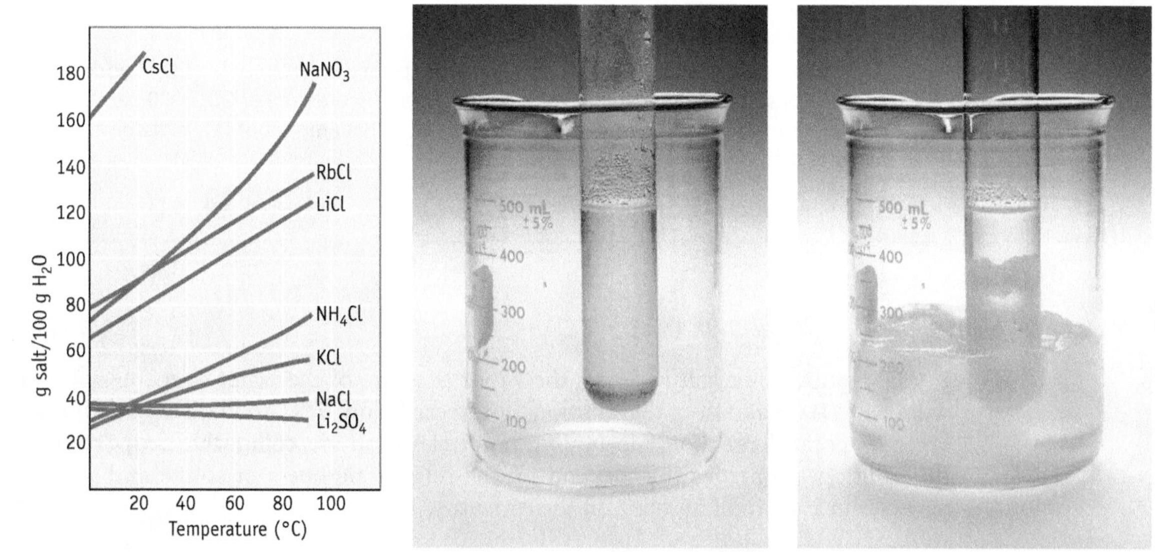

(a) Temperature dependence of the solubility of some ionic compounds.

(b) NH_4Cl dissolved in water.

(c) NH_4Cl precipitates when the solution is cooled in ice.

Photos: © Cengage Learning/Charles D. Winters

FIGURE 13.11 **The temperature dependence of the solubility of some ionic compounds in water.** The solubility of most ionic compounds increases with increasing temperature. This is illustrated using NH_4Cl (parts b and c).

Chemists take advantage of the variation of solubility with temperature to purify compounds. An impure sample of a compound that is more soluble at higher temperatures is dissolved by heating the solution. The solution is then cooled to decrease the solubility (Figure 13.11c). When the limit of solubility is reached at the lower temperature, crystals of the pure compound form. If the process is done slowly and carefully, it is sometimes possible to obtain very large crystals.

A CLOSER LOOK Growing Crystals

The very large crystal you see in the photo was grown at the Lawrence Livermore Laboratory in California. It weighs 318 kg and measures 66 × 53 × 58 cm. The crystal was grown by suspending a thumbnail-sized seed crystal in a 6-foot tank of saturated KH_2PO_4. The temperature of the solution was gradually reduced from 65 °C over a period of about 50 days. The crystals are sliced into thin plates, which are used to convert light from a giant laser from infrared to ultraviolet.

You can grow crystals from chemicals you can find in the supermarket. Alum (potassium aluminum sulfate) is a particularly good choice. Heat about 100 mL of water and then add the alum until no more will dissolve. Allow the mixture to cool undisturbed overnight. The next day small "seed" crystals will have formed. Remove one small crystal that appears well formed, and then pour the saturated solution into another clean jar. Carefully tie a thread or a piece of nylon fishing line around the seed crystal and suspend it in the saturated solution. (Don't let it touch the sides or the bottom.) Cover the jar lightly and put it aside in a place where it can sit undisturbed for a few days or weeks, and a well-formed crystal will form.

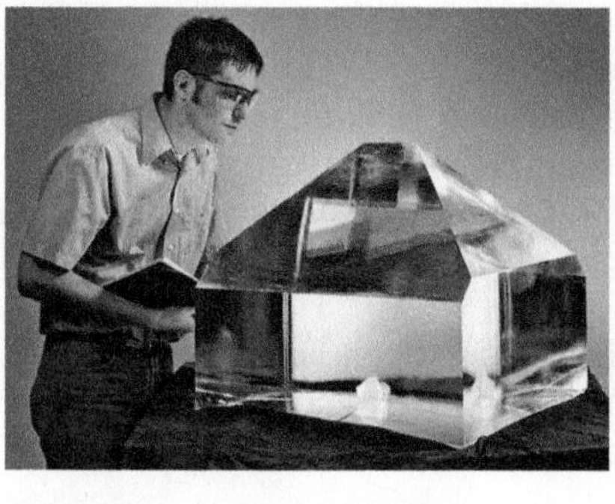

Courtesy of Lawrence Livermore National Laboratory

Giant crystal of potassium dihydrogen phosphate.

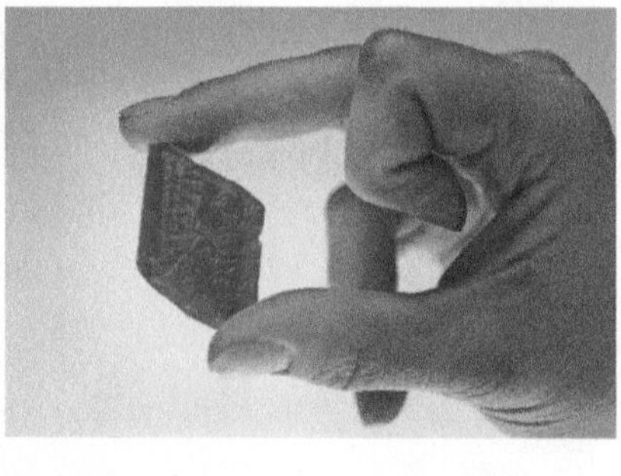

© Cengage Learning/Charles D. Winters

A copper sulfate crystal grown by a student.

REVIEW & CHECK FOR SECTION 13-3

1. Soft drinks are carbonated by adding CO_2 under pressure. Assume that CO_2 is added to a bottle of soft drink containing 710 g of diet soda. The pressure of CO_2 is 4.0 bar. (CO_2 obeys Henry's law at pressures up to about 5 bar.) What amount of CO_2 is dissolved in 710 g of diet soda?

   (a) 0.14 mol (b) 0.097 mol (c) 0.034 mol (d) 0.13 mol

13-4 Colligative Properties

If you dissolve some salt in water, the vapor pressure of the water over the solution will decrease. In addition, the solution will freeze below 0 °C and boil above 100 °C. Freezing point depression and boiling point elevation are **colligative properties** of the solution, properties that depend on the relative numbers of solute and solvent particles in a solution and not on their identity.

Changes in Vapor Pressure: Raoult's Law

Equilibrium Vapor Pressure
Recall the equilibrium vapor pressure of a liquid is defined as the pressure of the vapor when the liquid and the vapor are in equilibrium (Section 11-6).

When a non-volatile solute dissolves in a liquid, the vapor pressure of the solvent is lowered. Experiments show that the vapor pressure of the solvent, $P_{solvent}$, is proportional to the mole fraction of the solvent. We can write an equation, called **Raoult's law**, for the equilibrium vapor pressure of the solvent over a solution:

$$P_{solvent} = X_{solvent}\, P°_{solvent} \tag{13.5}$$

Raoult's law tells us that the vapor pressure of solvent over a solution ($P_{solvent}$) is some fraction of the pure solvent equilibrium vapor pressure ($P°_{solvent}$). For example, if 95% of the molecules in a solution are solvent molecules ($X_{solvent} = 0.95$), then the vapor pressure of the solvent ($P_{solvent}$) is 95% of $P°_{solvent}$.

An **ideal solution** is defined as one that obeys Raoult's law precisely. However, just as no gas is truly ideal, no solution is truly ideal. Nonetheless, Raoult's law is a good approximation of solution behavior in most instances, especially at low solute concentration.

For Raoult's law to apply, the forces of attraction between solute and solvent molecules must be the same as those between solvent molecules in the pure solvent. This is frequently the case when molecules with similar structures are involved. Thus, solutions of one hydrocarbon in another (hexane, C_6H_{14}, dissolved in octane, C_8H_{18}, for example) follow Raoult's law quite closely. However, with other solutions deviations from Raoult's law are observed. If solvent–solute interactions are stronger than solvent–solvent interactions, the measured vapor pressure will be lower than the value calculated by Raoult's law. If the solvent–solute interactions are weaker than solvent–solvent interactions, the vapor pressure will be higher.

Raoult's law can be modified to give another useful equation that allows us to calculate the *lowering* of the vapor pressure of the *solvent*, $\Delta P_{solvent}$, as a function of the mole fraction of the *solute*.

$$\Delta P_{solvent} = P_{solvent} - P°_{solvent}$$

Substituting Raoult's law for $P_{solvent}$, we have

$$\Delta P_{solvent} = (X_{solvent}\, P°_{solvent}) - P°_{solvent} = -(1 - X_{solvent})P°_{solvent}$$

In a solution that has only the volatile solvent and one nonvolatile solute, the sum of the mole fraction of solvent and solute must be 1:

$$X_{solvent} + X_{solute} = 1$$

Therefore, $1 - X_{solvent} = X_{solute}$, and the equation for $\Delta P_{solvent}$ can be rewritten as

$$\Delta P_{solvent} = -X_{solute} P°_{solvent} \quad (13.6)$$

Thus, the *decrease* in the vapor pressure of the solvent is proportional to the mole fraction (the relative number of particles) of solute.

EXAMPLE 13.4

Using Raoult's Law

Problem You dissolve 651 g of ethylene glycol, $HOCH_2CH_2OH$, in 1.50 kg of water. What is the vapor pressure of the water over the solution at 90 °C? Assume ideal behavior for the solution.

What Do You Know? This is a Raoult's law problem where you want to know $P_{solvent}$. To calculate $P_{solvent}$ you need the mole fraction of solvent and the vapor pressure of the pure solvent. You can calculate the mole fraction of solute from the masses of solute and solvent and the molar masses of these species. The vapor pressure of pure water at 90 °C (= 525.8 mm Hg) is found in Appendix G.

Strategy First calculate the mole fraction of the solvent (water) and then combine that with the vapor pressure of pure solvent at the specified temperature using Raoult's law (Equation 13.5).

Solution

(a) Calculate the amounts of water and ethylene glycol and, from these, the mole fraction of water.

$$\text{Amount of water} = 1.50 \times 10^3 \text{ g} \left(\frac{1 \text{ mol}}{18.02 \text{ g}}\right) = 83.2 \text{ mol water}$$

$$\text{Amount of ethylene glycol} = 651 \text{ g} \left(\frac{1 \text{ mol}}{62.07 \text{ g}}\right) = 10.5 \text{ mol glycol}$$

$$X_{water} = \frac{83.2 \text{ mol water}}{83.2 \text{ mol water} + 10.5 \text{ mol glycol}} = 0.888$$

(b) Next apply Raoult's law.

$$P_{water} = X_{water}P°_{water} = (0.888)(525.8 \text{ mm Hg}) = 467 \text{ mm Hg}$$

Think about Your Answer Although a substantial mass of ethylene glycol was added to the water, the decrease in the vapor pressure of the solvent was only 59 mm Hg, or about 11%:

$$\Delta P_{water} = P_{water} - P°_{water} = 467 \text{ mm Hg} - 525.8 \text{ mm Hg} = -59 \text{ mm Hg}$$

Ethylene glycol is ideal for use as antifreeze. It dissolves easily in water, is noncorrosive, and is relatively inexpensive. Because of its high boiling point, it will not evaporate readily. It is, however, toxic to animals, so it is being replaced by less toxic propylene glycol.

Check Your Understanding

Assume you dissolve 10.0 g of sucrose ($C_{12}H_{22}O_{11}$) in 225 mL (225 g) of water and warm the water to 60 °C. What is the vapor pressure of the water over this solution? (Appendix G lists $P°(H_2O)$ at various temperatures.)

Boiling Point Elevation

Suppose you have a solution of a nonvolatile solute in the volatile solvent benzene. If the solute concentration is 0.200 mol in 100. g of benzene (C_6H_6) (= 2.00 mol/kg), this means that $X_{benzene} = 0.865$. Using $X_{benzene}$ and applying Raoult's law, we can calculate that the vapor pressure of the solvent at 60 °C will drop from 400. mm Hg for the pure solvent to 346 mm Hg for the solution:

$$P_{benzene} = X_{benzene}\, P°_{benzene} = (0.865)(400.\text{ mm Hg}) = 346 \text{ mm Hg}$$

This point is marked on the vapor pressure graph in Figure 13.12. Now, what is the vapor pressure when the temperature of the solution is raised another 10 °C? The vapor pressure of pure benzene, $P°_{benzene}$, becomes larger with increasing temperature, so $P_{benzene}$ for the solution must also become larger. This new point, and additional ones calculated in the same way for other temperatures, define the vapor pressure curve for the solution (the lower curve in Figure 13.12).

An important observation we can make in Figure 13.12 is that the vapor pressure lowering caused by the nonvolatile solute leads to an increase in the boiling point. The normal boiling point of a liquid is the temperature at which its vapor pressure is equal to 1 atm or 760 mm Hg (◀ Section 11-6). In Figure 13.12, we see that the normal boiling point of pure benzene (at 760 mm Hg) is about 80 °C. Tracing the vapor pressure curve for the solution, it is apparent that the vapor pressure reaches 760 mm Hg at a temperature about 5 °C higher than this value.

An important question is how the boiling point of the solution varies with solute concentration. In fact, a simple relationship exists: the boiling point elevation, ΔT_{bp}, is directly proportional to the molality of the solute.

$$\text{Elevation in boiling point} = \Delta T_{bp} = K_{bp} \cdot m_{solute} \qquad (13.7)$$

In this equation, $\boldsymbol{K_{bp}}$ is a proportionality constant called the **molal boiling point elevation constant**. It has the units of degrees/molal (°C/m). Values for K_{bp} are determined experimentally, and different solvents have different values (Table 13.3). Formally, the value of K_{bp} corresponds to the elevation in boiling point for a 1 m solution.

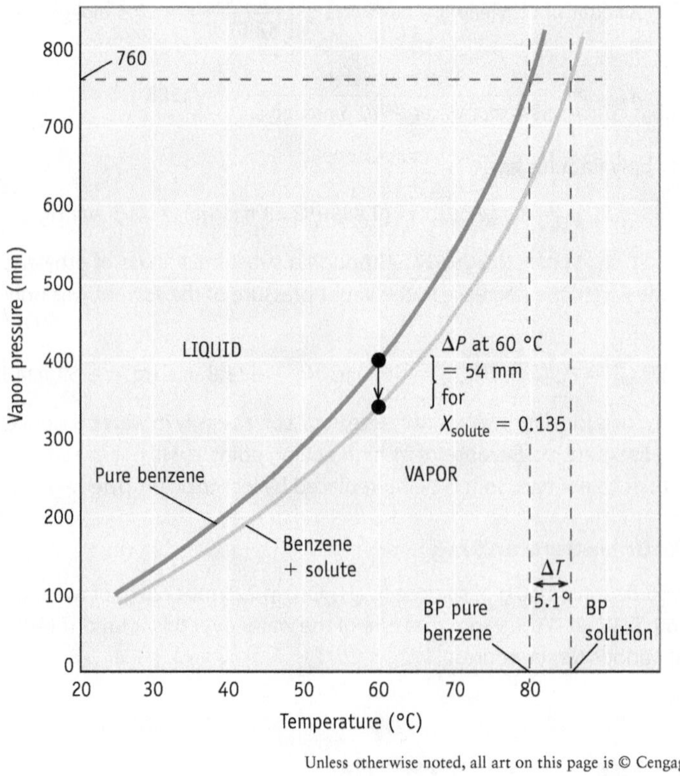

FIGURE 13.12 Lowering the vapor pressure of benzene by addition of a nonvolatile solute. The curve drawn in red represents the vapor pressure of pure benzene, and the curve in blue represents the vapor pressure of a solution containing 0.200 mol of a solute dissolved in 0.100 kg of solvent (2.00 m). This graph was created by doing a series of calculations such as the one shown in the text. As an alternative, the graph could be created by measuring various vapor pressures for the solution in a laboratory experiment.

Table 13.3 Some Boiling Point Elevation and Freezing Point Depression Constants

Solvent	Normal Boiling Point (°C) Pure Solvent	K_{bp} (°C/m)	Normal Freezing Point (°C) Pure Solvent	K_{fp} (°C/m)
Water	100.00	+0.5121	0.0	−1.86
Benzene (C_6H_6)	80.10	+2.53	5.50	−5.12
Camphor ($C_{10}H_{16}O$)	207.4	+5.611	179.75	−39.7
Chloroform ($CHCl_3$)	61.70	+3.63	—	—

EXAMPLE 13.5

Boiling Point Elevation

Problem Eugenol, a compound found in nutmeg and cloves, has the formula $C_{10}H_{12}O_2$. What is the boiling point of a solution containing 0.144 g of this compound dissolved in 10.0 g of benzene?

What Do You Know? You know the identity and mass of both the solute and the solvent. You will need to look up the boiling point for pure benzene and the value of K_{bp}.

Strategy

- Calculate the solution concentration (molality, m, in mol/kg) from the amount of eugenol and the mass of solvent (kg).
- Calculate the change in boiling point using Equation 13.7 (with a value of K_{bp} from Table 13.3).
- Add the change to the boiling temperature of pure benzene to obtain the new boiling point.

Solution

(a) Solution concentration

$$0.144 \text{ g eugenol}\left(\frac{1 \text{ mol eugenol}}{164.2 \text{ g}}\right) = 8.77 \times 10^{-4} \text{ mol eugenol}$$

$$c_{eugenol} = \frac{8.77 \times 10^{-4} \text{ mol eugenol}}{0.0100 \text{ kg benzene}} = 8.77 \times 10^{-2}\ m$$

(b) Boiling point elevation

$$\Delta T_{bp} = (2.53\ °C/m)(0.0877\ m) = 0.222\ °C$$

Because the boiling point rises relative to that of the pure solvent, the boiling point of the solution is

$$80.10\ °C + 0.222\ °C = 80.32\ °C$$

Think about Your Answer Boiling point elevation is proportional to the solute concentration so sizable increases in boiling point are possible at high concentrations.

Check Your Understanding

What quantity of ethylene glycol, $HOCH_2CH_2OH$, must be added to 125 g of water to raise the boiling point by 1.0 °C? Express the answer in grams.

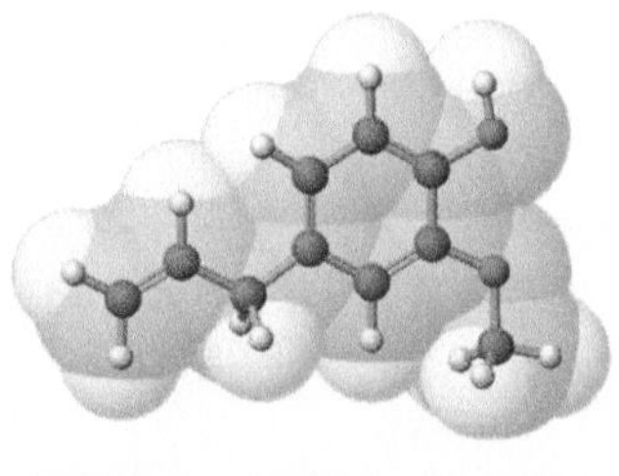

Eugenol, $C_{10}H_{12}O_2$, is an important component in oil of cloves, a commonly used spice.

Strategy Map 13.5

PROBLEM

Calculate **boiling point** of solution.

↓

DATA/INFORMATION

- Mass of ***compound*** and ***solvent***
- K_{bp} and T(bp solvent) from Table 13.3

↓ STEP 1. Calculate c_{solute} = (mol compound/kg solvent).

Concentration of solute (mol/kg)

↓ STEP 2. Use $\Delta T_{bp} = K_{bp}m$.

Change in boiling point (ΔT_{bp})

↓ STEP 3. ΔT_{bp} = T(bp solution) − T(bp solvent).

T(bp solution)

Why Is the Boiling Point of a Solution Elevated and Its Freezing Point Depressed? The answer to this question is related to entropy, a thermodynamic function discussed in Chapter 18. You can consult a website that has a discussion of entropy (entropysite.oxy.edu) or the specific site at which colligative properties are discussed: http://entropysite.oxy.edu/entropy_is_simple/index.html.

The elevation of the boiling point of a solvent on adding a solute has many practical consequences. One of them is the summer protection your car's engine receives from "all-season" antifreeze. The main ingredient of commercial antifreeze is ethylene glycol, $HOCH_2CH_2OH$. The car's radiator and cooling system are sealed to keep the coolant under pressure, ensuring that it will not vaporize at normal engine temperatures. When the air temperature is high in the summer, however, the radiator could "boil over" if it were not protected with "antifreeze." By adding this nonvolatile liquid, the solution in the radiator has a higher boiling point than that of pure water.

Freezing Point Depression

Another consequence of dissolving a solute in a solvent is that the freezing point of the solution is lower than that of the pure solvent (Figure 13.13). For an ideal solution, the depression of the freezing point is given by an equation similar to that for the elevation of the boiling point:

$$\text{Freezing point depression} = \Delta T_{fp} = K_{fp} m_{solute} \quad (13.8)$$

where K_{fp} is the **molal freezing point depression constant** in degrees Celsius per molal (°C/m). Values of K_{fp} for a few common solvents are given in Table 13.3. The values are negative quantities, so the result of the calculation is a negative value for ΔT_{fp}, signifying a decrease in temperature.

The practical aspects of freezing point changes from pure solvent to solution are similar to those for boiling point elevation. The very name of the liquid you add to the radiator in your car, antifreeze, indicates its purpose (Figure 13.13a). The label on the container of antifreeze tells you, for example, to add 6 qt (5.7 L) of antifreeze to a 12-qt (11.4-L) cooling system to lower the freezing point to −34 °C and to raise the boiling point to +109 °C.

FIGURE 13.13 Freezing a solution.

(a) Adding antifreeze to water prevents the water from freezing. Here, a jar of pure water *(left)* and a jar of water to which automobile antifreeze had been added *(right)* were kept overnight in the freezing compartment of a home refrigerator.

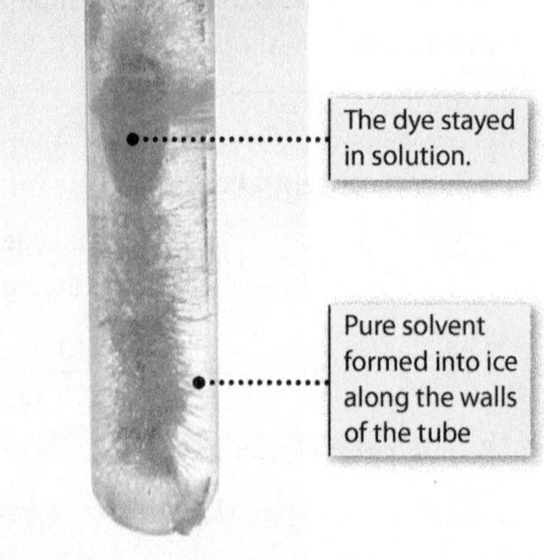

(b) When a solution freezes, it is pure solvent that solidifies. Here, water containing a purple dye was frozen slowly. Pure ice formed along the walls of the tube, and the dye stayed in solution. The dye concentration increased as more and more solvent was frozen out, and the resulting solution had a lower and lower freezing point. Eventually, the system contained pure, colorless ice along the walls of the tube and a concentrated solution of dye in the center of the tube.

EXAMPLE 13.6

Freezing Point Depression

Problem What mass of ethylene glycol, $HOCH_2CH_2OH$, must be added to 5.50 kg of water to lower the freezing point of the water from 0.0 °C to −10.0 °C?

What Do You Know? In some ways this is the reverse of Example 13.5. Here you know the change in freezing point, but wish to know how much solute is needed to produce that value of ΔT.

Strategy The solution concentration (molality, m) can be calculated from ΔT_{fp} and K_{fp} (Table 13.3) using Equation 13.8. Combine the concentration with the mass of solvent to obtain the amount of solute and then its mass.

Solution

(a) Calculate the solute concentration in a solution with a freezing point depression of −10.0 °C.

$$\text{Solute concentration } (m) = \frac{\Delta T_{fp}}{K_{fp}} = \frac{-10.0\ °C}{-1.86\ °C/m} = 5.38\ m$$

(b) Calculate the amount of solute from the concentration and solvent mass.

$$\left(\frac{5.38 \text{ mol glycol}}{1.00 \text{ kg water}}\right)(5.50 \text{ kg water}) = 29.6 \text{ mol glycol}$$

(c) Calculate the mass of the solute, ethylene glycol.

$$29.6 \text{ mol glycol}\left(\frac{62.07 \text{ g}}{1 \text{ mol}}\right) = 1840 \text{ g glycol}$$

Think about Your Answer The value of K_{fp} tells us that the freezing point of water is lower by 1.86 °C for a 1 molal solution. In this particular problem, the freezing point depression was −10.0 °C, so a molality around 5 m is reasonable. The density of ethylene glycol is 1.11 kg/L, so the volume of glycol to be added is (1.84 kg)(1 L/1.11 kg) = 1.66 L.

Check Your Understanding

In the northern United States, summer cottages are usually closed up for the winter. When doing so, the owners "winterize" the plumbing by putting antifreeze in the toilet tanks, for example. Will adding 525 g of $HOCH_2CH_2OH$ to 3.00 kg of water ensure that the water will not freeze at −25 °C?

Osmotic Pressure

Osmosis is the movement of solvent molecules through a semipermeable membrane from a region of lower solute concentration to a region of higher solute concentration. This movement can be demonstrated with a simple experiment. The beaker in Figure 13.14 contains pure water, and the bag and tube hold a concentrated sugar solution. The liquids are separated by a semipermeable membrane, a thin sheet of material (such as a vegetable tissue or cellophane) through which only certain types of molecules can pass. Here, water molecules can pass through the membrane, but larger sugar molecules (or hydrated ions) cannot (Figure 13.15). When the experiment is begun, the liquid levels in the beaker and the tube are the same. Over time, however, the level of the sugar solution inside the tube rises, the level of pure water in the beaker falls, and the sugar solution becomes more dilute. Eventually, no further net change occurs; equilibrium is reached.

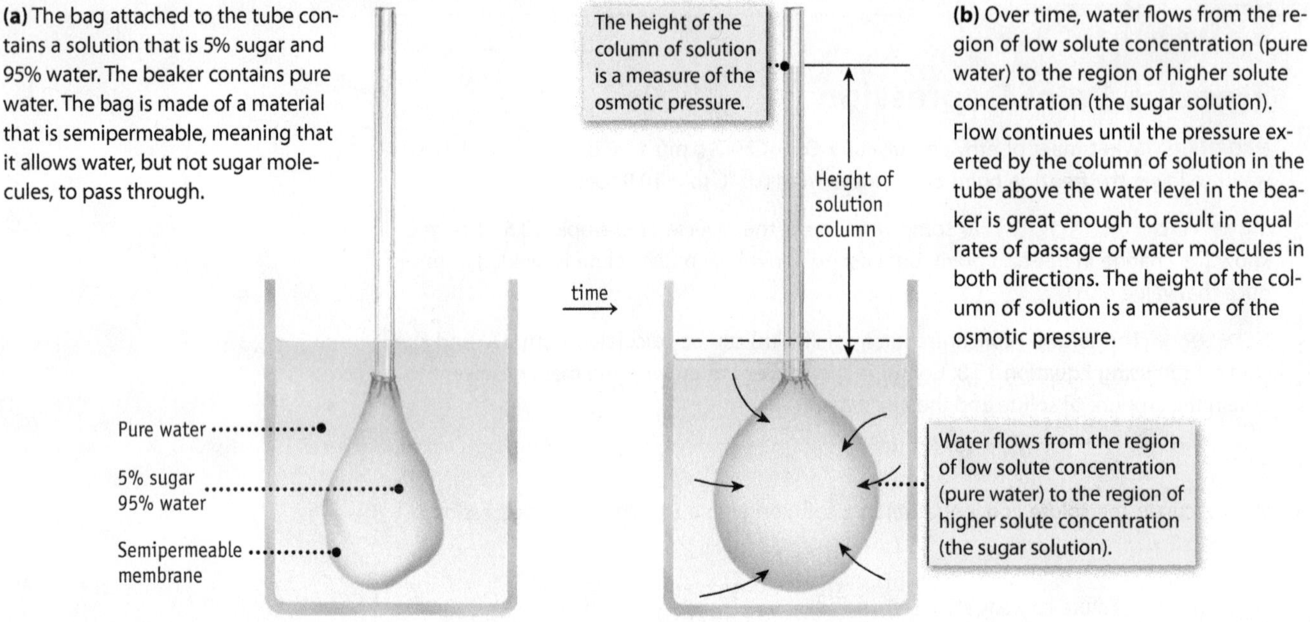

FIGURE 13.14 **The process of osmosis.**

From a molecular point of view, the semipermeable membrane does not present a barrier to the movement of water molecules, so they move through the membrane in both directions. Over time, more water molecules pass through the membrane from the pure water side to the solution side than in the opposite direction. The net effect is that water molecules move from regions of low solute concentration to regions of high solute concentration. The same is true for any solvent, as long as the membrane allows solvent molecules but not solute molecules or ions to pass through.

Why does the system eventually reach equilibrium? Clearly, the solution in the tube in Figure 13.14 can never reach zero sugar or salt concentration, which would be required to equalize the concentrations of solute on both sides of the membrane. The answer lies in the fact that the solution moves higher and higher in the tube as water moves into the sugar solution. Eventually, the pressure exerted by this column

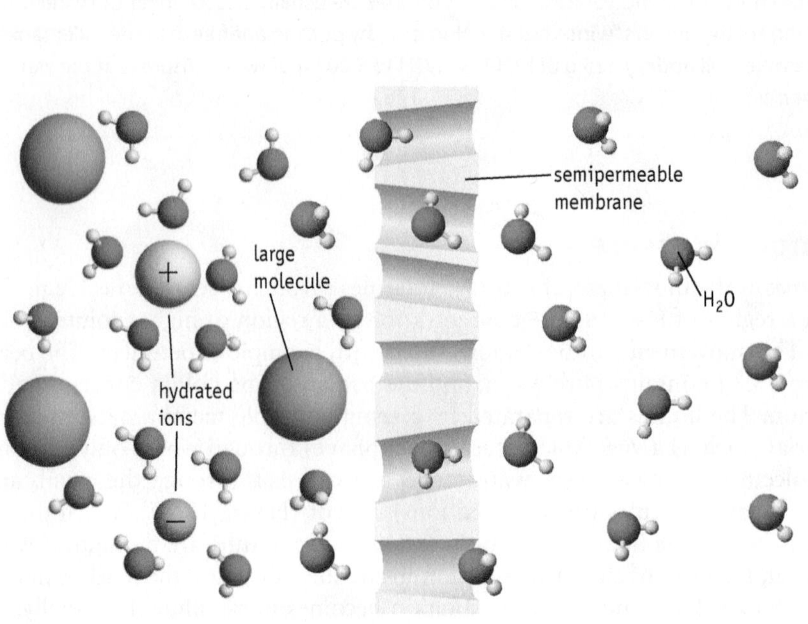

FIGURE 13.15 **Osmosis at the particulate level.** Osmotic flow through a membrane that is selectively permeable (semipermeable) to water. Dissolved substances such as hydrated ions or large sugar molecules cannot diffuse through the membrane.

of solution counterbalances the pressure exerted by the water moving through the membrane from the pure water side, and no further *net* movement of water occurs. An equilibrium of forces is achieved. The pressure created by the column of solution for the system at equilibrium is a measure of the **osmotic pressure**, Π. That is, the osmotic pressure is the difference between the height of the solution in the tube and the level of pure water in the beaker.

From experimental measurements on dilute solutions, it is known that osmotic pressure and concentration (c) are related by the equation

$$\Pi = cRT \qquad (13.9)$$

In this equation, c is the molar concentration (in moles per liter); R is the gas constant; and T is the absolute temperature (in kelvins). Using a value for the gas law constant of 0.082057 L·atm/K·mol allows calculation of the osmotic pressure Π in atmospheres. This equation is analogous to the ideal gas law ($PV = nRT$), with Π taking the place of P and c being equivalent to n/V.

Even solutions with low solute concentrations have a significant osmotic pressure. For example, the osmotic pressure of a 1.00×10^{-3} M solution at 298 K is 18.5 mm Hg. Low pressures such as this are easily and accurately measured, so concentrations of very dilute solutions can be determined by this technique. (Compare this to the effect of a solute on freezing point, for example. A dilute aqueous solution of similar concentration, 1.00×10^{-3} mol/kg solvent, would be expected to lower the freezing point by about 0.002 °C, too small to measure accurately.) For this reason determining a molar mass by measuring the osmotic pressure of a solution is a particularly useful technique when dealing with compounds having a very high molar mass such as polymers and large biomolecules.

Other examples of osmosis are shown in Figure 13.16. In this case, the egg's membrane serves as the semipermeable membrane. Osmosis occurs in one direction if the concentration of solute is greater inside the egg than in the exterior solution and occurs in the other direction if the concentration of the solution is less inside the egg than in the exterior solution. In both cases, solvent flows from the region of low solute concentration to the region of high solute concentration.

(a) A fresh egg is placed in dilute acetic acid. The acid reacts with the $CaCO_3$ of the shell but leaves the egg membrane intact.

(b) If the egg, with its shell removed, is placed in pure water, the egg swells.

(c) If the egg, with its shell removed, is placed in a concentrated sugar solution, the egg shrivels.

FIGURE 13.16 **An experiment to observe osmosis.** You can try this experiment in your kitchen. In the first step, use vinegar as a source of acetic acid.

A CLOSER LOOK

Reverse Osmosis for Pure Water

Finding sources of freshwater for humans and agriculture has been a constant battle for centuries, and, if we continue using Earth's water at the present rate, those problems may increase. Although the Earth has abundant water, 97% of it is too salty to drink or to use on crops. A large portion of the remaining 3% is locked in the form of ice in the polar regions and is not easily obtained.

Andy Sotiriou/Getty Images

A reverse osmosis plant.

One of the oldest ways to obtain freshwater from seawater is by evaporation. This is, however, very energy-intensive, and the salt and other materials left behind may not be useful.

Reverse osmosis is another method of obtaining freshwater from seawater or groundwater. In this technique a pressure greater than the osmotic pressure of the impure water is applied to force water through a semipermeable membrane from a region of high solute concentration to one of lower solute concentration, that is, in the reverse direction that the water would move by osmosis.

Although reverse osmosis has been known for over 200 years, only in the last few decades has it been exploited. Now some municipalities obtain drinking water this way, and pharmaceutical companies use it to obtain highly purified water. More than 15,000 reverse osmosis plants are in operation or in the planning stage worldwide.

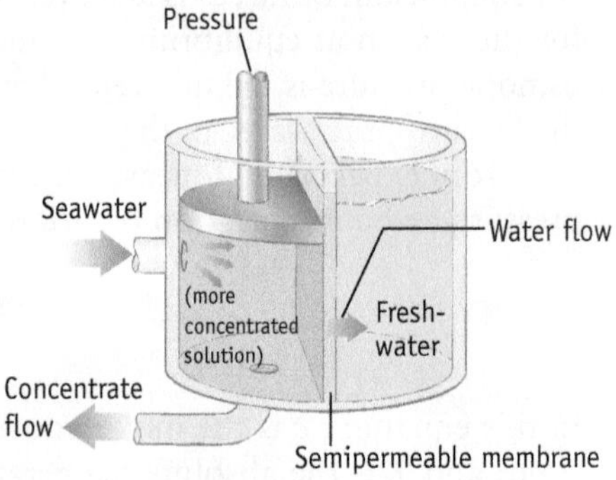

Reverse osmosis. Drinking water can be produced from seawater by reverse osmosis. The osmotic pressure of seawater is approximately 27 atm. To obtain freshwater at a reasonable rate, reverse osmosis requires a pressure of about 50 atm. For comparison, bicycle tires usually have an air pressure of 2–3 atm.

EXAMPLE 13.7

Determining the Osmotic Pressure of a Solution of a Polymer

Problem Polyvinyl alcohol is a water soluble polymer with an average molar mass of 28,000. You dissolve 1.844 g of this polymer in water to give 150. mL of solution. What is the osmotic pressure, measured at 27 °C?

What Do You Know? Osmotic pressure is calculated by Equation 13.9, $\Pi = cRT$. You are given the mass and molar mass of the polymer and the temperature and will need the gas law constant.

Strategy Calculate the concentration of the polymer, c, in mol/L. The temperature must be expressed in kelvins. Substitute these values into Equation 13.9 to solve for the osmotic pressure.

Solution

$$c = 1.844 \text{ g}(1 \text{ mol}/28{,}000 \text{ g})/(0.150 \text{ L}) = 4.4 \times 10^{-4} \text{ mol/L}$$

$$\Pi = cRT$$

$$\Pi = (4.4 \times 10^{-4} \text{ mol/L})(0.08206 \text{ L} \cdot \text{atm/mol} \cdot \text{K})(300 \text{ K})$$

$$\Pi = 0.011 \text{ atm } (= 8.2 \text{ mm Hg})$$

Think about Your Answer If the osmotic pressure is measured in a device similar to that shown in Figure 13.14, the height of the column of aqueous solution supported would be about 110 mm (8.2 mm × 13.5 mm H_2O/mm Hg = 110 mm). This would be easily measurable in the laboratory.

Check Your Understanding

Bradykinin is a small peptide (9 amino acids; 1060 g/mol) that lowers blood pressure by causing blood vessels to dilate. What is the osmotic pressure of a solution of this protein at 20 °C if 0.033 g of the peptide is dissolved in water to give 50.0 mL of solution?

Colligative Properties and Molar Mass Determination

Earlier in this book you learned how to calculate a molecular formula from an empirical formula when given the molar mass. But how do you know the molar mass of an unknown compound? An experiment must be carried out to find this crucial piece of information, and one way to do so is to use a colligative property of a solution of the compound. The strategy map used with Example 13.8 represents the basic approach for each of the colligative properties studied.

EXAMPLE 13.8

Determining Molar Mass from Boiling Point Elevation

Problem A solution prepared from 1.25 g of oil of wintergreen (methyl salicylate) in 99.0 g of benzene has a boiling point of 80.31 °C. Determine the molar mass of methyl salicylate.

What Do You Know? The molar mass of a compound is the quotient of the mass of a sample (g) and the amount (mol) represented by that sample. Here you know the mass of the sample (1.25 g), so you need to find the amount (moles) that corresponds to this mass.

Strategy

- Determine ΔT_{bp} from the given boiling point of the solution. (The boiling point of pure benzene and K_{bp} for benzene are given in Table 13.3.) Use the equation $\Delta T_{bp} = K_{bp} \cdot m$ to calculate the solution concentration in units of mol/kg.
- Knowing the mass of solvent, calculate the amount of solute (mol).
- Combine the mass and amount of solute to give the molar mass [molar mass = mass (g)/amount (mol)].

Strategy Map 13.8

PROBLEM

Calculate **molar mass** of unknown.

↓

DATA/INFORMATION

- **Mass** of unknown and solvent
- **Boiling point** of solution (80.31 °C)

↓ STEP 1. Use $\Delta T_{bp} = K_{bp}m$.

Concentration of solute (mol/kg)

↓ STEP 2. Mol solute = (mol/kg)(kg solvent).

Amount of solute (mol)

↓ STEP 3. Molar mass = g solute/mol solute.

Molar mass of unknown **(g/mol)**

Solution

(a) Use the boiling point elevation to calculate the solution concentration:

$$\text{Boiling point elevation } (\Delta T_{bp}) = 80.31\ °C - 80.10\ °C = 0.21\ °C$$

$$c_{solute} = \frac{\Delta T_{bp}}{K_{bp}} = \frac{0.21\ °C}{2.53\ °C/m} = 0.083\ m$$

(b) Calculate the amount of solute in the solution from the solution concentration:

$$\text{Amount of solute} = \left(\frac{0.083\ \text{mol}}{1.00\ \text{kg}}\right)(0.099\ \text{kg solvent}) = 0.0082\ \text{mol solute}$$

(c) Combine the amount of solute with its mass to obtain its molar mass.

$$\frac{1.25\ \text{g}}{0.0082\ \text{mol}} = 150\ \text{g/mol}$$

A CLOSER LOOK — Osmosis and Medicine

Osmosis is of practical significance for people in the health professions. Patients who become dehydrated through illness often need to be given water and nutrients intravenously. Water cannot simply be dripped into a patient's vein, however. Rather, the intravenous solution must have the same overall solute concentration as the patient's blood: the solution must be iso-osmotic or **isotonic** (Figure B, middle). If pure water was used, the inside of a blood cell would have a higher solute concentration (lower water concentration), and water would flow into the cell. This **hypotonic** situation would cause the red blood cells to burst (lyse) (Figure B, right). The opposite situation, **hypertonicity**, occurs if the intravenous solution is more concentrated than the contents of the blood cell (Figure B, left). In this case, the cell would lose water and shrivel up (crenate). To combat this, a dehydrated patient is rehydrated in the hospital with a sterile saline solution that is 0.16 M NaCl, a solution that is isotonic with the cells of the body.

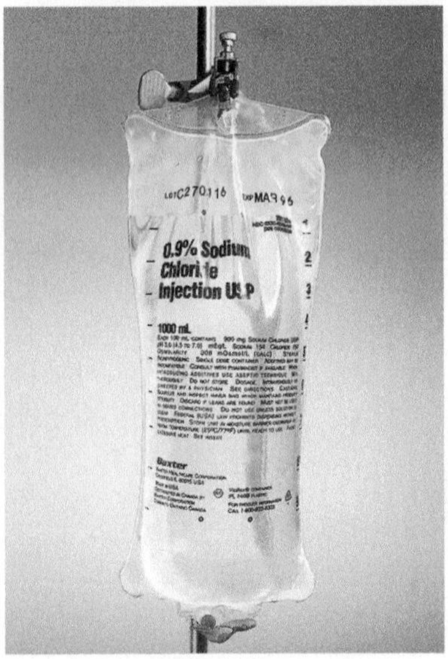

© Cengage Learning/Charles D. Winters

FIGURE A **An isotonic saline solution.** This solution has the same molality as body fluids.

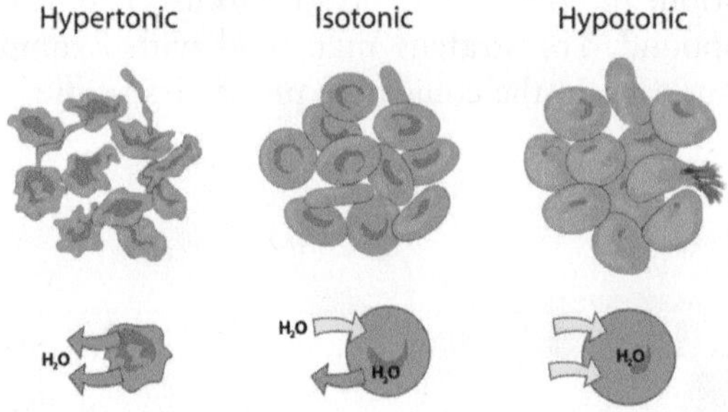

FIGURE B **Osmosis and living cells.** *(middle)* A cell placed in an isotonic solution. The net movement of water into and out of the cell is zero because the concentration of solutes inside and outside the cell is the same. *(left)* In a hypertonic solution, the concentration of solutes outside the cell is greater than that inside. There is a net flow of water out of the cell, causing the cell to dehydrate, shrink, and perhaps die. *(right)* In a hypotonic solution, the concentration of solutes outside the cell is less than that inside. There is a net flow of water into the cell, causing the cell to swell and perhaps to burst (or lyse).

Think about Your Answer Methyl salicylate has the formula $C_8H_8O_3$ and a molar mass of 152.14 g/mol. Given that ΔT has only two significant figures, the calculated value is acceptably close to the actual value.

Check Your Understanding

An aluminum-containing compound has the empirical formula $(C_2H_5)_2AlF$. Find the molecular formula if 0.448 g of the compound dissolved in 23.46 g of benzene has a freezing point of 5.265 °C.

EXAMPLE 13.9

Osmotic Pressure and Molar Mass

Problem Beta-carotene is the most important of the A vitamins. Calculate the molar mass of β-carotene if 10.0 mL of a solution in chloroform containing 7.68 mg of β-carotene has an osmotic pressure of 26.57 mm Hg at 25.0 °C.

What Do You Know? The molar mass of a compound is the quotient of the mass of a sample and the amount represented by that sample. Here you know the mass of the sample (7.68 mg), so you need to find the amount (moles) equivalent to this mass.

Strategy

- Use Equation 13.9 to calculate the solution concentration from the osmotic pressure.
- Use the volume and concentration of the solution to calculate the amount of solute.
- Find the molar mass of the solute from its mass and amount.

Solution

(a) Calculate the concentration of β-carotene from Π, R, and T.

$$\text{Concentration (mol/L)} = \frac{\Pi}{RT} = \frac{(26.57\text{ mm Hg})\left(\dfrac{1\text{ atm}}{760\text{ mm Hg}}\right)}{(0.082057\text{ L}\cdot\text{atm/K}\cdot\text{mol})(298.2\text{ K})}$$

$$= 1.429 \times 10^{-3}\text{ mol/L}$$

(b) Calculate the amount of β-carotene dissolved in 10.0 mL of solvent.

$$(1.429 \times 10^{-3}\text{ mol/L})(0.0100\text{ L}) = 1.43 \times 10^{-5}\text{ mol}$$

(c) Combine the amount of solute with its mass to calculate its molar mass:

$$\frac{7.68 \times 10^{-3}\text{ g}}{1.43 \times 10^{-5}\text{ mol}} = 538\text{ g/mol}$$

Think about Your Answer Beta-carotene is a hydrocarbon with the formula $C_{40}H_{56}$ (molar mass = 536.9 g/mol).

Check Your Understanding

A 1.40-g sample of polyethylene, a common plastic, is dissolved in enough organic solvent to give 100.0 mL of solution. What is the average molar mass of the polymer if the measured osmotic pressure of the solution is 1.86 mm Hg at 25 °C?

Colligative Properties of Solutions Containing Ions

In the northern United States, it is common practice to scatter salt on snowy or icy roads or sidewalks in the winter. When the Sun shines on the snow or patch of ice, a small amount melts, and some salt dissolves in the water. As a result of the dissolved solute, the freezing point of the solution is lower than 0 °C. The solution "eats" its way through the ice, breaking it up, and the icy patch is no longer dangerous for drivers or walkers.

Salt (NaCl) is the most common substance used on roads because it is inexpensive and dissolves readily in water. Its relatively low molar mass means that the effect per gram is large. In addition, salt is especially effective because it is an electrolyte. That is, it dissolves to give ions in solution:

$$NaCl(s) \rightarrow Na^+(aq) + Cl^-(aq)$$

Recall that *colligative properties depend not on what is dissolved but on the number of particles of solute per solvent particle.* When 1 mol of NaCl dissolves, 2 mol of ions form, which means that the effect on the freezing point of water should be twice as large as that expected for a mole of sugar. A 0.100 m solution of NaCl really contains two solutes, 0.100 m Na^+ and 0.100 m Cl^-. What we should use to estimate the freezing point depression is the *total* molality of solute particles:

$$m_{\text{total}} = m(Na^+) + m(Cl^-) = (0.100 + 0.100)\text{ mol/kg} = 0.200\text{ mol/kg}$$

$$\Delta T_{\text{fp}} = (-1.86\text{ °C}/m)(0.200\ m) = -0.372\text{ °C}$$

To estimate the freezing point depression for an ionic compound, first find the molality of solute from the mass and molar mass of the compound and the mass of

Table 13.4 Freezing Point Depressions of Some Ionic Solutions

Mass %	m (mol/kg)	ΔT_{fp} (measured, °C)	ΔT_{fp} (calculated, °C)	ΔT_{fp}, measured / ΔT_{fp}, calculated
NaCl				
0.00700	0.0120	−0.0433	−0.0223	1.94
0.500	0.0860	−0.299	−0.160	1.87
1.00	0.173	−0.593	−0.322	1.84
2.00	0.349	−1.186	−0.649	1.83
Na_2SO_4				
0.00700	0.00493	−0.0257	−0.00917	2.80
0.500	0.0354	−0.165	−0.0658	2.51
1.00	0.0711	−0.320	−0.132	2.42
2.00	0.144	−0.606	−0.268	2.26

the solvent. Then, multiply the molality by the number of ions in the formula: two for NaCl, three for Na_2SO_4, four for $LaCl_3$, five for $Al_2(SO_4)_3$, and so on.

Table 13.4 shows that as the concentration of NaCl decreases, ΔT_{fp} for NaCl approaches but does not quite reach a value that is two times larger than the value determined assuming no dissociation. Likewise, ΔT_{fp} for Na_2SO_4 approaches but does not reach a value that is three times larger. The ratio of the experimentally observed value of ΔT_{fp} to the value calculated, assuming no dissociation, is called the **van't Hoff factor** after Jacobus Henrikus van't Hoff (1852–1911), who studied this phenomenon. The van't Hoff factor is represented by i.

$$i = \frac{\Delta T_{fp}\text{, measured}}{\Delta T_{fp}\text{, calculated}} = \frac{\Delta T_{fp}\text{, measured}}{K_{fp} \times m}$$

or

$$\Delta T_{fp}\text{ measured} = K_{fp} \times m \times i \qquad (13.10)$$

The numbers in the last column of Table 13.4 are van't Hoff factors. These values can be used in calculations of any colligative property. Vapor pressure lowering, boiling point elevation, freezing point depression, and osmotic pressure are all larger for electrolytes than for nonelectrolytes of the same molality.

The van't Hoff factor approaches a whole number (2, 3, and so on) only with very dilute solutions. In more concentrated solutions, the experimental freezing point depressions indicate that there are fewer ions in solution than expected. This behavior, which is typical of all ionic compounds, is a consequence of the strong attractions between ions. The result is as if some of the positive and negative ions are paired, decreasing the total molality of particles. Indeed, in more concentrated solutions, and especially in solvents less polar than water, ions are extensively associated in ion pairs and in even larger clusters.

EXAMPLE 13.10

Freezing Point and Ionic Solutions

Problem A 0.0200 m aqueous solution of an ionic compound, $Co(NH_3)_4Cl_3$, freezes at −0.0640 °C. How many moles of ions does 1 mol of the salt produce on being dissolved in water?

What Do You Know? You know the freezing point depression (−0.0640 °C), the solution concentration, and K_{fp}.

Strategy The van't Hoff factor, *i*, is the ratio of the measured ΔT_{fp} to the calculated freezing point depression. First, calculate ΔT_{fp} expected for a solution in which no ions are produced. Compare this value with the actual value of ΔT_{fp}. The ratio (= *i*) will reflect the number of ions produced.

Solution

(a) Calculate the freezing-point depression expected for a 0.0200 *m* solution assuming that the salt does not dissociate into ions.

$$\Delta T_{fp} \text{ calculated} = K_{fp}m = (-1.86\ °\text{C})(0.0200\ m) = -0.0372\ °\text{C}$$

(b) Compare the calculated freezing point depression with the measured depression. This gives the van't Hoff factor:

$$i = \frac{\Delta T_{fp}\text{, measured}}{\Delta T_{fp}\text{, calculated}} = \frac{-0.0640\ °\text{C}}{-0.0372\ °\text{C}} = 1.72$$

The *i* value is much greater than 1 and is approaching 2. Therefore, we assume each formula unit of $Co(NH_3)_4Cl_3$ produces 2 ions in solution.

Think about Your Answer We find *i* is approaching 2, meaning that the complex dissociates into two ions: $[Co(NH_3)_4Cl_2]^+$ and Cl^-. As you will see in Chapter 22, the cation is a Co^{3+} ion surrounded octahedrally by 4 NH_3 molecules and two Cl^- ions.

Check Your Understanding

Calculate the freezing point of 525 g of water that contains 25.0 g of NaCl. Assume *i*, the van't Hoff factor, is 1.85 for NaCl.

REVIEW & CHECK FOR SECTION 13-4

1. *Vapor pressure:* Arrange the following aqueous solutions in order of increasing vapor pressure at 25 °C: 0.35 *m* $C_2H_4(OH)_2$ (ethylene glycol, nonvolatile solute); 0.50 *m* sugar; 0.20 *m* KBr; and 0.20 *m* Na_2SO_4.

   (a) $C_2H_4(OH)_2$ < sugar < KBr < Na_2SO_4
   (b) Na_2SO_4 < sugar < KBr < $C_2H_4(OH)_2$
   (c) sugar < $C_2H_4(OH)_2$ < KBr < Na_2SO_4
   (d) KBr < sugar < Na_2SO_4 < $C_2H_4(OH)_2$

2. One gram (1.00 g) of each of the listed substances is dissolved in 50 g of benzene. Which of the solutions has the lowest freezing point?

   (a) buckyballs, C_{60}
   (b) acetaminophen, $C_8H_9NO_2$
   (c) trinitrotoluene, $C_7H_5(NO_2)_3$
   (d) naphthalene, $C_{10}H_8$

3. Samples of each of the substances listed below are dissolved in 125 g of water. Which of the solutions has the highest boiling point?

   (a) 3.0 g sucrose, $C_{12}H_{22}O_{11}$
   (b) 1.0 g glycerol, $C_3H_5(OH)_3$
   (c) 1.0 g propylene glycol, $C_3H_6(OH)_2$
   (d) 2.0 g glucose, $C_6H_{12}O_6$

4. *Molar mass:* Erythritol is a compound that occurs naturally in algae and fungi. It is about twice as sweet as sucrose. A solution of 2.50 g of erythritol in 50.0 g of water freezes at −0.762 °C. What is the molar mass of the compound?

   (a) 26.9 g/mol
   (b) 35.5 g/mol
   (c) 122 g/mol
   (d) 224 g/mol

Learning Objectives: LO 2.10

13-5 Colloids

Earlier in this chapter, we defined a solution broadly as a homogeneous mixture of two or more substances in a single phase. To this definition we should add that, in a true solution, no settling of the solute should be observed and the solute particles should be in the form of ions or relatively small molecules. Thus, NaCl and sugar form true solutions in water. You are also familiar with suspensions, which result, for example, if a handful of fine sand is added to water and shaken vigorously. Sand particles are still visible and gradually settle to the bottom of the beaker or bottle. **Colloidal dispersions**, also called **colloids**, represent a state intermediate between a solution and a suspension (Figure 13.17). Colloids include many of the foods you eat and the materials around you; among them are JELL-O®, milk, fog, and porcelain (Table 13.5).

FIGURE 13.17 **Gold colloid.** A water-soluble salt of $[AuCl_4]^-$ is reduced to give colloidal gold metal. The colloidal gold gives the dispersion its red color (when the particles have a length or diameter of less than 100 nm). (Similarly, colloidal gold is used to give a beautiful red color to glass.) Since the days of alchemy, some have claimed that drinking a colloidal gold solution was good for the mind.

Around 1860, the British chemist Thomas Graham (1805–1869) found that substances such as starch, gelatin, glue, and albumin from eggs diffused only very slowly when placed in water, compared with sugar or salt. In addition, the former substances differed significantly in their ability to diffuse through a thin membrane: Sugar molecules can diffuse through many membranes, but the very large molecules that make up starch, gelatin, glue, and albumin do not. Moreover, Graham found that he could not crystallize these substances, whereas he could crystallize sugar, salt, and other materials that form true solutions. Graham coined the word "colloid" (from the Greek, meaning "glue") to describe this class of substances that are distinctly different from true solutions and suspensions.

We now know that it is possible to crystallize some colloidal substances, albeit with difficulty, so there really is no sharp dividing line between these classes based on this property. Colloids do, however, have several distinguishing characteristics. First, many of the substances that form colloids have high molar masses; this is true of proteins such as hemoglobin that have molar masses in the thousands. Second, the particles of a colloid are relatively large (say, several hundred nanometers in diameter). As a consequence, they exhibit the **Tyndall effect**; they scatter visible light when dispersed in a solvent, making the mixture appear cloudy (Figure 13.18). Third, even though colloidal particles are large, they are not so large that they settle out.

Graham also gave us the words **sol** for a colloidal dispersion of a solid substance in a fluid medium and **gel** for a colloidal dispersion that has a structure that prevents it from being mobile. JELL-O® is a sol when the solid is first mixed with boiling water, but it becomes a gel when cooled. Other examples of gels are the gelatinous precipitates of $Al(OH)_3$, $Fe(OH)_3$, and $Cu(OH)_2$ (Figure 13.19).

Table 13.5 Types of Colloids

Type	Dispersing Medium	Dispersed Phase	Examples
Aerosol	Gas	Liquid	Fog, clouds, aerosol sprays
Aerosol	Gas	Solid	Smoke, airborne viruses, automobile exhaust
Foam	Liquid	Gas	Shaving cream, whipped cream
Foam	Solid	Gas	Styrofoam, marshmallow
Emulsion	Liquid	Liquid	Mayonnaise, milk, face cream
Gel	Solid	Liquid	Jelly, JELL-O®, cheese, butter
Sol	Liquid	Solid	Gold in water, milk of magnesia, mud
Solid sol	Solid	Solid	Milkglass

Photos: © Cengage Learning/Charles D. Winters

Dust in the air scatters the light coming through the trees in a forest along the Oregon coast.

A narrow beam of light from a laser is passed through an NaCl solution *(left)* and then a colloidal mixture of gelatin and water *(right)*.

FIGURE 13.18 **The Tyndall effect.** Colloidal dispersions scatter light, a phenomenon known as the Tyndall effect.

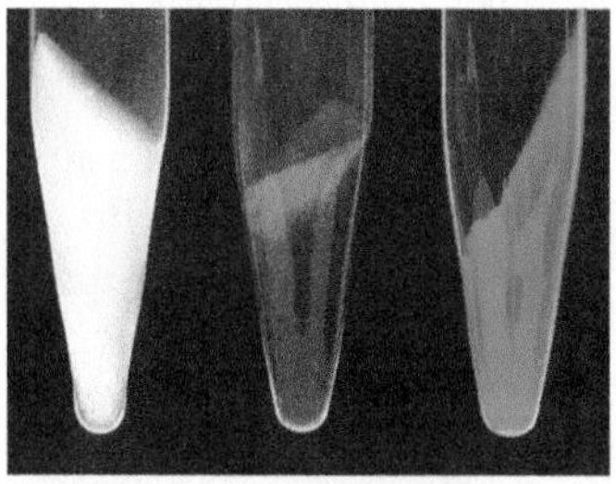

© Cengage Learning/Charles D. Winters

FIGURE 13.19 **Gelatinous precipitates.** *(left)* $Al(OH)_3$, *(center)* $Fe(OH)_3$, and *(right)* $Cu(OH)_2$.

Because of the small size of the particles in a colloidal dispersion, they can have a very high surface area. For example, if you have one millionth of a mole of colloidal particles, each assumed to be a sphere with a diameter of 1000 nm, the total surface area of the particles would be on the order of 2 million cm^2. It is not surprising, therefore, that many of the properties of colloids depend on the properties of surfaces.

Types of Colloids

Colloids are classified according to the state of the dispersed phase and the dispersing medium. Table 13.5 lists several types of colloids and gives examples of each.

Colloids with water as the dispersing medium can be classified as **hydrophobic** (from the Greek, meaning "water-fearing") or **hydrophilic** ("water-loving"). A *hydrophobic colloid* is one in which only weak attractive forces exist between the water and the surfaces of the colloidal particles. Examples include dispersions of metals (see Figure 13.17) and of nearly insoluble salts in water. When compounds like AgCl precipitate, the result is often a colloidal dispersion. The precipitation reaction occurs too rapidly for ions to gather from long distances and make large crystals, so the ions aggregate to form small particles that remain suspended in the liquid.

Why don't the particles come together (coagulate) and form larger particles? The answer is that the colloidal particles carry electric charges. To see how this happens, suppose AgCl ion pairs come together to form a tiny particle. If Ag^+ ions are still present in substantial concentration in the solution, these positive ions could be attracted to negative Cl^- ions on the surface of the particle. Thus the original clump of AgCl ion pairs becomes positively charged, allowing it to attract a secondary layer of anions. The particles, now surrounded by layers of ions, repel one another and are prevented from coming together to form a precipitate (Figure 13.20).

Soil particles are often carried by water in rivers and streams as hydrophobic colloids. When river water carrying large amounts of colloidal particles meets seawater with its high concentration of salts, the particles coagulate to form the silt seen at the mouth of the river (Figure 13.21). Municipal water treatment plants often add salts such as $Al_2(SO_4)_3$ to clarify water. In aqueous solution, aluminum ions exist as $[Al(H_2O)_6]^{3+}$ cations, which neutralize the charge on the hydrophobic colloidal soil particles, causing these particles to aggregate and settle out.

Hydrophilic colloids are strongly attracted to water molecules. They often have groups such as —OH and —NH_2 on their surfaces. These groups form strong hydrogen bonds to water, thereby stabilizing the colloid. Proteins and starch are

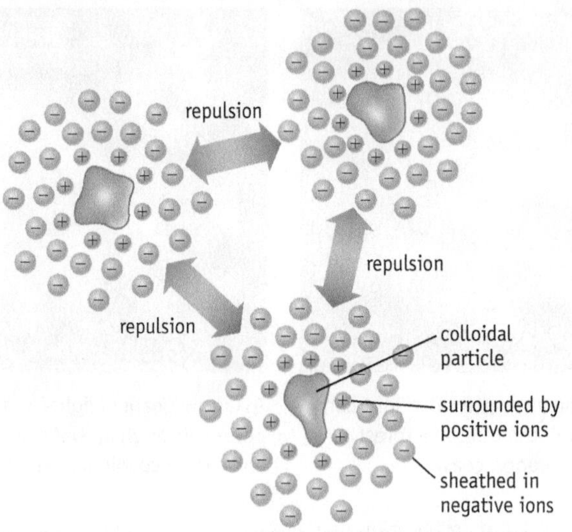

FIGURE 13.20 **Hydrophobic colloids.** A hydrophobic colloid is stabilized by positive ions adsorbed onto each particle and a secondary layer of negative ions. Because the particles bear similar charges, they repel one another, and precipitation is prevented.

NASA Earth Observatory image by Robert Simmon, using Landsat 5 data from the U.S. Geological Survey Global Visualization Viewer

FIGURE 13.21 **Formation of silt.** Silt forms at a river delta as colloidal soil particles come in contact with saltwater in the ocean. Here, the Connecticut River empties into the Long Island Sound. The high concentration of ions in seawater causes the colloidal soil particles to coagulate.

important examples of hydrophilic colloids, and homogenized milk is the most familiar example.

Emulsions are colloidal dispersions of one liquid in another, such as oil or fat in water. Familiar examples include salad dressing, mayonnaise, and milk. If vegetable oil and vinegar are mixed to make a salad dressing, the mixture quickly separates into two layers because the nonpolar oil molecules do not interact with the polar water and acetic acid (CH_3CO_2H) molecules. So why are milk and mayonnaise apparently homogeneous mixtures that do not separate into layers? The answer is that they contain an **emulsifying agent** such as soap or a protein. Lecithin, found in egg yolks, can act as an emulsifying agent, so mixing egg yolks with oil and vinegar stabilizes the colloidal dispersion known as mayonnaise. To understand this process further, let us look into the functioning of soaps and detergents, substances known as surfactants.

Surfactants

Soaps and detergents are emulsifying agents. Soap is made by heating a fat with sodium or potassium hydroxide, which produces anions of long chain carboxylic acids, sometimes referred to as fatty acids. An example is sodium stearate.

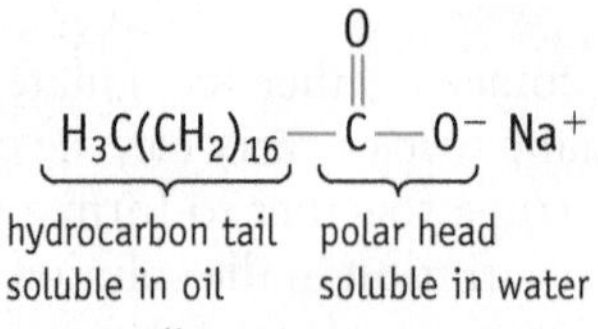

sodium stearate, a soap

The fatty acid anion has a split personality: It has a nonpolar, hydrophobic hydrocarbon tail that is soluble in other similar hydrocarbons and a polar, hydrophilic head that is soluble in water.

Oil cannot be readily washed away from dishes or clothing with water because oil is nonpolar and thus insoluble in water. Instead, we add soap to the water to clean away the oil. The nonpolar molecules of the oil interact with the nonpolar hydrocarbon tails of the soap molecules, leaving the polar heads of the soap to interact with surrounding water molecules. The oil and water then mix (Figure 13.22), and the oil can then be washed away.

Substances such as soaps that affect the properties of surfaces, and therefore affect the interaction between two phases, are called surface-active agents, or **surfactants**, for short. A surfactant used for cleaning is called a **detergent**. One

Soaps and Surfactants Sodium soaps are solid at room temperature, whereas potassium soaps are usually liquids. About 30 million tons of household and toilet soap, and synthetic and soap-based laundry detergents, are produced annually worldwide.

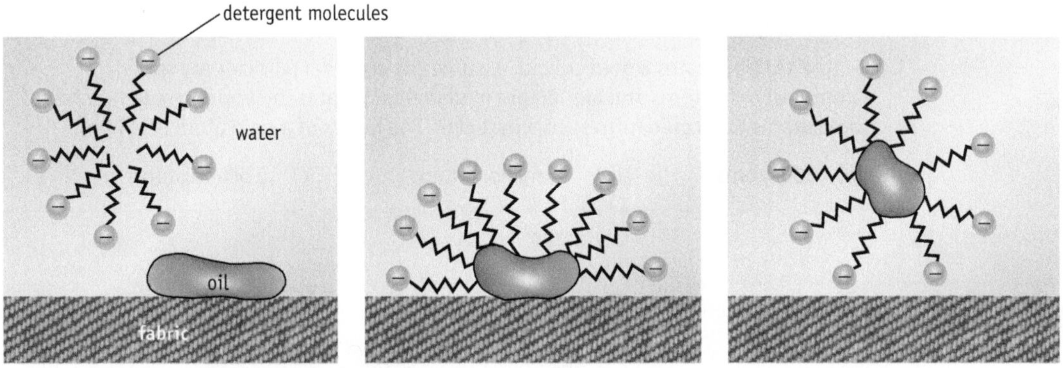

FIGURE 13.22 **The cleaning action of soap.** Soap molecules interact with water through the charged, hydrophilic end of the molecule. The long, hydrocarbon end of the molecule is hydrophobic, but it can bind through dispersion forces with hydrocarbons and other nonpolar substances.

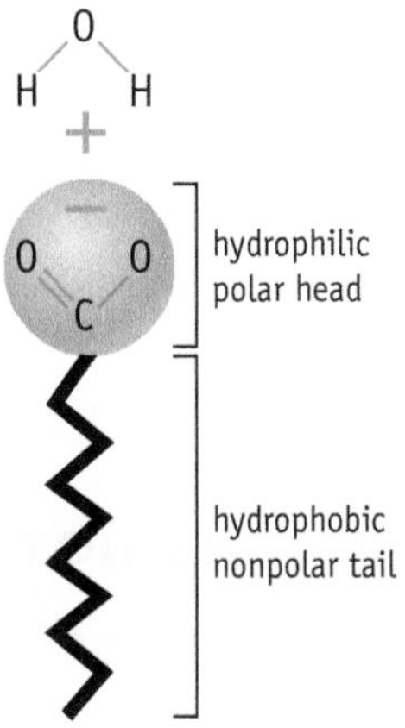

function of a surfactant is to lower the surface tension of water, which enhances the cleansing action of the detergent (Figure 13.23).

Many detergents used in the home and industry are synthetic. One example is sodium laurylbenzenesulfonate, a biodegradable compound.

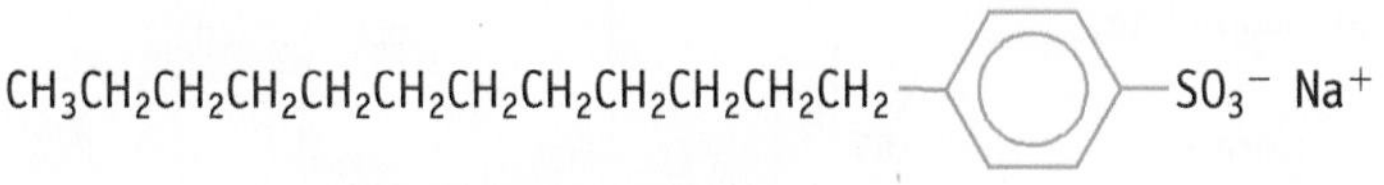

sodium laurylbenzenesulfonate

In general, synthetic detergents use the sulfonate group, —SO_3^-, as the polar head instead of the carboxylate group, —CO_2^-. The carboxylate anions form an insoluble precipitate with any Ca^{2+} or Mg^{2+} ions present in water. Because hard water is characterized by high concentrations of these ions, using soaps containing carboxylates produces bathtub rings and telltale gray clothing. The synthetic sulfonate detergents have the advantage that they do not form such precipitates because their calcium salts are more soluble in water.

FIGURE 13.23 **Effect of a detergent on the surface tension of water.**

Sulfur (density = 2.1 g/cm^3) is carefully placed on the surface of water (density, 1.0 g/cm^3). The surface tension of the water keeps the denser sulfur afloat.

Several drops of detergent are then placed on the surface of the water. The surface tension of the water is reduced, and the sulfur sinks to the bottom of the beaker.

REVIEW & CHECK FOR SECTION 13-5

1. Figure 13.17 illustrates a gold colloid. Assume the colloidal particles are spherical clumps of gold atoms and are 100 nm in diameter. What is the approximate number of gold atoms that could form such a particle? (The radius of a gold atom is 144 pm.)

   (a) 300 atoms (b) 40 million atoms (c) 2 billion atoms

APPLYING CHEMICAL PRINCIPLES

Distillation

Distillation is a means of separating components of a mixture based upon differences in volatility. Because petroleum consists of a large number of compounds of widely varying volatility, distillation is a key process used to produce gasoline and related products (Figure A). How does this process work?

If a mixture is composed of one volatile component and one or more nonvolatile components, a complete separation of the volatile component is possible. But, when two or more components in a mixture have nonzero vapor pressures at the mixture's boiling point, the result of a simple distillation is an incomplete separation.

Fractional distillation uses repetitive evaporation–condensation cycles to improve the separation of volatile compounds. When a mixture is boiled, the vapor above the liquid has a higher concentration of the more volatile components than the liquid. If this vapor is condensed, then boiled again, the resulting vapor is further enriched in more volatile material.

The temperature–composition diagram for a hexane–heptane mixture is shown in Figure B. The lower curved line indicates the boiling point of the mixture as a function of the mole fraction of the more volatile component, hexane. The upper curve indicates the mole fraction of hexane in the vapor phase above the boiling solution. The blue line represents the change in composition of the mixture in the course of the fractional distillation of a mixture with an initial hexane mole fraction of 0.20. The solution may be heated until it reaches its boiling point of 90 °C. At this temperature, the mole fraction of hexane in the vapor phase can be determined by drawing a horizontal line at 90 °C that intersects the top curve. This indicates that the vapor phase has a mole fraction of hexane of 0.38 at this temperature.

FIGURE A **Equipment used for fractional distillation of petroleum in an oil refinery.**

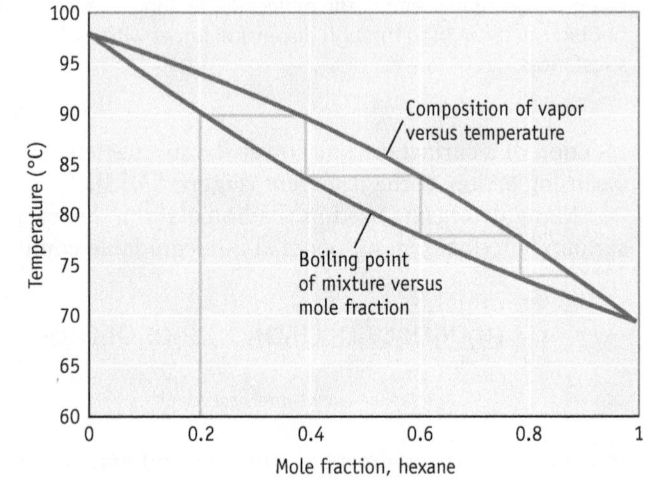

FIGURE B **A temperature–composition diagram for hexane (C_6H_{14})-heptane (C_7H_{16}) mixtures.**

The efficiency of a fractional distillation column is expressed in terms of *theoretical plates*. Each evaporation–condensation cycle requires one theoretical plate. The greater the number of theoretical plates, the better the separation for most mixtures.

QUESTIONS:

1. The blue line on the diagram illustrates the effect of using fractional distillation to separate a mixture of hexane (C_6H_{14}) and heptane (C_7H_{16}). If one starts a fractional distillation with a 0.20 mole fraction of hexane, what is the approximate mole fraction of hexane in the vapor phase after two evaporation–condensation cycles?
2. How many theoretical plates are required to produce a solution with a mole fraction of hexane greater than 0.90?
3. What is the mass percent of hexane in a mixture with heptane if the mole fraction of hexane is 0.20?
4. The vapor pressure of pure heptane is 361.5 mm Hg at 75.0 °C and its normal boiling point is 98.4 °C. Use the Clausius–Clapeyron equation (see page 427) to determine the enthalpy of vaporization of heptane.

CHAPTER GOALS REVISITED

Now that you have studied this chapter, you should ask whether you have met the chapter goals.

UNDERSTAND

- The energetics of the solution process (Section 13-2).
- The basis of the "like dissolves like" rule (Section 13-2).
- How changes in pressure and temperature affect solubility (Section 13-3).
- How solutes in solution affect a solvent's vapor pressure, freezing point, and boiling point, and the osmotic pressure of the solution (colligative properties) (Section 13-4).

DO

- Use the units of solution concentration (Section 13-1).
  - **a.** Use the following concentration units: molality, mole fraction, and weight percent (Section 13-1). Study Questions: 1–12.
- Calculate the enthalpy of solution from thermodynamic data (Section 13-2). Study Questions: 15, 16, 71.
- Use Henry's law (Section 13-3).
  - **a.** Use Henry's law to calculate the solubility of a gas in a solvent (Section 13-3). Study Questions: 19–24, 69, 83, 84.
- Use Le Chatelier's principle to predict qualitatively the effect of stresses on systems at equilibrium (Section 13-3). Study Questions: 17, 18, 20, 23, 24, 84.
- Calculate changes in vapor pressure, freezing point, and boiling point as solute is added to a solvent (colligative properties) (Section 13-4).
  - **a.** Calculate the mole fraction of a solvent ($X_{solvent}$) and the effect of a solute on solvent vapor pressure ($P_{solvent}$) using Raoult's law. Study Questions: 25-28, 75, 76, 100, 103.
  - **b.** Calculate the boiling point elevation or freezing point depression caused by a solute in a solvent. Study Questions: 29–36, 47, 55, 62.
  - **c.** Characterize the effect of ionic solutes on colligative properties. Study Questions: 49, 50, 54, 55, 62, 63, 95.
- Calculate the osmotic pressure of a solution (Section 13-4). Study Questions: 37–40, 80, 90.
- Use colligative properties to determine the molar mass of a solute (Section 13-4). Study Questions: 41–46, 66, 91, 92.
- Apply the van't Hoff factor in calculations involving ionic solutes (Section 13-4). Study Questions: 38, 47, 48, 64, 65, 77, 79, 81, 82, 104.

REMEMBER

- The difference between molarity (M) and molality (*m*) (Section 13-1).
- Le Chatelier's principle, which predicts how systems at equilibrium respond to stresses (Section 13-3).
- Henry's law, the relationship of pressure and gas solubility (Section 13-3).
- The effect of solutes on the properties of a solution (Section 13-4).

- The importance and properties of colloids (Section 13-5).
- The terminology of solutions and their behavior.
  a. Define the terms solution, solvent, solute, and colligative properties.
  b. Understand the distinctions between saturated, unsaturated, and supersaturated solutions (Section 13-2). Study Questions: 17, 18.
  c. Define and illustrate the terms *miscible* and *immiscible* (Section 13-2). Study Questions: 13, 98.

KEY EQUATIONS

Equation 13.1 (page 471) Molality is defined as the amount of solute per kilogram of solvent.

$$\text{Concentration } (c, \text{ mol/kg}) = \text{molality of solute} = \frac{\text{amount of solute (mol)}}{\text{mass of solvent (kg)}}$$

Equation 13.2 (page 471) The mole fraction, X, of a solution component is defined as the number of moles of a given component of a mixture (n_A, mol) divided by the total number of moles of all of the components of the mixture.

$$\text{Mole fraction of A } (X_A) = \frac{n_A}{n_A + n_B + n_C + \ldots}$$

Equation 13.3 (page 472) Weight percent is the mass of one component divided by the total mass of the mixture (multiplied by 100%).

$$\text{Weight \% A} = \frac{\text{mass of A}}{\text{mass of A} + \text{mass of B} + \text{mass of C} + \ldots} \times 100\%$$

Equation 13.4 (page 479) Henry's law: The solubility of a gas, S_g, is equal to the product of the partial pressure of the gaseous solute (P_g) and a constant (k_H) characteristic of the solute and solvent.

$$S_g = k_H P_g$$

Equation 13.5 (page 484) Raoult's law: The equilibrium vapor pressure of a solvent over a solution at a given temperature, $P_{solvent}$, is the product of the mole fraction of the solvent ($X_{solvent}$) and the vapor pressure of the pure solvent ($P°_{solvent}$).

$$P_{solvent} = X_{solvent} P°_{solvent}$$

Equation 13.6 (page 485) The decrease in the vapor pressure of the solvent over a solution, $\Delta P_{solvent}$, depends on the mole fraction of the solute (X_{solute}) and the vapor pressure of the pure solvent ($P°_{solvent}$).

$$\Delta P_{solvent} = -X_{solute} P°_{solvent}$$

Equation 13.7 (page 486) The elevation in boiling point of the solvent in a solution, ΔT_{bp}, is the product of the molality of the solute, m_{solute}, and a constant characteristic of the solvent, K_{bp}.

$$\text{Elevation in boiling point} = \Delta T_{bp} = K_{bp} m_{solute}$$

Equation 13.8 (page 488) The depression of the freezing point of the solvent in a solution, ΔT_{fp}, is the product of the molality of the solute, m_{solute}, and a constant characteristic of the solvent, K_{fp}.

$$\text{Freezing point depression} = \Delta T_{fp} = K_{fp} m_{solute}$$

Equation 13.9 (page 491) The osmotic pressure, Π, is the product of the solute concentration *c* (in mol/L), the universal gas constant *R* (0.082057 L · atm/K · mol), and the temperature *T* (in kelvins).

$$\Pi = cRT$$

Equation 13.10 (page 496) This modified equation for freezing point depression accounts for the possible dissociation of a solute. The van't Hoff factor, *i*, the ratio of the measured freezing point depression and the freezing point depression calculated assuming no solute dissociation, is related to the relative number of particles produced by a dissolved solute.

$$\Delta T_{fp} \text{ measured} = K_{fp} \times m \times i$$

©Rich Carey/Shutterstock.com

STUDY QUESTIONS

▲ denotes challenging questions.

Blue-numbered questions have answers in Appendix N and fully worked solutions in the *Student Solutions Manual.*

Practicing Skills

Concentration

(See Section 13-1 and Example 13.1.)

1. You dissolve 2.56 g of succinic acid, $C_2H_4(CO_2H)_2$, in 500. mL of water. Assuming that the density of water is 1.00 g/cm^3, calculate the molality, mole fraction, and weight percent of acid in the solution.

2. You dissolve 45.0 g of camphor, $C_{10}H_{16}O$, in 425 mL of ethanol, C_2H_5OH. Calculate the molality, mole fraction, and weight percent of camphor in this solution. (The density of ethanol is 0.785 g/mL.)

3. Fill in the blanks in the table. Aqueous solutions are assumed.

Compound	Molality	Weight Percent	Mole Fraction
NaI	0.15	_____	_____
C_2H_5OH	_____	5.0	_____
$C_{12}H_{22}O_{11}$	0.15	_____	_____

4. Fill in the blanks in the table. Aqueous solutions are assumed.

Compound	Molality	Weight Percent	Mole Fraction
KNO_3	_____	10.0	_____
CH_3CO_2H	0.0183	_____	_____
$HOCH_2CH_2OH$	_____	18.0	_____

5. What mass of Na_2CO_3 must you add to 125 g of water to prepare 0.200 *m* Na_2CO_3? What is the mole fraction of Na_2CO_3 in the resulting solution?

6. What mass of $NaNO_3$ must be added to 500. g of water to prepare a solution that is 0.0512 *m* in $NaNO_3$? What is the mole fraction of $NaNO_3$ in the solution?

7. You wish to prepare an aqueous solution of glycerol, $C_3H_5(OH)_3$, in which the mole fraction of the solute is 0.093. What mass of glycerol must you add to 425 g of water to make this solution? What is the molality of the solution?

8. You want to prepare an aqueous solution of ethylene glycol, $HOCH_2CH_2OH$, in which the mole fraction of solute is 0.125. What mass of ethylene glycol, in grams, should you combine with 955 g of water? What is the molality of the solution?

9. Hydrochloric acid is sold as a concentrated aqueous solution. If the concentration of commercial HCl is 12.0 M and its density is 1.18 g/cm^3, calculate the following:

   (a) the molality of the solution
   (b) the weight percent of HCl in the solution

10. Concentrated sulfuric acid has a density of 1.84 g/cm^3 and is 95.0% by weight H_2SO_4. What is the molality of this acid? What is its molarity?

11. The average lithium ion concentration in seawater is 0.18 ppm. What is the molality of Li^+ in seawater?

12. Silver ion has an average concentration of 28 ppb (parts per billion) in U.S. water supplies.

(a) What is the molality of the silver ion?
(b) If you wanted 1.0×10^2 g of silver and could recover it chemically from water supplies, what volume of water in liters, would you have to treat? (Assume the density of water is 1.0 g/cm^3.)

The Solution Process

(See Section 13-2 and Example 13.2.)

13. Which pairs of liquids will be miscible?

(a) H_2O and $CH_3CH_2CH_2CH_3$
(b) C_6H_6 (benzene) and CCl_4
(c) H_2O and CH_3CO_2H

14. Acetone, CH_3COCH_3, is quite soluble in water. Explain why this should be so.

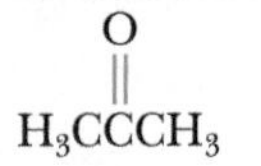

Acetone

15. Use the data of Table 13.1 to calculate the enthalpy of solution of LiCl.

16. Use the following data to calculate the enthalpy of solution of sodium perchlorate, $NaClO_4$:

$$\Delta_f H°(s) = -382.9 \text{ kJ/mol} \quad \text{and} \quad \Delta_f H°(aq, 1\ m) = -369.5 \text{ kJ/mol}$$

17. You make a saturated solution of NaCl at 25 °C. No solid is present in the beaker holding the solution. What can be done to increase the amount of dissolved NaCl in this solution? (See Figure 13.11.)

(a) Add more solid NaCl.
(b) Raise the temperature of the solution.
(c) Raise the temperature of the solution, and add some NaCl.
(d) Lower the temperature of the solution, and add some NaCl.

18. Some lithium chloride, LiCl, is dissolved in 100 mL of water in one beaker, and some Li_2SO_4 is dissolved in 100 mL of water in another beaker. Both are at 10 °C, and both are saturated solutions; some solid remains undissolved in each beaker. Describe what you would observe as the temperature is raised. The following data are available to you from a handbook of chemistry:

	Solubility (g/100 mL)	
Compound	**10 °C**	**40 °C**
Li_2SO_4	35.5	33.7
LiCl	74.5	89.8

Henry's Law

(See Section 13-3 and Example 13.3.)

19. The partial pressure of O_2 in your lungs varies from 25 mm Hg to 40 mm Hg. What mass of O_2 can dissolve in 1.0 L of water at 25 °C if the partial pressure of O_2 is 40 mm Hg?

20. The Henry's law constant for O_2 in water at 25 °C is given in Table 13.2. Which of the following is a reasonable constant when the temperature is 50 °C? Explain the reason for your choice.

(a) 6.7×10^{-4} mol/kg·bar
(b) 2.6×10^{-3} mol/kg·bar
(c) 1.3×10^{-3} mol/kg·bar
(d) 6.4×10^{-2} mol/kg·bar

21. An unopened soda can has an aqueous CO_2 concentration of 0.0506 *m* at 25 °C. What is the pressure of CO_2 gas in the can?

22. Hydrogen gas has a Henry's law constant of 7.8×10^{-4} mol/kg·bar at 25 °C when dissolving in water. If the total pressure of gas (H_2 gas plus water vapor) over water is 1.00 bar, what is the concentration of H_2 in the water in grams per milliliter? (See Appendix G for the vapor pressure of water.)

Le Chatelier's Principle

(See Section 13-3.)

23. A sealed flask contains water and oxygen gas at 25 °C. The O_2 gas has a partial pressure of 1.5 atm.

(a) What is the concentration of O_2 in the water?
(b) If the pressure of O_2 in the flask is raised to 1.7 atm, what happens to the amount of dissolved O_2? What happens to the amount of dissolved O_2 when the pressure of O_2 gas drops to 1.0 atm?

24. Butane, C_4H_{10}, has been suggested as the refrigerant in household compressors such as those found in air conditioners.

(a) To which extent is butane soluble in water? Calculate the butane concentration in water if the pressure of the gas is 0.21 atm. (k_H = 0.0011 mol/kg·bar at 25 °C)
(b) If the pressure of butane is increased to 1.0 atm, does the butane concentration increase or decrease?

Raoult's Law

(See Section 13-4 and Example 13.4.)

25. A 35.0-g sample of ethylene glycol, $HOCH_2CH_2OH$, is dissolved in 500.0 g of water. The vapor pressure of water at 32 °C is 35.7 mm Hg. What is the vapor pressure of the water–ethylene glycol solution at 32 °C? (Ethylene glycol is nonvolatile.)

26. Urea, $(NH_2)_2CO$, which is widely used in fertilizers and plastics, is quite soluble in water. If you dissolve 9.00 g of urea in 10.0 mL of water, what is the vapor pressure of the solution at 24 °C? Assume the density of water is 1.00 g/mL.

27. Pure ethylene glycol, $HOCH_2CH_2OH$, is added to 2.00 kg of water in the cooling system of a car. The vapor pressure of the water in the system when the temperature is 90 °C is 457 mm Hg. What mass of glycol was added? (Assume the solution is ideal. See Appendix G for the vapor pressure of water.)

28. Pure iodine (105 g) is dissolved in 325 g of CCl_4 at 65 °C. Given that the vapor pressure of CCl_4 at this temperature is 531 mm Hg, what is the vapor pressure of the CCl_4–I_2 solution at 65 °C? (Assume that I_2 does not contribute to the vapor pressure.)

Boiling Point Elevation

(See Section 13-4 and Example 13.5.)

29. What is the boiling point of a solution containing 0.200 mol of a nonvolatile solute in 125 g of benzene (C_6H_6)?

30. What is the boiling point of a solution composed of 15.0 g of urea, $(NH_2)_2CO$, in 0.500 kg of water?

31. What is the boiling point of a solution composed of 15.0 g of $CHCl_3$ and 0.515 g of the nonvolatile solute acenaphthene, $C_{12}H_{10}$, a component of coal tar?

32. A solution of glycerol, $C_3H_5(OH)_3$, in 735 g of water has a boiling point of 104.4 °C at a pressure of 760 mm Hg. What is the mass of glycerol in the solution? What is the mole fraction of the solute?

Freezing Point Depression

(See Section 13-4 and Example 13.6.)

33. A mixture of ethanol, C_2H_5OH, and water has a freezing point of -16.0 °C.
   (a) What is the molality of the alcohol?
   (b) What is the weight percent of alcohol in the solution?

34. Some ethylene glycol, $HOCH_2CH_2OH$, is added to your car's cooling system along with 5.0 kg of water. If the freezing point of the water–glycol solution is -15.0 °C, what mass of $HOCH_2CH_2OH$ must have been added?

35. You dissolve 15.0 g of sucrose, $C_{12}H_{22}O_{11}$, in a cup of water (225 g). What is the freezing point of the solution?

36. A typical bottle of wine consists of an 11% solution (by weight) of ethanol (C_2H_5OH) in water. If the wine is chilled to -20 °C, will the solution begin to freeze?

Osmosis

(See Section 13-4 and Example 13.7.)

37. An aqueous solution contains 3.00% phenylalanine ($C_9H_{11}NO_2$) by mass. (Phenylalanine is nonionic and nonvolatile.) Find the following:
   (a) the freezing point of the solution
   (b) the boiling point of the solution
   (c) the osmotic pressure of the solution at 25 °C

   In your view, which of these values is most easily measurable in the laboratory?

38. Estimate the osmotic pressure of human blood at 37 °C. Assume blood is isotonic with a 0.154 M NaCl solution, and assume the van't Hoff factor, *i*, is 1.90 for NaCl.

39. An aqueous solution containing 1.00 g of bovine insulin (a protein, not ionized) per liter has an osmotic pressure of 3.1 mm Hg at 25 °C. Calculate the molar mass of bovine insulin.

40. Calculate the osmotic pressure of a 0.0120 M solution of NaCl in water at 0 °C. Assume the van't Hoff factor, *i*, is 1.94 for this solution.

Colligative Properties and Molar Mass Determination

(See Section 13-4 and Examples 13.8 and 13.9.)

41. You add 0.255 g of an orange, crystalline compound whose empirical formula is $C_{10}H_8Fe$ to 11.12 g of benzene. The boiling point of the benzene rises from 80.10 °C to 80.26 °C. What are the molar mass and molecular formula of the compound?

42. Butylated hydroxyanisole (BHA) is used in margarine and other fats and oils. (It is used as an antioxidant and prolongs the shelf life of the food.) What is the molar mass of BHA if 0.640 g of the compound, dissolved in 25.0 g of chloroform, produces a solution whose boiling point is 62.22 °C?

43. Benzyl acetate is one of the active components of oil of jasmine. If 0.125 g of the compound is added to 25.0 g of chloroform ($CHCl_3$), the boiling point of the solution is 61.82 °C. What is the molar mass of benzyl acetate?

44. Anthracene, a hydrocarbon obtained from coal, has an empirical formula of C_7H_5. To find its molecular formula, you dissolve 0.500 g in 30.0 g of benzene. The boiling point of pure benzene is 80.10 °C, whereas the solution has a boiling point of 80.34 °C. What is the molecular formula of anthracene?

45. An aqueous solution contains 0.180 g of an unknown, nonionic solute in 50.0 g of water. The solution freezes at -0.040 °C. What is the molar mass of the solute?

46. Aluminon, an organic compound, is used as a reagent to test for the presence of the aluminum ion in aqueous solution. A solution of 2.50 g of aluminon in 50.0 g of water freezes at -0.197 °C. What is the molar mass of aluminon?

Colligative Properties of Ionic Compounds

(See Section 13-4 and Example 13.10.)

47. If 52.5 g of LiF is dissolved in 306 g of water, what is the expected freezing point of the solution? (Assume the van't Hoff factor, *i*, for LiF is 2.)

48. To make homemade ice cream, you cool the milk and cream by immersing the container in ice and a concentrated solution of rock salt (NaCl) in water. If you want to have a water–salt solution that freezes at $-10.$ °C, what mass of NaCl must you add to 3.0 kg of water? (Assume the van't Hoff factor, *i*, for NaCl is 1.85.)

49. List the following aqueous solutions in order of increasing melting point. (The last three are all assumed to dissociate completely into ions in water.)
   (a) 0.1 *m* sugar
   (b) 0.1 *m* NaCl
   (c) 0.08 *m* $CaCl_2$
   (d) 0.04 *m* Na_2SO_4

50. Arrange the following aqueous solutions in order of decreasing freezing point. (The last three are all assumed to dissociate completely into ions in water.)

(a) 0.20 *m* ethylene glycol (nonvolatile, nonelectrolyte)
(b) 0.12 *m* K_2SO_4
(c) 0.10 *m* $MgCl_2$
(d) 0.12 *m* KBr

Colloids

(See Section 13-5.)

51. When solutions of $BaCl_2$ and Na_2SO_4 are mixed, the mixture becomes cloudy. After a few days, a white solid is observed on the bottom of the beaker with a clear liquid above it.

(a) Write a balanced equation for the reaction that occurs.
(b) Why is the solution cloudy at first?
(c) What happens during the few days of waiting?

52. The dispersed phase of a certain colloidal dispersion consists of spheres of diameter 1.0×10^2 nm.

(a) What are the volume ($V = \frac{4}{3}\pi r^3$) and surface area ($A = 4\pi r^2$) of each sphere?
(b) How many spheres are required to give a total volume of 1.0 cm^3? What is the total surface area of these spheres in square meters?

General Questions

These questions are not designated as to type or location in the chapter. They may combine several concepts.

53. Phenylcarbinol is used in nasal sprays as a preservative. A solution of 0.52 g of the compound in 25.0 g of water has a melting point of −0.36 °C. What is the molar mass of phenylcarbinol?

54. (a) Which aqueous solution is expected to have the higher boiling point: 0.10 *m* Na_2SO_4 or 0.15 *m* sugar?
(b) For which aqueous solution is the vapor pressure of water higher: 0.30 *m* NH_4NO_3 or 0.15 *m* Na_2SO_4?

55. Arrange the following aqueous solutions in order of (i) increasing vapor pressure of water and (ii) increasing boiling point.

(a) 0.35 *m* $HOCH_2CH_2OH$ (a nonvolatile solute)
(b) 0.50 *m* sugar
(c) 0.20 *m* KBr (a strong electrolyte)
(d) 0.20 *m* Na_2SO_4 (a strong electrolyte)

56. Making homemade ice cream is one of life's great pleasures. Fresh milk and cream, sugar, and flavorings are churned in a bucket suspended in an ice–water mixture, the freezing point of which has been lowered by adding salt. One manufacturer of home ice cream freezers recommends adding 2.50 lb (1130 g) of salt (NaCl) to 16.0 lb of ice (7250 g) in a 4-qt freezer. For the solution when this mixture melts, calculate the following:

(a) the weight percent of NaCl
(b) the mole fraction of NaCl
(c) the molality of the solution

57. Dimethylglyoxime [DMG, $(CH_3CNOH)_2$] is used as a reagent to precipitate nickel ion. Assume that 53.0 g of DMG has been dissolved in 525 g of ethanol (C_2H_5OH).

The red, insoluble compound formed between nickel(II) ion and dimethylglyoxime (DMG) is precipitated when DMG is added to a basic solution of Ni^{2+}(aq).

(a) What is the mole fraction of DMG?
(b) What is the molality of the solution?
(c) What is the vapor pressure of the ethanol over the solution at ethanol's normal boiling point of 78.4 °C?
(d) What is the boiling point of the solution? (DMG does not produce ions in solution.) (K_{bp} for ethanol = +1.22 °C/*m*)

58. A 10.7 *m* solution of NaOH has a density of 1.33 g/cm^3 at 20 °C. Calculate the following:

(a) the mole fraction of NaOH
(b) the weight percent of NaOH
(c) the molarity of the solution

59. Concentrated aqueous ammonia has a molarity of 14.8 mol/L and a density of 0.90 g/cm^3. What is the molality of the solution? Calculate the mole fraction and weight percent of NH_3.

60. If you dissolve 2.00 g of $Ca(NO_3)_2$ in 750 g of water, what is the molality of $Ca(NO_3)_2$? What is the total molality of ions in solution? (Assume total dissociation of the ionic solid.)

61. If you want a solution that is 0.100 *m* in ions, what mass of Na_2SO_4 must you dissolve in 125 g of water? (Assume total dissociation of the ionic solid.)

62. Consider the following aqueous solutions: (i) 0.20 *m* $HOCH_2CH_2OH$ (nonvolatile, nonelectrolyte); (ii) 0.10 *m* $CaCl_2$; (iii) 0.12 *m* KBr; and (iv) 0.12 *m* Na_2SO_4.

(a) Which solution has the highest boiling point?
(b) Which solution has the lowest freezing point?
(c) Which solution has the highest water vapor pressure?

63. (a) Which solution is expected to have the higher boiling point: 0.20 *m* KBr or 0.30 *m* sugar?
(b) Which aqueous solution has the lower freezing point: 0.12 *m* NH_4NO_3 or 0.10 *m* Na_2CO_3?

64. The solubility of NaCl in water at 100 °C is 39.1 g/100. g of water. Calculate the boiling point of this solution. (Assume *i* = 1.85 for NaCl.)

65. Instead of using NaCl to melt the ice on your sidewalk, you decide to use $CaCl_2$. If you add 35.0 g of $CaCl_2$ to 150. g of water, what is the freezing point of the solution? (Assume $i = 2.7$ for $CaCl_2$.)

66. The smell of ripe raspberries is due to 4-(*p*-hydroxyphenyl)-2-butanone, which has the empirical formula C_5H_6O. To find its molecular formula, you dissolve 0.135 g in 25.0 g of chloroform, $CHCl_3$. The boiling point of the solution is 61.82 °C. What is the molecular formula of the solute?

67. Hexachlorophene has been used in germicidal soap. What is its molar mass if 0.640 g of the compound, dissolved in 25.0 g of chloroform, produces a solution whose boiling point is 61.93 °C?

68. The solubility of ammonium formate, NH_4CHO_2, in 100. g of water is 102 g at 0 °C and 546 g at 80 °C. A solution is prepared by dissolving NH_4CHO_2 in 200. g of water until no more will dissolve at 80 °C. The solution is then cooled to 0 °C. What mass of NH_4CHO_2 precipitates? (Assume that no water evaporates and that the solution is not supersaturated.)

69. How much N_2 can dissolve in water at 25 °C if the N_2 partial pressure is 585 mm Hg?

70. Cigars are best stored in a "humidor" at 18 °C and 55% relative humidity. This means the pressure of water vapor should be 55% of the vapor pressure of pure water at the same temperature. The proper humidity can be maintained by placing a solution of glycerol $[C_3H_5(OH)_3]$ and water in the humidor. Calculate the percent by mass of glycerol that will lower the vapor pressure of water to the desired value. (The vapor pressure of glycerol is negligible.)

71. An aqueous solution containing 10.0 g of starch per liter has an osmotic pressure of 3.8 mm Hg at 25 °C.
    (a) What is the average molar mass of starch? (The result is an average because not all starch molecules are identical.)
    (b) What is the freezing point of the solution? Would it be easy to determine the molecular weight of starch by measuring the freezing point depression? (Assume that the molarity and molality are the same for this solution.)

72. Vinegar is a 5% solution (by weight) of acetic acid in water. Determine the mole fraction and molality of acetic acid. What is the concentration of acetic acid in parts per million (ppm)? Explain why it is not possible to calculate the molarity of this solution from the information provided.

73. Calculate the enthalpies of solution for Li_2SO_4 and K_2SO_4. Are the solution processes exothermic or endothermic? Compare them with LiCl and KCl. What similarities or differences do you find?

Compound	$\Delta_fH°$(s) (kJ/mol)	$\Delta_fH°$(aq, 1 *m*) (kJ/mol)
Li_2SO_4	−1436.4	−1464.4
K_2SO_4	−1437.7	−1413.0

74. ▲ Water at 25 °C has a density of 0.997 g/cm³. Calculate the molality and molarity of pure water at this temperature.

75. ▲ If a volatile solute is added to a volatile solvent, both substances contribute to the vapor pressure over the solution. Assuming an ideal solution, the vapor pressure of each is given by Raoult's law, and the total vapor pressure is the sum of the vapor pressures for each component. A solution, assumed to be ideal, is made from 1.0 mol of toluene ($C_6H_5CH_3$) and 2.0 mol of benzene (C_6H_6). The vapor pressures of the pure solvents are 22 mm Hg and 75 mm Hg, respectively, at 20 °C. What is the total vapor pressure of the mixture? What is the mole fraction of each component in the liquid and in the vapor?

76. A solution is made by adding 50.0 mL of ethanol (C_2H_5OH, d = 0.789 g/mL) to 50.0 mL of water (d = 0.998 g/mL). What is the total vapor pressure over the solution at 20 °C? (See Study Question 75.) The vapor pressure of ethanol at 20 °C is 43.6 mm Hg.

77. A 2.0% (by mass) aqueous solution of novocainium chloride ($C_{13}H_{21}ClN_2O_2$) freezes at −0.237 °C. Calculate the van't Hoff factor, *i*. How many moles of ions are in the solution per mole of compound?

78. A solution is 4.00% (by mass) maltose and 96.00% water. It freezes at −0.229 °C.
    (a) Calculate the molar mass of maltose (which is not an ionic compound).
    (b) The density of the solution is 1.014 g/mL. Calculate the osmotic pressure of the solution.

79. ▲ The following table lists the concentrations of the principal ions in seawater:

Ion	Concentration (ppm)
Cl^-	1.95×10^4
Na^+	1.08×10^4
Mg^{2+}	1.29×10^3
SO_4^{2-}	9.05×10^2
Ca^{2+}	4.12×10^2
K^+	3.80×10^2
Br^-	67

    (a) Calculate the freezing point of seawater.
    (b) Calculate the osmotic pressure of seawater at 25 °C. What is the minimum pressure needed to purify seawater by reverse osmosis?

80. ▲ A tree is 10.0 m tall.
    (a) What must be the total molarity of the solutes if sap rises to the top of the tree by osmotic pressure at 20 °C? Assume the groundwater outside the tree is pure water and that the density of the sap is 1.0 g/mL. (1 mm Hg = 13.6 mm H_2O.)
    (b) If the only solute in the sap is sucrose, $C_{12}H_{22}O_{11}$, what is its percent by mass?

81. A 2.00% solution of H_2SO_4 in water freezes at −0.796 °C.
(a) Calculate the van't Hoff factor, *i*.
(b) Which of the following best represents sulfuric acid in a dilute aqueous solution: H_2SO_4, $H_3O^+ + HSO_4^-$, or $2\ H_3O^+ + SO_4^{2-}$?

82. A compound is known to be a potassium halide, KX. If 4.00 g of the salt is dissolved in exactly 100 g of water, the solution freezes at −1.28 °C. Identify the halide ion in this formula.

83. Nitrous oxide, N_2O, laughing gas, is used as an anesthetic. Its Henry's law constant is 2.4×10^{-2} mol/kg·bar. Determine the mass of N_2O that will dissolve in 500. mL of water, under an N_2O pressure of 1.00 bar. What is the concentration of N_2O in this solution, expressed in ppm (d (H_2O) = 1.00 g/mL)?

84. If a carbonated beverage is bottled under 1.5 bar CO_2 pressure, what will be the concentration of dissolved CO_2 in that beverage? (k_H for CO_2 is 0.034 mol/kg bar.) After the pressure is released what fraction of the dissolved gas will escape before equilibrium with the CO_2 in the atmosphere is reached?

85. You are given a flask filled with a colored liquid. Suggest several tests that would allow you to determine whether this is a solution or a colloid.

86. If one is very careful, it is possible to float a needle on the surface of water. (If the needle is magnetized, it will turn to point north and south and become a makeshift compass.) What would happen to the needle if a drop of liquid soap is added to the solution? Explain the observation.

In the Laboratory

87. ▲ A solution of benzoic acid in benzene has a freezing point of 3.1 °C and a boiling point of 82.6 °C. (The freezing point of pure benzene is 5.50 °C, and its boiling point is 80.1 °C.) The structure of benzoic acid is

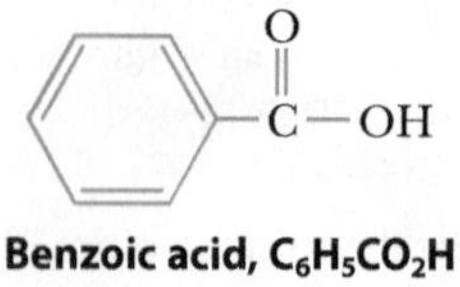

Benzoic acid, $C_6H_5CO_2H$

What can you conclude about the state of the benzoic acid molecules at the two different temperatures? Recall the discussion of hydrogen bonding in Section 11-3.

88. ▲ You dissolve 5.0 mg of iodine, I_2, in 25 mL of water. You then add 10.0 mL of CCl_4 and shake the mixture. If I_2 is 85 times more soluble in CCl_4 than in H_2O (on a volume basis), what are the masses of I_2 in the water and CCl_4 layers after shaking? (See Figure 13.5.)

89. ▲ A solution of 5.00 g of acetic acid in 100. g of benzene freezes at 3.37 °C. A solution of 5.00 g of acetic acid in 100. g of water freezes at −1.49 °C. Find the molar mass of acetic acid from each of these experiments. What can you conclude about the state of the acetic acid molecules dissolved in each of these solvents? Recall the discussion of hydrogen bonding in Section 11-3, and propose a structure for the species in benzene solution.

90. ▲ In a police forensics lab, you examine a package that may contain heroin. However, you find the white powder is not pure heroin but a mixture of heroin ($C_{21}H_{23}O_5N$) and lactose ($C_{12}H_{22}O_{11}$). To determine the amount of heroin in the mixture, you dissolve 1.00 g of the white powdery mixture in water in a 100.0-mL volumetric flask. You find that the solution has an osmotic pressure of 539 mm Hg at 25 °C. What is the composition of the mixture?

91. An organic compound contains carbon (71.17%), hydrogen (5.12%) with the remainder nitrogen. Dissolving 0.177 g of the compound in 10.0 g of benzene gives a solution with a vapor pressure of 94.16 mm Hg at 25 °C. (The vapor pressure of pure benzene at this temperature is 95.26 mm Hg.) What is the molecular formula for the compound?

92. In chemical research we often send newly synthesized compounds to commercial laboratories for analysis. These laboratories determine the weight percent of C and H by burning the compound and collecting the evolved CO_2 and H_2O. They determine the molar mass by measuring the osmotic pressure of a solution of the compound. Calculate the empirical and molecular formulas of a compound, C_xH_yCr, given the following information:
(a) The compound contains 73.94% C and 8.27% H; the remainder is chromium.
(b) At 25 °C, the osmotic pressure of a solution containing 5.00 mg of the unknown dissolved in exactly 100 mL of chloroform solution is 3.17 mm Hg.

Summary and Conceptual Questions

The following questions may use concepts from this and previous chapters.

93. When salts of Mg^{2+}, Ca^{2+}, and Be^{2+} are placed in water, the positive ion is hydrated (as is the negative ion). Which of these three cations is most strongly hydrated? Which one is least strongly hydrated?

94. Explain why a cucumber shrivels up when it is placed in a concentrated solution of salt.

95. If you dissolve equal molar amounts of NaCl and $CaCl_2$ in water, the $CaCl_2$ lowers the freezing point of the water almost 1.5 times as much as the NaCl. Why?

96. A 100.-gram sample of sodium chloride (NaCl) is added to 100. mL of water at 0 °C. After equilibrium is reached, about 64 g of solid remains undissolved. Describe the equilibrium that exists in this system at the particulate level.

97. Which of the following substances is/are likely to dissolve in water, and which is/are likely to dissolve in benzene (C_6H_6)?
(a) $NaNO_3$
(b) diethyl ether, $CH_3CH_2OCH_2CH_3$

(c) NH_4Cl
(d) naphthalene, $C_{10}H_8$

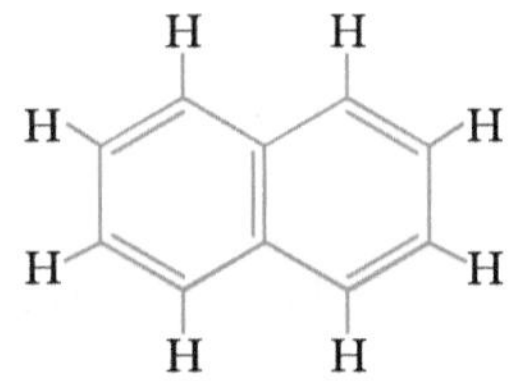

Naphthalene, $C_{10}H_8$

98. Account for the fact that alcohols such as methanol (CH_3OH) and ethanol (C_2H_5OH) are quite miscible with water, whereas an alcohol with a long-carbon chain, such as octanol ($C_8H_{17}OH$), is poorly soluble in water.

99. Starch contains C—C, C—H, C—O, and O—H bonds. Hydrocarbons have only C—C and C—H bonds. Both starch and hydrocarbons can form colloidal dispersions in water. Which dispersion is classified as hydrophobic? Which is hydrophilic? Explain briefly.

100. Which substance would have the greater influence on the vapor pressure of water when added to 1000. g of water: 10.0 g of sucrose ($C_{12}H_{22}O_{11}$) or 10.0 g of ethylene glycol ($HOCH_2CH_2OH$)?

101. You have two aqueous solutions separated by a semipermeable membrane. One contains 5.85 g of NaCl dissolved in 100. mL of solution, and the other contains 8.88 g of KNO_3 dissolved in 100. mL of solution. In which direction will solvent flow: from the NaCl solution to the KNO_3 solution, or from KNO_3 to NaCl? Explain briefly.

102. A protozoan (single-celled animal) that normally lives in the ocean is placed in freshwater. Will it shrivel or burst? Explain briefly.

103. ▲ In the process of distillation, a mixture of two (or more) volatile liquids is first heated to convert the volatile materials to the vapor state. Then the vapor is condensed, reforming the liquid. The net result of this liquid → vapor → liquid conversion is to enrich the fraction of a more volatile component in the mixture in the condensed vapor. We can describe how this occurs using Raoult's law. Imagine that you have a mixture of 12% (by weight) ethanol and water (as formed, for example, by fermentation of grapes).

(a) What are the mole fractions of ethanol and water in this mixture?
(b) This mixture is heated to 78.5 °C (the normal boiling point of ethanol). What are the equilibrium vapor pressures of ethanol and water at this temperature, assuming Raoult's law (ideal) behavior? (You will need to derive the equilibrium vapor pressure of water at 78.5 °C from data in Appendix G.)
(c) What are the mole fractions of ethanol and water in the vapor?
(d) After this vapor is condensed to a liquid, to what extent has the mole fraction of ethanol been enriched? What is the mass fraction of ethanol in the condensed vapor?

104. Sodium chloride (NaCl) is commonly used to melt ice on roads during the winter. Calcium chloride ($CaCl_2$) is sometimes used for this purpose too. Let us compare the effectiveness of equal masses of these two compounds in lowering the freezing point of water, by calculating the freezing point depression of solutions containing 200. g of each salt in 1.00 kg of water. (An advantage of $CaCl_2$ is that it acts more quickly because it is hygroscopic, that is, it absorbs moisture from the air to give a solution and begin the process. A disadvantage is that this compound is more costly.)

105. Review the trend in values of the van't Hoff factor i as a function of concentration (Table 13.4). Use the following data to calculate the van't Hoff factor for a NaCl concentration of 5.00% (by weight) (for which $\Delta T = -3.05$ °C) and a Na_2SO_4 concentration of 5.00% (by weight) (for which $\Delta T = -1.36$ °C). Are these values in line with your expectations based on the trend in the values given in Table 13.4? Speculate on why this trend is seen.

106. The table below gives experimentally determined values for freezing points of 1.00% solutions (mass %) of a series of acids.

(a) Calculate the molality of each solution, determine the calculated freezing points, and then calculate the values of the van't Hoff factor i. Fill these values into the table.

Acid (1.00 mass %)	Molality (mol/kg H_2O)	$T_{measured}$ (°C)	$T_{calculated}$ (°C)	i
HNO_3	____	−0.56	____	____
CH_3CO_2H	____	−0.32	____	____
H_2SO_4	____	−0.42	____	____
$H_2C_2O_4$	____	−0.30	____	____
HCO_2H	____	−0.42	____	____
CCl_3CO_2H	____	−0.21	____	____

(b) Analyze the results, comparing the values of i for the various acids. How do these data relate to acid strengths? (The discussion of strong and weak acids in Section 3-6 will assist you to answer this question.)

107. It is interesting how the Fahrenheit temperature scale was established. One report, given by Fahrenheit in a paper in 1724, stated that the value of 0 °F was established as the freezing temperature of saturated solutions of sea salt. From the literature we find that the freezing point of a 20% by mass solution of NaCl is −16.46 °C (This is the lowest freezing temperature reported for solutions of NaCl.) Does this value lend credence to this story of the establishment of the Fahrenheit scale?

108. The osmotic pressure exerted by seawater at 25 °C is about 27 atm. Calculate the concentration of ions dissolved in seawater that is needed to give an osmotic pressure of this magnitude. (Desalinization of seawater is accomplished by reverse osmosis. In this process an applied pressure forces water through a membrane against a concentration gradient. The minimum external force needed for this process will be 27 atm. Actually, to accomplish the process at a reasonable rate, the applied pressure needs to be about twice this value.)

AP Multiple-Choice Review Questions

1. Which of the following conditions most favors the process of dissolution?

Strength of Attraction between Different Substances

	Solvent–Solvent	Solvent–Solute	Solute–Solute
(A)	Weak	Weak	Weak
(B)	Weaker	Weaker	Stronger
(C)	Weaker	Stronger	Weaker
(D)	Stronger	Weaker	Weaker

2. Determine the molarity of a solution that is made by dissolving 20.0 g of ammonium nitrate, NH_4NO_3, in enough water to make 250.0 mL of solution.

(A) 0.250 *M*
(B) 1.00 *M*
(C) 2.00 *M*
(D) 4.00 *M*

3. Nonpolar solutes dissolve more readily in nonpolar solvents than polar solvents because

(A) the induced dipole of the solute molecule creates an induced dipole in the solvent molecule and London dispersion forces occur.
(B) the induced dipole of the solute molecule creates a permanent dipole in the solvent molecule and London dispersion forces occur.
(C) the permanent dipole of the solute molecule creates an induced dipole in the solvent molecule and London dispersion forces occur.
(D) the permanent dipole of the solute molecule creates a permanent dipole in the solvent and London dispersion forces occur.

4. Predict what effect increasing the charge of the metal ion has on the solubility in water of KCl compared with $CaCl_2$.

(A) The solubility of KCl is less than that of $CaCl_2$ due to stronger Coulombic forces in the KCl.
(B) The solubility of KCl is less than that of $CaCl_2$ due to weaker Coulombic forces in the KCl.
(C) The solubility of KCl is greater than that of $CaCl_2$ due to stronger Coulombic forces in the KCl.
(D) The solubility of KCl is greater than that of $CaCl_2$ due to weaker Coulombic forces in the KCl.

5. Which of the following is the best explanation of how the ions in KCl interact with a polar solvent in the process of dissolution?

(A) The K^+ ions are attracted to the negative end of the polar solvent, and the Cl^- ions are attracted to the positive end.
(B) The K^+ ions are attracted to the positive end of the polar solvent, and the Cl^- ions are attracted to the negative end.
(C) Both the K^+ and the Cl^- ions are attracted to the negative end of the polar solvent.
(D) Both the K^+ and the Cl^- ions are attracted to the positive end of the polar solvent.

6. Iodine crystals dissolve in hexane more readily than in water. However, if the iodine crystals are left in the water for an extended time period, they will dissolve at the interface. This can best be explained because

(A) iodine, although nonpolar in nature, has permanent dipoles that can interact with the polar water molecules.
(B) iodine, although nonpolar in nature, has momentary dipoles that can then interact with the polar water molecules.
(C) iodine, although nonpolar in nature, has a large molar mass, which allows it to interact with the polar water molecules.
(D) iodine, although nonpolar in nature, has a relatively low melting point, which allows it to interact with the polar water molecules.

7. Arrange the hydroxides from least soluble to most soluble based on their relative K_{sp} values.

KOH	K_{sp} = very large
$Ca(OH)_2$	$K_{sp} = 5.0 \times 10^{-6}$
$Al(OH)_3$	$K_{sp} = 3.0 \times 10^{-34}$

(A) KOH, $Al(OH)_3$, $Ca(OH)_2$
(B) KOH, $Ca(OH)_2$, $Al(OH)_3$
(C) $Al(OH)_3$, $Ca(OH)_2$, KOH
(D) $Ca(OH)_2$, $Al(OH)_3$, KOH

8. A student attempted to dissolve a liquid ionic solute in a nonpolar solvent. The resulting mixture showed three distinct layers. This would be classified as a

(A) chemical change because the ionic solute and nonpolar solvent did not mix.

(B) physical change because the ionic solute and nonpolar solvent did not mix.

(C) chemical change because three distinct layers were formed.

(D) physical change because three distinct layers were formed.

9. Which compound would be expected to be the most soluble in water?

(A) C_6H_6

(B) $CHBr_3$

(C) C_6H_{14}

(D) CH_3NH_2

10. A student dissolved 30 g of an unknown compound in 50 g of water at 39 °C. What is the unknown compound?

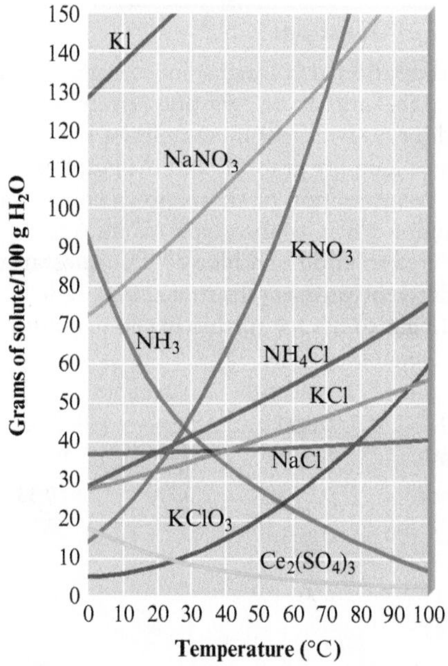

(A) $Ce_2(SO_4)_3$

(B) KCl

(C) NH_4Cl

(D) KNO_3

11. A 10-lane Olympic-sized swimming pool contains 2.5×10^6 kg of water. If the water is at 0 °C, how many kilojoules of energy must be removed to freeze the water in this pool? ΔH_{fus} for H_2O = 334 J/g

(A) 7.5×10^3 kJ

(B) 8.4×10^5 kJ

(C) 7.5×10^6 kJ

(D) 8.4×10^8 kJ

AP Free Response Review Questions

Question Format: Long

Category of Question: Lab 2

The concentration of colored solutions can be determined by measuring the amount of light of a certain wavelength that is absorbed (or transmitted) by samples of known concentrations. These data are graphed and the graph is used to determine the concentration of an unknown concentration of the same solution when its absorbance is measured.

A diluted solution of a blue-colored substance was tested at four different wavelengths to determine the best wavelength of light to use for further experimentation. The following data were obtained.

Color and Wavelength	Violet 430 nm	Blue 470 nm	Green 565 nm	Red 635 nm
Absorbance	0.25	0.28	0.33	0.40

Questions

(a) Which wavelength should be used for further study? Why?

Five standard solutions of the same blue-colored substance were prepared with the following concentrations: 0.10 *M*, 0.20 *M*, 0.30 *M*, 0.40 *M*, and 0.50 *M*.

(b) The standard solutions that were prepared were measured spectrophotometrically. The absorbance data at the chosen wavelength are shown below. Graph the data and draw a best-fit line through the data points. Be sure to label the axes and provide a descriptive title for the graph.

Concentration	0.10 *M*	0.20 *M*	0.30 *M*	0.40 *M*	0.50 *M*
Absorbance	0.12	0.38	0.63	0.86	1.05

A stock solution of the compound with unknown concentration was diluted by the following process. A 25.00 mL sample of the stock solution was pipeted into a 100 mL volumetric flask. The flask was then filled with distilled water and the resulting solution was mixed carefully. A 25.00 mL sample of the diluted solution was then pipeted into a 50.0 mL volumetric flask and thoroughly mixed. A 5.00 mL sample of this final solution was analyzed spectrophotometrically at the same wavelength as was used with the known solutions. The absorbance of the unknown solution was found to be 0.54.

(c) What is the concentration of the diluted unknown?

(d) What is the concentration of the original stock solution?

When added to a copper penny, nitric acid dissolves the copper and zinc that make up the penny. The zinc nitrate solution produced is colorless, but the copper(II) nitrate solution is blue.

(e) How can the % copper in the penny be determined using this procedure? Briefly describe the procedure and calculations that must be done.

Fading of the color of phenolphthalein with time

(elapsed time about 3 minutes)

The reaction of the acid–base indicator phenolphthalein with sodium hydroxide.

Chemical Kinetics: The Rates of Chemical Reactions

Chapter Outline

WHERE DID THE INDICATOR GO?

The titration of an acid with a base is a common laboratory experiment (◀ Section 4-7), and you may use phenolphthalein as an indicator to tell you when the amount of added base exactly matches the amount of acid that was in the solution. Students are told that the equivalence point is indicated when the color of the phenolphthalein changes from colorless to the faintest pink and that the color should persist for 30 seconds or more. We find, though, that some students are over-exuberant and add the base too quickly. They overrun the equivalence point, and the color of the solution turns a beautiful magenta. However, the color fades quickly on shaking the solution. The students therefore think the equivalence point has not been reached and mistakenly add even more base. The solution is again bright magenta, but again the color fades quickly. What is happening in the solution?

The predominant form of phenolphthalein in a basic solution is its anion. However, if a solution containing phenolphthalein has a pH higher than about 12, the red color fades, and the solution becomes colorless. This is

Chapter Goals

See Chapter Goals Revisited (page 551) for Study Questions keyed to these goals.

UNDERSTAND

- Rates of reaction and the conditions affecting rates.
- The collision theory of reaction rates and the role of activation energy.

DO

- Derive a rate equation, rate constant, and reaction order from experimental data.
- Use integrated rate laws.
- Determine the order of a reaction by graphing appropriate functions of concentration vs. time.
- Relate reaction mechanisms and rate laws.

REMEMBER

- The definition of the rate of reaction.
- The half-life of a reaction is the time required for the concentration of a reactant to decrease to one-half its initial value.
- A reaction can proceed no faster than the slowest step in the reaction mechanism.

due to the chemical reaction of hydroxide ion with the anion of phenolphthalein as shown in the equation. The rate of this reaction can be measured by monitoring the change in the intensity of color of the solution by using the spectroscopic techniques described in Section 4-8.

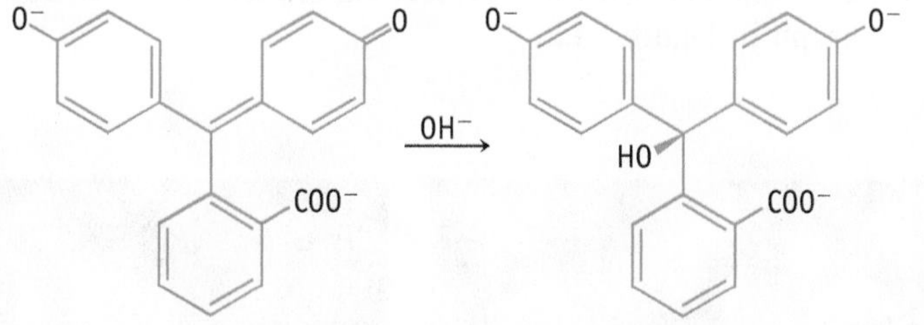

This chapter is about a fundamental area of chemistry: *chemical kinetics*. This encompasses the study of reaction rates and their interpretation based on reaction mechanisms.

A Study Question related to this story is: 14.81.

When carrying out a chemical reaction, chemists are often concerned with two issues: the *extent* to which the reaction is product-favored at equilibrium and the *rate* at which the reaction proceeds. Chapter 5 began to address the first question, and Chapters 15 and 18 will develop that topic further. This chapter deals with the second question: the rates of chemical reactions.

Chemical kinetics is the study of the rates of chemical reactions. On the *macroscopic level*, the field of chemical kinetics addresses what reaction rate means, how

Kinetics and Thermodynamics The extent to which a reaction occurs, whether it is product-favored at equilibrium (see Section 3-3), is related to thermodynamics (Chapter 18). Kinetics studies the speed of reactions. There is no connection between the speed of a reaction and whether it is or is not product-favored at equilibrium.

to determine a reaction rate experimentally, and how factors such as temperature and reactant concentrations influence rates. At the *particulate level*, the concern is with the **reaction mechanism**, the detailed pathway taken by atoms and molecules as a reaction proceeds. The goal is to use data from the macroscopic world of chemistry to understand how chemical reactions occur at the particulate level—and then to apply this information to control important reactions.

14-1 Rates of Chemical Reactions

You have encountered the concept of rates in your daily lives. The speed of an automobile, for example, is the distance traveled per unit time (for example, kilometers per hour) and the rate of flow of water from a faucet is the volume delivered per unit time (perhaps liters per minute). In each case, a change is measured over an interval of time. Similarly, the rate of a chemical reaction refers to the change in concentration of a reactant or product per unit of time.

$$\text{Reaction rate} = \frac{\text{change in concentration}}{\text{change in time}}$$

Calculating a Rate

The average speed of an automobile is the distance traveled divided by the time elapsed, or Δ(distance)/Δ(time). If an automobile travels 3.9 km in 4.5 min (0.075 h), its average speed is (3.9 km/0.075 h), or 52 km/h. Average rates of chemical reactions can be determined similarly. Two quantities, concentration and time, are measured. Concentrations can be determined in a variety of ways, such as by measuring the absorbance of light by a solution, a property that can be related to the concentration of a species in solution (Figure 14.1). The average rate of the reaction is the change in the concentration per unit time.

Let's consider the decomposition of N_2O_5 in a solvent. This reaction occurs according to the following equation:

$$N_2O_5 \rightarrow 2\ NO_2 + \tfrac{1}{2}\ O_2$$

Concentrations and time elapsed for a typical experiment done at 30.0 °C are illustrated by the graph in Figure 14.2.

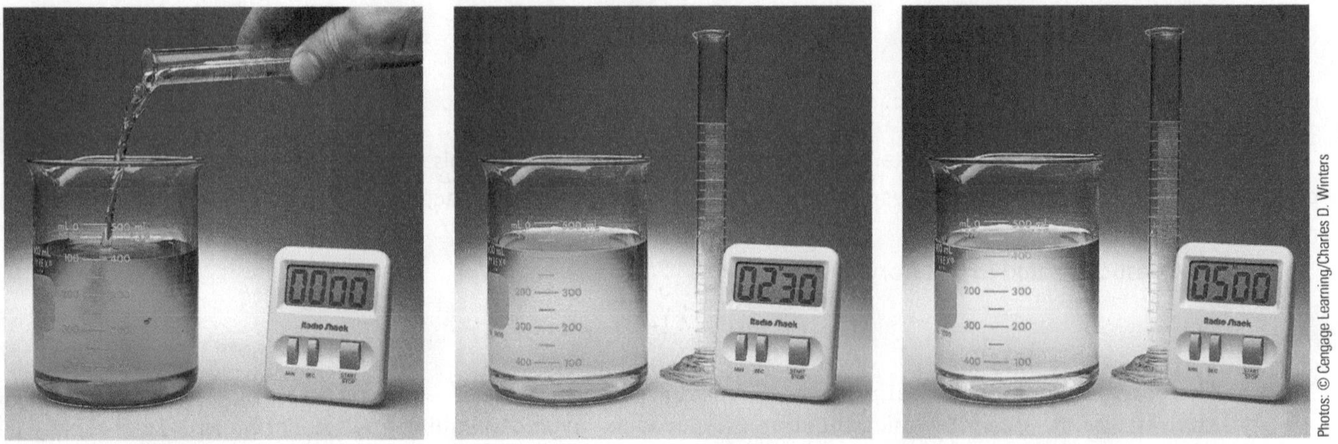

Photos: © Cengage Learning/Charles D. Winters

A few drops of blue food dye were added to water, followed by a solution of bleach.

The color fades as the dye reacts with the bleach.

FIGURE 14.1 **An experiment to measure rate of reaction.** The absorbance of the solution, and thus the dye concentration, can be measured at various times using a spectrophotometer. As described in Section 4-8, the absorbance is related directly to the dye concentration through Beer's Law.

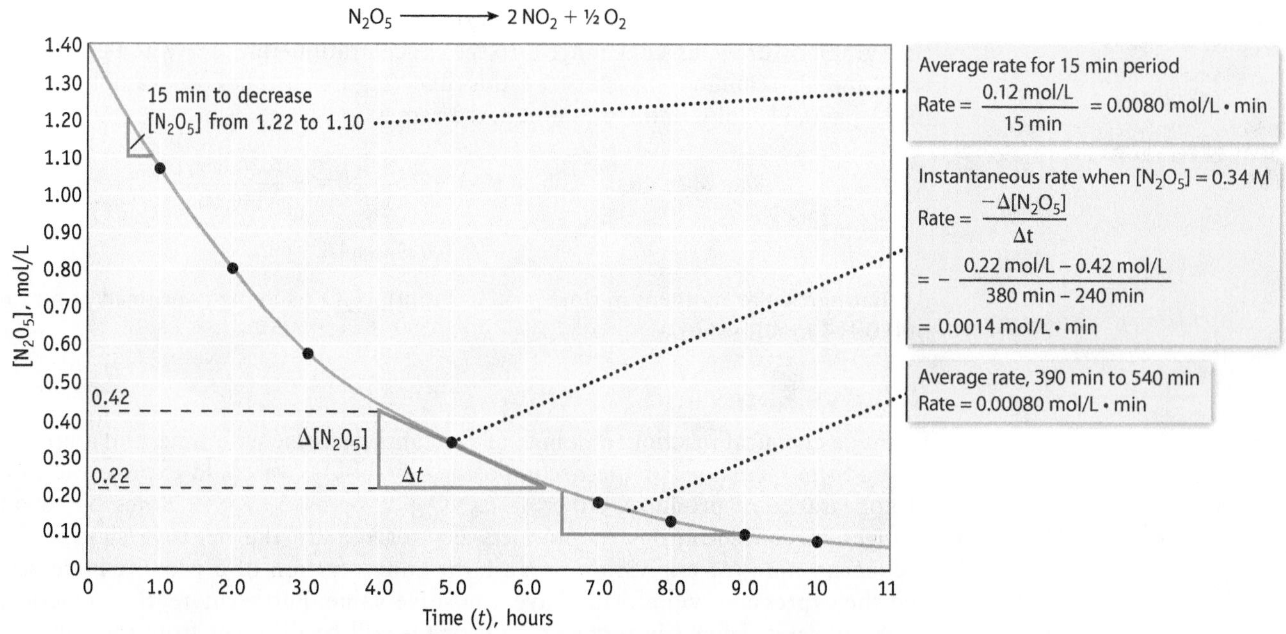

FIGURE 14.2 **A plot of reactant concentration versus time for the decomposition of N_2O_5.**

The *average* rate of this reaction for any interval of time can be expressed as the negative of the change in concentration of N_2O_5 divided by the change in time:

$$\text{Rate of decomposition of } N_2O_5 = -\frac{\text{change in } [N_2O_5]}{\text{change in time}} = -\frac{\Delta[N_2O_5]}{\Delta t}$$

The negative sign is required because N_2O_5 is a reactant and its concentration decreases with time (that is, $\Delta[N_2O_5] = [N_2O_5](\text{final}) - [N_2O_5](\text{initial})$ is negative), but rate is always expressed as a positive quantity. For example, using data from Figure 14.2, the average rate of disappearance of N_2O_5 between 40 and 55 minutes is given by

$$\text{Rate} = -\frac{\Delta[N_2O_5]}{\Delta t} = -\frac{(1.10 \text{ mol/L}) - (1.22 \text{ mol/L})}{55 \text{ min} - 40 \text{ min}} = +\frac{0.12 \text{ mol/L}}{15 \text{ min}}$$

$$\text{Rate} = 0.0080 \text{ mol } N_2O_5 \text{ consumed/L} \cdot \text{min}$$

Calculating Changes When calculating a change in a quantity, we always subtract the initial quantity from the final quantity: $\Delta c = c_{\text{final}} - c_{\text{initial}}$.

Note the units for reaction rates; if concentration is expressed in mol/L, the units for rate will be mol/(L · time). Also notice that the average rate for the decomposition of N_2O_5 is the negative of the slope of a line connecting the two points of interest on the concentration-time graph.

The rate of the reaction changes during the course of the reaction. The concentration of N_2O_5 decreases rapidly at the beginning of the reaction but more slowly near the end. We can verify this by comparing the average rate of disappearance of N_2O_5 calculated previously (when the concentration decreased by 0.12 mol/L in 15 minutes) to the average rate of reaction calculated for the time interval from 390 min to 540 min (when the concentration drops by 0.12 mol/L in 150 minutes). The average rate in this later stage of this reaction is only one tenth of the previous value.

$$-\frac{\Delta[N_2O_5]}{\Delta t} = -\frac{(0.10 \text{ mol/L}) - (0.22 \text{ mol/L})}{540 \text{ min} - 390 \text{ min}} = +\frac{0.12 \text{ mol/L}}{150 \text{ min}}$$

$$= 0.00080 \text{ mol/L} \cdot \text{min}$$

We might also ask what the *instantaneous* rate is at a single point in time. In an automobile, the instantaneous rate can be read from the speedometer. For a

The Slope of a Line The instantaneous rate in Figure 14.2 can be determined from the slope of the tangent line. See *Let's Review: The Tools of Quantitative Chemistry* (pages 39–41), for more on finding the slope of a line.

chemical reaction, we can extract the instantaneous rate from the concentration–time graph by drawing a line tangent to the concentration–time curve at a particular time and determining the slope of this line (Figure 14.2). For example, when $[N_2O_5] = 0.34$ mol/L and $t = 300$ min, the rate is

$$\text{Rate when } [N_2O_5] \text{ is } 0.34\ M = -\frac{\Delta[N_2O_5]}{\Delta t} = +\frac{0.20 \text{ mol/L}}{140 \text{ min}}$$

$$= 0.0014 \text{ mol/L} \cdot \text{min}$$

At that particular moment in time ($t = 300$ min), N_2O_5 is being consumed at a rate of 0.0014 mol/L · min.

Relative Rates and Stoichiometry

During a chemical reaction, amounts of reactants decrease with time, and amounts of products increase. For the decomposition of N_2O_5, we could express the rate of appearance of products, either as $\Delta[NO_2]/\Delta t$ or as $\Delta[O_2]/\Delta t$. Rates based on changes in concentrations of products do not require the negative sign in the Δ(concentration)/Δt expression because the concentration of a product increases, and the expression will already have a positive value. Furthermore, the numerical values of rates defined in terms of NO_2 or O_2 will be different from the value of $\Delta[N_2O_5]/\Delta t$ due to the different stoichiometric coefficients for the substances in the chemical equation. For example, the rate of appearance of NO_2 will be *twice* the rate of disappearance of N_2O_5 because the stoichiometry requires *two* NO_2 molecules to be formed for each N_2O_5 molecule consumed. To take the stoichiometry into account when defining the rate of a reaction, we include a factor for each reactant and product of $1/x$ where x is the substance's stoichiometric coefficient. This gives us a single value of the reaction rate regardless of which reactant or product is being monitored. For the general reaction

$$a\text{ A} + b\text{ B} \rightarrow c\text{ C} + d\text{ D}$$

the reaction rate is defined as

$$\text{Reaction rate} = -\frac{1}{a}\frac{\Delta[A]}{\Delta t} = -\frac{1}{b}\frac{\Delta[B]}{\Delta t} = +\frac{1}{c}\frac{\Delta[C]}{\Delta t} = +\frac{1}{d}\frac{\Delta[D]}{\Delta t}$$

Note that this gives us the reaction rate on a "per mole of reaction" basis. In our example above using the decomposition of N_2O_5 reaction, the rate expression relating all of the reactants and products is

$$\text{Reaction rate} = -\frac{\Delta[N_2O_5]}{\Delta t} = +\frac{1}{2}\frac{\Delta[NO_2]}{\Delta t} = +2\frac{\Delta[O_2]}{\Delta t}$$

EXAMPLE 14.1

Rate of Reaction

Problem Data collected on the concentration of a dye as a function of time (Figure 14.1) are given in the graph below. Using these data estimate the value of (a) the average rate of change of the dye concentration over the first 2 minutes, (b) the average rate of change during the fifth minute (from $t = 4.0$ minutes to $t = 5.0$ minutes), and (c) the instantaneous rate at 4.0 minutes.

What Do You Know? The concentration of dye as a function of time is presented as a graph. From this curve you can identify the concentration of dye at a specific time.

Strategy To find the average rate, calculate the difference in concentration at the beginning and end of a time period ($\Delta c = c_{final} - c_{initial}$) and divide by the elapsed time. To find the instantaneous rate at 4 minutes, draw a line tangent to the graph at the specified time. The negative of the slope of the line is the instantaneous rate.

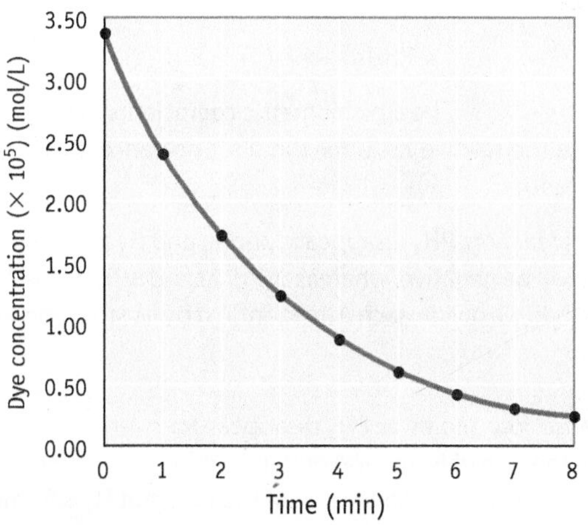

Solution

(a) Average rate over first 2 minutes: The concentration of dye decreases from 3.4×10^{-5} mol/L at $t = 0$ minutes to 1.7×10^{-5} mol/L at $t = 2.0$ minutes. The average rate of the reaction in this interval of time is

$$\text{Average rate} = -\frac{\Delta[\text{Dye}]}{\Delta t} = -\frac{(1.7 \times 10^{-5}\ \text{mol/L}) - (3.4 \times 10^{-5}\ \text{mol/L})}{2.0\ \text{min}}$$

$$\text{Average rate} = 8.5 \times 10^{-6}\ \text{mol/L} \cdot \text{min}$$

(b) Average rate during the fifth minute: The concentration of dye decreases from 0.90×10^{-5} mol/L at $t = 4.0$ minutes to 0.60×10^{-5} mol/L at $t = 5.0$ minutes. The average rate of the reaction in this interval of time is

$$\text{Average rate} = -\frac{\Delta[\text{Dye}]}{\Delta t} = -\frac{(0.60 \times 10^{-5}\ \text{mol/L}) - (0.90 \times 10^{-5}\ \text{mol/L})}{1.0\ \text{min}}$$

$$\text{Average rate} = 3.0 \times 10^{-6}\ \text{mol/L} \cdot \text{min}$$

(c) Instantaneous rate at 4.0 minutes: A line tangent to the curve is drawn at time = 4.0 min. Two points on the line are chosen and the slope of the line is calculated. The instantaneous rate at 4.0 min is the negative of this slope and has a value of 3.5×10^{-6} mol/L · min.

Think about Your Answer Notice that the rate of reaction decreases as the concentration of dye decreases. This tells us that the rate of the reaction is related to the concentration of dye.

Check Your Understanding

Sucrose decomposes to fructose and glucose in acid solution. A plot of the concentration of sucrose as a function of time is given in the margin. What is the rate of change of the sucrose concentration over the first 2 hours? What is the rate of change over the last 2 hours? Estimate the instantaneous rate at 4 hours.

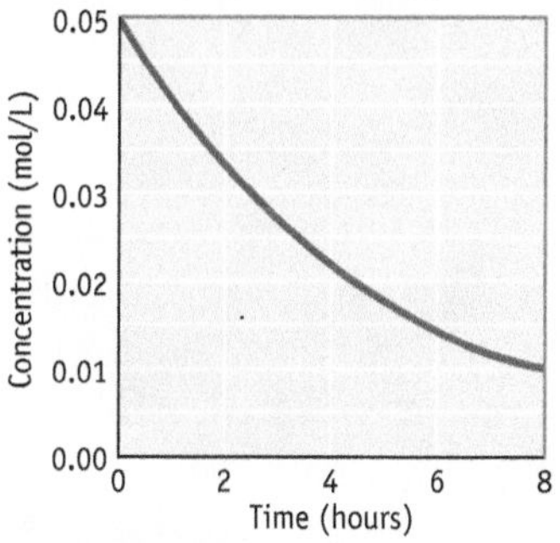

Concentration versus time for the decomposition of sucrose. ("Check Your Understanding" in Example 14.1.)

EXAMPLE 14.2

Relative Rates and Stoichiometry

Problem Relate the rates for the disappearance of reactants and formation of products for the following reaction:

$$4\ PH_3(g) \rightarrow P_4(g) + 6\ H_2(g)$$

What Do You Know? The stoichiometric coefficients in the balanced equation can be used to evaluate the relative rates for the disappearance of the starting material and formation of the products.

Strategy In this reaction, PH_3 disappears, and P_4 and H_2 are formed. Consequently, the value of $\Delta[PH_3]/\Delta t$ will be negative, whereas $\Delta[P_4]/\Delta t$ and $\Delta[H_2]/\Delta t$ will be positive. To relate the rates to each other, we divide each Δ[reagent]/Δt by its stoichiometric coefficient in the balanced equation.

Solution Because four moles of PH_3 disappear for every one mole of P_4 formed, the numerical value of the rate of formation of P_4 is one fourth of the rate of disappearance of PH_3. Similarly, P_4 is formed at only one sixth of the rate that H_2 is formed.

$$\text{Reaction rate} = -\frac{1}{4}\left(\frac{\Delta[PH_3]}{\Delta t}\right) = +\frac{\Delta[P_4]}{\Delta t} = +\frac{1}{6}\left(\frac{\Delta[H_2]}{\Delta t}\right)$$

Think about Your Answer In determining the rate of a chemical reaction you should take into account (1) whether a substance is a reactant or product and (2) the stoichiometric coefficient of the substance in the balanced chemical equation for the reaction.

Check Your Understanding

What are the relative rates of appearance or disappearance of each product and reactant in the decomposition of nitrosyl chloride, NOCl?

$$2\ NOCl(g) \rightarrow 2\ NO(g) + Cl_2(g)$$

REVIEW & CHECK FOR SECTION 14-1

1. Compare the rates of disappearance of NO(g) and O_2(g) for the reaction $2\ NO(g) + O_2(g) \rightarrow 2\ NO_2(g)$.

   (a) The rates are equal.

   (b) The rate of disappearance of NO(g) is twice the rate of disappearance of O_2(g).

   (c) The rate of disappearance of NO(g) is one half the rate of disappearance of O_2(g).

   (d) The rates are not related.

2. Use the graph provided in Example 14.1 to estimate the average rate of disappearance of dye for the period 1–3 minutes.

   (a) 0.6 mol/L · min

   (b) 1.2×10^{-5} mol/L · min

   (c) 0.6×10^{-5} mol/L · min

   (d) 1.2 mol/L · min

14-2 Reaction Conditions and Rate

Learning Objectives: LO 4.1 (see APEC Lab 10 "Investigating Reaction Rates")

Several factors—reactant concentrations, temperature, and presence of catalysts—affect the rate of a reaction. If the reactant is a solid, the surface area available for reaction is also a factor.

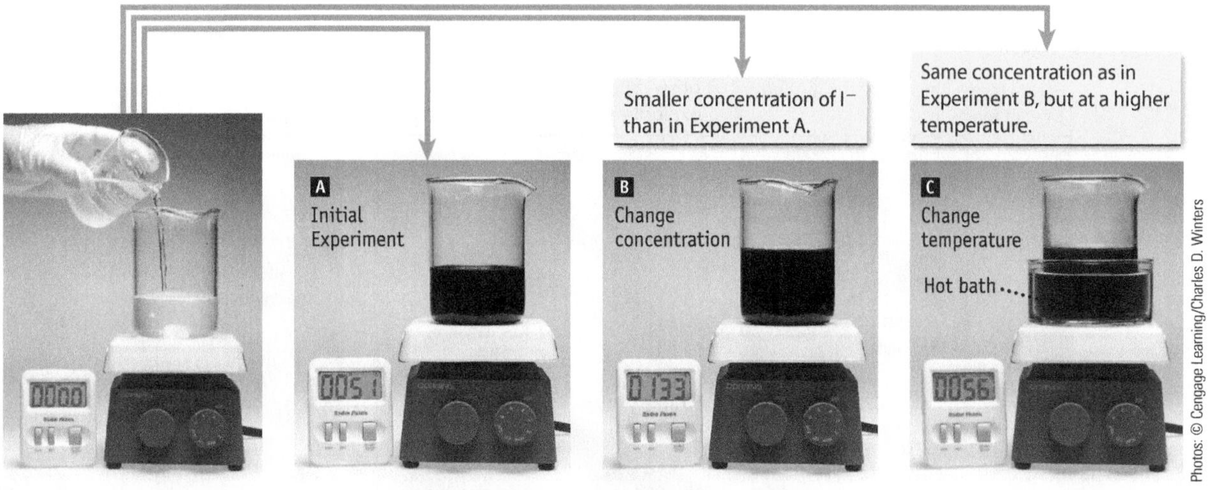

Solutions containing vitamin C, H_2O_2, I^-, and starch are mixed.

Initial Experiment The blue color of the starch-iodine complex develops in 51 seconds.

Change Concentration The blue color of the starch-iodine complex develops in 1 minute 33 seconds when the solution is less concentrated than in A.

Change Temperature The blue color of the starch-iodine complex develops in 56 seconds when the solution is the same concentration as in B but at a higher temperature.

FIGURE 14.3 **The iodine clock reaction.** This reaction illustrates the effects of concentration and temperature on reaction rate. (You can do these experiments yourself with reagents available in the supermarket. For details, see S. W. Wright: "The vitamin C clock reaction," *Journal of Chemical Education*, Vol. 79, p. 41, 2002.)

The "iodine clock reaction" (Figure 14.3) illustrates the **effects of concentration and temperature**. The reaction mixture contains hydrogen peroxide (H_2O_2), iodide ion (I^-), ascorbic acid (vitamin C), and starch (which is an indicator of the presence of iodine, I_2). A sequence of reactions begins with the slow oxidation of iodide ion to I_2 by H_2O_2.

$$H_2O_2(aq) + 2\ I^-(aq) + 2\ H_3O^+(aq) \rightarrow 4\ H_2O(\ell) + I_2(aq)$$

As soon as I_2 is formed in the solution, vitamin C rapidly reduces it back to I^-.

$$2\ H_2O(\ell) + I_2(aq) + C_6H_8O_6(aq) \rightarrow C_6H_6O_6(aq) + 2\ H_3O^+(aq) + 2\ I^-(aq)$$

When all of the vitamin C has been consumed, I_2 remains in solution and forms a blue-black complex with starch. The time it takes for the given amount of vitamin C to react is measured. For the first experiment (A in Figure 14.3) the time required is 51 seconds. When the concentration of iodide ion is smaller (B), the time required for the vitamin C to be consumed is longer, 1 minute 33 seconds. Finally, when the concentrations are again the same as in experiment B but the reaction mixture is heated, the reaction occurs more rapidly (56 seconds). This experiment illustrates two features that are true of most reactions:

- If the concentration of a reactant is increased, the reaction rate will increase as well.
- Chemical reactions occur more rapidly at higher temperatures.

Catalysts are substances that accelerate chemical reactions but are not themselves consumed. Consider the effect of a catalyst on the decomposition of hydrogen peroxide, H_2O_2, to form water and oxygen.

$$2\ H_2O_2(aq) \rightarrow O_2(g) + 2\ H_2O(\ell)$$

This decomposition is very slow; a solution of H_2O_2 can be stored for many months with only minimal change in concentration. Adding manganese(IV) oxide, an iodide-containing salt, or a compound called catalase—a biological catalyst or *enzyme*—causes this reaction to occur rapidly, as shown by vigorous bubbling as gaseous oxygen escapes from the solution (Figure 14.4).

The rate of decomposition of hydrogen peroxide is increased by the catalyst MnO_2. Here, H_2O_2 (as a 30% aqueous solution) is poured onto the black solid MnO_2 and rapidly decomposes to O_2 and H_2O.

A bombardier beetle uses the catalyzed decomposition of H_2O_2 as a defense mechanism.

The enzyme catalase, found in potatoes, is used to catalyze H_2O_2 decomposition.

FIGURE 14.4 **Catalyzed decomposition of H_2O_2.**

The *surface area* of a solid reactant can also affect the reaction rate. Only molecules at the surface of a solid can come in contact with other reactants. The smaller the particles of a solid, the more molecules are found on the solid's surface. With very small particles, the effect of surface area on rate can be quite dramatic (Figure 14.5). Farmers know that fine dust particles (suspended in the air in an enclosure used for grain storage such as a silo or a feed mill) represent a major explosion hazard.

REVIEW & CHECK FOR SECTION 14-2

1. Which of the following will not usually increase the rate of a chemical reaction?
   (a) crushing a solid reactant
   (b) decreasing the concentration of one of the reactants
   (c) increasing the temperature

FIGURE 14.5 **The contrasting rates of combustion of lycopodium powder in bulk and finely powdered form.**

The spores of the common lycopodium clubmoss burn only with difficulty when piled in a dish.

If the spores are ground to a fine powder and sprayed into a flame, combustion is rapid.

14-3 Effect of Concentration on Reaction Rate

One important goal in studying the kinetics of a reaction is to determine its mechanism; that is, how the reaction occurs at the molecular level. The place to begin is to learn, by experiment, how reactant concentrations affect the reaction rate. The resulting relationship between reactant concentrations and reaction rate is expressed by an equation called a **rate equation**, or **rate law**.

Rate Equations

The effect of concentration can be determined by evaluating how the rate is affected when the concentrations of the reactants are varied (with the temperature held constant). Consider, for example, the decomposition of N_2O_5 to NO_2 and O_2. Figure 14.2 presented data on the concentration of N_2O_5 as a function of time. We previously calculated that, when $[N_2O_5] = 0.34$ mol/L, the instantaneous rate of disappearance of N_2O_5 is 0.0014 mol/L · min. An evaluation of the instantaneous rate of the reaction when $[N_2O_5] = 0.68$ mol/L reveals a rate of 0.0028 mol/L · min. That is, doubling the concentration of N_2O_5 doubles the reaction rate. A similar exercise shows that if $[N_2O_5]$ is 0.17 mol/L (half of 0.34 mol/L), the reaction rate is also halved. From these results, we know that the rate for this reaction must be directly proportional to the N_2O_5 concentration:

$$N_2O_5 \longrightarrow 2\ NO_2 + \tfrac{1}{2}\ O_2$$

$$\text{Rate of reaction} \propto [N_2O_5]$$

where the symbol $\propto$ means "proportional to." This proportionality is expressed by the rate equation

$$\text{Rate of reaction} = -\Delta[N_2O_5]/\Delta t = k[N_2O_5]$$

where the proportionality constant, k, is called the **rate constant**. This rate equation tells us that this reaction rate is proportional to the concentration of the reactant. Based on this equation, we can determine that when $[N_2O_5]$ is doubled, the reaction rate doubles.

Generally, for a reaction such as

$$a\ A + b\ B \longrightarrow x\ X$$

the rate equation has the form

$$\text{Rate of reaction} = k[A]^m[B]^n$$

The rate equation expresses the fact that the rate of reaction is proportional to the reactant concentrations, each concentration being raised to some power. The exponents in this equation are often positive whole numbers, but they can also be negative numbers, fractions, or zero. They must be determined by experiment.

If a homogeneous catalyst is present, its concentration might also be included in the rate equation, even though the catalytic species is not a product or reactant in the equation for the reaction. Consider, for example, the decomposition of hydrogen peroxide in the presence of a catalyst such as iodide ion.

$$H_2O_2(aq) \xrightarrow{I^-(aq)} H_2O(\ell) + \tfrac{1}{2}\ O_2(g)$$

Experiments show that this reaction has the following rate equation:

$$\text{Reaction rate} = -\Delta[H_2O_2]/\Delta t = k[H_2O_2][I^-]$$

Here, the concentration of the catalyst, I^-, appears in the rate law, even though it is not part of the balanced equation.

Exponents on Reactant Concentrations and Reaction Stoichiometry It is important to recognize that the exponents m and n are not necessarily the stoichiometric coefficients (a and b) for the balanced chemical equation.

The Nature of Catalysts A catalyst does not appear as a reactant in the balanced, overall equation for the reaction, but it may appear in the rate expression. A common practice is to identify catalysts by name or symbol above the reaction arrow, as shown in the example. A *homogeneous* catalyst is one in the same phase as the reactants. For example, both H_2O_2 and I^- are dissolved in water.

The Order of a Reaction

The **order** of a reaction with respect to a particular reactant is the exponent of its concentration term in the rate law expression, and the **overall reaction order** is the sum of the exponents on all concentration terms. For example, the reaction of NO and Cl_2:

$$NO(g) + \tfrac{1}{2} Cl_2(g) \rightarrow NOCl(g)$$

has the following experimentally determined rate law:

$$\text{Reaction rate} = -\Delta[NO]/\Delta t = k[NO]^2[Cl_2]$$

This reaction is second-order in NO, first-order in Cl_2, and third-order overall.

While first- and second-order reactions are common, other reaction orders are also observed, including zero-order reactions. An example of a zero-order reaction is the decomposition of ammonia on a platinum surface at 856 °C.

$$NH_3(g) \rightarrow \tfrac{1}{2} N_2(g) + \tfrac{3}{2} H_2(g)$$

When the concentration of ammonia is high, the reaction rate is independent of NH_3 concentration. The rate law for this reaction is

$$\text{Reaction rate} = k[NH_3]^0 = k$$

Reaction order is important because it gives some insight into the most interesting question of all—how the reaction occurs. This is described further in Section 14-6.

The Rate Constant, *k*

The rate constant, k, is a proportionality constant that relates rate and concentration *at a given temperature.* It is an important quantity because it enables you to find the reaction rate for a new set of concentrations. To see how to use k, consider the substitution of Cl^- ion by water in the cancer chemotherapy agent cisplatin, $Pt(NH_3)_2Cl_2$.

$$Pt(NH_3)_2Cl_2(aq) + H_2O(\ell) \longrightarrow [Pt(NH_3)_2(H_2O)Cl]^+(aq) + Cl^-(aq)$$

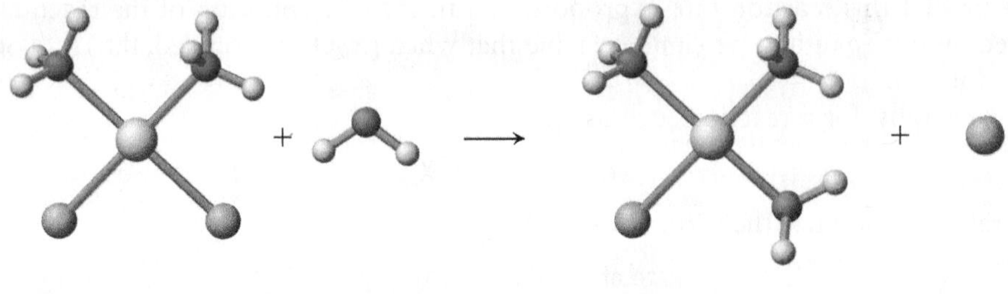

Pseudo-First Order Reaction Actually, the reaction of cisplatin and water is a second-order reaction where Rate = $k[Pt(NH_3)_2Cl_2][H_2O]$. If the reaction is done in a great excess of water, however, the concentration of water does not change by a significant amount over the course of the reaction, that is, $[H_2O]$ = constant. Under such circumstances, the reaction is said to be run under *pseudo-first-order conditions*, and the rate law is given by the equation Rate = $k'[Pt(NH_3)_2Cl_2]$ where $k' = k[H_2O]$.

The rate law for this reaction is

$$\text{Reaction rate} = -\Delta[Pt(NH_3)_2Cl_2]/\Delta t = k[Pt(NH_3)_2Cl_2]$$

and the rate constant, k, is 0.27/h at 25 °C. Knowing k allows you to calculate the rate at a particular reactant concentration—for example, when $[Pt(NH_3)_2Cl_2]$ = 0.018 mol/L:

$$\text{Reaction rate} = (0.27/\text{h})(0.018\ \text{mol/L}) = 0.0049\ \text{mol/L} \cdot \text{h}$$

As noted earlier, reaction rates have units of mol/L · time when concentrations are given as moles per liter. Rate constants must have units consistent with the units for the other terms in the rate equation.

- First-order reactions: The units of k are 1/time.
- Second-order reactions: The units of k are L/mol · time.
- Zero-order reaction: The units of k are mol/L · time.

Time and Rate Constants The time in a rate constant can be seconds, minutes, hours, days, years, or whatever time unit is appropriate. The fraction 1/time can also be written as $time^{-1}$. For example, 1/y is equivalent to y^{-1}, and 1/s is equivalent to s^{-1}.

Finally, you should recognize that reactions can range from excruciatingly slow to lightning fast, and this is reflected in wide-ranging values of k. The platinum reaction above has a value of k of 0.27/h at 25 °C. In contrast, sucrose decomposes in a first-order reaction to fructose and glucose with a rate constant of 0.0036/h at

25 °C. And the very rapid combination of I atoms to form I_2 molecules in the gas phase has $k = 4 \times 10^{11}$ L/mol · s at 23 °C.

Determining a Rate Equation

One way to determine a rate equation is by using the "method of initial rates." *The initial rate is the instantaneous reaction rate at the start of the reaction* (the rate at $t = 0$). An approximate value of the initial rate can be obtained by mixing the reactants and determining the reaction rate after 1% to 2% of the limiting reactant has been consumed. Measuring the rate during the initial stage of a reaction is convenient because initial concentrations are known.

As an example of the determination of a reaction rate by the method of initial rates, let us consider the following reaction of nitrogen monoxide with chlorine.

$$NO(g) + \tfrac{1}{2}\, Cl_2(g) \rightarrow NOCl(g)$$

Reactant concentrations and initial rates for this reaction for several experiments at 50 °C are collected in the table below.

	Initial Concentrations (mol/L)		
Experiment	**[NO]**	**[Cl_2]**	**Initial Rate, $-\Delta[NO]/\Delta t$ (mol/L · s)**
1	0.250	0.250	1.43×10^{-6}
	↓ × 2	↓ No change	↓ × 4
2	0.500	0.250	5.72×10^{-6}
3	0.250	0.500	2.86×10^{-6}
4	0.500	0.500	11.4×10^{-6}

- *Compare Experiments 1 and 2:* Here, [Cl_2] is held constant, and [NO] is doubled. This change in [NO] by a factor of 2 leads to a reaction rate increase by a factor of 4; that is, the rate is proportional to the *square* of the NO concentration.
- *Compare Experiments 1 and 3:* In experiments 1 and 3, [NO] is held constant, and [Cl_2] is doubled, causing the rate to double. That is, the rate is proportional to [Cl_2].

The rate law that reflects these experimental observations is

$$\text{Reaction rate} = -\Delta[NO]/\Delta t = k[NO]^2[Cl_2]$$

Using this equation, we can predict that doubling both concentrations at the same time should cause the rate to go up by a factor of 8, as is determined if experiments 1 and 4 are compared [(1.43×10^{-6} mol/L · s) × 8 = 11.4×10^{-6} mol/L · s].

If the rate equation is known, the value of k, the rate constant, can be found by substituting values for the rate and concentration into the rate equation. Using the data for the NO/Cl_2 reaction from the first experiment, we have

$$\text{Reaction rate} = 1.43 \times 10^{-6}\ \text{mol/L} \cdot \text{s} = k(0.250\ \text{mol/L})^2(0.250\ \text{mol/L})$$

$$k = \frac{1.43 \times 10^{-6}\ \text{mol/L} \cdot \text{s}}{(0.250\ \text{mol/L})^2(0.250\ \text{mol/L})} = 9.15 \times 10^{-5}\ \text{L}^2/\text{mol}^2 \cdot \text{s}$$

EXAMPLE 14.3

Determining a Rate Equation

Problem The rate of the reaction between CO and NO_2 at 540 K

$$CO(g) + NO_2(g) \rightarrow CO_2(g) + NO(g)$$

was measured starting with various concentrations of CO and NO_2. Determine the rate equation and the value of the rate constant.

	INITIAL CONCENTRATIONS (mol/L)		
EXPERIMENT	**[CO]**	**[NO_2]**	**INITIAL RATE (mol/L · h)**
1	5.10×10^{-4}	0.350×10^{-4}	3.4×10^{-8}
2	5.10×10^{-4}	0.700×10^{-4}	6.8×10^{-8}
3	5.10×10^{-4}	0.175×10^{-4}	1.7×10^{-8}
4	1.02×10^{-3}	0.350×10^{-4}	6.8×10^{-8}
5	1.53×10^{-3}	0.350×10^{-4}	10.2×10^{-8}

What Do You Know? The table contains concentrations of the two reactants and initial rates for five experiments.

Strategy For a reaction involving several reactants, the general approach is to keep the concentration of one reactant constant and then decide how the rate of reaction changes as the concentration of the other reagent is varied. The rate is proportional to the concentration of a reactant, R, raised to some power *n* (the reaction order)

$$\text{Rate} \propto [R]^n$$

If [R] is doubled and the rate doubles from experiment 1 to experiment 2, then $n = 1$. If [R] doubles and the rate goes up by a factor of 4, then $n = 2$. If the rate is unchanged, then $n = 0$.

Strategy Map 14.3

PROBLEM
Derive the **rate equation** and **value of *k*** for a given reaction.

↓

DATA/INFORMATION
5 experiments measuring ***initial rate*** as a function of **reactant concentration**

STEP 1. **Compare rates** for two experiments where the concentration of reactant **A** is ***constant*** and reactant **B** is ***varied.***

↓

Gives the **dependence of rate** on one reactant **(B)**

STEP 2. **Compare rates** for two experiments where the concentration of reactant **B** is ***constant*** and reactant **A** is ***varied.***

↓

Gives the **dependence of rate** on the other reactant **(A)**

STEP 3. Use the ***rate dependence*** on **A** and **B** to write the **rate equation.**

↓

$\text{Rate} = k\,[A]^n[B]^m$

STEP 4. Substitute the **rate data** for one experiment into the **rate equation** to calculate ***k***.

↓

Value of rate constant ***k***

Solution In the first three experiments, the concentration of CO is held constant. In the second experiment, the NO_2 concentration has been doubled relative to experiment 1, leading to a twofold increase in the rate. Because the rate has doubled, the reaction is first-order in NO_2.

This finding is confirmed by experiment 3. Decreasing [NO_2] in experiment 3 to half its original value causes the rate to decrease by half.

The data in experiments 1 and 4 (with constant [NO_2]) show that doubling [CO] doubles the rate, and the data from experiments 1 and 5 show that tripling the concentration of CO triples the rate. These results mean that the reaction is first-order in [CO]. Thus, we now know the rate equation is

$$\text{Reaction rate} = k[CO][NO_2]$$

The rate constant, *k*, can be found by inserting data for one of the experiments into the rate equation. Using data from experiment 1, for example,

$$\text{Rate} = 3.4 \times 10^{-8}\ \text{mol/L} \cdot \text{h} = k(5.10 \times 10^{-4}\ \text{mol/L})(0.350 \times 10^{-4}\ \text{mol/L})$$

$$k = 1.9\ \text{L/mol} \cdot \text{h}$$

Think about Your Answer To check your answer, calculate *k* for two or more of the experiments. If the values determined for *k* differ significantly, then you know that you have made a mistake in calculating the reaction orders. The same rate law would apply if the reaction were carried out at a different temperature, but the rate constant *k* would have a different value.

Check Your Understanding

The initial rate ($-\Delta[NO]/\Delta t$) of the reaction of nitrogen monoxide and oxygen

$$NO(g) + \frac{1}{2} O_2(g) \rightarrow NO_2(g)$$

was measured for various initial concentrations of NO and O_2 at 25 °C. Determine the rate equation from these data. What is the value of the rate constant, *k*, and what are its units?

	Initial Concentrations (mol/L)		
Experiment	**[NO]**	**[O_2]**	**Initial Rate (mol NO/L · s)**
1	0.020	0.010	0.028
2	0.020	0.020	0.057
3	0.020	0.040	0.114
4	0.040	0.020	0.227
5	0.010	0.020	0.014

EXAMPLE 14.4

Using a Rate Equation to Determine Rates

Problem Using the rate equation and rate constant determined for the reaction of CO and NO_2 at 540 K in Example 14.3, determine the initial rate of the reaction when $[CO] = 3.8 \times 10^{-4}$ mol/L and $[NO_2] = 0.650 \times 10^{-4}$ mol/L.

What Do You Know? The rate law and the value for the rate constant (1.9 L/mol · h) are both known. The concentrations of the two reactants are given.

Strategy A rate equation consists of three parts: a rate, a rate constant (*k*), and the concentration terms. If two of these parts are known (here *k* and the concentrations), the third can be calculated.

Solution Substitute *k* (= 1.9 L/mol · h) and the concentration of each reactant into the rate law determined in Example 14.3.

$$\text{Reaction rate} = k[CO][NO_2] = (1.9 \text{ L/mol} \cdot \text{h})(3.8 \times 10^{-4} \text{ mol/L})(0.650 \times 10^{-4} \text{ mol/L})$$

$$\text{Reaction rate} = 4.7 \times 10^{-8} \text{ mol/L} \cdot \text{h}$$

Think about Your Answer As a check on the calculated result, it is sometimes useful to make an educated guess at the answer before carrying out the mathematical solution. We know the reaction here is first-order in both reactants. Comparing the concentration values given in this problem with the concentration values in experiment 1 in Example 14.3, we notice that [CO] is about three fourths of the concentration value, whereas [NO_2] is almost twice the value. The effects do not precisely offset each other, but we might predict that the difference in rates between this experiment and experiment 1 will be fairly small, with the rate in this experiment being just a little greater. The calculated value bears this out.

Check Your Understanding

The rate constant, *k*, at 25 °C is 0.27/h for the reaction

$$Pt(NH_3)_2Cl_2(aq) + H_2O(\ell) \rightarrow [Pt(NH_3)_2(H_2O)Cl]^+(aq) + Cl^-(aq)$$

and the rate equation is

$$\text{Reaction rate} = k[Pt(NH_3)_2Cl_2]$$

Calculate the rate of reaction when the concentration of $Pt(NH_3)_2Cl_2$ is 0.020 M.

PROBLEM SOLVING TIP 14.1

Determining a Rate Equation

To determine the rate equation for a reaction involving several reactants, the general approach is to keep the concentration of one reactant constant and then decide how the rate of reaction changes as the concentration of the other reagent is varied. Because the rate of any reaction is proportional to the concentration of a reactant, R, raised to some power n (the reaction order)

$$\text{Rate} \propto [\text{R}]^n$$

we can write the following general equation for the ratio of rates in two experiments:

$$\frac{\text{Rate in experiment 2}}{\text{Rate in experiment 1}} = \frac{[\text{R}_2]^n}{[\text{R}_1]^n} = \left(\frac{[\text{R}_2]}{[\text{R}_1]}\right)^n$$

Consider the experiment in Example 14.3. In the second experiment, the NO_2 concentration has doubled relative to experiment 1, leading to a twofold increase in the rate. Putting the data into the general equation confirms the result that $n = 1$.

$$\frac{\text{Rate in experiment 2}}{\text{Rate in experiment 1}} = \frac{6.8 \times 10^{-8}\ \text{mol/L} \cdot \text{h}}{3.4 \times 10^{-8}\ \text{mol/L} \cdot \text{h}} = \left(\frac{0.700 \times 10^{-4}}{0.350 \times 10^{-4}}\right)^n$$

$$2 = (2)^n$$

$$n = 1 \text{ because } 2 = (2)^1$$

REVIEW & CHECK FOR SECTION 14-3

1. The reaction $NO(g) + 1/2\ Cl_2(g) \longrightarrow NOCl(g)$ is first-order in $[Cl_2]$ and second-order with respect to [NO]. Under a given set of conditions, the initial rate of this reaction is 6.20×10^{-6} mol/L · s. What is the rate of this reaction if the concentration of NO is doubled and the concentration of Cl_2 is reduced to half the original value?

   (a) 6.20×10^{-6} mol/L · s

   (b) 1.24×10^{-5} mol/L · s

   (c) 2.48×10^{-5} mol/L · s

   (d) 4.96×10^{-5} mol/L · s

Learning Objectives: LO 4.2 (see APEC Lab 11 "Rate Law Determination"), LO 4.3

14-4 Concentration–Time Relationships: Integrated Rate Laws

It is often important for a chemist to know how long a reaction must proceed to reach a predetermined concentration of some reactant or product, or what the reactant and product concentrations will be after some time has elapsed. For this reason it would be useful to have a mathematical equation that relates time and concentration—an equation that describes concentration–time curves like the one shown in Figure 14.2. With such an equation, we could calculate the concentration at any given time or the length of time needed for a given amount of reactant to react.

First-Order Reactions

Suppose the reaction "R → products" is first-order. This means the reaction rate is directly proportional to the concentration of R raised to the first power, or, mathematically,

$$-\frac{\Delta[\text{R}]}{\Delta t} = k[\text{R}]$$

This relationship can be transformed into a very useful equation called an **integrated rate equation** (because integral calculus is used in its derivation).

$$\ln \frac{[\text{R}]_t}{[\text{R}]_0} = -kt \qquad (14.1)$$

Here, $[R]_0$ and $[R]_t$ are concentrations of the reactant at time $t = 0$ and at a later time, t, respectively. The ratio of concentrations, $[R]_t/[R]_0$, *is the fraction of reactant that remains after a given time has elapsed.*

Equation 14.1 can be used to carry out many useful calculations. For example,

- If $[R]_t/[R]_0$ is measured in the laboratory after some amount of time has elapsed, then k can be determined.
- If $[R]_0$ and k are known, then the concentration of material remaining after a given amount of time ($[R]_t$) can be calculated.
- If k is known, then the time elapsed until a specific fraction ($[R]_t/[R]_0$) remains can be determined.

Finally, notice that *k for a first-order reaction is independent of concentration*; k has units of time^{-1} (y^{-1} or s^{-1}, for example). This means we can choose any convenient unit for $[R]_t$ and $[R]_0$: moles per liter, moles, grams, number of atoms, number of molecules, or gas pressure.

EXAMPLE 14.5

The First-Order Rate Equation

Problem In the past, cyclopropane, C_3H_6, was used in a mixture with oxygen as an anesthetic. (This practice has almost ceased today because the compound is flammable.) When heated, cyclopropane rearranges to propene in a first-order process.

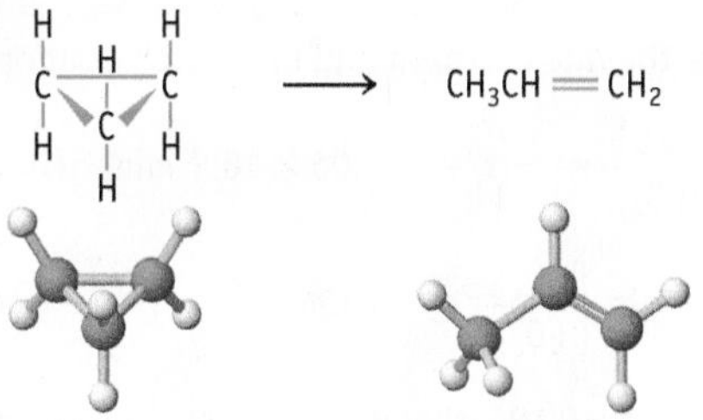

cyclopropane propene

$$\text{Rate} = k[\text{cyclopropane}] \qquad k = 2.42\ \text{h}^{-1} \text{ at } 500\ °\text{C}$$

If the initial concentration of cyclopropane is 0.050 mol/L, how much time (in hours) must elapse for its concentration to drop to 0.010 mol/L?

What Do You Know? The reaction is first-order in cyclopropane. You know the rate constant, k, and the initial and final concentrations of this reactant, [R] and $[R]_0$.

Strategy Use Equation 14.1 to calculate the time (t) elapsed to reach a concentration of 0.010 mol/L.

Solution Values for $[\text{cyclopropane}]_t$, $[\text{cyclopropane}]_0$, and k are substituted into Equation 14.1; t (time) is the unknown:

$$\ln\frac{[0.010]}{[0.050]} = -(2.42\ \text{h}^{-1})t$$

$$t = \frac{-\ln(0.20)}{2.42\ \text{h}^{-1}} = \frac{-(-1.61)}{2.42\ \text{h}^{-1}} = 0.665\ \text{h}$$

Think about Your Answer A carbon ring with only three or four CH_2 groups (a cycloalkane) is strained because the C—C—C bond angles cannot match the preferred 109.5°. Thus, the cyclopropane ring opens readily when energy is added.

Check Your Understanding

Sucrose, a sugar, decomposes in acid solution to give glucose and fructose. The reaction is first-order in sucrose, and the rate constant at 25 °C is $k = 0.21\ h^{-1}$. If the initial concentration of sucrose is 0.010 mol/L, what is its concentration after 5.0 h?

EXAMPLE 14.6

Using the First-Order Rate Equation

Problem Hydrogen peroxide decomposes in a dilute sodium hydroxide solution at 20 °C in a first-order reaction:

$$H_2O_2(aq) \rightarrow H_2O(\ell) + \tfrac{1}{2}\,O_2(g)$$

$$\text{Rate} = k[H_2O_2] \text{ with } k = 1.06 \times 10^{-3}\ \text{min}^{-1}$$

What is the fraction remaining after 100. min? What is the concentration of H_2O_2 after 100. minutes if the initial concentration of H_2O_2 is 0.020 mol/L?

What Do You Know? This is a first-order reaction. The rate constant *k*, initial concentration of H_2O_2, and elapsed time are given.

Strategy Because the reaction is first-order in H_2O_2, use Equation 14.1. Here, $[H_2O_2]_0$, k, and t are known, and you are asked to find the value of the fraction remaining, $[H_2O_2]_t/[H_2O_2]_0$. Once this value is known, and knowing $[H_2O_2]_0$, you can calculate $[H_2O_2]_t$.

Solution Substitute the rate constant and time into Equation 14.1.

$$\ln\frac{[H_2O_2]_t}{[H_2O_2]_0} = -kt = -(1.06 \times 10^{-3}\ \text{min}^{-1})(100.\ \text{min})$$

$$\ln\frac{[H_2O_2]_t}{[H_2O_2]_0} = -0.106$$

Taking the antilogarithm of −0.106 [that is, the inverse of the natural logarithm of −0.106 or $e^{-0.106}$], we find the fraction remaining to be 0.90.

$$\text{Fraction remaining} = \frac{[H_2O_2]_t}{[H_2O_2]_0} = 0.90$$

The calculated fraction remaining is 0.90, thus the concentration of H_2O_2 remaining is 90% of the initial concentration.

$$[H_2O_2]_t = 0.90\ [H_2O_2]_0 = 0.90\ (0.020\ \text{mol/L}) = 0.018\ \text{mol/L}$$

Think about Your Answer Although H_2O_2 is unstable, its rate of decomposition is very slow, particularly in a dilute solution. However, sodium hydroxide catalyzes the decomposition. The rate of the reaction can be studied by measuring the volume of O_2 gas evolved as a function of time.

Check Your Understanding

Gaseous azomethane ($CH_3N_2CH_3$) decomposes to ethane and nitrogen when heated:

$$CH_3N_2CH_3(g) \rightarrow CH_3CH_3(g) + N_2(g)$$

The decomposition of azomethane is a first-order reaction with $k = 3.6 \times 10^{-4}\ s^{-1}$ at 600 K.

(a) A sample of gaseous $CH_3N_2CH_3$ is placed in a flask and heated at 600 K for 150 seconds. What fraction of the initial sample remains after this time?

(b) How long must a sample be heated so that 99% of the sample has decomposed?

Second-Order Reactions

Suppose the reaction "R → products" is second-order. The rate equation is

$$-\frac{\Delta[\text{R}]}{\Delta t} = k[\text{R}]^2$$

Using calculus, this relationship can be transformed into the following equation that relates reactant concentration and time:

$$\frac{1}{[\text{R}]_t} - \frac{1}{[\text{R}]_0} = kt \qquad (14.2)$$

The same symbolism used with first-order reactions applies: $[\text{R}]_0$ is the concentration of reactant at time $t = 0$; $[\text{R}]_t$ is the concentration at a later time; and k is the second-order rate constant, which has the units of L/mol · time.

EXAMPLE 14.7

Using the Second-Order Integrated Rate Equation

Problem The gas-phase decomposition of HI

$$\text{HI(g)} \rightarrow \tfrac{1}{2}\,\text{H}_2\text{(g)} + \tfrac{1}{2}\,\text{I}_2\text{(g)}$$

has the rate equation

$$-\frac{\Delta[\text{HI}]}{\Delta t} = k[\text{HI}]^2$$

where k = 30. L/mol · min at 443 °C. How much time does it take for the concentration of HI to drop from 0.010 mol/L to 0.0050 mol/L at 443 °C?

What Do You Know? Equation 14.2 is used for a second-order reaction. The rate constant, k, and the initial and final concentrations of HI are given; the elapsed time is the unknown.

Strategy Substitute the values of $[\text{HI}]_0$, $[\text{HI}]_t$, and k into Equation 14.2, and solve for the unknown, t.

Solution Here, $[\text{HI}]_0$ = 0.010 mol/L and $[\text{HI}]_t$ = 0.0050 mol/L. Using Equation 14.2, we have

$$\frac{1}{0.0050\ \text{mol/L}} - \frac{1}{0.010\ \text{mol/L}} = (30.\ \text{L/mol} \cdot \text{min})t$$

$$(2.0 \times 10^2\ \text{L/mol}) - (1.0 \times 10^2\ \text{L/mol}) = (30.\ \text{L/mol} \cdot \text{min})t$$

$$t = 3.3\ \text{minutes}$$

Think about Your Answer In the solution of this problem, we kept track of the units for each quantity. This leads to an answer for time elapsed with the unit minutes.

Check Your Understanding

Using the rate constant for HI decomposition given in this example, calculate the concentration of HI after 12 minutes if $[\text{HI}]_0$ = 0.010 mol/L.

Zero-Order Reactions

If a reaction (R ⟶ products) is zero-order, the rate equation is

$$-\frac{\Delta[\text{R}]}{\Delta t} = k[\text{R}]^0$$

This equation leads to the integrated rate equation

$$[\text{R}]_0 - [\text{R}]_t = kt \qquad (14.3)$$

where the units of k are mol/L · s.

Graphical Methods for Determining Reaction Order and the Rate Constant

Finding the Slope of a Line See *Let's Review: Tools of Quantitative Chemistry* (pages 39–41), for a description of methods for finding the slope of a line.

Chemists find it is convenient to determine the order of a reaction and its rate constant using graphical methods. If rearranged slightly, Equations 14.1, 14.2, and 14.3 have the form $y = mx + b$. This is the equation for a straight line, where m is the slope of the line and b is the y-intercept. In each of these equations, $x = t$.

Zero-order	First-order	Second-order
$[\text{R}]_t = -kt + [\text{R}]_0$	$\ln[\text{R}]_t = -kt + \ln[\text{R}]_0$	$\frac{1}{[\text{R}]_t} = +kt + \frac{1}{[\text{R}]_0}$
↓ y ↓ mx ↓ b	↓ y ↓ mx ↓ b	↓ y ↓ mx ↓ b

As an example of the graphical method for determining reaction order, consider the decomposition of azomethane.

$$CH_3N_2CH_3(g) \longrightarrow CH_3CH_3(g) + N_2(g)$$

The decomposition of azomethane was followed at 600 K by observing the decrease in its partial pressure ($P(CH_3N_2CH_3)$) with time. (Recall from Chapter 10 that pressure is proportional to concentration at a given temperature and volume.) As shown in Figure 14.6a, a graph of $\ln P(CH_3N_2CH_3)$ versus time produces a straight line, which shows that the reaction is first-order in $CH_3N_2CH_3$. The slope of the line can be determined, and the negative of the slope equals the rate constant for the reaction, $3.6 \times 10^{-4}\ s^{-1}$.

The decomposition of NO_2 is a second-order process.

$$NO_2(g) \longrightarrow NO(g) + \tfrac{1}{2}\,O_2(g)$$

$$\text{Rate} = k[NO_2]^2$$

This fact can be verified by showing that a plot of $1/[NO_2]$ versus time is a straight line (Figure 14.6b). Here, the slope of the line is equal to k.

For a zero-order reaction (Figure 14.6c), a plot of concentration versus time gives a straight line with a slope equal to the negative of the rate constant.

Table 14.1 summarizes the relationships between concentration and time for first-, second-, and zero-order processes.

Table 14.1 Characteristic Properties of Reactions of the Type "R ⟶ Products"

Order	Rate Equation	Integrated Rate Equation	Straight-Line Plot	Slope	k Units
0	$-\Delta[\text{R}]/\Delta t = k[\text{R}]^0$	$[\text{R}]_0 - [\text{R}]_t = kt$	$[\text{R}]_t$ vs. t	$-k$	mol/L · time
1	$-\Delta[\text{R}]/\Delta t = k[\text{R}]^1$	$\ln([\text{R}]_t/[\text{R}]_0) = -kt$	$\ln[\text{R}]_t$ vs. t	$-k$	1/time
2	$-\Delta[\text{R}]/\Delta t = k[\text{R}]^2$	$(1/[\text{R}]_t) - (1/[\text{R}]_0) = kt$	$1/[\text{R}]_t$ vs. t	k	L/mol · time

Time (s)	$P \times 10^2$ atm	ln P
0	8.20	−2.50
1000	5.72	−2.86
2000	3.99	−3.22
3000	2.78	−3.58
4000	1.94	−3.94

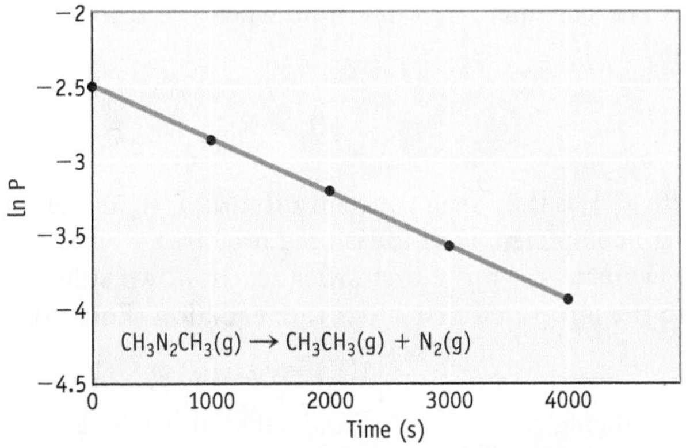

Rate = $k[CH_3N_2CH_3]$

$$\text{Slope} = -k = \frac{[(-3.76) - (-3.04)]}{(3500 - 1500)\text{ s}}$$

$$k = 3.6 \times 10^{-4}\text{ s}^{-1}$$

(a) First-order reaction. A plot of the natural logarithm of the $CH_3N_2CH_3$ pressure versus time for the decomposition of azomethane results in a straight line with a negative slope. The rate constant $k = -\text{slope}$.

Time (s)	$[NO_2]$ (mol/L)	$1/[NO_2]$ (L/mol)
0	0.020	50
30	0.015	67
60	0.012	83
90	0.010	100
120	0.0087	115

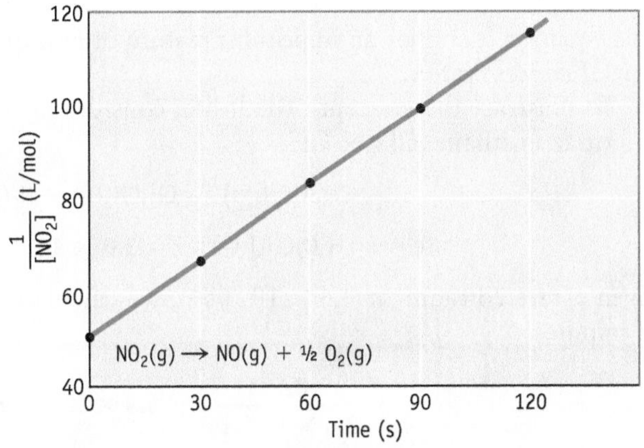

Rate = $k[NO_2]^2$

$$\text{Slope} = k = \frac{(105 - 61)\text{ mol/L}}{(100 - 20)\text{ s}}$$

$$k = 0.55\text{ L/mol}\cdot\text{s}$$

(b) Second-order reaction. A plot of $1/[NO_2]$ versus time for the decomposition of NO_2 results in a straight line. The rate constant $k = \text{slope}$.

Time (s)	$[NO_3]$ (mmol/L)
200	1.75
280	1.65
600	1.15
750	0.94
800	0.85
900	0.70

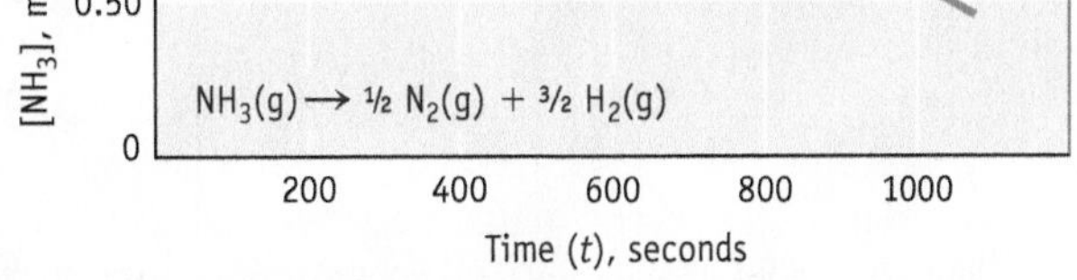

Rate = $k[NH_3]^0$

$$\text{Slope} = -k = \frac{(0.540 - 1.29)\text{ mmol/L}}{(1000 - 500)\text{ s}} = -1.5 \times 10^{-3}\text{ mmol/L}\cdot\text{s}$$

$$k = 1.5 \times 10^{-3}\text{ mmol/L}\cdot\text{s}$$

(c) Zero-order reaction. A plot of the concentration of ammonia, $[NH_3]_t$, against time for the decomposition of NH_3 on a metal surface at 856 °C is a straight line, indicating that this is a zero-order reaction. The rate constant $k = -\text{slope}$.

FIGURE 14.6 **Graphical methods for determining reaction order.**

Half-Life and First-Order Reactions

The **half-life, $t_{1/2}$,** of a reaction is the time required for the concentration of a reactant to decrease to one half its initial value. It is a convenient way to describe the rate at which a reactant is consumed in a chemical reaction: *The longer the half-life, the slower the reaction.*

The half-life, $t_{1/2}$, is the time when the fraction of the reactant R remaining is equal to 1/2.

$$[R]_t = \tfrac{1}{2}[R]_0 \quad \text{or} \quad \frac{[R]_t}{[R]_0} = \tfrac{1}{2}$$

Here, $[R]_0$ is the initial concentration, and $[R]_t$ is the concentration after the reaction is half completed. Half-life is used primarily when dealing with first-order processes. To evaluate $t_{1/2}$ for a first-order reaction, we substitute $[R]_t/[R]_0 = \tfrac{1}{2}$ and $t = t_{1/2}$ into the integrated first-order rate equation (Equation 14.1),

$$\ln(\tfrac{1}{2}) = -kt_{1/2} \quad \text{or} \quad \ln 2 = kt_{1/2}$$

Half-Life and Radioactivity
Half-life is a term often encountered when dealing with radioactive elements. Radioactive decay is a first-order process, and half-life is commonly used to describe how rapidly a radioactive element decays. See Chapter 25 and Example 14.9.

Rearranging this equation (and substituting ln 2 = 0.693) provides a useful equation that relates half-life and the first-order rate constant:

$$t_{1/2} = \frac{0.693}{k} \tag{14.4}$$

This equation identifies an important feature of first-order reactions: *$t_{1/2}$ is independent of concentration.*

To illustrate the concept of half-life, consider again the first-order decomposition of azomethane, $CH_3N_2CH_3$.

$$CH_3N_2CH_3(g) \rightarrow CH_3CH_3(g) + N_2(g)$$

$$\text{Rate} = k[CH_3N_2CH_3] \text{ with } k = 3.6 \times 10^{-4}\ s^{-1} \text{ at } 600\ K$$

Half-Life Equations for Other Reaction Orders
For a zero-order reaction, R → products

$$t_{1/2} = \frac{[R]_0}{2k}$$

For a second-order reaction, R → products

$$t_{1/2} = \frac{1}{k[R]_0}$$

Note that in both cases the half-life depends on the initial concentration.

Given a rate constant of $3.6 \times 10^{-4}\ s^{-1}$, we calculate a half-life of 1.9×10^3 s or 32 minutes.

$$t_{1/2} = \frac{0.693}{3.6 \times 10^{-4}\ s^{-1}} = 1.9 \times 10^3 \text{ s (or 32 min)}$$

The partial pressure of azomethane has been plotted as a function of time in Figure 14.7, and this graph shows that P(azomethane) decreases by half every 32 minutes. The initial pressure of azomethane was 820 mm Hg, but it dropped to 410 mm Hg in 32 minutes, and then dropped to 205 mm Hg in another 32 minutes. That is, after two half-lives (64 minutes), the partial pressure is $(\tfrac{1}{2}) \times (\tfrac{1}{2}) = (\tfrac{1}{2})^2 = \tfrac{1}{4}$ or 25% of the initial pressure. After three half-lives, the partial pressure has dropped further to

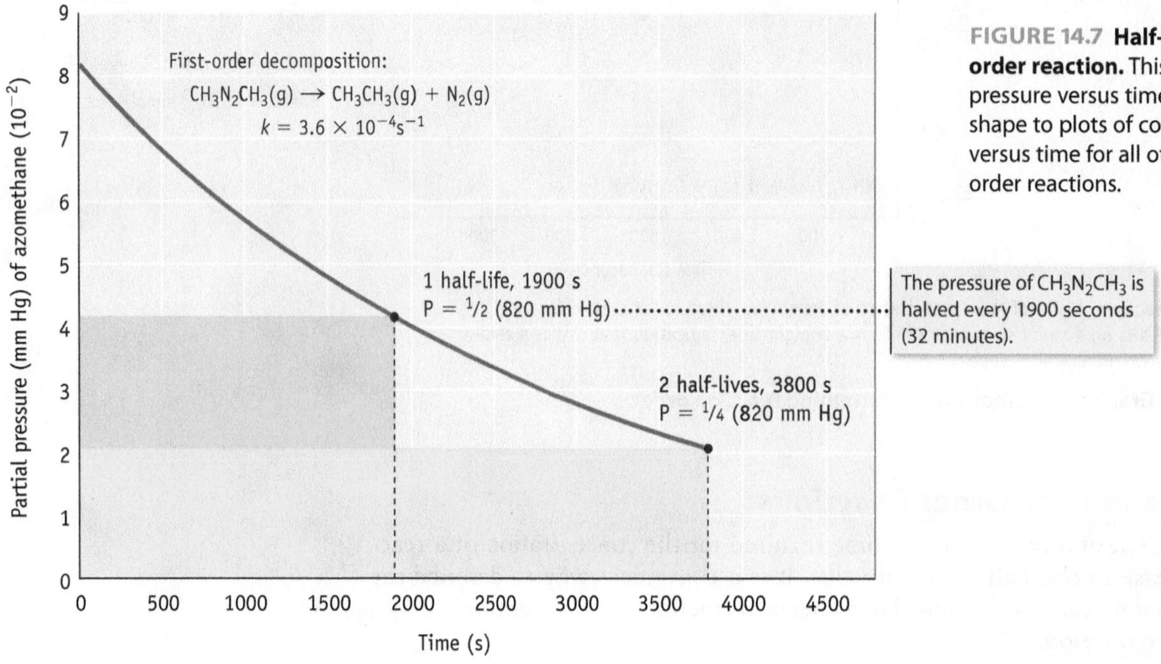

FIGURE 14.7 Half-life of a first-order reaction. This plot of pressure versus time is similar in shape to plots of concentration versus time for all other first-order reactions.

102 mm Hg or 12.5% of the initial value and is equal to $(\frac{1}{2}) \times (\frac{1}{2}) \times (\frac{1}{2}) = (\frac{1}{2})^3 = \frac{1}{8}$ of the initial value.

It can be hard to visualize whether a reaction is fast or slow from the rate constant value. Can you tell from the rate constant, $k = 3.6 \times 10^{-4}\ s^{-1}$, whether the azomethane decomposition will take seconds, hours, or days to reach completion? Probably not, but you can get a better sense of reaction rate from the value of the half-life for the reaction (32 minutes). Now you know that you would only have to wait a few hours for the reactant to be essentially consumed.

EXAMPLE 14.8

Half-Life and a First-Order Process

Problem Sucrose, $C_{12}H_{22}O_{11}$, decomposes to fructose and glucose in acid solution with the rate law

$$\text{Rate} = k[C_{12}H_{22}O_{11}] \qquad k = 0.216\ h^{-1} \text{ at } 25\ °C$$

(a) What is the half-life of $C_{12}H_{22}O_{11}$ at this temperature?

(b) What amount of time is required for 87.5% of the initial concentration of $C_{12}H_{22}O_{11}$ to decompose?

What Do You Know? The decomposition of sucrose is a first-order reaction. The rate constant for the reaction (at 25 °C) is given.

Strategy (a) Use Equation 14.4 to calculate the half-life from the rate constant. (b) After 87.5% of the $C_{12}H_{22}O_{11}$ has decomposed, 12.5% (or one eighth of the sample) remains. To reach this point, three half-lives are required.

HALF-LIFE	FRACTION REMAINING
1	0.5
2	0.25
3	0.125

Therefore, we multiply the half-life calculated in part (a) by 3.

Solution

(a) The half-life for the reaction is

$$t_{1/2} = 0.693/k = 0.693/(0.216\ h^{-1}) = 3.21 \text{ hours}$$

(b) Three half-lives must elapse before the fraction remaining is 0.125, so

$$\text{Time elapsed} = 3 \times 3.21\ h = 9.63 \text{ hours}$$

Think about Your Answer Half-life is a convenient way to describe the speed of a first-order reaction. In this example, you can quickly see that complete decomposition of a sample of sucrose requires many hours.

Check Your Understanding

The catalyzed decomposition of hydrogen peroxide is first-order in $[H_2O_2]$. It was found that the concentration of H_2O_2 decreased from 0.24 M to 0.060 M over a period of 282 minutes. What is the half-life of H_2O_2? What is the rate constant for this reaction? What is the initial rate of decomposition at the beginning of this experiment (when $[H_2O_2] = 0.24$ M)?

Strategy Map 14.9

PROBLEM

Find the **final number of atoms** of a radioactive isotope after a **given time period.**

DATA/INFORMATION

- Half-life for decay
- Initial number of atoms
- Time elapsed

STEP 1. Use Equation 14.4 to calculate k from $t_{1/2}$.

Value of k

STEP 2. Use Equation 14.1 where k, $[R]_0$, and t are known to calculate $[R]_t$.

Value of $[R]_t$, the ***final number of atoms*** of radioactive isotope after time t.

EXAMPLE 14.9

Half-Life and First-Order Processes

Problem Radioactive decay is a first-order process. Radioactive radon-222 gas (^{222}Rn) occurs naturally as a product of uranium decay. The half-life of ^{222}Rn is 3.8 days. Suppose a flask originally contained 4.0×10^{13} atoms of ^{222}Rn. How many atoms of ^{222}Rn will remain after one month (30. days)?

What Do You Know? This process follows first-order kinetics. The half-life of ^{222}Rn and the number of atoms initially present are known.

Strategy First, the rate constant, k, must be found from the half-life using Equation 14.4. Then, using Equation 14.1, and knowing the number of atoms at the beginning ($[R]_0$), the elapsed time (30. days), and the rate constant, we can calculate the number of atoms remaining ($[R]_t$).

Solution The rate constant, k, is

$$k = \frac{0.693}{t_{1/2}} = \frac{0.693}{3.8\ \text{d}} = 0.18\ \text{d}^{-1}$$

Now use Equation 14.1 to calculate the number of atoms remaining after 30. days.

$$\ln \frac{[\text{Rn}]_t}{4.0 \times 10^{13}\ \text{atoms}} = -(0.18\ \text{d}^{-1})(30.\ \text{d}) = -5.5$$

$$\frac{[\text{Rn}]_t}{4.0 \times 10^{13}\ \text{atoms}} = e^{-5.5} = 0.0042$$

$$[\text{Rn}]_t = 2 \times 10^{11}\ \text{atoms}$$

Think about Your Answer Thirty days is approximately 8 half-lives for this element. This means that the number of atoms present at the end of the month is approximately $(1/2)^8$ or $1/256$th of the original number.

Check Your Understanding

Americium is used in smoke detectors and in medicine for the treatment of certain malignancies. One isotope of americium, ^{241}Am, has a rate constant, k, for radioactive decay of $0.0016\ \text{y}^{-1}$. In contrast, radioactive iodine-125, which is used for studies of thyroid functioning, has a rate constant for decay of $0.011\ \text{d}^{-1}$.

(a) What are the half-lives of these isotopes?

(b) Which isotope decays faster?

(c) If you are given a dose of iodine-125 containing 1.6×10^{15} atoms, how many atoms remain after 2.0 days?

REVIEW & CHECK FOR SECTION 14-4

1. The decomposition of N_2O_5 is a first-order process. How many half-lives would be required to decompose 99% of the sample?

   (a) 7 (b) between 6 and 7 (c) 5 (d) between 5 and 6

2. Which of the following will confirm that the decomposition of SO_2Cl_2 (to form SO_2 and Cl_2) is a first-order process?

   (a) A graph of $[SO_2Cl_2]$ vs. time gives a curved line.

   (b) A graph of $\ln[SO_2Cl_2]$ vs. time gives a curved line.

A CLOSER LOOK Rate Laws, Rate Constants, and Reaction Stoichiometry

Qualitatively, the rate of a reaction is easy to understand: it represents the change in concentration of the reactants and products. When we deal with reaction rates quantitatively, however, we need to be specific about the reaction stoichiometry.

Consider the first-order decomposition of N_2O_5, a reaction we mentioned earlier.

$$N_2O_5(g) \rightarrow 2\ NO_2(g) + \tfrac{1}{2}\ O_2(g)$$

The rate of the reaction can be expressed (and measured in the lab) as

$$\text{Rate} = -\left(\frac{\Delta[N_2O_5]}{\Delta t}\right) = +\frac{1}{2}\left(\frac{\Delta[NO_2]}{\Delta t}\right) = +2\left(\frac{\Delta[O_2]}{\Delta t}\right)$$

If we were to follow the disappearance of N_2O_5 as a measure of reaction rate and base our definition of rate on the stoichiometry above, we should write the following differential form of the rate law.

$$\text{Rate} = -\left(\frac{\Delta[N_2O_5]}{\Delta t}\right) = k[N_2O_5]$$

From this definition, it also follows that the integrated rate equation is

$$\ln\frac{[N_2O_5]_t}{[N_2O_5]_0} = -kt$$

and the half-life equation is

$$t_{1/2} = 0.693/k$$

We can also, however, write the equation for the decomposition of N_2O_5 as follows:

$$2\ N_2O_5(g) \rightarrow 4\ NO_2(g) + O_2(g)$$

Following the reasoning above, the reaction rate would be written as follows:

$$\text{Rate} = -\frac{1}{2}\left(\frac{\Delta[N_2O_5]}{\Delta t}\right) = +\frac{1}{4}\left(\frac{\Delta[NO_2]}{\Delta t}\right) = +\left(\frac{\Delta[O_2]}{\Delta t}\right)$$

This leads to the following differential rate law:

$$\text{Rate} = -\frac{1}{2}\left(\frac{\Delta[N_2O_5]}{\Delta t}\right) = k'[N_2O_5]$$

Rearranging this to solve for the rate of disappearance of N_2O_5 yields the following equation:

$$-\left(\frac{\Delta[N_2O_5]}{\Delta t}\right) = 2k'[N_2O_5]$$

with the following integrated rate equation and half-life equation.

Integrated rate equation:

$$\ln\frac{[N_2O_5]_t}{[N_2O_5]_0} = -2k't$$

Half-life equation:

$$t_{1/2} = 0.693/2k'$$

Note that the differential and integrated rate laws derived based on the two different chemical equations have the same form, but k and k' do not have the same values; instead $k = 2k'$. Notice, however, that both calculations give the same value for the half-life, as they should; half-life does not depend on how the equation is written.

For more on these issues, see K. T. Quisenberry and J. Tellinghuisen, *Journal of Chemical Education*, Vol. 83, pp. 510–512, 2006.

(c) A graph of $1/[SO_2Cl_2]$ vs. time gives a straight line.

(d) A graph of $\ln[SO_2Cl_2]$ vs. time gives a straight line.

3. The equation for the decomposition of $NO_2(g)$ at 573 K is $2\ NO_2(g) \rightarrow 2\ NO(g) + O_2(g)$. Using the concentration–time data below, determine the order of the reaction with respect to $[NO_2]$.

$[NO_2]$, M	Time, min
0.20	0
0.095	5
0.063	10
0.047	15

(a) first-order (b) second-order (c) zero-order

14-5 A Microscopic View of Reaction Rates

Learning Objectives: LO 4.5, LO 4.6, LO 4.8, LO 4.9 (see Appendix O-2 "Acid Catalysts"), LO 5.18 (see Appendix O-3 "The Interplay of Kinetics and Thermodynamics")

Chemists often turn to the particulate level of chemistry to explain chemical phenomena, and rates of reaction are no exception. Looking at the way reactions occur at the atomic and molecular levels can give some insight into the various influences on rates of reactions.

Let us review the macroscopic observations we have made so far concerning reaction rates. There are wide differences in rates of reactions—from very fast reactions like the explosion that occurs when hydrogen and oxygen are exposed to a spark or flame (◀ Figure 1.15), to slow reactions like the formation of rust that occurs over days, weeks, or years. For a specific reaction, factors that influence reaction rate include the concentrations of the reactants, the temperature of the reaction system, and the presence of catalysts. Each of these influences can be explained using the **collision theory of reaction rates**, which states that three conditions must be met for a reaction to occur:

1. The reacting molecules must collide with one another.
2. The reacting molecules must collide with sufficient energy to initiate the process of breaking and forming bonds.
3. The molecules must collide in an orientation that can lead to rearrangement of the atoms and the formation of products.

Collision Theory: Concentration and Reaction Rate

Consider the gas-phase reaction of nitric oxide and ozone, an environmentally important reaction that contributes to both natural and human-caused ozone decomposition:

$$NO(g) + O_3(g) \rightarrow NO_2(g) + O_2(g)$$

The rate law for this product-favored reaction is first-order in each reactant: Rate = $k[NO][O_3]$. How can this reaction have this rate law?

Imagine a flask containing a mixture of NO and O_3 molecules in the gas phase. Both kinds of molecules are in rapid and random motion within the flask. They strike the walls of the vessel, but they also collide with other molecules. It is reasonable to propose that the rate of their reaction should be related to the number of collisions, which is in turn related to their concentrations (Figure 14.8). Doubling the concentration of one reactant in the NO + O_3 reaction, say NO, will lead to twice the number of molecular collisions. Figure 14.8a shows a single molecule of one of the reactants (NO) moving randomly among sixteen O_3 molecules. In a given time period, it might collide with two O_3 molecules. The number of NO—O_3 collisions will double, however, if the concentration of NO molecules is doubled (to 2, as shown in Figure 14.8b) or if the number of O_3 molecules is doubled (to 32, as in Figure 14.8c). Thus, the dependence of reaction rate on concentration can be explained: The number of collisions between the two reactant molecules is directly proportional to the concentration of each reactant, and the rate of the reaction shows a first-order dependence on each reactant.

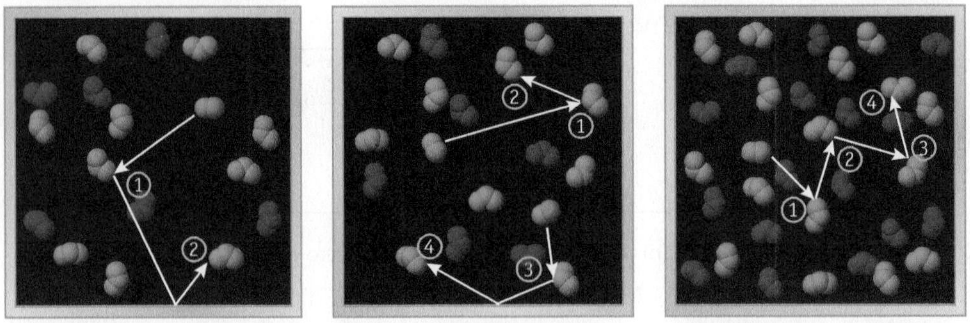

(a) 1 NO : 16 O_3 – *2 hits/second.*

A single NO molecule, moving among 16 O_3 molecules, is shown colliding with two of them per second.

(b) 2 NO : 16 O_3 – *4 hits/second.*

If two NO molecules move among 16 O_3 molecules, we would predict that four NO—O_3 collisions would occur per second.

(c) 1 NO : 32 O_3 – *4 hits/second.*

If the number of O_3 molecules is doubled (to 32), the frequency of NO—O_3 collisions is also doubled, to four per second.

FIGURE 14.8 **The effect of concentration on the frequency of molecular collisions.**

Collision Theory: Activation Energy

Molecules require some minimum energy to react. Chemists visualize this as an energy barrier that must be surmounted by the reactants for a reaction to occur (Figure 14.9). The energy required to cross the barrier is called the **activation energy, E_a**. If the barrier is low, the energy required is low, and a high proportion of the molecules in a sample may have sufficient energy to react. The reaction will be fast. If the barrier is high, the activation energy is high, and only a few reactant molecules in a sample may have enough energy. The reaction will be slow.

FIGURE 14.9 **An analogy to chemical activation energy.** For the volleyball to go over the net, the player must give it sufficient energy.

To further illustrate an activation energy barrier, consider the high temperature conversion of NO_2 and CO to NO and CO_2. At the molecular level, we imagine that the reaction involves the transfer of an O atom from an NO_2 molecule to a CO molecule.

$$NO_2(g) + CO(g) \rightleftharpoons NO(g) + CO_2(g)$$

We can describe this process by using an energy diagram or **reaction coordinate** diagram (Figure 14.10). The horizontal axis describes the reaction progress as the reaction proceeds, and the vertical axis represents the potential energy of the system during the reaction. When NO_2 and CO approach and O atom transfer begins, an N—O bond is being broken, and a C═O bond is forming. Energy input (the activation energy) is required for this to occur. The energy of the system reaches a maximum at the **transition state**. At the transition state, sufficient energy has been concentrated in the appropriate bonds; bonds in the reactants can now break, and new bonds can form to give products. The system is poised to go on to products, but it could return to the reactants. Because the transition state is at a maximum in potential energy, a molecular species with this structure cannot be isolated. Using computer molecular modeling techniques, however, chemists can describe what the transition state must look like.

In the NO_2 + CO reaction, 132 kJ/mol is required to reach the transition state, that is, the top of the energy barrier. As the reaction continues toward the products—as the N—O bond breaks and a C═O bond forms—the reaction evolves energy, 358 kJ/mol. The net energy change involved in this *exo*thermic reaction is −226 kJ/mol.

$$\Delta H = +132 \text{ kJ/mol} + (-358 \text{ kJ/mol}) = -226 \text{ kJ/mol}$$

What happens if the reverse reaction is carried out? That reaction requires 358 kJ/mol to reach the transition state, and 132 kJ/mol is evolved on proceeding

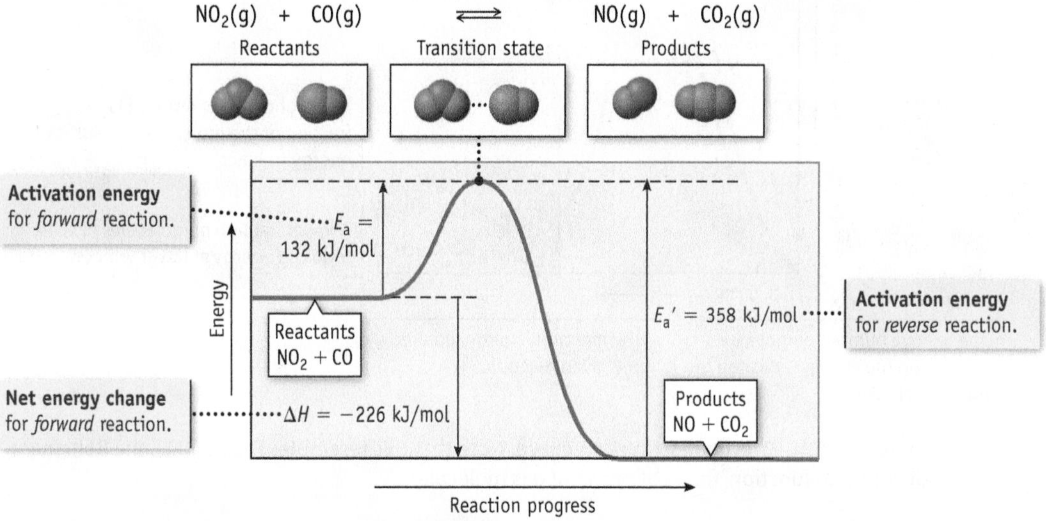

FIGURE 14.10 **Activation energy for the reaction of NO_2 and CO to give NO and CO_2.**

to the products, NO_2 and CO. The reaction in this direction is *endo*thermic, requiring a net input of +226 kJ/mol.

Collision Theory: Activation Energy and Temperature

In a laboratory or in the chemical industry, a chemical reaction is often carried out at elevated temperatures because this allows the reaction to occur more rapidly. Conversely, it is sometimes desirable to lower the temperature to slow down a chemical reaction (to avoid an uncontrollable reaction or a potentially dangerous explosion).

A discussion of the effect of temperature on reaction rate begins by recalling there is a distribution of energies for molecules in a sample of a gas or liquid. The molecules in a sample have a wide range of energies, described earlier as a Boltzmann distribution of energies (◀ Figure 10.13). In any sample of a gas or liquid, some molecules have very low energies; others have very high energies; but most have some intermediate energy. As the temperature increases, the average energy of the molecules in the sample increases, as does the fraction having higher energies. For example, in the reaction discussed above the conversion of NO_2 and CO to products at room temperature is slow because only a small fraction of the molecules have enough energy to reach the transition state. The rate can be increased by heating the sample. Raising the temperature increases the reaction rate by increasing the fraction of molecules with enough energy to surmount the activation energy barrier (Figure 14.11).

Collision Theory: Effect of Molecular Orientation on Reaction Rate

Not only must reacting molecules have sufficient energy to react, but the reactant molecules must also come together in the correct orientation. For the reaction of NO_2 and CO, we can imagine that the transition state structure has one of the O atoms of NO_2 beginning to bind to the C atom of CO in preparation for O atom

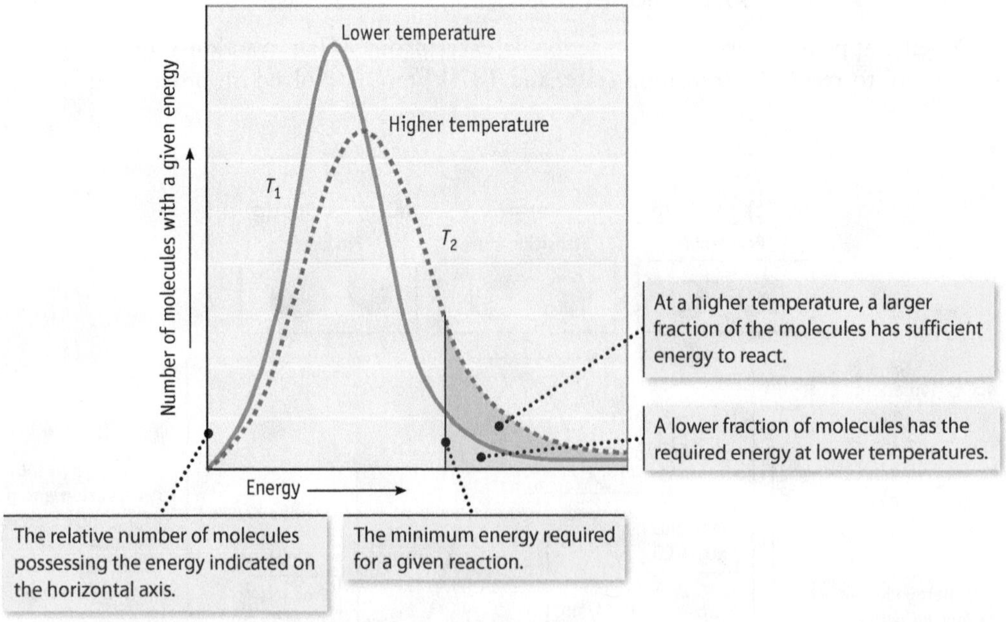

FIGURE 14.11 Energy distribution curve. Note that this resembles Figure 10.13, the Boltzmann distribution function, for a collection of gas molecules.

transfer (see Figure 14.10). The lower the probability of achieving the proper alignment, the smaller the value of k, and the slower the reaction.

Imagine what happens when two or more complicated molecules collide. In only a small fraction of the collisions will the molecules come together in exactly the right orientation. Thus, only a tiny fraction of the collisions can be effective. No wonder some reactions are slow. Conversely, it is amazing that so many are fast!

The Arrhenius Equation

The observation that reaction rates depend on the energy and frequency of collisions between reacting molecules, on the temperature, and on whether the collisions have the correct geometry is summarized by the **Arrhenius equation**:

$$k = \text{rate constant} = \underbrace{A}_{\text{Frequency factor}}\underbrace{e^{-E_a/RT}}_{\text{Fraction of molecules with minimum energy for reaction}} \qquad (14.5)$$

Interpreting the Arrhenius Equation
(a) The exponential term gives the fraction of molecules having sufficient energy for reaction and is a function of T.
(b) Although a complete understanding of the frequency factor goes beyond the level of this text, note that A becomes smaller as the reactants become larger. This reflects the fact that larger molecules have a smaller probability of coming together in the appropriate geometry.

In this equation, k is the rate constant, R is the gas constant with a value of 8.314462×10^{-3} kJ/K · mol, and T is the kelvin temperature. The parameter A is called the **frequency factor**. It is related to the number of collisions and to the fraction of collisions that have the correct geometry; A is specific to each reaction and is temperature dependent. The factor $e^{-E_a/RT}$, which always has a value less than 1, represents *the fraction of molecules having the minimum energy required for reaction*. As the following table shows, this fraction changes significantly with temperature.

TEMPERATURE (K)	VALUE OF $e^{-E_a/RT}$ FOR $E_a = 40$ kJ/mol-rxn
298	9.7×10^{-8}
400	5.9×10^{-6}
600	3.3×10^{-4}

The Arrhenius equation is significant because

- it can be used to calculate E_a from the temperature dependence of the rate constant.
- it can be used to calculate the rate constant, if E_a, T, and A are known.

E_a, Reaction Rates, and Temperature An often-used rule of thumb is that reaction rates double for every 10 °C rise in temperature in the vicinity of room temperature.

If rate constants for a given reaction are measured at several temperatures then you can use graphical techniques to determine the activation energy of a reaction. Taking the natural logarithm of each side of Equation 14.5, we have

$$\ln k = \ln A + \left(-\frac{E_a}{RT}\right)$$

Rearranging this expression slightly shows that ln k and $1/T$ are related linearly.

$$\ln k = -\frac{E_a}{R}\left(\frac{1}{T}\right) + \ln A \quad \leftarrow \text{Arrhenius equation} \qquad (14.6)$$

$$\begin{array}{ccccc} \downarrow & & \downarrow & & \downarrow \\ y & = & mx & & +\ b \end{array} \quad \leftarrow \text{Equation for straight line}$$

Temperature Dependence of the Rate Constant k Figure 14.11 illustrates the fact that the fraction of molecules in a reaction mixture that has the required energy for reaction increases with temperature. This temperature dependence is reflected in the temperature dependence of k (as given by the Arrhenius equation).

This means that, if the natural logarithm of k (ln k) is plotted versus $1/T$, the result is a downward-sloping straight line with a slope of $(-E_a/R)$. The activation energy, E_a, can be obtained from the slope of this line ($E_a = -R \times \text{slope}$).

EXAMPLE 14.10

Determination of E_a from the Arrhenius Equation

Problem Using the experimental data shown in the table, calculate the activation energy E_a for the reaction

$$2\ N_2O(g) \rightarrow 2\ N_2(g) + O_2(g)$$

EXPERIMENT	TEMPERATURE (K)	*k* (L/mol · s)
1	1125	11.59
2	1053	1.67
3	1001	0.380
4	838	0.0011

What Do You Know? Rate constants are given at several temperatures.

Strategy To solve this problem graphically, you first need to calculate ln *k* and 1/*T* for each data point. These data are then plotted, and E_a is calculated from the resulting straight line (slope $= -E_a/R$).

Solution First, calculate 1/*T* and ln *k*.

EXPERIMENT	$1/T$ (K^{-1})	ln *k*
1	8.889×10^{-4}	2.4501
2	9.497×10^{-4}	0.513
3	9.990×10^{-4}	−0.968
4	11.9×10^{-4}	−6.81

Plotting these data gives the graph shown in Figure 14.12. Choosing the large blue points on the graph, the slope is found to be

$$\text{Slope} = \frac{\Delta \ln k}{\Delta(1/T)} = \frac{2.0 - (-5.6)}{(9.0 - 11.5)(10^{-4})K^{-1}} = -3.0 \times 10^4\ \text{K}$$

The activation energy is evaluated from the slope.

$$\text{Slope} = -\frac{E_a}{R} = -\frac{E_a}{8.31 \times 10^{-3}\ \text{kJ/K} \cdot \text{mol}} = -3.0 \times 10^4\ \text{K}$$

$$E_a = 250\ \text{kJ/mol}$$

Think about Your Answer Notice the units of the answer. Using the value for $R = 8.31 \times 10^{-3}$ kJ/K · mol will give an answer with the units kJ/mol.

Check Your Understanding

Rate constants were determined for the decomposition of acetaldehyde (CH_3CHO) in the temperature range 700 to 1000 K. Use these data to determine E_a for the reaction using a graphical method.

T (K)	700	760	840	1000
k (L/mol · s)	0.011	0.105	2.17	145

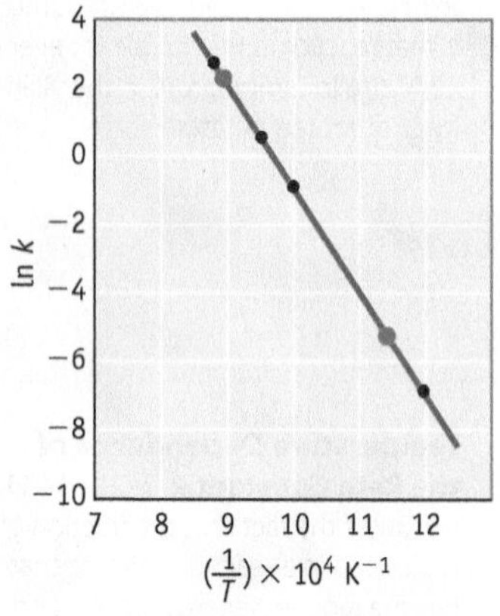

FIGURE 14.12 Arrhenius plot. A plot of ln *k* versus 1/*T* for the reaction $2\ N_2O(g) \rightarrow 2\ N_2(g) + O_2(g)$. The slope of the line can be used to calculate E_a. See Example 14.10.

The activation energy, E_a, for a reaction can be obtained algebraically if k is known at two different temperatures. You can write an equation for each set of these conditions:

$$\ln k_1 = -\left(\frac{E_a}{RT_1}\right) + \ln A \quad \text{and} \quad \ln k_2 = -\left(\frac{E_a}{RT_2}\right) + \ln A$$

If one of these equations is subtracted from the other, we have

$$\ln k_2 - \ln k_1 = \ln\frac{k_2}{k_1} = -\frac{E_a}{R}\left[\frac{1}{T_2} - \frac{1}{T_1}\right] \qquad (14.7)$$

Example 14.11 demonstrates the use of this equation.

EXAMPLE 14.11

Calculating E_a Numerically

Problem Use values of k determined at two different temperatures to calculate the value of E_a for the decomposition of HI:

$$2\,HI(g) \rightarrow H_2(g) + I_2(g)$$

$$k_1 = 2.15 \times 10^{-8}\ L/(mol \cdot s) \text{ at } 6.50 \times 10^2\ K\ (T_1)$$

$$k_2 = 2.39 \times 10^{-7}\ L/(mol \cdot s) \text{ at } 7.00 \times 10^2\ K\ (T_2)$$

What Do You Know? Values for the rate constant at two temperatures are given.

Strategy Substitute values of k_1, k_2, T_1, and T_2 into Equation 14.7 and solve for E_a.

Solution

$$\ln\frac{2.39 \times 10^{-7}\ L/(mol \cdot s)}{2.15 \times 10^{-8}\ L/(mol \cdot s)} = -\frac{E_a}{8.315 \times 10^{-3}\ kJ/K \cdot mol} \times \left[\frac{1}{7.00 \times 10^2\ K} - \frac{1}{6.50 \times 10^2\ K}\right]$$

Solving this equation gives $E_a = 180$ kJ/mol.

Think about Your Answer Another way to write the difference in fractions in brackets is

$$\left[\frac{1}{T_2} - \frac{1}{T_1}\right] = \frac{T_1 - T_2}{T_1 T_2}$$

This expression is sometimes easier to use.

Check Your Understanding

The colorless gas N_2O_4 decomposes to the brown gas NO_2 in a first-order reaction.

$$N_2O_4(g) \rightarrow 2\,NO_2(g)$$

The rate constant $k = 4.5 \times 10^3\ s^{-1}$ at 274 K and $k = 1.00 \times 10^4\ s^{-1}$ at 283 K. What is the activation energy, E_a?

Effect of Catalysts on Reaction Rate

A catalyst is a substance that speeds up the rate of a chemical reaction, and you have seen several examples of catalysts in earlier discussions in this chapter: MnO_2, iodide ion, the enzyme catalase in a potato, and hydroxide ion all catalyze the decomposition of hydrogen peroxide (see Figure 14.4).

A CLOSER LOOK — Thinking About Kinetics and Bond Energies

As you will see in Section 14-6, one of the most important uses of chemical kinetics is to give us an idea as to the reaction mechanism, the step-by-step process by which a chemical reaction occurs. These individual steps involve bond breaking and bond formation and guide the chemical reaction from reactants to products. Bond breaking requires energy, while bond formation evolves energy.

Consider the uncatalyzed conversion between *cis*- and *trans*-2-butene. The postulated mechanism for this reaction involves rotation around the double bond, which would occur if the two ends of the molecule twist out of alignment by 90° resulting in the π bond being broken. We can estimate the energy of the π bond in this species using data from the table of bond dissociation enthalpies (see Table 8.9). The average bond dissociation enthalpies of C=C double and C—C single bonds are 610 kJ/mol and 346 kJ/mol, respectively; the difference between these two values is 264 kJ/mol-rxn.

Note the correspondence between this value and the measured value for the activation energy of this reaction, 264 kJ/mol-rxn. Matching the estimated bond energy and the activation energy is taken to be evidence in support this mechanism.

Enzymes: Biological Catalysts Many natural systems are controlled by catalysts called enzymes. One example is catalase, whose function is to speed up the decomposition of hydrogen peroxide. This enzyme ensures that hydrogen peroxide, which is highly toxic, does not build up in the body. See *Case Study: Enzymes—Nature's Catalysts,* page 540.

Catalysts are not consumed in a chemical reaction. They are, however, intimately involved in the details of the reaction at the particulate level. Their function is to provide *a different pathway with a lower activation energy for the reaction.* To illustrate how a catalyst participates in a reaction, let us consider the isomerization of *cis*-2-butene to the slightly more stable isomer *trans*-2-butene.

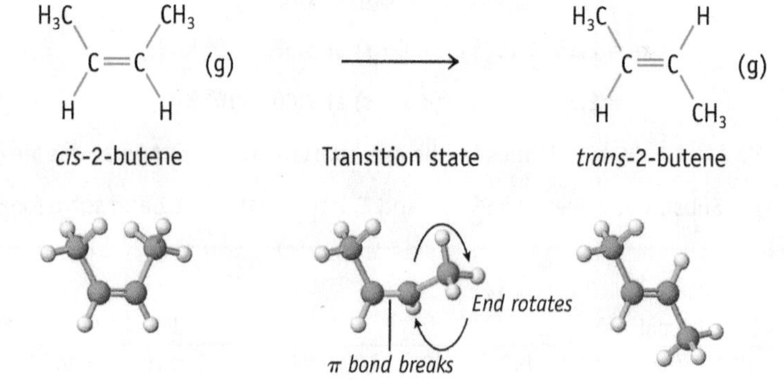

The activation energy for the uncatalyzed conversion is relatively large—264 kJ/mol—because the π bond must be broken to allow one end of the molecule to rotate into a new position. Because of the high activation energy, this is a slow reaction, and rather high temperatures are required for it to occur at a reasonable rate.

Catalysts and the Economy "One third of [the] material gross national product in the United States involves a catalytic process somewhere in the production chain." (Quoted in A. Bell, *Science,* Vol. 299, p. 1688, 2003.)

The *cis*- to *trans*-2-butene reaction is greatly accelerated by a catalyst, iodine, and the reaction can be carried out in the presence of iodine at a temperature several hundred degrees lower than for the uncatalyzed reaction. Iodine is not consumed (nor is it a product), and it does not appear in the overall balanced equation. It does appear in the reaction rate law, however; the rate of the reaction depends on the square root of the iodine concentration:

$$\text{Rate} = k[\textit{cis}\text{-2-butene}][I_2]^{1/2}$$

The presence of I_2 changes the way the butene isomerization reaction occurs; that is, it changes the mechanism of the reaction (Figure 14.13). The best hypothesis is that iodine molecules first dissociate to form iodine atoms (Step 1). This requires much less energy input than rotation of the C=C double bond. An iodine atom then adds to one of the C atoms of the C=C double bond (Step 2). This converts the double bond between the carbon atoms to a single bond (the π bond is broken) and allows the ends of the molecule to twist freely relative to each other (Step 3). If the iodine atom then dissociates from the intermediate, the double bond can re-form in the *trans* configuration (Step 4). The iodine atom is now free to add to another molecule of *cis*-2-butene. The result is a kind of chain reaction, as one molecule of

Acid Catalysis For information about acid catalysis of reactions, see Appendix O-2, "Acid Catalysts."

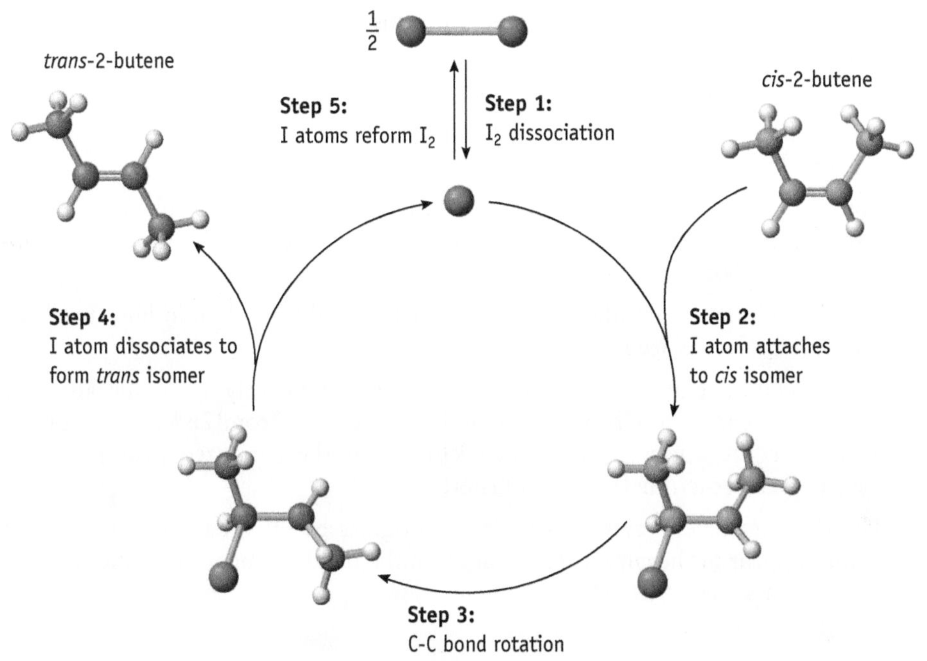

FIGURE 14.13 **The mechanism of the iodine-catalyzed isomerization of *cis*-2-butene to *trans*-2-butene.**

cis-2-butene after another is converted to the *trans* isomer. The chain is broken if the iodine atom recombines with another iodine atom to re-form molecular iodine.

An energy profile for the catalyzed reaction (Figure 14.14) shows that the overall energy barrier is much lower than for the uncatalyzed reaction. Five separate steps are identified for the mechanism in the energy profile. This proposed mechanism also includes a series of **reaction intermediates,** species formed in one step of the reaction and consumed in a later step. Iodine atoms are intermediates, as are the free radical species formed when an iodine atom adds to *cis*-2-butene.

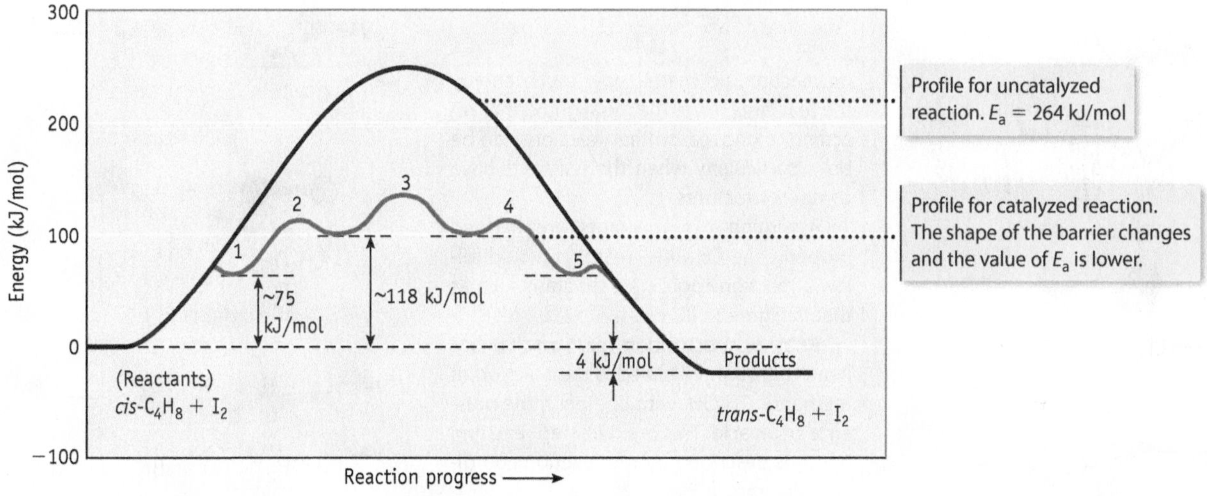

FIGURE 14.14 **Energy profile for the iodine-catalyzed reaction of *cis*-2-butene to form *trans*-2-butene.** A catalyst accelerates a reaction by altering the mechanism so that the activation energy is lowered. With a smaller barrier to overcome, more reacting molecules have sufficient energy to surmount the barrier, and the reaction occurs more rapidly.

Five important points are associated with this mechanism:

- Iodine molecules, I_2, dissociate to atoms and then re-form. On the macroscopic level, the concentration of I_2 is unchanged. Iodine does not appear in the balanced, stoichiometric equation even though it appears in the rate equation. This is generally true of catalysts.
- Both the catalyst I_2 and the reactant *cis*-2-butene are in the gas phase. If a catalyst is present in the same phase as the reacting substance, it is called a *homogeneous catalyst.*
- Iodine atoms and the radical species formed by addition of an iodine atom to a 2-butene molecule are intermediates.
- The activation energy barrier to reaction is significantly lower because the mechanism changed. Dropping the activation energy from 264 kJ/mol for the uncatalyzed reaction to about 150 kJ/mol for the catalyzed process makes the catalyzed reaction 10^{15} times faster!
- The diagram of energy-versus-reaction progress has five energy barriers (five humps appear in the curve). This feature in the diagram means that the reaction occurs in a series of five steps.

A CLOSER LOOK | More About Molecular Orientation and Reaction Coordinate Diagrams

The Arrhenius equation tells us, among other things, that the rate constant depends on the proper alignment of reactants. A reaction will occur only if the reactants are in the proper orientation. A well-studied example of this is the substitution of a halogen atom of CH_3Cl by an ion such as F^-. Here, the F^- ion attacks the molecule from the side opposite the Cl substituent. As F^- begins to form a bond to carbon, the C—Cl bond weakens, and the CH_3 portion of the molecule changes shape. As time progresses, the products CH_3F and Cl^- are formed.

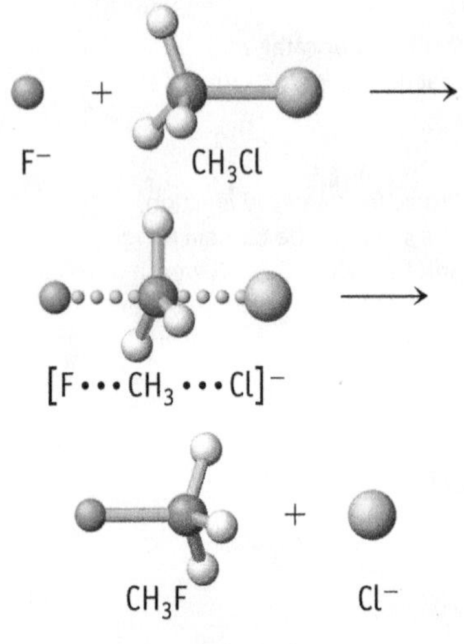

But what happens if F^- approaches from the side of the molecule with the Cl atom or along one of the C—H bonds? There will be no reaction, no matter how much energy the reactants have! The misalignment of reactants is one reason that reactions can be slow, particularly when the reactants have complex structures.

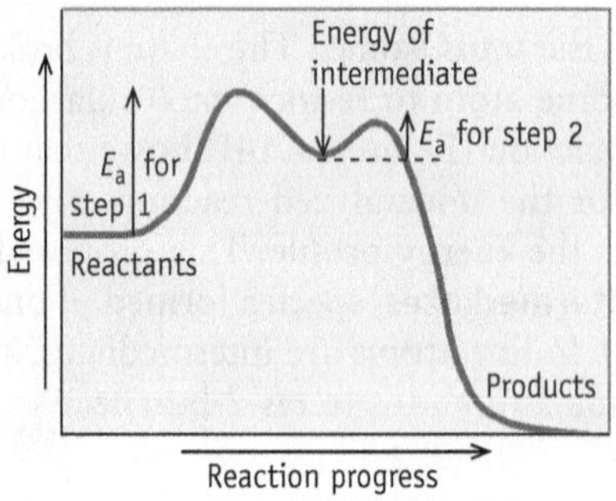

FIGURE A A reaction coordinate diagram for a two-step reaction, a process involving an intermediate.

Assuming the reactants are aligned properly, the CH_3Cl/F^- reaction would follow a reaction coordinate diagram such as that in Figure 14.10.

Another substitution reaction that has been thoroughly studied is the reaction of methanol, CH_3OH, with Br^- ion in the presence of an acid. This is a two-step reaction, which is described by the reaction coordinate diagram in Figure A.

In the first step, an H^+ ion attaches to the O of the C—O—H group in a rapid, reversible reaction. The energy of this protonated species, $CH_3OH_2^+$, a reaction intermediate, is higher than the energies of the reactants. The reaction intermediate is represented by the dip in the curve shown in Figure A. In the second step, a halide ion, say Br^-, attacks the intermediate to produce methyl bromide, CH_3Br, and water. There is an activation energy barrier in both the first step and second step.

Notice in Figure A, as in Figure 14.10, that the energy of the products is lower than the energy of the reactants. The reaction is exothermic.

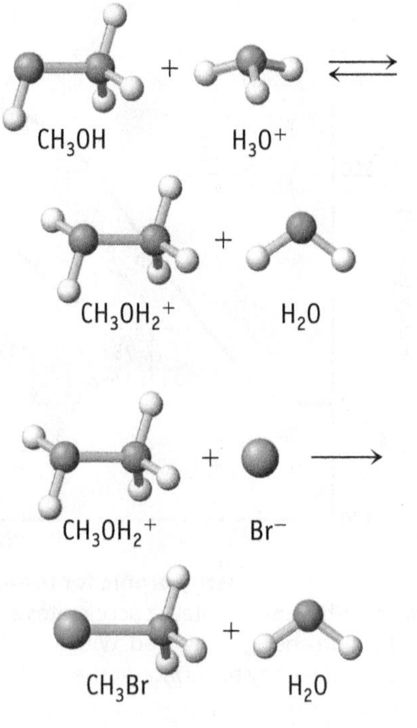

REVIEW & CHECK FOR SECTION 14-5

1. Which of the following graphs will produce a straight line?

   (a) k vs. T (b) $\ln E_a$ vs. T (c) $\ln k$ vs. $1/T$ (d) E_a vs. $1/T$

2. What is the primary reason that increasing the temperature causes an increase in reaction rate?

   (a) An increase in T lowers the activation energy.

   (b) A higher proportion of reactant molecules exceeds the activation energy.

   (c) In a closed vessel, increasing the temperature results in a higher pressure.

   (d) Increasing the temperature provides other reaction pathways.

14-6 Reaction Mechanisms

Learning Objectives: LO 4.4, LO 4.7

Why study chemical kinetics? Beyond simply telling us what factors influence the rate of a chemical reaction and how we might be able to speed up or slow down a particular reaction, chemical kinetics also gives us insight into how a chemical reaction actually occurs. The **reaction mechanism** for a chemical reaction is the sequence of bond-making and bond-breaking steps that occurs during the conversion of reactants to products. Based on the rate equation for a reaction, and by applying chemical intuition, chemists can often make an educated guess about the mechanism for a reaction.

In some reactions, the conversion of reactants to products in a single step is envisioned as the logical mechanism. For example, the uncatalyzed isomerization of *cis*-2-butene to *trans*-2-butene is best described as a single-step reaction (see Figure 14.14).

Most chemical reactions occur in a sequence of steps, however. A multiple-step mechanism was proposed for the iodine-catalyzed 2-butene isomerization reaction. Another example of a multistep reaction is the reaction of bromine and NO:

$$Br_2(g) + 2\ NO(g) \rightarrow 2\ BrNO(g)$$

A single-step reaction would require that three reactant molecules collide simultaneously in just the right orientation. The probability of this occurring is small; thus, it is reasonable to look for a mechanism that occurs in a series of steps, with each step involving only one or two molecules. In one possible mechanism, Br_2 and NO might combine in an initial step to produce an intermediate species, Br_2NO.

Step 1

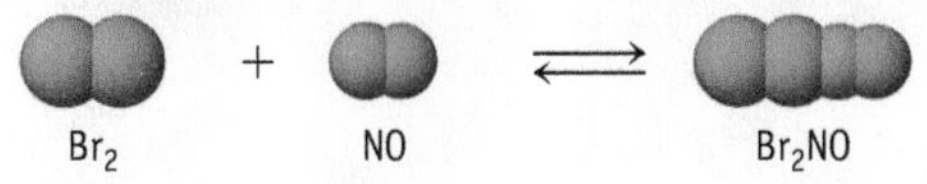

This intermediate would then react with another NO molecule to give the reaction products.

Step 2

The equation for the overall reaction is obtained by adding the equations for these two steps:

Step 1:	$Br_2(g) + NO(g) \rightleftharpoons Br_2NO(g)$
Step 2:	$NO(g) + Br_2NO(g) \rightarrow 2\ BrNO(g)$
Overall Reaction:	$Br_2(g) + 2\ NO(g) \rightarrow 2\ BrNO(g)$

CASE STUDY Enzymes—Nature's Catalysts

Within any living organism, there are untold numbers of chemical reactions occurring, many of them extremely rapidly. In many cases, enzymes, biological catalysts, speed up reactions that would normally move at a snail's pace from reactants to products. Typically, enzyme-catalyzed reactions are 10^7 to 10^{14} times faster than uncatalyzed reactions.

Enzymes are typically large proteins, often containing metal ions such as Zn^{2+}. They are thought to function by bringing the reactants together in just the right orientation in a site where specific bonds can be broken and/or made.

Carbonic anhydrase is one of many enzymes important in biological processes (Figure A). Carbon dioxide dissolves in water to a small extent to produce carbonic acid, which ionizes to give H_3O^+ and HCO_3^- ions.

$$CO_2(g) \rightleftharpoons CO_2(aq) \quad (1)$$

$$CO_2(aq) + H_2O(\ell) \rightleftharpoons H_2CO_3(aq) \quad (2)$$

$$H_2CO_3(aq) + H_2O(\ell) \rightleftharpoons H_3O^+(aq) + HCO_3^-(aq) \quad (3)$$

Carbonic anhydrase speeds up reactions 2 and 3. Many of the H_3O^+ ions produced by ionization of H_2CO_3 (reaction 3) are picked up by hemoglobin in the blood as hemoglobin loses O_2. The resulting HCO_3^- ions are transported back to the lungs. When hemoglobin again takes on O_2, it releases H_3O^+ ions. These ions and HCO_3^- re-form H_2CO_3, from which CO_2 is liberated and exhaled.

You can do an experiment that illustrates the effect of carbonic anhydrase. First, add a small amount of NaOH to a cold, aqueous solution of CO_2. The solution becomes basic immediately because there is not enough H_2CO_3 in the solution to use up the NaOH. After some seconds, however, dissolved CO_2 slowly produces more H_2CO_3, which consumes NaOH, and the solution is again acidic.

Now try the experiment again, this time adding a few drops of blood to the solution (Figure A). The solution becomes acidic very quickly. Carbonic anhydrase in blood speeds up the reaction of CO_2(aq) to HCO_3^-(aq) by a factor of about 10^7, as evidenced by the more rapid reaction under these conditions.

In 1913, Leonor Michaelis and Maud L. Menten proposed a general theory of enzyme action based on kinetic observations. They assumed that the substrate, S (the reactant), and the enzyme, E, form a complex, ES. This complex then breaks down, releasing the enzyme and the product, P.

$$E + S \rightleftharpoons ES$$

$$ES \rightarrow P + E$$

When the substrate concentration is low, the rate of the reaction is first order in S (Figure B). As [S] increases, however, the active sites in the enzyme become saturated with substrate, and the rate reaches its maximum value. Now the kinetics are zero order in substrate.

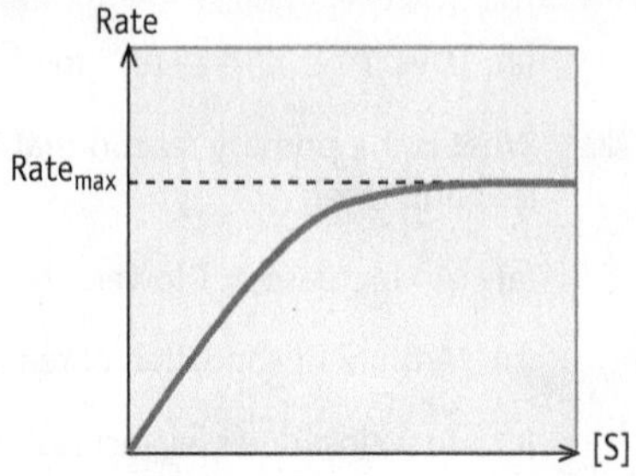

FIGURE B Rate of enzyme-catalyzed reaction. This plot of reaction velocity versus substrate concentration [S] is typical of reactions catalyzed by enzymes that follow the Michaelis–Menten model.

Questions:

1. Catalase can decompose hydrogen peroxide to O_2 and water about 10^7 times faster than the uncatalyzed reaction. If the latter requires one year, how much time is required by the enzyme-catalyzed reaction?
2. According to the Michaelis–Menten model, if 1/Rate is plotted versus 1/[S], the intercept of the plot (when 1/[S] = 0) is $1/Rate_{max}$. Find $Rate_{max}$ for a reaction involving carbonic anhydrase.

[S], mol/L	RATE, mmol/min
2.500	0.588
1.00	0.500
0.714	0.417
0.526	0.370
0.250	0.256

Answers to these questions are available in Appendix N.

Photos: © Cengage Learning/ Charles D. Winters

(a) $t = 0$

A few drops of blood are added to a cold solution of CO_2 in water.

(b) $t = 3$ sec

A few drops of a dye (bromthymol blue) are added to the solution, the yellow color indicating an acidic solution.

(c) $t = 15$ sec

A less-than-stoichiometric amount of sodium hydroxide is added, converting the H_2CO_3 to HCO_3^- (and CO_3^{2-}). The blue color of the dye indicates a basic solution.

(d) $t = 17$ sec

(e) $t = 21$ sec

The blue color begins to fade after some seconds as CO_2 forms more H_2CO_3. The amount of H_2CO_3 formed is finally sufficient to consume the added NaOH, and the solution is again acidic.

FIGURE A CO_2 in water.

Each step in a multistep reaction sequence is an **elementary step**, defined by a chemical equation that describes a single molecular event such as the formation or rupture of a chemical bond resulting from a molecular collision. Each step has its own activation energy, E_a, and rate constant, k. Adding the equations for each step must give the balanced equation for the overall reaction, and the time required to complete all of the steps defines the overall reaction rate. The series of steps constitutes a possible reaction mechanism.

Molecularity of Elementary Steps

Elementary steps are classified by the number of reactant molecules (or ions, atoms, or free radicals) that come together. This whole, positive number is called the **molecularity** of the elementary step. When one molecule is the only reactant in an elementary step, the reaction is a **unimolecular** process. A **bimolecular** elementary process involves two molecules, which may be identical (A + A → products) or different (A + B → products). The mechanism proposed for the decomposition of ozone in the stratosphere illustrates the use of these terms.

Step 1:	Unimolecular	$O_3(g) \rightarrow O_2(g) + O(g)$
Step 2:	Bimolecular	$O_3(g) + O(g) \rightarrow 2\ O_2(g)$
Overall Reaction:		$2\ O_3(g) \rightarrow 3\ O_2(g)$

A **termolecular** elementary step involves three molecules, which could be the same or different (3 A → products; 2 A + B → products; or A + B + C → products). Be aware, however, the simultaneous collision of three molecules has a low probability, unless one of the molecules involved is in high concentration, such as a solvent molecule. In fact, most termolecular processes involve the collision of two reactant molecules and a third, inert molecule. The function of the inert molecule is to absorb the excess energy produced when a new chemical bond is formed by the first two molecules. For example, N_2 is unchanged in a termolecular reaction between oxygen molecules and oxygen atoms that produces ozone in the upper atmosphere:

$$O(g) + O_2(g) + N_2(g) \rightarrow O_3(g) + \text{energetic } N_2(g)$$

The probability that four or more molecules will simultaneously collide with sufficient kinetic energy and proper orientation to react is so small that reaction molecularities greater than three are never proposed.

Before leaving this discussion of molecularity, let us go back to our previous description of collision theory. We can see how bimolecular or termolecular reactions can occur by collisions of reactant molecules with sufficient energy and in the correct orientation to react. But what about a unimolecular reaction? How can collisions be involved? In a unimolecular reaction, the reacting species must acquire enough energy to break apart. This energy can come from collisions of the reacting molecule with other molecules, such as with other molecules of the same kind, with solvent molecules, or with some high-energy background molecule. Atmospheric ozone, for example, disintegrates into O_2 molecules and O atoms by colliding with high-energy nitrogen molecules.

Rate Equations for Elementary Steps

The rate equation for a reaction must be determined by experiment; it cannot be predicted from the overall stoichiometry. In contrast, *the rate equation for any elementary step is defined by its reaction stoichiometry*. The rate equation of an elementary step is given by the product of its rate constant and the concentrations of

A CLOSER LOOK

Organic Bimolecular Substitution Reactions

Experimentally determined rate laws can be used to propose mechanisms and to eliminate other mechanisms from consideration. To decide among possible mechanisms, however, additional experimental information and chemical intuition are also required.

Consider the reaction between 2-bromooctane and iodide ion (Figure A) (a reaction similar to the reaction of fluoride ion and chloromethane (page 538)). This reaction follows second-order kinetics; it is first-order in each of the reagents, and from this we know that a single-step mechanism is one possibility. A possible single-step mechanism is shown in Figure B. This involves attack of iodide ion on the side of the carbon atom opposite to Br, which leads to breaking of the carbon-bromine bond concurrent with formation of a carbon-iodine bond.

Notice that the geometry around the carbon atom in 2-bromooctane inverts in the course of this mechanism. (The geometry around the carbon has been inverted like an umbrella inverts in a strong wind.) If this is the correct mechanism, and if we start with a compound having the geometry shown, then the product of the reaction should have the inverted geometry. This is exactly what is found in the laboratory and provides strong evidence in support of this mechanism.

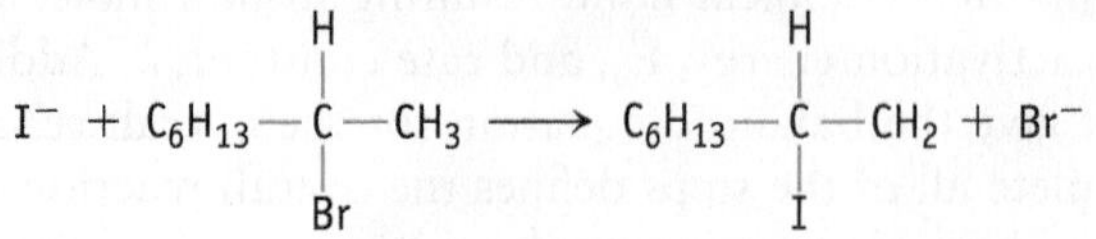

FIGURE A **Reaction of 2-Bromooctane with Iodide ion.**

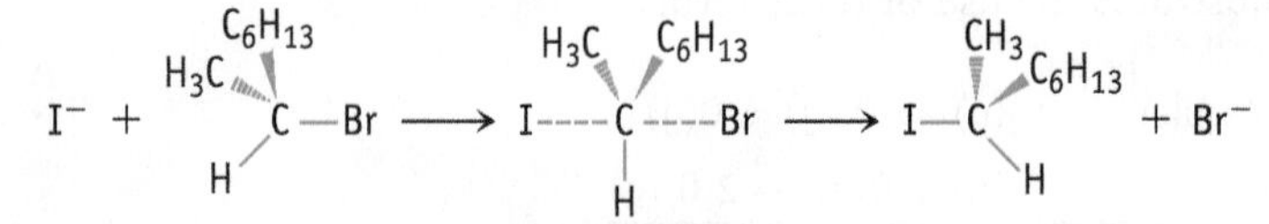

FIGURE B **Proposed Mechanism for the Reaction of 2-Bromooctane with Iodide ion.**

the reactants in that step. We can therefore write the rate equation for any elementary step, as shown by examples in the following table:

ELEMENTARY STEP	MOLECULARITY	RATE EQUATION
$A \rightarrow$ product	Unimolecular	Rate $= k[A]$
$A + B \rightarrow$ product	Bimolecular	Rate $= k[A][B]$
$A + A \rightarrow$ product	Bimolecular	Rate $= k[A]^2$
$2A + B \rightarrow$ product	Termolecular	Rate $= k[A]^2[B]$

For example, the rate laws for each of the two elementary steps in the decomposition of ozone are

$$\text{Rate for (unimolecular) Step 1} = k[O_3]$$

$$\text{Rate for (bimolecular) Step 2} = k'[O_3][O]$$

The two rate constants (k and k' in this example) are not expected to have the same value (nor the same units, because the two steps have different molecularities).

EXAMPLE 14.12

Elementary Steps

Problem The hypochlorite ion undergoes self-oxidation–reduction to give chlorate, ClO_3^-, and chloride ions.

$$3\ ClO^-(aq) \rightarrow ClO_3^-(aq) + 2\ Cl^-(aq)$$

This reaction is thought to occur in two steps:

Step 1: $ClO^-(aq) + ClO^-(aq) \rightarrow ClO_2^-(aq) + Cl^-(aq)$

Step 2: $ClO_2^-(aq) + ClO^-(aq) \rightarrow ClO_3^-(aq) + Cl^-(aq)$

What is the molecularity of each step? Write the rate equation for each elementary step. Show that the sum of these reactions gives the equation for the net reaction.

What Do You Know? A two-step mechanism for the reaction of ClO^- to form Cl^- and ClO_3^- is proposed.

Strategy The molecularity is the number of ions or molecules involved in a reaction step. The rate equation for each elementary step involves the concentration of each ion or molecule in the elementary step, raised to the power of its stoichiometric coefficient.

Solution Because two ions are involved in each elementary step, each step is bimolecular. The rate equation for any elementary step involves the product of the concentrations of the reactants. Thus, in this case, the rate equations are

Step 1: $\text{Rate} = k_1[ClO^-]^2$

Step 2: $\text{Rate} = k_2[ClO_2^-][ClO^-]$

From the equations for the two elementary steps, we see that the ClO_2^- ion is an intermediate, a product of the first step and a reactant in the second step. It therefore cancels out, and we are left with the balanced equation for the overall reaction:

Step 1: $ClO^-(aq) + ClO^-(aq) \rightarrow ClO_2^-(aq) + Cl^-(aq)$

Step 2: $ClO_2^-(aq) + ClO^-(aq) \rightarrow ClO_3^-(aq) + Cl^-(aq)$

Sum of steps: $3\ ClO^-(aq) \rightarrow ClO_3^-(aq) + 2\ Cl^-(aq)$

Think about Your Answer Other mechanisms are possible. The next question to ask is "What is the evidence that will let you decide between several different mechanisms?"

Check Your Understanding

Nitrogen monoxide is reduced by hydrogen to give nitrogen and water:

$$2\ NO(g) + 2\ H_2(g) \rightarrow N_2(g) + 2\ H_2O(g)$$

One possible mechanism for this reaction involves the following reactions:

$$2\ NO(g) \rightarrow N_2O_2(g)$$

$$N_2O_2(g) + H_2(g) \rightarrow N_2O(g) + H_2O(g)$$

$$N_2O(g) + H_2(g) \rightarrow N_2(g) + H_2O(g)$$

What is the molecularity of each of the three steps? What is the rate equation for the third step? Identify the intermediates in this reaction; how many different intermediates are there? Show that the sum of these elementary steps gives the equation for the overall reaction.

Reaction Mechanisms and Rate Equations

The dependence of rate on concentration is an experimental fact. Mechanisms, in contrast, are constructs of our imagination, intuition, and good "chemical sense." To describe a mechanism, we need to make a guess (a good guess, we hope) about how the reaction occurs at the particulate level. Several mechanisms can often be proposed that correspond to the observed rate equation. A good mechanism is a worthy goal because it allows us to understand the chemistry better and perhaps to predict how to control a reaction better and how to design new experiments.

One of the important guidelines of kinetics is that *products of a reaction can never be produced at a rate faster than the rate of the slowest step.* If one step in a multistep reaction is slower than the others, then *the rate of the overall reaction is limited by the combined rates of all elementary steps up through the slowest step in the mechanism.* Often the overall reaction rate and the rate of the slow step are nearly the same. If the slow step determines the rate of the reaction, it is called the **rate-determining step**, or rate-limiting step.

Imagine that a reaction takes place with a mechanism involving two sequential steps, and assume that we know the rates of both steps. The first step is slow and the second is fast:

Elementary Step 1:	$A + B \xrightarrow[\text{Slow, } E_a \text{ large}]{k_1} X + M$	
Elementary Step 2:	$M + A \xrightarrow[\text{Fast, } E_a \text{ small}]{k_2} Y$	
Overall Reaction:	$2A + B \longrightarrow X + Y$	

In the first step, A and B come together and slowly react to form one of the products (X) plus another reactive species, M. Almost as soon as M is formed, however, it is rapidly consumed by reacting with another molecule of A to form the second product Y. The rate-determining elementary step in this example is the first step. That is, the rate of the first step is equal to the rate of the overall reaction. This step is bimolecular and so it has the rate equation:

$$\text{Rate} = k_1[\text{A}][\text{B}]$$

where k_1 is the rate constant for that step. The overall reaction is expected to have this same second-order rate equation.

Let us apply these ideas to the mechanism of a real reaction: the second-order reaction of nitrogen dioxide with fluorine.

$$2\ NO_2(g) + F_2(g) \longrightarrow 2\ FNO_2(g)$$

$$\text{Rate} = k[NO_2][F_2]$$

The rate equation immediately rules out the possibility that the reaction occurs in a single step. If this was a single-step reaction, the rate law would have a second-order dependence on $[NO_2]$. Because a single-step reaction is ruled out, the mechanism must include at least two steps. We can also conclude from the rate law that the rate-determining elementary step must involve NO_2 and F_2 in a 1:1 ratio.

Can You Derive a Mechanism?
At this introductory level, you cannot be expected to derive reaction mechanisms. Given a mechanism, however, you can decide whether it agrees with experimental rate laws.

One possible mechanism for the NO_2/F_2 reaction proposes that NO_2 and F_2 first react to produce one molecule of the product (FNO_2) plus one F atom. In a second step, the fluorine atom produced in the first step reacts with additional NO_2 to give a second molecule of product. If the first, bimolecular step is rate determining, the rate equation would be "Rate = $k_1[NO_2][F_2]$," the same as the experimentally observed rate equation. The experimental rate constant would be the same as k_1.

Elementary Step 1:	Slow	$NO_2(g) + F_2(g) \xrightarrow{k_1} FNO_2(g) + F(g)$
Elementary Step 2:	Fast	$NO_2(g) + F(g) \xrightarrow{k_2} FNO_2(g)$
Overall Reaction:		$2\ NO_2(g) + F_2(g) \longrightarrow 2\ FNO_2(g)$

The fluorine atom formed in the first step of the NO_2/F_2 reaction is a reaction intermediate. It does not appear in the equation describing the overall reaction. Reaction intermediates usually have only a fleeting existence, but in some instances they have long enough lifetimes to be observed. When this is possible, the detection and identification of an intermediate provide strong evidence supporting the proposed mechanism.

EXAMPLE 14.13

Elementary Steps and Reaction Mechanisms

Problem Oxygen atom transfer from NO_2 to CO produces nitrogen monoxide and carbon dioxide.

$$NO_2(g) + CO(g) \rightarrow NO(g) + CO_2(g)$$

The mechanism for this reaction depends on the temperature with one mechanism followed at low temperatures (less than 500 K) and another mechanism followed at high temperatures. The rate equation for this reaction at temperatures less than 500 K is Rate = $k[NO_2]^2$. Can the low-temperature reaction occur in one bimolecular step?

What Do You Know? The reaction equation and the rate law for the reaction are given.

Strategy Write the rate law based on the equation for the NO_2 + CO reaction occurring as if it were an elementary step. If this rate law corresponds to the observed rate law, then a one-step mechanism is possible.

Solution If the reaction occurs by the collision of one NO_2 molecule with one CO molecule, the rate equation would be

$$\text{Rate} = k[NO_2][CO]$$

This does *not* agree with experiment, so the mechanism must involve more than a single step. In one possible mechanism, the reaction occurs in two bimolecular steps, the first one slow and the second one fast:

Elementary Step 1:	Slow, rate-determining	$2\ NO_2(g) \longrightarrow NO_3(g) + NO(g)$
Elementary Step 2:	Fast	$NO_3(g) + CO(g) \longrightarrow NO_2(g) + CO_2(g)$
Overall Reaction:		$NO_2(g) + CO(g) \longrightarrow NO(g) + CO_2(g)$

The first (rate-determining) step has a rate equation that agrees with experiment, so this is a possible mechanism.

Think about Your Answer Because the rate equation is second-order in $[NO_2]$, the rate-determining step in this multistep reaction must involve the collision of two NO_2 molecules.

Check Your Understanding

The Raschig reaction produces hydrazine, N_2H_4, an industrially important reducing agent, from NH_3 and OCl^- in basic, aqueous solution. A proposed mechanism is

Step 1: Fast $NH_3(aq) + OCl^-(aq) \rightarrow NH_2Cl(aq) + OH^-(aq)$

Step 2: Slow $NH_2Cl(aq) + NH_3(aq) \rightarrow N_2H_5^+(aq) + Cl^-(aq)$

Step 3: Fast $N_2H_5^+(aq) + OH^-(aq) \rightarrow N_2H_4(aq) + H_2O(\ell)$

(a) What is the overall equation?

(b) Which step of the three is rate determining?

(c) Write the rate equation for the rate-determining elementary step.

(d) What reaction intermediates are involved?

Reaction Mechanisms Involving an Initial Equilibrium Step

A common two-step reaction mechanism involves an initial fast reaction that produces an intermediate, followed by a slower second step in which the intermediate is converted to the final product. The rate of the reaction is determined by the second step, for which a rate law can be written. The rate of that step, however, depends on the concentration of the intermediate. An intermediate should not appear as a term in the overall rate equation because its concentration will probably not be measurable and because such a rate law cannot be compared directly with the experimentally determined rate law. Therefore, we must find a way to replace the expression for the intermediate with another expression in terms of quantities measurable in the lab.

The reaction of nitrogen monoxide and oxygen is an example of a two-step reaction where the first step is fast and the second step is rate determining.

$$2\ NO(g) + O_2(g) \rightarrow 2\ NO_2(g)$$

$$\text{Rate} = k[NO]^2[O_2]$$

The experimentally determined rate law shows second-order dependence on NO and first-order dependence on O_2. Although this rate law would be correct for a termolecular reaction, experimental evidence indicates that an intermediate is formed in this reaction. A possible two-step mechanism that proceeds through an intermediate is

Elementary Step 1:	Fast, equilibrium	$NO(g) + O_2(g) \underset{k_{-1}}{\overset{k_1}{\rightleftharpoons}} OONO(g)$ (intermediate)
Elementary Step 2:	Slow, rate-determining	$NO(g) + OONO(g) \xrightarrow{k_2} 2\ NO_2(g)$
Overall Reaction:		$2\ NO(g) + O_2(g) \rightarrow 2\ NO_2(g)$

The second step of this reaction is the slow step, and determines the overall rate. We can write a rate law for the second step, but this rate law cannot be compared directly with the experimental rate law because it contains the concentration of an intermediate, OONO:

$$\text{Rate} = k_2[NO][OONO]$$

To eliminate the concentration of intermediate from this rate expression, we look at the rapid first step, which involves an equilibrium between the intermediate species and the reactants.

Mechanisms with an Initial Equilibrium In this mechanism, the forward and reverse reactions in the first elementary step are so much faster than the second elementary step that equilibrium is established before any significant amount of OONO is consumed by NO to give NO_2. The state of equilibrium for the first step remains throughout the lifetime of the overall reaction.

At the beginning of the reaction, NO and O_2 react rapidly and produce the intermediate OONO. The rate of formation can be defined by a rate law with a rate constant k_1:

$$\text{Rate of production of OONO } (NO + O_2 \rightarrow OONO) = k_1[NO][O_2]$$

Because the intermediate is consumed only very slowly in the second step, it is possible for the OONO to revert to NO and O_2 before it reacts further:

$$\text{Rate of reverse reaction } (OONO \rightarrow NO + O_2) = k_{-1}[OONO]$$

As NO and O_2 form OONO, their concentrations drop, so the rate of the forward reaction decreases. At the same time, the concentration of OONO builds up, so the rate of the reverse reaction increases. At equilibrium, the rates of the forward and reverse reactions become the same.

$$\text{Rate of forward reaction} = \text{rate of reverse reaction}$$

$$k_1[NO][O_2] = k_{-1}[OONO]$$

Rearranging this equation, we find

$$\frac{k_1}{k_{-1}} = \frac{[OONO]}{[NO][O_2]} = K$$

Both k_1 and k_{-1} are constants (they will change only if the temperature changes). We can define a new constant K equal to the ratio of these two constants and called the **equilibrium constant**, which is equal to the quotient $[OONO]/[NO][O_2]$. From this, we can derive an expression for the concentration of OONO:

$$[OONO] = K[NO][O_2]$$

If $K[NO][O_2]$ is substituted for [OONO] in the rate law for the rate-determining elementary step, we have

$$\text{Rate} = k_2[NO][OONO] = k_2[NO]\{K[NO][O_2]\}$$
$$= k_2K[NO]^2[O_2]$$

Because both k_2 and K are constants, their product is another constant k', and we have

$$\text{Rate} = k'[NO]^2[O_2]$$

This is exactly the rate law derived from experiment. Thus, the sequence of reactions on which the rate law is based may be a reasonable mechanism for this reaction. It is not the only possible mechanism, however. This rate equation is also consistent with the reaction occurring in a single termolecular step, and another possible mechanism is illustrated in Example 14.14.

Equilibrium Constant The important concept of chemical equilibrium was introduced in Chapter 3 and will be described in more detail in Chapters 15–18.

EXAMPLE 14.14

Reaction Mechanism Involving an Equilibrium Step

Problem The NO + O_2 reaction described in the text could also occur by the following mechanism:

Elementary Step 1: Fast, equilibrium

$$NO(g) + NO(g) \underset{k_{-1}}{\overset{k_1}{\rightleftharpoons}} \underset{\text{intermediate}}{N_2O_2(g)}$$

Elementary Step 2: Slow, rate-determining

$$N_2O_2(g) + O_2(g) \xrightarrow{k_2} 2\ NO_2(g)$$

Overall Reaction: $2\ NO(g) + O_2(g) \rightarrow 2\ NO_2(g)$

Show that this mechanism leads to the following experimental rate law: Rate = $k[NO]^2[O_2]$.

What Do You Know? A possible mechanism for the reaction of NO and O_2 is given.

Strategy The rate law for the reaction is derived using the stoichiometry of the rate-determining step. If this step involves an intermediate, an expression for the concentration of this intermediate will need to be found that has only the concentrations of species in the overall balanced equation.

Solution The rate law for the rate-determining elementary step is

$$\text{Rate} = k_2[N_2O_2][O_2]$$

The intermediate N_2O_2 cannot appear in the final derived rate law. However, we can find an expression relating the concentration of the intermediate to the concentrations of the reactants, using the equilibrium constant expression for the first step. $[N_2O_2]$ and [NO] are related by the equilibrium constant.

$$\frac{k_1}{k_{-1}} = \frac{[N_2O_2]}{[NO]^2} = K$$

Solving this equation for $[N_2O_2]$ gives $[N_2O_2] = K[NO]^2$. When this is substituted into the derived rate law

$$\text{Rate} = k_2\{K[NO]^2\}[O_2]$$

the resulting equation is identical with the experimental rate law where $k_2K = k$.

Think about Your Answer Three mechanisms have been proposed for the $NO + O_2$ reaction. The challenge for chemists is to decide which is correct. In this case, further experimentation detected the species OONO as a short-lived intermediate, thus providing evidence for the mechanism involving this intermediate.

Check Your Understanding

One possible mechanism for the decomposition of nitryl chloride, NO_2Cl, is

Elementary Step 1: Fast, equilibrium $NO_2Cl(g) \underset{k_{-1}}{\overset{k_1}{\rightleftharpoons}} NO_2(g) + Cl(g)$

Elementary Step 2: Slow $NO_2Cl(g) + Cl(g) \xrightarrow{k_2} NO_2(g) + Cl_2(g)$

What is the overall reaction? What rate law would be derived from this mechanism? What effect does increasing the concentration of the product NO_2 have on the reaction rate?

Reaction Mechanisms Involving a Free-Radical Chain Reaction

A free-radical chain reaction has another type of commonly occurring reaction mechanism. An example of this type of process is the reaction of methane and chlorine, which results in the formation of chloroalkanes. This exothermic reaction requires either ultraviolet light or temperatures in the range of 300 °C to occur; the reaction does not occur when these reactants are mixed at room temperature and in

PROBLEM SOLVING TIP 14.2
Relating Rate Equations and Reaction Mechanisms

The connection between an experimental rate equation and the proposed reaction mechanism is important in chemistry.

1. Experiments are performed to determine the experimental rate equation.
2. A mechanism for the reaction is proposed on the basis of the experimental rate equation, the principles of stoichiometry, molecular structure and bonding, general chemical experience, and intuition.
3. The proposed reaction mechanism is used to derive a rate equation. This rate equation can contain only those species involved in the overall chemical reaction. If the derived and experimental rate equations are the same, the postulated mechanism *may* be a reasonable hypothesis.
4. If more than one mechanism can be proposed and they all predict derived rate equations in agreement with experiment, then more experiments must be done.

the dark. If the reactants are present in a 1:1 ratio, the products are mainly CH_3Cl and HCl, along with smaller amounts of CH_2Cl_2 and other chlorinated methanes.

$$CH_4(g) + Cl_2(g) \rightarrow HCl(g) + CH_3Cl(g)$$

(plus lesser amounts of CH_2Cl_2, $CHCl_3$, and CCl_4)

The mechanism is believed to involve a series of steps:

1. *Initiation Step.* Heat or UV light causes the chlorine molecule to dissociate into two chlorine atoms. Only a few chlorine atoms are needed to initiate the chain reaction.

$$Cl_2 \rightarrow 2 \cdot Cl \qquad \Delta H = 242 \text{ kJ/mol-rxn}$$

2. *Propagation Steps.* The highly energetic chlorine atom is a free radical (see Section 8-5). As the ·Cl atom moves randomly in the system, various molecular collisions with other species (CH_4, Cl_2, and Cl) are expected occur. Collision with a Cl_2 molecule is not productive, but collision with a methane molecule will result in the formation of a Cl—H bond concurrent with C—H bond breaking. An estimate of the enthalpy of this process using bond dissociation enthalpy values (see Table 8.8) indicates that this reaction should be slightly exothermic.

D, Bond Dissociation Enthalpy *D* is commonly used as a symbol for bond dissociation enthalpies.

$$CH_3\text{—}H + \cdot Cl \rightarrow \cdot CH_3 + HCl \qquad \Delta H = D(C\text{—}H) - D(H\text{—}Cl)$$

$$\Delta H = 413 \text{ kJ/mol-rxn} - 432 \text{ kJ/mol-rxn} = -19 \text{ kJ/mol-rxn}$$

The methyl radical, $\cdot CH_3$, generated in the previous step is also highly reactive. A collision with a Cl_2 molecule results in the formation of a C—Cl bond and a chlorine atom. This is also an exothermic reaction.

$$\cdot CH_3 + Cl\text{—}Cl \rightarrow CH_3Cl + \cdot Cl \qquad \Delta H = D(Cl\text{—}Cl) - D(C\text{—}Cl)$$

$$\Delta H = 242 \text{ kJ/mol-rxn} - 339 \text{ kJ/mol-rxn} = -97 \text{ kJ/mol-rxn}$$

The chlorine atom formed in this step is now available to react with another molecule of CH_4. The propagation steps can repeat over and over, a feature characteristic of a chain reaction.

As the reaction progresses, the concentration of CH_4 decreases and the concentration of the product, CH_3Cl, increases. With these changes, the probability of collisions between CH_3Cl and ·Cl atoms increases. These collisions lead to the formation of small amounts of CH_2Cl_2 and the other more highly chlorinated species.

3. *Termination Step.* The chain reaction will continue as long as the free radicals (·Cl or $\cdot CH_3$) are present. It will end if the radicals cease to be present. This will happen if two Cl radicals (or any two radicals) collide and react.

$$2 \cdot Cl \rightarrow Cl_2 \qquad \Delta H = -242 \text{ kJ/mol-rxn}$$

The concentration of the various radical species in these reactions is exceedingly small. Thus, the probability of such a reaction is fairly low and the radical chain reaction will have a long lifetime before it stops.

Summing the equations for the individual steps to give CH_3Cl gives the overall reaction equation. The enthalpy change for this reaction, $\Delta H = -116$ kJ/mol-rxn, is the sum of the enthalpies of the individual steps.

REVIEW & CHECK FOR SECTION 14-6

1. The rate equation for a reaction A + B → C was determined by experiment to be Rate = k[A][B]. From this we can conclude

   (a) the reaction occurs in a single elementary step

   (b) this reaction might occur in a single elementary step

   (c) this reaction must involve several elementary steps

2. A reaction is believed to occur by the following mechanism:

Step 1: $2\,A \rightleftharpoons I$ (Fast, equilibrium)

Step 2: $I + B \rightarrow C$ (Slow)

Overall: $2\,A + B \rightarrow C$

What experimentally determined rate law would lead to this mechanism?

(a) Rate = $k[A][B]$ (c) Rate = $k[A]^2[B]$

(b) Rate = $k[A]^2$ (d) Rate = $k[I][B]$

APPLYING CHEMICAL PRINCIPLES

Kinetics and Mechanisms: A 70-Year-Old Mystery Solved

Toward the end of the 19th century, the gas phase reaction of $H_2(g)$ with $I_2(s)$ was shown to be first-order for each reactant.

$$H_2(g) + I_2(g) \rightleftharpoons 2\,HI(g)$$

For approximately 70 years, the accepted mechanism was an elementary bimolecular collision that results in an exchange of atoms.

However, in 1967, John H. Sullivan determined that this single-step mechanism is incorrect. Sullivan provided evidence that the reaction actually occurs in two steps. The first step of the mechanism is the dissociation of elemental iodine into iodine atoms. The dissociation of I_2 is a fast equilibrium process that produces a relatively constant concentration of iodine atoms.

Fast equilibrium $I_2(g) \rightleftharpoons 2\,I(g)$

The second step of the mechanism is a slow termolecular reaction between two iodine atoms and elemental hydrogen.

Slow $H_2(g) + 2\,I(g) \rightarrow 2\,HI$

What was Sullivan's evidence for the revised mechanism? First, he worked at temperatures too low to allow thermal decomposition of I_2. At these temperatures, little or no hydrogen iodide is formed. Second, he used a technique called *flash photolysis* to create iodine atoms from I_2. In this technique a mixture of hydrogen and iodine was irradiated with a strong pulse of light. Sullivan found that the rate of the reaction was dependent on the square of the concentration of iodine atoms created by flash photolysis, which is consistent with the second elementary step in his reaction mechanism.

The story of the mechanism of the hydrogen-iodine reaction is a good lesson: chemists should not trust a proposed mechanism just because it fits with an experimentally determined reaction order. Verifying mechanisms often requires identifying intermediates during the course of a reaction. Sullivan was not only able to identify an intermediate, he controlled its production.

Colin Cuthbert/Science Source

An apparatus for carrying out flash photolysis experiments in the study of kinetics.

QUESTIONS:

1. Sullivan used 578-nm light to dissociate I_2 molecules to I atoms.
   a) What is the energy (in kJ/mol) of 578-nm light?
   b) Breaking an I_2 bond requires 151 kJ/mol of energy. What is the longest wavelength of light that has enough energy to dissociate I_2?
2. Show that the two-step mechanism proposed by Sullivan yields the correct (overall second-order) rate law.
3. Why is a termolecular elementary step likely to be the slowest in a mechanism?
4. Determine the activation energy for the reaction of H_2 and I_2 to produce HI, given the data in the table.

Temperature (°C)	Rate Constant ($M^{-1}\,s^{-1}$)
144.7	1.40×10^{-12}
207.5	1.52×10^{-9}
246.9	5.15×10^{-8}

REFERENCE:

J. H. Sullivan, *Journal of Chemical Physics*, Vol. 46, pp. 73–77, 1967.

CHAPTER GOALS REVISITED

Now that you have studied this chapter, you should ask whether you have met the chapter goals. In particular, you should be able to:

UNDERSTAND

- Rates of reaction and the conditions affecting rates.
  - **a.** Explain the concept of reaction rate (Section 14-1).
  - **b.** Derive the average and instantaneous rates of a reaction from concentration-time data (Section 14-1). Study Questions: 5, 6.
  - **c.** Describe factors that affect reaction rate (i.e., reactant concentrations, temperature, presence of a catalyst, and the state of the reactants) (Section 14-2). Study Questions: 8–10, 68, 88, 89, 93.
- The collision theory of reaction rates and the role of activation energy.
  - **a.** Describe the collision theory of reaction rates (Section 14-5).
  - **b.** Relate activation energy (E_a) to the rate of a reaction (Section 14-5). Study Questions: 37, 38, 40.
  - **c.** Use collision theory to describe the effect of reactant concentration on reaction rate (Section 14-5). Study Question: 92.
  - **d.** Understand the effect of molecular orientation on reaction rate (Section14-5).
  - **e.** Describe the effect of temperature on reaction rate using the collision theory of reaction rates and the Arrhenius equation (Section 14-5 and Equations 14.5–14.7). Study Question: 92.
  - **f.** Use Equations 14.5, 14.6, and 14.7 to calculate the activation energy from rate constants at different temperatures (Section 14-5). Study Questions: 37, 39, 40, 62, 69, 70.
  - **g.** Understand reaction coordinate diagrams (Section 14-5). Study Questions: 41, 42, 47, 95.

DO

- Derive a rate equation, rate constant, and reaction order from experimental data.
  - **a.** Define the various parts of a rate equation (the rate constant and order of reaction), and understand their significance (Section 14-3). Study Questions: 12–14.
  - **b.** Derive a rate equation using the method of initial rates (Section 14-3). Study Questions: 11–14, 52, 60.
- Use integrated rate laws.
  - **a.** Describe and use the relationships between reactant concentration and time for zero-order, first-order, and second-order reactions (Section 14-4 and Table 14.1). Study Questions: 15–24.
  - **b.** Use the concept of half-life ($t_{1/2}$), especially for first-order reactions (Section 14-4). Study Questions: 25–30, 64, 81.
- Determine the order of a reaction by graphing appropriate functions of concentration vs. time.
  - **a.** Apply graphical methods for determining reaction order and the rate constant from experimental data (Section 14-4 and Table 14.1). Study Questions: 31–36, 54, 55, 57.
- Relate reaction mechanisms and rate laws.
  - **a.** Describe the functioning of a catalyst and its effect on the activation energy and mechanism of a reaction (Section 14-5). Study Questions: 90, 96.

b. Understand the concept of a reaction mechanism (a proposed sequence of bond-making and bond-breaking steps that occurs during the conversion of reactants to products) and the relation of the mechanism to the overall, stoichiometric equation for a reaction (Section 14-6).

c. Describe the elementary steps of a mechanism, and give their molecularity (Section 14-6). Study Questions: 43–48, 84.

d. Define the rate-determining step in a mechanism, and identify any reaction intermediates (Section 14-6). Study Questions: 45, 48, 59, 67, 80, 90, 91.

REMEMBER

- The definition of the rate of reaction.
- The half-life of a reaction is the time required for the concentration of a reactant to decrease to one-half its initial value.
- A reaction can proceed no faster than the slowest step in the reaction mechanism.

KEY EQUATIONS

Equation 14.1 (page 520) Integrated rate equation for a first-order reaction (in which $-\Delta[R]/\Delta t = k[R]$).

$$\ln\frac{[R]_t}{[R]_0} = -kt$$

Here, $[R]_0$ and $[R]_t$ are concentrations of the reactant at time $t = 0$ and at a later time, t. The ratio of concentrations, $[R]_t/[R]_0$, is the fraction of reactant that remains after a given time has elapsed.

Equation 14.2 (page 523) Integrated rate equation for a second-order reaction (in which $-\Delta[R]/\Delta t = k[R]^2$).

$$\frac{1}{[R]_t} - \frac{1}{[R]_0} = kt$$

Equation 14.3 (page 524) Integrated rate equation for a zero-order reaction (in which $-\Delta[R]/\Delta t = k[R]^0$).

$$[R]_0 - [R]_t = kt$$

Equation 14.4 (page 526) The relation between the half-life ($t_{1/2}$) and the rate constant (k) for a first-order reaction.

$$t_{1/2} = \frac{0.693}{k}$$

Equation 14.5 (page 533) Arrhenius equation in exponential form.

$$k = \text{rate constant} = \underbrace{A}_{\text{Frequency factor}}\underbrace{e^{-E_a/RT}}_{\text{Fraction of molecules with minimum energy for reaction}}$$

A is the frequency factor; E_a is the activation energy; T is the temperature (in kelvins); and R is the gas constant ($= 8.314462 \times 10^{-3}$ kJ/K · mol).

Equation 14.6 (page 533) Expanded Arrhenius equation in logarithmic form.

$$\ln k = -\frac{E_a}{R}\left(\frac{1}{T}\right) + \ln A \longleftarrow \text{Arrhenius equation}$$

$$\downarrow \qquad \downarrow \qquad \downarrow$$

$$y \;=\; mx \;+\; b \longleftarrow \text{Equation for straight line}$$

Equation 14.7 (page 535) A version of the Arrhenius equation used to calculate the activation energy for a reaction when you know the values of the rate constant at two temperatures (in kelvins).

$$\ln k_2 - \ln k_1 = \ln\frac{k_2}{k_1} = -\frac{E_a}{R}\left[\frac{1}{T_2} - \frac{1}{T_1}\right]$$

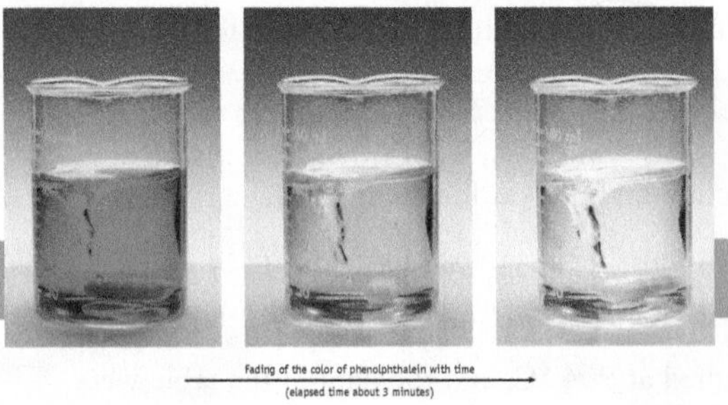

STUDY QUESTIONS

▲ denotes challenging questions.

Blue-numbered questions have answers in Appendix N and fully worked solutions in the *Student Solutions Manual.*

Practicing Skills

Reaction Rates

(See Section 14-1 and Examples 14.1–14.2.)

1. Give the relative rates of disappearance of reactants and formation of products for each of the following reactions.
   (a) $2\ O_3(g) \rightarrow 3\ O_2(g)$
   (b) $2\ HOF(g) \rightarrow 2\ HF(g) + O_2(g)$

2. Give the relative rates of disappearance of reactants and formation of products for each of the following reactions.
   (a) $2\ NO(g) + Br_2(g) \rightarrow 2\ NOBr(g)$
   (b) $N_2(g) + 3\ H_2(g) \rightarrow 2\ NH_3(g)$

3. In the reaction $2\ O_3(g) \rightarrow 3\ O_2(g)$, the rate of formation of O_2 is 1.5×10^{-3} mol/L·s. What is the rate of decomposition of O_3?

4. In the synthesis of ammonia, if $-\Delta[H_2]/\Delta t = 4.5 \times 10^{-4}$ mol/L·min, what is $\Delta[NH_3]/\Delta t$?

$$N_2(g) + 3\ H_2(g) \rightarrow 2\ NH_3(g)$$

5. Experimental data are listed here for the reaction $A \rightarrow 2\ B$.

Time (s)	[B] (mol/L)
0.00	0.000
10.0	0.326
20.0	0.572
30.0	0.750
40.0	0.890

   (a) Prepare a graph from these data; connect the points with a smooth line; and calculate the rate of change of [B] for each 10-second interval from 0.0 to 40.0 seconds. Does the rate of change decrease from one time interval to the next? Suggest a reason for this result.
   (b) How is the rate of change of [A] related to the rate of change of [B] in each time interval? Calculate the rate of change of [A] for the time interval from 10.0 to 20.0 seconds.
   (c) What is the instantaneous rate, $\Delta[B]/\Delta t$, when [B] = 0.750 mol/L?

6. Phenyl acetate, an ester, reacts with water according to the equation

$$\underset{\text{phenyl acetate}}{CH_3\overset{\overset{O}{\|}}{C}OC_6H_5} + H_2O \longrightarrow \underset{\text{acetic acid}}{CH_3\overset{\overset{O}{\|}}{C}OH} + \underset{\text{phenol}}{C_6H_5OH}$$

The data in the table were collected for this reaction at 5 °C.

Time (s)	[Phenyl acetate] (mol/L)
0	0.55
15.0	0.42
30.0	0.31
45.0	0.23
60.0	0.17
75.0	0.12
90.0	0.085

(a) Plot the phenyl acetate concentration versus time, and describe the shape of the curve observed.
(b) Calculate the rate of change of the phenyl acetate concentration during the period 15.0 seconds to 30.0 seconds and also during the period 75.0 seconds to 90.0 seconds. Why is one value smaller than the other?
(c) What is the rate of change of the phenyl acetate concentration during the time period 60.0 seconds to 75.0 seconds?
(d) What is the instantaneous rate at 15.0 seconds?

Concentration and Rate Equations

(See Section 14-3 and Examples 14.3–14.4.)

7. Using the rate equation Rate = $k[A]^2[B]$, define the order of the reaction with respect to A and B. What is the total order of the reaction?

8. A reaction has the experimental rate equation Rate = $k[A]^2$. How will the rate change if the concentration of A is tripled? If the concentration of A is halved?

9. The reaction between ozone and nitrogen dioxide at 231 K is first-order in both $[NO_2]$ and $[O_3]$.

$$2\ NO_2(g) + O_3(g) \rightarrow N_2O_5(g) + O_2(g)$$

(a) Write the rate equation for the reaction.
(b) If the concentration of NO_2 is tripled (and $[O_3]$ is not changed), what is the change in the reaction rate?
(c) What is the effect on reaction rate if the concentration of O_3 is halved (with no change in $[NO_2]$)?

10. Nitrosyl bromide, NOBr, is formed from NO and Br_2:

$$2\ NO(g) + Br_2(g) \rightarrow 2\ NOBr(g)$$

Experiments show that this reaction is second-order in NO and first-order in Br_2.

(a) Write the rate equation for the reaction.
(b) How does the initial reaction rate change if the concentration of Br_2 is changed from 0.0022 mol/L to 0.0066 mol/L?
(c) What is the change in the initial rate if the concentration of NO is changed from 0.0024 mol/L to 0.0012 mol/L?

11. The data in the table are for the reaction of NO and O_2 at 660 K.

$$NO(g) + \tfrac{1}{2}\ O_2(g) \rightarrow NO_2(g)$$

Reactant Concentration (mol/L)		Rate of Disappearance of NO
[NO]	$[O_2]$	(mol/L · s)
0.010	0.010	2.5×10^{-5}
0.020	0.010	1.0×10^{-4}
0.010	0.020	5.0×10^{-5}

(a) Determine the order of the reaction for each reactant.
(b) Write the rate equation for the reaction.
(c) Calculate the rate constant.
(d) Calculate the rate (in mol/L · s) at the instant when [NO] = 0.015 mol/L and $[O_2]$ = 0.0050 mol/L.
(e) At the instant when NO is reacting at the rate 1.0×10^{-4} mol/L · s, what is the rate at which O_2 is reacting and NO_2 is forming?

12. The reaction

$$2\ NO(g) + 2\ H_2(g) \rightarrow N_2(g) + 2\ H_2O(g)$$

was studied at 904 °C, and the data in the table were collected.

Reactant Concentration (mol/L)		Rate of Appearance of N_2
[NO]	$[H_2]$	(mol/L · s)
0.420	0.122	0.136
0.210	0.122	0.0339
0.210	0.244	0.0678
0.105	0.488	0.0339

(a) Determine the order of the reaction for each reactant.
(b) Write the rate equation for the reaction.
(c) Calculate the rate constant for the reaction.
(d) Find the rate of appearance of N_2 at the instant when [NO] = 0.350 mol/L and $[H_2]$ = 0.205 mol/L.

13. Data for the reaction $NO(g) + \tfrac{1}{2}\ O_2(g) \rightarrow NO_2(g)$ are given (for a particular temperature) in the table.

Experiment	Concentration (mol/L)		Initial Rate
	[NO]	$[O_2]$	(mol NO/L · h)
1	3.6×10^{-4}	5.2×10^{-3}	3.4×10^{-8}
2	3.6×10^{-4}	1.04×10^{-2}	6.8×10^{-8}
3	1.8×10^{-4}	1.04×10^{-2}	1.7×10^{-8}
4	1.8×10^{-4}	5.2×10^{-3}	?

(a) What is the rate law for this reaction?
(b) What is the rate constant for the reaction?
(c) What is the initial rate of the reaction in experiment 4?

14. Data for the following reaction are given in the table below.

$$CO(g) + NO_2(g) \rightarrow CO_2(g) + NO(g)$$

Experiment	Concentration (mol/L) [CO]	[NO_2]	Initial Rate (mol/L · h)
1	5.0×10^{-4}	0.36×10^{-4}	3.4×10^{-8}
2	5.0×10^{-4}	0.18×10^{-4}	1.7×10^{-8}
3	1.0×10^{-3}	0.36×10^{-4}	6.8×10^{-8}
4	1.5×10^{-3}	0.72×10^{-4}	?

(a) What is the rate law for this reaction?
(b) What is the rate constant for the reaction?
(c) What is the initial rate of the reaction in experiment 4?

Concentration–Time Relationships

(See Section 14-4 and Examples 14.5–14.7.)

15. The rate equation for the hydrolysis of sucrose to fructose and glucose

$$C_{12}H_{22}O_{11}(aq) + H_2O(\ell) \rightarrow 2\ C_6H_{12}O_6(aq)$$

is $-\Delta[\text{sucrose}]/\Delta t = k[C_{12}H_{22}O_{11}]$. After 27 minutes at 27 °C, the sucrose concentration decreased from 0.0146 M to 0.0132 M. Find the rate constant, k.

16. The decomposition of N_2O_5 in CCl_4 is a first-order reaction. If 2.56 mg of N_2O_5 is present initially and 2.50 mg is present after 4.26 minutes at 55 °C, what is the value of the rate constant, k?

17. The decomposition of SO_2Cl_2 is a first-order reaction:

$$SO_2Cl_2(g) \rightarrow SO_2(g) + Cl_2(g)$$

The rate constant for the reaction is 2.8×10^{-3} min^{-1} at 600 K. If the initial concentration of SO_2Cl_2 is 1.24×10^{-3} mol/L, how long will it take for the concentration to drop to 0.31×10^{-3} mol/L?

18. The conversion of cyclopropane to propene (see Example 14.5) occurs with a first-order rate constant of 2.42×10^{-2} h^{-1}. How long will it take for the concentration of cyclopropane to decrease from an initial concentration of 0.080 mol/L to 0.020 mol/L?

19. Hydrogen peroxide, $H_2O_2(aq)$, decomposes to $H_2O(\ell)$ and $O_2(g)$ in a reaction that is first-order in H_2O_2 and has a rate constant $k = 1.06 \times 10^{-3}$ min^{-1} at a given temperature.
(a) How long will it take for 15% of a sample of H_2O_2 to decompose?
(b) How long will it take for 85% of the sample to decompose?

20. The decomposition of nitrogen dioxide at a high temperature

$$NO_2(g) \rightarrow NO(g) + \tfrac{1}{2}\ O_2(g)$$

is second-order in this reactant. The rate constant for this reaction is 3.40 L/mol·min. Determine the time needed for the concentration of NO_2 to decrease from 2.00 mol/L to 1.50 mol/L.

21. At 573 K, gaseous $NO_2(g)$ decomposes, forming $NO(g)$ and $O_2(g)$. If a vessel containing $NO_2(g)$ has an initial concentration of 1.9×10^{-2} mol/L, how long will it take for 75% of the $NO_2(g)$ to decompose? The decomposition of $NO_2(g)$ is second-order in the reactant and the rate constant for this reaction, at 573 K, is 1.1 L/mol·s.

22. The dimerization of butadiene, C_4H_6, to form 1,5-cyclooctadiene is a second-order process that occurs when the diene is heated. In an experiment, a sample of 0.0087 mol of C_4H_6 was heated in a 1.0-L flask. After 600. seconds, 21% of the butadiene had dimerized. Calculate the rate constant for this reaction.

23. The decomposition of ammonia on a metal surface to form N_2 and H_2 is a zero-order reaction (Figure 14.6c). At 873 °C, the value of the rate constant is 1.5×10^{-3} mol/L·s. How long will it take to completely decompose 0.16 g of NH_3 in a 1.0-L flask?

24. Hydrogen iodide decomposes when heated, forming $H_2(g)$ and $I_2(g)$. The rate law for this reaction is $-\Delta[HI]/\Delta t = k[HI]^2$. At 443 °C, k = 30. L/mol · min. If the initial HI(g) concentration is 1.5×10^{-2} mol/L, what concentration of HI(g) will remain after 10. minutes?

Half-Life

(See Section 14-4 and Examples 14.8 and 14.9.)

25. The rate equation for the decomposition of N_2O_5 (giving NO_2 and O_2) is Rate = $k[N_2O_5]$. The value of k is 6.7×10^{-5} s^{-1} for the reaction at a particular temperature.
(a) Calculate the half-life of N_2O_5.
(b) How long does it take for the N_2O_5 concentration to drop to one tenth of its original value?

26. Gaseous azomethane, $CH_3N{=}NCH_3$, decomposes in a first-order reaction when heated:

$$CH_3N{=}NCH_3(g) \rightarrow N_2(g) + C_2H_6(g)$$

The rate constant for this reaction at 600 K is 0.0216 min^{-1}. If the initial quantity of azomethane in the flask is 2.00 g, how much remains after 0.0500 hour? What mass of N_2 is formed in this time?

27. The decomposition of SO_2Cl_2

$$SO_2Cl_2(g) \rightarrow SO_2(g) + Cl_2(g)$$

is first-order in SO_2Cl_2, and the reaction has a half-life of 245 minutes at 600 K. If you begin with 3.6×10^{-3} mol of SO_2Cl_2 in a 1.0-L flask, how long will it take for the amount of SO_2Cl_2 to decrease to 2.00×10^{-4} mol?

28. The compound $Xe(CF_3)_2$ decomposes in a first-order reaction to elemental Xe with a half-life of 30. minutes. If you place 7.50 mg of $Xe(CF_3)_2$ in a flask, how long must you wait until only 0.25 mg of $Xe(CF_3)_2$ remains?

29. The radioactive isotope ^{64}Cu is used in the form of copper(II) acetate to study Wilson's disease. The isotope has a half-life of 12.70 hours. What fraction of radioactive copper(II) acetate remains after 64 hours?

30. Radioactive gold-198 is used in the diagnosis of liver problems. The half-life of this isotope is 2.7 days. If you begin with a 5.6-mg sample of the isotope, how much of this sample remains after 1.0 day?

Graphical Analysis: Rate Equations and *k*

(See Section 14-4.)

31. Data for the decomposition of dinitrogen monoxide

$$N_2O(g) \rightarrow N_2(g) + \tfrac{1}{2} O_2(g)$$

on a gold surface at 900 °C are given below. Verify that the reaction is first-order by preparing a graph of ln[N_2O] versus time. Derive the rate constant from the slope of the line in this graph. Using the rate law and value of k, determine the decomposition rate at 900 °C when [N_2O] = 0.035 mol/L.

Time (min)	[N_2O] (mol/L)
15.0	0.0835
30.0	0.0680
80.0	0.0350
120.0	0.0220

32. Ammonia decomposes when heated according to the equation

$$NH_3(g) \rightarrow NH_2(g) + H(g)$$

The data in the table for this reaction were collected at a high temperature.

Time (h)	[NH_3] (mol/L)
0	8.00×10^{-7}
25	6.75×10^{-7}
50	5.84×10^{-7}
75	5.15×10^{-7}

Plot ln [NH_3] versus time and 1/[NH_3] versus time. What is the order of this reaction with respect to NH_3? Find the rate constant for the reaction from the slope.

33. Gaseous NO_2 decomposes at 573 K.

$$NO_2(g) \rightarrow NO(g) + \tfrac{1}{2} O_2(g)$$

The concentration of NO_2 was measured as a function of time. A graph of 1/[NO_2] versus time gives a straight line with a slope of 1.1 L/mol · s. What is the rate law for this reaction? What is the rate constant?

34. The decomposition of HOF occurs at 25 °C.

$$HOF(g) \rightarrow HF(g) + \tfrac{1}{2} O_2(g)$$

Using the data in the table below, determine the rate law, and then calculate the rate constant.

[HOF] (mol/L)	Time (min)
0.850	0
0.810	2.00
0.754	5.00
0.526	20.0
0.243	50.0

35. For the reaction $C_2F_4 \rightarrow \tfrac{1}{2} C_4F_8$, a graph of 1/[$C_2F_4$] versus time gives a straight line with a slope of +0.04 L/mol · s. What is the rate law for this reaction?

36. Butadiene, $C_4H_6(g)$, dimerizes when heated, forming 1,5-cyclooctadiene, C_8H_{12}. The data in the table were collected.

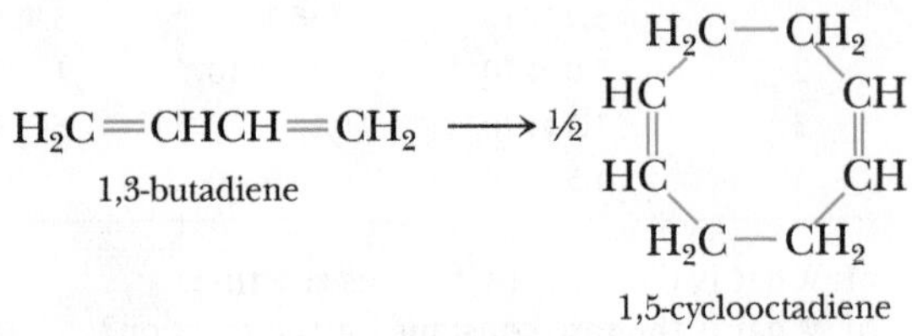

[C_4H_6] (mol/L)	Time (s)
1.0×10^{-2}	0
8.7×10^{-3}	200.
7.7×10^{-3}	500.
6.9×10^{-3}	800.
5.8×10^{-3}	1200.

(a) Use a graphical method to verify that this is a second-order reaction.
(b) Calculate the rate constant for the reaction.

Kinetics and Energy

(See Section 14-5 and Examples 14.10 and 14.11.)

37. Calculate the activation energy, E_a, for the reaction

$$2\ N_2O_5(g) \rightarrow 4\ NO_2(g) + O_2(g)$$

from the observed rate constants: k at 25 °C = $3.46 \times 10^{-5}\ s^{-1}$ and k at 55 °C = $1.5 \times 10^{-3}\ s^{-1}$.

38. If the rate constant for a reaction triples when the temperature rises from 3.00×10^2 K to 3.10×10^2 K, what is the activation energy of the reaction?

39. When heated to a high temperature, cyclobutane, C_4H_8, decomposes to ethylene:

$$C_4H_8(g) \rightarrow 2\ C_2H_4(g)$$

The activation energy, E_a, for this reaction is 260 kJ/mol. At 800 K, the rate constant k = 0.0315 s^{-1}. Determine the value of k at 850 K.

40. When heated, cyclopropane is converted to propene (see Example 14.5). Rate constants for this reaction at 470 °C and 510 °C are $k = 1.10 \times 10^{-4}\ s^{-1}$ and $k = 1.02 \times 10^{-3}\ s^{-1}$, respectively. Determine the activation energy, E_a, from these data.

41. The reaction of H_2 molecules with F atoms

$$H_2(g) + F(g) \rightarrow HF(g) + H(g)$$

has an activation energy of 8 kJ/mol and an enthalpy change of −133 kJ/mol. Draw a diagram similar to Figure 14.10 for this process. Indicate the activation energy and enthalpy change on this diagram.

42. Answer the following questions based on the diagram below.

(a) Is the reaction exothermic or endothermic?
(b) Does the reaction occur in more than one step? If so, how many?

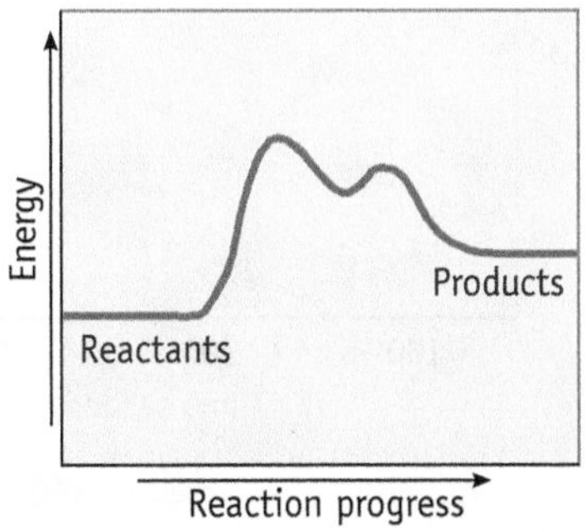

Reaction Mechanisms

(See Section 14-6 and Examples 14.12–14.14.)

43. What is the rate law for each of the following elementary reactions?

(a) $NO(g) + NO_3(g) \rightarrow 2\ NO_2(g)$
(b) $Cl(g) + H_2(g) \rightarrow HCl(g) + H(g)$
(c) $(CH_3)_3CBr(aq) \rightarrow (CH_3)_3C^+(aq) + Br^-(aq)$

44. What is the rate law for each of the following elementary reactions?

(a) $Cl(g) + ICl(g) \rightarrow I(g) + Cl_2(g)$
(b) $O(g) + O_3(g) \rightarrow 2\ O_2(g)$
(c) $2\ NO_2(g) \rightarrow N_2O_4(g)$

45. Ozone, O_3, in the Earth's upper atmosphere decomposes according to the equation

$$2\ O_3(g) \rightarrow 3\ O_2(g)$$

The mechanism of the reaction is thought to proceed through an initial fast, reversible step followed by a slow, second step.

Step 1: Fast, reversible $O_3(g) \rightleftharpoons O_2(g) + O(g)$

Step 2: Slow $O_3(g) + O(g) \rightarrow 2\ O_2(g)$

(a) Which of the steps is rate-determining?
(b) Write the rate equation for the rate-determining step.

46. The reaction of $NO_2(g)$ and $CO(g)$ is thought to occur in two steps to give NO and CO_2:

Step 1: Slow $NO_2(g) + NO_2(g) \rightarrow NO(g) + NO_3(g)$

Step 2: Fast $NO_3(g) + CO(g) \rightarrow NO_2(g) + CO_2(g)$

(a) Show that the elementary steps add up to give the overall, stoichiometric equation.
(b) What is the molecularity of each step?
(c) For this mechanism to be consistent with kinetic data, what must be the experimental rate equation?
(d) Identify any intermediates in this reaction.

47. A proposed mechanism for the reaction of NO_2 and CO is

Step 1: Slow, endothermic

$$2\ NO_2(g) \rightarrow NO(g) + NO_3(g)$$

Step 2: Fast, exothermic

$$NO_3(g) + CO(g) \rightarrow NO_2(g) + CO_2(g)$$

Overall Reaction: Exothermic

$$NO_2(g) + CO(g) \rightarrow NO(g) + CO_2(g)$$

(a) Identify each of the following as a reactant, product, or intermediate: $NO_2(g)$, $CO(g)$, $NO_3(g)$, $CO_2(g)$, $NO(g)$.
(b) Draw a reaction coordinate diagram for this reaction. Indicate on this drawing the activation energy for each step and the overall enthalpy change.

48. The mechanism for the reaction of CH_3OH and HBr is believed to involve two steps. The overall reaction is exothermic.

Step 1: Fast, endothermic

$$CH_3OH + H^+ \rightleftharpoons CH_3OH_2^+$$

Step 2: Slow

$$CH_3OH_2^+ + Br^- \rightarrow CH_3Br + H_2O$$

(a) Write an equation for the overall reaction.
(b) Draw a reaction coordinate diagram for this reaction.
(c) Show that the rate law for this reaction is Rate = $k[CH_3OH][H^+][Br^-]$.

General Questions

These questions are not designated as to type or location in the chapter. They may combine several concepts.

49. A reaction has the following experimental rate equation: Rate = $k[A]^2[B]$. If the concentration of A is doubled and the concentration of B is halved, what happens to the reaction rate?

50. For a first-order reaction, what fraction of reactant remains after five half-lives have elapsed?

51. To determine the concentration dependence of the rate of the reaction

$$H_2PO_3^-(aq) + OH^-(aq) \rightarrow HPO_3^{2-}(aq) + H_2O(\ell)$$

you might measure $[OH^-]$ as a function of time using a pH meter. (To do so, you would set up conditions under which $[H_2PO_3^-]$ remains constant by using a large excess of this reactant.) How would you prove a second-order rate dependence for $[OH^-]$?

52. Data for the following reaction are given in the table.

$$2\ NO(g) + Br_2(g) \rightarrow 2\ NOBr(g)$$

Experiment	[NO] (M)	$[Br_2]$ (M)	Initial Rate (mol/L · s)
1	1.0×10^{-2}	2.0×10^{-2}	2.4×10^{-2}
2	4.0×10^{-2}	2.0×10^{-2}	0.384
3	1.0×10^{-2}	5.0×10^{-2}	6.0×10^{-2}

What is the order of the reaction with respect to [NO] and [Br_2], and what is the overall order of the reaction?

53. Formic acid decomposes at 550 °C according to the equation

$$HCO_2H(g) \rightarrow CO_2(g) + H_2(g)$$

The reaction follows first-order kinetics. In an experiment, it is determined that 75% of a sample of HCO_2H has decomposed in 72 seconds. Determine $t_{1/2}$ for this reaction.

54. Isomerization of CH_3NC occurs slowly when CH_3NC is heated.

$$CH_3NC(g) \rightarrow CH_3CN(g)$$

To study the rate of this reaction at 488 K, data on [CH_3NC] were collected at various times. Analysis led to the graph below.

(a) What is the rate law for this reaction?
(b) What is the equation for the straight line in this graph?
(c) Calculate the rate constant for this reaction.
(d) How long does it take for half of the sample to isomerize?
(e) What is the concentration of CH_3NC after 1.0×10^4 s?

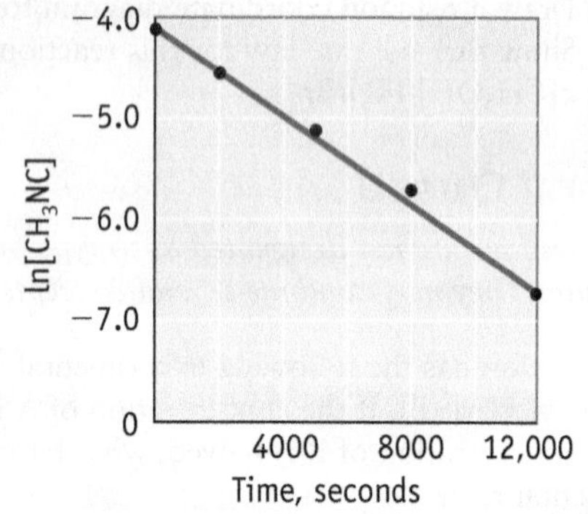

55. When heated, tetrafluoroethylene dimerizes to form octafluorocyclobutane.

$$C_2F_4(g) \rightarrow \tfrac{1}{2}\, C_4F_8(g)$$

To determine the rate of this reaction at 488 K, the data in the table were collected. Analysis was done graphically, as shown below:

[C_2F_4] (M)	Time (s)
0.100	0
0.080	56
0.060	150.
0.040	335
0.030	520.

(a) What is the rate law for this reaction?
(b) What is the value of the rate constant?
(c) What is the concentration of C_2F_4 after 600 s?
(d) How long will it take until the reaction is 90% complete?

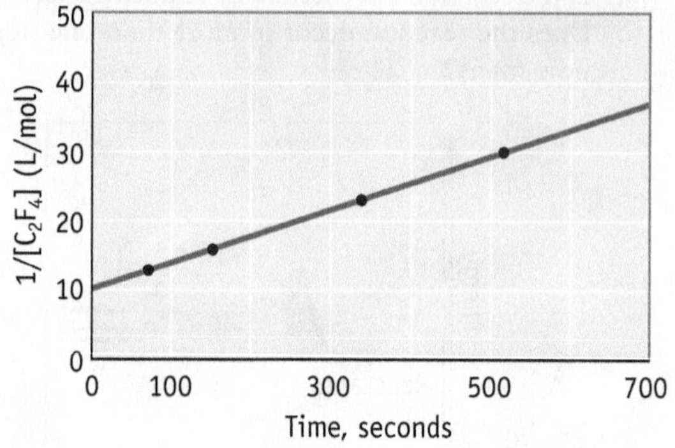

56. Data in the table were collected at 540 K for the following reaction:

$$CO(g) + NO_2(g) \rightarrow CO_2(g) + NO(g)$$

Initial Concentration (mol/L)		Initial Rate
[CO]	[NO_2]	(mol/L · h)
5.1×10^{-4}	0.35×10^{-4}	3.4×10^{-8}
5.1×10^{-4}	0.70×10^{-4}	6.8×10^{-8}
5.1×10^{-4}	0.18×10^{-4}	1.7×10^{-8}
1.0×10^{-3}	0.35×10^{-4}	6.8×10^{-8}
1.5×10^{-3}	0.35×10^{-4}	10.2×10^{-8}

Using the data in the table:

(a) Determine the reaction order with respect to each reactant.
(b) Derive the rate equation.
(c) Calculate the rate constant, giving the correct units for *k*.

57. Ammonium cyanate, NH_4NCO, rearranges in water to give urea, $(NH_2)_2CO$.

$$NH_4NCO(aq) \rightarrow (NH_2)_2CO(aq)$$

Time (min)	[NH_4NCO] (mol/L)
0	0.458
4.50×10^1	0.370
1.07×10^2	0.292
2.30×10^2	0.212
6.00×10^2	0.114

Using the data in the table:

(a) Decide whether the reaction is first-order or second-order.
(b) Calculate *k* for this reaction.
(c) Calculate the half-life of ammonium cyanate under these conditions.
(d) Calculate the concentration of NH_4NCO after 12.0 hours.

58. NO_x, a mixture of NO and NO_2, plays an essential role in the production of pollutants found in photochemical smog. The NO_x in the atmosphere is slowly broken down to N_2 and O_2 in a first-order reaction. The average half-life of NO_x in the smokestack emissions in a large city during daylight is 3.9 hours.

(a) Starting with 1.50 mg in an experiment, what quantity of NO_x remains after 5.25 hours?
(b) How many hours of daylight must have elapsed to decrease 1.50 mg of NO_x to 2.50×10^{-6} mg?

59. At temperatures below 500 K, the reaction between carbon monoxide and nitrogen dioxide

$$CO(g) + NO_2(g) \rightarrow CO_2(g) + NO(g)$$

has the following rate equation: Rate = $k[NO_2]^2$. Which of the three mechanisms suggested here best agrees with the experimentally observed rate equation?

Mechanism 1	Single, elementary step	
	$NO_2 + CO \rightarrow CO_2 + NO$	
Mechanism 2	Two steps	
Slow	$NO_2 + NO_2 \rightarrow NO_3 + NO$	
Fast	$NO_3 + CO \rightarrow NO_2 + CO_2$	
Mechanism 3	Two steps	
Slow	$NO_2 \rightarrow NO + O$	
Fast	$CO + O \rightarrow CO_2$	

60. ▲ Nitryl fluoride can be made by treating nitrogen dioxide with fluorine:

$$2\ NO_2(g) + F_2(g) \rightarrow 2\ NO_2F(g)$$

Use the rate data in the table to do the following:

(a) Write the rate equation for the reaction.
(b) Indicate the order of reaction with respect to each component of the reaction.
(c) Find the numerical value of the rate constant, *k*.

Experiment	Initial Concentrations (mol/L) $[NO_2]$	$[F_2]$	$[NO_2F]$	Initial Rate (mol F_2/L · s)
1	0.001	0.005	0.001	2.0×10^{-4}
2	0.002	0.005	0.001	4.0×10^{-4}
3	0.006	0.002	0.001	4.8×10^{-4}
4	0.006	0.004	0.001	9.6×10^{-4}
5	0.001	0.001	0.001	4.0×10^{-5}
6	0.001	0.001	0.002	4.0×10^{-5}

61. The decomposition of dinitrogen pentaoxide

$$N_2O_5(g) \rightarrow 2\ NO_2(g) + \tfrac{1}{2}\ O_2(g)$$

has the following rate equation: Rate = $k[N_2O_5]$. It has been found experimentally that the decomposition is 20.5% complete in 13.0 hours at 298 K. Calculate the rate constant and the half-life at 298 K.

62. The data in the table give the temperature dependence of the rate constant for the reaction $N_2O_5(g) \rightarrow 2\ NO_2(g) + \tfrac{1}{2}\ O_2(g)$. Plot these data in the appropriate way to derive the activation energy for the reaction.

T(K)	*k* (s^{-1})
338	4.87×10^{-3}
328	1.50×10^{-3}
318	4.98×10^{-4}
308	1.35×10^{-4}
298	3.46×10^{-5}
273	7.87×10^{-7}

63. The decomposition of gaseous dimethyl ether at ordinary pressures is first-order. Its half-life is 25.0 minutes at 500 °C:

$$CH_3OCH_3(g) \rightarrow CH_4(g) + CO(g) + H_2(g)$$

(a) Starting with 8.00 g of dimethyl ether, what mass remains (in grams) after 125 minutes and after 145 minutes?
(b) Calculate the time in minutes required to decrease 7.60 ng (nanograms) to 2.25 ng.
(c) What fraction of the original dimethyl ether remains after 150 minutes?

64. The decomposition of phosphine, PH_3, proceeds according to the equation

$$PH_3(g) \rightarrow \tfrac{1}{4}\ P_4(g) + \tfrac{3}{2}\ H_2(g)$$

It is found that the reaction has the following rate equation: Rate = $k[PH_3]$. The half-life of PH_3 is 37.9 seconds at 120 °C.

(a) How much time is required for three fourths of the PH_3 to decompose?
(b) What fraction of the original sample of PH_3 remains after 1.00 minute?

65. The thermal decomposition of diacetylene, C_4H_2, was studied at 950 °C. Use the following data (K. C. Hou and H. B. Palmer, *Journal of Physical Chemistry*, Vol. 69, p. 858, 1965) to determine the order of the reaction.

Time (ms)	Concentration of C_4H_2 (mol/L)
0	1.02×10^{-4}
50.	5.05×10^{-5}
100.	2.59×10^{-5}
150.	2.01×10^{-5}
200.	1.44×10^{-5}
250.	1.30×10^{-5}

66. Kinetic experiments were conducted to determine the value of the rate constant, k, for the thermal decomposition of diacetylene, C_4H_2, at temperatures below 1100 K (K. C. Hou and H. B. Palmer, *Journal of Physical Chemistry*, Vol. 69, p. 858, 1965). Calculate E_a for this reaction from a plot of ln k versus 1/T.

T(K)	k(L mol^{-1} min^{-1})
973	10.6
1023	29.8
1073	71.1

67. The ozone in the Earth's ozone layer decomposes according to the equation

$$2\ O_3(g) \rightarrow 3\ O_2(g)$$

The mechanism of the reaction is thought to proceed through an initial fast equilibrium and a slow step:

Step 1: Fast, reversible $O_3(g) \rightleftharpoons O_2(g) + O(g)$

Step 2: Slow $O_3(g) + O(g) \rightarrow 2\ O_2(g)$

Show that the mechanism agrees with this experimental rate law:

$$\text{Rate} = -(1/2)\Delta[O_3]/\Delta t = k[O_3]^2/[O_2].$$

68. Hundreds of different reactions occur in the stratosphere, among them reactions that destroy the Earth's ozone layer. The table below lists several (second-order) reactions of Cl atoms with ozone and organic compounds; each is given with its rate constant.

Reaction	Rate Constant (298 K, cm^3/molecule · s)
(a) $Cl + O_3 \rightarrow ClO + O_2$	1.2×10^{-11}
(b) $Cl + CH_4 \rightarrow HCl + CH_3$	1.0×10^{-13}
(c) $Cl + C_3H_8 \rightarrow HCl + C_3H_7$	1.4×10^{-10}
(d) $Cl + CH_2FCl \rightarrow HCl + CHFCl$	3.0×10^{-18}

For equal concentrations of Cl and the other reactant, which is the slowest reaction? Which is the fastest reaction?

69. Data for the reaction

$$[Mn(CO)_5(CH_3CN)]^+ + NC_5H_5 \longrightarrow [Mn(CO)_5(NC_5H_5)]^+ + CH_3CN$$

are given in the table. Calculate E_a from a plot of ln k versus $1/T$.

T(K)	k(min^{-1})
298	0.0409
308	0.0818
318	0.157

70. The gas-phase reaction

$$2\ N_2O_5(g) \rightarrow 4\ NO_2(g) + O_2(g)$$

has an activation energy of 103 kJ/mol, and the rate constant is 0.0900 min^{-1} at 328.0 K. Find the rate constant at 318.0 K.

71. A reaction that occurs in our atmosphere is the oxidation of NO to the brown gas NO_2.

$$2\ NO(g) + O_2(g) \rightarrow 2\ NO_2(g)$$

The mechanism of the reaction is thought to be

Step 1: $2\ NO(g) \rightleftharpoons N_2O_2(g)$ rapidly established equilibrium

Step 2: $N_2O_2(g) + O_2(g) \rightarrow 2\ NO_2(g)$ slow

Which is the rate determining step? Is there an intermediate in the reaction? If this is the correct mechanism for this reaction, what is the experimentally determined rate law?

72. The decomposition of SO_2Cl_2 to SO_2 and Cl_2 is first-order in SO_2Cl_2.

$$SO_2Cl_2(g) \rightarrow SO_2(g) + Cl_2(g)$$

$$\text{Rate} = k[SO_2Cl_2] \text{ where } k = 0.17/\text{hr}$$

(a) What is the rate of decomposition when $[SO_2Cl_2] =$ 0.010 M?
(b) What is the half-life of the reaction?
(c) If the initial pressure of SO_2Cl_2 in a flask is 0.050 atm, what is the pressure of all gases (i.e., the total pressure) in the flask after the reaction has proceeded for one half-life?

73. The decomposition of nitrogen dioxide at a high temperature

$$NO_2(g) \rightarrow NO(g) + \tfrac{1}{2}\ O_2(g)$$

is second-order in this reactant.

(a) Determine the rate constant for this reaction if it takes 1.76 min for the concentration of NO_2 to fall from 0.250 mol/L to 0.100 mol/L.
(b) If the chemical equation is written as

$$2\ NO_2(g) \rightarrow 2\ NO(g) + O_2(g)$$

what is the value of the rate constant?

74. Hydrogen peroxide, $H_2O_2(aq)$, decomposes to $H_2O(\ell)$ and $O_2(g)$

$$2\ H_2O_2(aq) \rightarrow 2\ H_2O(\ell) + O_2(g)$$

At a particular temperature, the following data were collected for the initial rate of appearance O_2.

$[H_2O_2]$ (mol/L)	Initial Reaction Rate (mol O_2/L · min)
0.0500	5.30×10^{-5}
0.100	1.06×10^{-4}
0.200	2.12×10^{-4}

(a) What is the rate law for this reaction?

(b) Calculate the value of the rate constant for this reaction.

(c) If the chemical equation for this reaction is written as

$$H_2O_2(aq) \rightarrow H_2O(\ell) + \frac{1}{2}\,O_2(g)$$

what is the value of the rate constant?

75. ▲ Egg protein albumin is precipitated when an egg is cooked in boiling (100 °C) water. E_a for this first-order reaction is 52.0 kJ/mol. Estimate the time to prepare a 3-minute egg at an altitude at which water boils at 90 °C.

76. ▲ The compound 1,3-butadiene (C_4H_6) forms 1,5-cyclooctadiene, C_8H_{12} at higher temperatures.

$$C_4H_6(g) \rightarrow \frac{1}{2}\,C_8H_{12}(g)$$

Use the following data to determine the order of the reaction and the rate constant, *k*. (Note that the total pressure is the pressure of the unreacted C_4H_6 at any time plus the pressure of the C_8H_{12}.)

Time (min)	Total Pressure (mm Hg)
0	436
3.5	428
11.5	413
18.3	401
25.0	391
32.0	382
41.2	371

77. ▲ Hypofluorous acid, HOF, is very unstable, decomposing in a first-order reaction to give HF and O_2, with a half-life of 30. minutes at room temperature:

$$HOF(g) \rightarrow HF(g) + \frac{1}{2}\,O_2(g)$$

If the partial pressure of HOF in a 1.00-L flask is initially 1.00×10^2 mm Hg at 25 °C, what are the total pressure in the flask and the partial pressure of HOF after exactly 30 minutes? After 45 minutes?

78. ▲ We know that the decomposition of SO_2Cl_2 is first-order in SO_2Cl_2,

$$SO_2Cl_2(g) \rightarrow SO_2(g) + Cl_2(g)$$

with a half-life of 245 minutes at 600 K. If you begin with a partial pressure of SO_2Cl_2 of 25 mm Hg in a 1.0-L flask, what is the partial pressure of each reactant and product after 245 minutes? What is the partial pressure of each reactant after 12 hours?

79. ▲ Nitramide, NO_2NH_2, decomposes slowly in aqueous solution according to the following reaction:

$$NO_2NH_2(aq) \rightarrow N_2O(g) + H_2O(\ell)$$

The reaction follows the experimental rate law

$$\text{Rate} = \frac{k[NO_2NH_2]}{[H_3O^+]}$$

(a) What is the apparent order of the reaction in a pH buffered solution? (In a pH buffered solution, the concentration of H_3O^+ is a constant.)

(b) Which of the following mechanisms is the most appropriate for the interpretation of this rate law? Explain. (Note that when writing the expression for *K*, the equilibrium constant, $[H_2O]$ is not involved. ▶ Chapter 15.)

Mechanism 1

$$NO_2NH_2 \xrightarrow{k_1} N_2O + H_2O$$

Mechanism 2

$$NO_2NH_2 + H_3O^+ \underset{k_2'}{\overset{k_2}{\rightleftharpoons}} NO_2NH_3^+ + H_2O \quad \text{(rapid equilibrium)}$$

$$NO_2NH_3^+ \xrightarrow{k_3} N_2O + H_3O^+ \quad \text{(rate-limiting step)}$$

Mechanism 3

$$NO_2NH_2 + H_2O \underset{k_4'}{\overset{k_4}{\rightleftharpoons}} NO_2NH^- + H_3O^+ \quad \text{(rapid equilibrium)}$$

$$NO_2NH^- \xrightarrow{k_5} N_2O + OH^- \quad \text{(rate-limiting step)}$$

$$H_3O^+ + OH^- \xrightarrow{k_6} 2\,H_2O \quad \text{(very fast reaction)}$$

(c) Show the relationship between the experimentally observed rate constant, *k*, and the rate constants in the selected mechanism.

(d) Based on the experimental rate law, will the reaction rate increase or decrease if the pH of the solution is increased?

80. Many biochemical reactions are catalyzed by acids. A typical mechanism consistent with the experimental results (in which HA is the acid and X is the reactant) is

Step 1: Fast, reversible: $HA \rightleftharpoons H^+ + A^-$

Step 2: Fast, reversible: $X + H^+ \rightleftharpoons XH^+$

Step 3: Slow $XH^+ \rightarrow \text{products}$

What rate law is derived from this mechanism? What is the order of the reaction with respect to HA? How would doubling the concentration of HA affect the reaction?

In the Laboratory

81. The color change accompanying the reaction of phenolphthalein with strong base is illustrated in the Chapter Opener (see page 506). The change in concentration of the dye can be followed by spectrophotometry

(see Section 4-8), and some data collected by that approach are given below. The initial concentrations were [phenolphthalein] = 0.0050 mol/L and $[OH^-]$ = 0.61 mol/L. (Data are taken from review materials for kinetics at chemed.chem.purdue.edu.) (For more details on this reaction see L. Nicholson, *Journal of Chemical Education*, Vol. 66, p. 725, 1989.)

Concentration of Phenolphthalein (mol/L)	Time (s)
0.0050	0.00
0.0045	10.5
0.0040	22.3
0.0035	35.7
0.0030	51.1
0.0025	69.3
0.0020	91.6
0.0015	120.4
0.0010	160.9
0.00050	230.3
0.00025	299.6

(a) Plot the data above as [phenolphthalein] versus time, and determine the average rate from $t = 0$ to $t = 15$ seconds and from $t = 100$ seconds to $t = 125$ seconds. Does the rate change? If so, why?
(b) What is the instantaneous rate at 50 seconds?
(c) Use a graphical method to determine the order of the reaction with respect to phenolphthalein. Write the rate law, and determine the rate constant.
(d) What is the half-life for the reaction?

82. ▲ You want to study the hydrolysis of the beautiful green, cobalt-based complex called *trans*-dichlorobis-(ethylenediamine)cobalt(III) ion,

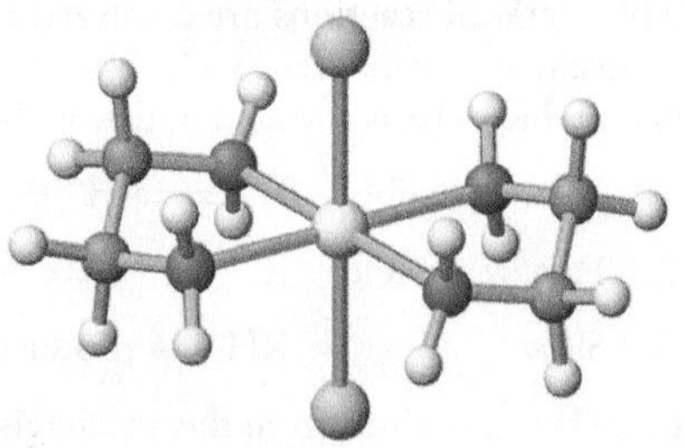

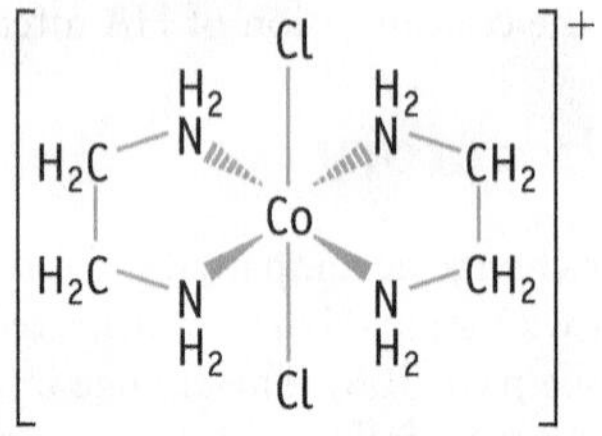

In this hydrolysis reaction, the green complex ion *trans*–$[Co(en)_2Cl_2]^+$ forms the red complex ion $[Co(en)_2(H_2O)Cl]^{2+}$ as a Cl^- ion is replaced with a water molecule on the Co^{3+} ion (en = $H_2NCH_2CH_2NH_2$).

$$\underset{\text{green}}{trans\text{–}[Co(en)_2Cl_2]^+(aq)} + H_2O(\ell) \rightarrow \underset{\text{red}}{[Co(en)_2(H_2O)Cl]^{2+}(aq)} + Cl^-(aq)$$

The reaction progress is followed by observing the color of the solution. The original solution is green, and the final solution is red, but at some intermediate stage when both the reactant and product are present, the solution is gray.

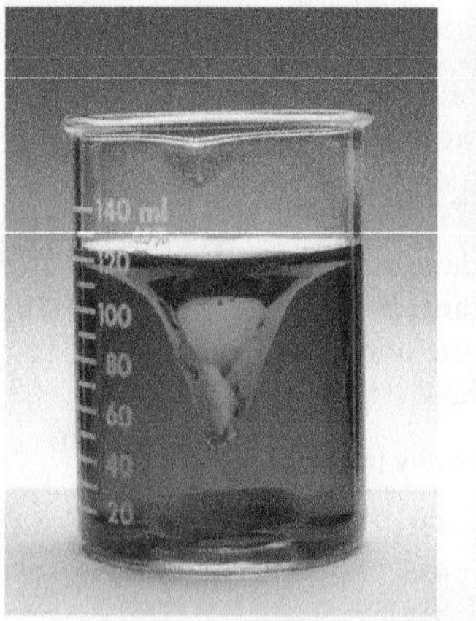

original solution

intermediate solution

final solution

Photos: © Cengage Learning/Charles D. Winters

Changes in color with time as Cl^- ion is replaced by H_2O in a cobalt(III) complex. The shape in the middle of the beaker is a vortex that arises because the solutions are being stirred using a magnetic stirring bar in the bottom of the beaker.

Reactions such as this have been studied extensively, and experiments suggest that the initial, slow step in the reaction is the breaking of the Co—Cl bond to give a five-coordinate intermediate. The intermediate is then attacked rapidly by water.

Slow: $trans\text{–}[Co(en)_2Cl_2]^+(aq) \rightarrow [Co(en)_2Cl]^{2+}(aq) + Cl-(aq)$

Fast: $[Co(en)_2Cl]^{2+}(aq) + H_2O(aq) \rightarrow [Co(en)_2(H_2O)Cl]^{2+}(aq)$

(a) Based on the reaction mechanism, what is the predicted rate law?

(b) As the reaction proceeds, the color changes from green to red with an intermediate stage where the color is gray. The gray color is reached at the same time, no matter what the concentration of the green starting material (at the same temperature). How does this show the reaction is first-order in the green form? Explain.

(c) The activation energy for a reaction can be found by plotting ln k versus $1/T$. However, here we do not need to measure k directly. Instead, because $k = -(1/t)\ln([R]/[R]_0)$, the time needed to achieve the gray color is a measure of k. Use the data below to find the activation energy.

Temperature (° C)	Time Needed to Achieve Gray Colors (for the Same Initial Concentration)
56	156 s
60	114 s
65	88 s
75	47 s

83. ▲ The enzyme chymotrypsin catalyzes the hydrolysis of a peptide containing phenylalanine. Using the data below at a given temperature, calculate the maximum rate of the reaction, Rate_{max}. (For more information on enzyme catalysis and the Michaelis–Menten model, see page 540.)

Peptide Concentration (mol/L)	Reaction Rate (mol/L · min)
2.5×10^{-4}	2.2×10^{-6}
5.0×10^{-4}	3.8×10^{-6}
10.0×10^{-4}	5.9×10^{-6}
15.0×10^{-4}	7.1×10^{-6}

84. The substitution of CO in $Ni(CO)_4$ by another molecule L [where L is an electron-pair donor such as $P(CH_3)_3$] was studied some years ago and led to an understanding of some of the general principles that govern the chemistry of compounds having metal–CO bonds. (See J. P. Day, F. Basolo, and R. G. Pearson: *Journal of the American Chemical Society*, Vol. 90, p. 6927, 1968.) A detailed study of the kinetics of the reaction led to the following mechanism:

Slow $Ni(CO)_4 \rightarrow Ni(CO)_3 + CO$

Fast $Ni(CO)_3 + L \rightarrow Ni(CO)_3L$

(a) What is the molecularity of each of the elementary reactions?

(b) Doubling the concentration of $Ni(CO)_4$ increased the reaction rate by a factor of 2. Doubling the concentration of L had no effect on the reaction rate. Based on this information, write the rate equation for the reaction. Does this agree with the mechanism described?

(c) The experimental rate constant for the reaction, when $L = P(C_6H_5)_3$, is $9.3 \times 10^{-3}\ s^{-1}$ at 20 °C. If the initial concentration of $Ni(CO)_4$ is 0.025 M, what is the concentration of the product after 5.0 minutes?

85. ▲ The oxidation of iodide ion by the hypochlorite ion in the presence of hydroxide ions

$$I^-(aq) + ClO^-(aq) \rightarrow IO^-(aq) + Cl^-(aq)$$

was studied at 25 °C, and the following initial rates data (Y. Chia and R. E. Connick, *Journal of Physical Chemistry*, Vol. 63, p. 1518, 1959) were collected:

Experiment	Initial Concentrations (mol/L) $[ClO^-]$	$[I^-]$	$[OH^-]$	Initial Rate (mol IO^-/L · s)
1	4.0×10^{-3}	2.0×10^{-3}	1.0	4.8×10^{-4}
2	2.0×10^{-3}	4.0×10^{-3}	1.0	5.0×10^{-4}
3	2.0×10^{-3}	2.0×10^{-3}	1.0	2.4×10^{-4}
4	2.0×10^{-3}	2.0×10^{-3}	0.50	4.6×10^{-4}

(a) Determine the rate law for this reaction.

(b) One mechanism that has been proposed for this reaction is the following:

Step 1 $ClO^- + H_2O \rightleftharpoons HOCl + OH^-$ fast, reversible

Step 2 $I^- + HOCl \rightarrow HOI + Cl^-$ slow

Step 3 $HOI + OH^- \rightarrow IO^- + H_2O$ fast

Show that the rate law predicted by this mechanism matches the experimentally-determined rate law in part a. (Note that when writing the expression for K, the equilibrium constant, $[H_2O]$ is not involved. ▶ Chapter 15.)

86. The acid-catalyzed iodination of acetone

$$CH_3COCH_3(aq) + I_2(aq) \rightarrow CH_3COCH_2I(aq) + HI(aq)$$

is a common laboratory experiment used in general chemistry courses to teach the method of initial rates. The reaction is followed spectrophotometrically by the disappearance of the color of iodine in the solution. The following data (J. P. Birk and D. L. Walters, *Journal of Chemical Education*, Vol. 69, p. 585, 1992) were collected at 23 °C for this reaction.

Experiment	Initial Concentrations (mol/L) $[CH_3COCH_3]$	$[H^+]$	$[I_2]$	Initial Rate (mol I_2/L · s)
1	1.33	0.162	0.00665	8.1×10^{-6}
2	1.33	0.323	0.00665	1.7×10^{-5}
3	0.667	0.323	0.00665	7.6×10^{-6}
4	0.333	0.323	0.00665	3.8×10^{-6}
5	0.333	0.323	0.00332	3.6×10^{-6}

Determine the rate law for this reaction.

Summary and Conceptual Questions

The following questions may use concepts from this and previous chapters.

87. Hydrogenation reactions, processes wherein H_2 is added to a molecule, are usually catalyzed. An excellent catalyst is a very finely divided metal suspended in the reaction solvent. Explain why finely divided rhodium, for example, is a much more efficient catalyst than a small block of the metal.

88. ▲ Suppose you have 1000 blocks, each of which is 1.0 cm on a side. If all 1000 of these blocks are stacked to give a cube that is 10. cm on a side, what fraction of the 1000 blocks have at least one surface on the outside surface of the cube? Next, divide the 1000 blocks into eight equal piles of blocks and form them into eight cubes, 5.0 cm on a side. What fraction of the blocks now have at least one surface on the outside of the cubes? How does this mathematical model pertain to Study Question 87?

89. The following statements relate to the reaction for the formation of HI:

$$H_2(g) + I_2(g) \rightarrow 2\ HI(g) \qquad \text{Rate} = k[H_2][I_2]$$

Determine which of the following statements are true. If a statement is false, indicate why it is incorrect.

(a) The reaction must occur in a single step.
(b) This is a second-order reaction overall.
(c) Raising the temperature will cause the value of k to decrease.
(d) Raising the temperature lowers the activation energy for this reaction.
(e) If the concentrations of both reactants are doubled, the rate will double.
(f) Adding a catalyst in the reaction will cause the initial rate to increase.

90. Chlorine atoms contribute to the destruction of the Earth's ozone layer by the following sequence of reactions:

$$Cl + O_3 \rightarrow ClO + O_2$$

$$ClO + O \rightarrow Cl + O_2$$

where the O atoms in the second step come from the decomposition of ozone by sunlight:

$$O_3(g) \rightarrow O(g) + O_2(g)$$

What is the net equation on summing these three equations? Why does this lead to ozone loss in the stratosphere? What is the role played by Cl in this sequence of reactions? What name is given to species such as ClO?

91. Describe each of the following statements as true or false. If false, rewrite the sentence to make it correct.

(a) The rate-determining elementary step in a reaction is the slowest step in a mechanism.
(b) It is possible to change the rate constant by changing the temperature.
(c) As a reaction proceeds at constant temperature, the rate remains constant.
(d) A reaction that is third-order overall must involve more than one step.

92. Identify which of the following statements are incorrect. If the statement is incorrect, rewrite it to be correct.

(a) Reactions are faster at a higher temperature because activation energies are lower.
(b) Rates increase with increasing concentration of reactants because there are more collisions between reactant molecules.
(c) At higher temperatures, a larger fraction of molecules have enough energy to get over the activation energy barrier.
(d) Catalyzed and uncatalyzed reactions have identical mechanisms.

93. The reaction cyclopropane → propene occurs on a platinum metal surface at 200 °C. (The platinum is a catalyst.) The reaction is first-order in cyclopropane. Indicate how the following quantities change (increase, decrease, or no change) as this reaction progresses, assuming constant temperature.

(a) [cyclopropane]
(b) [propene]
(c) [catalyst]
(d) the rate constant, k
(e) the order of the reaction
(f) the half-life of cyclopropane

94. Isotopes are often used as "tracers" to follow an atom through a chemical reaction, and the following is an example. Acetic acid reacts with methanol.

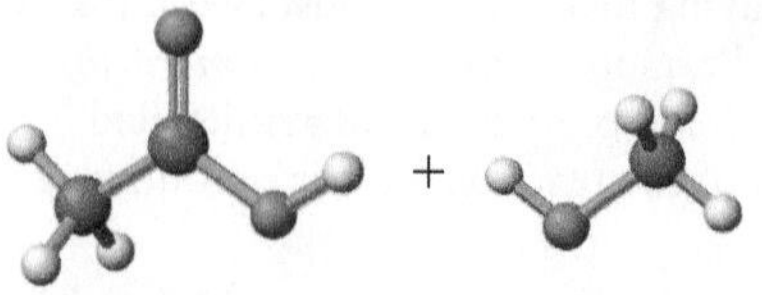

CH_3CO_2H + CH_3OH

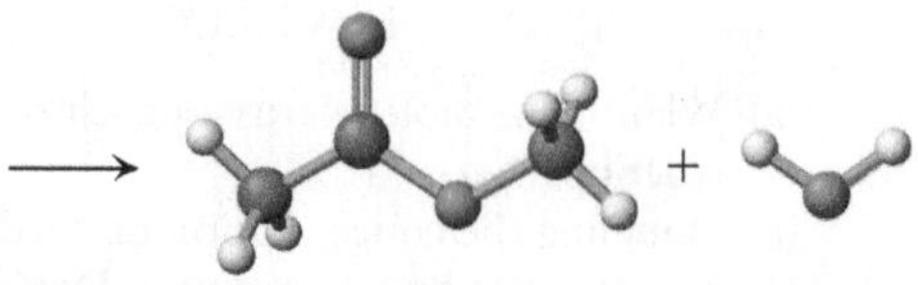

$CH_3CO_2CH_3$ + H_2O

Explain how you could use the isotope ^{18}O to show whether the oxygen atom in the water comes from the —OH of CH_3CO_2H or the —OH of CH_3OH.

95. Examine the reaction coordinate diagram given here.

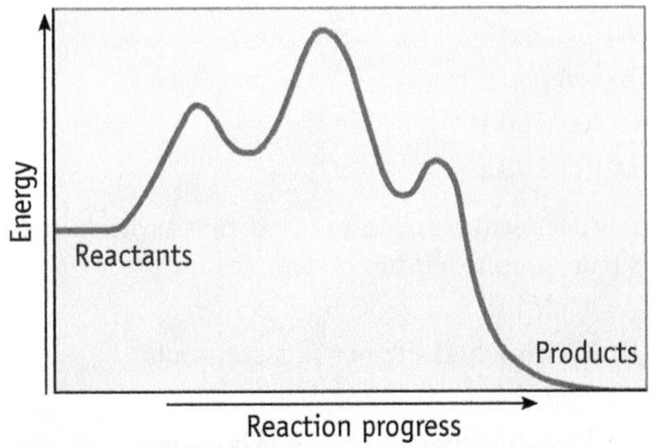

(a) How many steps are in the mechanism for the reaction described by this diagram?
(b) Is the reaction overall exothermic or endothermic?

96. Draw a reaction coordinate diagram for an exothermic reaction that occurs in a single step. Identify the activation energy and the net energy change for the reaction on this diagram. Draw a second diagram that represents the same reaction in the presence of a catalyst, assuming a single step reaction is involved here also. Identify the activation energy of this reaction and the energy change. Is the activation energy in the two drawings different? Does the energy evolved in the two reactions differ?

AP Multiple-Choice Review Questions

1. Magnesium reacts with hydrochloric acid to produce hydrogen gas. An experiment was set up to determine the rate of production of the hydrogen gas by measuring its change in volume over the first 60 seconds of the reaction. Magnesium ribbon was cut into squares of 0.5 cm^2 and 1.0 cm^2. The volume of hydrochloric acid solution and the total mass of magnesium were held constant in each trial. Which set of conditions would produce the highest rate of production of hydrogen gas?

(A) 1 *M* HCl, 0.5-cm^2 pieces of magnesium
(B) 1 *M* HCl, 1.0-cm^2 pieces of magnesium
(C) 3 *M* HCl, 1.0-cm^2 pieces of magnesium
(D) 3 *M* HCl, 0.5-cm^2 pieces of magnesium

Questions 2–4 refer to the following:

Given the reaction: $A + 2B \rightarrow C$

Trial #	$[A]_0$ (mol L^{-1})	$[B]_0$ (mol L^{-1})	Rate of formation of C (mol L^{-1} s^{-1})
1	1.2×10^{-2}	1.2×10^{-2}	1.8×10^{-4}
2	1.2×10^{-2}	2.4×10^{-2}	7.2×10^{-4}
3	2.4×10^{-2}	1.2×10^{-2}	3.6×10^{-4}

2. Based on the experimental data given in the table, what is the order of the reaction with respect to A?

(A) zero
(B) first
(C) second
(D) third

3. Based on the experimental data given in the table, what is the order of the reaction with respect to B?

(A) zero
(B) first
(C) second
(D) third

4. What is the rate of disappearance of B in trial 2?

(A) 2.4×10^{-2} mol L^{-1} s^{-1}
(B) 1.4×10^{-3} mol L^{-1} s^{-1}
(C) 3.6×10^{-4} mol L^{-1} s^{-1}
(D) 7.2×10^{-4} mol L^{-1} s^{-1}

5. What is the value of *k* for a first-order reaction with a half-life of 23.1 s?

(A) 16.0 s^{-1}
(B) 16.0 s
(C) 0.0300 s^{-1}
(D) 0.0300 s

6. In a chemical reaction that has first-order kinetics, which is true at constant temperature?

(A) Half-life and *k* are both constant.
(B) Neither half-life nor *k* is constant.
(C) Half-life is constant, but *k* changes.
(D) Half-life changes, but *k* is constant.

7. The reaction $Q + R_2 \rightarrow R_2Q$ is found to be first order in R_2 and zero order in Q. Which of these mechanisms is most likely for this reaction?

(A) $Q + R_2 \rightarrow R_2Q$ (slow)
(B) $2Q \rightarrow Q_2$ (slow)
$Q_2 + R_2 \rightarrow R_2Q + Q$ (fast)
(C) $Q + Z \rightarrow QZ$ (slow)
$QZ + R \rightarrow QR + Z$ (fast)
$QR + R \rightarrow R_2Q$ (fast)
(D) $R_2 \rightarrow 2R$ (slow)
$R + Q \rightarrow RQ$ (fast)
$RQ + R \rightarrow R_2Q$ (fast)

8. Which is true of the reaction diagram for an elementary reaction, such as the one shown?

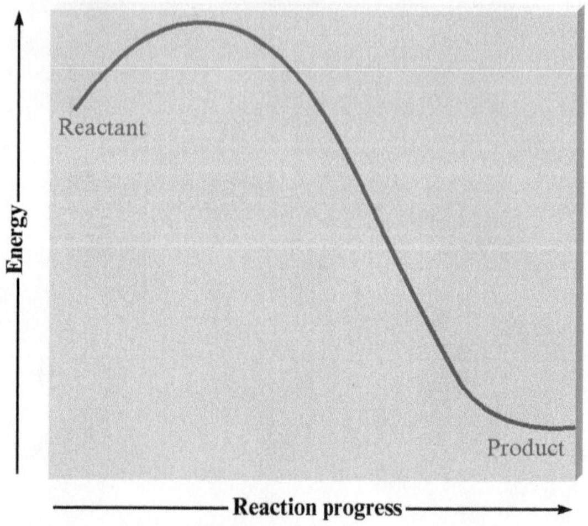

(A) It consists of zero transition states and zero intermediates.
(B) It has one transition state and zero intermediates.
(C) It has one transition state and one intermediate.
(D) It has two transition states and two intermediates.

9. Which is a correct explanation for why the reaction rate increases with increasing temperature?

(A) The reaction becomes more exothermic.
(B) The enthalpy change of the reaction increases.
(C) The activation energy of the reaction decreases.
(D) More of the colliding particles have the activation energy.

10. How would the net-ionic equation written for a catalyzed reaction differ from the net-ionic equation written for the same reaction without a catalyst?

(A) The net-ionic equation would be different because an additional reactant is needed.
(B) The net-ionic equation would be different because the catalyst should be shown on both the reactant and product side.
(C) The net-ionic equation would be the same because the catalyst is a spectator ion and would be left out of a net ionic equation.
(D) The net-ionic equation would be the same because a catalyst is neither a reactant nor a product.

11. The following reaction was determined to be elementary:

$$A + B \rightarrow C$$

What is the overall order of the reaction and the units of the rate constant, k?

(A) first order, time^{-1}
(B) second order, time^{-1}
(C) second order, $L/(mol \times time)$
(D) cannot determine the order and units of k without experimental data

12. The concentration of reactant versus time data were measured and plotted for a reaction with the rate law: Rate = $k[A]^2$. Which graph would result?

(A)
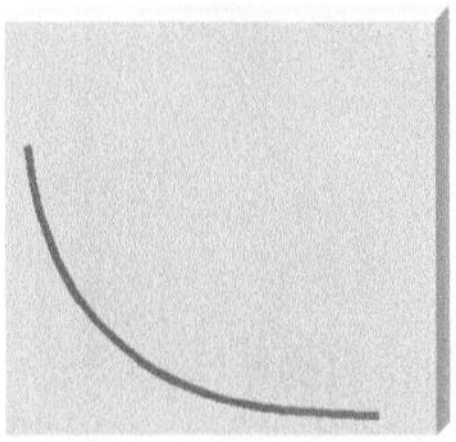
(B)
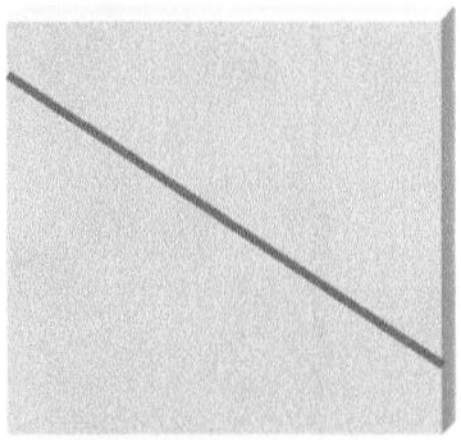
(C)
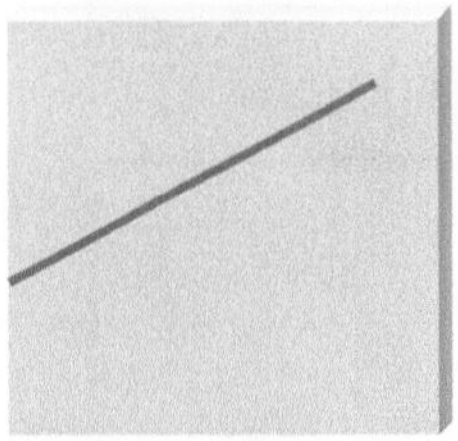
(D)

13. Many organic reactions, such as the two-step conversion of 2-butene to 1-butene as shown in the mechanism below, proceed at higher rates in the presence of an acid. What is the role of the H_3O^+ in this mechanism?

$$CH_3CH{=}CHCH_3 + H_3O^+ \rightleftharpoons CH_3CH_2\overset{+}{C}HCH_3 + H_2O$$
$$CH_3CH_2\overset{+}{C}HCH_3 + H_2O \rightleftharpoons CH_3CH_2CH{=}CH_2 + H_3O^+$$

(A) reactant
(B) catalyst
(C) inhibitor
(D) intermediate

14. A proposed mechanism for the reaction $W_2 + X_2 \rightarrow 2WX$ is:

Step 1: $W_2 \rightarrow 2W$ (slow)
Step 2: $W + X_2 \rightarrow WX + X$ (fast)
Step 3: $X + W \rightarrow WX$ (fast)

What rate law is supported by this mechanism?

(A) rate = $k[W_2]$
(B) rate = $k[W][X_2]$
(C) rate = $k[W_2][X_2]$
(D) rate = $k[W_2]^{1/2}[X_2]$

15. Which energy profile represents the reaction that would occur at the lowest rate at a given temperature?

(A)

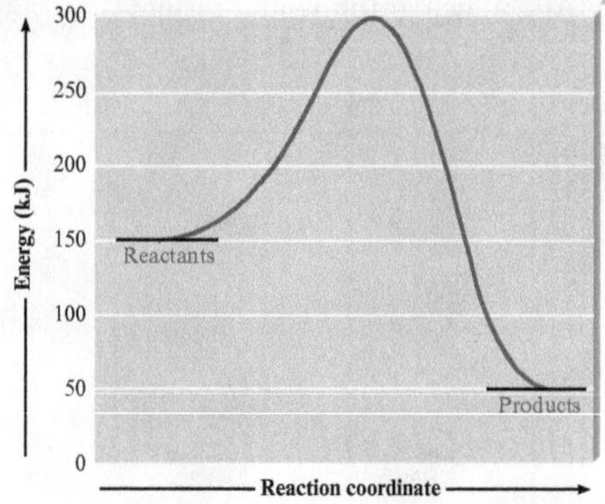

(B)

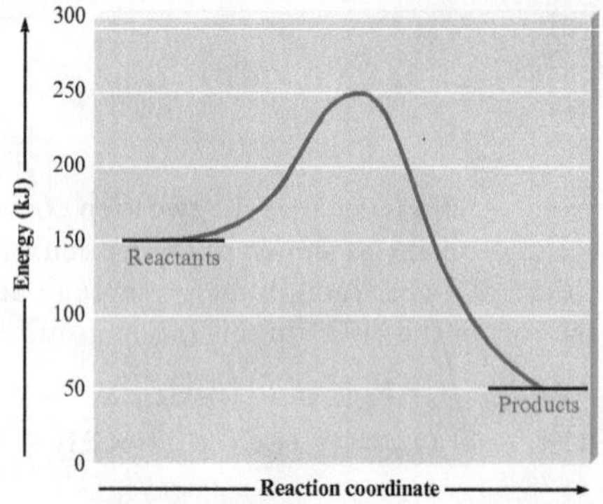

(C)

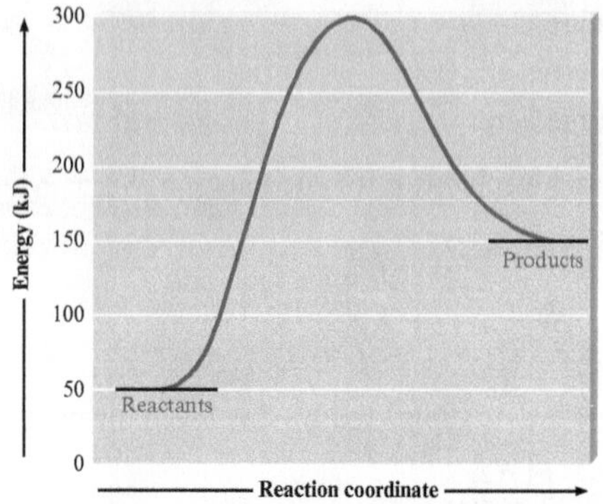

(D)

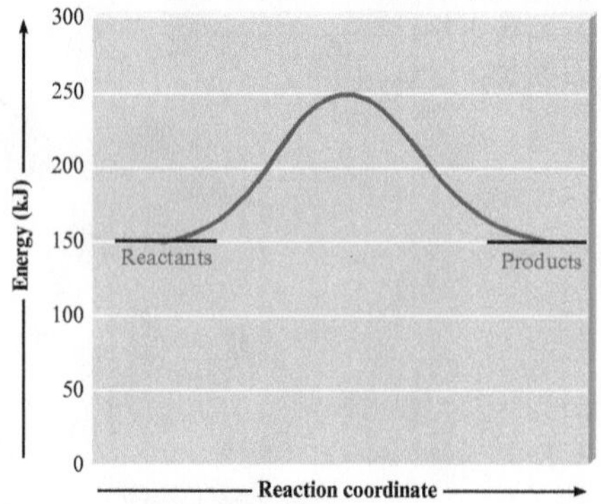

16. Which of the following graphs describes a pathway of reaction that is exothermic with a high activation energy?

(A)

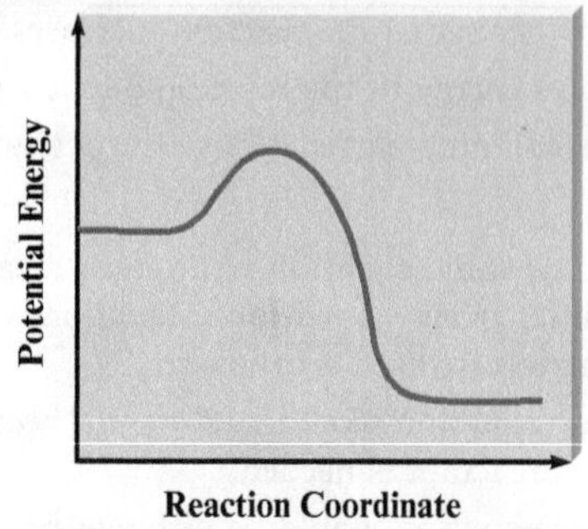

(B)

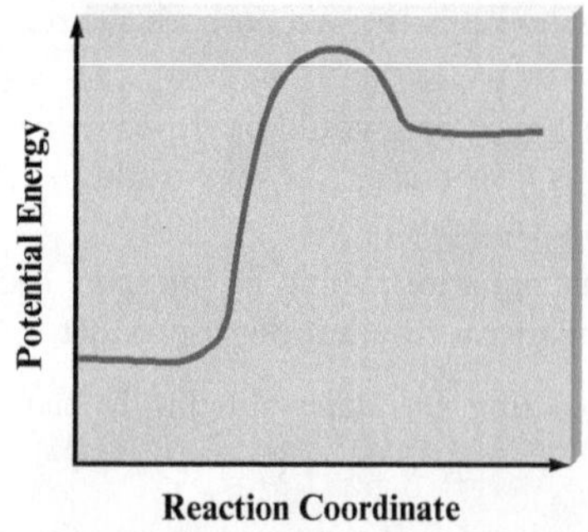

(C)

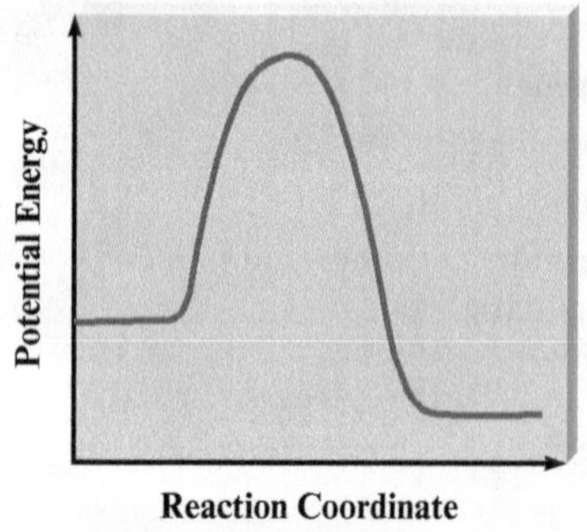

(D)

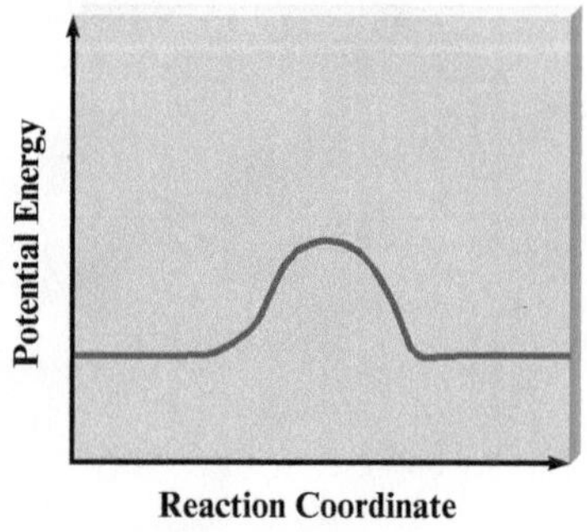

AP Free Response Review Questions

Question Format: Short

Category of Question: Representation 1

Graphical methods are used to determine certain kinetics information.

Questions

On the graph, draw a line that illustrates how data can be used to determine the half-life and specific rate constant, *k*, for a first-order chemical or nuclear decay reaction. Label each axis with name and appropriate unit and explain how the graph can be used to determine these values.

Question Format: Long

Category of Question: Lab 2

$$A(g) + B(g) \rightarrow C(g)$$

For the gas phase reaction above, the following data was obtained.

Experiment	[A] (mol/L)	[B] (mol/L)	Initial Rate (mol L^{-1} sec^{-1})
1	10.1	2.01	5
2	19.8	3.99	80
3	40.2	2.00	80
4	?	6.00	35

Questions

(a) Find the order with respect to A. Explain your reasoning.
(b) Find the order with respect to B. Explain your reasoning.
(c) Write the rate law for the overall reaction.
(d) Determine the value for k and specify its units.
(e) Determine the concentration of A for experiment 4.

A catalyst works in one of three ways: lowering the activation energy by changing the mechanism of the reaction, changing the geometry of the collisions to make them more favorable, or by doing a combination of the two. In order to determine how a catalyst affects the reaction above, a series of five experiments was conducted at different temperatures without a catalyst. Then the experiments were repeated using a catalyst. The resulting data was graphed to produce the following graph.

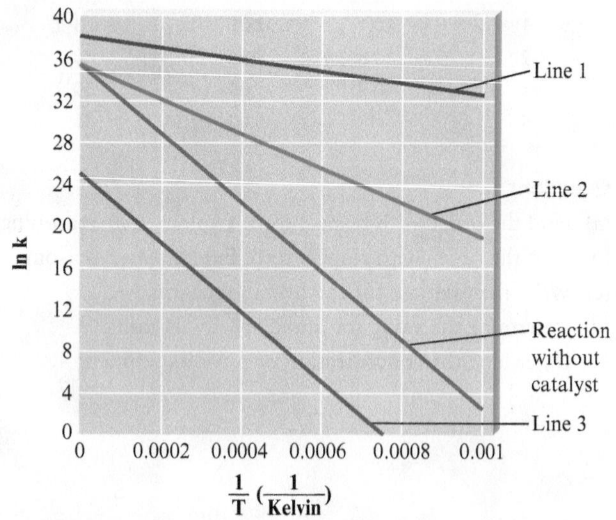

(f) Which line on the graph (line 1, 2, or 3) shows the effects of the catalyst only affecting the geometry of the collisions? Explain your reasoning.

Question Format: Long

Category of Question: Representation 1

There are several ways to speed up a chemical reaction. One of the most common is to increase the temperature at which the reaction proceeds. Two factors affect the rate of the reaction when temperature is changed.

Questions

(a) List the two factors.

(b) Briefly explain how each factor affects the rate of reaction.

(c) Of the two factors, which is more important in speeding up a chemical reaction?

Another way to increase the rate of a reaction is to use a catalyst. Enzymes are biological catalysts and are sensitive to extreme heat. The following graph shows the rate of an enzymatically catalyzed reaction at various temperatures.

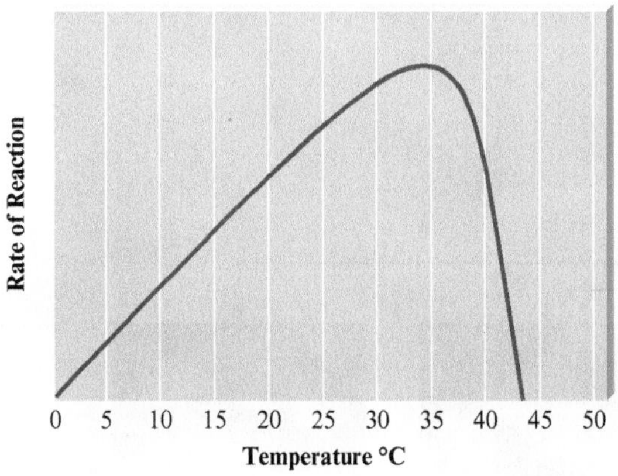

(d) Explain why the rate of reaction suddenly falls between 35 and 40 degrees.

(e) Explain one physiological affect this has on human beings.

A third way to change the rate of a reaction is to change the volume of its container.

(f) What types of reactions will this have an impact on?

(g) Why would it change the reaction rate?

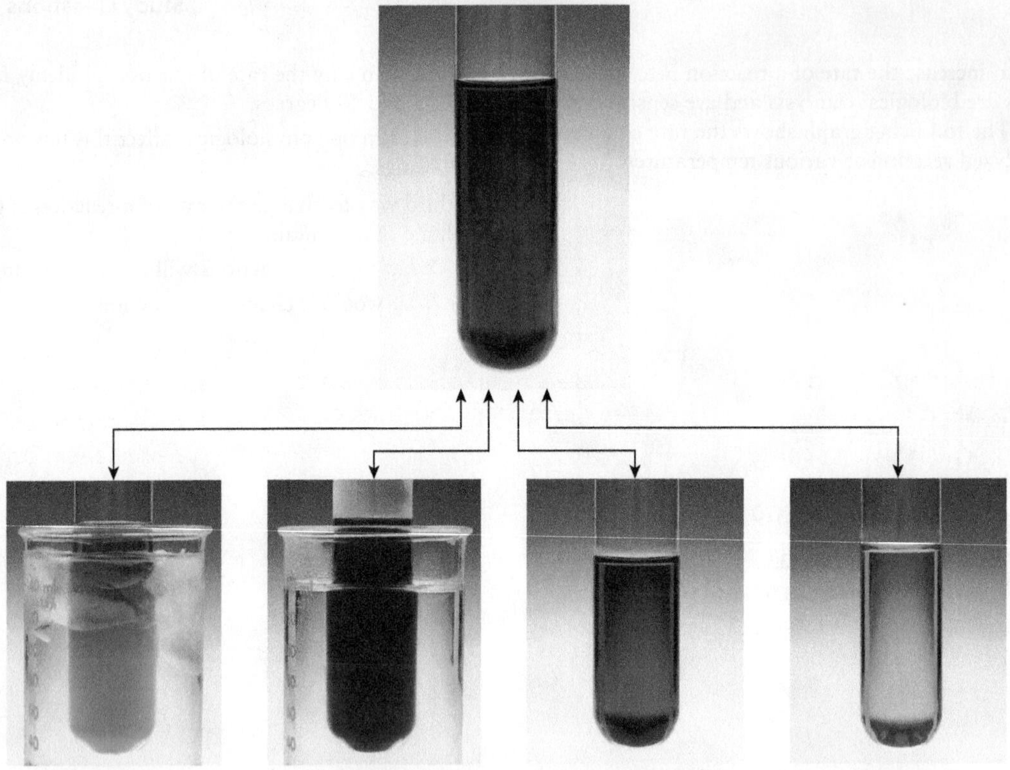

Equilibria in a solution containing cobalt(II) chloride and hydrochloric acid.

Principles of Chemical Reactivity: Equilibria

Chapter Outline

DYNAMIC AND REVERSIBLE! Chemical reactions are dynamic, as proved by experiments in which reactants and products can be interconverted by changing the conditions of the reaction. An experiment using a solution of cobalt(II) chloride in dilute hydrochloric acid demonstrates this aspect of chemical equilibria.

The photo at the top shows a solution prepared by dissolving cobalt(II) chloride, a red crystalline solid, in dilute hydrochloric acid. The solution is red-blue owing to the presence of an equilibrium mixture of the red octahedral cation $[Co(H_2O)_6]^{2+}$ and the blue tetrahedral anion $[CoCl_4]^{2-}$.

Chapter Goals

See Chapter Goals Revisited (page 582) for Study Questions keyed to these goals.

UNDERSTAND

- The nature and characteristics of chemical equilibria.
- The significance of the equilibrium constant, *K*, and the reaction quotient, *Q*.
- How an equilibrium will respond if the reaction conditions are changed (Le Chatelier's principle).

DO

- Write the equilibrium constant and reaction quotient expressions for a reaction.
- Calculate an equilibrium constant given the reactant and product concentrations.
- Use *Q* and *K* in quantitative studies of chemical equilibria.
- Derive a *K* value if different stoichiometric coefficients are used, if the chemical equation is reversed, or if several equations are added.
- Use Le Chatelier's principle.

REMEMBER

- The characteristics of chemical equilibria.
- The importance of the state of equilibrium in chemical systems.
- The mathematical formulation of the equilibrium constant.
- Le Chatelier's principle and how it is applied to chemical equilibria.

$$\underset{\text{red}}{[Co(H_2O)_6]^{2+}(aq)} + 4\ Cl^-(aq) \rightleftarrows \underset{\text{blue}}{[CoCl_4]^{2-}(aq)} + H_2O(\ell)$$

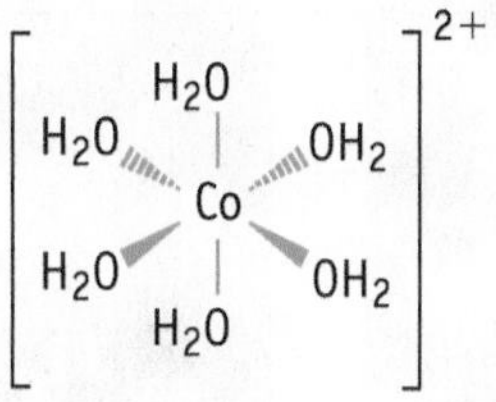

Red, $[Co(H_2O)_6]^{2+}$

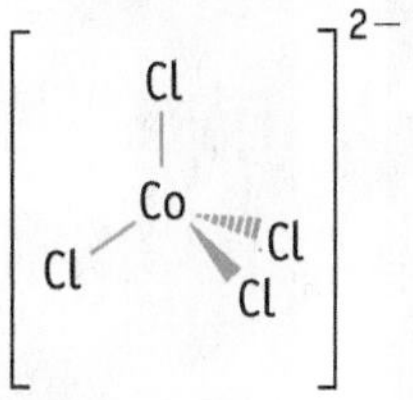

Blue, $[CoCl_4]^{2-}$

The equilibrium is affected both by changing the temperature and by addition of one of the reagents. When the solution is placed in ice, the color changes to red, indicating a shift in the equilibrium to favor the red cation. When the solution is placed in boiling water, however, the color changes to blue; the equilibrium has shifted to favor the blue anion.

The blue anion is also favored if more chloride ion (from hydrochloric acid) is added to the solution. Finally, adding water shifts the equilibrium back to the red cation.

To learn how we can account for these interesting observations, see Section 13-3 where Le Chatelier's principle is introduced and Section 15-6, Disturbing a Chemical Equilibrium.

Study Questions related to this story are: 15.66, 15.67, and 15.74.

The concept of an equilibrium, which is so fundamental in chemistry, was introduced in Chapter 3, and you have already encountered its importance in explaining phenomena such as solubility, acid–base behavior, and changes of state. These previous discussions emphasized the following concepts:

- chemical reactions are reversible,
- chemical reactions proceed spontaneously in the direction that leads toward equilibrium,
- in a closed system a state of equilibrium between reactants and products is achieved eventually, and
- outside forces can disturb the equilibrium.

A major goal of our further exploration of chemical equilibria in this and the next two chapters will be to describe chemical equilibria in quantitative terms.

Learning Objectives: LO 6.1

15-1 Chemical Equilibrium: A Review

If you mix solutions of $CaCl_2$ and $NaHCO_3$, a chemical reaction is immediately detected: a gas (CO_2) bubbles from the mixture, and an insoluble white solid, $CaCO_3$, forms (Figure 15.1a). The reaction occurring is

$$Ca^{2+}(aq) + 2\ HCO_3^-(aq) \rightarrow CaCO_3(s) + CO_2(g) + H_2O(\ell)$$

If you next add pieces of dry ice (solid CO_2) to the suspension of $CaCO_3$ (or if you bubble gaseous CO_2 into the mixture), the solid $CaCO_3$ dissolves (Figures 15.1b and 15.1c). This happens because a reaction occurs that is the reverse of the reaction that led to precipitation of $CaCO_3$; that is:

$$CaCO_3(s) + CO_2(g) + H_2O(\ell) \rightarrow Ca^{2+}(aq) + 2\ HCO_3^-(aq)$$

Photos: © Cengage Learning/Charles D. Winters

(a) Combining solutions of $NaHCO_3$ and $CaCl_2$ produces solid $CaCO_3$ and CO_2 gas.

(b) Dry ice (the white solid) is added to the slurry of $CaCO_3$ precipitated in (a).

(c) The calcium carbonate dissolves on adding sufficient dry ice (CO_2) to give $Ca^{2+}(aq)$ and $HCO_3^-(aq)$.

FIGURE 15.1 **The $CO_2/Ca^{2+}/H_2O$ system.** See Figure 3.5, which shows the same reaction and illustrates the chemistry of the system.

Now imagine what will happen if the solution of Ca^{2+} and HCO_3^- ions is in a *closed* container (unlike the reaction in Figure 15.1). As the reaction begins, Ca^{2+} and HCO_3^- react to give products at some rate. As the reactants are depleted, the rate of this reaction slows. At the same time, however, the reaction products ($CaCO_3$, CO_2, and H_2O) begin to combine to re-form Ca^{2+} and HCO_3^-. Eventually, the rate of the forward reaction, the formation of $CaCO_3$, and the rate of the reverse reaction, the redissolving of $CaCO_3$, become equal. Both the forward and reverse reactions continue to occur, but no further macroscopic change is observed. Equilibrium has been achieved.

We describe an equilibrium system with a chemical equation that connects reactants and products with double arrows. The double arrow symbol, $\rightleftharpoons$, indicates that the reaction is reversible and is a signal to you that the reaction will be studied using the concepts of chemical equilibria.

Cave Chemistry This same chemistry accounts for stalactites and stalagmites in caves (see Section 3-3).

$$Ca^{2+}(aq) + 2\ HCO_3^-(aq) \rightleftharpoons CaCO_3(s) + CO_2(g) + H_2O(\ell)$$

The calcium carbonate equilibrium illustrates an important feature of chemical reactions: *All chemical reactions are reversible, at least in principle*. This was a key point in our earlier discussion of equilibrium (◀ Chapter 3).

REVIEW & CHECK FOR SECTION 15-1

1. Once a chemical equilibrium has been established,
   (a) only the forward reaction occurs.
   (b) only the reverse reaction occurs.
   (c) the forward and reverse reactions occur at an equal rate.
   (d) the forward and reverse reactions stop.

15-2 The Equilibrium Constant and Reaction Quotient

Learning Objectives: LO 6.4, LO 6.7

The concentrations of reactants and products for a reaction at equilibrium are related by a mathematical equation. For example, for the reaction of hydrogen and iodine to produce hydrogen iodide, experiments have shown that at equilibrium the ratio of the square of the HI concentration to the product of the H_2 and I_2 concentrations is a constant.

$$H_2(g) + I_2(g) \rightleftharpoons 2\ HI(g)$$

$$\frac{[HI]^2}{[H_2][I_2]} = \text{constant } (K) \text{ at equilibrium}$$

This constant, ***K***, the **equilibrium constant**, is always the same within experimental error for all experiments done *at a given temperature*. Suppose, for example, the concentrations of H_2 and I_2 in a flask are each initially 0.0175 mol/L at 425 °C and no HI is present. Over time, the concentrations of H_2 and I_2 will decrease, and the concentration of HI will increase until a state of equilibrium is reached (Figure 15.2). If the gases in the flask are then analyzed, the observed concentrations would be $[H_2] = [I_2] = 0.0037$ mol/L and $[HI] = 0.0276$ mol/L. The following table—which we call an **ICE table** for **initial, change,** and **equilibrium concentrations**—summarizes these results:

ICE Table: Initial, Change, and Equilibrium Throughout our discussions of chemical equilibria, we shall express the quantitative information for reactions in an amounts table or ICE table (◀ Section 4-1). These tables show what the initial (*I*) concentrations are, how those concentrations change (*C*) on proceeding to equilibrium, and what the concentrations are at equilibrium (*E*).

EQUATION	$H_2(g)$	+	$I_2(g)$	$\rightleftharpoons$	$2\ HI(g)$
I = *Initial* concentration (M)	0.0175		0.0175		0
C = *Change* in concentration as reaction proceeds to equilibrium (M)	−0.0138		−0.0138		+0.0276
E = *Equilibrium* concentration (M)	0.0037		0.0037		0.0276

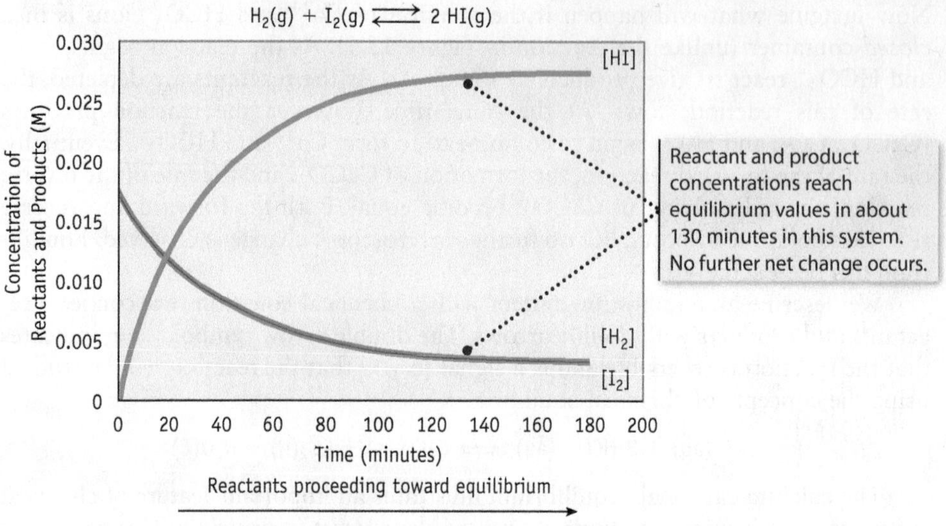

FIGURE 15.2 The reaction of H_2 and I_2 reaches equilibrium. The final concentrations of H_2, I_2, and HI depend on the initial concentrations of H_2 and I_2. If one begins with a different set of initial concentrations, the equilibrium concentrations will be different, but the quotient $[HI]^2/[H_2][I_2]$ will always be the same at a given temperature.

The second line in the table gives the change in concentration of reactants and products on proceeding to equilibrium. Changes are always equal to the difference between the equilibrium and initial concentrations.

Change in concentration = equilibrium concentration − initial concentration

Putting the equilibrium concentration values from the ICE table into the expression for the constant (K) gives a value of 56.

$$\frac{[HI]^2}{[H_2][I_2]} = \frac{(0.0276)^2}{(0.0037)(0.0037)} = 56$$

Other experiments can be done on the H_2/I_2 reaction with different concentrations of reactants or using mixtures of reactants and products. Regardless of the initial amounts, when equilibrium is achieved, the ratio $[HI]^2/[H_2][I_2]$ is always the same, 56, at this temperature.

The observation that the ratio of the product and reactant concentrations for the H_2 and I_2 reaction is always the same can be generalized to other reactions. For the general chemical reaction

$$aA + bB \rightleftharpoons cC + dD$$

we can define the equilibrium constant, K, which characterizes a reaction at equilibrium.

$$\text{Equilibrium constant} = K = \frac{[C]^c[D]^d}{[A]^a[B]^b} \qquad (15.1)$$

Equation 15.1 is called the **equilibrium constant expression.** If the ratio of products to reactants as defined by Equation 15.1 matches the equilibrium constant value, the system is at equilibrium. Conversely, if the ratio has a different value, the system is *not* at equilibrium. However, as you will see later in this section, you will be able to use this value to predict in which direction the reaction will proceed to reach equilibrium.

Writing Equilibrium Constant Expressions

In an equilibrium constant expression,

- all concentrations are equilibrium values.
- product concentrations appear in the numerator, and reactant concentrations appear in the denominator.

- each concentration is raised to the power of its stoichiometric coefficient in the balanced chemical equation.
- the value of the constant K depends on the particular reaction and on the temperature.
- values of K are dimensionless. (See *A Closer Look: Activities and Units of K.*)

FIGURE 15.3 Burning sulfur. Elemental sulfur burns in oxygen with a beautiful blue flame to give SO_2 gas.

Reactions Involving Solids

The concentrations of any solid reactants and products are not included in the equilibrium constant expression. The oxidation of solid, yellow sulfur produces colorless sulfur dioxide gas (Figure 15.3),

$$S(s) + O_2(g) \rightleftharpoons SO_2(g)$$

a reaction with the following equilibrium constant expression.

$$K = \frac{[SO_2]}{[O_2]}$$

In reactions involving solids, experiments show that the equilibrium concentrations of other reactants or products—here, O_2 and SO_2—do not depend on the amount of solid present (as long as some solid is present at equilibrium).

Reactions Involving Solid Reagents Although solids do not appear in an equilibrium constant expression, all reactants and products (including solids) must be present for a system to be at equilibrium.

Reactions in Solution

There are also special considerations for reactions occurring in solution when the solvent (water, for example) is either a reactant or a product. Consider ammonia, which is a weak base owing to its incomplete reaction with water.

$$NH_3(aq) + H_2O(\ell) \rightleftharpoons NH_4^+(aq) + OH^-(aq)$$

Because the water concentration is very high in a dilute ammonia solution, the concentration of water is essentially unchanged by the reaction. The general rule *for reactions in aqueous solution is that the concentration of water is not included in the equilibrium constant expression.* Thus, for the aqueous ammonia equilibrium we write

$$K = \frac{[NH_4^+][OH^-]}{[NH_3]}$$

Reactions Involving Gases: K_c and K_p

Concentration data can be used to calculate equilibrium constants for both aqueous and gaseous systems. In these cases, the symbol K is sometimes given the subscript "c" for "concentration," as in K_c. For gases, however, equilibrium constant expressions

Using Partial Pressures in Place of Concentrations If you rearrange the ideal gas law, [$PV = nRT$], and recognize that the "gas concentration," (n/V), is equivalent to P/RT. Thus, the partial pressure of a gas is proportional to its concentration [$P = (n/V)RT$].

A CLOSER LOOK: Activities and Units of K

In the text we state that "values of K are dimensionless." After all our care in using units in this book, this might seem sloppy. However, advanced thermodynamics informs us that equilibrium constants should really be calculated from the "activities" of reactants and products and not from their concentrations or partial pressures. Activities can be thought of as "effective" concentrations or partial pressures.

The activity of a substance in solution is obtained by calculating the ratio of its concentration, [X], relative to a standard concentration (1 M) and then multiplying this ratio by a correction factor called an *activity coefficient.* Because it involves a ratio of concentrations, the activity is dimensionless. (Likewise, the activity of a gas is obtained from the ratio of its partial pressure, P_X, relative to a standard pressure [1 atm or 1 bar] and then multiplying by an activity coefficient.) In general chemistry, we assume all the activity coefficients are equal to 1 and so the activity of a solute or a gas is numerically the same as its concentration or partial pressure, respectively. This assumption is best met for solutes in very dilute solutions or gases at low pressures. Regardless of the values of activity coefficients, values of K are properly calculated using dimensionless quantities and so they have no units.

Another consequence of using activities is that the "concentration" of solids does not appear in the K expression. This is because the activity of a solid is 1. Similarly, pure liquids and solvents are not included because their activities are also 1.

A CLOSER LOOK Equilibrium Constant Expressions for Gases—K_c and K_p

Many metal carbonates, such as limestone, decompose on heating to give the metal oxide and CO_2 gas.

$$CaCO_3(s) \rightleftharpoons CaO(s) + CO_2(g)$$

The equilibrium constant for this reaction can be expressed either in terms of the number of moles per liter of CO_2, $K_c = [CO_2]$, or in terms of the partial pressure of CO_2, $K_p = P_{CO_2}$. From the ideal gas law, you know that

$$P = (n/V)RT = (\text{concentration in mol/L}) \times RT$$

Therefore, for this reaction $K_p = P_{CO_2} = [CO_2]RT$. Because $K_c = [CO_2]$, this leads to the conclusion that $K_p = K_c(RT)$. That is, the values of K_p and K_c are not the same. For the decomposition of calcium carbonate, K_p is the product of K_c and the factor RT.

Consider the equilibrium constant for the reaction of N_2 and H_2 to produce ammonia in terms of partial pressures, K_p.

$$N_2(g) + 3\,H_2(g) \rightleftharpoons 2\,NH_3(g)$$

$$K_p = \frac{(P_{NH_3})^2}{(P_{N_2})(P_{H_2})^3}$$

Does K_c, the equilibrium constant in terms of concentrations, have the same value as, or a different value than, K_p? We can answer this question by substituting for each pressure in K_p the equivalent expression $[C](RT)$. That is,

$$K_p = \frac{\{[NH_3](RT)\}^2}{\{[N_2](RT)\}\{[H_2](RT)\}^3} = \frac{[NH_3]^2}{[N_2][H_2]^3} \times \frac{1}{(RT)^2} = \frac{K_c}{(RT)^2}$$

$$\text{or } K_p = K_c(RT)^{-2}$$

Once again, you see that K_p and K_c are not the same but are related by some function of RT.

Looking carefully at these examples and others, we find that

$$K_p = K_c(RT)^{\Delta n}$$

where Δn is the change in the number of moles of gas on going from reactants to products.

Δn = total moles of gaseous products − total moles of gaseous reactants

For the decomposition of $CaCO_3$,

$$\Delta n = 1 - 0 = 1$$

whereas the value of Δn for the ammonia synthesis is

$$\Delta n = 2 - 4 = -2$$

What about a reaction in which Δn is zero, such as the oxidation of NO by ozone?

$$NO(g) + O_3(g) \rightleftharpoons NO_2(g) + O_2(g)$$

Now $K_p = K_c$.

can also be written in terms of partial pressures of reactants and products. If reactant and product quantities are given in partial pressures (in atmospheres or in bars), then K is given the subscript "p," as in K_p.

$$H_2(g) + I_2(g) \rightleftharpoons 2\,HI(g)$$

$$K_p = \frac{P_{HI}^2}{P_{H_2}P_{I_2}}$$

Notice that the basic form of the equilibrium constant expression is the same as for K_c. In some cases, the numerical values of K_c and K_p are the same, but they are different when the numbers of moles of gaseous reactants and products are different. *A Closer Look: Equilibrium Constant Expressions for Gases—K_c and K_p* shows how K_c and K_p are related and how to convert from one to the other.

EXAMPLE 15.1

Writing Equilibrium Constant Expressions

Problem Write the equilibrium constant expressions (K_c) for the following reactions.

(a) $N_2(g) + 3\,H_2(g) \rightleftharpoons 2\,NH_3(g)$

(b) $H_2CO_3(aq) + H_2O(\ell) \rightleftharpoons HCO_3^-(aq) + H_3O^+(aq)$

What Do You Know? You have balanced chemical equations, from which you can write the equilibrium constant expressions.

Strategy Product concentrations always appear in the numerator and reactant concentrations appear in the denominator. Each concentration should be raised to a power equal to the stoichiometric coefficient in the balanced equation. In reaction (b), the water concentration does not appear in the equilibrium constant expression.

Solution

(a) $K_c = \frac{[NH_3]^2}{[N_2][H_2]^3}$

(b) $K_c = \frac{[HCO_3^-][H_3O^+]}{[H_2CO_3]}$

Think about Your Answer Always check to make sure you have the products in the numerator and reactants in the denominator. Confusing these is *a common source of student error.*

Check Your Understanding

Write the equilibrium constant expression for each of the following reactions in terms of concentrations.

(a) $CO_2(g) + C(s) \rightleftharpoons 2\,CO(g)$

(b) $[Cu(NH_3)_4]^{2+}(aq) \rightleftharpoons Cu^{2+}(aq) + 4\,NH_3(aq)$

(c) $CH_3CO_2H(aq) + H_2O(\ell) \rightleftharpoons CH_3CO_2^-(aq) + H_3O^+(aq)$

The Magnitude of the Equilibrium Constant, *K*

The magnitude of the equilibrium constant for a reaction, which provides a qualitative measure of how far the reaction has gone toward products when equilibrium is achieved, can vary from a very small to a very large value. A large value for the equilibrium constant means that the concentrations of the products are larger than the concentrations of the reactants at equilibrium. That is, the products are favored over the reactants at equilibrium.

$K > 1$: Reaction is product-favored at equilibrium. The concentrations of products are greater than the concentrations of the reactants at equilibrium.

An example is the reaction of nitrogen monoxide and ozone.

$$NO(g) + O_3(g) \rightleftharpoons NO_2(g) + O_2(g)$$

$$K_c = \frac{[NO_2][O_2]}{[NO][O_3]} = 6 \times 10^{34} \text{ at } 25\ °C$$

The large value of K indicates that, at equilibrium, $[NO_2][O_2] >> [NO][O_3]$. If stoichiometric amounts of NO and O_3 are mixed and allowed to come to equilibrium, virtually none of the reactants will be found. Essentially, all will have been converted to NO_2 and O_2. A chemist would say that "the reaction has gone to completion."

Conversely, a small value of K means that little of the products exists when equilibrium has been achieved. That is, the reactants are favored over the products at equilibrium.

$K < 1$: Reaction is reactant-favored at equilibrium. Concentrations of reactants are greater than concentrations of products at equilibrium.

This is true for the formation of ozone from oxygen.

$$3/2\ O_2(g) \rightleftharpoons O_3(g)$$

$$K_c = \frac{[O_3]}{[O_2]^{3/2}} = 2.5 \times 10^{-29} \text{ at } 25\ °C$$

The small value of K indicates that, at equilibrium, $[O_3] << [O_2]^{3/2}$. If O_2 is placed in a flask, little O_2 will have been converted to O_3 when equilibrium has been achieved.

When K is close to 1, it may not be immediately clear whether the reactant concentrations are larger than the product concentrations, or vice versa. It will depend on the form of the equilibrium expression and thus on the reaction stoichiometry. Calculations of the concentrations will have to be done.

The Reaction Quotient, Q

The equilibrium constant, K, for a reaction has a particular numerical value when the reactants and products are at equilibrium. When the reactants and products in a reaction are not at equilibrium, however, it is convenient to calculate the reaction quotient, Q. For the general reaction of A and B to give C and D,

$$aA + bB \rightleftharpoons cC + dD$$

the reaction quotient is defined as

$$\text{Reaction quotient} = Q = \frac{[C]^c[D]^d}{[A]^a[B]^b} \quad (15.2)$$

While this equation may look identical to the expression for K, there is an important distinction. When K is indicated, the concentrations *must* be those present *at equilibrium*. In contrast, the concentrations of reactants and products in the expression for Q are those that occur at any point as the reaction proceeds from reactants to an equilibrium mixture. Only when the system is at equilibrium does $Q = K$. For any system not at equilibrium the value of Q is different than K.

Determining a reaction quotient is useful for two reasons. First, it will tell you whether a system is at equilibrium (when $Q = K$) or is not at equilibrium (when $Q \neq K$). Second, by comparing Q and K, you can predict what changes will occur in reactant and product concentrations as the reaction proceeds to equilibrium.

Comparing Q and *K*

Relative Magnitude	Direction of Reaction
$Q < K$	Reactants → Products
$Q = K$	Reaction at equilibrium
$Q > K$	Reactants ← Products

- $Q < K$: If Q is less than K, some reactants must be converted to products for the reaction to reach equilibrium. This will decrease the reactant concentrations and increase the product concentrations. (This is the case for the system in Figure 15.4a.)
- $Q > K$: If Q is greater than K, some products must be converted to reactants for the reaction to reach equilibrium. This will increase the reactant concentrations and decrease the product concentrations (Figure 15.4c).

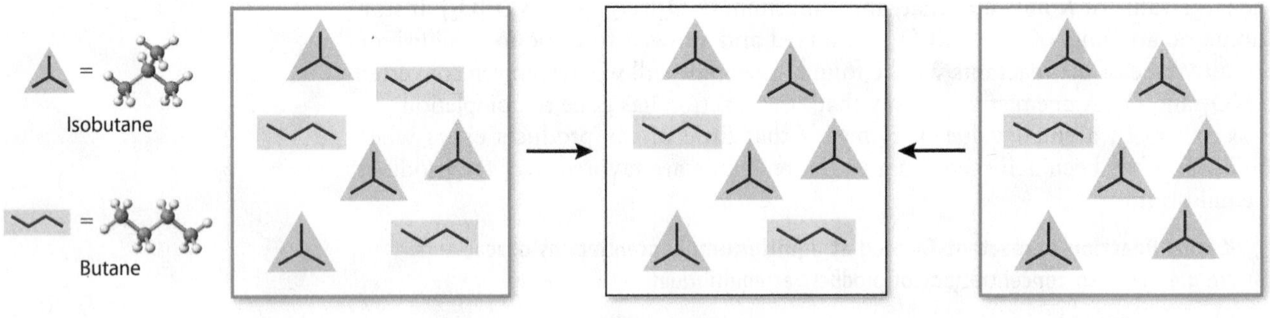

(a) Not at equilibrium.
$Q = 4/3 < K$.
Here, four isobutane molecules and three butane molecules are present. Reaction will proceed to convert butane into isobutane to reach equilibrium.

(b) At equilibrium.
$Q = 5/2 = K$.
Here, five isobutane molecules and two butane molecules are present. Reaction is at equilibrium.

(c) Not at equilibrium.
$Q = 6/1 > K$.
Here, six isobutane molecules and one butane molecule are present. Reaction will proceed to convert isobutane into butane to reach equilibrium.

FIGURE 15.4 **The interconversion of isobutane and butane.** Only when the concentrations of isobutane and butane are in the ratio [isobutane]/[butane] = 2.5 is the system at equilibrium (b). With any other ratio of concentrations, there will be a net conversion of one compound into the other until equilibrium is achieved.

To illustrate these points, let us consider the transformation of butane to isobutane (2-methylpropane).

$$\text{Butane} \rightleftharpoons \text{Isobutane}$$

$$CH_3CH_2CH_2CH_3 \rightleftharpoons CH_3CH(CH_3)CH_3$$

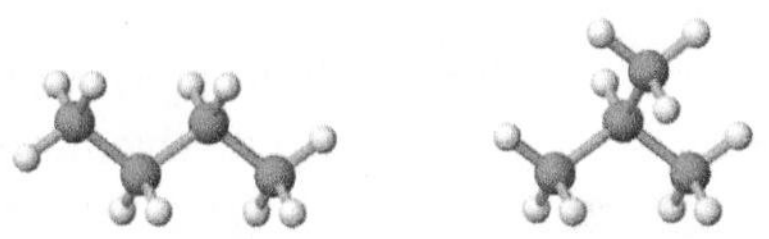

$$K_c = \frac{[\text{isobutane}]}{[\text{butane}]} = 2.50 \text{ at } 298 \text{ K}$$

Any mixture of butane and isobutane, whether at equilibrium or not, can be represented by the reaction quotient Q (=[isobutane]/[butane]). Suppose you have a mixture composed of 0.0030 mol/L of butane and 0.0040 mol/L of isobutane (at 298 K) (Figure 15.4a). This means that the reaction quotient, Q, is

$$Q = \frac{[\text{isobutane}]}{[\text{butane}]} = \frac{0.0040}{0.0030} = 1.3$$

This set of concentrations does not represent an equilibrium system because $Q < K_c$. To reach equilibrium, some butane molecules must be converted to molecules of isobutane, thereby lowering [butane] and raising [isobutane]. This transformation will continue until the ratio [isobutane]/[butane] = 2.5; that is, until $Q = K_c$ (Figure 15.4b).

What happens when there is too much isobutane in the system relative to the amount of butane? Suppose [isobutane] = 0.0060 mol/L but [butane] is only 0.0010 mol/L (Figure 15.4c). Now the reaction quotient Q is greater than K_c ($Q > K_c$), and the system is again not at equilibrium. It will proceed to equilibrium by converting isobutane molecules to butane molecules.

EXAMPLE 15.2

The Reaction Quotient

Problem The brown gas nitrogen dioxide, NO_2, can exist in equilibrium with the colorless gas N_2O_4. $K_c = 170$ at 298 K for the reaction

$$2\ NO_2(g) \rightleftharpoons N_2O_4(g) \quad K_c = 170$$

Suppose that the concentration of NO_2 is 0.015 M and the concentration of N_2O_4 is 0.025 M. Is Q larger than, smaller than, or equal to K_c? If the system is not at equilibrium, in which direction will the reaction proceed to achieve equilibrium?

What Do You Know? You are given the balanced chemical equation, the value of the equilibrium constant K_c, and concentrations of reactant and product.

Strategy

- Write the expression for the reaction quotient, Q, from the balanced equation.
- Substitute concentrations of reactant and product into the expression and calculate Q.
- Decide if Q is greater than, less than, or equal to K_c and in which direction the reaction will proceed.

Strategy Map 15.2

PROBLEM
Is a reaction at **equilibrium**? If not, which way does it proceed? Calculate ***Q***.

DATA/INFORMATION KNOWN
- Balanced equation
- Value of ***K***
- Concentrations of ***reactant*** and ***product***

STEP 1. Write ***Q*** **expression** and calculate ***Q***.

Calculated ***Q*** from reactant and product concentrations

STEP 2. Compare ***Q*** and ***K***.

Q (110) < ***K*** (170)
More product forms from reactant to reach equilibrium.

Solution

$$Q = \frac{[N_2O_4]}{[NO_2]^2} = \frac{(0.025)}{(0.015)^2} = 110$$

The value of Q is less than the value of K_c ($Q < K$), so the reaction is not at equilibrium. The system proceeds to equilibrium by converting NO_2 to N_2O_4, thereby increasing $[N_2O_4]$, and decreasing $[NO_2]$ until $Q = K_c$.

Think about Your Answer When calculating Q, make sure that you raise each concentration to the power corresponding to the stoichiometric coefficient.

Check Your Understanding

Answer the following questions regarding the butane $\rightleftharpoons$ isobutane equilibrium ($K_c = 2.50$ at 298 K).

(a) Is the system at equilibrium when [butane] = 0.00097 M and [isobutane] = 0.00218 M? If not, in which direction will the reaction proceed to achieve equilibrium?

(b) Is the system at equilibrium when [butane] = 0.00075 M and [isobutane] = 0.00260 M? If not, in which direction will the reaction proceed to achieve equilibrium?

REVIEW & CHECK FOR SECTION 15-2

1. Which of the following is the correct form of the equilibrium constant expression for the decomposition of SO_3 to SO_2 and O_2?

$$2\ SO_3(g) \rightleftharpoons 2\ SO_2(g) + O_2(g)$$

(a) $K_c = [SO_2][O_2]/[SO_3]$
(b) $K_c = [SO_2]^2[O_2]/[SO_3]^2$
(c) $K_c = [SO_3]^2/[SO_2]^2[O_2]$
(d) $K_c = [SO_2][O_2]^2$

2. At 2000 K the equilibrium constant for the formation of NO(g) is 4.0×10^{-4}.

$$N_2(g) + O_2(g) \rightleftharpoons 2\ NO(g)$$

You have a flask in which, at 2000 K, the concentration of N_2 is 0.050 mol/L, that of O_2 is 0.025 mol/L, and that of NO is 4.2×10^{-4} mol/L. Is the system at equilibrium?

(a) Yes, it is at equilibrium.

(b) No, it is not at equilibrium, and the reaction proceeds farther to the right.

(c) No, it is not at equilibrium, and the reaction proceeds to the left, turning products into reactants.

Learning Objectives: LO 6.5

15-3 Determining an Equilibrium Constant

When the concentrations of all of the reactants and products are known at equilibrium, an equilibrium constant can be calculated by substituting the data into the equilibrium constant expression. Assume a mixture of SO_2, O_2, and SO_3 is at equilibrium at 852 K.

$$2\ SO_2(g) + O_2(g) \rightleftharpoons 2\ SO_3(g)$$

The equilibrium concentrations are found to be $[SO_2] = 3.61 \times 10^{-3}$ mol/L, $[O_2] = 6.11 \times 10^{-4}$ mol/L, and $[SO_3] = 1.01 \times 10^{-2}$ mol/L. Substituting these data into the equilibrium constant expression, we can calculate the value of K_c.

$$K_c = \frac{[SO_3]^2}{[SO_2]^2[O_2]} = \frac{(1.01 \times 10^{-2})^2}{(3.61 \times 10^{-3})^2(6.11 \times 10^{-4})} = 1.28 \times 10^4 \text{ at 852 K}$$

(Notice that K_c has a large value; at equilibrium, the oxidation of sulfur dioxide is product-favored at 852 K.)

More commonly, an experiment will provide information on the initial quantities of reactants and the concentration at equilibrium of only one of the reactants or of one of the products. The equilibrium concentrations of the rest of the reactants and products must then be calculated based on the reaction stoichiometry. As an example, let's again consider the oxidation of sulfur dioxide to sulfur trioxide and suppose that 0.00100 mol each of SO_2 and O_2 are placed in a 1.00-L flask at a high temperature. When equilibrium has been achieved, 0.00054 mol of SO_3 has been formed. Let us use this information to calculate the equilibrium constant for the reaction. After writing the equilibrium constant expression in terms of concentrations, we set up an ICE table (◀ Section 4-1 and Section 15-2) showing the initial concentrations, the changes in those concentrations on proceeding to equilibrium, and the concentrations at equilibrium.

Equation	$2\ SO_2(g)$	+ $O_2(g)$	⇌ $2\ SO_3(g)$
Initial (M)	0.00100	0.00100	0
Change (M)	$-2x$	$-x$	$+2x$
Equilibrium (M)	$0.00100 - 2x$	$0.00100 - x$	$2x$
	$0.00100 - 0.00054$ $= 0.00046$	$0.00100 - 0.00054/2$ $= 0.00073$	$= 0.00054$

The quantities in the ICE table result from the following analysis:

- Line 1: Initial concentrations.
- Line 2: The amount of O_2 consumed is designated as $-x$ mol/L. We give it a minus sign because O_2 is consumed. It then follows from the reaction stoichiometry that the amount of SO_2 consumed is $-2x$, and the amount of SO_3 produced is $+2x$.
- Line 3:
  (a) We know from experiment that $[SO_3]$ at equilibrium is 0.00054 M. Therefore, $2x = 0.00054$ M.
  (b) The equilibrium concentration of SO_2 is equal to the initial concentration minus what was consumed. Therefore, $[SO_2]$ is $(0.00100 - 2x)$ M or 0.00046 M.
  (c) The amount of O_2 consumed is half of the amount of SO_3 produced or x (= 0.00027 mol/L). Therefore, the equilibrium concentration of O_2 is 0.00073.

With the equilibrium concentrations now known, it is possible to calculate K_c.

$$K_c = \frac{[SO_3]^2}{[SO_2]^2[O_2]} = \frac{(0.00054)^2}{(0.00046)^2(0.00073)} = 1.9 \times 10^3$$

EXAMPLE 15.3

Calculating an Equilibrium Constant (K_c) Using Concentrations

Problem In aqueous solution iron(III) ions react with iodide ions to give iron(II) ions and triiodide ions, I_3^-. Suppose the initial concentration of Fe^{3+} ions is 0.200 M, the initial I^- ion concentration is 0.300 M, and the equilibrium concentration of I_3^- ions is 0.0866 M. What is the value of K_c?

$$2\ Fe^{3+}(aq) + 3\ I^-(aq) \rightleftharpoons 2\ Fe^{2+}(aq) + I_3^-(aq)$$

Strategy Map 15.3

PROBLEM

Calculate K_c for reaction of Fe^{3+} with I^- to give Fe^{2+} and I_3^-.

DATA/INFORMATION KNOWN

- Balanced equation
- **Initial concentrations** of reactants
- **Equilibrium concentration** of one product

STEP 1. Organize information.

Write K_c **expression**, set up **ICE table**, and enter ***known concentrations*** in the table.

STEP 2. Enter ***concentration changes*** in ICE table and derive **equilibrium concentrations.**

Complete **ICE table** with equilibrium concentrations known.

STEP 3. Enter **equilibrium concentrations** in K_c **expression** and solve for K_c.

Value of K_c

What Do You Know? You are given the balanced equation (from which the equilibrium constant expression can be written), initial concentrations of the reactants, and the concentration of one product (I_3^-) after equilibrium has been reached.

Strategy

- Set up an ICE table and enter the initial concentrations.
- Decide how each concentration changes. Let us begin by saying that x mol/L of I_3^- ions are produced on proceeding to equilibrium. Based on the reaction stoichiometry, this means that $2x$ mol/L of Fe^{2+} must also be produced, $2x$ mol/L of Fe^{3+} ions are consumed, and $3x$ mol/L of I^- ions are consumed.
- The equilibrium concentration of I_3^- is known (0.0866 M), so this is the quantity x.
- Knowing that $x = 0.0866$ M, calculate the equilibrium concentrations for each species.
- Enter the equilibrium concentrations of reactants and products into the equilibrium constant expression and solve for K_c.

Solution The strategy outlined leads to the ICE table below.

EQUATION	$2\,Fe^{3+}$	+	$3\,I^-$	$\rightleftarrows$	$2\,Fe^{2+}$	+	I_3^-
Initial (M)	0.200		0.300		0		0
Change (M)	$-2x$		$-3x$		$+2x$		$+x$
Equilibrium (M)	0.200 − 2(0.0866) = 0.027		0.300 − 3(0.0866) = 0.040		2(0.0866) = 0.173		0.0866

The concentration of each substance at equilibrium is now known, and K_c can be calculated.

$$K_c = \frac{[Fe^{2+}]^2[I_3^-]}{[Fe^{3+}]^2[I^-]^3} = \frac{(0.173)^2(0.0866)}{(0.027)^2(0.040)^3} = 5.6 \times 10^4$$

Think about Your Answer The key to this problem is that the concentration of one product, I_3^-, was known at equilibrium. The concentrations of the other product and of the reactants could be derived from this based on the reaction stoichiometry. Also notice that the calculated K_c is much greater than one, so the reaction is product-favored at equilibrium. This is consistent with the equilibrium concentrations calculated in the ICE table.

Check Your Understanding

A solution is prepared by dissolving 0.050 mol of diiodocyclohexane, $C_6H_{10}I_2$, in the solvent CCl_4. The total solution volume is 1.00 L. When the reaction

$$C_6H_{10}I_2 \rightleftarrows C_6H_{10} + I_2$$

has come to equilibrium at 35 °C, the concentration of I_2 is 0.035 mol/L.

(a) What are the concentrations of $C_6H_{10}I_2$ and C_6H_{10} at equilibrium?

(b) Calculate K_c, the equilibrium constant.

REVIEW & CHECK FOR SECTION 15-3

1. You place 0.010 mol of $N_2O_4(g)$ in a 2.0-L flask at 200 °C. After reaching equilibrium, $[N_2O_4] = 0.0042$ M. Calculate K_c for the following reaction: $N_2O_4(g) \rightleftarrows 2\,NO_2(g)$

   (a) 1640
   (b) 6.1×10^{-4}
   (c) 3.1×10^{-4}
   (d) 8.8×10^{-6}

15-4 Using Equilibrium Constants in Calculations

Learning Objectives: LO 6.6

Suppose the value of K_c and the initial concentrations of reactants are known, and you want to know the equilibrium concentrations. As we look at several examples of this situation, we will again use ICE tables that summarize the initial conditions, the changes occurring on proceeding to equilibrium, and the final conditions.

EXAMPLE 15.4

Calculating Equilibrium Concentrations

Problem The equilibrium constant K_c (= 55.64) for

$$H_2(g) + I_2(g) \rightleftharpoons 2\ HI(g)$$

has been determined at 425 °C. If 0.130 mol each of H_2 and I_2 is placed in a 25.0-L flask at 425 °C, what are the concentrations of H_2, I_2, and HI when equilibrium has been achieved?

What Do You Know? You are given the balanced equation (from which the equilibrium constant expression can be written), the value of K_c, and the initial amounts of the reactants and the volume of the container (from which initial concentrations of the reactants can be calculated).

Strategy

- Write the equilibrium constant expression and set up an ICE table.
- Enter the initial concentrations of H_2 and I_2 on the first line (I).
- Assign the variable x to represent changes in concentration. Based on the reaction stoichiometry the change in $[H_2]$ and $[I_2]$ is $-x$ and the change in [HI] is $+2x$. Enter these values into the change (C) line of the table.
- Enter the expressions for the final equilibrium concentrations of all three species on the third line (E) of the ICE table, and then transfer these expressions to the equilibrium constant expression and solve for x.
- Use the calculated value of x to solve for the final concentration of each species.

Strategy Map 15.4

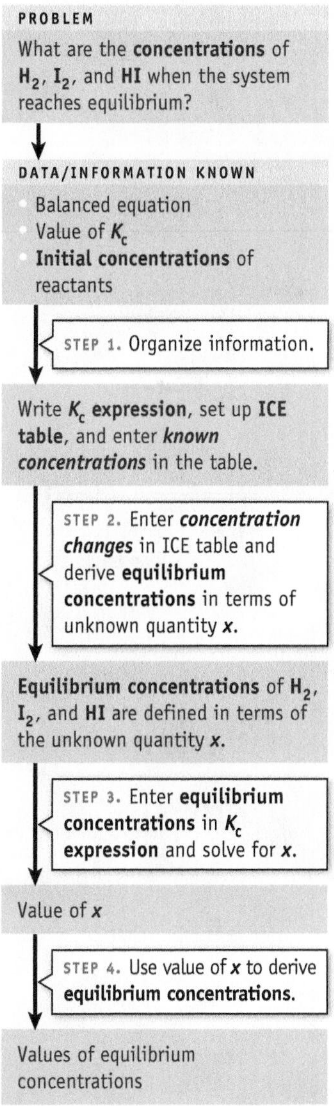

Solution Write the equilibrium constant expression

$$K_c = \frac{[HI]^2}{[H_2][I_2]} = 55.64$$

and then set up the ICE table as outlined in the Strategy.

EQUATION	$H_2(g)$	+	$I_2(g)$	$\rightleftharpoons$	2 HI(g)
Initial (M)	0.130 mol/25.0 L = 5.20×10^{-3} M		0.130 mol/25.0 L = 5.20×10^{-3} M		0
Change (M)	$-x$		$-x$		$+2x$
Equilibrium (M)	5.20×10^{-3} M $- x$		5.20×10^{-3} M $- x$		$2x$

Now the expressions for the equilibrium concentrations can be substituted into the equilibrium constant expression.

$$55.64 = \frac{(2x)^2}{(5.20 \times 10^{-3} - x)(5.20 \times 10^{-3} - x)} = \frac{(2x)^2}{(5.20 \times 10^{-3} - x)^2}$$

In this case, you can solve for the unknown quantity x by taking the square root of both sides of the equation,

$$\sqrt{K_c} = 7.459 = \frac{2x}{5.20 \times 10^{-3} - x}$$

$$7.459\,(5.20 \times 10^{-3} - x) = 0.0388 - 7.459x = 2x$$

$$0.0388 = 9.459x$$

$$x = 4.10 \times 10^{-3}$$

With x known, you can solve for the equilibrium concentrations of the reactants and products.

$$[H_2] = [I_2] = 5.20 \times 10^{-3} - x = 1.10 \times 10^{-3}\ M$$

$$[HI] = 2x = 8.20 \times 10^{-3}\ M$$

Think about Your Answer It is always wise to verify the answer by substituting the value of each concentration back into the equilibrium constant expression to see if your calculated K_c agrees with the one given in the problem. In this case, $(8.20 \times 10^{-3})^2/(1.10 \times 10^{-3})^2 = 55.6$, which agrees quite well with the value of K_c.

Check Your Understanding

At some temperature, $K_c = 33$ for the reaction

$$H_2(g) + I_2(g) \rightleftharpoons 2\ HI(g)$$

Assume the initial concentrations of both H_2 and I_2 are 6.00×10^{-3} mol/L. Find the concentration of each reactant and product at equilibrium.

Calculations Where the Solution Involves a Quadratic Expression

Suppose you are studying the decomposition of PCl_5 to form PCl_3 and Cl_2. You know that $K_c = 1.20$ at a given temperature.

$$PCl_5(g) \rightleftharpoons PCl_3(g) + Cl_2(g)$$

If the initial concentration of PCl_5 is 0.0920 M, what will be the concentrations of reactant and products when the system reaches equilibrium? Following the procedures outlined in Example 15.4, you would set up an ICE table to define the equilibrium concentrations of reactants and products.

Reaction	$PCl_5(g)$	$\rightleftharpoons$	$PCl_3(g)$	+	$Cl_2(g)$
Initial (M)	0.0920		0		0
Change (M)	$-x$		$+x$		$+x$
Equilibrium (M)	$0.0920 - x$		x		x

Substituting into the equilibrium constant expression, we have

$$K_c = 1.20 = \frac{[PCl_3][Cl_2]}{[PCl_5]} = \frac{(x)(x)}{0.0920 - x}$$

Expanding the algebraic expression results in a quadratic equation,

$$x^2 + 1.20x - 0.110 = 0$$

Using the quadratic formula (Appendix A; $a = 1$, $b = 1.20$, and $c = -0.110$), we find two roots to the equation: $x = 0.0859$ and -1.29. Because a negative value of

x (which represents a negative concentration) is not chemically meaningful, the answer is $x = 0.0859$. Therefore, at equilibrium we have

$$[PCl_5] = 0.0920 - 0.0859 = 0.0061\ M$$

$$[PCl_3] = [Cl_2] = 0.0859\ M$$

Although a solution to a quadratic equation can always be obtained using the quadratic formula, in many instances an acceptable answer can be obtained by using a realistic approximation to simplify the equation. To illustrate this, consider another equilibrium, the dissociation of I_2 molecules to form I atoms, for which $K_c = 5.6 \times 10^{-12}$ at 500 K.

$$I_2(g) \rightleftharpoons 2\ I(g)$$

$$K_c = \frac{[I]^2}{[I_2]} = 5.6 \times 10^{-12}$$

Assuming the initial I_2 concentration is 0.45 M and setting up the ICE table in the usual manner, we have

Reaction	$I_2(g)$	$\rightleftharpoons$	$2\ I(g)$
Initial (M)	0.45		0
Change (M)	$-x$		$+2x$
Equilibrium (M)	$0.45 - x$		$2x$

For the equilibrium constant expression, we again arrive at a quadratic equation.

$$K_c = 5.6 \times 10^{-12} = \frac{(2x)^2}{(0.45 - x)}$$

This could be solved using the quadratic formula, but there is a simpler way to reach an answer. Notice that the value of K_c is very small, indicating that the change in I_2 concentration is very small. In fact, K_c is so small that subtracting x from the original reactant concentration (0.45 mol/L) in the denominator of the equilibrium constant expression will leave the denominator essentially unchanged. That is, $(0.45 - x)$ is essentially equal to 0.45. Thus, we drop x in the denominator and have a simpler equation to solve.

Solving Quadratic Equations
Quadratic equations are usually solved using the quadratic formula (Appendix A). An alternative is the *method of successive approximations,* also outlined in Appendix A. Most equilibrium expressions can be solved quickly by this method, and you are urged to try it. This will remove the uncertainty of whether K expressions need to be solved exactly. (There are, however, rare cases in which this does not work; this is explained more fully in Appendix A.)

$$K_c = 5.6 \times 10^{-12} = \frac{(2x)^2}{(0.45)}$$

The solution to this equation gives $x = 7.9 \times 10^{-7}$. From this value, we can determine that $[I_2] = 0.45 - x = 0.45$ mol/L and $[I] = 2x = 1.6 \times 10^{-6}$ mol/L. Notice that the answer confirms the assumption the dissociation of I_2 is so small that $[I_2]$ at equilibrium is essentially equal to the initial concentration.

When is it possible to simplify a quadratic equation? The decision depends on both the value of the initial concentration of the reactant and the value of x, which is in turn related to the value of K. Consider the general reaction

$$A \rightleftharpoons B + C$$

where $K = [B][C]/[A]$. Assume that there is no B or C initially present, that you know K and the initial concentration of A ($= [A]_0$) and wish to find the equilibrium concentrations of B and C ($= x$). The equilibrium constant expression now is

$$K_c = \frac{[B][C]}{[A]} = \frac{(x)(x)}{[A]_0 - x}$$

When K_c is very small, the value of x will be much less than $[A]_0$, so $[A]_0 - x \cong [A]_0$. Therefore, we can write the following expression.

$$K_c = \frac{[B][C]}{[A]} \approx \frac{(x)(x)}{[A]_0} \quad (15.3)$$

A good guideline to follow is: *If $100 \times K_c < [A]_0$, the approximate expression will give acceptable values of equilibrium concentrations* (to two significant figures). For more about this, see *Problem Solving Tip 15.1*.

EXAMPLE 15.5

Calculating Equilibrium Concentrations Using an Equilibrium Constant

Problem The reaction

$$N_2(g) + O_2(g) \rightleftharpoons 2\ NO(g)$$

contributes to air pollution whenever a fuel is burned in air at a high temperature, as in a gasoline engine. At 1500 K, $K_c = 1.0 \times 10^{-5}$. Suppose a sample of air has $[N_2] = 0.080$ mol/L and $[O_2] = 0.020$ mol/L before any reaction occurs. Calculate the equilibrium concentrations of reactants and products after the mixture has been heated to 1500 K.

What Do You Know? As in Example 15.4, you know the value of K_c and can write the equilibrium expression from the balanced equation. You also know the initial concentrations of the reactants and can define the equilibrium concentrations in terms of the amounts of N_2 and O_2 consumed ($= x$).

Strategy Set up an ICE table, and then substitute the equilibrium concentrations into the equilibrium constant expression. The result will be a quadratic equation. This expression can be solved using the methods outlined in Appendix A or by using the guideline in the text to simplify the calculation.

Strategy Map 15.5

PROBLEM
What are the **equilibrium concentrations** of N_2, O_2, and **NO** in formation of NO from N_2 and O_2?

DATA/INFORMATION KNOWN
- Balanced equation
- Value of K_c
- **Initial concentrations** of reactants

STEP 1. Enter ***concentration changes*** in ICE table and derive **equilibrium concentrations** in terms of unknown quantity ***x***.

Equilibrium concentrations of N_2, O_2, and **NO** are defined in terms of the unknown quantity ***x***.

STEP 2. Enter **equilibrium concentrations** in K_c **expression** and solve for ***x***.

Value of ***x***

STEP 3. Use value of ***x*** to derive **equilibrium concentrations.**

Values of equilibrium concentrations

Solution We first set up an ICE table where the amounts of N_2 and O_2 consumed are designated as x.

EQUATION	$N_2(g)$	+	$O_2(g)$	$\rightleftharpoons$	2 NO(g)
Initial (M)	0.080		0.020		0
Change (M)	$-x$		$-x$		$+2x$
Equilibrium (M)	$0.080 - x$		$0.020 - x$		$2x$

Next, the equilibrium concentrations are substituted into the equilibrium constant expression.

$$K_c = 1.0 \times 10^{-5} = \frac{[NO]^2}{[N_2][O_2]} = \frac{[2x]^2}{(0.080 - x)(0.020 - x)}$$

We refer to the guideline (Equation 15.3) to decide whether an approximate solution is acceptable. Here, $100 \times K_c$ ($= 1.0 \times 10^{-3}$) is smaller than either of the initial reactant concentrations (0.080 and 0.020). This means we can use the approximate expression.

$$K_c = 1.0 \times 10^{-5} = \frac{[NO]^2}{[N_2][O_2]} = \frac{(2x)^2}{(0.080)(0.020)}$$

PROBLEM SOLVING TIP 15.1

When Do You Need to Use the Quadratic Equation?

In most equilibrium calculations, the quantity x may be neglected in the denominator of the equation $K = x^2/([A]_0 - x)$ if x is less than 10% of the concentration of reactant initially present ($= [A]_0$). The guideline presented in the text for making the approximation that $[A]_0 - x = [A]_0$ when $100 \times K < [A]_0$ reflects this fact.

In general, when K is about 1 or greater, the approximation cannot be made. If K is much less than 1 and $100 \times K < [A]_0$ (you will see many such cases in Chapter 16), the approximate expression ($K = x^2/[A]_0$) gives an acceptable answer. If you are not certain, first make the assumption that the unknown (x) is small, and solve the approximate expression ($K = (x)^2/[A]_0$). Next, compare the "approximate" value of x with $[A]_0$. If x has a value equal to or less than 10% of $[A]_0$, there is no need to solve the full equation using the quadratic formula.

Solving this expression, we find

$$1.6 \times 10^{-8} = 4x^2$$

$$x = 6.3 \times 10^{-5}$$

Therefore, the reactant and product concentrations at equilibrium are

$$[N_2] = 0.080 - 6.3 \times 10^{-5} \approx 0.080 \text{ M}$$

$$[O_2] = 0.020 - 6.3 \times 10^{-5} \approx 0.020 \text{ M}$$

$$[NO] = 2x = 1.3 \times 10^{-4} \text{ M}$$

Think about Your Answer The value of x obtained using the approximation is the same as that obtained from the quadratic formula.

Check Your Understanding

The decomposition of $PCl_5(g)$ to form $PCl_3(g)$ and $Cl_2(g)$ has $K_c = 33.3$ at a high temperature. If the initial concentration of PCl_5 is 0.1000 M, what are the equilibrium concentrations of the reactants and products?

REVIEW & CHECK FOR SECTION 15-4

1. Graphite and carbon dioxide are kept at constant volume at 1000 K until the reaction

$$C(\text{graphite}) + CO_2(g) \rightleftharpoons 2\ CO(g)$$

has come to equilibrium. At this temperature, $K_c = 0.021$. The initial concentration of CO_2 is 0.012 mol/L. Calculate the equilibrium concentration of CO.

(a) 0.012 M (b) 0.011 M (c) 0.0057 M

15-5 More about Balanced Equations and Equilibrium Constants

Learning Objectives: LO 6.2

Using Different Stoichiometric Coefficients

Chemical equations can be balanced using different sets of stoichiometric coefficients. For example, the equation for the oxidation of carbon to give carbon monoxide can be written

$$C(s) + \tfrac{1}{2}\ O_2(g) \rightleftharpoons CO(g)$$

for which the equilibrium constant expression would be

$$K_1 = \frac{[CO]}{[O_2]^{1/2}} = 4.6 \times 10^{23} \text{ at } 25\ °C$$

You can write the chemical equation equally well, however, as

$$2\ C(s) + O_2(g) \rightleftharpoons 2\ CO(g)$$

and the equilibrium constant expression would now be

$$K_2 = \frac{[CO]^2}{[O_2]} = 2.1 \times 10^{47} \text{ at } 25\ °C$$

When you compare the two equilibrium constant expressions you find that $K_2 = (K_1)^2$; that is,

$$K_2 = \frac{[CO]^2}{[O_2]} = \left\{\frac{[CO]}{[O_2]^{1/2}}\right\}^2 = K_1^2$$

When the stoichiometric coefficients of a balanced equation are multiplied by some factor, the equilibrium constant for the new equation (K_{new}) is the old equilibrium constant (K_{old}) raised to the power of the multiplication factor.

In the case of the oxidation of carbon, the second equation was obtained by multiplying the first equation by two. Therefore, K_2 is the *square* of K_1 ($K_2 = K_1^2$).

Reversing a Chemical Equation

Let us consider what happens if a chemical equation is reversed. Here, we will compare the value of K_c for formic acid transferring an H^+ ion to water

$$HCO_2H(aq) + H_2O(\ell) \rightleftharpoons HCO_2^-(aq) + H_3O^+(aq)$$

$$K_1 = \frac{[HCO_2^-][H_3O^+]}{[HCO_2H]} = 1.8 \times 10^{-4} \text{ at } 25\ °C$$

with the opposite reaction, the gain of an H^+ ion by the formate ion, HCO_2^-.

$$HCO_2^-(aq) + H_3O^+(aq) \rightleftharpoons HCO_2H(aq) + H_2O(\ell)$$

$$K_2 = \frac{[HCO_2H]}{[HCO_2^-][H_3O^+]} = 5.6 \times 10^3 \text{ at } 25\ °C$$

Here, $K_2 = 1/K_1$.

The equilibrium constants for a reaction and its reverse are the reciprocals of one another.

Adding Two Chemical Equations

It is often useful to add two equations to obtain the equation for a net process. As an example, consider the reactions that take place when silver chloride dissolves in water (to a *very* small extent) and ammonia is added to the solution. Ammonia reacts with silver ions to form a water-soluble compound, $Ag(NH_3)_2Cl$ (Figure 15.5). Adding the equation for dissolving solid AgCl to the equation for the reaction of Ag^+ ions with ammonia gives the equation for the net reaction, dissolving solid AgCl in aqueous ammonia. (All equilibrium constants are given at 25 °C.)

$AgCl(s) \rightleftharpoons Ag^+(aq) + Cl^-(aq)$ $\qquad K_1 = [Ag^+][Cl^-] = 1.8 \times 10^{-10}$

$Ag^+(aq) + 2\ NH_3(aq) \rightleftharpoons [Ag(NH_3)_2]^+(aq)$ $\qquad K_2 = \frac{[Ag(NH_3)_2^+]}{[Ag^+][NH_3]^2} = 1.1 \times 10^7$

Net equation:

$AgCl(s) + 2\ NH_3(aq) \rightleftharpoons [Ag(NH_3)_2]^+(aq) + Cl^-(aq)$

FIGURE 15.5 **Dissolving silver chloride in aqueous ammonia.** *(left)* A precipitate of AgCl(s) is suspended in water. *(right)* When aqueous ammonia is added, the ammonia reacts with the trace of silver ion in solution, the equilibrium shifts, and the silver chloride dissolves.

To obtain the equilibrium constant for the net reaction, K_{net}, we *multiply* the equilibrium constants for the two reactions, $K_1 \times K_2$.

$$K_{net} = K_1 \times K_2 = [\cancel{Ag^+}][Cl^-] \times \frac{[Ag(NH_3)_2^+]}{[\cancel{Ag^+}][NH_3]^2} = \frac{[Ag(NH_3)_2^+][Cl^-]}{[NH_3]^2}$$

$$K_{net} = K_1 \times K_2 = 2.0 \times 10^{-3}$$

When two or more chemical equations are added to produce a net equation, the equilibrium constant for the net equation is the product of the equilibrium constants for the added equations.

EXAMPLE 15.6

Balanced Equations and Equilibrium Constants

Problem A mixture of nitrogen, hydrogen, and ammonia is brought to equilibrium. When the equation is written using whole-number coefficients, as follows, the value of K_c is 3.5×10^8 at 25 °C.

Equation 1: $N_2(g) + 3\ H_2(g) \rightleftharpoons 2\ NH_3(g)$ $\quad K_1 = 3.5 \times 10^8$

However, the equation can also be written as given in Equation 2. What is the value of K_2?

Equation 2: $\frac{1}{2}\ N_2(g) + \frac{3}{2}\ H_2(g) \rightleftharpoons NH_3(g)$ $\quad K_2 = ?$

The decomposition of ammonia to the elements (Equation 3) is the reverse of its formation (Equation 1). What is the value of K_3?

Equation 3: $2\ NH_3(g) \rightleftharpoons N_2(g) + 3\ H_2(g)$ $\quad K_3 = ?$

What Do You Know? You know the value of K_c for a given balanced equation. You want to know how the value of K_c changes as the stoichiometric coefficients change or when the equation is reversed.

Strategy Determine how the desired reaction is related to the given reaction(s). (Was a given chemical reaction multiplied by a factor? Was a reaction reversed? Were two or more reactions added?) Use the relationships discussed to determine the effect(s) of these transformations on the given K value(s). See also *Problem Solving Tip 15.2.*

PROBLEM SOLVING TIP 15.2

Balanced Equations and Equilibrium Constants

You should now know

1. how to write an equilibrium constant expression from the balanced equation, recognizing that the concentrations of solids and liquids used as solvents do not appear in the expression.
2. that when the stoichiometric coefficients in a balanced equation are changed by a factor of n, $K_{new} = (K_{old})^n$.
3. that when a balanced equation is reversed, $K_{new} = 1/K_{old}$.
4. that when several balanced equations (each with its own equilibrium constant, K_1, K_2, etc.) are added to obtain a net, balanced equation, $K_{net} = K_1 \times K_2 \times K_3 \times \ldots$.

Solution Equation 2 can be obtained by multiplying Equation 1 by 1/2. Thus K_2 is equal to K_1 raised to the one-half power, $K_1^{1/2}$. To confirm this relationship between K_1 and K_2, write the equilibrium constant expressions for these two balanced equations.

$$K_1 = \frac{[NH_3]^2}{[N_2][H_2]^3} \qquad K_2 = \frac{[NH_3]}{[N_2]^{1/2}[H_2]^{3/2}}$$

Writing these expressions makes it clear that K_2 is the square root of K_1.

$$K_2 = (K_1)^{1/2} = \sqrt{K_1} = \sqrt{3.5 \times 10^8} = 1.9 \times 10^4$$

Equation 3 is the reverse of Equation 1, and its equilibrium constant expression is

$$K_3 = \frac{[N_2][H_2]^3}{[NH_3]^2}$$

In this case, K_3 is the reciprocal of K_1. That is, $K_3 = 1/K_1$.

$$K_3 = \frac{1}{K_1} = \frac{1}{3.5 \times 10^8} = 2.9 \times 10^{-9}$$

Think about Your Answer Notice that the production of ammonia from the elements has a large equilibrium constant and is product-favored (see Section 15-2). As expected, the reverse reaction, the decomposition of ammonia to its elements, has a small equilibrium constant and is reactant-favored.

Check Your Understanding

The conversion of oxygen to ozone has a very small equilibrium constant.

$$3/2\ O_2(g) \rightleftharpoons O_3(g) \qquad K = 2.5 \times 10^{-29}$$

(a) What is the value of K when the equation is written using whole-number coefficients?

$$3\ O_2(g) \rightleftharpoons 2\ O_3(g)$$

(b) What is the value of K for the conversion of ozone to oxygen?

$$2\ O_3(g) \rightleftharpoons 3\ O_2(g)$$

REVIEW & CHECK FOR SECTION 15-5

1. The following equilibrium constants are given at 500 K:

$H_2(g) + Br_2(g) \rightleftharpoons 2\ HBr(g)$ $\qquad K_p = 7.9 \times 10^{11}$

$H_2(g) \rightleftharpoons 2\ H(g)$ $\qquad K_p = 4.8 \times 10^{-41}$

$Br_2(g) \rightleftharpoons 2\ Br$ $\qquad K_p = 2.2 \times 10^{-15}$

What is the value of K_p for the reaction $H + Br \rightleftharpoons HBr$?

(a) $K_p = 8.3 \times 10^{-44}$ (b) $K_p = 7.5 \times 10^{66}$ (c) $K_p = 2.7 \times 10^{33}$

15-6 Disturbing a Chemical Equilibrium

Learning Objectives: LO 6.3, LO 6.8, LO 6.9 (see APEC Lab 13 "Le Châtelier's Principle"), LO 6.10

The equilibrium between reactants and products may be disturbed in three ways: (1) by changing the temperature, (2) by changing the concentration of a reactant or product, or (3) by changing the volume (for systems involving gases) (Table 15.1). *A change in any of the factors that determine the equilibrium conditions of a system will cause the system to change in such a manner as to reduce or counteract the effect of the change.* This statement is often referred to as *Le Chatelier's principle* (◀ Section 13-3). It is a shorthand way of describing how the quantities of reactants and products are adjusted so that equilibrium is restored, that is, so that the reaction quotient is once again equal to the equilibrium constant.

Le Chatelier's Principle and Chemical Kinetics One way to understand the shift in equilibrium when a reactant or product concentration changes is to recall that reaction rates depend on reactant concentrations. If a system is at equilibrium the rate of conversion of reactants to products is equal to the rate of conversion of products to reactants. (See page 546.) But suppose the reactant concentration suddenly increases. Now the rate of reactant → product exceeds the rate for product → reactant, and the system is no longer at equilibrium. The reaction returns to equilibrium when the product and reactant concentrations are such that the forward and reverse rates are again equal.

Effect of the Addition or Removal of a Reactant or Product

Consider the following experiment: You have a chemical system initially at equilibrium. To this you add (or take away) one or more of the reactants or products. The system will no longer be at equilibrium. When the system returns to equilibrium the new equilibrium concentrations of reactants and products will be different, but the value of the equilibrium constant expression will still equal K (Table 15.1). To illustrate this, let us return to the butane/isobutane equilibrium (with $K_c = 2.5$).

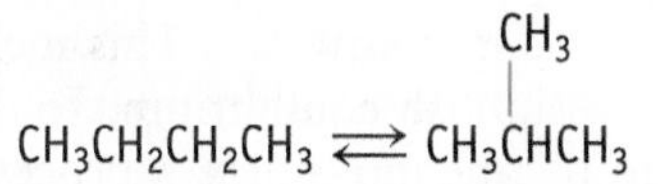

butane isobutane

$K_c = 2.5$

Table 15.1 Effects of Disturbances on Equilibrium Composition

Disturbance	Change as Mixture Returns to Equilibrium	Effect on Equilibrium	Effect on K
Reactions Involving Solids, Liquids, or Gases			
Rise in temperature	Energy is consumed by system	Shift in endothermic direction	Change
Drop in temperature	Energy is generated by system	Shift in exothermic direction	Change
Addition of reactant*	Some of added reactant is consumed	Product concentration increases	No change
Addition of product*	Some of added product is consumed	Reactant concentration increases	No change
Reactions Involving Gases			
Decrease in volume, increase in pressure	Pressure decreases	Composition changes to reduce total number of gas molecules	No change
Increase in volume, decrease in pressure	Pressure increases	Composition changes to increase total number of gas molecules	No change

*Does not apply when an insoluble solid reactant or product is added. Their "concentrations" do not appear in the reaction quotient.

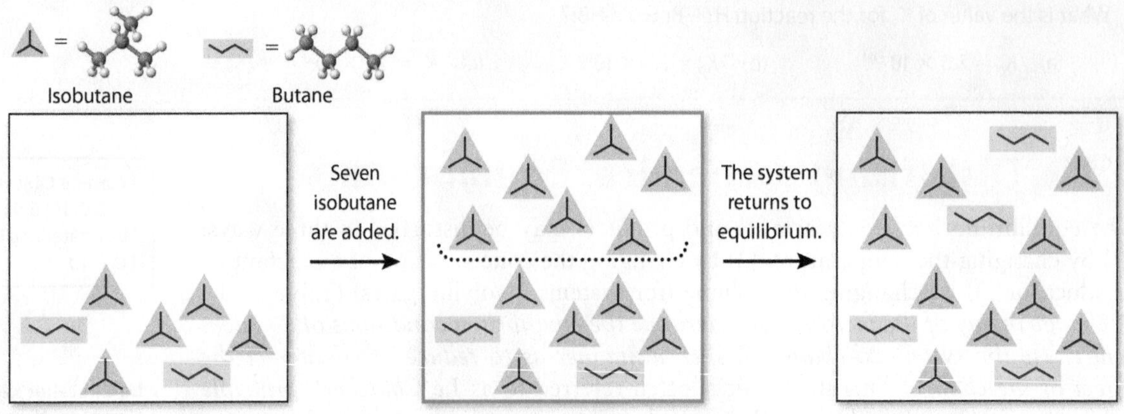

$Q = 5/2 = K$
An equilibrium mixture of five isobutane molecules and two butane molecules.

$Q = 12/2 > K$
Seven isobutane molecules are added, so the system is no longer at equilibrium.

$Q = 10/4 = K$
A net of two isobutane molecules has changed to butane molecules, to once again give an equilibrium mixture where the ratio of isobutane to butane is 5:2 (or 2.5:1).

FIGURE 15.6 Addition of more reactant or product to an equilibrium system.

Suppose the equilibrium mixture consists of two molecules of butane and five molecules of isobutane (Figure 15.6). The reaction quotient, Q, is 5/2 (or 2.5/1), the value of the equilibrium constant for the reaction. Now we add seven more molecules of isobutane to the mixture to give a ratio of 12 isobutane molecules to two butane molecules. The reaction quotient is now 6/1. This means Q is greater than K, and the system will change to reestablish equilibrium. To do so, some molecules of isobutane must be changed into butane molecules, a process that continues until the ratio [isobutane]/[butane] is once again 2.5/1. In this particular case, if two of the 12 isobutane molecules change to butane, the ratio of isobutane to butane is again equal to K_c (= 10/4 = 2.5/1), and equilibrium is reestablished.

EXAMPLE 15.7

Effect of Concentration Changes on Equilibrium

Problem Assume equilibrium has been established in a 1.00-L flask with [butane] = 0.00500 mol/L and [isobutane] = 0.0125 mol/L.

$$\text{Butane} \rightleftharpoons \text{Isobutane} \qquad K_c = 2.50$$

Then 0.0150 mol of butane is added. What are the concentrations of butane and isobutane when equilibrium is reestablished?

What Do You Know? Here you know the value of K_c, the balanced equation, the original equilibrium concentrations of reactant and product, and the amount of reactant added to the system at equilibrium.

Strategy After adding excess butane, $Q < K_c$. To reestablish equilibrium, the concentration of butane must decrease by an amount x and that of isobutane must increase, also by an amount x. Use an ICE table to track the changes.

Solution First organize the information in a modified ICE table (and convert amounts to concentrations).

EQUATION	BUTANE	$\rightleftarrows$	ISOBUTANE
Initial (M)	0.00500		0.0125
Concentration immediately on adding butane (M)	0.00500 + 0.0150		0.0125
Change in concentration to reestablish equilibrium (M)	$-x$		$+x$
Equilibrium (M)	$0.00500 + 0.0150 - x$		$0.0125 + x$

The entries in this table were obtained as follows:

(a) The concentration of butane when equilibrium is reestablished is the original equilibrium concentration *plus* what was added (0.0150 mol/L) *minus* the concentration of butane that is converted to isobutane to reestablish equilibrium. The concentration of butane converted to isobutane is unknown and so is designated as x.

(b) The concentration of isobutane when equilibrium is reestablished is the concentration that was already present (0.0125 mol/L) plus the concentration formed (x mol/L) on reestablishing equilibrium.

Having defined [butane] and [isobutane] when equilibrium is reestablished and remembering that K_c is a constant (= 2.50), we can write

$$K_c = 2.50 = \frac{[\text{isobutane}]}{[\text{butane}]}$$

We now calculate the new equilibrium composition:

$$2.50 = \frac{0.0125 + x}{0.00500 + 0.0150 - x} = \frac{0.0125 + x}{0.0200 - x}$$

$$2.50\,(0.0200 - x) = 0.0125 + x$$

$$x = 0.0107 \text{ mol/L}$$

$$[\text{butane}] = 0.00500 + 0.0150 - x = 0.0093 \text{ M and } [\text{isobutane}] = 0.0125 + x = 0.0232 \text{ M}$$

Answer check: new ratio [isobutane]/[butane] = 0.0232/0.0093 = 2.5

Think about Your Answer As predicted by Le Chatelier's principle, the added "stress" on the system of adding excess butane is relieved by converting some butane to isobutane to achieve a new equilibrium mixture where Q again equals K_c. In the new equilibrium mixture the butane concentration lies between its initial value and its value immediately upon the addition of excess butane, and the isobutane concentration is greater than the original value.

Check Your Understanding

Equilibrium exists between butane and isobutane when [butane] = 0.020 M and [isobutane] = 0.050 M. An additional 0.0200 mol/L of isobutane is added to the mixture. What are the concentrations of butane and isobutane after equilibrium has again been attained?

Strategy Map 15.7

PROBLEM

What are the **equilibrium concentrations** of reactant and product after adding **excess reactant**?

DATA/INFORMATION KNOWN

- Balanced equation
- Value of K_c
- **Initial concentrations** of ***reactant*** and ***product*** and amount of ***excess reactant*** added

STEP 1. Enter ***concentration changes*** in ICE table and derive **equilibrium concentrations** in terms of unknown quantity x.

Equilibrium concentrations of ***reactant*** and ***product*** are defined in terms of the unknown quantity x.

STEP 2. Enter **equilibrium concentrations** in K_c **expression** and solve for x.

Value of x

STEP 3. Use value of x to derive **equilibrium concentrations.**

Values of equilibrium concentrations

Effect of Volume Changes on Gas-Phase Equilibria

For a reaction that involves gases, what happens to equilibrium concentrations or pressures if the size of the container is changed? (Such a change occurs, for example, when fuel and air are compressed in an automobile engine.) The answer to this is that the gas concentrations must also change if the container volume changes. And, if the concentrations change, then, depending on the stoichiometry, the equilibrium composition can change. As an example, consider the following equilibrium:

$$\underset{\text{brown gas}}{2\ NO_2(g)} \rightleftharpoons \underset{\text{colorless gas}}{N_2O_4(g)}$$

$$K_c = \frac{[N_2O_4]}{[NO_2]^2} = 170 \text{ at } 298 \text{ K}$$

What happens if the volume of the flask holding the gases is suddenly halved? The immediate result is that the concentrations of both gases will double. For example, assume equilibrium is initially established when $[N_2O_4]$ is 0.0280 mol/L and $[NO_2]$ is 0.0128 mol/L. When the volume is halved, $[N_2O_4]$ becomes 0.0560 mol/L, and $[NO_2]$ is 0.0256 mol/L. The reaction quotient, Q, under these circumstances is $(0.0560)/(0.0256)^2 = 85.4$. Now, Q is less than K, and to return to equilibrium the quantity of product must increase at the expense of the reactant. Thus, the new equilibrium composition will have a higher concentration of N_2O_4 than immediately after the volume change.

$$2\ NO_2(g) \rightleftharpoons N_2O_4(g)$$

$$\xrightarrow[\substack{NO_2 \text{ is converted to } N_2O_4 \\ \text{until equilibrium is attained}}]{\text{decrease volume of container}}$$

In returning to equilibrium the concentration of NO_2 decreases twice as much as the concentration of N_2O_4 increases because one molecule of N_2O_4 is formed by consuming two molecules of NO_2. This occurs until the reaction quotient, $Q = [N_2O_4]/[NO_2]^2$, is once again equal to K_c. The net effect of the volume decrease is to decrease the number of molecules in the gas phase.

The conclusions for the NO_2/N_2O_4 equilibrium can be generalized:

- For reactions involving gases, the stress of a volume decrease (a pressure increase) will be counterbalanced by a change in the equilibrium composition to one having a smaller number of gas molecules.
- For a volume increase (a pressure decrease), the equilibrium composition will favor the side of the reaction with the larger number of gas molecules.
- For a reaction in which there is no change in the number of gas molecules in proceeding from reactants to products, such as in the reaction of H_2 and I_2 to produce HI $[H_2(g) + I_2(g) \rightleftharpoons 2\ HI(g)]$, a volume change will have no effect.

Effect of Temperature Changes on Equilibrium Composition

Changing the temperature of a system at equilibrium is different from other equilibrium disturbances because the value of the equilibrium constant changes with temperature. Predicting the exact changes in equilibrium compositions with temperature is beyond the scope of this text, but you can make a qualitative prediction about the effect if you know whether the reaction is exothermic or endothermic. As an example, consider the endothermic reaction of N_2 with O_2 to give NO.

$$N_2(g) + O_2(g) \rightleftharpoons 2\ NO(g) \qquad \Delta_r H° = +180.6 \text{ kJ/mol-rxn}$$

$$K_c = \frac{[NO]^2}{[N_2][O_2]}$$

Le Chatelier's principle allows you to predict how the value of K will vary with temperature. The formation of NO from N_2 and O_2 is endothermic; that is, energy must be provided as heat for the reaction to occur. You might imagine that heat is a "reactant." If the system is at equilibrium and the temperature then increases, the system will adjust to alleviate this "stress." The way to counteract the energy input is to use up some of the energy added as heat by consuming N_2 and O_2 and

CASE STUDY | Applying Equilibrium Concepts—The Haber-Bosch Ammonia Process

Nitrogen-containing substances are used around the world to stimulate the growth of field crops. Farmers from Portugal to Tibet have used animal waste for centuries as a "natural" fertilizer. In the 19th century, industrialized countries imported nitrogen-rich marine bird manure from Peru, Bolivia, and Chile, but the supply of this material was clearly limited. In 1898, William Ramsay (the discoverer of the noble gases, *Applying Chemical Principles*, Chapter 2) pointed out that the amount of "fixed nitrogen" in the world was being depleted and predicted that world food shortages would occur by the mid-20th century as a result. That Ramsay's prediction failed to materialize was due in part to the work of Fritz Haber (1868–1934). In about 1908, Haber developed a method to make ammonia directly from the elements,

$$N_2(g) + 3\ H_2(g) \rightleftharpoons 2\ NH_3(g)$$

and, a few years later, Carl Bosch (1874–1940) perfected the industrial scale synthesis. Ammonia is now made for pennies per kilogram and is consistently ranked in the top five chemicals produced in the United States, with 15–20 billion kilograms produced annually. Not only is ammonia used directly as a fertilizer, but it is also a starting material for making nitric acid and ammonium nitrate, among other things.

The manufacture of ammonia (Figure A) is a good example of the role that kinetics and chemical equilibria play in practical chemistry.

The $N_2 + H_2$ reaction is exothermic and product-favored at 25 °C ($K_c > 1$).

At 25 °C, K_c (calc'd value) $= 3.5 \times 10^8$ and $\Delta_r H° = -92.2$ kJ/mol-rxn

Unfortunately, the reaction at 25 °C is slow, so it is necessary to carry out the reaction at a higher temperature to increase the reaction rate. The problem with this, however, is that the equilibrium constant declines with temperature, as predicted by Le Chatelier's principle.

At 450 °C, K_c (experimental value) $= 0.16$ and $\Delta_r H° = -111.3$ kJ/mol-rxn

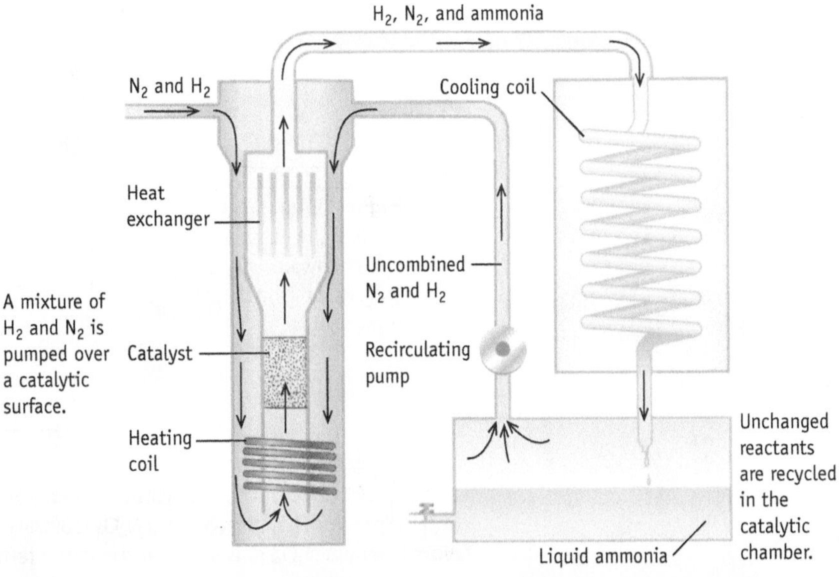

FIGURE A **The Haber-Bosch process for ammonia synthesis.** A mixture of H_2 and N_2 is pumped over a catalytic surface. The NH_3 is collected as a liquid (at −33 °C), and unchanged reactants are recycled in the catalytic chamber.

Thus, the yield declines with increasing temperature.

There are two things that can be done. The first is to raise the pressure. This does not change the value of *K*, but an increase in pressure can be compensated by converting 4 mol of reactants to 2 mol of product, and thereby increasing the percent conversion to NH_3.

In an industrial ammonia plant, conditions are chosen that balance reaction rate (improved at higher temperature) with product yield (*K* is smaller at higher temperatures). Additionally, a catalyst is often used to accelerate the reaction. An effective catalyst for the Haber-Bosch process is Fe_3O_4 mixed with KOH, SiO_2, and Al_2O_3 (all inexpensive chemicals). Because the catalyst is not effective below 400 °C, the process is carried out at 450–500 °C and 250 atm pressure.

Questions:

1. Anhydrous ammonia is used directly as a fertilizer, but much of it is also converted to other fertilizers, ammonium nitrate and urea.
   (a) How is NH_3 converted to ammonium nitrate?
   (b) Urea is formed in the reaction of ammonia and CO_2.

   $$2\ NH_3(g) + CO_2(g) \rightleftharpoons (NH_2)_2CO(s) + H_2O(g)$$

   Which would favor urea production, high temperature or high pressure? ($\Delta_f H°$ for solid urea $= -333.1$ kJ/mol-rxn)
2. Hydrogen is used in the Haber-Bosch process, and this is made from natural gas in a process called *steam reforming.*

   $$CH_4(g) + H_2O(g) \rightarrow CO(g) + 3\ H_2(g)$$
   $$CO(g) + H_2O(g) \rightarrow CO_2(g) + H_2(g)$$

   (a) Are the two reactions above endo- or exothermic?
   (b) To obtain the H_2 necessary to manufacture 15 billion kilograms of NH_3, what mass of CH_4 is required, and what mass of CO_2 is produced as a by-product (assuming complete conversion of the CH_4)?

Answers to these questions are available in Appendix N.

producing more NO as the system returns to equilibrium. This raises the value of the numerator ($[NO]^2$) and lowers the value of the denominator ($[N_2][O_2]$) in the reaction quotient, *Q*, resulting in a higher value of K_c.

The prediction regarding the $N_2/O_2/NO$ reaction is correct as you see in the following table of equilibrium constants at various temperatures. The equilibrium

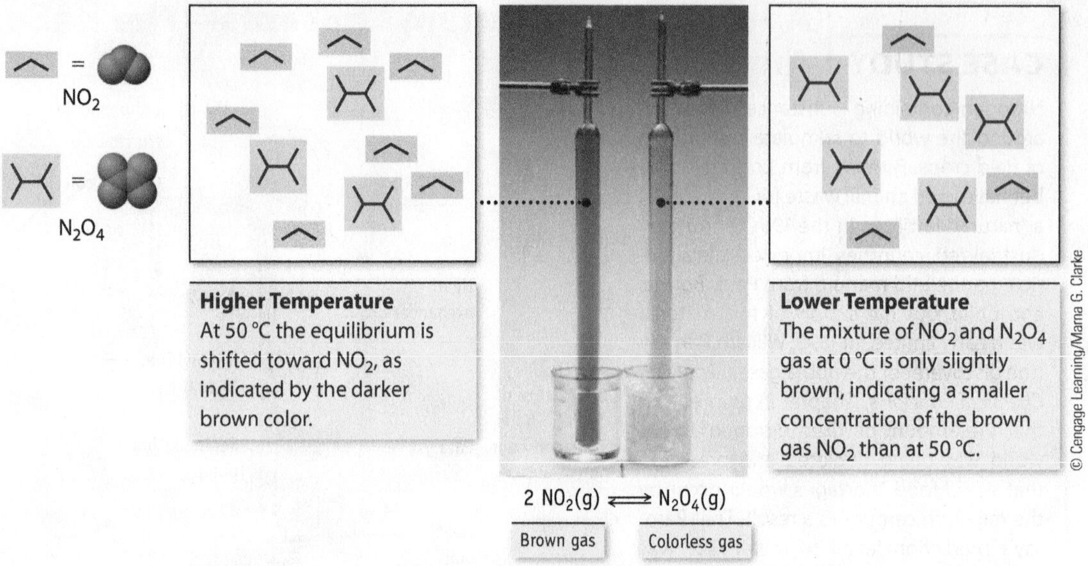

FIGURE 15.7 **Effect of temperature on an equilibrium.** The tubes in the photograph both contain gaseous NO_2 (brown) and N_2O_4 (colorless) at equilibrium. Because the equilibrium favors colorless N_2O_4, K_c is larger at the lower temperature.

constant and thus the proportion of NO in the equilibrium mixture increases with temperature.

Equilibrium Constant, K_c	Temperature (K)
4.5×10^{-31}	298
6.7×10^{-10}	900
1.7×10^{-3}	2300

As another example, consider the combination of molecules of the brown gas NO_2 to form colorless N_2O_4. An equilibrium between these compounds is readily achieved in a closed system (Figure 15.7).

$$2\ NO_2(g) \rightleftharpoons N_2O_4(g) \qquad \Delta_r H° = -57.1\ \text{kJ/mol-rxn}$$

$$K_c = \frac{[N_2O_4]}{[NO_2]^2}$$

Equilibrium Constant, K_c	Temperature (K)
1300	273
170	298

Here, the reaction is exothermic, so we might imagine heat as being a reaction "product." By lowering the temperature of the system, as in Figure 15.7, some energy is removed as heat. The removal of energy can be counteracted if the reaction produces energy as heat by the combination of NO_2 molecules to give more N_2O_4. Thus, the equilibrium concentration of NO_2 decreases; the concentration of N_2O_4 increases; and the value of K is larger at lower temperatures.

In summary,

- when the temperature of a system at equilibrium increases, the equilibrium will shift in the direction that absorbs energy as heat (Table 15.1)—that is, in the endothermic direction.

- if the temperature decreases, the equilibrium will shift in the direction that releases energy as heat—that is, in the exothermic direction.
- changing the temperature changes the value of *K*.

REVIEW & CHECK FOR SECTION 15-6

The formation of ammonia from its elements is an important industrial process.

$$3\ H_2(g) + N_2(g) \rightleftharpoons 2\ NH_3(g)$$

1. Does the reaction shift to the right or to the left, or does it remain unchanged, when extra H_2 is added?

   (a) shift left
   (b) shift right
   (c) unchanged

2. Does the reaction shift to the right or to the left, or does it remain unchanged, when the volume of the system is increased?

   (a) shift left
   (b) shift right
   (c) unchanged

3. For the equilibrium $2\ SO_2(g) + O_2(g) \rightleftharpoons 2\ SO_3(g)$, K_c has the following values: 4.0×10^{24} at 300 K, 2.5×10^{10} at 500 K, and 3.0×10^{4} at 700 K. Is this reaction exothermic or endothermic?

   (a) exothermic
   (b) endothermic

APPLYING CHEMICAL PRINCIPLES

Trivalent Carbon

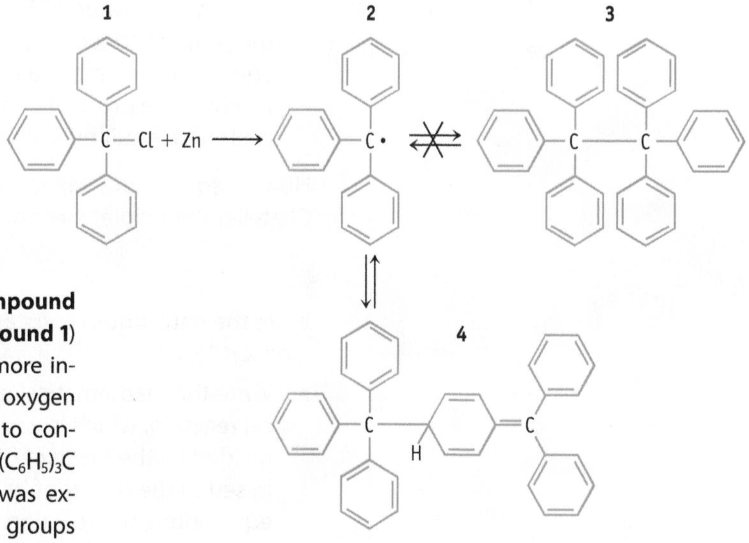

The octet rule is a guiding principle in organic chemistry. As a result, when someone discovers a molecule that does not obey the octet rule, organic chemists are always interested. The synthesis of the triphenylmethyl radical, $(C_6H_5)_3C$ was one such event.

The triphenylmethyl radical (**compound 2**), the first known persistent organic free radical, was discovered over 100 years ago by Moses Gomberg, a chemist at the University of Michigan. Gomberg set out to make hexaphenylethane [$(C_6H_5)_3C{-}C(C_6H_5)_3$] (**compound 3**). When he combined the reactants $(C_6H_5)_3CCl$ (**compound 1**) and Zn, he obtained a yellow solution that became more intensely yellow when heated and was reactive toward oxygen and halogens. This extreme reactivity led Gomberg to conclude that the yellow color was due to the presence of $(C_6H_5)_3C$ in solution. The existence of the stable free radical was explained by the fact that there are three large phenyl groups around a carbon atom, which prevents the radical from undergoing the expected dimerization to hexaphenylethane.

Actually, the triphenylmethyl radical does dimerize, but not the way Gomberg had expected. A diamagnetic, white solid crystalline dimer (**compound 4**) can be isolated from the solutions containing the radical. The dimerization occurs between a methyl carbon radical on one molecule and the phenyl ring on a second. When redissolved in benzene, the original yellow solution forms.

Studies determined that compounds **4** and **2** exist in solution in equilibrium. The value of K_c for the dimer-monomer equilibrium (**4** $\rightleftharpoons$ **2**) in benzene is 4.1×10^{-4} at 20 °C.

Interestingly, Gomberg finished his initial publication with the following statement: "This work will be continued and I wish to reserve the field for myself." In the United States, chemical research is competitive and Gomberg's wish was not respected.

QUESTIONS:

1. Freezing point depression is one means of determining the molar mass of a compound. The freezing point depression constant of benzene is –5.12 °C/*m*.
   a) When a 0.503 g sample of the white crystalline dimer is dissolved in 10.0 g benzene, the freezing point of benzene is decreased by 0.542 °C. Verify that the molar mass of the dimer is 475 g/mol when determined by freezing point depression. Assume no dissociation of the dimer occurs.
   b) The correct molar mass of the dimer is 487 g/mol. Explain why the dissociation equilibrium causes the freezing point depression calculation to yield a lower molar mass for the dimer.
2. What concentration of the monomer (**2**) will exist at equilibrium with 0.015 mol/L of the dimer (**4**) in benzene at 20 °C?
3. A 0.64 g sample of the white crystalline dimer (**4**) is dissolved in 25.0 mL of benzene at 20 °C. Use the equilibrium constant to calculate the concentrations of monomer (**2**) and dimer (**4**) in this solution.
4. Predict whether the dissociation of the dimer to the monomer is exothermic or endothermic, based on the fact that at higher temperatures the yellow color of the solution intensifies.
5. Which of the organic species mentioned in this story is paramagnetic?
   a) triphenylmethyl chloride
   b) triphenylmethyl radical
   c) the triphenylmethyl dimer

REFERENCE:

M. Gomberg, *Journal of the American Chemical Society*, Vol. 22, pp. 757-771, 1900.

CHAPTER GOALS REVISITED

Now that you have studied this chapter, you should ask whether you have met the chapter goals. In particular, you should be able to:

UNDERSTAND

- The nature and characteristics of chemical equilibria.
- The significance of the equilibrium constant, *K*, and the reaction quotient, *Q*.
  a. Predict whether a reaction is product-favored or reactant-favored at equilibrium. A large value of *K* ($K > 1$) means the reaction is product-favored, and the product concentrations are greater than the reactant concentrations at equilibrium. A small value of *K* ($K < 1$) indicates a reactant-favored reaction in which the product concentrations are smaller than the reactant concentrations at equilibrium (Section 15-2). Study Questions: 68, 70, 71.
- How an equilibrium will respond if the reaction conditions are changed (Le Chatelier's principle) (Section 15-6).

DO

- Write the equilibrium constant and reaction quotient expressions for a reaction (Section 15-2).
  a. Write the mathematical expression for the reaction quotient, *Q*, for a chemical reaction, which is equal to the product of the product concentrations divided by the product of the reactant concentrations, each concentration raised to the power of its stoichiometric coefficient. When the system is at equilibrium, the reaction quotient is equal to the equilibrium constant *K* (Equation 15.1). Study Questions: 1–4.
  b. Know that concentrations of solids, pure liquids, and solvents (e.g., water) are not included in the equilibrium constant expression.
  c. Designate equilibrium constants as being K_c or K_p and convert between values of K_c and K_p. Equilibrium concentrations may be expressed in terms of reactant and product concentrations (in moles per liter) and that *K* is then sometimes designated as K_c. Alternatively, concentrations of gases may be represented by partial pressures, and *K* is designated K_p. Study Questions: 25, 26, 55, 62.

- Calculate an equilibrium constant given the reactant and product concentrations (Section 15-3). Study Questions: 7–11, 31, 35, 36, 46, 60, 63.
- Use Q and K in quantitative studies of chemical equilibria.
  - **a.** Use the reaction quotient (Q) to decide whether a reaction is at equilibrium ($Q = K$), or if there will be a net conversion of reactants to products ($Q < K$) or products to reactants ($Q > K$) to attain equilibrium (Section 15-2). Study Questions: 3–6, 37, 38, 64.
  - **b.** Use equilibrium constants to calculate the concentration (or pressure) of a reactant or a product at equilibrium (Section 15-4). Study Questions: 16, 17, 34, 38, 44, 48–58, 61, 63.
- Derive a K value if different stoichiometric coefficients are used, if the chemical equation is reversed, or if several equations are added (Section 15-5). Study Questions: 19–24, 33, 39.
- Use Le Chatelier's principle.
  - **a.** Predict the effect of a disturbance on a chemical equilibrium—a change in temperature, a change in concentrations, or a change in volume or pressure for a reaction involving gases (Section 15-6 and Table 15.1). Study Questions: 27–30, 41–43, 64.

REMEMBER

- The characteristics of chemical equilibria (Sections 15-1 and 15-2).
- The importance of the state of equilibrium in chemical systems (Sections 15-1 and 15-2).
- The mathematical formulation of the equilibrium constant (Section 15-2).
- Le Chatelier's principle and how it is applied to chemical equilibria (Section 15-6).

KEY EQUATIONS

Equation 15.1 (page 558) The equilibrium constant expression. At equilibrium, the ratio of products to reactants (each raised to the power corresponding to its stoichiometric coefficient) has a constant value, K (at a particular temperature). For the general reaction $aA + bB \rightleftharpoons cC + dD$,

$$\text{Equilibrium constant} = K = \frac{[C]^c[D]^d}{[A]^a[B]^b}$$

Equation 15.2 (page 562) For the general reaction $aA + bB \rightleftharpoons cC + dD$, the ratio of product to reactant concentrations at any point in the reaction is the reaction quotient, Q.

$$\text{Reaction quotient} = Q = \frac{[C]^c[D]^d}{[A]^a[B]^b}$$

Equation 15.3 (page 570) This approximation is used to solve for the equilibrium concentrations of B and C ($= x$) in the general reaction $A \rightleftharpoons B + C$ when the value of $100 \times K$ is less than the original concentration of $A (= [A]_0)$.

$$K = \frac{[B][C]}{[A]} \approx \frac{(x)(x)}{[A]_0}$$

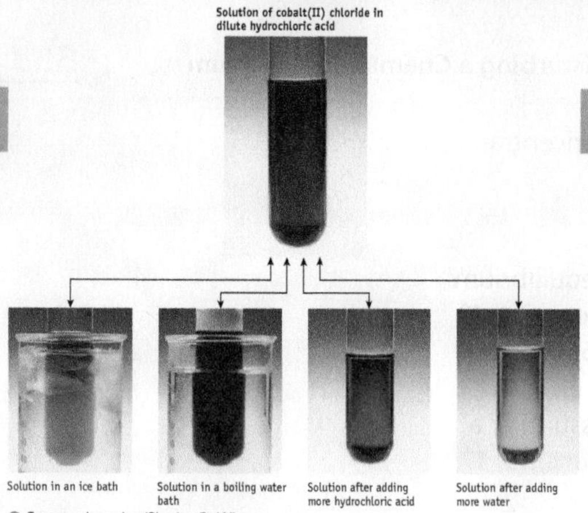

STUDY QUESTIONS

▲ denotes challenging questions.

Blue-numbered questions have answers in Appendix N and fully worked solutions in the *Student Solutions Manual.*

Practicing Skills

Writing Equilibrium Constant Expressions

(See Section 15-2 and Example 15.1.)

1. Write equilibrium constant expressions for the following reactions. For gases, use either pressures or concentrations.
   (a) $2\ H_2O_2(g) \rightleftharpoons 2\ H_2O(g) + O_2(g)$
   (b) $CO(g) + \frac{1}{2}\ O_2(g) \rightleftharpoons CO_2(g)$
   (c) $C(s) + CO_2(g) \rightleftharpoons 2\ CO(g)$
   (d) $NiO(s) + CO(g) \rightleftharpoons Ni(s) + CO_2(g)$

2. Write equilibrium constant expressions for the following reactions. For gases, use either pressures or concentrations.
   (a) $3\ O_2(g) \rightleftharpoons 2\ O_3(g)$
   (b) $Fe(s) + 5\ CO(g) \rightleftharpoons Fe(CO)_5(g)$
   (c) $(NH_4)_2CO_3(s) \rightleftharpoons 2\ NH_3(g) + CO_2(g) + H_2O(g)$
   (d) $Ag_2SO_4(s) \rightleftharpoons 2\ Ag^+(aq) + SO_4^{2-}(aq)$

The Equilibrium Constant and Reaction Quotient

(See Section 15-2 and Example 15.2.)

3. $K_c = 5.6 \times 10^{-12}$ at 500 K for the dissociation of iodine molecules to iodine atoms.

$$I_2(g) \rightleftharpoons 2\ I(g)$$

A mixture has $[I_2] = 0.020$ mol/L and $[I] = 2.0 \times 10^{-8}$ mol/L. Is the reaction at equilibrium (at 500 K)? If not, which way must the reaction proceed to reach equilibrium?

4. The reaction

$$2\ NO_2(g) \rightleftharpoons N_2O_4(g)$$

has an equilibrium constant, K_c, of 170 at 25 °C. If 2.0×10^{-3} mol of NO_2 is present in a 10.-L flask along with 1.5×10^{-3} mol of N_2O_4, is the system at equilibrium? If it is not at equilibrium, does the concentration of NO_2 increase or decrease as the system proceeds to equilibrium?

5. A mixture of SO_2, O_2, and SO_3 at 1000 K contains the gases at the following concentrations: $[SO_2] = 5.0 \times 10^{-3}$ mol/L, $[O_2] = 1.9 \times 10^{-3}$ mol/L, and $[SO_3] = 6.9 \times 10^{-3}$ mol/L. Is the reaction at equilibrium? If not, which way will the reaction proceed to reach equilibrium?

$$2\ SO_2(g) + O_2(g) \rightleftharpoons 2\ SO_3(g) \quad K_c = 279$$

6. The equilibrium constant, K_c, for the reaction

$$2\ NOCl(g) \rightleftharpoons 2\ NO(g) + Cl_2(g)$$

is 3.9×10^{-3} at 300 °C. A mixture contains the gases at the following concentrations: $[NOCl] = 5.0 \times 10^{-3}$ mol/L, $[NO] = 2.5 \times 10^{-3}$ mol/L, and $[Cl_2] = 2.0 \times 10^{-3}$ mol/L. Is the reaction at equilibrium at 300 °C? If not, in which direction does the reaction proceed to come to equilibrium?

Calculating an Equilibrium Constant

(See Section 15-3 and Example 15.3.)

7. The reaction

$$PCl_5(g) \rightleftharpoons PCl_3(g) + Cl_2(g)$$

was examined at 250 °C. At equilibrium, $[PCl_5] = 4.2 \times 10^{-5}$ mol/L, $[PCl_3] = 1.3 \times 10^{-2}$ mol/L, and $[Cl_2] = 3.9 \times 10^{-3}$ mol/L. Calculate K_c for the reaction.

8. An equilibrium mixture of SO_2, O_2, and SO_3 at a high temperature contains the gases at the following concentrations: $[SO_2] = 3.77 \times 10^{-3}$ mol/L, $[O_2] = 4.30 \times 10^{-3}$ mol/L, and $[SO_3] = 4.13 \times 10^{-3}$ mol/L. Calculate the equilibrium constant, K_c, for the reaction.

$$2\ SO_2(g) + O_2(g) \rightleftharpoons 2\ SO_3(g)$$

9. The reaction

$$C(s) + CO_2(g) \rightleftharpoons 2\ CO(g)$$

occurs at high temperatures. At 700 °C, a 200.0-L tank contains 1.0 mol of CO, 0.20 mol of CO_2, and 0.40 mol of C at equilibrium.
   (a) Calculate K_c for the reaction at 700 °C.
   (b) Calculate K_c for the reaction, also at 700 °C, if the amounts at equilibrium in the 200.0-L tank are 1.0 mol of CO, 0.20 mol of CO_2, and 0.80 mol of C.
   (c) Compare the results of (a) and (b). Does the quantity of carbon affect the value of K_c? Explain.

10. Hydrogen and carbon dioxide react at a high temperature to give water and carbon monoxide.

$$H_2(g) + CO_2(g) \rightleftharpoons H_2O(g) + CO(g)$$

(a) Laboratory measurements at 986 °C show that there are 0.11 mol each of CO and H_2O vapor and 0.087 mol each of H_2 and CO_2 at equilibrium in a 50.0-L container. Calculate the equilibrium constant for the reaction at 986 °C.
(b) Suppose 0.010 mol each of H_2 and CO_2 are placed in a 200.0-L container. When equilibrium is achieved at 986 °C, what amounts of CO(g) and H_2O(g), in moles, would be present? [Use the value of K_c from part (a).]

11. A mixture of CO and Cl_2 is placed in a reaction flask: [CO] = 0.0102 mol/L and [Cl_2] = 0.00609 mol/L. When the reaction

$$CO(g) + Cl_2(g) \rightleftharpoons COCl_2(g)$$

has come to equilibrium at 600 K, [Cl_2] = 0.00301 mol/L.

(a) Calculate the concentrations of CO and $COCl_2$ at equilibrium.
(b) Calculate K_c.

12. You place 0.0300 mol of pure SO_3 in an 8.00-L flask at 1150 K. At equilibrium, 0.0058 mol of O_2 has been formed. Calculate K_c for the reaction at 1150 K.

$$2\ SO_3(g) \rightleftharpoons 2\ SO_2(g) + O_2(g)$$

Using Equilibrium Constants

(See Section 15-4 and Examples 15.4 and 15.5.)

13. The value of K_c for the interconversion of butane and isobutane is 2.5 at 25 °C.

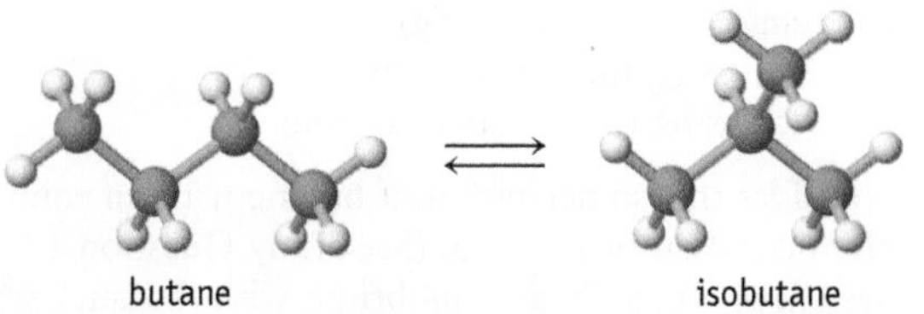

If you place 0.017 mol of butane in a 0.50-L flask at 25 °C and allow equilibrium to be established, what will be the equilibrium concentrations of the two forms of butane?

14. Cyclohexane, C_6H_{12}, a hydrocarbon, can isomerize or change into methylcyclopentane, a compound of the same formula ($C_5H_9CH_3$) but with a different molecular structure.

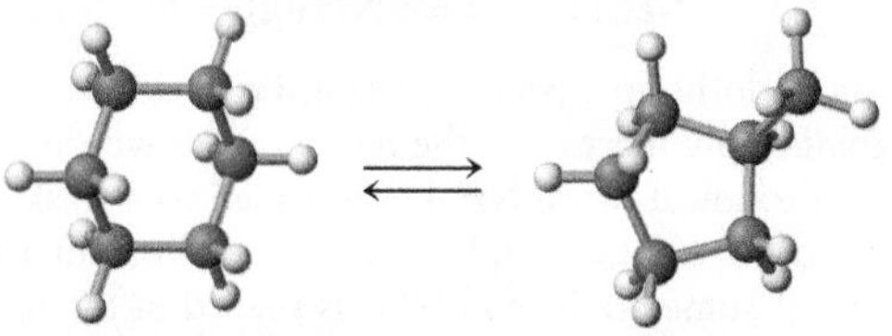

The equilibrium constant has been estimated to be 0.12 at 25 °C. If you had originally placed 0.045 mol of cyclohexane in a 2.8-L flask, what would be the concentrations of cyclohexane and methylcyclopentane when equilibrium is established?

15. The equilibrium constant for the dissociation of iodine molecules to iodine atoms

$$I_2(g) \rightleftharpoons 2\ I(g)$$

is 3.76×10^{-3} at 1000 K. Suppose 0.105 mol of I_2 is placed in a 12.3-L flask at 1000 K. What are the concentrations of I_2 and I when the system comes to equilibrium?

16. The equilibrium constant, K_c, for the reaction

$$N_2O_4(g) \rightleftharpoons 2\ NO_2(g)$$

at 25 °C is 170. Suppose 15.6 g of N_2O_4 is placed in a 5.000-L flask at 25 °C. Calculate the following:
(a) the amount of NO_2 (mol) present at equilibrium;
(b) the percentage of the original N_2O_4 that is dissociated.

17. Carbonyl bromide decomposes to carbon monoxide and bromine.

$$COBr_2(g) \rightleftharpoons CO(g) + Br_2(g)$$

K_c is 0.190 at 73 °C. If you place 0.0500 mol of $COBr_2$ in a 2.00-L flask and heat it to 73 °C, what are the equilibrium concentrations of $COBr_2$, CO, and Br_2? What percentage of the original $COBr_2$ decomposed at this temperature?

18. Iodine dissolves in water, but its solubility in a nonpolar solvent such as CCl_4 is greater.

Extracting iodine (I_2) from water with the nonpolar solvent CCl_4. I_2 is more soluble in CCl_4 and, after shaking a mixture of water and CCl_4, the I_2 has accumulated in the more dense CCl_4 layer.

The equilibrium constant is 85.0 for the process

$$I_2(aq) \rightleftharpoons I_2(CCl_4)$$

You place 0.0340 g of I_2 in 100.0 mL of water. After shaking it with 10.0 mL of CCl_4, how much I_2 remains in the water layer?

Manipulating Equilibrium Constant Expressions

(See Section 15-5 and Example 15.6.)

19. Which of the following correctly relates the equilibrium constants for the two reactions shown?

$$A + B \rightleftharpoons 2\,C \qquad K_1$$
$$2\,A + 2\,B \rightleftharpoons 4\,C \qquad K_2$$

(a) $K_2 = 2K_1$
(b) $K_2 = K_1^2$
(c) $K_2 = 1/K_1$
(d) $K_2 = 1/K_1^2$

20. Which of the following correctly relates the equilibrium constants for the two reactions shown?

$$A + B \rightleftharpoons 2\,C \qquad K_1$$
$$C \rightleftharpoons \tfrac{1}{2}\,A + \tfrac{1}{2}\,B \qquad K_2$$

(a) $K_2 = 1/(K_1)^{1/2}$
(b) $K_2 = 1/K_1$
(c) $K_2 = K_1^2$
(d) $K_2 = -K_1^{1/2}$

21. Consider the following equilibria involving $SO_2(g)$ and their corresponding equilibrium constants.

$$SO_2(g) + \tfrac{1}{2}\,O_2(g) \rightleftharpoons SO_3(g) \qquad K_1$$
$$2\,SO_3(g) \rightleftharpoons 2\,SO_2(g) + O_2(g) \qquad K_2$$

Which of the following expressions relates K_1 to K_2?

(a) $K_2 = K_1^2$
(b) $K_2^2 = K_1$
(c) $K_2 = K_1$
(d) $K_2 = 1/K_1$
(e) $K_2 = 1/K_1^2$

22. The equilibrium constant K for the reaction

$$CO_2(g) \rightleftharpoons CO(g) + \tfrac{1}{2}\,O_2(g)$$

is 6.66×10^{-12} at 1000 K. Calculate K for the reaction

$$2\,CO(g) + O_2(g) \rightleftharpoons 2\,CO_2(g)$$

23. Calculate K for the reaction

$$SnO_2(s) + 2\,CO(g) \rightleftharpoons Sn(s) + 2\,CO_2(g)$$

given the following information:

$$SnO_2(s) + 2\,H_2(g) \rightleftharpoons Sn(s) + 2\,H_2O(g) \qquad K = 8.12$$
$$H_2(g) + CO_2(g) \rightleftharpoons H_2O(g) + CO(g) \qquad K = 0.771$$

24. Calculate K for the reaction

$$Fe(s) + H_2O(g) \rightleftharpoons FeO(s) + H_2(g)$$

given the following information:

$$H_2O(g) + CO(g) \rightleftharpoons H_2(g) + CO_2(g) \qquad K = 1.6$$
$$FeO(s) + CO(g) \rightleftharpoons Fe(s) + CO_2(g) \qquad K = 0.67$$

25. Relationship of K_c and K_p:

(a) K_p for the following reaction is 0.16 at 25 °C. What is the value of K_c?

$$2\,NOBr(g) \rightleftharpoons 2\,NO(g) + Br_2(g)$$

(b) The equilibrium constant, K_c, for the following reaction is 1.05 at 350 K. What is the value of K_p?

$$2\,CH_2Cl_2(g) \rightleftharpoons CH_4(g) + CCl_4(g)$$

26. Relationship of K_c and K_p:

(a) The equilibrium constant, K_c, for the following reaction at 25 °C is 170. What is the value of K_p?

$$N_2O_4(g) \rightleftharpoons 2\,NO_2(g)$$

(b) K_c for the decomposition of ammonium hydrogen sulfide is 1.8×10^{-4} at 25 °C. What is the value of K_p?

$$NH_4HS(s) \rightleftharpoons NH_3(g) + H_2S(g)$$

Disturbing a Chemical Equilibrium

(See Section 15-6 and Example 15.7.)

27. Dinitrogen trioxide decomposes to NO and NO_2 in an endothermic process ($\Delta_r H° = 40.5$ kJ/mol-rxn).

$$N_2O_3(g) \rightleftharpoons NO(g) + NO_2(g)$$

Predict the effect of the following changes on the position of the equilibrium; that is, state which way the equilibrium will shift (left, right, or no change) when each of the following changes is made.

(a) adding more $N_2O_3(g)$
(b) adding more $NO_2(g)$
(c) increasing the volume of the reaction flask
(d) lowering the temperature

28. K_p for the following reaction is 0.16 at 25 °C:

$$2\,NOBr(g) \rightleftharpoons 2\,NO(g) + Br_2(g)$$

The enthalpy change for the reaction at standard conditions is +16.3 kJ/mol-rxn. Predict the effect of the following changes on the position of the equilibrium; that is, state which way the equilibrium will shift (left, right, or no change) when each of the following changes is made.

(a) adding more $Br_2(g)$
(b) removing some NOBr(g)
(c) decreasing the temperature
(d) increasing the container volume

29. Consider the isomerization of butane with an equilibrium constant of $K = 2.5$. (See Study Question 13.) The system is originally at equilibrium with [butane] = 1.0 M and [isobutane] = 2.5 M.

(a) If 0.50 mol/L of isobutane is suddenly added and the system shifts to a new equilibrium position, what is the equilibrium concentration of each gas?
(b) If 0.50 mol/L of butane is added to the original equilibrium mixture and the system shifts to a new equilibrium position, what is the equilibrium concentration of each gas?

30. The decomposition of NH_4HS

$$NH_4HS(s) \rightleftharpoons NH_3(g) + H_2S(g)$$

is an endothermic process. Using Le Chatelier's principle, explain how increasing the temperature would affect the equilibrium. If more NH_4HS is added to a flask in which this equilibrium exists, how is the equilibrium affected? What if some additional NH_3 is placed in the flask? What will happen to the pressure of NH_3 if some H_2S is removed from the flask?

General Questions

These questions are not designated as to type or location in the chapter. They may combine several concepts.

31. Suppose 0.086 mol of Br_2 is placed in a 1.26-L flask and heated to 1756 K, a temperature at which the halogen dissociates to atoms.

$$Br_2(g) \rightleftharpoons 2\ Br(g)$$

If Br_2 is 3.7% dissociated at this temperature, calculate K_c.

32. The equilibrium constant for the reaction

$$N_2(g) + O_2(g) \rightleftharpoons 2\ NO(g)$$

is 1.7×10^{-3} at 2300 *K*.

(a) What is *K* for the reaction when written as follows?

$$\tfrac{1}{2}\ N_2(g) + \tfrac{1}{2}\ O_2(g) \rightleftharpoons NO(g)$$

(b) What is *K* for the following reaction?

$$2\ NO(g) \rightleftharpoons N_2(g) + O_2(g)$$

33. K_p for the formation of phosgene, $COCl_2$, is 6.5×10^{11} at 25 °C.

$$CO(g) + Cl_2(g) \rightleftharpoons COCl_2(g)$$

What is the value of K_p for the dissociation of phosgene?

$$COCl_2(g) \rightleftharpoons CO(g) + Cl_2(g)$$

34. The equilibrium constant, K_c, for the following reaction is 1.05 at 350 K.

$$2\ CH_2Cl_2(g) \rightleftharpoons CH_4(g) + CCl_4(g)$$

If an equilibrium mixture of the three gases at 350 K contains 0.0206 M $CH_2Cl_2(g)$ and 0.0163 M CH_4, what is the equilibrium concentration of CCl_4?

35. Carbon tetrachloride can be produced by the following reaction:

$$CS_2(g) + 3\ Cl_2(g) \rightleftharpoons S_2Cl_2(g) + CCl_4(g)$$

Suppose 0.12 mol of CS_2 and 0.36 mol of Cl_2 are placed in a 10.0-L flask. After equilibrium has been achieved, the mixture contains 0.090 mol CCl_4. Calculate K_c.

36. Equal numbers of moles of H_2 gas and I_2 vapor are mixed in a flask and heated to 700 °C. The initial concentration of each gas is 0.0088 mol/L, and 78.6% of the I_2 is consumed when equilibrium is achieved according to the equation

$$H_2(g) + I_2(g) \rightleftharpoons 2\ HI(g)$$

Calculate K_c for this reaction.

37. The equilibrium constant for the butane $\rightleftharpoons$ isobutane isomerization reaction is 2.5 at 25 °C. If 1.75 mol of butane and 1.25 mol of isobutane are mixed, is the system at equilibrium? If not, when it proceeds to equilibrium, which reagent increases in concentration? Calculate the concentrations of the two compounds when the system reaches equilibrium.

38. At 2300 K the equilibrium constant for the formation of NO(g) is 1.7×10^{-3}.

$$N_2(g) + O_2(g) \rightleftharpoons 2\ NO(g)$$

(a) Analysis shows that the concentrations of N_2 and O_2 are both 0.25 M, and that of NO is 0.0042 M under certain conditions. Is the system at equilibrium?
(b) If the system is not at equilibrium, in which direction does the reaction proceed?
(c) When the system is at equilibrium, what are the equilibrium concentrations?

39. Which of the following correctly relates the two equilibrium constants for the two reactions shown?

$$NOCl(g) \rightleftharpoons NO(g) + \tfrac{1}{2}\ Cl_2(g) \qquad K_1$$

$$2\ NO(g) + Cl_2(g) \rightleftharpoons 2\ NOCl(g) \qquad K_2$$

(a) $K_2 = -K_1^2$
(b) $K_2 = 1/(K_1)^{1/2}$
(c) $K_2 = 1/K_1^2$
(d) $K_2 = 2K_1$

40. Consider the following equilibrium:

$$COBr_2(g) \rightleftharpoons CO(g) + Br_2(g) \qquad K_c = 0.190 \text{ at } 73\ °C$$

(a) A 0.50 mol sample of $COBr_2$ is transferred to a 9.50-L flask and heated until equilibrium is attained. Calculate the equilibrium concentrations of each species.
(b) The volume of the container is decreased to 4.5 L and the system allowed to return to equilibrium. Calculate the new equilibrium concentrations. (*Hint*: The calculation will be easier if you view this as a new problem with 0.5 mol of $COBr_2$ transferred to a 4.5-L flask.)
(c) What is the effect of decreasing the container volume from 9.50 L to 4.50 L?

41. Heating a metal carbonate leads to decomposition.

$$BaCO_3(s) \rightleftharpoons BaO(s) + CO_2(g)$$

Predict the effect on the equilibrium of each change listed below. Answer by choosing (i) no change, (ii) shifts left, or (iii) shifts right.

(a) add $BaCO_3$
(b) add CO_2
(c) add BaO
(d) raise the temperature
(e) increase the volume of the flask containing the reaction

42. Carbonyl bromide decomposes to carbon monoxide and bromine.

$$COBr_2(g) \rightleftharpoons CO(g) + Br_2(g)$$

K_c is 0.190 at 73 °C. Suppose you place 0.500 mol of $COBr_2$ in a 2.00-L flask and heat it to 73 °C (see Study Question 17). After equilibrium has been achieved, you add an additional 2.00 mol of CO.

(a) How is the equilibrium mixture affected by adding more CO?
(b) When equilibrium is reestablished, what are the new equilibrium concentrations of $COBr_2$, CO, and Br_2?
(c) How has the addition of CO affected the percentage of $COBr_2$ that decomposed?

43. Phosphorus pentachloride decomposes at elevated temperatures.

$$PCl_5(g) \rightleftharpoons PCl_3(g) + Cl_2(g)$$

An equilibrium mixture at some temperature consists of 3.120 g of PCl_5, 3.845 g of PCl_3, and 1.787 g of Cl_2 in a 10.0-L flask. If you add 1.418 g of Cl_2, how will the equilibrium be affected? What will the concentrations of PCl_5, PCl_3, and Cl_2 be when equilibrium is reestablished?

44. Ammonium hydrogen sulfide decomposes on heating.

$$NH_4HS(s) \rightleftharpoons NH_3(g) + H_2S(g)$$

If K_p for this reaction is 0.11 at 25 °C (when the partial pressures are measured in atmospheres), what is the total pressure in the flask at equilibrium?

45. Ammonium iodide dissociates reversibly to ammonia and hydrogen iodide if the salt is heated to a sufficiently high temperature.

$$NH_4I(s) \rightleftharpoons NH_3(g) + HI(g)$$

Some ammonium iodide is placed in a flask, which is then heated to 400 °C. If the total pressure in the flask when equilibrium has been achieved is 705 mm Hg, what is the value of K_p (when partial pressures are in atmospheres)?

46. When solid ammonium carbamate sublimes, it dissociates completely into ammonia and carbon dioxide according to the following equation:

$$(NH_4)(H_2NCO_2)(s) \rightleftharpoons 2\ NH_3(g) + CO_2(g)$$

At 25 °C, experiment shows that the total pressure of the gases in equilibrium with the solid is 0.116 atm. What is the equilibrium constant, K_p?

47. The equilibrium reaction $N_2O_4(g) \rightleftharpoons 2\ NO_2(g)$ has been thoroughly studied (Figure 15.7).

(a) If the total pressure in a flask containing NO_2 and N_2O_4 gas at 25 °C is 1.50 atm and the value of K_p at this temperature is 0.148, what fraction of the N_2O_4 has dissociated to NO_2?

(b) What happens to the fraction dissociated if the volume of the container is increased so that the total equilibrium pressure falls to 1.00 atm?

48. In the gas phase, acetic acid exists as an equilibrium of monomer and dimer molecules. (The dimer consists of two molecules linked through hydrogen bonds.)

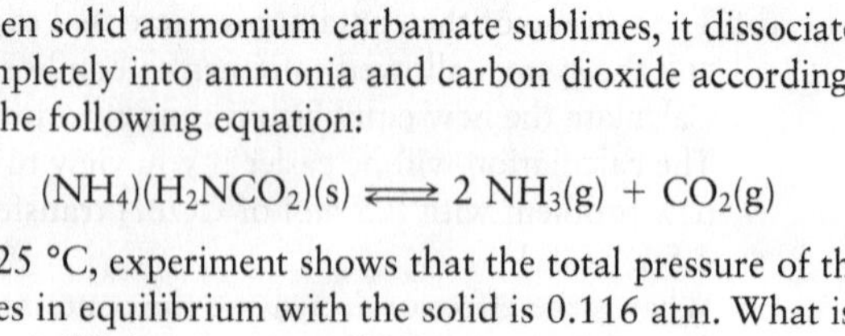

The equilibrium constant, K_c, at 25 °C for the monomer–dimer equilibrium

$$2\ CH_3CO_2H \rightleftharpoons (CH_3CO_2H)_2$$

has been determined to be 3.2×10^4. Assume that acetic acid is present initially at a concentration of 5.4×10^{-4} mol/L at 25 °C and that no dimer is present initially.

(a) What percentage of the acetic acid is converted to dimer?

(b) As the temperature increases, in which direction does the equilibrium shift? (Recall that hydrogen-bond formation is an exothermic process.)

49. Assume 3.60 mol of ammonia is placed in a 2.00-L vessel and allowed to decompose to the elements at 723 K.

$$2\ NH_3(g) \rightleftharpoons N_2(g) + 3\ H_2(g)$$

If the experimental value of K_c is 6.3 for this reaction at the temperature in the reactor, calculate the equilibrium concentration of each reagent. What is the total pressure in the flask?

50. The total pressure for a mixture of N_2O_4 and NO_2 is 0.15 atm. If $K_p = 7.1$ (at 25 °C), calculate the partial pressure of each gas in the mixture.

$$2\ NO_2(g) \rightleftharpoons N_2O_4(g)$$

51. K_c for the decomposition of ammonium hydrogen sulfide is 1.8×10^{-4} at 25 °C.

$$NH_4HS(s) \rightleftharpoons NH_3(g) + H_2S(g)$$

(a) When the pure salt decomposes in a flask, what are the equilibrium concentrations of NH_3 and H_2S?

(b) If NH_4HS is placed in a flask already containing 0.020 mol/L of NH_3 and then the system is allowed to come to equilibrium, what are the equilibrium concentrations of NH_3 and H_2S?

52. ▲ $COCl_2$ decomposes to CO and Cl_2 at high temperatures. K_c at 600 K for the reaction is 0.0071.

$$COCl_2(g) \rightleftharpoons CO(g) + Cl_2(g)$$

If 0.050 mol of $COCl_2$ is placed in a 12.5-L flask, what is the total pressure at equilibrium at 600 K?

53. ▲ A 15-L flask at 300 K contains 6.44 g of a mixture of NO_2 and N_2O_4 in equilibrium. What is the total pressure in the flask? (K_p for $2\ NO_2(g) \rightleftharpoons N_2O_4(g)$ is 7.1.)

54. ▲ Lanthanum oxalate decomposes when heated to lanthanum(III) oxide, CO, and CO_2.

$$La_2(C_2O_4)_3(s) \rightleftharpoons La_2O_3(s) + 3\ CO(g) + 3\ CO_2(g)$$

(a) If, at equilibrium, the total pressure in a 10.0-L flask is 0.200 atm, what is the value of K_p?

(b) Suppose 0.100 mol of $La_2(C_2O_4)_3$ was originally placed in the 10.0-L flask. What quantity of $La_2(C_2O_4)_3$ remains unreacted at equilibrium at 373 K?

55. ▲ The reaction of hydrogen and iodine to give hydrogen iodide has an equilibrium constant, K_c, of 56 at 435 °C.

(a) What is the value of K_p?

(b) Suppose you mix 0.045 mol of H_2 and 0.045 mol of I_2 in a 10.0-L flask at 425 °C. What is the total pressure of the mixture before and after equilibrium is achieved?

(c) What is the partial pressure of each gas at equilibrium?

56. Sulfuryl chloride, SO_2Cl_2, is used as a reagent in the synthesis of organic compounds. When heated to a sufficiently high temperature, it decomposes to SO_2 and Cl_2.

$$SO_2Cl_2(g) \rightleftharpoons SO_2(g) + Cl_2(g) \qquad K_c = 0.045 \text{ at } 375\ °C$$

(a) A 10.0-L flask containing 6.70 g of SO_2Cl_2 is heated to 375 °C. What is the concentration of each of the compounds in the system when equilibrium is achieved? What fraction of SO_2Cl_2 has dissociated?
(b) What are the concentrations of SO_2Cl_2, SO_2, and Cl_2 at equilibrium in the 10.0-L flask at 375 °C if you begin with a mixture of SO_2Cl_2 (6.70 g) and Cl_2 (0.10 atm)? What fraction of SO_2Cl_2 has dissociated?
(c) Compare the fractions of SO_2Cl_2 in parts (a) and (b). Do they agree with your expectations based on Le Chatelier's principle?

57. ▲ Hemoglobin (Hb) can form a complex with both O_2 and CO. For the reaction

$$HbO_2(aq) + CO(g) \rightleftharpoons HbCO(aq) + O_2(g)$$

at body temperature, K is about 200. If the ratio $[HbCO]/[HbO_2]$ comes close to 1, death is probable. What partial pressure of CO in the air is likely to be fatal? Assume the partial pressure of O_2 is 0.20 atm.

58. ▲ Limestone decomposes at high temperatures.

$$CaCO_3(s) \rightleftharpoons CaO(s) + CO_2(g)$$

At 1000 °C, $K_p = 3.87$. If pure $CaCO_3$ is placed in a 5.00-L flask and heated to 1000 °C, what quantity of $CaCO_3$ must decompose to achieve the equilibrium pressure of CO_2?

59. At 1800 K, oxygen dissociates very slightly into its atoms.

$$O_2(g) \rightleftharpoons 2\ O(g) \qquad K_p = 1.2 \times 10^{-10}$$

If you place 0.050 mol of O_2 in a 10.-L vessel and heat it to 1800 K, how many O atoms are present in the flask?

60. ▲ Nitrosyl bromide, NOBr, dissociates readily at room temperature.

$$NOBr(g) \rightleftharpoons NO(g) + \tfrac{1}{2}\ Br_2(g)$$

Some NOBr is placed in a flask at 25 °C and allowed to dissociate. The total pressure at equilibrium is 190 mm Hg and the compound is found to be 34% dissociated. What is the value of K_p?

61. ▲ Boric acid and glycerin form a complex

$$B(OH)_3(aq) + \text{glycerin}(aq) \rightleftharpoons B(OH)_3 \cdot \text{glycerin}(aq)$$

with an equilibrium constant of 0.90. If the concentration of boric acid is 0.10 M, how much glycerin should be added, per liter, so that 60.% of the boric acid is in the form of the complex?

62. ▲ The dissociation of calcium carbonate has an equilibrium constant of $K_p = 1.16$ at 800 °C.

$$CaCO_3(s) \rightleftharpoons CaO(s) + CO_2(g)$$

(a) What is K_c for the reaction?
(b) If you place 22.5 g of $CaCO_3$ in a 9.56-L container at 800 °C, what is the pressure of CO_2 in the container?
(c) What percentage of the original 22.5-g sample of $CaCO_3$ remains undecomposed at equilibrium?

63. ▲ A sample of N_2O_4 gas with a pressure of 1.00 atm is placed in a flask. When equilibrium is achieved, 20.0% of the N_2O_4 has been converted to NO_2 gas.

(a) Calculate K_p.
(b) If the original pressure of N_2O_4 is 0.10 atm, what is the percent dissociation of the gas? Is the result in agreement with Le Chatelier's principle?

64. ▲ A reaction important in smog formation is

$$O_3(g) + NO(g) \rightleftharpoons O_2(g) + NO_2(g) \qquad K_c = 6.0 \times 10^{34}$$

(a) If the initial concentrations are $[O_3] = 1.0 \times 10^{-6}$ M, $[NO] = 1.0 \times 10^{-5}$ M, $[NO_2] = 2.5 \times 10^{-4}$ M, and $[O_2] = 8.2 \times 10^{-3}$ M, is the system at equilibrium? If not, in which direction does the reaction proceed?
(b) If the temperature is increased, as on a very warm day, will the concentrations of the products increase or decrease? (*Hint*: You may have to calculate the enthalpy change for the reaction to find out if it is exothermic or endothermic.)

In the Laboratory

65. ▲ The ammonia complex of trimethylborane, $(NH_3)B(CH_3)_3$, dissociates at 100 °C to its components with $K_p = 4.62$ (when the pressures are in atmospheres).

$$(NH_3)B(CH_3)_3(g) \rightleftharpoons B(CH_3)_3(g) + NH_3(g)$$

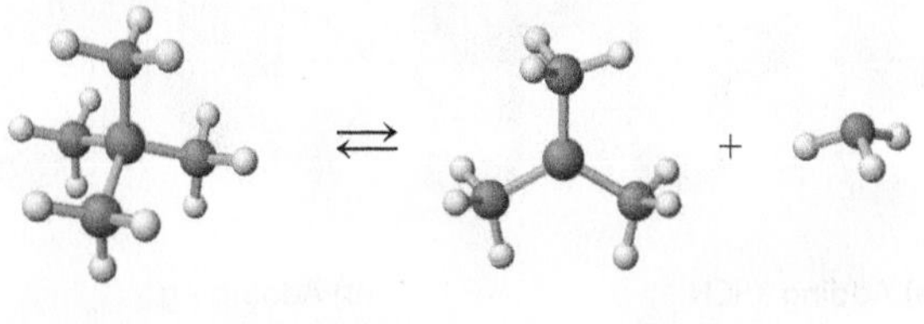

If NH_3 is changed to some other molecule, the equilibrium constant is different.

For $[(CH_3)_3P]B(CH_3)_3$ $\qquad K_p = 0.128$

For $[(CH_3)_3N]B(CH_3)_3$ $\qquad K_p = 0.472$

(a) If you begin an experiment by placing 0.010 mol of each complex in a flask, which would have the largest partial pressure of $B(CH_3)_3$ at 100 °C?
(b) If 0.73 g (0.010 mol) of $(NH_3)B(CH_3)_3$ is placed in a 1.25-L flask and heated to 100 °C, what is the partial pressure of each gas in the equilibrium mixture, and what is the total pressure? What is the percent dissociation of $(NH_3)B(CH_3)_3$?

66. The photographs below show what occurs when a solution of potassium chromate is treated with a few drops of concentrated hydrochloric acid. Some of the bright yellow chromate ion is converted to the orange dichromate ion.

$$2\ CrO_4^{2-}(aq) + 2\ H_3O^+(aq) \rightleftharpoons Cr_2O_7^{2-}(aq) + 3\ H_2O(\ell)$$

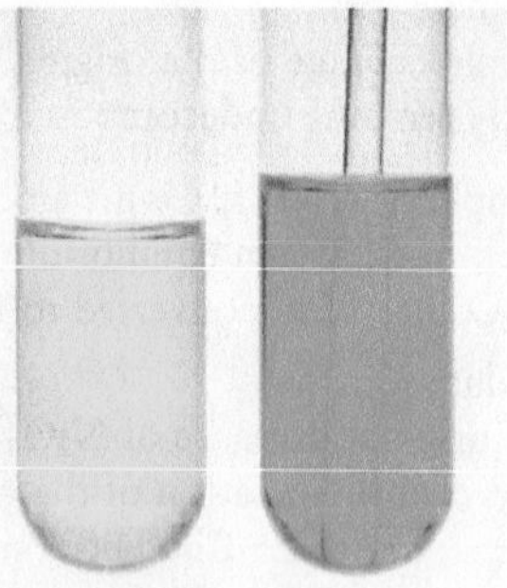

Photos: © Cengage Learning/Charles D. Winters

(a) Explain this experimental observation in terms of Le Chatelier's principle.
(b) What would you observe if you treated the orange solution with sodium hydroxide? Explain your observation.

67. The photograph below (a) shows what occurs when a solution of iron(III) nitrate is treated with a few drops of aqueous potassium thiocyanate. The nearly colorless iron(III) ion is converted to a red $[Fe(H_2O)_5SCN]^{2+}$ ion. (This is a classic test for the presence of iron(III) ions in solution.)

$$[Fe(H_2O)_6]^{3+}(aq) + SCN^-(aq) \rightleftharpoons [Fe(H_2O)_5SCN]^{2+}(aq) + H_2O(\ell)$$

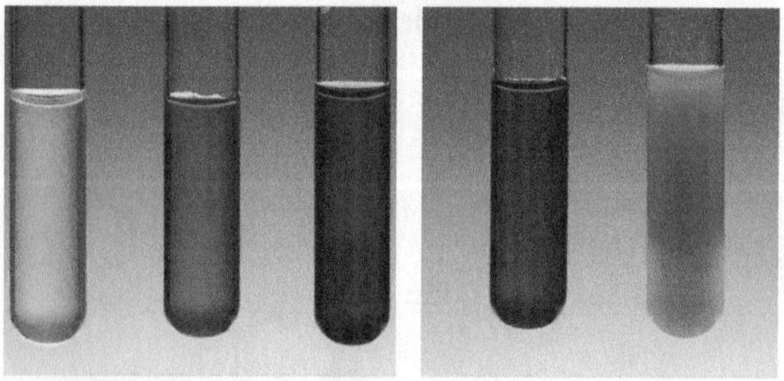

Photos: © Cengage Learning/Charles D. Winters

(a) Adding KSCN **(b)** Adding Ag^+

(a) As more KSCN is added to the solution, the color becomes even more red. Explain this observation.
(b) Silver ions form a white precipitate with SCN^- ions. What would you observe on adding a few drops of aqueous silver nitrate to a red solution of $[Fe(H_2O)_5SCN]^+$ ions? Explain your observation.

68. ▲ The photographs on the next page show what occurs when you add ammonia to aqueous nickel(II) nitrate and then add ethylenediamine ($NH_2CH_2CH_2NH_2$) to the intermediate blue-purple solution.

$[Ni(H_2O)_6]^{2+}(aq)$ (green) $+ 6\ NH_3(aq) \rightleftharpoons [Ni(NH_3)_6]^{2+}(aq)$ (blue-purple) $+ 6\ H_2O(\ell)$ K_1

$[Ni(NH_3)_6]^{2+}(aq)$ (blue-purple) $+ 3\ NH_2CH_2CH_2NH_2(aq) \rightleftharpoons [Ni(NH_2CH_2CH_2NH_2)_3]^{2+}(aq)$ (violet) $+ 6\ NH_3(aq)$ K_2

(a) Write a chemical equation for the formation of $[Ni(NH_2CH_2CH_2NH_2)_3]^{2+}$ from $[Ni(H_2O)_6]^{2+}$ and ethylenediamine, and relate the value of K for this reaction to K_1 and K_2.
(b) Which species, $[Ni(NH_2CH_2CH_2NH_2)_3]^{2+}$, $[Ni(NH_3)_6]^{2+}$, or $[Ni(H_2O)_6]^{2+}$ is the most stable? Explain.

Summary and Conceptual Questions

The following questions may use concepts from this and previous chapters.

69. Decide whether each of the following statements is true or false. If false, change the wording to make it true.
(a) The magnitude of the equilibrium constant is always independent of temperature.
(b) When two chemical equations are added to give a net equation, the equilibrium constant for the net equation is the product of the equilibrium constants of the summed equations.
(c) The equilibrium constant for a reaction has the same value as K for the reverse reaction.
(d) Only the concentration of CO_2 appears in the equilibrium constant expression for the reaction $CaCO_3(s) \rightleftharpoons CaO(s) + CO_2(g)$.
(e) For the reaction $CaCO_3(s) \rightleftharpoons CaO(s) + CO_2(g)$, the value of K is numerically the same, whether the amount of CO_2 is expressed as moles/liter or as gas pressure.

70. Neither $PbCl_2$ nor PbF_2 is appreciably soluble in water. If solid $PbCl_2$ and solid PbF_2 are placed in equal amounts of water in separate beakers, in which beaker is the concentration of Pb^{2+} greater? Equilibrium constants for these solids dissolving in water are as follows:

$PbCl_2(s) \rightleftharpoons Pb^{2+}(aq) + 2\ Cl^-(aq)$ $K_c = 1.7 \times 10^{-5}$

$PbF_2(s) \rightleftharpoons Pb^{2+}(aq) + 2\ F^-(aq)$ $K_c = 3.7 \times 10^{-8}$

71. Characterize each of the following as product- or reactant-favored at equilibrium.
(a) $CO(g) + \frac{1}{2}\ O_2(g) \rightleftharpoons CO_2(g)$ $K_p = 1.2 \times 10^{45}$
(b) $H_2O(g) \rightleftharpoons H_2(g) + \frac{1}{2}\ O_2(g)$ $K_p = 9.1 \times 10^{-41}$
(c) $CO(g) + Cl_2(g) \rightleftharpoons COCl_2(g)$ $K_p = 6.5 \times 10^{11}$

72. ▲ The size of a flask containing colorless $N_2O_4(g)$ and brown $NO_2(g)$ at equilibrium is rapidly reduced to half the original volume.

$$N_2O_4(g) \rightleftharpoons 2\ NO_2(g)$$

(a) What color change (if any) is observed immediately upon halving the flask size?

(b) What color change (if any) is observed during the process in which equilibrium is reestablished in the flask?

73. Describe an experiment that would allow you to prove that the system $3\ H_2(g) + N_2(g) \rightleftharpoons 2\ NH_3(g)$ is a dynamic equilibrium. (*Hint:* Consider using a stable isotope such as ^{15}N or ^{2}H.)

74. Equilibria in a solution of cobalt(II) chloride (introduction to Chapter 15).

(a) Is the conversion of the red cation to the blue anion exothermic or endothermic?

(b) Account for the effect of adding hydrochloric acid and more water.

(c) How do these observations prove the reaction is reversible?

75. Suppose a tank initially contains H_2S at a pressure of 10.00 atm and a temperature of 800 K. When the reaction has come to equilibrium, the partial pressure of S_2 vapor is 0.020 atm. Calculate K_p.

$$2\ H_2S(g) \rightleftharpoons 2\ H_2(g) + S_2(g)$$

76. Pure PCl_5 gas is placed in a 2.00-L flask. After heating to 250 °C the pressure of PCl_5 is initially 2.000 atm. However, the gas slowly but only partially decomposes to gaseous PCl_3 and Cl_2. When equilibrium is reached, the partial pressure of Cl_2 is 0.814 atm. Calculate K_p for the decomposition.

AP Multiple-Choice Review Questions

1. Consider the dissolution of an ionic salt in water. Which of the following statements best explains why this process is considered a physical change?
(A) The ionic salt can be recovered by evaporation of the water.
(B) The ionic salt can be recovered by solidification of the water.
(C) Dissolution of an ionic salt is mostly a physical change, and all physical changes are reversible.
(D) Dissolution of an ionic salt is mostly a chemical change, and all chemical changes are reversible.

2. For the reaction $A \rightleftharpoons B$, for which value of K is the concentration of the reactants greater than the concentration of the products?
(A) K equals 0
(B) K equals 1
(C) K is less than 1
(D) K is greater than 1

3. A solution with initial concentrations of 6.00 M Fe^{3+} and 10.0 M SCN^- is allowed to reach equilibrium. At equilibrium it is found that the concentration of $FeSCN^{2+}$ is 4.00 M. What are the equilibrium concentrations of the Fe^{3+} and SCN^-?

$$Fe^{3+}(aq) + SCN^-(aq) \rightleftharpoons FeSCN^{2+}(aq)$$

(A) $[Fe^{3+}] = 4.00\ M$; $[SCN^-] = 4.00\ M$
(B) $[Fe^{3+}] = 2.00\ M$; $[SCN^-] = 6.00\ M$
(C) $[Fe^{3+}] = 6.00\ M$; $[SCN^-] = 2.00\ M$
(D) $[Fe^{3+}] = 2.00\ M$; $[SCN^-] = 2.00\ M$

4. Hydrogen gas at a pressure of 9.0 atm is added to a container containing 5.0 atm of iodine vapor. The resulting reaction is allowed to come to equilibrium, and it is found that the final pressure of iodine vapor is 2.0 atm. What is the K_p value for the following reaction?

$$H_2(g) + I_2(g) \rightleftharpoons 2HI(g)$$

(A) 0.25
(B) 0.33
(C) 3.0
(D) 4.0

5. Dinitrogen pentoxide is added to an evacuated rigid container at 25 °C. Given that the initial pressure is 1.00 atm and at equilibrium the pressure is 0.500 atm, determine the final pressure in the reaction vessel at equilibrium.

$$2N_2O_5(g) \rightleftharpoons 4NO_2(g) + O_2(g)$$

(A) 0.750 atm
(B) 1.00 atm
(C) 1.25 atm
(D) 1.75 atm

6. Determine the K_p for the following reaction if at equilibrium half of the initial SO_2 reacted to form 2.00 atm of SO_3. The initial partial pressure of SO_2 and O_2 was equal.

$$2SO_2(g) + O_2(g) \rightleftharpoons 2SO_3(g)$$

(A) 0.250 atm
(B) 0.333 atm
(C) 0.500 atm
(D) 1.00 atm

7. An initial mixture of 5.00 M N_2 and 5.00 M H_2 is placed in a reaction vessel and allowed to come to equilibrium. The equilibrium concentration of the NH_3 is determined to be 2.00 M. Determine K for the reaction below.

$$N_2(g) + 3H_2(g) \rightleftharpoons 2NH_3(g)$$

(A) 0.125
(B) 0.250
(C) 0.500
(D) 1.00

Questions 8–12 refer to the following:

Hydrogen gas, iodine vapor, and hydrogen iodide gas are added to an evacuated flask until the concentrations of H_2 and I_2 are both 2.0 M and that of HI equals 8.0 M.

$$H_2(g) + I_2(g) \rightleftharpoons 2\ HI(g) \qquad (\text{At } 425\ °C,\ K = 9.00)$$

8. Determine the value of Q.
(A) 2.0
(B) 4.0
(C) 8.0
(D) 16

9. The reaction vessel is heated to 675 °C, where the equilibrium concentration of the HI is determined to be 6.0 M. What is the K value at 675 °C?
(A) ~~6.0~~ 4.0
(B) 9.0
(C) 24
(D) 36

10. Once the system reaches equilibrium at 675 °C, additional H_2 is added and the temperature is held constant. Which statement best describes how this affects the value of K?
(A) The value of K increases because the formation of products is favored.
(B) The value of K decreases because the formation of reactants is favored.
(C) The value of K remains unchanged because the temperature remained constant.
(D) The value of K cannot be determined until the equilibrium concentrations are determined.

11. In a separate experiment to determine the rate law for this reaction, the data given in the table below were produced. Determine the rate law for this reaction.

Initial $[H_2]$ (mol L^{-1})	Initial $[I_2]$ (mol L^{-1})	Initial rate of appearance of HI (mol L^{-1} min^{-1})
1.0	2.0	5.00
1.0	4.0	10.0
2.0	4.0	20.0

(A) rate $= k[H_2]$
(B) rate $= k[I_2]$
(C) rate $= k[H_2][I_2]$
(D) rate $= k[H_2]^2[I_2]$

12. This reaction has been considered to occur as a single elementary, bimolecular mechanism. However, in a recent laboratory investigation, the mixture was irradiated with light. When the wavelength used supplied the energy needed to dissociate the iodine bond, this caused the reaction rate to increase significantly. This would support the following mechanism:

$$I_2(g) \rightarrow 2I(g) \qquad \text{step 1}$$
$$2I(g) + H_2(g) \rightarrow H_2I_2(g) \qquad \text{step 2}$$
$$H_2I_2(g) \rightarrow 2HI(g) \qquad \text{step 3}$$

Which step in the mechanism would be the rate-determining step?

(A) step 1
(B) step 2
(C) step 3
(D) cannot determine the rate-determining step without knowing the rate law

13. Consider the decomposition of potassium chlorate according to the reaction below. Which expression is needed to find the pressure of the O_2 if 61.2 g of the potassium chlorate (molar mass = 122.4 g/mol) decomposes in a rigid 2.5-L container at a temperature of 525°C? (Assume all the chlorate decomposed to form the products.)

$$2KClO_3(s) \rightarrow 2KCl(s) + 3O_2(g)$$

(A) $\dfrac{(0.75)(0.0821)(525)}{2.5}$

(B) $\dfrac{(0.75)(0.0821)(525 + 273)}{2.5}$

(C) $(0.75)(0.0821)(525)(2.5)$

(D) $\dfrac{(0.75)(0.0821)}{(2.5)(525 + 273)}$

Questions 14 and 15 refer to the following reaction at equilibrium:

$$2SO_2(g) + O_2(g) \rightleftharpoons 2SO_3(g) \qquad \Delta H = -198 \text{ kJ}$$

14. Which of the following occurs after the addition of O_2?

(A) The rate of the forward reaction increases, and the value of K increases.
(B) The rate of the forward reaction decreases, and the value of K increases.
(C) The rate of the forward reaction decreases, and the value of K remains the same.
(D) The rate of the forward reaction increases, and the value of K remains the same.

15. Which of the following changes to the system at equilibrium would result in an increase in the concentration of O_2?

(A) an increase in the concentration of SO_2 and an increase in the temperature
(B) an increase in the concentration of SO_2 and a decrease in the temperature
(C) an increase in the concentration of SO_3 and a decrease in the temperature
(D) an increase in the concentration of SO_3 and an increase in the temperature

16. It is found that the value of the reaction quotient is 12 for a given reaction, whereas the equilibrium constant is 8.0. Which statement best describes how the system will respond?

(A) Since $Q > K$, the forward reaction is favored and the equilibrium shifts to the right.
(B) Since $Q < K$, the forward reaction is favored and the equilibrium shifts to the right.
(C) Since $Q < K$, the reverse reaction is favored and the equilibrium shifts to the left.
(D) Since $Q > K$, the reverse reaction is favored and the equilibrium shifts to the left.

AP Free Response Review Questions

Question Format: Short

Category of Question: Quantitative

$$3\ H_2(g) + N_2(g) \rightleftharpoons 2\ NH_3(g)$$

In the Haber Process for producing ammonia, 150.0 atm of hydrogen gas and 50.0 atm nitrogen gas are reacted in a very high pressure reaction chamber. The total pressure of the gases is monitored throughout the process and the results are recorded in the table below.

Time (hours)	Total Pressure of Gases in Container at 615 K (atm)
0.0	200.0
2.0	170.0
4.0	150.0
6.0	140.0
8.0	130.0
10.0	130.0

Questions

(a) Write the expression for the equilibrium constant, K_p, for the reaction.

(b) For the reaction mixture at equilibrium at 615 K, calculate

(i) the partial pressure of $NH_3(g)$, and

(ii) the value of the equilibrium constant, K_p, at 615 K

Question Format: Long

Category of Question: Representation 2

Ten molecules of XY react according to the following equation:

$$XY \rightleftharpoons X + Y \qquad K_c = 1.0 \times 10^{-1} \text{ at } 125\ °C$$
$$\Delta H_{rxn} = -24.5\ kJ/mol_{rxn}$$

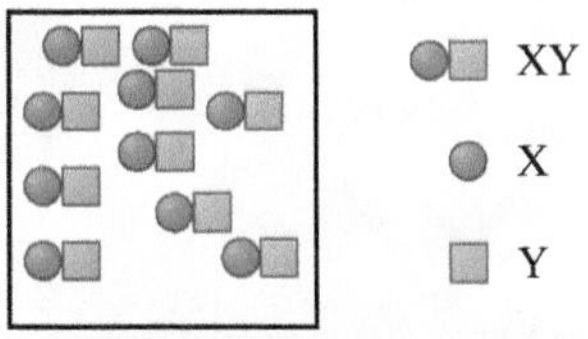

Before Reaction

Questions

(a) Sketch the reactants and products as they would appear when equilibrium has been reached.

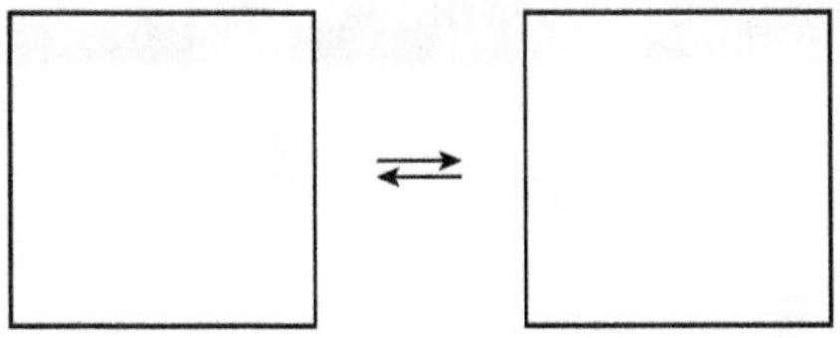
Reactants Products

(b) The temperature of the reaction is decreased from 125 °C to 25 °C. Draw a possible new molecular diagram to represent any changes that would occur in concentrations.

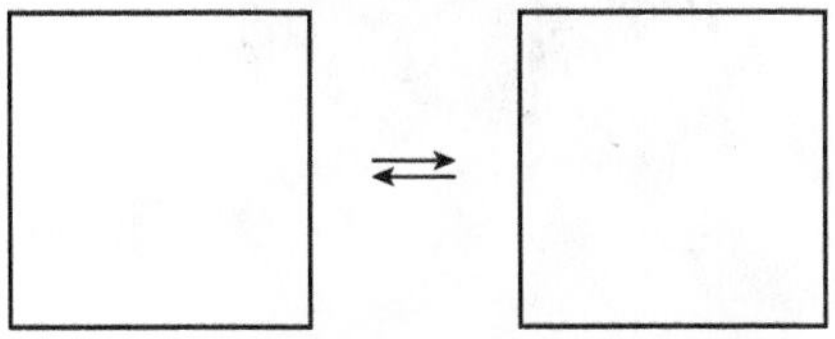
Reactants Products

(c) Will the equilibrium constant value increase, decrease, or remain the same when the temperature is decreased? Explain.

(d) How will lowering the temperature affect the value of ΔH? Explain.

(e) A catalyst is added to the reaction.

(i) How will the concentrations of reactants and products at equilibrium change? Explain your reasoning.

(ii) How will the addition of a catalyst affect the value of ΔH? Explain your reasoning.

(f) Determine the equilibrium constant for the reaction $X + Y \rightleftharpoons XY$ at 125 °C.

(g) What is the value for ΔH_{rxn} for the reaction in part (f) above?

The pufferfish is the source of a deadly poison, tetrodotoxin, a weak base.

Principles of Chemical Reactivity: The Chemistry of Acids and Bases

Chapter Outline

ALKALOIDS AND TOXINS You are probably familiar with some naturally occurring acids such as citric acid in citrus fruits, malic acid in apples, and tartaric acid in grapes. There are many naturally occurring bases, as well, and a number of these are classified as *alkaloids.* These are molecules where the basic sites are nitrogen atoms. Unlike naturally occurring acids, which are generally benign, alkaloids can cause a wide range of physiological effects on animals and humans.

A particularly interesting alkaloid is tetrodotoxin. It is present in pufferfish, as well as a handful of other marine animals. In Japan, the pufferfish (known as fugu) is an expensive and dangerous delicacy. If it is properly

Chapter Goals

See Chapter Goals Revisited (page 628) for Study Questions keyed to these goals.

UNDERSTAND

- The similarities and differences between Brønsted–Lowry acid–base and Lewis acid–base theories.
- The influence of structure and bonding on acid–base properties.

DO

- Use the Brønsted–Lowry and Lewis theories of acids and bases.
- Apply the principles of chemical equilibrium to acids and bases in aqueous solution.
- Understand how Brønsted–Lowry theory is used to predict the outcome of reactions of acids and bases.
- Calculate pH from the concentration of hydronium ion in solution.
- Given values of K_a and K_b, calculate the concentration of species in solution.

REMEMBER

- Brønsted–Lowry acids are proton donors and Brønsted–Lowry bases are proton acceptors.
- Lewis acids are electron-pair acceptors and Lewis bases are electron-pair donors.
- pH is a measure of hydronium ion concentration.

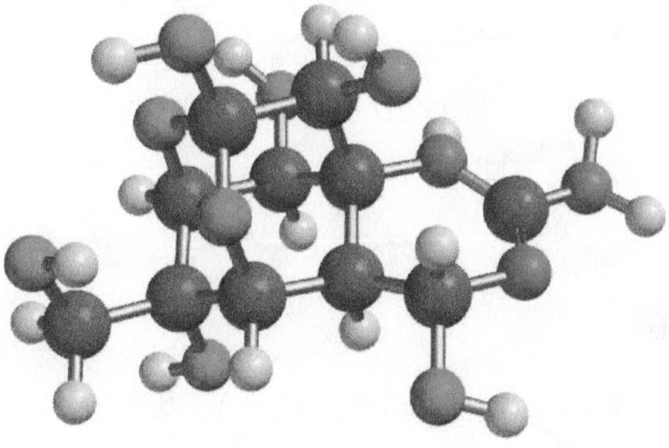

Tetrodotoxin, $C_{11}H_{17}N_3O_8$

prepared, a diner will feel a tingling sensation on the lips and tongue while eating. The sensation is due to the tetrodotoxin, a neurotoxin so toxic that consumption of as little as 1 to 2 milligrams can be fatal. Preparation of pufferfish should be left to specially trained and licensed chefs because the toxin is present in lethal quantities in the organs of the pufferfish. Each year, dozens of people become seriously ill after eating pufferfish, and deaths are not uncommon. A lethal dose may take hours to kill its victim as the toxin spreads through the body, attacking the nervous system and paralyzing muscles. During this period, the paralyzed victim remains conscious because the toxin does not cross the blood-brain barrier.

Tetrodotoxin is a nitrogen heterocycle, a compound in which one or more nitrogen atoms are part of a ring structure. A large number of drugs are also nitrogen heterocycles. Examples include common stimulants such as caffeine and nicotine, controlled pharmaceuticals such as codeine and morphine, and illegal drugs such as cocaine and heroin. Scientists continue to seek out new alkaloids in hopes of developing them into new drugs.

Study Questions related to this story are: 16.93, 16.94, and 16.100.

Acids and bases are among the most common substances in nature. Amino acids are the building blocks of proteins. The repository of genetic information in your cells is DNA, deoxyribonucleic acid. The pH of the lakes, rivers, and oceans is affected by dissolved acids and bases, and many bodily functions depend on acids and bases. You were introduced to acids and bases and to some of their chemistry in Chapter 3, but this chapter and the next explore the chemistry of this important class of substances in more detail.

Learning Objectives: LO 3.7

16-1 The Brønsted–Lowry Concept of Acids and Bases

Brønsted–Lowry Theory This chapter has limited the discussion to aqueous solutions. However, the theory applies equally well to non-aqueous systems.

In Chapter 3, you were introduced to two definitions of acids and bases: the Arrhenius definition and the Brønsted–Lowry definition. According to the Arrhenius definition, an acid is any substance that, when dissolved in water, increases the concentration of hydrogen ions, H^+. An Arrhenius base is any substance that increases the concentration of hydroxide ions, OH^-, when dissolved in water.

The Brønsted–Lowry definition of acids and bases is more general and views acid–base behavior in terms of proton transfer from one substance to another. *A Brønsted–Lowry acid is a proton (H^+) donor, and a Brønsted–Lowry base is a proton acceptor.* This definition extends the list of acids and bases and the scope of acid–base reactions, and it helps chemists make predictions of product- or reactant-favorability based on acid and base strength.

A wide variety of Brønsted–Lowry acids is known. These include some molecular compounds such as nitric acid,

$$\underset{\text{acid}}{HNO_3(aq)} + H_2O(\ell) \rightleftharpoons NO_3^-(aq) + H_3O^+(aq)$$

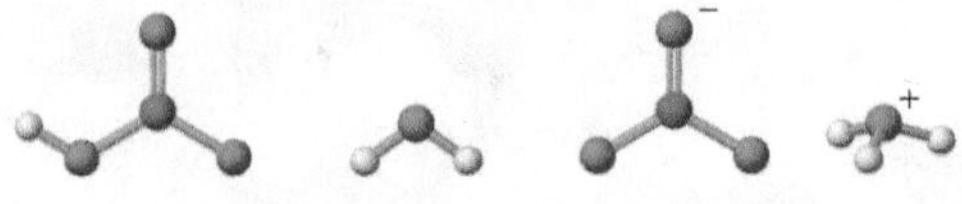

cations such as NH_4^+,

$$\underset{\text{acid}}{NH_4^+(aq)} + H_2O(\ell) \rightleftharpoons NH_3(aq) + H_3O^+(aq)$$

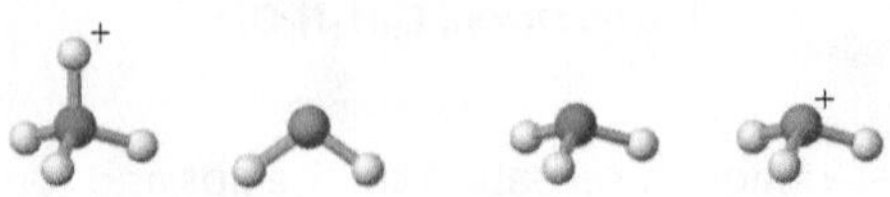

anions such as $H_2PO_4^-$,

$$H_2PO_4^-(aq) + H_2O(\ell) \rightleftharpoons HPO_4^{2-}(aq) + H_3O^+(aq)$$

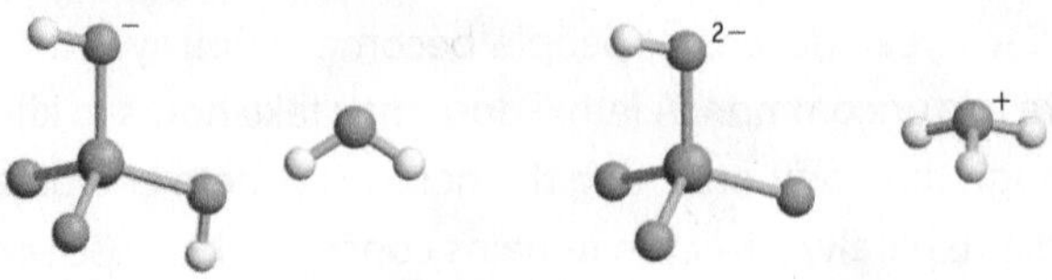

and hydrated metal cations.

$$[Fe(H_2O)_6]^{3+}(aq) + H_2O(\ell) \rightleftharpoons [Fe(H_2O)_5(OH)]^{2+}(aq) + H_3O^+(aq)$$

Similarly, many different types of species can act as Brønsted–Lowry bases in their reactions with water. These include some molecular compounds,

$$\underset{\text{base}}{NH_3(aq)} + H_2O(\ell) \rightleftharpoons NH_4^+(aq) + OH^-(aq)$$

and anions.

$$CO_3^{2-}(aq) + H_2O(\ell) \rightleftharpoons HCO_3^-(aq) + OH^-(aq)$$

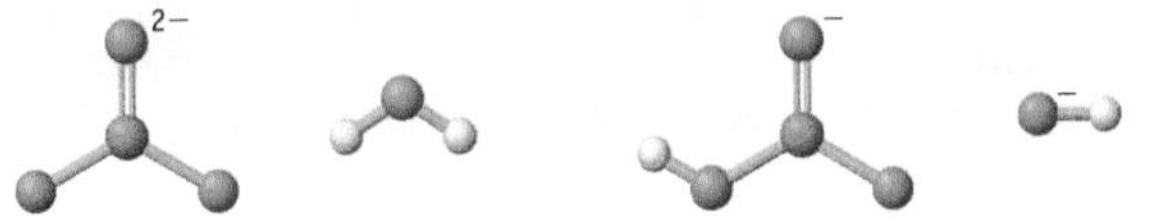

Acids such as HF, HCl, HNO_3, and CH_3CO_2H (acetic acid) are all capable of donating one proton and so are called **monoprotic acids.** Other acids, called **polyprotic acids** (Table 16.1), are capable of donating two or more protons. Sulfuric acid is a familiar example of a polyprotic acid.

$$H_2SO_4(aq) + H_2O(\ell) \rightleftharpoons HSO_4^-(aq) + H_3O^+(aq)$$

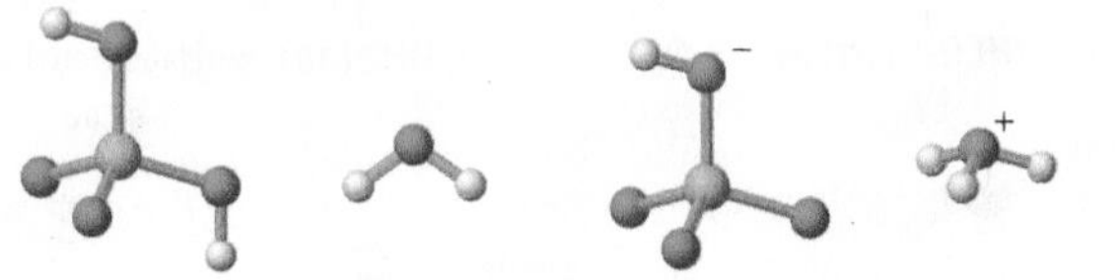

$$HSO_4^-(aq) + H_2O(\ell) \rightleftharpoons SO_4^{2-}(aq) + H_3O^+(aq)$$

Just as there are acids that can donate more than one proton, so there are **polyprotic bases** that can accept more than one proton. The fully deprotonated anions of polyprotic acids are polyprotic bases; examples include SO_4^{2-}, PO_4^{3-}, CO_3^{2-}, and $C_2O_4^{2-}$. The carbonate ion, for example, can accept two protons.

$$\underset{\text{base}}{CO_3^{2-}(aq)} + H_2O(\ell) \rightleftharpoons HCO_3^-(aq) + OH^-(aq)$$

$$\underset{\text{base}}{HCO_3^-(aq)} + H_2O(\ell) \rightleftharpoons H_2CO_3(aq) + OH^-(aq)$$

Some molecules (such as water) and ions can behave either as Brønsted acids or bases and are referred to as being **amphiprotic** (see Section 3-6). An example of an amphiprotic anion is the dihydrogen phosphate ion (Table 16.1).

$$\underset{\text{acid}}{H_2PO_4^-(aq)} + H_2O(\ell) \rightleftharpoons H_3O^+(aq) + HPO_4^{2-}(aq)$$

$$\underset{\text{base}}{H_2PO_4^-(aq)} + H_2O(\ell) \rightleftharpoons H_3PO_4(aq) + OH^-(aq)$$

© Cengage Learning/Charles D. Winters

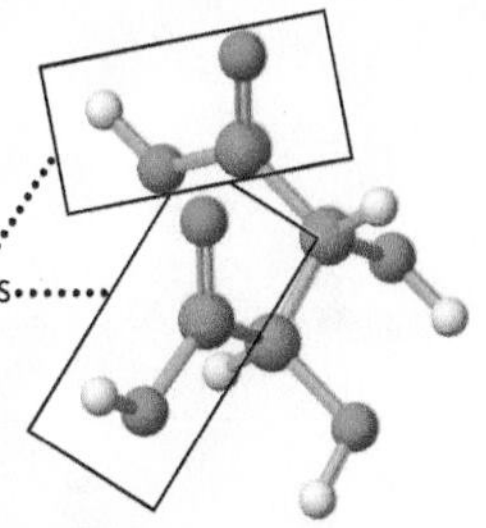

Tartaric acid, $H_2C_4H_4O_6$, is a naturally occurring diprotic acid. Tartaric acid and its potassium salt are found in grapes and other fruits. The acidic protons are the H atoms of the —CO_2H or carboxylic acid groups.

Table 16.1 Polyprotic Acids and Bases

ACID FORM	AMPHIPROTIC FORM	BASE FORM
H_2S (hydrosulfuric acid or hydrogen sulfide)	HS^- (hydrogen sulfide ion)	S^{2-} (sulfide ion)
H_3PO_4 (phosphoric acid)	$H_2PO_4^-$ (dihydrogen phosphate ion) HPO_4^{2-} (hydrogen phosphate ion)	PO_4^{3-} (phosphate ion)
H_2CO_3 (carbonic acid)	HCO_3^- (hydrogen carbonate ion or bicarbonate ion)	CO_3^{2-} (carbonate ion)
$H_2C_2O_4$ (oxalic acid)	$HC_2O_4^-$ (hydrogen oxalate ion)	$C_2O_4^{2-}$ (oxalate ion)

As you will learn in Chapter 17 (*Case Study: Take a Deep Breath*), amphiprotic ions such as HCO_3^- and $H_2PO_4^-$ are particularly important in biochemical systems.

Conjugate Acid–Base Pairs

The reaction of the hydrogen carbonate ion and water exemplifies a feature of Brønsted acid–base chemistry: *The reaction of a Brønsted acid and base produces a new acid and base.*

conjugate pair 1

conjugate pair 2

$$\underset{\text{base}}{HCO_3^-(aq)} + \underset{\text{acid}}{H_2O(\ell)} \rightleftharpoons \underset{\text{base}}{OH^-(aq)} + \underset{\text{acid}}{H_2CO_3(aq)}$$

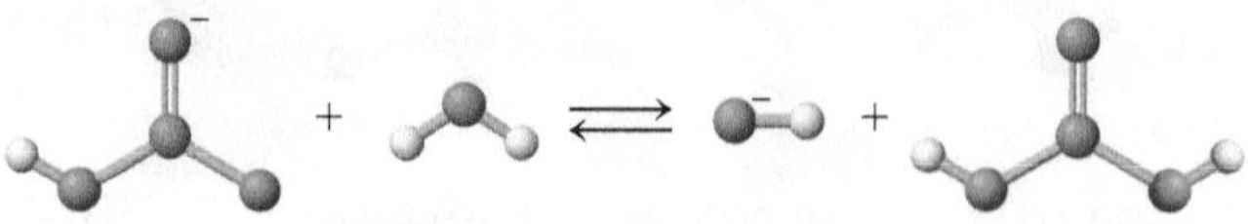

In the forward direction, HCO_3^- is the Brønsted base because it captures H^+ from the Brønsted acid, H_2O. The products are a new Brønsted acid and base. In the reverse direction, the H_2CO_3 is the acid, and OH^- is the base.

A **conjugate acid–base pair** consists of two species that differ from each other by the presence of one hydrogen ion. Thus, H_2CO_3 and HCO_3^- are a conjugate acid–base pair. In this pair, HCO_3^- is the conjugate base of the acid H_2CO_3, and H_2CO_3 is the conjugate acid of the base HCO_3^-. There is a second conjugate acid–base pair in this reaction: H_2O and OH^-. In fact, *every reaction between a Brønsted acid and a Brønsted base involves two conjugate acid–base pairs.*

REVIEW & CHECK FOR SECTION 16-1

1. H_3PO_4, phosphoric acid, can donate two protons to water to form the hydrogen phosphate ion, HPO_4^{2-}. Is the ion an acid or a base, or is it amphiprotic?

   (a) acid (b) base (c) amphiprotic

2. The cyanide ion, CN^-, accepts a proton from water to form HCN. Is CN^- a Brønsted acid or base or is it amphiprotic?

   (a) acid (b) base (c) amphiprotic

3. In the following reaction, identify the acid on the left and its conjugate base on the right.

$$HNO_3(aq) + NH_3(aq) \rightleftharpoons NH_4^+(aq) + NO_3^-(aq)$$

   (a) acid = NH_3 and conjugate base = NH_4^+

   (b) acid = HNO_3 and conjugate base = NO_3^-

Similarly, identify the base on the left and its conjugate acid on the right.

(a) base = NH_3 and conjugate acid = NH_4^+

(b) base = HNO_3 and conjugate acid = NO_3^-

4. Identify the conjugate acid/base pairs in the reaction of HF and acetic acid.

$$HF(aq) + CH_3CO_2^-(aq) \rightleftharpoons F^-(aq) + CH_3CO_2H(aq)$$

(a) $HF/CH_3CO_2^-$ and F^-/CH_3CO_2H

(b) HF/CH_3CO_2H and $F^-/CH_3CO_2^-$

(c) HF/F^- and $CH_3CO_2H/CH_3CO_2^-$

16-2 Water and the pH Scale

Learning Objectives: LO 6.14

Because we generally use aqueous solutions of acids and bases and because the acid–base reactions in your body occur in your aqueous interior, we want to consider the behavior of water in terms of chemical equilibria.

Water Autoionization and the Water Ionization Constant, K_w

An acid such as HCl does not need to be present for the hydronium ion to exist in water. In pure water, an equilibrium exists between water and the hydronium and hydroxide ions.

$$2\ H_2O(\ell) \rightleftharpoons H_3O^+(aq) + OH^-(aq)$$

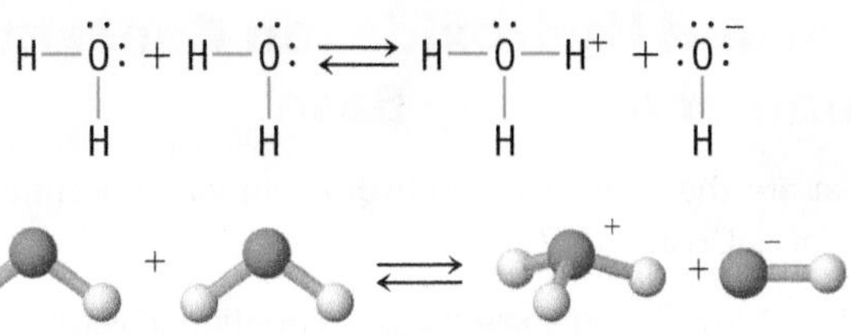

This **autoionization** reaction of water was demonstrated over a century ago by Friedrich Kohlrausch (1840–1910). He found that, even after water is painstakingly purified, it still conducts electricity to a small extent. We now know this is because autoionization produces very low concentrations of H_3O^+ and OH^- ions. *Water autoionization is the cornerstone of our concepts of aqueous acid–base behavior.*

The water autoionization equilibrium is very reactant-favored at equilibrium. In fact, in pure water at 25 °C, only about two out of a billion (10^9) water molecules are ionized at any instant. To express this idea more quantitatively, we can write the equilibrium constant expression for autoionization.

$$K_w = [H_3O^+][OH^-] = 1.0 \times 10^{-14} \text{ at } 25\ °C \quad (16.1)$$

There are several important aspects of this equation.

- Based on the rules for writing equilibrium constants, we do not include the concentration of water.
- The equilibrium constant is given a special symbol, K_w, and is known as the **autoionization constant for water.**
- Because autoionization is the only source of hydronium and hydroxide ions in pure water, we know that $[H_3O^+]$ must be equal to $[OH^-]$. Electrical conductivity measurements of pure water show that $[H_3O^+] = [OH^-] = 1.0 \times 10^{-7}$ M at 25 °C, so K_w has a value of 1.0×10^{-14} at 25 °C.

K_w and Temperature The equation $K_w = [H_3O^+][OH^-]$ is valid for pure water and for any aqueous solution. The numerical value for K_w, however, is temperature dependent. Because the autoionization reaction is endothermic, K_w increases with temperature. And notice that this means a neutral solution at a temperature other than 25 °C will have a different value of pH.

T (°C)	K_w
10	0.29×10^{-14}
15	0.45×10^{-14}
20	0.68×10^{-14}
25	1.01×10^{-14}
30	1.47×10^{-14}
50	5.48×10^{-14}

The Magnitude of [H_3O^+] in Pure Water The ionization of two water molecules out of a billion produces an H_3O^+ concentration of 1×10^{-7} M. To have an sense of this tiny amount, this would be like identifying just 14 people out of the current population of the Earth, about 7 billion.

In pure water, the hydronium ion and hydroxide ion concentrations are equal, and the water is said to be neutral. If some acid or base is added to pure water, however, the equilibrium

$$2\ H_2O(\ell) \rightleftharpoons H_3O^+(aq) + OH^-(aq)$$

is disturbed. Adding acid raises the concentration of the H_3O^+ ions, so the solution is acidic. To oppose this increase, Le Chatelier's principle (◀ Section 15-6) predicts that a small fraction of the H_3O^+ ions will react with OH^- ions from water autoionization to form water. This lowers [OH^-] until the product of [H_3O^+] and [OH^-] is again equal to 1.0×10^{-14} at 25 °C. Similarly, adding a base to pure water gives a basic solution because the OH^- ion concentration has increased. Le Chatelier's principle predicts that some of the added OH^- ions will react with H_3O^+ ions present in the solution from water autoionization, thereby lowering [H_3O^+] until the value of the product of [H_3O^+] and [OH^-] equals 1.0×10^{-14} at 25 °C.

Thus, for aqueous solutions at 25 °C,

- In a neutral solution, $[H_3O^+] = [OH^-]$.
  Both are equal to 1.0×10^{-7} M.
- In an acidic solution, $[H_3O^+] > [OH^-]$.
  $[H_3O^+] > 1.0 \times 10^{-7}$ M and $[OH^-] < 1.0 \times 10^{-7}$ M.
- In a basic solution, $[H_3O^+] < [OH^-]$.
  $[H_3O^+] < 1.0 \times 10^{-7}$ M and $[OH^-] > 1.0 \times 10^{-7}$ M.

EXAMPLE 16.1

Hydronium and Hydroxide Ion Concentrations in a Solution of a Strong Base

Problem What are the hydroxide and hydronium ion concentrations in a 0.0012 M aqueous solution of NaOH at 25 °C?

What Do You Know? You know the concentration of NaOH and that it is a strong base, 100% dissociated into ions in water.

Strategy Because NaOH is a strong base we assume that the OH^- ion concentration is the same as the NaOH concentration. The H_3O^+ ion concentration can then be calculated using Equation 16.1.

Solution The initial concentration of OH^- is 0.0012 M.

$$0.0012 \text{ mol NaOH per liter} \rightarrow 0.0012\text{ M } Na^+(aq) + 0.0012\text{ M } OH^-(aq)$$

Substituting the OH^- concentration into Equation 16.1, we have

$$K_w = 1.0 \times 10^{-14} = [H_3O^+][OH^-] = [H_3O^+](0.0012)$$

and so

$$[H_3O^+] = \frac{1.0 \times 10^{-14}}{0.0012} = 8.3 \times 10^{-12}\text{ M}$$

Think about Your Answer Why didn't we take into account the ions produced by water autoionization when we calculated the concentration of hydroxide ions? It should add OH^- and H_3O^+ ions to the solution. If x is equal to the concentration of OH^- ions generated by the autoionization of water, then, when equilibrium is achieved,

$$[OH^-] = (0.0012\text{ M} + OH^- \text{ from water autoionization}) = (0.0012\text{ M} + x)$$

In pure water, the concentration of OH^- ion generated by autoionization is 1.0×10^{-7} M. Le Chatelier's principle (◀ Section 15-6) suggests, however, that the concentration should be even smaller when OH^- ions are already present in solution from NaOH; that is, x should be much less than 1.0×10^{-7} M. This means x in the term $(0.0012 + x)$ is insignificant compared with 0.0012. (Following the rules for significant figures, the sum of 0.0012 and a number even smaller than 1.0×10^{-7} is 0.0012.) Thus, the equilibrium concentration of OH^- is equivalent to the concentration of NaOH in the solution.

Check Your Understanding

What are the hydronium ion and hydroxide ion concentrations in 4.0×10^{-3} M HCl(aq) at 25 °C? (Recall that because HCl is a strong acid, it is 100% ionized in water.)

The pH Scale

The concentration of hydronium ion in an aqueous solution can vary from less than 10^{-15} M in concentrated strong bases to greater that 10 M in concentrated strong acids—in other words, over 16 orders of magnitude. The **pH** scale compresses this range of concentrations to values from roughly −1 to 15. The pH of a solution is defined as the negative of the base-10 logarithm (log) of the hydronium ion concentration (◀ Section 4-6).

$$\text{pH} = -\log[H_3O^+] \qquad \textbf{(4.3 and 16.2)}$$

Working with Logarithms See Appendix A for more on using logarithms.

In a similar way, we can define the pOH of a solution as the negative of the base-10 logarithm of the hydroxide ion concentration.

$$\text{pOH} = -\log[OH^-] \qquad \textbf{(16.3)}$$

In pure water, the hydronium and hydroxide ion concentrations are both 1.0×10^{-7} M. Therefore, for pure water at 25 °C

$$\text{pH} = -\log(1.0 \times 10^{-7}) = 7.00$$

In the same way, you can show that the pOH of pure water is also 7.00 at 25 °C.

If we take the negative logarithms of both sides of the expression $K_w = [H_3O^+][OH^-]$, we obtain another useful equation.

$$K_w = 1.0 \times 10^{-14} = [H_3O^+][OH^-]$$

$$-\log K_w = -\log(1.0 \times 10^{-14}) = -\log([H_3O^+][OH^-])$$

$$pK_w = 14.00 = -\log([H_3O^+]) + (-\log[OH^-])$$

$$pK_w = 14.00 = \text{pH} + \text{pOH} \qquad \textbf{(16.4)}$$

The sum of the pH and pOH of a solution must be equal to 14.00 at 25 °C.

As illustrated in Figures 4.9 and 16.1, solutions with pH less than 7.00 (at 25 °C) are acidic, whereas solutions with pH greater than 7.00 are basic. Solutions with pH = 7.00 at 25 °C are neutral.

Calculating pH

The calculation of pH from the hydronium ion concentration, or the concentration of hydronium ion from pH, was introduced in Chapter 4. The *Review & Check* questions review those calculations.

FIGURE 16.1 pH and pOH. This figure illustrates the relationship of hydronium ion and hydroxide ion concentrations and of pH and pOH at 25 °C.

	pH	$[H_3O^+]$	$[OH^-]$	pOH
Basic	14.00	1.0×10^{-14}	1.0×10^{0}	0.00
	10.00	1.0×10^{-10}	1.0×10^{-4}	4.00
Neutral	7.00	1.0×10^{-7}	1.0×10^{-7}	7.00
Acidic	4.00	1.0×10^{-4}	1.0×10^{-10}	10.00
	0.00	1.0×10^{0}	1.0×10^{-14}	14.00

REVIEW & CHECK FOR SECTION 16-2

1. What is the pH of a 0.0012 M NaOH solution at 25 °C?

   (a) 2.92 (b) 11.08 (c) 8.67

2. The pH of a diet soda is 4.32 at 25 °C. What is the hydronium ion concentration in the soda?

   (a) 4.8×10^{-5} M (b) 2.1×10^{-10} M (c) 2.1×10^{-4} M

3. If the pH of a solution containing the strong base $Sr(OH)_2$ is 10.46 at 25 °C, what is the concentration of $Sr(OH)_2$?

   (a) 3.5×10^{-11} M (b) 2.9×10^{-4} M (c) 6.9×10^{-11} M (d) 1.4×10^{-4} M

Learning Objectives: LO 6.11, LO 6.12

16-3 Equilibrium Constants for Acids and Bases

In Chapter 3, it was stated that acids and bases can be divided roughly into those that are strong electrolytes (such as HCl, HNO_3, and NaOH) and those that are weak electrolytes (such as CH_3CO_2H and NH_3) (Figure 16.2) (◀ Table 3.1, Common Acids and Bases). Hydrochloric acid is a strong acid, so 100% of the acid ionizes to produce hydronium and chloride ions. In contrast, acetic acid is a weak electrolyte because it ionizes only to a small extent in water.

$$CH_3CO_2H(aq) + H_2O(\ell) \rightleftharpoons H_3O^+(aq) + CH_3CO_2^-(aq)$$

(a) Hydrochloric acid, a strong acid, is sold for household use as "muriatic acid." The acid completely ionizes in water.

(b) Vinegar is a solution of acetic acid, a weak acid that ionizes only to a small extent in water.

(c) Ammonia is a weak base, ionizing to a small extent in water.

FIGURE 16.2 Strong and weak acids and bases.

The acid, its anion, and the hydronium ion are all present at equilibrium in solution, but the ions are present in low concentration relative to the acid concentration. For example, in a 0.100 M solution of acetic acid, $[H_3O^+]$ and $[CH_3CO_2^-]$ are each about 0.0013 M whereas that of un-ionized acetic acid, $[CH_3CO_2H]$, is 0.099 M.

Similarly, ammonia is a weak base.

$$NH_3(aq) + H_2O(\ell) \rightleftharpoons NH_4^+(aq) + OH^-(aq)$$

Only about 1% of ammonia molecules in a 0.100 M solution react with water to produce the ammonium and hydroxide ions.

One way to define the relative strengths of a series of acids is to measure the pH of solutions of acids of equal concentration: the lower the pH, the greater the concentration of hydronium ion, the stronger the acid. Similarly, for a series of weak bases, $[OH^-]$ will increase, and the pH will increase as the bases become stronger.

- For a strong monoprotic acid, $[H_3O^+]$ in solution is equal to the original acid concentration. Similarly, for a strong monoprotic base, $[OH^-]$ is equal to the original base concentration.
- For a weak acid, $[H_3O^+]$ is much less than the original acid concentration. That is, $[H_3O^+]$ is smaller than if the acid were a strong acid of the same concentration. Similarly, a weak base gives a smaller $[OH^-]$ than if the base were a strong base of the same concentration.
- For a series of weak monoprotic acids (of the type HA) of the same concentration, $[H_3O^+]$ increases (and the pH will decline) as the acids become stronger. Similarly, for a series of weak bases, $[OH^-]$ increases (and the pH increases) as the bases become stronger.

Strong Acids, Weak Acids, and pH

1. For strong acids, the greater the concentration, the lower the pH.
2. For a group of weak acids of the same concentration, the stronger the acid, the lower the pH.
3. If a strong acid and a weak acid have the same concentration, the strong acid will have the lower pH (as there are many more H_3O^+ ions in solution per mole of strong acid).
4. If a strong acid and a weak acid have the same pH, the strong acid concentration must be less than the weak acid concentration.

The relative strength of an acid or base in water can also be expressed quantitatively with an equilibrium constant, often called an **ionization constant.** For the general acid HA, we can write

$$HA(aq) + H_2O(\ell) \rightleftharpoons H_3O^+(aq) + A^-(aq)$$

$$K_a = \frac{[H_3O^+][A^-]}{[HA]} \quad (16.5)$$

where the equilibrium constant, K, has a subscript "a" to indicate that it is an equilibrium constant for an acid in water. For weak acids, the value of K_a is less than 1 because the product $[H_3O^+][A^-]$ is less than the equilibrium concentration of the weak acid [HA]. For a series of acids, the acid strength increases as the value of K_a increases.

Similarly, we can write the equilibrium expression for a weak base B in water. Here, we label K with a subscript "b." Its value is less than 1 for weak bases.

$$B(aq) + H_2O(\ell) \rightleftharpoons BH^+(aq) + OH^-(aq)$$

$$K_b = \frac{[BH^+][OH^-]}{[B]} \quad (16.6)$$

Some acids and bases are listed in Table 16.2, each with its value of K_a or K_b. The following are important concepts concerning this table.

- A large value of K indicates that ionization products are strongly favored, whereas a small value of K indicates that reactants are favored.
- The strongest acids are at the upper left. They have the largest K_a values. K_a values become smaller on descending the chart as acid strength declines.
- The strongest bases are at the lower right. They have the largest K_b values. K_b values become larger on descending the chart as base strength increases.

PROBLEM SOLVING TIP 16.1

Strong or Weak?

How can you tell whether an acid or a base is weak? The easiest way is to remember those few that are strong. All others are probably weak.

Common strong acids include the following:

Hydrohalic acids: HCl, HBr, and HI (but not HF)

Nitric acid: HNO_3

Sulfuric acid: H_2SO_4 (for loss of first H^+ only)

Perchloric acid: $HClO_4$

Some common strong bases include the following:

All Group 1A hydroxides: LiOH, NaOH, KOH, RbOH, CsOH

Group 2A hydroxides: $Sr(OH)_2$ and $Ba(OH)_2$. [Neither $Mg(OH)_2$ nor $Ca(OH)_2$ dissolve appreciably in water. However, some texts consider them strong bases.]

- *The weaker the acid, the stronger its conjugate base.* That is, the smaller the value of K_a, the larger the value of K_b.
- Some acids or bases are listed as having K_a or K_b values that are large or very small. Aqueous acids that are stronger than H_3O^+ are completely ionized (HNO_3, for example), so their K_a values are "large." Their conjugate bases (such as NO_3^-) do not produce meaningful concentrations of OH^- ions, so their K_b values are "very small." Similar arguments follow for strong bases and their conjugate acids.

To illustrate some of these ideas, let us compare some common acids and bases. For example, HF is a stronger acid than HClO, which is in turn stronger than HCO_3^-,

Increasing acid strength →

HCO_3^-	HClO	HF
$K_a = 4.8 \times 10^{-11}$	$K_a = 3.5 \times 10^{-8}$	$K_a = 7.2 \times 10^{-4}$

and their conjugate bases become stronger from F^- to ClO^- to CO_3^{2-}.

← Increasing base strength

CO_3^{2-}	ClO^-	F^-
$K_b = 2.1 \times 10^{-4}$	$K_b = 2.9 \times 10^{-7}$	$K_a = 1.4 \times 10^{-11}$

Acids and bases are abundant in nature (Figure 16.3). Many naturally occurring acids contain the carboxyl group ($—CO_2H$), and a few are illustrated here. Notice that the organic portion of the molecule has an effect on its relative strength (as described further in Section 16-9).

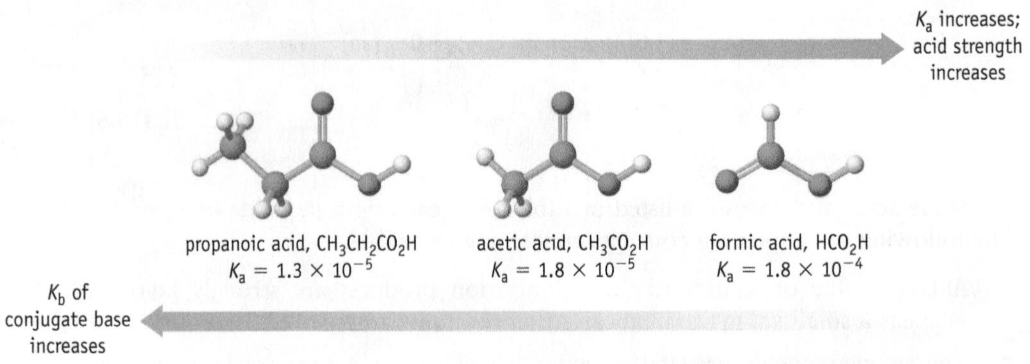

There are many naturally occurring weak bases as well (Figure 16.3). Ammonia and its conjugate acid, the ammonium ion, are part of the nitrogen cycle in the environment (► Section 20-1). Biological systems reduce nitrate ion to NH_3 and NH_4^+

Table 16.2 Ionization Constants for Some Acids and Their Conjugate Bases at 25 °C

Acid Name	Acid	K_a	Base	K_b	Base Name
Perchloric acid	$HClO_4$	Large	ClO_4^-	Very small	Perchlorate ion
Sulfuric acid	H_2SO_4	Large	HSO_4^-	Very small	Hydrogen sulfate ion
Hydrochloric acid	HCl	Large	Cl^-	Very small	Chloride ion
Nitric acid	HNO_3	Large	NO_3^-	Very small	Nitrate ion
Hydronium ion	H_3O^+	1.0	H_2O	1.0×10^{-14}	Water
Sulfurous acid	H_2SO_3	1.2×10^{-2}	HSO_3^-	8.3×10^{-13}	Hydrogen sulfite ion
Hydrogen sulfate ion	HSO_4^-	1.2×10^{-2}	SO_4^{2-}	8.3×10^{-13}	Sulfate ion
Phosphoric acid	H_3PO_4	7.5×10^{-3}	$H_2PO_4^-$	1.3×10^{-12}	Dihydrogen phosphate ion
Hexaaquairon(III) ion	$[Fe(H_2O)_6]^{3+}$	6.3×10^{-3}	$[Fe(H_2O)_5OH]^{2+}$	1.6×10^{-12}	Pentaaquahydroxoiron(III) ion
Hydrofluoric acid	HF	7.2×10^{-4}	F^-	1.4×10^{-11}	Fluoride ion
Nitrous acid	HNO_2	4.5×10^{-4}	NO_2^-	2.2×10^{-11}	Nitrite ion
Formic acid	HCO_2H	1.8×10^{-4}	HCO_2^-	5.6×10^{-11}	Formate ion
Benzoic acid	$C_6H_5CO_2H$	6.3×10^{-5}	$C_6H_5CO_2^-$	1.6×10^{-10}	Benzoate ion
Acetic acid	CH_3CO_2H	1.8×10^{-5}	$CH_3CO_2^-$	5.6×10^{-10}	Acetate ion
Propanoic acid	$CH_3CH_2CO_2H$	1.3×10^{-5}	$CH_3CH_2CO_2^-$	7.7×10^{-10}	Propanoate ion
Hexaaquaaluminum ion	$[Al(H_2O)_6]^{3+}$	7.9×10^{-6}	$[Al(H_2O)_5OH]^{2+}$	1.3×10^{-9}	Pentaaquahydroxoaluminum ion
Carbonic acid	H_2CO_3	4.2×10^{-7}	HCO_3^-	2.4×10^{-8}	Hydrogen carbonate ion
Hexaaquacopper(II) ion	$[Cu(H_2O)_6]^{2+}$	1.6×10^{-7}	$[Cu(H_2O)_5OH]^+$	6.3×10^{-8}	Pentaaquahydroxocopper(II) ion
Hydrogen sulfide	H_2S	1×10^{-7}	HS^-	1×10^{-7}	Hydrogen sulfide ion
Dihydrogen phosphate ion	$H_2PO_4^-$	6.2×10^{-8}	HPO_4^{2-}	1.6×10^{-7}	Hydrogen phosphate ion
Hydrogen sulfite ion	HSO_3^-	6.2×10^{-8}	SO_3^{2-}	1.6×10^{-7}	Sulfite ion
Hypochlorous acid	$HClO$	3.5×10^{-8}	ClO^-	2.9×10^{-7}	Hypochlorite ion
Hexaaqualead(II) ion	$[Pb(H_2O)_6]^{2+}$	1.5×10^{-8}	$[Pb(H_2O)_5OH]^+$	6.7×10^{-7}	Pentaaquahydroxolead(II) ion
Hexaaquacobalt(II) ion	$[Co(H_2O)_6]^{2+}$	1.3×10^{-9}	$[Co(H_2O)_5OH]^+$	7.7×10^{-6}	Pentaaquahydroxocobalt(II) ion
Boric acid	$B(OH)_3(H_2O)$	7.3×10^{-10}	$B(OH)_4^-$	1.4×10^{-5}	Tetrahydroxoborate ion
Ammonium ion	NH_4^+	5.6×10^{-10}	NH_3	1.8×10^{-5}	Ammonia
Hydrocyanic acid	HCN	4.0×10^{-10}	CN^-	2.5×10^{-5}	Cyanide ion
Hexaaquairon(II) ion	$[Fe(H_2O)_6]^{2+}$	3.2×10^{-10}	$[Fe(H_2O)_5OH]^+$	3.1×10^{-5}	Pentaaquahydroxoiron(II) ion
Hydrogen carbonate ion	HCO_3^-	4.8×10^{-11}	CO_3^{2-}	2.1×10^{-4}	Carbonate ion
Hexaaquanickel(II) ion	$[Ni(H_2O)_6]^{2+}$	2.5×10^{-11}	$[Ni(H_2O)_5OH]^+$	4.0×10^{-4}	Pentaaquahydroxonickel(II) ion
Hydrogen phosphate ion	HPO_4^{2-}	3.6×10^{-13}	PO_4^{3-}	2.8×10^{-2}	Phosphate ion
Water	H_2O	1.0×10^{-14}	OH^-	1.0	Hydroxide ion
Hydrogen sulfide ion*	HS^-	1×10^{-19}	S^{2-}	1×10^{5}	Sulfide ion
Ethanol	C_2H_5OH	Very small	$C_2H_5O^-$	Large	Ethoxide ion
Ammonia	NH_3	Very small	NH_2^-	Large	Amide ion
Hydrogen	H_2	Very small	H^-	Large	Hydride ion

Increasing Acid Strength ↑ (upward along the table)

Increasing Base Strength ↓ (downward along the table)

*The values of K_a for HS^- and K_b for S^{2-} are estimates.

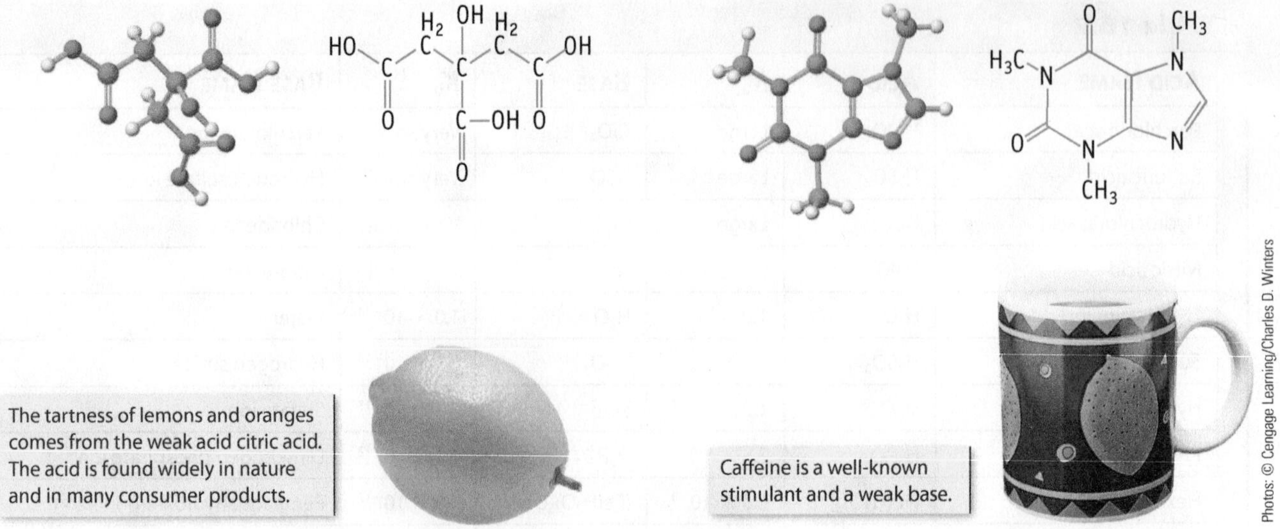

FIGURE 16.3 Natural acids and bases. Hundreds of acids and bases occur in nature. Our foods contain a wide variety, and biochemically important molecules are often acids and bases.

and incorporate nitrogen into amino acids and proteins. Many bases are derived from NH_3 by replacement of the H atoms with organic groups.

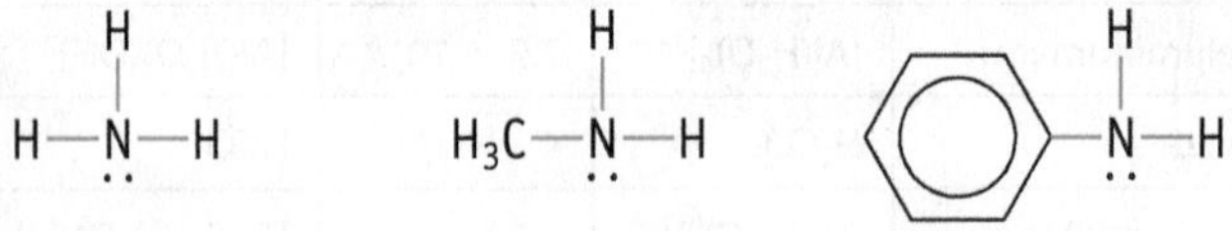

ammonia	methylamine	aniline
$K_b = 1.8 \times 10^{-5}$	$K_b = 5.0 \times 10^{-4}$	$K_b = 4.0 \times 10^{-10}$

Ammonia is a weaker base than methylamine (K_b for $NH_3 < K_b$ for CH_3NH_2). This means that the conjugate acid of ammonia, NH_4^+ ($K_a = 5.6 \times 10^{-10}$), is stronger than the methylammonium ion, the conjugate acid of methylamine, $CH_3NH_3^+$ ($K_a = 2.0 \times 10^{-11}$).

K_a and K_b Values for Polyprotic Acids

Like all polyprotic acids, phosphoric acid ionizes in a series of steps, three in this case.

First ionization step: $K_{a1} = 7.5 \times 10^{-3}$

$$H_3PO_4(aq) + H_2O(\ell) \rightleftharpoons H_2PO_4^-(aq) + H_3O^+(aq)$$

Second ionization step: $K_{a2} = 6.2 \times 10^{-8}$

$$H_2PO_4^-(aq) + H_2O(\ell) \rightleftharpoons HPO_4^{2-}(aq) + H_3O^+(aq)$$

Third ionization step: $K_{a3} = 3.6 \times 10^{-13}$

$$HPO_4^{2-}(aq) + H_2O(\ell) \rightleftharpoons PO_4^{3-}(aq) + H_3O^+(aq)$$

We observe that the K_a value for each successive step becomes smaller because it is more difficult to remove H^+ from a negatively charged ion, such as $H_2PO_4^-$, than from a neutral molecule, such as H_3PO_4. Similarly, the larger the negative charge of the anionic acid, the more difficult it is to remove H^+. Finally, for many inorganic polyprotic acids, K_a values become smaller by about 10^5 for each proton removed.

Similarly, successive base equilibrium expressions can be written for phosphate ion, PO_4^{3-}, in water.

First step: $K_{b1} = 2.8 \times 10^{-2}$

$$PO_4^{3-}(aq) + H_2O(\ell) \rightleftharpoons HPO_4^{2-}(aq) + OH^-(aq)$$

Second step: $K_{b2} = 1.6 \times 10^{-7}$

$$HPO_4^{2-}(aq) + H_2O(\ell) \rightleftharpoons H_2PO_4^-(aq) + OH^-(aq)$$

Third step: $K_{b3} = 1.3 \times 10^{-12}$

$$H_2PO_4^-(aq) + H_2O(\ell) \rightleftharpoons H_3PO_4(aq) + OH^-(aq)$$

In a trend that is similar to polyprotic acid dissociation, the K_b value for each successive step becomes smaller by about 10^5.

Logarithmic Scale of Relative Acid Strength, pK_a

Many chemists and biochemists use a logarithmic scale to report and compare relative acid strengths.

$$pK_a = -\log K_a \tag{16.7}$$

The pK_a of an acid is the negative log of the K_a value (just as pH is the negative log of the hydronium ion concentration). For example, acetic acid has a pK_a value of 4.74.

$$pK_a = -\log (1.8 \times 10^{-5}) = 4.74$$

The pK_a value becomes smaller as the acid strength increases.

Acid strength increases →

Propanoic Acid	Acetic Acid	Formic Acid
$CH_3CH_2CO_2H$	CH_3CO_2H	HCO_2H
$K_a = 1.3 \times 10^{-5}$	$K_a = 1.8 \times 10^{-5}$	$K_a = 1.8 \times 10^{-4}$
pK_a = 4.89	pK_a = 4.74	pK_a = 3.74

pK_a decreases →

Relating the Ionization Constants for an Acid and Its Conjugate Base

Let us look again at Table 16.2. From the top of the table to the bottom, the strengths of the acids decline (K_a becomes smaller), and the strengths of their conjugate bases increase (the values of K_b increase). Indeed these observations are connected: the product of K_a for an acid and K_b for its conjugate base is equal to a constant, specifically K_w.

$$K_a \times K_b = K_w \tag{16.8}$$

A Relation Among p*K* Values
A useful relationship for an acid–conjugate base pair follows from Equation 16.8:

$$pK_w = pK_a + pK_b$$

Consider the specific case of the ionization of a weak acid, say HCN, and the interaction of its conjugate base, CN^-, with H_2O.

Weak acid:	$HCN(aq) + H_2O(\ell) \rightleftharpoons H_3O^+(aq) + CN^-(aq)$	$K_a = 4.0 \times 10^{-10}$
Conjugate base:	$CN^-(aq) + H_2O(\ell) \rightleftharpoons HCN(aq) + OH^-(aq)$	$K_b = 2.5 \times 10^{-5}$
	$2\ H_2O(\ell) \rightleftharpoons H_3O^+(aq) + OH^-(aq)$	$K_w = 1.0 \times 10^{-14}$

Adding the equations gives the chemical equation for the autoionization of water, and the product of K_a and K_b is indeed 1.0×10^{-14}. That is,

$$K_a \times K_b = \left(\frac{[H_3O^+][\cancel{CN^-}]}{[\cancel{HCN}]}\right)\left(\frac{[\cancel{HCN}][OH^-]}{[\cancel{CN^-}]}\right) = [H_3O^+][OH^-] = K_w$$

Equation 16.8 is useful because K_b can be calculated from K_a. The value of K_b for the cyanide ion, for example, is

$$K_b \text{ for } CN^- = \frac{K_w}{K_a \text{ for HCN}} = \frac{1.0 \times 10^{-14}}{4.0 \times 10^{-10}} = 2.5 \times 10^{-5}$$

REVIEW & CHECK FOR SECTION 16-3

Use Table 16.2 to answer the following questions.

1. Which of the following is the strongest acid?

   (a) HF (b) H_2S (c) HOCl (d) CH_3CO_2H

2. Which acid has the strongest conjugate base?

   (a) HNO_2 (b) $C_6H_5CO_2H$ (c) HCN (d) HCl

3. Which of the following has a pK_a value of 4.20?

   (a) $C_6H_5CO_2H$ (b) CH_3CO_2H (c) HCO_2H (d) HF

4. What is the pK_a for the conjugate acid of ammonia?

   (a) 4.74 (b) 9.25 (c) 5.60 (d) 7.00

5. K_a for lactic acid, $CH_3CHOHCO_2H$, is 1.4×10^{-4}. What is the pK_b for the conjugate base of this acid, $CH_3CHOHCO_2^-$?

   (a) 3.85 (b) 7.00 (c) 10.15 (d) 12.60

16-4 Acid–Base Properties of Salts

A number of the acids and bases listed in Table 16.2 are cations or anions. As described earlier, anions can act as Brønsted bases because they can accept a proton from an acid to form the conjugate acid of the ion.

$$CO_3^{2-}(aq) + H_2O(\ell) \rightleftharpoons HCO_3^-(aq) + OH^-(aq)$$
$$K_b = 2.1 \times 10^{-4}$$

You should also notice that many metal cations in water are Brønsted acids.

$$[Al(H_2O)_6]^{3+}(aq) + H_2O(\ell) \rightleftharpoons [Al(H_2O)_5(OH)]^{2+}(aq) + H_3O^+(aq)$$
$$K_a = 7.9 \times 10^{-6}$$

Hydrolysis Reactions and Hydrolysis Constants Chemists often say that, when ions interact with water to produce acidic or basic solutions, the ions "hydrolyze" in water, or they undergo "hydrolysis." Thus, some books refer to the K_a and K_b values of ions as "hydrolysis constants," K_h.

Table 16.3 summarizes the acid–base properties of some common cations and anions in aqueous solution. As you look over this table, notice the following points:

- Anions that are conjugate bases of strong acids (for example, Cl^- and NO_3^-) are such weak bases that they have no effect on solution pH.
- There are numerous basic anions (such as $CH_3CO_2^-$). All are the conjugate bases of weak acids.
- The acid–base behavior of anions of polyprotic acids depends on the extent of deprotonation. For example, a fully deprotonated anion (such as CO_3^{2-}) will be basic. A partially deprotonated anion (such as HCO_3^-) is amphiprotic and is capable of undergoing both acid and base reactions with water. A solution may be acidic or basic depending on the relative strengths of the anion as an acid or as a base.

Table 16.3 Acid and Base Properties of Some Ions in Aqueous Solution

	NEUTRAL	BASIC	ACIDIC
Anions	Cl^-, NO_3^-, Br^-, ClO_4^-, I^-	$CH_3CO_2^-$, CN^-, SO_4^{2-}, HCO_2^-, PO_4^{3-}, HPO_4^{2-}, CO_3^{2-}, HCO_3^-, SO_3^{2-}, S^{2-}, HS^-, OCl^-, F^-, NO_2^-	HSO_4^-, $H_2PO_4^-$, HSO_3^-
Cations	Li^+, Na^+, Ca^{2+}, K^+, Ba^{2+}	$[Al(H_2O)_5(OH)]^{2+}$ (for example)	$[Al(H_2O)_6]^{3+}$ and hydrated transition metal cations (such as $[Fe(H_2O)_6]^{3+}$) NH_4^+

- Alkali metal and alkaline earth cations have no measurable effect on solution pH.
- Basic cations are conjugate bases of acidic cations such as $[Al(H_2O)_6]^{3+}$.
- Acidic cations fall into two categories: (a) metal cations with 2+ and 3+ charges and (b) ammonium ions (and its organic derivatives). All metal cations are hydrated in water, forming ions such as $[M(H_2O)_6]^{n+}$. However, only when M is a 2+ or 3+ ion, particularly a transition metal ion, does the ion act as an acid.

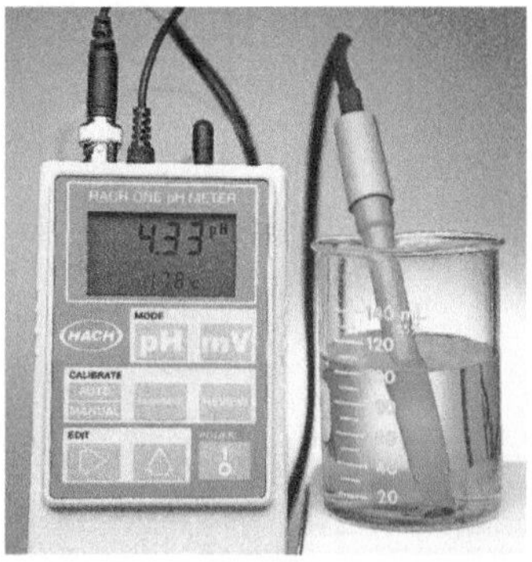

© Cengage Learning/Charles D. Winters

Many aqueous metal cations in salts are Brønsted acids. A pH measurement of a dilute solution of copper(II) sulfate shows that the solution is clearly acidic. Among the common cations, Al^{3+} and transition metal ions form acidic solutions in water.

EXAMPLE 16.2

Acid–Base Properties of Salts

Problem Decide whether each of the following will give rise to an acidic, basic, or neutral solution in water.

(a) $NaNO_3$
(b) K_3PO_4
(c) $FeCl_2$
(d) $NaHCO_3$
(e) NH_4F

What Do You Know? You know the salt formulas and, from Tables 16.2 and 16.3, you know the effect of the constituent ions on pH.

Strategy First, identify the cation and anion in each salt. Next, use Tables 16.2 and 16.3 to describe the acid–base properties of each ion. Finally, decide on the overall acid–base properties of the salt.

Solution

(a) $NaNO_3$: This salt gives a neutral, aqueous solution (pH = 7). Neither the sodium ion, Na^+, nor the nitrate ion, NO_3^- (the very weak conjugate base of a strong acid), affects the solution pH.

(b) K_3PO_4: An aqueous solution of K_3PO_4 should be basic (pH > 7) because PO_4^{3-} is the conjugate base of the weak acid HPO_4^{2-}. The K^+ ion, like the Na^+ ion, does not affect the solution pH.

(c) $FeCl_2$: An aqueous solution of $FeCl_2$ should be weakly acidic (pH < 7). The Fe^{2+} ion in water, $[Fe(H_2O)_6]^{2+}$, is a Brønsted acid. In contrast, Cl^- is the very weak conjugate base of the strong acid HCl, so it does not contribute OH^- ions to the solution.

(d) $NaHCO_3$: Some additional information is needed concerning salts of amphiprotic anions such as HCO_3^-. Because they have an ionizable hydrogen, they can act as acids,

$$HCO_3^-(aq) + H_2O(\ell) \rightleftharpoons CO_3^{2-}(aq) + H_3O^+(aq) \qquad K_a = 4.8 \times 10^{-11}$$

Strategy Map 16.2

PROBLEM
Decide whether a salt is **acidic**, **basic**, or **neutral**.

DATA/INFORMATION KNOWN
- The formula of the salt: K_3PO_4

STEP 1. Identify the **cation** and **anion**.

Cation = K^+, anion = PO_4^{3-}

STEP 2. Identify the nature of the **cation**.

K^+ is a **neutral** cation.

STEP 3. Identify the nature of the **anion**.

PO_4^{3-} is a ***relatively strong*** **base**.

STEP 4. Decide on the acid–base properties of the salt.

K_3PO_4 is **basic**.

but because they are anions, they can also act as bases and accept an H^+ ion from water.

$$HCO_3^-(aq) + H_2O(\ell) \rightleftharpoons H_2CO_3(aq) + OH^-(aq) \qquad K_b = 2.4 \times 10^{-8}$$

Whether the solution is acidic or basic will depend on the relative magnitude of K_a and K_b. In the case of the hydrogen carbonate anion, K_b is larger than K_a, so $[OH^-]$ is larger than $[H_3O^+]$, and an aqueous solution of $NaHCO_3$ will be slightly basic.

(e) NH_4F: What happens if you have a salt based on an acidic cation and a basic anion? One example is ammonium fluoride. Here, the ammonium ion would decrease the pH, and the fluoride ion would increase the pH.

$$NH_4^+(aq) + H_2O(\ell) \rightleftharpoons H_3O^+(aq) + NH_3(aq) \qquad K_a\ (NH_4^+) = 5.6 \times 10^{-10}$$

$$F^-(aq) + H_2O(\ell) \rightleftharpoons HF(aq) + OH^-(aq) \qquad K_b\ (F^-) = 1.4 \times 10^{-11}$$

Because $K_a\ (NH_4^+) > K_b\ (F^-)$, the ammonium ion is a stronger acid than the fluoride ion is a base. The resulting solution should be slightly acidic.

Think about Your Answer There are several important points here:

- Anions that are conjugate bases of strong acids—such as Cl^- and NO_3^-—have no effect on solution pH.
- To determine whether a salt is acidic, basic, or neutral, we must take into account both the cation and the anion. When a salt has an acidic cation and a basic anion, the pH of the solution will be determined by the ion that is the stronger acid or base.

Check Your Understanding

For each of the following salts in water, predict whether the pH will be greater than, less than, or equal to 7.

(a) KBr (b) NH_4NO_3 (c) $AlCl_3$ (d) Na_2HPO_4

REVIEW & CHECK FOR SECTION 16-4

1. Adding NaH_2PO_4 to water will cause the pH to
   (a) increase (b) decrease (c) stay the same
2. Adding KCN to water will cause the pH to
   (a) increase (b) decrease (c) stay the same

PROBLEM SOLVING TIP 16.2
Aqueous Solutions of Salts

It is useful to be able to predict acid and base properties of salts. Information on the pH of an aqueous solution of a salt is summarized in Table 16.3. Consider also the following examples:

Cation	Anion	pH of the Solution
From strong base (Na^+)	From strong acid (Cl^-)	= 7 (neutral)
From strong base (K^+)	From weak acid ($CH_3CO_2^-$)	> 7 (basic)
From weak base (NH_4^+)	From strong acid (Cl^-)	< 7 (acidic)
From any weak base (BH^+)	From any weak acid (A^-)	Depends on relative acid strength of BH^+ and base strength of A^-

Learning Objectives: LO 6.12

16-5 Predicting the Direction of Acid–Base Reactions

According to the Brønsted–Lowry theory, all acid–base reactions can be written as equilibria involving the acid and base and their conjugates.

$$\text{Acid} + \text{base} \rightleftharpoons \text{conjugate base of the acid} + \text{conjugate acid of the base}$$

In Sections 16-3 and 16-4, we used equilibrium constants to provide information about the relative strengths of acids and bases. Now we want to show how these constants can be used to decide whether a particular acid–base reaction is product- or reactant-favored at equilibrium.

Hydrochloric acid is a strong acid. Its equilibrium constant for reaction with water is very large, with the equilibrium lying completely to the right.

$$HCl(aq) + H_2O(\ell) \rightleftharpoons H_3O^+(aq) + Cl^-(aq)$$

$$\text{Strong acid } (\approx 100\% \text{ ionized}),\ K_a >> 1$$

$$[H_3O^+] \approx \text{initial concentration of the acid}$$

Of the two acids here, HCl is stronger than H_3O^+. Of the two bases, H_2O and Cl^-, water is the stronger base and wins out in the competition for the proton. Notice that *the equilibrium lies to the side of the chemical equation having the weaker acid and base.*

conjugate pair 1

conjugate pair 2

$$HCl(aq) + H_2O(\ell) \underset{K>1}{\rightleftharpoons} H_3O^+(aq) + Cl^-(aq)$$

$HCl(aq)$	$H_2O(\ell)$	$H_3O^+(aq)$	$Cl^-(aq)$
stronger acid than H_3O^+	stronger base than Cl^-	weaker acid than HCl	weaker base than H_2O

In contrast to HCl and other strong acids, acetic acid, a *weak* acid, ionizes to only a very small extent (Table 16.2).

$$CH_3CO_2H(aq) + H_2O(\ell) \rightleftharpoons H_3O^+(aq) + CH_3CO_2^-(aq)$$

$$\text{Weak acid } (< 100\% \text{ ionized}),\ K_a = 1.8 \times 10^{-5}$$

$$[H_3O^+] << \text{initial concentration of the acid}$$

When equilibrium is achieved in a 0.1 M aqueous solution of CH_3CO_2H, the concentrations of $H_3O^+(aq)$ and $CH_3CO_2^-(aq)$ are each only about 0.001 M. Approximately 99% of the acetic acid is not ionized.

conjugate pair 1

conjugate pair 2

$$CH_3CO_2H(aq) + H_2O(\ell) \underset{K<1}{\rightleftharpoons} H_3O^+(aq) + CH_3CO_2^-(aq)$$

$CH_3CO_2H(aq)$	$H_2O(\ell)$	$H_3O^+(aq)$	$CH_3CO_2^-(aq)$
weaker acid than H_3O^+	weaker base than $CH_3CO_2^-$	stronger acid than CH_3CO_2H	stronger base than H_2O

Again, the equilibrium lies toward the side of the reaction having the weaker acid and base.

These two examples of the relative extent of acid–base reactions illustrate a general principle:

> All proton transfer reactions proceed from the stronger acid and base to the weaker acid and base.

General Principle of Reactivity
A general principle in chemistry is that more reactive substances react to form less reactive substances. Here you see the result of this for acid–base reactions: The stronger acid and stronger base always react to form the weaker acid and weaker base.

Using this principle and Table 16.2, you can predict which reactions are product-favored and which are reactant-favored at equilibrium. Consider the possible reaction of phosphoric acid and acetate ion to give acetic acid and the dihydrogen phosphate ion. Table 16.2 informs us that H_3PO_4 is a stronger acid ($K_a = 7.5 \times 10^{-3}$) than acetic acid ($K_a = 1.8 \times 10^{-5}$), and the acetate ion ($K_b = 5.6 \times 10^{-10}$) is a stronger base than the dihydrogen phosphate ion ($K_b = 1.3 \times 10^{-12}$).

Brønsted acids

Brønsted bases

$$H_3PO_4(aq) + CH_3CO_2^-(aq) \rightleftharpoons H_2PO_4^-(aq) + CH_3CO_2H(aq)$$

$H_3PO_4(aq)$	$CH_3CO_2^-(aq)$	$H_2PO_4^-(aq)$	$CH_3CO_2H(aq)$
stronger acid than CH_3CO_2H	stronger base than $H_2PO_4^-$	weaker base than $CH_3CO_2^-$	weaker acid than H_3PO_4

Thus, mixing phosphoric acid with sodium acetate will produce a significant amount of dihydrogen phosphate ion and acetic acid. That is, the equilibrium is predicted to lie to the right because the reaction proceeds from the stronger acid–base combination to the weaker acid–base combination.

EXAMPLE 16.3

Reactions of Acids and Bases

Problem Write a balanced, net ionic equation for the reaction that occurs between acetic acid and sodium bicarbonate. Decide whether the equilibrium lies predominantly to the left or to the right.

What Do You Know? You know the identity of the acid, and you know that the other reactant, $NaHCO_3$, is a water-soluble salt that forms Na^+ and HCO_3^- ions in water. You also know that the HCO_3^- ion is amphiprotic, but it must act as a base toward acetic acid in this reaction. You need to know the ionization constants for acetic acid and the HCO_3^- ion and for their conjugates.

Strategy

- Identify the products of the acid–base reaction (which arise by H^+ transfer from acetic acid to the base, HCO_3^-). That is, identify the conjugate base of acetic acid and the conjugate acid of HCO_3^-.
- Write a balanced chemical equation for the equilibrium between the acid and base and their conjugate base and acid.
- Use Table 16.2 to decide which is the weaker of the two acids (or the weaker of the two bases). The equilibrium will favor the weaker acid and base.

Solution The conjugate base of acetic acid is the acetate ion, $CH_3CO_2^-$, and the conjugate acid of the base HCO_3^- is H_2CO_3. Hydrogen ion transfer from the acid to the base occurs by the following net ionic equation:

$$\underset{K_a = 1.8 \times 10^{-5}}{CH_3CO_2H(aq)} + \underset{K_b = 2.4 \times 10^{-8}}{HCO_3^-(aq)} \rightleftharpoons \underset{K_b = 5.6 \times 10^{-10}}{CH_3CO_2^-(aq)} + \underset{K_a = 4.2 \times 10^{-7}}{H_2CO_3(aq)}$$

The value of K_a or K_b (from Table 16.2) is given for each reactant and product. The equilibrium constants show that H_2CO_3 is a weaker acid than CH_3CO_2H, and $CH_3CO_2^-$ is a weaker base than HCO_3^-. The reaction favors the side having the weaker acid and base—that is, the equilibrium lies to the right.

Think about Your Answer One product of the reaction of acetic acid and $NaHCO_3$ is H_2CO_3, which dissociates into CO_2 and H_2O. As you can see in the photograph in the margin, CO_2 bubbles out of the solution. The equilibrium for the dissociation of H_2CO_3 to form CO_2 and H_2O lies far to the right.

$$H_2CO_3(aq) \rightleftharpoons CO_2(g) + H_2O(\ell)$$

© Cengage Learning/Charles D. Winters

Reaction of vinegar and baking soda. This reaction involves the weak acid acetic acid and the weak base HCO_3^- from sodium hydrogen carbonate. Based on the values of the equilibrium constants, the reaction is predicted to proceed to the right to produce acetate ion, CO_2, and water.

The loss of a product, CO_2, causes the equilibrium to shift farther to the right. See the discussion of gas-forming reactions in Section 3-7 and of Le Chatelier's principle in Section 15-6.

Check Your Understanding

(a) Which is the stronger Brønsted acid, HCO_3^- or NH_4^+? Which has the stronger conjugate base?

(b) Is a reaction between HCO_3^- ions and NH_3 product- or reactant-favored at equilibrium?

$$HCO_3^-(aq) + NH_3(aq) \rightleftharpoons CO_3^{2-}(aq) + NH_4^+(aq)$$

(c) You mix solutions of sodium hydrogen phosphate and ammonia. The net ionic equation for a possible reaction is

$$HPO_4^{2-}(aq) + NH_3(aq) \rightleftharpoons PO_4^{3-}(aq) + NH_4^+(aq)$$

Does the equilibrium lie to the left or to the right for this reaction?

REVIEW & CHECK FOR SECTION 16-5

1. Is the reaction of NaCN and HCl in water product- or reactant-favored at equilibrium?

   (a) reactant-favored (b) product-favored

2. In the following reaction, does the equilibrium lie predominantly to the left or to the right?

$$HS^-(aq) + H_3PO_4(aq) \rightleftharpoons H_2S(aq) + H_2PO_4^-(aq)$$

   (a) left (b) right

16-6 Types of Acid–Base Reactions

Learning Objectives: LO 6.12, LO 6.15

The reaction of hydrochloric acid and sodium hydroxide is the classic example of a strong acid–strong base reaction, whereas the reaction of citric acid and bicarbonate ion represents the reaction of a weak acid and weak base (Figure 16.4). These are two of four general types of acid–base reactions (Table 16.4). Because acid–base reactions are among the most important classes of chemical reactions, it is useful for you to know the outcome of the various types of these reactions.

FIGURE 16.4 Reaction of a weak acid with a weak base. The bubbles coming from the tablet are carbon dioxide. This arises from the reaction of a weak Brønsted acid (citric acid) with a weak Brønsted base (HCO_3^-). The reaction is driven to completion by gas evolution.

The Reaction of a Strong Acid with a Strong Base

Strong acids and bases are effectively 100% ionized in solution. Therefore, the complete ionic equation for the reaction of HCl (strong acid) and NaOH (strong base) is

$$H_3O^+(aq) + Cl^-(aq) + Na^+(aq) + OH^-(aq) \rightleftharpoons 2\ H_2O(\ell) + Na^+(aq) + Cl^-(aq)$$

which leads to the following net ionic equation

$$H_3O^+(aq) + OH^-(aq) \rightleftharpoons 2\ H_2O(\ell) \qquad K = 1/K_w = 1.0 \times 10^{14}$$

The net ionic equation for the reaction of any strong acid with any strong base is always simply the reaction of hydronium ion and hydroxide ion to give water (◀ Section 3-6). Because this reaction is the reverse of the autoionization of water, it has an equilibrium constant of $1/K_w$. This very large value of K shows that, for all practical purposes, the reactants are completely consumed to form products. Thus, if equal numbers of moles of NaOH and HCl are mixed, the result is just a solution of NaCl in water. The constituents of NaCl, Na^+ and Cl^- ions, which arise from a strong base and a strong acid, respectively, produce a neutral aqueous solution. For this reason, reactions of strong acids and bases are often called "neutralizations."

Mixing equal amounts (moles) of a strong monoprotic base and a strong monoprotic acid produces a neutral solution (pH = 7.00 at 25 °C).

The Reaction of a Weak Acid with a Strong Base

Formic Acid + NaOH The equilibrium constant for the reaction of formic acid and sodium hydroxide is 1.8×10^{10}. Can you confirm this? (See Study Question 16.103.)

Consider the reaction of the naturally occurring weak acid formic acid, HCO_2H, with sodium hydroxide. The net ionic equation is

$$HCO_2H(aq) + OH^-(aq) \rightleftharpoons H_2O(\ell) + HCO_2^-(aq)$$

In this reaction, OH^- is a much stronger base than HCO_2^- ($K_b = 5.6 \times 10^{-11}$), and the reaction is predicted to proceed to the right. If equal amounts of weak acid and base are mixed, the final solution will contain sodium formate ($NaHCO_2$), a salt that is 100% dissociated in water. The Na^+ ion is a Group IA cation and so gives a neutral solution. The formate ion, however, is the conjugate base of a weak acid (Table 16.2), so the solution is basic. This example leads to a useful general conclusion:

Mixing equal amounts (moles) of a strong base and a weak acid produces a salt whose anion is the conjugate base of the weak acid. The solution is basic, with the pH depending on K_b for the anion.

The Reaction of a Strong Acid with a Weak Base

Ammonia + HCl The equilibrium constant for the reaction of a strong acid with aqueous ammonia is 1.8×10^9. Can you confirm this? (See Study Question 16.102.)

The net ionic equation for the reaction of the strong acid HCl and the weak base NH_3 is

$$H_3O^+(aq) + NH_3(aq) \rightleftharpoons H_2O(\ell) + NH_4^+(aq)$$

The hydronium ion, H_3O^+, is a much stronger acid than NH_4^+ ($K_a = 5.6 \times 10^{-10}$), and NH_3 is a stronger base ($K_b = 1.8 \times 10^{-5}$) than H_2O. Therefore, the reaction is predicted to proceed to the right and to reach completion. Thus, after mixing equal amounts of HCl and NH_3, the solution contains the salt ammonium chloride, NH_4Cl. The Cl^- ion has no effect on the solution pH (Tables 16.2 and 16.3). However, the NH_4^+ ion is the conjugate acid of the weak base NH_3, so the solution at the conclusion of the reaction is acidic. In general, we can conclude that

Mixing equal amounts (moles) of a strong acid and a weak base produces a salt whose cation is the conjugate acid of the weak base. The solution is acidic, with the pH depending on K_a for the cation.

The Reaction of a Weak Acid with a Weak Base

***K* for Reaction of Weak Acid and Weak Base** The equilibrium constant for the reaction between a weak acid and a weak base is $K_{net} = K_w/(K_a \cdot K_b)$. (See Study Question 16.127.)

If acetic acid, a weak acid, is mixed with ammonia, a weak base, the following reaction occurs.

$$CH_3CO_2H(aq) + NH_3(aq) \rightleftharpoons NH_4^+(aq) + CH_3CO_2^-(aq)$$

You know that the reaction is product-favored because CH_3CO_2H is a stronger acid than NH_4^+ and NH_3 is a stronger base than $CH_3CO_2^-$ (Table 16.2). Thus, if equal amounts of the acid and base are mixed, the resulting solution contains ammonium acetate, $NH_4CH_3CO_2$. Is this solution acidic or basic? In Example 16.2(e) you learned that this depends on the relative values of K_a for the conjugate acid (here, NH_4^+; $K_a = 5.6 \times 10^{-10}$) and K_b for the conjugate base (here, $CH_3CO_2^-$;

Table 16.4 Characteristics of Acid–Base Reactions

Type	Example	Net Ionic Equation	Species Present after Equal Amounts Are Mixed; pH
Strong acid + strong base	$HCl + NaOH$	$H_3O^+(aq) + OH^-(aq) \rightleftharpoons 2\ H_2O(\ell)$	Cl^-, Na^+, pH = 7
Strong acid + weak base	$HCl + NH_3$	$H_3O^+(aq) + NH_3(aq) \rightleftharpoons NH_4^+(aq) + H_2O(\ell)$	Cl^-, NH_4^+, pH < 7
Weak acid + strong base	$HCO_2H + NaOH$	$HCO_2H(aq) + OH^-(aq) \rightleftharpoons HCO_2^-(aq) + H_2O(\ell)$	HCO_2^-, Na^+, pH > 7
Weak acid + weak base	$HCO_2H + NH_3$	$HCO_2H(aq) + NH_3(aq) \rightleftharpoons HCO_2^-(aq) + NH_4^+(aq)$	HCO_2^-, NH_4^+, pH dependent on K_a and K_b of conjugate acid and base

$K_b = 5.6 \times 10^{-10}$). In this case, the values of K_a and K_b are the same, so the solution is predicted to be neutral.

Mixing equal amounts (moles) of a weak acid and a weak base produces a salt whose cation is the conjugate acid of the weak base and whose anion is the conjugate base of the weak acid. The solution pH depends on the relative K_a and K_b values.

REVIEW & CHECK FOR SECTION 16-6

1. Equal amounts (moles) of HCl(aq) and NaCN(aq) are mixed. The resulting solution is

   (a) acidic (b) basic (c) neutral

2. Equal amounts (moles) of acetic acid(aq) and sodium sulfite, Na_2SO_3(aq), are mixed. The resulting solution is

   (a) acidic (b) basic (c) neutral

3. Equal amounts (moles) of NaOH(aq) and NaH_2PO_4(aq) are mixed. The resulting solution is

   (a) acidic (b) basic (c) neutral

16-7 Calculations with Equilibrium Constants

Learning Objectives: LO 6.16, LO 6.17

Determining *K* from Initial Concentrations and Measured pH

The K_a and K_b values found in Table 16.2 and in the more extensive tables in Appendices H and I were all determined by experiment. There are several experimental methods available, but one approach, illustrated by the following example, is to determine the pH of the solution.

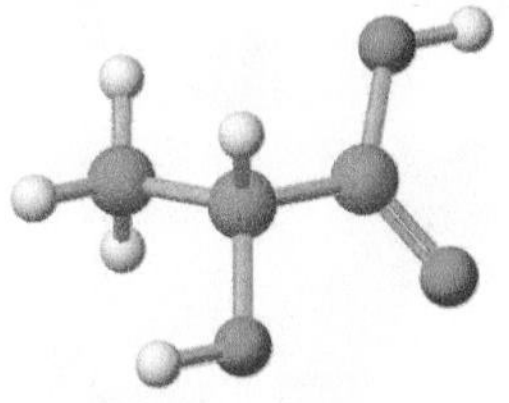

lactic acid, $CH_3CHOHCO_2H$

Lactic acid, $CH_3CHOHCO_2H$. Lactic acid is a weak monoprotic acid that occurs naturally in sour milk and arises from metabolism in the human body.

EXAMPLE 16.4

Calculating a K_a Value from a Measured pH

Problem A 0.10 M aqueous solution of lactic acid, $CH_3CHOHCO_2H$, has a pH of 2.43. What is the value of K_a for lactic acid?

What Do You Know? You need to know the equilibrium concentration of each species to calculate K_a. The pH of the solution allows you to calculate the equilibrium concentration of H_3O^+, and you can derive the other equilibrium concentrations from this.

Strategy Map 16.4

PROBLEM

Calculate K_a for the ionization of **lactic acid**, a weak acid.

↓

DATA/INFORMATION KNOWN

- Acid concentration
- Solution pH

↓ STEP 1. Write **balanced equation** and **K_a expression** and set up **ICE table.**

K_a expression and ICE table

↓ STEP 2. Enter **equilibrium concentrations** in ICE table.

At equilibrium:
$[H_3O^+]$ = [Conjugate base] = x
[Lactic acid] = original conc. − x

↓ STEP 3. Convert **pH** to **$[H_3O^+]$** and solve for **x**.

Equilibrium concentrations of **lactic acid, hydronium ion,** and **lactate ion**

↓ STEP 4. Enter **equilibrium concentrations** into **K_a expression** and solve.

Value of K_a

Strategy

- Write the equilibrium constant expression, set up an ICE table, and convert pH to $[H_3O^+]$, the hydronium ion equilibrium concentration.
- Enter the initial concentration of $CH_3CHOHCO_2H$ on the initial (I) line of the ICE table.
- Assign the variable x to represent changes in concentration. Based on the reaction stoichiometry the change in $[CH_3CHOHCO_2H]$ is $-x$ and the change in $[CH_3CHOHCO_2^-]$ is $+x$. Enter these values in the change (C) line of the table.
- Recognize that the hydronium ion equilibrium concentration, $[H_3O^+]$, is equal to x.
- Enter the expressions for the final equilibrium concentrations of all three species on the E line of the ICE table. Using this, determine the values of the other equilibrium concentrations.
- Use the equilibrium concentrations to solve for K_a.

Solution The equation for the reaction of lactic acid with water and its equilibrium constant expression are

$$\underset{\text{lactic acid}}{CH_3CHOHCO_2H(aq)} + H_2O(\ell) \rightleftharpoons \underset{\text{lactate ion}}{CH_3CHOHCO_2^-(aq)} + H_3O^+(aq)$$

$$K_a \text{ (lactic acid)} = \frac{[H_3O^+][CH_3CHOHCO_2^-]}{[CH_3CHOHCO_2H]}$$

Begin by converting the pH to $[H_3O^+]$:

$$[H_3O^+] = 10^{-pH} = 10^{-2.43} = 3.7 \times 10^{-3}\text{ M}$$

Enter in the ICE table the concentrations before equilibrium is established, the change that occurs as the reaction proceeds to equilibrium, and the concentrations when equilibrium has been achieved. (See Examples 15.2–15.5.)

EQUILIBRIUM	$CH_3CHOHCO_2H$ + H_2O ⇌	$CH_3CHOHCO_2^-$ +	H_3O^+
Initial (M)	0.10	0	0
Change (M)	$-x$	$+x$	$+x$
Equilibrium (M)	$(0.10 - x)$	x	x

The following points can be made concerning the ICE table.

- The quantity x represents the equilibrium concentrations of hydronium ion and lactate ion. That is, at equilibrium $x = [H_3O^+] = [CH_3CHOHCO_2^-] = 3.7 \times 10^{-3}$ M.
- By stoichiometry, x is also the concentration of acid that ionized on proceeding to equilibrium.

With these points in mind, we can calculate K_a for lactic acid.

$$K_a \text{ (lactic acid)} = \frac{[H_3O^+][CH_3CHOHCO_2^-]}{[CH_3CHOHCO_2H]}$$

$$= \frac{(3.7 \times 10^{-3})(3.7 \times 10^{-3})}{0.10 - 0.0037} = 1.4 \times 10^{-4}$$

Comparing this value of K_a with others in Table 16.2, we see lactic acid is similar to formic acid in its strength.

Think about Your Answer Hydronium ion, H_3O^+, is present in solution from lactic acid ionization and from water autoionization. Le Chatelier's principle informs us that the H_3O^+ from lactic acid will suppress the H_3O^+ coming from the water autoionization.

Because $[H_3O^+]$ from water must be less than 10^{-7} M, the pH is almost completely a reflection of H_3O^+ from lactic acid. (See Example 16.1.)

Check Your Understanding

A solution prepared from 0.055 mol of butanoic acid dissolved in sufficient water to give 1.0 L of solution has a pH of 2.72. Determine K_a for butanoic acid. The acid ionizes according to the balanced equation

$$CH_3CH_2CH_2CO_2H(aq) + H_2O(\ell) \rightleftharpoons H_3O^+(aq) + CH_3CH_2CH_2CO_2^-(aq)$$

There is an important point to notice in Example 16.4. The lactic acid concentration at equilibrium was given by $(0.10 - x)$ where x was found from the solution pH to be 3.7×10^{-3} M. By the usual rules governing significant figures $(0.10 - 0.0037)$ is equal to 0.10. The acid is weak, so very little of it ionizes (approximately 4%), and the equilibrium concentration of lactic acid is essentially equal to the initial acid concentration. Neglecting to subtract 0.0037 from 0.10 has no effect on the answer, which is known only to two significant figures.

Like lactic acid, most weak acids (HA) are so weak that the equilibrium concentration of the acid, [HA], is effectively its initial concentration ($= [HA]_0$). This leads to the useful conclusion that the denominator in the equilibrium constant expression for dilute solutions of most weak acids is simply $[HA]_0$, the original or initial concentration of the weak acid.

$$HA(aq) + H_2O(\ell) \rightleftharpoons H_3O^+(aq) + A^-(aq)$$

$$K_a = \frac{[H_3O^+][A^-]}{[HA]_0 - [H_3O^+]} \approx \frac{[H_3O^+][A^-]}{[HA]_0}$$

Analysis shows that

> The approximation that
>
> $$[HA]_{equilibrium} = [HA]_0 - [H_3O^+] \approx [HA]_0$$
>
> is valid whenever $[HA]_0$ is greater than or equal to $100 \times K_a$.

This is the same approximation we used in Chapter 15 when deciding whether we needed to solve quadratic equations exactly (◀ Problem Solving Tip 15.1).

What Is the pH of an Aqueous Solution of a Weak Acid or Base?

Knowing values of the equilibrium constants for weak acids and bases enables us to calculate the pH of a solution of a weak acid or base.

EXAMPLE 16.5

Calculating Equilibrium Concentrations and pH from K_a

Problem Calculate the pH of a 0.020 M solution of benzoic acid ($C_6H_5CO_2H$) given that $K_a = 6.3 \times 10^{-5}$ for the acid.

$$C_6H_5CO_2H(aq) + H_2O(\ell) \rightleftharpoons H_3O^+(aq) + C_6H_5CO_2^-(aq)$$

Strategy Map 16.5

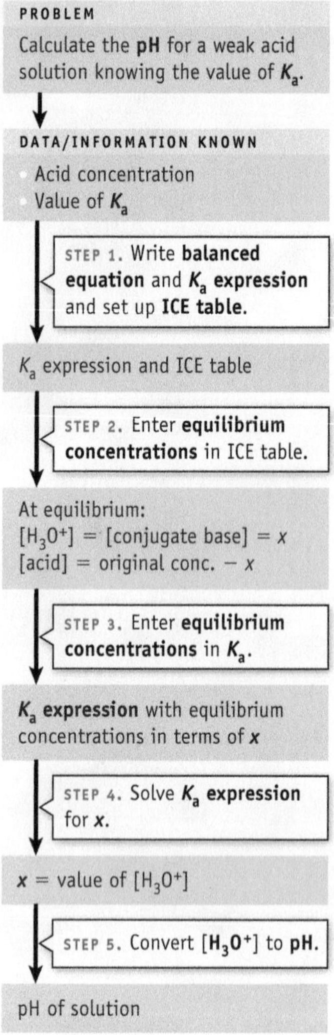

What Do You Know? You know the value of K_a for the acid and its initial concentration. You need to find the equilibrium concentration of H_3O^+ in order to calculate the pH.

Strategy This is similar to Examples 15.4 and 15.5, where you wanted to find the concentration of a reaction product. The strategy is the same:

- Write the equilibrium constant expression and set up an ICE table.
- Enter the initial concentration of $C_6H_5CO_2H$ on the initial (I) line of the ICE table.
- The variable x represents changes in concentration, so the change in $[C_6H_5CO_2H]$ is $-x$ and the change in product concentrations is $+x$. Enter these values in the change (C) line of the table.
- Enter the expressions for the final equilibrium concentrations of all three species on the E line of the ICE table, and then transfer these expressions to the equilibrium constant expression and solve for x.
- Convert $[H_3O^+]$ ($= x$) to pH.

Solution Organize the information in an ICE table.

EQUILIBRIUM	$C_6H_5CO_2H$	+ H_2O $\rightleftharpoons$	$C_6H_5CO_2^-$	+ H_3O^+
Initial (M)	0.020		0	0
Change (M)	$-x$		$+x$	$+x$
Equilibrium (M)	$(0.020 - x)$		x	x

According to reaction stoichiometry,

$$[H_3O^+] = [C_6H_5CO_2^-] = x \text{ at equilibrium}$$

the concentration of acid ionized is x. Thus, the benzoic acid concentration at equilibrium is

$$[C_6H_5CO_2H] = \text{initial acid concentration} - \text{concentration of acid that ionized}$$

$$[C_6H_5CO_2H] = 0.020 - x$$

Substituting these equilibrium concentrations into the K_a expression, we have

$$K_a = \frac{[H_3O^+][C_6H_5CO_2^-]}{[C_6H_5CO_2H]}$$

$$6.3 \times 10^{-5} = \frac{(x)(x)}{0.020 - x}$$

The value of x is small compared with 0.020 (because $[HA]_0 > 100 \times K_a$; $0.020\text{ M} > 6.3 \times 10^{-3}$). Therefore, you can use the approximate expression.

$$K_a = 6.3 \times 10^{-5} = \frac{x^2}{0.020}$$

Solving for x, we have

$$x = \sqrt{K_a \times (0.020)} = 0.0011\text{ M}$$

and we find that

$$[H_3O^+] = [C_6H_5CO_2^-] = 0.0011\text{ M}$$

Finally, the pH of the solution is found to be

$$\text{pH} = -\log(1.1 \times 10^{-3}) = \mathbf{2.96}$$

Think about Your Answer We made the approximation that $(0.020 - x) \approx 0.020$. If the approximation is not made and the exact expression is solved, $x = [H_3O^+] = 0.0011$ M. This is the same answer to two significant figures that we obtained from the "approximate" expression. Finally, notice that any H_3O^+ that arises from water ionization was again ignored.

Check Your Understanding

What are the equilibrium concentrations of acetic acid, the acetate ion, and H_3O^+ for a 0.10 M solution of acetic acid ($K_a = 1.8 \times 10^{-5}$)? What is the pH of the solution?

EXAMPLE 16.6

Calculating Equilibrium Concentrations and pH from K_a and Using the Method of Successive Approximations

Problem What is the pH of a 0.0010 M solution of formic acid? What is the concentration of formic acid at equilibrium? The acid is moderately weak, with $K_a = 1.8 \times 10^{-4}$.

$$HCO_2H(aq) + H_2O(\ell) \rightleftharpoons HCO_2^-(aq) + H_3O^+(aq)$$

What Do You Know? You know the value of K_a for the acid and its initial concentration. You need to find the equilibrium concentration of H_3O^+ in order to calculate the pH.

Strategy This is similar to Example 16.5, where you wanted to find the concentration of a reaction product, except that an approximate solution will not be possible. The strategy is the same:

- Write the equilibrium constant expression and set up an ICE table.
- Enter the initial concentration of HCO_2H on the initial (I) line of the ICE table.
- The variable x represents changes in concentration, so the change in $[HCO_2H]$ is $-x$ and the change in product concentrations is $+x$. Enter these values in the change (C) line of the table.
- Enter the expressions for the final equilibrium concentrations of all three species on the E line of the ICE table, and then transfer these expressions to the equilibrium constant expression and solve for x.
- Convert $[H_3O^+]$ ($= x$) to pH.

Solution The ICE table is as follows.

EQUILIBRIUM	HCO_2H	+	H_2O	$\rightleftharpoons$	HCO_2^-	+	H_3O^+
Initial (M)	0.0010				0		0
Change (M)	$-x$				$+x$		$+x$
Equilibrium (M)	$(0.0010 - x)$				x		x

Substituting the values in the table into the K_a expression we have

$$K_a = \frac{[H_3O^+][HCO_2^-]}{[HCO_2H]} = 1.8 \times 10^{-4} = \frac{(x)(x)}{0.0010 - x}$$

In this example, $[HA]_0$ ($= 0.0010$ M) is *not* greater than $100 \times K_a$ ($= 1.8 \times 10^{-2}$), so the usual approximation is not reasonable. Thus, we have to find the equilibrium concentrations by solving the "exact" expression. This can be solved with the quadratic formula or by successive approximations (Appendix A). Let us use the successive approximation method here.

To use the **successive approximations approach**, begin by solving the approximate expression for x.

$$1.8 \times 10^{-4} = \frac{(x)(x)}{0.0010}$$

Solving this, we find $x = 4.2 \times 10^{-4}$. Put this value into the expression for x in the denominator of the exact expression.

$$1.8 \times 10^{-4} = \frac{(x)(x)}{0.0010 - x} = \frac{(x)(x)}{0.0010 - 4.2 \times 10^{-4}}$$

Solving this equation for x, we now find $x = 3.2 \times 10^{-4}$. Again, put this value into the denominator, and solve for x.

$$1.8 \times 10^{-4} = \frac{(x)(x)}{0.0010 - x} = \frac{(x)(x)}{0.0010 - 3.2 \times 10^{-4}}$$

Continue this procedure until the value of x does not change from one cycle to the next. In this case, two more cycles give us the result that

$$x = [H_3O^+] = [HCO_2^-] = 3.4 \times 10^{-4}\ M$$

Thus,

$$[HCO_2H] = 0.0010 - x \approx 0.0007\ M$$

and the pH of the formic acid solution is

$$pH = -\log(3.4 \times 10^{-4}) = 3.47$$

Think about Your Answer If we had used the approximate expression to find the H_3O^+ concentration, we would have obtained a value of $[H_3O^+] = 4.2 \times 10^{-4}$ M. The simplifying assumption led to a large error, about 24%. The approximate solution fails in this case because (a) the acid concentration is small and (b) the acid is not all that weak.

Check Your Understanding

What are the equilibrium concentrations of HF, F^- ion, and H_3O^+ ion in a 0.00150 M solution of HF? What is the pH of the solution?

Just as acids can be molecular species or ions, so too can bases be ionic or molecular (Figures 16.3–16.5). Many molecular bases are based on nitrogen, with ammonia being the simplest. Many other nitrogen-containing bases occur naturally; caffeine and nicotine are well known, tetrodotoxin (see the introductory story for this chapter) is less well known. The anionic conjugate bases of weak acids make up another group of bases. The following example describes the calculation of the pH for a solution of sodium acetate.

EXAMPLE 16.7

The pH of a Solution of a Weakly Basic Salt, Sodium Acetate

Problem What is the pH of a 0.015 M solution of sodium acetate, $NaCH_3CO_2$?

What Do You Know? You know sodium acetate is basic in water because the acetate ion, the conjugate base of a weak acid, acetic acid, reacts with water to form OH^-

(Tables 16.2 and 16.3). (You also know that the sodium ion of sodium acetate does not affect the solution pH.) Finally, you know the value of K_b for the acetate ion (Table 16.2) and its initial concentration. You need to find the equilibrium concentration of H_3O^+ in order to calculate the pH.

Strategy This is similar to Examples 16.5 and 16.6, where you wanted to find the concentration of a reaction product.

- Write the balanced equation and the equilibrium constant expression, and set up an ICE table.
- Enter the initial concentration of $CH_3CO_2^-$ on the initial (I) line of the ICE table.
- The variable x represents changes in concentration, so the change in $[CH_3CO_2^-]$ is $-x$ and the change in product concentrations is $+x$. Enter these values in the change (C) line of the table.
- Enter the expressions for the equilibrium concentrations of all three species on the E line of the ICE table, and then transfer these to the equilibrium constant expression and solve for x.
- The value of $x = [OH^-]$. Determine $[H_3O^+]$ from this value using the expression $K_w = [H_3O^+][OH^-]$, then calculate pH from $[H_3O^+]$.

Solution The value of K_b for the acetate ion is 5.6×10^{-10} (Table 16.2).

$$CH_3CO_2^-(aq) + H_2O(\ell) \rightleftharpoons CH_3CO_2H(aq) + OH^-(aq)$$

Set up an ICE table to summarize the initial and equilibrium concentrations of the species in solution.

Equilibrium	$CH_3CO_2^-$	+	H_2O	$\rightleftharpoons$	CH_3CO_2H	+	OH^-
Initial (M)	0.015				0		0
Change (M)	$-x$				$+x$		$+x$
Equilibrium (M)	$(0.015 - x)$				x		x

Strategy Map 16.7

PROBLEM
Calculate the **pH** for a weak base knowing the value of K_b.

DATA/INFORMATION KNOWN
- Base concentration
- Value of K_b

STEP 1. Write **balanced equation** and K_b **expression** and set up **ICE table.**

K_b expression and ICE table

STEP 2. Enter **equilibrium concentrations** in ICE table.

At equilibrium:
$[OH^-]$ = [conjugate acid] = x
[base] = original conc. − x

STEP 3. Enter **equilibrium concentrations** in K_b.

K_b **expression** with equilibrium concentrations in terms of x

STEP 4. Solve K_b **expression** for x.

x = value of $[OH^-]$

STEP 5. Using $[OH^-]$ and K_w, calculate $[H_3O^+]$ and then **pH.**

pH of solution

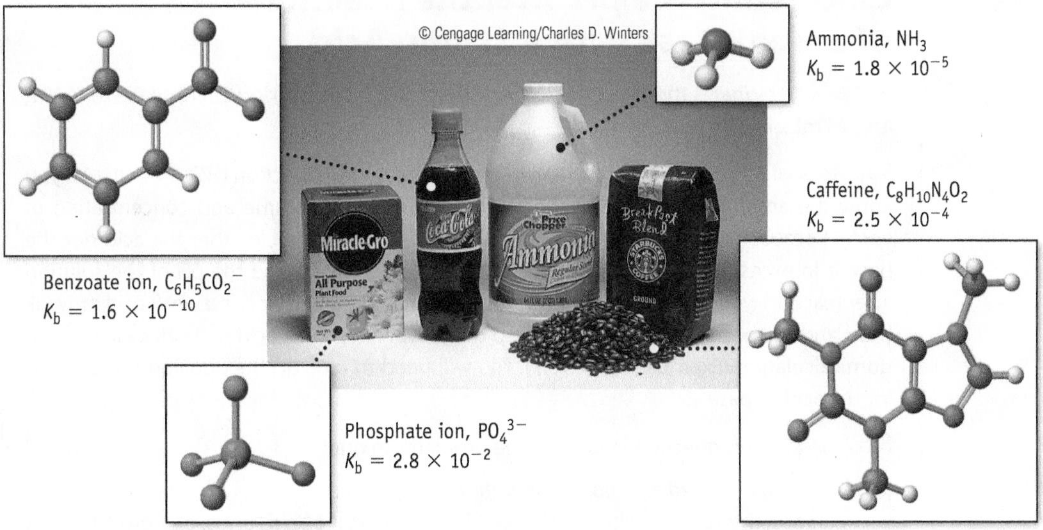

FIGURE 16.5 **Examples of weak bases.** Weak bases in water include molecules having one or more N atoms capable of accepting an H^+ ion and anions of weak acids such as benzoate and phosphate.

Next, substitute the values in the table into the K_b expression.

$$K_b = 5.6 \times 10^{-10} = \frac{[CH_3CO_2H][OH^-]}{[CH_3CO_2^-]} = \frac{x^2}{0.015 - x}$$

The acetate ion, a weak base, has a very small value of K_b. Therefore, we assume that x, the concentration of hydroxide ion generated by reaction of acetate ion with water, is very small, and we use the approximate expression to solve for x.

$$K_b = 5.6 \times 10^{-10} = \frac{x^2}{0.015}$$

$$x = [OH^-] = [CH_3CO_2H] = \sqrt{(5.6 \times 10^{-10})(0.015)} = 2.9 \times 10^{-6}\ M$$

To calculate the pH of the solution, we need the hydronium ion concentration. In aqueous solutions, it is always true that, at 25 °C,

$$K_w = 1.0 \times 10^{-14} = [H_3O^+][OH^-]$$

$$[H_3O^+] = \frac{K_w}{[OH^-]} = \frac{1.0 \times 10^{-14}}{2.9 \times 10^{-6}} = 3.5 \times 10^{-9}\ M$$

$$\text{Therefore, pH} = -\log(3.5 \times 10^{-9}) = 8.46$$

The acetate ion gives rise to a weakly basic solution as expected for the conjugate base of a weak acid.

Think about Your Answer The hydroxide ion concentration (x) is indeed quite small relative to the initial acetate ion concentration so the approximate expression is appropriate. (Note that $100 \times K_b$ is less than the initial base concentration.)

Check Your Understanding

The weak base, ClO^- (hypochlorite ion), is used in the form of NaClO as a disinfectant in swimming pools and water treatment plants. What are the concentrations of HClO and OH^- and the pH of a 0.015 M solution of NaClO?

EXAMPLE 16.8

Calculating the pH after the Reaction of a Weak Base with a Strong Acid

Problem What is the pH of the solution that results from mixing 25 mL of 0.016 M NH_3 and 25 mL of 0.016 M HCl?

What Do You Know? You know this is an acid–base reaction (HCl + NH_3), and you know the amount of each reactant (calculated from the volume and concentration of each). Because equal volumes and concentrations are involved, neither the acid nor the base is in excess, and none will remain after the reaction. To find the pH of the solution after reaction, you need to know the amount of product, whether it is a weak acid or weak base, and its concentration. The final step then involves a weak acid or weak base equilibrium calculation (Examples 16.5–16.7). You will need to look up the equilibrium constant for the acid or base.

Strategy This question involves three problems in one:

(a) *Writing a balanced equation:* First write a balanced equation for the reaction that occurs and then decide whether the reaction products are acids or bases. Here, the weak acid NH_4^+ is the product of interest.

(b) *Stoichiometry problem:* Finding the "initial" NH_4^+ concentration is a stoichiometry problem. The amount of NH_4^+ (in moles) produced in the HCl + NH_3 reaction is divided by the volume of the resulting solution.

(c) *Equilibrium problem:* Calculating the pH involves first solving an equilibrium problem. Needed for this calculation is the "initial" concentration of NH_4^+ from part (b) and the value of K_a for NH_4^+.

Solution If equal amounts (moles) of base (NH_3) and acid (HCl) are mixed, the result should be an acidic solution because the significant species remaining in solution upon completion of the reaction is NH_4^+, the conjugate acid of the weak base ammonia (see Tables 16.2 and 16.4).

(a) *Writing balanced equations*

The equation for the product-favored reaction of HCl (the supplier of hydronium ion) with NH_3 to give NH_4^+:

$$NH_3(aq) + H_3O^+(aq) \rightarrow NH_4^+(aq) + H_2O(\ell)$$

The equation for the reactant-favored reaction of NH_4^+, the product, with water:

$$NH_4^+(aq) + H_2O(\ell) \rightleftharpoons H_3O^+(aq) + NH_3(aq)$$

(b) *Stoichiometry problem*

Amount of HCl and NH_3 consumed:

$$(0.025 \text{ L HCl})(0.016 \text{ mol/L}) = 4.0 \times 10^{-4} \text{ mol HCl}$$

$$(0.025 \text{ L } NH_3)(0.016 \text{ mol/L}) = 4.0 \times 10^{-4} \text{ mol } NH_3$$

Amount of NH_4^+ produced upon completion of the reaction:

$$4.0 \times 10^{-4} \text{ mol } NH_3 \left(\frac{1 \text{ mol } NH_4^+}{1 \text{ mol } NH_3}\right) = 4.0 \times 10^{-4} \text{ mol } NH_4^+$$

Concentration of NH_4^+: Combining 25 mL each of HCl and NH_3 gives a total solution volume of 50. mL. Therefore, the concentration of NH_4^+ is

$$[NH_4^+] = \frac{4.0 \times 10^{-4} \text{ mol}}{0.050 \text{ L}} = 8.0 \times 10^{-3} \text{ M}$$

(c) *Acid–base equilibrium problem*

With the initial concentration of ammonium ion known, set up an ICE table to find the equilibrium concentration of hydronium ion.

EQUILIBRIUM	NH_4^+	+	H_2O	$\rightleftharpoons$	NH_3	+	H_3O^+
Initial (M)	0.0080				0		0
Change (M)	$-x$				$+x$		$+x$
Equilibrium (M)	$(0.0080 - x)$				x		x

Next, substitute the values in the table into the K_a expression for the ammonium ion. Thus, we have

$$K_a = 5.6 \times 10^{-10} = \frac{[H_3O^+][NH_3]}{[NH_4^+]} = \frac{(x)(x)}{0.0080 - x}$$

The ammonium ion is a very weak acid, as reflected by the very small value of K_a. Therefore, x, the concentration of hydronium ion generated by reaction of ammonium ion with water, is assumed to be very small, and the approximate expression is used to solve for x. (Here $100 \times K_a$ is much less than the original acid concentration.)

Strategy Map 16.8

PROBLEM

Calculate **pH** of solution after the reaction of a **weak base** and a **strong acid.**

DATA/INFORMATION KNOWN

- Reactant concentrations
- Reactant volumes

STEP 1. Write **balanced equation** and solve **stoichiometry problem.**

Know **amounts of reactants** and derive **amount of product.**

STEP 2. Decide if product is **weak acid** or **weak base.**

Product is a **weak acid (NH_4^+)**

STEP 3. Calculate concentration of **NH_4^+.**

Concentration of weak acid whose K_a is known.

STEP 4. Solve for **[H_3O^+]** as in Examples 16.5 - 16.7.

Value of [H_3O^+]

STEP 5. Convert **[H_3O^+]** to **pH.**

pH of solution

$$K_a = 5.6 \times 10^{-10} = \frac{x^2}{0.0080}$$

$$x = \sqrt{(5.6 \times 10^{-10})(0.0080)}$$

$$= [H_3O^+] = [NH_3] = 2.1 \times 10^{-6}\ M$$

$$pH = -\log(2.1 \times 10^{-6}) = 5.67$$

Think about Your Answer As predicted (Table 16.4), the solution after mixing equal amounts of a strong acid and weak base is weakly acidic.

Check Your Understanding

Calculate the pH after mixing 15 mL of 0.12 M acetic acid with 15 mL of 0.12 M NaOH. What are the major species in solution at equilibrium (besides water), and what are their concentrations?

CASE STUDY Would You Like Some Belladonna Juice in Your Drink?

The belladonna plant produces black, cherry-sized berries that look good enough to eat. But you should think twice because the plant is also called *deadly nightshade.* The berries contain atropine, a base, which is toxic and has been used by women and men for centuries to eliminate old lovers and political enemies.

The name for the plant, *belladonna*, comes from the Italian meaning "beautiful woman." Courtesans and actresses in Venice in the 16th century would put a drop or two of the juice in their eyes. It would dilate the pupils and give them a "fashionable, doe-like" appearance that could last several days.

Atropine was used for some years by physicians to dilate the eye, and it is used to treat such conditions as bradycardia, an extremely low heart rate. It is also an antidote for sarin, a nerve gas. In fact, victims of a sarin gas attack in Japan in the 1990s were treated with atropine, and soldiers in the first Gulf War in 1990–1991 carried atropine as an antidote in the event of a nerve gas attack.

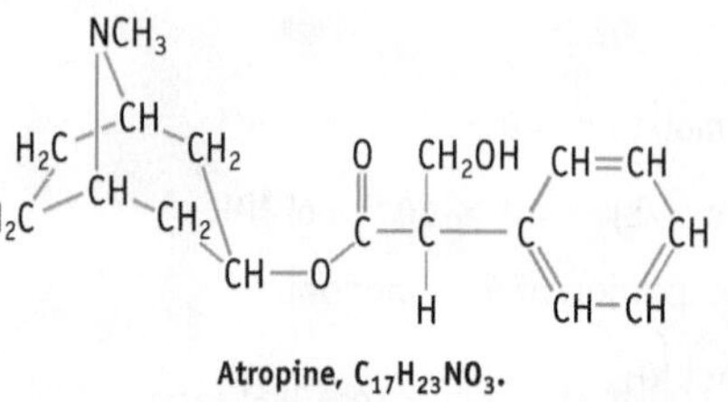

Atropine, $C_{17}H_{23}NO_3$.

© WILDLIFE GmbH/Alamy

Berries of the belladonna plant, a source of atropine

But atropine is mostly remembered in history as a poison. A fatal dose is around 100 mg. One legend is that Cleopatra at first wanted to commit suicide by taking atropine. She had a slave try it first, but the slave's death was not pleasant, so she opted for the bite of an asp, a deadly snake.

At the height of the Roman Empire, atropine and other agents were so often used as poisons that a law was passed in 82 BC to "suppress domestic poisoning." It apparently had little effect.

The symptoms of atropine poisoning are well known. Physicians say the patient is "red as a beet" because the blood vessels dilate. Or you can be "blind as a bat" because the pupils are so dilated that vision is blurred. "Dry as a bone" is another symptom arising from the suppression of the salivary glands. In addition, you can be "hot as a hare" because your body temperature goes up and stays up for some hours. Finally, you can be "mad as a hatter" (like the hatter in *Alice in Wonderland*) because you act like a drunk person.

Atropine is not very soluble in water. However, because atropine is a base it reacts with acids. For example, reaction with sulfuric acid forms the sulfate salt. This salt is so soluble that 1 mL of a saturated solution of this compound contains many times the amount needed for a fatal dose.

If you are interested in the history of atropine as a murder weapon, be sure to read about the attempted murder of Alexandra Agutter by her husband in Scotland in the 1990s. Just like an episode of *CSI*!

Questions:

1. If a fatal dose of atropine is 100. mg, what amount of compound (moles) is this?
2. When atropine is added to sulfuric acid, a proton attaches to the molecule. What is the site of attachment?
3. The pK_a of the conjugate acid of atropine is 4.35. How does this compare with the pK_a values for the conjugate acids of ammonia, methylamine, and aniline?

Answers to these questions are available in Appendix N.

Reference:

J. Emsley, *Molecules of Murder*, Royal Society of Chemistry, London, 2008.

PROBLEM SOLVING TIP 16.3

What Is the pH After Mixing Equal Numbers of Moles of an Acid and a Base

Table 16.4 summarizes the outcome of mixing various types of acids and bases. But how do you calculate a numerical value for the pH, particularly in the case of mixing a weak acid with a strong base or a weak base with a strong acid? The strategy (Example 16.8) is to recognize that this involves two calculations: a stoichiometry calculation and an equilibrium calculation. The key is that you need to know the concentration of the weak acid or weak base produced when the acid and base are mixed. Answering the following questions will guide you to an answer:

(a) What amounts of acid and base are used (in moles)? (This is a stoichiometry problem.)

(b) What is the total volume of the solution after mixing the acid and base solutions?

(c) What is the concentration of the weak acid or base produced on mixing the acid and base solutions?

(d) Using the concentration found in Step (c), what is the hydronium ion concentration in the solution? (This is an equilibrium problem.) Determine the pH from the hydronium ion concentration.

REVIEW & CHECK FOR SECTION 16-7

1. What is $[H_3O^+]$ in a 0.10 M solution of HCN at 25 °C? (K_a for HCN $= 4.0 \times 10^{-10}$)

   (a) 1.6×10^{-9} M
   (b) 6.3×10^{-6} M
   (c) 2.0×10^{-5} M
   (d) 4.0×10^{-11} M

2. A 0.040 M solution of an acid, HA, has a pH of 3.02 at 25 °C. What is K_a for this acid?

   (a) 2.3×10^{-5}
   (b) 5.7×10^{-4}
   (c) 2.4×10^{-2}
   (d) 4.3×10^{-10}

3. What are the pH and ion concentrations in a solution of 0.10 M sodium formate, $NaCHO_2$? K_b for the formate ion, HCO_2^- is 5.6×10^{-11}.

	pH	$[Na^+]$	$[CHO_2^-]$	$[OH^-]$
(a)	5.63	0.10	0.10	2.4×10^{-6}
(b)	8.37	0.10	0.10	2.4×10^{-6}
(c)	8.22	0.050	0.050	1.7×10^{-6}
(d)	5.63	0.10	0.10	4.2×10^{-9}

4. You mix 0.40 g of NaOH with 100 mL of 0.10 M acetic acid. What is the pH of the resulting solution?

   (a) less than 7
   (b) equal to 7
   (c) greater than 7

16-8 Polyprotic Acids and Bases

Learning Objectives: LO 6.17

Because polyprotic acids are capable of donating more than one proton, they present us with additional challenges when predicting the pH of their solutions. For many inorganic polyprotic acids, such as phosphoric acid, carbonic acid, and hydrosulfuric acid (H_2S), the ionization constant for each successive loss of a proton is about 10^4 to 10^6 smaller than the previous ionization step. This means that the first ionization step of a polyprotic acid produces up to about a million times more H_3O^+

ions than the second step. For this reason, *the pH of many inorganic polyprotic acids depends primarily on the hydronium ion generated in the first ionization step; the hydronium ion produced in the second step can be neglected.* The same principle applies to the fully deprotonated conjugate bases of polyprotic acids. This is illustrated by the calculation of the pH of a solution of carbonate ion, an important base in our environment (Example 16.9).

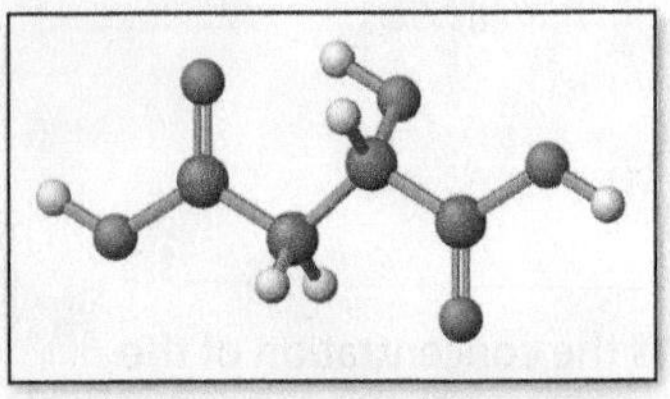

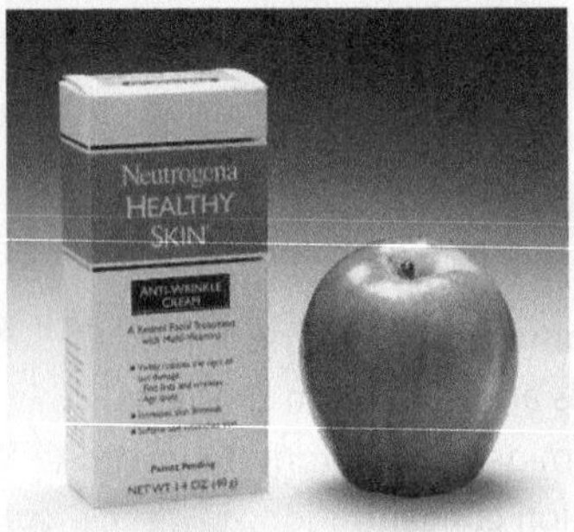

A polyprotic acid. Malic acid, $C_4H_4O_4$, is a diprotic acid occurring in apples. It is also classified as an alpha-hydroxy acid because it has an OH group on the C atom next to the CO_2H (in the alpha position). It is one of a large group of natural alpha-hydroxy acids such as lactic acid, citric acid, and ascorbic acid. Alpha-hydroxy acids have been touted as an ingredient in "anti-aging" skin creams. They work by accelerating the natural process by which skin replaces the outer layer of cells with new cells.

EXAMPLE 16.9

Calculating the pH of the Solution of a Polyprotic Base

Problem The carbonate ion, CO_3^{2-}, is a base in water, forming the hydrogen carbonate ion, which in turn can form carbonic acid.

$$CO_3^{2-}(aq) + H_2O(\ell) \rightleftharpoons HCO_3^-(aq) + OH^-(aq) \qquad K_{b1} = 2.1 \times 10^{-4}$$

$$HCO_3^-(aq) + H_2O(\ell) \rightleftharpoons H_2CO_3(aq) + OH^-(aq) \qquad K_{b2} = 2.4 \times 10^{-8}$$

What is the pH of a 0.10 M solution of Na_2CO_3?

What Do You Know? You know the balanced equations and the values of K_b for the ions as well as the concentration of the carbonate ion.

Strategy The first ionization constant, K_{b1}, is much larger than the second, K_{b2}, so the hydroxide ion concentration in the solution results almost entirely from the first step. Therefore, you can calculate the OH^- concentration produced by considering only the first ionization step, but we will want to test the conclusion that OH^- produced in the second step is negligible.

Solution Set up an ICE table for the reaction of the carbonate ion (Equilibrium Table 1).

Equilibrium Table 1—Reaction of CO_3^{2-} Ion

EQUILIBRIUM	CO_3^{2-}	+	H_2O	$\rightleftharpoons$	HCO_3^-	+	OH^-
Initial (M)	0.10				0		0
Change	$-x$				$+x$		$+x$
Equilibrium (M)	$(0.10 - x)$				x		x

Based on this table, the equilibrium concentration of OH^- ($= x$) can then be calculated.

$$K_{b1} = 2.1 \times 10^{-4} = \frac{[HCO_3^-][OH^-]}{[CO_3^{2-}]} = \frac{x^2}{0.10 - x}$$

Because K_{b1} is relatively small, it is reasonable to make the approximation that $(0.10 - x) \approx 0.10$. Therefore,

$$x = [HCO_3^-] = [OH^-] = \sqrt{(2.1 \times 10^{-4})(0.10)} = 4.6 \times 10^{-3}\ M$$

Using this value of $[OH^-]$, you can calculate the pOH of the solution,

$$pOH = -\log(4.6 \times 10^{-3}) = 2.34$$

and then use the relationship pH + pOH = 14 to calculate the pH.

$$pH = 14 - pOH = 11.66$$

Finally, you can conclude that the concentration of the carbonate ion is, to a good approximation, 0.10 M.

$$[CO_3^{2-}] = 0.10 - 0.0046 \approx 0.10\ M$$

The HCO_3^- ion produced in the first step could acquire another proton to give H_2CO_3 and this could affect the pH. But does this occur to a meaningful extent? To test this, set up a second ICE Table.

Equilibrium Table 2—Reaction of HCO_3^- Ion

EQUILIBRIUM	HCO_3^-	+ $H_2O \rightleftharpoons$	H_2CO_3	+	OH^-
Initial (M)	4.6×10^{-3}		0		4.6×10^{-3}
Change (M)	$-y$		$+y$		$+y$
Equilibrium (M)	$(4.6 \times 10^{-3} - y)$		y		$(4.6 \times 10^{-3} + y)$

Because K_{b2} is so small, the second step occurs to a much smaller extent than the first step. This means the amount of H_2CO_3 and OH^- produced in the second step ($= y$) is much smaller than 4.6×10^{-3} M. Therefore, it is reasonable that both $[HCO_3^-]$ and $[OH^-]$ are very close to 4.6×10^{-3} M.

$$K_{b2} = 2.4 \times 10^{-8} = \frac{[H_2CO_3][OH^-]}{[HCO_3^-]} = \frac{(y)(4.6 \times 10^{-3})}{4.6 \times 10^{-3}}$$

Because $[HCO_3^-]$ and $[OH^-]$ have nearly identical values, they cancel from the expression, and we find that $[H_2CO_3]$ is simply equal to K_{b2}.

$$y = [H_2CO_3] = K_{b2} = 2.4 \times 10^{-8}\ M$$

The amount of OH^- produced in this reaction is negligible. The hydroxide ion is essentially all produced in the first equilibrium process.

Think about Your Answer It is almost always the case that the pH of a solution of an inorganic polyprotic acid is due to the hydronium ion generated in the first ionization step. Similarly, the pH of a polyprotic base is due to the OH^- ion produced in the first hydrolysis step.

Check Your Understanding

What is the pH of a 0.10 M solution of oxalic acid, $H_2C_2O_4$? What are the concentrations of H_3O^+, $HC_2O_4^-$, and the oxalate ion, $C_2O_4^{2-}$? (See Appendix H for K_a values.)

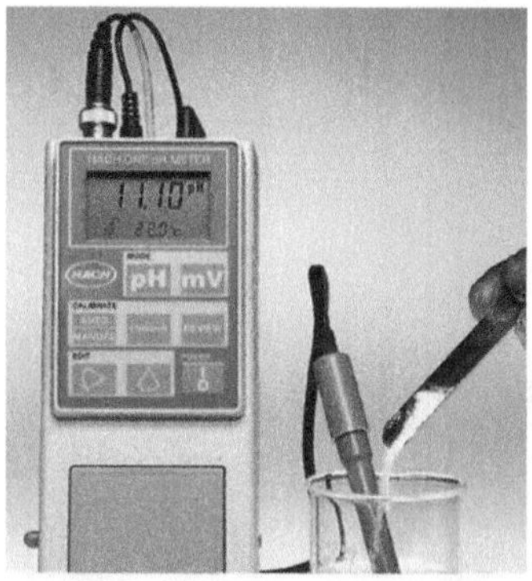

© Cengage Learning/Charles D. Winters

Sodium carbonate, a polyprotic base. This common substance is a base in aqueous solution. Its primary use is in the glass industry. Although it used to be manufactured, it is now mined as the mineral trona, $Na_2CO_3 \cdot NaHCO_3 \cdot 2\,H_2O$.

REVIEW & CHECK FOR SECTION 16-8

1. Hydrazine (N_2H_4) is like CO_3^{2-} in that it is a polyprotic base ($K_{b1} = 8.5 \times 10^{-7}$ and $K_{b2} = 8.9 \times 10^{-16}$). The two conjugate acids are $N_2H_5^+$ and $N_2H_6^{2+}$. What is the expected pH of a 0.025 M solution of N_2H_4?

   (a) 3.83 (b) 8.32 (c) 10.16

16-9 Molecular Structure, Bonding, and Acid–Base Behavior

Learning Objectives: LO 2.2

One of the most interesting aspects of chemistry is the correlation between a molecule's structure and bonding and its chemical properties. Because acids and bases play such a key role in chemistry, it is especially useful to see if there are some general principles governing acid–base behavior.

Acid Strength of the Hydrogen Halides, HX

Aqueous HF is a weak Brønsted acid in water, whereas the other hydrohalic acids—aqueous HCl, HBr, and HI—are all strong acids. Experiments show that the acid strength increases in the order HF << HCl < HBr < HI. A detailed analysis of the

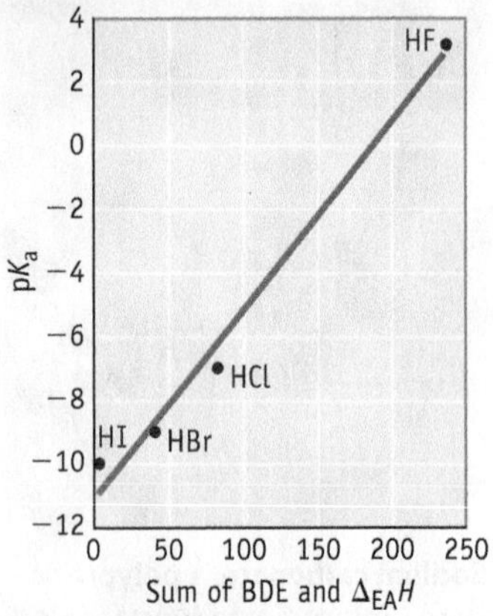

FIGURE 16.6 The effect of H—X bond enthalpy and X electron attachment enthalpy on acid strength. Stronger acids have weaker H—X bonds and X atoms with more negative electron attachment enthalpies. (BDE is the bond dissociation enthalpy of the H—X bond, and $\Delta_{EA}H$ is the electron attachment enthalpy of the halogen atom.) See M. Moran, *Journal of Chemical Education,* Vol. 83, pp. 800–803, 2006.

factors that lead to these differences in acid strength in this group is informative (see *A Closer Look: Acid Strengths and Molecular Structure*). Predictions about relative acid strength can be made based on the sum of two energy quantities, the energy required to break the H—X bond (the bond dissociation enthalpy) and the electron attachment enthalpy of the halogen. That is, when a hydrohalic acid HX ionizes in water,

$$HX(aq) + H_2O(\ell) \rightarrow H_3O^+(aq) + X^-(aq)$$

the sum of the two energy terms

$$\text{Change in energy} \propto \text{HX bond dissociation enthalpy} + \text{electron attachment enthalpy of X}$$

correlates with acid strength. Stronger acids should result when the H—X bond is more easily broken (as signaled by a smaller, positive value of ΔH for bond dissociation) and when there is a more negative value for the electron attachment enthalpy of X.

The bond dissociation enthalpy and electron attachment enthalpy effects can work together (a weak H—X bond and a large, negative electron attachment enthalpy of the X group) to produce a strong acid, but they can also work in opposite directions. The balance of the two effects is important. Let us examine some data for the Group 7A binary acids, HX.

Increasing acid strength →

	HF	HCl	HBr	HI
pK_a	+3.14	−7	−9	−10
H—X bond strength (kJ/mol)	565	432	366	299
Electron attachment enthalpy of *X* (kJ/mol)	−328	−349	−325	−295
Sum (kJ/mol)	237	83	41	4

In this series of acids, the bond enthalpy factor dominates: the weakest acid, HF, has the strongest H—X bond, and the strongest acid, HI, has the weakest H—X bond. However, the electron attachment enthalpy of X is most negative with Cl, less so with F and Br, and much less so with I. A less negative electron attachment enthalpy should lead to a weaker acid, but it is the *sum* of the two effects that leads to the observation that HI is the strongest acid. In Figure 16.6 you see there is a good correlation between an acid's pK_a and the *sum* of the enthalpies for bond dissociation and electron attachment enthalpy.

Table 16.5 Oxoacids

Acid	pK_a
Cl-Based Oxoacids	
HOCl	7.46
HOClO ($HClO_2$)	~2
$HOClO_2$ ($HClO_3$)	~ −3
$HOClO_3$ ($HClO_4$)	~ −8
S-Based Oxoacids	
$(HO)_2SO$ [H_2SO_3]	1.92, 7.21
$(HO)_2SO_2$ [H_2SO_4]	~ −3, 1.92

Linus Pauling stated the general relationship that, for oxoacids with the general formula $(HO)_nE(O)_m$, the value of pK_a is about 8–5*m*. When $n > 1$, the pK_a increases by about 5 for each successive loss of a proton.

Comparing Oxoacids: HNO_2 and HNO_3

Nitrous acid (HNO_2) and nitric acid (HNO_3) are representative of several series of **oxoacids.** Oxoacids contain an atom (usually a nonmetal atom) bonded to one or more oxygen atoms, some with hydrogen atoms attached. Besides those based on N, you are familiar with the sulfur- and chlorine-based oxoacids (Table 16.5). In all these series of related compounds, the acid strength increases as the number of oxygen atoms bonded to the central element increases. Thus, nitric acid (HNO_3) is a stronger acid than nitrous acid (HNO_2).

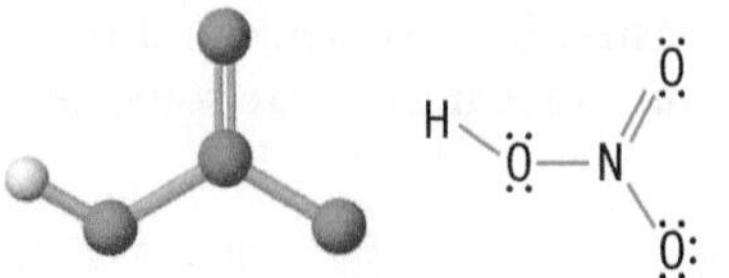

HNO_3, strong acid, $pK_a = -1.4$

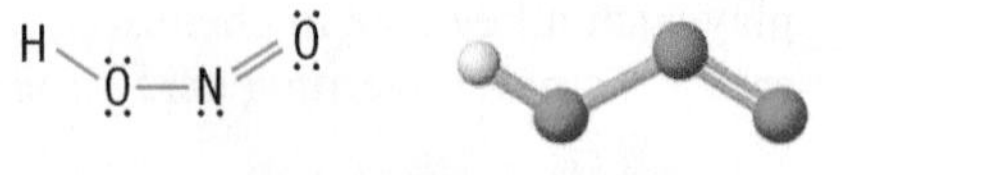

HNO_2, weak acid, $pK_a = +3.35$

A CLOSER LOOK Acid Strengths and Molecular Structure

Although predictions about acid strength in aqueous solution are fairly simple to make, a complete explanation can be complicated. When evaluating the strength of an acid HX(aq), we are looking at the following reaction:

$$HX(aq) + H_2O(\ell) \rightleftharpoons H_3O^+(aq) + X^-(aq)$$

Acid strength is sometimes correlated with the strength and the polarity of the H—X bond, readily identifiable characteristics derived from the structure of the acid. To fully explain the extent of ionization, we must also consider characteristics of the conjugate base of the acid, X^-. The ability of the anion to spread out the negative charge across the ion and the solvation of the anion by the solvent are among the issues that also have some relevance in an explanation of the strength of the acid.

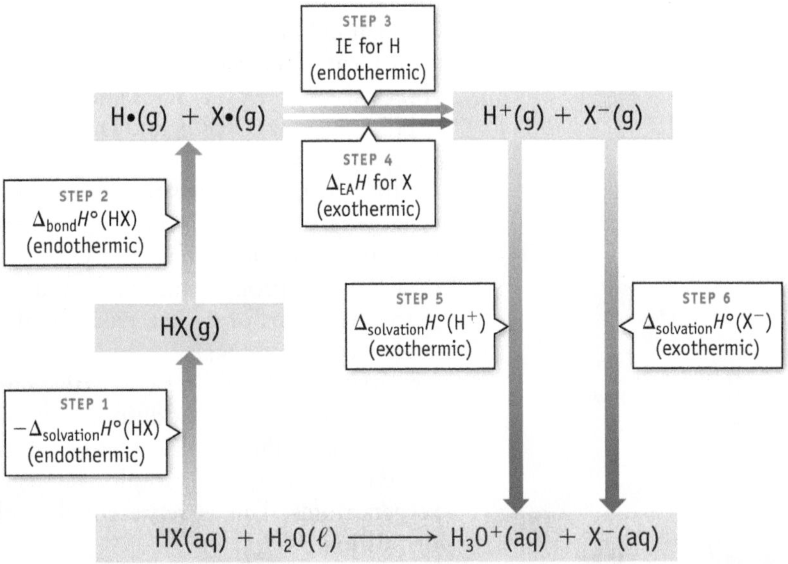

How enthalpy changes contribute to acid strength can be assessed using a thermochemical cycle (such as the one used to evaluate a lattice enthalpy, ◀ Section 12-3). Consider the relative acid strengths of the hydrogen halides. The enthalpy change for the ionization of an acid in water can be related to other enthalpy changes as shown in the diagram. The ionization energy (Step 3) and the solvation of H^+ (Step 5) are common to all of the hydrogen halides and therefore do not contribute to the differences among their enthalpies for ionization, but the four remaining terms are different. For the hydrogen halides, the bond dissociation enthalpy (Step 2) of HF is much larger than the bond dissociation enthalpies of the other hydrogen halides and contributes significantly to the reason why HF is a weak acid whereas the others are strong acids. However, it is compensated for significantly by the enthalpy of solvation of the anion (Step 6), which for the fluoride ion is much more exothermic than the solvation energies of the other halide ions. The electron attachment enthalpy (Step 4) is also a contributor to the differences in overall enthalpy changes; their values vary among the halogens, but to a smaller extent than the variation in bond energy and the enthalpy of solvation of the halide ion. Differences in solvation energy for the molecular species (Step 1) are minimal.

We noted earlier (◀ Section 13-2) that entropy plays an important role in solution chemistry. It should not be surprising then that entropy also has a role in determining acid strength. Indeed, differences in entropy changes are significant in accounting for the differences in acid strength of the hydrogen halides. Entropy has yet to be discussed in this text in detail (▶ Chapter 18) but a complete analysis of strengths of acids in aqueous solution will include consideration of both enthalpies and entropies.

Although all of these terms contribute to acid strength, it can often be correlated with a subset of this information, as can be seen by the examples presented in this section. Correlations, however, while sometimes highly useful to a chemist because they can be used to make important predictions, are at best only partial explanations.

Let's apply the bond enthalpy/electron attachment enthalpy analysis to HNO_3 and HNO_2.

Increasing acid strength ⟶	**HNO_2**	**HNO_3**
pK_a	+3.35	−1.4
H—O bond strength (kJ/mol)	328	423
Electron attachment enthalpy of X (kJ/mol)	−219	−377
Sum (kJ/mol)	109	46

As in the case of the Group 7A acids, we again see that acid strength correlates with the sum of the enthalpies for bond breaking and X group (NO_2 or NO_3) electron attachment enthalpy.

Analysis of the Group 7A acids showed that the H—X bond strength was the more important factor; as the H—X bond became weaker, the acid became stronger. However, the data for HNO_3 and HNO_2 show this is not true here. The O—H bond is stronger in the stronger acid HNO_3. Instead, the electron attachment term is the more important term in this correlation. These same effects are observed for other oxyacids such as the chlorine-based oxoacids HOCl < HOClO < $HOClO_2$ < $HOClO_3$ and the S-based oxoacids (Table 16.5). How is this to be interpreted?

In HNO_3, there are two other oxygen atoms bonded to the central nitrogen atom, whereas in HNO_2 only one other oxygen is bonded to the nitrogen atom. By attaching more electronegative O atoms to nitrogen, we are increasing the electron affinity of the group attached to hydrogen, and anything that increases the affinity of the X group for an electron should also make HX a stronger acid and X^- a weaker conjugate base. This is another way of saying that if X^- has a way to accommodate and stabilize a negative charge, it will be a weaker conjugate base. In the case of oxoacids, additional oxygen atoms have the effect of stabilizing the anion because the negative charge on the anion can be dispersed over more atoms. In the nitrate ion, for example, the negative charge is shared equally over the three oxygen atoms. This is represented symbolically by the three resonance structures for this ion.

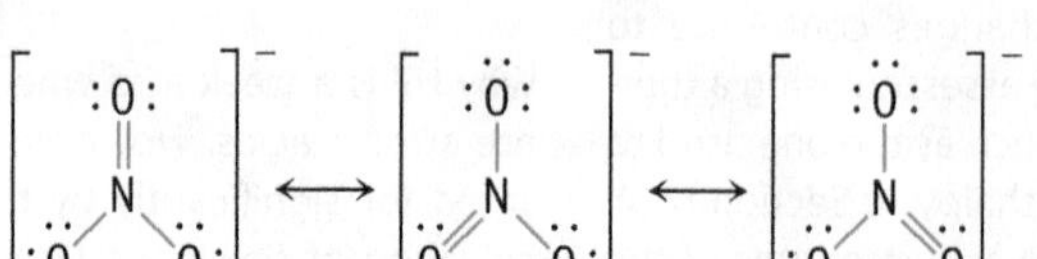

In nitrite ion, only two atoms share the negative charge. Therefore, NO_2^- is a stronger conjugate base than NO_3^-. *In general, greater stabilization of the products formed by ionizing the acid contributes to increased acidity.*

It is also found that in a series of related acids, the larger the formal charge on the central atom, the stronger the acid and the weaker the conjugate base. For example, the N atom formal charge in the weak acid HNO_2 is 0, whereas it is +1 in the strong acid HNO_3, and these are reflected by the results of theoretical calculations cited in Figure 16.7. In oxoacids, the formal charge on the central atom increases as the number of oxygen atom attached to the central atom increases. The results are shown below for two pairs of oxoacids.

	Central Atom Formal Charge	pK_a
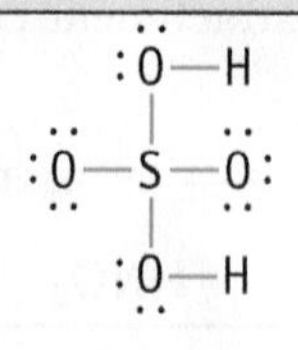	+2	−3
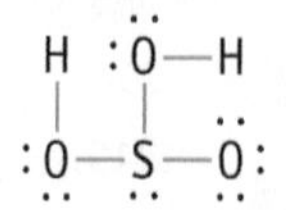	+1	1.92
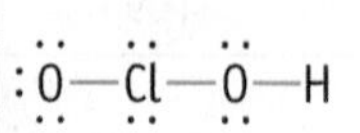	+1	2
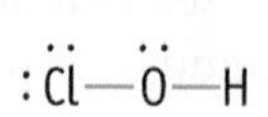	0	7.46

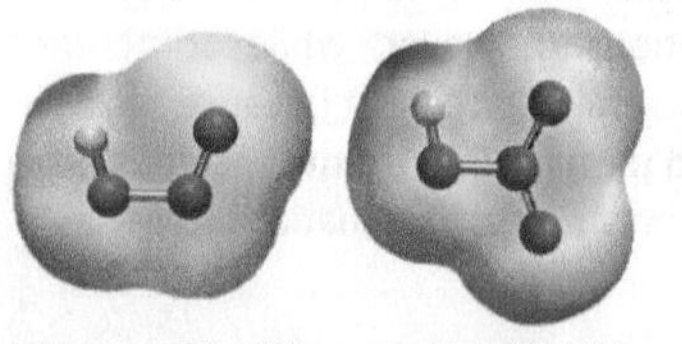

FIGURE 16.7 Electrostatic potential surfaces for the nitrogen oxoacids. Both surfaces show the O—H bond is quite polar. More importantly, calculations show that the OH bond becomes more polar as more O atoms are added to N.

Partial Charges

Molecule	H Atom	O Atom of OH	N Atom
HNO_2	+0.39	−0.35	+0.14
HNO_3	+0.41	−0.47	+0.76

In summary, molecules such as the oxoacids can behave as stronger Brønsted acids when the anion created by loss of H^+ is better able to accommodate the negative charge. These conditions are promoted by

- the presence of electronegative atoms attached to the central atom.
- the possibility of resonance structures for the anion, which lead to delocalization of the negative charge over the anion and thus to a more stable ion.
- greater positive formal charge of the central atom.

FIGURE 16.8 Electrostatic potential surface and partial charges for acetic acid. The H atoms of the molecule are all positively charged, but the H atom of the OH is much more highly charged. As expected, both of the electronegative O atoms have a partial negative charge.

Atom or Group	Calculated Partial Charge
H of OH	+0.43
O of OH	−0.62
H of CH_3	+0.23

Why Are Carboxylic Acids Brønsted Acids?

There is a large class of organic acids, typified by acetic acid (CH_3CO_2H) (Figure 16.8), called *carboxylic acids* because all have the carboxylic acid group, $—CO_2H$ (▶ Section 23-4). The arguments used to explain the acidity of oxoacids can also be applied to carboxylic acids. The O—H bond in these compounds is polar, a prerequisite for ionization.

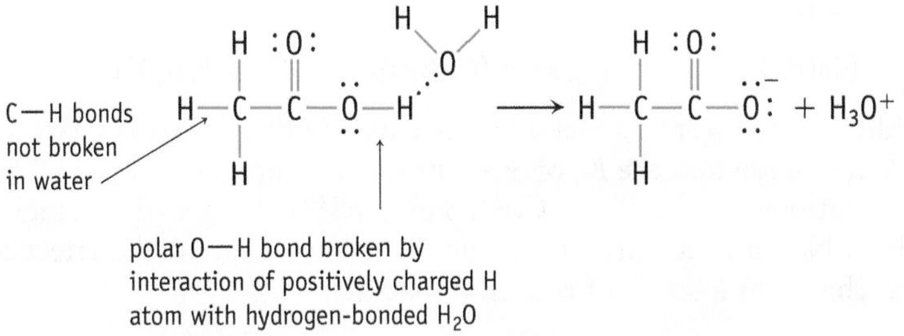

In addition, carboxylate anions are stabilized by delocalizing the negative charge over the two oxygen atoms.

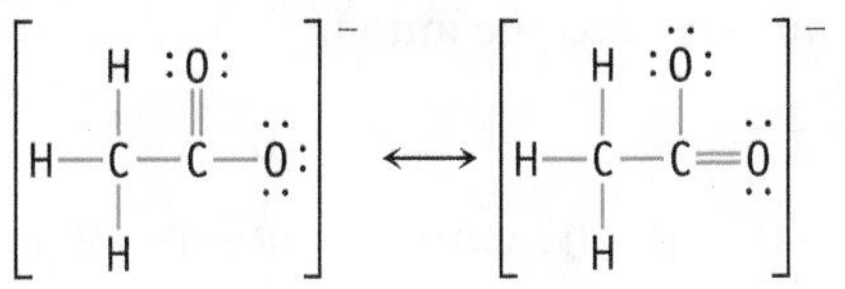

The simple carboxylic acids, RCO_2H in which R is a hydrocarbon group, do not differ markedly in acid strength (compare acetic acid, $pK_a = 4.74$, and propanoic acid, $pK_a = 4.89$, Table 16.2). The acidity of carboxylic acids is enhanced, however, if electronegative substituents replace the hydrogens in the alkyl ($—CH_3$ or $—C_2H_5$) group. Compare, for example, the pK_a values of a series of acetic acids in which hydrogen is replaced sequentially by the more electronegative element chlorine.

Acid		pK_a Value	
CH_3CO_2H	Acetic acid	4.74	Increasing acid strength ↓
$ClCH_2CO_2H$	Chloroacetic acid	2.85	
Cl_2CHCO_2H	Dichloroacetic acid	1.49	
Cl_3CCO_2H	Trichloroacetic acid	0.7	

As in the nitrogen oxoacids, increasingly electronegative substituents lead to an increase in acid strength. One argument is that electronegative substituents stabilize the negative charge of the anion. That is, the $Cl_3CCO_2^-$ anion is more stable than the $H_3CCO_2^-$ anion, so the formation of $Cl_3CCO_2^-$ is more favored than the formation of $CH_3CO_2^-$. Thus, the $Cl_3CCO_2^-$ anion is a weaker base than the $CH_3CO_2^-$ anion.

Finally, why are the C—H hydrogens of carboxylic acids not dissociated as H^+ instead of (or in addition to) the O—H hydrogen atom? The calculated partial positive charges listed in Figure 16.8 show that the H atoms of the CH_3 group have a much smaller positive partial charge than the O—H hydrogen atom. Furthermore, in carboxylic acids, the C atom of the CH_3 group is not sufficiently electronegative to accommodate the negative charge left if the bond breaks as C—H → C:$^-$ + H^+, and the product anion is not well stabilized.

Why Are Hydrated Metal Cations Brønsted Acids?

Polarization of O—H Bonds Water molecules attached to a metal cation have strongly polarized O—H bonds.

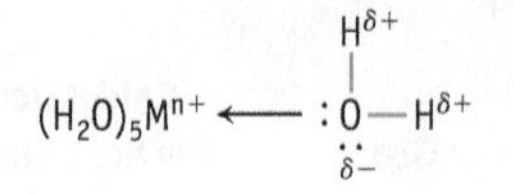

When a coordinate covalent bond is formed between a metal cation and a water molecule, the positive charge of the metal ion and its small size means that the electrons of the $H_2O \rightarrow M^{n+}$ bond are very strongly attracted to the metal (Section 16-10). As a result, the O—H bonds of the bound water molecules are polarized, just as in oxoacids and carboxylic acids. The net effect is that a hydrogen atom of a coordinated water molecule is removed as H^+ more readily than in an uncoordinated water molecule. Thus, a hydrated metal cation functions as a Brønsted acid or proton donor.

$$[Cu(H_2O)_6]^{2+} + H_2O(\ell) \rightleftharpoons [Cu(H_2O)_5(OH)]^+(aq) + H_3O^+(aq)$$

The acidity of the hydrated metal ion increases with increasing charge. Consulting Table 16.2, you see that the K_a of +3 ions (for example Al^{3+} and Fe^{3+}) is greater than for +2 cations (Cu^{2+}, Pb^{2+}, Co^{2+}, Fe^{2+}, Ni^{2+}). Ions with a single positive charge such as Na^+ and K^+ are not acidic. (This is similar to the effect of central atom formal charge in a series of related oxoacids.)

Why Are Anions Brønsted Bases?

Anions, particularly oxoanions such as PO_4^{3-}, are Brønsted bases. The negatively charged anion interacts with the positively charged H atom of a polar water molecule, and an H^+ ion is transferred to the anion.

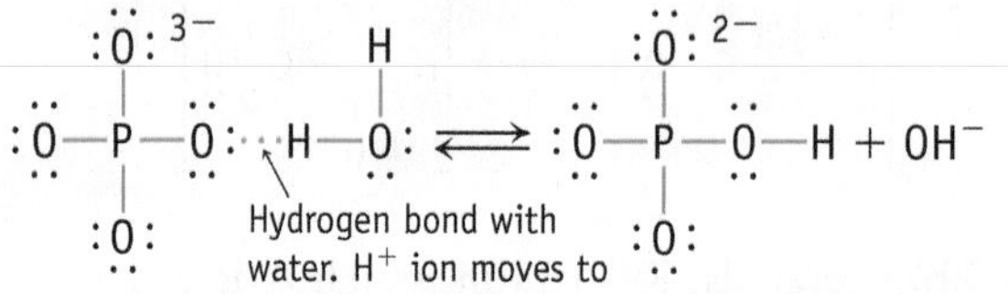

The data in Table 16.6 show that, in a series of related anions, the basicity of an anionic base increases as the negative charge of the anion increases.

Table 16.6 Basic Oxoanions

ANION	pK_b
PO_4^{3-}	1.55
HPO_4^{2-}	6.80
$H_2PO_4^-$	11.89
CO_3^{2-}	3.68
HCO_3^-	7.62
SO_3^{2-}	6.80
HSO_3^-	12.08

REVIEW & CHECK FOR SECTION 16-9

1. Which of the following is the stronger acid?

   (a) H_2SeO_4 (b) H_2SeO_3

2. Which of the following should be the stronger acid?

   (a) $[Fe(H_2O)_6]^{2+}$ (b) $[Fe(H_2O)_6]^{3+}$

3. Which of the following should be the stronger acid?

   (a) HOCl (b) HOBr

16-10 The Lewis Concept of Acids and Bases

The concept of acid–base behavior advanced by Brønsted and Lowry in the 1920s works well for reactions involving proton transfer. However, a more general acid–base concept was developed by Gilbert N. Lewis in the 1930s (◀ Section 8-2). This concept is based on the sharing of electrons pairs between an acid and a base.

> A **Lewis acid** is a substance that can accept a pair of electrons from another atom to form a new bond, and a **Lewis base** is a substance that can donate a pair of electrons to another atom to form a new bond.

The product of a Lewis acid–base reaction is called an **acid–base adduct.**

$$\underset{\text{acid}}{A} + \underset{\text{base}}{B:} \rightarrow \underset{\text{adduct}}{B{\rightarrow}A}$$

In Section 8-5, this type of chemical bond was called a *coordinate covalent bond.*

All Brønsted–Lowry acid–base reactions can be characterized as Lewis acid–base reactions. Formation of a hydronium ion from H^+ and water, and the formation of the ammonium ion from H^+ and ammonia, are good examples of a Lewis acid–base reaction.

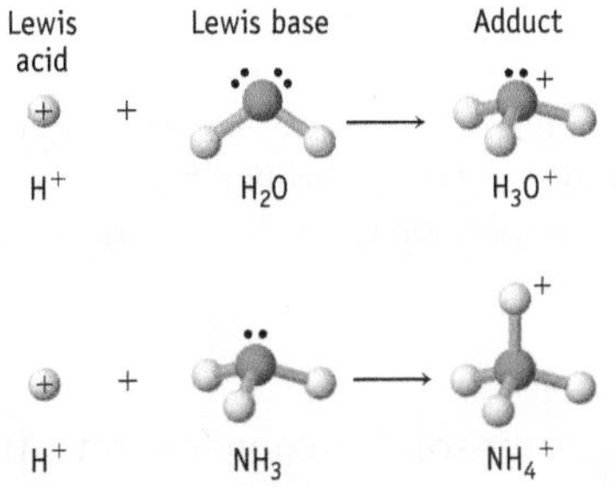

The H^+ ion has no electrons in its valence (1*s*) shell, and the water molecule has two unshared pairs of electrons (located in sp^3 hybrid orbitals). One of the lone pairs of a water molecule oxygen atom can be shared with an H^+ ion, thus forming an O—H bond in an H_3O^+ ion. A similar interaction occurs between H^+ and the nitrogen lone pair on ammonia to form the ammonium ion.

Lewis acid–base reactions are very common. In general, they involve Lewis acids that are cations or neutral molecules with an available, empty valence orbital and bases that are anions or neutral molecules with a lone electron pair.

Cationic Lewis Acids

Just as H^+ and water form a Lewis acid–base adduct, metal cations interact with water molecules to form hydrated cations. In these species, coordinate covalent bonds form between the metal cation and a lone pair of electrons on the O atom of each water. For example, an iron(II) ion, Fe^{2+}, forms six coordinate-covalent bonds to water.

$$Fe^{2+}(aq) + 6\ H_2O(\ell) \rightarrow [Fe(H_2O)_6]^{2+}(aq)$$

Solutions of transition metal cations are generally very colorful (Figures 16.9 and 16.10 and Section 22-3). Chemists call the species formed by coordination of water to a metal ion **complex ions** or, because of the presence of coordinate covalent bonds, **coordination complexes**. Several are listed in Table 16.2 as acids, and their behavior is described further in Chapter 22.

Ammonia is a typical Lewis base and, like water, it also combines with metal cations to give coordination complexes, which are often very colorful. For example, copper(II) ions, light blue in aqueous solution (Figure 16.9), react with ammonia to give a deep blue adduct with four ammonia molecules surrounding each Cu^{2+} ion.

Hydroxide ion, OH^-, is an excellent Lewis base and binds readily to metal cations to give metal hydroxides. An important feature of the chemistry of some metal hydroxides is that they are **amphoteric.** An amphoteric metal hydroxide can behave as an acid or a base (Table 16.7), and the chemistry of aluminum hydroxide, $Al(OH)_3$, is one of the best examples of this behavior. Adding OH^- to a precipitate

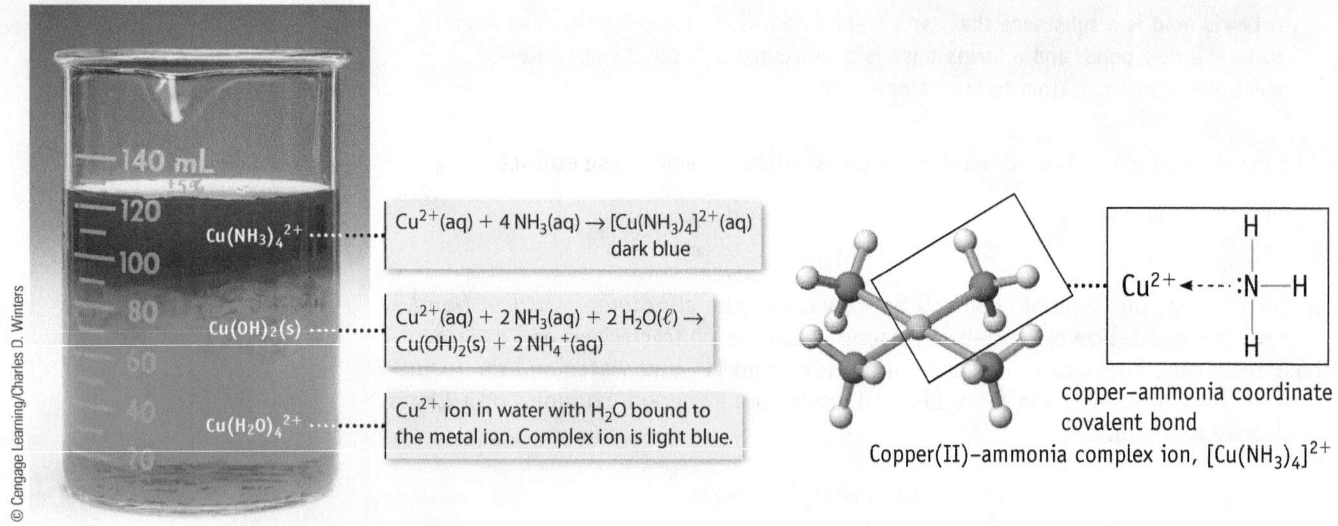

FIGURE 16.9 The Lewis acid–base complex ion $[Cu(NH_3)_4]^{2+}$. Aqueous ammonia was added to aqueous $CuSO_4$ in a beaker (the light blue solution at the bottom of the beaker). The small concentration of OH^- in $NH_3(aq)$ first led to the formation of insoluble blue-white $Cu(OH)_2$. With additional NH_3, however, the dark blue, soluble complex ion formed. Ammonia is bound to the Cu^{2+} ion by a coordinate-covalent bond.

of $Al(OH)_3$ produces the water-soluble complex ion $[Al(OH)_4]^-$ (Figure 16.11). In this reaction, $Al(OH)_3$ is acting as a Lewis acid.

$$\underset{\text{acid}}{Al(OH)_3(s)} + \underset{\text{base}}{OH^-(aq)} \rightarrow [Al(OH)_4]^-(aq)$$

If acid is added to the $Al(OH)_3$ precipitate, it again dissolves. This time, however, aluminum hydroxide is acting as a base.

$$\underset{\text{base}}{Al(OH)_3(s)} + \underset{\text{acid}}{3\,H_3O^+(aq)} \rightarrow Al^{3+}(aq) + 6\,H_2O(\ell)$$

Molecular Lewis Acids

Lewis's acid–base concept also accounts for the fact that oxides of nonmetals such as CO_2 and SO_2 behave as acids (◀ Section 3-6). Because oxygen is more electronegative than C, the C—O bonding electrons in CO_2 are polarized away from carbon and toward oxygen. This causes the carbon atom to be slightly positive, and it

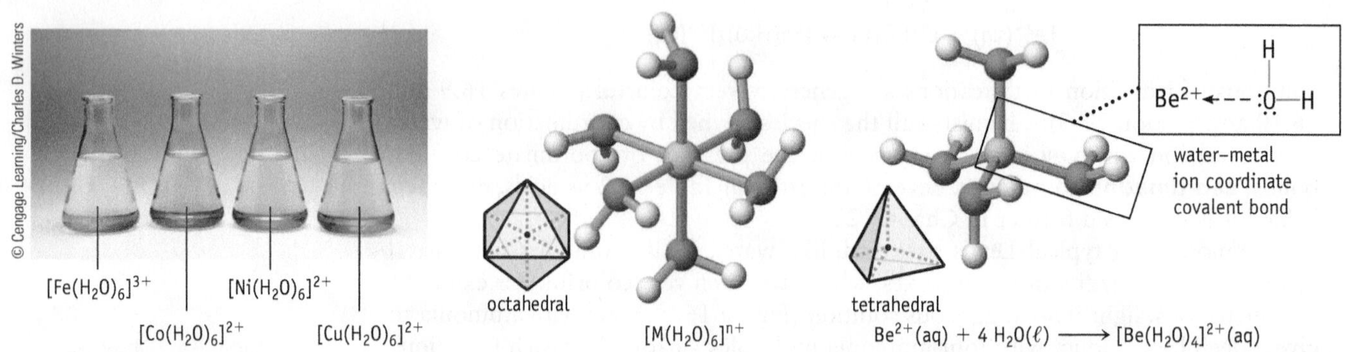

Solutions of the nitrate salts of iron(III), cobalt(II), nickel(II), and copper(II) all have characteristic colors.

Models of complex ions (Lewis acid–base adducts) formed between a metal cation and water molecules. Such complexes often have six or four water molecules arranged octahedrally or tetrahedrally around the metal cation.

FIGURE 16.10 Metal cations in water.

Table 16.7 Some Common Amphoteric Metal Hydroxides

HYDROXIDE	REACTION AS A BASE*	REACTION AS AN ACID
$Al(OH)_3$	$Al(OH)_3(s) + 3\ H_3O^+(aq) \rightleftharpoons Al^{3+}(aq) + 6\ H_2O(\ell)$	$Al(OH)_3(s) + OH^-(aq) \rightleftharpoons [Al(OH)_4]^-(aq)$
$Zn(OH)_2$	$Zn(OH)_2(s) + 2\ H_3O^+(aq) \rightleftharpoons Zn^{2+}(aq) + 4\ H_2O(\ell)$	$Zn(OH)_2(s) + 2\ OH^-(aq) \rightleftharpoons [Zn(OH)_4]^{2-}(aq)$
$Sn(OH)_4$	$Sn(OH)_4(s) + 4\ H_3O^+(aq) \rightleftharpoons Sn^{4+}(aq) + 8\ H_2O(\ell)$	$Sn(OH)_4(s) + 2\ OH^-(aq) \rightleftharpoons [Sn(OH)_6]^{2-}(aq)$
$Cr(OH)_3$	$Cr(OH)_3(s) + 3\ H_3O^+(aq) \rightleftharpoons Cr^{3+}(aq) + 6\ H_2O(\ell)$	$Cr(OH)_3(s) + OH^-(aq) \rightleftharpoons [Cr(OH)_4]^-(aq)$

*The aqueous metal cations are best described as $[M(H_2O)_6]^{n+}$.

is this atom that the negatively charged Lewis base OH^- can attack to give, ultimately, the bicarbonate ion.

CO_2 in Basic Solution This reaction of CO_2 with OH^- is the first step in the precipitation of $CaCO_3$ when CO_2 is bubbled into a solution of $Ca(OH)_2$ (see Figure 3.5).

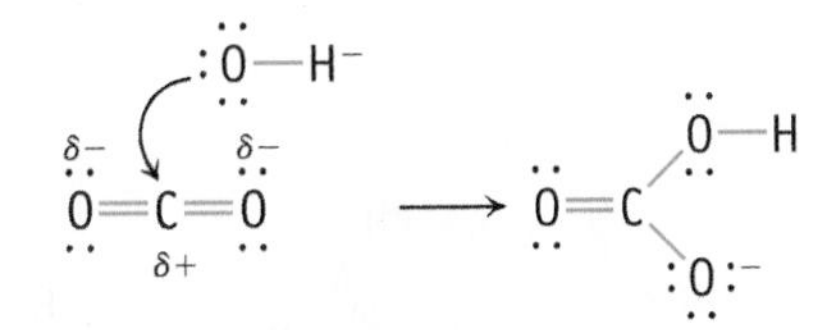

Similarly, SO_2 reacts with aqueous OH^- to form the HSO_3^- ion.

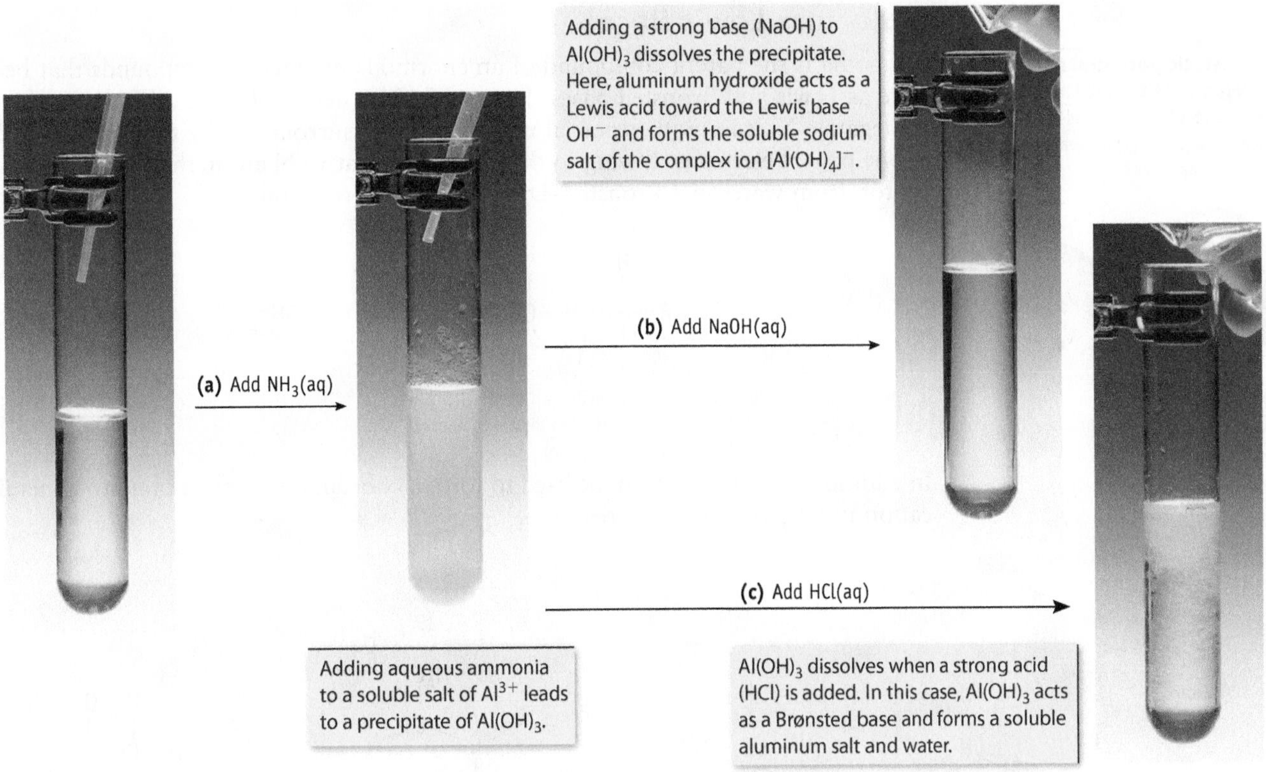

FIGURE 16.11 **The amphoteric nature of $Al(OH)_3$.** Aluminum hydroxide is formed by the reaction of aqueous Al^{3+} and ammonia.

$$Al^{3+}(aq) + 3\ NH_3(aq) + 3\ H_2O(\ell) \rightleftharpoons Al(OH)_3(s) + 3\ NH_4^+(aq)$$

Reactions of solid $Al(OH)_3$ with aqueous NaOH and HCl demonstrate that aluminum hydroxide is amphoteric.

Compounds based on the Group 3A elements boron and aluminum are among the most-studied Lewis acids. One example is a reaction in organic chemistry that is catalyzed by the Lewis acid $AlCl_3$. The mechanism of this important reaction—called the *Friedel-Crafts reaction*—is illustrated here.

STEP 1 A Lewis base, the Cl^- ion, transfers from the reactant, here CH_3COCl, to the Lewis acid to give $[AlCl_4]^-$ and an organic cation.

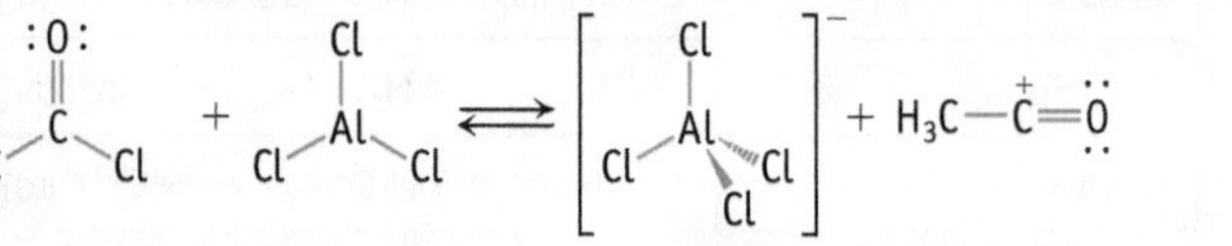

STEP 2 The organic cation attacks a benzene molecule to give a cationic intermediate.

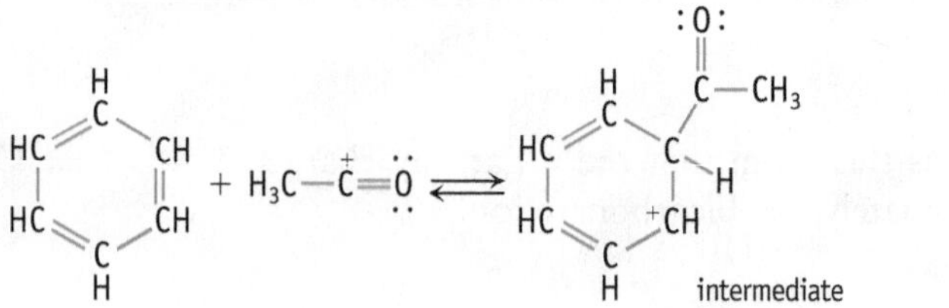

STEP 3 The cationic intermediate interacts with $[AlCl_4]^-$ to produce HCl and the final organic product. The catalyst is regenerated.

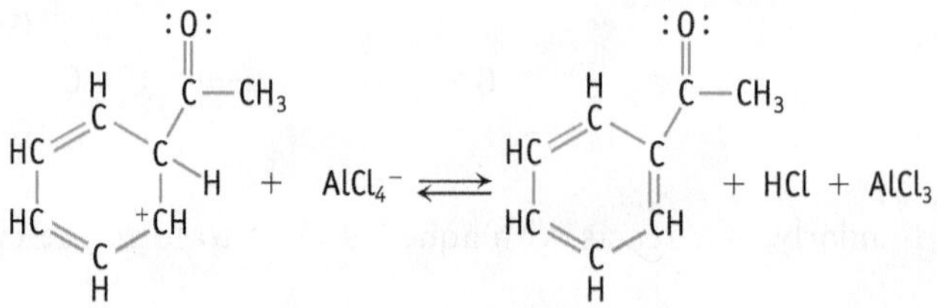

Molecular Lewis Bases

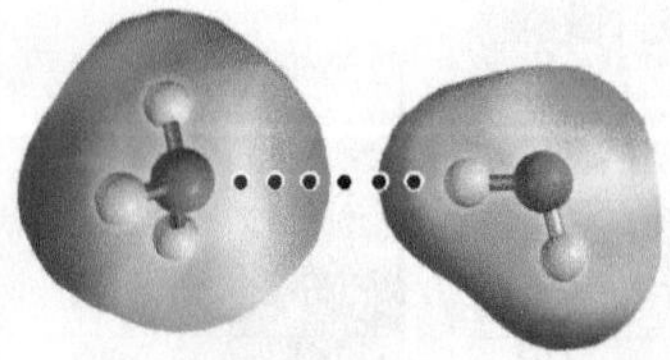

Electrostatic potential surfaces for NH_3 and H_2O. The NH_3 is both a Lewis and a Brønsted base and can remove the proton from water to form NH_4^+ and OH^-.

Ammonia is the parent compound of an enormous number of compounds that behave as Lewis and Brønsted bases (Figure 16.12). These molecules all have an electronegative N atom with a partial negative charge surrounded by three bonds and a lone pair of electrons. Owing to this partially negative N atom, they can extract a proton from water in a Brønsted–Lowry acid–base reaction.

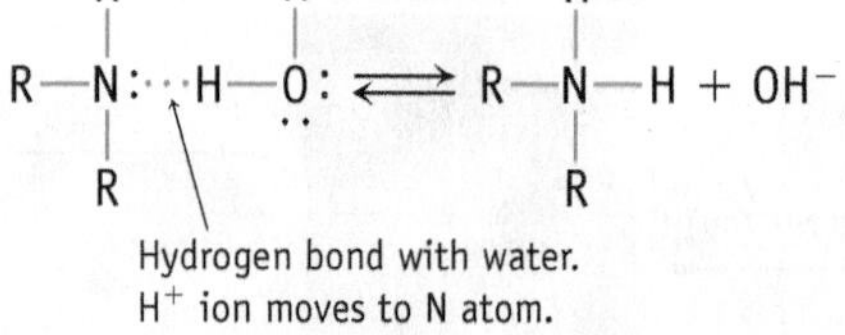

In addition, the lone pair can be used to form a coordinate covalent bond to a metal cation in a Lewis acid–base reaction.

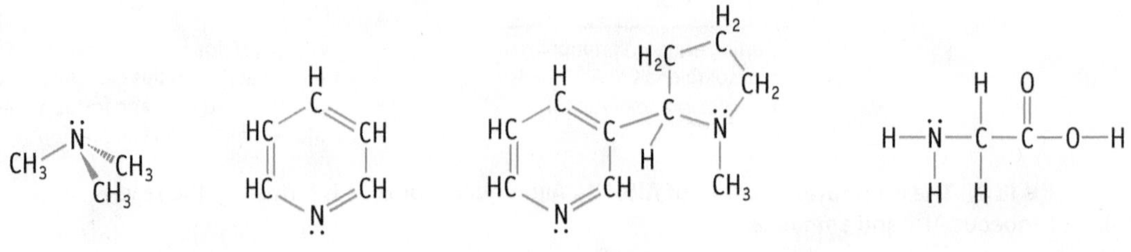

trimethylamine pyridine nicotine glycine, an amino acid

FIGURE 16.12 **Nitrogen-based Lewis and Brønsted bases.** All have an N atom surrounded by three bonds and a lone pair of electrons. Tetrodotoxin, the subject of the introductory story for this chapter, is in this broad class of compounds.

REVIEW & CHECK FOR SECTION 16-10

1. Which of the following can act as a Lewis acid? (*Hint:* In each case, draw the Lewis electron dot structure of the molecule or ion. Are there lone pairs of electrons on the central atom? If so, it can be a Lewis base. Does the central atom lack an electron pair? If so, it can behave as a Lewis acid.)

   (a) PH_3 (b) BCl_3 (c) H_2S (d) HS^-

2. The molecule whose structure is illustrated here is amphetamine, a stimulant. Which description best fits this molecule? (*Note:* There may be more than one answer.)

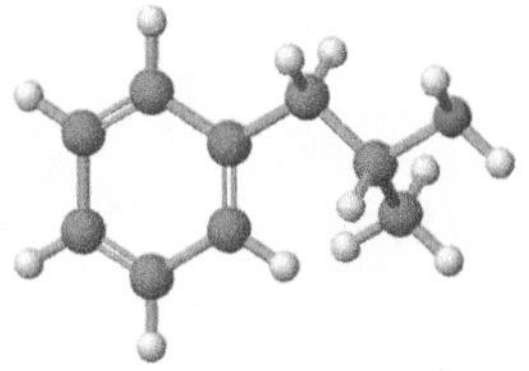

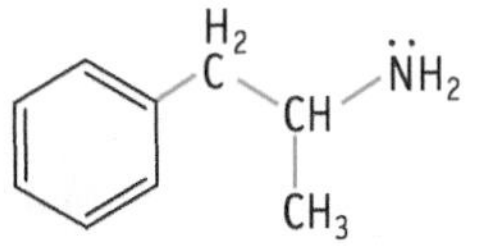

   (a) Brønsted acid (b) Lewis acid (c) Brønsted base (d) Lewis base

APPLYING CHEMICAL PRINCIPLES

The Leveling Effect, Nonaqueous Solvents, and Superacids

What is the strongest Brønsted acid that can exist in water? The answer is the hydronium ion. Although the common strong acids (HCl, HBr, HI, HNO_3, $HClO_4$, and H_2SO_4) are all stronger acids than H_3O^+, these acids ionize completely in water. The result is that all Brønsted acids with acidities above a certain value are equally acidic in water and, thus, their acid strength is indistinguishable. This is referred to as the *leveling effect* of water.

Similarly, the strongest base that can exist in water is OH^-. Any base that is stronger than OH^- will react completely with water to give OH^-. The amide ion, NH_2^-, and the oxide ion, O^{2-}, both stronger bases than OH^-, react completely with water, giving OH^-.

Although strong acids behave identically in water, they are not equally strong. One means of differentiating the strengths of these acids is to measure the degree of their ionization in solvents other than water. These solvents, like water, must be Brønsted bases. Additionally, the solvents must be weaker bases than water so that they are not fully protonated by a strong acid. One such solvent is acetic acid. Pure acetic acid—known as *glacial acetic acid*—is similar to water in that it can both donate or accept protons. Dissolution of hydrochloric acid in acetic acid, for example, yields the following chemical reaction:

$$HCl + CH_3CO_2H \rightleftharpoons CH_3CO_2H_2^+ + Cl^-$$

Unlike the ionization of HCl in water, this reaction does not go to completion; the p*K* value of this reaction is 8.8. Two other important acids, $HClO_4$ and H_2SO_4 (first proton only), have p*K* values of 5.3 and 6.8, respectively.

Other acids are even stronger, and are often called *superacids*. One superacid is fluorosulfonic acid (HSO_3F), which is about 1000 times stronger than sulfuric acid. Even this acid pales in comparison to a mixture of HSO_3F and SbF_5, which, depending on the concentrations, may be over 10^{16} times stronger than 100% sulfuric acid. It is sold under a suitable name, "Magic Acid."

George Olah

George Olah (1927–present). Much of the early research on superacids was done by Olah, and he received the Nobel Prize in Chemistry for this work in 1994.

QUESTIONS:

1. Convert the p*K* values to *K* values for the ionization of HCl, $HClO_4$, and H_2SO_4 in glacial acetic acid. Rank these acids in order from strongest to weakest.
2. Other solvents also undergo autoionization.
   a) Write a chemical equation for the autoionization of glacial acetic acid.
   b) The equilibrium constant for the autoionization of glacial acetic acid is 3.2×10^{-15} at 25°C. Determine the concentration of $[CH_3CO_2H_2]^+$ in acetic acid at 25°C.

3. Write an equation for the reaction of the amide ion (a stronger base than OH^-) and water. Does the equilibrium favor products or reactants?
4. Will a solution of $HClO_4$ in glacial acetic acid be a strong conductor of electricity, a weak conductor, or a nonconductor?
5. To measure the relative strengths of bases stronger than OH^-, it is necessary to choose a solvent that is a weaker acid than water. One such solvent is liquid ammonia.
   a) Write a chemical equation for the autoionization of ammonia.
   b) What is the strongest acid and base that can exist in liquid ammonia?
   c) Will a solution of HCl in liquid ammonia be a strong electrical conductor, a weak conductor, or a nonconductor?
   d) Oxide ion (O^{2-}) is a stronger base than the amide ion (NH_2^-). Write an equation for the reaction of O^{2-} with NH_3 in liquid ammonia. Will the equilibrium favor products or reactants?

CHAPTER GOALS REVISITED

Now that you have studied this chapter, you should ask whether you have met the chapter goals. In particular, you should be able to:

UNDERSTAND

- The similarities and differences between Brønsted–Lowry acid–base and Lewis acid–base theories.
  - **a.** Classify acids and bases according to Brønsted–Lowry and Lewis acid–base theories (Sections 16-1 and 16-10). Study Questions: 78, 115, 117.
- The influence of structure and bonding on acid–base properties.
  - **a.** Appreciate the connection between the structure of a compound and its acidity or basicity (Section 16-9). Study Questions: 75–78, 80, 120.
  - **b.** Characterize a compound as a Lewis base (an electron-pair donor) or a Lewis acid (an electron-pair acceptor) (Section 16-10). Study Questions: 79–82, 114.

DO

- Use the Brønsted–Lowry and Lewis theories of acids and bases.
  - **a.** Define and use the Brønsted concept of acids and bases (Sections 16-1).
  - **b.** Recognize common monoprotic and polyprotic acids and bases, and write balanced equations for their ionization in water (Section 16-1). Study Questions: 21, 22, 67, 68.
  - **c.** Appreciate when a substance can be amphiprotic (Section 16-1). Study Questions: 5, 6.
  - **d.** Recognize the Brønsted acid and base in a reaction, and identify the conjugate partner of each (Section 16-1). Study Questions: 1–4, 7, 8.
  - **e.** Use the water ionization constant, K_w (Section 16-2). Study Questions: 31–34.
  - **f.** Identify common strong acids and bases (Tables 3.1 and 16.2).
  - **g.** Recognize some common weak acids and understand that they can be neutral molecules (such as acetic acid), cations (NH_4^+ or hydrated metal ions such as $[Fe(H_2O)_6]^{2+}$, or anions (such as HCO_3^-) (Table 16.2).
- Apply the principles of chemical equilibrium to acids and bases in aqueous solution.
  - **a.** Write equilibrium constant expressions for weak acids and bases (Section 16-3).
  - **b.** Calculate pK_a from K_a (or K_a from pK_a), and understand how pK_a is correlated with acid strength (Section 16-3). Study Questions: 25–30, 110, 112.
  - **c.** Understand the relationship between K_a for a weak acid and K_b for its conjugate base (Section 16-3). Study Questions: 17, 18, 31–34.
  - **d.** Write equations for acid–base reactions, and decide whether they are product- or reactant-favored at equilibrium (Section 16-5 and Table 16.4). Study Questions: 35–42, 87.

e. Calculate the equilibrium constant for a weak acid (K_a) or a weak base (K_b) from experimental information (such as pH, $[H_3O^+]$, or $[OH^-]$) (Section 16-7 and Example 16.4). Study Questions: 43–46, 91, 113.
f. Describe the acid–base properties of salts, and calculate the pH of a solution of a salt of a weak acid or of a weak base (Section 16-4 and Example 16.7). Study Questions: 59–62, 90, 98, 99, 109, 127.

- Understand how Brønsted–Lowry theory is used to predict the outcome of reactions of acids and bases.
  a. Recognize the type of acid–base reaction, and describe its result (Section 16-6). Study Questions: 65, 66.
- Calculate pH from the concentration of hydronium ion in solution.
  a. Use the pH concept (Section 16-2). Study Questions: 9–14.
  b. Calculate the pH after an acid–base reaction (Section 16-6 and Example 16.8). Study Questions: 63, 64, 104.
- Given values of K_a and K_b, calculate the concentration of species in solution.
  a. Use the equilibrium constant and other information to calculate the pH of a solution of a weak acid or weak base (Section 16-7 and Examples 16.5 and 16.6). Study Questions: 49–58, 71, 72, 95, 97.

REMEMBER

- Brønsted–Lowry acids are proton donors and Brønsted–Lowry bases are proton acceptors.
- Lewis acids are electron-pair acceptors and Lewis bases are electron-pair donors.
- pH is a measure of hydronium ion concentration.

KEY EQUATIONS

Equation 16.1 (page 589) Water ionization constant.

$$K_w = [H_3O^+][OH^-] = 1.0 \times 10^{-14} \text{ at } 25 \text{ °C}$$

Equation 16.2 (page 591) Definition of pH.

$$pH = -\log[H_3O^+]$$

Equation 16.3 (page 591) Definition of pOH.

$$pOH = -\log[OH^-]$$

Equation 16.4 (page 591) Definition of $pK_w = pH + pOH$ (= 14.00 at 25 °C).

$$pK_w = 14.00 = pH + pOH$$

Equation 16.5 (page 593) Equilibrium expression for a general acid, HA, in water.

$$K_a = \frac{[H_3O^+][A^-]}{[HA]}$$

Equation 16.6 (page 593) Equilibrium expression for a general base, B, in water.

$$K_b = \frac{[BH^+][OH^-]}{[B]}$$

Equation 16.7 (page 597) Definition of pK_a.

$$pK_a = -\log K_a$$

Equation 16.8 (page 597) Relationship of K_a, K_b, and K_w, where K_a and K_b are for a conjugate acid–base pair.

$$K_a \times K_b = K_w$$

©Beth Swanson/Shutterstock.com

▲ denotes challenging questions.

Blue-numbered questions have answers in Appendix N and fully worked solutions in the *Student Solutions Manual.*

Practicing Skills

The Brønsted Concept

(See Section 16-1.)

1. Write the formula and give the name of the conjugate base of each of the following acids.
   (a) HCN (b) HSO_4^- (c) HF

2. Write the formula and give the name of the conjugate acid of each of the following bases.
   (a) NH_3 (b) HCO_3^- (c) Br^-

3. What are the products of each of the following acid–base reactions? Indicate the acid and its conjugate base and the base and its conjugate acid.
   (a) $HNO_3 + H_2O \rightarrow$
   (b) $HSO_4^- + H_2O \rightarrow$
   (c) $H_3O^+ + F^- \rightarrow$

4. What are the products of each of the following acid–base reactions? Indicate the acid and its conjugate base and the base and its conjugate acid.
   (a) $HClO_4 + H_2O \rightarrow$
   (b) $NH_4^+ + H_2O \rightarrow$
   (c) $HCO_3^- + OH^- \rightarrow$

5. Write balanced equations showing how the hydrogen oxalate ion, $HC_2O_4^-$, can be both a Brønsted acid and a Brønsted base.

6. Write balanced equations showing how the HPO_4^{2-} ion of sodium hydrogen phosphate, Na_2HPO_4, can be a Brønsted acid or a Brønsted base.

7. In each of the following acid–base reactions, identify the Brønsted acid and base on the left and their conjugate partners on the right.
   (a) $HCO_2H(aq) + H_2O(\ell) \rightleftharpoons HCO_2^-(aq) + H_3O^+(aq)$
   (b) $NH_3(aq) + H_2S(aq) \rightleftharpoons NH_4^+(aq) + HS^-(aq)$
   (c) $HSO_4^-(aq) + OH^-(aq) \rightleftharpoons SO_4^{2-}(aq) + H_2O(\ell)$

8. In each of the following acid–base reactions, identify the Brønsted acid and base on the left and their conjugate partners on the right.
   (a) $C_5H_5N(aq) + CH_3CO_2H(aq) \rightleftharpoons C_5H_5NH^+(aq) + CH_3CO_2^-(aq)$
   (b) $N_2H_4(aq) + HSO_4^-(aq) \rightleftharpoons N_2H_5^+(aq) + SO_4^{2-}(aq)$
   (c) $[Al(H_2O)_6]^{3+}(aq) + OH^-(aq) \rightleftharpoons [Al(H_2O)_5OH]^{2+}(aq) + H_2O(\ell)$

pH Calculations

(See Section 16-2 and Examples 4.8 and 16.1.)

9. An aqueous solution has a pH of 3.75. What is the hydronium ion concentration of the solution? Is it acidic or basic?

10. A saturated solution of milk of magnesia, $Mg(OH)_2$, has a pH of 10.52. What is the hydronium ion concentration of the solution? What is the hydroxide ion concentration? Is the solution acidic or basic?

11. What is the pH of a 0.0075 M solution of HCl? What is the hydroxide ion concentration of the solution?

12. What is the pH of a 1.2×10^{-4} M solution of KOH? What is the hydronium ion concentration of the solution?

13. What is the pH of a 0.0015 M solution of $Ba(OH)_2$?

14. The pH of a solution of $Ba(OH)_2$ is 10.66 at 25 °C. What is the hydroxide ion concentration in the solution? If the solution volume is 125 mL, what mass of $Ba(OH)_2$ must have been dissolved?

Equilibrium Constants for Acids and Bases

(See Sections 16-3 and 16-4 and Example 16.2.)

15. Several acids are listed here with their respective equilibrium constants:

$$C_6H_5OH(aq) + H_2O(\ell) \rightleftharpoons H_3O^+(aq) + C_6H_5O^-(aq) \quad K_a = 1.3 \times 10^{-10}$$

$$HCO_2H(aq) + H_2O(\ell) \rightleftharpoons H_3O^+(aq) + HCO_2^-(aq) \quad K_a = 1.8 \times 10^{-4}$$

$$HC_2O_4^-(aq) + H_2O(\ell) \rightleftharpoons H_3O^+(aq) + C_2O_4^{2-}(aq) \quad K_a = 6.4 \times 10^{-5}$$

   (a) Which is the strongest acid? Which is the weakest acid?
   (b) Which acid has the weakest conjugate base?
   (c) Which acid has the strongest conjugate base?

16. Several acids are listed here with their respective equilibrium constants.

$$HF(aq) + H_2O(\ell) \rightleftharpoons H_3O^+(aq) + F^-(aq) \quad K_a = 7.2 \times 10^{-4}$$

$$HPO_4^{2-}(aq) + H_2O(\ell) \rightleftharpoons H_3O^+(aq) + PO_4^{3-}(aq) \quad K_a = 3.6 \times 10^{-13}$$

$$CH_3CO_2H(aq) + H_2O(\ell) \rightleftharpoons H_3O^+(aq) + CH_3CO_2^-(aq) \quad K_a = 1.8 \times 10^{-5}$$

(a) Which is the strongest acid? Which is the weakest acid?
(b) What is the conjugate base of the acid HF?
(c) Which acid has the weakest conjugate base?
(d) Which acid has the strongest conjugate base?

17. Which of the following ions or compounds has the strongest conjugate base? Briefly explain your choice.

(a) HSO_4^- (b) CH_3CO_2H (c) HOCl

18. Which of the following compounds or ions has the weakest conjugate base? Briefly explain your choice.

(a) HCN (b) HClO (c) NH_4^+

19. Which of the following compounds or ions has the weakest conjugate acid? Briefly explain your choice.

(a) HCO_3^- (b) F^- (c) NO_2^-

20. Which of the following compounds or ions has the strongest conjugate acid? Briefly explain your choice.

(a) CN^- (b) NH_3 (c) SO_4^{2-}

21. Dissolving K_2CO_3 in water gives a basic solution. Write a balanced equation showing how can occur.

22. Dissolving ammonium bromide in water gives an acidic solution. Write a balanced equation showing how this can occur.

23. If each of the salts listed here were dissolved in water to give a 0.10 M solution, which solution would have the highest pH? Which would have the lowest pH?

(a) Na_2S
(b) Na_3PO_4
(c) NaH_2PO_4
(d) NaF
(e) $NaCH_3CO_2$
(f) $AlCl_3$

24. Which of the following common food additives would give a basic solution when dissolved in water?

(a) $NaNO_3$ (used as a meat preservative)
(b) $NaC_6H_5CO_2$ (sodium benzoate; used as a soft-drink preservative)
(c) Na_2HPO_4 (used as an emulsifier in the manufacture of pasteurized cheese)

pK_a: A Logarithmic Scale of Acid Strength

(See Section 16-3.)

25. A weak acid has a K_a of 6.5×10^{-5}. What is the value of pK_a for the acid?

26. If K_a for a weak acid is 2.4×10^{-11}, what is the value of pK_a?

27. Epinephrine hydrochloride has a pK_a value of 9.53. What is the value of K_a? Where does the acid fit in Table 16.2?

28. An organic acid has pK_a = 8.95. What is its K_a value? Where does the acid fit in Table 16.2?

29. Which is the stronger of the following two acids?

(a) benzoic acid, $C_6H_5CO_2H$, pK_a = 4.20
(b) 2-chlorobenzoic acid, $ClC_6H_4CO_2H$, pK_a = 2.90

30. Which is the stronger of the following two acids?

(a) acetic acid, CH_3CO_2H, $K_a = 1.8 \times 10^{-5}$
(b) chloroacetic acid, $ClCH_2CO_2H$, pK_a = 2.85

Ionization Constants for Weak Acids and Their Conjugate Bases

(See Section 16-3.)

31. Chloroacetic acid ($ClCH_2CO_2H$) has $K_a = 1.41 \times 10^{-3}$. What is the value of K_b for the chloroacetate ion ($ClCH_2CO_2^-$)?

32. A weak base has $K_b = 1.5 \times 10^{-9}$. What is the value of K_a for the conjugate acid?

33. The trimethylammonium ion, $(CH_3)_3NH^+$, is the conjugate acid of the weak base trimethylamine, $(CH_3)_3N$. A chemical handbook gives 9.80 as the pK_a value for $(CH_3)_3NH^+$. What is the value of K_b for $(CH_3)_3N$?

34. The chromium(III) ion in water, $[Cr(H_2O)_6]^{3+}$, is a weak acid with pK_a = 3.95. What is the value of K_b for its conjugate base, $[Cr(H_2O)_5OH]^{2+}$?

Predicting the Direction of Acid–Base Reactions

(See Section 16-5 and Example 16.3.)

35. Acetic acid and sodium hydrogen carbonate, $NaHCO_3$, are mixed in water. Write a balanced equation for the acid–base reaction that could, in principle, occur. Using Table 16.2, decide whether the equilibrium lies predominantly to the right or to the left.

36. Ammonium chloride and sodium dihydrogen phosphate, NaH_2PO_4, are mixed in water. Write a balanced equation for the acid–base reaction that could, in principle, occur. Using Table 16.2, decide whether the equilibrium lies predominantly to the right or to the left.

37. For each of the following reactions, predict whether the equilibrium lies predominantly to the left or to the right. Explain your predictions briefly.

(a) $NH_4^+(aq) + Br^-(aq) \rightleftharpoons NH_3(aq) + HBr(aq)$
(b) $HPO_4^{2-}(aq) + CH_3CO_2^-(aq) \rightleftharpoons PO_4^{3-}(aq) + CH_3CO_2H(aq)$
(c) $[Fe(H_2O)_6]^{3+}(aq) + HCO_3^-(aq) \rightleftharpoons [Fe(H_2O)_5(OH)]^{2+}(aq) + H_2CO_3(aq)$

38. For each of the following reactions, predict whether the equilibrium lies predominantly to the left or to the right. Explain your predictions briefly.

(a) $H_2S(aq) + CO_3^{2-}(aq) \rightleftharpoons HS^-(aq) + HCO_3^-(aq)$

(b) $HCN(aq) + SO_4^{2-}(aq) \rightleftharpoons CN^-(aq) + HSO_4^-(aq)$

(c) $SO_4^{2-}(aq) + CH_3CO_2H(aq) \rightleftharpoons HSO_4^-(aq) + CH_3CO_2^-(aq)$

Types of Acid–Base Reactions

(See Section 16-6.)

39. Equal molar quantities of sodium hydroxide and sodium hydrogen phosphate (Na_2HPO_4) are mixed.

(a) Write the balanced, net ionic equation for the acid–base reaction that can, in principle, occur.

(b) Does the equilibrium lie to the right or left?

40. Equal molar quantities of hydrochloric acid and sodium hypochlorite (NaClO) are mixed.

(a) Write the balanced, net ionic equation for the acid–base reaction that can, in principle, occur.

(b) Does the equilibrium lie to the right or left?

41. Equal molar quantities of acetic acid and sodium hydrogen phosphate (Na_2HPO_4) are mixed.

(a) Write a balanced, net ionic equation for the acid–base reaction that can, in principle, occur.

(b) Does the equilibrium lie to the right or left?

42. Equal molar quantities of ammonia and sodium dihydrogen phosphate (NaH_2PO_4) are mixed.

(a) Write a balanced, net ionic equation for the acid–base reaction that can, in principle, occur.

(b) Does the equilibrium lie to the right or left?

Using pH to Calculate Ionization Constants

(See Section 16-7 and Example 16.4.)

43. A 0.015 M solution of hydrogen cyanate, HOCN, has a pH of 2.67.

(a) What is the hydronium ion concentration in the solution?

(b) What is the ionization constant, K_a, for the acid?

44. A 0.10 M solution of chloroacetic acid, $ClCH_2CO_2H$, has a pH of 1.95. Calculate K_a for the acid.

45. A 0.025 M solution of hydroxylamine has a pH of 9.11. What is the value of K_b for this weak base?

$$H_2NOH(aq) + H_2O(\ell) \rightleftharpoons H_3NOH^+(aq) + OH^-(aq)$$

46. Methylamine, CH_3NH_2, is a weak base.

$$CH_3NH_2(aq) + H_2O(\ell) \rightleftharpoons CH_3NH_3^+(aq) + OH^-(aq)$$

If the pH of a 0.065 M solution of the amine is 11.70, what is the value of K_b?

47. A 2.5×10^{-3} M solution of an unknown acid has a pH of 3.80 at 25 °C.

(a) What is the hydronium ion concentration of the solution?

(b) Is the acid a strong acid, a moderately weak acid (K_a of about 10^{-5}), or a very weak acid (K_a of about 10^{-10})?

48. A 0.015 M solution of a base has a pH of 10.09.

(a) What are the hydronium and hydroxide ion concentrations of this solution?

(b) Is the base a strong base, a moderately weak base (K_b of about 10^{-5}), or a very weak base (K_b of about 10^{-10})?

Using Ionization Constants

(See Section 16-7 and Examples 16.5–16.6.)

49. What are the equilibrium concentrations of hydronium ion, acetate ion, and acetic acid in a 0.20 M aqueous solution of acetic acid?

50. The ionization constant of a very weak acid, HA, is 4.0×10^{-9}. Calculate the equilibrium concentrations of H_3O^+, A^-, and HA in a 0.040 M solution of the acid.

51. What are the equilibrium concentrations of H_3O^+, CN^-, and HCN in a 0.025 M solution of HCN? What is the pH of the solution?

52. Phenol (C_6H_5OH), commonly called *carbolic acid*, is a weak organic acid.

$$C_6H_5OH(aq) + H_2O(\ell) \rightleftharpoons C_6H_5O^-(aq) + H_3O^+(aq) \quad K_a = 1.3 \times 10^{-10}$$

If you dissolve 0.195 g of the acid in enough water to make 125 mL of solution, what is the equilibrium hydronium ion concentration? What is the pH of the solution?

53. What are the equilibrium concentrations of NH_3, NH_4^+, and OH^- in a 0.15 M solution of ammonia? What is the pH of the solution?

54. A hypothetical weak base has $K_b = 5.0 \times 10^{-4}$. Calculate the equilibrium concentrations of the base, its conjugate acid, and OH^- in a 0.15 M solution of the base.

55. The weak base methylamine, CH_3NH_2, has $K_b = 4.2 \times 10^{-4}$. It reacts with water according to the equation

$$CH_3NH_2(aq) + H_2O(\ell) \rightleftharpoons CH_3NH_3^+(aq) + OH^-(aq)$$

Calculate the equilibrium hydroxide ion concentration in a 0.25 M solution of the base. What are the pH and pOH of the solution?

56. Calculate the pH of a 0.12 M aqueous solution of the base aniline, $C_6H_5NH_2$ ($K_b = 4.0 \times 10^{-10}$).

$$C_6H_5NH_2(aq) + H_2O(\ell) \rightleftharpoons C_6H_5NH_3^+(aq) + OH^-(aq)$$

57. Calculate the pH of a 0.0010 M aqueous solution of HF.

58. A solution of hydrofluoric acid, HF, has a pH of 2.30. Calculate the equilibrium concentrations of HF, F^-, and H_3O^+, and calculate the amount of HF originally dissolved per liter.

Acid–Base Properties of Salts

(See Sections 16-4 and 16-7 and Example 16.8.)

59. Calculate the hydronium ion concentration and pH in a 0.20 M solution of ammonium chloride, NH_4Cl.

60. ▲ Calculate the hydronium ion concentration and pH for a 0.015 M solution of sodium formate, $NaHCO_2$.

61. Sodium cyanide is the salt of the weak acid HCN. Calculate the concentrations of H_3O^+, OH^-, HCN, and Na^+ in a solution prepared by dissolving 10.8 g of NaCN in enough water to make 5.00×10^2 mL of solution at 25 °C.

62. The sodium salt of propanoic acid, $NaCH_3CH_2CO_2$, is used as an antifungal agent by veterinarians. Calculate the equilibrium concentrations of H_3O^+ and OH^-, and the pH, for a solution of 0.10 M $NaCH_3CH_2CO_2$.

pH after an Acid–Base Reaction

(See Example 16.7.)

63. Calculate the hydronium ion concentration and pH of the solution that results when 22.0 mL of 0.15 M acetic acid, CH_3CO_2H, is mixed with 22.0 mL of 0.15 M NaOH.

64. Calculate the hydronium ion concentration and the pH when 50.0 mL of 0.40 M NH_3 is mixed with 50.0 mL of 0.40 M HCl.

65. For each of the following cases, decide whether the pH is less than 7, equal to 7, or greater than 7.
(a) Equal volumes of 0.10 M acetic acid, CH_3CO_2H, and 0.10 M KOH are mixed.
(b) 25 mL of 0.015 M NH_3 is mixed with 25 mL of 0.015 M HCl.
(c) 150 mL of 0.20 M HNO_3 is mixed with 75 mL of 0.40 M NaOH.

66. For each of the following cases, decide whether the pH is less than 7, equal to 7, or greater than 7.
(a) 25 mL of 0.45 M H_2SO_4 is mixed with 25 mL of 0.90 M NaOH.
(b) 15 mL of 0.050 M formic acid, HCO_2H, is mixed with 15 mL of 0.050 M NaOH.
(c) 25 mL of 0.15 M $H_2C_2O_4$ (oxalic acid) is mixed with 25 mL of 0.30 M NaOH. (Both H^+ ions of oxalic acid are removed with NaOH.)

Polyprotic Acids and Bases

(See Section 16-8 and Example 16.9.)

67. Oxalic acid, $H_2C_2O_4$, is a diprotic acid. Write a chemical equilibrium expression for each ionization step in water.

68. Sodium carbonate is a diprotic base. Write a chemical equilibrium expression for each of the two successive base reactions with water.

69. Prove that $K_{a1} \times K_{b2} = K_w$ for oxalic acid, $H_2C_2O_4$, by adding the chemical equilibrium expressions that correspond to first ionization step of the acid in water with the second step of the reaction of the fully deprotonated base, $C_2O_4^{2-}$, with water.

70. Prove that $K_{a3} \times K_{b1} = K_w$ for phosphoric acid, H_3PO_4, by adding the chemical equilibrium expressions that correspond to third ionization step of the acid in water with the first of the three successive steps of the reaction of phosphate ion, PO_4^{3-}, with water.

71. Sulfurous acid, H_2SO_3, is a weak acid capable of providing two H^+ ions.
(a) What is the pH of a 0.45 M solution of H_2SO_3?
(b) What is the equilibrium concentration of the sulfite ion, SO_3^{2-}, in the 0.45 M solution of H_2SO_3?

72. Ascorbic acid (vitamin C, $C_6H_8O_6$) is a diprotic acid ($K_{a1} = 6.8 \times 10^{-5}$ and $K_{a2} = 2.7 \times 10^{-12}$). What is the pH of a solution that contains 5.0 mg of acid per milliliter of solution?

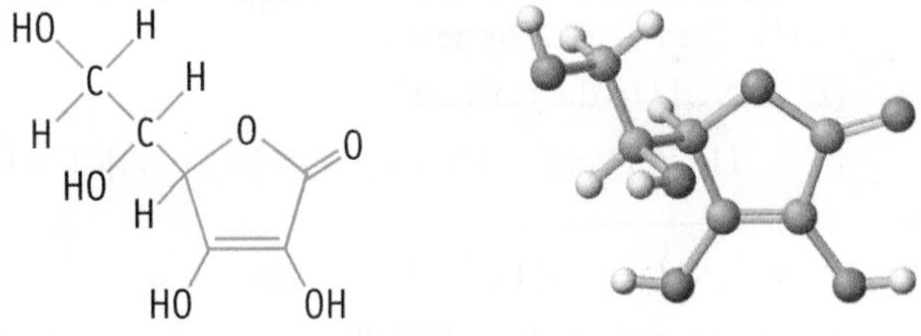

Ascorbic acid

73. Hydrazine, N_2H_4, can interact with water in two steps.

$$N_2H_4(aq) + H_2O(\ell) \rightleftharpoons N_2H_5^+(aq) + OH^-(aq) \quad K_{b1} = 8.5 \times 10^{-7}$$

$$N_2H_5^+(aq) + H_2O(\ell) \rightleftharpoons N_2H_6^{2+}(aq) + OH^-(aq) \quad K_{b2} = 8.9 \times 10^{-16}$$

(a) What is the concentration of OH^-, $N_2H_5^+$, and $N_2H_6^{2+}$ in a 0.010 M aqueous solution of hydrazine?
(b) What is the pH of the 0.010 M solution of hydrazine?

74. Ethylenediamine, $H_2NCH_2CH_2NH_2$, can interact with water in two steps, forming OH^- in each step (▶ Appendix I). If you have a 0.15 M aqueous solution of the amine, calculate the concentrations of $[H_3NCH_2CH_2NH_3]^{2+}$ and OH^-.

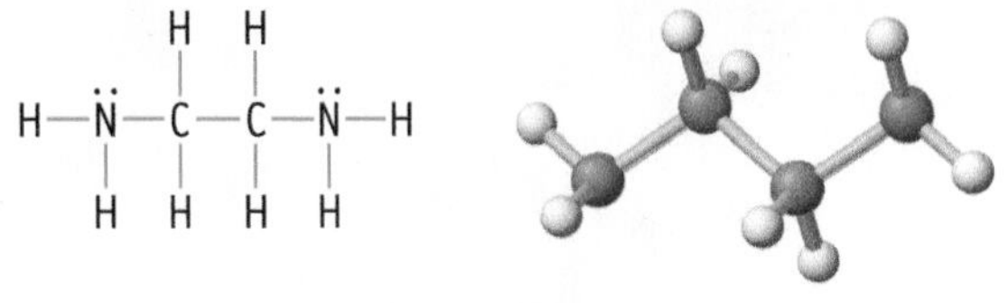

Ethylenediamine

Molecular Structure, Bonding, and Acid–Base Behavior

(See Section 16-9.)

75. Which should be the stronger acid, HOCN or HCN? Explain briefly. (In HOCN, the H^+ ion is attached to the O atom of the OCN^- ion.)

76. Which should be the stronger Brønsted acid, $[V(H_2O)_6]^{2+}$ or $[V(H_2O)_6]^{3+}$?

77. Explain why benzenesulfonic acid is a Brønsted acid.

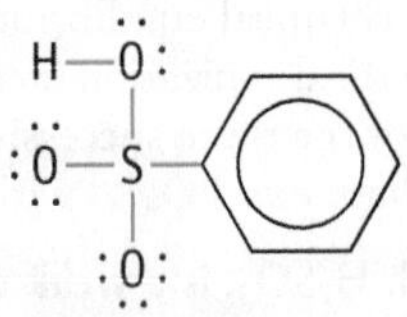

benzenesulfonic acid

78. The structure of ethylenediamine is illustrated in Study Question 74. Is this compound a Brønsted acid, a Brønsted base, a Lewis acid, or a Lewis base, or some combination of these?

Lewis Acids and Bases

(See Section 16-10.)

79. Decide whether each of the following substances should be classified as a Lewis acid or a Lewis base.

(a) H_2NOH in the reaction

$$H_2NOH(aq) + HCl(aq) \longrightarrow [H_3NOH]Cl(aq)$$

(b) Fe^{2+}

(c) CH_3NH_2 (*Hint:* Draw the electron dot structure.)

80. Decide whether each of the following substances should be classified as a Lewis acid or a Lewis base.

(a) BCl_3 (*Hint:* Draw the electron dot structure.)

(b) H_2NNH_2, hydrazine (*Hint:* Draw the electron dot structure.)

(c) the reactants in the reaction

$$Ag^+(aq) + 2\ NH_3(aq) \rightleftharpoons [Ag(NH_3)_2]^+(aq)$$

81. Carbon monoxide forms complexes with low-valent metals. For example, $Ni(CO)_4$ and $Fe(CO)_5$ are well known. CO also forms complexes with the iron(II) ion in hemoglobin, which prevents the hemoglobin from acting in its normal way. Is CO a Lewis acid or a Lewis base?

82. Trimethylamine, $(CH_3)_3N$, is a common reagent. It interacts readily with diborane gas, B_2H_6. The latter dissociates to BH_3, and this forms a complex with the amine, $(CH_3)_3N{\rightarrow}BH_3$. Is the BH_3 fragment a Lewis acid or a Lewis base?

General Questions

These questions are not designated as to type or location in the chapter. They may combine several concepts.

83. About this time, you may be wishing you had an aspirin. Aspirin is an organic acid with a K_a of 3.27×10^{-4} for the reaction

$$HC_9H_7O_4(aq) + H_2O(\ell) \rightleftharpoons C_9H_7O_4^-(aq) + H_3O^+(aq)$$

If you have two tablets, each containing 0.325 g of aspirin (mixed with a neutral "binder" to hold the tablet together), and you dissolve them in a glass of water to give 225 mL of solution, what is the pH of the solution?

84. Consider the following ions: NH_4^+, CO_3^{2-}, Br^-, S^{2-}, and ClO_4^-.

(a) Which of these ions in water gives an acidic solution and which gives a basic solution?

(b) Which of these anions will have no effect on the pH of an aqueous solution?

(c) Which ion is the strongest base?

(d) Write a chemical equation for the reaction of each basic anion with water.

85. A 2.50-g sample of a solid that could be $Ba(OH)_2$ or $Sr(OH)_2$ was dissolved in enough water to make 1.00 L of solution. If the pH of the solution is 12.61, what is the identity of the solid?

86. ▲ In a particular solution, acetic acid is 11% ionized at 25 °C. Calculate the pH of the solution and the mass of acetic acid dissolved to yield 1.00 L of solution.

87. Hydrogen sulfide, H_2S, and sodium acetate, $NaCH_3CO_2$, are mixed in water. Using Table 16.2, write a balanced equation for the acid–base reaction that could, in principle, occur. Does the equilibrium lie toward the products or the reactants?

88. For each of the following reactions, predict whether the equilibrium lies predominantly to the left or to the right. Explain your prediction briefly.

(a) $HCO_3^-(aq) + SO_4^{2-}(aq) \rightleftharpoons CO_3^{2-}(aq) + HSO_4^-(aq)$

(b) $HSO_4^-(aq) + CH_3CO_2^-(aq) \rightleftharpoons SO_4^{2-}(aq) + CH_3CO_2H(aq)$

(c) $[Co(H_2O)_6]^{2+}(aq) + CH_3CO_2^-(aq) \rightleftharpoons [Co(H_2O)_5(OH)]^+(aq) + CH_3CO_2H(aq)$

89. A monoprotic acid HX has $K_a = 1.3 \times 10^{-3}$. Calculate the equilibrium concentrations of HX and H_3O^+ and the pH for a 0.010 M solution of the acid.

90. Arrange the following 0.10 M solutions in order of increasing pH.

(a) NaCl

(b) NH_4Cl

(c) HCl

(d) $NaCH_3CO_2$

(e) KOH

91. *m*-Nitrophenol, a weak acid, can be used as a pH indicator because it is yellow at a pH above 8.6 and colorless at a pH below 6.8. If the pH of a 0.010 M solution of the compound is 3.44, calculate its pK_a.

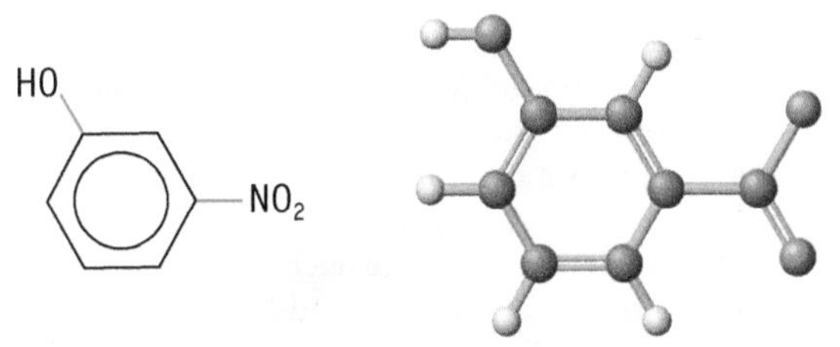

***m*-Nitrophenol**

92. The butylammonium ion, $C_4H_9NH_3^+$, has a K_a of 2.3×10^{-11}.

$$C_4H_9NH_3^+(aq) + H_2O(\ell) \rightleftharpoons H_3O^+(aq) + C_4H_9NH_2(aq)$$

(a) Calculate K_b for the conjugate base, $C_4H_9NH_2$ (butylamine).
(b) Place the butylammonium ion and its conjugate base in Table 16.2. Name an acid weaker than $C_4H_9NH_3^+$ and a base stronger than $C_4H_9NH_2$.
(c) What is the pH of a 0.015 M solution of butylammonium chloride?

93. The local anesthetic novocaine is the hydrogen chloride salt of an organic base, procaine.

$$\underset{\text{procaine}}{C_{13}H_{20}N_2O_2(aq)} + HCl(aq) \longrightarrow \underset{\text{novocaine}}{[HC_{13}H_{20}N_2O_2]^+Cl^-(aq)}$$

The pK_a for novocaine is 8.85. What is the pH of a 0.0015 M solution of novocaine?

94. Pyridine is a weak organic base and readily forms a salt with hydrochloric acid.

$$\underset{\text{pyridine}}{C_5H_5N(aq)} + HCl(aq) \longrightarrow \underset{\text{pyridinium ion}}{C_5H_5NH^+(aq)} + Cl^-(aq)$$

What is the pH of a 0.025 M solution of pyridinium hydrochloride, $[C_5H_5NH^+]Cl^-$?

95. The base ethylamine ($CH_3CH_2NH_2$) has a K_b of 4.3×10^{-4}. A closely related base, ethanolamine ($HOCH_2CH_2NH_2$), has a K_b of 3.2×10^{-5}.

(a) Which of the two bases is stronger?
(b) Calculate the pH of a 0.10 M solution of the stronger base.

96. Chloroacetic acid, $ClCH_2CO_2H$, is a moderately weak acid ($K_a = 1.40 \times 10^{-3}$). If you dissolve 94.5 mg of the acid in water to give 125 mL of solution, what is the pH of the solution?

97. Saccharin ($HC_7H_4NO_3S$) is a weak acid with $pK_a = 2.32$ at 25 °C. It is used in the form of sodium saccharide, $NaC_7H_4NO_3S$. What is the pH of a 0.10 M solution of sodium saccharide at 25 °C?

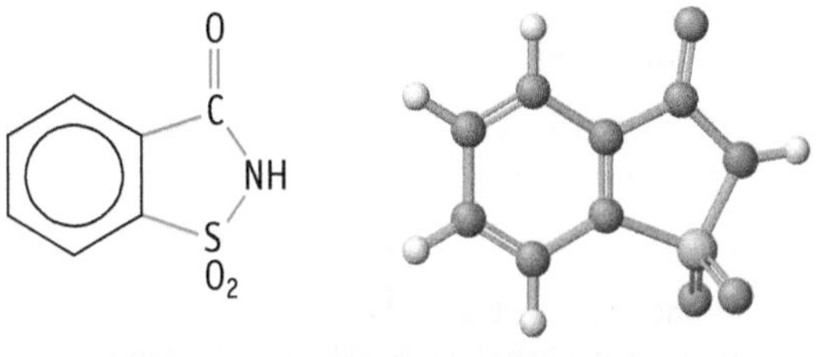

Saccharin

98. Given the following solutions:

(a) 0.1 M NH_3
(b) 0.1 M Na_2CO_3
(c) 0.1 M NaCl
(d) 0.1 M CH_3CO_2H
(e) 0.1 M NH_4Cl
(f) 0.1 M $NaCH_3CO_2$
(g) 0.1 M $NH_4CH_3CO_2$

(i) Which of the solutions are acidic?
(ii) Which of the solutions are basic?
(iii) Which of the solutions is most acidic?

99. For each of the following salts, predict whether a 0.10 M solution has a pH less than, equal to, or greater than 7.

(a) $NaHSO_4$
(b) NH_4Br
(c) $KClO_4$
(d) Na_2CO_3
(e) $(NH_4)_2S$
(f) $NaNO_3$
(g) Na_2HPO_4
(h) LiBr
(i) $FeCl_3$

Which solution has the highest pH? The lowest pH?

100. Nicotine, $C_{10}H_{14}N_2$, has two basic nitrogen atoms (Figure 16.12), and both can react with water.

$$Nic(aq) + H_2O(\ell) \rightleftharpoons NicH^+(aq) + OH^-(aq)$$

$$NicH^+(aq) + H_2O(\ell) \rightleftharpoons NicH_2^{2+}(aq) + OH^-(aq)$$

K_{b1} is 7.0×10^{-7} and K_{b2} is 1.1×10^{-10}. Calculate the approximate pH of a 0.020 M solution.

101. Oxalic acid is a relatively weak diprotic acid. Calculate the equilibrium constant for the reaction shown below from K_{a1} and K_{a2}. (See Appendix H for the required K_a values.)

$$H_2C_2O_4(aq) + 2\ H_2O(\ell) \rightleftharpoons C_2O_4^{2-}(aq) + 2\ H_3O^+(aq)$$

102. ▲ The equilibrium constant for the reaction of hydrochloric acid and ammonia is 1.8×10^9 (page 604). Confirm this value.

103. ▲ The equilibrium constant for the reaction of formic acid and sodium hydroxide is 1.8×10^{10} (page 604). Confirm this value.

104. ▲ Calculate the pH of the solution that results from mixing 25.0 mL of 0.14 M formic acid and 50.0 mL of 0.070 M sodium hydroxide.

105. ▲ To what volume should 1.00×10^2 mL of any weak acid, HA, with a concentration 0.20 M be diluted to double the percentage ionization?

106. ▲ The hydrogen phthalate ion, $C_8H_5O_4^-$, is a weak acid with $K_a = 3.91 \times 10^{-6}$.

$$C_8H_5O_4^-(aq) + H_2O(\ell) \rightleftharpoons C_8H_4O_4^{2-}(aq) + H_3O^+(aq)$$

What is the pH of a 0.050 M solution of potassium hydrogen phthalate, $KC_8H_5O_4$? *Note*: To find the pH for a solution of the anion, we must take into account that the ion is amphiprotic. It can be shown that, for most cases of amphiprotic ions, the H_3O^+ concentration is

$$[H_3O^+] = \sqrt{K_{a1} \times K_{a2}}$$

For phthalic acid, $C_8H_6O_4$, K_1 is 1.12×10^{-3}, and K_2 is 3.91×10^{-6}.

107. ▲ You prepare a 0.10 M solution of oxalic acid, $H_2C_2O_4$. What molecules and ions exist in this solution? List them in order of decreasing concentration.

108. ▲ You mix 30.0 mL of 0.15 M NaOH with 30.0 mL of 0.15 M acetic acid. What molecules and ions exist in this solution? List them in order of decreasing concentration.

In the Laboratory

109. Describe an experiment that will allow you to place the following three bases in order of increasing base strength: NaCN, CH_3NH_2, Na_2CO_3.

110. The data below compare the strength of acetic acid with a related series of acids, where the H atoms of the CH_3 group in acetic acid are successively replaced by Br.

Acid	pK_a
CH_3CO_2H	4.74
$BrCH_2CO_2H$	2.90
Br_2CHCO_2H	1.39
Br_3CCO_2H	−0.147

(a) What trend in acid strength do you observe as H is successively replaced by Br? Can you suggest a reason for this trend?

(b) Suppose each of the acids above was present as a 0.10 M aqueous solution. Which would have the highest pH? The lowest pH?

111. ▲ You have three solutions labeled A, B, and C. You know only that each contains a different cation—Na^+, NH_4^+, or H_3O^+. Each has an anion that does not contribute to the solution pH (e.g., Cl^-). You also have two other solutions, Y and Z, each containing a different anion, Cl^- or OH^-, with a cation that does not influence solution pH (e.g., K^+). If equal amounts of B and Y are mixed, the result is an acidic solution. Mixing A and Z gives a neutral solution, whereas B and Z give a basic solution. Identify the five unknown solutions. (Adapted from D. H. Barouch: *Voyages in Conceptual Chemistry*, Boston, Jones and Bartlett, 1997.)

	Y	Z
A		neutral
B	acidic	basic
C		

112. A hydrogen atom in the organic base pyridine, C_5H_5N, can be substituted by various atoms or groups to give XC_5H_4N, where X is an atom such as Cl or a group such as CH_3. The following table gives K_a values for the conjugate acids of a variety of substituted pyridines.

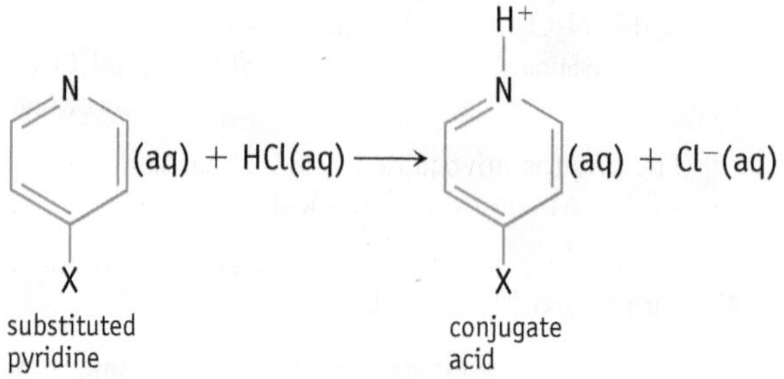

Atom or Group X	K_a of Conjugate Acid
NO_2	5.9×10^{-2}
Cl	1.5×10^{-4}
H	6.8×10^{-6}
CH_3	1.0×10^{-6}

(a) Suppose each conjugate acid is dissolved in sufficient water to give a 0.050 M solution. Which solution would have the highest pH? The lowest pH?

(b) Which of the substituted pyridines is the strongest Brønsted base? Which is the weakest Brønsted base?

113. Nicotinic acid, $C_6H_5NO_2$, is found in minute amounts in all living cells, but appreciable amounts occur in liver, yeast, milk, adrenal glands, white meat, and corn. Whole-wheat flour contains about 60. μg per gram of flour. One gram (1.00 g) of the acid dissolves in water to give 60. mL of solution having a pH of 2.70. What is the approximate value of K_a for the acid?

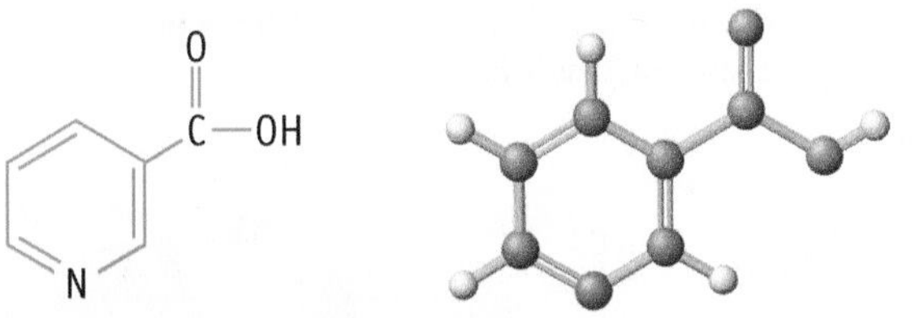

Nicotinic acid

114. ▲ Equilibrium constants can be measured for the dissociation of Lewis acid–base complexes such as the dimethyl ether complex of BF_3, $(CH_3)_2O{\rightarrow}BF_3$. The value of K (here K_p) for the reaction is 0.17 at 125 °C.

$$(CH_3)_2O{\rightarrow}BF_3(g) \rightleftharpoons BF_3(g) + (CH_3)_2O(g)$$

(a) Describe each product as a Lewis acid or a Lewis base.

(b) If you place 1.00 g of the complex in a 565-mL flask at 125 °C, what is the total pressure in the flask when equilibrium is established? What are the equilibrium partial pressures of the Lewis acid, the Lewis base, and the complex?

115. ▲ Sulfanilic acid, which is used in making dyes, is made by reacting aniline with sulfuric acid.

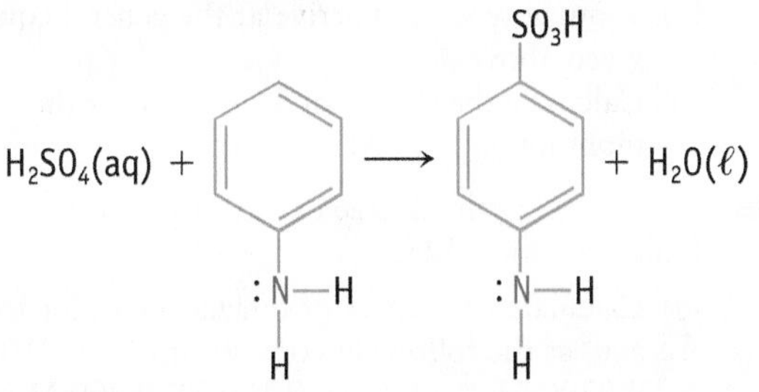

aniline sulfanilic acid

(a) Is aniline a Brønsted base, a Lewis base, or both? Explain, using its possible reactions with HCl, BF_3, or other acid.

(b) Sulfanilic acid has a pK_a value of 3.23. The sodium salt of the acid, $Na(H_2NC_6H_4SO_3)$, is quite soluble in water. If you dissolve 1.25 g of the salt in water to give 125 mL of solution, what is the pH of the solution?

116. Amino acids are an important group of compounds. At low pH, both the carboxylic acid group ($—CO_2H$) and the amine group (—NHR) are protonated. However, as the pH of the solution increases (say by adding base), the carboxylic acid proton is removed, usually at a pH between 2 and 3. In a middle range of pHs, therefore, the amine group is protonated, but the carboxylic acid group has lost the proton. (This is called a *zwitterion.*) At more basic pH values, the amine proton is dissociated.

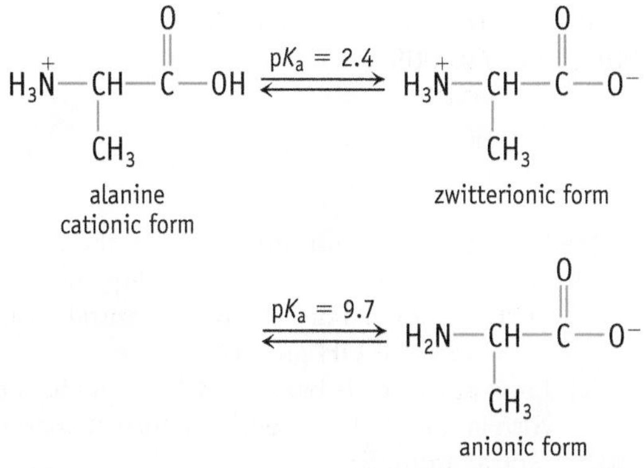

What is the pH of a 0.20 M solution of alanine hydrochloride, $[NH_3CHCH_3CO_2H]Cl$?

Summary and Conceptual Questions

The following questions may use concepts from this and previous chapters.

117. How can water be both a Brønsted base and a Lewis base? Can water be a Brønsted acid? A Lewis acid?

118. The nickel(II) ion exists as $[Ni(H_2O)_6]^{2+}$ in aqueous solution. Why is this solution acidic? As part of your answer, include a balanced equation depicting what happens when $[Ni(H_2O)_6]^{2+}$ interacts with water.

119. The halogens form three stable, weak acids, HOX.

Acid	pK_a
HOCl	7.46
HOBr	8.7
HOI	10.6

(a) Which is the strongest of these acids?

(b) Explain why the acid strength changes as the halogen atom is changed.

120. The acidity of the oxoacids was described in Section 16-9, and a larger number of acids are listed in the table below.

$E(OH)_m$	pK_a	$EO(OH)_m$	pK_a	$EO_2(OH)_m$	pK_a	$EO_3(OH)_m$	pK_a
Very weak		**Weak**		**Strong**		**Very strong**	
Cl(OH)	7.5	ClO(OH)	2	$ClO_2(OH)$	−3	$ClO_3(OH)$	−10
Br(OH)	8.7	NO(OH)	3.4	$NO_2(OH)$	−1.4		
I(OH)	10.6	IO(OH)	1.6	$IO_2(OH)$	0.8		
$Si(OH)_4$	9.7	$SO(OH)_2$	1.8	$SO_2(OH)_2$	−3		
$Sb(OH)_3$	11.0	$SeO(OH)_2$	2.5	$SeO_2(OH)_2$	−3		
$As(OH)_3$	9.2	$AsO(OH)_3$	2.3				
		$PO(OH)_3$	2.1				
		$HPO(OH)_2$	1.8				
		$H_2PO(OH)$	2.0				

(a) What general trends do you see in these data?
(b) What has a greater effect on acidity, the number of O atoms bonded directly to the central atom E or the number of OH groups?
(c) Look at the acids based on Cl, N, and S. Is there a correlation of acidity with the formal charge on the central atom, E?
(d) The acid H_3PO_3 has a pK_a of 1.8, and this led to some insight into its structure. If the structure of the acid were $P(OH)_3$, what would be its predicted pK_a value? Given that this is a diprotic acid, which H atoms are lost as H^+ ions?

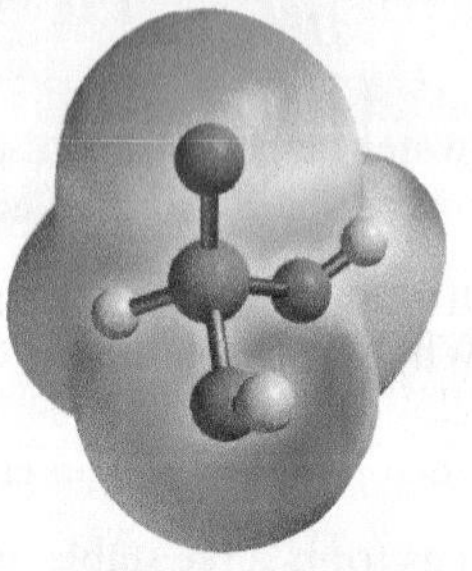

The acid H_3PO_3

121. Perchloric acid behaves as an acid, even when it is dissolved in sulfuric acid.
(a) Write a balanced equation showing how perchloric acid can transfer a proton to sulfuric acid.
(b) Draw a Lewis electron dot structure for sulfuric acid. How can sulfuric acid function as a base?

122. You purchase a bottle of water. On checking its pH, you find that it is not neutral, as you might have expected. Instead, it is slightly acidic. Why?

123. Iodine, I_2, is much more soluble in an aqueous solution of potassium iodide, KI, than it is in pure water. The anion found in solution is I_3^-.
(a) Draw an electron dot structure for I_3^-.
(b) Write an equation for this reaction, indicating the Lewis acid and the Lewis base.

124. ▲ Uracil is a base found in RNA. Indicate sites in the molecule where hydrogen bonding is possible or that are sites of Lewis basicity.

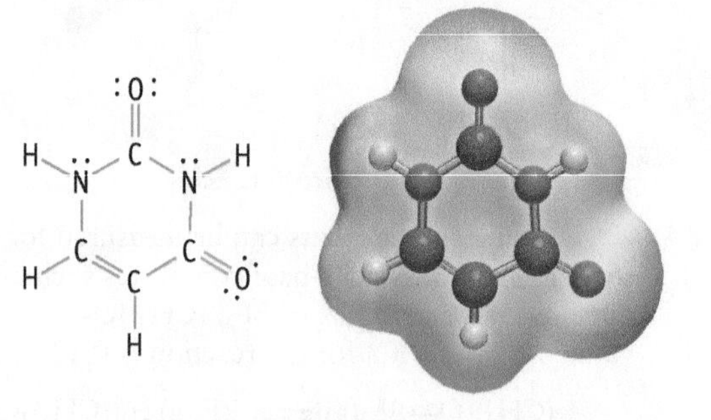

Uracil

125. Chemists often refer to the *degree of ionization* of a weak acid or base and give it the symbol α. The equilibrium constant in terms of α and C_o, the initial acid or base concentration, is given by the useful equation

$$K = \frac{\alpha^2 C_o}{(1 - \alpha)}$$

As an example, the degree of ionization for 0.010 M acetic acid is 0.0103.
(a) Show how we can arrive at the general equation given above.
(b) Calculate the degree of ionization for the ammonium ion in 0.10 M NH_4Cl.

126. ▲ Exploring the degree of ionization equation in Study Question 125:
(a) Calculate the degree of ionization, α, for formic acid at the following concentrations: 0.0100 M, 0.0200 M, 0.0400 M, 0.100 M, 0.200 M, 0.400 M, 1.00 M, 2.00 M, and 4.00 M.
(b) Plot the results of the calculation as α versus formic acid concentration. Is there a linear relationship? If not, try plotting the logarithm of C_o versus α.
(c) What can you conclude about the relationship of the degree of ionization and the initial acid or base concentration?

127. ▲ Consider a salt of a weak base and a weak acid such as ammonium cyanide. Both the NH_4^+ and CN^- ions interact with water in aqueous solution, but the net reaction can be considered as a proton transfer from NH_4^+ to CN^-.

$$NH_4^+(aq) + CN^-(aq) \rightleftharpoons NH_3(aq) + HCN(aq)$$

(a) Show that the equilibrium constant for this reaction, K_{net}, is

$$K_{net} = \frac{K_w}{K_a K_b}$$

where K_a is the ionization constant for the weak acid HCN and K_b is the constant for the weak base NH_3.

(b) Calculate K_{net} values for each of the following: NH_4CN, $NH_4CH_3CO_2$, and NH_4F. Which salt has the largest value of K_{net} and why?

(c) Predict whether a solution of each of the compounds in (b) is acidic or basic. Explain how you made this prediction. (You do not need a calculation to make this prediction.)

AP Multiple-Choice Review Questions

Questions 1–3 refer to the following:

$HF(aq) + H_2O(\ell) \rightleftharpoons H_3O^+(aq) + F^-(aq) \quad K = 7.2 \times 10^{-4}$

1. Which species are considered to be Brønsted-Lowry acids?

(A) Only HF is a Brønsted-Lowry acid because it donates a proton.

(B) HF and H_3O^+ are both Brønsted-Lowry acids because they both donate protons.

(C) HF and F^- are both Brønsted-Lowry acids because HF gains a proton while F^- donates a proton.

(D) HF and H_2O are both Brønsted-Lowry acids because HF donates a proton while H_2O gains a proton.

2. If the concentration of the HF in the reaction above is 0.1 *M*, what is an approximate pH of the solution?

(A) 1

(B) 2

(C) 7

(D) 9

3. Which is the strongest base in this reaction?

(A) F^-

(B) H_2O

(C) HF

(D) H_3O^+

4. Which of the following correctly ranks the species from weakest to strongest base?

HF ($K_a = 7.1 \times 10^{-4}$)
HCN ($K_a = 6.2 \times 10^{-10}$)
$HClO_2$ ($K_a = 1.2 \times 10^{-2}$)
NH_4^+ ($K_a = 5.6 \times 10^{-10}$)

(A) $CN^- < NH_3 < F^- < ClO_2^- < H_2O < NO_3^-$

(B) $CN^- < NH_3 < F^- < ClO_2^- < NO_3^- < H_2O$

(C) $H_2O < NO_3^- < ClO_2^- < F^- < NH_3 < CN^-$

(D) $NO_3^- < H_2O < ClO_2^- < F^- < NH_3 < CN^-$

5. At the normal body temperature of a human, 37 °C, the equilibrium constant for the dissociation of water is higher than it is at 25 °C, as shown in the equilibrium expression.

$$K_w = [H^+][OH^-] = 2.42 \times 10^{-14}$$

What is true of pure water at 37 °C?

(A) Water is neutral because the hydrogen and hydroxide ion concentrations are equal.

(B) Water is basic because the hydroxide ion concentration is greater than 1×10^{-7} *M*.

(C) Water is acidic because the hydrogen ion concentration is greater than 1×10^{-7} *M*.

(D) Water is neutral because the hydrogen and hydroxide ion concentrations are each 1×10^{-7} *M*.

6. The acid strength of the oxyacids of chlorine is as follows:

$$HClO_4 > HClO_3 > HClO_2 > HClO$$

Which statement best explains this trend?

(A) The electrons in the H—O bond are pulled away from the hydrogen by the more electronegative oxygen, making the bond weaker. Additional oxygen atoms intensify this effect, making the H—O bond even weaker and increasing the degree of ionization.

(B) Oxygen is less electronegative than hydrogen. Additional oxygen atoms provide greater repulsion of the electrons and cause them to be even closer to the hydrogen atom, making the H—O bond weaker and increasing the degree of ionization.

(C) Extra electrons are always attracted to the central atom in a molecule. With more oxygen atoms, additional electrons are transferred to the chlorine atom. This weakens the H—O bond and increases the degree of ionization.

(D) Oxygen has six valence electrons. Each oxygen atom needs two additional electrons to fulfill its octet. These electrons are pulled from the H—O bond and cause the acid to ionize. More oxygen atoms require more electrons, so the degree of ionization increases.

Questions 7–9 refer to the following solutions:

Beaker #1	Beaker #2	Beaker #3
HCl(*aq*)	HNO_2(*aq*)	HI(*aq*)

Each beaker contains 100 mL of the indicated acidic solution, all with a pH of 3.00.

$$K_a \text{ for } HNO_2 = 4.0 \times 10^{-4}$$

7. Which beaker would have the highest hydrogen ion concentration?

(A) Beaker 1 has the highest hydrogen ion concentration.

(B) Beaker 2 has the highest hydrogen ion concentration.

(C) Beaker 1 and 3 are equally high.

(D) All have the same hydrogen ion concentration.

8. Which solution has the highest percent ionization?

(A) Beaker 1 has the highest percent ionization.

(B) Beaker 2 has the highest percent ionization.

(C) Beakers 1 and 3 are equally high.

(D) All have the same percent ionization.

9. If 50 mL of 0.1 M NaOH was added to each beaker, which resulting solution would have the lowest pH?
(A) Beaker 1 would have the lowest pH.
(B) Beaker 2 would have the lowest pH.
(C) Beakers 1 and 3 are equally low.
(D) All would have the same pH.

10. A solution is prepared by mixing 500 mL of 1 M HCl with 500 mL of 0.01 M HNO_3. What is the pH of the resulting solution?
(A) 0.0
(B) between 0.0 and 1.0
(C) 1.0
(D) greater than 1.0

11. In a research project, a scientist adds 0.1 mole of HCN, 0.1 mole of H_3O^+, and 0.1 mole of CN^- to water to make a total volume of 1 L. Will this reaction proceed to a greater extent in the forward direction or in the reverse direction?

$$HCN + H_2O \rightleftharpoons H_3O^+ + CN^- \qquad K_a = 6.2 \times 10^{-10}$$

(A) Forward; acids always dissociate in water.
(B) Forward; the K value is less than 1.
(C) Reverse; the K value is less than 1.
(D) Reverse; water cannot be a reactant.

12. What is the conjugate acid of HPO_4^{2-}?
(A) H_3O^+
(B) PO_4^{3-}
(C) $H_2PO_4^-$
(D) H_3PO_4

13. Bromothymol blue is a chemical indicator that turns blue at pH values greater than 7. In which of these solutions would a blue color be observed if 2 drops of bromothymol blue were added? The concentration of each solution is 0.10 M. K_a for $HC_2H_3O_2(aq) = 1.8 \times 10^{-5}$; K_b for $NH_3(aq) = 1.8 \times 10^{-5}$.
(A) NH_4Cl
(B) $NaNO_3$
(C) $NH_4C_2H_3O_2$
(D) $NaC_2H_3O_2$

14. A weak acid, HZ, has a K_a of 1.0×10^{-7}. What is the pH of a 0.10 M solution of HZ?
(A) 1.00
(B) 3.50
(C) 4.00
(D) 7.00

15. HA is a weak, monoprotic acid that dissociated according to the equation

$$HA(aq) \rightleftharpoons H^+(aq) + A^-(aq) \text{ and } K_a = 4.0 \times 10^{-9}$$

If the initial concentration of HA is 0.10 M, find the concentration of H^+.
(A) 2.0×10^{-4} M
(B) 2.0×10^{-5} M
(C) 7.5×10^{-8} M
(D) 8.5×10^{-10} M

Questions 16 and 17 refer to the following reaction:

$$CH_3NH_2(aq) + H_2O(\ell) \rightleftharpoons CH_3NH_3^+(aq) + OH^-(aq) \qquad K_b = 4.00 \times 10^{-4}$$

16. Determine the $[OH^-]$ for 0.25 M methylamine, CH_3NH_2.
(A) 2.0×10^{-7} M
(B) 6.0×10^{-5} M
(C) 1.0×10^{-4} M
(D) 1.0×10^{-2} M

17. Determine the pH of the methylamine solution.
(A) 4.00
(B) 6.00
(C) 10.00
(D) 12.00

18. Solution A consists of 1.0 M $HC_2H_3O_2$ ($K_a = 1.8 \times 10^{-5}$), and Solution B consists of 1.0 M $HC_2H_3O_2$ and 1.0 M $NaC_2H_3O_2$. Which of the following statements is true?
(A) $HC_2H_3O_2$ undergoes a greater percent dissociation in Solution A than Solution B, and the pH of Solution A is lower than that of Solution B.
(B) $HC_2H_3O_2$ undergoes a greater percent dissociation in Solution A than Solution B, and the pH of Solution A is higher than that of Solution B.
(C) $HC_2H_3O_2$ undergoes a lower percent dissociation in Solution A than Solution B, and the pH of Solution A is lower than that of Solution B.
(D) $HC_2H_3O_2$ undergoes a lower percent dissociation in Solution A than Solution B, and the pH of Solution A is higher than that of Solution B.

Questions 19 and 20 refer to the following information:

0.01 M HX	$K_a = 1.0 \times 10^{-4}$
0.01 M HA	$K_a = 1.0 \times 10^{-8}$

19. Which acid solution has a greater pH?
(A) HA because it dissociates less than HX
(B) HA because it dissociates more than HX
(C) HX because it dissociates less than HA
(D) HX because it dissociates more than HA

20. How would diluting HA from 0.15 M to 0.005 M affect the pH of the solution?
(A) The pH would decrease because the $[H^+]$ decreases.
(B) The pH would decrease because the $[H^+]$ increases.
(C) The pH would increase because the $[H^+]$ decreases.
(D) The pH would increase because the $[H^+]$ increases.

AP Free Response Review Questions

Question Format: Short

Category of Question: Quantitative

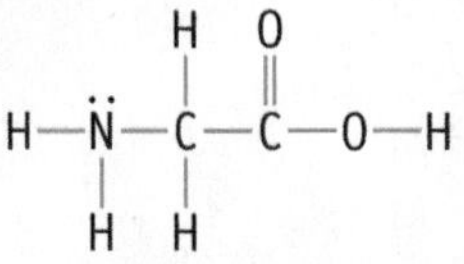

The simplest amino acid is glycine, whose structure is shown above. An aqueous solution of glycine is prepared by dissolving 0.329 g in 150. mL of water at a temperature of 25 °C. The resulting solution has a pH of 2.02.

Questions

(a) Calculate the molarity of the solution.

(b) Calculate the percent ionization of this solution of glycine.

(c) Calculate the K_a for glycine.

Question Format: Short

Category of Question: Quantitative

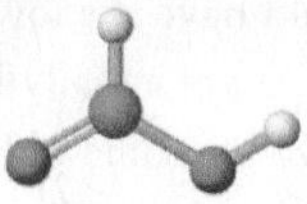

Formic acid, as shown in the model above, is a weak acid with a K_a value of 1.8×10^{-4} at 25 °C. A solution with a concentration of 0.424 *M* formic acid is prepared in the laboratory.

Questions

(a) Write the ionization equation for an aqueous solution of formic acid.

(b) Determine the pH of the solution prepared above.

Question Format: Long

Category of Question: Representation 2

Below are six representations of aqueous solutions of acids or bases, all with equal molarities. Small spheres represent hydrogen ions. Larger spheres and rectangles represent other ions or molecules. Answer the following questions about the representations.

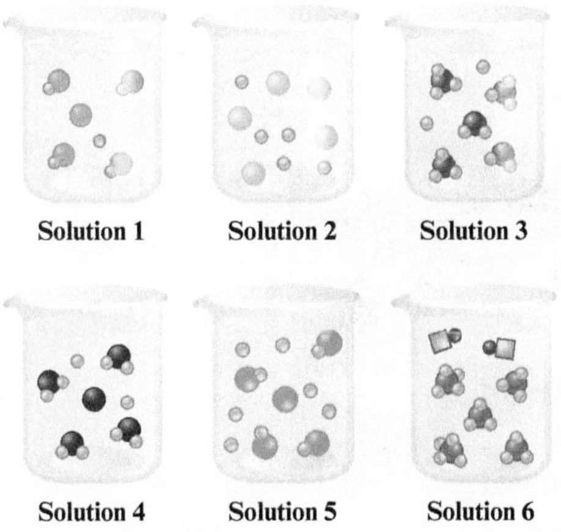

Questions

(a) Which solution is the most accurate representation of $HCl(aq)$? Explain your reasoning.

(b) Which solution is the most accurate representation of $NH_3(aq)$? Explain your reasoning.

(c) Which solution is the most accurate representation of $H_2SO_4(aq)$? Explain your reasoning.

(d) Which solution is the most accurate representation of $HC_2H_3O_2(aq)$? Explain your reasoning.

(e) Which solution would have the lowest pH? Explain your reasoning.

Rhubarb makes a good pie and is a very good source of oxalic acid, a weak acid.

Principles of Chemical Reactivity: Other Aspects of Aqueous Equilibria

Chapter Outline

NATURE'S ACIDS Many people grow rhubarb in gardens because the stalks of the plant, when stewed with sugar, make a wonderful dessert or filling for a pie or tart. But the leaves can make you sick! Why?

Rhubarb leaves are a source of at least seven organic acids, among them acetic and citric acids. But the most abundant is oxalic acid, $H_2C_2O_4$.

$$H_2C_2O_4(aq) + H_2O(\ell) \rightleftharpoons H_3O^+(aq) + HC_2O_4^-(aq)$$
$$HC_2O_4^-(aq) + H_2O(\ell) \rightleftharpoons H_3O^+(aq) + C_2O_4^{2-}(aq)$$

Rhubarb leaves contain between 0.1% and 1.4% by weight oxalic acid; other leafy vegetables such as cabbage, spinach, and beet tops have lesser amounts.

While oxalic acid and other acids give the tart taste many of us enjoy with rhubarb, there is a problem with ingesting it: oxalic acid interferes with essential elements in the body such as iron, magnesium, and, especially, calcium. The Ca^{2+} ion and oxalic acid react to form insoluble calcium oxalate, CaC_2O_4.

Chapter Goals

See Chapter Goals Revisited (page 675) for Study Questions keyed to these goals.

UNDERSTAND

- The common ion effect.
- The control of pH in aqueous solutions with buffers.

DO

- Calculate the pH of buffer solutions.
- Evaluate the pH in the course of acid–base titrations.
- Apply chemical equilibrium concepts to the solubility of ionic compounds.

REMEMBER

- Acid–base buffers are composed of weak acids and their conjugate bases.
- Acid–base buffers are resistant to changes in pH.
- The pH of a buffer is close to the pK_a of its weak acid.
- Insoluble salts in which the anion is the conjugate base of a weak acid dissolve in strong acids.

$$Ca^{2+}(aq) + H_2C_2O_4(aq) + 2\ H_2O(\ell) \rightarrow CaC_2O_4(s) + 2\ H_3O^+(aq)$$

Not only does this effectively remove calcium ions from the body, but calcium oxalate crystals can also grow into painful kidney and bladder stones. Because of this, people susceptible to kidney stones are put on a low-oxalic acid diet. They also have to be careful of taking too much vitamin C, a compound that can be turned into oxalic acid in the body. People have died from accidentally drinking antifreeze because the ethylene glycol in the antifreeze is converted into oxalic acid in the body. Symptoms of oxalic acid poisoning include nausea, vomiting, abdominal pain, and hemorrhages.

Because oxalic acid also occurs in other edible substances, including cocoa, peanuts, and tea, the average person consumes about 150 mg of oxalic acid a day. But will it kill you? For a person weighing about 68 kg (150 pounds), the lethal dose is around 24 grams of pure oxalic acid. You would have to eat a field of rhubarb leaves or drink an

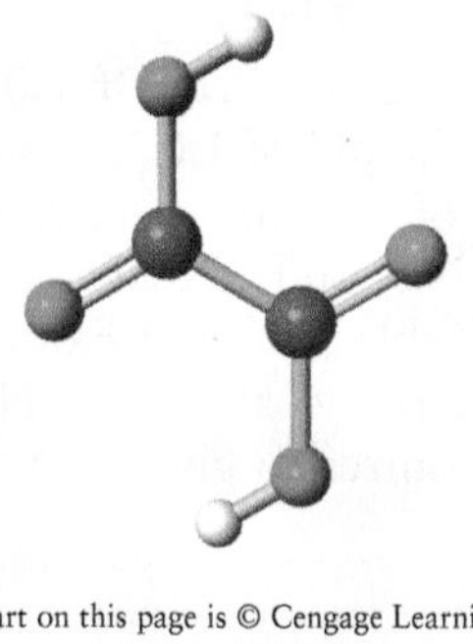

A model of oxalic acid, $H_2C_2O_4$, the acid in rhubarb.

ocean of tea to come close to a fatal dose of oxalic acid. What would happen first, however, is that you may have severe diarrhea. Your gut recognizes oxalic acid as something to be eliminated and is stimulated to get rid of it.

In spite of the minor health risk from eating too much rhubarb, this plant and others have been cultivated for thousands of years for their healthful properties. The Chinese particularly have used rhubarb in traditional medicine for centuries. Indeed, emperors of China in the 18th and 19th centuries forbade its export because it was so important. Rhubarb was also cultivated in Russia and later in England. It made first its appearance in the United States in about 1800.

When you enjoy a slice of rhubarb pie, think about the topics in this chapter: the chemistry of acids and bases and of insoluble substances.

Study Questions related to this story are: 17.93 and 17.94.

In Chapter 3, four fundamental types of chemical reactions are described: acid–base reactions, precipitation reactions, gas-forming reactions, and oxidation-reduction reactions. In the present chapter, the principles of chemical equilibria are applied to the first two kinds of reactions.

With regard to acid–base reactions, the goals are to answer the following questions:

- How can the pH of a solution be controlled?
- What happens when an acid and base are mixed in any amount?

Precipitation reactions can also be understood in terms of chemical equilibria. The following questions are discussed in this chapter:

- If aqueous solutions of two ionic compounds are mixed, will precipitation occur?
- To what extent does an "insoluble" substance actually dissolve?
- What chemical reactions can be used to dissolve a precipitate?

17-1 The Common Ion Effect

In the previous chapter, you studied the behavior of weak acids and bases in aqueous solution. But what happens to the pH of an acetic acid solution to which you add a significant concentration of its conjugate base, the acetate ion? The answer is that the pH of such a solution—weak acid + conjugate base or weak base + conjugate acid—is different than the pH of a solution of the weak acid or base by itself. The effect on the pH that is produced by having a significant concentration of acetate ion in an acetic acid solution, for example, is called the **common ion effect**. The name comes from the fact that the added acetate ion is "common" to the ionization equilibrium reaction of acetic acid.

$$CH_3CO_2H(aq) + H_2O(\ell) \rightleftharpoons H_3O^+(aq) + CH_3CO_2^-(aq)$$

Exploring this aspect of acid–base chemistry here will be important in understanding *buffer solutions* (see Section 17-2).

How does the common ion effect work (Figure 17.1)? If 1.0 L of a 0.25 M acetic acid solution has a pH of 2.67, what is the pH of 1.0 L of solution prepared with 0.25 mol of acetic acid and 0.10 mol of sodium acetate? Sodium acetate, $NaCH_3CO_2$, is 100% dissociated into its ions, Na^+ and $CH_3CO_2^-$, in water. Sodium ion has no effect on the pH of a solution (◀ Table 16.3 and Example 16.2). Thus, the important components of the solution are the weak acid (CH_3CO_2H) and its conjugate base ($CH_3CO_2^-$). Assume the acid ionizes to give H_3O^+ and $CH_3CO_2^-$,

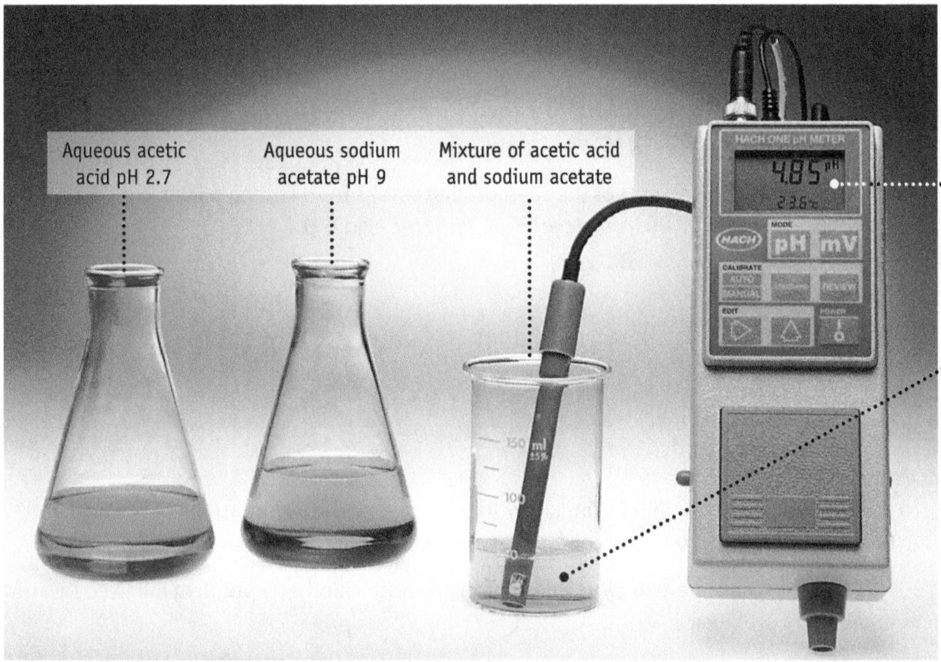

FIGURE 17.1 **The common ion effect.** The acetic acid and sodium acetate solutions each had about the same concentration. Each solution contains universal indicator. This dye is red in low pH, yellow in slightly acidic media, and green in neutral to weakly basic media.

both in the concentration x. This means that, relative to their initial concentrations, CH_3CO_2H decreases in concentration slightly (by a concentration x) and $CH_3CO_2^-$ increases slightly (by a concentration x).

EQUATION	CH_3CO_2H	+	H_2O	$\rightleftharpoons$	H_3O^+	+	$CH_3CO_2^-$
Initial (M)	0.25				0		0.10
Change (M)	$-x$				$+x$		$+x$
Equilibrium (M)	$(0.25 - x)$				x		$0.10 + x$

The Common Ion Effect In this ICE table, the first row (Initial) reflects the assumption that no ionization of the acid (or hydrolysis of the conjugate base) has yet occurred. Ionization of the acid in the presence of the conjugate base then produces x mol/L of hydronium ion and x mol/L more of the conjugate base.

Because the equilibrium concentrations of all species are related through the variable x and the acid dissociation constant (K_a) is known, the hydronium ion concentration ($= x$) can be calculated from the equilibrium constant expression.

$$K_a = 1.8 \times 10^{-5} = \frac{[H_3O^+][CH_3CO_2^-]}{[CH_3CO_2H]} = \frac{(x)(0.10 + x)}{0.25 - x}$$

Next, assume x is quite small because acetic acid is a weak acid and because it is ionizing in the presence of a significant concentration of its conjugate base. That is, it is reasonable to assume that $(0.10 + x)$M $\approx$ 0.10 M and that $(0.25 - x)$M $\approx$ 0.25 M. This leads to the "approximate" expression.

$$K_a = 1.8 \times 10^{-5} = \frac{[H_3O^+][CH_3CO_2^-]}{[CH_3CO_2H]} = \frac{(x)(0.10)}{0.25}$$

Solving this expression yields $x = [H_3O^+] = 4.5 \times 10^{-5}$ M and the pH is 4.35. (Note that the simplifying assumptions were valid.)

Equilibrium Constants and Temperature Unless specified otherwise, all equilibrium constants and all calculations in this chapter are at 25 °C.

Without added $NaCH_3CO_2$, which provides the "common ion" $CH_3CO_2^-$, the ionization of 0.25 M acetic acid will produce H_3O^+ and $CH_3CO_2^-$ ions in a concentration of 0.0021 M (pH = 2.67). Le Chatelier's principle, however, predicts that the added common ion causes the reaction to proceed less far to the right. Hence, as calculated above, $[H_3O^+]$ is less than 0.0021 M in the presence of added acetate ion.

Strategy Map 17.1

PROBLEM

Calculate **pH** after combining solutions of **NaOH** and **lactic acid.**

↓

DATA/INFORMATION KNOWN

- Solution concentrations
- Solution volumes
- Value of acid K_a

↓ STEP 1. Stoichiometry problem.

Concentrations of **lactic acid** and **lactate ion** after acid–base reaction

↓ STEP 2. Enter **equilibrium concentrations** in ICE table.

At equilibrium:
$[H_3O^+] = x$
[Lactic acid] = original conc. − x
[Lactate ion] = original conc. + x

↓ STEP 3. Enter **equilibrium concentrations** in K_a.

K_a expression with equilibrium concentrations in terms of ***x***

↓ STEP 4. Solve **K_a expression** for ***x***.

Value of $[H_3O^+]$

↓ STEP 5. Convert $[H_3O^+]$ to **pH.**

pH of solution

EXAMPLE 17.1

Reaction of Lactic Acid with a Deficiency of Sodium Hydroxide

Problem What is the pH of the solution that results from adding 25.0 mL of 0.0500 M NaOH to 25.0 mL of 0.100 M lactic acid? (K_a for lactic acid = 1.4×10^{-4})

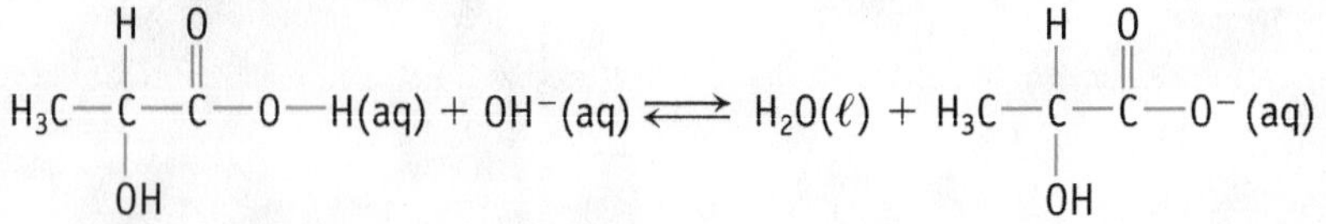

lactic acid ($HC_3H_5O_3$)
$K_a = 1.4 \times 10^{-4}$

lactate ion ($C_3H_5O_3^-$)

What Do You Know? You know the volumes and concentrations of the acid and base, and the ionization constant for the weak acid.

Strategy There are two parts to this problem: a stoichiometry problem followed by an equilibrium problem.

Part 1: *Stoichiometry Problem*

(a) Determine the initial amounts of acid and base from their volumes and concentrations.

(b) Work a limiting reactant problem (in moles) to determine the amounts of lactic acid and lactate ion remaining in solution after the reaction between lactic acid and sodium hydroxide.

(c) Calculate the concentrations of lactic acid and lactate ion that are present from the amounts of lactic acid and lactate ion calculated in step (b) and the total volume of solution.

Part 2: *Equilibrium Problem*

(a) Set up an ICE table where the initial acid and conjugate base concentrations are known and the changes in the concentration of acid consumed and concentration of conjugate base produced are defined as x.

(b) Insert the equilibrium concentrations in the K_a expression for lactic acid and solve for x, then calculate the pH from the equilibrium hydronium ion concentration (= x).

Solution

Part 1: *Stoichiometry Problem*

(a) Amounts of NaOH and lactic acid used in the reaction

$$(0.0250 \text{ L NaOH})(0.0500 \text{ mol/L}) = 1.25 \times 10^{-3} \text{ mol NaOH}$$

$$(0.0250 \text{ L lactic acid})(0.100 \text{ mol/L}) = 2.50 \times 10^{-3} \text{ mol lactic acid}$$

(b) Amount of lactate ion produced by the acid–base reaction

Recognizing that NaOH is the limiting reactant, you have

$$(1.25 \times 10^{-3} \text{ mol NaOH})\left(\frac{1 \text{ mol lactate ion}}{1 \text{ mol NaOH}}\right) = 1.25 \times 10^{-3} \text{ mol lactate ion produced}$$

Amount of lactic acid consumed

$$(1.25 \times 10^{-3} \text{ mol NaOH})\left(\frac{1 \text{ mol lactic acid}}{1 \text{ mol NaOH}}\right) = 1.25 \times 10^{-3} \text{ mol lactic acid consumed}$$

Amount of lactic acid remaining when reaction is complete.

$$2.50 \times 10^{-3} \text{ mol lactic acid available} - 1.25 \times 10^{-3} \text{ mol lactic acid consumed}$$
$$= 1.25 \times 10^{-3} \text{ mol lactic acid remaining}$$

(c) Concentrations of lactic acid and lactate ion after reaction. Note that the total solution volume after reaction is 50.0 mL or 0.0500 L.

$$[\text{Lactic acid}] = \frac{1.25 \times 10^{-3} \text{ mol lactic acid}}{0.0500 \text{ L}} = 2.50 \times 10^{-2} \text{ M}$$

Because the amount of lactic acid remaining is the same as the amount of lactate ion produced, you have

$$[\text{Lactic acid}] = [\text{lactate ion}] = 2.50 \times 10^{-2} \text{ M}$$

Part 2: *Equilibrium Problem*

(a) The concentrations just determined are used as the initial concentrations in an ICE table.

Equilibrium	$HC_3H_5O_3$	+	H_2O	$\rightleftarrows$	H_3O^+	+	$C_3H_5O_3^-$
Initial (M)	0.0250				0		0.0250
Change (M)	$-x$				$+x$		$+x$
Equilibrium (M)	$(0.0250 - x)$				x		$(0.0250 + x)$

(b) Substituting the concentrations into the equilibrium constant expression, you have

$$K_a \text{ (lactic acid)} = 1.4 \times 10^{-4} = \frac{[H_3O^+][C_3H_5O_2^-]}{[HC_3H_5O_2]} = \frac{(x)(0.0250 + x)}{0.0250 - x}$$

Making the assumption that x is small with respect to 0.0250 M, you see that

$$K_a = 1.4 \times 10^{-4} \text{ M} = x = [H_3O^+], \text{ which gives a pH of } 3.85.$$

Think about Your Answer There are several observations to be made:

- The assumption that $x << 0.0250$ in Part 2 is valid.
- By a separate calculation, it can be shown that a 0.025 M lactic acid solution has a pH of 2.73. The presence of 0.025 M lactate ion (a Brønsted base) in this solution has resulted in an increase of the pH to 3.85.
- Here a base was added to the acidic solution. A useful observation is that *adding base to any solution will always result in an increase in pH.*

Check Your Understanding

You have a 0.30 M solution of formic acid (HCO_2H) and have added enough sodium formate ($NaHCO_2$) to make the solution 0.10 M in the salt. Calculate the pH of the formic acid solution before and after adding solid sodium formate.

REVIEW & CHECK FOR SECTION 17-1

1. What is the pH of the solution that results from adding 30.0 mL of 0.100 M NaOH to 45.0 mL of 0.100 M acetic acid?

   (a) 2.87 (b) 5.05 (c) 7.00

Learning Objectives: LO 6.18 (see APEC Lab 15 "Buffers and Buffered Systems"), LO 6.19, LO 6.20 (see APEC Lab 16 "Acids, Bases, and Buffers")

17-2 Controlling pH: Buffer Solutions

The addition of a small quantity of strong acid or base, say 0.010 mol, to a liter of human blood leads to a change in pH of only about 0.1 pH units from the normal pH of about 7.4. In comparison, if you add 0.010 mol of HCl to 1.0 L of pure water, the pH drops from 7 to 2. Addition of 0.010 mol of NaOH to pure water increases the pH from 7 to 12. Blood, and many other body fluids, are said to be buffered. *A buffered solution is resistant to a change in pH when an acid or base is added* (Figure 17.2).

There are two requirements for a buffer:

- Two substances are needed: an acid capable of reacting with added OH^- ions and a base that can consume added H_3O^+ ions.
- The acid and base must not react with each another.

Buffers and the Common Ion Effect The common ion effect is observed for an acid (or base) ionizing in the presence of its conjugate base (or acid). A buffer is a solution of a weak acid and its conjugate base.

These requirements mean a buffer is usually prepared from a conjugate acid–base pair (such as acetic acid and acetate ion). Some buffers commonly used in the laboratory are given in Table 17.1.

To see how a buffer works, consider an acetic acid/acetate ion buffer. Acetic acid, a weak acid, is needed to consume any added hydroxide ions.

$$CH_3CO_2H(aq) + OH^-(aq) \rightleftharpoons CH_3CO_2^-(aq) + H_2O(\ell) \qquad K = 1.8 \times 10^9$$

The equilibrium constant for the reaction is very large because OH^- is a much stronger base than acetate ion, $CH_3CO_2^-$ (◀ Section 16-5 and Table 16.2). This means that any OH^- entering the solution from an outside source is consumed completely. In a similar way, any hydronium ion added to the solution reacts completely with the acetate ion present in the buffer.

$$H_3O^+(aq) + CH_3CO_2^-(aq) \rightleftharpoons H_2O(\ell) + CH_3CO_2H(aq) \qquad K = 5.6 \times 10^4$$

The equilibrium constant for this reaction is also quite large because H_3O^+ is a much stronger acid than CH_3CO_2H.

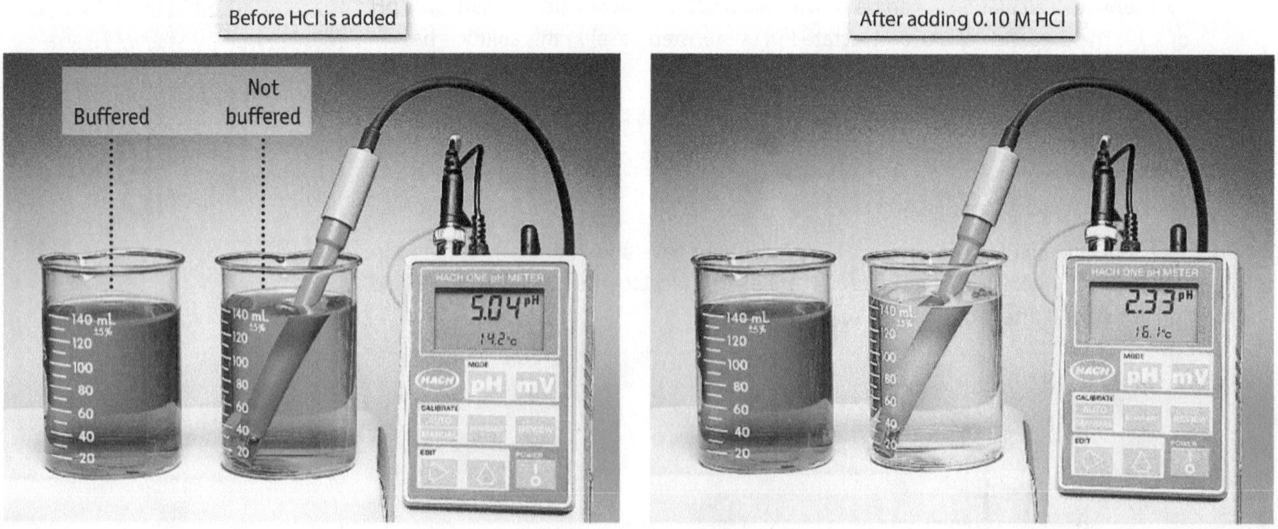

Photos: © Cengage Learning/Charles D. Winters

(a) The pH electrode is indicating the pH of water that contains a trace of acid (and bromphenol blue acid–base indicator). The solution at the left is a buffer solution with a pH of about 7. (It also contains bromphenol blue dye.)

(b) When 5 mL of 0.10 M HCl is added to each solution, the pH of the water drops several units, whereas the pH of the buffer stays essentially constant, as implied by the fact that the indicator color does not change.

FIGURE 17.2 **Buffer solutions.**

Table 17.1 Some Commonly Used Buffer Systems

Weak Acid	Conjugate Base	Acid K_a (pK_a)	Useful pH Range
Phthalic acid, $C_6H_4(CO_2H)_2$	Hydrogen phthalate ion, $C_6H_4(CO_2H)(CO_2)^-$	1.3×10^{-3} (2.89)	1.9–3.9
Acetic acid, CH_3CO_2H	Acetate ion, $CH_3CO_2^-$	1.8×10^{-5} (4.74)	3.7–5.8
Dihydrogen phosphate ion, $H_2PO_4^-$	Hydrogen phosphate ion, HPO_4^{2-}	6.2×10^{-8} (7.21)	6.2–8.2
Hydrogen phosphate ion, HPO_4^{2-}	Phosphate ion, PO_4^{3-}	3.6×10^{-13} (12.44)	11.4–13.4

The next several examples illustrate how to calculate the pH of a buffer solution, how to prepare a buffer, and how a buffer can control the pH of a solution.

EXAMPLE 17.2

pH of a Buffer Solution

Problem What is the pH of an acetic acid/sodium acetate buffer with $[CH_3CO_2H] = 0.700$ M and $[CH_3CO_2^-] = 0.600$ M?

What Do You Know? The hydronium ion concentration (and so the pH) of a buffer can be calculated if you know the concentrations of the weak acid, its conjugate base, and K_a, as is the case here.

Strategy

- Write the balanced equation and the equilibrium constant expression.
- Set up an ICE table where the initial concentrations of acid and conjugate base are known, and the change in their concentrations is designated by x.
- Use the K_a expression to solve for the hydronium ion concentration.

Solution

Equilibrium	CH_3CO_2H	+	H_2O	$\rightleftarrows$	H_3O^+	+	$CH_3CO_2^-$
Initial (M)	0.700				0		0.600
Change (M)	$-x$				$+x$		$+x$
Equilibrium (M)	$0.700 - x$				x		$0.600 + x$

The appropriate equilibrium constant expression is

$$K_a = 1.8 \times 10^{-5} = \frac{[H_3O^+][CH_3CO_2^-]}{[CH_3CO_2H]} = \frac{(x)(0.600 + x)}{0.700 - x}$$

The value of x will be very small with respect to 0.700 or 0.600, so you can use the "approximate expression" to find x, the hydronium ion concentration.

$$K_a = 1.8 \times 10^{-5} = \frac{[H_3O^+][CH_3CO_2^-]}{[CH_3CO_2H]} = \frac{(x)(0.600)}{0.700}$$

$$x = 2.1 \times 10^{-5}\ \text{M}$$

$$\text{pH} = -\log(2.1 \times 10^{-5}) = 4.68$$

Strategy Map 17.2

PROBLEM
Calculate **pH** of a **buffer solution.**

DATA/INFORMATION KNOWN
- Concentration of **weak acid**
- Concentration of **conjugate base**
- Value of acid K_a

STEP 1. Write **balanced equation** and **K_a expression** and set up **ICE table.**

K_a expression and ICE table

STEP 2. Enter **equilibrium concentrations** in ICE table.

At equilibrium:
$[H_3O^+] = x$
[Weak acid] = original conc. − x
[Conjugate base] = original conc. + x

STEP 3. Enter **equilibrium concentrations** in K_a.

K_a expression with equilibrium concentrations in terms of x

STEP 4. Solve **K_a expression** for x.

Value of $[H_3O^+]$

STEP 5. Convert **$[H_3O^+]$** to **pH**.

pH of solution

Think about Your Answer If a buffer is composed of equal amounts of a weak acid and its conjugate base, its pH will be equal to the pK_a for the weak acid. It takes a 10-fold change in the ratio of acid to base to change the pH of a buffer by 1.00. In this example, the concentrations of the weak acid and conjugate base are similar and, thus, the pH is near the pK_a for the acid (4.74).

Check Your Understanding

What is the pH of a buffer solution composed of 0.50 M formic acid (HCO_2H) and 0.70 M sodium formate ($NaHCO_2$)?

General Expressions for Buffer Solutions

In Example 17.2, the hydronium ion concentration of the acetic acid/acetate ion buffer solution was found by solving for x in the equation

$$K_a = 1.8 \times 10^{-5} = \frac{[H_3O^+][CH_3CO_2^-]}{[CH_3CO_2H]} = \frac{(x)(0.600)}{0.700}$$

Rearrangement of this equation results in a useful equation that can help you better understand how a buffer works.

$$[H_3O^+] = \frac{[CH_3CO_2H]}{[CH_3CO_2^-]} \times K_a$$

That is, the hydronium ion concentration in the acetic acid/acetate ion buffer is given by the ratio of the acid and conjugate base concentrations at equilibrium times the acid ionization constant. Indeed, this is true for all solutions of *a weak acid and its conjugate base*.

Buffer Solutions You will find it generally useful to consider all buffer solutions as composed of a weak acid and its conjugate base. Suppose, for example, you have a solution containing the weak base ammonia and its conjugate acid ammonium ion. The hydronium ion concentration can be found from Equation 17.1 or 17.2 by assuming the buffer is composed of the weak acid NH_4^+ and its conjugate base, NH_3.

$$[H_3O^+] = \frac{[\text{acid}]}{[\text{conjugate base}]} \times K_a \qquad (17.1)$$

It is often convenient to use Equation 17.1 in a different form. If you take the negative logarithm of each side of the equation, you have

$$-\log[H_3O^+] = \left\{-\log\frac{[\text{acid}]}{[\text{conjugate base}]}\right\} + (-\log K_a)$$

You know that $-\log[H_3O^+]$ is defined as pH, and $-\log K_a$ is defined as pK_a (◀ Sections 16-2 and 16-3). Furthermore, because

$$-\log\frac{[\text{acid}]}{[\text{conjugate base}]} = +\log\frac{[\text{conjugate base}]}{[\text{acid}]}$$

the preceding equation can be rewritten as

$$\text{pH} = \text{p}K_a + \log\frac{[\text{conjugate base}]}{[\text{acid}]} \qquad (17.2)$$

This equation is known as the **Henderson–Hasselbalch equation**. The equation is simply a rearrangement of the equilibrium expression for the ionization of an acid. But, *to use the Henderson-Hasselbalch equation you assume that the equilibrium concentrations of the acid and its conjugate base are approximately equal to their initial concentrations*. This criterion is met when:

- *the pH of the buffer falls within a pH range of 3 to 11*. The pH of a buffer will be close to the pK_a for the weak acid. If K_a for a weak acid is greater than 10^{-3} (pK_a < 3), a significant fraction of the acid will dissociate in water and, thus, the equilibrium concentrations of the acid and the conjugate base will differ from their initial concentrations. Likewise, for buffers with pH values above 11, K_b for the weak base is greater than 10^{-3} and the base reacts to a significant extent with water.

- *the initial concentrations of the acid and the conjugate base are large* so that a small amount of dissociation of the acid (or the conjugate base) will not result in an appreciable change in concentration.

The Henderson-Hasselbalch equation shows that *the pH of a buffer solution is controlled by two factors:*

- the strength of the acid (as expressed by K_a or pK_a)
- and the relative amounts of acid and conjugate base

The solution pH is established primarily by the value of pK_a, and the pH can be fine-tuned by adjusting the acid-to-conjugate base ratio.

When the concentrations of conjugate base and acid are the same in a solution, the ratio [conjugate base]/[acid] is 1. The log of 1 is zero, so $pH = pK_a$ under these circumstances. If there is more of the conjugate base in the solution than acid, for example, then $pH > pK_a$. Conversely, if there is more acid than conjugate base in solution, then $pH < pK_a$.

EXAMPLE 17.3

Using the Henderson–Hasselbalch Equation

Problem Benzoic acid ($C_6H_5CO_2H$, 2.00 g) and sodium benzoate ($NaC_6H_5CO_2$, 2.00 g) are dissolved in enough water to make 1.00 L of solution. Calculate the pH of the solution using the Henderson–Hasselbalch equation.

What Do You Know? You know the masses of weak acid and conjugate base and the volume of solution. You also know the K_a for the weak acid (Table 16.2 or Appendix H), from which you can calculate the required pK_a for the acid.

Strategy Calculate the acid and conjugate base concentrations and substitute these into the Henderson–Hasselbalch equation along with the value of pK_a for the acid.

Solution

K_a for benzoic acid is 6.3×10^{-5}. Therefore, $pK_a = -\log(6.3 \times 10^{-5}) = 4.20$

Next, you need the concentrations of the acid (benzoic acid) and its conjugate base (benzoate ion).

$$2.00 \text{ g benzoic acid} \left(\frac{1 \text{ mol}}{122.1 \text{ g}}\right) = 0.0164 \text{ mol benzoic acid}$$

$$2.00 \text{ g sodium benzoate} \left(\frac{1 \text{ mol}}{144.1 \text{ g}}\right) = 0.0139 \text{ mol sodium benzoate}$$

Because the solution volume is 1.00 L, the concentrations are [benzoic acid] = 0.0164 M and [benzoate ion] = 0.0139 M. Therefore, using Equation 17.2, you have

$$pH = 4.20 + \log\frac{0.0139}{0.0164} = 4.20 + \log(0.848) = 4.13$$

Think about Your Answer Notice that the pH is less than the pK_a because the concentration of acid is greater than the concentration of the conjugate base (and so the ratio of conjugate base to acid concentration is less than 1).

Check Your Understanding

Use the Henderson–Hasselbalch equation to calculate the pH of 1.00 L of a buffer solution containing 15.0 g of $NaHCO_3$ and 18.0 g of Na_2CO_3. (Consider this buffer as a solution of the weak acid HCO_3^- and its conjugate base, CO_3^{2-}.)

Preparing Buffer Solutions

To be useful, a buffer solution must have two characteristics:

- *pH Control:* It should control the pH at the desired value. The Henderson–Hasselbalch equation shows us how this can be done.

$$\mathrm{pH} = \mathrm{p}K_a + \log \frac{[\text{conjugate base}]}{[\text{acid}]}$$

  First, an acid is chosen whose pK_a (or K_a) is near the intended value of pH (or $[H_3O^+]$). Second, the exact value of pH (or $[H_3O^+]$) is then achieved by adjusting the conjugate base-to-acid ratio. (Example 17.4 illustrates this approach.)

- *Buffer capacity:* The buffer should have the ability to keep the pH approximately constant after the addition of reasonable amounts of acid and base. For example, the concentration of acetic acid in an acetic acid/acetate ion buffer must be sufficient to consume all the hydroxide ion that may be added and still control the pH (see Example 17.4). Buffers are often prepared as 0.10 M to 1.0 M solutions of reagents. However, any buffer will lose its ability to moderate changes if too much strong acid or base is added.

EXAMPLE 17.4

Preparing a Buffer Solution

Problem You wish to prepare 1.0 L of a buffer solution with a pH of 4.30. A list of possible acids (and their conjugate bases) follows:

ACID	CONJUGATE BASE	K_a	pK_a
CH_3CO_2H	$CH_3CO_2^-$	1.8×10^{-5}	4.74
$H_2PO_4^-$	HPO_4^{2-}	6.2×10^{-8}	7.21
HCO_3^-	CO_3^{2-}	4.8×10^{-11}	10.32

Which combination should be selected, and what should be the ratio of acid to conjugate base?

What Do You Know? You know the desired pH of the buffer, and you have a list of possible acid/conjugate base combinations.

Strategy Use either the general equation for a buffer (Equation 17.1) or the Henderson–Hasselbalch equation (Equation 17.2). Equation 17.1 informs you that $[H_3O^+]$ should be close to the acid K_a value, and Equation 17.2 tells you that pH should be close to the acid pK_a value. Either will establish which acid you should use. Having decided which acid to use, convert pH to $[H_3O^+]$ to use Equation 17.1. If you use Equation 17.2, use the pK_a value in the table. Finally, calculate the ratio of acid to conjugate base.

Solution The hydronium ion concentration for the buffer is found from the targeted pH.

$$\mathrm{pH} = 4.30, \text{ so } [H_3O^+] = 10^{-\mathrm{pH}} = 10^{-4.30} = 5.0 \times 10^{-5}\ \mathrm{M}$$

Of the acids given, only acetic acid (CH_3CO_2H) has a K_a value close to that of the desired $[H_3O^+]$ (or a pK_a close to a pH of 4.30). Now you need only to adjust the ratio $[CH_3CO_2H]/[CH_3CO_2^-]$ to achieve the desired hydronium ion concentration.

$$[H_3O^+] = 5.0 \times 10^{-5}\ M = \frac{[CH_3CO_2H]}{[CH_3CO_2^-]}(1.8 \times 10^{-5})$$

Rearrange this equation to find the ratio $[CH_3CO_2H]/[CH_3CO_2^-]$.

$$\frac{[CH_3CO_2H]}{[CH_3CO_2^-]} = \frac{[H_3O^+]}{K_a} = \frac{5.0 \times 10^{-5}}{1.8 \times 10^{-5}} = \frac{2.8\ mol/L}{1.0\ mol/L}$$

Therefore, if you add 0.28 mol of acetic acid and 0.10 mol of sodium acetate (or any other pair of molar quantities in the ratio 2.8/1) to enough water to prepare 1.0 L of solution, the buffer solution will have a pH of 4.30.

Think about Your Answer If you prefer to use the Henderson–Hasselbalch equation, you would have

$$pH = 4.30 = 4.74 + \log\frac{[CH_3CO_2^-]}{[CH_3CO_2H]}$$

$$\log\frac{[CH_3CO_2^-]}{[CH_3CO_2H]} = 4.30 - 4.74 = -0.44$$

$$\frac{[CH_3CO_2^-]}{[CH_3CO_2H]} = 10^{-0.44} = 0.36$$

The ratio of conjugate base to acid, $[CH_3CO_2^-]/[CH_3CO_2H]$, is 0.36. The reciprocal of this ratio $\{= [CH_3CO_2H]/[CH_3CO_2^-] = 1/0.36)\}$ is 2.8/1. This is the same result obtained previously using Equation 17.1.

Check Your Understanding

Using an acetic acid/sodium acetate buffer solution, what ratio of conjugate base to acid will you need to maintain the pH at 5.00? Describe how you would prepare such a solution.

Example 17.4 illustrates several important points concerning buffer solutions. The hydronium ion concentration depends not only on the K_a value of the acid but also on the ratio of acid and conjugate base concentrations. However, even though the ratios are written in terms of reagent concentrations, it is *the relative number of moles of acid and conjugate base that is important in determining the pH of a buffer solution.* Because both reagents are dissolved in the same solution, their concentrations

PROBLEM SOLVING TIP 17.1
Buffer Solutions

The following is a summary of important aspects of buffer solutions.

- A buffer resists changes in pH on adding small quantities of acid or base.
- A buffer consists of a weak acid and its conjugate base.
- The hydronium ion concentration of a buffer solution can be calculated from Equation 17.1,

$$[H_3O^+] = \frac{[acid]}{[conjugate\ base]} \times K_a$$

or the pH can be calculated from the Henderson–Hasselbalch equation (Equation 17.2).

$$pH = pK_a + \log\frac{[conjugate\ base]}{[acid]}$$

- The pH depends primarily on the K_a of the weak acid and secondarily on the relative amounts of acid and conjugate base.
- The function of the weak acid of a buffer is to consume added base, and the function of the conjugate base is to consume added acid. Such reactions change the relative quantities of weak acid and its conjugate base. Because this ratio of acid to its conjugate base has only a secondary effect on the pH, the pH can be maintained relatively constant.
- The buffer must have sufficient capacity to react with reasonable quantities of added acid or base.

depend on the same solution volume. In Example 17.4, the ratio 2.8/1 for acetic acid and sodium acetate implies that 2.8 times as many moles of acid were dissolved per liter as moles of sodium acetate.

$$\frac{[CH_3CO_2H]}{[CH_3CO_2^-]} = \frac{2.8 \text{ mol } CH_3CO_2H/L}{1.0 \text{ mol } CH_3CO_2^-/L} = \frac{2.8 \text{ mol } CH_3CO_2H}{1.0 \text{ mol } CH_3CO_2^-}$$

Notice that on dividing one concentration by the other, the volumes "cancel." This means that you only need to ensure that the ratio of moles of acid to moles of conjugate base is 2.8 to 1 in this example. The acid and its conjugate base could have been dissolved in any reasonable amount of water. This also means that *diluting a buffer solution will not change its pH.* Commercially available buffer solutions are often sold as premixed, dry reagents. To use them, you only need to mix the reagents in some volume of pure water (Figure 17.3).

How Does a Buffer Maintain pH?

Now let us explore quantitatively how a given buffer solution can maintain the pH of a solution after a small amount of strong acid has been added.

If too much water is added, the acid and conjugate base concentrations will be too low, and the buffer capacity could be exceeded. Buffer solutions usually have solute concentrations around 0.1 M to 1.0 M.

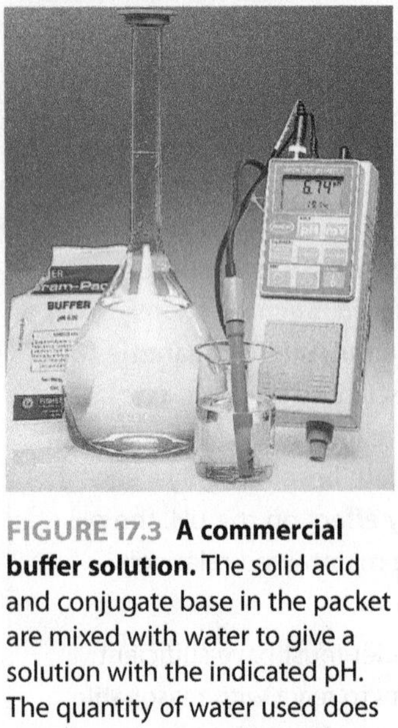

© Cengage Learning/Charles D. Winters

FIGURE 17.3 A commercial buffer solution. The solid acid and conjugate base in the packet are mixed with water to give a solution with the indicated pH. The quantity of water used does not matter because the ratio [acid]/[conjugate base] does not depend on the solution volume.

EXAMPLE 17.5

How Does a Buffer Maintain a Constant pH?

Problem What is the change in pH when 1.00 mL of 1.00 M HCl is added to (1) 1.000 L of pure water and to (2) 1.000 L of acetic acid/sodium acetate buffer with $[CH_3CO_2H] = 0.700$ M and $[CH_3CO_2^-] = 0.600$ M? (The pH of this acetic acid/acetate ion buffer is 4.68. See Example 17.2.)

What Do You Know? You know HCl is a strong acid and ionizes completely to supply H_3O^+ ions. In the first problem, when HCl is added to pure water, the concentration of HCl in the solution determines the pH. In the second problem, the conjugate base of the weak acid will react with the added HCl. Therefore, you need to perform a stoichiometry calculation to determine the new weak acid/conjugate base concentrations before you can calculate the pH.

Strategy

Part 1: *involves two steps:*

- Find the H_3O^+ concentration when adding 1.00 mL of acid to 1.000 L of pure water.
- Convert the value of $[H_3O^+]$ for the dilute solution to pH.

Part 2: *involves three steps:*

- Calculate the concentrations of acid and conjugate base after adding H_3O^+.
- Find $[H_3O^+]$ for a buffer solution knowing the concentrations of CH_3CO_2H and $CH_3CO_2^-$.
- Convert the value of $[H_3O^+]$ for the solution to pH.

Solution

Part 1: *Adding Acid to Pure Water*

1.00 mL of 1.00 M HCl represents 0.00100 mol of acid. If this is added to 1.000 L of pure water, the H_3O^+ concentration of the water changes from 10^{-7} to almost 10^{-3},

$$c_1 \times V_1 = c_2 \times V_2$$

$$(1.00 \text{ M})(0.00100 \text{ L}) = c_2 \times (1.001 \text{ L})$$

$$c_2 = [H_3O^+] \text{ in diluted solution} = 9.99 \times 10^{-4} \text{ M}$$

and so the pH falls from 7.00 to 3.00.

Part 2: *Adding Acid to an Acetic Acid/Acetate Buffer Solution*

HCl is a strong acid that is 100% ionized in water and supplies H_3O^+, which reacts completely with the base (acetate ion) in the buffer solution according to the following equation:

$$H_3O^+(aq) + CH_3CO_2^-(aq) \rightarrow H_2O(\ell) + CH_3CO_2H(aq)$$

	H_3O^+ FROM ADDED HCl	$CH_3CO_2^-$ FROM BUFFER	CH_3CO_2H FROM BUFFER
Initial amount of acid or base (mol $= c \times V$)	0.00100	0.600	0.700
Change (mol)	−0.00100	−0.00100	+0.00100
After reaction (mol)	0	0.599	0.701
Concentrations after reaction (c = mol/V)	0	0.598	0.700

Because the added HCl reacts completely with acetate ion to produce acetic acid, the solution after this reaction (with $V = 1.001$ L) is once again a buffer containing only the weak acid and its salt. Now you only need to use Equation 17.1 (or the Henderson–Hasselbalch equation) to find $[H_3O^+]$ and the pH in the buffer solution as in Examples 17.2 and 17.3.

EQUILIBRIUM	CH_3CO_2H	+	H_2O	$\rightleftharpoons$	H_3O^+	+	$CH_3CO_2^-$
Initial (M)	0.700				0		0.598
Change (M)	$-x$				$+x$		$+x$
Equilibrium (M)	$0.700 - x$				x		$0.598 + x$

As usual, you can make the approximation that x, the concentration of H_3O^+ formed by ionizing acetic acid in the presence of acetate ion, is very small compared with 0.700 M or 0.598 M. Using Equation 17.1, you should get a pH of 4.68.

$$[H_3O^+] = x = \frac{[CH_3CO_2H]}{[CH_3CO_2^-]} \times K_a = \left(\frac{0.700\ \text{mol}}{0.598\ \text{mol}}\right)(1.8 \times 10^{-5}) = 2.1 \times 10^{-5}\ \text{M}$$

$$\text{pH} = 4.68$$

Think about Your Answer Within the number of significant figures allowed, the pH of the buffer solution does not change after adding this amount of HCl. The buffer solution contains the conjugate base of the weak acid, and the base consumed the added HCl. In contrast, the pH changed by 4 units when the same amount of HCl was added to 1.0 L of pure water. That is, $[H_3O^+]$ went up by 10^4.

Check Your Understanding

Calculate the pH of 0.500 L of a buffer solution composed of 0.50 M formic acid (HCO_2H) and 0.70 M sodium formate ($NaHCO_2$) before and after adding 10.0 mL of 1.0 M HCl.

REVIEW & CHECK FOR SECTION 17-2

1. Which choice would be a good buffer solution?

   (a) 0.20 M KCH_3CO_2 and 0.20 M CH_3CO_2H (c) 0.20 M CH_3CO_2H and 0.10 M HCO_2H

   (b) 0.20 M HCl and 0.10 M KOH (d) 0.10 HCl and 0.010 M KCl

2. If an acetic acid/sodium acetate buffer solution is prepared from 100. mL of 0.10 M acetic acid, what volume of 0.10 M sodium acetate must be added to have a pH of 4.00?

   (a) 100. mL (b) 50. mL (c) 36 mL (d) 18 mL

3. What is the pH of a buffer composed of 100. mL of 0.20 M NH_4Cl and 200. mL of 0.10 M NH_3?

(a) 4.85 (c) 7.00 (e) 10.05

(b) 9.25 (d) 5.65

4. To prepare a buffer containing CH_3CO_2H and $NaCH_3CO_2$ and having a pH of 5, the ratio of the concentration of CH_3CO_2H to that of $NaCH_3CO_2$ should be about

(a) 1/1 (b) 1.8/1 (c) 1/1.8 (d) 5.0/1

Learning Objectives: LO 6.13 (see APEC Lab 14 "Titration Curves")

17-3 Acid–Base Titrations

A titration is one of the most useful ways of determining accurately the quantity of an acid, a base, or some other substance in a mixture. You learned how to perform the stoichiometry calculations involved in titrations in Chapter 4 (◀ Section 4-7). In Chapter 16, the following points were emphasized regarding acid–base reactions (◀ Section 16-6):

- The pH at the equivalence point of a strong acid–strong base titration is 7. The solution at the equivalence point is truly "neutral" *only* when a strong acid is titrated with a strong base and vice versa.
- If the substance being titrated is a weak acid or base, then the pH at the equivalence point is not 7 (◀ Table 16.4).
  (a) A weak acid titrated with a strong base leads to a pH > 7 at the equivalence point due to the conjugate base of the weak acid.
  (b) A weak base titrated with a strong acid leads to a pH < 7 at the equivalence point due to the conjugate acid of the weak base.

Equivalence Point The equivalence point for a reaction is the point at which one reactant has been completely consumed upon addition of another reactant (see Section 4-7).

You will now see how what you have learned about how to calculate the pH of various types of solutions can be applied to understanding how the pH changes in the course of an acid–base reaction.

Titration of a Strong Acid with a Strong Base

Weak Acid–Weak Base Titrations Titrations combining a weak acid and weak base are generally not done because the equivalence point often cannot be accurately judged.

Figure 17.4 illustrates what happens to the pH as 0.100 M NaOH is slowly added to 50.0 mL of 0.100 M HCl.

$$HCl(aq) + NaOH(aq) \rightarrow NaCl(aq) + H_2O(\ell)$$

$$\text{Net ionic equation: } H_3O^+(aq) + OH^-(aq) \rightarrow 2\ H_2O(\ell)$$

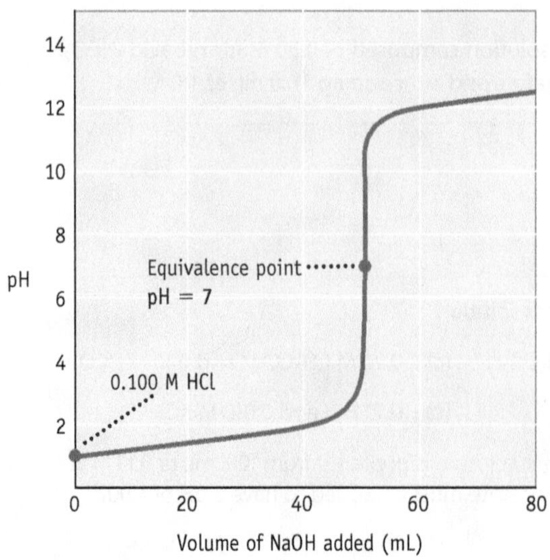

50.0 mL of 0.100 M HCl titrated with 0.100 M NaOH	
Volume of base added	pH
0.0	1.00
10.0	1.18
20.0	1.37
40.0	1.95
45.0	2.28
48.0	2.69
49.0	3.00
50.0	7.00
51.0	11.00
55.0	11.68
60.0	11.96
80.0	12.36
100.0	12.52
very large amount	13.00 (maximum)

FIGURE 17.4 **The change in pH as a strong acid is titrated with a strong base.** In this case, 50.0 mL of 0.100 M HCl is titrated with 0.100 M NaOH. The pH at the equivalence point is 7.0 for the reaction of a strong acid with a strong base.

CASE STUDY — Take a Deep Breath

Maintenance of pH is vital to the cells of all living organisms because enzyme activity is influenced by pH. The primary protection against harmful pH changes in cells is provided by buffer systems, which maintain the intracellular pH of most cells between 6.9 and 7.4. Two important biological buffer systems control pH in this range: the bicarbonate/carbonic acid system (HCO_3^-/H_2CO_3) and the phosphate system ($HPO_4^{2-}/H_2PO_4^-$).

The bicarbonate/carbonic acid buffer is important in blood plasma, where three equilibria are important.

$$CO_2(g) \rightleftharpoons CO_2(\text{dissolved})$$

$$CO_2(\text{dissolved}) + H_2O(\ell) \rightleftharpoons H_2CO_3(aq)$$

$$H_2CO_3(aq) + H_2O(\ell) \rightleftharpoons H_3O^+(aq) + HCO_3^-(aq)$$

The overall equilibrium for the second and third steps has $pK_{overall} = 6.3$ at 37 °C, the temperature of the human body. Thus,

$$7.4 = 6.3 + \log\frac{[HCO_3^-]}{[CO_2(\text{dissolved})]}$$

Although the value of $pK_{overall}$ is about 1 pH unit away from the blood pH, the natural partial pressure of CO_2 in the alveoli of the lungs (about 40 mm Hg) is sufficient to keep $[CO_2(\text{dissolved})]$ at about 1.2×10^{-3} M and $[HCO_3^-]$ at about 1.5×10^{-2} M as required to maintain this pH.

If blood pH rises above about 7.45, you can suffer from a condition called *alkalosis*. *Respiratory alkalosis* can arise from hyperventilation when a person breathes quickly to expel CO_2 from the lungs. This has the effect of lowering the CO_2 concentration, which in turn leads to a lower H_3O^+ concentration and a higher pH. This same condition can also arise from severe anxiety or from an oxygen deficiency at high altitude. It can ultimately lead to overexcitability of

© Cengage Learning/Charles D. Winters

the central nervous system, muscle spasms, convulsions, and death. One way to treat acute respiratory alkalosis is to breathe into a paper bag. The CO_2 you exhale is recycled. This raises the blood CO_2 level and causes the equilibria above to shift to the right, thus raising the hydronium ion concentration and lowering the pH.

Metabolic alkalosis can occur if you take large amounts of sodium bicarbonate to treat stomach acid (which is mostly HCl at a pH of about 1 to 2). It also commonly occurs when a person vomits profusely. This depletes the body of hydronium ions, which leads to an increase in bicarbonate ion concentration.

Athletes can use the H_2CO_3/HCO_3^- equilibrium to enhance their performance. Strenuous activity produces high levels of lactic acid, and this can lower blood pH and cause muscle cramps. To counteract this, athletes will prepare before a race by hyperventilating for some seconds to raise blood pH, thereby helping to neutralize the acidity from the lactic acid.

Acidosis is the opposite of alkalosis. There was a case of a toddler who came to the hospital with viral gastroenteritis and *metabolic acidosis*. He had severe diarrhea, was dehydrated, and had a high rate of respiration. One function of the bicarbonate ion is to neutralize stomach acid in the intestines. However, because of his diarrhea, the toddler was losing bicarbonate ions in his stool, and his blood pH was too low. To compensate, the toddler was breathing rapidly and blowing off CO_2 through the lungs (the effect of which is to lower $[H_3O^+]$ and raise the pH).

Respiratory acidosis results from a buildup of CO_2 in the body. This can be caused by pulmonary problems, by head injuries, or by drugs such as anesthetics and sedatives. It can be reversed by breathing rapidly and deeply. Doubling the breathing rate increases the blood pH by about 0.23 units.

Questions:

Phosphate ions are abundant in cells, both as the ions themselves and as important substituents on organic molecules. Most importantly, the pK_a for the $H_2PO_4^-$ ion is 7.20, which is very close to the normal pH in the body.

$$H_2PO_4^-(aq) + H_2O(\ell) \rightleftharpoons H_3O^+(aq) + HPO_4^{2-}(aq)$$

1. What should the ratio $[HPO_4^{2-}]/[H_2PO_4^-]$ be to control the pH at 7.4?
2. A typical total phosphate concentration in a cell, $[HPO_4^{2-}] + [H_2PO_4^-]$, is 2.0×10^{-2} M. What are the concentrations of HPO_4^{2-} and $H_2PO_4^-$ at pH 7.4?

Answers to these questions are available in Appendix N.

Let us focus on four regions on this plot.

- pH of the initial solution
- pH as NaOH is added to the HCl solution before the equivalence point
- pH at the equivalence point
- pH after the equivalence point

Before beginning the titration, the 0.100 M solution of HCl has a pH of 1.00. As NaOH is added to the acid solution, the amount of HCl declines, and the acid remaining is dissolved in an ever-increasing volume of solution. Thus, $[H_3O^+]$

decreases, and the pH slowly increases. As an example, let us find the pH of the solution after 10.0 mL of 0.100 M NaOH has been added to 50.0 mL of 0.100 M HCl. Here, a table is created to list the amounts of acid and base before reaction, the changes in those amounts, and the amounts remaining after reaction. Be sure to notice that the volume of the solution after reaction is the sum of the combined volumes of NaOH and HCl (60.0 mL or 0.0600 L in this example).

Titrations, Stoichiometry, and Limiting Reactants In the titration of an acid with a base (as in Figure 17.4) the limiting reactant is the base before the equivalence point. After the equivalence point it will be the acid.

	$H_3O^+(aq)$	+	$OH^-(aq)$	→	$2\ H_2O(\ell)$
Initial amount (mol = $c \times V$)	0.00500		0.00100		
Change (mol)	−0.00100		−0.00100		
After reaction (mol)	0.00400		0		
After reaction (c = mol/V)	0.00400 mol/0.0600 L = 0.0667 M		0		

After addition of 10.0 mL of NaOH, the final solution has a hydronium ion concentration of 0.0667 M, and so the pH is

$$pH = -\log[H_3O^+] = -\log(0.0667) = 1.176$$

After 49.5 mL of base has been added—that is, just before the equivalence point—the same approach can be used to show that the pH is 3.3. The solution being titrated is still quite acidic, even very close to the equivalence point.

The pH of the equivalence point in an acid–base titration is the value at the steepest point in the vertical portion of the pH versus volume of titrant curve. (The **titrant** is the substance being added during the titration.) In the HCl/NaOH titration illustrated in Figure 17.4, you see that the pH increases very rapidly near the equivalence point. In fact, in this case the pH rises 7 units (the H_3O^+ concentration decreases by a factor of 10 million!) when only a drop or two of the NaOH solution is added, and the steepest point of the vertical portion of the curve is at a pH of 7.00.

The pH of the solution at the equivalence point in a monoprotic strong acid–strong base reaction is always 7.00 (at 25 °C) because the solution contains a neutral salt.

After all of the HCl has been consumed and the slightest excess of NaOH has been added, the solution will be basic, and the pH will continue to increase as more NaOH is added (and the solution volume increases). For example, if you calculate the pH of the solution after 55.0 mL of 0.100 M NaOH has been added to 50.0 mL of 0.100 M HCl, you find

	$H_3O^+(aq)$	+	$OH^-(aq)$	→	$2\ H_2O(\ell)$
Initial amount (mol = $c \times V$)	0.00500		0.00550		
Change (mol)	−0.00500		−0.00500		
After reaction (mol)	0		0.00050		
After reaction (c = mol/V)	0		0.00050 mol/0.1050 L = 0.0048 M		

At this point, the solution has a hydroxide ion concentration of 0.0048 M. Calculate the pOH from this value, then use this to calculate pH.

$$pOH = -\log[OH^-] = -\log(0.0048) = 2.32$$

$$pH = 14.00 - pOH = 11.68$$

FIGURE 17.5 **The change in pH during the titration of a weak acid with a strong base.** Here, 100.0 mL of 0.100 M acetic acid is titrated with 0.100 M NaOH.

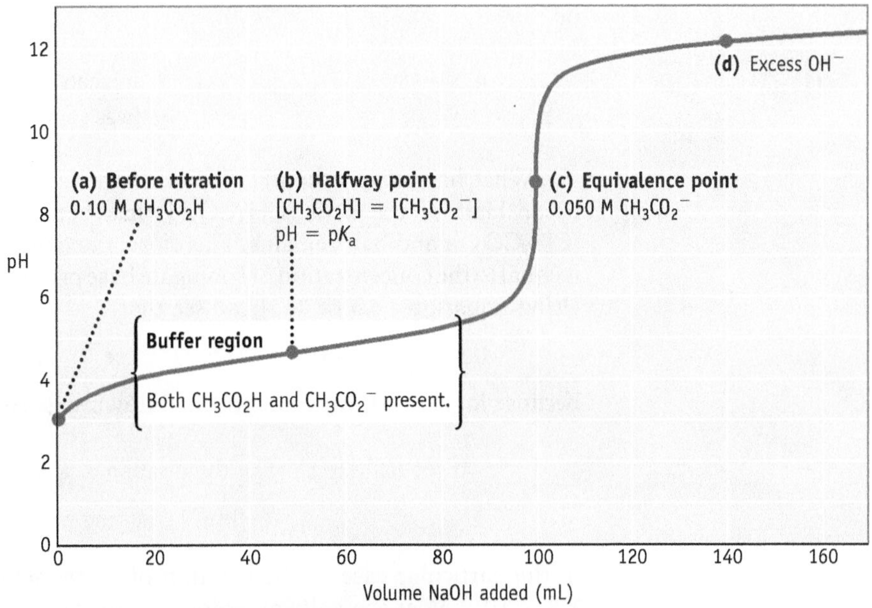

(a) Before titration. A 0.100 M solution of acetic acid has a pH of 2.87.

(b) Halfway point. The pH at the point at which half the acid has reacted with base is equal to the pK_a for the acid (pH = pK_a = 4.74).

(c) Equivalence point. The solution contains the acetate ion, a weak base. Therefore, the solution is basic, with a pH of 8.72.

(d) After the equivalence point. The pH is determined from the moles of excess NaOH and total volume of solution.

Titration of a Weak Acid with a Strong Base

The titration of a weak acid with a strong base is somewhat different from the strong acid–strong base titration. Look carefully at the curve for the titration of 100.0 mL of 0.100 M acetic acid with 0.100 M NaOH (Figure 17.5),

$$CH_3CO_2H(aq) + NaOH(aq) \longrightarrow NaCH_3CO_2(aq) + H_2O(\ell)$$

and focus on four points on this curve:

- *The pH before titration begins.* The pH before any base is added can be calculated from the weak acid K_a value and the acid concentration (◀ Example 16.5).
- *The pH in the buffer region and, in particular, at the halfway point (half-equivalence point) of the titration.* At the halfway point, the pH is equal to the pK_a of the weak acid, a conclusion discussed in more detail in following paragraphs.
- *The pH at the equivalence point.* At the equivalence point, the solution contains only sodium acetate, the CH_3CO_2H and NaOH having been consumed. The pH is controlled by the acetate ion, and is thus basic.
- *The pH after the equivalence point.* The pH can be calculated using the amount of NaOH added after the equivalence point and the total volume of solution.

As NaOH is added to acetic acid, they are consumed and sodium acetate is produced. Thus, at every point between the beginning of the titration (when only acetic acid is present) and the equivalence point (when only sodium acetate is present), the solution contains both acetic acid and its salt, sodium acetate. These are the components of a *buffer solution*, and the hydronium ion concentration can be calculated from Equation 17.3 or 17.4.

$$[H_3O^+] = \frac{[\text{weak acid remaining}]}{[\text{conjugate base produced}]} \times K_a \quad (17.3)$$

or

$$pH = pK_a + \log\frac{[\text{conjugate base produced}]}{[\text{weak acid remaining}]} \quad (17.4)$$

What happens to the pH when *exactly* half of the acid has been consumed by base? Half of the acid (CH_3CO_2H) has been converted to the conjugate base ($CH_3CO_2^-$), and half remains. Therefore, the concentration of weak acid remaining is equal to the concentration of conjugate base produced ($[CH_3CO_2H] = [CH_3CO_2^-]$). Using Equation 17.3 or 17.4, we see that

$$[H_3O^+] = (1) \times K_a \quad \text{or} \quad pH = pK_a + \log(1)$$

Because $\log(1) = 0$, we come to the following general conclusion:

At the halfway point in the titration of a weak acid with a strong base

$$[H_3O^+] = K_a \text{ and } pH = pK_a \quad (17.5)$$

In the particular case of the titration of acetic acid with a strong base, $[H_3O^+] = 1.8 \times 10^{-5}$ M at the halfway point, and so the pH is 4.74. This is equal to the pK_a of acetic acid.

Acid–Base Titrations See Problem Solving Tip 17.2: Calculating the pH at Various Stages in an Acid–Base Titration.

EXAMPLE 17.6

Titration of Acetic Acid with Sodium Hydroxide

Problem Consider the titration of 100.0 mL of 0.100 M acetic acid with 0.100 M NaOH (see Figure 17.5).

$$CH_3CO_2H(aq) + OH^-(aq) \rightarrow CH_3CO_2^-(aq) + H_2O(\ell)$$

(a) What is the pH of the solution when 90.0 mL of 0.100 M NaOH has been added to 100.0 mL of 0.100 M acetic acid?

(b) What is the pH at the equivalence point?

(c) What is the pH after 110.0 mL of NaOH has been added?

What Do You Know? You know the concentrations and volumes of the acid and base and the balanced equation for the reaction. For part (a) you know K_a of acetic acid and for part (b) you know K_b for the acetate ion (◀ Table 16.2). You should also recognize that part (a) is similar to Example 17.1.

Strategy Each part of the problem has at least two steps:

(1) The first step in each part involves a limiting-reactant stoichiometry calculation to determine the amounts of acetic acid, sodium hydroxide, and acetate ion present after the acid–base reaction has gone to completion.

(2) **Part (a):** Before the equivalence point, do an equilibrium calculation to find $[H_3O^+]$ for a buffer solution where the amounts of CH_3CO_2H and $CH_3CO_2^-$ are known from the stoichiometry calculation. (See Example 17.1.)

Part (b): Only the acetate ion remains at the equivalence point. (See Example 16.7.) Determine the concentration of this ion after the acid–base reaction goes to completion. Using the balanced equation for the reaction of the acetate ion with water and its corresponding K_b, determine the equilibrium hydroxide ion concentration. Convert this to the equilibrium hydronium ion concentration and calculate the pH.

Part (c): After the equivalence point, the solution contains both the acetate ion and excess NaOH, but the latter controls the pH. Determine the concentration of excess NaOH (and $[OH^-]$), and then convert $[OH^-]$ to pH.

Solution

Part (a): *pH before the Equivalence Point*

First calculate the amounts of reactants before reaction (= concentration × volume) and then use the principles of stoichiometry to calculate the amounts of reactants and products after reaction. The limiting reactant is NaOH, so some CH_3CO_2H remains along with the product, $CH_3CO_2^-$.

EQUATION	CH_3CO_2H	+ OH^-	$\rightleftharpoons$ $CH_3CO_2^-$	+ H_2O
Initial (mol)	0.0100	0.00900	0	
Change (mol)	−0.00900	−0.00900	+0.00900	
After reaction (mol)	0.0010	0	0.00900	

The ratio of amounts (moles) of acid to conjugate base is the same as the ratio of their concentrations. Therefore, you can use the amounts of weak acid remaining and conjugate base formed to find the pH from Equation 17.3.

$$[H_3O^+] = \frac{\text{mol } CH_3CO_2H}{\text{mol } CH_3CO_2^-} \times K_a = \left(\frac{0.0010 \text{ mol}}{0.0090 \text{ mol}}\right)(1.8 \times 10^{-5}) = 2.0 \times 10^{-6} \text{ M}$$

$$\text{pH} = -\log(2.0 \times 10^{-6}) = 5.70$$

The pH is 5.70, in agreement with Figure 17.5. Notice that this pH is appropriate for a point after the halfway point (4.74) but before the equivalence point (8.72; see below).

Part (b): *pH at the Equivalence Point*

To reach the equivalence point, 0.0100 mol of NaOH has been added to 0.0100 mol of CH_3CO_2H and 0.0100 mol of $CH_3CO_2^-$ has been formed.

EQUATION	CH_3CO_2H	+ OH^-	$\rightarrow$ $CH_3CO_2^-$	+ H_2O
Initial (mol)	0.0100	0.0100	0	
Change (mol)	−0.0100	−0.0100	+0.0100	
After reaction (mol)	0	0	0.0100	

Because two solutions, each with a volume of 100.0 mL, have been combined, the concentration of $CH_3CO_2^-$ at the equivalence point is (0.0100 mol/0.200 L) = 0.0500 M. Next, set up an ICE table for the reaction of this weak base with water,

EQUATION	$CH_3CO_2^-$	+ H_2O	$\rightleftharpoons$ CH_3CO_2H	+ OH^-
Initial (M)	0.0500		0	0
Change (M)	$-x$		$+x$	$+x$
After reaction (M)	$0.0500 - x$		x	x

and calculate the concentration of OH^- ion using K_b for the weak base.

$$K_b \text{ for } CH_3CO_2^- = 5.6 \times 10^{-10} = \frac{[CH_3CO_2H][OH^-]}{[CH_3CO_2^-]} = \frac{(x)(x)}{0.0500 - x}$$

Strategy Map 17.6

PROBLEM — *Part (b)*

Calculate **pH** at the ***equivalence point*** for a titration of **acetic acid** with **NaOH**.

↓

DATA/INFORMATION KNOWN

- Solution concentrations
- Solution volumes
- Value of conjugate base K_b

↓ STEP 1. Stoichiometry problem

Concentration of **acetate ion** at ***equivalence point*** of acid–base titration

↓ STEP 2. Enter **equilibrium concentrations** in ICE table.

At equilibrium:
$[OH^-]$ = [Acetic acid] = x
[Acetate ion] = original conc. − x

↓ STEP 3. Enter **equilibrium concentrations** in K_b.

K_b **expression** with equilibrium concentrations in terms of x

↓ STEP 4. Solve K_b **expression** for x.

Value of $[OH^-]$

↓ STEP 5. Convert $[OH^-]$ to **pH**.

pH of solution

Making the usual assumption that x is small with respect to 0.0500 M,

$$x = [OH^-] = 5.3 \times 10^{-6}\text{ M and so the pOH} = 5.28$$

$$pH = 14.00 - 5.28 = 8.72$$

***Part (c):** pH after the Equivalence Point*

Now the limiting reactant is CH_3CO_2H, and the solution contains excess OH^- ion from the unused NaOH as well as from the hydrolysis of $CH_3CO_2^-$.

EQUATION	CH_3CO_2H	+	OH^-	→	$CH_3CO_2^-$	+	H_2O
Initial (mol)	0.0100		0.0110		0		
Change (mol)	−0.0100		−0.0100		+0.0100		
After reaction (mol)	0		0.0010		0.0100		

The amount of OH^- produced by $CH_3CO_2^-$ hydrolysis is very small [see part (b)], so the pH of the solution after the equivalence point is determined by the excess NaOH (in 210 mL of solution).

$$[OH^-] = 0.0010\text{ mol}/0.210\text{ L} = 4.8 \times 10^{-3}\text{ M (pOH} = 2.32)$$

$$pH = 14.00 - 2.32 = 11.68$$

Think about Your Answer The pH at the equivalence point (8.72) indicates the solution is mildly basic, as expected for a solution of the anion of a weak acid. As more NaOH is added past the equivalence point the solution becomes substantially more basic (pH = 11.68).

Check Your Understanding

The titration of 0.100 M acetic acid with 0.100 M NaOH is described in the text. What is the pH of the solution when 35.0 mL of the base has been added to 100.0 mL of 0.100 M acetic acid?

Titration of Weak Polyprotic Acids

The titrations illustrated thus far have been for the reaction of a monoprotic acid (HA) with a base such as NaOH. It is possible to extend the discussion of titrations to polyprotic acids such as oxalic acid, $H_2C_2O_4$.

$$H_2C_2O_4(aq) + H_2O(\ell) \rightleftharpoons HC_2O_4^-(aq) + H_3O^+(aq) \qquad K_{a1} = 5.9 \times 10^{-2}$$

$$HC_2O_4^-(aq) + H_2O(\ell) \rightleftharpoons C_2O_4^{2-}(aq) + H_3O^+(aq) \qquad K_{a2} = 6.4 \times 10^{-5}$$

Figure 17.6 illustrates the curve for the titration of 100 mL of 0.100 M oxalic acid with 0.100 M NaOH. The first significant rise in pH is experienced when 100 mL of base has been added, indicating that the first proton of the acid has been titrated.

$$H_2C_2O_4(aq) + OH^-(aq) \rightleftharpoons HC_2O_4^-(aq) + H_2O(\ell)$$

When the second proton of oxalic acid is titrated, the pH again rises significantly.

$$HC_2O_4^-(aq) + OH^-(aq) \rightleftharpoons C_2O_4^{2-}(aq) + H_2O(\ell)$$

The pH at this second equivalence point is controlled by the oxalate ion, $C_2O_4^{2-}$.

$$C_2O_4^{2-}(aq) + H_2O(\ell) \rightleftharpoons HC_2O_4^-(aq) + OH^-(aq)$$

$$K_b = K_w/K_{a2} = 1.6 \times 10^{-10}$$

Calculation of the pH at the equivalence point indicates that it should be about 8.4, as observed.

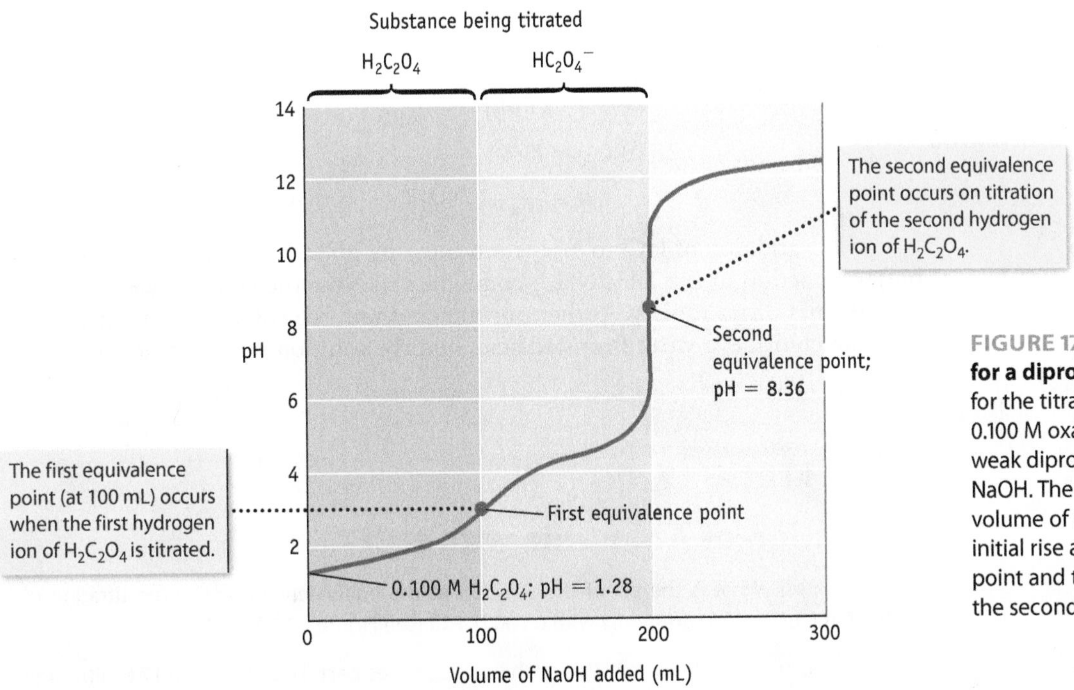

FIGURE 17.6 Titration curve for a diprotic acid. The curve for the titration of 100.0 mL of 0.100 M oxalic acid ($H_2C_2O_4$, a weak diprotic acid) with 0.100 M NaOH. The curve for pH versus volume of NaOH added shows an initial rise at the first equivalence point and then another rise at the second equivalence point.

Titration of a Weak Base with a Strong Acid

Finally, it is useful to consider the titration of a weak base with a strong acid. Figure 17.7 illustrates the pH curve for the titration of 100.0 mL of 0.100 M NH_3 with 0.100 M HCl.

$$NH_3(aq) + H_3O^+(aq) \rightleftharpoons NH_4^+(aq) + H_2O(\ell)$$

The initial pH for a 0.100 M NH_3 solution is 11.13. As the titration progresses, the important species in solution are the weak acid NH_4^+ and its conjugate base, NH_3.

$$NH_4^+(aq) + H_2O(\ell) \rightleftharpoons NH_3(aq) + H_3O^+(aq) \qquad K_a = 5.6 \times 10^{-10}$$

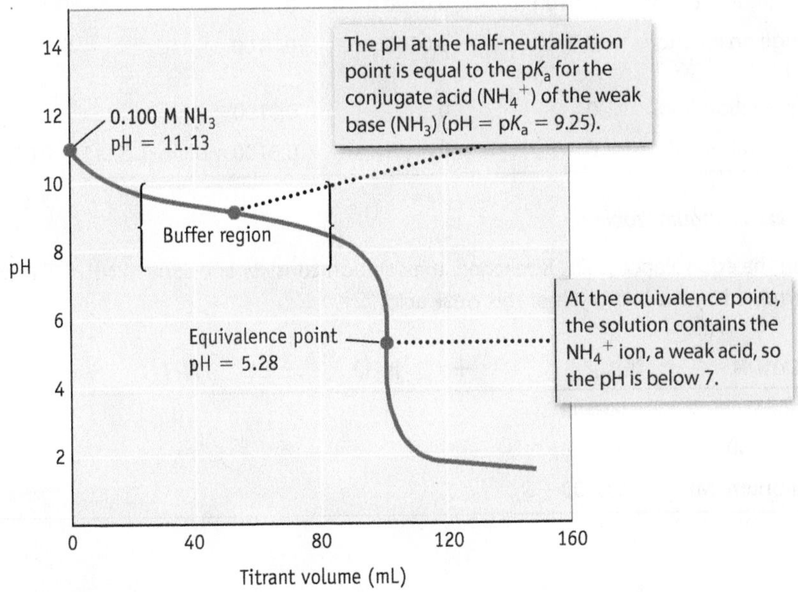

FIGURE 17.7 Titration of a weak base with a strong acid. The change in pH during the titration of a weak base (100.0 mL of 0.100 M NH_3) with a strong acid (0.100 M HCl).

At the halfway point, the concentrations of NH_4^+ and NH_3 are the same, so

$$[H_3O^+] = \frac{[NH_4^+]}{[NH_3]} \times K_a = 5.6 \times 10^{-10}$$

$$[H_3O^+] = K_a$$

$$pH = pK_a = -\log(5.6 \times 10^{-10}) = 9.25$$

As the addition of HCl to NH_3 continues, the pH declines slowly because of the buffering action of the NH_3/NH_4^+ combination. Near the equivalence point, however, the pH drops rapidly. At the equivalence point, the solution contains only ammonium chloride, a weak Brønsted acid, and the solution is weakly acidic.

EXAMPLE 17.7

Titration of Ammonia with HCl

Problem What is the pH of the solution at the equivalence point in the titration of 100.0 mL of 0.100 M ammonia with 0.100 M HCl (see Figure 17.7)?

What Do You Know? This problem resembles part (b) of Example 17.6, although here you are titrating a weak base with a strong acid. In both examples you know the quantities of reagents and want to know the pH at the equivalence point. Here you need to know the K_a value for NH_4^+, the conjugate acid of the weak base, NH_3.

Strategy As in Example 17.6, this problem has two steps: (a) a stoichiometry calculation to find the concentration of NH_4^+ at the equivalence point, and (b) an equilibrium calculation to find $[H_3O^+]$ for a solution of the weak acid NH_4^+.

Solution

Part 1: *Stoichiometry Problem*

Here, you are titrating 0.0100 mol of NH_3 ($= c \times V$), so 0.0100 mol of HCl is required. Thus, 100.0 mL of 0.100 M HCl (= 0.0100 mol HCl) must be used in the titration, and the solution volume at the equivalence point is 200.0 mL.

EQUATION	NH_3	+ H_3O^+	→ NH_4^+ + H_2O
Initial (mol = $c \times V$)	0.0100	0.0100	0
Change on reaction (mol)	−0.0100	−0.0100	+0.0100
After reaction (mol)	0	0	0.0100
Concentration (M)	0	0	0.0100 mol (in 0.200L) = 0.0500 M

Part 2: *Equilibrium Problem*

When the equivalence point is reached, the solution consists of 0.0500 M NH_4^+. The pH is determined by the hydrolysis of this weak acid.

EQUATION	NH_4^+	+ H_2O	⇌ NH_3	+ H_3O^+
Initial (M)	0.0500		0	0
Change (M)	$-x$		$+x$	$+x$
Equilibrium (M)	$0.0500 - x$		x	x

Using K_a for the weak acid NH_4^+, you have

$$K_a = 5.6 \times 10^{-10} = \frac{[NH_3][H_3O^+]}{[NH_4^+]} = \frac{x^2}{0.0500 - x}$$

$$\text{Simplifying, } x = [H_3O^+] = \sqrt{(5.6 \times 10^{-10})(0.0500)} = 5.3 \times 10^{-6}\text{ M}$$

$$pH = 5.28$$

Think about Your Answer The pH at the equivalence point (5.28) indicates the solution is mildly acidic, as expected for a solution of the conjugate acid of a weak base.

Check Your Understanding

Calculate the pH after 75.0 mL of 0.100 M HCl has been added to 100.0 mL of 0.100 M NH_3 (see Figure 17.7).

Roses are a natural indicator.

(a) The pigment in red rose petals was extracted with ethanol; the extract was a faint red.

(b) After adding one drop of 6 M HCl, the color changed to a vivid red.

(c) Adding two drops of 6 M NH_3 produced a green color, and

(d) adding 1 drop each of HCl and NH_3 (to give a buffer solution) gave a blue solution.

(e) Finally, adding a few milligrams of $Al(NO_3)_3$ turned the solution deep purple.

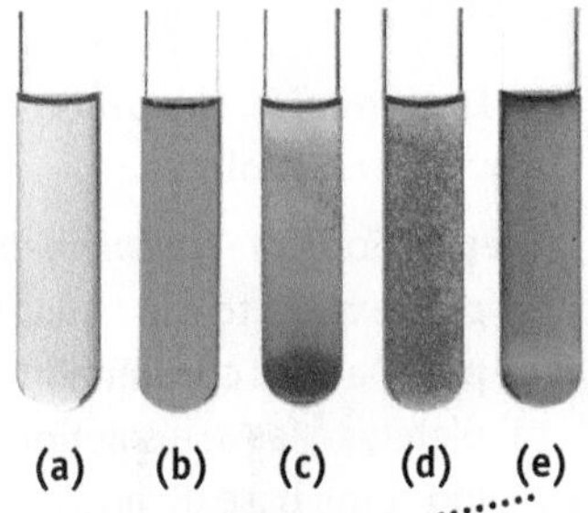

The deep purple color with aluminum ions was so intense that the solution had to be diluted significantly to take the photo.

pH Indicators

Many organic compounds, both natural and synthetic, have a color that changes with pH (Figure 17.8). Not only does this add beauty and variety to our world, but it is also a useful property in chemistry.

You may have done an acid–base titration in the laboratory, and, before starting the titration, you added an **indicator**. The acid–base indicator is usually an organic compound that is itself a weak acid or weak base (as are many compounds that give flowers their colors). In aqueous solution, the acid form is in equilibrium with its conjugate base. Abbreviating the indicator's acid formula as HInd and the formula of its conjugate base as Ind^-, you can write the equilibrium equation

$$HInd(aq) + H_2O(\ell) \rightleftharpoons H_3O^+(aq) + Ind^-(aq)$$

The important characteristic of acid–base indicators is that the acid form of the compound (HInd) has one color and the conjugate base (Ind^-) has another. To see how such compounds can be used as equivalence point indicators, let us write the

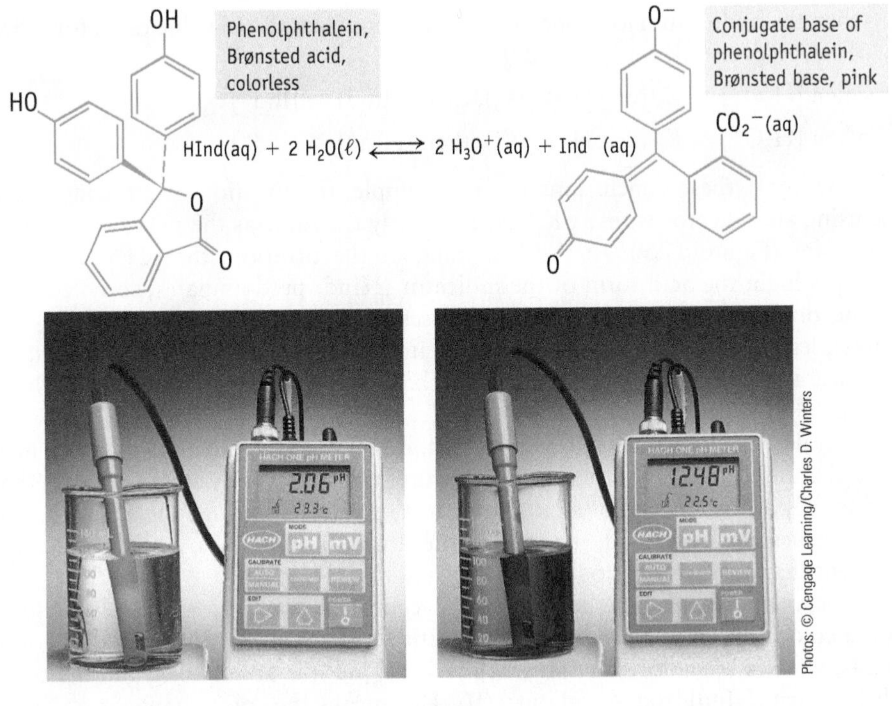

FIGURE 17.8 Phenolphthalein, a common acid–base indicator. Phenolphthalein, a weak acid, is colorless. As the pH increases, the pink conjugate base form predominates, and the color of the solution changes. The change in color is most noticeable around pH 9. The dye is commonly used for strong acid + strong base or weak acid + strong base titrations because the pH changes from about 3 to about 10 in these cases. For other suitable indicator dyes, see Figure 17.10.

PROBLEM SOLVING TIP 17.2

Calculating the pH at Various Stages in an Acid–Base Titration

Finding the pH at or before the equivalence point for an acid–base reaction always involves several calculation steps. There are no shortcuts. Consider the *titration of a weak base, B, with a strong acid* as in Example 17.7. (The same principles apply to other acid–base reactions.)

$$H_3O^+(aq) + B(aq) \rightleftarrows BH^+(aq) + H_2O(\ell)$$

A: Determining the pH before the equivalence point.

Step 1. *Solve the stoichiometry problem.* Up to the equivalence point, acid is consumed completely to leave a solution containing some base (B) and its conjugate acid (BH^+). Use the principles of stoichiometry to calculate (a) the amount of acid added, (b) the amount of base remaining, and (c) the amount of conjugate acid (BH^+) formed.

Step 2. Calculate the concentrations of B and BH^+. Recognize that the volume of the solution at any point is the sum of the original volume of base solution plus the volume of acid solution added.

Step 3. *Calculate the pH.* At any point before the equivalence point, the solution is a buffer solution because both B and BH^+ are present. Calculate $[H_3O^+]$ using the concentrations of Step 2 and the value of K_a for the conjugate acid of the weak base.

B: Determining the pH at the equivalence point.

Calculate the concentration of the conjugate acid using the procedure of Part A. Use the value of K_a for the conjugate acid of the weak base and the procedure outlined in Example 17.7. (For a titration of a weak acid with a strong base, use the value of K_b for the conjugate base of the acid and follow the procedure outlined in Example 17.6.)

usual equilibrium constant expressions for the dependence of hydronium ion concentration or pH on the indicator's ionization constant (K_a) and on the relative quantities of the acid and conjugate base.

$$[H_3O^+] = \frac{[HInd]}{[Ind^-]} \times K_a \quad \text{or} \quad pH = pK_a + \log\frac{[Ind^-]}{[HInd]}$$

These equations inform us that

- when the hydronium ion concentration is equivalent to the value of K_a (or when $pH = pK_a$), then $[HInd] = [Ind^-]$
- when $[H_3O^+] > K_a$ (or $pH < pK_a$), then $[HInd] > [Ind^-]$
- when $[H_3O^+] < K_a$ (or $pH > pK_a$), then $[HInd] < [Ind^-]$

Now apply these conclusions to, for example, the titration of an acid with a base using an indicator whose pK_a value is nearly the same as the pH at the equivalence point (Figure 17.9). At the beginning of the titration, the pH is low and $[H_3O^+]$ is high; the acid form of the indicator (HInd) predominates, so its color is the one observed. As the titration progresses and the pH increases ($[H_3O^+]$ decreases), less of the acid HInd and more of its conjugate base exist in solution. Finally, just after the equivalence point is reached, $[Ind^-]$ is much larger than [HInd], and the color of $[Ind^-]$ is observed.

Several questions remain to be answered. If you are trying to analyze for an acid and add an indicator that is a weak acid, won't this affect the analysis? Recall that you use only a tiny amount of an indicator in a titration. Although the acidic indicator molecules also react with the base as the titration progresses, so little indicator is present that any error is not significant.

Another question is whether you could accurately determine the pH by observing the color change of an indicator. In practice, your eyes are not quite that good. Usually, you see the color of HInd when $[HInd]/[Ind^-]$ is about 10/1, and the color of Ind^- when $[HInd]/[Ind^-]$ is about 1/10. This means the color change is observed over a hydronium ion concentration interval of about 2 pH units. However, as you

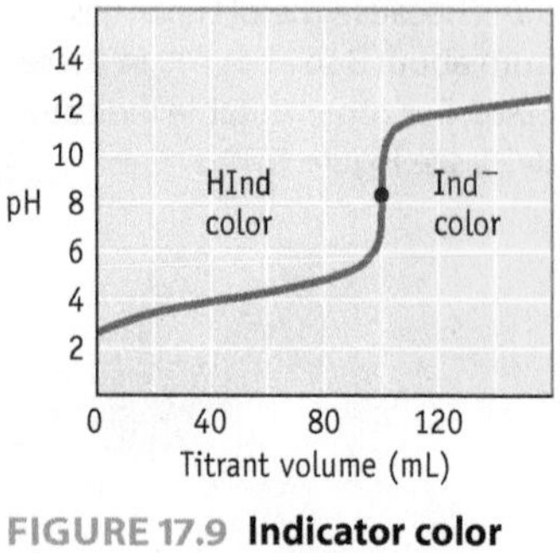

FIGURE 17.9 **Indicator color changes in the course of a titration when the pK_a of the indicator HInd is about 8.**

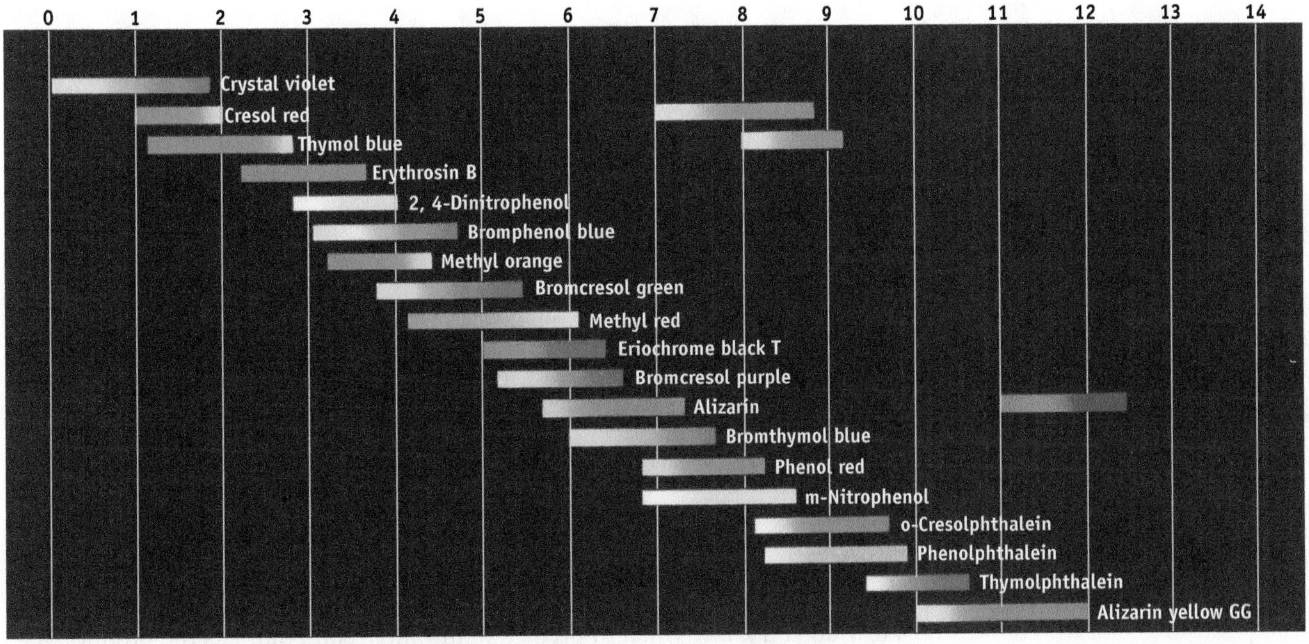

FIGURE 17.10 **Common acid–base indicators.** The color changes occur over a range of pH values. Notice that a few indicators have color changes over two different pH ranges.

can see in Figures 17.4–17.7, on passing through the equivalence point of these titrations, the pH changes by as many as 7 units.

As Figure 17.10 shows, a variety of indicators is available, each changing color in a different pH range. If you are analyzing an acid or base by titration, you must choose an indicator that changes color in a range that includes the pH to be observed at the equivalence point. For the titration of a strong acid with a strong base an indicator that changes color in the pH range 7 ± 2 should be used. On the other hand, the pH at the equivalence point in the titration of a weak acid with a strong base is greater than 7, and you should choose an indicator that changes color at a pH near the anticipated equivalence point.

REVIEW & CHECK FOR SECTION 17-3

1. What is the pH after 25.0 mL of 0.100 M NaOH has been added to 50.0 mL of 0.100 M HCl?

   (a) 1.00 (b) 1.48 (c) 7.00 (d) 13.00

2. What is the pH at the equivalence point in the titration of 25.0 mL of 0.090 M phenol ($K_a = 1.3 \times 10^{-10}$) with 0.108 M NaOH?

   (a) 7.00 (b) 5.65 (c) 8.98 (d) 11.29

3. Use Figure 17.10 to decide which indicator is best to use in the titration of NH_3 with HCl shown in Figure 17.7.

   (a) crystal violet (b) thymol blue (c) methyl red (d) phenolphthalein

17-4 Solubility of Salts

Learning Objectives: LO 6.21, LO 6.22, LO 6.23

Precipitation reactions (◀ Section 3-5) are exchange reactions in which one of the products is a water-insoluble compound such as $CaCO_3$,

$$CaCl_2(aq) + Na_2CO_3(aq) \longrightarrow CaCO_3(s) + 2\ NaCl(aq)$$

that is, a compound having a water solubility of less than about 0.01 mol of dissolved material per liter of solution (Figure 17.11).

Crocoite, lead(II) chromate, $PbCrO_4$

Rhodochrosite, manganese(II) carbonate, $MnCO_3$

Copper(II) minerals: green malachite, $CuCO_3 \cdot Cu(OH)_2$, and blue azurite, $2\,CuCO_3 \cdot Cu(OH)_2$

FIGURE 17.11 **Some insoluble substances.**

How do you know when to predict an insoluble compound as the product of a reaction? In Chapter 3, some guidelines are listed for predicting solubility (◀ Figure 3.10). Now we want to make our estimates of solubility more quantitative and to explore conditions under which some compounds precipitate and others do not.

The Solubility Product Constant, K_{sp}

If some AgBr is placed in pure water, a tiny amount of the compound dissolves, and an equilibrium is established.

$$\text{AgBr(s)} \rightleftharpoons \text{Ag}^+(\text{aq}, 7.35 \times 10^{-7}\ \text{M}) + \text{Br}^-(\text{aq}, 7.35 \times 10^{-7}\ \text{M})$$

When sufficient AgBr has dissolved and equilibrium is attained, the solution is said to be **saturated** (◀ Section 13-2), and experiments show that the concentrations of the silver and bromide ions in the solution are each about 7.35×10^{-7} M at 25 °C. The extent to which an insoluble salt dissolves can be expressed in terms of the equilibrium constant for the dissolving process. In this case, the appropriate expression is

$$K_{sp} = [\text{Ag}^+][\text{Br}^-]$$

Writing Equilibrium Constant Expressions Solids are not included in these equations.

The equilibrium constant that reflects the solubility of a compound is referred to as its **solubility product constant**. Chemists frequently use the notation K_{sp} for such constants, the subscript "sp" denoting a "solubility product."

The water solubility of a compound, and thus its K_{sp} value, can be estimated by determining the concentration of the cation or anion when the compound dissolves. For example, if you find that AgBr dissolves to give a silver ion concentration of 7.35×10^{-7} mol/L, you know that 7.35×10^{-7} mol of AgBr must have dissolved per liter of solution (and that the bromide ion concentration also equals 7.35×10^{-7} M). Therefore, the value of the equilibrium constant for AgBr is

$$K_{sp} = [\text{Ag}^+][\text{Br}^-] = (7.35 \times 10^{-7})(7.35 \times 10^{-7}) = 5.40 \times 10^{-13} \text{ (at 25 °C)}$$

Equilibrium constants for dissolving other insoluble salts can be calculated in the same manner.

The solubility product constant, K_{sp}, for any salt always has the form

$$\text{A}_x\text{B}_y\text{(s)} \rightleftharpoons x\ \text{A}^{y+}(\text{aq}) + y\ \text{B}^{x-}(\text{aq}) \qquad K_{sp} = [\text{A}^{y+}]^x[\text{B}^{x-}]^y \qquad (17.6)$$

For example,

$$CaF_2(s) \rightleftharpoons Ca^{2+}(aq) + 2\ F^-(aq) \qquad K_{sp} = [Ca^{2+}][F^-]^2 = 5.3 \times 10^{-11}$$

$$Ag_2SO_4(s) \rightleftharpoons 2\ Ag^+(aq) + SO_4^{2-}(aq) \qquad K_{sp} = [Ag^+]^2[SO_4^{2-}] = 1.2 \times 10^{-5}$$

The numerical values of K_{sp} for a few salts are given in Table 17.2, and more values are collected in Appendix J.

Do not confuse the *solubility* of a compound with its *solubility product constant.* The *solubility* of a salt is the quantity or amount present in some volume of a saturated solution, expressed in grams per 100 mL, moles per liter, or other units. The *solubility product constant* is an equilibrium constant. Nonetheless, there is a connection between them: If one is known, the other can, in principle, be calculated.

Relating Solubility and K_{sp}

Solubility product constants are determined by careful laboratory measurements of the concentrations of ions in solution.

EXAMPLE 17.8

K_{sp} from Solubility Measurements

Problem Calcium fluoride, the main component of the mineral fluorite, dissolves to a slight extent in water.

$$CaF_2(s) \rightleftharpoons Ca^{2+}(aq) + 2\ F^-(aq) \qquad K_{sp} = [Ca^{2+}][F^-]^2$$

Calculate the K_{sp} value for CaF_2 if the calcium ion concentration has been found to be 2.3×10^{-4} mol/L.

What Do You Know? You know the balanced equation for the process, the Ca^{2+} concentration, and the K_{sp} expression.

Strategy

- Calculate the fluoride ion concentration from $[Ca^{2+}]$ and stoichiometry.
- Insert the values for $[F^-]$ and $[Ca^{2+}]$ into the K_{sp} expression and calculate the value of K_{sp}.

Solution When CaF_2 dissolves in water, the balanced equation shows that the concentration of F^- ion must be twice the Ca^{2+} ion concentration.

$$\text{If } [Ca^{2+}] = 2.3 \times 10^{-4}\ M, \text{ then } [F^-] = 2 \times [Ca^{2+}] = 4.6 \times 10^{-4}\ M$$

This means the solubility product constant is

$$K_{sp} = [Ca^{2+}][F^-]^2 = (2.3 \times 10^{-4})(4.6 \times 10^{-4})^2 = 4.9 \times 10^{-11}$$

Think about Your Answer A common student error is to forget the reaction stoichiometry. Be sure to notice that for every Ca^{2+} ion in solution there are two F^- ions.

Check Your Understanding

The barium ion concentration, $[Ba^{2+}]$, in a saturated solution of barium fluoride is 3.6×10^{-3} M. Calculate the value of the K_{sp} for BaF_2.

$$BaF_2(s) \rightleftharpoons Ba^{2+}(aq) + 2\ F^-(aq)$$

Strategy Map 17.8

PROBLEM
Calculate K_{sp} of CaF_2 from its **solubility.**

↓

DATA/INFORMATION KNOWN
- Concentration of Ca^{2+}
- Form of K_{sp}
- Balanced equation

↓ **STEP 1.** Calculate F^- **concentration.**

$[F^-] = 2 \times [Ca^{2+}]$

↓ **STEP 2.** Enter **equilibrium concentrations** in K_{sp} expression and calculate K_{sp}.

Value of K_{sp}

K_{sp} values for insoluble salts can be used to calculate the solubility of a solid salt or to determine whether a solid will precipitate when solutions of its anion and cation are mixed. Let us first look at an example of the calculation of the solubility of a salt from its K_{sp} value.

Table 17.2 Some Common Insoluble Compounds and Their K_{sp} Values*

FORMULA	NAME	K_{sp} (25 °C)	COMMON NAMES/USES
$CaCO_3$	Calcium carbonate	3.4×10^{-9}	Calcite, iceland spar
$MnCO_3$	Manganese(II) carbonate	2.3×10^{-11}	Rhodochrosite (forms rose-colored crystals)
$FeCO_3$	Iron(II) carbonate	3.1×10^{-11}	Siderite
CaF_2	Calcium fluoride	5.3×10^{-11}	Fluorite (source of HF and other inorganic fluorides)
$AgCl$	Silver chloride	1.8×10^{-10}	Chlorargyrite
$AgBr$	Silver bromide	5.4×10^{-13}	Used in photographic film
$CaSO_4$	Calcium sulfate	4.9×10^{-5}	Hydrated form is commonly called *gypsum*
$BaSO_4$	Barium sulfate	1.1×10^{-10}	Barite (used in "drilling mud" and as a component of paints)
$SrSO_4$	Strontium sulfate	3.4×10^{-7}	Celestite
$Ca(OH)_2$	Calcium hydroxide	5.5×10^{-5}	Slaked lime

*The values in this table were taken from *Lange's Handbook of Chemistry,* 15th edition, McGraw-Hill Publishers, New York, NY (1999). Additional K_{sp} values are given in Appendix J.

EXAMPLE 17.9

Solubility from K_{sp}

Problem The K_{sp} for the mineral barite ($BaSO_4$, Figure 17.12) is 1.1×10^{-10} at 25 °C. Calculate the solubility of barium sulfate in pure water in (a) moles per liter and (b) grams per liter.

What Do You Know? You know the formula for the mineral and its K_{sp} value.

A CLOSER LOOK

Minerals and Gems—The Importance of Solubility

Minerals and gems are among nature's most beautiful creations. Many, such as rubies, are metal oxides, and the various types of quartz are based on silicon dioxide. Another large class of gemstones consists largely of metal silicates. These include emerald, topaz, aquamarine, and tourmaline.

Carbonates represent another large class of minerals and a few gemstones. Rhodochrosite, one of the most beautiful red stones, is manganese(II) carbonate. And one of the most abundant minerals on Earth is limestone, calcium carbonate, which is also a major component of sea shells and corals.

Hydroxides are represented by azurite, which is a mixed carbonate/hydroxide with the formula $Cu_3(OH)_2(CO_3)_2$. Turquoise is a mixed hydroxide/phosphate based on copper(II), the source of the blue color of turquoise.

Among the most common minerals are sulfides such as golden iron pyrite (FeS_2), black stibnite (Sb_2S_3), red cinnabar (HgS), and yellow orpiment (As_2S_3).

Other smaller classes of minerals exist; one of the smallest is the class based on the halides, and the best example is fluorite. Fluorite, CaF_2, exhibits a wide range of colors from purple to green to yellow.

What do all of these minerals and gems have in common? They are all insoluble or poorly soluble in water. If they were more soluble, they would be dissolved in the world's lakes and oceans.

Mineral samples (clockwise from the top center): red rhodochrosite, yellow orpiment, golden iron pyrite, green-blue turquoise, black stibnite, purple fluorite, and blue azurite. Formulas are in the text (see also Figure 17.11).

(a) A sample of the mineral barite, which is mostly barium sulfate. "Drilling mud," used in drilling oil wells, consists of clay, barite, and calcium carbonate.

© Cengage Learning/Charles D. Winters

(b) Barium sulfate is opaque to x-rays, so it is used by physicians to examine the digestive tract. A patient drinks a "cocktail" containing $BaSO_4$, and the progress of the $BaSO_4$ through the digestive organs can be followed by x-ray analysis. This photo is an x-ray of the gastrointestinal tract after a person ingested barium sulfate.

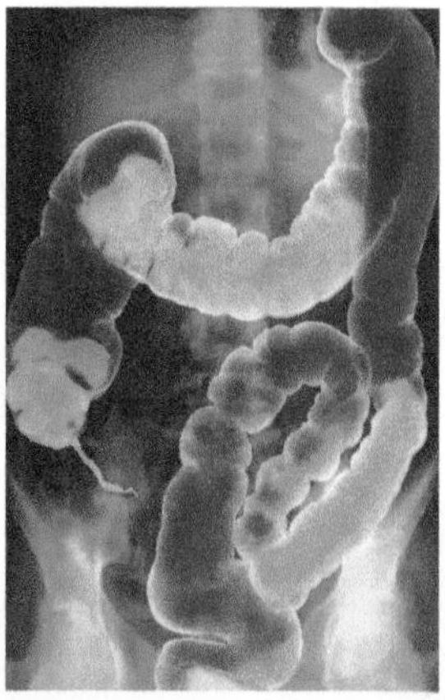

CNRI/Science Source

FIGURE 17.12 **Barium sulfate.** Barium sulfate, a white solid, is quite insoluble in water ($K_{sp} = 1.1 \times 10^{-10}$) (see Example 17.9).

Strategy When $BaSO_4$ dissolves, equimolar amounts of Ba^{2+} ions and SO_4^{2-} ions are produced. Thus, the solubility of $BaSO_4$ can be estimated by calculating the equilibrium concentration of either Ba^{2+} or SO_4^{2-} from the solubility product constant.

- Write the balanced equation and the K_{sp} expression.
- Set up an ICE table, designating the unknown concentrations of Ba^{2+} and SO_4^{2-} in solution as x.
- Using x for $[Ba^{2+}]$ and $[SO_4^{2-}]$ in the K_{sp} expression, solve for x.

Solution The equation for the solubility of $BaSO_4$ and its K_{sp} expression are

$$BaSO_4(s) \rightleftharpoons Ba^{2+}(aq) + SO_4^{2-}(aq) \qquad K_{sp} = [Ba^{2+}][SO_4^{2-}] = 1.1 \times 10^{-10}$$

Denote the solubility of $BaSO_4$ (in mol/L) by x; that is, x moles of $BaSO_4$ dissolve per liter. Therefore, both $[Ba^{2+}]$ and $[SO_4^{2-}]$ must also equal x at equilibrium.

Equation	**$BaSO_4$(s)**	$\rightleftharpoons$	**Ba^{2+}(aq)**	+	**SO_4^{2-}(aq)**
Initial (M)			0		0
Change (M)			$+x$		$+x$
Equilibrium (M)			x		x

Because K_{sp} is the product of the barium ion and sulfate ion concentrations, K_{sp} is the square of the solubility, x,

$$K_{sp} = [Ba^{2+}][SO_4^{2-}] = 1.1 \times 10^{-10} = (x)(x) = x^2$$

and so the value of x is

$$x = [Ba^{2+}] = [SO_4^{2-}] = \sqrt{K_{sp}} = \sqrt{1.1 \times 10^{-10}} = 1.0 \times 10^{-5}\ M$$

The solubility of $BaSO_4$ in pure water is 1.0×10^{-5} mol/L. To find its solubility in g/L, you only need to multiply by the molar mass of $BaSO_4$.

$$\text{Solubility in g/L} = (1.0 \times 10^{-5}\ \text{mol/L})(233\ \text{g/mol}) = 0.0024\ \text{g/L}$$

Think about Your Answer As noted in Figure 17.12, $BaSO_4$ is used to investigate the digestive tract. It is fortunate the compound is so insoluble, because water- and acid-soluble barium salts are toxic.

Check Your Understanding

Calculate the solubility of AgCN in moles per liter and grams per liter. K_{sp} for AgCN is 6.0×10^{-17}.

Strategy Map 17.9

PROBLEM

Calculate **solubility** of **$BaSO_4$** from **K_{sp}**.

DATA/INFORMATION KNOWN

- K_{sp} for $BaSO_4$
- Balanced equation

STEP 1. Write the **balanced equation** and **K_{sp} expression** and set up **ICE table.**

At equilibrium: $[Ba^{2+}] = [SO_4^{2-}] = x$

STEP 2. Enter **equilibrium concentrations** in K_{sp} expression.

K_{sp} expression with equilibrium concentrations in terms of **x**

STEP 3. Solve **K_{sp} expression** for **x**.

x = Solubility = $[Ba^{2+}] = [SO_4^{2-}]$

EXAMPLE 17.10

Solubility from K_{sp}

Problem Knowing that the K_{sp} value for MgF_2 is 5.2×10^{-11}, calculate the solubility of the salt in (a) moles per liter and (b) grams per liter.

What Do You Know? You know the formula for magnesium fluoride and its K_{sp} value.

Strategy The solubility must be defined in terms that will allow you to solve the K_{sp} expression for the concentration of one ion. From stoichiometry, you can say that if x mol of MgF_2 dissolves, then x mol of Mg^{2+} and $2x$ mol of F^- appear in solution. This means the MgF_2 solubility (in moles dissolved per liter) is equivalent to the concentration of Mg^{2+} ions in the solution.

- Write the balanced equation and the K_{sp} expression.
- Set up an ICE table, designating the unknown concentrations of Mg^{2+} and F^- in solution as x and $2x$, respectively.
- Using x for $[Mg^{2+}]$ and $2x$ for $[F^-]$ in the K_{sp} expression, solve for x.

Solution

$$MgF_2(s) \rightleftharpoons Mg^{2+}(aq) + 2\ F^-(aq) \qquad K_{sp} = [Mg^{2+}][F^-]^2 = 5.2 \times 10^{-11}$$

EQUATION	$MgF_2(s)$	$\rightleftharpoons$	$Mg^{2+}(aq)$	+	$2\ F^-(aq)$
Initial (M)			0		0
Change (M)			$+x$		$+2x$
Equilibrium (M)			x		$2x$

Substituting the equilibrium concentrations for $[Mg^{2+}]$ and $[F^-]$ into the K_{sp} expression, you find

$$K_{sp} = [Mg^{2+}][F^-]^2 = (x)(2x)^2 = 4x^3$$

Solving the equation for x,

$$x = \sqrt[3]{\frac{K_{sp}}{4}} = \sqrt[3]{\frac{5.2 \times 10^{-11}}{4}} = 2.4 \times 10^{-4}$$

you find that 2.4×10^{-4} moles of MgF_2 dissolve per liter. The solubility of MgF_2 in grams per liter is

$$(2.4 \times 10^{-4}\ \text{mol/L})(62.3\ \text{g/mol}) = 0.015\ \text{g}\ MgF_2\text{/L}$$

Think about Your Answer Problems like this one might provoke our students to ask the question, "Aren't you counting things twice when you multiply x by 2 and then square it as well?" in the expression $K_{sp} = (x)(2x)^2$. The answer is no. The 2 in the $2x$ term is based on the stoichiometry of the compound. The exponent of 2 on the F^- ion concentration arises from the rules for writing equilibrium expressions.

Check Your Understanding

Calculate the solubility of $Ca(OH)_2$ in moles per liter and grams per liter ($K_{sp} = 5.5 \times 10^{-5}$).

The *relative* solubilities of salts can often be deduced by comparing values of solubility product constants, but you must be careful! For example, the K_{sp} for silver chloride is

$$AgCl(s) \rightleftharpoons Ag^+(aq) + Cl^-(aq) \qquad K_{sp} = 1.8 \times 10^{-10}$$

whereas that for silver chromate is

$$Ag_2CrO_4(s) \rightleftharpoons 2\ Ag^+(aq) + CrO_4^{2-}(aq) \qquad K_{sp} = 9.0 \times 10^{-12}$$

In spite of the fact that Ag_2CrO_4 has a smaller numerical K_{sp} value than AgCl, the chromate salt is about 10 times *more* soluble than the chloride salt. If you determine solubilities from K_{sp} values as in the examples above, you would find the solubility of AgCl is 1.3×10^{-5} mol/L, whereas that of Ag_2CrO_4 is 1.3×10^{-4} mol/L. From this example and countless others, we conclude that

> Direct comparisons of the solubility of two salts on the basis of their K_{sp} values can be made only for salts having the same cation-to-anion ratio.

This means, for example, that you can directly compare solubilities of 1:1 salts such as the silver halides by comparing their K_{sp} values.

$$AgI\ (K_{sp} = 8.5 \times 10^{-17}) < AgBr\ (K_{sp} = 5.4 \times 10^{-13}) < AgCl\ (K_{sp} = 1.8 \times 10^{-10})$$

increasing K_{sp} and increasing solubility ⟶

Similarly, you could compare 1:2 salts such as the lead halides,

$$PbI_2\ (K_{sp} = 9.8 \times 10^{-9}) < PbBr_2\ (K_{sp} = 6.6 \times 10^{-6}) < PbCl_2\ (K_{sp} = 1.7 \times 10^{-5})$$

increasing K_{sp} and increasing solubility ⟶

but you cannot directly compare the solubility of a 1:1 salt (AgCl) with a 2:1 salt (Ag_2CrO_4) by only comparing the K_{sp} values.

Solubility and the Common Ion Effect

The test tube on the left in Figure 17.13 contains a precipitate of silver acetate, $AgCH_3CO_2$, in water. The solution is saturated, and the silver ions and acetate ions in the solution are in equilibrium with solid silver acetate.

$$AgCH_3CO_2(s) \rightleftharpoons Ag^+(aq) + CH_3CO_2^-(aq)$$

But what would happen if the silver ion concentration is increased, say by adding silver nitrate? Le Chatelier's principle (◀ Section 15-6) suggests—and observations confirm—that more silver acetate precipitate should form because a product ion has been added, causing the equilibrium to shift to form more silver acetate.

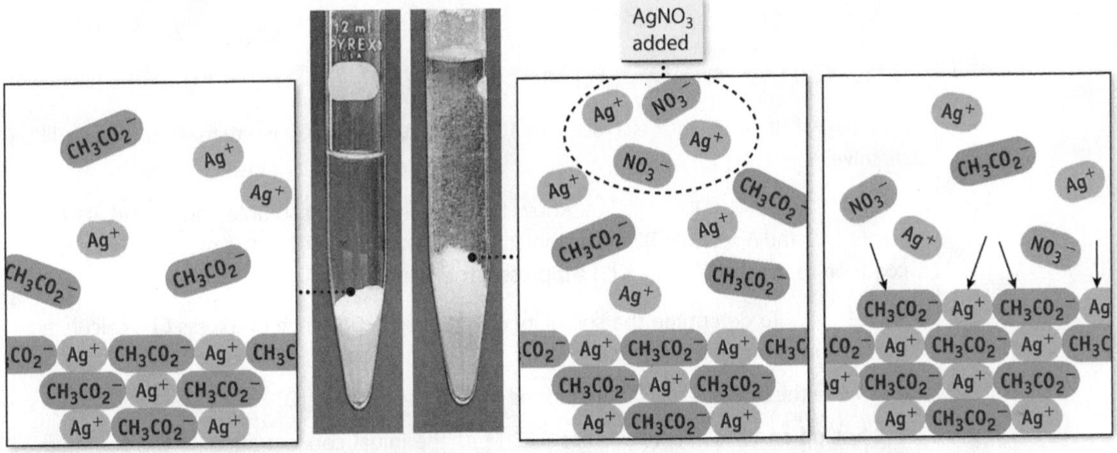

Photos: © Cengage Learning/Charles D. Winters

FIGURE 17.13 **The common ion effect.** The tube at the *left* contains a saturated solution of silver acetate, $AgCH_3CO_2$. When 1.0 M $AgNO_3$ is added to the tube *(right)*, more solid silver acetate forms.

A CLOSER LOOK

Solubility Calculations

The K_{sp} value reported for lead(II) chloride, $PbCl_2$, is 1.7×10^{-5}. If we assume the appropriate equilibrium in solution is

$$PbCl_2(s) \rightleftharpoons Pb^{2+}(aq) + 2\ Cl^-(aq)$$

the calculated solubility of $PbCl_2$ is 0.016 M. The experimental value for the solubility of the salt, however, is 0.036 M, more than twice the calculated value! The problem is that the chemical behavior is often much more complicated than the equation defining K_{sp}.

The main problem in the lead(II) chloride case, and in many others, is that the compound dissolves but is not 100% dissociated into its constituent ions. Instead, it dissolves as the undissociated salt or forms ion pairs.

Other problems that lead to discrepancies between calculated and experimental solubilities are the reactions of ions (particularly anions) with water and complex ion formation. An example of the former effect is the product-favored reaction of sulfide ion with water, that is, *hydrolysis*.

$$S^{2-}(aq) + H_2O(\ell) \rightleftharpoons HS^-(aq) + OH^-(aq)$$

$$PbCl_2(aq) \xrightleftharpoons{K = 0.63} PbCl^+(aq) + Cl^-(aq)$$

undissociated salt dissolved in water — ion pairs

$PbCl_2(aq) \rightleftharpoons PbCl_2(s)$: $K = 0.0011$

$PbCl^+(aq) + Cl^-(aq) \rightleftharpoons Pb^{2+}(aq) + 2\ Cl^-(aq)$: $K = 0.026$

$$PbCl_2(s) \xrightleftharpoons{K_{sp} = 1.7 \times 10^{-5}} Pb^{2+}(aq) + 2\ Cl^-(aq)$$

slightly soluble salt — 100% dissociated into ions

This means that the solubility of a metal sulfide is better described by a chemical equation such as

$$NiS(s) + H_2O(\ell) \rightleftharpoons Ni^{2+}(aq) + HS^-(aq) + OH^-(aq)$$

Complex ion formation is illustrated by the fact that lead chloride is more soluble in the presence of excess chloride ion, owing to the formation of the complex ion $PbCl_4^{2-}$.

$$PbCl_2(s) + 2\ Cl^-(aq) \rightleftharpoons PbCl_4^{2-}(aq)$$

Hydrolysis and complex ion formation are discussed further on pages 655–656 and 670–674, respectively.

References:

- L. Meites, J. S. F. Pode, and H. C. Thomas: *Journal of Chemical Education*, Vol. 43, pp. 667–672, 1966.
- S. J. Hawkes: *Journal of Chemical Education*, Vol. 75, pp. 1179–1181, 1998.
- R. W. Clark and J. M. Bonicamp: *Journal of Chemical Education*, Vol. 75, pp. 1182–1185, 1998.
- R. J. Myers: *Journal of Chemical Education*, Vol. 63, pp. 687–690, 1986.

The ionization of weak acids and bases is affected by the presence of an ion common to the equilibrium process (Section 17-1), and the effect of adding silver ions to a saturated silver acetate solution is another example of the common ion effect. Adding a common ion to a saturated solution of a salt will lower the salt solubility (unless a complex ion can form; see *A Closer Look: Solubility Calculations*).

EXAMPLE 17.11

The Common Ion Effect and Salt Solubility

Problem If solid AgCl is placed in 1.00 L of 0.55 M NaCl, what mass of AgCl will dissolve?

What Do You Know? You know the formula of the insoluble compound, its K_{sp} (Table 17.2 and Appendix J), and its molar mass. You also know that the presence of an ion common to the equilibrium (Cl^-) suppresses the solubility of AgCl.

Strategy To determine the solubility of AgCl in the presence of excess Cl^-, calculate the concentration of the Ag^+ ion.

- Write the balanced equation and the K_{sp} expression for AgCl.
- Set up an ICE table, and enter 0.55 M as the initial concentration of the common ion, Cl^-.

- Define the solubility of AgCl as *x*. This is the increase in the concentration of Ag^+ and Cl^- in solution as AgCl dissolves. Enter this information on the change (C) line in the ICE table.
- Fill in the last line (E) of the ICE table with *x* for $[Ag^+]$ and $(0.55 + x)$ for $[Cl^-]$. Solve the K_{sp} expression for *x*.

Solution Set up an ICE table to show the concentrations of Ag^+ and Cl^- when equilibrium is attained.

EQUATION	AgCl(s)	⇌	$Ag^+(aq)$	+	$Cl^-(aq)$
Initial (M)			0		0.55
Change (M)			$+x$		$+x$
Equilibrium (M)			x		$0.55 + x$

The equilibrium concentrations from the table are substituted into the K_{sp} expression,

$$K_{sp} = 1.8 \times 10^{-10} = [Ag^+][Cl^-] = (x)(0.55 + x)$$

This is a quadratic equation and can be solved by the methods in Appendix A. An easier approach, however, is to make the approximation that *x* is very small with respect to 0.55 [and so $(0.55 + x) \approx 0.55$]. This is a reasonable assumption because you know that the solubility is very small without the common ion Cl^- and that it will be even smaller in the presence of added Cl^-. Therefore,

$$K_{sp} = 1.8 \times 10^{-10} = (x)(0.55)$$

$$x = [Ag^+] = 3.3 \times 10^{-10}\ M$$

The solubility in grams per liter is then

$$(3.3 \times 10^{-10}\ mol/L)(143\ g/mol) = 4.7 \times 10^{-8}\ g/L$$

As predicted by Le Chatelier's principle, the solubility of AgCl in the presence of added Cl^- is much less (3.3×10^{-10} M) than in pure water (1.3×10^{-5} M).

Think about Your Answer The approximation you made here is similar to the approximations you make in acid–base equilibrium problems. However, as a final step, you should check its validity by substituting the calculated value of *x* into the exact expression $K_{sp} = (x)(0.55 + x)$. If the product $(x)(0.55 + x)$ is the same as the given value of K_{sp}, the approximation is valid.

$$K_{sp} = (x)(0.55 + x) = (3.3 \times 10^{-10})(0.55 + 3.3 \times 10^{-10}) = 1.8 \times 10^{-10}$$

Check Your Understanding

Calculate the solubility of $BaSO_4$ (a) in pure water and (b) in the presence of 0.010 M $Ba(NO_3)_2$. K_{sp} for $BaSO_4$ is 1.1×10^{-10}.

EXAMPLE 17.12

The Common Ion Effect and Salt Solubility

Problem Calculate the solubility of silver chromate, Ag_2CrO_4, at 25 °C in the presence of 0.0050 M K_2CrO_4 solution.

$$Ag_2CrO_4(s) \rightleftharpoons 2\ Ag^+(aq) + CrO_4^{2-}(aq)$$

$$K_{sp} = [Ag^+]^2[CrO_4^{2-}] = 9.0 \times 10^{-12}$$

For comparison, the solubility of Ag_2CrO_4 in pure water is 1.3×10^{-4} mol/L.

What Do You Know? You know the formula and K_{sp} value for Ag_2CrO_4.

Strategy In the presence of chromate ion from the water-soluble salt K_2CrO_4, the concentration of Ag^+ ions produced by Ag_2CrO_4 will be less than in pure water. Assume the solubility of Ag_2CrO_4 is x mol/L. This means the concentration of Ag^+ ions will be $2x$ mol/L, whereas the concentration of CrO_4^{2-} ions will be x mol/L plus the concentration of CrO_4^{2-} already in the solution.

- Write the balanced equation and the K_{sp} expression for Ag_2CrO_4.
- Set up an ICE table, and enter 0.0050 M as the initial concentration of CrO_4^{2-}.
- Designate the increase in the concentration of the CrO_4^{2-} ion in solution as x and the increase in $[Ag^+]$ as $2x$.
- Using $2x$ for $[Ag^+]$ and $(0.0050 + x)$ for $[CrO_4^{2-}]$ in the K_{sp} expression, solve for x.

Solution

EQUATION	$Ag_2CrO_4(s)$	$\rightleftharpoons$	$2\ Ag^+(aq)$	+	$CrO_4^{2-}(aq)$
Initial (M)			0		0.0050
Change (M)			$+2x$		$+x$
Equilibrium (M)			$2x$		$0.0050 + x$

Substituting the equilibrium concentrations into the K_{sp} expression, you have

$$K_{sp} = 9.0 \times 10^{-12} = [Ag^+]^2[CrO_4^{2-}]$$

$$K_{sp} = (2x)^2(0.0050 + x)$$

As in Example 17.11, you can make the approximation that x is very small with respect to 0.0050, and so $(0.0050 + x) \approx 0.0050$. Therefore, the approximate expression is

$$K_{sp} = 9.0 \times 10^{-12} = [Ag^+]^2[CrO_4^{2-}] = (2x)^2(0.0050)$$

Solving, you find x, the solubility of silver chromate in the presence of excess chromate ion, is

$$x = \text{Solubility of } Ag_2CrO_4 = 2.1 \times 10^{-5}\ M$$

Think about Your Answer The silver ion concentration in the presence of the common ion is

$$[Ag^+] = 2x = 4.2 \times 10^{-5}\ M$$

This silver ion concentration is indeed less than its value in pure water (2.6×10^{-4} M), owing to the presence of an ion "common" to the equilibrium.

Check Your Understanding

Calculate the solubility of $Zn(CN)_2$ at 25 °C (a) in pure water and (b) in the presence of 0.10 M $Zn(NO_3)_2$. K_{sp} for $Zn(CN)_2$ is 8.0×10^{-12}.

There are two important general ideas from Examples 17.11 and 17.12:

- The solubility of a salt will be reduced by the presence of a common ion, in accordance with Le Chatelier's principle.
- We made the approximation that the amount of common ion added to the solution was very large in comparison with the amount of that ion coming from the insoluble salt, and this allowed us to simplify our calculations. This is almost always the case, but you should check to be sure.

The Effect of Basic Anions on Salt Solubility

The next time you are tempted to wash a supposedly insoluble salt down the kitchen or laboratory drain, stop and consider the consequences. Many metal ions such as lead, chromium, and mercury are toxic in the environment. Even if a so-called insoluble salt of one of these cations does not appear to dissolve, its solubility in water may be greater than you think, in part owing to the possibility that the anion of the salt is a weak base or the cation is a weak acid.

Lead(II) sulfide, PbS, which is found in nature as the mineral galena (Figure 17.14), provides an example of the effect of the acid–base properties of an ion on salt solubility. When placed in water, a trace amount dissolves,

$$PbS(s) \rightleftharpoons Pb^{2+}(aq) + S^{2-}(aq)$$

and one product of the reaction is the sulfide ion, which is itself a strong base.

$$S^{2-}(aq) + H_2O(\ell) \rightleftharpoons HS^-(aq) + OH^-(aq) \qquad K_{b1} = 1 \times 10^5$$

The sulfide ion undergoes extensive hydrolysis (reaction with water) (◀ Table 16.3), which decreases its concentration, and the equilibrium process for dissolving PbS shifts to the right. Thus, the lead ion concentration in solution is greater than expected from the simple dissociation of the salt.

The lead(II) sulfide example leads to the following general observation:

> Any salt containing an anion that is the conjugate base of a weak acid will dissolve in water to a greater extent than given by K_{sp}.

Metal Sulfide Solubility The true solubility of a metal sulfide is better represented by a modified solubility product constant, K'_{sp}, which is defined as follows:

$MS(s) \rightleftharpoons M^{2+}(aq) + S^{2-}(aq)$

$K_{sp} = [M^{2+}][S^{2-}]$

$S^{2-}(aq) + H_2O(\ell) \rightleftharpoons HS^-(aq) + OH^-(aq)$

$K_b = [HS^-][OH^-]/[S^{2-}]$

Net reaction:

$MS(s) + H_2O(\ell) \rightleftharpoons HS^-(aq) + M^{2+}(aq) + OH^-(aq)$

$K'_{sp} = [M^{2+}][HS^-][OH^-] = K_{sp} \times K_b$

Values for K'_{sp} for several metal sulfides are included in Appendix J (Table 18B).

This means that salts of phosphate, acetate, carbonate, and cyanide, as well as sulfide, can be affected, because all of these anions undergo the general hydrolysis reaction

$$X^-(aq) + H_2O(\ell) \rightleftharpoons HX(aq) + OH^-(aq)$$

The observation that ions from insoluble salts can undergo hydrolysis is related to another useful, general conclusion:

> Insoluble salts in which the anion is the conjugate base of a weak acid dissolve in strong acids.

Insoluble salts containing anions such as acetate, carbonate, hydroxide, phosphate, and sulfide dissolve in strong acids. For example, you know that if a strong acid is added to a water-insoluble metal carbonate such as $CaCO_3$, the salt dissolves (◀ Section 3-7).

$$CaCO_3(s) + 2\ H_3O^+(aq) \rightarrow Ca^{2+}(aq) + 3\ H_2O(\ell) + CO_2(g)$$

You can think of this as the result of a series of reactions.

$$CaCO_3(s) \rightleftharpoons Ca^{2+}(aq) + CO_3^{2-}(aq) \qquad K_{sp} = 3.4 \times 10^{-9}$$

$$CO_3^{2-}(aq) + H_3O^+(aq) \rightleftharpoons HCO_3^-(aq) + H_2O(\ell) \qquad 1/K_{a2} = 1/4.8 \times 10^{-11} = 2.1 \times 10^{10}$$

$$HCO_3^-(aq) + H_3O^+(aq) \rightleftharpoons H_2CO_3(aq) + H_2O(\ell) \qquad 1/K_{a1} = 1/4.2 \times 10^{-7} = 2.4 \times 10^6$$

$$\text{Overall: } CaCO_3(s) + 2\ H_3O^+(aq) \rightleftharpoons Ca^{2+}(aq) + 2\ H_2O(\ell) + H_2CO_3(aq)$$

$$K_{net} = (K_{sp})(1/K_{a2})(1/K_{a1}) = 1.7 \times 10^8$$

Carbonic acid, a product of this reaction, is not stable,

$$H_2CO_3(aq) \rightleftharpoons CO_2(g) + H_2O(\ell) \qquad K \approx 10^5$$

and you see CO_2 bubbling out of the solution, a process that moves the $CaCO_3 + H_3O^+$ equilibrium even further to the right. Calcium carbonate dissolves completely in strong acid!

FIGURE 17.14 **Lead(II) sulfide (galena).** This and other metal sulfides dissolve in water to a greater extent than expected because the sulfide ion reacts with water to form HS^- and OH^-.

$PbS(s) + H_2O(\ell) \rightleftharpoons Pb^{2+}(aq) + HS^-(aq) + OH^-(aq)$

The model of PbS shows that the unit cell is cubic, a feature reflected by the cubic crystals of the mineral galena.

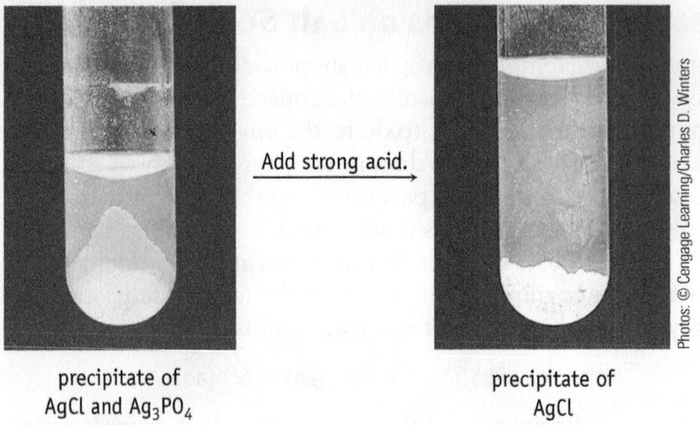

FIGURE 17.15 The effect of the anion on salt solubility in acid. *(left)* A precipitate of AgCl (white) and Ag_3PO_4 (yellow). *(right)* Adding a strong acid (HNO_3) dissolves Ag_3PO_4 (and leaves insoluble AgCl). The basic anion PO_4^{3-} reacts with acid to give H_3PO_4, whereas Cl^- is too weakly basic to form HCl.

Many metal sulfides are also soluble in strong acids

$$FeS(s) + 2\ H_3O^+(aq) \rightleftharpoons Fe^{2+}(aq) + H_2S(aq) + 2\ H_2O(\ell)$$

as are metal phosphates (Figure 17.15),

$$Ag_3PO_4(s) + 3\ H_3O^+(aq) \rightleftharpoons 3\ Ag^+(aq) + H_3PO_4(aq) + 3\ H_2O(\ell)$$

and metal hydroxides.

$$Mg(OH)_2(s) + 2\ H_3O^+(aq) \rightleftharpoons Mg^{2+}(aq) + 4\ H_2O(\ell)$$

In general, the solubility of a salt containing the conjugate base of a weak acid is increased by addition of a stronger acid to the solution. In contrast, salts are not soluble in strong acid if the anion is the conjugate base of a strong acid. For example, AgCl is not soluble in strong acid

$$AgCl(s) \rightleftharpoons Ag^+(aq) + Cl^-(aq) \qquad K_{sp} = 1.8 \times 10^{-10}$$

$$H_3O^+(aq) + Cl^-(aq) \rightleftharpoons HCl(aq) + H_2O(\ell) \qquad K << 1$$

because Cl^- is a very weak base (◀ Table 16.2), and so its concentration is not lowered by a reaction with the strong acid H_3O^+ (Figure 17.15). This same conclusion would also apply to insoluble salts of Br^- and I^-.

REVIEW & CHECK FOR SECTION 17-4

1. What is the K_{sp} expression for silver carbonate?

   (a) $K_{sp} = [Ag^+][CO_3^{2-}]$ (c) $K_{sp} = [Ag^+][CO_3^{2-}]^2$

   (b) $K_{sp} = [Ag^+]^2[CO_3^{2-}]$

2. Using K_{sp} values, predict which salt in each pair is more soluble in water.

   (a) AgCl ($K_{sp} = 1.8 \times 10^{-10}$) or AgCN ($K_{sp} = 6.0 \times 10^{-17}$)

   (b) $Mg(OH)_2$ ($K_{sp} = 5.6 \times 10^{-12}$) or $Ca(OH)_2$ ($K_{sp} = 5.5 \times 10^{-5}$)

   (c) $Ca(OH)_2$ ($K_{sp} = 5.5 \times 10^{-5}$) or $CaSO_4$ ($K_{sp} = 4.9 \times 10^{-5}$)

3. What is the solubility of $PbSO_4$ in water at 25 °C? (K_{sp} for $PbSO_4 = 2.5 \times 10^{-8}$)

   (a) 2.5×10^{-8} M (b) 1.6×10^{-4} M (c) 6.3×10^{-16} M

4. What is the solubility of $PbSO_4$ in water at 25 °C if the solution already contains 0.25 M Na_2SO_4? (K_{sp} for $PbSO_4 = 2.5 \times 10^{-8}$)

   (a) 1.0×10^{-7} M (b) 1.6×10^{-4} M (c) 6.3×10^{-9} M

5. Which compound should be more soluble in 0.1 M HCl?

   (a) $FeCO_3$ ($K_{sp} = 3.1 \times 10^{-11}$) (b) AgCl ($K_{sp} = 1.8 \times 10^{-10}$)

17-5 Precipitation Reactions

Metal-bearing ores contain the metal in the form of an insoluble salt (Figure 17.16), and, to complicate matters, ores often contain several such metal salts. Many industrial methods for separating metals from their ores involve dissolving metal salts to obtain the metal ion or ions in solution. The solution is then concentrated in some manner, and a precipitating agent is added to precipitate selectively only one type of metal ion as an insoluble salt. In the case of nickel, for example, the Ni^{2+} ion can be precipitated as insoluble nickel(II) sulfide or nickel(II) carbonate.

$$Ni^{2+}(aq) + HS^-(aq) + H_2O(\ell) \rightleftharpoons NiS(s) + H_3O^+(aq) \qquad K = 1.7 \times 10^{18}$$

$$Ni^{2+}(aq) + CO_3^{2-}(aq) \rightleftharpoons NiCO_3(s) \qquad K = 7.1 \times 10^{6}$$

After separating the insoluble salt, the final step in obtaining the metal itself is to reduce the metal cation to the metal either chemically or electrochemically (▶ Chapter 19).

Our immediate goal in this section is to work out methods to determine whether a precipitate will form under a given set of conditions.

FIGURE 17.16 Minerals. Minerals are insoluble salts. The minerals shown here are light purple fluorite (calcium fluoride), black hematite [iron(III) oxide], and rust brown goethite, a mixture of iron(III) oxide and iron(III) hydroxide.

K_{sp} and the Reaction Quotient, Q

Silver chloride dissolves to a very small extent in water and has a correspondingly small value of K_{sp}.

$$AgCl(s) \rightleftharpoons Ag^+(aq) + Cl^-(aq) \qquad K_{sp} = [Ag^+][Cl^-] = 1.8 \times 10^{-10}$$

But look at the problem from the other direction: If a solution contains Ag^+ and Cl^- ions at some concentration, will AgCl precipitate from solution? This is the same question we asked in Section 15-2 when we wanted to know if a given mixture of reactants and products was an equilibrium mixture, if the reactants continued to form products, or if products would revert to reactants. The procedure was to calculate the reaction quotient, Q.

For silver chloride, the expression for the reaction quotient, Q, is

$$Q = [Ag^+][Cl^-]$$

Recall that *the difference between Q and K is that the concentrations in the reaction quotient expression, Q, may or may not be those at equilibrium.* For the case of a slightly soluble salt such as AgCl, we can reach the following conclusions (◀ Section 15-2).

1. If $Q = K_{sp}$, the solution is saturated.

When $Q = K_{sp}$ the ion concentrations have reached their maximum value.

2. If $Q < K_{sp}$, the solution is not saturated.

This can mean either of two things: (i) If solid AgCl is present, more will dissolve until equilibrium is achieved (when $Q = K_{sp}$). (ii) If solid AgCl is not already present, more $Ag^+(aq)$ or more $Cl^-(aq)$ (or both) could be added to the solution until precipitation of solid AgCl begins (when $Q > K_{sp}$).

3. If $Q > K_{sp}$, the solution is oversaturated and precipitation will occur.

If $Q > K_{sp}$, then precipitation will occur until $Q = K_{sp}$.

Strategy Map 17.13

PROBLEM

Does **AgCl** precipitate at specified values of **[Ag⁺]** and **[Cl⁻]**?

DATA/INFORMATION KNOWN

- K_{sp} value for AgCl
- Ag^+ concentration
- Cl^- concentration

STEP 1. Write expression for ***Q***, the reaction quotient.

$Q = [Ag^+][Cl^-]$

STEP 2. Enter concentrations in ***Q* expression** and solve.

$Q < K_{sp}$, so more AgCl will dissolve.

EXAMPLE 17.13

Solubility and the Reaction Quotient

Problem Solid AgCl has been placed in a beaker of water. After some time, the concentrations of Ag^+ and Cl^- are each 1.2×10^{-5} mol/L. Has the system reached equilibrium? If not, will more AgCl dissolve?

What Do You Know? You know the balanced equation for dissolving the AgCl, its value of K_{sp}, and the Ag^+ and Cl^- concentrations.

Strategy

- Write the balanced equation for dissolving the salt and then write the expression for the reaction quotient, Q.
- Use the experimental ion concentrations to calculate the reaction quotient Q. Compare Q and K_{sp} to decide if the system is at equilibrium (that is, if $Q = K_{sp}$).

Solution

$$AgCl(s) \rightleftharpoons Ag^+(aq) + Cl^-(aq) \qquad K_{sp} = [Ag^+][Cl^-] = 1.8 \times 10^{-10}$$

$$Q = [Ag^+][Cl^-] = (1.2 \times 10^{-5})(1.2 \times 10^{-5}) = 1.4 \times 10^{-10}$$

Here, Q is less than K_{sp} (1.8×10^{-10}). The solution is not yet saturated, and AgCl will continue to dissolve until $Q = K_{sp}$, at which point $[Ag^+] = [Cl^-] = 1.3 \times 10^{-5}$ M. That is, an additional 0.1×10^{-5} mol of AgCl will dissolve per liter.

Think about Your Answer Dissolving is often a fairly slow process. If you measure the ion concentrations at a particular time, they may not have yet reached an equilibrium value, as is the case here. In contrast, acid–base reactions generally proceed rapidly to equilibrium.

Check Your Understanding

Solid PbI_2 ($K_{sp} = 9.8 \times 10^{-9}$) is placed in a beaker of water. After a period of time, the lead(II) concentration is measured and found to be 1.1×10^{-3} M. Has the system reached equilibrium? That is, is the solution saturated? If not, will more PbI_2 dissolve?

K_{sp}, the Reaction Quotient, and Precipitation Reactions

Using the reaction quotient and the solubility product constant, we can decide (1) if a precipitate will form when the ion concentrations are known or (2) what concentrations of ions are required to begin the precipitation of an insoluble salt.

Suppose the concentration of magnesium ion in an aqueous solution is 1.5×10^{-6} M. If enough NaOH is added to make the solution 1.0×10^{-4} M in hydroxide ion, OH^-, will precipitation of $Mg(OH)_2$ occur ($K_{sp} = 5.6 \times 10^{-12}$)? If not, will it occur if the concentration of OH^- is increased to 1.0×10^{-2} M?

Our strategy is similar to that in Example 17.13. That is, use the ion concentrations to calculate the value of Q and then compare Q with K_{sp} to decide if the system is at equilibrium. We begin with the equation for the dissolution of $Mg(OH)_2$.

$$Mg(OH)_2(s) \rightleftharpoons Mg^{2+}(aq) + 2\ OH^-(aq)$$

When the concentrations of magnesium and hydroxide ions are the first ones stated above, we find that Q is less than K_{sp}.

$$Q = [Mg^{2+}][OH^-]^2 = (1.5 \times 10^{-6})(1.0 \times 10^{-4})^2 = 1.5 \times 10^{-14}$$

$$Q\ (1.5 \times 10^{-14}) < K_{sp}\ (5.6 \times 10^{-12})$$

This means the solution is not yet saturated, and precipitation does not occur.

When $[OH^-]$ is increased to 1.0×10^{-2} M, the reaction quotient is 1.5×10^{-10},

$$Q = (1.5 \times 10^{-6})(1.0 \times 10^{-2})^2$$

$$Q = 1.5 \times 10^{-10} > K_{sp}\ (5.6 \times 10^{-12})$$

and the reaction quotient is now *larger* than K_{sp}. Precipitation of $Mg(OH)_2$ occurs and will continue until the Mg^{2+} and OH^- ion concentrations have decreased to the point where their product is equal to K_{sp}.

Now let us turn to a similar problem: deciding how much of the precipitating agent is required to begin the precipitation of an ion at a given concentration level.

EXAMPLE 17.14

Ion Concentrations Required to Begin Precipitation

Problem The concentration of barium ion, Ba^{2+}, in a solution is 0.010 M.

(a) What concentration of sulfate ion, SO_4^{2-}, is required to begin the precipitation of $BaSO_4$?

(b) When the concentration of sulfate ion in the solution reaches 0.015 M, what concentration of barium ion will remain in solution?

What Do You Know? There are three terms in the K_{sp} expression: K_{sp} and the anion and cation concentrations. Here, you know K_{sp} (1.1×10^{-10}) and one of the ion concentrations. You can then calculate the other ion concentration.

Strategy

- Write the balanced equation for dissolving $BaSO_4$ and the K_{sp} expression.
- **Part (a):** Use the K_{sp} expression to calculate $[SO_4^{2-}]$ when $[Ba^{2+}] = 0.010$ M.
- **Part (b):** Use the K_{sp} expression to calculate $[Ba^{2+}]$ when $[SO_4^{2-}] = 0.015$ M.

Solution

$$BaSO_4(s) \rightleftharpoons Ba^{2+}(aq) + SO_4^{2-}(aq) \qquad K_{sp} = [Ba^{2+}][SO_4^{2-}] = 1.1 \times 10^{-10}$$

(a) When the product of the ion concentrations exceeds the K_{sp} ($= 1.1 \times 10^{-10}$)—that is, when $Q > K_{sp}$—precipitation will occur. The Ba^{2+} ion concentration is known (0.010 M), so the SO_4^{2-} ion concentration necessary for precipitation can be calculated.

$$[SO_4^{2-}] = \frac{K_{sp}}{[Ba^{2+}]} = \frac{1.1 \times 10^{-10}}{0.010} = 1.1 \times 10^{-8}\ \text{M}$$

The result tells us that if the sulfate ion concentration is just slightly greater than 1.1×10^{-8} M, $BaSO_4$ will begin to precipitate.

(b) If the sulfate ion concentration is increased to 0.015 M, the maximum concentration of Ba^{2+} ion that can exist in solution (in equilibrium with $BaSO_4$) is

$$[Ba^{2+}] = \frac{K_{sp}}{[SO_4^{2-}]} = \frac{1.1 \times 10^{-10}}{0.015} = 7.3 \times 10^{-9}\ \text{M}$$

Think about Your Answer The fact that the barium ion concentration is so small when $[SO_4^{2-}] = 0.015$ M means that the Ba^{2+} ion has been essentially removed from solution. (It began at 0.010 M and has decreased by a factor of about 1 million.)

Check Your Understanding

What is the minimum concentration of I^- that can cause precipitation of PbI_2 from a 0.050 M solution of $Pb(NO_3)_2$? K_{sp} for PbI_2 is 9.8×10^{-9}. What concentration of Pb^{2+} ions remains in solution when the concentration of I^- is 0.0015 M?

Strategy Map 17.14

PROBLEM

What concentration of SO_4^{2-} is required to begin precipitation of $BaSO_4$?

DATA/INFORMATION KNOWN

- K_{sp} value for $BaSO_4$
- Initial $[Ba^{2+}]$

STEP 1. Write **expression** for K_{sp}.

$K_{sp} = [Ba^{2+}][SO_4^{2-}]$

STEP 2. Enter Ba^{2+} **concentration** and solve for $[SO_4^{2-}]$.

$BaSO_4$ begins to precipitate when $[SO_4^{2-}]$ exceeds calculated value.

EXAMPLE 17.15

K_{sp} and Precipitations

Problem Suppose you mix 100.0 mL of 0.0200 M $BaCl_2$ with 50.0 mL of 0.0300 M Na_2SO_4. Will $BaSO_4$ ($K_{sp} = 1.1 \times 10^{-10}$) precipitate?

What Do You Know? You know the concentration of two different compounds in solutions of differing volumes. You know that $BaCl_2$ and Na_2SO_4 will combine to give a precipitate, $BaSO_4$, if they are mixed in sufficient concentration. You also know the K_{sp} value for $BaSO_4$.

Strategy Here, you mix two solutions, one containing Ba^{2+} ions and the other SO_4^{2-} ions, both with known concentration and volume, and insoluble $BaSO_4$ may be formed.

- Find the concentration of each of these ions after mixing.
- Knowing the ion concentrations in the combined solution, calculate Q and compare it with the K_{sp} value for $BaSO_4$ to decide if $BaSO_4$ will precipitate under these circumstances.

Solution First, use the equation $c_1V_1 = c_2V_2$ (◀ Section 4-5) to calculate c_2, the concentration of the Ba^{2+} and SO_4^{2-} ions after mixing, to give a new solution with a volume of 150.0 mL (= V_2).

$$[Ba^{2+}] \text{ after mixing} = \frac{(0.0200 \text{ mol/L})(0.1000 \text{ L})}{0.1500 \text{ L}} = 0.0133 \text{ M}$$

$$[SO_4^{2-}] \text{ after mixing} = \frac{(0.0300 \text{ mol/L})(0.0500 \text{ L})}{0.1500 \text{ L}} = 0.0100 \text{ M}$$

The equilibrium governing the reaction that can occur is

$$BaSO_4(s) \rightleftharpoons Ba^{2+}(aq) + SO_4^{2-}(aq) \qquad K_{sp} = [Ba^{2+}][SO_4^{2-}] = 1.1 \times 10^{-10}$$

Now the reaction quotient can be calculated.

$$Q = [Ba^{2+}][SO_4^{2-}] = (0.0133)(0.0100) = 1.33 \times 10^{-4}$$

Q is much larger than K_{sp}, so $BaSO_4$ precipitates.

Think about Your Answer The K_{sp} value for $BaSO_4$ is very small, so mixing solutions with Ba^{2+} and SO_4^{2-} ions, even in very low concentration, can lead to the precipitation of $BaSO_4$.

Check Your Understanding

You have 100.0 mL of 0.0010 M silver nitrate. Will AgCl precipitate if you add 5.0 mL of 0.025 M HCl?

REVIEW & CHECK FOR SECTION 17-5

1. Will $SrSO_4$ precipitate from a solution containing 2.5×10^{-4} M strontium ion, Sr^{2+}, if enough of the soluble salt Na_2SO_4 is added to make the solution 2.5×10^{-4} M in SO_4^{2-}? K_{sp} for $SrSO_4$ is 3.4×10^{-7}.

   (a) yes (b) no (c) can't decide

Complex Ions Complex ions are prevalent in chemistry and are the basis of such biologically important substances as hemoglobin and vitamin B_{12}. They are described in more detail in Chapter 22. See also Section 16-10.

17-6 Equilibria Involving Complex Ions

Metal ions exist in aqueous solution as complex ions (◀ Section 16-10). Complex ions consist of the metal ion and other molecules or ions bound into a single entity. In water, metal ions are always surrounded by water molecules, with the negative end of the polar water molecule, the oxygen atom, attracted to the positive metal ion. In the case of Ni^{2+}, the ion exists as $[Ni(H_2O)_6]^{2+}$ in water. On adding ammonia, water molecules are displaced successively, and in the presence of a high enough concentration of ammonia, the complex ion $[Ni(NH_3)_6]^{2+}$ is formed. Many organic molecules also form complex ions with metal ions, one example being the complex with the dimethylglyoximate ion in Figure 17.17.

The molecules or ions that bind to metal ions are called **ligands** (▶ Chapter 22). In aqueous solution, metal ions and ligands exist in equilibrium, and the equilibrium constants for these reactions are referred to as **formation constants, K_f** (Appendix K). For example,

$$Cu^{2+}(aq) + NH_3(aq) \rightleftharpoons [Cu(NH_3)]^{2+}(aq) \qquad K_{f1} = 2.0 \times 10^4$$

$$[Cu(NH_3)]^{2+}(aq) + NH_3(aq) \rightleftharpoons [Cu(NH_3)_2]^{2+}(aq) \qquad K_{f2} = 4.7 \times 10^3$$

$$[Cu(NH_3)_2]^{2+}(aq) + NH_3(aq) \rightleftharpoons [Cu(NH_3)_3]^{2+}(aq) \qquad K_{f3} = 1.1 \times 10^3$$

$$[Cu(NH_3)_3]^{2+}(aq) + NH_3(aq) \rightleftharpoons [Cu(NH_3)_4]^{2+}(aq) \qquad K_{f4} = 2.0 \times 10^2$$

In these reactions, Cu^{2+} begins as $[Cu(H_2O)_4]^{2+}$, but ammonia successively displaces the water molecules. Overall, the formation of the tetraammine copper(II) complex ion has an equilibrium constant of 2.1×10^{13} ($= K_{f1} \times K_{f2} \times K_{f3} \times K_{f4}$).

$$Cu^{2+}(aq) + 4\ NH_3(aq) \rightleftharpoons [Cu(NH_3)_4]^{2+}(aq) \qquad K_f = 2.1 \times 10^{13}$$

Dimethylglyoximate complex of Ni^{2+} ion

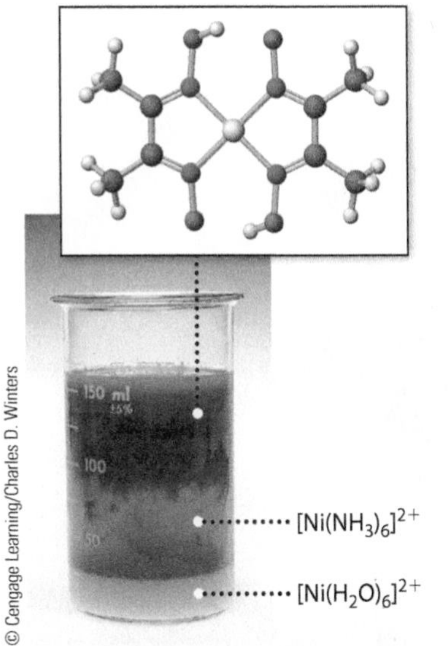

FIGURE 17.17 Complex ions. The green solution contains soluble $Ni(H_2O)_6^{2+}$ ions in which water molecules are bound to Ni^{2+} ions by ion–dipole forces. This complex ion gives the solution its green color. The Ni^{2+}-ammonia complex ion is purple. The red, insoluble solid is the dimethylglyoximate complex of the Ni^{2+} ion $[Ni(C_4H_7O_2N_2)_2]$ (model at top). Formation of this beautiful red insoluble compound is the classical test for the presence of the aqueous Ni^{2+} ion.

EXAMPLE 17.16

Complex Ion Equilibria

Problem What is the concentration of Cu^{2+} ions in a solution prepared by adding 0.00100 mol of $Cu(NO_3)_2$ to 1.00 L of 1.50 M NH_3? K_f for the copper-ammonia complex ion $[Cu(NH_3)_4]^{2+}$ is 2.1×10^{13}.

What Do You Know? Here you know the concentration of the species that form the complex ion (Cu^{2+} and NH_3), and you know the formation constant for the complex ion.

Strategy The formation constant for the complex ion is very large, so you start with the assumption that all of the Cu^{2+} ions react with NH_3 to form $[Cu(NH_3)_4]^{2+}$. That is, the initial concentration of the complex ion, $[Cu(NH_3)_4]^{2+}$ is 0.00100 M. This cation then dissociates to produce Cu^{2+} ions and additional NH_3 in solution. The equilibrium constant for the dissociation of $[Cu(NH_3)_4]^{2+}$ is the reciprocal of K_f because the dissociation of the ion is the reverse of its formation.

- Write a balanced equation for the dissociation of the complex ion that formed in solution and set up an ICE table.
- Assume that all of the Cu^{2+} ions in the solution are in the form of $[Cu(NH_3)_4]^{2+}$ (0.00100 M). This means that $[NH_3]$ = original concentration − 4 × 0.00100 M.
- Assume the concentration of complex ion dissociated at equilibrium is x, so x mol/L of Cu^{2+} are released to solution as are $4x$ mol/L of NH_3.
- Use the equilibrium concentrations of the ions in the expression for $K_{dissociation}$ ($= 1/K_f$) and solve for x (which is the concentration of Cu^{2+} at equilibrium).

Solution Set up an ICE table for the dissociation of $[Cu(NH_3)_4]^{2+}$.

EQUATION	$[Cu(NH_3)_4]^{2+}(aq)$ ⇌	$Cu^{2+}(aq)$ +	$4\ NH_3(aq)$
Initial (M)	0.00100	0	1.50 − 0.00400 M
Change (M)	$-x$	$+x$	$+4x$
Equilibrium (M)	$0.00100 - x$ ≈ 0.00100	x	$1.50 - 0.00400 + 4x$ ≈ 1.50

Here you assume that x is so small that the concentration of the complex ion is very nearly 0.00100 M and that the NH_3 concentration at equilibrium is essentially what was there originally.

$$K_{dissociation} = \frac{1}{K_f} = \frac{1}{2.1 \times 10^{13}} = \frac{[Cu^{2+}][NH_3]^4}{\{[Cu(NH_3)_4]^{2+}\}} = \frac{(x)(1.50)^4}{0.00100}$$

$$x = [Cu^{2+}] = 9.4 \times 10^{-18}\ M$$

Think about Your Answer Make sure to test your assumption that x is so small it can be neglected in determining the equilibrium concentrations of $[Cu(NH_3)_4]^{2+}$ and NH_3. It certainly is in this case.

Check Your Understanding

Silver nitrate (0.0050 mol) is added to 1.00 L of 1.00 M NH_3. What is the concentration of Ag^+ ions at equilibrium?

$$Ag^+(aq) + 2\ NH_3(aq) \rightleftharpoons [Ag(NH_3)_2]^+(aq) \qquad K_f = 1.1 \times 10^7$$

REVIEW & CHECK FOR SECTION 17-6

1. Iron(II) chloride (0.0025 mol) is added to 1.00 L of 0.500 M NaCN. What is the concentration of Fe^{2+} ions at equilibrium? K_f for $[Fe(CN)_6]^{4-}$ is 1.0×10^{35}.

   (a) 1.0×10^{-35} M (b) 1.9×10^{-36} M (c) 5.2×10^{-38} M

Learning Objectives: LO 5.17

17-7 Solubility and Complex Ions

Silver chloride does not dissolve either in water or in strong acid, but it does dissolve in ammonia because it forms a water-soluble complex ion, $[Ag(NH_3)_2]^+$ (Figure 17.18).

$$AgCl(s) + 2\ NH_3(aq) \rightleftharpoons [Ag(NH_3)_2]^+(aq) + Cl^-(aq)$$

Dissolving AgCl(s) can be viewed as a two-step process. First, AgCl dissolves minimally in water, giving Ag^+(aq) and Cl^-(aq) ion. Then, the Ag^+(aq) ion combines with NH_3 to give the ammonia complex. Lowering the Ag^+(aq) concentration through complexation with NH_3 shifts the solubility equilibrium to the right, and more solid AgCl dissolves.

$$AgCl(s) \rightleftharpoons Ag^+(aq) + Cl^-(aq) \qquad K_{sp} = 1.8 \times 10^{-10}$$

$$Ag^+(aq) + 2\ NH_3(aq) \rightleftharpoons [Ag(NH_3)_2]^+(aq) \qquad K_f = 1.1 \times 10^7$$

This is an example of combining or "coupling" two (or more) equilibria where one is a product-favored reaction and the other is reactant-favored.

The large value of the formation constant for $[Ag(NH_3)_2]^+$ means that the equilibrium lies well to the right, and AgCl can dissolve in the presence of NH_3. If you combine K_f with K_{sp}, you obtain the net equilibrium constant for the interaction of AgCl and aqueous ammonia.

$$K_{net} = K_{sp} \times K_f = (1.8 \times 10^{-10})(1.1 \times 10^7) = 2.0 \times 10^{-3}$$

$$K_{net} = 2.0 \times 10^{-3} = \frac{\{[Ag(NH_3)_2]^+\}[Cl^-]}{[NH_3]^2}$$

Even though the value of K_{net} seems small, if you use a large concentration of NH_3, the concentration of $[Ag(NH_3)_2]^+$ in solution can be appreciable. Silver chloride is thus much more soluble in the presence of ammonia than in pure water.

$AgCl(s)$, $K_{sp} = 1.8 \times 10^{-10}$

(a) AgCl precipitates on adding NaCl(aq) to $AgNO_3(aq)$.

$[Ag(NH_3)_2]^+(aq)$

(b) The precipitate of AgCl dissolves on adding aqueous NH_3 to give water-soluble $[Ag(NH_3)_2]^+$.

$AgBr(s)$, $K_{sp} = 5.4 \times 10^{-13}$

(c) The silver-ammonia complex ion is changed to insoluble AgBr on adding NaBr(aq).

$[Ag(S_2O_3)_2]^{3-}(aq)$

(d) Solid AgBr is dissolved on adding $Na_2S_2O_3(aq)$. The product is the water-soluble complex ion $[Ag(S_2O_3)_2]^{3-}$.

FIGURE 17.18 **Forming and dissolving precipitates.** Insoluble compounds often dissolve upon addition of a complexing agent.

The stabilities of various complex ions involving silver(I) can be compared by comparing values of their formation constants.

Formation Equilibrium	K_f
$Ag^+(aq) + 2\ Cl^-(aq) \rightleftharpoons [AgCl_2]^-(aq)$	1.1×10^5
$Ag^+(aq) + 2\ S_2O_3^{2-}(aq) \rightleftharpoons [Ag(S_2O_3)_2]^{3-}(aq)$	2.9×10^{13}
$Ag^+(aq) + 2\ CN^-(aq) \rightleftharpoons [Ag(CN)_2]^-(aq)$	1.3×10^{21}

The formation of all three silver complexes is strongly product-favored, and the cyanide complex ion $[Ag(CN)_2]^-$ is the most stable of the three.

Figure 17.18 shows what happens as complex ions are formed. Beginning with a precipitate of AgCl, adding aqueous ammonia dissolves the precipitate to give the soluble complex ion $[Ag(NH_3)_2]^+$. Silver bromide is even more stable than $[Ag(NH_3)_2]^+$, so AgBr ($K_{sp} = 5.4 \times 10^{-13}$) forms in preference to the complex ion on adding bromide ion. If thiosulfate ion, $S_2O_3^{2-}$, is then added, AgBr dissolves due to the formation of $[Ag(S_2O_3)_2]^{3-}$, a complex ion with a large formation constant (2.9×10^{13}).

EXAMPLE 17.17

Complex Ions and Solubility

Problem What is the value of the equilibrium constant, K_{net}, for dissolving AgBr in a solution containing the thiosulfate ion, $S_2O_3^{2-}$ (Figure 17.18)? Does AgBr dissolve readily on adding aqueous sodium thiosulfate to the solid?

What Do You Know? There are two equilibria here. One is for dissolving AgBr in water to give Ag^+ and Br^- ions, and its equilibrium constant is K_{sp}. The other is the formation of $[Ag(S_2O_3)_2]^{3-}$ ions from Ag^+ and $S_2O_3^{2-}$ ions; its equilibrium constant is K_f.

Strategy Summing several equilibrium processes gives the net chemical equation. K_{net} is the product of the values of K of the summed chemical equations (◀ Section 15-5).

Solution The overall reaction for dissolving AgBr in the presence of the thiosulfate anion is the sum of two equilibrium processes.

$$AgBr(s) \rightleftharpoons Ag^+(aq) + Br^-(aq) \qquad K_{sp} = 5.0 \times 10^{-13}$$

$$Ag^+(aq) + 2\ S_2O_3^{2-}(aq) \rightleftharpoons [Ag(S_2O_3)_2]^{3-}(aq) \qquad K_f = 2.9 \times 10^{13}$$

Net chemical equation:

$$AgBr(s) + 2\ S_2O_3^{2-}(aq) \rightleftharpoons [Ag(S_2O_3)_2]^{3-}(aq) + Br^-(aq) \qquad K_{net} = K_{sp} \times K_f = 15$$

AgBr is predicted to dissolve readily in aqueous $Na_2S_2O_3$, as observed (Figure 17.18).

Think about Your Answer The value of K_{net} is greater than 1, indicating a product-favored reaction at equilibrium.

Check Your Understanding

Calculate the value of the equilibrium constant, K_{net}, for dissolving $Cu(OH)_2$ in aqueous ammonia (to form the complex ion $[Cu(NH_3)_4]^{2+}$) (◀ Figure 16.9).

REVIEW & CHECK FOR SECTION 17-7

1. What is the equilibrium constant for the process of dissolving AgI by the addition of aqueous NaCN? K_{sp} for AgI is 8.5×10^{-17}, and K_f for $[Ag(CN)_2]^-$ is 1.3×10^{21}.

   (a) 6.5×10^{-4} (b) 8.7×10^4 (c) 1.1×10^5

APPLYING CHEMICAL PRINCIPLES

Everything That Glitters . . .

For thousands of years gold has been used in jewelry and for currency. Gold does not tarnish, and it can be drawn into wires or hammered into sheets. In modern society, the most important application of this element may be in electronics, where its high conductivity and resistance to corrosion make it invaluable for wires and connectors.

Gold mining evokes images of miners panning for gold in mountain streams or chopping rocks with pick axes. However, the percentage of gold in most deposits is too low for these extraction methods to be feasible. Today's miners blast and crush enormous quantities of gold-bearing ore and then dissolve gold from the ore using a chemical process involving cyanide ion and oxygen.

$$4\ Au(s) + 8\ NaCN(aq) + O_2(g) + 2\ H_2O(\ell) \rightarrow 4\ NaAu(CN)_2(aq) + 4\ NaOH(aq)$$

The solution containing the soluble complex ion $[Au(CN)_2]^-$ is filtered to separate it from the solids. Metallic gold is then recovered by reacting the cyanide complex with zinc. The zinc reduces the gold(I) complex to elemental gold and then joins with the cyanide to form $[Zn(CN)_4]^{2-}$.

Large volumes of 0.035% aqueous sodium cyanide are used for gold extraction. Unfortunately, unsafe disposal and accidental discharges have resulted in environmental disasters. In 2000, the collapse of dams in Baia Mare, Romania, resulted in millions of liters of cyanide waste entering the Tisza and Danube river. All aquatic life for miles downstream was killed.

© Dennis Hallinan/Alamy

John C. Kotz

Using gold. *(left)* Much of current gold use today is in electronic devices. The microprocessor connector pins are coated with a thin film of gold. *(right)* The dome of St. Isaac's Cathedral in St. Petersburg, Russia, is covered with 100 kg of pure gold. (It was completed in 1858.)

Although research into safer extraction methods is ongoing, extraction by cyanide ion is still the primary means of obtaining gold.

QUESTIONS:

1. Approximately 0.10 g of sodium cyanide is fatal to humans. What volume (in mL) of 0.035 mass percent NaCN solution contains a fatal dose of sodium cyanide? Assume the density of the solution is 1.0 g/mL.
2. What is the minimum volume of 0.0071 M NaCN(aq) necessary to dissolve the gold from 1.0 metric ton (1000 kg) of ore if the ore contains 0.012% gold?
3. Use the formation constant of $[Au(CN)_2]^-$ in Appendix K to determine the equilibrium concentration of Au^+(aq) in a solution that is 0.0071 M CN^- and 1.1×10^{-4} M $[Au(CN)_2]^-$. Is it reasonable to conclude that 100% of the gold in solution is present as the $[Au(CN)_2]^-$ complex ion? Explain.
4. Silver undergoes similar reactions as those shown for gold. Both metals react with cyanide ion in the presence of oxygen to form soluble complexes, and both are reduced by zinc. The reaction of Ag^+ with cyanide ion may be viewed as two sequential steps:

$$(1)\ Ag^+(aq) + CN^-(aq) \rightleftharpoons AgCN(s)$$
$$(2)\ AgCN(s) + CN^-(aq) \rightleftharpoons [Ag(CN)_2]^-(aq)$$
$$Ag^+(aq) + 2\ CN^-(aq) \rightleftharpoons [Ag(CN)_2]^-(aq)$$
$$K_f = 1.3 \times 10^{21}$$

(a) Use the solubility product equilibrium constant (Appendix J) of AgCN(s) to determine the equilibrium constant for step 1.

(b) Use the equilibrium constants from Step 1 and the overall reaction to determine the equilibrium constant for Step 2.

(c) Excess AgCN(s) is combined with 1.0 L of 0.0071 M CN^-(aq) and allowed to equilibrate. Calculate the equilibrium concentrations of CN^- and $[Ag(CN)_2]^-$ using the equilibrium constant for step 2. Assume no change in volume occurs.

5. Write a balanced chemical equation for the reaction of $NaAu(CN)_2$(aq) and Zn(s).

CHAPTER GOALS REVISITED

Now that you have studied this chapter, you should ask whether you have met the chapter goals. In particular, you should be able to:

UNDERSTAND

- The common ion effect.
  - **a.** Predict the effect of the addition of a "common ion" on the pH of the solution of a weak acid or base (Section 17-1). Study Questions: 1–4, 8-10, 85, 87.
- The control of pH in aqueous solutions with buffers (Section 17-2).

DO

- Calculate the pH of buffer solutions.
  - **a.** Use the Henderson–Hasselbalch equation (Equation 17.2) to calculate the pH of a buffer solution of given composition. Study Questions: 5–8, 11, 12, 15, 16.
  - **b.** Describe how a buffer solution of a given pH can be prepared. Study Questions: 9, 10, 17–22, 89, 90, 109, 110, 107.
  - **c.** Calculate the pH of a buffer solution before and after adding acid or base. Study Questions: 23–26.
- Evaluate the pH in the course of acid–base titrations.
  - **a.** Predict the pH of an acid–base reaction at its equivalence point (Section 17-3; see also Sections 17-6 and 17-7). Study Questions: 27–34, 106, 107, 116.

ACID	BASE	pH AT EQUIVALENCE POINT
Strong	Strong	= 7 (neutral)
Strong	Weak	< 7 (acidic)
Weak	Strong	> 7 (basic)

b. Understand the differences between the titration curves for a strong acid–strong base titration and titrations in which one of the substances is weak.
c. Describe how an indicator functions in an acid–base titration. Study Questions: 35, 105–107.

- Apply chemical equilibrium concepts to the solubility of ionic compounds.
  a. Write the equilibrium constant expression—relating concentrations of ions in solutions to K_{sp}—for any insoluble salt (Section 17-4). Study Questions: 41, 42.
  b. Calculate K_{sp} values from experimental data (Section 17-4). Study Questions: 43–48.
  c. Estimate the solubility of a salt from the value of K_{sp} (Section 17-4). Study Questions: 49–52, 104, 113.
  d. Calculate the solubility of a salt in the presence of a common ion (Section 17-4). Study Questions: 57–62.
  e. Understand how hydrolysis of basic anions affects the solubility of a salt (Section 17-4). Study Questions: 63, 64, 120.
  f. Decide if a precipitate will form when the ion concentrations are known Section 17-5). Study Questions: 65–68, 79, 96, 97.
  g. Calculate the ion concentrations that are required to begin the precipitation of an insoluble salt (Section 17-5). Study Questions: 69, 84, 95–97.
  h. Understand that the formation of a complex ion can increase the solubility of an insoluble salt (Sections 17-6 and 17-7). Study Questions: 71–76, 92, 100.

REMEMBER

- Acid–base buffers are composed of weak acids and their conjugate bases.
- Acid–base buffers are resistant to changes in pH.
- The pH of a buffer is close to the pK_a of its weak acid.
- Insoluble salts in which the anion is the conjugate base of a weak acid dissolve in strong acids.

KEY EQUATIONS

Equation 17.1 (page 638) Hydronium ion concentration in a buffer solution composed of a weak acid and its conjugate base.

$$[H_3O^+] = \frac{[\text{acid}]}{[\text{conjugate base}]} \times K_a$$

Equation 17.2 (page 638) Henderson–Hasselbalch equation. To calculate the pH of a buffer solution composed of a weak acid and its conjugate base.

$$pH = pK_a + \log \frac{[\text{conjugate base}]}{[\text{acid}]}$$

Equation 17.3 (page 647) Equation to calculate the hydronium ion concentration before the equivalence point in the titration of a weak acid with a strong base. See also Equation 17.4 for the version of the equation based on the Henderson–Hasselbalch equation.

$$[H_3O^+] = \frac{[\text{weak acid remaining}]}{[\text{conjugate base produced}]} \times K_a$$

Equation 17.5 (page 648) The relationship between the pH of the solution and the pK_a of the weak acid (or [H_3O^+] and K_a) at the halfway or half-neutralization point in the titration of a weak acid with a strong base (or of a weak base with a strong acid).

$$[H_3O^+] = K_a \text{ and } pH = pK_a$$

Equation 17.6 (page 656) The general equilibrium constant expression, K_{sp} (solubility constant) for dissolving a poorly soluble salt, A_xB_y.

$$A_xB_y(s) \rightleftharpoons x\,A^{y+}(aq) + y\,B^{x-}(aq) \qquad K_{sp} = [A^{y+}]^x[B^{x-}]^y$$

© Cengage Learning/Charles D. Winters

STUDY QUESTIONS

▲ denotes challenging questions.

Blue-numbered questions have answers in Appendix N and fully worked solutions in the *Student Solutions Manual.*

Practicing Skills

The Common Ion Effect and Buffer Solutions

(See Sections 17-1 and 17-2 and Examples 17.1 and 17.2.)

1. Does the pH of the solution increase, decrease, or stay the same when you
   (a) add solid ammonium chloride to a dilute aqueous solution of NH_3?
   (b) add solid sodium acetate to a dilute aqueous solution of acetic acid?
   (c) add solid NaCl to a dilute aqueous solution of NaOH?

2. Does the pH of the solution increase, decrease, or stay the same when you
   (a) add solid sodium oxalate, $Na_2C_2O_4$, to 50.0 mL of 0.015 M oxalic acid, $H_2C_2O_4$?
   (b) add solid ammonium chloride to 75 mL of 0.016 M HCl?
   (c) add 20.0 g of NaCl to 1.0 L of 0.10 M sodium acetate, $NaCH_3CO_2$?

3. What is the pH of a solution that consists of 0.20 M ammonia, NH_3, and 0.20 M ammonium chloride, NH_4Cl?

4. What is the pH of 0.15 M acetic acid to which 1.56 g of sodium acetate, $NaCH_3CO_2$, has been added?

5. What is the pH of the solution that results from adding 30.0 mL of 0.015 M KOH to 50.0 mL of 0.015 M benzoic acid?

6. What is the pH of the solution that results from adding 25.0 mL of 0.12 M HCl to 25.0 mL of 0.43 M NH_3?

7. What is the pH of the buffer solution that contains 2.2 g of NH_4Cl in 250 mL of 0.12 M NH_3? Is the final pH lower or higher than the pH of the 0.12 M ammonia solution?

8. Lactic acid ($CH_3CHOHCO_2H$) is found in sour milk, in sauerkraut, and in muscles after activity. (K_a for lactic acid = 1.4×10^{-4}.)
   (a) If 2.75 g of $NaCH_3CHOHCO_2$, sodium lactate, is added to 5.00×10^2 mL of 0.100 M lactic acid, what is the pH of the resulting buffer solution?
   (b) Is the pH of the buffered solution lower or higher than the pH of the lactic acid solution?

9. What mass of sodium acetate, $NaCH_3CO_2$, must be added to 1.00 L of 0.10 M acetic acid to give a solution with a pH of 4.50?

10. What mass of ammonium chloride, NH_4Cl, must be added to exactly 5.00×10^2 mL of 0.10 M NH_3 solution to give a solution with a pH of 9.00?

Using the Henderson–Hasselbalch Equation

(See Section 17-2 and Example 17.3.)

11. Calculate the pH of a solution that has an acetic acid concentration of 0.050 M and a sodium acetate concentration of 0.075 M.

12. Calculate the pH of a solution that has an ammonium chloride concentration of 0.050 M and an ammonia concentration of 0.045 M.

13. What must the ratio of acetic acid to acetate ion be to have a buffer with a pH value of 5.00?

14. What must the ratio of $H_2PO_4^-$ to HPO_4^{2-} be to have a buffer with a pH value of 7.00?

15. A buffer is composed of formic acid and its conjugate base, the formate ion.

(a) What is the pH of a solution that has a formic acid concentration of 0.050 M and a sodium formate concentration of 0.035 M?
(b) What must the ratio of acid to conjugate base be to have a pH value 0.50 units higher than the value calculated in part (a)?

16. A buffer solution is composed of 1.360 g of KH_2PO_4 and 5.677 g of Na_2HPO_4.

(a) What is the pH of the buffer solution?
(b) What mass of KH_2PO_4 must be added to decrease the buffer solution pH by 0.50 unit from the value calculated in part (a)?

Preparing a Buffer Solution

(See Section 17-2 and Example 17.4.)

17. Which of the following combinations would be the best to buffer the pH of a solution at approximately 9?

(a) HCl and NaCl
(b) NH_3 and NH_4Cl
(c) CH_3CO_2H and $NaCH_3CO_2$

18. Which of the following combinations would be the best to buffer the pH of a solution at approximately 7?

(a) H_3PO_4 and NaH_2PO_4
(b) NaH_2PO_4 and Na_2HPO_4
(c) Na_2HPO_4 and Na_3PO_4

19. Describe how to prepare a buffer solution from NaH_2PO_4 and Na_2HPO_4 to have a pH of 7.5.

20. Describe how to prepare a buffer solution from NH_3 and NH_4Cl to have a pH of 9.5.

21. Determine the volume (in mL) of 1.00 M NaOH that must be added to 250 mL of 0.50 M CH_3CO_2H to produce a buffer with a pH of 4.50.

22. Determine the volume (in mL) of 1.00 M HCl that must be added to 750 mL of 0.50 M HPO_4^{2-} to produce a buffer with a pH of 7.00.

Adding an Acid or a Base to a Buffer Solution

(See Section 17-2 and Example 17.5.)

23. A buffer solution was prepared by adding 4.95 g of sodium acetate, $NaCH_3CO_2$, to 2.50×10^2 mL of 0.150 M acetic acid, CH_3CO_2H.

(a) What is the pH of the buffer?
(b) What is the pH of 1.00×10^2 mL of the buffer solution if you add 82 mg of NaOH to the solution?

24. You dissolve 0.425 g of NaOH in 2.00 L of a buffer solution that has $[H_2PO_4^-] = [HPO_4^{2-}] = 0.132$ M. What is the pH of the solution before adding NaOH? After adding NaOH?

25. A buffer solution is prepared by adding 0.125 mol of ammonium chloride to 5.00×10^2 mL of 0.500 M solution of ammonia.

(a) What is the pH of the buffer?
(b) If 0.0100 mol of HCl gas is bubbled into 5.00×10^2 mL of the buffer, what is the new pH of the solution?

26. What is the pH change when 20.0 mL of 0.100 M NaOH is added to 80.0 mL of a buffer solution consisting of 0.169 M NH_3 and 0.183 M NH_4Cl?

More about Acid–Base Reactions: Titrations

(See Section 17-3 and Examples 17.6 and 17.7.)

27. Phenol, C_6H_5OH, is a weak organic acid. Suppose 0.515 g of the compound is dissolved in enough water to make 125 mL of solution. The resulting solution is titrated with 0.123 M NaOH.

$$C_6H_5OH(aq) + OH^-(aq) \rightleftharpoons C_6H_5O^-(aq) + H_2O(\ell)$$

(a) What is the pH of the original solution of phenol?
(b) What are the concentrations of all of the following ions at the equivalence point: Na^+, H_3O^+, OH^-, and $C_6H_5O^-$?
(c) What is the pH of the solution at the equivalence point?

28. Assume you dissolve 0.235 g of the weak acid benzoic acid, $C_6H_5CO_2H$, in enough water to make 1.00×10^2 mL of solution and then titrate the solution with 0.108 M NaOH.

$$C_6H_5CO_2H(aq) + OH^-(aq) \rightleftharpoons C_6H_5CO_2^-(aq) + H_2O(\ell)$$

(a) What was the pH of the original benzoic acid solution?
(b) What are the concentrations of all of the following ions at the equivalence point: Na^+, H_3O^+, OH^-, and $C_6H_5CO_2^-$?
(c) What is the pH of the solution at the equivalence point?

29. You require 36.78 mL of 0.0105 M HCl to reach the equivalence point in the titration of 25.0 mL of aqueous ammonia.

(a) What was the concentration of NH_3 in the original ammonia solution?
(b) What are the concentrations of H_3O^+, OH^-, and NH_4^+ at the equivalence point?
(c) What is the pH of the solution at the equivalence point?

30. A titration of 25.0 mL of a solution of the weak base aniline, $C_6H_5NH_2$, requires 25.67 mL of 0.175 M HCl to reach the equivalence point.

$$C_6H_5NH_2(aq) + H_3O^+(aq) \rightleftharpoons C_6H_5NH_3^+(aq) + H_2O(\ell)$$

(a) What was the concentration of aniline in the original solution?
(b) What are the concentrations of H_3O^+, OH^-, and $C_6H_5NH_3^+$ at the equivalence point?
(c) What is the pH of the solution at the equivalence point?

Titration Curves and Indicators

(See Section 17-3 and Figures 17.4–17.10.)

31. Without doing detailed calculations, sketch the curve for the titration of 30.0 mL of 0.10 M NaOH with 0.10 M HCl. Indicate the approximate pH at the beginning of the titration and at the equivalence point. What is the total solution volume at the equivalence point?

32. Without doing detailed calculations, sketch the curve for the titration of 50 mL of 0.050 M pyridine, C_5H_5N (a weak base), with 0.10 M HCl. Indicate the approximate pH at the beginning of the titration and at the equivalence point. What is the total solution volume at the equivalence point?

33. You titrate 25.0 mL of 0.10 M NH_3 with 0.10 M HCl.
(a) What is the pH of the NH_3 solution before the titration begins?
(b) What is the pH at the equivalence point?
(c) What is the pH at the halfway point of the titration?
(d) What indicator in Figure 17.10 could be used to detect the equivalence point?
(e) Calculate the pH of the solution after adding 5.00, 15.0, 20.0, 22.0, and 30.0 mL of the acid. Combine this information with that in parts (a)–(c) and plot the titration curve.

34. Construct a rough plot of pH versus volume of base for the titration of 25.0 mL of 0.050 M HCN with 0.075 M NaOH.
(a) What is the pH before any NaOH is added?
(b) What is the pH at the halfway point of the titration?
(c) What is the pH when 95% of the required NaOH has been added?
(d) What volume of base, in milliliters, is required to reach the equivalence point?
(e) What is the pH at the equivalence point?
(f) What indicator would be most suitable for this titration? (See Figure 17.10.)
(g) What is the pH when 105% of the required base has been added?

35. Using Figure 17.10, suggest an indicator to use in each of the following titrations:
(a) The weak base pyridine is titrated with HCl.
(b) Formic acid is titrated with NaOH.
(c) Ethylenediamine, a weak diprotic base, is titrated with HCl.

36. Using Figure 17.10, suggest an indicator to use in each of the following titrations.
(a) $NaHCO_3$ is titrated to CO_3^{2-} with NaOH.
(b) Hypochlorous acid is titrated with NaOH.
(c) Trimethylamine is titrated with HCl.

Solubility Guidelines

(See Sections 3-4 and 3-5, Figure 3.10, and Example 3.2.)

37. Name two insoluble salts of each of the following ions.
(a) Cl^- (b) Zn^{2+} (c) Fe^{2+}

38. Name two insoluble salts of each of the following ions.
(a) SO_4^{2-} (b) Ni^{2+} (c) Br^-

39. Using the solubility guidelines (◀ Figure 3.10), predict whether each of the following is insoluble or soluble in water.
(a) $(NH_4)_2CO_3$ (c) NiS
(b) $ZnSO_4$ (d) $BaSO_4$

40. Predict whether each of the following is insoluble or soluble in water.
(a) $Pb(NO_3)_2$ (c) $ZnCl_2$
(b) $Fe(OH)_3$ (d) CuS

Writing Solubility Product Constant Expressions

(See Section 17-4.)

41. For each of the following insoluble salts, (1) write a balanced equation showing the equilibrium occurring when the salt is added to water, and (2) write the K_{sp} expression.
(a) AgCN (b) $NiCO_3$ (c) $AuBr_3$

42. For each of the following insoluble salts, (1) write a balanced equation showing the equilibrium occurring when the salt is added to water, and (2) write the K_{sp} expression.
(a) $PbSO_4$ (b) BaF_2 (c) Ag_3PO_4

Calculating K_{sp}

(See Section 17-4 and Example 17.8.)

43. When 1.55 g of solid thallium(I) bromide is added to 1.00 L of water, the salt dissolves to a small extent.

$$TlBr(s) \rightleftharpoons Tl^+(aq) + Br^-(aq)$$

The thallium(I) and bromide ions in equilibrium with TlBr each have a concentration of 1.9×10^{-3} M. What is the value of K_{sp} for TlBr?

44. At 20 °C, a saturated aqueous solution of silver acetate, $AgCH_3CO_2$, contains 1.0 g of the silver compound dissolved in 100.0 mL of solution. Calculate K_{sp} for silver acetate.

$$AgCH_3CO_2(s) \rightleftharpoons Ag^+(aq) + CH_3CO_2^-(aq)$$

45. When 250 mg of SrF_2, strontium fluoride, is added to 1.00 L of water, the salt dissolves to a very small extent.

$$SrF_2(s) \rightleftharpoons Sr^{2+}(aq) + 2\ F^-(aq)$$

At equilibrium, the concentration of Sr^{2+} is found to be 1.03×10^{-3} M. What is the value of K_{sp} for SrF_2?

46. Calcium hydroxide, $Ca(OH)_2$, dissolves in water to the extent of 1.78 g per liter. What is the value of K_{sp} for $Ca(OH)_2$?

$$Ca(OH)_2(s) \rightleftharpoons Ca^{2+}(aq) + 2\ OH^-(aq)$$

47. You add 0.979 g of $Pb(OH)_2$ to 1.00 L of pure water at 25 °C. The pH is 9.15. Estimate the value of K_{sp} for $Pb(OH)_2$.

48. You place 1.234 g of solid $Ca(OH)_2$ in 1.00 L of pure water at 25 °C. The pH of the solution is found to be 12.68. Estimate the value of K_{sp} for $Ca(OH)_2$.

Estimating Salt Solubility from K_{sp}

(See Section 17-4 and Examples 17.9 and 17.10.)

49. Estimate the solubility of silver iodide in pure water at 25 °C (a) in moles per liter and (b) in grams per liter.

$$AgI(s) \rightleftharpoons Ag^+(aq) + I^-(aq)$$

50. What is the molar concentration of $Au^+(aq)$ in a saturated solution of AuCl in pure water at 25 °C?

$$AuCl(s) \rightleftharpoons Au^+(aq) + Cl^-(aq)$$

51. Estimate the solubility of calcium fluoride, CaF_2, (a) in moles per liter and (b) in grams per liter of pure water.

$$CaF_2(s) \rightleftharpoons Ca^{2+}(aq) + 2\ F^-(aq)$$

52. Estimate the solubility of lead(II) bromide (a) in moles per liter and (b) in grams per liter of pure water.

53. The K_{sp} value for radium sulfate, $RaSO_4$, is 4.2×10^{-11}. If 25 mg of radium sulfate is placed in 1.00×10^2 mL of water, does all of it dissolve? If not, how much dissolves?

54. If 55 mg of lead(II) sulfate is placed in 250 mL of pure water, does all of it dissolve? If not, how much dissolves?

55. Use K_{sp} values to decide which compound in each of the following pairs is more soluble. (▶ Appendix J.)
(a) $PbCl_2$ or $PbBr_2$
(b) HgS or FeS
(c) $Fe(OH)_2$ or $Zn(OH)_2$

56. Use K_{sp} values to decide which compound in each of the following pairs is more soluble. (▶ Appendix J.)
(a) AgBr or AgSCN
(b) $SrCO_3$ or $SrSO_4$
(c) AgI or PbI_2
(d) MgF_2 or CaF_2

The Common Ion Effect and Salt Solubility

(See Section 17-4 and Examples 17.11 and 17.12.)

57. Calculate the molar solubility of silver thiocyanate, AgSCN, in pure water and in water containing 0.010 M NaSCN.

58. Calculate the solubility of silver bromide, AgBr, in moles per liter, in pure water. Compare this value with the molar solubility of AgBr in 225 mL of water to which 0.15 g of NaBr has been added.

59. Compare the solubility, in milligrams per milliliter, of silver iodide, AgI, (a) in pure water and (b) in water that is 0.020 M in $AgNO_3$.

60. What is the solubility, in milligrams per milliliter, of BaF_2, (a) in pure water and (b) in water containing 5.0 mg/mL KF?

61. Calculate the solubility, in moles per liter, of iron(II) hydroxide, $Fe(OH)_2$, in a solution buffered to a pH of 7.00.

62. Calculate the solubility, in moles per liter, of calcium hydroxide, $Ca(OH)_2$, in a solution buffered to a pH of 12.60.

The Effect of Basic Anions on Salt Solubility

63. Which insoluble compound in each pair should be more soluble in nitric acid than in pure water?
(a) $PbCl_2$ or PbS
(b) Ag_2CO_3 or AgI
(c) $Al(OH)_3$ or AgCl

64. Which compound in each pair is more soluble in water than is predicted by a calculation from K_{sp}?
(a) AgI or Ag_2CO_3
(b) $PbCO_3$ or $PbCl_2$
(c) AgCl or AgCN

Precipitation Reactions

(See Section 17-5 and Examples 17.13–17.15.)

65. You have a solution that has a lead(II) ion concentration of 0.0012 M. If enough soluble chloride-containing salt is added so that the Cl^- concentration is 0.010 M, will $PbCl_2$ precipitate?

66. Sodium carbonate is added to a solution in which the concentration of Ni^{2+} ion is 0.0024 M. Will precipitation of $NiCO_3$ occur (a) when the concentration of the carbonate ion is 1.0×10^{-6} M or (b) when it is 100 times greater (1.0×10^{-4} M)?

67. If the concentration of Zn^{2+} in 10.0 mL of water is 1.63×10^{-4} M, will zinc hydroxide, $Zn(OH)_2$, precipitate when 4.0 mg of NaOH is added?

68. You have 95 mL of a solution that has a lead(II) concentration of 0.0012 M. Will $PbCl_2$ precipitate when 1.20 g of solid NaCl is added?

69. If the concentration of Mg^{2+} ion in seawater is 1350 mg/L, what OH^- concentration is required to precipitate $Mg(OH)_2$?

70. Will a precipitate of $Mg(OH)_2$ form when 25.0 mL of 0.010 M NaOH is combined with 75.0 mL of a 0.10 M solution of magnesium chloride?

Equilibria Involving Complex Ions

(See Sections 17-6 and 17-7 and Examples 17.16 and 17.17.)

71. Zinc hydroxide is amphoteric (◀ Section 16-10). Use equilibrium constants to show that, given sufficient OH^-, $Zn(OH)_2$ can dissolve in NaOH.

72. Solid silver iodide, AgI, can be dissolved by adding aqueous sodium cyanide. Calculate K_{net} for the following reaction.

$$AgI(s) + 2\ CN^-(aq) \rightleftharpoons [Ag(CN)_2]^-(aq) + I^-(aq)$$

73. ▲ What amount of ammonia (moles) must be added to dissolve 0.050 mol of AgCl suspended in 1.0 L of water?

74. Can you dissolve 15.0 mg of AuCl in 100.0 mL of water if you add 15.0 mL of 6.00 M NaCN?

75. What is the solubility of AgCl (a) in pure water and (b) in 1.0 M NH_3?

76. The chemistry of silver(I) cyanide:

(a) Calculate the solubility of AgCN(s) in water from the K_{sp} value.

(b) Calculate the value of the equilibrium constant for the reaction

$$AgCN(s) + CN^-(aq) \rightleftharpoons [Ag(CN)_2]^-(aq)$$

from K_{sp} and K_f values and predict from this value whether AgCN(s) would dissolve in KCN(aq).

(c) Determine the equilibrium constant for the reaction

$$AgCN(s) + 2\ S_2O_3^{2-}(aq) \rightleftharpoons [Ag(S_2O_3)_2]^{3-}(aq) + CN^-(aq)$$

Calculate the solubility of AgCN in a solution containing 0.10 M $S_2O_3^{2-}$ and compare the value to the solubility in water [part (a)].

General Questions

These questions are not designated as to type or location in the chapter. They may combine several concepts.

77. In each of the following cases, decide whether a precipitate will form when mixing the indicated reagents, and write a balanced equation for the reaction.

(a) $NaBr(aq) + AgNO_3(aq)$
(b) $KCl(aq) + Pb(NO_3)_2(aq)$

78. In each of the following cases, decide whether a precipitate will form when mixing the indicated reagents, and write a balanced equation for the reaction.

(a) $Na_2SO_4(aq) + Mg(NO_3)_2(aq)$
(b) $K_3PO_4(aq) + FeCl_3(aq)$

79. If you mix 48 mL of 0.0012 M $BaCl_2$ with 24 mL of 1.0×10^{-6} M Na_2SO_4, will a precipitate of $BaSO_4$ form?

80. Calculate the hydronium ion concentration and the pH of the solution that results when 20.0 mL of 0.15 M acetic acid, CH_3CO_2H, is mixed with 5.0 mL of 0.17 M NaOH.

81. Calculate the hydronium ion concentration and the pH of the solution that results when 50.0 mL of 0.40 M NH_3 is mixed with 25.0 mL of 0.20 M HCl.

82. For each of the following cases, decide whether the pH is less than 7, equal to 7, or greater than 7.

(a) Equal volumes of 0.10 M acetic acid, CH_3CO_2H, and 0.10 M KOH are mixed.
(b) 25 mL of 0.015 M NH_3 is mixed with 12 mL of 0.015 M HCl.
(c) 150 mL of 0.20 M HNO_3 is mixed with 75 mL of 0.40 M NaOH.
(d) 25 mL of 0.45 M H_2SO_4 is mixed with 25 mL of 0.90 M NaOH.

83. Rank the following compounds in order of increasing solubility in water: Na_2CO_3, $BaCO_3$, Ag_2CO_3.

84. A sample of hard water contains about 2.0×10^{-3} M Ca^{2+}. A soluble fluoride-containing salt such as NaF is added to "fluoridate" the water (to aid in the prevention of dental cavities). What is the maximum concentration of F^- that can be present without precipitating CaF_2?

© Cengage Learning/Charles D. Winters

Dietary sources of fluoride ion. Adding fluoride ion to drinking water (or toothpaste) prevents the formation of dental cavities.

85. What is the pH of a buffer solution prepared from 5.15 g of NH_4NO_3 and 0.10 L of 0.15 M NH_3? What is the new pH if the solution is diluted with pure water to a volume of 5.00×10^2 mL?

86. If you place 5.0 mg of $SrSO_4$ in 1.0 L of pure water, will all of the salt dissolve before equilibrium is established, or will some salt remain undissolved?

© Cengage Learning/Charles D. Winters

Celestite, $SrSO_4$
Strontium sulfate

87. Describe the effect on the pH of the following actions or explain why there is not an effect:

(a) Adding sodium acetate, $NaCH_3CO_2$, to 0.100 M CH_3CO_2H
(b) Adding $NaNO_3$ to 0.100 M HNO_3

88. What volume of 0.120 M NaOH must be added to 100. mL of 0.100 M $NaHC_2O_4$ to reach a pH of 4.70?

89. ▲ A buffer solution is prepared by dissolving 1.50 g each of benzoic acid, $C_6H_5CO_2H$, and sodium benzoate, $NaC_6H_5CO_2$, in 150.0 mL of solution.

(a) What is the pH of this buffer solution?
(b) Which buffer component must be added, and in what quantity, to change the pH to 4.00?
(c) What quantity of 2.0 M NaOH or 2.0 M HCl must be added to the buffer to change the pH to 4.00?

90. What volume of 0.200 M HCl must be added to 500.0 mL of 0.250 M NH_3 to have a buffer with a pH of 9.00?

91. What is the equilibrium constant for the following reaction?

$$AgCl(s) + I^-(aq) \rightleftharpoons AgI(s) + Cl^-(aq)$$

Does the equilibrium lie predominantly to the left or to the right? Will AgI form if iodide ion, I^-, is added to a saturated solution of AgCl?

92. Calculate the equilibrium constant for the following reaction.

$$Zn(OH)_2(s) + 2\ CN^-(aq) \rightleftharpoons Zn(CN)_2(s) + 2\ OH^-(aq)$$

Does the equilibrium lie predominantly to the left or to the right?

93. Suppose you eat 28 grams of rhubarb leaves with an oxalic acid content of 1.2% by weight.

(a) What volume of 0.25 M NaOH is required to titrate completely the oxalic acid in the leaves?
(b) What mass of calcium oxalate could be formed from the oxalic acid in these leaves?

94. The solubility product constant for calcium oxalate is estimated to be 4×10^{-9}. What is its solubility in grams per liter?

95. ▲ In principle, the ions Ba^{2+} and Ca^{2+} can be separated by the difference in solubility of their fluorides, BaF_2 and CaF_2. If you have a solution that is 0.10 M in both Ba^{2+} and Ca^{2+}, CaF_2 will begin to precipitate first as fluoride ion is added slowly to the solution.

(a) What concentration of fluoride ion will precipitate the maximum amount of Ca^{2+} ion without precipitating BaF_2?
(b) What concentration of Ca^{2+} remains in solution when BaF_2 just begins to precipitate?

96. ▲ A solution contains 0.10 M iodide ion, I^-, and 0.10 M carbonate ion, CO_3^{2-}.

(a) If solid $Pb(NO_3)_2$ is slowly added to the solution, which salt will precipitate first, PbI_2 or $PbCO_3$?
(b) What will be the concentration of the first ion that precipitates (CO_3^{2-} or I^-) when the second, more soluble salt begins to precipitate?

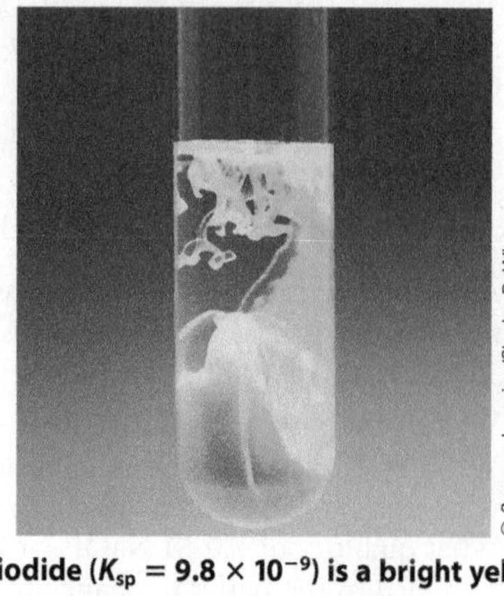

Lead(II) iodide ($K_{sp} = 9.8 \times 10^{-9}$) is a bright yellow solid.

97. ▲ A solution contains Ca^{2+} and Pb^{2+} ions, both at a concentration of 0.010 M. You wish to separate the two ions from each other as completely as possible by precipitating one but not the other using aqueous Na_2SO_4 as the precipitating agent.

(a) Which will precipitate first as sodium sulfate is added, $CaSO_4$ or $PbSO_4$?
(b) What will be the concentration of the first ion that precipitates (Ca^{2+} or Pb^{2+}) when the second, more soluble salt begins to precipitate?

98. Buffer capacity is defined as the number of moles of a strong acid or strong base that is required to change the pH of 1 L of the buffer solution by one unit. What is the buffer capacity of a solution that is 0.10 M in acetic acid and 0.10 M in sodium acetate?

99. The Ca^{2+} ion in hard water can be precipitated as $CaCO_3$ by adding soda ash, Na_2CO_3. If the calcium ion concentration in hard water is 0.010 M and if the Na_2CO_3 is added until the carbonate ion concentration is 0.050 M, what percentage of the calcium ions has been removed from the water? (You may neglect carbonate ion hydrolysis.)

This sample of calcium carbonate ($K_{sp} = 3.4 \times 10^{-9}$) was deposited in a cave formation.

100. Some photographic film is coated with crystals of AgBr suspended in gelatin. Some of the silver ions are reduced to silver metal on exposure to light. Unexposed AgBr is then dissolved with sodium thiosulfate in the "fixing" step.

$$AgBr(s) + 2\ S_2O_3^{2-}(aq) \rightleftharpoons [Ag(S_2O_3)_2]^{3-}(aq) + Br^-(aq)$$

(a) What is the equilibrium constant for this reaction?
(b) What mass of $Na_2S_2O_3$ must be added to dissolve 1.00 g of AgBr suspended in 1.00 L of water?

In the Laboratory

101. Each pair of ions below is found together in aqueous solution. Using the table of solubility product constants in Appendix J, devise a way to separate these ions by adding a reagent to precipitate one of the ions as an insoluble salt and leaving the other in solution.

(a) Ba^{2+} and Na^+ (b) Ni^{2+} and Pb^{2+}

102. Each pair of ions below is found together in aqueous solution. Using the table of solubility product constants in Appendix J, devise a way to separate these ions by adding a reagent to precipitate one of the ions as an insoluble salt and leave the other in solution.

(a) Cu^{2+} and Ag^+ (b) Al^{3+} and Fe^{3+}

103. ▲ The cations Ba^{2+} and Sr^{2+} can be precipitated as very insoluble sulfates.

(a) If you add sodium sulfate to a solution containing these metal cations, each with a concentration of 0.10 M, which is precipitated first, $BaSO_4$ or $SrSO_4$?

(b) What will be the concentration of the first ion that precipitates (Ba^{2+} or Sr^{2+}) when the second, more soluble salt begins to precipitate?

104. ▲ You will often work with salts of Fe^{3+}, Pb^{2+}, and Al^{3+} in the laboratory. (All are found in nature, and all are important economically.) If you have a solution containing these three ions, each at a concentration of 0.10 M, what is the order in which their hydroxides precipitate as aqueous NaOH is slowly added to the solution?

105. Aniline hydrochloride, $(C_6H_5NH_3)Cl$, is a weak acid. (Its conjugate base is the weak base aniline, $C_6H_5NH_2$.) The acid can be titrated with a strong base such as NaOH.

$$C_6H_5NH_3^+(aq) + OH^-(aq) \rightleftharpoons C_6H_5NH_2(aq) + H_2O(\ell)$$

Assume 50.0 mL of 0.100 M aniline hydrochloride is titrated with 0.185 M NaOH. (K_a for aniline hydrochloride is 2.4×10^{-5}.)

(a) What is the pH of the $(C_6H_5NH_3)Cl$ solution before the titration begins?

(b) What is the pH at the equivalence point?

(c) What is the pH at the halfway point of the titration?

(d) Which indicator in Figure 17.10 could be used to detect the equivalence point?

(e) Calculate the pH of the solution after adding 10.0, 20.0, and 30.0 mL of base.

(f) Combine the information in parts (a), (b), (c), and (e), and plot an approximate titration curve.

106. The weak base ethanolamine, $HOCH_2CH_2NH_2$, can be titrated with HCl.

$$HOCH_2CH_2NH_2(aq) + H_3O^+(aq) \rightleftharpoons HOCH_2CH_2NH_3^+(aq) + H_2O(\ell)$$

Assume you have 25.0 mL of a 0.010 M solution of ethanolamine and titrate it with 0.0095 M HCl. (K_b for ethanolamine is 3.2×10^{-5}.)

(a) What is the pH of the ethanolamine solution before the titration begins?

(b) What is the pH at the equivalence point?

(c) What is the pH at the halfway point of the titration?

(d) Which indicator in Figure 17.10 would be the best choice to detect the equivalence point?

(e) Calculate the pH of the solution after adding 5.00, 10.0, 20.0, and 30.0 mL of the acid.

(f) Combine the information in parts (a), (b), (c), and (e), and plot an approximate titration curve.

107. For the titration of 50.0 mL of 0.150 M ethylamine, $C_2H_5NH_2$, with 0.100 M HCl, find the pH at each of the following points, and then use that information to sketch the titration curve and decide on an appropriate indicator.

(a) At the beginning, before HCl is added

(b) At the halfway point in the titration

(c) When 75% of the required acid has been added

(d) At the equivalence point

(e) When 10.0 mL more HCl has been added than is required

(f) Sketch the titration curve.

(g) Suggest an appropriate indicator for this titration.

108. A buffer solution with a pH of 12.00 consists of Na_3PO_4 and Na_2HPO_4. The volume of solution is 200.0 mL.

(a) Which component of the buffer is present in a larger amount?

(b) If the concentration of Na_3PO_4 is 0.400 M, what mass of Na_2HPO_4 is present?

(c) Which component of the buffer must be added to change the pH to 12.25? What mass of that component is required?

109. To have a buffer with a pH of 2.50, what volume of 0.150 M NaOH must be added to 100. mL of 0.230 M H_3PO_4?

110. ▲ What mass of Na_3PO_4 must be added to 80.0 mL of 0.200 M HCl to obtain a buffer with a pH of 7.75?

111. You have a solution that contains $AgNO_3$, $Pb(NO_3)_2$, and $Cu(NO_3)_2$. Devise a separation method that results in having Ag^+ in one test tube, Pb^{2+} in another, and Cu^{2+} in a third test tube. Use solubility guidelines and K_{sp} and K_f values.

112. Once you have separated the three salts in Study Question 111 into three test tubes, you now need to confirm their presence.

(a) For Pb^{2+} ion, one way to do this is to treat a precipitate of $PbCl_2$ with K_2CrO_4 to produce the bright yellow insoluble solid, $PbCrO_4$. Using K_{sp} values, confirm that the chloride salt should be converted to the chromate salt.

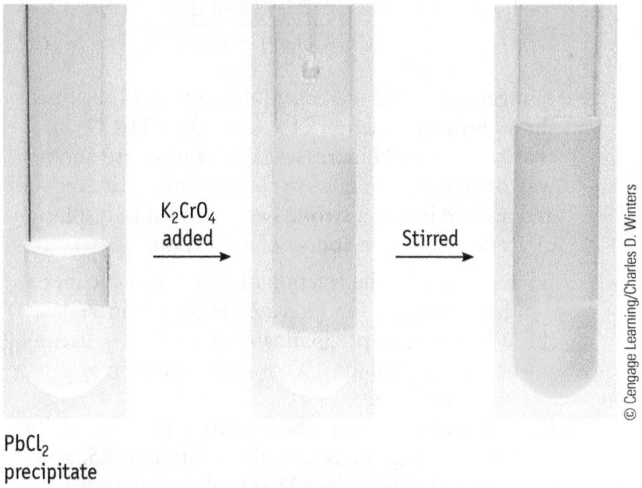

White $PbCl_2$ is converted to yellow $PbCrO_4$ on adding K_2CrO_4.

(b) Suggest a method for confirming the presence of Ag^+ and Cu^{2+} ions using complex ions.

Summary and Conceptual Questions

The following questions may use concepts from this and previous chapters.

113. Suggest a method for separating a precipitate consisting of a mixture of solid CuS and solid $Cu(OH)_2$.

114. Which of the following barium salts should dissolve in a strong acid such as HCl: $Ba(OH)_2$, $BaSO_4$, or $BaCO_3$?

115. Explain why the solubility of Ag_3PO_4 can be greater in water than is calculated from the K_{sp} value of the salt.

116. Two acids, each approximately 0.01 M in concentration, are titrated separately with a strong base. The acids show the following pH values at the equivalence point: HA, pH = 9.5, and HB, pH = 8.5.

(a) Which is the stronger acid, HA or HB?

(b) Which of the conjugate bases, A^- or B^-, is the stronger base?

117. Composition diagrams, commonly known as "alpha plots," are often used to visualize the species in a solution of an acid or base as the pH is varied. The diagram for 0.100 M acetic acid is shown here.

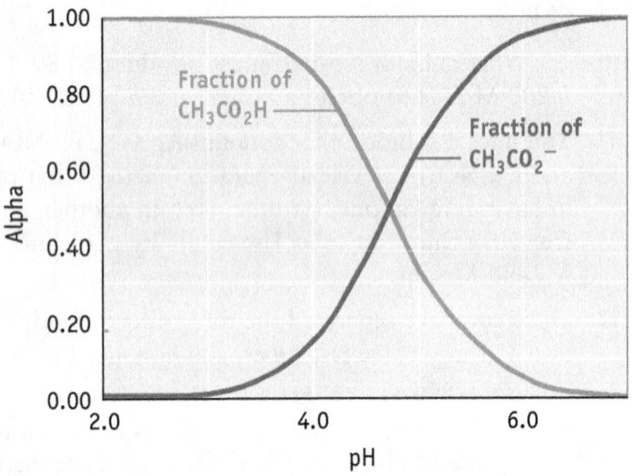

The plot shows how the fraction [alpha (α)] of acetic acid in solution,

$$\alpha = \frac{[CH_3CO_2H]}{[CH_3CO_2H] + [CH_3CO_2^-]}$$

changes as the pH increases (blue curve). (The red curve shows how the fraction of acetate ion, $CH_3CO_2^-$, changes as the pH increases.) Alpha plots are another way of viewing the relative concentrations of acetic acid and acetate ion as a strong base is added to a solution of acetic acid in the course of a titration.

(a) Explain why the fraction of acetic acid declines and that of acetate ion increases as the pH increases.

(b) Which species predominates at a pH of 4, acetic acid or acetate ion? What is the situation at a pH of 6?

(c) Consider the point where the two lines cross. The fraction of acetic acid in the solution is 0.5, and so is that of acetate ion. That is, the solution is half acid and half conjugate base; their concentrations are equal. At this point, the graph shows the pH is 4.74. Explain why the pH at this point is 4.74.

118. The composition diagram, or alpha plot, for the important acid–base system of carbonic acid, H_2CO_3, is illustrated below. (See Study Question 117 for more information on such diagrams.)

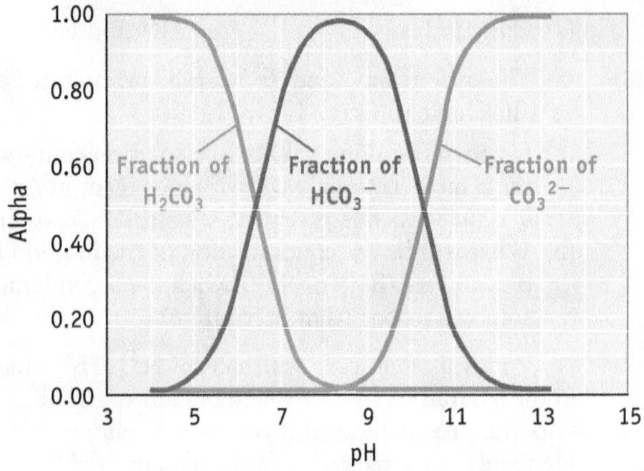

(a) Explain why the fraction of bicarbonate ion, HCO_3^-, rises and then falls as the pH increases.

(b) What is the composition of the solution when the pH is 6.0? When the pH is 10.0?

(c) If you wanted to buffer a solution at a pH of 11.0, what should be the ratio of HCO_3^- to CO_3^{2-}?

119. The chemical name for aspirin is acetylsalicylic acid. It is believed that the analgesic and other desirable properties of aspirin are due not to the aspirin itself but rather to the simpler compound salicylic acid, $C_6H_4(OH)CO_2H$, which results from the breakdown of aspirin in the stomach.

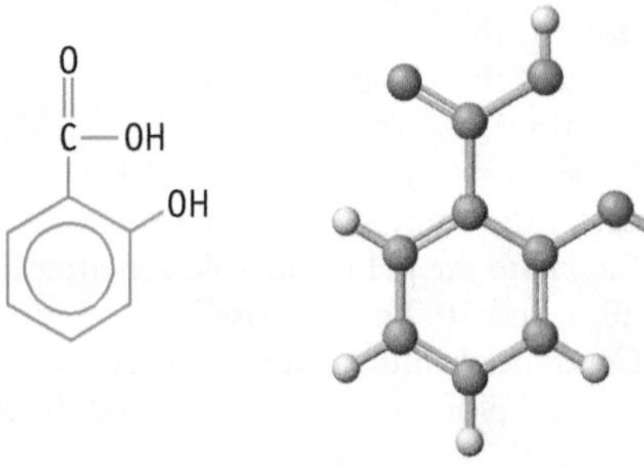

Salicylic acid

(a) Give approximate values for the following bond angles in the acid: (i) C—C—C in the ring; (ii) O—C=O; (iii) either of the C—O—H angles; and (iv) C—C—H.

(b) What is the hybridization of the C atoms of the ring? Of the C atom in the $—CO_2H$ group?

(c) Experiment shows that 1.00 g of the acid will dissolve in 460 mL of water. If the pH of this solution is 2.4, what is K_a for the acid?

(d) If you have salicylic acid in your stomach and if the pH of gastric juice is 2.0, calculate the percentage of salicylic acid that will be present in the stomach in the form of the salicylate ion, $C_6H_4(OH)CO_2^-$.

(e) Assume you have 25.0 mL of a 0.014 M solution of salicylic acid and titrate it with 0.010 M NaOH. What is the pH at the halfway point of the titration? What is the pH at the equivalence point?

120. Aluminum hydroxide reacts with phosphoric acid to give $AlPO_4$. The substance is used industrially in adhesives, binders, and cements.

(a) Write the balanced equation for the preparation of $AlPO_4$ from aluminum hydroxide and phosphoric acid.

(b) If you begin with 152 g of aluminum hydroxide and 3.00 L of 0.750 M phosphoric acid, what is the theoretical yield of $AlPO_4$?

(c) If you place 25.0 g of $AlPO_4$ in 1.00 L of water, what are the concentrations of Al^{3+} and PO_4^{3-} at equilibrium? (Neglect hydrolysis of aqueous Al^{3+} and PO_4^{3-} ions.) K_{sp} for $AlPO_4$ is 1.3×10^{-20}.

(d) Does the solubility of $AlPO_4$ increase or decrease on adding HCl? Explain.

This is a sample of hydrated aluminum phosphate, a mineral known as augelite.

AP Multiple-Choice Review Questions

1. A 0.010-mole sample of K_2SO_4 is added to 1.0 L of each of two different solutions. One solution contains 2.0×10^{-3} *M* $Ba(NO_3)_2$, and the other contains 2.0×10^{-3} *M* $AgNO_3$. Which statement best describes what is observed? K_{sp} for $BaSO_4 = 1.5 \times 10^{-9}$; K_{sp} for $Ag_2SO_4 = 1.2 \times 10^{-5}$.

(A) $BaSO_4$ would precipitate, but Ag_2SO_4 would not.
(B) Ag_2SO_4 would precipitate, but $BaSO_4$ would not.
(C) Both would precipitate.
(D) Neither would precipitate.

2. For which of the following can we directly compare their K_{sp} values to determine their relative solubilities?

(A) Ag_2CrO_4 and AgBr
(B) Ag_2SO_4 and $CaSO_4$
(C) $PbCl_2$ and $PbSO_4$
(D) ZnS and AgI

3. The salt MX_2 has a solubility of 1.0×10^{-4} *M*. Determine the K_{sp} for MX_2.

(A) 1.0×10^{-4}
(B) 1.0×10^{-8}
(C) 1.0×10^{-12}
(D) 4.0×10^{-12}

4. Three ionic salts, AX, BX_2, and CX_3, each have a solubility of 2×10^{-5} *M*. Which of the following correctly ranks the K_{sp} of the three salts from least to greatest?

(A) $CX_3 < BX_2 < AX$
(B) $AX < BX_2 < CX_3$
(C) $BX_2 < CX_3 < AX$
(D) $AX < CX_3 < BX_2$

5. Aqueous solutions of NaCl and Na_2CrO_4 are mixed and they do not react. To this mixture an aqueous solution of $AgNO_3$ is added (dropwise). At first, a white solid forms. As the $AgNO_3$ solution continues to be added, a yellow solid begins to form. AgCl(*s*) is white in color and Ag_2CrO_4(*s*) is yellow. Which of the following is the most accurate conclusion based on these results?

(A) The molar solubility of the NaCl is greater than the molar solubility of Na_2CrO_4 because the white solid formed first.
(B) The molar solubility of the NaCl is less than the molar solubility of Na_2CrO_4 because the white solid formed first.
(C) The molar solubility of AgCl is greater than the molar solubility of Ag_2CrO_4 because the white solid formed first.
(D) The molar solubility of AgCl is less than the molar solubility of Ag_2CrO_4 because the white solid formed first.

6. Barium iodate has a K_{sp} of 4.0×10^{-9}. What is the iodate ion concentration in a saturated solution of barium iodate?

(A) 1.0×10^{-3} *M*
(B) 2.0×10^{-3} *M*
(C) 6.3×10^{-5} *M*
(D) 2.0×10^{-9} *M*

7. Which of these salts would have increased solubility in a 0.10 *M* solution of HNO_3, compared with their solubilities in pure water at the same temperature?

(A) AgBr
(B) Hg_2Cl_2
(C) $Mg(OH)_2$
(D) PbI_2

8. When 0.10 mole of solid $Ag_2C_2O_4$ is added to 1 L of pure water at 25 °C, a saturated solution results. The solubility of $Ag_2C_2O_4$ is 2.1×10^{-4} *M*. Which would be the correct setup to calculate the K_{sp} of $Ag_2C_2O_4$?

(A) $K_{sp} = (2.1 \times 10^{-4})(2.1 \times 10^{-4})$
(B) $K_{sp} = (2.1 \times 10^{-4})^2(2.1 \times 10^{-4})$
(C) $K_{sp} = \dfrac{(2.1 \times 10^{-4})(2.1 \times 10^{-4})}{0.10}$
(D) $K_{sp} = \dfrac{(2.1 \times 10^{-4})^2(2.1 \times 10^{-4})}{0.10}$

9. Ten grams of $Ca(OH)_2$(*s*) are added, with stirring, to 100 mL of water, producing a saturated solution with solid $Ca(OH)_2$ on the bottom of the beaker. Which is true?

(A) The addition of 30 drops of 3 *M* HCl will cause the K_{sp} of the reaction to decrease.
(B) The addition of 0.1 mole of solid $Ca(NO_3)_2$ will cause some additional $Ca(OH)_2$ to form.
(C) The addition of 0.1 mole of solid NaOH will cause some additional $Ca(OH)_2$ to dissolve.
(D) The addition of 0.1 mole of solid $Ca(OH)_2$ will cause the K_{sp} of the reaction to increase.

10. Solid sodium chloride was added to pure water slowly, with stirring, at 25 °C until no more sodium chloride would dissolve. Solid remained on the bottom of the container, even after the solution was stirred repeatedly over 8 hours. After the solid was allowed to settle, some of the clear, colorless solution was carefully poured off into a flask. This flask was placed in a refrigerator at a temperature of 4 °C for 2 hours. When the flask was removed from the refrigerator, a small amount of white solid was found to have appeared in the flask. What is the best explanation for this?

(A) Solids settle out of solutions over time.
(B) NaCl has an exothermic heat of solution.
(C) The K_{sp} of NaCl decreases with decreasing temperature.
(D) The K_{sp} of NaCl increases with decreasing temperature.

11. Which of the following statements is true concerning the relative solubility of silver chloride? All samples are at the same temperature.
   (A) AgCl is less soluble in 1.0 *M* $AgNO_3$ than it is in pure water.
   (B) AgCl is less soluble in 1.0 *M* HNO_3 than it is in pure water.
   (C) AgCl is more soluble in 1.0 *M* $AgNO_3$ than it is in pure water.
   (D) AgCl is more soluble in 1.0 *M* HNO_3 than it is in pure water.

12. The K_{sp} of a hypothetical metallic hydroxide, MOH, is 1.0×10^{-4}. What is the pH of a saturated solution of MOH?
   (A) 4.00
   (B) 8.00
   (C) 10.00
   (D) 12.00

13. The solubility equations and K_{sp} values for two different chloride salts are shown below.

$$NaCl(s) \rightleftharpoons Na^+(aq) + Cl^-(aq) \quad K_{sp} = 36$$
$$AgCl(s) \rightleftharpoons Ag^+(aq) + Cl^-(aq) \quad K_{sp} = 1.6 \times 10^{-10}$$

   What can be interpreted from this information?
   (A) The K_{sp} of AgCl is so small that AgCl is completely insoluble.
   (B) The K_{sp} of NaCl is so large that the reaction is not reversible.
   (C) With NaCl, the forward reaction is favored. The relatively large equilibrium constant tells us that the products are favored.
   (D) With AgCl, the forward reaction is favored. The relatively small equilibrium constant tells us that the products are favored.

14. The mineral fluorite is the main source of calcium fluoride. CaF_2 has a solubility of 2.2×10^{-4} *M* in pure water. Which is a correct explanation for what occurs when solid CaF_2 is dissolved in an acidic solution, rather than in pure water?
   (A) The solubility increases because HF is a weak acid.
   (B) The solubility increases because HF is a strong acid.
   (C) The solubility decreases because HF is a weak acid.
   (D) The solubility decreases because HF is a strong acid.

15. Aqueous solutions of Na_2CO_3 and $Ca(NO_3)_2$, 0.10 *M* each, are combined. A white precipitate is observed in the container after mixing. The precipitate is filtered and carefully rinsed with distilled water to remove other ions. A sample of the precipitate is added to 100 mL of 0.1 *M* NaCl. A second sample of the precipitate is then added to 100 mL of 0.1 *M* HCl. What would be observed in each case?

	Observation upon Addition of Precipitate to NaCl(*aq*)	Observation upon Addition of Precipitate to HCl(*aq*)
(A)	Additional precipitate forms.	No visible reaction occurs.
(B)	No visible reaction occurs.	Gas is produced, and some precipitate dissolves.
(C)	No visible reaction occurs.	No visible reaction occurs.
(D)	Additional precipitate forms.	Gas is produced, and some precipitate dissolves.

16. Arrange the hydroxides from least soluble to most soluble based on their relative K_{sp} values.

KOH	K_{sp} = very large
$Ca(OH)_2$	$K_{sp} = 5.0 \times 10^{-6}$
$Al(OH)_3$	$K_{sp} = 3.0 \times 10^{-34}$

   (A) KOH, $Al(OH)_3$, $Ca(OH)_2$
   (B) KOH, $Ca(OH)_2$, $Al(OH)_3$
   (C) $Al(OH)_3$, $Ca(OH)_2$, KOH
   (D) $Ca(OH)_2$, $Al(OH)_3$, KOH

17. A 25.0-mL sample of an unknown monoprotic acid was titrated with 0.12 *M* NaOH. The student added 31.6 mL of NaOH and went past the equivalence point. Which procedure could be performed next to more accurately determine the concentration of the unknown acid?
   (A) Back-titrate with additional NaOH to neutralize the additional HCl that was added.
   (B) Back-titrate with additional HCl to neutralize the additional NaOH that was added.
   (C) Start over again, being careful to stop the titration just before the equivalence point.
   (D) Perform an additional two trials and average the volumes of the NaOH for all three trials.

18. A student uses acetic acid to titrate a solution of copper(I) hydroxide to determine the concentration of the copper(I) hydroxide. If 30.0 mL of 0.250 *M* acetic acid is needed to neutralize 15.0 mL copper(I) hydroxide, what is the molarity of the copper(I) hydroxide?

(A) 0.125 *M*
(B) 0.250 *M*
(C) 0.375 *M*
(D) 0.500 *M*

19. Consider 100.0 mL of 0.100 *M* aqueous solutions of each of the following acids: HCN ($K_a = 6.2 \times 10^{-10}$), HF ($K_a = 7.2 \times 10^{-4}$), HCl, $HC_2H_3O_2$ ($K_a = 1.8 \times 10^{-5}$). Each acid is titrated with 0.100 *M* NaOH(*aq*). Once the equivalence point is reached for each solution, rank the pH values from highest to lowest.

(A) HCl, HCN, HF, $HC_2H_3O_2$
(B) HCN, $HC_2H_3O_2$, HF, HCl
(C) HCl, HF, $HC_2H_3O_2$, HCN
(D) $HC_2H_3O_2$, HCN, HCl, HF

20. You are asked to make 1.00 L of a solution buffered at a pH of 9.00. You are given 1.00 *M* HCN ($K_a = 6.2 \times 10^{-10}$) and 1.00 *M* NaCN. Which of the following statements correctly describes the relative volumes of each solution to make such a buffer?

(A) The volumes of the 1.00 *M* HCN and the 1.00 *M* NaCN are equal.
(B) The volume of the 1.00 *M* HCN must be less than the volume of the 1.00 *M* NaCN.
(C) The volume of the 1.00 *M* HCN must be greater than the volume of the 1.00 *M* NaCN.
(D) There is no way to make a buffer solution at a pH of 9.00 with HCN and NaCN.

21. You are asked to make a buffered solution with a pH as close to 7.00 as possible by mixing equal volumes of 1.00 *M* solutions. Which of the following mixtures is the best choice?

(A) HF ($K_a = 7.2 \times 10^{-4}$) and NaF
(B) HCN ($K_a = 6.2 \times 10^{-10}$) and NaCN
(C) HOCl ($K_a = 3.5 \times 10^{-8}$) and NaOCl
(D) $HC_2H_3O_2$ ($K_a = 1.8 \times 10^{-5}$) and $NaC_2H_3O_2$

22. A certain buffer solution has a pH of 4.6. The weak acid used to make this solution, HA, has a pK_a of 3.2. Which statement best describes the relationship between the concentration of hydrogen ion, $[H^+]$, and the concentration of A^-, $[A^-]$?

(A) $[H^+] > [A^-]$ because $pH > pK_a$
(B) $[H^+] > [A^-]$ because $pH < pK_a$
(C) $[H^+] < [A^-]$ because $pH > pK_a$
(D) $[H^+] < [A^-]$ because $pH < pK_a$

23. Strong acids do not make good buffered solutions because

(A) strong acids dissociate completely and the equilibrium lies far to the right.
(B) strong acids dissociate completely and the equilibrium lies far to the left.
(C) strong acids react completely with any base and the equilibrium lies far to the right.
(D) strong acids react completely with any base and the equilibrium lies far to the left.

24. A 25.0-mL sample of 0.10 *M* $HC_2H_3O_2$ is titrated with 0.10 *M* NaOH. What is the pH after 25.0 mL of NaOH have been added? The K_a value for $HC_2H_3O_2$ is 1.8×10^{-5}.

(A) 4.57
(B) 6.24
(C) 7.00
(D) 8.72

25. A 0.10 *M* HCl solution may be titrated with two different bases: 0.10 *M* NaOH or 0.10 *M* $Ca(OH)_2$. Which statement best describes the volumes of the bases necessary to reach the equivalence point?

(A) Half as much NaOH is needed.
(B) Equal volumes of NaOH and $Ca(OH)_2$ are needed.
(C) Twice as much $Ca(OH)_2$ is needed.
(D) Twice as much NaOH is needed.

AP Free Response Review Questions

Question Format: Short

Category of Question: Quantitative

A 500.0 mL sample of saturated nickel(II) phosphate solution was analyzed spectrophotometrically and found to contain 1.88×10^{-5} g of nickel.

Questions

(a) Determine the molarity of the nickel(II) phosphate solution.

(b) Calculate the solubility product constant, K_{sp}, for nickel(II) phosphate.

Question Format: Long

Category of Question: Lab 1

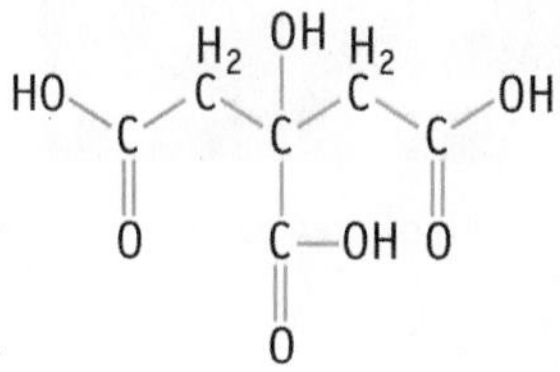

Lemon juice is acidic because of the presence of citric acid, a weak triprotic acid with the formula $C_6H_8O_7$ (molar mass 192.12 g), and structure as shown above. The acidity of a lemon varies with both the variety and the growing conditions with the average being approximately 5% citric acid. This percentage is represented as grams of citric acid per 100 mL of lemon juice.

Available Equipment and Supplies (not all will necessarily be used):

- 50.00 mL buret
- buret clamp and stand
- 250 mL Erlenmeyer flask
- 250 mL of standardized NaOH solution
- 50 mL of juice from a lemon (freshly squeezed and filtered)
- pH meter
- phenolphthalein
- wash bottle
- freshly distilled water
- 10.00 mL volumetric pipet
- 100 mL graduated cylinder

Questions

(a) Circle the hydrogen atoms that are able to ionize in the citric acid structure.

(b) Write a complete balanced molecular equation to show the neutralization of the citric acid by sodium hydroxide.

(c) When the NaOH solution was standardized, 1.2582 g of potassium hydrogen phthalate, a monoprotic weak acid (molar mass = 204.22 g) neutralized a 22.43 mL sample of the sodium hydroxide solution. Determine the molarity of the sodium hydroxide solution.

(d) Design an experiment to determine the citric acid content of a sample of lemon juice. List the steps of the lab procedure.

(e) Describe all calculations that would be necessary in this experiment.

(f) Many commercial lemon-flavored drink mixes include both sodium citrate and citric acid. Suggest a reason that the sodium citrate is included.

Question Format: Long

Category of Question: Quantitative

The solubility of insoluble substances changes depending on the nature of the solution. Below are two solutions in which $Cu(OH)_2$ is dissolved; in each case, the solubility is not the same as it is in pure water.

Questions

(a) For each solution state whether the solubility is greater than or less than that of pure water and briefly account for the change in solubility.

  (i) 1-molar $HCl(aq)$

  (ii) 1-molar $Cu(NO_3)_2(aq)$

A saturated solution of lead(II) iodide in pure water has a lead ion concentration of 1.3×10^{-3} mole per liter at 25 °C.

(b) Calculate the value for the solubility-product constant of PbI_2 at 25 °C.

(c) Calculate the molar solubility of PbI_2 in a 0.10 M $Pb(NO_3)_2$ solution at 25 °C.

(d) To 333 milliliters of a 0.12 M $Pb(NO_3)_2$ solution, 667 milliliters of 0.015 M KI is added. Does a precipitate form? Support your answer with calculations.

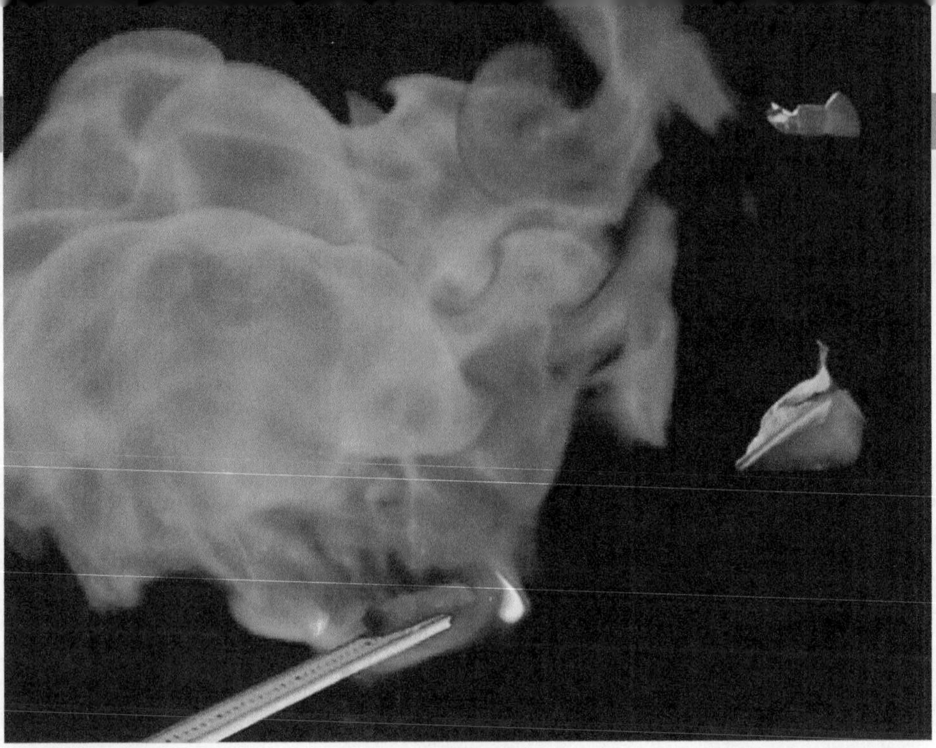

The Combustion of Hydrogen Gas. The exothermic reaction of hydrogen with oxygen to form water. (A hydrogen-filled balloon was ignited with a candle.)

Principles of Chemical Reactivity: Entropy and Free Energy

Chapter Outline

18-1 Spontaneity and Energy Transfer as Heat

18-2 Dispersal of Energy: Entropy

18-3 Entropy: A Microscopic Understanding

18-4 Entropy Measurement and Values

18-5 Entropy Changes and Spontaneity

18-6 Gibbs Free Energy

18-7 Calculating and Using Free Energy

HYDROGEN FOR THE FUTURE? Hydrogen could be an excellent energy source in the future. Sources of the element, such as water and hydrocarbons, are abundant. As the photo above shows, the combustion of hydrogen is very exothermic. Interestingly, this reaction can also be run without a flame using fuel cell technology (Section 19-3). Regardless of how the reaction is run, the product of the combustion reaction is simply water!

There are many challenges, however, that still remain to be solved. The cost for a hydrogen fuel system is currently much higher than that for a gasoline engine. Scientists and engineers have yet to find a way to store enough hydrogen on a vehicle so it can travel 300 miles or so without needing to refuel. New infrastructure would need to be built to provide hydrogen at sufficient locations. And overcoming the public's perception of hydrogen as exceptionally dangerous is a hurdle. While it is true

Chapter Goals

See Chapter Goals Revisited (page 710) for Study Questions keyed to these goals.

UNDERSTAND

- The concept of entropy and its relationship to reaction spontaneity.
- The relationship between enthalpy, entropy, and free energy changes for a reaction.

DO

- Calculate the change in entropy for a system, its surroundings, and the universe to determine whether a process is spontaneous under standard conditions.
- Use the change in Gibbs free energy to predict reaction spontaneity.
- Calculate the standard free energy change for a reaction from free energy of formation data.
- Calculate an equilibrium constant for a process from its standard free energy change.

REMEMBER

- The entropy of the universe increases in a spontaneous change.
- The Gibbs free energy change for a spontaneous reaction is negative.

that hydrogen is flammable over a wider range of concentrations in air than is gasoline, hydrogen requires a higher temperature to ignite.

A major problem with hydrogen is that it takes energy to obtain hydrogen in the first place. One way is to pass an electric current through water to produce hydrogen and oxygen. The resulting hydrogen would then be recombined with oxygen in a fuel cell, releasing energy in the process. In Chapter 5, you learned that the first law of thermodynamics states that energy is conserved in the universe. Thus, the best we could hope for is to get the same amount of energy back from hydrogen combustion as was originally used to decompose water.

But there is another problem. In this chapter, you will learn about the second law of thermodynamics, which states that it is not possible to have 100% of the energy in a process transferred as work. Because of this, the usable energy from hydrogen combustion would be less than needed to generate the hydrogen. One potential solution is to use a renewable energy source such as solar or wind energy to decompose water. The laws of thermodynamics still apply, but it is not as important that less energy is obtained than was needed to generate the hydrogen because the input of energy came from an abundant and renewable energy resource.

Scientists are actively seeking ways to make hydrogen a useful, economical, and safe fuel for the future. Underlying this search, chemistry and the laws of thermodynamics play essential roles.

Study Questions related to this story are: 18.85 and 18.86.

© Cengage Learning/Charles D. Winters

FIGURE 18.1 A spontaneous process. The heated metal cylinder is placed in water. Energy transfers as heat spontaneously from the metal to water, that is, from the hotter object to the cooler object.

Change is central to chemistry, so it is important to understand the factors that determine whether a change will occur. In chemistry, we encounter many examples of chemical change (chemical reactions) and physical change (the formation of mixtures, expansion of gases, and changes of state, to name a few). Chemists use the term **spontaneous** to represent a change that occurs without outside intervention. *Spontaneous changes occur only in the direction that leads to equilibrium.* Whether or not the process is spontaneous does not tell us anything about the rate of the change or the extent to which a process will occur before equilibrium is reached. Saying a change is spontaneous means only that the change will occur in a specific direction (toward equilibrium) and will occur naturally and unaided.

If a piece of hot metal is placed in a beaker of cold water (Figure 18.1), energy is transferred as heat spontaneously from the hot metal to the cooler water, and energy transfer will continue until thermal equilibrium is attained, that is, until the two objects are at the same temperature. Similarly, chemical reactions proceed spontaneously until equilibrium is reached, regardless of whether the position of the equilibrium favors products or reactants. We readily recognize that, starting with pure reactants, all product-favored reactions must be spontaneous. Be aware, though, that reactant-favored reactions are also spontaneous until equilibrium is achieved. Even though the dissolution of $CaCO_3$ is reactant-favored at equilibrium, if you place a handful of $CaCO_3$ in water, the process of dissolving will proceed spontaneously until equilibrium is reached.

Systems never change spontaneously in a direction that takes them farther from equilibrium. Given two objects at the same temperature, in contact but thermally isolated from their surroundings, one will never heat up while the other becomes colder. Gas molecules will never spontaneously congregate at one end of a flask. Similarly, once equilibrium is established, the small amount of dissolved $CaCO_3$ in equilibrium with solid $CaCO_3$ will not spontaneously precipitate from solution, nor will a greater amount of $CaCO_3$ spontaneously dissolve.

The factors that determine the directionality and extent of change are among the topics of this chapter.

PROBLEM SOLVING TIP 18.1
A Review of Concepts of Thermodynamics

To understand the thermodynamic concepts introduced in this chapter, be sure to review these ideas from Chapter 5.

System: The part of the universe under study.

Surroundings: The rest of the universe exclusive of the system, capable of exchanging energy and/or matter with the system.

Exothermic: Energy transfers as heat from the system to the surroundings.

Endothermic: Energy transfers as heat from the surroundings to the system.

First law of thermodynamics: The law of conservation of energy; energy cannot be created or destroyed. The change in internal energy of a system is the sum of energy transferred into or out of the system as heat and/or as work, $\Delta U = q + w$.

Enthalpy change: The energy transferred as heat under conditions of constant pressure.

State function: A quantity whose value depends only on the state of the system; changes in a state function can be calculated by taking into account the initial and final states of a system.

Standard conditions: Pressure of 1 bar (1 bar = 0.98692 atm) and solution concentration of 1 *m*.

Standard enthalpy of formation, $\Delta_f H°$: The enthalpy change occurring when 1 mol of a compound is formed from its elements in their standard states.

18-1 Spontaneity and Energy Transfer as Heat

We can readily recognize many chemical reactions that are spontaneous, such as hydrogen and oxygen combining to form water, methane burning to give CO_2 and H_2O, Na and Cl_2 reacting to form NaCl, and HCl(aq) and NaOH(aq) reacting to form H_2O and NaCl(aq). A common feature of these reactions is that they are exothermic, so it would be tempting to conclude that evolution of energy as heat is the criterion that determines whether a reaction or process is spontaneous. Further inspection, however, reveals significant flaws in this reasoning. This is especially evident when we consider some common spontaneous changes that are endothermic or energy neutral:

- *Dissolving NH_4NO_3.* The ionic compound NH_4NO_3 dissolves spontaneously in water. The process is endothermic ($\Delta_r H° = +25.7$ kJ/mol).
- *Expansion of a gas into a vacuum.* A system is set up with two flasks connected by a valve (Figure 18.2). One flask is filled with a gas, and the other is evacuated. When the valve is opened, the gas flows spontaneously from one flask to the other until the pressure is the same throughout. The expansion of an ideal gas is energy neutral (although expansion of most real gases is endothermic).
- *Phase changes.* Melting of ice is an endothermic process. Above 0 °C, ice melts spontaneously. Below 0 °C, melting is not spontaneous. At 0 °C, no net change will occur; liquid water and ice coexist at equilibrium. This example illustrates that temperature can have a role in determining spontaneity and that equilibrium is somehow an important aspect of the problem.
- *Energy transfer as heat.* The temperature of cold water sitting in a warm environment will rise until it reaches the ambient temperature. The energy required for this endothermic process comes from the surroundings. Energy transfer as heat from a hotter object (the surroundings) to a cooler object (the water) is spontaneous.
- *Chemical Reactions.* The reaction of H_2 and I_2 to form HI is endothermic, and the reverse reaction, the decomposition of HI to form H_2 and I_2, is exothermic. If $H_2(g)$ and $I_2(g)$ are mixed, a reaction forming HI will occur [$H_2(g) + I_2(g) \rightleftharpoons 2\ HI(g)$] until equilibrium is reached. Furthermore, if HI(g) is placed in a container, there will also be a reaction, but in the reverse direction, until equilibrium is achieved. Notice that approach to equilibrium occurs spontaneously from either direction.

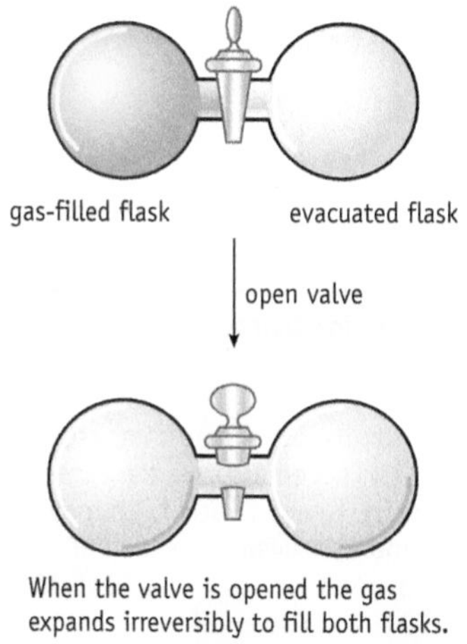

FIGURE 18.2 Spontaneous expansion of a gas.

On further reflection, it is logical to conclude that evolution of heat cannot be a sufficient criterion in determining spontaneity. The first law of thermodynamics tells us that in any process energy must be conserved. If energy is transferred out of a system, then the same amount of energy must be transferred to the surroundings. Exothermicity of the system is always accompanied by an endothermic change in the surroundings. If energy evolution were the only factor determining whether a change is spontaneous, then for every spontaneous process there would be a corresponding nonspontaneous change in the surroundings. We must search further than the first law of thermodynamics to determine whether a change is spontaneous.

REVIEW & CHECK FOR SECTION 18-1

1. A process is spontaneous in the direction that moves it

   (a) away from equilibrium (b) toward equilibrium

2. A process that is reactant-favored at equilibrium can never be spontaneous. This statement is

   (a) true (b) false

3. Endothermic processes are
   (a) always spontaneous
   (b) sometimes spontaneous
   (c) never spontaneous

Learning Objectives: LO 5.12

18-2 Dispersal of Energy: Entropy

Entropy For a more complete discussion of entropy, see the papers by F. L. Lambert, such as "Entropy Is Simple, Qualitatively," *Journal of Chemical Education*, Vol. 79, pp. 1241–1246, 2002, and references therein. See also Lambert's website: entropysite.oxy.edu

Second Law of Thermodynamics For a spontaneous process, $\Delta S(\text{universe}) > 0$.

We have shown that we cannot use energy itself as an indicator of spontaneity because energy is conserved in any process; we always end up with the same amount of energy as we had at the beginning. Consider again placing a piece of hot metal in a beaker of cold water. Energy transfers as heat spontaneously from the metal to the water until the temperature of the metal and the water is the same. In accord with the first law of thermodynamics, the total amount of energy in the combination of the piece of metal and the water is conserved, but there is directionality to this process. Energy transfers as heat from a hotter object to a colder object; you will never see a net flow of energy in the opposite direction, from a colder object to a hotter object. Is there a way to predict the directionality of this energy transfer?

Let us consider the initial and final states for the process of adding the hot metal to the cold water. Initially, energy is concentrated in the piece of metal. At the end of the process, this energy has been dispersed between the metal and the water. This is the indicator for which we have been searching. *In a spontaneous process, energy goes from being more concentrated to being more dispersed.*

There is a state function called **entropy (*S*)** that allows us to quantify the dispersal of energy. The **second law of thermodynamics** states that *a spontaneous process is one that results in an increase of the entropy of the universe. In a spontaneous process ΔS(universe) is greater than zero; this is a measure of the dispersal of energy in the process.*

Because thermal energy is the result of the random motion of particles, potential energy is dispersed when it is converted to thermal energy. This conversion occurs when energy is transferred as heat, q. It is therefore not surprising that q is a part of the mathematical definition of ΔS. In addition, the effect of a given quantity of energy transferred as heat on energy dispersal is different at different temperatures. It

A CLOSER LOOK — Reversible and Irreversible Processes

To determine entropy changes experimentally, the energy transferred by heating and cooling must be measured for a reversible process. But what is a reversible process?

The test for reversibility is that after carrying out a change along a given path (for example, energy added as heat), it must be possible to return to the starting point by the same path (energy taken away as heat) without altering the surroundings. Melting of ice and freezing of water at 0 °C are examples of reversible processes. Given a mixture of ice and water at equilibrium, adding energy as heat in small increments will convert ice to water; removing energy as heat in small increments will convert water back to ice.

Reversibility is closely associated with equilibrium. Assume that we have a system at equilibrium. Reversible changes can be made by very slightly perturbing the equilibrium and letting the system readjust.

Spontaneous processes are not reversible. Suppose a gas is allowed to expand into a vacuum. No work is done in this process because there is no force to resist expansion. To return the system to its original state, it is necessary to compress the gas. Doing so means doing work on the system, however, because the system will not return to its original state on its own. In this process, the energy of the surroundings decreases by the amount of work expended by the surroundings. The system can be restored to its original state, but the surroundings will be altered in the process.

In summary, there are two important points concerning reversibility:

- At every step along a reversible pathway between two states, the system remains at equilibrium.
- Spontaneous processes often follow irreversible pathways and involve nonequilibrium conditions.

To determine the entropy change for a process, it is necessary to identify a reversible pathway. Only then can an entropy change for the process be calculated from q_{rev} and the Kelvin temperature.

turns out that a given q has a greater effect on ΔS at a lower temperature than at a higher temperature; that is, the extent of energy dispersal is inversely proportional to the temperature.

Our proposed definition for ΔS is thus related to the quotient q/T, but we must be a little more specific about q. The value of q used in the calculation of an entropy change must be the energy transferred as heat under what are called *reversible conditions*, which we symbolize as q_{rev} (see *A Closer Look: Reversible and Irreversible Processes*). The mathematical definition of ΔS is therefore q_{rev} divided by the absolute (Kelvin) temperature:

$$\Delta S = \frac{q_{rev}}{T} \quad (18.1)$$

As expected from this equation, the units for ΔS are J/K.

REVIEW & CHECK FOR SECTION 18-2

1. In a spontaneous process, ΔS(universe) is

   (a) < 0 (b) $= 0$ (c) > 0

2. Which of the following is true for a spontaneous process but not for a nonspontaneous process? Energy in the universe is

   (a) concentrated (b) conserved (c) dispersed (d) not conserved

3. For a particular system, q_{rev} at 25 °C is equal to + 950. J. What is ΔS for this system?

   (a) 38 J/K (b) 3.19 J/K (c) −3.19 J/K (d) −38 J/K

18-3 Entropy: A Microscopic Understanding

Entropy is a measure of the extent of energy dispersal. In all spontaneous physical and chemical processes, energy changes from being localized or concentrated to being more dispersed or spread out. *In a spontaneous process, the change in entropy, ΔS, of the universe indicates the extent to which energy is dispersed.* So far, however, we have not explained why dispersal of energy occurs. In order to do this, we need to consider energy in its quantized form and matter on the atomic level.

Dispersal of Energy

We can explore the dispersal of energy using a simple example: energy being transferred as heat between hot and cold gaseous atoms. Consider an experiment involving two containers, one holding hot atoms and the other with cold atoms. Because they have translational energy, the atoms move randomly in each container and collide with the walls. When the containers are in contact, energy is transferred through the container walls. Eventually, both containers will be at the same temperature; the energy originally localized in the hotter atoms is distributed over a greater number of atoms; and the atoms in each container will have the same distribution of energies.

For further insight, we shall use a statistical explanation to show why energy is dispersed in a system. With statistical arguments, systems must include large numbers of particles for the arguments to be accurate. It will be easiest, however, if we look first at simple examples to understand the underlying concepts and then extrapolate our conclusions to larger systems.

Consider the system in Figure 18.3 in which, initially, there is one atom (1) with two discrete packets, or quanta, of energy and three other atoms (2, 3, and 4) with

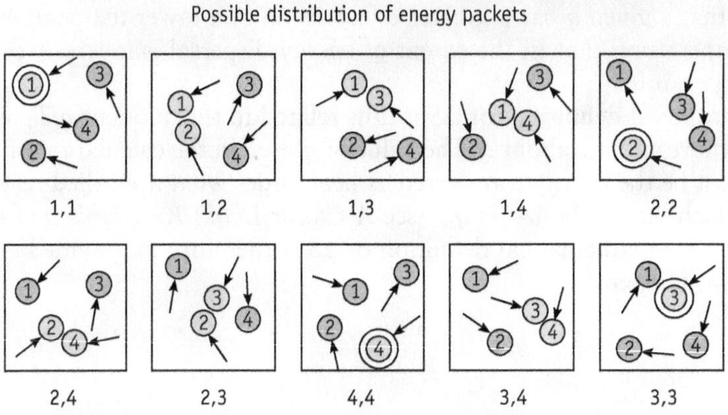

FIGURE 18.3 Energy dispersal. Possible ways of distributing two packets of energy among four atoms. To keep our analysis simple, we assume that initially there is one atom with two quanta of energy (1) and three atoms (2, 3, and 4) with no energy. There are 10 different ways to distribute the two quanta of energy among the four atoms.

no energy. Collisions among the atoms allow energy to be transferred so that, over time, all distributions of the two packets of energy over the four atoms are seen. There are 10 different ways to distribute these 2 quanta of energy over the four atoms. Each of these 10 different ways to distribute the energy is called a **microstate**. In only one of these microstates do the 2 quanta remain on atom 1. In fact, only in 4 of the 10 microstates [1,1; 2,2; 3,3; and 4,4] is the energy concentrated on a single atom. In the majority of cases, 6 out of 10, the energy is distributed to two different atoms. Even in this small sample (four atoms) with only two packets of energy, it is more likely that at any given time the energy will be distributed to two atoms rather than concentrated on a single atom. There is a distinct preference that the energy will be dispersed over a greater number of atoms.

Let us now add more atoms to our system. We again begin with one atom (1) having 2 quanta of energy but now have five other atoms (2, 3, 4, 5, and 6) with no energy. Collisions let the energy be transferred between the atoms, and we now find there are 21 possible microstates (Figure 18.4). There are six microstates in which the energy is concentrated on one atom, including one in which the energy is still on atom 1, but there are now 15 out of 21 microstates (or 71.4%) in which the energy is present on two different atoms. As the number of particles increases, the number of microstates available increases dramatically, and the fraction of microstates in which the energy is concentrated rather than dispersed goes down dramatically. It is much more likely that the energy will be dispersed rather than concentrated.

FIGURE 18.4 Distributing 2 quanta of energy among six atoms. (Atoms are labeled 1 to 6.) There are 21 ways—21 microstates—of distributing 2 quanta of energy among six atoms.

Number of Microstates	Distribution of 2 Quanta of Energy Among Six Atoms					
6	1:1	2:2	3:3	4:4	5:5	6:6
5	1:2	2:3	3:4	4:5	5:6	
4	1:3	2:4	3:5	4:6		
3	1:4	2:5	3:6			
2	1:5	2:6				
1	1:6					

Now let us return to an example using a total of four atoms but increase the quantity of energy from 2 quanta to 6 quanta. Assume that we start with two atoms having 3 quanta of energy each. The other two atoms initially have zero energy (Figure 18.5). Through collisions, energy can be transferred to achieve different distributions of energy among the four atoms. In all, there are 84 microstates, falling into nine basic patterns. For example, one possible arrangement has one atom with 3 quanta of energy, and three atoms with 1 quantum each. There are four microstates in which this is true (Figure 18.5c). Increasing the number of quanta from 2 to 6 with the same number of atoms increased the number of possible microstates from 10 to 84. In this case, increasing the amount of energy that is dispersed resulted in an increase in the number of microstates.

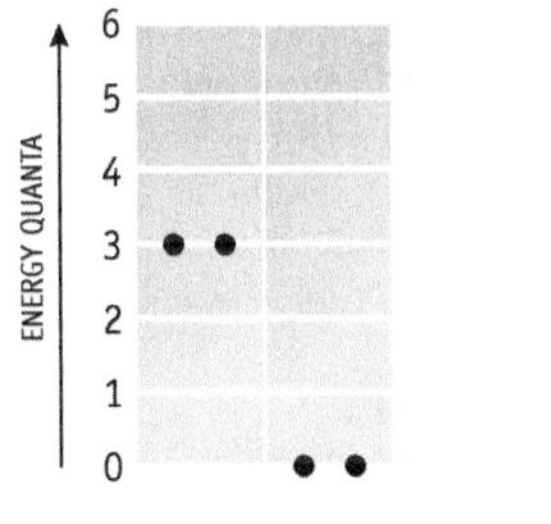

(a) Initially, four particles are separated from each other. Two particles each have 3 quanta of energy, and the other two have none. A total of 6 quanta of energy will be distributed once the four particles interact.

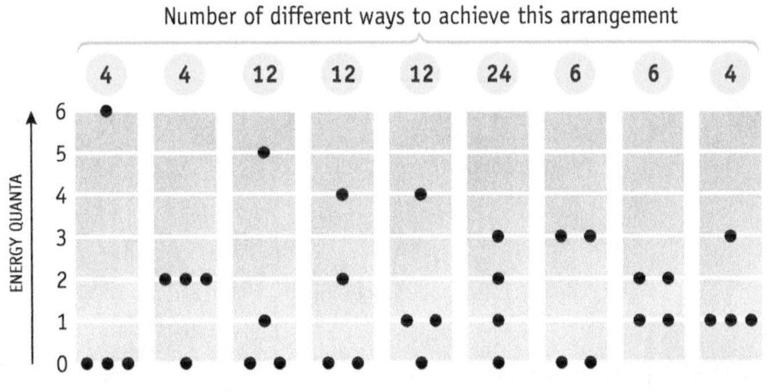

(b) Once the particles begin to interact, there are nine ways to distribute the 6 available quanta. Each of these arrangements will have multiple ways of distributing the energy among the four atoms. Part (c) shows how the arrangement on the right can be achieved four ways.

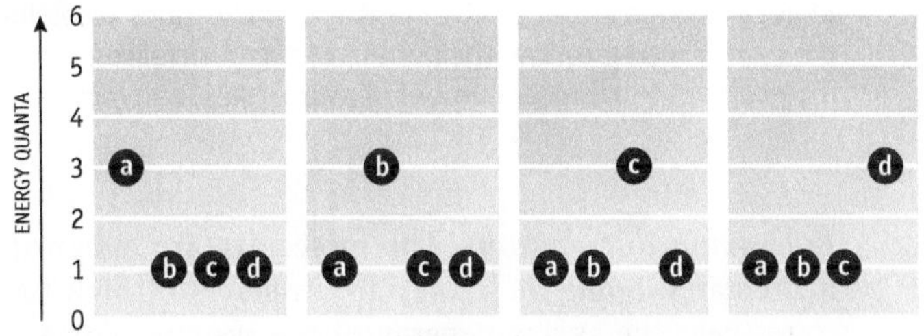

(c) There are four different ways to have four particles (a, b, c, and d) such that one particle has 3 quanta of energy and the other three each have 1 quantum of energy.

FIGURE 18.5 **Energy dispersal.** Possible ways of distributing 6 quanta of energy among four atoms. A total of 84 microstates is possible.

Statistical analyses for larger aggregates of atoms and energy quanta become increasingly complex, but the conclusions are even more compelling. As the number of particles and/or quanta increases, the number of energy microstates grows rapidly. This larger number of microstates allows the energy to be dispersed to a greater extent. Ludwig Boltzmann proposed that the entropy of a system (the dispersal of energy at a given temperature) results from the number of microstates available. *As the number of microstates increases, so does the entropy of the system.* He expressed this idea in the equation

$$S = k \ln W \tag{18.2}$$

which states that the entropy of a system, S, is proportional to the natural logarithm of the number of accessible microstates, W, that belong to a given energy of a system or substance. (The proportionality constant, k, is now known as **Boltzmann's constant** and has a value of 1.381×10^{-23} J/K.) Within these microstates, it turns out that those states that disperse energy over the largest number of atoms are vastly more probable than the others.

Oesper Collection in the History of Chemistry/University of Cincinnati

Ludwig Boltzmann (1844–1906). Engraved on his tombstone in Vienna, Austria, is his equation defining entropy. The constant k is now known as Boltzmann's constant.

How Many Microstates? To give you a sense of the number of microstates available to a substance, consider a mole of ice at 273 K, where $S° = 41.3$ J/K · mol. Using Boltzmann's equation, we find that $W = 10^{1,299,000,000,000,000,000,000,000}$. That is, there are many, many more microstates for 1 mol of ice than there are atoms in the universe (about 10^{80}).

Dispersal of Matter: Dispersal of Energy Revisited

In many processes, it appears that the dispersal of matter also contributes to spontaneity. We shall see, however, that these effects can also be explained in terms of energy dispersal. Let us examine a specific case, the expansion of a gas into a vacuum (see Figure 18.2). How is this spontaneous expansion of a gas related to energy dispersal and entropy?

We begin with the premise that all energy is quantized and that this applies to any system, including gas molecules in a room or in a reaction flask. You know from the previous discussion of kinetic-molecular theory that the molecules in a gas sample have a distribution of energies (◀ Figure 10.14) (often referred to as *a*

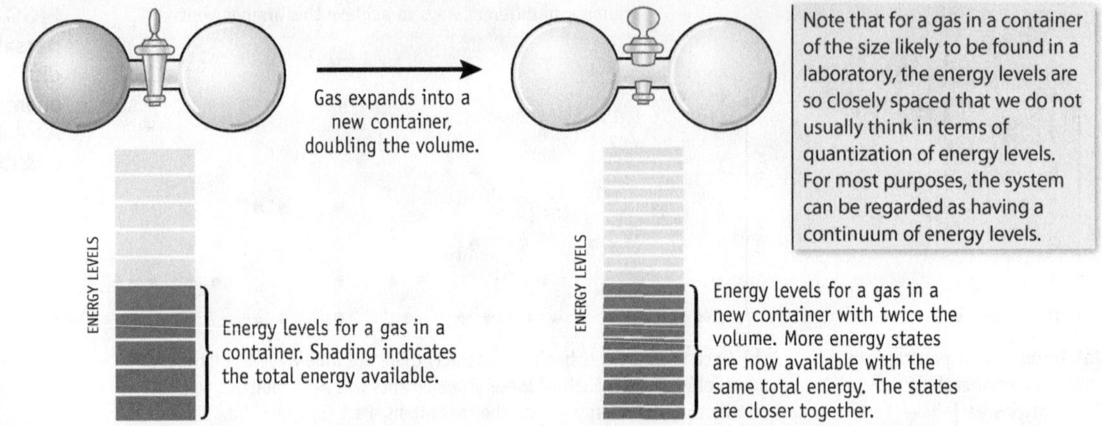

FIGURE 18.6 **Energy (and matter) dispersal.** As the size of the container for the chemical or physical change increases, the number of microstates accessible to the atoms or molecules of the system increases, and the density of states increases. A consequence of the distribution of molecules over a greater number of microstates is an increase in entropy.

Boltzmann distribution). The molecules are assigned to (or "occupy") quantized microstates. Some molecules are in states of high or low energy, but most are in states near the average energy of the system. (For a gas in a laboratory-sized container, the energy levels are so closely spaced that, for most purposes, there is a continuum of energy states.)

Statistical Thermodynamics
The arguments presented here come from a branch of chemistry called *statistical thermodynamics*. See H. Jungermann, *Journal of Chemical Education*, Vol. 83, pp. 1686–1694, 2006.

When the gas expands to fill a larger container, the average energy of the sample and the energy for the particles in a given energy range are constant. However, quantum mechanics show (for now, you will have to take our word for it) that as a consequence of having a larger volume in which the molecules can move in the expanded state, there is an increase in the number of microstates and that those microstates are even more closely spaced than before (Figure 18.6). The result of this greater density of microstates is that the number of microstates available to the gas particles increases when the gas expands. Gas expansion, a dispersal of matter, leads to the dispersal of energy over a larger number of microstates and thus to an increase in entropy.

The logic applied to the expansion of a gas into a vacuum can be used to rationalize the mixing of two gases, the mixing of two liquids, or the dissolution of a solid in a liquid (Figure 18.7). For example, if flasks containing O_2 and N_2 are connected (in an experimental setup like that in Figure 18.6), the two gases diffuse together, eventually leading to a mixture in which O_2 and N_2 molecules are evenly distributed throughout the total volume. A mixture of O_2 and N_2 will never separate into samples of each component of its own accord. The gases spontaneously move toward a situation in which each gas and its energy are maximally dispersed. The energy of the system is dispersed over a larger number of microstates, and the

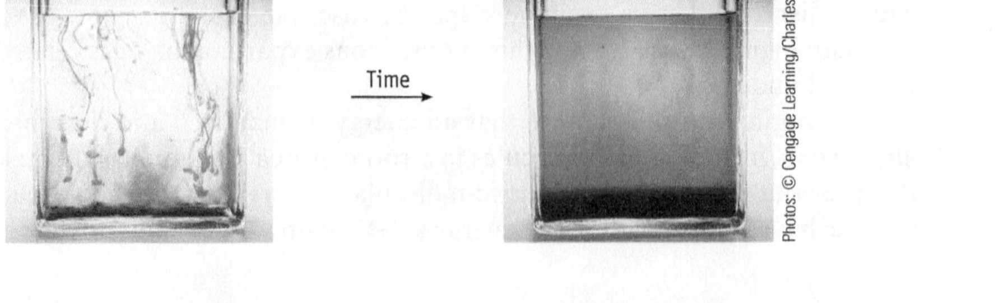

FIGURE 18.7 **Dissolving $KMnO_4$ in water.** A small quantity of solid, purple $KMnO_4$ is added to water *(left)*. With time, the solid dissolves, and the highly colored MnO_4^- ions (and the K^+ ions) become dispersed throughout the solution. Entropy makes a large contribution to the mixing of liquids and solutions (see Section 13-2).

entropy of the system increases. Indeed, this is a large part of the explanation for the fact that similar liquids (such as oil and gasoline or water and ethanol) will readily form homogeneous solutions. Recall the rule of thumb that "like dissolves like" (◀ Section 13-2).

A Summary: Entropy, Entropy Change, and Energy Dispersal

According to Boltzmann's equation (Equation 18.2), entropy is proportional to the number of ways energy can be dispersed in a substance, that is, to the number of microstates available to the system *(W)*. The number of microstates increases with an increased number of particles, with an increase in energy, and with an increase in volume. There will be a change in entropy, ΔS, if there is a change in the number of microstates over which energy can be dispersed.

$$\Delta S = S_{\text{final}} - S_{\text{initial}} = k\,(\ln W_{\text{final}} - \ln W_{\text{initial}}) = k\,\ln(W_{\text{final}}/W_{\text{initial}})$$

Our focus as chemists is on ΔS, and we shall be concerned mainly with the dispersion of energy in systems and surroundings during a physical or chemical change.

Entropy Change on Gas Expansion The entropy change for a gas expansion can be calculated from

$$\Delta S = nR\ln(V_{\text{final}}/V_{\text{initial}})$$

At a given temperature, V is proportional to the number of microstates, so the equation is related to $k\ln(W_{\text{final}}/W_{\text{initial}})$.

REVIEW & CHECK FOR SECTION 18-3

1. As the number of microstates over which energy can be distributed in a system increases, its entropy

   (a) decreases (b) increases (c) remains constant

2. Calculate the change in entropy for a system in going from a condition with 5 accessible microstates to 30 accessible microstates.

   (a) -2.5×10^{-23} J/K (c) 2.5×10^{-23} J/K

   (b) 9.4×10^{-24} J/K (d) 8.3×10^{-23} J/K

18-4 Entropy Measurement and Values

Learning Objectives: LO 5.12

A numerical value for entropy can be determined for any substance under a given set of conditions. The greater the dispersal of energy, the greater the entropy and the larger the value of S. The point of reference for entropy values is established by the **third law of thermodynamics.** Defined by Ludwig Boltzmann, the third law states that *a perfect crystal at 0 K has zero entropy; that is, $S = 0$.* The entropy of an element or compound under any other set of conditions is the entropy gained by converting the substance from 0 K to those conditions. To determine the value of S, it is necessary to measure the energy transferred as heat under reversible conditions for the conversion from 0 K to the defined conditions and then to use Equation 18.1 ($\Delta S = q_{\text{rev}}/T$). Because it is necessary to add energy as heat to raise the temperature, *all substances have positive entropy values at temperatures above 0 K.* Negative values of entropy cannot occur. Recognizing that entropy is directly related to energy added as heat allows us to predict several general features of entropy values:

- Raising the temperature of a substance corresponds to adding energy as heat. Thus, the entropy of a substance will increase with an increase in temperature.
- Conversions from solid to liquid and from liquid to gas typically require large inputs of energy as heat. Consequently, there is a large increase in entropy in conversions involving changes of state (Figure 18.8).

Negative Entropy Values A glance at thermodynamic tables indicates that ions in aqueous solution can and do have negative entropy values listed. However, these are not absolute entropies. For ions, the entropy of $H^+(aq)$ is arbitrarily assigned a standard entropy of zero, and the entropy values for other ions are assigned relative to this value.

Standard Entropy Values, $S°$

We introduced the concept of standard states into the earlier discussion of enthalpy (◀ Section 5-4), and we can similarly define the entropy of any substance in its standard state. The **standard molar entropy,** $S°$, of a substance is the entropy gained

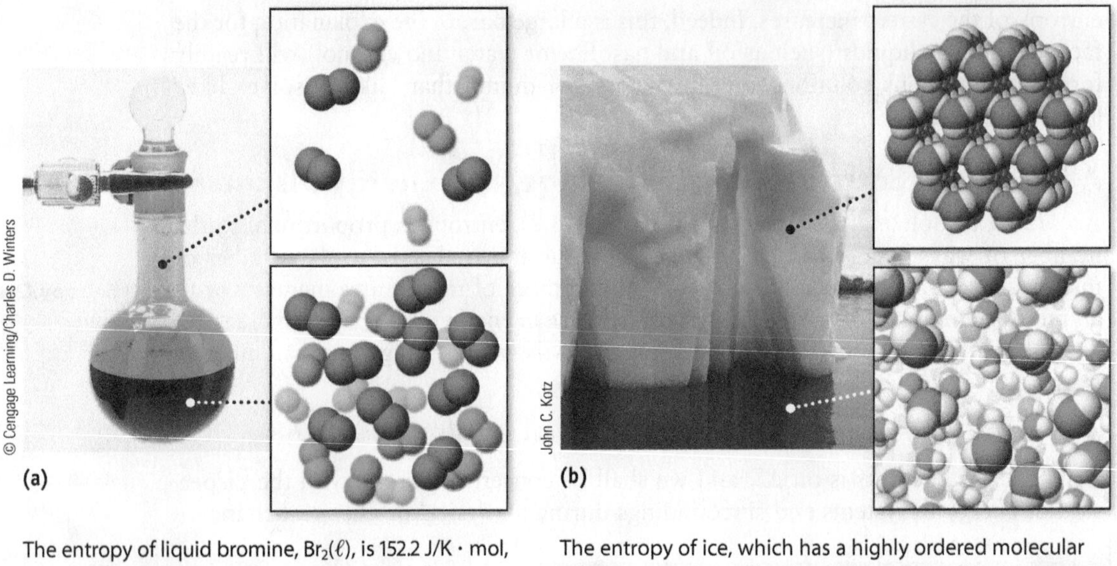

The entropy of liquid bromine, $Br_2(\ell)$, is 152.2 J/K · mol, and that for bromine vapor is 245.47 J/K · mol.

The entropy of ice, which has a highly ordered molecular arrangement, is smaller than the entropy of liquid water.

FIGURE 18.8 Entropy and states of matter.

by converting 1 mol of it from a perfect crystal at 0 K to standard state conditions (1 bar, 1 molal for a solution) at the specified temperature. The units for standard molar entropy values are J/K · mol. Generally, values of $S°$ found in tables of data refer to a temperature of 298 K. Appendix L lists many standard molar entropies at 298 K. More extensive lists of $S°$ values can be found in standard reference sources such as the NIST tables (**webbook.nist.gov**).

$S°$ (J/K · mol)

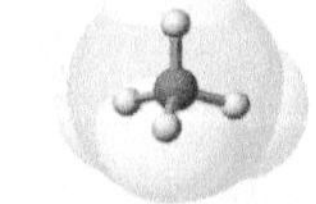
methane 186.3

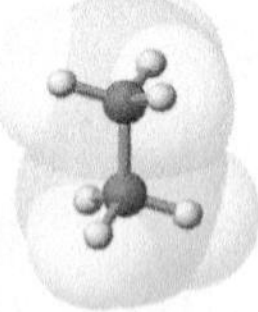
ethane 229.2

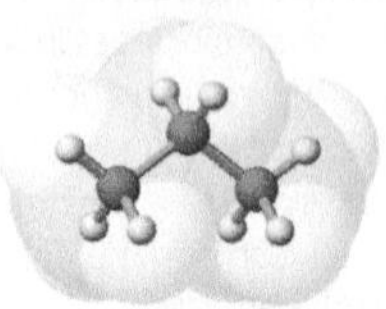
propane 270.3

Scanning a list of standard entropies (such as those in Appendix L) will show that *large molecules generally have larger entropies than small molecules.* With a larger molecule, there are more ways for the molecule to rotate and vibrate, which provides a larger number of energy microstates over which energy can be distributed. As an example, consider the standard entropies for methane (CH_4), ethane (C_2H_6), and propane (C_3H_8), whose values are 186.3, 229.2, and 270.3 J/K · mol, respectively. Also, *molecules with more complex structures have larger entropies than molecules with simpler structures.* The effect of molecular structure can also be seen when comparing atoms or molecules of similar molar mass: Gaseous argon, CO_2, and C_3H_8 have entropies of 154.9, 213.7, and 270.3 J/K · mol, respectively.

Tables of entropy values also show that *entropies of gases are larger than those for liquids, and entropies of liquids are larger than those for solids.* In a solid, the particles have fixed positions in the solid lattice. When a solid melts, these particles have more freedom to assume different positions, resulting in an increase in the number of microstates available and an increase in entropy. When a liquid evaporates, constraints due to forces between the particles nearly disappear, the volume increases greatly, and a large entropy increase occurs. For example, the standard entropies of $I_2(s)$, $Br_2(\ell)$, and $Cl_2(g)$ are 116.1, 152.2, and 223.1 J/K · mol, respectively.

Finally, as illustrated in Figure 18.8, *for a given substance, a large increase in entropy accompanies changes of state,* reflecting the relatively large energy transfer as heat required to carry out these processes (as well as the dispersion of energy over a larger number of available microstates). For example, the entropies of liquid and gaseous water are 69.95 and 188.84 J/K · mol, respectively.

PROBLEM SOLVING TIP 18.2

A List of Common Entropy-Favored Processes

The discussion to this point allows the listing of several general principles involving entropy changes:

- The entropy of a substance will increase in going from a solid to a liquid to a gas.
- The entropy of any substance increases as the temperature is raised. Energy must be added to a system to increase its temperature (that is, $q > 0$), so q_{rev}/T is necessarily positive.
- The entropy of a gas increases with an increase in volume. A larger volume provides a larger number of energy states over which to disperse energy.
- Reactions that increase the number of moles of gases in a system are accompanied by an increase in entropy.

EXAMPLE 18.1

Entropy Comparisons

Problem Which substance has the higher entropy under standard conditions at 25 °C? Explain your reasoning. Check your answer against data in Appendix L.

(a) NO_2(g) or N_2O_4(g)

(b) I_2(g) or I_2(s)

What Do You Know? Larger molecules of related substances have greater entropies than smaller molecules, and entropy decreases in the order gas > liquid > solid.

Strategy For each part, identify the difference between the two substances and relate this to the general rules for entropy given above.

Solution

(a) Both NO_2 and N_2O_4 are gases. N_2O_4 is a larger molecule than NO_2 and so is expected to have the higher standard entropy.

(b) For a given substance, gases have higher entropies than solids, so I_2(g) is expected to have the greater standard entropy.

Think about Your Answer $S°$ values in Appendix L confirm these predictions. At 25 °C, $S°$ for NO_2(g) is 240.04 J/K · mol, and $S°$ for N_2O_4(g) is 304.38 J/K · mol. $S°$ for I_2(g) is 260.69 J/K · mol; $S°$ for I_2(s) is 116.135 J/K · mol.

Check Your Understanding

Predict which substance in each pair has the higher entropy and explain your reasoning.

(a) O_2(g) or O_3(g)

(b) $SnCl_4(\ell)$ or $SnCl_4$(g)

Determining Entropy Changes in Physical and Chemical Processes

It is possible to use standard molar entropy values quantitatively to calculate the change in entropy that occurs in various processes under standard conditions. The standard entropy change for a reaction ($\Delta_r S°$) is the sum of the standard molar entropies of the products, each multiplied by its stoichiometric coefficient, minus the

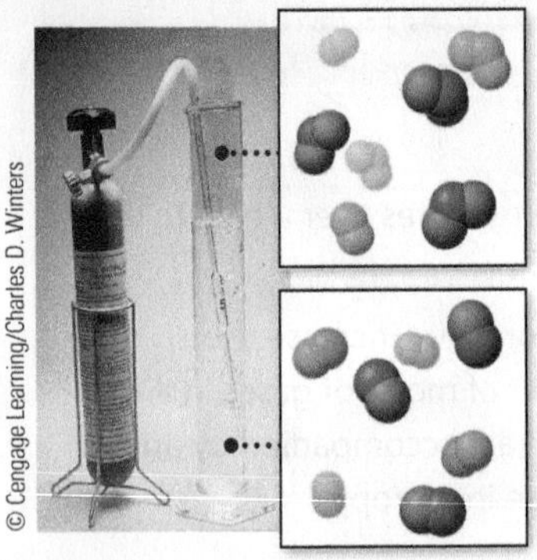

The reaction of NO with O_2. The entropy of the system decreases when two molecules of gas are produced from three molecules of gaseous reactants.

sum of the standard molar entropies of the reactants, each multiplied by its stoichiometric coefficient.

$$\Delta_r S° = \Sigma n S°(\text{products}) - \Sigma n S°(\text{reactants}) \quad \textbf{(18.3)}$$

This equation allows us to calculate entropy changes for a *system* in which reactants are completely converted to products, under standard conditions. To illustrate, let us calculate $\Delta_r S°$ for the oxidation of NO with O_2.

$$2\ NO(g) + O_2(g) \rightarrow 2\ NO_2(g)$$

$$\begin{aligned}\Delta_r S° &= (2\text{ mol }NO_2/\text{mol-rxn})\ S°[NO_2(g)] - \\ &\quad \{(2\text{ mol NO(g)/mol-rxn})\ S°[NO(g)] + (1\text{ mol }O_2/\text{mol-rxn})\ S°[O_2(g)]\} \\ &= (2\text{ mol }NO_2/\text{mol-rxn})(240.0\text{ J/K}\cdot\text{mol}) - \\ &\quad [(2\text{ mol NO(g)/mol-rxn})(210.8\text{ J/K}\cdot\text{mol}) + (1\text{ mol }O_2/\text{mol-rxn})(205.1\text{ J/K}\cdot\text{mol})] \\ &= -146.7\text{ J/K}\cdot\text{mol-rxn}\end{aligned}$$

The entropy of the system decreases, as is generally observed when some number of gaseous reactants has been converted to fewer molecules of gaseous products.

Strategy Map 18.2

PROBLEM

Calculate $\Delta_r S°$ for a reaction.

DATA/INFORMATION

- Balanced chemical equation
- $S°$ values (Appendix L)

STEP 1. Calculate $\Delta_r S°$ using Equation 18.3.

$\Delta_r S°$ for the reaction

EXAMPLE 18.2

Predicting and Calculating $\Delta_r S°$ for a Reaction

Problem Using standard molar entropies, calculate the standard entropy changes for the following processes.

(a) Evaporation of 1.00 mol of liquid ethanol to ethanol vapor:

$$C_2H_5OH(\ell) \rightarrow C_2H_5OH(g)$$

(b) Formation of ammonia from hydrogen and nitrogen based on the following equation:

$$N_2(g) + 3\ H_2(g) \rightarrow 2\ NH_3(g)$$

What Do You Know? For each part, you are given a balanced chemical equation and asked to determine the standard entropy change for the reaction ($\Delta_r S°$). Values of standard molar entropies for the substances can be found in Appendix L.

Strategy Entropy changes for each system can be calculated from values of standard entropies (Appendix L) using Equation 18.3.

Solution

(a) Evaporation of ethanol

$$\begin{aligned}\Delta_r S° &= \Sigma n S°(\text{products}) - \Sigma n S°(\text{reactants}) \\ &= (1\text{ mol }C_2H_5OH(g)/\text{mol-rxn})\ S°[C_2H_5OH(g)] - \\ &\quad (1\text{ mol }C_2H_5OH(\ell)/\text{mol-rxn})\ S°[C_2H_5OH(\ell)] \\ &= (1\text{ mol }C_2H_5OH(g)/\text{mol-rxn})(282.7\text{ J/K}\cdot\text{mol}) - \\ &\quad (1\text{ mol }C_2H_5OH(\ell)/\text{mol-rxn})(160.7\text{ J/K}\cdot\text{mol}) \\ &= +122.0\text{ J/K}\cdot\text{mol-rxn}\end{aligned}$$

(b) Formation of ammonia

$$\Delta_r S° = \Sigma nS°(\text{products}) - \Sigma nS°(\text{reactants})$$

$$= (2\text{ mol }NH_3(g)/\text{mol-rxn})\ S°[NH_3(g)] - \{(1\text{ mol }N_2(g)/\text{mol-rxn})\ S°[N_2(g)] + (3\text{ mol }H_2(g)/\text{mol-rxn})\ S°[H_2(g)]\}$$

$$= (2\text{ mol }NH_3(g)/\text{mol-rxn})(192.77\text{ J/K}\cdot\text{mol}) - [(1\text{ mol }N_2(g)/\text{mol-rxn})(191.56\text{ J/K}\cdot\text{mol}) + (3\text{ mol }H_2(g)/\text{mol-rxn})(130.7\text{ J/K}\cdot\text{mol})]$$

$$= -198.1\text{ J/K}\cdot\text{mol-rxn}$$

Think about Your Answer Predictions for the signs of these entropy changes can be made using the guidelines given in the text. In part (a), a large positive value for the entropy change is expected because the process converts ethanol from a liquid to a vapor. In part (b), a decrease in entropy is predicted because the number of moles of gases decreases from four to two.

Check Your Understanding

Calculate the standard entropy changes for the following processes using the entropy values in Appendix L. Are the signs of the calculated values of $\Delta_r S°$ in accord with predictions?

(a) Dissolving 1 mol of $NH_4Cl(s)$ in water: $NH_4Cl(s) \rightarrow NH_4Cl(aq)$

(b) Oxidation of ethanol: $C_2H_5OH(g) + 3\ O_2(g) \rightarrow 2\ CO_2(g) + 3\ H_2O(g)$

Amount of Substance and Thermodynamic Calculations
In the calculation here and in all others in this chapter, when we write, for example,

282.70 J/K · mol

for the standard entropy of ethanol at 298 K, we mean

282.70 J/K · mol $C_2H_5OH(\ell)$

The identifying formula has been left off for the sake of simplicity.

REVIEW & CHECK FOR SECTION 18-4

1. Without looking up their standard entropies in reference tables, identify which of the following lists the materials in order of increasing entropy.

   (a) $H_2O(\ell) < NaCl(s) < NH_3(g)$
   (b) $H_2O(\ell) < NH_3(g) < NaCl(s)$
   (c) $NaCl(s) < H_2O(\ell) < NH_3(g)$
   (d) $NH_3(g) < H_2O(\ell) < NaCl(s)$

2. Without doing any calculations, predict the sign of $\Delta_r S°$ for the following reaction:

   $$Zn(s) + 2\ HCl(aq) \rightarrow ZnCl_2(aq) + H_2(g)$$

   (a) $\Delta_r S° < 0$ (b) $\Delta_r S° = 0$ (c) $\Delta_r S° > 0$

3. Calculate $\Delta_r S°$ for the following reaction at 25 °C.

   $$2\ H_2(g) + O_2(g) \rightarrow 2\ H_2O(\ell)$$

   (a) −326.6 J/K · mol-rxn
   (b) −139.9 J/K · mol-rxn
   (c) 139.9 J/K · mol-rxn
   (d) 326.6 J/K · mol-rxn

18-5 Entropy Changes and Spontaneity

Learning Objectives: LO 5.13

As illustrated by Example 18.2, the standard entropy change *for the system* in a physical or chemical change can be either positive (evaporation of ethanol) or negative (synthesis of ammonia from nitrogen and hydrogen). How does this information contribute to determining the spontaneity of the process?

As discussed previously (Section 18-2), spontaneity is determined by the *second law of thermodynamics,* which states that *a spontaneous process is one that results in an increase of entropy in the universe.* The universe has two parts: the system and its surroundings (◀ Section 5-1), and so the entropy change for the universe is the sum of the entropy changes for the system and the surroundings. Under standard conditions, the entropy change for the universe, $\Delta S°$(universe) is

$$\Delta S°(\text{universe}) = \Delta S°(\text{system}) + \Delta S°(\text{surroundings}) \quad \textbf{(18.4)}$$

The calculation in Example 18.2 gave us the entropy change under standard conditions for a system, only half of the information needed. We will also have to determine how the change being studied affects the entropy of the surroundings so that we can find the entropy change for the universe.

The value of $\Delta S°$(universe) calculated from Equation 18.4 is the entropy change when reactants are converted *completely* to products, with all species at standard conditions. *A process is spontaneous under standard conditions if* $\Delta S°$*(universe) is greater than zero.* As an example of the determination of reaction spontaneity, let us calculate $\Delta S°$(universe) for the reaction currently used to manufacture methanol, CH_3OH.

Using $\Delta S°$(universe) For a process that is spontaneous under standard conditions:

$$\Delta S°(\text{universe}) > 0$$

For a process at equilibrium under standard conditions:

$$\Delta S°(\text{universe}) = 0$$

For a process that is not spontaneous under standard conditions:

$$\Delta S°(\text{universe}) < 0$$

Note that these conclusions refer to the *complete* conversion of reactants to products.

$$CO(g) + 2\ H_2(g) \rightarrow CH_3OH(\ell)$$

If $\Delta S°$(universe) is positive, the conversion of 1 mol of CO(g) and 2 mol of H_2(g) to 1 mol of $CH_3OH(\ell)$ will be spontaneous under standard conditions.

Calculating $\Delta S°$(system) To calculate $\Delta S°$(system), we start by defining the system to include the reactants and products. This means that $\Delta S°$(system) corresponds to the entropy change for the reaction, $\Delta_r S°$. Calculation of this entropy change follows the procedure given in Example 18.2.

$$\begin{aligned}
\Delta S°(\text{system}) = \Delta_r S° &= \Sigma n S°(\text{products}) - \Sigma n S°(\text{reactants}) \\
&= (1\ \text{mol CH}_3\text{OH}(\ell)/\text{mol-rxn})\ S°[\text{CH}_3\text{OH}(\ell)] - \\
&\quad \{(1\ \text{mol CO(g)/mol-rxn})\ S°[\text{CO(g)}] + (2\ \text{mol H}_2\text{(g)/mol-rxn})\ S°[\text{H}_2\text{(g)}]\} \\
&= (1\ \text{mol CH}_3\text{OH}(\ell)/\text{mol-rxn})(127.2\ \text{J/K}\cdot\text{mol}) - \\
&\quad [(1\ \text{mol CO(g)/mol-rxn})(197.7\ \text{J/K}\cdot\text{mol}) + \\
&\quad (2\ \text{mol H}_2\text{(g)/mol-rxn})(130.7\ \text{J/K}\cdot\text{mol})] \\
&= -331.9\ \text{J/K}\cdot\text{mol-rxn}
\end{aligned}$$

A decrease in entropy for the system is expected because three moles of gaseous reactants are converted to one mole of a liquid product.

Calculating $\Delta S°$(surroundings) We now need to calculate the entropy change for the surroundings. Recall from Equation 18.1 that for a reversible change, ΔS is equal to q_{rev}/T. Under constant pressure conditions and assuming a reversible process, the entropy change in the surroundings results from the fact that the enthalpy change for the reaction ($q_{rev} = \Delta_r H$) affects the surroundings. That is, the energy associated with an exothermic chemical reaction is dispersed into the surroundings. Recognizing that $\Delta H°$(surroundings) $= -\Delta_r H°$(system), the entropy change for the surroundings can be calculated by the equation

$$\Delta S°(\text{surroundings}) = \Delta H°(\text{surroundings})/T = -\Delta_r H°(\text{system})/T$$

For the synthesis of methanol by the reaction given, the enthalpy change can be calculated from enthalpy of formation data using Equation 5.6.

$$\begin{aligned}
\Delta H°(\text{system}) &= \Sigma n \Delta_f H°(\text{products}) - \Sigma n \Delta_f H°(\text{reactants}) \\
&= (1\ \text{mol CH}_3\text{OH}(\ell)/\text{mol-rxn})\ \Delta_f H°[\text{CH}_3\text{OH}(\ell)] - \\
&\quad \{(1\ \text{mol CO(g)/mol-rxn})\ \Delta_f H°[\text{CO(g)}] + \\
&\quad (2\ \text{mol H}_2\text{(g)/mol-rxn})\ \Delta_f H°[\text{H}_2\text{(g)}]\} \\
&= (1\ \text{mol CH}_3\text{OH}(\ell)/\text{mol-rxn})(-238.4\ \text{kJ/mol}) - \\
&\quad [(1\ \text{mol CO(g)/mol-rxn})(-110.5\ \text{kJ/mol}) + \\
&\quad (2\ \text{mol H}_2\text{(g)/mol-rxn})(0\ \text{kJ/ mol})] \\
&= -127.9\ \text{kJ/mol-rxn}
\end{aligned}$$

Assuming that the process is reversible and occurs at a constant temperature and pressure, the entropy change for the surroundings in the methanol synthesis is +429.2 J/K · mol-rxn, calculated as follows.

$$\Delta S°(\text{surroundings}) = -\Delta_r H°(\text{system})/T$$
$$= -[(-127.9 \text{ kJ/mol-rxn})/298 \text{ K})](1000 \text{ J/kJ})$$
$$= +429.2 \text{ J/K} \cdot \text{mol-rxn}$$

Calculating ΔS°(universe), the Entropy Change for the System and Surroundings
The pieces are now in place to calculate the entropy change in the universe. For the formation of $CH_3OH(\ell)$ from CO(g) and $H_2(g)$, ΔS°(universe) is

$$\Delta S°(\text{universe}) = \Delta S°(\text{system}) + \Delta S°(\text{surroundings})$$
$$= -331.9 \text{ J/K} \cdot \text{mol-rxn} + 429.2 \text{ J/K} \cdot \text{mol-rxn}$$
$$= +97.3 \text{ J/K} \cdot \text{mol-rxn}$$

The positive value indicates an increase in the entropy of the universe. It follows from the second law of thermodynamics that this reaction is spontaneous under standard conditions.

EXAMPLE 18.3

Determining Whether a Process Is Spontaneous

Problem Calculate ΔS°(universe) for the process of dissolving NaCl in water at 298 K.

What Do You Know? The process occurring is NaCl(s) → NaCl(aq). ΔS°(universe) is equal to the sum of ΔS°(system) and ΔS°(surroundings). Values of S° and $\Delta_f H°$ for NaCl(s) and NaCl(aq) are given in Appendix L.

Strategy The entropy change for the system, ΔS°(system), can be calculated from values of S° for the two species using Equation 18.3. $\Delta_r H°$ can be calculated from values of $\Delta_f H°$ for the two species using Equation 5.6. ΔS°(surroundings) is determined by dividing $-\Delta_r H°$ for the process by the Kelvin temperature. The sum of ΔS°(system) and ΔS°(surroundings) is ΔS°(universe). If this value is positive, then the process is spontaneous under standard conditions.

Solution

Calculate ΔS°(system)

$$\Delta S°(\text{system}) = \Sigma nS°(\text{products}) - \Sigma nS°(\text{reactants})$$
$$= (1 \text{ mol NaCl(aq)/mol-rxn})\ S°[\text{NaCl(aq)}] - (1 \text{ mol NaCl(s)/mol-rxn})\ S°[\text{NaCl(s)}]$$
$$= (1 \text{ mol NaCl(aq)/mol-rxn})(115.5 \text{ J/K} \cdot \text{mol}) - (1 \text{ mol NaCl(s)/mol-rxn})(72.11 \text{ J/K} \cdot \text{mol})$$
$$= +43.4 \text{ J/K} \cdot \text{mol-rxn}$$

Calculate ΔS°(surroundings)

$$\Delta_r H°(\text{system}) = \Sigma n\Delta_f H°(\text{products}) - \Sigma n\Delta_f H°(\text{reactants})$$
$$= (1 \text{ mol NaCl(aq)/mol-rxn})\ \Delta_f H°[\text{NaCl(aq)}] - (1 \text{ mol NaCl(s)/mol-rxn})\ \Delta_f H°[\text{NaCl(s)}]$$
$$= (1 \text{ mol NaCl(aq)/mol-rxn})(-407.27 \text{ kJ/mol}) - (1 \text{ mol NaCl(s)/mol-rxn})(-411.12 \text{ kJ/mol})$$
$$= +3.85 \text{ kJ/mol-rxn}$$

The entropy change of the surroundings is determined by dividing $-\Delta_r H°$(system) by the Kelvin temperature.

$$\Delta S°(\text{surroundings}) = -\Delta_r H°(\text{system})/T$$
$$= (-3.85 \text{ kJ/mol-rxn}/298 \text{ K})(1000 \text{ J}/1 \text{ kJ})$$
$$= -12.9 \text{ J/K} \cdot \text{mol-rxn}$$

Calculate $\Delta S°$(universe)

The overall entropy change—the change of entropy in the universe—is the sum of the values for the system and the surroundings.

$$\Delta S°(\text{universe}) = \Delta S°(\text{system}) + \Delta S°(\text{surroundings})$$
$$= (+43.4 \text{ J/K} \cdot \text{mol-rxn}) + (-12.9 \text{ J/K} \cdot \text{mol-rxn})$$
$$= +30.5 \text{ J/K} \cdot \text{mol-rxn}$$

Think about Your Answer The sum of the two entropy quantities is positive, indicating that the entropy in the universe increases; thus, the process is spontaneous under standard conditions. Notice that the spontaneity of the process results from $\Delta S°$(system) and not from $\Delta S°$(surroundings).

Check Your Understanding

Is the reaction of hydrogen and chlorine to give hydrogen chloride gas predicted to be spontaneous under standard conditions (at 298 K)?

$$H_2(g) + Cl_2(g) \rightarrow 2\ HCl(g)$$

Predict the spontaneity of the reaction based on $\Delta_r H°$ and $\Delta_r S°$, and then calculate $\Delta S°$(universe) to verify your prediction.

In Summary: Spontaneous or Not?

$\Delta S°$(universe), Spontaneity, and Standard Conditions It is important to reiterate that $\Delta H°$ and $\Delta S°$ values for a reaction are for the *complete* conversion of reactants to products under standard conditions. If $\Delta S°$(universe) is > 0, the reaction as written is spontaneous *under standard conditions*. However, one can calculate values for ΔS(universe) (without the superscript zero) for *nonstandard* conditions. If ΔS(universe) is > 0, the reaction is spontaneous under those conditions.

In the preceding examples, predictions about the spontaneity of a process under standard conditions were made using values of $\Delta S°$(system) and $\Delta H°$(system) calculated from tables of thermodynamic data. It will be useful to look at all possibilities that result from the interplay of these two quantities. There are four possible outcomes when these two quantities are paired (Table 18.1). In two, $\Delta H°$(system) and

Table 18.1 Predicting Whether a Reaction Will Be Spontaneous Under Standard Conditions

Reaction Type	$\Delta H°$(system)	$\Delta S°$(system)	Spontaneous Process? (Standard Conditions)
1	Exothermic, < 0	Positive, > 0	Spontaneous at all temperatures. $\Delta S°$(universe) > 0.
2	Exothermic, < 0	Negative, < 0	Depends on relative magnitudes of $\Delta H°$ and $\Delta S°$. Spontaneous at lower temperatures.
3	Endothermic, > 0	Positive, > 0	Depends on relative magnitudes of $\Delta H°$ and $\Delta S°$. Spontaneous at higher temperatures.
4	Endothermic, > 0	Negative, < 0	Not spontaneous at any temperature. $\Delta S°$(universe) < 0.

$\Delta S°$(system) work in concert (Types 1 and 4 in Table 18.1). In the other two, the two quantities are opposed (Types 2 and 3).

Processes in which both the standard enthalpy and entropy changes favor energy dispersal (Type 1) are always spontaneous under standard conditions. Processes disfavored by both their standard enthalpy and entropy changes in the system (Type 4) can *never* be spontaneous under standard conditions. Let us consider examples that illustrate each situation.

Combustion reactions are always exothermic and often produce a larger number of gaseous product molecules from a few reactant molecules. They are Type 1 reactions. The equation for the combustion of butane is an example.

$$2\ C_4H_{10}(g) + 13\ O_2(g) \rightarrow 8\ CO_2(g) + 10\ H_2O(g)$$

For this reaction, $\Delta_r H° = -5315.1$ kJ/mol-rxn, and $\Delta_r S° = 312.4$ J/K · mol-rxn. Both contribute to this reaction being spontaneous under standard conditions.

Hydrazine, N_2H_4, is used as a high-energy rocket fuel. Synthesis of N_2H_4 from gaseous N_2 and H_2 would be attractive because these reactants are inexpensive.

$$N_2(g) + 2\ H_2(g) \rightarrow N_2H_4(\ell)$$

However, this reaction fits into the Type 4 category. The reaction is endothermic ($\Delta_r H° = +50.63$ kJ/mol-rxn), and the entropy change is negative ($\Delta_r S° = -331.4$ J/K · mol-rxn) (1 mol of liquid is produced from 3 mol of gases), so the reaction is not spontaneous under standard conditions, and complete conversion of reactants to products will not occur without outside intervention.

In the two other possible outcomes, entropy and enthalpy changes oppose each other. A process could be favored by the enthalpy change but disfavored by the entropy change (Type 2), or vice versa (Type 3). In either instance, whether a process is spontaneous depends on which factor is more important.

Temperature also influences the value of $\Delta S°$(universe). Because the enthalpy change for the surroundings is divided by the temperature to obtain $\Delta S°$(surroundings), the numerical value of $\Delta S°$(surroundings) will be smaller (either less positive or less negative) at higher temperatures. In contrast, $\Delta S°$(system) and $\Delta H°$(system) do not vary much with temperature. Thus, the effect of $\Delta S°$(surroundings) relative to $\Delta S°$(system) is diminished at higher temperature. Stated another way, at higher temperature, the enthalpy change becomes a less important factor in determining the overall entropy change. Consider the two cases where $\Delta H°$(system) and $\Delta S°$(system) are in opposition (Table 18.1):

- Type 2: Exothermic processes with $\Delta S°(\text{system}) < 0$. Such processes become less favorable with an increase in temperature.
- Type 3: Endothermic processes with $\Delta S°(\text{system}) > 0$. These processes become more favorable as the temperature increases.

The effect of temperature is illustrated by two examples. The first is the reaction of N_2 and H_2 to form NH_3. The reaction is exothermic, and thus it is favored by energy dispersal to the surroundings. The entropy change for the system is unfavorable, however, because the reaction, $N_2(g) + 3\ H_2(g) \rightarrow 2\ NH_3(g)$, converts four moles of gaseous reactants to two moles of gaseous products. The favorable enthalpy effect [$\Delta_r S°(\text{surroundings}) = -\Delta_r H°(\text{system})/T$] becomes less important at higher temperatures. It is therefore reasonable to expect that the reaction will not be spontaneous if the temperature is high enough.

The second example considers the thermal decomposition of NH_4Cl (Figure 18.9). At room temperature, NH_4Cl is a stable, white, crystalline salt. When heated strongly, it decomposes to $NH_3(g)$ and $HCl(g)$. The reaction is endothermic (enthalpy-disfavored) but entropy-favored because of the formation of two moles of gas from one mole of a solid reactant. The reaction is increasingly favored at higher temperatures.

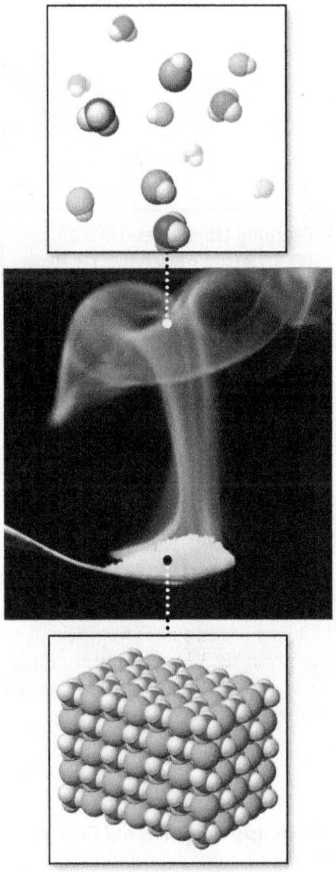

FIGURE 18.9 Thermal decomposition of $NH_4Cl(s)$. White, solid ammonium chloride, $NH_4Cl(s)$, is heated in a spoon. At high temperatures, decomposition to form $NH_3(g)$ and $HCl(g)$ is spontaneous. At lower temperatures, the reverse reaction, forming $NH_4Cl(s)$, is spontaneous. As gaseous $HCl(g)$ and $NH_3(g)$ cool, they recombine to form solid NH_4Cl, the white "smoke" seen in this photo.

REVIEW & CHECK FOR SECTION 18-5

1. Calculate $\Delta_r S°$ for the following reaction at 25 °C:

$$N_2(g) + 2\ O_2(g) \rightarrow 2\ NO_2(g)$$

(a) −480.1 J/K · mol-rxn
(b) −121.6 J/K · mol-rxn
(c) 121.6 J/K · mol-rxn
(d) 480.1 J/K · mol-rxn

2. Calculate $\Delta S°$(universe) for the following reaction at 25.0 °C:

$$C(graphite) + O_2(g) \rightarrow CO_2(g)$$

(a) −1317 J/K · mol-rxn
(b) 3.1 J/K · mol-rxn
(c) 4.4 J/K · mol-rxn
(d) 1320 J/K · mol-rxn

3. If $\Delta_r H° = +467.9$ kJ/mol-rxn and $\Delta_r S° = +560.7$ J/K · mol-rxn for the following reaction

$$2\ Fe_2O_3(s) + 3\ C(graphite) \rightarrow 4\ Fe(s) + 3\ CO_2(g)$$

then, under standard conditions, this reaction will be spontaneous

(a) at all temperatures
(b) at higher temperatures
(c) at lower temperatures
(d) at no temperature

Learning Objectives: LO 5.13, LO 5.18 (see Appendix O-3 "The Interplay of Kinetics and Thermodynamics"), LO 6.25

18-6 Gibbs Free Energy

The method used so far to determine whether a process is spontaneous required evaluation of two quantities, $\Delta S°$(system) and $\Delta S°$(surroundings). Wouldn't it be convenient to have a single thermodynamic function that serves the same purpose? A function associated with the system only—one that does not require assessment of the surroundings—would be even better. Such a function exists. It is called the **Gibbs free energy**, with the name honoring J. Willard Gibbs (1839–1903). Gibbs free energy, *G*, often referred to simply as "free energy," is defined mathematically as

$$G = H - TS$$

© INTERFOTO/Alamy

J. Willard Gibbs (1839–1903)
Gibbs received a Ph.D. from Yale University in 1863. His was the first Ph.D. in science awarded from an American university.

where *H* is enthalpy, *T* is the Kelvin temperature, and *S* is entropy. In this equation, *G*, *H*, and *S* all refer to the system. Because enthalpy and entropy are state functions (◀ Section 5-4), free energy is also a state function.

Every substance possesses free energy, but the actual quantity is seldom known. Instead, just as with enthalpy (*H*) and internal energy (*U*), we are concerned with *changes* in free energy, ΔG, that occur in chemical and physical processes.

Let us first see how to use free energy as a way to determine whether a reaction is spontaneous. We can then ask further questions about the meaning of the term "free energy" and its use in deciding whether a reaction is product- or reactant-favored.

Enthalpy and Internal Energy
In the AP curriculum, internal energy and enthalpy are treated as equivalent.

The Change in the Gibbs Free Energy, ΔG

Recall the equation defining the entropy change for the universe:

$$\Delta S(\text{universe}) = \Delta S(\text{surroundings}) + \Delta S(\text{system})$$

The entropy change of the surroundings equals the negative of the change in enthalpy of the system divided by *T*. Thus,

$$\Delta S(\text{universe}) = -\Delta H(\text{system})/T + \Delta S(\text{system})$$

Multiplying through this equation by $-T$, gives the equation

$$-T\Delta S(\text{universe}) = \Delta H(\text{system}) - T\Delta S(\text{system})$$

Gibbs defined the free energy function so that ΔG(system) $= -T\Delta S$(universe). Thus, the general expression relating changes in free energy to the enthalpy and entropy changes in the system is the following:

$$\Delta G = \Delta H - T\Delta S$$

Under standard conditions, we can rewrite this, the Gibbs free energy equation, as

$$\Delta G° = \Delta H° - T\Delta S° \quad (18.5)$$

Exergonic and Endergonic When the amount of energy transferred as heat, ΔH, is of interest, we use the terms "exothermic" and "endothermic." When we are referring to values of ΔG, we sometimes refer to reactions as being exergonic ($\Delta G < 0$) or endergonic ($\Delta G > 0$).

Gibbs Free Energy, Spontaneity, and Chemical Equilibrium

Because ΔG is related directly to ΔS(universe), the Gibbs free energy can be used as a criterion of spontaneity for physical and chemical changes. To better understand the Gibbs function, let us examine the diagrams in Figure 18.10, diagrams that will form the basis for our understanding of free energy and its relation to reaction spontaneity and the criterion of equilibrium.

In Figure 18.10 the free energy of pure, unmixed reactants is indicated on the left, and the free energy of the pure, unmixed products is indicated on the right. The extent of reaction, plotted on the x-axis, goes from zero to one. *$\Delta G°$ is the change in free energy accompanying the complete conversion of reactants into products under standard conditions.* Mathematically, it is the numerical difference in free energy between the products and the reactants under standard conditions ($\Delta G° = G°_{products} - G°_{reactants}$). It has units of kJ.

A closely related parameter, $\Delta_r G°$, is the *change of $G°$ as a function of the reaction composition on going from reactants to products.* It has units of kJ/mol-rxn. As you shall see below, $\Delta_r G°$ is related to the equilibrium constant, K.

As a chemical reaction (the curves in Figure 18.10) begins to occur, the reactants mix and begin producing products. The free energy of the system is no longer given by $G°$ but is instead G. At any one point along the way from reactants to products the difference between the free energy of the system at that point and another is ΔG.

Free Energy, Spontaneity, and Equilibrium $\Delta_r G°$ is an intensive quantity that describes how $G°$ changes per mole of reaction. For more on these relationships, see J. Quilez, *Journal of Chemical Education,* Vol. 89, pages 87–93, 2012.

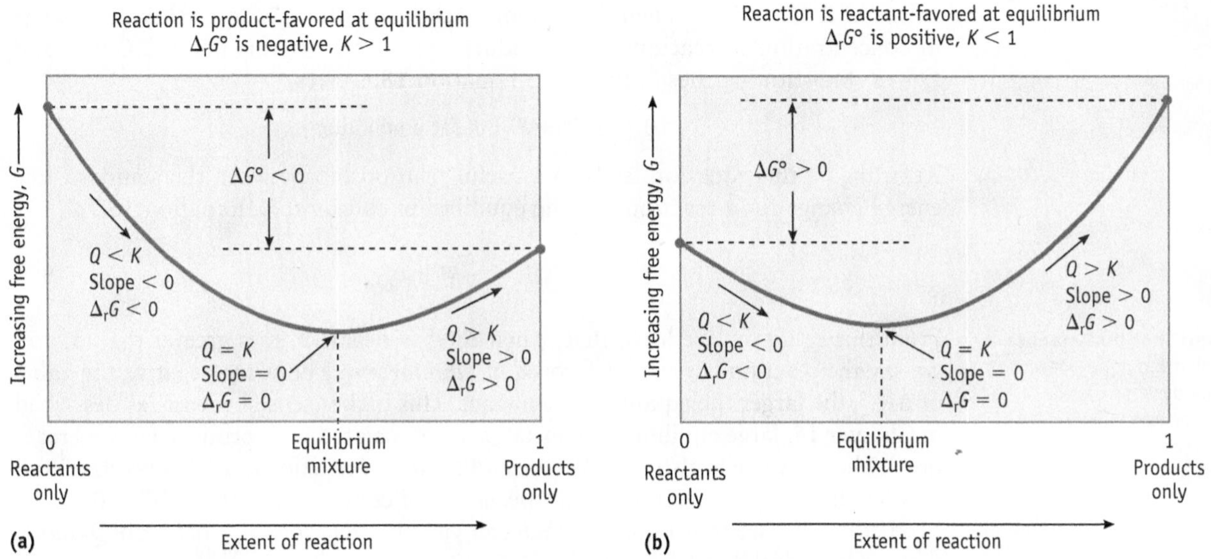

FIGURE 18.10 **Free energy changes in the course of a reaction.** The difference in free energy between the pure reactants in their standard states and the pure products in their standard states is $\Delta G°$. Here, Q is the reaction quotient, and K is the equilibrium constant.

In both cases in Figure 18.10, the free energy initially declines as reactants begin to form products; it reaches a minimum at equilibrium and then increases again as we move from the equilibrium position to pure products. *The free energy at equilibrium, where there is a mixture of reactants and products, is always lower than the free energy of the pure reactants and of the pure products. A reaction proceeds spontaneously toward the minimum in free energy, which corresponds to equilibrium.*

Now let us consider what happens to the instantaneous slope of the curve in Figure 18.10 as the reaction proceeds spontaneously toward equilibrium. Initially, this slope is negative. That is, the *change* in G for the reaction, $\Delta_r G$, has a negative value. *For all spontaneous reactions* $\Delta_r G < 0$.

Eventually the free energy reaches a minimum. At this point, the instantaneous slope of the graph is zero and $\Delta_r G = 0$; the reaction has reached equilibrium.

If we move past the equilibrium point, the instantaneous slope is positive ($\Delta_r G > 0$). Proceeding further toward products is *not* spontaneous. In fact, the reverse reaction will occur spontaneously (because $\Delta_r G$ will be negative in the reverse direction), and the reaction will once again proceed toward equilibrium.

An important observation in Figure 18.10a is that the equilibrium position occurs closer to the product side than to the reactant side. This is a product-favored reaction at equilibrium, and there is a connection between this observation and the quantity $\Delta_r G°$. That is, *a reaction with* $\Delta_r G° < 0$ *is product-favored at equilibrium.*

In Figure 18.10b, we find the opposite. The reaction is reactant-favored at equilibrium. A reaction with $\Delta_r G° > 0$ is reactant-favored at equilibrium.

We have introduced terms for the extent of change in free energy under standard conditions ($\Delta_r G°$) or nonstandard conditions ($\Delta_r G$). It turns out there is a very useful relationship between them (Equation 18.6).

$$\Delta_r G = \Delta_r G° + RT \ln Q \quad (18.6)$$

where R is the universal gas constant, T is the temperature in kelvins, and Q is the reaction quotient (◀ Section 15-2). For a general reaction, $a\text{A} + b\text{B} \rightarrow c\text{C} + d\text{D}$:

$$Q = \frac{[C]^c[D]^d}{[A]^a[B]^b}$$

Equation 18.6 informs us that, at a given temperature, $\Delta_r G$ is determined by the values of $\Delta_r G°$ and Q. When the system reaches equilibrium, no further net change in concentration of reactants and products will occur; at this point $\Delta_r G = 0$ and $Q = K$. Substituting these values into Equation 18.6 gives

$$0 = \Delta_r G° + RT \ln K \text{ (at equilibrium)}$$

Rearranging this equation leads to a useful relationship between the standard free energy change for a reaction and the equilibrium constant, K, Equation 18.7:

$$\Delta_r G° = -RT \ln K \quad (18.7)$$

Kinetics and Thermodynamics For information about the kinetic versus thermodynamic control of reactions, see Appendix O-3 "The Interplay of Kinetics and Thermodynamics."

From this equation, we learn that, when $\Delta_r G°$ is negative, K is greater than 1, and we say the reaction is *product-favored at equilibrium*. The more negative the value of $\Delta_r G°$, the larger the equilibrium constant. This makes sense because, as described in Chapter 15, large equilibrium constants are associated with product-favored reactions. The converse is also true: For *reactant-favored* reactions, $\Delta_r G°$ is positive, and K is less than 1. Finally, if $K = 1$ (a special set of conditions), then $\Delta_r G° = 0$.

Let us now see that Equation 18.6 can yield the relationships between Q and K that we introduced in Chapter 15.

$$\Delta_r G = \Delta_r G° + RT \ln Q$$

Substituting $-RT\ln K$ for $\Delta_r G°$ (Equation 18.7) gives

$$\Delta_r G = -RT \ln K + RT \ln Q$$

This equation can be rearranged as follows:

$$\Delta_r G = RT (\ln Q - \ln K)$$

$$\Delta_r G = RT \ln (Q/K)$$

This means that for a spontaneous reaction where $\Delta_r G$ is negative, Q must be less than K ($Q < K$), just as has been stated earlier. A similar analysis shows that if $\Delta_r G$ is positive, then $Q > K$.

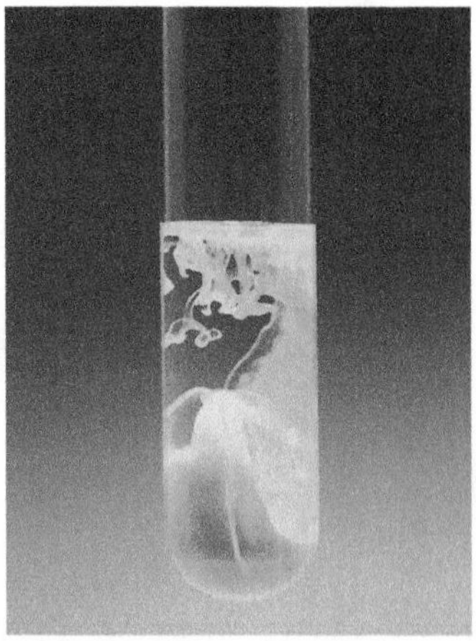

© Cengage Learning/Charles D. Winters

A reactant-favored process. If a sample of yellow lead(II) iodide is placed in pure water, a small amount of the compound will dissolve spontaneously ($\Delta_r G < 0$ and $Q < K$) until equilibrium is reached. Because PbI_2 is quite insoluble ($K_{sp} = 9.8 \times 10^{-9}$), however, the process of dissolving the compound is reactant-favored at equilibrium. We may conclude, therefore, that the value of $\Delta_r G°$ is positive.

A Summary: Gibbs Free Energy ($\Delta_r G$ and $\Delta_r G°$), the Reaction Quotient (Q) and Equilibrium Constant (K), and Reaction Favorability

Let us summarize the relationships among $\Delta_r G°$, $\Delta_r G$, Q, and K.

- In Figure 18.10, you see that free energy decreases to a minimum as a system approaches equilibrium. The free energy of the mixture of reactants and products at equilibrium is always lower than the free energy of the pure reactants or of the pure products.
- When $\Delta_r G < 0$, the reaction is proceeding spontaneously toward equilibrium and $Q < K$.
- When $\Delta_r G > 0$, the reaction is not spontaneous and $Q > K$. It will be spontaneous in the reverse direction.
- When $\Delta_r G = 0$, the reaction is at equilibrium; $Q = K$.
- A reaction for which $\Delta_r G° < 0$ will proceed to an equilibrium position at which point the products will dominate in the reaction mixture because $K > 1$. That is, the reaction is *product-favored* at equilibrium.
- A reaction for which $\Delta_r G° > 0$ will proceed to an equilibrium position at which point the reactants will dominate in the equilibrium mixture because $K < 1$. That is, the reaction is *reactant-favored* at equilibrium.
- For the special condition where a reaction has $\Delta_r G° = 0$, the reaction is at equilibrium at standard conditions, with $K = 1$.

What Is "Free" Energy?

The term *free energy* was not arbitrarily chosen. In any given process, the free energy represents the maximum energy available to do useful work (mathematically, $\Delta G = w_{max}$). In this context, the word *free* means "available."

To illustrate the reasoning behind this relationship, consider a reaction carried out under standard conditions and in which energy is evolved as heat ($\Delta_r H° < 0$) and entropy decreases ($\Delta_r S° < 0$).

$$2\ H_2(g) + O_2(g) \rightarrow 2\ H_2O(g)$$

$$\Delta_r H° = -483.6 \text{ kJ/mol-rxn and } \Delta_r S° = -88.8 \text{ J/K} \cdot \text{mol-rxn}$$

$$\Delta_r G° = -483.6 \text{ kJ/mol-rxn} - (298 \text{ K})(-0.0888 \text{ kJ/mol-rxn}) = -457.2 \text{ kJ/mol-rxn}$$

At first glance, it might seem reasonable that all the energy released as heat (−483.6 kJ/mol-rxn) would be available. This energy could be transferred to the surroundings and would thus be available to do work. This is not the case, however. A negative entropy change in this reaction means that energy is less dispersed in the products than in the reactants. A portion of the energy released from the reaction must be used to reverse energy dispersal in the system; that is, to concentrate energy in the product. The energy left over is "free," or available to perform work. Here, the free energy change amounts to −457.2 kJ/mol-rxn.

REVIEW & CHECK FOR SECTION 18-6

1. For a reaction to be spontaneous, $\Delta_r G$ will be ________ than zero and Q will be ________ than K.

   (a) greater, greater (b) greater, less (c) less, greater (d) less, less

2. A reaction for which $\Delta_r G° < 0$ is

   (a) product-favored at equilibrium (b) reactant-favored at equilibrium

Learning Objectives: LO 5.14, LO 5.15

18-7 Calculating and Using Free Energy

Standard Free Energy of Formation

The standard free energy of formation of a compound, $\Delta_f G°$, is the free energy change that occurs to form one mole of the compound from the component elements, with products and reactants in their standard states. By defining $\Delta_f G°$ in this way, *the free energy of formation of an element in its standard state is zero.*

Just as the standard enthalpy or entropy change for a reaction can be calculated using values of $\Delta_f H°$ (Equation 5.6) or $S°$ (Equation 18.3), the standard free energy change for a reaction can be calculated from values of $\Delta_f G°$ using a similar equation, where n represents the stoichiometric coefficient of the material in the balanced chemical equation under consideration:

$$\Delta_r G° = \Sigma n\Delta_f G°(\text{products}) - \Sigma n\Delta_f G°(\text{reactants}) \quad (18.8)$$

Calculating $\Delta_r G°$, the Free Energy Change for a Reaction Under Standard Conditions

The free energy change for a reaction under standard conditions can be calculated from thermodynamic data in two ways, either from standard enthalpy and entropy changes using values of $\Delta_f H°$ and $S°$ (as we did on the previous page for the formation of H_2O) or directly from values of $\Delta_f G°$ found in tables. These calculations are illustrated in the following two examples.

EXAMPLE 18.4

Calculating $\Delta_r G°$ from $\Delta_r H°$ and $\Delta_r S°$

Problem Calculate the standard free energy change, $\Delta_r G°$, for the formation of methane from carbon and hydrogen at 298 K, using tabulated values of $\Delta_f H°$ and $S°$. Is the reaction product-favored or reactant-favored at equilibrium?

$$\text{C(graphite)} + 2\ H_2(g) \rightarrow CH_4(g)$$

What Do You Know? You are given a balanced chemical equation. Standard molar enthalpies of formation and standard molar entropies can be found in Appendix L.

Strategy The values of $\Delta_f H°$ *and* $S°$ are first combined to find $\Delta_r H°$ *and* $\Delta_r S°$. With these values known, $\Delta_r G°$ can be calculated using Equation 18.5. (Remember that $S°$ values are given in units of J/K · mol, whereas $\Delta_f H°$ values are given in units of kJ/mol.)

Solution

	C(graphite)	+	$2\ H_2(g)$	→	$CH_4(g)$
$\Delta_f H°$ (kJ/mol)	0		0		−74.9
$S°$ (J/K·mol)	+5.6		+130.7		+186.3

From these values, we can find both $\Delta_r H°$ and $\Delta_r S°$ for the reaction:

$$\Delta_r H° = \Sigma n \Delta_f H°(\text{products}) - \Sigma n \Delta_f H°(\text{reactants})$$

$$= (1 \text{ mol } CH_4(g)/\text{mol-rxn})\ \Delta_f H°[CH_4(g)] - \{(1 \text{ mol C(graphite)/mol-rxn})\ \Delta_f H°[\text{C(graphite)}] + (2 \text{ mol } H_2(g)/\text{mol-rxn})\ \Delta_f H°[H_2(g)]\}$$

$$= (1 \text{ mol } CH_4(g)/\text{mol-rxn})(-74.9 \text{ kJ/mol}) - [(1 \text{ mol C(graphite)/mol-rxn})(0 \text{ kJ/mol}) + (2 \text{ mol } H_2(g)/\text{mol-rxn})(0 \text{ kJ/mol})]$$

$$= -74.9 \text{ kJ/mol-rxn}$$

$$\Delta_r S° = \Sigma n S°(\text{products}) - \Sigma n S°(\text{reactants})$$

$$= (1 \text{ mol } CH_4(g)/\text{mol-rxn})\ S°[CH_4(g)] - \{(1 \text{ mol C(graphite)/mol-rxn})\ S°[\text{C(graphite)}] + (2 \text{ mol } H_2(g)/\text{mol-rxn})\ S°[H_2(g)]\}$$

$$= (1 \text{ mol } CH_4(g)/\text{mol-rxn})(186.3 \text{ J/K} \cdot \text{mol}) - [1 \text{ mol C(graphite)/mol-rxn}](5.6 \text{ J/K} \cdot \text{mol}) + (2 \text{ mol } H_2(g)/\text{mol-rxn})(130.7 \text{ J/K} \cdot \text{mol})]$$

$$= -80.7 \text{ J/K} \cdot \text{mol-rxn}$$

Combining the values of $\Delta_r H°$ and $\Delta_r S°$ using Equation 18.5 gives $\Delta_r G°$.

$$\Delta_r G° = \Delta_r H° - T\Delta_r S°$$

$$= -74.9 \text{ kJ/mol-rxn} - [(298 \text{ K})(-80.7 \text{ J/K} \cdot \text{mol-rxn})](1 \text{ kJ}/1000 \text{ J})$$

$$= -50.9 \text{ kJ/mol-rxn}$$

$\Delta_r G°$ is negative at 298 K, so the reaction is predicted to be product-favored at equilibrium.

Think about Your Answer One of the most common mistakes students make is to forget to use $\Delta_r H°$ and $\Delta_r S°$ in the same energy unit (in this case, kJ). In this example, the product $T\Delta_r S°$ is negative (−24.0 kJ/mol-rxn) and disfavors the reaction. However, the entropy change is relatively small, and $\Delta_r H° = -74.9$ kJ/mol-rxn is the dominant term. Chemists call this an *enthalpy-driven reaction.*

Check Your Understanding

Using values of $\Delta_f H°$ and $S°$ to find $\Delta_r H°$ and $\Delta_r S°$, calculate the free energy change, $\Delta_r G°$, for the formation of 2 mol of $NH_3(g)$ from the elements at standard conditions and 25 °C.

$$N_2(g) + 3\ H_2(g) \rightarrow 2\ NH_3(g)$$

EXAMPLE 18.5

Calculating $\Delta_r G°$ Using Free Energies of Formation

Problem Calculate the standard free energy change for the combustion of one mole of methane using values for standard free energies of formation of the products and reactants. Is the reaction product-favored or reactant-favored at equilibrium?

Strategy Map 18.5

PROBLEM

Calculate $\Delta_r G°$ for a reaction.

KNOWN DATA/INFORMATION

- Description of chemical reaction
- $\Delta_f G°$ values (Appendix L)

STEP 1. Write a **balanced chemical equation.**

Balanced chemical equation

STEP 2. Calculate $\Delta_r G°$ using Equation 18.8.

$\Delta_r G°$

What Do You Know? You are asked to determine the standard free energy change for a reaction ($\Delta_r G°$). Values of standard molar free energies of formation for the substances involved in the reaction can be found in Appendix L.

Strategy Write a balanced equation for the reaction. Then, use Equation 18.8 with values of $\Delta_f G°$ obtained from Appendix L.

Solution The balanced equation and values of $\Delta_f G°$ for each reactant and product are

	$CH_4(g)$	+	$2\ O_2(g)$	→	$2\ H_2O(g)$	+	$CO_2(g)$
$\Delta_f G°$(kJ/mol)	−50.8		0		−228.6		−394.4

These values can then be substituted into Equation 18.8.

$$\Delta_r G° = \Sigma n\Delta_f G°(\text{products}) - \Sigma n\Delta_f G°(\text{reactants})$$

$$= \{(2\ \text{mol}\ H_2O(g)/\text{mol-rxn})\ \Delta_f G°[H_2O(g)] + (1\ \text{mol}\ CO_2(g)/\text{mol-rxn})\ \Delta_f G°[CO_2(g)]\}$$
$$- \{(1\ \text{mol}\ CH_4(g)/\text{mol-rxn})\ \Delta_f G°[CH_4(g)] + (2\ \text{mol}\ O_2(g)/\text{mol-rxn})\ \Delta_f G°[O_2(g)]\}$$

$$= [(2\ \text{mol}\ H_2O(g)/\text{mol-rxn})(-228.6\ \text{kJ/mol}) + (1\ \text{mol}\ CO_2(g)/\text{mol-rxn})(-394.4\ \text{kJ/mol})]$$
$$- [(1\ \text{mol}\ CH_4(g)/\text{mol-rxn})(-50.8\ \text{kJ/mol}) + (2\ \text{mol}\ O_2(g)/\text{mol-rxn})(0\ \text{kJ/mol})]$$

$$= -800.8\ \text{kJ/mol-rxn}$$

The large negative value of $\Delta_r G°$ indicates that the reaction is product-favored at equilibrium.

Think about Your Answer Common errors made by students in this calculation are (1) overlooking the stoichiometric coefficients in the equation and (2) confusing the signs for the terms when using Equation 18.8.

Check Your Understanding

Calculate the standard free energy change for the oxidation of 1.00 mol of $SO_2(g)$ to form $SO_3(g)$ using values of $\Delta_f G°$.

Free Energy and Temperature

The definition of free energy, $G = H - TS$, informs us that free energy is a function of temperature, so $\Delta_r G°$ will change as the temperature changes (Figure 18.11). A consequence of this dependence on temperature is that, in certain instances, reactions can be product-favored at equilibrium at one temperature and reactant-favored at another. Those instances arise when the $\Delta_r H°$ and $T\Delta_r S°$ terms work in opposite directions:

- Processes that are entropy-favored ($\Delta_r S° > 0$) and enthalpy-disfavored ($\Delta_r H° > 0$)
- Processes that are enthalpy-favored ($\Delta_r H° < 0$) and entropy-disfavored ($\Delta_r S° < 0$)

Let us explore the relationship of $\Delta_r G°$ and T further and illustrate how it can be used to advantage.

Calcium carbonate is the primary component of limestone, marble, and seashells. Heating $CaCO_3$ produces lime, CaO, an important chemical, along with gaseous CO_2. The data below from Appendix L are at 298 K (25 °C).

	$CaCO_3(s)$	→	$CaO(s)$	+	$CO_2(g)$
$\Delta_f G°$ (kJ/mol)	−1129.16		−603.42		−394.36
$\Delta_f H°$ (kJ/mol)	−1207.6		−635.09		−393.51
$S°$ (J/K · mol)	91.7		38.2		213.74

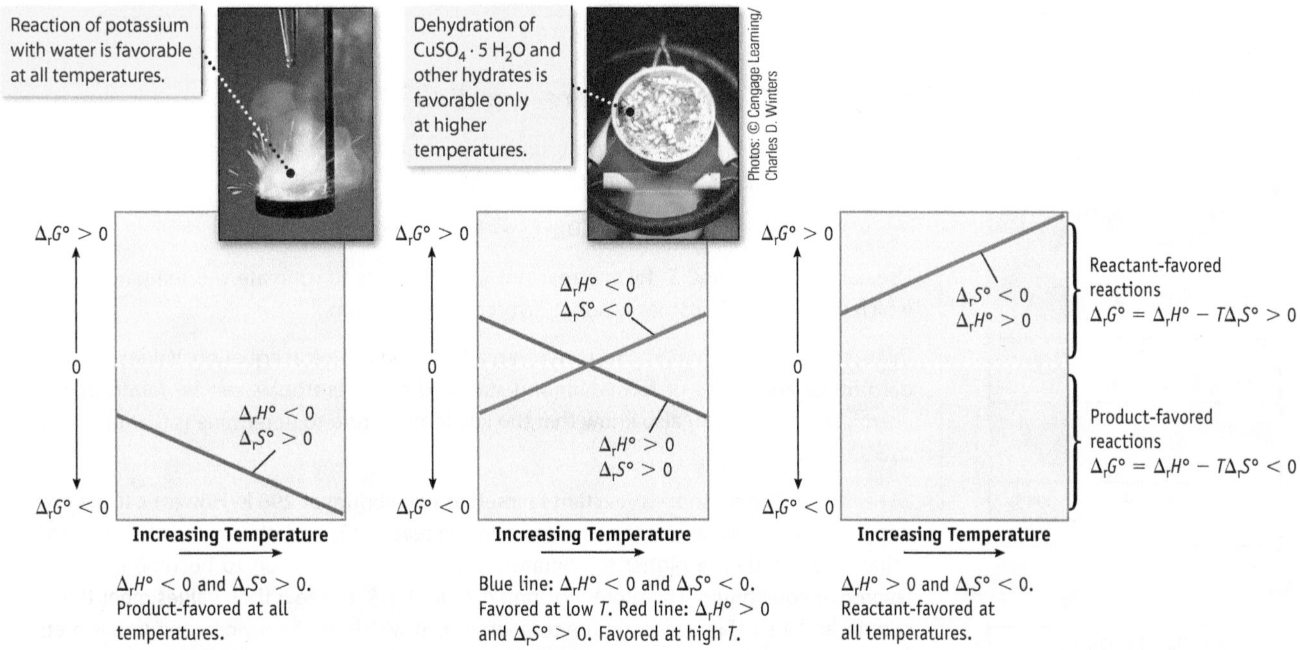

FIGURE 18.11 **The variation in $\Delta_rG°$ with temperature.**

For the conversion of 1 mol of $CaCO_3$(s) to 1 mol of CaO(s) under standard conditions, $\Delta_rG° = +131.38$ kJ, $\Delta_rH° = +179.0$ kJ, and $\Delta_rS° = +160.2$ J/K. Although the reaction is entropy-favored, the large positive and unfavorable enthalpy change dominates at 298 K. Thus, the standard free energy change is positive at 298 K and 1 bar, indicating that the reaction is reactant-favored at equilibrium.

The temperature dependence of $\Delta_rG°$ provides a means to turn the $CaCO_3$ decomposition into a product-favored reaction. Notice that the entropy change in the reaction is positive as a result of the formation of CO_2 gas in the reaction. Thus, raising the temperature results in the value of $T\Delta_rS°$ becoming increasingly large. At a high enough temperature, $T\Delta_rS°$ will outweigh the enthalpy effect, and the process will become product-favored at equilibrium.

How high must the temperature be for this reaction to become product-favored? An estimate of the temperature can be obtained using Equation 18.5, by calculating the temperature at which $\Delta_rG° = 0$. Above that temperature, $\Delta_rG°$ will have a negative value.

$$\Delta_rG° = \Delta_rH° - T\Delta_rS°$$
$$0 = (179.0\ \text{kJ/mol-rxn})(1000\ \text{J/kJ}) - T(160.2\ \text{J/K} \cdot \text{mol-rxn})$$
$$T = 1117\ \text{K (or 844 °C)}$$

$CaCO_3$ Decomposition Experiments show that the pressure of CO_2 in an equilibrium system [$CaCO_3(s) \rightleftharpoons CaO(s) + CO_2(g)$] is 1 bar at about 900 °C ($K = 1$ and $\Delta G° = 0$), close to our estimated temperature.

How accurate is this result? As noted earlier, this answer is only an estimate of the temperature needed. One source of error is the assumption that $\Delta_rH°$ and $\Delta_rS°$ do not vary with temperature, an assumption that is not strictly true. There is always a small variation in these values when the temperature changes—not large enough to be important if the temperature range is narrow, but potentially a problem over wider temperature ranges such as seen in this example. As an estimate, however, a temperature in the range of 850 °C for this reaction is reasonable.

Strategy Map 18.6

PROBLEM

Determine the **temperature** above which a chemical reaction is ***product-favored*** at **equilibrium.**

KNOWN DATA/INFORMATION

- Balanced chemical equation
- Temperature
- Values of $\Delta_f H°$ and $S°$

STEP 1. Calculate $\Delta_r H°$ using Equation 5.6.

$\Delta_r H°$

STEP 2. Calculate $\Delta_r S°$ using Equation 18.3.

$\Delta_r S°$

STEP 3. Use the equation $\Delta_r G° = \Delta_r H° - T\Delta_r S°$ to determine the temperature at which $\Delta_r G° = 0$.

Temperature above which the reaction is ***product-favored*** at **equilibrium.**

EXAMPLE 18.6

Effect of Temperature on $\Delta_r G°$

Problem The decomposition of liquid $Ni(CO)_4$ to produce nickel metal and carbon monoxide has a $\Delta_r G°$ value of 40 kJ/mol-rxn at 25 °C.

$$Ni(CO)_4(\ell) \rightarrow Ni(s) + 4\ CO(g)$$

Use values of $\Delta_f H°$ and $S°$ for the reactant and products to estimate the temperature at which the reaction becomes product-favored at equilibrium.

What Do You Know? You are given a balanced chemical equation. Values of standard molar enthalpies of formation and standard molar entropies can be found in the chemical literature. You also know that the key temperature to determine is that at which $\Delta_r G°$ is zero.

Strategy The reaction is reactant-favored at equilibrium at 298 K. However, if the entropy change is positive for the reaction and the reaction is endothermic (with a positive value of $\Delta_r H°$), then a higher temperature may allow the reaction to become product-favored at equilibrium. Therefore, first find $\Delta_r H°$ and $\Delta_r S°$ to see if their values meet these criteria, and if so, then calculate the temperature at which the following condition is met: $0 = \Delta_r H° - T\Delta_r S°$.

Solution Values for $\Delta_f H°$ and $S°$ are obtained from the chemical literature for the substances involved.

	$Ni(CO)_4(\ell)$	$\rightarrow$	$Ni(s)$	+	$4\ CO(g)$
$\Delta_f H°$(kJ/mol)	−632.0		0		−110.525
$S°$(J/K · mol)	320.1		29.87		197.67

For a process in which 1 mol of liquid $Ni(CO)_4$ is converted to 1 mol of Ni(s) and 4 mol of CO(g), we find

$$\Delta_r H° = +189.9 \text{ kJ/mol-rxn}$$

$$\Delta_r S° = +500.5 \text{ J/K mol-rxn}$$

We use these values of $\Delta_r H°$ and $\Delta_r S°$ to find the temperature at which $\Delta_r G° = 0$.

$$\Delta_r G° = \Delta_r H° - T\Delta_r S°$$

$$0 = (189.9 \text{ kJ/mol-rxn})(1000 \text{ J/kJ}) - T(500.5 \text{ J/K} \cdot \text{mol-rxn})$$

$$T = 379.4 \text{ K (or 106.2 °C)}$$

Think about Your Answer At 298 K, the reaction is reactant-favored at equilibrium largely because it is quite endothermic. However, the positive entropy change allows the reaction to be product-favored at equilibrium at a higher temperature.

Check Your Understanding

Oxygen was first prepared by Joseph Priestley (1733–1804) by heating HgO. Use data in Appendix L to estimate the temperature required to decompose HgO(s) into Hg(ℓ) and O_2(g).

Using the Relationship between $\Delta_r G°$ and K

Equation 18.7 provides a direct route to determine the standard free energy change from experimentally determined equilibrium constants. Alternatively, it allows calculation of an equilibrium constant from thermochemical data contained in tables or obtained from an experiment.

EXAMPLE 18.7

Calculating K_p from $\Delta_r G°$

Problem Determine the standard free energy change, $\Delta_r G°$, for the formation of 1.00 mol of $NH_3(g)$ from nitrogen and hydrogen, and use this value to calculate the equilibrium constant for this reaction at 25 °C.

What Do You Know? You are given enough information so you can write a balanced chemical equation for the desired chemical reaction. Values of $\Delta_f G°$ are given in Appendix L.

Strategy The free energy of formation of ammonia represents the free energy change to form 1.00 mol of $NH_3(g)$ from the elements. The equilibrium constant for this reaction is calculated from $\Delta_r G°$ using Equation 18.7. Because the reactants and products are gases, the calculated value will be K_p.

Solution Begin by specifying a balanced equation for the chemical reaction under investigation.

$$\tfrac{1}{2}\,N_2(g) + \tfrac{3}{2}\,H_2(g) \rightleftharpoons NH_3(g)$$

The free energy change for this reaction is −16.37 kJ/mol-rxn ($\Delta_r G° = \Delta_f G°$ for $NH_3(g)$; Appendix L). In a calculation of K_p using Equation 18.7, we will need consistent units. If we use the gas constant, R, in units of 8.3145 J/K · mol, then the value of $\Delta_r G°$ must be in J/mol-rxn (and not kJ/mol-rxn). The temperature is 25 °C (298.15 K).

$$\Delta_r G° = -RT \ln K$$

$$-16{,}370 \text{ J/mol-rxn} = (-8.3145 \text{ J/K} \cdot \text{mol-rxn})(298.15 \text{ K}) \ln K_p$$

$$\ln K_p = 6.604$$

$$K_p = 738$$

Think about Your Answer The value of $\Delta_r G°$ is less than zero, indicating that this reaction is product-favored at equilibrium. The value of K_p calculated is greater than 1 as it should be for such a process. This example illustrates how to calculate equilibrium constants from thermodynamic data. In fact, many equilibrium constants you find in the chemical literature are not experimentally determined but are instead calculated from thermodynamic data in this way.

Check Your Understanding

Determine the value of the equilibrium constant, K_p, for the decomposition of calcium carbonate to calcium oxide and carbon dioxide gas at 298.15 K.

K and $\Delta_r G°$ For an equation that allows you to calculate the value of K given the value of $\Delta_r G°$, see Appendix O-4 "The Relationship of the Equilibrium Constant and the Standard Gibbs Free Energy Change."

Strategy Map 18.7

PROBLEM

Determine the **equilibrium constant** for a reaction using **thermodynamic data.**

KNOWN DATA/INFORMATION

- Information to write a balanced chemical equation
- The values of $\Delta_f G°$
- Temperature

STEP 1. Write the **balanced chemical equation.**

Balanced chemical equation

STEP 2. Calculate $\Delta_r G°$ using values of $\Delta_f G°$ in Equation 18.8.

$\Delta_r G°$

STEP 3. Use the equation $\Delta_r G° = -RT \ln K$ to determine the value of K.

Equilibrium constant, K

EXAMPLE 18.8

Calculating $\Delta_r G°$ from K_{sp} for an Insoluble Solid

Problem The value of K_{sp} for AgCl(s) at 25 °C is 1.8×10^{-10}. Determine $\Delta_r G°$ for the process $Ag^+(aq) + Cl^-(aq) \rightleftharpoons AgCl(s)$ at 298.15 K.

What Do You Know You are given the value of K_{sp}. The process of interest is the reverse of the chemical equation for K_{sp}. You also know the temperature.

Strategy The chemical equation given is the opposite of the equation used to define K_{sp}; therefore, the equilibrium constant for this reaction is $1/K_{sp}$. This value is used in Equation 18.7 to calculate $\Delta_r G°$.

CASE STUDY
Thermodynamics and Living Things

The laws of thermodynamics apply to all chemical reactions. It should come as no surprise, therefore, that issues of spontaneity and calculations involving $\Delta_r G$ also arise in studies of biochemical reactions. For biochemical processes, however, a different standard state is often used. Most of the usual definition is retained: 1 bar pressure for gases and 1 *m* concentration for aqueous solutes with the exception of one very important solute. Rather than using a standard state of 1 molal for hydronium ions (corresponding to a pH of about 0), biochemists use a hydronium concentration of 1×10^{-7} M, corresponding to a pH of 7. This pH is more useful for biochemical reactions. When biochemists use this as the standard state, they write the symbol ′ next to the thermodynamic function. For example, they would write $\Delta G°'$ (pronounced *delta G zero prime*).

Living things require energy to perform their many functions. One of the main reactions providing this energy is that of adenosine triphosphate (ATP) with water, a reaction for which $\Delta_r G°' = -30.5$ kJ/mol-rxn.

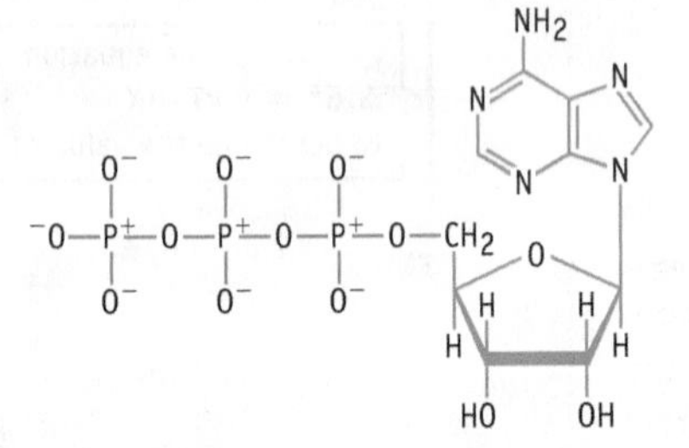

ATP, adenosine triphosphate

One of the key functions of the process of respiration is to produce molecules of ATP for our bodies to use. ATP is produced in the reaction of adenosine diphosphate (ADP) with hydrogen phosphate ($HP_i = HPO_4^{2-}$),

$$ADP + HP_i + H^+ \rightarrow ATP + H_2O \quad \Delta_r G°' = +30.5 \text{ kJ/mol-rxn}$$

John C. Kotz

a reaction that is reactant-favored at equilibrium. How then do our bodies get this reaction to occur? The answer is to couple the production of ATP with another reaction that is even more product-favored than ATP production is reactant-favored. For example, organisms carry out the oxidation of carbohydrates in a multistep process, producing energy. One of the compounds produced in the process called *glycolysis* is phosphoenolpyruvate (PEP).

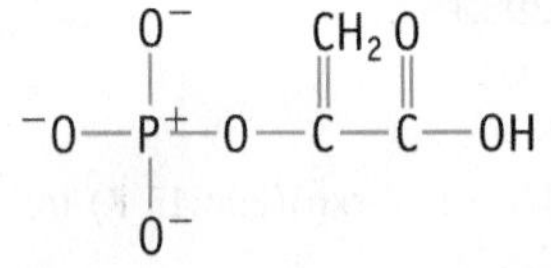

PEP, phosphoenolpyruvate

Its reaction with water is product-favored at equilibrium

$$PEP + H_2O \rightarrow Pyruvate + HP_i \quad \Delta_r G°' = -61.9 \text{ kJ/mol-rxn}$$

This reaction and ATP formation are linked through the HP_i that is produced in the PEP reaction. If both reactions are carried out, we obtain the following:

$$PEP + H_2O \rightarrow Pyruvate + HP_i \quad \Delta_r G°' = -61.9 \text{ kJ/mol-rxn}$$

$$ADP + HP_i + H^+ \rightarrow ATP + H_2O \quad \Delta_r G°' = +30.5 \text{ kJ/mol-rxn}$$

$$PEP + ADP + H^+ \rightarrow Pyruvate + ATP \quad \Delta_r G°' = -31.4 \text{ kJ/mol-rxn}$$

The overall reaction has a negative value for $\Delta_r G°'$ and thus is product-favored at equilibrium. ATP is formed in this process.

The coupling of reactions to produce a system that is product-favored is used in a multitude of reactions that occur in our bodies.

Questions:

1. Consider the hydrolysis reactions of creatine phosphate and adenosine-5′-monophosphate.

   $$\text{Creatine Phosphate} + H_2O \rightarrow \text{Creatine} + HP_i \quad \Delta_r G°' = -43.3 \text{ kJ/mol-rxn}$$

   $$\text{Adenosine-5'-Monophosphate} + H_2O \rightarrow \text{Adenosine} + HP_i \quad \Delta_r G°' = -9.2 \text{ kJ/mol-rxn}$$

   Which of the following combinations produces a reaction that is product-favored at equilibrium: for creatine phosphate to transfer phosphate to adenosine or for adenosine-5′-monophosphate to transfer phosphate to creatine?
2. Assume the reaction $A(aq) + B(aq) \rightarrow C(aq) + H_3O^+(aq)$ produces one hydronium ion. What is the mathematical relationship between $\Delta_r G°'$ and $\Delta_r G°$ at 25 °C? (*Hint:* Use the equation $\Delta_r G = \Delta_r G° + RT \ln Q$ and substitute $\Delta_r G°'$ for $\Delta_r G$.)

Answers to these questions are available in Appendix N.

Solution

For $Ag^+(aq) + Cl^-(aq) \rightleftharpoons AgCl(s)$,

$$K = 1/K_{sp} = 1/\,1.8 \times 10^{-10} = 5.6 \times 10^9$$

$$\Delta_r G° = -RT \ln K = -(8.3145 \text{ J/K} \cdot \text{mol-rxn})(298.15 \text{ K}) \ln(5.6 \times 10^9)$$

$$= -56{,}000 \text{ J/mol-rxn} = -56 \text{ kJ/mol-rxn}$$

Think about Your Answer The negative value of $\Delta_r G°$ indicates that the precipitation of AgCl from Ag^+(aq) and Cl^-(aq) is product-favored at equilibrium.

Check Your Understanding

Determine the value of $\Delta_r G°$ for the reaction C(s) + CO_2(g) $\rightleftharpoons$ 2 CO(g) from data in Appendix L. Use this result to calculate the equilibrium constant.

Calculating $\Delta_r G$, the Free Energy Change for a Reaction Using $\Delta_r G°$ and the Reaction Quotient

Equation 18.6 allows you to calculate the value of $\Delta_r G$, the free energy change for a reaction at nonstandard conditions, given the values of $\Delta_r G°$ and the reaction quotient, Q.

EXAMPLE 18.9

Calculating $\Delta_r G$ from $\Delta_r G°$ and Q

Problem Gaseous iodine monochloride can be decomposed into iodine and chlorine gases according to the following chemical equation

$$2\ ICl(g) \rightarrow I_2(g) + Cl_2(g)$$

(a) Calculate $\Delta_r G°$ for this reaction at 298 K using values for the standard free energies of formation of the products and reactant. Is this reaction reactant-favored or product-favored at equilibrium?

(b) Calculate the value of $\Delta_r G$ at 298 K for this reaction if the reactant and products are mixed with the following partial pressures: 1.0 atm ICl, 1.0×10^{-3} atm I_2, and 1.0×10^{-3} atm Cl_2. Is the reaction spontaneous under these conditions?

What Do You Know? You are given a balanced chemical equation. Standard free energies of formation are listed in Appendix L.

Strategy For part (a), use Equation 18.8 with values of $\Delta_f G°$ to obtain the value of $\Delta_r G°$. For part (b), use Equation 18.6 to obtain the value of $\Delta_r G$ under the conditions given.

Solution

(a)

	2 ICl(g)	→	I_2(g)	+	Cl_2(g)
$\Delta_f G°$ (kJ/mol)	−5.73		19.33		0

These values can be substituted into Equation 18.8.

$$\Delta_r G° = \Sigma n\Delta_f G°(\text{products}) - \Sigma n\Delta_f G°(\text{reactants})$$

$$= \{(1\ \text{mol}\ I_2(g)/\text{mol-rxn})\ \Delta_f G°[I_2(g)] + (1\ \text{mol}\ Cl_2(g)/\text{mol-rxn})\ \Delta_f G°[Cl_2(g)]\} - (2\ \text{mol}\ ICl(g)/\text{mol-rxn})\ \Delta_f G°[ICl(g)]$$

$$= [(1\ \text{mol}\ I_2(g)/\text{mol-rxn})(19.33\ \text{kJ/mol}) + (1\ \text{mol}\ Cl_2(g)/\text{mol-rxn})(0\ \text{kJ/mol})] - (2\ \text{mol}\ ICl(g)/\text{mol-rxn})(-5.73\ \text{kJ/mol})$$

$$= 30.79\ \text{kJ/mol-rxn}$$

$\Delta_r G°$ is positive at 298 K, so the reaction is predicted to be reactant-favored at equilibrium.

(b) Equation 18.6 can be used to calculate $\Delta_r G$ for this reaction under the given conditions.

$$\Delta_r G = \Delta_r G° + RT\ln Q$$
$$= \Delta_r G° + RT\ln(P_{I_2}P_{Cl_2}/P_{ICl}^2)$$
$$= 30.79 \text{ kJ/mol-rxn} + (0.0083145 \text{ kJ/K} \cdot \text{mol-rxn})(298 \text{ K})\ln[(1.0 \times 10^{-3})(1.0 \times 10^{-3})/(1.0)^2]$$
$$= -3.44 \text{ kJ/mol-rxn}$$

$\Delta_r G$ is negative at 298 K, so the reaction will proceed spontaneously until the reactant-favored equilibrium position is reached.

Think about Your Answer Even though the equilibrium position for this reaction favors the reactants, the reaction is spontaneous under the conditions presented in part (b) of the question. Even a reactant-favored reaction is spontaneous until equilibrium is attained.

Check Your Understanding

Nitrogen and oxygen can react to form nitrogen monoxide according to the following chemical equation

$$N_2(g) + O_2(g) \rightarrow 2\ NO(g)$$

(a) Calculate $\Delta_r G°$ for this reaction at 298 K using values for the standard free energies of formation of the product and reactants. Is this reaction reactant-favored or product-favored at equilibrium?

(b) Calculate the value of $\Delta_r G$ at 298 for this reaction if the reactants and product are mixed with the following partial pressures: 0.10 atm N_2, 0.10 atm O_2, and 0.010 atm NO. Is this reaction spontaneous under these conditions?

REVIEW & CHECK FOR SECTION 18-7

1. Given that $\Delta_r H° = -2219$ kJ/mol-rxn and that $\Delta_r S° = -216$ J/K · mol-rxn at 25 °C, determine the value of $\Delta_r G°$ at 25 °C for the reaction

$$C_3H_8(g) + 5\ O_2(g) \rightarrow 3\ CO_2(g) + 4\ H_2O(\ell)$$

(a) −2283 kJ/mol-rxn
(b) −2214 kJ/mol-rxn
(c) −2155 kJ/mol-rxn
(d) 6.218×10^4 kJ/mol-rxn

2. Using values of $\Delta_f G°$, determine the value of $\Delta_r G°$ at 25 °C for the reaction

$$2\ KClO_3(s) \rightarrow 2\ KCl(s) + 3\ O_2(g)$$

(a) −225 kJ/mol-rxn
(b) −112 kJ/mol-rxn
(c) 112 kJ/mol-rxn
(d) 225 kJ/mol-rxn

3. The value of K_p for the following reaction at 425 °C is 0.018. What is the value of $\Delta_r G°$ at this temperature?

$$2\ HI(g) \rightleftharpoons H_2(g) + I_2(g)$$

(a) 1.0×10^1 kJ/mol-rxn
(b) −14 kJ/mol-rxn
(c) 23 kJ/mol-rxn
(d) 240 kJ/mol-rxn

APPLYING CHEMICAL PRINCIPLES

Are Diamonds Forever?

Natural diamonds are created over 150 kilometers beneath the Earth's surface. At these depths, enormous pressures and high temperatures convert graphite, the more stable allotrope of carbon at lower pressure, into diamond. It is believed that volcanic eruptions then push diamonds to the Earth's surface. If a diamond is pushed to the surface quickly, it will cool before it has a chance to revert to graphite. Although diamonds are thermodynamically unstable at room temperature, the activation barrier for conversion is too high for the process to occur.

Diamonds have been synthesized in laboratories since the 1950s by duplicating the conditions that exist deep underground. To produce a synthetic diamond, a seed crystal of diamond is combined with graphite and nickel (or chromium), then subjected to pressures greater than 50,000 atmospheres and temperatures around 1500 °C. The nickel, now molten, simultaneously acts as a solvent for carbon and a catalyst for the formation of diamond. If conditions are maintained near the equilibrium line between diamond and graphite (Figure 1), single crystals of synthetic diamonds may be grown to sizes larger than one carat in approximately three days. Synthetic diamonds may be produced in a variety of colors. One of the most common colors is yellow, which results from a small amount of nitrogen replacing carbon in diamond's lattice. Is this a problem? Probably not. Natural yellow diamonds are extremely rare and sell for high prices.

Currently, a technique known as *chemical vapor deposition* (CVD) is being used to grow diamonds in a vacuum and at lower temperatures (800 °C). In CVD, methane and hydrogen gases are atomized above a diamond seed crystal. Hydrogen atoms bond with carbon atoms on the diamond's surface, preventing the carbon atoms from forming double bonds with its neighbors. Carbon radicals, from the decomposed methane, slowly replace the hydrogen atoms on the diamond's surface, building a larger diamond, one atom layer at a time. In addition to gemstones, the CVD method may be used to create diamond windows or thin diamond films over a variety of substrates (Figure 2).

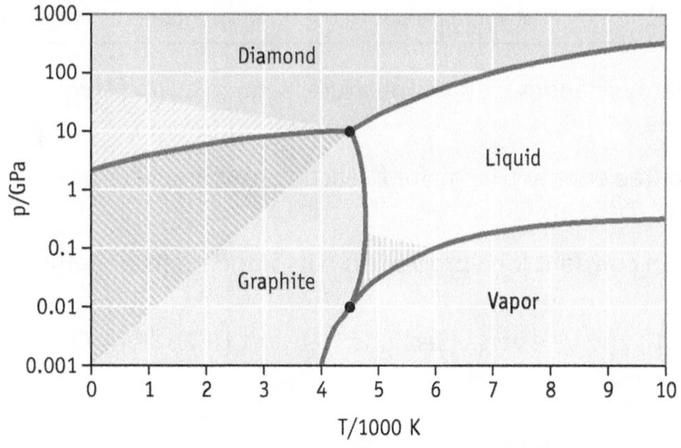

FIGURE 1 **Phase diagram for carbon.** The hatched areas are regions where the two phases can coexist. Pressures are in gigapascals (where 1 GPa is about 9900 atm).

AFP PHOTO/Toshifumi KITAMURA/Newscom

FIGURE 2 **Diamond wafers.** The chemical vapor deposition (CVD) technique allows the synthesis of diamond in the shape of extended disks or wafers. Under optimized growth conditions the properties of these disks approach those of perfect diamond single crystals.

QUESTIONS:

1. The decomposition of diamond to graphite [C(diamond) $\rightarrow$ C(graphite)] is thermodynamically favored, but occurs slowly at room temperature.
   (a) Use $\Delta_f G°$ values from Appendix L to calculate $\Delta_r G°$ and K_{eq} for the reaction under standard conditions and 298.15 K.
   (b) Use $\Delta_f H°$ and $S°$ values from Appendix L to calculate $\Delta_r G°$ and K_{eq} for the reaction at 1000 K. Assume that enthalpy and entropy values are valid at these temperatures. Does heating shift the equilibrium toward the formation of diamond or graphite?
   (c) Why is the formation of diamond favored at high pressures?
   (d) The phase diagram shows that diamond is thermodynamically favored over graphite at 20,000 atmospheres pressure (about 2 GPa) at room temperature. Why is this conversion actually done at much higher temperatures and pressures?
2. It has been demonstrated that buckminsterfullerene (C_{60}), another allotrope of carbon (Section 2-5), may be converted into diamond at room temperature and 20,000 atmospheres pressure (about 2 GPa). The standard enthalpy of formation, $\Delta_f H°$, for buckminsterfullerene is 2320 kJ/mol at 298.2 K.
   (a) Calculate $\Delta_r H°$ for the conversion of C_{60} to diamond at standard state conditions and 298.2 K.
   (b) Assuming that the standard entropy per mole of carbon in both C_{60} and diamond is comparable (both about 2.3 J/K mol), is the conversion of C_{60} to diamond product-favored at room temperature?

CHAPTER GOALS REVISITED

Now that you have studied this chapter, you should ask whether you have met the chapter goals. In particular, you should be able to:

UNDERSTAND

- The concept of entropy and its relationship to reaction spontaneity.
  - **a.** Understand that entropy is a measure of energy dispersal (Section 18-2). Study Questions: 1, 2.
  - **b.** Recognize that an entropy change is the energy transferred as heat for a reversible process divided by the Kelvin temperature (*A Closer Look: Reversible and Irreversible Processes,* Section 18-2 and Equation 18.1). Study Questions: 42–44.
  - **c.** Identify common processes that are entropy-favored (Section 18-4). Study Question: 47.
- The relationship between enthalpy, entropy, and free energy changes for a reaction (Section 18-6). Study Questions: 15, 16.

DO

- Calculate the change in entropy for a system, its surroundings, and the universe to determine whether a process is spontaneous under standard conditions.
  - **a.** Calculate entropy changes from tables of standard entropy values (Section 18-4). Study Questions: 3–8.
  - **b.** Use standard entropy and enthalpy changes to predict whether a reaction will be spontaneous under standard conditions (Section 18-5 and Table 18.1). Study Questions: 9–12.
  - **c.** Recognize how temperature influences whether a reaction is spontaneous (Section 18-5). Study Questions: 13, 14, 23–26.
- Use the change in Gibbs free energy to predict reaction spontaneity.
  - **a.** Calculate the change in free energy at standard conditions for a reaction from the enthalpy and entropy changes under standard conditions (Section 18-7). Study Questions: 15-18, 48, 49, 57, 58.
  - **b.** Understand the relationship of $\Delta_r G$, Q, K, and reaction spontaneity (Section 18-6).

Q	**ΔG**	**SPONTANEOUS?**
$Q < K$	$\Delta_r G < 0$	Spontaneous to the right as the equation is written
$Q = K$	$\Delta_r G = 0$	Reaction is at equilibrium
$Q > K$	$\Delta_r G > 0$	Not spontaneous to the right; spontaneous to the left

  - **c.** Know how free energy changes with temperature (Section 18-7). Study Questions: 23–26, 59, 61, 72.
- Calculate the standard free energy change for a reaction from free energy of formation data (Section 18-7). Study Questions: 19, 20, 54, 55, 65.
- Calculate an equilibrium constant for a process from its standard free energy change.
  - **a.** Calculate K from $\Delta_r G°$ and vice versa (Sections 18-6 and 18-7). Study Questions: 27–30, 50, 52–54, 63.

b. Understand the relationship between $\Delta_r G°$ and whether a reaction is reactant- or product-favored at equilibrium. (Section 18-6).

K	$\Delta G°$	Reactant-Favored or Product-Favored at Equilibrium?
$K >> 1$	$\Delta_r G° < 0$	Product-favored
$K = 1$	$\Delta_r G° = 0$	$[C]^c[D]^d = [A]^a[B]^b$ at equilibrium
$K << 1$	$\Delta_r G° > 0$	Reactant-favored

REMEMBER

- The entropy of the universe increases in a spontaneous change.
- The Gibbs free energy change for a spontaneous reaction is negative.

KEY EQUATIONS

Equation 18.1 (page 683) Calculate the entropy change from the energy transferred as heat for a reversible process and the temperature at which it occurs.

$$\Delta S = \frac{q_{rev}}{T}$$

Equation 18.2 (page 685) The Boltzmann equation: The entropy of a system, *S*, is proportional to the number of accessible microstates, *W*, belonging to a given energy of a system or substance.

$$S = k \ln W$$

Equation 18.3 (page 690) Calculate the standard entropy change for a process from the tabulated entropies of the products and reactants and the stoichiometric coefficients (n) of the substances in the balanced chemical equation for the reaction.

$$\Delta_r S° = \Sigma n S°(\text{products}) - \Sigma n S°(\text{reactants})$$

Equation 18.4 (page 692) Calculate the total entropy change for a system and its surroundings, to determine whether a process is spontaneous under standard conditions.

$$\Delta S°(\text{universe}) = \Delta S°(\text{system}) + \Delta S°(\text{surroundings})$$

Equation 18.5 (page 697) Calculate the free energy change for a process from enthalpy and entropy changes.

$$\Delta_r G° = \Delta_r H° - T\Delta_r S°$$

Equation 18.6 (page 698) Calculate the free energy change under nonstandard conditions ($\Delta_r G$) from the standard free energy change ($\Delta_r G°$) and the reaction quotient Q.

$$\Delta_r G = \Delta_r G° + RT \ln Q$$

Equation 18.7 (page 698) Calculate the standard free energy change for a reaction from its equilibrium constant.

$$\Delta_r G° = -RT \ln K$$

Equation 18.8 (page 700) Calculate the standard free energy change for a reaction using tabulated values of $\Delta_f G°$ and the stoichiometric coefficients (n) of the substances in the balanced chemical equation for the reaction.

$$\Delta_r G° = \Sigma n \Delta_f G°(\text{products}) - \Sigma n \Delta_f G°(\text{reactants})$$

© Cengage Learning/Charles D. Winters

STUDY QUESTIONS

▲ denotes challenging questions.

Blue-numbered questions have answers in Appendix N and fully worked solutions in the *Student Solutions Manual.*

Practicing Skills

Entropy

(See Sections 18-2–18-4 and Examples 18.1 and 18.2.)

1. Which substance has the higher entropy?
   (a) dry ice (solid CO_2) at −78 °C or CO_2(g) at 0 °C
   (b) liquid water at 25 °C or liquid water at 50 °C
   (c) pure alumina, Al_2O_3(s), or ruby (ruby is Al_2O_3 in which some Al^{3+} ions in the crystalline lattice are replaced with Cr^{3+} ions)
   (d) one mole of N_2(g) at 1 bar pressure or one mole of N_2(g) at 10 bar pressure (both at 298 K)

2. Which substance has the higher entropy?
   (a) a sample of pure silicon (to be used in a computer chip) or a piece of silicon containing a trace of another element such as boron or phosphorus
   (b) O_2(g) at 0 °C or O_2(g) at −50 °C
   (c) I_2(s) or I_2(g), both at room temperature
   (d) one mole of O_2(g) at 1 bar pressure or one mole of O_2(g) at 0.01 bar pressure (both at 298 K)

3. Use $S°$ values to calculate the standard entropy change, $\Delta_r S°$, for each of the following processes and comment on the sign of the change.
   (a) $KOH(s) \rightarrow KOH(aq)$
   (b) $Na(g) \rightarrow Na(s)$
   (c) $Br_2(\ell) \rightarrow Br_2(g)$
   (d) $HCl(g) \rightarrow HCl(aq)$

4. Use $S°$ values to calculate the standard entropy change, $\Delta_r S°$, for each of the following processes, and comment on the sign of the change.
   (a) $NH_4Cl(s) \rightarrow NH_4Cl(aq)$
   (b) $CH_3OH(\ell) \rightarrow CH_3OH(g)$
   (c) $CCl_4(g) \rightarrow CCl_4(\ell)$
   (d) $NaCl(s) \rightarrow NaCl(g)$

5. Calculate the standard entropy change for the formation of 1.0 mol of the following compounds from the elements at 25 °C.
   (a) $HCl(g)$ (b) $Ca(OH)_2(s)$

6. Calculate the standard entropy change for the formation of 1.0 mol of the following compounds from the elements at 25 °C.
   (a) $H_2S(g)$ (b) $MgCO_3(s)$

7. Calculate the standard entropy change for the following reactions at 25 °C. Comment on the sign of $\Delta_r S°$.
   (a) $2\ Al(s) + 3\ Cl_2(g) \rightarrow 2\ AlCl_3(s)$
   (b) $2\ CH_3OH(\ell) + 3\ O_2(g) \rightarrow 2\ CO_2(g) + 4\ H_2O(g)$

8. Calculate the standard entropy change for the following reactions at 25 °C. Comment on the sign of $\Delta_r S°$.
   (a) $2\ Na(s) + 2\ H_2O(\ell) \rightarrow 2\ NaOH(aq) + H_2(g)$
   (b) $Na_2CO_3(s) + 2\ HCl(aq) \rightarrow 2\ NaCl(aq) + H_2O(\ell) + CO_2(g)$

$\Delta_r S°$(universe) and Spontaneity

(See Sections 18-2–18-5 and Example 18.3.)

9. Is the reaction $Si(s) + 2\ Cl_2(g) \rightarrow SiCl_4(g)$ spontaneous under standard conditions at 298.15 K? Answer this question by calculating $\Delta S°$(system), $\Delta S°$(surroundings), and $\Delta S°$(universe). (Define reactants and products as the system.)

10. Is the reaction $Si(s) + 2\ H_2(g) \rightarrow SiH_4(g)$ spontaneous under standard conditions at 298.15 K? Answer this question by calculating $\Delta S°$(system), $\Delta S°$(surroundings), and $\Delta S°$(universe). (Define reactants and products as the system.)

11. Calculate $\Delta S°$(universe) for the decomposition of 1 mol of liquid water to form gaseous hydrogen and oxygen. Is this reaction spontaneous under standard conditions at 25 °C? Explain your answer briefly.

12. Calculate $\Delta S°$(universe) for the formation of 1 mol HCl(g) from gaseous hydrogen and chlorine. Is this reaction spontaneous under standard conditions at 25 °C? Explain your answer briefly.

13. Classify each of the reactions according to one of the four reaction types summarized in Table 18.1.
   (a) $Fe_2O_3(s) + 2\ Al(s) \rightarrow 2\ Fe(s) + Al_2O_3(s)$
   $\Delta_r H° = -851.5$ kJ/mol-rxn
   $\Delta_r S° = -375.2$ J/K · mol-rxn
   (b) $N_2(g) + 2\ O_2(g) \rightarrow 2\ NO_2(g)$
   $\Delta_r H° = 66.2$ kJ/mol-rxn
   $\Delta_r S° = -121.6$ J/K · mol-rxn

14. Classify each of the reactions according to one of the four reaction types summarized in Table 18.1.
   (a) $C_6H_{12}O_6(s) + 6\ O_2(g) \rightarrow 6\ CO_2(g) + 6\ H_2O(\ell)$
   $\Delta_r H° = -673$ kJ/mol-rxn
   $\Delta_r S° = 60.4$ J/K · mol-rxn
   (b) $MgO(s) + C(graphite) \rightarrow Mg(s) + CO(g)$
   $\Delta_r H° = 490.7$ kJ/mol-rxn
   $\Delta_r S° = 197.9$ J/K · mol-rxn

Gibbs Free Energy

(See Sections 18-6 and 18-7 and Example 18.4.)

15. Using values of $\Delta_f H°$ and $S°$, calculate $\Delta_r G°$ for each of the following reactions at 25 °C.

(a) $2\ Pb(s) + O_2(g) \rightarrow 2\ PbO(s)$
(b) $NH_3(g) + HNO_3(aq) \rightarrow NH_4NO_3(aq)$

Which of these reactions is (are) predicted to be product-favored at equilibrium? Are the reactions enthalpy- or entropy-driven?

16. Using values of $\Delta_f H°$ and $S°$, calculate $\Delta_r G°$ for each of the following reactions at 25 °C.

(a) $2\ Na(s) + 2\ H_2O(\ell) \rightarrow 2\ NaOH(aq) + H_2(g)$
(b) $6\ C(graphite) + 3\ H_2(g) \rightarrow C_6H_6(\ell)$

Which of these reactions is (are) predicted to be product-favored at equilibrium? Are the reactions enthalpy- or entropy-driven?

17. Using values of $\Delta_f H°$ and $S°$, calculate the standard molar free energy of formation, $\Delta_f G°$, for each of the following compounds:

(a) $CS_2(g)$
(b) $NaOH(s)$
(c) $ICl(g)$

Compare your calculated values of $\Delta_f G°$ with those listed in Appendix L. Which of these formation reactions are predicted to be product-favored at equilibrium at 25 °C?

18. Using values of $\Delta_f H°$ and $S°$, calculate the standard molar free energy of formation, $\Delta_f G°$, for each of the following:

(a) $Ca(OH)_2(s)$
(b) $Cl(g)$
(c) $Na_2CO_3(s)$

Compare your calculated values of $\Delta_f G°$ with those listed in Appendix L. Which of these formation reactions are predicted to be product-favored at equilibrium at 25 °C?

Free Energy of Formation

(See Section 18-7 and Example 18.5.)

19. Using values of $\Delta_f G°$, calculate $\Delta_r G°$ for each of the following reactions at 25 °C. Which are product-favored at equilibrium?

(a) $2\ K(s) + Cl_2(g) \rightarrow 2\ KCl(s)$
(b) $2\ CuO(s) \rightarrow 2\ Cu(s) + O_2(g)$
(c) $4\ NH_3(g) + 7\ O_2(g) \rightarrow 4\ NO_2(g) + 6\ H_2O(g)$

20. Using values of $\Delta_f G°$, calculate $\Delta_r G°$ for each of the following reactions at 25 °C. Which are product-favored at equilibrium?

(a) $HgS(s) + O_2(g) \rightarrow Hg(\ell) + SO_2(g)$
(b) $2\ H_2S(g) + 3\ O_2(g) \rightarrow 2\ H_2O(g) + 2\ SO_2(g)$
(c) $SiCl_4(g) + 2\ Mg(s) \rightarrow 2\ MgCl_2(s) + Si(s)$

21. For the reaction $BaCO_3(s) \rightarrow BaO(s) + CO_2(g)$, $\Delta_r G° = +219.7$ kJ. Using this value and other data available in Appendix L, calculate the value of $\Delta_f G°$ for $BaCO_3(s)$.

22. For the reaction $TiCl_2(s) + Cl_2(g) \rightarrow TiCl_4(\ell)$, $\Delta_r G° = -272.8$ kJ. Using this value and other data available in Appendix L, calculate the value of $\Delta_f G°$ for $TiCl_2(s)$.

Effect of Temperature on ΔG

(See Section 18-7 and Example 18.6.)

23. Determine whether the reactions listed below are entropy-favored or disfavored under standard conditions. Predict how an increase in temperature will affect the value of $\Delta_r G°$.

(a) $N_2(g) + 2\ O_2(g) \rightarrow 2\ NO_2(g)$
(b) $2\ C(s) + O_2(g) \rightarrow 2\ CO(g)$
(c) $CaO(s) + CO_2(g) \rightarrow CaCO_3(s)$
(d) $2\ NaCl(s) \rightarrow 2\ Na(s) + Cl_2(g)$

24. Determine whether the reactions listed below are entropy-favored or disfavored under standard conditions. Predict how an increase in temperature will affect the value of $\Delta_r G°$.

(a) $I_2(g) \rightarrow 2\ I(g)$
(b) $2\ SO_2(g) + O_2(g) \rightarrow 2\ SO_3(g)$
(c) $SiCl_4(g) + 2\ H_2O(\ell) \rightarrow SiO_2(s) + 4\ HCl(g)$
(d) $P_4(s, white) + 6\ H_2(g) \rightarrow 4\ PH_3(g)$

25. Heating some metal carbonates, among them magnesium carbonate, leads to their decomposition.

$$MgCO_3(s) \rightarrow MgO(s) + CO_2(g)$$

(a) Calculate $\Delta_r G°$ and $\Delta_r S°$ for the reaction.
(b) Is the reaction product-favored at equilibrium at 298 K?
(c) Is the reaction predicted to be product-favored at equilibrium at higher temperatures?

26. Calculate $\Delta_r H°$ and $\Delta_r S°$ for the reaction of tin(IV) oxide with carbon.

$$SnO_2(s) + C(s) \rightarrow Sn(s) + CO_2(g)$$

(a) Is the reaction product-favored at equilibrium at 298 K?
(b) Is the reaction predicted to be product-favored at equilibrium at higher temperatures?

Free Energy and Equilibrium Constants

(See Section 18-7 and Examples 18.7 and 18.8.)

27. The standard free energy change, $\Delta_r G°$, for the formation of NO(g) from its elements is +86.58 kJ/mol at 25 °C. Calculate K_p at this temperature for the equilibrium

$$\tfrac{1}{2}\ N_2(g) + \tfrac{1}{2}\ O_2(g) \rightleftharpoons NO(g)$$

Comment on the sign of $\Delta_r G°$ and the magnitude of K_p.

28. The standard free energy change, $\Delta_r G°$, for the formation of $O_3(g)$ from $O_2(g)$ is +163.2 kJ/mol at 25 °C. Calculate K_p at this temperature for the equilibrium

$$3\ O_2(g) \rightleftharpoons 2\ O_3(g)$$

Comment on the sign of $\Delta_r G°$ and the magnitude of K_p.

29. Calculate $\Delta_r G°$ at 25 °C for the formation of 1.00 mol of $C_2H_6(g)$ from $C_2H_4(g)$ and $H_2(g)$. Use this value to calculate K_p for the equilibrium.

$$C_2H_4(g) + H_2(g) \rightleftharpoons C_2H_6(g)$$

Comment on the sign of $\Delta_r G°$ and the magnitude of K_p.

30. Calculate $\Delta_r G°$ at 25 °C for the formation of 1.00 mol of $C_2H_5OH(g)$ from $C_2H_4(g)$ and $H_2O(g)$. Use this value to calculate K_p for the equilibrium.

$$C_2H_4(g) + H_2O(g) \rightleftharpoons C_2H_5OH(g)$$

Comment on the sign of $\Delta_r G°$ and the magnitude of K_p.

Free Energy and Reaction Conditions

(See Section 18-7 and Example 18.9.)

31. For the synthesis of ammonia from its elements at 25 °C,

$$N_2(g) + 3\ H_2(g) \rightarrow 2\ NH_3(g)$$

(a) Calculate $\Delta_r G°$ using values of $\Delta_f G°$. Is the reaction product-favored at equilibrium?
(b) Calculate $\Delta_r G$ when the reactants and product are each present at a partial pressure of 0.10 atm. Is the reaction spontaneous under these conditions?

32. For the decomposition of solid calcium carbonate at 25 °C,

$$CaCO_3(s) \rightarrow CaO(s) + CO_2(g)$$

(a) Calculate $\Delta_r G°$ using values of $\Delta_f G°$. Is the reaction product-favored at equilibrium?
(b) Calculate $\Delta_r G$ when the partial pressure of carbon dioxide is 0.10 atm in the presence of both calcium carbonate and calcium oxide. Is the reaction spontaneous under these conditions?

General Questions

These questions are not designated as to type or location in the chapter. They may combine several concepts.

33. Compare the compounds in each set below and decide which is expected to have the higher entropy. Assume all are at the same temperature. Check your answers using data in Appendix L.

(a) HF(g), HCl(g), or HBr(g)
(b) $NH_4Cl(s)$ or $NH_4Cl(aq)$
(c) $C_2H_4(g)$ or $N_2(g)$ (two substances with the same molar mass)
(d) NaCl(s) or NaCl(g)

34. Using standard entropy values, calculate $\Delta_r S°$ for the formation of 1.0 mol of $NH_3(g)$ from $N_2(g)$ and $H_2(g)$ at 25 °C.

35. About 5 billion kilograms of benzene, C_6H_6, are made each year. Benzene is used as a starting material for many other compounds and as a solvent (although it is also a carcinogen, and its use is restricted). One compound that can be made from benzene is cyclohexane, C_6H_{12}.

$$C_6H_6(\ell) + 3\ H_2(g) \rightarrow C_6H_{12}(\ell)$$

$$\Delta_r H° = -206.7\ \text{kJ/mol-rxn};\ \Delta_r S° = -361.5\ \text{J/K} \cdot \text{mol-rxn}$$

Is this reaction predicted to be product-favored at equilibrium at 25 °C? Is the reaction enthalpy- or entropy-driven?

36. Hydrogenation, the addition of hydrogen to an organic compound, is an industrially important reaction. Calculate $\Delta_r H°$, $\Delta_r S°$, and $\Delta_r G°$ for the hydrogenation of octene, C_8H_{16}, to give octane, C_8H_{18}, at 25 °C. Is the reaction product- or reactant-favored at equilibrium?

$$C_8H_{16}(g) + H_2(g) \rightarrow C_8H_{18}(g)$$

Along with data in Appendix L, the following information is needed for this calculation.

Compound	$\Delta_f H°$ (kJ/mol)	$S°$ (J/K · mol)
Octene	−82.93	462.8
Octane	−208.45	463.639

37. Is the combustion of ethane, C_2H_6, product-favored at equilibrium at 25 °C?

$$C_2H_6(g) + \tfrac{7}{2}\ O_2(g) \rightarrow 2\ CO_2(g) + 3\ H_2O(g)$$

Answer the question by calculating the value of $\Delta S°$(universe) at 298 K, using values of $\Delta_f H°$ and $S°$ in Appendix L. Does the answer agree with your preconceived idea of this reaction?

38. Write a balanced equation that depicts the formation of 1 mol of $Fe_2O_3(s)$ from its elements. What is the standard free energy of formation of 1.00 mol of $Fe_2O_3(s)$? What is the value of $\Delta G°$ when 454 g (1 lb) of $Fe_2O_3(s)$ is formed from the elements?

39. When vapors from hydrochloric acid and aqueous ammonia come in contact, they react, producing a white "cloud" of solid NH_4Cl (Figure 18.9).

$$HCl(g) + NH_3(g) \rightleftharpoons NH_4Cl(s)$$

Defining the reactants and products as the system under study:

(a) Predict whether $\Delta S°$(system), $\Delta S°$(surroundings), $\Delta S°$(universe), $\Delta_r H°$, and $\Delta_r G°$ (at 298 K) are greater than zero, equal to zero, or less than zero; and explain your prediction. Verify your predictions by calculating values for each of these quantities.
(b) Calculate the value of K_p for this reaction at 298 K.

40. Calculate $\Delta S°$(system), $\Delta S°$(surroundings), and $\Delta S°$(universe) for each of the following processes at 298 K, and comment on how these systems differ.

(a) $HNO_3(g) \rightarrow HNO_3(aq)$
(b) $NaOH(s) \rightarrow NaOH(aq)$

41. Methanol is now widely used as a fuel in race cars. Consider the following reaction as a possible synthetic route to methanol.

$$C(graphite) + \tfrac{1}{2} O_2(g) + 2\ H_2(g) \rightleftharpoons CH_3OH(\ell)$$

Calculate K_p for the formation of methanol at 298 K using this reaction. Would this reaction be more product-favored at a different temperature?

42. The enthalpy of vaporization of liquid diethyl ether, $(C_2H_5)_2O$, is 26.0 kJ/mol at the boiling point of 35.0 °C. Calculate $\Delta S°$ for a vapor-to-liquid transformation at 35.0 °C.

43. Calculate the entropy change, $\Delta_r S°$, for the vaporization of ethanol, C_2H_5OH, at its normal boiling point, 78.0 °C. The enthalpy of vaporization of ethanol is 39.3 kJ/mol.

44. Using thermodynamic data, estimate the normal boiling point of ethanol. (Recall that liquid and vapor are in equilibrium at 1.0 atm pressure at the normal boiling point.) The actual normal boiling point is 78 °C. How well does your calculated result agree with the actual value?

45. The following reaction is reactant-favored at equilibrium at room temperature.

$$COCl_2(g) \rightarrow CO(g) + Cl_2(g)$$

Will raising or lowering the temperature make it product-favored?

46. When calcium carbonate is heated strongly, CO_2 gas is evolved. The equilibrium pressure of CO_2 is 1.00 bar at 897 °C, and $\Delta_r H°$ at 298 K is 179.0 kJ/mol-rxn.

$$CaCO_3(s) \rightarrow CaO(s) + CO_2(g)$$

Estimate the value of $\Delta_r S°$ at 897 °C for the reaction.

47. Sodium reacts violently with water according to the equation

$$Na(s) + H_2O(\ell) \rightarrow NaOH(aq) + \tfrac{1}{2} H_2(g)$$

Without doing calculations, predict the signs of $\Delta_r H°$ and $\Delta_r S°$ for the reaction. Verify your prediction with a calculation.

48. Yeast can produce ethanol by the fermentation of glucose $(C_6H_{12}O_6)$, which is the basis for the production of most alcoholic beverages.

$$C_6H_{12}O_6(aq) \rightarrow 2\ C_2H_5OH(\ell) + 2\ CO_2(g)$$

Calculate $\Delta_r H°$, $\Delta_r S°$, and $\Delta_r G°$ for the reaction at 25 °C. Is the reaction product- or reactant-favored at equilibrium? In addition to the thermodynamic values in Appendix L, you will need the following data for $C_6H_{12}O_6(aq)$:

$\Delta_f H° = -1260.0$ kJ/mol; $S° = 289$ J/K · mol; and $\Delta_f G° = -918.8$ kJ/mol.

49. Elemental boron, in the form of thin fibers, can be made by reducing a boron halide with H_2.

$$BCl_3(g) + \tfrac{3}{2} H_2(g) \rightarrow B(s) + 3\ HCl(g)$$

Calculate $\Delta_r H°$, $\Delta_r S°$, and $\Delta_r G°$ at 25 °C for this reaction. Is the reaction predicted to be product-favored at equilibrium at 25 °C? If so, is it enthalpy- or entropy-driven? [$S°$ for B(s) is 5.86 J/K · mol.]

50. ▲ Estimate the vapor pressure of ethanol at 37 °C using thermodynamic data. Express the result in millimeters of mercury.

51. The equilibrium constant, K_p, for $N_2O_4(g) \rightleftharpoons 2\ NO_2(g)$ is 0.14 at 25 °C. Calculate $\Delta_r G°$ for the conversion of $N_2O_4(g)$ to $NO_2(g)$ from this constant, and compare this value with that determined from the $\Delta_f G°$ values in Appendix L.

52. ▲ Estimate the boiling point of water in Denver, Colorado (where the altitude is 1.60 km and the atmospheric pressure is 630 mm Hg or 0.840 bar).

53. The equilibrium constant for the butane $\rightleftharpoons$ isobutane equilibrium at 25 °C is 2.50. Calculate $\Delta_r G°$ at this temperature in units of kJ/mol.

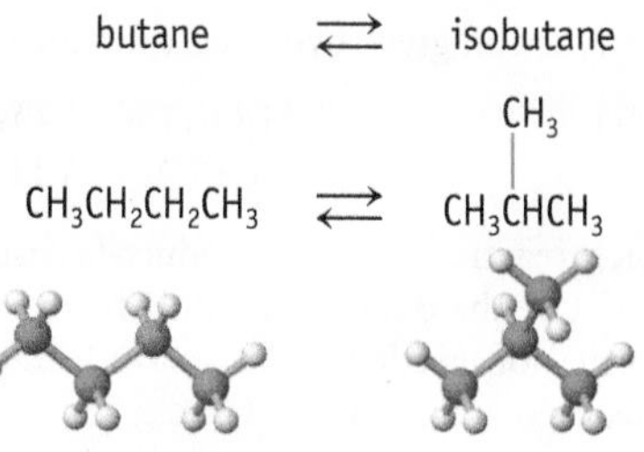

$$K_c = \frac{[\text{isobutane}]}{[\text{butane}]} = 2.50 \text{ at } 298\ K$$

54. A crucial reaction for the production of synthetic fuels is the production of H_2 by the reaction of coal with steam. The chemical reaction is

$$C(s) + H_2O(g) \rightarrow CO(g) + H_2(g)$$

(a) Calculate $\Delta_r G°$ for this reaction at 25 °C, assuming C(s) is graphite.
(b) Calculate K_p for the reaction at 25 °C.
(c) Is the reaction predicted to be product-favored at equilibrium at 25 °C? If not, at what temperature will it become so?

55. Calculate $\Delta_r G°$ for the decomposition of sulfur trioxide to sulfur dioxide and oxygen.

$$2\ SO_3(g) \rightleftharpoons 2\ SO_2(g) + O_2(g)$$

(a) Is the reaction product-favored at equilibrium at 25 °C?
(b) If the reaction is not product-favored at 25 °C, is there a temperature at which it will become so? Estimate this temperature.
(c) Estimate the equilibrium constant for the reaction at 1500 °C.

56. Methanol can be made by partial oxidation of methane by $O_2(g)$.

$$CH_4(g) + \frac{1}{2} O_2(g) \rightleftharpoons CH_3OH(\ell)$$

(a) Determine $\Delta S°$(system), $\Delta S°$(surroundings), and $\Delta S°$(universe) for this process.
(b) Is this reaction product-favored at equilibrium at 25 °C?

57. A cave in Mexico was recently discovered to have some interesting chemistry. Hydrogen sulfide, H_2S, reacts with oxygen in the cave to give sulfuric acid, which drips from the ceiling in droplets with a pH less than 1. The reaction occurring is

$$H_2S(g) + 2\ O_2(g) \rightarrow H_2SO_4(\ell)$$

Calculate $\Delta_r H°$, $\Delta_r S°$, and $\Delta_r G°$. Is the reaction product-favored at equilibrium at 25 °C? Is it enthalpy- or entropy-driven?

58. Wet limestone is used to scrub SO_2 gas from the exhaust gases of power plants. One possible reaction gives hydrated calcium sulfite:

$$CaCO_3(s) + SO_2(g) + \frac{1}{2} H_2O(\ell) \rightleftharpoons CaSO_3 \cdot \frac{1}{2} H_2O(s) + CO_2(g)$$

Another reaction gives hydrated calcium sulfate:

$$CaCO_3(s) + SO_2(g) + \frac{1}{2} H_2O(\ell) + \frac{1}{2} O_2(g) \rightleftharpoons CaSO_4 \cdot \frac{1}{2} H_2O(s) + CO_2(g)$$

(a) Which reaction is more product-favored at equilibrium? Use the data in the table below and any other information needed in Appendix L to calculate $\Delta_r G°$ for each reaction at 25 °C.

	$CaSO_3 \cdot \frac{1}{2} H_2O(s)$	$CaSO_4 \cdot \frac{1}{2} H_2O(s)$
$\Delta_f H°$ (kJ/mol)	−1311.7	−1574.65
$S°$ (J/K · mol)	121.3	134.8

(b) Calculate $\Delta_r G°$ for the reaction

$$CaSO_3 \cdot \frac{1}{2} H_2O(s) + \frac{1}{2} O_2(g) \rightleftharpoons CaSO_4 \cdot \frac{1}{2} H_2O(s)$$

Is this reaction product- or reactant-favored at equilibrium?

59. Sulfur undergoes a phase transition between 80 and 100 °C.

$$S_8(\text{rhombic}) \rightarrow S_8(\text{monoclinic})$$

$$\Delta_r H° = 3.213 \text{ kJ/mol-rxn} \quad \Delta_r S° = 8.7 \text{ J/K} \cdot \text{mol-rxn}$$

(a) Estimate $\Delta_r G°$ for the transition at 80.0 °C and 110.0 °C. What do these results tell you about the stability of the two forms of sulfur at each of these temperatures?
(b) Calculate the temperature at which $\Delta_r G° = 0$. What is the significance of this temperature?

60. Calculate the entropy change for dissolving HCl gas in water at 25 °C. Is the sign of $\Delta_r S°$ what you expected? Why or why not?

In the Laboratory

61. Some metal oxides can be decomposed to the metal and oxygen under reasonable conditions. Is the decomposition of silver(I) oxide product-favored at equilibrium at 25 °C?

$$2\ Ag_2O(s) \rightarrow 4\ Ag(s) + O_2(g)$$

If not, can it become so if the temperature is raised? At what temperature does the reaction become product-favored at equilibrium?

62. Copper(II) oxide, CuO, can be reduced to copper metal with hydrogen at higher temperatures.

$$CuO(s) + H_2(g) \rightarrow Cu(s) + H_2O(g)$$

Is this reaction product- or reactant-favored at equilibrium at 298 K?

© Cengage Learning/Charles D. Winters

If copper metal is heated in air, a black film of CuO forms on the surface. In this photo, the heated bar, covered with a black CuO film, has been bathed in hydrogen gas. Black, solid CuO is reduced rapidly to copper at higher temperatures.

63. Calculate $\Delta_f G°$ for HI(g) at 350 °C, given the following equilibrium partial pressures: $P(H_2) = 0.132$ bar, $P(I_2) = 0.295$ bar, and $P(HI) = 1.61$ bar. At 350 °C and 1 bar, I_2 is a gas.

$$\frac{1}{2} H_2(g) + \frac{1}{2} I_2(g) \rightleftharpoons HI(g)$$

64. Calculate the equilibrium constant for the formation of NiO at 1627 °C. Can the reaction proceed in the forward direction if the initial pressure of O_2 is below 1.00 mm Hg? {$\Delta_f G°$ [NiO(s)] = −72.1 kJ/mol at 1627 °C}

$$Ni(s) + \frac{1}{2} O_2(g) \rightleftharpoons NiO(s)$$

65. Titanium(IV) oxide is converted to titanium carbide with carbon at a high temperature.

$$TiO_2(s) + 3\ C(s) \rightarrow 2\ CO(g) + TiC(s)$$

Compound	Free Energies of Formation at 727 °C, kJ/mol
$TiO_2(s)$	−757.8
TiC(s)	−162.6
CO(g)	−200.2

(a) Calculate $\Delta_r G°$ and K at 727 °C
(b) Is the reaction product-favored at equilibrium at this temperature?
(c) How can the reactant or product concentrations be adjusted for the reaction to proceed at 727 °C?

66. Cisplatin [*cis*-diamminedichloroplatinum(II)] is a potent treatment for certain types of cancers, but the *trans* isomer is not effective. What is the equilibrium constant at 298 K for the transformation of the *cis* to the *trans* isomer? Which is the favored isomer at 298 K, the *cis* or the *trans* isomer?

Compound	$\Delta_f H°$ (kJ/mol, 298 K)	$\Delta_f G°$ (kJ/mol, 298 K)
Cis-$Pt(NH_3)_2Cl_2$	−467.4	−228.7
Trans-$Pt(NH_3)_2Cl_2$	−480.3	−222.8

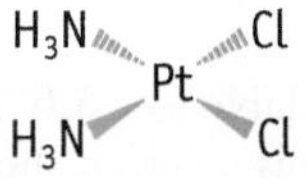

cis isomer

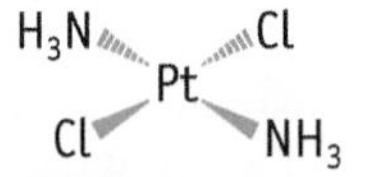

trans isomer

Summary and Conceptual Questions

The following questions may use concepts from this and previous chapters.

67. ▲ Mercury vapor is dangerous because breathing it brings this toxic element into the lungs. We wish to estimate the vapor pressure of mercury at two different temperatures from the following data:

	$\Delta_f H°$ (kJ/mol)	$S°$ (J/K · mol)	$\Delta_f G°$ (kJ/mol)
Hg(ℓ)	0	76.02	0
Hg(g)	61.38	174.97	31.88

Estimate the temperature at which K_p for the process Hg(ℓ) ⇌ Hg(g) is equal to 1.00 (and the vapor pressure of Hg is 1.00 bar). Next, estimate the temperature at which the vapor pressure is (1/760) bar. (Experimental vapor pressures are 1.00 mm Hg at 126.2 °C and 1.00 bar at 356.6 °C.) (*Note:* The temperature at which $P = 1.00$ bar can be calculated from thermodynamic data. To find the other temperature, you will need to use the temperature for $P = 1.00$ bar and the Clausius–Clapeyron equation in Section 11-6.)

68. Explain why each of the following statements is incorrect.

(a) Entropy increases in all spontaneous reactions.
(b) Reactions with a negative free energy change ($\Delta_r G° < 0$) are product-favored and occur with rapid transformation of reactants to products.
(c) All spontaneous processes are exothermic.
(d) Endothermic processes are never spontaneous.

69. Decide whether each of the following statements is true or false. If false, rewrite it to make it true.

(a) The entropy of a substance increases on going from the liquid to the vapor state at any temperature.
(b) An exothermic reaction will always be spontaneous.
(c) Reactions with a positive $\Delta_r H°$ and a positive $\Delta_r S°$ can never be product-favored.
(d) If $\Delta_r G°$ for a reaction is negative, the reaction will have an equilibrium constant greater than 1.

70. Under what conditions is the entropy of a pure substance 0 J/K · mol? Could a substance at standard conditions at 25 °C have a value of 0 J/K · mol? A negative entropy value? Are there any conditions under which a substance will have negative entropy? Explain your answer.

71. In Chapter 13, you learned that entropy, as well as enthalpy, plays a role in the solution process. If $\Delta H°$ for the solution process is zero, explain how the process can be driven by entropy.

72. ▲ Consider the formation of NO(g) from its elements.

$$N_2(g) + O_2(g) \rightleftharpoons 2\ NO(g)$$

(a) Calculate K_p at 25 °C. Is the reaction product-favored at equilibrium at this temperature?
(b) Assuming $\Delta_r H°$ and $\Delta_r S°$ are nearly constant with temperature, calculate $\Delta_r G°$ at 700 °C. Estimate K_p from the new value of $\Delta_r G°$ at 700 °C. Is the reaction product-favored at equilibrium at 700 °C?
(c) Using K_p at 700 °C, calculate the equilibrium partial pressures of the three gases if you mix 1.00 bar each of N_2 and O_2.

73. Write a chemical equation for the oxidation of $C_2H_6(g)$ by $O_2(g)$ to form $CO_2(g)$ and $H_2O(g)$. Defining this as the system:

(a) Predict whether the signs of $\Delta S°$(system), $\Delta S°$(surroundings), and $\Delta S°$(universe) will be greater than zero, equal to zero, or less than zero. Explain your prediction.
(b) Predict the signs of $\Delta_r H°$ and $\Delta_r G°$. Explain how you made this prediction.
(c) Will the value of K_p be very large, very small, or near 1? Will the equilibrium constant, K_p, for this system be larger or smaller at temperatures greater than 298 K? Explain how you made this prediction.

74. The normal melting point of benzene, C_6H_6, is 5.5 °C. For the process of melting, what is the sign of each of the following?

(a) $\Delta_r H°$
(b) $\Delta_r S°$
(c) $\Delta_r G°$ at 5.5 °C
(d) $\Delta_r G°$ at 0.0 °C
(e) $\Delta_r G°$ at 25.0 °C

75. Calculate the standard molar entropy change, $\Delta_r S°$, for each of the following reactions at 25 °C:

1. $C(s) + 2\ H_2(g) \rightarrow CH_4(g)$
2. $CH_4(g) + \frac{1}{2}\ O_2(g) \rightarrow CH_3OH(\ell)$
3. $C(s) + 2\ H_2(g) + \frac{1}{2}\ O_2(g) \rightarrow CH_3OH(\ell)$

Verify that these values are related by the equation $\Delta_r S°(1) + \Delta_r S°(2) = \Delta_r S°(3)$. What general principle is illustrated here?

76. For each of the following processes, predict the algebraic sign of $\Delta_r H°$, $\Delta_r S°$, and $\Delta_r G°$. No calculations are necessary; use your common sense.

(a) The decomposition of liquid water to give gaseous oxygen and hydrogen, a process that requires a considerable amount of energy.
(b) Dynamite is a mixture of nitroglycerin, $C_3H_5N_3O_9$, and diatomaceous earth. The explosive decomposition of nitroglycerin gives gaseous products such as water, CO_2, and others; much heat is evolved.
(c) The combustion of gasoline in the engine of your car, as exemplified by the combustion of octane.

$$2\ C_8H_{18}(g) + 25\ O_2(g) \rightarrow 16\ CO_2(g) + 18\ H_2O(g)$$

77. "Heater Meals" are food packages that contain their own heat source. Just pour water into the heater unit, wait a few minutes, and voilà! You have a hot meal.

$$Mg(s) + 2\ H_2O(\ell) \rightarrow Mg(OH)_2(s) + H_2(g)$$

© Cengage Learning/Charles D. Winters

The heat for the heater unit is produced by the reaction of magnesium with water.

(a) Confirm that this is a product-favored reaction at equilibrium at 25 °C.
(b) What mass of magnesium is required to produce sufficient energy to heat 225 mL of water (density = 0.995 g/mL) from 25 °C to the boiling point?

78. Use values of $\Delta_f G°$ for solid and gaseous iodine at 25 °C (Appendix L) to calculate the equilibrium vapor pressure of iodine at this temperature.

© Cengage Learning/Charles D. Winters

Iodine, I_2, readily sublimes at room temperature.

79. Oxygen dissolved in water can cause corrosion in hot-water heating systems. To remove oxygen, hydrazine (N_2H_4) is often added. Hydrazine reacts with dissolved O_2 to form water and N_2.

(a) Write a balanced chemical equation for the reaction of hydrazine and oxygen. Identify the oxidizing and reducing agents in this redox reaction.
(b) Calculate $\Delta_r H°$, $\Delta_r S°$, and $\Delta_r G°$ for this reaction involving 1 mol of N_2H_4 at 25 °C.
(c) Because this is an exothermic reaction, energy is evolved as heat. What temperature change is expected in a heating system containing 5.5×10^4 L of water? (Assume no energy is lost to the surroundings.)
(d) The mass of a hot-water heating system is 5.5×10^4 kg. What amount of O_2 (in moles) would be present in this system if it is filled with water saturated with O_2? (The solubility of O_2 in water at 25 °C is 0.000434 g per 100 g of water.)
(e) Assume hydrazine is available as a 5.0% solution in water. What mass of this solution should be added to totally consume the dissolved O_2 [described in part (d)]?
(f) Assuming the N_2 escapes as a gas, calculate the volume of $N_2(g)$ (measured at 273 K and 1.00 atm) that will be produced.

80. The formation of diamond from graphite is a process of considerable importance.

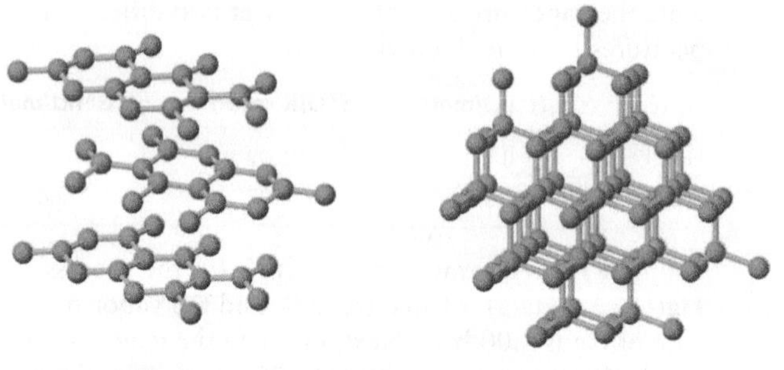

graphite diamond

(a) Using data in Appendix L, calculate $\Delta_r S°$, $\Delta_r H°$, and $\Delta_r G°$ for this process at 25 °C.
(b) The calculations will suggest that this process is not possible at any temperature. However, the synthesis of diamonds by this reaction is a commercial process. How can this contradiction be rationalized? (*Note:* In the industrial synthesis, high pressure and high temperatures are used.)

81. Iodine, I_2, dissolves readily in carbon tetrachloride. For this process, $\Delta H° = 0$ kJ/mol.

$$I_2(s) \rightarrow I_2\ (\text{in } CCl_4 \text{ solution})$$

What is the sign of $\Delta_r G°$? Is the dissolving process entropy-driven or enthalpy-driven? Explain briefly.

82. Write an equation for the reaction of $Fe_2O_3(s)$ and C(s) to give Fe(s) and CO(g) (one of the reactions occurring in a blast furnace). How does $\Delta_r G°$ vary with temperature? Is there a temperature at which the reaction is product-favored at equilibrium?

83. Write an equation for the decomposition of 1.0 mol of gaseous methanol to the elements in their standard states.

(a) How does the value of $\Delta_r G°$ change as the the temperature increases?
(b) Is there a temperature between 400 K and 1000 K at which the decomposition is product-favored at equilibrium?

84. Consider the reaction of NO and Cl_2 to produce NOCl.

(a) What is $\Delta S°$(system) for this reaction?
(b) Does $\Delta S°$(system) change with temperature?
(c) Does $\Delta S°$(surroundings) change with temperature?
(d) Does $\Delta S°$(universe) always change with an increase in temperature?
(e) Do exothermic reactions always lead to positive values of $\Delta S°$(universe)?
(f) Is the NO + Cl_2 reaction spontaneous at 298 K? At 700 K?

85. Two processes that can be used to generate hydrogen are the electrolysis of water

$$2\ H_2O(\ell) \rightarrow 2\ H_2(g) + O_2(g)$$

and the reaction of methane with steam

$$CH_4(g) + H_2O(g) \rightarrow 3\ H_2(g) + CO(g)$$

(a) Calculate $\Delta_r G°$ for each reaction.
(b) For each reaction, calculate $\Delta G°$ per mole of hydrogen produced.
(c) Which process do you think is better to use to obtain hydrogen? Explain.

86. Hydrogen and methane are two possible replacements for gasoline in automobiles. The reactions for their combustion are as follows:

$$H_2(g) + \tfrac{1}{2}\ O_2(g) \rightarrow H_2O(\ell)$$

$$CH_4(g) + 2\ O_2(g) \rightarrow CO_2(g) + 2\ H_2O(\ell)$$

(a) Calculate $\Delta_r G°$ for each reaction.
(b) Calculate $\Delta G°$ for each fuel on a per gram basis.
(c) Which is a better fuel? Explain.

87. ▲ The Haber–Bosch process for the production of ammonia is one of the key industrial processes in developed countries.

$$N_2(g) + 3\ H_2(g) \rightleftharpoons 2\ NH_3(g)$$

(a) Calculate $\Delta_r G°$ for the reaction at 298 K, 800 K, and 1300 K. Data at 298 K are given in Appendix L. Data for the other temperatures are as follows:

Temperature	$\Delta_r H°$ (kJ/mol)	$\Delta_r S°$ (J/K · mol)
800 K	−107.4	−225.4
1300 K	−112.4	−228.0

How does the $\Delta_r G°$change with temperature?
(b) Calculate the equilibrium constant for the reaction at 298 K, 800 K, and 1300 K.
(c) At what temperature (298 K, 800 K, or 1300 K) is the mole fraction of NH_3 the greatest?

88. ▲ Muscle cells need energy to contract. One biochemical pathway for energy transfer is the breakdown of glucose to pyruvate in a process called *glycolysis*. In the presence of sufficient oxygen in the cell, pyruvate is oxidized to CO_2 and H_2O to make further energy available. However, under extreme conditions not enough oxygen can be supplied to the cells, so muscle cells produce lactate ion according to the reaction

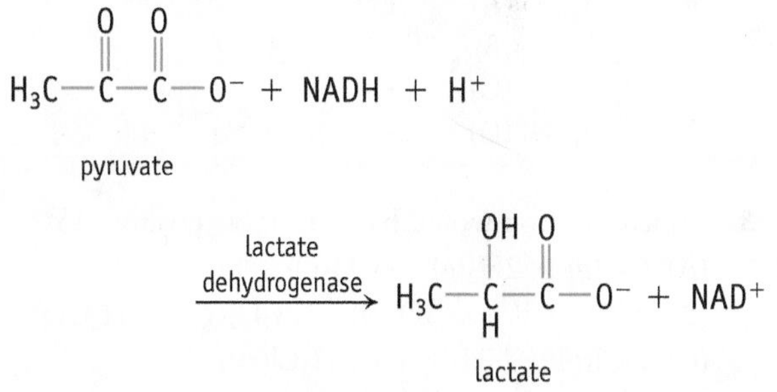

where $\Delta_r G°' = -25.1$ kJ/mol. In living cells, the pH value is about 7. The hydronium ion concentration is constant and is included in $\Delta G°$, which is then called $\Delta_r G°'$ (as explained on page 706). *(This problem is taken from the problems for the 36th International Chemistry Olympiad for high school students held in Kiel, Germany, in 2004.)*

(a) Calculate $\Delta_r G°$ for the reaction at 25 °C.
(b) Calculate the equilibrium constant K'. (The hydronium ion concentration is included in the constant. That is, $K' = K \cdot [H_3O^+]$ for the reaction at 25 °C and pH = 7.0.)
(c) $\Delta_r G°'$ is the free energy change under standard conditions; that is, the concentrations of all reactants (except H_3O^+) are 1.00 mol/L. Calculate $\Delta_r G'$ at 25 °C, assuming the following concentrations in the cell: pyruvate, 380 μmol/L; NADH, 50 μmol/L; lactate ion, 3700 μmol/L; and NAD^+ ion, 540 μmol/L.

AP Multiple-Choice Review Questions

1. Consider the freezing of liquid water at −10 °C and 1 atm. For this process, what are the signs for ΔH, ΔS, and ΔG?

	ΔH	ΔS	ΔG
(A)	+	−	0
(B)	−	+	0
(C)	+	+	−
(D)	−	−	−

2. A 100-mL sample of water is placed in a coffee-cup calorimeter. Solid NaCl is then dissolved in the water. The temperature of the water decreases from 20.5 °C to 19.7 °C and is then allowed to return to room temperature (20.5 °C). Determine the signs for ΔH and ΔS for the process of dissolving NaCl and ΔG for the entire process at constant temperature.

	ΔH	ΔS	ΔG
(A)	+	−	0
(B)	−	+	0
(C)	+	+	−
(D)	−	−	−

3. Which reaction would have the most positive $\Delta S°$?

(A) $CO(g) + 2H_2(g) \rightarrow CH_3OH(\ell)$

(B) $2CH_3OH(g) + 3O_2(g) \rightarrow 2CO_2(g) + 4H_2O(g)$

(C) $HCl(g) + NH_3(g) \rightarrow NH_4Cl(s)$

(D) $Ba(OH)_2 \cdot 8H_2O(s) + 2NH_4NO_3(s) \rightarrow Ba(NO_3)_2(s) + 2NH_3(g) + 10H_2O(\ell)$

4. Solutions A and B are both clear and colorless. When Solution A is mixed with Solution B, the temperature of the mixture increases and a yellow precipitate is observed. What can be concluded from these observations?

(A) The reaction is thermodynamically favored (spontaneous) at all temperatures.

(B) The reaction is thermodynamically favored (spontaneous) only at high temperatures.

(C) The reaction is thermodynamically favored (spontaneous) only at low temperatures.

(D) The reaction is not thermodynamically favored (spontaneous) at any temperature.

Questions 5–8 refer to the following information:

The removal of copper from metallic ores has been a challenge since ancient times. Strong heating of copper(II) carbonate results in the formation of copper(II) oxide.

Although the decomposition of copper(II) oxide into copper metal and oxygen gas is not thermodynamically favorable under standard conditions, it may be made favorable by adding carbon to the mixture.

The resulting reaction is: $2CuO(s) + C(s) \rightarrow 2Cu(s) + CO_2(g)$.

$CuO(s) \rightarrow Cu(s) + \frac{1}{2}O_2(g)$ $\Delta G° = 128$ kJ/mol

$C(s) + O_2(g) \rightarrow CO_2(g)$ $\Delta G° = -394$ kJ/mol

5. Calculate $\Delta G°$ for the overall reaction.

(A) −138 kJ/mol

(B) −266 kJ/mol

(C) 522 kJ/mol

(D) 650 kJ/mol

6. Predict and justify the sign of $\Delta S°$ for the reaction $CuO(s) \rightarrow Cu(s) + \frac{1}{2}O_2(g)$.

(A) ΔS is positive because ΔG is positive.

(B) ΔS is negative because ΔG is positive.

(C) ΔS is positive because the products have more moles of gas than the reactant.

(D) ΔS is negative because the products have more moles of gas than the reactant.

7. Why is the overall process thermodynamically favorable?

(A) Carbon serves as a catalyst to lower the activation energy of the reaction.

(B) The process involves coupling a very thermodynamically favorable reaction with one that is not thermodynamically favored.

(C) When two reactions are coupled, free energy is always released.

(D) The addition of carbon speeds up the reaction because powdered carbon has a large surface area.

8. Which statement is correct about the value of K for the reaction $2CuO(s) + C(s) \rightarrow 2Cu(s) + CO_2(g)$ at standard conditions?

(A) K will be less than 1.

(B) K will be 0.

(C) K will be between 0 and 1.

(D) K will be greater than 1.

9. Under normal conditions, an iron nail rusts so slowly that the reaction is not easily observed. What must be true?

(A) The reaction occurs, but very slowly.

(B) The product of the reaction is an invisible gas.

(C) The reaction does not occur without a catalyst.

(D) The reaction is not thermodynamically favorable.

10. Calculate the $\Delta G°$ for the following equation: $2SO_2(g) + O_2(g) \rightarrow 2SO_3(g)$

$\Delta G_f°$ for $SO_2 = -300$ kJ/mol

$\Delta G_f°$ for $SO_3 = -371$ kJ/mol

(A) −71 kJ/mol

(B) −142 kJ/mol

(C) 71 kJ/mol

(D) 671 kJ/mol

AP Free Response Review Questions

Question Format: Short

Category of Question: Quantitative

Ethyne, $C_2H_2(g)$, is reacted with chlorine gas to make tetrachloroethane, $C_2H_2Cl_4(\ell)$, which is the refrigerant R-130.

Questions

(a) Write a balanced chemical equation for this reaction.

(b) Predict the sign of ΔS for this reaction and explain your reasoning.

At low temperatures, this reaction is thermodynamically favored, while at higher temperatures the reaction becomes thermodynamically unfavored.

(c) Predict the sign of ΔH for this reaction and explain your reasoning.

1C2H2 + 2Cl2 → 1C2H2Cl4

ΔG = ΔH − TΔS

−G = ΔH − TΔ−S

+

Q=mHf

Question Format: Long

Category of Question: Quantitative

Below is the phase change diagram for water.

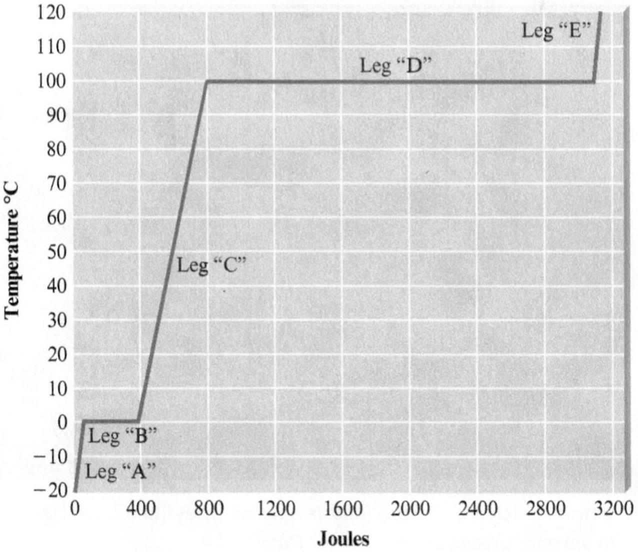

Questions

(a) What is occurring on "leg D" and what is the temperature?

(b) What is the value of ΔG for "leg D"? Explain your answer.

(c) Using the information in the table below, determine each of the following values for "leg D," going from left to right across the chart.

(i) ΔH_{rxn}

(ii) ΔS_{rxn}

	$\Delta H°_f$ (kJ/mol)	$S°$ (J/mol K)
H_2O (liquid)	−285.83	69.95
H_2O (gas)	−241.83	188.84

(d) Calculate the boiling point of water using your answers from part (C).

(e) Account for the fact that your answer from part (D) and the temperature from reading the graph are not the same.

ΔG = ΔH − TΔS

neg. bc exothermic

none

ΔG = (−) − (+)

Courtesy Tesla Motors

Electric vehicles. The Tesla Motors Roadster uses lithium-ion batteries for propulsion. (For more on lithium-ion batteries see *Case Study: Lithium and "Green Cars"* in Chapter 12.)

Principles of Chemical Reactivity: Electron Transfer Reactions

Chapter Outline

BATTERY POWER The 20th century was the century of the use and abuse of petroleum. The 21st century has to be the century of the discovery and use of alternative energy sources. Many of these will involve electrochemistry, the use of chemical reactions to produce electricity (batteries), or the use of electricity to produce chemical change (electrolysis).

The lithium-ion battery in your laptop computer or your phone, or the nickel-metal hydride battery in your hybrid car, works because redox reactions release chemical energy. (When you recharge the battery, you use electric energy to rejuvenate the chemicals in the battery.) But don't for a moment think that everything is understood about batteries or how to make them smaller, cheaper, or more efficient. Researchers at companies and universities around the world are searching for new battery designs that are lightweight, inexpensive, safe, environmentally kind, and that produce sufficient energy.

Chapter Goals

See Chapter Goals Revisited (page 759) for Study Questions keyed to these goals.

UNDERSTAND

- The principles underlying voltaic cells.
- How to use electrochemical potentials.
- Electrical energy is used to produce chemical change in electrolysis.

DO

- Balance equations for oxidation–reduction reactions in acidic or basic solutions using the half-reaction approach.
- Relate the quantity of a substance oxidized or reduced to the amount of current and the time the current flows.
- Use the relationships between cell voltage ($E°_{cell}$) and free energy ($\Delta_r G°$) and between $E°_{cell}$ and an equilibrium constant for the cell reaction.

REMEMBER

- Voltaic cells use chemical reactions to produce electric current; electrolysis cells use electric current to bring about chemical change.
- Oxidation occurs at an anode and reduction occurs at a cathode.
- The differences between primary and secondary batteries.

One of the most important areas of battery research today is the development of lithium-based, rechargeable batteries. Two physical properties of lithium make it an ideal choice for batteries: lithium has the lowest molar mass, and it produces the highest voltages of all metals. Lithium's molar mass (6.941 g/mol) is significantly lower than that of other metals commonly used in batteries. (The molar mass of lead, the metal used in most automobile batteries, is 207.2 g/mol.) The oxidation of only 7 grams of lithium produces one mole of electrons, whereas 104 grams of lead is required to produce an equivalent amount of electrons. Lithium also produces a greater voltage than other batteries. Lithium-ion battery cells produce approximately 3.7 volts, nearly twice the voltage of a lead-acid battery cell. This combination of low mass and high voltage enables lithium batteries to produce the highest energy density (often measured in watt·hours/kg) of any currently produced batteries. Finally, lithium-ion batteries may be discharged and recharged through many cycles with minimal loss in functionality.

You may be wondering why lithium-ion batteries have not entirely replaced other types of rechargeable batteries, especially in the transportation industry where lighter weight vehicles translate into lower fuel costs. A major problem is that when lithium-ion batteries fail, they sometimes fail catastrophically. Heat generated from overcharging the batteries or from internal short-circuiting can destroy the batteries and even cause fires. In early 2013 Boeing Airline's entire fleet of new 787 aircraft was grounded due to two separate lithium-ion battery failures. In one incident a battery overheated and emitted smoke while the airplane was in flight. In the second, a battery erupted in flames while the plane was parked at a terminal. Events such as these illustrate why further research into making lithium-ion batteries safer is necessary.

Study Questions related to this story are: 19.97 and 19.98.

Let us introduce you to electrochemistry and electron transfer reactions with a simple experiment. Place a piece of copper in an aqueous solution of silver nitrate. After a short time, metallic silver deposits on the copper, and the solution takes on the blue color typical of aqueous Cu^{2+} ions (Figure 19.1). The following oxidation–reduction (redox) reaction has occurred:

$$Cu(s) + 2\ Ag^+(aq) \rightarrow Cu^{2+}(aq) + 2\ Ag(s)$$

At the particulate level, Ag^+ ions in solution come into direct contact with the copper surface where the transfer of electrons occurs. Two electrons are transferred from a Cu atom to two Ag^+ ions. Copper ions, Cu^{2+}, enter the solution, and silver atoms are deposited on the copper surface. This product-favored reaction continues until one or both of the reactants is consumed.

Could the reaction between copper metal and silver ions be used to generate an electric current? When the reactants, Cu(s) and $Ag^+(aq)$, are in direct contact, electrons are transferred directly from copper atoms to silver ions, and an increase in temperature (heating) rather than electrical work results. Instead, the reaction must be run in an apparatus that allows electrons to be transferred from one reactant to the other through an electrical circuit. The movement of electrons through the circuit would constitute an electric current that could be used to light a lightbulb or to run a motor.

Devices that use chemical reactions to produce an electric current are called **voltaic cells** or **galvanic cells**, names honoring Count Alessandro Volta (1745–1827) and Luigi Galvani (1737–1798). All voltaic cells work in the same general way: They use product-favored redox reactions, and the electrons from the species being

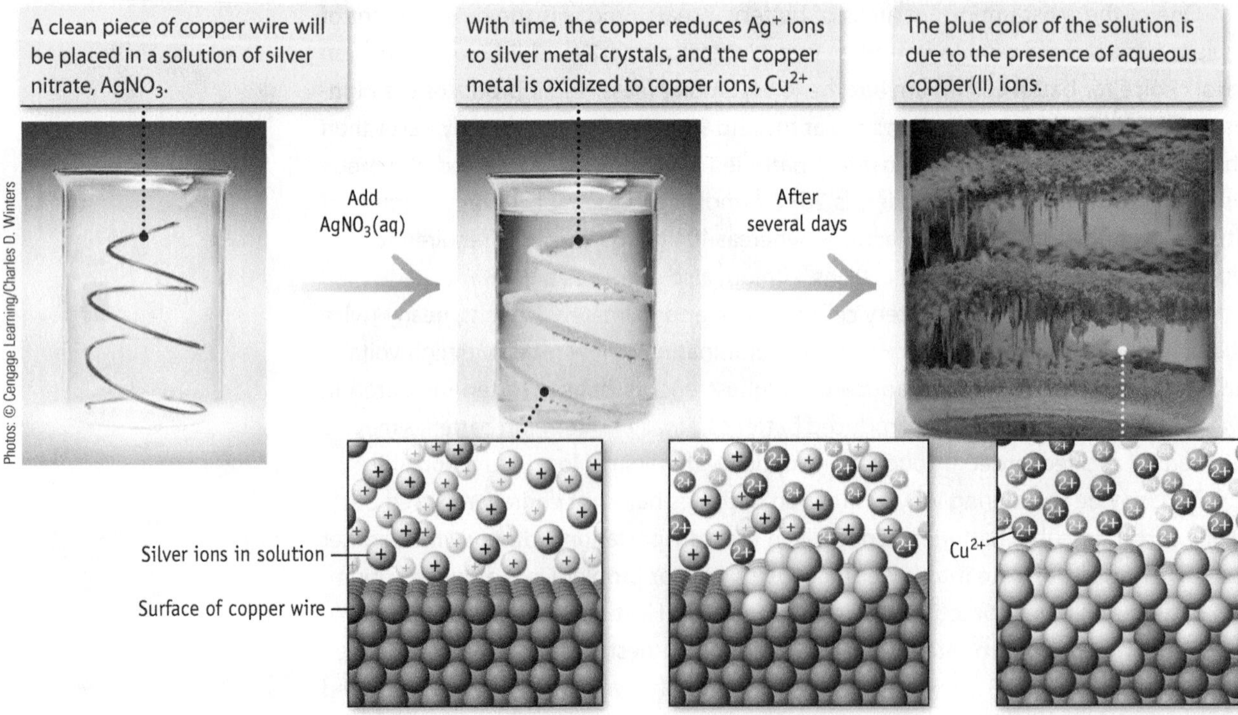

FIGURE 19.1 The oxidation of copper by silver ions. For clarity, water molecules are not shown.

oxidized (the reducing agent) are transferred through an electric circuit to the species being reduced.

A voltaic cell converts chemical energy to electrical energy. The opposite process, the use of electric energy to effect a chemical change, occurs in **electrolysis**. An example is the electrolysis of water, in which electrical energy is used to split water into its component elements, hydrogen and oxygen. Electrolysis is also used to electroplate one metal onto another, to obtain aluminum from its common ore (bauxite, mostly Al_2O_3), and to prepare important chemicals such as chlorine.

Electrochemistry is the field of chemistry that studies chemical reactions that produce or are caused by electrical energy. Because all electrochemical reactions are oxidation–reduction (redox) reactions, we begin our exploration of this subject by first describing electron transfer reactions in more detail.

Two Types of Electrochemical Processes
- Chemical change can produce an electric current in a voltaic cell.
- Electric energy can cause chemical change in the process of electrolysis.

19-1 Oxidation–Reduction Reactions

Learning Objectives: LO 3.2

In an oxidation–reduction reaction, electron transfer occurs between a reducing agent and an oxidizing agent (◀ Section 3-8). The essential features of all electron transfer reactions are as follows:

- One reactant is oxidized, and one is reduced.
- The extent of oxidation and reduction must balance.
- The oxidizing agent (the chemical species causing oxidation) is reduced.
- The reducing agent (the chemical species causing reduction) is oxidized.

Oxidation Numbers Oxidation numbers (see Section 3-8) can be used to determine whether a substance is oxidized or reduced. An element is oxidized if its oxidation number increases. The oxidation number decreases in a reduction.

These aspects of oxidation–reduction or redox reactions are illustrated for the reaction of copper metal and silver ion (see Figure 19.1).

Cu oxidized, oxidation number increases; Cu is the reducing agent.

$$Cu(s) + 2\ Ag^+(aq) \longrightarrow Cu^{2+}(aq) + 2\ Ag(s)$$

Ag^+ reduced, oxidation number decreases; Ag^+ is the oxidizing agent.

Balancing Oxidation–Reduction Equations

All equations for oxidation–reduction reactions must be balanced for both mass and charge. The same number of atoms appear in the products and reactants of an equation, and the sum of electric charges of all the species on each side of the equation arrow must be the same. Charge balance guarantees that the number of electrons produced in oxidation equals the number of electrons consumed in reduction.

Balancing some redox equations can be complicated, but fortunately some systematic procedures can be used in these cases. Here, we describe the **half-reaction method**, a procedure that involves writing separate, balanced equations for the oxidation and reduction processes. One half-reaction describes the oxidation part of the reaction, and a second half-reaction describes the reduction part.

When a reaction has been determined to involve oxidation and reduction (by noting, for example, that oxidation state changes have occurred), the equation is separated into two half-reactions, which are then balanced for mass and charge. The equation for the overall reaction is then the sum of these two balanced half-reactions, after adjustments have been made (if necessary) in one or both half-reaction equations so that the numbers of electrons transferred from reducing agent to oxidizing agent balance. For example, the half-reactions for the reaction of copper metal with silver ions are

Reduction half-reaction: $Ag^+(aq) + e^- \rightarrow Ag(s)$

Oxidation half-reaction: $Cu(s) \rightarrow Cu^{2+}(aq) + 2\ e^-$

FIGURE 19.2 Reduction of Cu^{2+} by Al. Aluminum always has a thin coating of Al_2O_3 on the surface, which protects the metal from further reaction. However, in the presence of Cl^- ion, the coating is breached, and reaction occurs (see Example 19.1).

(a) A ball of aluminum foil is added to a solution of $Cu(NO_3)_2$ and NaCl.

(b) A coating of copper is soon seen on the surface of the aluminum, and the reaction generates a significant amount of energy as heat.

Notice that the equations for the half-reactions are themselves balanced for mass and charge. In the copper half-reaction, there is one Cu atom on each side of the equation (mass balance). The electric charge on the right side of the equation is 0 (the sum of +2 for the ion and −2 for two electrons), as it is on the left side (charge balance).

To produce the net chemical equation, we will add the two half-reactions. First, however, we must multiply the silver half-reaction by 2.

$$2\ Ag^+(aq) + 2\ e^- \rightarrow 2\ Ag(s)$$

Each mole of copper atoms produces two moles of electrons, and two moles of Ag^+ ions are required to consume those electrons.

Finally, adding the two half-reactions and canceling electrons from both sides leads to the net ionic equation for the reaction.

Reduction half-reaction:	$2\ [Ag^+(aq) + e^- \rightarrow Ag(s)]$
Oxidation half-reaction:	$Cu(s) \rightarrow Cu^{2+}(aq) + 2\ e^-$
Net ionic equation	$Cu(s) + 2\ Ag^+(aq) \rightarrow Cu^{2+}(aq) + 2\ Ag(s)$

The resulting net ionic equation is balanced for mass and charge.

EXAMPLE 19.1

Balancing Oxidation–Reduction Equations

Problem Balance the following net ionic equation

$$Al(s) + Cu^{2+}(aq) \rightarrow Al^{3+}(aq) + Cu(s)$$

Identify the oxidizing agent, the reducing agent, the substance oxidized, and the substance reduced. Write balanced half-reactions and the balanced net ionic equation. See Figure 19.2 for photographs of this reaction.

What Do You Know? You know that Al metal is producing Al^{3+} ions, and Cu^{2+} ions are producing copper metal.

Strategy

- Make sure the reaction is an oxidation–reduction reaction by checking each element to see whether the oxidation numbers change.

- Separate the equation into half-reactions, identifying what has been reduced (oxidizing agent) and what has been oxidized (reducing agent). (You may wish to review oxidation numbers and oxidation–reduction reactions in Section 3-8.)
- Balance the half-reactions, first for mass and then for charge.
- Add the two half-reactions, after ensuring that the reducing agent half-reaction involves the same number of electrons as the oxidizing agent half-reaction.

Solution

Step 1. *Recognize the Reaction as an Oxidation–Reduction Reaction.*

Here, the oxidation number for aluminum changes from 0 to +3, and the oxidation number of copper changes from +2 to 0. Aluminum is oxidized and serves as the reducing agent. Copper(II) ions are reduced, and Cu^{2+} is the oxidizing agent.

Step 2. *Separate the Process into Half-Reactions.*

Reduction: $Cu^{2+}(aq) \rightarrow Cu(s)$
(Oxidation number of Cu decreases.)

Oxidation: $Al(s) \rightarrow Al^{3+}(aq)$
(Oxidation number of Al increases.)

Step 3. *Balance Each Half-Reaction for Mass.*

Both half-reactions are already balanced for mass.

Step 4. *Balance Each Half-Reaction for Charge.*

To balance the equations for charge, add electrons to the more positive side of each half-reaction to bring the charge on that side of the equation down to the same value as is present on the other side.

Reduction: $2\,e^- + Cu^{2+}(aq) \rightarrow Cu(s)$
(Each Cu^{2+} ion requires two electrons.)

Oxidation: $Al(s) \rightarrow Al^{3+}(aq) + 3\,e^-$
(Each Al atom releases three electrons.)

Step 5. *Multiply Each Half-Reaction by an Appropriate Factor.*

The reducing agent must donate as many electrons as the oxidizing agent acquires. Three Cu^{2+} ions are required to take on the six electrons produced by two Al atoms. Thus, we multiply the Cu^{2+}/Cu half-reaction by 3 and the Al/Al^{3+} half-reaction by 2.

Reduction: $3[2\,e^- + Cu^{2+}(aq) \rightarrow Cu(s)]$

Oxidation: $2[Al(s) \rightarrow Al^{3+}(aq) + 3\,e^-]$

Step 6. *Add the Half-Reactions to Produce the Overall Balanced Equation.*

Reduction: $6\,e^- + 3\,Cu^{2+}(aq) \rightarrow 3\,Cu(s)$

Oxidation: $2\,Al(s) \rightarrow 2\,Al^{3+}(aq) + 6\,e^-$

Net ionic equation: $3\,Cu^{2+}(aq) + 2\,Al(s) \rightarrow 3\,Cu(s) + 2\,Al^{3+}(aq)$

Step 7. *Simplify by Eliminating Reactants and Products That Appear on Both Sides.*

This step is not required here.

Think about Your Answer You should always check the overall equation to ensure there is mass and charge balance. In this case, three Cu atoms and two Al atoms appear on each side. The net electric charge on each side is +6. The equation is balanced.

Strategy Map 19.1

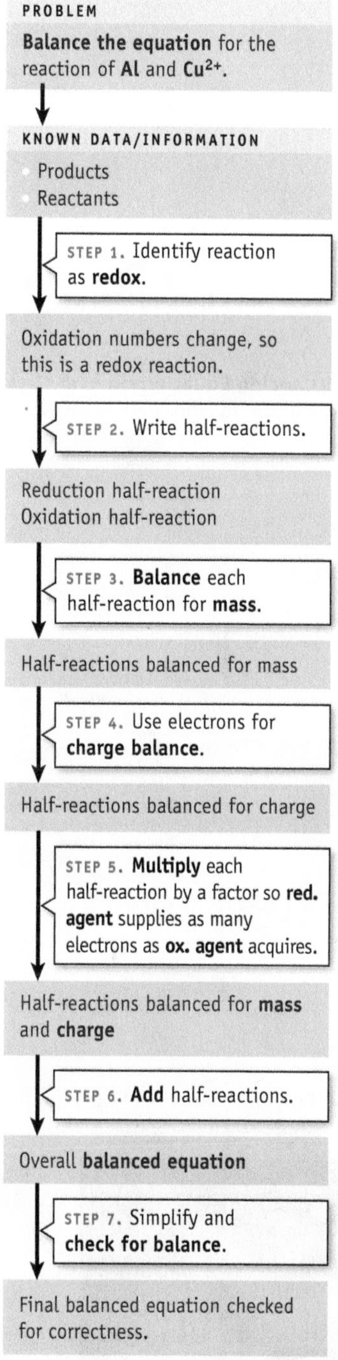

Check Your Understanding

Aluminum reacts with nonoxidizing acids to give Al^{3+}(aq) and H_2(g). The (unbalanced) equation is

$$Al(s) + H^+(aq) \rightarrow Al^{3+}(aq) + H_2(g)$$

Write balanced equations for the half-reactions and the balanced net ionic equation. Identify the oxidizing agent, the reducing agent, the substance oxidized, and the substance reduced.

Balancing Equations in Acid Solution

Balancing Equations in Acid Solution To simplify equations, we shall use H^+ instead of H_3O^+ when balancing equations in acid solution.

When balancing equations for redox reactions in aqueous solution, it is sometimes necessary to add water molecules (H_2O) and either H^+(aq) in acidic solution or OH^-(aq) in basic solution to the equation. Equations that include oxoanions such as SO_4^{2-}, NO_3^-, ClO^-, CrO_4^{2-}, and MnO_4^- and organic compounds fall into this category. The process is outlined in Example 19.2 for the reduction of an oxocation in acid solution and in Example 19.3 for a reaction in basic solution.

EXAMPLE 19.2

Balancing Equations for Oxidation–Reduction Reactions in Acid Solution

Problem Balance the net ionic equation for the reaction of the dioxovanadium(V) ion, VO_2^+, with zinc in acid solution to form VO^{2+} (Figure 19.3).

$$VO_2^+(aq) + Zn(s) \rightarrow VO^{2+}(aq) + Zn^{2+}(aq)$$

FIGURE 19.3 **Reduction of vanadium(V) with zinc.** See Example 19.2 for the balanced equation for the first reaction in this sequence.

What Do You Know? You know that the VO_2^+ ions produce VO^{2+} ions, and Zn metal produces Zn^{2+} ions. You know that H^+ ions and water are used to balance the O atoms involved in the reaction.

Strategy Follow the strategy outlined in the text and Example 19.1. Note that water and H^+ ions will appear in the half-reaction for the reduction of VO_2^+ ion.

Solution

Step 1. *Recognize the Reaction as an Oxidation–Reduction Reaction.*

The oxidation number of V changes from +5 in VO_2^+ to +4 in VO^{2+}. The oxidation number of Zn changes from 0 in the metal to +2 in Zn^{2+}.

Step 2. *Separate the Process into Half-Reactions.*

Oxidation: $Zn(s) \rightarrow Zn^{2+}(aq)$
(Zn(s) is oxidized and is the reducing agent.)

Reduction: $VO_2^+(aq) \rightarrow VO^{2+}(aq)$
($VO_2^+(aq)$ is reduced and is the oxidizing agent.)

Step 3. *Balance the Half-Reactions for Mass.*

Begin by balancing all atoms except H and O. (These atoms are always the last to be balanced because they often appear in more than one reactant or product.)

Zinc half-reaction: $Zn(s) \rightarrow Zn^{2+}(aq)$

The zinc half-reaction is already balanced for mass.

Vanadium half-reaction: $VO_2^+(aq) \rightarrow VO^{2+}(aq)$

The V atoms in this half-reaction are already balanced. An oxygen-containing species must be added to the right side of the equation to achieve an O atom balance, however.

$$VO_2^+(aq) \rightarrow VO^{2+}(aq) + \text{(need 1 O atom)}$$

In acid solution, add H_2O to the side requiring O atoms, one H_2O molecule for each O atom required.

$$VO_2^+(aq) \rightarrow VO^{2+}(aq) + H_2O(\ell)$$

There are now two unbalanced H atoms on the right. Because the reaction occurs in an acidic solution, H^+ ions are present. Therefore, a mass balance for H can be achieved by adding H^+ to the side of the equation deficient in H atoms. Here, two H^+ ions are added to the left side of the equation, and the equation is balanced for mass.

$$2\ H^+(aq) + VO_2^+(aq) \rightarrow VO^{2+}(aq) + H_2O(\ell)$$

Step 4. *Balance the Half-Reactions for Charge by Adding Electrons to the More Positive Side to Make the Charges Equal on Both Sides.*

Two electrons are added to the right side of the zinc half-reaction to bring its charge down to the same value as is present on the left side (in this case, zero).

Zinc half-reaction: $Zn(s) \rightarrow Zn^{2+}(aq) + 2\ e^-$

The mass-balanced VO_2^+ equation has a net charge of 3+ on the left side and 2+ on the right. Therefore, 1 e^- is added to the more positive left side.

Vanadium half-reaction: $e^- + 2\ H^+(aq) + VO_2^+(aq) \rightarrow VO^{2+}(aq) + H_2O(\ell)$

As a check on your work, notice that the vanadium atom changes in oxidation number from +5 to +4 and so needs to acquire one electron for each vanadium atom reduced.

Strategy Map 19.2

PROBLEM
Balance the equation for the reaction of **Zn** and $\mathbf{VO_2^+}$ in acid solution.

KNOWN DATA/INFORMATION
- Products
- Reactants

STEP 1. Identify reaction as **redox.**

Oxidation numbers change, so this is a redox reaction.

STEP 2. **Write** half-reactions.

Reduction half-reaction
Oxidation half-reaction

STEP 3. **Balance** each half-reaction for **mass.** Use $\mathbf{H^+}$ and $\mathbf{H_2O}$ as reactants or products if necessary for mass balance.

Half-reactions **balanced for mass.** May include H^+ and H_2O in addition to original reactants and products.

STEP 4. Use electrons for **charge balance.**

Half-reactions balanced for charge.

STEP 5. **Multiply** each half-reaction by a factor so **red. agent** supplies as many electrons as **ox. agent** acquires.

Half-reactions balanced for **mass** and **charge.**

STEP 6. **Add** half-reactions.

Overall **balanced equation**

STEP 7. Simplify and **check for balance.**

Final equation checked for correctness.

***Step 5.** Multiply the Half-Reactions by Appropriate Factors so That the Reducing Agent Supplies as Many Electrons as the Oxidizing Agent Consumes.*

Here, the oxidation half-reaction supplies two electrons per Zn atom, and the reduction half-reaction consumes one electron per VO_2^+ ion. Therefore, the reduction half-reaction must be multiplied by two. Now two ions of the oxidizing agent (VO_2^+) consume the two electrons provided per atom of the reducing agent (Zn).

$$Zn(s) \longrightarrow Zn^{2+}(aq) + 2\,e^-$$

$$2[e^- + 2\,H^+(aq) + VO_2^+(aq) \longrightarrow VO^{2+}(aq) + H_2O(\ell)]$$

***Step 6.** Add the Half-Reactions to Give the Balanced, Overall Equation.*

Oxidation half-reaction: $Zn(s) \longrightarrow Zn^{2+}(aq) + 2\,e^-$

Reduction half-reaction: $2\,e^- + 4\,H^+(aq) + 2\,VO_2^+(aq) \longrightarrow 2\,VO^{2+}(aq) + 2\,H_2O(\ell)$

Net ionic equation: $Zn(s) + 4\,H^+(aq) + 2\,VO_2^+(aq) \longrightarrow Zn^{2+}(aq) + 2\,VO^{2+}(aq) + 2\,H_2O(\ell)$

***Step 7.** Simplify by Eliminating Reactants and Products That Appear on Both Sides.*

This step is not required here.

Think about Your Answer Check the overall equation to ensure that there is a mass and charge balance.

Mass balance: 1 Zn, 2 V, 4 H, and 4 O on each side of the equation.

Charge balance: Each side has a net charge of +6.

Check Your Understanding

1. The yellow dioxovanadium(V) ion, $VO_2^+(aq)$, is reduced by zinc metal in three steps. The first step reduces it to blue $VO^{2+}(aq)$. This ion is further reduced to green $V^{3+}(aq)$ in the second step, and V^{3+} can be reduced to violet $V^{2+}(aq)$ in a third step. In each step, zinc is oxidized to $Zn^{2+}(aq)$. Write balanced net ionic equations for Steps 2 and 3. (This reduction sequence is shown in Figure 19.3.)

PROBLEM SOLVING TIP 19.1
Balancing Oxidation–Reduction Equations: A Summary

- Hydrogen balance can be achieved only with H^+/H_2O (in acid) or OH^-/H_2O (in base). Never add H or H_2 to balance hydrogen.
- Use H_2O or OH^- as appropriate to balance oxygen. Never add O atoms, O^{2-} ions, or O_2 for O balance.
- Never include $H^+(aq)$ and $OH^-(aq)$ in the same equation. A solution can be either acidic or basic, never both.
- The number of electrons in a half-reaction reflects the change in oxidation number of the element being oxidized or reduced.
- Electrons are always a component of half-reactions but should never appear in the overall equation.
- Include charges in the formulas for ions. Omitting the charge, or writing the charge incorrectly, is one of the most common errors seen on student papers.
- The best way to become competent in balancing redox equations is to practice, practice, practice.

2. A common laboratory analysis for iron is to titrate aqueous iron(II) ion with a solution of potassium permanganate of precisely known concentration. Use the half-reaction method to write the balanced net ionic equation for the reaction in acid solution.

$$MnO_4^-(aq) + Fe^{2+}(aq) \rightarrow Mn^{2+}(aq) + Fe^{3+}(aq)$$

Identify the oxidizing agent, the reducing agent, the substance oxidized, and the substance reduced (see Figure 19.4).

© Cengage Learning/Charles D. Winters

FIGURE 19.4 The reaction of purple permanganate ion (MnO_4^-) with iron(II) ions in acid solution. The products are the nearly colorless Mn^{2+} and Fe^{3+} ions.

Balancing Equations in Basic Solution

Example 19.2 illustrates the technique of balancing equations for redox reactions that occur in acid solution. In these reactions, H^+ ion or the H^+/H_2O pair can be used to achieve a balanced equation if required. However, in basic solution, only OH^- ion or the OH^-/H_2O pair can be used.

EXAMPLE 19.3

Balancing Equations for Oxidation–Reduction Reactions in Basic Solution

Problem Aluminum metal is oxidized in aqueous base, with water serving as the oxidizing agent. The products of the reaction are $[Al(OH)_4]^-(aq)$ and $H_2(g)$. Write a balanced net ionic equation for this reaction.

What Do You Know? You know the reactants and products. Here the reaction is in basic solution, so the balanced equation may require OH^- and H_2O.

Strategy The strategy is basically that of Examples 19.1 and 19.2 with the exception that you will need to decide if OH^- ions are involved and if H_2O is also included in the half-reactions.

Solution

Step 1. *Recognize the Reaction as an Oxidation–Reduction Reaction.*

The unbalanced equation is

$$Al(s) + H_2O(\ell) \rightarrow [Al(OH)_4]^-(aq) + H_2(g)$$

Here, aluminum is oxidized, with its oxidation number changing from 0 to +3. Hydrogen is reduced, with its oxidation number decreasing from +1 to zero.

Step 2. *Separate the Process into Half-Reactions.*

Oxidation half-reaction: $Al(s) \rightarrow [Al(OH)_4]^-(aq)$
(Al oxidation number increased from 0 to +3.)

Reduction half-reaction: $H_2O(\ell) \rightarrow H_2(g)$
(H oxidation number decreased from +1 to 0.)

Step 3. *Balance the Half-Reactions for Mass.*

Addition of OH^- or OH^- and H_2O is required for mass balance in both half-reactions. In the case of the aluminum half-reaction, we simply add OH^- ions to the left side.

Oxidation half-reaction: $Al(s) + 4\ OH^-(aq) \rightarrow [Al(OH)_4]^-(aq)$

To balance the half-reaction for water reduction, notice that an oxygen-containing species must appear on the right side of the equation. Because H_2O is a reactant, we use OH^-, which is present in this basic solution, as the other product.

Reduction half-reaction: $2\ H_2O(\ell) \rightarrow H_2(g) + 2\ OH^-(aq)$

Step 4. *Balance the Half-Reactions for Charge.*

Electrons are added to balance charge.

Oxidation half-reaction: $Al(s) + 4\ OH^-(aq) \rightarrow [Al(OH)_4]^-(aq) + 3\ e^-$

Reduction half-reaction: $2\ H_2O(\ell) + 2\ e^- \rightarrow H_2(g) + 2\ OH^-(aq)$

Step 5. *Multiply the Half-Reactions by Appropriate Factors so That the Reducing Agent Donates as Many Electrons as the Oxidizing Agent Consumes.*

Here, electron balance is achieved by using two Al atoms to provide six electrons which are then acquired by six H_2O molecules.

Oxidation half-reaction: $2[Al(s) + 4\ OH^-(aq) \rightarrow [Al(OH)_4]^-(aq) + 3\ e^-]$

Reduction half-reaction: $3[2\ H_2O(\ell) + 2\ e^- \rightarrow H_2(g) + 2\ OH^-(aq)]$

Step 6. *Add the Half-Reactions.*

$$2\ Al(s) + 8\ OH^-(aq) \rightarrow 2\ [Al(OH)_4]^-(aq) + 6\ e^-$$

$$6\ H_2O(\ell) + 6\ e^- \rightarrow 3\ H_2(g) + 6\ OH^-(aq)$$

Net equation: $2\ Al(s) + 8\ OH^-(aq) + 6\ H_2O(\ell) \rightarrow 2\ [Al(OH)_4]^-(aq) + 3\ H_2(g) + 6\ OH^-(aq)$

Step 7. *Simplify by Eliminating Reactants and Products That Appear on Both Sides.*

Six OH^- ions can be canceled from the two sides of the equation:

$$2\ Al(s) + 2\ OH^-(aq) + 6\ H_2O(\ell) \rightarrow 2\ [Al(OH)_4]^-(aq) + 3\ H_2(g)$$

Think about Your Answer The final equation is balanced for mass and charge.

Mass balance: 2 Al, 14 H, and 8 O on each side of the equation.

Charge balance: There is a net −2 charge on each side.

Check Your Understanding

Voltaic cells based on the reduction of sulfur are under development. One such cell involves the reaction of sulfur with aluminum under basic conditions.

$$Al(s) + S(s) \rightarrow Al(OH)_3(s) + HS^-(aq)$$

(a) Balance this equation, showing each balanced half-reaction.

(b) Identify the oxidizing and reducing agents, the substance oxidized, and the substance reduced.

REVIEW & CHECK FOR SECTION 19-1

1. Copper(II) sulfide reacts with nitric acid according to the balanced equation:

$$3\ CuS(s) + 8\ H^+(aq) + 2\ NO_3^-(aq) \rightarrow 3\ Cu^{2+}(aq) + 3\ S(s) + 4\ H_2O(\ell) + 2\ NO(g)$$

The substance oxidized is

(a) CuS (b) H^+ (c) NO_3^-

2. The balanced half-reaction for $NO_3^- \rightarrow NO$ in acid solution is

(a) $NO_3^- \rightarrow NO + e^-$
(b) $2\ H^+ + e^- + NO_3^- \rightarrow NO + 2\ H_2O$
(c) $NO_3^- \rightarrow NO + O^{2-} + e^-$
(d) $4\ H^+ + 3\ e^- + NO_3^- \rightarrow NO + 2\ H_2O$

PROBLEM SOLVING TIP 19.2

An Alternative Method of Balancing Equations in Basic Solution

Balancing redox equations in basic solution, which may require you to use OH^- ions and H_2O, can sometimes be more challenging than balancing equations in acidic solution. Rather than learn a separate method for balancing equations in basic solution, some students find it easier to first balance an equation as if it were in acidic solution and then add enough OH^- ions to *both sides* of the equation so that H^+ ions are converted to water. Let us show how this works for balancing the reaction of hypochlorite ion with manganese(IV) oxide to form chloride ion and permanganate ion.

(a) Balance the equation as if the reaction were carried out in acid by following Steps 1–7 in Example 19.2:

$$3\,ClO^-(aq) + H_2O(\ell) + 2\,MnO_2(s) \rightarrow 3\,Cl^-(aq) + 2\,MnO_4^-(aq) + 2\,H^+(aq)$$

(b) To adjust for the fact that this reaction is carried out in base rather than in acid, the same number of hydroxide ions (two) are added to both sides of the equation as there are $H^+(aq)$ ions. On the side that had the $H^+(aq)$ ions, the $H^+(aq)$ ions and $OH^-(aq)$ ions will form $H_2O(\ell)$.

$$3\,ClO^-(aq) + H_2O(\ell) + 2\,MnO_2(s) + 2\,OH^-(aq) \rightarrow 3\,Cl^-(aq) + 2\,MnO_4^-(aq) + 2\,H^+(aq) + 2\,OH^-(aq)$$

$$3\,ClO^-(aq) + H_2O(\ell) + 2\,MnO_2(s) + 2\,OH^-(aq) \rightarrow 3\,Cl^-(aq) + 2\,MnO_4^-(aq) + 2\,H_2O(\ell)$$

(c) Simplify the equation.

$$3\,ClO^-(aq) + 2\,MnO_2(s) + 2\,OH^-(aq) \rightarrow 3\,Cl^-(aq) + 2\,MnO_4^-(aq) + H_2O(\ell)$$

3. The balanced half-reaction for $Br_2 \rightarrow BrO_3^-$ in basic solution is

(a) $3\,OH^- + Br_2 \rightarrow 2\,BrO_3^- + H_2O + e^-$

(b) $12\,OH^- + Br_2 \rightarrow 2\,BrO_3^- + 6\,H_2O + 10\,e^-$

(c) $e^- + OH^- + Br_2 \rightarrow 2\,BrO_3^- + H_2O$

(d) $10\,e^- + Br_2 + 6\,H_2O \rightarrow 2\,BrO_3^- + 6\,OH^-$

19-2 Simple Voltaic Cells

Learning Objectives: LO 3.12, LO 3.13

The reaction of copper metal and silver ions (see Figure 19.1) can be used as the basis of a voltaic cell. By placing the components of the two half-reactions in separate compartments (Figure 19.5), electrons can only be transferred from copper metal to silver ions through an external circuit, and useful work can potentially be done.

The copper half-cell (on the left in Figure 19.5) consists of copper metal that serves as one electrode and a solution containing copper(II) ions. The half-cell on the right uses a silver electrode and a solution containing silver(I) ions. Important features of this simple cell are as follows:

- *The two half-cells are connected with a* **salt bridge** *that allows cations and anions to move between the two half-cells.* The electrolyte chosen for the salt bridge should contain ions that will not react with chemical reagents in both half-cells. In the example in Figure 19.5, $NaNO_3$ is used.
- *In all electrochemical cells, the* **anode** *is the electrode at which oxidation occurs. The electrode at which reduction occurs is always the* **cathode**. (In Figure 19.5, the copper electrode is the anode, and the silver electrode is the cathode.)
- *A negative sign can be assigned to the anode in a voltaic cell, and the cathode is marked with a positive sign.* The chemical oxidation, which occurs at the anode and produces electrons, gives it a negative charge.
- *In all electrochemical cells, electrons flow in the external circuit from the anode to the cathode.* Electric current in the external circuit of a voltaic cell consists of electrons moving from the negative to the positive electrode.

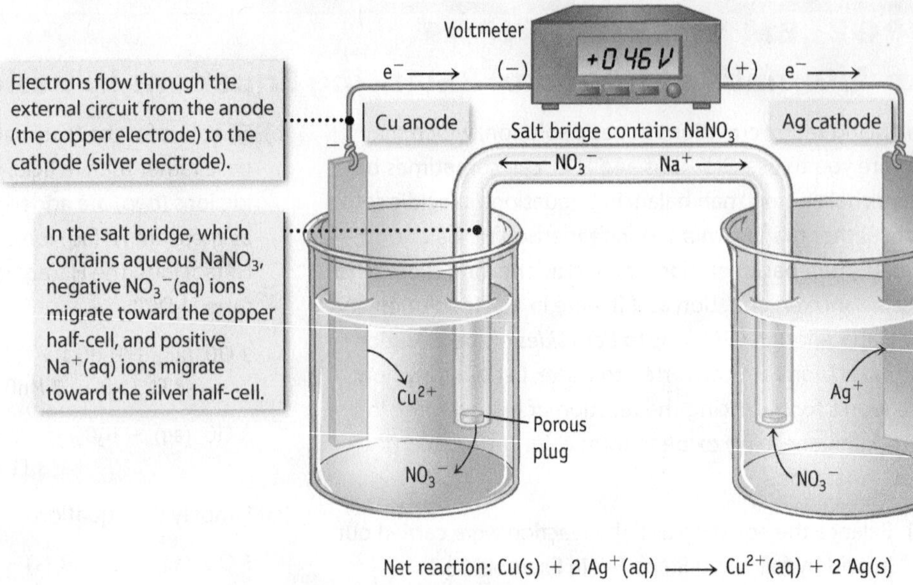

FIGURE 19.5 A voltaic cell using $Cu(s)|Cu^{2+}(aq)$ and $Ag(s)|Ag^{+}(aq)$ half-cells.

The chemistry occurring in the cell pictured in Figure 19.5 is summarized by the following half-reactions and net ionic equation:

Cathode, reduction:	$2\ Ag^{+}(aq) + 2\ e^{-} \rightarrow 2\ Ag(s)$
Anode, oxidation:	$Cu(s) \rightarrow Cu^{2+}(aq) + 2\ e^{-}$
Net ionic equation:	$Cu(s) + 2\ Ag^{+}(aq) \rightarrow Cu^{2+}(aq) + 2\ Ag(s)$

Salt Bridges A simple salt bridge can be made by adding gelatin to a solution of an electrolyte. Gelatin makes the contents semi-rigid so that the salt bridge is easier to handle. Porous glass disks and ion-permeable membranes are alternatives to a salt bridge. These devices allow ions to traverse from one half-cell to the other while keeping the two solutions from mixing.

The salt bridge is required in a voltaic cell for the reaction to proceed. In the Cu/Ag^{+} voltaic cell, anions move in the salt bridge toward the copper half-cell, and cations move toward the silver half-cell (Figure 19.5). As $Cu^{2+}(aq)$ ions are formed in the copper half-cell by oxidation of copper metal, negative ions enter that cell from the salt bridge (and positive ions leave the cell) so that the numbers of positive and negative charges in the half-cell compartment remain in balance. The silver half-cell contains $AgNO_3$, so, as $Ag^{+}(aq)$ ions are reduced to silver metal, negative ions (NO_3^{-}) move out of the half-cell into the salt bridge, and positive ions move from anode to cathode through the salt bridge. A complete circuit is required for current to flow. If the salt bridge is removed, reactions at the electrodes will cease.

In Figure 19.5, the electrodes are connected by wires to a voltmeter. In an alternative setup, the connections might be to a lightbulb or other device that uses electricity. Electrons are produced by oxidation of copper, and $Cu^{2+}(aq)$ ions enter the solution. The electrons traverse the external circuit to the silver electrode, where they reduce $Ag^{+}(aq)$ ions to silver metal. The main features of this and of all other voltaic cells are summarized in Figure 19.6.

EXAMPLE 19.4

Electrochemical Cells

Problem Describe how to set up a voltaic cell to generate an electric current using the reaction

$$Fe(s) + Cu^{2+}(aq) \rightarrow Cu(s) + Fe^{2+}(aq)$$

Which electrode is the anode, and which is the cathode? In which direction do electrons flow in the external circuit? In which direction do the positive and negative ions flow in the salt bridge? Write equations for the half-reactions that occur at each electrode.

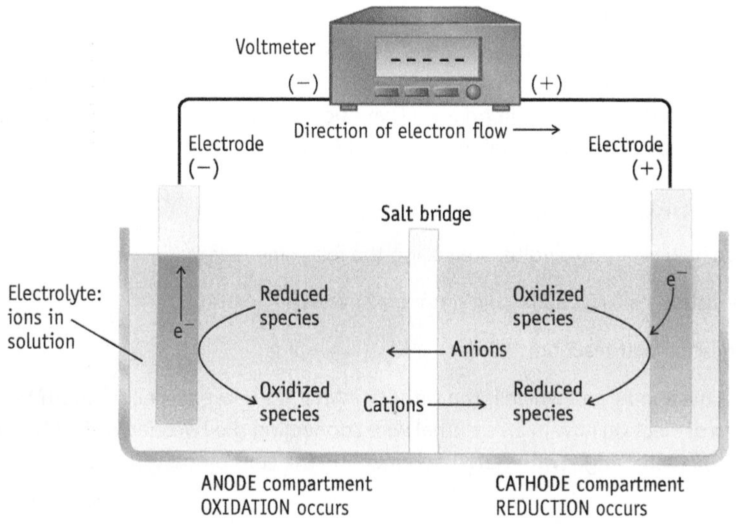

FIGURE 19.6 Summary of terms used in a voltaic cell. Electrons move from the anode, the site of oxidation, through the external circuit to the cathode, the site of reduction. Charge balance in each half-cell is achieved by migration of ions through the salt bridge. Negative ions move from the reduction half-cell to the oxidation half-cell and positive ions move in the opposite direction.

What Do You Know? You are told the reaction proceeds in the direction written. You also know that the half-reaction occurring in one half-cell will involve an iron electrode and a solution containing Fe^{2+}(aq) ions. The other half-cell consists of a copper electrode and solution containing Cu^{2+}(aq) ion.

Strategy First, identify the two different half-cells that make up the cell. Next, these two half-cells are linked together with a salt bridge and an external circuit.

Solution This voltaic cell is similar to the one diagrammed in Figure 19.5. Here we assume the two half-cells are linked with a salt bridge containing KNO_3 as the electrolyte.

Iron is oxidized, so the iron electrode is the anode:

Oxidation, anode: $Fe(s) \rightarrow Fe^{2+}(aq) + 2\,e^-$

Because copper(II) ions are reduced, the copper electrode is the cathode. The cathodic half-reaction is

Reduction, cathode: $Cu^{2+}(aq) + 2\,e^- \rightarrow Cu(s)$

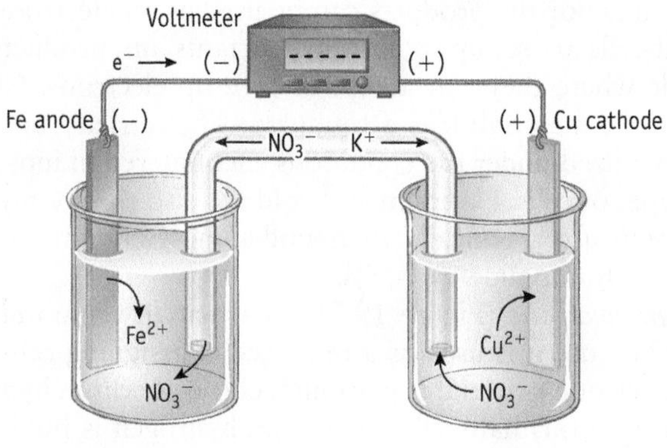

In the external circuit, electrons flow from the iron electrode (anode) to the copper electrode (cathode). In the salt bridge, negative ions flow toward the iron/iron(II) half-cell, and positive ions flow in the opposite direction.

Think about Your Answer A good strategy to understand voltaic cells is to focus on the movement of the negative species in the cell (electron flow in the external circuit and anion flow in the salt bridge). These species always move in a circular fashion:

electrons from anode to cathode, and anions in the salt bridge in the opposite direction. If you establish which reactant is oxidized (provides electrons), you then know which electrode is the anode, in which direction electrons move in the external circuit, and in which direction anions flow in the salt bridge. (That said, don't ignore the fact that cations flow in the opposite direction to the anions in the salt bridge.)

Check Your Understanding

Describe how to set up a voltaic cell using the following half-reactions:

Reduction half-reaction: $Ag^+(aq) + e^- \rightarrow Ag(s)$

Oxidation half-reaction: $Ni(s) \rightarrow Ni^{2+}(aq) + 2\,e^-$

Which is the anode, and which is the cathode? What is the overall cell reaction? What is the direction of electron flow in an external wire connecting the two electrodes? Describe the ion flow in a salt bridge (with $NaNO_3$) connecting the cell compartments.

Voltaic Cells with Inert Electrodes

In the half-cells described so far, the metal used as an electrode is also a reactant or a product in the redox reaction. Not all half-reactions involve a metal as a reactant or product, however. With the exception of carbon in the form of graphite, nonmetals are unsuitable as electrode materials because they do not conduct electricity. It is not possible to make an electrode from a gas, a liquid (except mercury), or a solution. Ionic solids do not make satisfactory electrodes because the ions are locked tightly in a crystal lattice, and these materials do not conduct electricity.

In situations where reactants and products cannot serve as the electrode material, an inert or chemically unreactive electrode must be used. Such electrodes are made of materials that conduct an electric current but that are neither oxidized nor reduced in the cell.

Consider constructing a voltaic cell to accommodate the following product-favored reaction:

$$2\,Fe^{3+}(aq) + H_2(g) \rightarrow 2\,Fe^{2+}(aq) + 2\,H^+(aq)$$

Reduction half-reaction: $Fe^{3+}(aq) + e^- \rightarrow Fe^{2+}(aq)$

Oxidation half-reaction: $H_2(g) \rightarrow 2\,H^+(aq) + 2\,e^-$

Neither the reactants nor the products can be used as an electrode material. Therefore, the two half-cells are set up so that the reactants and products come in contact with an electrode where they can accept or give up electrons. Graphite is a commonly used electrode material: It is a conductor of electricity, and it is inexpensive and not readily oxidized under the conditions encountered in most cells. Mercury is used in certain types of cells. Platinum and gold are also commonly used in the laboratory because both are chemically inert under most circumstances, but they are generally too costly for commercial cells.

The *hydrogen electrode* (Figure 19.7) is particularly important in the field of electrochemistry because it is used as a reference in assigning cell voltages (see Section 19-4). The electrode material is platinum, chosen because hydrogen adsorbs on the metal's surface. In this half-cell's operation, hydrogen is bubbled over the electrode, and adsorption on the large surface area maximizes the contact of the gas and the electrode. The aqueous solution contains $H^+(aq)$. The half-reactions involving $H^+(aq)$ and $H_2(g)$

$$2\,H^+(aq) + 2\,e^- \rightarrow H_2(g) \quad \text{or} \quad H_2(g) \rightarrow 2\,H^+(aq) + 2\,e^-$$

take place at the electrode surface, and the electrons involved in the reaction are conducted to or from the reaction site by the metal electrode.

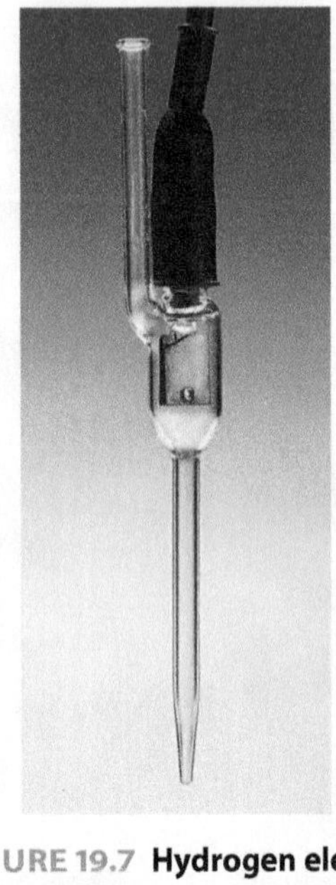

© Cengage Learning/Charles D. Winters

FIGURE 19.7 **Hydrogen electrode.** Hydrogen gas is bubbled over a platinum electrode in a solution containing H^+ ions. Often, platinum wires are woven into a gauze, or the metal surface is roughened either by abrasion or by chemical treatment to increase the surface area.

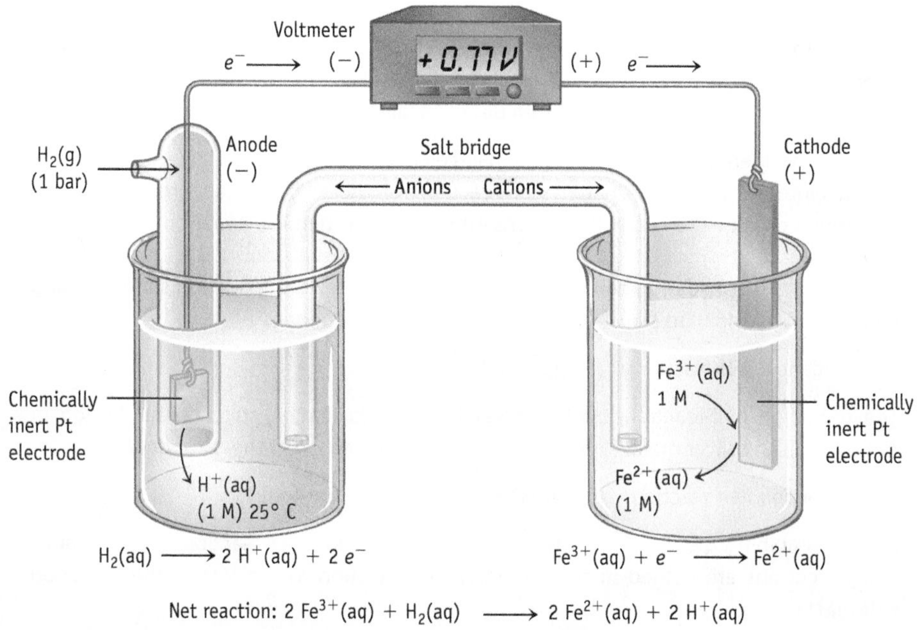

FIGURE 19.8 **A voltaic cell with a hydrogen electrode.** This cell has Fe^{2+}(aq, 1.0 M) and Fe^{3+}(aq, 1.0 M) in the cathode compartment and H_2(g) and H^+(aq, 1.0 M) in the anode compartment. At 25 °C, the cell generates 0.77 V. (The hydrogen electrode in the anode compartment in this illustration is a simplified schematic. See Figure 19.7 for a photograph of a commercial hydrogen electrode.)

A half-cell using the reduction of Fe^{3+}(aq) to Fe^{2+}(aq) can also be set up with a platinum electrode. In this case, the solution surrounding the electrode contains iron ions in two different oxidation states. Transfer of electrons to or from the reactant occurs at the electrode surface.

A voltaic cell involving the reduction of Fe^{3+}(aq, 1.0 M) to Fe^{2+}(aq, 1.0 M) with H_2 gas is illustrated in Figure 19.8. In this cell, the hydrogen electrode is the anode (H_2 is oxidized to H^+), and the iron-containing compartment is the cathode (Fe^{3+} is reduced to Fe^{2+}). The cell produces 0.77 V.

Electrochemical Cell Notations

Chemists use a shorthand notation to simplify cell descriptions. For example, the cell involving the reduction of silver ion with copper metal is written as

$$\underbrace{Cu(s)\,|\,Cu^{2+}(aq,\ 1.0\ M)}_{\text{Anode information}}\ ||\ \underbrace{Ag^+(aq,\ 1.0\ M)\,|\,Ag(s)}_{\text{Cathode information}}$$

The cell using H_2 gas to reduce Fe^{3+} ions is written as

$$\underbrace{Pt\,|\,H_2(P = 1\ bar)\,|\,H^+(aq,\ 1.0\ M)}_{\text{Anode information}}\ ||\ \underbrace{Fe^{3+}(aq,\ 1.0\ M),\ Fe^{2+}(aq,\ 1.0\ M)\,|\,Pt}_{\text{Cathode information}}$$

By convention, on the left we write the anode and information with respect to the solution with which it is in contact. A single vertical line (|) indicates a phase boundary, and double vertical lines (||) indicate a salt bridge.

EXAMPLE 19.5

Electrochemical Cell Notation

Problem Determine the oxidation and reduction half-reactions and the overall chemical equation for the following electrochemical cell:

$$Pt\,|\,H_2(P = 1\ bar))\,|\,H^+(aq,\ 1.0\ M)\ ||\ Br^-(aq,\ 1.0\ M)\,|\ AgBr(s)\,|\,Ag(s)$$

What Do You Know? You know that oxidation takes place in the half-cell that contains hydrogen gas and hydronium ions in contact with an inert Pt electrode. (In the shorthand description, the oxidation half-cell is on the left.) The cell in which reduction takes place, contains bromide ion, silver bromide, and a silver electrode.

Strategy Identify an element in each half-cell that is present in two different oxidation states. Write a balanced oxidation half-reaction for the oxidation and reduction half-reactions. Combine the two half-reactions into an overall chemical equation.

Solution The oxidation half-reaction involves hydrogen gas (oxidation state = 0) and hydrogen ion (oxidation state = +1). The reaction at the anode is:

Oxidation half-reaction: $H_2(g) \longrightarrow 2\ H^+(aq) + 2\ e^-$

The reduction half-reaction involves silver bromide (oxidation state of the Ag ion in AgBr = +1) and silver metal (oxidation state= 0). The reaction at the cathode is:

Reduction half-reaction: $AgBr(s) + e^- \longrightarrow Ag(s) + Br^-(aq)$

Before combining the half-reactions, multiply the reduction half-reaction by 2 so that as many electrons are gained in the reduction half-reaction as are lost in the oxidation half-reaction.

Overall chemical equation: $2\ AgBr(s) + H_2(g) \longrightarrow 2\ Ag(s) + 2\ H^+(aq) + 2\ Br^-(aq)$

Think about Your Answer Verify that the overall chemical equation is balanced for each type of atom, as well as for charge.

Check Your Understanding

The following overall chemical reaction occurs in an electrochemical cell.

Overall chemical equation: $Zn(s) + PbSO_4(s) \longrightarrow Zn^{2+}(aq) + Pb(s) + SO_4^{2-}(aq)$

Use cell notation to describe the electrochemical cell.

REVIEW & CHECK FOR SECTION 19-2

Choose the correct responses based on the cell below in which the following reaction occurs:

$$Ni^{2+}(aq) + Cd(s) \longrightarrow Ni(s) + Cd^{2+}(aq)$$

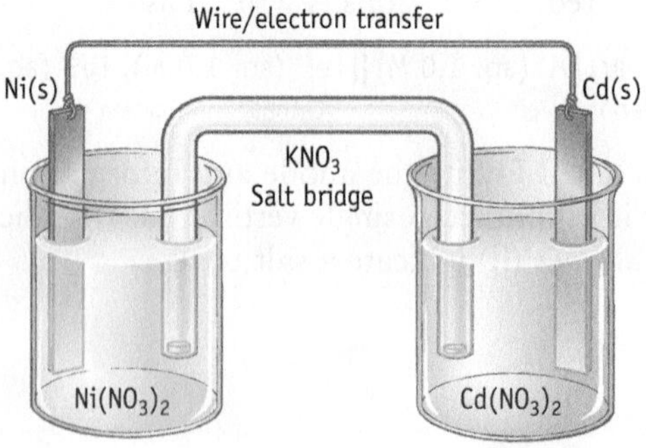

1. Electron transfer:

   (a) Electrons transfer from Ni to Cd
   (b) Electrons transfer from Cd to Ni

2. Electrodes:

   (a) Cd is the anode and is negative
   (b) Cd is the anode and is positive
   (c) Cd is the cathode and is negative
   (d) Cd is the cathode and is positive

3. Salt bridge (which contains K^+ and NO_3^- ions):

   (a) NO_3^- ions move from the Cd half-cell to the Ni half-cell and K^+ ions move from the Ni half-cell to the Cd half-cell.

   (b) NO_3^- ions move from the Ni half-cell to the Cd half-cell and K^+ ions move from the Cd half-cell to the Ni half-cell.

19-3 Commercial Voltaic Cells

The cells described so far are unlikely to have practical use. They are neither compact nor robust. In most situations, it is also important that the cell produce a constant voltage, even while current is drawn from the cell. A problem with the cells described so far is that the voltage produced varies as the concentrations of reactants and products change (see Section 19-5). Drawing a current results in a decrease in the voltage if reactant concentrations near the anode or the cathode are depleted faster than they can be replenished from the bulk of the solution. Similarly, a decrease in voltage occurs if product concentrations increase near the electrodes faster than they move into the bulk solution.

The electrical work that can be drawn from a voltaic cell depends on the quantity of reagents consumed. A voltaic cell must have a large mass of reactants to produce current over a prolonged period. In addition, a voltaic cell that can be recharged is attractive. Recharging a cell means returning the reagents to their original sites in the cell. In many types of electrochemical cells, the movement of ions in the cell mixes the reagents, and they cannot be "unmixed" after the cell has been running.

Batteries can be classified as primary and secondary. **Primary batteries** cannot be returned to their original state by recharging, so when the reactants are consumed, the battery is "dead" and must be discarded. **Secondary batteries** are often called **storage batteries** or **rechargeable batteries.** The reactions in these batteries can be reversed, so the batteries can be recharged.

Years of development have led to many different commercial voltaic cells to meet specific needs (Figure 19.9), and several common ones are described below. All adhere to the principles that have been developed in earlier discussions.

Batteries The word *battery* has become part of our common language, designating any self-contained device that generates an electric current. The term battery has a more precise scientific meaning, however. It refers to a collection of two or more voltaic cells. For example, the 12-volt battery used in automobiles is made up of six voltaic cells. Each voltaic cell develops a voltage of 2 volts. Six cells connected in series produce 12 volts.

© Cengage Learning/Charles D. Winters

FIGURE 19.9 **Some commercial voltaic cells.** Commercial voltaic cells provide energy for a wide range of devices, come in a myriad of sizes and shapes, and produce different voltages. Some are rechargeable; others are discarded after use. One might think that there is nothing further to learn about batteries, but this is not true. Research on these devices is actively pursued in the chemical community.

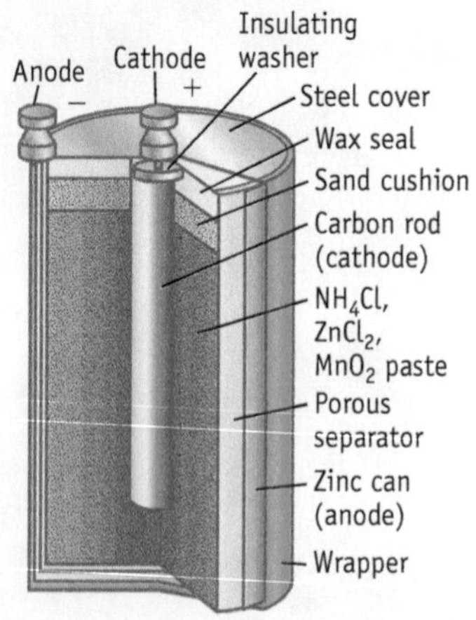

FIGURE 19.10 The common dry cell battery. Sometimes called the *zinc-carbon battery.*

Primary Batteries: Dry Cells and Alkaline Batteries

If you buy an inexpensive flashlight battery or dry cell battery, it might be a modern version of a voltaic cell invented by George LeClanché in 1866 (Figure 19.10). Zinc serves as the anode, and the cathode is a graphite rod placed down the center of the device. These cells are often called "dry cells" because there is no visible liquid phase. However, the cell contains a moist paste of NH_4Cl, $ZnCl_2$, and MnO_2, so water is present. The moisture is necessary because the ions present must be able to migrate from one electrode to the other. The cell generates a potential of 1.5 V using the following half-reactions:

Cathode, reduction: $2\ NH_4^+(aq) + 2\ e^- \rightarrow 2\ NH_3(g) + H_2(g)$

Anode, oxidation: $Zn(s) \rightarrow Zn^{2+}(aq) + 2\ e^-$

The products at the cathode are gases, which could build up pressure in the cell and cause it to rupture. The problem is avoided, however, by two other reactions that take place in the cell. Ammonia molecules bind to Zn^{2+} ions, and hydrogen gas is oxidized by MnO_2 to water.

$$Zn^{2+}(aq) + 2\ NH_3(g) + 2\ Cl^-(aq) \rightarrow Zn(NH_3)_2Cl_2(s)$$

$$2\ MnO_2(s) + H_2(g) \rightarrow Mn_2O_3(s) + H_2O(\ell)$$

Zinc-carbon dry cells were widely used because of their low cost, but they have several disadvantages. If current is drawn from the battery rapidly, the gaseous products cannot be consumed rapidly enough, so the cell resistance rises, and the voltage drops. In addition, the zinc electrode and ammonium ions are in contact in the cell, and these chemicals react slowly. The ammonium ion, NH_4^+, is a weak Brønsted acid and reacts slowly with zinc to form Zn^{2+} and hydrogen gas. Because of this reaction, these voltaic cells cannot be stored indefinitely, a fact you may have learned from experience. When the zinc outer shell deteriorates, the contents of the battery can leak and perhaps damage the appliance in which it is contained.

At the present time, you are more likely to use **alkaline batteries** in your camera or flashlight because they generate current up to 50% longer than a dry cell of the same size. The chemistry of alkaline cells is similar to that in a zinc-carbon dry cell, except that the material inside the cell is basic (alkaline). Alkaline cells use the oxidation of zinc and the reduction of MnO_2 to generate a current, but NaOH or KOH is used in the cell instead of the acidic salt NH_4Cl.

Cathode, reduction: $2\ MnO_2(s) + H_2O(\ell) + 2\ e^- \rightarrow Mn_2O_3(s) + 2\ OH^-(aq)$

Anode, oxidation: $Zn(s) + 2\ OH^-(aq) \rightarrow ZnO(s) + H_2O(\ell) + 2\ e^-$

Alkaline cells, which produce 1.54 V (approximately the same voltage as the zinc-carbon dry cell), have the further advantage that the cell potential does not decline under high current loads because no gases are formed.

Prior to 2000, mercury-containing batteries were widely used in calculators, cameras, watches, heart pacemakers, and other devices. However, these small batteries were banned in the United States in the 1990s because of environmental problems. They have been replaced by several other types of batteries, such as silver oxide batteries and zinc-oxygen batteries. Both operate under alkaline conditions, and both have zinc anodes. In the silver oxide battery, which produces a voltage of about 1.5 V, the cell reactions are

Cathode, reduction: $Ag_2O(s) + H_2O(\ell) + 2\ e^- \rightarrow 2\ Ag(s) + 2\ OH^-(aq)$

Anode, oxidation: $Zn(s) + 2\ OH^-(aq) \rightarrow ZnO(s) + H_2O(\ell) + 2\ e^-$

The zinc-oxygen battery, which produces about 1.15–1.35 V, is unique in that atmospheric oxygen and not a metal oxide is the oxidizing agent.

Cathode, reduction: $O_2(g) + 2\ H_2O(\ell) + 4\ e^- \rightarrow 4\ OH^-(aq)$

Anode, oxidation: $Zn(s) + 2\ OH^-(aq) \rightarrow ZnO(s) + H_2O(\ell) + 2\ e^-$

These batteries are used in hearing aids, pagers, and medical devices.

Secondary or Rechargeable Batteries

When a zinc-carbon dry cell or an alkaline cell ceases to produce a usable electric current, it is discarded. In contrast, some types of cells can be recharged, often hundreds of times. Recharging requires applying an electric current from an external source to restore the cell to its original state. There are a number of well-known types of secondary batteries in common use.

Lead Storage Battery

An automobile battery—the lead storage battery—is probably the best-known rechargeable battery (Figure 19.11). The 12-V version of this battery contains six voltaic cells, each generating about 2 V. The lead storage battery can produce a large initial current, an essential feature when starting an automobile engine.

The anode of a lead storage battery is metallic lead. The cathode is also made of lead, but it is covered with a layer of compressed, insoluble lead(IV) oxide, PbO_2. The electrodes, arranged alternately in a stack and separated by thin fiberglass sheets, are immersed in aqueous sulfuric acid. When the cell supplies electrical energy, the lead anode is oxidized to lead(II) sulfate, an insoluble substance that adheres to the electrode surface. The two electrons produced per lead atom move through the external circuit to the cathode, where PbO_2 is reduced to Pb^{2+} ions that, in the presence of H_2SO_4, also form lead(II) sulfate.

Cathode, reduction: $PbO_2(s) + 4\ H^+(aq) + SO_4^{2-}(aq) + 2\ e^- \rightarrow PbSO_4(s) + 2\ H_2O(\ell)$

Anode, oxidation: $Pb(s) + SO_4^{2-}(aq) \rightarrow PbSO_4(s) + 2\ e^-$

Net ionic equation: $Pb(s) + PbO_2(s) + 2\ H_2SO_4(aq) \rightarrow 2\ PbSO_4(s) + 2\ H_2O(\ell)$

When current is generated, sulfuric acid is consumed and water is formed. Because water is less dense than sulfuric acid, the density of the solution decreases during this process. Therefore, one way to determine whether a lead storage battery needs to be recharged is to measure the density of the solution.

A lead storage battery is recharged by supplying electrical energy. The $PbSO_4$ coating the surfaces of the electrodes is converted back to metallic lead and PbO_2, and sulfuric acid is regenerated. Recharging this battery is possible because the reactants and products remain attached to the electrode surface. The lifetime of a lead storage battery is limited, however, because, with time, the coatings of PbO_2 and $PbSO_4$ flake off of the surface and fall to the bottom of the battery case.

Scientists and engineers would like to find an alternative to lead storage batteries, especially for use in cars. Lead storage batteries have the disadvantage of being large and heavy. In addition, lead and its compounds are toxic and their disposal adds a further complication. Nevertheless, at this time, the advantages of lead storage batteries often outweigh their disadvantages.

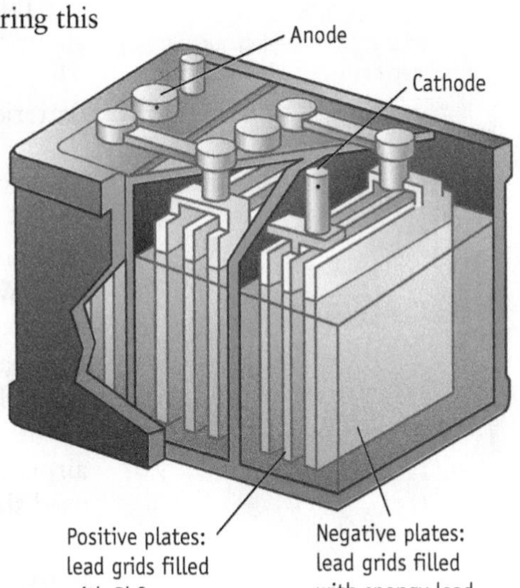

FIGURE 19.11 Lead storage battery, a secondary or rechargeable battery. Each cell of the battery generates 2 V.

Nickel-Cadmium Batteries

Nickel-cadmium ("Ni-cad") batteries, used in a variety of cordless appliances such as telephones, video camcorders, and cordless power tools, are lightweight and rechargeable. The chemistry of the cell is based on the oxidation of cadmium and the reduction of nickel(III) oxide under basic conditions. As with the lead storage battery, the reactants and products formed when producing a current are solids that adhere to the electrodes.

Cathode, reduction: $NiO(OH)(s) + H_2O(\ell) + e^- \rightarrow Ni(OH)_2(s) + OH^-(aq)$

Anode, oxidation: $Cd(s) + 2\ OH^-(aq) \rightarrow Cd(OH)_2(s) + 2\ e^-$

Ni-cad batteries produce a nearly constant voltage (1.2 V). However, their cost is relatively high, and there are restrictions on their disposal because cadmium compounds are toxic and present an environmental hazard.

Nickel-Metal Hydride

Rechargeable nickel-metal hydride batteries (NiMH) are now in common use. You may have them in your camera or portable music player. Their most important use, however, is in electric or hybrid cars.

In the nickel-metal hydride battery, electrons are generated when H atoms interact with OH^- ions at the metal alloy anode.

$$Alloy(H) + OH^- \rightarrow Alloy + H_2O + e^-$$

The reaction at the cathode is the same as in Ni-cad batteries.

$$NiO(OH) + H_2O + e^- \rightarrow Ni(OH)_2 + OH^-$$

The "alloy" in NiMH batteries is generally a mixture of a rare earth metal such as lanthanum, cerium, or neodymium and another metal such as nickel, cobalt, manganese, or aluminum. These batteries also generate 1.2 V.

Lithium Batteries

Be Alert: Children Can Ingest Lithium Batteries! Very small lithium batteries are used in many devices such as toys, musical greeting cards, and appliances. Unfortunately, because they are small and shiny, children put them in their mouths and can swallow them. In 2010 the *New York Times* (June 1, 2010, page D5) reported that an increasing number of children have died from reactions induced by the battery's current when the battery was swallowed.

Much research on batteries now focuses on lithium batteries. (See the introduction to this chapter.) There are two types in common use: lithium-ion and a variant, lithium-ion polymer batteries. The chemistry of both is the same.

Cathode, reduction: $Li_{1-x}CoO_2(s) + x\ Li^+ + x\ e^- \rightarrow LiCoO_2(s)$

Anode, oxidation: $Li_xC_6(s) \rightarrow x\ Li^+ + x\ e^- + 6\ C(s)$

Lithium-ion polymer batteries are popular because they can be made in any shape and so fit into products such as Amazon's Kindle and Apple's portable devices. They generate a 3.6-V potential, deliver a higher current density than lithium-ion batteries, and can be charged and discharged through many cycles.

An important reason for the development of lithium-based batteries is their light weight. Lithium has a much lower molar mass (6.941 g/mol) than cadmium (112.4 g/mol), nickel (58.69 g/mol), or lead (207.2 g/mol). The oxidation of 7 grams of lithium produces the same number of electrons as the oxidation of 104 grams of lead. When the masses of all the components of lithium-ion and lead-acid batteries are taken into account, lithium ion batteries can deliver the same energy as a lead-acid battery at approximately a quarter of the mass. This is important not only in portable devices where people do not want to carry around heavy objects but also in the automobile and aircraft industry. A lighter weight for a battery in a car or airplane results in more of the energy going into moving the vehicle and less being used simply to transport the battery.

Fuel Cells

An advantage of voltaic cells is that they are small and portable, but their size is also a limitation. The amount of electric current produced is limited by the quantity of reagents contained in the cell. When one of the reactants is completely consumed, the cell will no longer generate a current. Fuel cells avoid this limitation because the reactants (fuel and oxidant) can be supplied continuously to the cell from an external reservoir.

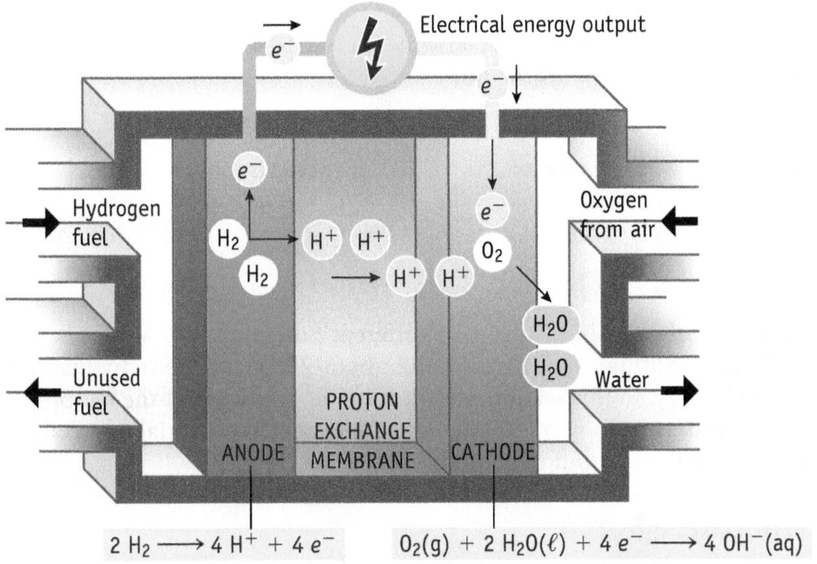

FIGURE 19.12 **Fuel cell design.** Hydrogen gas is oxidized to $H^+(aq)$ at the anode surface. On the other side of the proton exchange membrane (PEM), oxygen gas is reduced to $OH^-(aq)$. The $H^+(aq)$ ions travel through the PEM and combine with $OH^-(aq)$, forming water.

Although the first fuel cells were constructed more than 150 years ago, little was done to develop this technology until the space program rekindled interest in these devices. Hydrogen-oxygen fuel cells have been used in NASA's Gemini, Apollo, and Space Shuttle programs. Not only are they lightweight and efficient, but they also have the added benefit that they generate drinking water for the ship's crew.

In a hydrogen-oxygen fuel cell (Figure 19.12), hydrogen is pumped onto the anode of the cell, and O_2 (or air) is directed to the cathode where the following reactions occur:

Cathode, reduction: $O_2(g) + 2\ H_2O(\ell) + 4\ e^- \rightarrow 4\ OH^-(aq)$

Anode, oxidation: $H_2(g) \rightarrow 2\ H^+(aq) + 2\ e^-$

The two halves of the cell are separated by a special material called a proton exchange membrane (PEM). Protons, $H^+(aq)$, formed at the anode traverse the PEM and react with the hydroxide ions produced at the cathode, forming water. The net reaction in the cell is thus the formation of water from H_2 and O_2. Cells currently in use produce about 0.9 V.

Hydrogen-oxygen fuel cells operate at 40–60% efficiency and meet most of the requirements for use in automobiles: They operate at room temperature or slightly above, start rapidly, and develop a high-current density. However, cost is a serious problem as is the absence of an economical, carbon-free way of making hydrogen. These faults, and the cost and difficulty of building a nationwide infrastructure for distributing hydrogen, remain major stumbling blocks that would need to be overcome before hydrogen fuel cells could be adopted for widespread use in automobiles.

Energy for Automobiles Energy available from systems that can be used to power an automobile.

Chemical System	W · h/kg* (1 W · h = 3600 J)
Lead-acid battery	18–56
Nickel-cadmium battery	33–70
Sodium-sulfur battery	80–140
Lithium polymer battery	150
Gasoline-air combustion engine	12,200

*watt-hour/kilogram

REVIEW & CHECK FOR SECTION 19-3

1. Which of the following statements is correct for the following half-reaction that occurs in an automobile lead-acid battery?

$$PbO_2(s) + 4\ H^+(aq) + SO_4^{2-}(aq) + 2\ e^- \rightarrow PbSO_4(s) + 2\ H_2O(\ell)$$

(a) Lead(IV) oxide is oxidized.
(b) Lead(IV) oxide is reduced.
(c) Hydrogen ions are oxidized.
(d) Hydrogen ions are reduced.

2. You can determine if an automobile lead-based battery is no longer working by checking the density of the solution in the battery. If the density is low, then the battery is "dead." This works because

(a) PbO_2 is consumed.
(b) Sulfuric acid is consumed.
(c) Water evaporates.
(d) Lead is consumed.

Learning Objectives: LO 3.12, LO 3.13

19-4 Standard Electrochemical Potentials

Different electrochemical cells produce different potentials: 1.5 V for alkaline cells, about 3.7 V for a lithium-ion battery, and about 2.0 V for the individual cells in a lead storage battery. In this section, we want to identify some of the factors affecting cell voltages and develop ways to calculate the expected potential of a cell based on the chemistry in the cell and the conditions used.

Electromotive Force

Electrochemical Units

- The coulomb (abbreviated C) is the standard (SI) unit of electrical charge (Appendix C, Table 6).
- 1 joule = 1 volt × 1 coulomb.
- 1 coulomb = 1 ampere × 1 second.

Electrons generated at the anode of an electrochemical cell move through the external circuit toward the cathode, and the force needed to move the electrons arises from a difference in the potential energy of electrons at the two electrodes. This difference in potential energy per electrical charge is called the **electromotive force** or **emf**, which literally means the "force causing electrons to move." Emf has units of volts (V); 1 volt is the potential difference needed to impart one joule of energy to an electric charge of one coulomb (1 V = 1 J / 1 C). *One coulomb is the quantity of charge that passes a point in an electric circuit when a current of 1 ampere flows for 1 second (1 C = 1 A × 1 s).*

Measuring Standard Potentials

Imagine you planned to study cell voltages in a laboratory with two objectives: (1) to understand the factors that affect these values and (2) to be able to predict the potential of a voltaic cell. You might construct a number of different half-cells, link them together in various combinations to form voltaic cells (as in Figure 19.13), and measure the cell potentials. After a few experiments, it would become apparent that cell potentials depend on a number of factors: the half-cells used (i.e., the reaction in each half-cell and the overall or net reaction in the cell), the concentrations of reactants and products in solution, the pressure of gaseous reactants, and the temperature.

To simplify matters for now, let us consider only cell potentials measured under **standard conditions**:

- Reactants and products are present in their standard states.
- Solutes in aqueous solution have a concentration of 1.0 M.
- Gaseous reactants or products have a pressure of 1.0 bar.

A CLOSER LOOK

EMF, Cell Potential, and Voltage

Electromotive force (emf) and cell potential (E_{cell}) are often used synonymously, but the two are subtly different. E_{cell} is a measured quantity, so its value is affected by how the measurement is made. To understand this point, consider as an analogy water in a pipe under pressure. Water pressure can be viewed as analogous to emf; it represents a force that will cause water in the pipe to move. If we open a faucet, water will flow. Opening the faucet will, however, decrease the pressure in the system.

Emf is the potential difference when no current flows. To measure E_{cell}, a voltmeter is placed in the external circuit. Although voltmeters have high internal resistance to minimize current flow, a small current flows nonetheless. As a result, the value of E_{cell} will be slightly different than the emf.

Finally, there is a difference between a *potential* and a *voltage*. The voltage of a cell has a magnitude but no sign. In contrast, the potential of a half-reaction or a cell has a sign (+ or −) and a magnitude.

A cell potential measured under these conditions is called the **standard potential** and is denoted by $\boldsymbol{E°_{cell}}$. Unless otherwise specified, all values of $E°_{cell}$ refer to measurements at 298 K (25 °C).

Suppose you set up a number of standard half-cells and connect each in turn to a **standard hydrogen electrode (SHE)**. Your apparatus would look like the voltaic cell in Figure 19.13b. For now, we will concentrate on three aspects of this cell:

1. *The reaction that occurs.* The reaction occurring in the cell pictured in Figure 19.13 could be *either* the reduction of Zn^{2+} ions with H_2 gas

$$Zn^{2+}(aq) + H_2(g) \rightarrow Zn(s) + 2\ H^+(aq)$$

$Zn^{2+}(aq)$ is the oxidizing agent, and H_2 is the reducing agent.
Standard hydrogen electrode would be the anode (negative electrode).

or the reduction of $H^+(aq)$ ions by Zn(s).

$$Zn(s) + 2\ H^+(aq) \rightarrow Zn^{2+}(aq) + H_2(g)$$

Zn is the reducing agent, and $H^+(aq)$ is the oxidizing agent.
Standard hydrogen electrode would be the cathode (positive electrode).

The reaction that actually occurs is the one that is product-favored at equilibrium. In this case we know the product-favored reaction is the reduction of H^+ ions by zinc metal (Figure 19.13a).

2. *Direction of electron flow in the external circuit.* In a voltaic cell, electrons always flow from the anode (negative electrode) to the cathode (positive electrode). We can tell the direction of electron movement—and therefore which is the anode and which is the cathode—by placing a voltmeter in the circuit. A positive potential is observed if the voltmeter terminal with a plus sign (+) is connected to the positive electrode or cathode [and the terminal with the minus sign (−) is connected to the negative electrode or anode]. Connected in the opposite way (plus to minus and minus to plus), the voltmeter will indicate a negative potential.

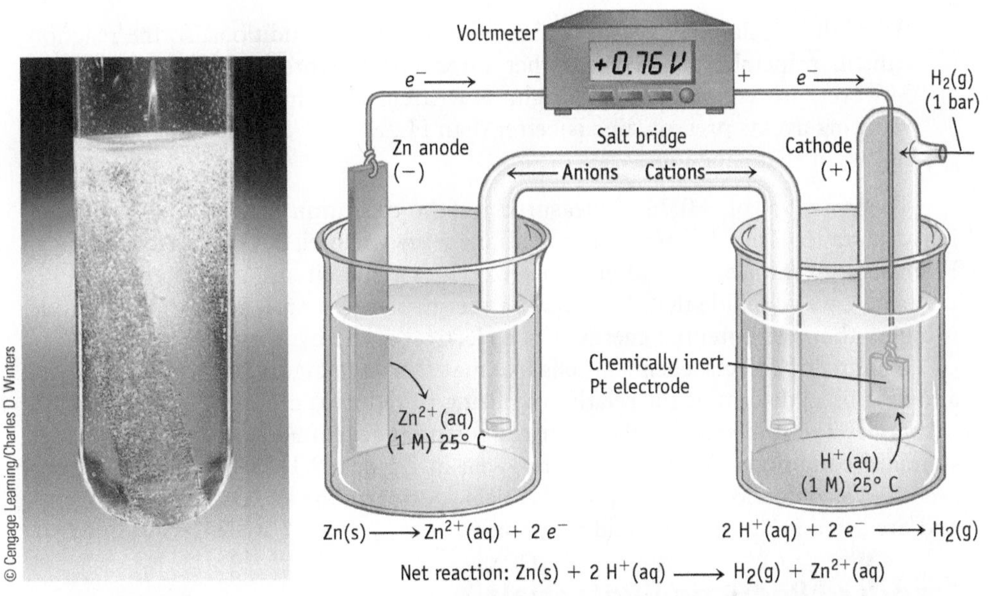

(a) The product-favored reaction of aqueous hydrogen ions with zinc produces $H_2(g)$ and Zn^{2+} ions.

(b) A voltaic cell that makes use of the product-favored reduction of aqueous hydrogen ions by zinc.

FIGURE 19.13 **A voltaic cell using Zn | Zn^{2+}(aq, 1.0 M) and H_2 | H^+(aq, 1.0 M) half-cells.**
- When zinc and acid are combined in an electrochemical cell, the cell generates a potential of 0.76 V under standard conditions.
- The electrode in the H_2 | H^+(aq, 1.0 M) half-cell is the cathode, and the Zn electrode is the anode.
- Electrons flow in the external circuit to the hydrogen half-cell from the zinc half-cell.
- The positive sign of the measured voltage indicates that the hydrogen electrode is the cathode or positive electrode.

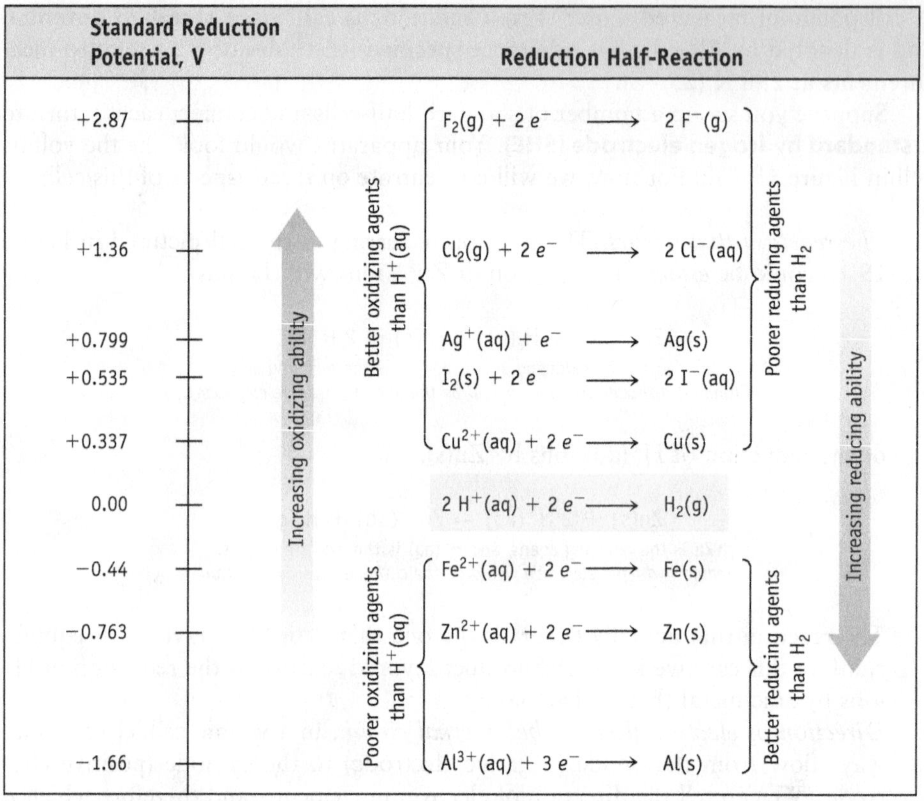

FIGURE 19.14 A potential ladder for reduction half-reactions.

- The position of a half-reaction on this potential ladder reflects the relative ability of the species at the left to act as an oxidizing agent.
- The higher the compound or ion is in the list, the better it is as an oxidizing agent. Conversely, the atoms or ions on the right are reducing agents. The lower they are in the list, the better they are as a reducing agent.
- The potential for each half-reaction is given with its standard reduction potential, $E°_{reduction}$.
- For more information see J. R. Runo and D. G. Peters, *Journal of Chemical Education*, Vol. 70, p. 708, 1993.

3. *Cell potential.* In Figure 19.13, the voltmeter is hooked up with its positive terminal connected to the hydrogen half-cell, and a reading of +0.76 V is observed. The hydrogen electrode is thus the positive electrode or cathode, and the reactions occurring in this cell must be

Reduction, cathode:	$2H^+(aq) + 2e^- \rightarrow H_2(g)$
Oxidation, anode:	$Zn(s) \rightarrow Zn^{2+}(aq) + 2e^-$
Net cell reaction:	$Zn(s) + 2H^+(aq) \rightarrow Zn^{2+}(aq) + H_2(g)$

All of the species are present in the cell at standard conditions, so the reaction can, in principle, proceed in either direction. The product-favored reaction, however, proceeds from left to right as written. This shows us that, of the two reducing agents present, zinc is better than H_2, and H^+ ions are a better oxidizing agent than zinc ions.

The potential of +0.76 V measured for the oxidation of zinc with hydrogen ions also reflects the difference in potential energy of an electron at each electrode. From the direction of flow of electrons in the external circuit (Zn electrode → H_2 electrode), we conclude that the potential energy of an electron at the zinc electrode is higher than the potential energy of the electron at the hydrogen electrode.

Hundreds of electrochemical cells like that shown in Figure 19.13 can be set up, allowing us to determine the relative oxidizing or reducing ability of various chemical species and to determine the electrical potential generated by the reaction under standard conditions. A few results are given in Figure 19.14, where half-reactions are listed as reductions. That is, the chemical species on the left are oxidizing agents and are listed in descending oxidizing ability.

Standard Reduction Potentials

By doing experiments such as that illustrated by Figure 19.13, we not only learn the relative oxidizing and reducing abilities of various chemical species, but we can also rank them quantitatively.

If $E°_{cell}$ is a measure of the standard potential for the cell, then $E°_{cathode}$ and $E°_{anode}$ can be taken as measures of electrode potential. Because $E°_{cell}$ reflects the *difference* in electrode potentials, $E°_{cell}$ must be the difference between $E°_{cathode}$ and $E°_{anode}$.

$$E°_{cell} = E°_{cathode} - E°_{anode} \quad (19.1)$$

Equation 19.1 Equation 19.1 is another example of calculating a change from $X_{final} - X_{initial}$. Electrons move to the cathode (the "final" state) from the anode (the "initial" state). Thus, Equation 19.1 resembles equations you have seen previously in this book (such as Equations 5.6 and 6.5).

Here, $E°_{cathode}$ and $E°_{anode}$ are the standard *reduction* potentials for the half-cell reactions that occur at the cathode and anode, respectively. Equation 19.1 is important for three reasons:

- If you have values for $E°_{cathode}$ and $E°_{anode}$, you can calculate the standard potential, $E°_{cell}$, for a voltaic cell.
- *When the calculated value of $E°_{cell}$ is positive, the reaction as written is predicted to be product-favored at equilibrium.* Conversely, if the calculated value of $E°_{cell}$ is negative, the reaction is predicted to be reactant-favored at equilibrium. Such a reaction will be product-favored at equilibrium in a direction opposite to the way it is written.
- If you measure $E°_{cell}$ and know either $E°_{cathode}$ or $E°_{anode}$, you can calculate the other value. This value would tell you how one half-cell reaction compares with others in terms of relative oxidizing or reducing ability.

But here is a dilemma. Individual half-cell potentials cannot be measured. Just as values for $\Delta_f H°$ and $\Delta_f G°$ were established by choosing a reference point (the elements in their standard states), scientists have selected a reference point for half-reactions. A potential of exactly 0 V is assigned to the half-reaction that occurs at a standard hydrogen electrode (SHE).

$$2\ H^+(aq,\ 1\ M) + 2\ e^- \rightarrow H_2(g,\ 1\ bar)\quad E° = 0.00\ V$$

With this standard, we can now determine $E°$ values for half-cells by measuring $E°_{cell}$ in experiments such as those described in Figures 19.8 and 19.13, where one of the electrodes is the SHE. We can then quantify the information with reduction potential tables such as Figure 19.14 and use these values to make predictions about $E°_{cell}$ for new voltaic cells.

Tables of Standard Reduction Potentials

The experimental approach just described leads to lists of $E°$ values such as seen in Figure 19.14, Table 19.1, and Appendix M. Let us list some important points concerning these tables and then illustrate them in the discussion and examples that follow.

***E°* Values** An extensive listing of $E°$ values is found in Appendix M, and still larger tables of data can be found in chemistry reference books. A common convention, used in Appendix M, lists standard reduction potentials in two groups, one for acid and neutral solutions and the other for basic solutions.

1. The half-reactions are written as "oxidized form + electrons → reduced form." The species on the left side of the reaction arrow is an oxidizing agent, and the species on the right side of the reaction arrow is a reducing agent. Therefore, *all potentials are for reduction reactions*, and the potentials (in volts versus SHE) are called *standard reduction potentials*.
2. The more positive the value of $E°$ for the reactions, the better the oxidizing ability of the ion or compound on the left side of the reaction. This means *$F_2(g)$ is the best oxidizing agent in the table.* Lithium ion at the lower-left corner of Table 19.1 is the poorest oxidizing agent because its $E°$ value is the most negative.
3. The more negative the value of the reduction potential, $E°$, the less likely the half-reaction will occur as a reduction, and the more likely the reverse half-reaction will occur (as an oxidation). Thus, Li(s) is the strongest reducing agent in the table, and F^- is the weakest reducing agent. The reducing agents in the table (the ions, elements, and compounds at the right) increase in strength from the top to the bottom.

Table 19.1 Standard Reduction Potentials in Aqueous Solution at 25 °C*

REDUCTION HALF-REACTION		$E°$ (V)
$F_2(g) + 2\,e^-$	$\rightarrow 2\,F^-(aq)$	+2.87
$H_2O_2(aq) + 2\,H^+(aq) + 2\,e^-$	$\rightarrow 2\,H_2O(\ell)$	+1.77
$PbO_2(s) + SO_4^{2-}(aq) + 4\,H^+(aq) + 2\,e^-$	$\rightarrow PbSO_4(s) + 2\,H_2O(\ell)$	+1.685
$MnO_4^-(aq) + 8\,H^+(aq) + 5\,e^-$	$\rightarrow Mn^{2+}(aq) + 4\,H_2O(\ell)$	+1.51
$Au^{3+}(aq) + 3\,e^-$	$\rightarrow Au(s)$	+1.50
$Cl_2(g) + 2\,e^-$	$\rightarrow 2\,Cl^-(aq)$	+1.36
$Cr_2O_7^{2-}(aq) + 14\,H^+(aq) + 6\,e^-$	$\rightarrow 2\,Cr^{3+}(aq) + 7\,H_2O(\ell)$	+1.33
$O_2(g) + 4\,H^+(aq) + 4\,e^-$	$\rightarrow 2\,H_2O(\ell)$	+1.229
$Br_2(\ell) + 2\,e^-$	$\rightarrow 2\,Br^-(aq)$	+1.08
$NO_3^-(aq) + 4\,H^+(aq) + 3\,e^-$	$\rightarrow NO(g) + 2\,H_2O(\ell)$	+0.96
$OCl^-(aq) + H_2O(\ell) + 2\,e^-$	$\rightarrow Cl^-(aq) + 2\,OH^-(aq)$	+0.89
$Hg^{2+}(aq) + 2\,e^-$	$\rightarrow Hg(\ell)$	+0.855
$Ag^+(aq) + e^-$	$\rightarrow Ag(s)$	+0.799
$Hg_2^{2+}(aq) + 2\,e^-$	$\rightarrow 2\,Hg(\ell)$	+0.789
$Fe^{3+}(aq) + e^-$	$\rightarrow Fe^{2+}(aq)$	+0.771
$I_2(s) + 2\,e^-$	$\rightarrow 2\,I^-(aq)$	+0.535
$O_2(g) + 2\,H_2O(\ell) + 4\,e^-$	$\rightarrow 4\,OH^-(aq)$	+0.40
$Cu^{2+}(aq) + 2\,e^-$	$\rightarrow Cu(s)$	+0.337
$Sn^{4+}(aq) + 2\,e^-$	$\rightarrow Sn^{2+}(aq)$	+0.15
$2\,H^+(aq) + 2\,e^-$	$\rightarrow H_2(g)$	0.00
$Sn^{2+}(aq) + 2\,e^-$	$\rightarrow Sn(s)$	−0.14
$Ni^{2+}(aq) + 2\,e^-$	$\rightarrow Ni(s)$	−0.25
$V^{3+}(aq) + e^-$	$\rightarrow V^{2+}(aq)$	−0.255
$PbSO_4(s) + 2\,e^-$	$\rightarrow Pb(s) + SO_4^{2-}(aq)$	−0.356
$Cd^{2+}(aq) + 2\,e^-$	$\rightarrow Cd(s)$	−0.40
$Fe^{2+}(aq) + 2\,e^-$	$\rightarrow Fe(s)$	−0.44
$Zn^{2+}(aq) + 2\,e^-$	$\rightarrow Zn(s)$	−0.763
$2\,H_2O(\ell) + 2\,e^-$	$\rightarrow H_2(g) + 2\,OH^-(aq)$	−0.8277
$Al^{3+}(aq) + 3\,e^-$	$\rightarrow Al(s)$	−1.66
$Mg^{2+}(aq) + 2\,e^-$	$\rightarrow Mg(s)$	−2.37
$Na^+(aq) + e^-$	$\rightarrow Na(s)$	−2.714
$K^+(aq) + e^-$	$\rightarrow K(s)$	−2.925
$Li^+(aq) + e^-$	$\rightarrow Li(s)$	−3.045

Increasing strength of oxidizing agents (↑)

Increasing strength of reducing agents (↓)

*In volts (V) versus the standard hydrogen electrode.

4. The reaction between any substance on the left in this table (an oxidizing agent) with any substance *lower* than it on the right (a reducing agent) is product-favored at equilibrium. This has been called the *northwest–southeast rule*: For example, Zn can reduce Fe^{2+}, H^+, Cu^{2+}, and I_2, but, of the species on this list, Cu can reduce only I_2.

Northwest–Southeast Rule This guideline is a reflection of the idea of moving down a potential energy "ladder" in a product-favored reaction.

Reduction Half-Reaction

$$I_2(s) + 2\,e^- \longrightarrow 2\,I^-(aq)$$
$$Cu^{2+}(aq) + 2\,e^- \longrightarrow Cu(s)$$
$$2\,H^+(aq) + 2\,e^- \longrightarrow H_2(g)$$
$$Fe^{2+}(aq) + 2\,e^- \longrightarrow Fe(s)$$
$$Zn^{2+}(aq) + 2\,e^- \longrightarrow Zn(s)$$

The northwest–southeast rule: The reducing agent always lies to the southeast of the oxidizing agent in a product-favored reaction.

5. The + or − sign of the half-reaction reduction potential is the sign of the electrode when it is attached to the H_2/H^+ standard cell (see Figures 19.8 and 19.13).
6. Electrochemical potentials depend on the nature of the reactants and products and their concentrations, not on the quantities of material used. Therefore, changing the stoichiometric coefficients for a half-reaction does not change the value of $E°$. For example, the reduction of Fe^{3+} has an $E°$ of +0.771 V, whether the reaction is written as

$$Fe^{3+}(aq,\ 1\ M) + e^- \rightarrow Fe^{2+}(aq,\ 1\ M) \qquad E° = +0.771\ V$$

or as

$$2\,Fe^{3+}(aq,\ 1\ M) + 2\,e^- \rightarrow 2\,Fe^{2+}(aq,\ 1\ M) \qquad E° = +0.771\ V$$

Changing Stoichiometric Coefficients The volt is defined as "energy/charge" (V = J/C). Multiplying a reaction by some number causes both the energy and the charge to be multiplied by that number. Thus, the ratio "energy/charge = volt" does not change.

Using Tables of Standard Reduction Potentials

Tables or "ladders" of standard reduction potentials are very useful. They allow you to predict the potential of a new voltaic cell (under standard conditions), provide information that can be used to balance redox equations, and help predict which redox reactions are product-favored.

Calculating Standard Cell Potentials, $E°_{cell}$

The standard reduction potentials for half-reactions were obtained by measuring cell potentials. It makes sense, therefore, that these values can be used to calculate the potential of some new cell.

The net reaction occurring in a voltaic cell using silver and copper half-cells is

$$2\,Ag^+(aq) + Cu(s) \rightarrow 2\,Ag(s) + Cu^{2+}(aq)$$

The silver electrode is the cathode, and the copper electrode is the anode. We know this because silver ion is reduced (to silver metal) and copper metal is oxidized (to Cu^{2+} ions). (Recall that oxidations always occur at the anode and reductions at the cathode.) Also notice that Cu is "southeast" of Ag^+ in the potential ladder (see Figure 19.14 and Table 19.1).

$$E°_{cathode} = +0.799\ V \qquad Ag^+(aq) + e^- \longrightarrow Ag(s)$$

"Distance" from $E°_{cathode}$ to $E°_{anode}$ is 0.799 V − 0.337 V = 0.462 V.

Cu is "southeast" of Ag^+

$$E°_{anode} = +0.337\ V \qquad Cu^{2+}(aq) + 2\,e^- \longrightarrow Cu(s)$$

The potential for the voltaic cell is the difference between the standard reduction potentials for the two half-reactions.

$$E^\circ_{cell} = E^\circ_{cathode} - E^\circ_{anode}$$
$$E^\circ_{cell} = (+0.799\ V) - (+0.337\ V)$$
$$E^\circ_{cell} = +0.462\ V$$

Notice that the value of E°_{cell} is related to the "distance" between the cathode and anode reactions on the potential ladder. The products have a lower potential energy than the reactants, and the cell potential, E°_{cell}, has a positive value.

A positive potential calculated for the $Ag^+|Ag$ and $Cu^{2+}|Cu$ cell ($E^\circ_{cell} = +0.462$ V) confirms that the reduction of silver ions in water with copper metal is product-favored at equilibrium (see Figure 19.1). We might ask, however, about the value of E°_{cell} if a reactant-favored equation had been selected. For example, what is E°_{cell} for the reduction of copper(II) ions with silver metal?

Cathode, reduction:	$Cu^{2+}(aq) + 2\ e^- \rightarrow Cu(s)$
Anode, oxidation:	$2\ Ag(s) \rightarrow 2\ Ag^+(aq) + 2\ e^-$
Net ionic equation:	$2\ Ag(s) + Cu^{2+}(aq) \rightarrow 2\ Ag^+(aq) + Cu(s)$

Cell Voltage Calculation

$$E^\circ_{cathode} = +0.337\ V \text{ and } E^\circ_{anode} = +0.799\ V$$
$$E^\circ_{cell} = E^\circ_{cathode} - E^\circ_{anode} = (+0.337\ V) - (0.799\ V)$$
$$E^\circ_{cell} = -0.462\ V$$

The negative sign for E°_{cell} indicates that the reaction as written is reactant-favored at equilibrium. The products of the reaction (Ag^+ and Cu) have a higher potential energy than the reactants (Ag and Cu^{2+}). For the indicated reaction to occur, a potential of at least 0.462 V would have to be imposed on the system by an external source of electricity (see Section 19-7).

Relative Strengths of Oxidizing and Reducing Agents

Five half-reactions, selected from Appendix M, are arranged from the half-reaction with the highest (most positive) E° value to the one with the lowest (most negative) value.

E°, V		Reduction Half-Reaction
+1.36	Increasing strength as oxidizing agents ↑	$Cl_2(g) + 2\ e^- \longrightarrow 2\ Cl^-(aq)$
+0.80		$Ag^+(aq) + e^- \longrightarrow Ag(s)$
+0.00		$2\ H^+(aq) + 2\ e^- \longrightarrow H_2(g)$
−0.25		$Ni^{2+}(aq) + 2\ e^- \longrightarrow Ni(s)$
−0.76		$Zn^{2+}(aq) + 2\ e^- \longrightarrow Zn(s)$

- The list on the left is headed by Cl_2, an element that is a strong oxidizing agent and thus is easily reduced. At the bottom of the list is $Zn^{2+}(aq)$, an ion not easily reduced and thus a poor oxidizing agent.
- On the right, the list is headed by $Cl^-(aq)$, an ion that can be oxidized to Cl_2 only with difficulty. It is a very poor reducing agent. At the bottom of the list is zinc metal, which is readily oxidized and is a good reducing agent.

A CLOSER LOOK — An Electrochemical Toothache

It was reported a few years ago that a 66-year-old woman had intense pain that was traced to her dental work (*New England Journal of Medicine,* Vol. 342, p. 2000, 2003). A root canal procedure had moved a mercury amalgam filling on one tooth slightly closer to a gold alloy crown on an adjacent tooth. Eating acidic foods caused her intense pain. When dental amalgams of dissimilar metals come in contact with saliva, a voltaic cell is formed that generates potentials up to several hundred millivolts—and you feel it! You can do it, too, if you chew an aluminum foil gum wrapper with teeth that have been filled with a dental amalgam. Ouch!

By arranging these half-reactions based on $E°$ values, we have also arranged the chemical species on the two sides of the equation in order of their strengths as oxidizing or reducing agents. In this list, from strongest to weakest, the order is

$$\text{Oxidizing agents: } Cl_2 > Ag^+ > H^+ > Ni^{2+} > Zn^{2+}$$
$$\textit{strong} \longrightarrow \textit{weak}$$

$$\text{Reducing agents: } Zn > Ni > H_2 > Ag > Cl^-$$
$$\textit{strong} \longrightarrow \textit{weak}$$

Finally, notice that the value of $E°_{cell}$ is greater the farther apart the oxidizing and reducing agents are on the potential ladder. For example,

$$Zn(s) + Cl_2(g) \rightarrow Zn^{2+}(aq) + 2\ Cl^-(aq) \qquad E° = +2.12\ V$$

is more strongly product-favored than the reduction of hydrogen ions with nickel metal.

$$Ni(s) + 2\ H^+(aq) \rightarrow Ni^{2+}(aq) + H_2(g) \qquad E° = +0.25\ V$$

EXAMPLE 19.6

Ranking Oxidizing and Reducing Agents

Problem Use the table of standard reduction potentials (Table 19.1) to do the following:

(a) Rank the halogens in order of their strength as oxidizing agents.

(b) Decide whether hydrogen peroxide (H_2O_2) in acid solution is a stronger oxidizing agent than Cl_2.

(c) Decide which of the halogens is capable of oxidizing gold metal to $Au^{3+}(aq)$.

What Do You Know? A table of electrode potentials, such as Table 19.1 or Appendix M, contains the information needed to answer these questions.

Strategy The ability of a species on the left side of a reduction potential table to function as an oxidizing agent declines on descending the list (see points 2 and 3, page 737).

Solution

(a) Ranking halogens according to oxidizing ability: The halogens (F_2, Cl_2, Br_2, and I_2) appear in the upper-left portion of Table 19.1, with F_2 being highest, followed in order by the other three species. Their strengths as oxidizing agents are $F_2 > Cl_2 > Br_2 > I_2$. (The ability of bromine to oxidize iodide ions to molecular iodine is illustrated in Figure 19.15.)

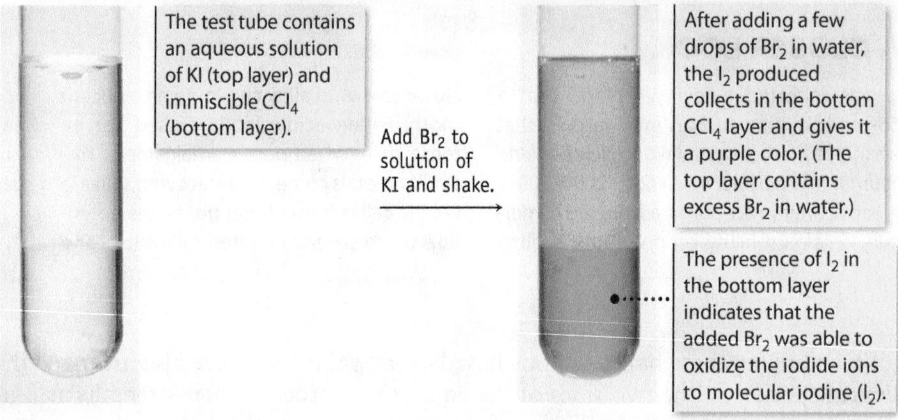

Photos: © Cengage Learning/Charles D. Winters

FIGURE 19.15 The reaction of bromine and iodide ion. This experiment proves that Br_2 is a better oxidizing agent than I_2.

(b) Comparing hydrogen peroxide and chlorine: H_2O_2 lies just below F_2 but well above Cl_2 in the potential ladder (Table 19.1). Thus, H_2O_2 is a weaker oxidizing agent than F_2 but a stronger one than Cl_2. (Note that the $E°$ value for H_2O_2 refers to an acidic solution and standard conditions.)

(c) Which halogen will oxidize gold metal to gold(III) ions? The $Au^{3+}|Au$ half-reaction is listed below the $F_2|F^-$ half-reaction and just above the $Cl_2|Cl^-$ half-reaction. This tells us that, among the halogens, only F_2 is capable of oxidizing Au to Au^{3+} under standard conditions. That is, for the reaction of Au and F_2,

Oxidation, anode:	$2[Au(s) \rightarrow Au^{3+}(aq) + 3\ e^-]$
Reduction, cathode:	$3[F_2(g) + 2\ e^- \rightarrow 2\ F^-(aq)]$
Net ionic equation:	$3\ F_2(g) + 2\ Au(s) \rightarrow 6\ F^-(aq) + 2\ Au^{3+}(aq)$

$$E°_{cell} = E°_{cathode} - E°_{anode} = +2.87\ V - (+1.50\ V) = +1.37\ V$$

F_2 is a stronger oxidizing agent than Au^{3+}, so the reaction proceeds from left to right as written. (This is confirmed by a positive value of $E°_{cell}$.) For the reaction of Cl_2 and Au, Table 19.1 shows us that Cl_2 is a weaker oxidizing agent than Au^{3+}, so the reaction would be expected to proceed in the opposite direction under standard conditions.

Oxidation, anode:	$2[Au(s) \rightarrow Au^{3+}(aq) + 3\ e^-]$
Reduction, cathode:	$3[Cl_2(aq) + 2\ e^- \rightarrow 2\ Cl^-(aq)]$
Net ionic equation:	$3\ Cl_2(aq) + 2\ Au(s) \rightarrow 6\ Cl^-(aq) + 2\ Au^{3+}(aq)$

$$E°_{cell} = E°_{cathode} - E°_{anode} = +1.36\ V - (+1.50\ V) = -0.14\ V$$

This is confirmed by the negative value for $E°_{cell}$.

Think about Your Answer In part (c), we calculated $E°_{cell}$ for two reactions. To achieve a balanced net ionic equation, we added the half-reactions, but only after multiplying the gold half-reaction by 2 and the halogen half-reaction by 3. (This means 6 mol of electrons were transferred from 2 mol Au to 3 mol Cl_2.) Notice that this multiplication does not change the value of $E°$ for the half-reactions because cell potentials do not depend on the quantity of material.

Check Your Understanding

(a) Rank the following metals in their ability to function as reducing agents: Hg, Sn, and Pb.

(b) Which halogens will oxidize mercury to mercury(II)?

CASE STUDY Manganese in the Oceans

Manganese is a key component of some oxidation–reduction cycles in the oceans. According to an article in the journal *Science*, it "can perform this role because it exists in multiple oxidation states and is recycled rapidly between these states by bacterial processes."

Figure A shows how this cycle is thought to work. Manganese(II) ions in subsurface water are oxidized to form manganese(IV) oxide, MnO_2. Particles of this insoluble solid sink toward the ocean floor. However, some encounter hydrogen sulfide, which is produced in the ocean depths, and rises toward the surface. Another redox reaction occurs, producing sulfur and manganese(II) ions. The newly formed Mn^{2+} ions diffuse upward, where they are again oxidized.

The manganese cycle had been thought to involve only the +2 and +4 oxidation states of manganese, and analyses of water samples assumed the dissolved manganese existed only as Mn^{2+} ions. One reason for this is that the intermediate oxidation state, Mn^{3+}, is not predicted to be stable in water. It should disproportionate to the +2 and +4 states.

$$2\ Mn^{3+}(aq) + 2\ H_2O(\ell) \longrightarrow Mn^{2+}(aq) + MnO_2(s) + 4\ H^+(aq)$$

It is known, however, that Mn^{3+} can exist when complexed with species such as pyrophosphate ions, $P_2O_7^{4-}$.

Several years ago, geochemists suggested that Mn^{3+} ions could exist in natural water. They could be produced by bacterial action and stabilized by phosphate from ATP or ADP. They speculated that the Mn^{3+} ion could play an important part in the natural manganese cycle.

Now, other researchers have indeed discovered that, in oxygen-poor waters, the manganese(III) ion, Mn^{3+}, can persist. These ions were found in anoxic zones (zones without dissolved oxygen) below 100 m in the Black Sea and below about 15 m in the Chesapeake Bay. It is now clear that Mn^{3+} ions, which had previously been known only in the laboratory, can exist in natural waters under the right circumstances and that the manganese cycle may have to be revised.

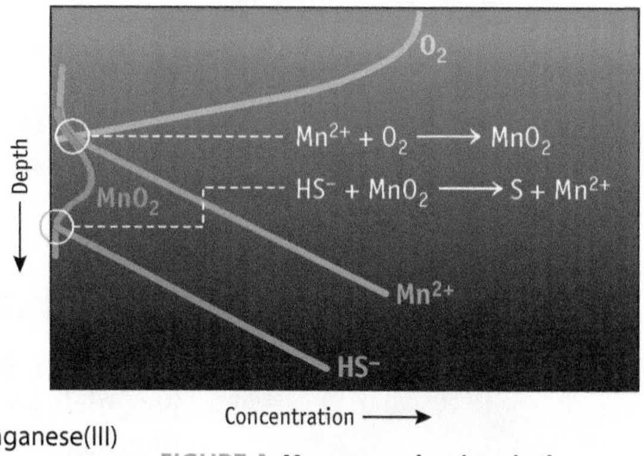

FIGURE A **Manganese chemistry in the oceans.** Relative concentrations of important species as a function of depth in the oceans. See K. S. Johnson, *Science*, Vol. 313, p. 1896, 2006 and R. E. Trouwborst, B. G. Clement, B. M. Tebor, B. T. Glazer, and G. W. Luther, III, *Science*, Vol. 313, pp. 1955–1957, 2006.

Questions:

1. Given the following reduction potentials, show that Mn^{3+} should disproportionate to Mn^{2+} and MnO_2 under standard conditions.

$$4\ H^+(aq) + MnO_2(s) + e^- \longrightarrow Mn^{3+}(aq) + 2\ H_2O(\ell)$$

$E° = 0.95$ V

$$Mn^{3+}(aq) + e^- \longrightarrow Mn^{2+}(aq)$$

$E° = 1.50$ V

2. Balance the following equations in acid solution.
   (a) Reduction of MnO_2 with HS^- to Mn^{2+} and S
   (b) Oxidation of Mn^{2+} with O_2 to MnO_2
3. Calculate $E°$ for the oxidation of Mn^{2+} with O_2 to MnO_2.

Answers to these questions are available in Appendix N.

REVIEW & CHECK FOR SECTION 19-4

1. The net reaction that occurs in a voltaic cell is $Zn(s) + 2\ Ag^+(aq) \rightarrow Zn^{2+}(aq) + 2\ Ag(s)$.

   Calculate a potential for the cell assuming standard conditions.

   (a) 1.562 V (b) 0.0360 V (c) 2.361 V

2. Which metal in the following list is easiest to oxidize: Fe, Ag, Zn, Mg, Au?

   (a) Fe (c) Zn (e) Au

   (b) Ag (d) Mg

3. Determine which of the following redox equations are product-favored at equilibrium.

   (i) $Ni^{2+}(aq) + H_2(g) \rightarrow Ni(s) + 2\ H^+(aq)$

   (ii) $2\ Fe^{3+}(aq) + 2\ I^-(aq) \rightarrow 2\ Fe^{2+}(aq) + I_2(s)$

   (iii) $Br_2(\ell) + 2\ Cl^-(aq) \rightarrow 2\ Br^-(aq) + Cl_2(g)$

   (iv) $Cr_2O_7^{2-}(aq) + 6\ Fe^{2+}(aq) + 14\ H^+(aq) \rightarrow 2\ Cr^{3+}(aq) + 6\ Fe^{3+}(aq) + 7\ H_2O(\ell)$

   (a) ii and iv (b) i and iii (c) iv only (d) all

Learning Objectives: LO 3.12, LO 3.13

19-5 Electrochemical Cells under Nonstandard Conditions

Electrochemical cells seldom operate under standard conditions in the real world. Even if the cell is constructed with all dissolved species at 1 M, reactant concentrations decrease and product concentrations increase in the course of the reaction. Changing concentrations of reactants and products, as well as the temperature, will affect the cell voltage. Therefore, we need to examine what happens to cell potentials under nonstandard conditions.

The Nernst Equation

Based on both theory and experimental results, it has been determined that cell potentials are related to concentrations of reactants and products and to temperature, as follows:

$$E = E° - (RT/nF)\ \ln Q \qquad (19.2)$$

In this equation, which is known as the **Nernst equation**, R is the gas constant (8.314472 J/K · mol); T is the temperature (K); and n is the number of moles of electrons transferred between oxidizing and reducing agents (as determined by the balanced equation for the reaction). The symbol F represents the **Faraday constant** (9.6485337×10^4 C/mol). *One Faraday is the quantity of electric charge carried by one mole of electrons.* The term Q is the reaction quotient (◀ Equation 15.2, Section 15-2). Substituting values for the constants in Equation 19.2, and using 298 K as the temperature, gives

$$E = E° - \frac{0.0257}{n} \ln Q \quad \text{at 25 °C} \qquad (19.3)$$

or, in a commonly used form using base-10 logarithms,

$$E = E° - \frac{0.0592}{n} \log Q$$

In essence, the term $(RT/nF)\ln Q$ "corrects" the standard potential $E°$ for nonstandard conditions or concentrations.

EXAMPLE 19.7

Using the Nernst Equation

Problem A voltaic cell is set up at 25 °C with the half-cells Al^{3+}(0.0010 M)|Al and Ni^{2+}(0.50 M)|Ni. Write an equation for the reaction that occurs when the cell generates an electric current and determine the cell potential.

What Do You Know? You know the temperature and the identity and concentrations of the reactants and products.

Strategy

- Determine which substance is oxidized (Al or Ni) by looking at the appropriate half-reactions in Table 19.1 and deciding which is the better reducing agent (Example 19.6).
- Add the half-reactions to determine the net ionic equation and calculate $E°_{cell}$.
- Use the Nernst equation to calculate E, the potential.

Solution Aluminum metal is a stronger reducing agent than Ni metal. (Conversely, Ni^{2+} is a better oxidizing agent than Al^{3+}.) Therefore, Al is oxidized, and the $Al^{3+}|Al$ compartment is the anode.

Cathode, reduction:	$3\,[Ni^{2+}(aq) + 2\,e^- \rightarrow Ni(s)]$
Anode, oxidation:	$2\,[Al(s) \rightarrow Al^{3+}(aq) + 3\,e^-]$
Net ionic equation:	$2\,Al(s) + 3\,Ni^{2+}(aq) \rightarrow 2\,Al^{3+}(aq) + 3\,Ni(s)$

$$E°_{cell} = E°_{cathode} - E°_{anode}$$

$$E°_{cell} = (-0.25\text{ V}) - (-1.66\text{ V}) = 1.41\text{ V}$$

The expression for Q is written based on the cell reaction. In the net reaction, $Al^{3+}(aq)$ has a coefficient of 2, so this concentration is squared. Similarly, $[Ni^{2+}(aq)]$ is cubed. Solids are not included in the expression for Q (◀ Section 15-2).

$$Q = \frac{[Al^{3+}]^2}{[Ni^{2+}]^3}$$

The net equation requires transfer of six moles of electrons from two moles of Al atoms to three moles of Ni^{2+} ions, so $n = 6$, and the Nernst equation gives

$$E_{cell} = E°_{cell} - \frac{0.0257}{n}\ln\frac{[Al^{3+}]^2}{[Ni^{2+}]^3}$$

$$= +1.41\text{ V} - \frac{0.0257}{6}\ln\frac{[0.0010]^2}{[0.50]^3}$$

$$= +1.41\text{ V} - 0.00428\ln(8.0 \times 10^{-6})$$

$$= +1.41\text{ V} - 0.00428\,(-11.74)$$

$$= 1.46\text{ V}$$

Think about Your Answer The concentrations of Al^{3+} and Ni^{2+} both affect the cell potential. Analysis of the $\ln Q$ term in the Nernst equation shows that if $[Ni^{2+}] = 1$ M but $[Al^{3+}] < 1$ M, then $E_{cell} > E°_{cell}$. The reaction is more product-favored in this situation. The reverse situation (with $[Ni^{2+}] < 1$ M and $[Al^{3+}] = 1$ M) would lead to $E_{cell} < E°_{cell}$. In this example, the very low value of $[Al^{3+}]$ has the greater effect, and E_{cell} is greater than $E°_{cell}$.

Check Your Understanding

A voltaic cell is set up with an aluminum electrode in a 0.025 M $Al(NO_3)_3(aq)$ solution and an iron electrode in a 0.50 M $Fe(NO_3)_2(aq)$ solution. Determine the cell potential, E_{cell}, at 298 K.

Strategy Map 19.7

PROBLEM

Write an equation for the reaction involving **Al** and **Al^{3+}** with **Ni** and **Ni^{2+}**. Calculate E_{cell}.

KNOWN DATA/INFORMATION

- Concentrations of **Al^{3+}** and **Ni^{2+}**
- Look up **$E°$ values** for the half-reactions.

STEP 1. Decide which half-reactions occur at the **anode** and **cathode** based on **$E°$ values.**

Cathode reaction (reduction of Ni^{2+}) and **anode reaction** (oxidation of Al)

STEP 2. Add half-reactions to obtain **net cell reaction.**

Net cell reaction

STEP 3. Calculate $E°_{cell}$.

$E°_{cell} = E°_{cathode} - E°_{anode}$

STEP 4. Use **Nernst equation** with known ion concentrations, calculated $E°_{cell}$, and **n value** to calculate E_{cell}.

E_{cell} under nonstandard conditions

Example 19.7 demonstrated the calculation of a cell potential if concentrations are known. It is also useful to apply the Nernst equation in the opposite sense, using a measured cell potential to determine an unknown concentration.

EXAMPLE 19.8

Variation of Cell Potential with Concentration

Problem A voltaic cell is set up with copper and hydrogen half-cells. Standard conditions are employed in the copper half-cell, Cu^{2+}(aq, 1.00 M)|Cu(s). The hydrogen gas pressure is 1.00 bar, and $[H^+(aq)]$ in the hydrogen half-cell is the unknown. A value of 0.490 V is recorded for E_{cell} at 298 K. Determine the pH of the solution.

What Do You Know? You know the temperature, the identity of the reactants and products, the concentration of the Cu^{2+} ion, the partial pressure of H_2, and E_{cell}.

Strategy

- Determine which is the better oxidizing and reducing agent in order to decide what net reaction is occurring in the cell. Write a balanced equation for the reaction.
- Calculate $E°_{cell}$ from values of $E°$ (Table 19.1).
- Use the Nernst equation with the given Cu^{2+} ion concentration to calculate the hydrogen ion concentration.
- Calculate the pH.

Solution Based on their positions in a table of standard reduction potentials, Cu^{2+} is a better oxidizing agent than H^+, so $Cu(s)|Cu^{2+}(aq, 1.00\ M)$ is the cathode, and $H_2(g, 1.00\ bar)|H^+(aq, ?\ M)$ is the anode.

Cathode, reduction: $Cu^{2+}(aq) + 2\ e^- \rightarrow Cu(s)$

Anode, oxidation: $H_2(g) \rightarrow 2\ H^+(aq) + 2\ e^-$

Net ionic equation: $H_2(g) + Cu^{2+}(aq) \rightarrow Cu(s) + 2\ H^+(aq)$

$$E°_{cell} = E°_{cathode} - E°_{anode}$$

$$E°_{cell} = (+0.337\ V) - (0.00\ V) = +0.337\ V$$

The reaction quotient, Q, is derived from the balanced net ionic equation.

$$Q = \frac{[H^+]^2}{[Cu^{2+}]P_{H_2}}$$

The net equation requires the transfer of two moles of electrons, so $n = 2$. The value of $[Cu^{2+}]$ is 1.00 M, and the pressure of H_2 is 1.0 bar, but $[H^+]$ is unknown. Substitute this information into the Nernst equation (and do not overlook the fact that $[H^+]$ is squared in the expression for Q).

$$E = E° - \frac{0.0257}{n}\ln\frac{[H^+]^2}{[Cu^{2+}]P_{H_2}}$$

$$0.490\ V = 0.337\ V - \frac{0.0257}{2}\ln\frac{[H^+]^2}{(1.00)(1.00)}$$

$$-11.9 = \ln[H^+]^2$$

$$[H^+] = 3 \times 10^{-3}\ M$$

$$pH = 2.6$$

Think about Your Answer Be sure to write the balanced equation. Without it you may not have the correct exponents in the term for Q in the Nernst equation.

Check Your Understanding

The half-cells $Fe^{2+}(aq, 0.024\ M)|Fe(s)$ and $H^+(aq, 0.056\ M)|H_2(1.0\ bar)$ are linked by a salt bridge to create a voltaic cell. Determine the cell potential, E_{cell}, at 298 K.

A pH meter is a device that a uses a measured cell potential to determine an unknown concentration (Figure 19.16). In an electrochemical cell in which $H^+(aq)$ is a reactant or product, the cell voltage will vary predictably with the hydrogen ion concentration. The cell voltage is measured and the value used to calculate pH. Example 19.8 illustrates how E_{cell} *varies with the hydrogen ion concentration in a simple cell.*

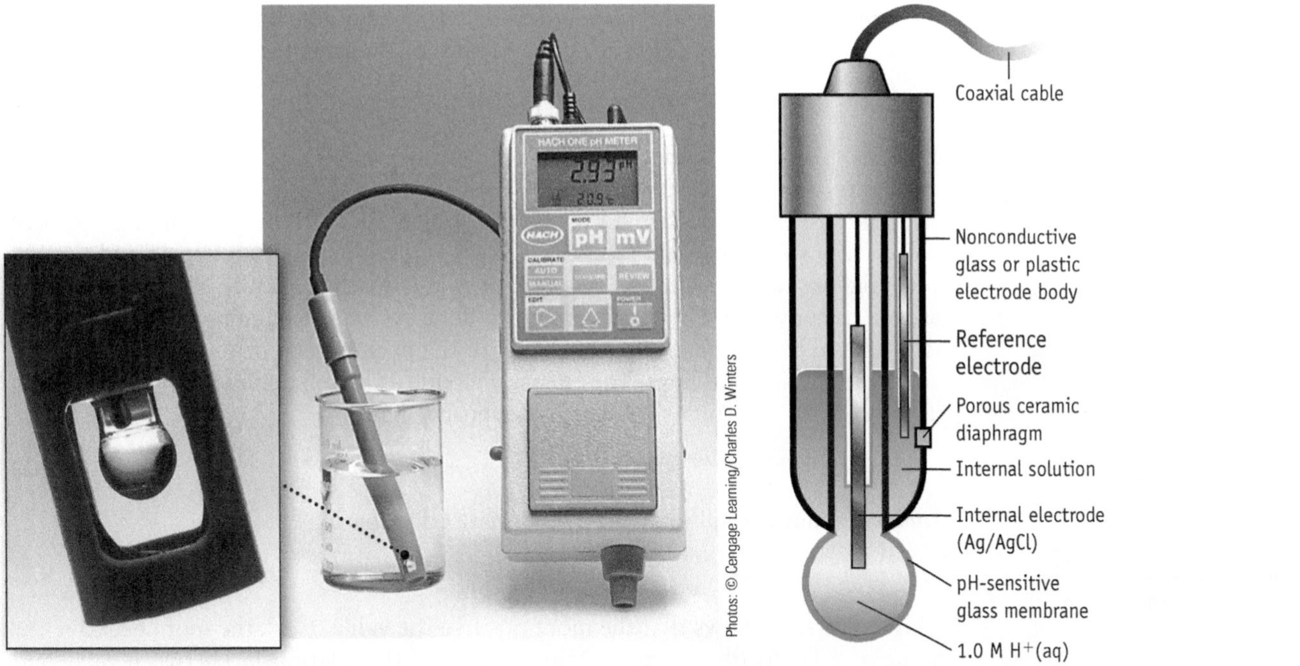

FIGURE 19.16 **Measuring pH.**

In the real world, using a hydrogen electrode in a pH meter is not practical. The apparatus is clumsy; it is anything but robust; and platinum (for the electrode) is costly. Common pH meters use a glass electrode, so called because it contains a thin glass membrane separating the cell from the solution whose pH is to be measured (Figure 19.16). Inside the glass electrode is a silver wire coated with AgCl and a solution of HCl; outside is the solution of unknown pH to be evaluated. An Ag/AgCl or calomel electrode—the latter a common reference electrode using a mercury(I)–mercury redox couple (Hg_2Cl_2 | Hg)—serves as the second electrode of the cell. The potential across the glass membrane depends on [H^+]. Common pH meters give a direct readout of pH.

REVIEW & CHECK FOR SECTION 19-5

1. Calculate E_{cell} at 298 K for a cell involving Sn and Cu and their ions:

$$Sn(s) \,|\, Sn^{2+}(aq, 0.25\ M) \,||\, Cu^{2+}(aq, 0.10\ M) \,|\, Cu(s)$$

(a) 0.47 V (b) 0.49 V (c) 0.50 V

19-6 Electrochemistry and Thermodynamics

Learning Objectives: LO 3.12, LO 3.13

Work and Free Energy

The first law of thermodynamics states that the internal energy change in a system (ΔU) is related to two quantities, heat (q) and work (w): $\Delta U = q + w$ (◀ Section 5-4). This equation also applies to chemical changes that occur in a voltaic cell. As current flows, energy is transferred from the system (the voltaic cell) to the surroundings.

In a voltaic cell, the decrease in internal energy in the system will manifest itself ideally as electrical work done on the surroundings by the system. In practice, however, some energy is usually evolved as heat by the voltaic cell. The maximum work done by an electrochemical system (ideally, assuming no heat is generated) is proportional to the potential difference (volts) and the quantity of charge (coulombs):

$$w_{max} = nFE \quad (19.4)$$

In this equation, E is the cell potential, and nF is the quantity of electric charge transferred from anode to cathode.

The free energy change for a process is, by definition, the maximum amount of work that can be obtained (Section 18-6). Because the maximum work and the cell potential are related, $E°$ and $\Delta_r G°$ can be related mathematically (taking care to assign signs correctly). The maximum work done on the surroundings when electricity is produced by a voltaic cell is $+nFE$, with the positive sign denoting an increase in energy in the surroundings. The energy content of the cell decreases by this amount. Thus, $\Delta_r G$ for the voltaic cell has the opposite sign.

$$\Delta_r G = -nFE \quad (19.5)$$

Under standard conditions, the appropriate equation is

$$\Delta_r G° = -nFE° \quad (19.6)$$

Units in Equation 19.6 n has units of mol e^-, and F has units of (C/mol e^-). Therefore, nF has units of coulombs (C). Because 1 J = 1 C · V, the product nFE will have units of energy (J).

This expression shows that the more positive the value of $E°$, the more negative the value of $\Delta_r G°$ for the reaction. Also, because of the relationship between $\Delta_r G°$ and K, the farther apart the half-reactions are on the potential ladder, the more strongly product-favored the reaction is at equilibrium.

EXAMPLE 19.9

Relating $E°$ and $\Delta_r G°$

Problem The standard cell potential, $E°_{cell}$, for the reduction of silver ions with copper metal (Figure 19.5) is +0.462 V at 25 °C. Calculate $\Delta_r G°$ for this reaction.

What Do You Know? You know the cell potential under standard conditions and therefore know to use Equation 19.6 to calculate the change in free energy. In this equation F is a known constant, but n has to be determined from the balanced equation for the cell reaction.

Strategy Use Equation 19.6 where $E°_{cell}$ and F are known. The value of n, the number of moles of electrons transferred between copper metal and silver ions, comes from the balanced equation.

Solution In this cell, copper is the anode, and silver is the cathode. The overall cell reaction is

$$Cu(s) + 2\ Ag^+(aq) \rightarrow Cu^{2+}(aq) + 2\ Ag(s)$$

which means that each mole of copper transfers 2 mol of electrons to 2 mol of Ag^+ ions. That is, $n = 2$. Now use Equation 19.6.

$$\Delta_r G° = -nFE° = -(2 \text{ mol } e^-)(96{,}485 \text{ C/mol } e^-)(0.462 \text{ V}) = -89{,}200 \text{ C} \cdot \text{V}$$

Because 1 C · V = 1 J, we have

$$\Delta_r G° = -89{,}200 \text{ J or } -89.2 \text{ kJ}$$

Think about Your Answer This example demonstrates an effective method of obtaining thermodynamic values from electrochemical experiments. Keep in mind that a positive $E°$ implies a negative $\Delta_r G°$.

Check Your Understanding

The following reaction has an $E°$ value of −0.76 V:

$$H_2(g) + Zn^{2+}(aq) \rightarrow Zn(s) + 2\,H^+(aq)$$

Calculate $\Delta_r G°$ for this reaction. Is the reaction product- or reactant-favored at equilibrium?

$E°$ and the Equilibrium Constant

When a voltaic cell produces an electric current, the reactant concentrations decrease, and the product concentrations increase. The cell voltage also changes. As reactants are converted to products, the value of E_{cell} decreases and the cell potential eventually reaches zero; no further net reaction occurs, and equilibrium is achieved.

This situation can be analyzed using the Nernst equation. When $E_{cell} = 0$, the reactants and products are at equilibrium, and the reaction quotient, Q, is equal to the equilibrium constant, K. Substituting the appropriate symbols and values into the Nernst equation,

$$E = 0 = E° - \frac{0.0257}{n} \ln K$$

and collecting terms gives an equation that relates the cell potential and equilibrium constant:

$$\ln K = \frac{nE°}{0.0257} \quad \text{at 25 °C (298 K)} \qquad \textbf{(19.7)}$$

Equation 19.7 can be used to determine values for equilibrium constants, as illustrated in Example 19.10.

EXAMPLE 19.10

$E°$ and Equilibrium Constants

Problem Calculate the equilibrium constant for the reaction at 298 K:

$$Fe(s) + Cd^{2+}(aq) \rightleftharpoons Fe^{2+}(aq) + Cd(s)$$

What Do You Know? You have the balanced chemical equation and know that Equation 19.7 is required. You need to determine $E°$ (from standard reduction potential values in Table 19.1) and n, the number of electrons transferred.

Strategy First, determine $E°_{cell}$ from $E°$ values for the two half-reactions and from those the value of n, the other parameter required in Equation 19.7.

Solution The half-reactions and $E°$ values are

Cathode, reduction: $Cd^{2+}(aq) + 2\,e^- \rightarrow Cd(s)$

Anode, oxidation: $Fe(s) \rightarrow Fe^{2+}(aq) + 2\,e^-$

Net ionic equation: $Fe(s) + Cd^{2+}(aq) \rightleftharpoons Fe^{2+}(aq) + Cd(s)$

$$E°_{cell} = E°_{cathode} - E°_{anode}$$

$$E°_{cell} = (-0.40\ V) - (-0.44\ V) = +0.04\ V$$

Strategy Map 19.10

PROBLEM

Calculate an **equilibrium constant** using ***electrochemical data.***

KNOWN DATA/INFORMATION

- Balanced equation

STEP 1. Calculate $E°_{cell}$ based on $E°$ **values** of the oxidation and reduction half-reactions.

$E°_{cell} = E°_{cathode} - E°_{anode}$

STEP 2. Use Equation 19.7 with calculated $E°_{cell}$ and n **value** to calculate **ln*K***.

Calculated **ln*K***

STEP 3. Convert **ln*K*** to ***K***.

Equilibrium constant, ***K***

Now substitute $n = 2$ and $E°_{cell}$ into Equation 19.7.

$$\ln K = \frac{nE°}{0.0257} = \frac{(2)(0.04\text{ V})}{0.0257} = 3.1$$

$$K = 20$$

Think about Your Answer The relatively small positive voltage (0.04 V) for the cell indicates that the cell reaction is only mildly product-favored. A value of 20 for the equilibrium constant is in accord with this observation.

Check Your Understanding

Calculate the equilibrium constant at 25 °C for the reaction

$$2\text{ Ag}^+(aq) + \text{Hg}(\ell) \rightleftharpoons 2\text{ Ag}(s) + \text{Hg}^{2+}(aq)$$

E°, K, and Q The standard electrochemical potential for a reaction, *E°*, depends only on the nature of the reactants and products. However, *E*, the potential under nonstandard conditions, does depend on the concentrations of the materials as well as their nature. As a battery discharges, the concentrations of the reactants decrease while the concentrations of the products increase. As the ratio of the products to reactants grows, *Q* becomes larger and larger, ln *Q* becomes more positive, and *E* approaches the value of *E°*. Eventually, when $Q = K$, the reaction reaches equilibrium, *E* equals zero. As there is no longer any net reaction occurring, the battery is "dead."

The relationships between $E°$, K, and $\Delta_r G°$ are summarized in Table 19.2. Values of $E°$ can be used to obtain equilibrium constants for many different chemical systems. One example is the determination of solubility product constants, K_{sp}. Let us begin with an electrode in which an insoluble ionic compound, AgCl, is a component of a half-cell. Figure 19.17 illustrates how the potential for the reduction of AgCl in the presence of Cl^- ion (1.00 M) can be determined.

$$\text{AgCl}(s) + e^- \rightarrow \text{Ag}(s) + \text{Cl}^-(aq) \qquad E° = +0.222\text{ V}$$

When paired with the standard hydrogen electrode, the standard reduction potential for the AgCl|Ag half-cell is +0.222 V. If this half-reaction is then paired with that for a standard silver electrode in a hypothetical voltaic cell, the cell reactions could be written as

Cathode, reduction: $\text{AgCl}(s) + e^- \rightarrow \text{Ag}(s) + \text{Cl}^-(aq)$

Anode, oxidation: $\text{Ag}(s) \rightarrow \text{Ag}^+(aq) + e^-$

Net ionic equation: $\text{AgCl}(s) \rightarrow \text{Ag}^+(aq) + \text{Cl}^-(aq)$

The equation for the net reaction represents the equilibrium of solid AgCl and its ions. The cell potential is negative,

$$E°_{cell} = E°_{cathode} - E°_{anode} = (+0.222\text{ V}) - (+0.799\text{ V}) = -0.577\text{ V}$$

indicating a reactant-favored process, as would be expected based on the low solubility of AgCl. Using Equation 19.7, the value of K_{sp} can then be obtained from $E°_{cell}$.

$$\ln K = \frac{nE°}{0.0257} = \frac{(1)(-0.577\text{ V})}{0.0257} = -22.5$$

$$K_{sp} = e^{-22.5} = 2 \times 10^{-10}$$

Table 19.2 Summary of the Relationship of K, $\Delta_r G°$, and $E°$

K	$\Delta_r G°$	$E°$	Reactant-Favored or Product-Favored at Equilibrium?
$K >> 1$	$\Delta_r G° < 0$	$E° > 0$	Product-favored
$K = 1$	$\Delta_r G° = 0$	$E° = 0$	$[C]^c[D]^d = [A]^a[B]^b$ at equilibrium
$K << 1$	$\Delta_r G° > 0$	$E° < 0$	Reactant-favored

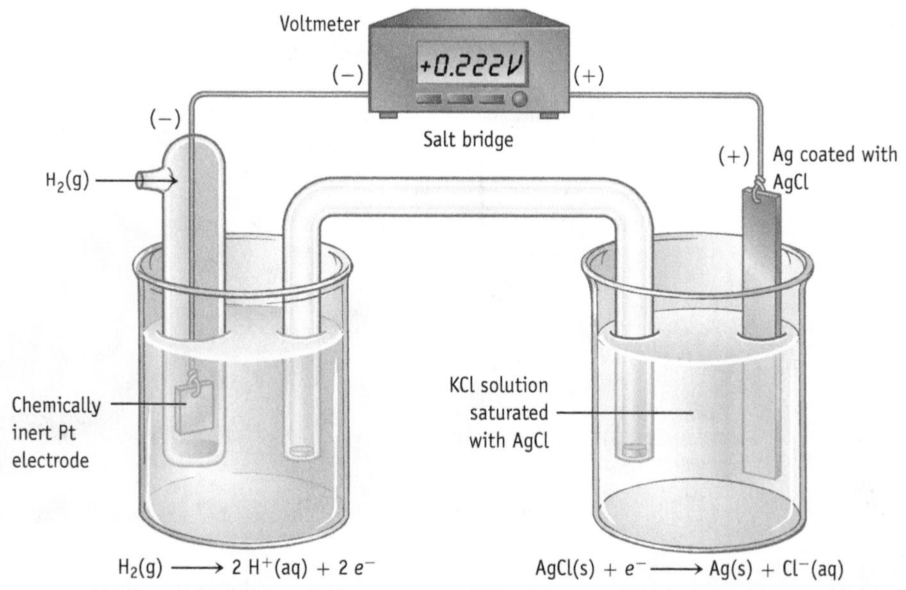

FIGURE 19.17 Measurement of the standard electrode potential for the Ag | AgCl electrode.

REVIEW & CHECK FOR SECTION 19-6

1. In Appendix M, the following standard reduction potential is reported:

$$[Zn(CN)_4]^{2-}(aq) + 2\ e^- \rightarrow Zn(s) + 4\ CN^-(aq) \qquad E° = -1.26\ V$$

Use this information, along with the data on the $Zn^{2+}(aq)|Zn$ half-cell, to calculate the equilibrium constant for the reaction

$$Zn^{2+}(aq) + 4\ CN^-(aq) \rightleftharpoons [Zn(CN)_4]^{2-}(aq)$$

What is the value for the formation constant for this complex ion at 25 °C?

(a) 2.8×10^8 (b) 6.3×10^{16} (c) 1.9×10^{68}

19-7 Electrolysis: Chemical Change Using Electrical Energy

Learning Objectives: LO 3.12, LO 3.13, LO 5.15

Thus far, we have described electrochemical cells that use product-favored redox reactions to generate an electric current. Equally important, however, is the opposite process, **electrolysis**, the use of electrical energy to bring about chemical change.

Electrolysis of water is a classic chemistry experiment, and the electroplating of metals is another example of electrolysis (Figure 19.18). In electroplating, an electric current is passed through a solution containing a salt of the metal to be plated. The object to be plated is the cathode, and when metal ions in solution are reduced, they deposit on the object's surface.

Electrolysis is also important because it is widely used in refining metals such as aluminum and in producing chemicals such as chlorine.

Electrolysis of Molten Salts

All electrolysis experiments are set up in a similar manner. The material to be electrolyzed, either a molten salt or a solution, is contained in an electrolysis cell. As was the case with voltaic cells, ions must be present in the liquid or solution for a current to flow as it is the movement of ions within the cell that constitutes the electric current. The cell has two electrodes that are connected to a source of DC (direct-current) voltage. If the applied voltage is high enough, chemical reactions occur at the two electrodes. Reduction occurs at the negatively charged cathode, with electrons being transferred from that electrode to a chemical species in the cell.

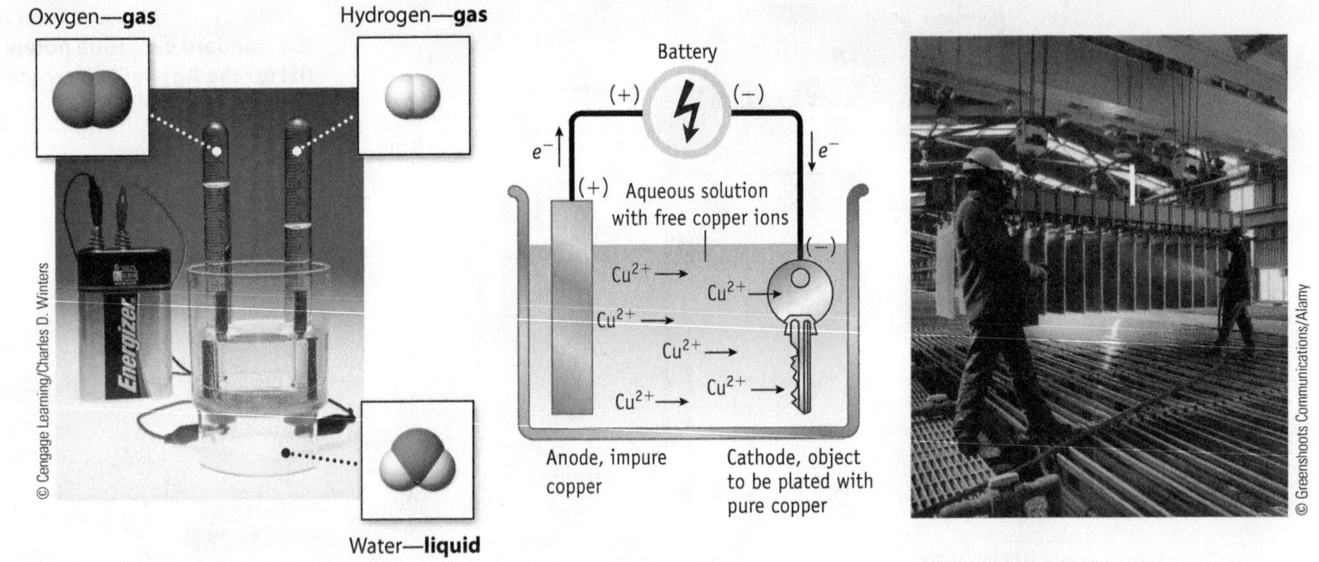

(a) Electrolysis of water produces hydrogen (at the cathode) and oxygen gas (at the anode).

(b) Purifying copper by electrolysis. Copper ions are produced at an anode made of impure copper. The ions migrate to the cathode where they are reduced to copper metal. (*Right.* A photo of a commercial electrolysis unit producing copper.)

FIGURE 19.18 **Electrolysis.**

Oxidation occurs at the positive anode, with electrons from a chemical species being transferred to that electrode.

Let us focus our attention on the chemical reactions that occur at each electrode in the electrolysis of a molten salt. Sodium chloride melts at about 800 °C, and in the molten state sodium ions (Na^+) and chloride ions (Cl^-) are freed from their rigid arrangement in the crystalline lattice. If a potential is applied to the electrodes, sodium ions are attracted to the negative electrode, and chloride ions are attracted to the positive electrode (Figure 19.19). If the potential is high enough, chemical reactions occur at each electrode. At the negative cathode, Na^+ ions accept electrons and are reduced to sodium metal (a liquid at this temperature). Simultaneously, at the positive anode, chloride ions give up electrons and form elemental chlorine.

Cathode (−), reduction:	$2\ Na^+ + 2\ e^- \rightarrow 2\ Na(\ell)$
Anode (+), oxidation:	$2\ Cl^- \rightarrow Cl_2(g) + 2\ e^-$
Net ionic equation:	$2\ Na^+ + 2\ Cl^- \rightarrow 2\ Na(\ell) + Cl_2(g)$

Electrons move through the external circuit under the force exerted by the applied potential, and the movement of positive and negative ions in the molten salt constitutes the current within the cell. Finally, it is important to recognize that the reaction

PROBLEM SOLVING TIP 19.3
Electrochemical Conventions: Voltaic Cells and Electrolysis Cells

Whether you are describing a voltaic cell or an electrolysis cell, the terms *anode* and *cathode* always refer to the electrodes at which oxidation and reduction occur, respectively. However, the electrodes in the two types of electrochemical cells have different polarities.

TYPE OF CELL	ELECTRODE	FUNCTION	POLARITY
Voltaic	Anode	Oxidation	−
	Cathode	Reduction	+
Electrolysis	Anode	Oxidation	+
	Cathode	Reduction	−

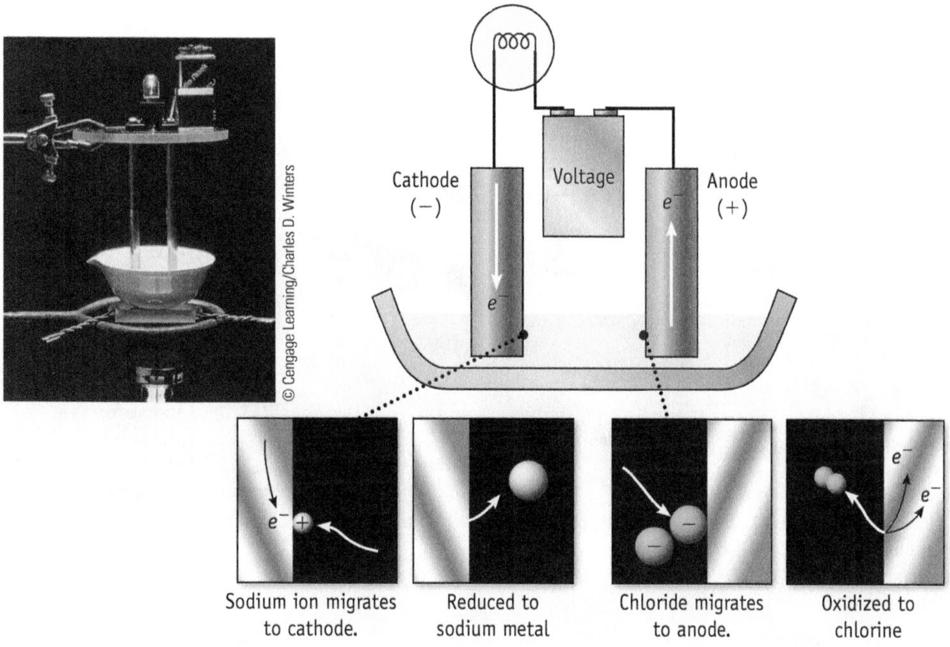

FIGURE 19.19 **The preparation of sodium and chlorine by the electrolysis of molten NaCl.** In the molten state, sodium ions migrate to the negative cathode, where they are reduced to sodium metal. Chloride ions migrate to the positive anode, where they are oxidized to elemental chlorine.

is not spontaneous. The energy required for this reaction to occur has been provided by the electric current.

Electrolysis of Aqueous Solutions

Sodium ions (Na^+) and chloride ions (Cl^-) are the primary species present in molten NaCl. Only chloride ions can be oxidized, and only sodium ions can be reduced. Electrolysis of a substance in aqueous solution is more complicated than the electrolysis of a molten salt, however, because water is now present. Water is an *electroactive* substance; that is, it can be oxidized or reduced in an electrochemical process.

Consider the electrolysis of aqueous sodium iodide (Figure 19.20). In this experiment, the electrolysis cell contains $Na^+(aq)$, $I^-(aq)$, and H_2O molecules. Possible *reduction reactions* at the *negative cathode* include

$$Na^+(aq) + e^- \rightarrow Na(s)$$

$$2\ H_2O(\ell) + 2\ e^- \rightarrow H_2(g) + 2\ OH^-(aq)$$

Possible *oxidation reactions* at the *positive anode* are

$$2\ I^-(aq) \rightarrow I_2(aq) + 2\ e^-$$

$$2\ H_2O(\ell) \rightarrow O_2(g) + 4\ H^+(aq) + 4\ e^-$$

In the electrolysis of aqueous NaI, $H_2(g)$ and $OH^-(aq)$ are formed by water reduction at the cathode, and iodine is formed at the anode. Thus, the overall cell process can be summarized by the following equations:

Cathode (−), reduction:	$2\ H_2O(\ell) + 2\ e^- \rightarrow H_2(g) + 2\ OH^-(aq)$
Anode (+), oxidation:	$2\ I^-(aq) \rightarrow I_2(aq) + 2\ e^-$
Net ionic equation:	$2\ H_2O(\ell) + 2\ I^-(aq) \rightarrow H_2(g) + 2\ OH^-(aq) + I_2(aq)$

where $E°_{cell}$ has a negative value.

$$E°_{cell} = E°_{cathode} - E°_{anode} = (-0.8277\ V) - (+0.621\ V) = -1.449\ V$$

This process is not spontaneous under standard conditions, and a potential of *at least* 1.45 V must be *applied* to the cell for these reactions to occur. If the process had involved the oxidation of water instead of iodide ion at the anode, the required potential

FIGURE 19.20 Electrolysis of aqueous NaI.

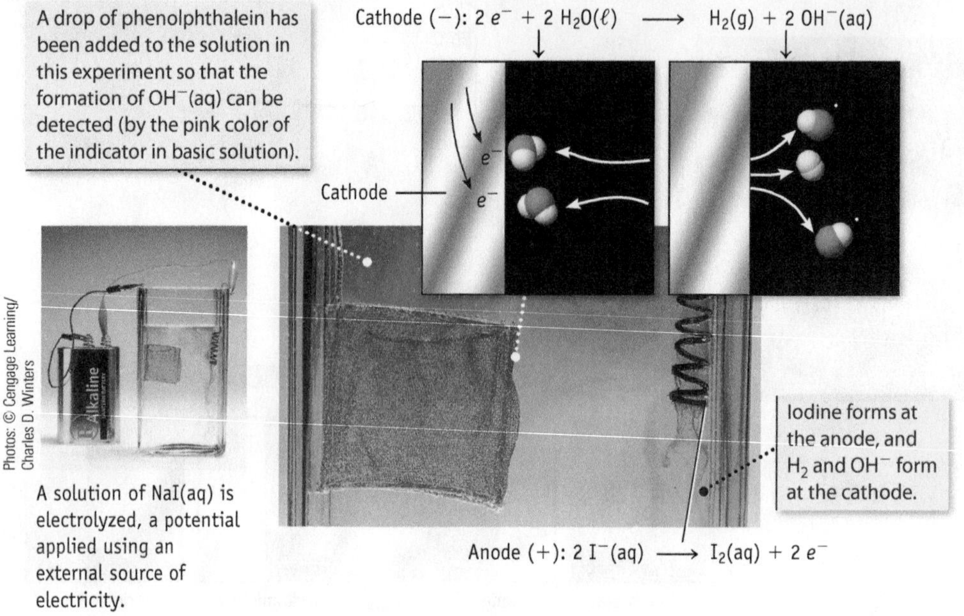

would be −2.057 V [$E°_{cathode} - E°_{anode} = (-0.8277\text{ V}) - (+1.229\text{ V})$], and if the reaction involving the reduction of Na^+ and the oxidation of I^- had occurred, the required potential would be −3.335 V [$E°_{cathode} - E°_{anode} = (-2.714\text{ V}) - (+0.621\text{ V})$]. The reaction occurring is the one requiring the smallest applied potential, so the net cell reaction in the electrolysis of NaI(aq) is the oxidation of iodide and reduction of water.

What happens if an aqueous solution of some other metal halide such as $SnCl_2$ is electrolyzed? Consult Appendix M, and consider all possible half-reactions. In this case, aqueous Sn^{2+} ion is much more easily reduced ($E° = -0.14$ V) than water

A CLOSER LOOK Electrochemistry and Michael Faraday

The terms *anion, cation, electrode,* and *electrolyte* originated with Michael Faraday (1791–1867), one of the most influential people in the history of chemistry. Faraday was apprenticed to a bookbinder in London when he was 13. This situation suited him perfectly, as he enjoyed reading the books sent to the shop for binding. By chance, one of these volumes was a small book on chemistry, which whetted his appetite for science, and he began performing experiments on electricity. In 1812, a patron of the shop invited Faraday to accompany him to the Royal Institution to attend a lecture by one of the most famous chemists of the day, Sir Humphry Davy. Faraday was intrigued by Davy's lecture and wrote to ask Davy for a position as an assistant. His request was granted and he began work in 1813. Faraday was so talented that his work proved extraordinarily fruitful, and only 12 years later he was made the director of the laboratory of the Royal Institution.

It has been said that Faraday's contributions were so enormous that, had there been Nobel Prizes when he was alive, he would have received at least six. These could have been awarded for discoveries such as the following:

- Electromagnetic induction, which led to the first transformer and electric motor
- The laws of electrolysis (the effect of electric current on chemicals)
- The magnetic properties of matter
- Benzene and other organic chemicals (which led to important chemical industries)
- The "Faraday effect" (the rotation of the plane of polarized light by a magnetic field)
- The introduction of the concept of electric and magnetic fields

Michael Faraday (1791–1867)

In addition to making discoveries that had profound effects on science, Faraday was an educator. He wrote and spoke about his work in memorable ways, especially in lectures to the general public that helped to popularize science.

A transcript of Faraday's lectures, *The Chemical History of a Candle*, was published in 1867. This small book, still widely available, is a beautiful and readable account of scientific thinking.

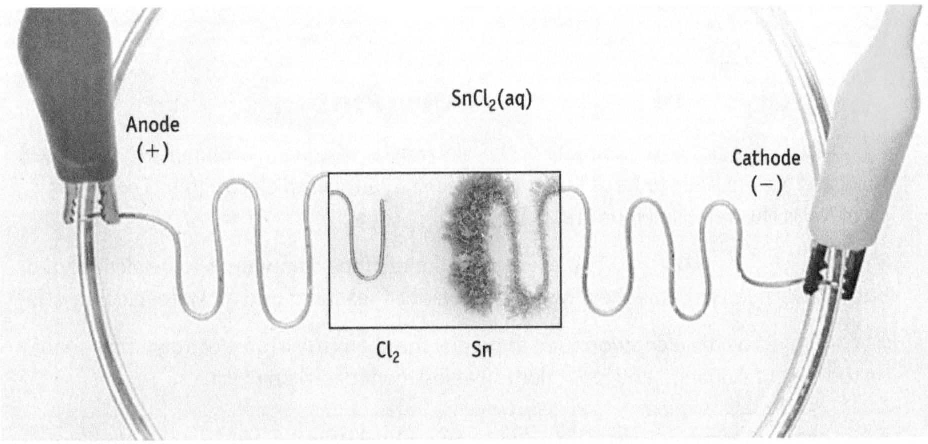

FIGURE 19.21 **Electrolysis of aqueous tin(II) chloride.** Tin metal collects at the negative cathode. Chlorine gas is formed at the positive anode. Elemental chlorine is formed in the cell, in spite of the fact that the potential for the oxidation of Cl^- is more negative than that for oxidation of water. (That is, chlorine should be less easily oxidized than water.) This is the result of chemical kinetics and illustrates the complexity of some aqueous electrochemistry.

($E° = -0.83$ V) at the cathode, so tin metal is produced. At the anode, two oxidations are possible: Cl^-(aq) to Cl_2(g) or $H_2O(\ell)$ to O_2(g). Experiments show that chloride ion is oxidized in preference to water, so the reactions occurring on electrolysis of aqueous tin(II) chloride are (Figure 19.21)

Cathode (−), reduction:	$Sn^{2+}(aq) + 2\,e^- \rightarrow Sn(s)$
Anode (+), oxidation:	$2\,Cl^-(aq) \rightarrow Cl_2(g) + 2\,e^-$
Net ionic equation:	$Sn^{2+}(aq) + 2\,Cl^-(aq) \rightarrow Sn(s) + Cl_2(g)$

$$E°_{cell} = E°_{cathode} - E°_{anode} = (-0.14\text{ V}) - (+1.36\text{ V}) = -1.50\text{ V}$$

Formation of Cl_2 at the anode in the electrolysis of $SnCl_2$(aq) is contrary to a prediction based on $E°$ values. If the electrode reactions were

Cathode (−), reduction:	$Sn^{2+}(aq) + 2\,e^- \rightarrow Sn(s)$
Anode (+), oxidation:	$2\,H_2O(\ell) \rightarrow O_2(g) + 4\,H^+(aq) + 4\,e^-$

$$E°_{cell} = (-0.14\text{ V}) - (+1.23\text{ V}) = -1.37\text{ V}$$

a smaller applied potential is required. To explain the formation of chlorine instead of oxygen, we must take into account rates of reaction. The oxidation of Cl^-(aq) is much more rapid than the oxidation of H_2O.

This "problem" is used to advantage in the commercially important electrolysis of aqueous NaCl, where a voltage high enough to oxidize both Cl^- and H_2O is used. However, because chloride ion is oxidized much faster than H_2O, Cl_2 is the major product in this electrolysis. This is the predominant means by which chlorine is produced for commercial use.

Overvoltage Voltages higher than the minimum are typically used to speed up reactions that would otherwise be slow. The term *overvoltage* is often used and refers to the voltage needed to make a reaction occur at a reasonable rate.

Another instance in which rates are important concerns electrode materials. Graphite, commonly used to make inert electrodes, can be oxidized. For the half-reaction $CO_2(g) + 4\,H^+(aq) + 4\,e^- \rightarrow C(s) + 2\,H_2O(\ell)$, $E°$ is $+0.20$ V, indicating that carbon is slightly easier to oxidize than copper ($E° = +0.34$ V). Based on this value, oxidation of a graphite electrode might reasonably be expected to occur during an electrolysis. And indeed it does, albeit slowly; graphite electrodes used in electrolysis cells slowly deteriorate and eventually have to be replaced.

One other factor—the concentration of electroactive species in solution—must be taken into account when discussing electrolyses. As shown in Section 19-5, the potential at which a species in solution is oxidized or reduced depends on concentration. Unless standard conditions are used, predictions based on $E°$ values are merely qualitative. In addition, the rate of a half-reaction depends on the concentration of the electroactive substance at the electrode surface. At a very low concentration, the rate of the redox reaction may depend on the rate at which an ion diffuses from the solution to the electrode surface.

EXAMPLE 19.11

Electrolysis of Aqueous Solutions

Problem Predict how products of the electrolysis of aqueous solutions of NaF, NaCl, NaBr, and NaI are likely to be different and predict $E°_{cell}$ for each electrolysis. (The electrolysis of NaI is illustrated in Figure 19.20.)

What Do You Know? You know the identity of the compounds to be electrolyzed, but you will need to know the $E°$ values for their half-reactions and for water electrolysis.

Strategy The main criterion used to predict the chemistry in an electrolytic cell should be the ease of oxidation and reduction, an assessment based on $E°$ values.

Solution The cathode reaction presents no problem: Water is reduced to hydroxide ion and H_2 gas in preference to reduction of $Na^+(aq)$ (as in the electrolysis of aqueous NaI). Thus, the primary cathode reaction in all cases is

$$2\ H_2O(\ell) + 2\ e^- \rightarrow H_2(g) + 2\ OH^-(aq)$$

$$E°_{cathode} = -0.83\ V$$

At the anode, you need to assess the ease of oxidation of the halide ions relative to water. Based on $E°$ values, this should be $I^-(aq) > Br^-(aq) > Cl^-(aq) >> F^-(aq)$. Fluoride ion is much more difficult to oxidize than water, and electrolysis of an aqueous solution containing this ion results exclusively in O_2 formation. That is, the primary anode reaction for NaF(aq) is

$$2\ H_2O(\ell) \rightarrow O_2(g) + 4\ H^+(aq) + 4\ e^-$$

$$E°_{anode} = +1.23\ V$$

Therefore, in this case,

$$E°_{cell} = (-0.83\ V) - (+1.23\ V) = -2.06\ V$$

Recall that chlorine is the primary product at the anode in the electrolysis of aqueous solutions of chloride salts (as in Figure 19.21). Therefore, the primary anode reaction in NaCl(aq) is

$$2\ Cl^-(aq) \rightarrow Cl_2(g) + 2\ e^-$$

$$E°_{cell} = (-0.83\ V) - (+1.36\ V) = -2.19\ V$$

Bromide ions are considerably easier to oxidize than chloride ions, so Br_2 may be expected as the primary product in the electrolysis of aqueous NaBr. For NaBr(aq), the primary anode reaction is

$$2\ Br^-(aq) \rightarrow Br_2(\ell) + 2\ e^-$$

so $E°_{cell}$ is

$$E°_{cell} = (-0.83\ V) - (+1.08\ V) = -1.91\ V$$

Thus, the electrolysis of NaBr resembles that of NaI (Figure 19.20) in producing the halogen, hydrogen gas, and hydroxide ion. The half-reactions and the cell potential for aqueous NaI were given on page 753.

Think about Your Answer As described above, you would predict from $E°$ values the ease of oxidation of halide ions is $I^-(aq) > Br^-(aq) > Cl^-(aq) >> F^-(aq)$. This is confirmed by the results.

Check Your Understanding

Predict the chemical reactions that will occur at the two electrodes in the electrolysis of an aqueous sodium hydroxide solution.

REVIEW & CHECK FOR SECTION 19-7

1. You have a solution containing several metal ions, K^+, Fe^{2+}, Al^{3+}, Ag^+. Which ion will require the lowest potential to plate out on the cathode?

(a) K^+ (b) Fe^{2+} (c) Al^{3+} (d) Ag^+

19-8 Counting Electrons

Learning Objectives: LO 3.12, LO 3.13

In the electrolysis of aqueous $AgNO_3$, one mole of electrons is required to produce one mole of silver. In contrast, two moles of electrons are required to produce one mole of tin (see Figure 19.21):

$$Sn^{2+}(aq) + 2\ e^- \rightarrow Sn(s)$$

It follows that if the number of moles of electrons flowing through the electrolysis cell could be measured, the number of moles of silver or tin produced could be calculated. Conversely, if the amount of silver or tin produced is known, then the number of moles of electrons moving through the circuit could be calculated.

The number of moles of electrons consumed or produced in an electron transfer reaction is obtained by measuring the current flowing in the external electric circuit in a given time. The **current** flowing in an electrical circuit is the amount of charge (in units of coulombs, C) per unit time, and the usual unit for current is the ampere (A). One ampere equals the passage of one coulomb of charge per second.

$$\text{Current (amperes, A)} = \frac{\text{electric charge (coulombs, C)}}{\text{time, } t \text{ (seconds, s)}} \quad \textbf{(19.8)}$$

The current passing through an electrochemical cell and the time for which the current flows are easily measured quantities. Therefore, the charge (in coulombs) that passes through a cell can be obtained by multiplying the current (in amperes) by the time (in seconds). Knowing the charge and using the Faraday constant as a conversion factor, we can calculate the number of moles of electrons that passed through an electrochemical cell. In turn, we can use this quantity to calculate the quantities of reactants and products. The following example illustrates this type of calculation.

Faraday Constant The Faraday constant is the charge carried by 1 mol of electrons: 9.6485337×10^4 C/mol e^-.

EXAMPLE 19.12

Using the Faraday Constant

Problem A current of 2.40 A is passed through a solution containing Cu^{2+}(aq) for 30.0 minutes, with copper metal being deposited at the cathode. What mass of copper, in grams, is deposited?

What Do You Know? You know the current passed through the cell and the time over which it was passed.

Strategy The current and time can be used to calculate the amount of charge that passed through the cell. The Faraday constant can then be used to relate this to the amount (moles) of electrons that were used. This in turn can be related to the amount of copper metal deposited and finally to the mass of copper.

Solution

1. Calculate the charge (number of coulombs) passing through the cell in 30.0 minutes.

$$\begin{aligned}\text{Charge (C)} &= \text{current (A)} \times \text{time (s)}\\ &= (2.40\ \text{A})(30.0\ \text{min})(60.0\ \text{s/min})\\ &= 4.32 \times 10^3\ \text{C}\end{aligned}$$

Strategy Map 19.12

PROBLEM

Calculate the **mass of copper** deposited in electrolysis cell.

KNOWN DATA/INFORMATION

- Current in cell
- Time

STEP 1. Use **current × time** to calculate **charge**.

Charge passing through cell (in **coulombs**)

STEP 2. Use **Faraday constant** to calculate **moles of electrons** passed.

Moles of electrons passed in **given time**

STEP 3. Relate moles of **electrons** to moles of **metal**.

Amount of metal **(mol)** produced

STEP 4. Convert **amount** to **mass**.

Mass of metal **(g)** produced

2. Calculate the number of moles of electrons (i.e., the number of Faradays of electricity).

$$(4.32 \times 10^3\ \text{C})\left(\frac{1\ \text{mol}\ e^-}{96,485\ \text{C}}\right) = 4.48 \times 10^{-2}\ \text{mol}\ e^-$$

3. Calculate the amount of copper and, from this, the mass of copper.

$$\text{mass of copper} = (4.48 \times 10^{-2}\ \text{mol}\ e^-)\left(\frac{1\ \text{mol Cu}}{2\ \text{mol}\ e^-}\right)\left(\frac{63.55\ \text{g Cu}}{1\ \text{mol Cu}}\right) = 1.42\ \text{g}$$

Think about Your Answer The key relation in this calculation is "current = charge/time." Most situations will involve knowing two of these three quantities from experiment and calculating the third.

Check Your Understanding

1. Calculate the mass of O_2 produced in the electrolysis of water, using a current of 0.445 A for a period of 45 minutes.
2. In the commercial production of sodium by electrolysis, the cell operates at 7.0 V and a current of 25×10^3 A. What mass of sodium can be produced in 1 hour?

REVIEW & CHECK FOR SECTION 19-8

1. If you wish to convert 0.0100 mol of Au^{3+}(aq) ions into Au(s) in a "gold-plating" process, how long must you electrolyze a solution if the current passing through the circuit is 2.00 amps?

   (a) 483 seconds
   (b) 4.83×10^4 seconds
   (c) 965 seconds
   (d) 1450 seconds

APPLYING CHEMICAL PRINCIPLES

Sacrifice!

In the latter half of the 18th century the British sheathed the hulls of their naval fleet with copper to protect the hulls from deterioration. Unfortunately, the copper corroded in sea water, so the navy called upon Sir Humphry Davy to determine the cause of the corrosion and to find a cure. Although Davy initially assumed that impurities in the copper caused the corrosion, he soon learned that high-purity copper corroded faster. Turning his attention to the sea water, Davy determined that the copper is oxidized by oxygen in the sea water. The overall reaction,

$$Cu(s) + \tfrac{1}{2}\,O_2(g) + H_2O(\ell) \rightarrow Cu(OH)_2(s)$$

produces copper(II) hydroxide which falls from the hull to the sea floor.

Davy, a pioneer in the field of electrochemistry, quickly determined that the corrosion of copper can be prevented by attaching small pieces of a more easily oxidized metal (such as zinc, tin, or iron) to the copper sheathing. The quantity of the metal may be small in comparison to the copper, but, to be effective, the metal must be positioned below the water line and in direct electrical contact with the copper.

Why is corrosion prevented by attaching a small piece of metal, such as zinc, to the copper? When the two different metals are submerged in sea water they form a galvanic cell. The copper serves as the cathode and the zinc as a "sacrificial" anode. The zinc anode is oxidized instead of the copper. Although the zinc anodes corrode over time and must be replaced, the cost is cheaper than replacing the copper on an entire ship's hull.

In modern fleets, copper-sheathed hulls have given way to steel hulls. Though surface coatings, such as paint, provide some protection against corrosion, sacrificial anodes are still used to protect the steel from corrosion. In addition, sacrificial anodes are now used to protect the steel in underground pipes, as well as in home water heaters, outboard motors, and boilers.

QUESTIONS:

1. If an electrically insulating material, such as paint, is placed between the zinc and the copper, the zinc will still corrode in seawater, but it will not protect the copper from corrosion. Explain.

2. Use standard reduction potentials to determine which of the following metals could serve as a sacrificial anode on a copper-sheathed hull. Indicate all correct responses.
(a) tin (c) iron (e) chromium
(b) silver (d) nickel
3. Use standard reduction potentials to determine which of the following metals could serve as a sacrificial anode on a steel hull. Assume the standard reduction potential for steel is the same as that of iron. Indicate all correct responses.
(a) tin (c) iron (e) chromium
(b) silver (d) nickel
4. The overall reaction for the production of $Cu(OH)_2$ from Cu in oxygenated water can be broken into three steps: an oxidation half-reaction, a reduction half-reaction, and a precipitation reaction.
(a) Complete and balance the two missing half-reactions to give the overall equation for the oxidation of copper in seawater.

1. Oxidation half-reaction: ?
2. Reduction half-reaction: ?
3. Precipitation: $Cu^{2+}(aq) + 2\ OH^-(aq) \rightarrow Cu(OH)_2(s)$
4. Overall: $Cu(s) + \frac{1}{2}\ O_2(g) + H_2O(\ell) \rightarrow Cu(OH)_2(s)$

(b) Determine the equilibrium constant for the overall reaction at 25 °C using standard reduction potentials and the solubility product constant (K_{sp}) of $Cu(OH)_2(s)$.

5. Assume the following electrochemical cell simulates the galvanic cell formed by copper and zinc in seawater at pH 7.90 and 25 °C.

$$Zn\,|\,Zn(OH)_2(s)\,|\,OH^-(aq)\,||\,Cu(OH)_2(s)\,|\,Cu(s)$$

(a) Write a balanced equation for the reaction that occurs at the cathode.
(b) Write a balanced equation for the reaction that occurs at the anode.
(c) Write a balanced chemical equation for the overall reaction.
(d) Determine the potential (in volts) of the cell.

© cliverivers/Alamy

Sacrificial anodes attached to a steel-hulled ship. The "patches" are zinc blocks. Sacrificial anodes of aluminum or magnesium are also used in home electric hot-water heaters to prevent corrosion in the heater.

CHAPTER GOALS REVISITED

Now that you have studied this chapter, you should ask whether you have met the chapter goals. In particular, you should be able to:

UNDERSTAND

- The principles underlying voltaic cells.
  a. In a voltaic cell, identify the half-reactions occurring at the anode and the cathode, the polarity of the electrodes, the direction of electron flow in the external circuit, and the direction of ion flow in the salt bridge (Section 19-2). Study Questions: 7–10, 55.
  b. Appreciate the chemistry and advantages and disadvantages of dry cells, alkaline batteries, lead storage batteries, lithium batteries, and Ni-cad batteries (Section 19-3). Study Questions: 15, 16.
  c. Understand how fuel cells work, and recognize the difference between batteries and fuel cells (Section 19-3). Study Question: 107.
- How to use electrochemical potentials.
  a. Understand the process by which standard reduction potentials are determined, and identify standard conditions as applied to electrochemistry (Section 19-4).
  b. Describe the standard hydrogen electrode ($E° = 0.00$ V), and explain how it is used as the standard to determine the standard potentials of half-reactions (Section 19-4).
  c. Know how to use standard reduction potentials to determine cell voltages for cells under standard conditions (Equation 19.1). Study Questions: 17–20.

d. Know how to use a table of standard reduction potentials (Table 19.1 and Appendix M) to rank the strengths of oxidizing and reducing agents, to predict which substances can reduce or oxidize another species, and to predict whether redox reactions will be product-favored or reactant-favored at equilibrium (Section 19-4). Study Questions: 21–28, 59, 60.

e. Use the Nernst equation (Equations 19.2 and 19.3) to calculate the cell potential under nonstandard conditions (Section 19-5). Study Questions: 29–32, 79–83.

f. Explain how cell voltage allows the determination of pH (Section 19-5) and other ion concentrations. Study Questions: 33, 34.

- Electrical energy is used to produce chemical change in electrolysis.
  a. Describe the chemical processes occurring in an electrolysis. Recognize the factors that determine which substances are oxidized and reduced at the electrodes (Section 19-7). Study Questions: 41–46, 78.

DO

- Balance equations for oxidation–reduction reactions in acidic or basic solutions using the half-reaction approach (Section 19-1). Study Questions: 1–6, 19, 20, 53, 54, 88, 89.
- Relate the quantity of a substance oxidized or reduced to the amount of current and the time the current flows (Section 19-8). Study Questions: 47–52, 63, 68–70.
- Use the relationships between cell voltage ($E°_{cell}$) and free energy ($\Delta_r G°$) and between $E°_{cell}$ and an equilibrium constant for the cell reaction (Section 19-6 and Table 19.2). Study Questions: 35–40, 64, 65, 67, 82, 84–87.

REMEMBER

- Voltaic cells use chemical reactions to produce electric current; electrolysis cells use electric current to bring about chemical change.
- Oxidation occurs at an anode and reduction occurs at a cathode.
- The differences between primary and secondary batteries.

KEY EQUATIONS

Equation 19.1 (page 737) Calculating a standard cell potential, $E°_{cell}$, from standard half-cell potentials.

$$E°_{cell} = E°_{cathode} - E°_{anode}$$

Equation 19.2 (page 744) The Nernst equation, the relationship of the cell potential under nonstandard conditions (E) to that under standard conditions ($E°$). R is the gas constant (8.314462 J/K · mol); T is the temperature (K); and n is the number of moles of electrons transferred between oxidizing and reducing agents. F is the **Faraday constant** (9.6485337×10^4 C/mol of e^-), and Q is the reaction quotient.

$$E = E° - (RT/nF) \ln Q$$

Equation 19.3 (page 744) Nernst equation (at 298 K).

$$E = E° - \frac{0.0257}{n} \ln Q$$

Equation 19.4 (page 748) The amount of work done (w) by an electrochemical system.

$$w_{max} = nFE$$

Equations 19.5 and 19.6 (page 748) Relationship between free energy change and the cell potential under nonstandard or standard conditions, respectively.

$$\Delta_r G = -nFE \text{ or } \Delta_r G° = -nFE°$$

Equation 19.7 (page 749) Relationship between the equilibrium constant and the standard cell potential for a reaction (at 298 K).

$$\ln K = \frac{nE°}{0.0257}$$

Equation 19.8 (page 757) Relationship between current, electric charge, and time.

$$\text{Current (amperes, A)} = \frac{\text{electric charge (coulombs, C)}}{\text{time, } t \text{ (seconds, s)}}$$

Courtesy Tesla Motors

STUDY QUESTIONS

▲ denotes challenging questions.

Blue-numbered questions have answers in Appendix N and fully worked solutions in the *Student Solutions Manual.*

Practicing Skills

Balancing Equations for Oxidation–Reduction Reactions

(See Section 19-1 and Examples 19.1–19.3.)

When balancing the following redox equations, it may be necessary to add $H^+(aq)$ or $H^+(aq)$ plus H_2O for reactions in acid, and $OH^-(aq)$ or $OH^-(aq)$ plus H_2O for reactions in base.

1. Write balanced equations for the following half-reactions. Specify whether each is an oxidation or reduction.
   (a) $Cr(s) \rightarrow Cr^{3+}(aq)$ (in acid)
   (b) $AsH_3(g) \rightarrow As(s)$ (in acid)
   (c) $VO_3^-(aq) \rightarrow V^{2+}(aq)$ (in acid)
   (d) $Ag(s) \rightarrow Ag_2O(s)$ (in base)

2. Write balanced equations for the following half-reactions. Specify whether each is an oxidation or reduction.
   (a) $H_2O_2(aq) \rightarrow O_2(g)$ (in acid)
   (b) $H_2C_2O_4(aq) \rightarrow CO_2(g)$ (in acid)
   (c) $NO_3^-(aq) \rightarrow NO(g)$ (in acid)
   (d) $MnO_4^-(aq) \rightarrow MnO_2(s)$ (in base)

3. Balance the following redox equations. All occur in acid solution.
   (a) $Ag(s) + NO_3^-(aq) \rightarrow NO_2(g) + Ag^+(aq)$
   (b) $MnO_4^-(aq) + HSO_3^-(aq) \rightarrow Mn^{2+}(aq) + SO_4^{2-}(aq)$
   (c) $Zn(s) + NO_3^-(aq) \rightarrow Zn^{2+}(aq) + N_2O(g)$
   (d) $Cr(s) + NO_3^-(aq) \rightarrow Cr^{3+}(aq) + NO(g)$

4. Balance the following redox equations. All occur in acid solution.
   (a) $Sn(s) + H^+(aq) \rightarrow Sn^{2+}(aq) + H_2(g)$
   (b) $Cr_2O_7^{2-}(aq) + Fe^{2+}(aq) \rightarrow Cr^{3+}(aq) + Fe^{3+}(aq)$
   (c) $MnO_2(s) + Cl^-(aq) \rightarrow Mn^{2+}(aq) + Cl_2(g)$
   (d) $CH_2O(aq) + Ag^+(aq) \rightarrow HCO_2H(aq) + Ag(s)$

5. Balance the following redox equations. All occur in basic solution.

(a) $Al(s) + H_2O(\ell) \rightarrow Al(OH)_4^-(aq) + H_2(g)$
(b) $CrO_4^{2-}(aq) + SO_3^{2-}(aq) \rightarrow Cr(OH)_3(s) + SO_4^{2-}(aq)$
(c) $Zn(s) + Cu(OH)_2(s) \rightarrow [Zn(OH)_4]^{2-}(aq) + Cu(s)$
(d) $HS^-(aq) + ClO_3^-(aq) \rightarrow S(s) + Cl^-(aq)$

6. Balance the following redox equations. All occur in basic solution.

(a) $Fe(OH)_3(s) + Cr(s) \rightarrow Cr(OH)_3(s) + Fe(OH)_2(s)$
(b) $NiO_2(s) + Zn(s) \rightarrow Ni(OH)_2(s) + Zn(OH)_2(s)$
(c) $Fe(OH)_2(s) + CrO_4^{2-}(aq) \rightarrow Fe(OH)_3(s) + [Cr(OH)_4]^-(aq)$
(d) $N_2H_4(aq) + Ag_2O(s) \rightarrow N_2(g) + Ag(s)$

Constructing Voltaic Cells

(See Section 19-2 and Examples 19.4 and 19.5.)

7. A voltaic cell is constructed using the reaction of chromium metal and iron(II) ions.

$$2\ Cr(s) + 3\ Fe^{2+}(aq) \rightarrow 2\ Cr^{3+}(aq) + 3\ Fe(s)$$

Complete the following sentences: Electrons in the external circuit flow from the ____ electrode to the ____ electrode. Negative ions move in the salt bridge from the ____ half-cell to the ____ half-cell. The half-reaction at the anode is ____, and that at the cathode is ____.

8. A voltaic cell is constructed using the reaction

$$Mg(s) + 2\ H^+(aq) \rightarrow Mg^{2+}(aq) + H_2(g)$$

(a) Write equations for the oxidation and reduction half-reactions.
(b) Which half-reaction occurs in the anode compartment, and which occurs in the cathode compartment?
(c) Complete the following sentences: Electrons in the external circuit flow from the ____ electrode to the ____ electrode. Negative ions move in the salt bridge from the ____ half-cell to the ____ half-cell. The half-reaction at the anode is ____, and that at the cathode is ____.

9. The half-cells $Fe^{2+}(aq)|Fe(s)$ and $O_2(g)|H_2O$ (in acid solution) are linked to create a voltaic cell.

(a) Write equations for the oxidation and reduction half-reactions and for the overall (cell) reaction.
(b) Which half-reaction occurs in the anode compartment, and which occurs in the cathode compartment?
(c) Complete the following sentences: Electrons in the external circuit flow from the ____ electrode to the ____ electrode. Negative ions move in the salt bridge from the ____ half-cell to the ____ half-cell.

10. The half-cells $Sn^{2+}(aq)|Sn(s)$ and $Cl_2(g)|Cl^-(aq)$ are linked to create a voltaic cell.

(a) Write equations for the oxidation and reduction half-reactions and for the overall (cell) reaction.
(b) Which half-reaction occurs in the anode compartment, and which occurs in the cathode compartment?
(c) Complete the following sentences: Electrons in the external circuit flow from the ____ electrode to the ____ electrode. Negative ions move in the salt bridge from the ____ half-cell to the ____ half-cell.

11. For each of the following electrochemical cells, write equations for the oxidation and reduction half-reactions and for the overall reaction.

(a) $Cu(s)|Cu^{2+}(aq)||Fe^{3+}(aq), Fe^{2+}(aq)|Pt(s)$
(b) $Pb(s)|PbSO_4(s)|SO_4^{2-}(aq)||Fe^{3+}(aq), Fe^{2+}(aq)|Pt(s)$

12. For each of the following electrochemical cells, write equations for the oxidation and reduction half-reactions and for the overall reaction.

(a) $Pb(s)|Pb^{2+}(aq)||Sn^{4+}(aq), Sn^{2+}(aq)|C(s)$
(b) $Hg(\ell)|Hg_2Cl_2(s)|Cl^-(aq)||Ag^+(aq)|Ag(s)$

13. Use cell notation to depict an electrochemical cell based upon the following, product-favored reaction.

$$Cu(s) + Cl_2(g) \rightarrow 2\ Cl^-(aq) + Cu^{2+}(aq)$$

14. Use cell notation to depict an electrochemical cell based upon the following, product-favored reaction.

$$Fe^{3+}(aq) + Ag(s) + Cl^-(aq) \rightarrow Fe^{2+}(aq) + AgCl(s)$$

Commercial Electrochemical Cells

(See Section 19-3.)

15. What are the similarities and differences between dry cells, alkaline batteries, and Ni-cad batteries?

16. What reactions occur when a lead storage battery is recharged?

Standard Electrochemical Potentials

(See Section 19-4 and Example 19.6.)

17. Calculate the value of $E°$ for each of the following reactions. Decide whether each is product-favored in the direction written.

(a) $2\ I^-(aq) + Zn^{2+}(aq) \rightarrow I_2(s) + Zn(s)$
(b) $Zn^{2+}(aq) + Ni(s) \rightarrow Zn(s) + Ni^{2+}(aq)$
(c) $2\ Cl^-(aq) + Cu^{2+}(aq) \rightarrow Cu(s) + Cl_2(g)$
(d) $Fe^{2+}(aq) + Ag^+(aq) \rightarrow Fe^{3+}(aq) + Ag(s)$

18. Calculate the value of $E°$ for each of the following reactions. Decide whether each is product-favored in the direction written. [Reaction (d) is carried out in basic solution.]

(a) $Br_2(\ell) + Mg(s) \rightarrow Mg^{2+}(aq) + 2\ Br^-(aq)$
(b) $Zn^{2+}(aq) + Mg(s) \rightarrow Zn(s) + Mg^{2+}(aq)$
(c) $Sn^{2+}(aq) + 2\ Ag^+(aq) \rightarrow Sn^{4+}(aq) + 2\ Ag(s)$
(d) $2\ Zn(s) + O_2(g) + 2\ H_2O(\ell) + 4\ OH^-(aq) \rightarrow 2\ [Zn(OH)_4]^{2-}(aq)$

19. Balance each of the following unbalanced equations; then calculate the standard potential, $E°$, and decide whether each is product-favored as written. (All reactions are carried out in acid solution.)

(a) $Sn^{2+}(aq) + Ag(s) \rightarrow Sn(s) + Ag^+(aq)$
(b) $Al(s) + Sn^{4+}(aq) \rightarrow Sn^{2+}(aq) + Al^{3+}(aq)$
(c) $ClO_3^-(aq) + Ce^{3+}(aq) \rightarrow Cl_2(g) + Ce^{4+}(aq)$
(d) $Cu(s) + NO_3^-(aq) \rightarrow Cu^{2+}(aq) + NO(g)$

20. Balance each of the following unbalanced equations; then calculate the standard potential, $E°$, and decide whether each is product-favored as written. (All reactions are carried out in acid solution.)

(a) $I_2(s) + Br^-(aq) \rightarrow I^-(aq) + Br_2(\ell)$
(b) $Fe^{2+}(aq) + Cu^{2+}(aq) \rightarrow Cu(s) + Fe^{3+}(aq)$
(c) $Fe^{2+}(aq) + Cr_2O_7^{2-}(aq) \rightarrow Fe^{3+}(aq) + Cr^{3+}(aq)$
(d) $MnO_4^-(aq) + HNO_2(aq) \rightarrow Mn^{2+}(aq) + NO_3^-(aq)$

Ranking Oxidizing and Reducing Agents

(See Section 19-4 and Example 19.6. Use a table of standard reduction potentials [Table 19.1 or Appendix M] to answer Study Questions 21–28.)

21. Consider the following half-reactions:

Half-Reaction	$E°$(V)
$Cu^{2+}(aq) + 2\ e^- \rightarrow Cu(s)$	+0.34
$Sn^{2+}(aq) + 2\ e^- \rightarrow Sn(s)$	−0.14
$Fe^{2+}(aq) + 2\ e^- \rightarrow Fe(s)$	−0.44
$Zn^{2+}(aq) + 2\ e^- \rightarrow Zn(s)$	−0.76
$Al^{3+}(aq) + 3\ e^- \rightarrow Al(s)$	−1.66

(a) Based on $E°$ values, which metal is the most easily oxidized?
(b) Which metals on this list are capable of reducing $Fe^{2+}(aq)$ to Fe(s)?
(c) Write a balanced chemical equation for the reaction of $Fe^{2+}(aq)$ with Sn(s). Is this reaction product-favored or reactant-favored?
(d) Write a balanced chemical equation for the reaction of $Zn^{2+}(aq)$ with Sn(s). Is this reaction product-favored or reactant-favored?

22. Consider the following half-reactions:

Half-Reaction	$E°$(V)
$MnO_4^-(aq) + 8\ H^+(aq) + 5\ e^- \rightarrow Mn^{2+}(aq) + 4\ H_2O(\ell)$	+1.51
$BrO_3^-(aq) + 6\ H^+(aq) + 6\ e^- \rightarrow Br^-(aq) + 3\ H_2O(\ell)$	+1.47
$Cr_2O_7^{2-}(aq) + 14\ H^+(aq) + 6\ e^- \rightarrow 2\ Cr^{3+}(aq) + 7\ H_2O(\ell)$	+1.33
$NO_3^-(aq) + 4\ H^+(aq) + 3\ e^- \rightarrow NO(g) + 2\ H_2O(\ell)$	+0.96
$SO_4^{2-}(aq) + 4\ H^+(aq) + 2\ e^- \rightarrow SO_2(g) + 2\ H_2O(\ell)$	+0.20

(a) Choosing from among the reactants in these half-reactions, identify the strongest and weakest oxidizing agents.
(b) Which of the oxidizing agents listed is (are) capable of oxidizing $Br^-(aq)$ to $BrO_3^-(aq)$ (in acid solution)?
(c) Write a balanced chemical equation for the reaction of $Cr_2O_7^{2-}(aq)$ with $SO_2(g)$ in acid solution. Is this reaction product-favored or reactant-favored?
(d) Write a balanced chemical equation for the reaction of $Cr_2O_7^{2-}(aq)$ with $Mn^{2+}(aq)$. Is this reaction product-favored or reactant-favored?

23. Which of the following elements is the best reducing agent under standard conditions?

(a) Cu
(b) Zn
(c) Fe
(d) Ag
(e) Cr

24. From the following list, identify those elements that are easier to oxidize than $H_2(g)$.

(a) Cu
(b) Zn
(c) Fe
(d) Ag
(e) Cr

25. Which of the following ions is most easily reduced?

(a) $Cu^{2+}(aq)$
(b) $Zn^{2+}(aq)$
(c) $Fe^{2+}(aq)$
(d) $Ag^+(aq)$
(e) $Al^{3+}(aq)$

26. From the following list, identify the ions that are more easily reduced than $H^+(aq)$.

(a) $Cu^{2+}(aq)$
(b) $Zn^{2+}(aq)$
(c) $Fe^{2+}(aq)$
(d) $Ag^+(aq)$
(e) $Al^{3+}(aq)$

27. (a) Which halogen is most easily reduced in acidic solution: F_2, Cl_2, Br_2, or I_2?
(b) Identify the halogens that are better oxidizing agents in acidic solution than $MnO_2(s)$.

28. (a) Which ion is most easily oxidized to the elemental halogen in acidic solution: F^-, Cl^-, Br^-, or I^-?
(b) Identify the halide ions that are more easily oxidized in acidic solution than $H_2O(\ell)$.

Electrochemical Cells under Nonstandard Conditions

(See Section 19-5 and Examples 19.7 and 19.9.)

29. Calculate the potential delivered by a voltaic cell using the following reaction if all dissolved species are 2.5×10^{-2} M and the pressure of H_2 is 1.0 bar.

$$Zn(s) + 2\ H_2O(\ell) + 2\ OH^-(aq) \rightarrow [Zn(OH)_4]^{2-}(aq) + H_2(g)$$

30. Calculate the potential developed by a voltaic cell using the following reaction if all dissolved species are 0.015 M.

$$2\ Fe^{2+}(aq) + H_2O_2(aq) + 2\ H^+(aq) \rightarrow 2\ Fe^{3+}(aq) + 2\ H_2O(\ell)$$

31. One half-cell in a voltaic cell is constructed from a silver wire electrode in a 0.25 M solution of $AgNO_3$. The other half-cell consists of a zinc electrode in a 0.010 M solution of $Zn(NO_3)_2$. Calculate the cell potential.

32. One half-cell in a voltaic cell is constructed from a copper wire electrode in a 4.8×10^{-3} M solution of $Cu(NO_3)_2$. The other half-cell consists of a zinc electrode in a 0.40 M solution of $Zn(NO_3)_2$. Calculate the cell potential.

33. One half-cell in a voltaic cell is constructed from a silver wire electrode in a $AgNO_3$ solution of unknown concentration. The other half-cell consists of a zinc electrode in a 1.0 M solution of $Zn(NO_3)_2$. A potential of 1.48 V is measured for this cell. Use this information to calculate the concentration of $Ag^+(aq)$.

34. One half-cell in a voltaic cell is constructed from an iron electrode in an $Fe(NO_3)_2$ solution of unknown concentration. The other half-cell is a standard hydrogen electrode. A potential of 0.49 V is measured for this cell. Use this information to calculate the concentration of Fe^{2+}(aq).

Electrochemistry, Thermodynamics, and Equilibrium

(See Section 19-6 and Examples 19.9 and 19.10.)

35. Calculate $\Delta_r G°$ and the equilibrium constant for the following reactions.

(a) $2\ Fe^{3+}(aq) + 2\ I^-(aq) \rightleftharpoons 2\ Fe^{2+}(aq) + I_2(aq)$
(b) $I_2(aq) + 2\ Br^-(aq) \rightleftharpoons 2\ I^-(aq) + Br_2(\ell)$

36. Calculate $\Delta_r G°$ and the equilibrium constant for the following reactions.

(a) $Zn^{2+}(aq) + Ni(s) \rightleftharpoons Zn(s) + Ni^{2+}(aq)$
(b) $Cu(s) + 2\ Ag^+(aq) \rightleftharpoons Cu^{2+}(aq) + 2\ Ag(s)$

37. Use standard reduction potentials (Appendix M) for the half-reactions $AgBr(s) + e^- \rightarrow Ag(s) + Br^-(aq)$ and $Ag^+(aq) + e^- \rightarrow Ag(s)$ to calculate the value of K_{sp} for AgBr.

38. Use the standard reduction potentials (Appendix M) for the half-reactions $Hg_2Cl_2(s) + 2\ e^- \rightarrow 2\ Hg(\ell) + 2\ Cl^-(aq)$ and $Hg_2^{2+}(aq) + 2\ e^- \rightarrow 2\ Hg(\ell)$ to calculate the value of K_{sp} for Hg_2Cl_2.

39. Use the standard reduction potentials (Appendix M) for the half-reactions $[AuCl_4]^-(aq) + 3\ e^- \rightarrow Au(s) + 4\ Cl^-(aq)$ and $Au^{3+}(aq) + 3\ e^- \rightarrow Au(s)$ to calculate the value of $K_{formation}$ for the complex ion $[AuCl_4]^-(aq)$.

40. Use the standard reduction potentials (Appendix M) for the half-reactions $[Zn(OH)_4]^{2-}(aq) + 2\ e^- \rightarrow Zn\ (s) + 4\ OH^-(aq)$ and $Zn^{2+}(aq) + 2\ e^- \rightarrow Zn(s)$ to calculate the value of $K_{formation}$ for the complex ion $[Zn(OH)_4]^{2-}$.

Electrolysis

(See Section 19-7 and Example 19.11.)

41. Diagram the apparatus used to electrolyze molten NaCl. Identify the anode and the cathode. Trace the movement of electrons through the external circuit and the movement of ions in the electrolysis cell.

42. Diagram the apparatus used to electrolyze aqueous $CuCl_2$. Identify the reaction products, the anode, and the cathode. Trace the movement of electrons through the external circuit and the movement of ions in the electrolysis cell.

43. Which product, O_2 or F_2, is more likely to form at the anode in the electrolysis of an aqueous solution of KF? Explain your reasoning.

44. Which product, Ca or H_2, is more likely to form at the cathode in the electrolysis of $CaCl_2$? Explain your reasoning.

45. An aqueous solution of KBr is placed in a beaker with two inert platinum electrodes. When the cell is attached to an external source of electrical energy, electrolysis occurs.

(a) Hydrogen gas and hydroxide ion form at the cathode. Write an equation for the half-reaction that occurs at this electrode.
(b) Bromine is the primary product at the anode. Write an equation for its formation.

46. An aqueous solution of Na_2S is placed in a beaker with two inert platinum electrodes. When the cell is attached to an external battery, electrolysis occurs.

(a) Hydrogen gas and hydroxide ion form at the cathode. Write an equation for the half-reaction that occurs at this electrode.
(b) Sulfur is the primary product at the anode. Write an equation for its formation.

Counting Electrons

(See Section 19-8 and Example 19.12.)

47. In the electrolysis of a solution containing Ni^{2+}(aq), metallic Ni(s) deposits on the cathode. Using a current of 0.150 A for 12.2 minutes, what mass of nickel will form?

48. In the electrolysis of a solution containing Ag^+(aq), metallic Ag(s) deposits on the cathode. Using a current of 1.12 A for 2.40 hours, what mass of silver forms?

49. Electrolysis of a solution of $CuSO_4$(aq) to give copper metal is carried out using a current of 0.66 A. How long should electrolysis continue to produce 0.50 g of copper?

50. Electrolysis of a solution of $Zn(NO_3)_2$(aq) to give zinc metal is carried out using a current of 2.12 A. How long should electrolysis continue in order to prepare 2.5 g of zinc?

51. A voltaic cell can be built using the reaction between Al metal and O_2 from the air. If the Al anode of this cell consists of 84 g of aluminum, how many hours can the cell produce 1.0 A of electricity, assuming an unlimited supply of O_2?

52. Assume the specifications of a Ni-Cd voltaic cell include delivery of 0.25 A of current for 1.00 hour. What is the minimum mass of the cadmium that must be used to make the anode in this cell?

General Questions

These questions are not designated as to type or location in the chapter. They may combine several concepts.

53. Write balanced equations for the following half-reactions.

(a) $UO_2^+(aq) \rightarrow U^{4+}(aq)$ (acid solution)
(b) $ClO_3^-(aq) \rightarrow Cl^-(aq)$ (acid solution)
(c) $N_2H_4(aq) \rightarrow N_2(g)$ (basic solution)
(d) $ClO^-(aq) \rightarrow Cl^-(aq)$ (basic solution)

54. Balance the following equations.

(a) $Zn(s) + VO^{2+}(aq) \rightarrow Zn^{2+}(aq) + V^{3+}(aq)$ (acid solution)

(b) $Zn(s) + VO_3^-(aq) \rightarrow V^{2+}(aq) + Zn^{2+}(aq)$ (acid solution)

(c) $Zn(s) + ClO^-(aq) \rightarrow Zn(OH)_2(s) + Cl^-(aq)$ (basic solution)

(d) $ClO^-(aq) + [Cr(OH)_4]^-(aq) \rightarrow Cl^-(aq) + CrO_4^{2-}(aq)$ (basic solution)

55. Magnesium metal is oxidized, and silver ions are reduced in a voltaic cell using Mg^{2+}(aq, 1 M)|Mg and Ag^+(aq, 1 M)|Ag half-cells.

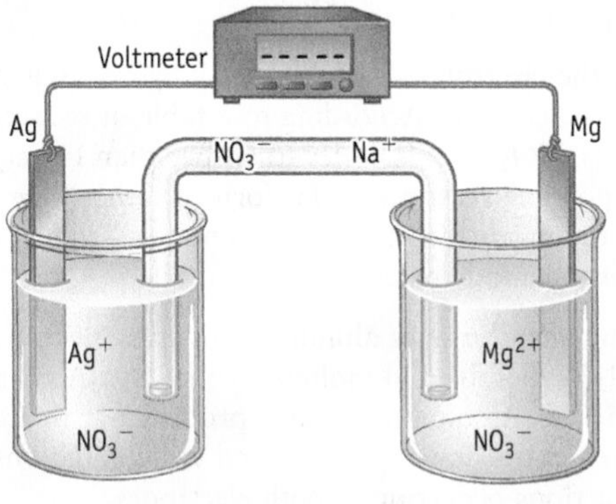

(a) Label each part of the cell.
(b) Write equations for the half-reactions occurring at the anode and the cathode, and write an equation for the net reaction in the cell.
(c) Trace the movement of electrons in the external circuit. Assuming the salt bridge contains $NaNO_3$, trace the movement of the Na^+ and NO_3^- ions in the salt bridge that occurs when a voltaic cell produces current. Why is a salt bridge required in a cell?

56. You want to set up a series of voltaic cells with specific cell potentials. A Zn^{2+}(aq, 1.0 M)|Zn(s) half-cell is in one compartment. Identify several half-cells that you could use so that the cell potential will be close to (a) 1.1 V and (b) 0.50 V. Consider cells in which the zinc cell can be either the cathode or the anode.

57. You want to set up a series of voltaic cells with specific cell potentials. The Ag^+(aq, 1.0 M)|Ag(s) half-cell is one of the compartments. Identify several half-cells that you could use so that the cell potential will be close to (a) 1.7 V and (b) 0.50 V. Consider cells in which the silver cell can be either the cathode or the anode.

58. Which of the following reactions is (are) product-favored?

(a) $Zn(s) + I_2(s) \rightarrow Zn^{2+}(aq) + 2\ I^-(aq)$
(b) $2\ Cl^-(aq) + I_2(s) \rightarrow Cl_2(g) + 2\ I^-(aq)$
(c) $2\ Na^+(aq) + 2\ Cl^-(aq) \rightarrow 2\ Na(s) + Cl_2(g)$
(d) $2\ K(s) + 2\ H_2O(\ell) \rightarrow 2\ K^+(aq) + H_2(g) + 2\ OH^-(aq)$

59. In the table of standard reduction potentials, locate the half-reactions for the reductions of the following metal ions to the metal: Sn^{2+}(aq), Au^+(aq), Zn^{2+}(aq), Co^{2+}(aq), Ag^+(aq), Cu^{2+}(aq). Among the metal ions and metals that make up these half-reactions:

(a) Which metal ion is the weakest oxidizing agent?
(b) Which metal ion is the strongest oxidizing agent?
(c) Which metal is the strongest reducing agent?
(d) Which metal is the weakest reducing agent?
(e) Will Sn(s) reduce Cu^{2+}(aq) to Cu(s)?
(f) Will Ag(s) reduce Co^{2+}(aq) to Co(s)?
(g) Which metal ions on the list can be reduced by Sn(s)?
(h) What metals can be oxidized by Ag^+(aq)?

60. ▲ In the table of standard reduction potentials, locate the half-reactions for the reductions of the following nonmetals: F_2, Cl_2, Br_2, I_2 (reduction to halide ions), and O_2, S, Se (reduction to H_2X in aqueous acid). Among the elements, ions, and compounds that make up these half-reactions:

(a) Which element is the weakest oxidizing agent?
(b) Which ion or H_2X is the weakest reducing agent?
(c) Which of the elements listed is (are) capable of oxidizing H_2O to O_2?
(d) Which of these elements listed is (are) capable of oxidizing H_2S to S?
(e) Is O_2 capable of oxidizing I^- to I_2, in acid solution?
(f) Is S capable of oxidizing I^- to I_2?
(g) Is the reaction $H_2S(aq) + Se(s) \rightarrow H_2Se(aq) + S(s)$ product-favored?
(h) Is the reaction $H_2S(aq) + I_2(s) \rightarrow 2\ H^+(aq) + 2\ I^-(aq) + S(s)$ product-favored?

61. Four voltaic cells are set up. In each, one half-cell contains a standard hydrogen electrode. The second half-cell is one of the following:

(i) Cr^{3+}(aq, 1.0 M)|Cr(s)
(ii) Fe^{2+}(aq, 1.0 M)|Fe(s)
(iii) Cu^{2+}(aq, 1.0 M)|Cu(s)
(iv) Mg^{2+}(aq, 1.0 M)|Mg(s)

(a) In which of the voltaic cells does the hydrogen electrode serve as the cathode?
(b) Which voltaic cell produces the highest potential? Which produces the lowest potential?

62. The following half-cells are available:

(i) Ag^+(aq, 1.0 M)|Ag(s)
(ii) Zn^{2+}(aq, 1.0 M)|Zn(s)
(iii) Cu^{2+}(aq, 1.0 M)|Cu(s)
(iv) Co^{2+}(aq, 1.0 M)|Co(s)

Linking any two half-cells makes a voltaic cell. Given four different half-cells, six voltaic cells are possible. These are labeled, for simplicity, Ag-Zn, Ag-Cu, Ag-Co, Zn-Cu, Zn-Co, and Cu-Co.

(a) In which of the voltaic cells does the copper electrode serve as the cathode? In which of the voltaic cells does the cobalt electrode serve as the anode?
(b) Which combination of half-cells generates the highest potential? Which combination generates the lowest potential?

63. The reaction occurring in the cell in which Al_2O_3 and aluminum salts are electrolyzed is $Al^{3+}(aq) + 3\,e^- \rightarrow Al(s)$. If the electrolysis cell operates at 5.0 V and 1.0×10^5 A, what mass of aluminum metal can be produced in a 24-hour day?

64. ▲ A cell is constructed using the following half-reactions:

$$Ag^+(aq) + e^- \rightarrow Ag(s)$$

$$Ag_2SO_4(s) + 2\,e^- \rightarrow 2\,Ag(s) + SO_4^{2-}(aq) \qquad E° = 0.653\text{ V}$$

(a) What reactions should be observed at the anode and cathode?
(b) Calculate the solubility product constant, K_{sp}, for Ag_2SO_4.

65. ▲ A potential of 0.142 V is recorded (under standard conditions) for a voltaic cell constructed using the following half reactions:

Cathode: $Pb^{2+}(aq) + 2\,e^- \rightarrow Pb(s)$
Anode: $PbCl_2(s) + 2\,e^- \rightarrow Pb(s) + 2\,Cl^-(aq)$
Net: $Pb^{2+}(aq) + 2\,Cl^-(aq) \rightarrow PbCl_2(s)$

(a) What is the standard reduction potential for the anode reaction?
(b) Calculate the solubility product, K_{sp}, for $PbCl_2$.

66. What is the value of $E°$ for the following half-reaction?

$$Ag_2CrO_4(s) + 2\,e^- \rightarrow 2\,Ag(s) + CrO_4^{2-}(aq)$$

67. The standard potential, $E°$, for the reaction of Zn(s) and $Cl_2(g)$ is +2.12 V. What is the standard free energy change, $\Delta_r G°$, for the reaction?

68. ▲ An electrolysis cell for aluminum production operates at 5.0 V and a current of 1.0×10^5 A. Calculate the number of kilowatt-hours of energy required to produce 1 metric ton (1.0×10^3 kg) of aluminum. (1 kWh = 3.6×10^6 J and 1 J = 1 C · V)

69. ▲ Electrolysis of molten NaCl is done in cells operating at 7.0 V and 4.0×10^4 A. What mass of Na(s) and $Cl_2(g)$ can be produced in 1 day in such a cell? What is the energy consumption in kilowatt-hours? (1 kWh = 3.6×10^6 J and 1 J = 1 C · V)

70. ▲ A current of 0.0100 A is passed through a solution of rhodium sulfate, causing reduction of the metal ion to the metal. After 3.00 hours, 0.038 g of Rh has been deposited. What is the charge on the rhodium ion, Rh^{n+}? What is the formula for rhodium sulfate?

71. ▲ A current of 0.44 A is passed through a solution of ruthenium nitrate causing reduction of the metal ion to the metal. After 25.0 minutes, 0.345 g of Ru has been deposited. What is the charge on the ruthenium ion, Ru^{n+}? What is the formula for ruthenium nitrate?

72. The total charge that can be delivered by a large dry cell battery before its voltage drops too low is usually about 35 amp-hours. (One amp-hour is the charge that passes through a circuit when 1 A flows for 1 hour.) What mass of Zn is consumed when 35 amp-hours are drawn from the cell?

73. Chlorine gas is obtained commercially by electrolysis of brine (a concentrated aqueous solution of NaCl). If the electrolysis cells operate at 4.6 V and 3.0×10^5 A, what mass of chlorine can be produced in a 24-hour day?

74. Write equations for the half-reactions that occur at the anode and cathode in the electrolysis of *molten* KBr. What are the products formed at the anode and cathode in the electrolysis of *aqueous* KBr?

75. The products formed in the electrolysis of aqueous $CuSO_4$ are Cu(s) and $O_2(g)$. Write equations for the anode and cathode reactions.

76. Predict the products formed in the electrolysis of an aqueous solution of $CdSO_4$.

77. In the electrolysis of $HNO_3(aq)$, hydrogen is produced at the cathode. According to a table of reduction potentials, $NO_3^-(aq)$ is easier to reduce than $H^+(aq)$. Suggest a possible reason why H_2 formed rather than NO. What is the product formed at the anode? Write an equation for the anode reaction.

78. The metallurgy of aluminum involves electrolysis of Al_2O_3 dissolved in molten cryolite (Na_3AlF_6) at about 950 °C. Aluminum metal is produced at the cathode. Predict the anode product and write equations for the reactions occurring at both electrodes.

79. Two half-cells, Pt|Fe^{3+}(aq, 0.50 M), Fe^{2+}(aq, 1.0×10^{-5} M) and Hg^{2+}(aq, 0.020 M)|Hg, are constructed and then linked together to form a voltaic cell. Which electrode is the anode? What will be the potential of the voltaic cell at 298 K?

80. A voltaic cell is set up utilizing the reaction

$$Cu(s) + 2\,Ag^+(aq) \rightarrow Cu^{2+}(aq) + 2\,Ag(s)$$

$$Cu(s)|Cu^{2+}(aq, 1.0\text{ M})||Ag^+(aq, 0.001\text{ M})|Ag(s)$$

Under standard conditions, the expected potential is 0.45 V. Predict whether the potential for the voltaic cell will be higher, lower, or the same as the standard potential. Verify your prediction by calculating the new cell potential.

81. Calculate the cell potential for the following cell:

$$Pt|H_2(P = 1\text{ bar})|H^+(aq, 1.0\text{ M})|| Fe^{3+}(aq, 1.0M), Fe^{2+}(aq, 1.0M)|Pt$$

Will this reaction be more or less favorable at lower pH? To determine this, calculate the cell potential for a reaction in which $[H^+(aq)]$ is 1.0×10^{-7} M.

82. A voltaic cell set up utilizing the reaction

$$Cu(s) + 2\,Ag^+(aq) \rightarrow Cu^{2+}(aq) + 2\,Ag(s)$$

has a cell potential of 0.45 at 298 K. Describe how the potential of this cell will change as the cell is discharged. At what point does the cell potential reach a constant value? Explain your answer.

83. Two $Ag^+(aq)|Ag(s)$ half-cells are constructed. The first has $[Ag^+] = 1.0$ M, the second has $[Ag^+] = 1.0 \times 10^{-5}$ M. When linked together with a salt bridge and external circuit, a cell potential is observed. (This kind of voltaic cell is referred to as a *concentration cell.*)
   (a) Draw a picture of this cell, labeling all components. Indicate the cathode and the anode, and indicate in which direction electrons flow in the external circuit.
   (b) Calculate the cell potential at 298 K.

84. Calculate equilibrium constants for the following reactions at 298 K. Indicate whether the equilibrium as written is reactant- or product-favored.
   (a) $Co(s) + Ni^{2+}(aq) \rightleftharpoons Co^{2+}(aq) + Ni(s)$
   (b) $Fe^{3+}(aq) + Cr^{2+}(aq) \rightleftharpoons Cr^{3+}(aq) + Fe^{2+}(aq)$

85. Calculate equilibrium constants for the following reactions at 298 K. Indicate whether the equilibrium as written is reactant- or product-favored.
   (a) $2\ Cl^-(aq) + Br_2(\ell) \rightleftharpoons Cl_2(aq) + 2\ Br^-(aq)$
   (b) $Fe^{2+}(aq) + Ag^+(aq) \rightleftharpoons Fe^{3+}(aq) + Ag(s)$

86. Use the table of standard reduction potentials (Appendix M) to calculate $\Delta_rG°$ for the following reactions at 298 K.
   (a) $ClO_3^-(aq) + 5\ Cl^-(aq) + 6\ H^+(aq) \rightarrow 3\ Cl_2(g) + 3\ H_2O(\ell)$
   (b) $AgCl(s) + Br^-(aq) \rightarrow AgBr(s) + Cl^-(aq)$

87. Use the table of standard reduction potentials (Appendix M) to calculate $\Delta_rG°$ for the following reactions at 298 K.
   (a) $3\ Cu(s) + 2\ NO_3^-(aq) + 8\ H^+(aq) \rightarrow 3\ Cu^{2+}(aq) + 2\ NO(g) + 4\ H_2O(\ell)$
   (b) $H_2O_2(aq) + 2\ Cl^-(aq) + 2\ H^+(aq) \rightarrow Cl_2(g) + 2\ H_2O(\ell)$

88. ▲ Write balanced equations for the following reduction half-reactions involving organic compounds.
   (a) $HCO_2H \rightarrow CH_2O$ (acid solution)
   (b) $C_6H_5CO_2H \rightarrow C_6H_5CH_3$ (acid solution)
   (c) $CH_3CH_2CHO \rightarrow CH_3CH_2CH_2OH$ (acid solution)
   (d) $CH_3OH \rightarrow CH_4$ (acid solution)

89. ▲ Balance the following equations involving organic compounds.
   (a) $Ag^+(aq) + C_6H_5CHO(aq) \rightarrow Ag(s) + C_6H_5CO_2H(aq)$ (acid solution)
   (b) $CH_3CH_2OH + Cr_2O_7^{2-}(aq) \rightarrow CH_3CO_2H(aq) + Cr^{3+}(aq)$ (acid solution)

90. A voltaic cell is constructed in which one half-cell consists of a silver wire in an aqueous solution of $AgNO_3$. The other half-cell consists of an inert platinum wire in an aqueous solution containing $Fe^{2+}(aq)$ and $Fe^{3+}(aq)$.
   (a) Calculate the cell potential, assuming standard conditions.
   (b) Write the net ionic equation for the reaction occurring in the cell.
   (c) Which electrode is the anode and which is the cathode?
   (d) If $[Ag^+]$ is 0.10 M, and $[Fe^{2+}]$ and $[Fe^{3+}]$ are both 1.0 M, what is the cell potential? Is the net cell reaction still that used in part (a)? If not, what is the net reaction under the new conditions?

91. An expensive but lighter alternative to the lead storage battery is the silver-zinc battery.

$$Ag_2O(s) + Zn(s) + H_2O(\ell) \rightarrow Zn(OH)_2(s) + 2\ Ag(s)$$

The electrolyte is 40% KOH, and silver–silver oxide electrodes are separated from zinc–zinc hydroxide electrodes by a plastic sheet that is permeable to hydroxide ions. Under normal operating conditions, the battery has a potential of 1.59 V.
   (a) How much energy can be produced per gram of reactants in the silver-zinc battery? Assume the battery produces a current of 0.10 A.
   (b) How much energy can be produced per gram of reactants in the standard lead storage battery? Assume the battery produces a current of 0.10 A at 2.0 V.
   (c) Which battery (silver-zinc or lead storage) produces the greater energy per gram of reactants?

92. The specifications for a lead storage battery include delivery of a steady 1.5 A of current for 15 hours.
   (a) What is the minimum mass of lead that will be used in the anode?
   (b) What mass of PbO_2 must be used in the cathode?
   (c) Assume that the volume of the battery is 0.50 L. What is the minimum molarity of H_2SO_4 necessary?

93. Manganese may play an important role in chemical cycles in the oceans (page 743). Two reactions involving manganese (in acid solution) are the reduction of nitrate ions (to NO) with Mn^{2+} ions and the oxidation of ammonium ions (to N_2) with MnO_2.
   (a) Write balanced chemical equations for these reactions (in acid solution).
   (b) Calculate $E°_{cell}$ for the reactions. (One half-reaction potential you need is for the reduction of N_2 to NH_4^+, $E° = -0.272$ V.)

94. ▲ You want to use electrolysis to plate a cylindrical object (radius = 2.50 and length = 20.00 cm) with a coating of nickel metal, 4.0 mm thick. You place the object in a bath containing a salt (Na_2SO_4). One electrode is impure nickel, and the other is the object to be plated. The electrolyzing potential is 2.50 V.
   (a) Which is the anode and which is the cathode in the experiment? What half-reaction occurs at each electrode?
   (b) Calculate the number of kilowatt-hours (kWh) of energy required to carry out the electrolysis. ($1\ kWh = 3.6 \times 10^6$ J and $1\ J = 1\ C \times 1\ V$)

95. ▲ Iron(II) ion undergoes a disproportionation reaction to give Fe(s) and the iron(III) ion. That is, iron(II) ion is both oxidized and reduced within the same reaction.

$$3\ Fe^{2+}(aq) \rightleftharpoons Fe(s) + 2\ Fe^{3+}(aq)$$

(a) What two half-reactions make up the disproportionation reaction?
(b) Use the values of the standard reduction potentials for the two half-reactions in part (a) to determine whether this disproportionation reaction is product-favored.
(c) What is the equilibrium constant for this reaction?

96. ▲ Copper(I) ion disproportionates to copper metal and copper(II) ion. (See Study Question 95.)

$$2\ Cu^{+}(aq) \rightleftharpoons Cu(s) + Cu^{2+}(aq)$$

(a) What two half-reactions make up the disproportionation reaction?
(b) Use values of the standard reduction potentials for the two half-reactions in part (a) to determine whether this disproportionation reaction is product-favored at equilibrium.
(c) What is the equilibrium constant for this reaction? If you have a solution that initially contains 0.10 mol of Cu^{+} in 1.0 L of water, what are the concentrations of Cu^{+} and Cu^{2+} at equilibrium?

97. The simplest way to write the reaction for discharge in a lithium-ion battery is

$$\text{Li(on carbon)(s)} + CoO_2(s) \rightarrow 6\ C(s) + LiCoO_2(s)$$

(a) What are the oxidation numbers for cobalt in the two substances in the battery?
(b) In such a battery, what reaction occurs at the cathode? At the anode?
(c) An electrolyte is needed for ion conduction within the battery. From what you know about lithium chemistry, can the electrolyte in the battery be dissolved in water?

98. A lithium-ion camera battery is rated at 7500 mAh. That is, it can deliver 7500 milliamps (mA) or 7.5 amps of steady current for an hour.

(a) How many moles of electrons can the battery deliver in one hour?
(b) What mass of lithium is oxidized under these conditions in 1.0 hour?

In the Laboratory

99. Consider an electrochemical cell based on the half-reactions $Ni^{2+}(aq) + 2\ e^{-} \rightarrow Ni(s)$ and $Cd^{2+}(aq) + 2\ e^{-} \rightarrow Cd(s)$.

(a) Diagram the cell, and label each of the components (including the anode, cathode, and salt bridge).
(b) Use the equations for the half-reactions to write a balanced, net ionic equation for the overall cell reaction.
(c) What is the polarity of each electrode?
(d) What is the value of $E°_{cell}$?
(e) In which direction do electrons flow in the external circuit?
(f) Assume that a salt bridge containing $NaNO_3$ connects the two half-cells. In which direction do the $Na^{+}(aq)$ ions move? In which direction do the $NO_3^{-}(aq)$ ions move?
(g) Calculate the equilibrium constant for the reaction.
(h) If the concentration of Cd^{2+} is reduced to 0.010 M and $[Ni^{2+}] = 1.0$ M, what is the value of E_{cell}? Is the net reaction still the reaction given in part (b)?
(i) If 0.050 A is drawn from the battery, how long can it last if you begin with 1.0 L of each of the solutions and each was initially 1.0 M in dissolved species? Each electrode weighs 50.0 g in the beginning.

100. An old method of measuring the current flowing in a circuit was to use a "silver coulometer." The current passed first through a solution of $Ag^{+}(aq)$ and then into another solution containing an electroactive species. The amount of silver metal deposited at the cathode was weighed. From the mass of silver, the number of atoms of silver was calculated. Since the reduction of a silver ion requires one electron, this value equaled the number of electrons passing through the circuit. If the time was noted, the average current could be calculated. If, in such an experiment, 0.052 g of Ag is deposited during 450 s, what was the current flowing in the circuit?

101. A "silver coulometer" (Study Question 100) was used in the past to measure the current flowing in an electrochemical cell. Suppose you found that the current flowing through an electrolysis cell deposited 0.089 g of Ag metal at the cathode after exactly 10 min. If this same current then passed through a cell containing gold(III) ion in the form of $[AuCl_4]^{-}$, how much gold was deposited at the cathode in that electrolysis cell?

102. ▲ Four metals, A, B, C, and D, exhibit the following properties:

(i) Only A and C react with 1.0 M hydrochloric acid to give $H_2(g)$.
(ii) When C is added to solutions of the ions of the other metals, metallic B, D, and A are formed.
(iii) Metal D reduces B^{n+} to give metallic B and D^{n+}.

Based on this information, arrange the four metals in order of increasing ability to act as reducing agents.

103. ▲ A solution of KI is added dropwise to a pale blue solution of $Cu(NO_3)_2$. The solution changes to a brown color, and a precipitate of CuI forms. In contrast, no change is observed if solutions of KCl and KBr are added to aqueous $Cu(NO_3)_2$. Consult the table of standard reduction potentials to explain the dissimilar results seen with the different halides. Write an equation for the reaction that occurs when solutions of KI and $Cu(NO_3)_2$ are mixed.

104. ▲ The amount of oxygen, O_2, dissolved in a water sample at 25 °C can be determined by titration. The first step is to add solutions of $MnSO_4$ and NaOH to the water to convert the dissolved oxygen to MnO_2. A solution of H_2SO_4 and KI is then added to convert the MnO_2 to Mn^{2+}, and the iodide ion is converted to I_2. The I_2 is then titrated with standardized $Na_2S_2O_3$.

(a) Balance the equation for the reaction of Mn^{2+} ions with O_2 in basic solution.
(b) Balance the equation for the reaction of MnO_2 with I^- in acid solution.
(c) Balance the equation for the reaction of $S_2O_3^{2-}$ with I_2.
(d) Calculate the amount of O_2 in 25.0 mL of water if the titration requires 2.45 mL of 0.0112 M $Na_2S_2O_3$ solution.

Summary and Conceptual Questions

The following questions may use concepts from this and previous chapters.

105. Fluorinated organic compounds are used as herbicides, flame retardants, and fire-extinguishing agents, among other things. A reaction such as

$$CH_3SO_2F + 3\ HF \rightarrow CF_3SO_2F + 3\ H_2$$

is carried out electrochemically in liquid HF as the solvent.

(a) If you electrolyze 150 g of CH_3SO_2F, what mass of HF is required, and what mass of each product can be isolated?
(b) Is H_2 produced at the anode or the cathode of the electrolysis cell?
(c) A typical electrolysis cell operates at 8.0 V and 250 A. How many kilowatt-hours of energy does one such cell consume in 24 hours?

106. ▲ The free energy change for a reaction, $\Delta_rG°$, is the maximum energy that can be extracted from the process as work, whereas $\Delta_rH°$ is the total chemical potential energy change. The efficiency of a fuel cell is the ratio of these two quantities.

$$\text{Efficiency} = \frac{\Delta_rG°}{\Delta_rH°} \times 100\%$$

Consider the hydrogen-oxygen fuel cell, where the net reaction is

$$H_2(g) + \tfrac{1}{2}\ O_2(g) \rightarrow H_2O(\ell)$$

(a) Calculate the efficiency of the fuel cell under standard conditions.
(b) Calculate the efficiency of the fuel cell if the product is water vapor instead of liquid water.
(c) Does the efficiency depend on the state of the reaction product? Why or why not?

107. A hydrogen-oxygen fuel cell operates on the simple reaction

$$H_2(g) + \tfrac{1}{2}\ O_2(g) \rightarrow H_2O(\ell)$$

If the cell is designed to produce 1.5 A of current and if the hydrogen is contained in a 1.0-L tank at 200 atm pressure at 25 °C, how long can the fuel cell operate before the hydrogen runs out? (Assume there is an unlimited supply of O_2.)

108. ▲ (a) Is it easier to reduce water in acid or base? To evaluate this, consider the half-reaction

$$2\ H_2O(\ell) + 2\ e^- \rightarrow 2\ OH^-(aq) + H_2(g) \qquad E° = -0.83\ V$$

(b) What is the reduction potential for water for solutions at pH = 7 (neutral) and pH = 1 (acid)? Comment on the value of $E°$ at pH = 1.

109. ▲ Living organisms derive energy from the oxidation of food, typified by glucose.

$$C_6H_{12}O_6(aq) + 6\ O_2(g) \rightarrow 6\ CO_2(g) + 6\ H_2O(\ell)$$

Electrons in this redox process are transferred from glucose to oxygen in a series of at least 25 steps. It is instructive to calculate the total daily current flow in a typical organism and the rate of energy expenditure (power). (See T. P. Chirpich: *Journal of Chemical Education*, Vol. 52, p. 99, 1975.)

(a) The molar enthalpy of combustion of glucose is −2800 kJ/mol-rxn. If you are on a typical daily diet of 2400 Cal (kilocalories), what amount of glucose (in moles) must be consumed in a day if glucose is the only source of energy? What amount of O_2 must be consumed in the oxidation process?
(b) How many moles of electrons must be supplied to reduce the amount of O_2 calculated in part (a)?
(c) Based on the answer in part (b), calculate the current flowing, per second, in your body from the combustion of glucose.
(d) If the average standard potential in the electron transport chain is 1.0 V, what is the rate of energy expenditure in watts?

AP Multiple-Choice Review Questions

Questions 1–3 refer to the following:

Alcohols are organic compounds containing a hydroxyl (—OH) group. When a solution containing dichromate ions is added to most alcohols, chromium(III) ions are formed. The color of the solution changes from bright orange to green.

$$CH_3CH_2OH(\ell) + Cr_2O_7^{2-}(aq) \rightarrow CH_3COOH(aq) + Cr^{3+}(aq)$$

The *unbalanced* reaction above shows ethanol reacting with the dichromate ion to produce acetic acid and the chromium(III) ion. This reaction occurs in acidic solution and is the chemical reaction used in a Breathalyzer that determines a person's blood alcohol level from the ethanol vapor present in his or her breath.

A kinetic study was conducted to determine the order of the $Cr_2O_7^{2-}$ ion in the rate law. A large excess of alcohol and hydrogen ions was used to ensure that their concentrations did not limit the reaction. The concentration of dichromate was followed spectrophotometrically, and the absorbance and time values were recorded.

1. What is the coefficient for water in the balanced redox reaction?

(A) 6

(B) 11

(C) 14

(D) 19

2. Which element is oxidized in the reaction?

(A) C

(B) Cr

(C) H

(D) O

3. In the kinetic study, the natural logarithms of the absorbance values were plotted versus time, resulting in a straight line. What does this indicate about the order of the reaction with respect to the dichromate ion?

(A) The reaction is zero order in dichromate.

(B) The reaction is first order in dichromate.

(C) The reaction is second order in dichromate.

(D) The order cannot be determined from this graph.

4. How many moles of solid chromium can be deposited from a $CrCl_3$ solution when a steel wrench is electroplated with a current of 3.0 amps for 965 seconds?

(A) 3.3×10^{-4} mol

(B) 5.0×10^{-4} mol

(C) 1.0×10^{-3} mol

(D) 3.0×10^{-3} mol

Questions 5–9 refer to the following electrochemical cell and reduction potentials:

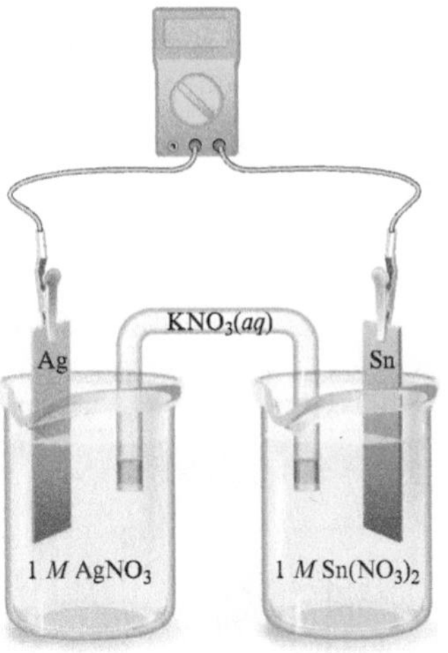

$Ag^+(aq) + e^- \rightarrow Ag(s)$ $\mathscr{E}° = 0.80$ V

$Sn^{2+}(aq) + 2e^- \rightarrow Sn(s)$ $\mathscr{E}° = -0.14$ V

$Zn^{2+}(aq) + 2e^- \rightarrow Zn(s)$ $\mathscr{E}° = -0.76$ V

5. Determine the $\mathscr{E}°_{cell}$ for the voltaic cell pictured above.
(A) 0.66V
(B) 0.94V
(C) −0.94V
(D) 1.74V

6. Which of these changes would increase the value of $\mathscr{E}_{cell}$?
(A) Add 50.0 mL of water to each beaker.
(B) Add 0.10 mole of NaCl(*s*) to the left beaker, producing a precipitate.
(C) Increase the temperature of each solution by 20 °C.
(D) Add 1.5 g of $AgNO_3(s)$ to the left beaker.

7. Which of the following is true regarding the salt bridge in this voltaic cell?
(A) Electrons travel through the salt bridge from the cathode to the anode.
(B) Electrons travel through the salt bridge from the anode to the cathode.
(C) Potassium ions travel to the anode, and nitrate ions travel to the cathode.
(D) Potassium ions travel to the cathode, and nitrate ions travel to the anode.

8. If the reverse reaction was desired, how could it be obtained in the laboratory?
(A) Increase the temperature and increase the concentration of the Sn^{2+}.
(B) Apply an electrical potential less than the $\mathscr{E}°_{cell}$ for the forward reaction.
(C) Apply an electrical potential greater than the $\mathscr{E}°_{cell}$ for the forward reaction.
(D) The reverse reaction is not thermodynamically favored and cannot occur.

9. If the tin electrode was replaced with a strip of zinc, how would the cell voltage change?
(A) increase
(B) decrease
(C) no change
(D) become zero

10. When electricity is passed through molten sodium chloride, solid sodium metal is formed at the cathode and chlorine gas is formed at the anode. Which of the following is true regarding this reaction?
(A) ΔG is positive.
(B) The reaction is at equilibrium.
(C) Electrons travel from the cathode to the anode.
(D) The equilibrium constant has a value greater than 1.

AP Free Response Review Questions

Question Format: Short

Category of Question: Quantitative

A metal "M" is combined with fluorine gas to form the compound MF_2. A sample of MF_2 is melted and electrolyzed by the passage of 2538 Coulombs of electricity, resulting in the formation of 1.478 g of solid M.

Questions

(a) Determine the molar mass of M and give the actual formula of MF_2.

(b) Using principles of bonding, explain how MF_2 can conduct electricity when molten.

Question Format: Long

Category of Question: Representation 1

A standard galvanic cell is constructed from zinc metal, zinc nitrate solution, silver, and silver nitrate solution. The cell potentials needed for this problem are shown below:

Reaction	$E°$ (V)
$Zn \rightarrow Zn^{2+} + 2e^-$	0.76
$Ag \rightarrow Ag^+ + e^-$	−0.80

Questions

(a) Write a balanced net ionic equation for the spontaneous reaction that occurs as the cell operates.

(b) Calculate the standard cell potential $E°_{cell}$ as the cell operates.

(c) Identify which species is oxidized.

(d) What happens to the mass of the silver electrode as the cell operates? Explain your answer.

(e) A partial diagram of the cell is shown below.

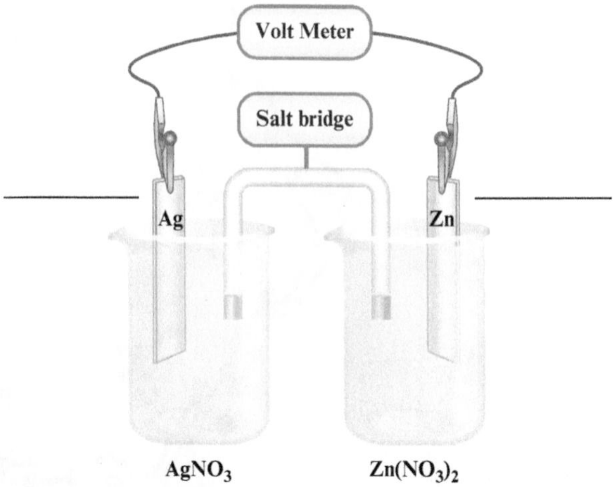

(i) Label the anode and the cathode on the lines next to each of the electrodes.

(ii) What are the concentrations of $Zn(NO_3)_2(aq)$ and $AgNO_3(aq)$ that are needed to generate $E°$?

(iii) Clearly indicate on the diagram the flow of electrons as the cell operates.

(iv) What function does the salt bridge serve?

(f) If the cell operates for 1216 seconds, 2.88 g of Ag is either reduced or oxidized. Calculate the current, in amps.

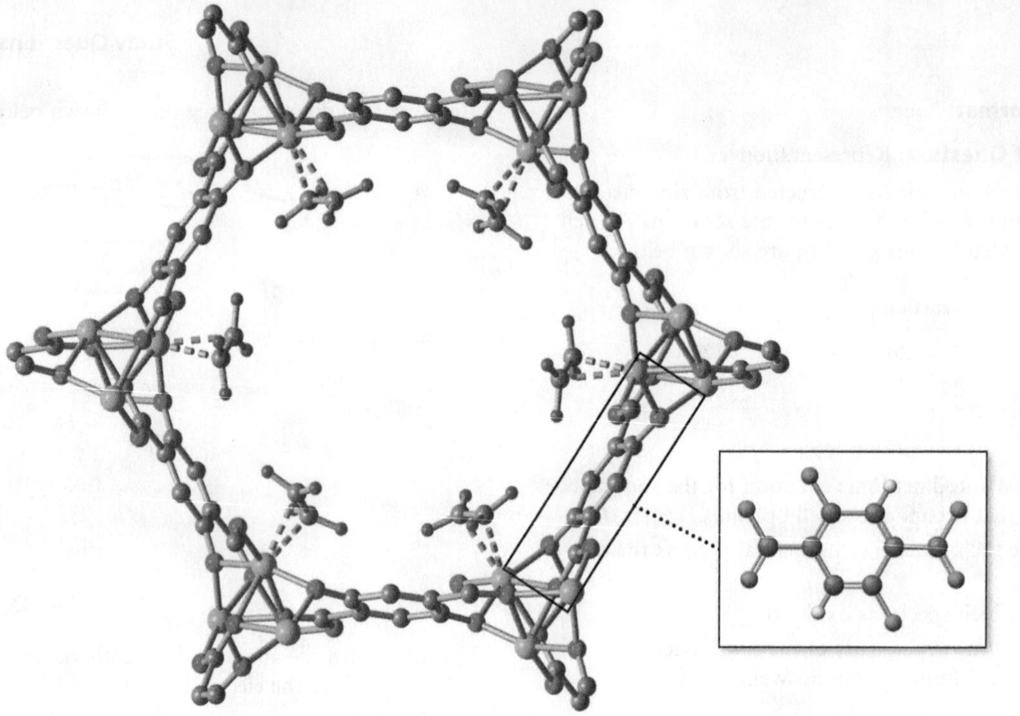

A portion of a MOF, a metal-organic framework. Recently discovered MOFs may be valuable in separating and storing small gaseous molecules. (Here the orange spheres are Fe^{2+} ions, and six ethylene molecules are within the framework. H atoms attached to C atoms in the framework are not shown. Jeffrey Long, Department of Chemistry, University of CA-Berkeley. Reproduced from *Science* vol. 335, page 1606, issue 6076, March 2012.)

Environmental Chemistry—Earth's Environment, Energy, and Sustainability

Chapter Outline

SAVING ENERGY WITH MOFs Metal-organic frameworks (MOFs) consist of a three-dimensional organic framework with embedded metal ions—in essence a giant molecule. Because of their interesting structures and potential uses, the synthesis and study of MOFs are active areas of chemical research. Nearly 1000 new MOFs are reported every year.

MOFs have open structures with large cavities within the framework and have an enormous surface area, often over 5000 m^2/g. The metal ions in the framework can attract and bond gaseous molecules that enter the framework, and, because of this feature, MOFs have the potential to trap and store small molecules such as C_2H_4, CH_4, and CO_2.

Chapter Goals

See Chapter Goals Revisited (page 800) for Study Questions keyed to these goals.

UNDERSTAND

- How human activity contributes to air and water pollution and what is being done to address these problems.
- Current energy resources and implications for the future.
- Efforts by the chemistry community to support green chemistry.
- Important current issues concerning the environment.

DO

- Calculate enthalpy changes, or use enthalpy changes, associated with burning of fossil fuels or with reactions in the environment.
- Apply the principles of stoichiometry, chemical bonding, gas and solution behavior, chemical equilibria, and kinetics to substances important in the environment.

REMEMBER

- The composition of the atmosphere and the aqua sphere.
- The identity of chemical pollutants in air and water and their effects on human life.
- The procedures by which water is purified.
- Renewable and nonrenewable energy resources.

The MOF illustrated here is based on iron(II) ions held together by a −4 charged organic anion, 2,5-dioxido-1,4-benzenedicarboxylate. In the illustrated structure there are also embedded ethylene molecules (C_2H_4).

Iron(II) ions in most compounds are surrounded octahedrally by six atoms. In this MOF, however, five of the six positions are oxygen atoms from the organic species but the sixth site is open. This makes it possible for small molecules such as ethylene to bond to the open site, and it is this ability that has led to so much interest in MOFs.

Ethylene (C_2H_4) and propene ($CH_3CH{=}CH_2$) are key molecules in our economy—they are used to make the polymers polyethylene and polypropylene, respectively—and they are made by "cracking" or thermally decomposing higher molecular weight hydrocarbons at high temperatures. In this process not only are these molecules formed but so also are ethane (C_2H_6) and propane (C_3H_8), among others. The separation of the various hydrocarbons from each other in the mixture is normally done in a complicated distillation process, which, according to the study published in *Science* magazine, "is among the most energy intensive separations carried out at large scale in the chemical industry." However, because ethylene and propene can bind to the MOF, but ethane and propane cannot, near perfect separation of ethane from ethylene, or of propane from propene, can be achieved without a complex distillation process and at the mild temperature of 45 °C.

While the molecule in this study is not yet used in a commercial process, the idea shows considerable promise. This and many others MOFs are relatively easily synthesized, are available in quantity, have interesting and useful properties, and may help us move to a "greener" chemical industry.

Planet Earth can be discussed from many points of view: geological, political, historical, and environmental. The last of these has now become a main topic of concern in the world today, and a background in chemistry is essential to discuss, understand, and evaluate issues pertaining to the environment.

In this chapter, we look at those parts of the environment that are most susceptible to change, the atmosphere and the aqua sphere (water). These are vitally important to our well-being, and yet human activities appear to be causing significant change.

The atmosphere is of major interest. Its composition is being changed by human activities, and the resulting effects on climate are well established. The water of the planet is also of concern: We often pollute it, and we need to purify it. And yet another major concern is energy. In addition to providing sufficient energy resources for the future, our choices of energy sources interact with, and affect, the atmosphere, the oceans, and our fresh water supplies.

Finally, "sustainability" or "sustainable development" is an underlying concern. In 1987 a commission of the United Nations defined sustainable development as "development that meets the needs of the present without compromising the ability of future generations to meet their own needs." This is a complex topic, but there appears to be a consensus that achieving sustainable development requires the interaction of environmental, societal, and economic factors.

Table 20.1 The Gases of the Atmosphere*

Gases	Concentration (ppm)
Nitrogen (N_2)	780,840
Oxygen (O_2)	209,460
Argon (Ar)	9,340
Carbon dioxide (CO_2)	397
Neon (Ne)	18
Helium (He)	5.2
Methane (CH_4)	1.8
Krypton (Kr)	1.1
Hydrogen (H_2)	0.5
Ozone (O_3)	0.4
Dinitrogen monoxide (nitrous oxide, N_2O)	0.3
Carbon monoxide (CO)	0.1
Xenon (Xe)	0.09
Radon (Rn)	traces

*Data on gas concentrations refer to relative numbers of particles in dry air (and hence are related to mole fractions).

20-1 The Atmosphere

The atmosphere may be the least weighty part of the environment, but it is complex and has a disproportionately large influence on our planet.

The major components of the atmosphere are listed in Table 20.1 (where the values in the table are for dry air at sea level). Normally, air also contains water vapor, which can vary considerably from place to place and from day to day. It can be as high as 40,000 ppm (parts per million) but is generally about half this value or less.

There are many more components of the atmosphere than those listed in the table. These include trace amounts of chemicals emitted by plants, animals, and microbes, as well as from burning coal, oil, and gas to generate electricity, from vehicle exhausts, from industry, and from our day-to-day activities.

You might imagine that air is a homogeneous mixture of gases because it is constantly being stirred by the motion of the planet and the heat of the Sun. In fact, mixing is far from complete. There is relatively little exchange of air between the north and south regions of the planet, and there are distinct layers in the atmosphere (◀ Chapter 10; *A Closer Look: The Earth's Atmosphere*). As far as humans are concerned, the most important layer is the lower layer in which we live—the troposphere, which goes up to about 7 km at the poles and 17 km at the equator. Above the troposphere is the stratosphere; this extends to about 30 km, getting less dense as altitude increases. There are even higher regions, but in this chapter, we concern ourselves only with the troposphere and the stratosphere.

The total mass of the atmosphere is estimated to be around 5.15×10^{18} kg (5.15×10^{15} metric tons, or 5.15×10^{6} gigatons). Three quarters of the mass of the atmosphere is in the troposphere, and there its average temperature is 14 °C. It can be as low as −89 °C, the lowest temperature ever recorded, in Antarctica in 1983, or as high as 58 °C, the highest temperature ever recorded, in North Africa in 1922. After temperature, the next most obvious property of the atmosphere is the pressure it exerts, which at sea level is around 101 kPa (1 atmosphere) and about 25 kPa (1/4 atmosphere) at 35,000 feet, the altitude used by passenger aircraft.

Gigatons are often used in environmental studies because the masses involved are so large. A *metric ton* is 1000 kg, but a gigaton is a billion metric tons, that is, 10^9 metric tons.

Some of the gases of the atmosphere are unreactive, notably the noble gases: helium, neon, argon, krypton, and xenon. Helium and argon are added continuously to the atmosphere because they are products of radioactive decay—helium comes from alpha particles emitted by naturally occurring elements such as uranium, and argon is produced by decay of ^{40}K, a long-lived radioactive isotope of potassium.

The other gases of the atmosphere, particularly oxygen, nitrogen, and carbon dioxide, are chemically reactive and can be changed into other molecules by reactions driven by lightning, ultraviolet rays from the Sun, or the influence of living things.

The atmosphere has undergone significant changes over the lifetime of our planet, and it is still changing. The well-publicized increase of CO_2 in the atmosphere and the decrease of ozone in the stratosphere are probably the best-known changes, but human activity is contributing new chemicals to the environment as well. We need to understand what these changes mean for the future.

Nitrogen and Nitrogen Oxides

Nitrogen in the atmosphere, N_2, arose from the out-gassing of Earth when it was simply a molten mass. Even today, some nitrogen escapes when volcanoes erupt. Every living thing on the planet has nitrogen in its cells in the form of proteins and in DNA and RNA, among other compounds. Gaseous N_2 is not the direct source of this element in living beings, however; to be taken up by plants, nitrogen must be in the form of a usable nitrogen compound, such as ammonia or ammonium or nitrate ions.

In the environment, atmospheric N_2 molecules are converted to other compounds by a number of natural processes. Some of this conversion is carried out within the nitrogen cycle, shown in Figure 20.1, which charts the processes that convert between various N-containing molecules and ions in nature.

Humans also influence the nitrogen cycle. On a global scale, the conversion of nitrogen to its various compounds is accomplished to the extent of around 50% by biological processes and 10% by lightning. However, about 30% comes from burning fossil fuels and 10% from manufactured fertilizers. Indeed, a recent paper in *Science* using $^{14/15}$N isotope analysis found that nitrogen inputs to the environment from fossil fuel combustion and large-scale biomass burning accelerated greatly beginning about 1895, and another shift was seen beginning about 1970 as massive amounts of N-containing fertilizer were increasingly produced.

Let us now focus on the various nitrogen oxides that are present in the atmosphere, among them dinitrogen monoxide (nitrous oxide, N_2O), nitrogen monoxide (nitric oxide, NO), and nitrogen dioxide (NO_2). Collectively, nitrogen oxides are referred to as NO_x compounds. Although the nitrogen cycle does produce some of these oxides in the atmosphere, the majority of NO_x molecules are produced by human activities.

The most abundant nitrogen oxide in the atmosphere is the least reactive one, dinitrogen monoxide,

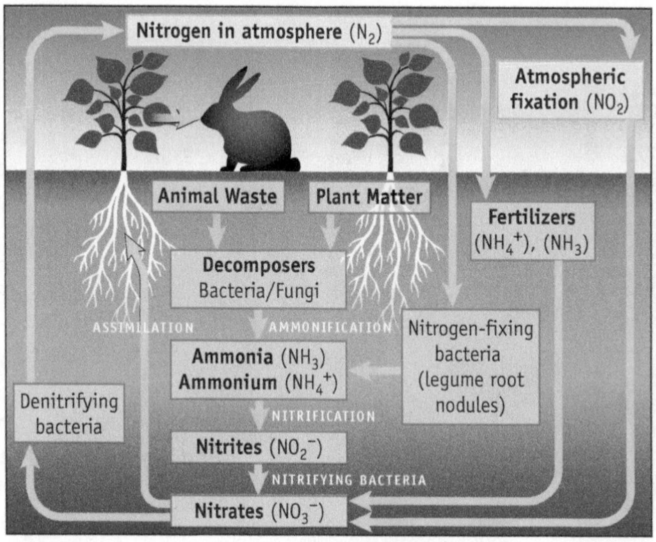

FIGURE 20.1 **The nitrogen cycle.** The nitrogen cycle involves nitrogen fixation by soil bacteria or, in aquatic environments, by cyanobacteria. The NH_4^+ ions produced are converted to nitrate ions, the main form of nitrogen absorbed by plants. Nitrogen is returned to the atmosphere by denitrifying bacteria, which convert nitrate ions to N_2.

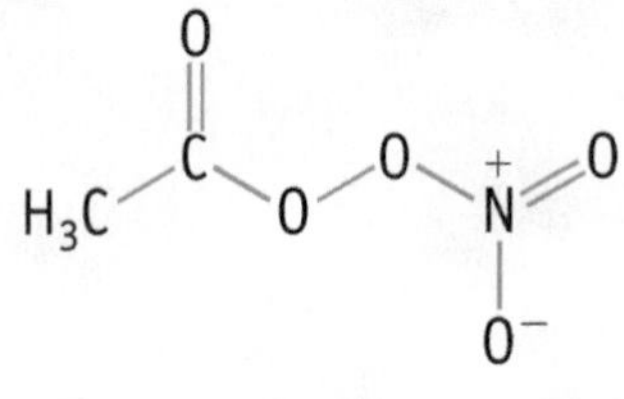

Peroxyacetyl nitrate, an air pollutant. It is an oxidant more powerful than ozone and is a lachrymator (it makes your eyes tear). It is formed in the atmosphere when ethanol is used as a fuel, so the more ethanol is used, the more its formation could be a problem. It is a member of a class of compounds called PANs or peroxyacyl nitrates.

N_2O. Its current average abundance is 0.3 ppm; however, the percent of this gas in the atmosphere has been increasing slowly for 250 years. The other nitrogen oxides make up only 0.00005 ppm of the atmosphere. Although 100 million tons of NO and NO_2 are generated by human processes annually, the concentration of these materials in the atmosphere is low because they are quickly washed out of the atmosphere by rain (where they contribute to "acid rain"). But, NO_x compounds can linger in certain situations, particularly over cities in sunny climates. There they can react with hydrocarbons in the atmosphere, such as traces of unburned fuel, to produce irritating photochemical smog. Among the most polluting components of smog are PANs, peroxyacyl nitrates. PANs are formed by photochemical (light-induced) reactions in smog involving organic compounds, O_3, and NO_x. They are toxic and irritating. At low concentrations, they irritate the eyes, but at higher concentrations they can cause more serious damage to both animals and vegetation. They are relatively stable; thus, it is possible they can persist for some time and travel considerable distance from where they are formed.

Oxygen

Over the lifetime of our planet, plant life has had a dramatic effect on the atmosphere, changing it from a reducing to an oxidizing one, that is, from there being no oxygen present to one where O_2 is the second most abundant species present in the atmosphere. This change meant that life had to change. Those species that could not live in the presence of oxygen either died out or were relegated to regions where oxygen is blocked out. The concentration of oxygen in the air is now midway between two extremes that would make life on Earth impossible for humans: below 17% we would suffocate, and above 25% all organic material would burn easily.

The total mass of oxygen in the atmosphere is a million gigatons. Even though the burning of 7 gigatons of fossil fuel carbon per year consumes 18 gigatons of oxygen, this makes almost no discernible difference to the amount of oxygen in the atmosphere.

Oxygen is a by-product of plant **photosynthesis**. Carbon dioxide is the source of the carbon that plants need and that they capture from the air and turn into carbohydrates such as glucose ($C_6H_{12}O_6$) by photosynthesis. The overall chemical reaction is

$$6\ CO_2 + 6\ H_2O \rightarrow C_6H_{12}O_6 + 6\ O_2$$

and the net result is the release of an oxygen molecule back into the atmosphere for each CO_2 absorbed. Oxygen molecules released by photosynthesis remain in the atmosphere, on average, for around 3000 years before being consumed through respiration in living beings or through other oxidation reactions.

Blue-green algae, or cyanobacteria (Figure 20.2), first began producing oxygen as long ago as 3.5 billion years. But, mysteriously, hundreds of millions of years elapsed before a significant amount of oxygen was present in the atmosphere. Astrobiologists are not certain why this occurred, but it does seem plausible that the oxygen first produced did not remain in the atmosphere because it reacted with metals, especially converting abundant iron to iron(II) ions and iron(III) ions. (Iron is the fourth most abundant element in the Earth's crust, where it is found primarily in the form of iron(III) oxides.) The concentration of oxygen remained low until about 2 billion years ago when it rose relatively rapidly to around 20% and the first land plants started to appear.

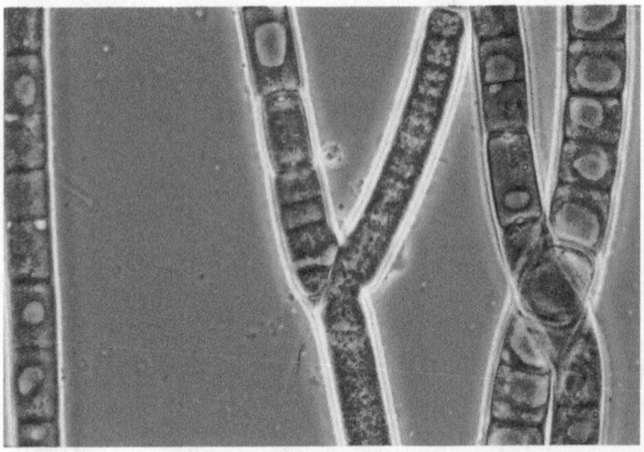

Michael Abbey/Science Source

FIGURE 20.2 **Cyanobacteria.** The importance of cyanobacteria, also known as blue-green algae, lies in their production of oxygen by photosynthesis and their participation in the nitrogen cycle.

There are three naturally occurring isotopes of oxygen: oxygen-16 accounts for 99.76% of O atoms, oxygen-17 for a mere 0.04%, and oxygen-18 for 0.2%. The ratio of oxygen-18 to oxygen-16 in the world's oceans has varied slightly over geological time, and this has left an imprint on parts of the environment, providing evidence of past climates. When the world is in a cooler period, water molecules with the lighter isotope, oxygen-16, evaporate more easily from the oceans than their heavier oxygen-18 counterpart. Thus, precipitation in the form of snow is slightly richer in oxygen-16, and the water that remains in the oceans is slightly richer in oxygen-18. Marine creatures therefore lay down shells that have more oxygen-18 than expected, and these are preserved in sediments. Analyzing the ratio of the two isotopes in such deposits reveals the cycle of global cooling and warming that has characterized the past half million years with its five ice ages.

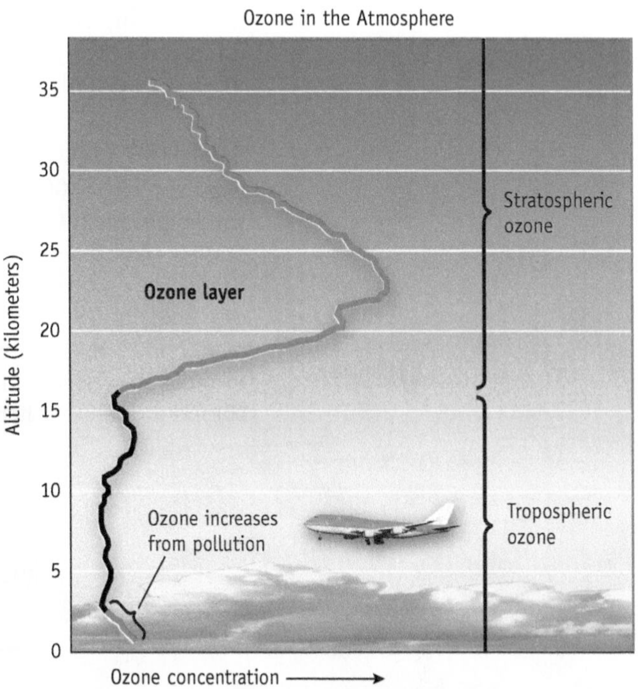

FIGURE 20.3 The ozone layer. About 90% of the ozone in the atmosphere is contained in the stratosphere (roughly 15–50 km above the surface). Concentrations there range from 2 to 8 ppm.

Ozone

Ozone (O_3) plays a key role in life on this planet, but it is also a threat. In the troposphere, it is a pollutant, whereas in the stratosphere it acts as a shield, protecting the planet from damaging ultraviolet rays from the Sun. This shield is known as the **ozone layer** (Figure 20.3).

Ozone is formed in lightning storms, so there is a natural low level of ozone in the air we breathe, about 0.02 ppm. In summer, however, the level can increase to 0.1 ppm or more as a result of sunlight acting on the nitrogen dioxide emitted by vehicles. The ultraviolet component of sunlight causes the dissociation of NO_2 to NO and O atoms. The resulting O atoms then react with O_2 (in the presence of a third molecule acting as an energy "sink") to produce ozone.

$$NO_2 + \text{energy } (\lambda < 240 \text{ nm}) \rightarrow NO + O$$

$$O + O_2 \rightarrow O_3$$

Because ozone damages the lungs, a legal limit for exposure to ozone in the workplace, 0.1 ppm, has been established. Some growing plants are also susceptible to the gas, and even though they do not show visible signs of stress, their growth is reduced in proportion to the level of ozone in the air.

In contrast to ozone in the troposphere, O_3 in the stratosphere is vital to the planet because the molecules absorb ultraviolet radiation before it reaches Earth's surface. Ozone is formed in the stratosphere when radiation with wavelengths shorter than 240 nm interacts with O_2 molecules and cleaves them into two O atoms. Each O atom combines with another O_2 molecule to produce an ozone molecule.

$$O_2 + \text{energy} \rightleftharpoons O + O$$

$$O + O_2 \rightarrow O_3$$

Ozone in turn absorbs ultraviolet radiation with wavelengths less than 320 nm, and the O_3 is decomposed to O_2 and O atoms.

$$O_3 + \text{energy } (\lambda < 320 \text{ nm}) \rightleftharpoons O_2 + O$$

$$O + O_3 \rightarrow 2\, O_2$$

Without the ozone layer, dangerous radiation capable of harming living cells would penetrate to Earth's surface. An increase in radiation could lead to an increased incidence of skin cancer and cataracts and suppression of the human immune response system. Damage to crops and marine phytoplankton and weathering of plastics can also result from increased levels of ultraviolet radiation.

The "Ozone Hole"

From the late 1800s until about 1930, ammonia (NH_3), chloromethane (CH_3Cl), and sulfur dioxide (SO_2) were widely used as refrigerants. However, leakage from refrigerators caused several fatal accidents in the 1920s, so three American corporations, Frigidaire, General Motors, and DuPont, collaborated on the search for a less dangerous fluid. In 1928, Thomas Midgley, Jr., and his coworkers discovered a "miracle compound" as a substitute. This compound, dichlorodifluoromethane (CCl_2F_2), is a member of a large family of compounds called chlorofluorocarbons (CFCs). The two compounds shown here are CFC-114 ($C_2Cl_2F_4$) and CFC-12 (CCl_2F_2).

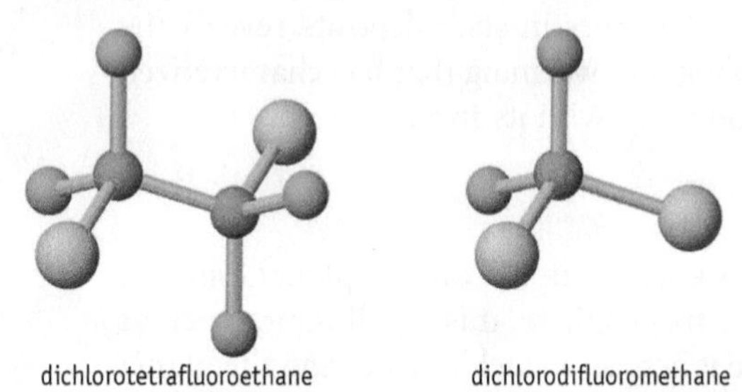

dichlorotetrafluoroethane   dichlorodifluoromethane

These compounds had exactly the physical and chemical properties needed for a refrigerant: appropriate critical temperatures and pressures, no toxicity, and apparent chemical inertness.

The uses of CFCs grew dramatically, not only in air conditioning and refrigeration equipment but also in applications such as propellants for aerosol cans, foaming agents in the production of expanded plastic foams, and inhalers for asthma sufferers.

Unfortunately, the properties that made CFCs so useful also led to environmental problems. CFCs are unreactive in Earth's troposphere, which allows them to remain there for hundreds of years. Over time, however, they slowly diffuse into the stratosphere where they are decomposed by solar radiation.

$$CF_2Cl_2(g) + \text{UV radiation} \rightarrow \cdot CF_2Cl(g) + \cdot Cl(g)$$

The Cl atoms released in the decomposition of CFCs and other chlorine-containing compounds could then destroy large numbers of ozone molecules. This occurs because Cl atoms catalyze the decomposition of O_3 molecules and produce the radical species ClO (Step 1). This in turn intercepts O atoms (Step 2) from the decomposition of O_3 molecules (Step 3), to produce Cl atoms, which then continue the cycle.

Step 1	$O_3(g) + \cdot Cl(g) \rightarrow \cdot ClO(g) + O_2(g)$
Step 2	$\cdot ClO(g) + \cdot O(g) \rightarrow \cdot Cl(g) + O_2(g)$
Step 3	$O_3(g) + \text{solar radiation} \rightarrow \cdot O(g) + O_2(g)$
Net reaction:	$2\,O_3(g) \rightarrow 3\,O_2(g)$

The equations above represent steps in a *chain reaction* (◀ Section 14-6), which, when repeated over and over, lead to the destruction of many ozone molecules per chlorine atom.

In 1985 three British scientists of the British Antarctic Survey discovered that there was a significant reduction in the ozone concentration over the Antarctic continent in the late winter and early spring, which has since been referred to as the "ozone hole" (Figure 20.4). In 1986, a team from the U.S. National Center for Atmospheric Research went to Antarctica to investigate the "hole" and found that this hole indeed had higher levels of the reaction intermediate, ·ClO, than expected in the stratosphere.

NOAA

FIGURE 20.4 The "ozone hole" over the Antarctic continent. During the Antarctic winter, when there are 24 hours of darkness, aerosols of HCl and $ClONO_2$ freeze and accumulate in the polar stratospheric clouds. During the Antarctic spring, these crystals melt, and Cl and ClO radicals are rapidly formed and lead to a depletion of stratospheric ozone over the continent.

The "ozone hole" occurrence is tied not only to ·Cl and ·ClO radicals, but also to NO_x chemistry. Ozone destruction over Antarctica is partly affected in certain seasons by the reaction of ·ClO and $·NO_2$ to give the compound $ClONO_2$.

$$\cdot ClO(g) + \cdot NO_2(g) \rightarrow ClONO_2(g)$$

In the Antarctic winter this compound and others such as HCl are frozen in stratospheric clouds. In the spring, at warmer temperatures, the problem begins when reactions such as the following occur:

$$ClONO_2(g) + H_2O(g) \rightarrow HOCl(g) + HNO_3(g)$$

$$ClONO_2(g) + HCl(g) \rightarrow Cl_2(g) + HNO_3(g)$$

Both HOCl and Cl_2 can be decomposed by solar radiation to give ·Cl atoms, which then lead to ozone destruction.

Because of the damage caused to the stratospheric ozone layer by CFCs and related compounds, the United States banned the use of CFCs as aerosol propellants in 1978, and 68 nations had followed suit by 1987. In 1990, the United States and 140 other countries agreed to a complete halt in CFC manufacture as of December 31, 1995. Continuous monitoring indicates the ozone hole is slowly closing at this time.

Carbon Dioxide and Methane

No element is more essential to life than carbon because only carbon has the ability to form stable compounds consisting of long chains and rings of atoms. This is the basis of the structures for many compounds that comprise the living cell. The food we eat—carbohydrates, oils, proteins, and fiber—is made up of compounds of carbon, and this carbon eventually returns to the atmosphere as CO_2 as part of the natural carbon cycle (Figure 20.5). This cycle moves over 200 gigatons of carbon every year between various compartments of the terrestrial ecosphere and so rules the tempo of life on Earth.

Some years ago scientists began to notice increasing levels of CO_2 in the atmosphere, so the *Intergovernmental Panel on Climate Change* (IPCC) was set up in 1988 by members of the United Nations Environment Program and the World Meteorological Organization. In the four Assessment Reports issued to date, a significant increase in the atmospheric carbon dioxide concentration has been reported, from around 280 ppm in 1750 to 396.8 ppm in March 2013 (Figure 20.6). The fourth IPCC report states that "Today's CO_2 concentration has not been exceeded during the past 420,000 years and likely not during the past 20 million years. The rate of increase over the past century is unprecedented, at least during the past 20,000 years." As described in Section 20-6, there has been significant debate about the origin of this increase and its effects on the planet's climate.

Climate Change Carbon dioxide and methane have significant effects on the environment (see Section 20-6, Environmental Impact of Fossil Fuels).

Methane is formed and released into the atmosphere by biological processes in enormous amounts. Some methane is produced in nature by anaerobic bacteria (that is, those that do not use oxygen) at the bottom of lakes and swamps, in termite mounds, and in the guts of animals such as cows and humans. Landfill sites are also contributors of methane due to the decomposition of organic materials in the absence of significant oxygen. The release of methane as the result of human activities such as coal mining or the processing and use of natural gas also contributes to CH_4 in the atmosphere. Finally, the increasing use of "fracking" (hydraulic fracturing, page 779) to obtain poorly accessible gas and oil has also led to significant concerns that even more CH_4 will be released to the atmosphere.

Methane hydrates are another source of methane (page 783). There are vast amounts of methane hydrates in the depths of the ocean, but they may be expensive to recover. The hydrates are also found in the Arctic, locked in the permafrost. There is also some concern that these deposits could release more methane directly into the atmosphere if warming of these regions continues.

The methane concentration in the atmosphere is now around 1.7 ppm. Based on studies of air bubbles trapped in ice sheets, we also know that methane is now

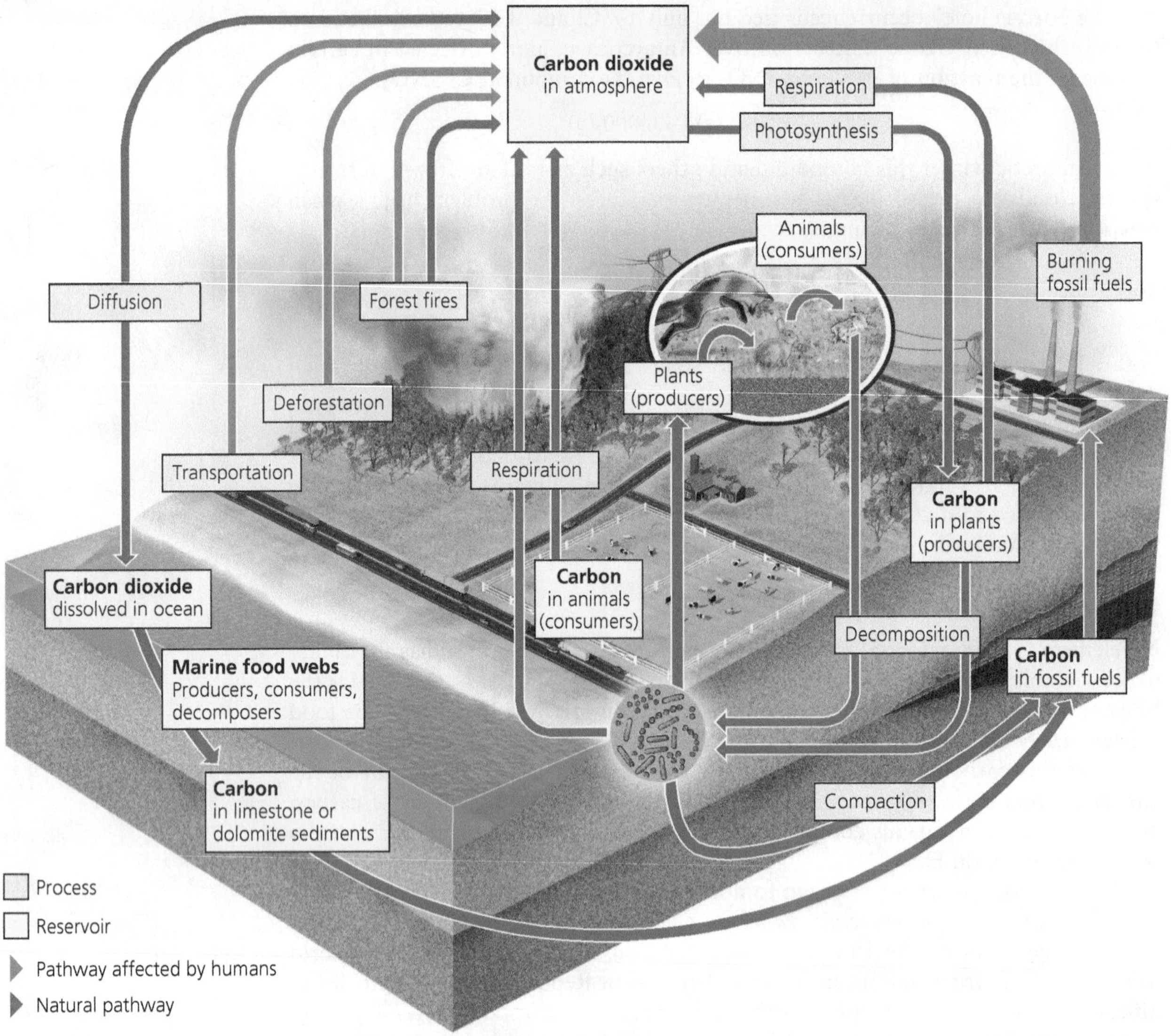

FIGURE 20.5 **The carbon cycle.** This diagram shows the movement of carbon between land, atmosphere, and oceans.

FIGURE 20.6 **Mean monthly concentrations of CO_2 at Mauna Loa, Hawaii.** Notice the yearly cycle of CO_2 concentration. It declines in the summer when photosynthesis is at its peak. In March 2013 the atmospheric concentration of CO_2 was 396.8 ppm, corresponding to an increase of 5 ppm in one year.

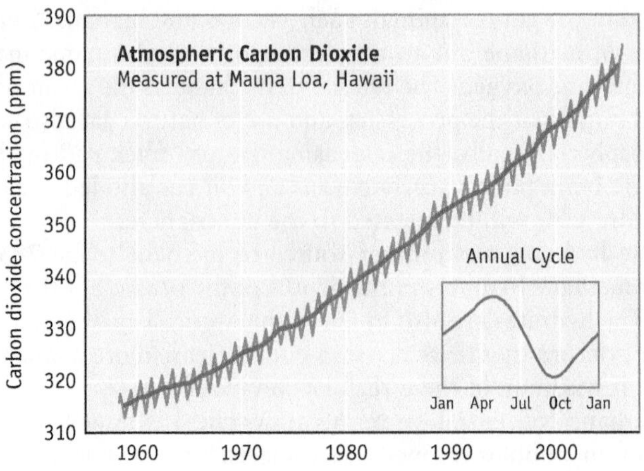

more abundant in Earth's atmosphere than at any time in the last 400,000 years. Concerns about methane in the atmosphere arise because it is a powerful greenhouse gas (page 791). In fact, CH_4 is about 21 times better at atmospheric warming than CO_2 by weight.

REVIEW & CHECK FOR SECTION 20-1

1. Which of the following atmospheric gases is present in highest concentration in dry air?

   (a) N_2O (b) CH_4 (c) O_3 (d) CO

2. Many chemical reactions that occur in the atmosphere and stratosphere involve free radicals. Free radical formation occurs when a photon of light is absorbed and the energy of the radiation being absorbed causes a chemical bond in the compound to break. Which of the following bonds requires the most energy (and the most energetic radiation) to be broken?

   (a) The oxygen—oxygen bond in O_2
   (b) The oxygen—oxygen bond in O_3
   (c) The chlorine—carbon bond in CCl_2F_2

20-2 The Aqua Sphere (Water)

There is an abundance of water on our planet, in the oceans, lakes, rivers, and underground aquifers, locked in minerals, in ice and snow in arctic regions, and water vapor in the atmosphere. This is fortunate because life as we know it cannot exist without water. Right now, however, there are serious problems associated with this valuable resource. Some locations are deprived of sufficient water, whereas there is an overabundance in other places. There are huge variations in the purity and quality of available water supplies, and evidence suggests these problems will continue to increase in the future.

People want water for drinking, for washing themselves and their clothing, for watering crops, and for flushing the lavatory. Agriculture and industry require even larger amounts of water than the amounts used by individuals. Most water that we use comes from available groundwater, rivers, lakes, underground aquifers, and rainwater collected and stored in reservoirs above or below ground. However, climate changes are even now affecting the amount and distribution of water resources in the world. In addition, we need to recognize that the amount of water required will increase with continuing growth in global population.

Already 500 million people worldwide are affected at some level by water shortages, although most of these problems have not yet seriously affected people in the United States. However, in the Great Plains underground aquifers are becoming seriously depleted, and some lakes and rivers are drying up. For example, Lake Mead, which was created by the Hoover Dam (on the Colorado River on the border between Nevada and Arizona) is now around 20 meters (60 feet) or more below the level of water it held in the 1980s. (Figure 20.7). The Colorado River no longer reaches the sea; much of its water is being drawn off for use in surrounding communities, especially for agriculture to irrigate crops.

Water quality is always an essential underlying issue when talking about water. There is a lot of water on Earth, but 97% of it is in the oceans and unsuitable for most uses until it is separated from dissolved salts. Much of the remaining 3% is also unsuitable for human consumption.

We contribute to pollution of water resources in much of what we do. For centuries humans have treated lakes, rivers, and oceans as the easiest place to dump waste. All too often, what appear to be benign human activities have unintended consequences for water supplies. For example, agricultural and industrial chemicals and drugs from discarded medications sometimes appear in water supplies. The presence of dissolved materials in water supplies then requires complex and expensive purification processes if the water is to be used.

Water Use In the United States, the average daily indoor per capita water use is 69.3 gallons. This is much greater than in any other country. In some third world countries, the per capita use is one tenth of this amount or less.

Check Your Water Supply In the United States, tap water from a municipality must meet standards at least as strict as those for bottled water. All municipalities publish annual reports of the water quality, many of them on the Internet. Check the quality of the tap water in your municipality.

FIGURE 20.7 **Lake Mead, a symbol of a crisis in water supply.** Lake Mead is the largest man-made lake and reservoir in the United States. It is located on the Colorado River in the states of Nevada and Arizona. Aqueducts carry the water to Las Vegas, Los Angeles, San Diego, and other communities in the Southwest. This view of the lake from Hoover Dam shows the drop in the lake level, which used to cover the white rocks on the mountainsides. The Scripps Institute of Oceanography set the odds of Lake Mead drying up by 2021 at 50-50.

The Oceans

The oceans cover 71% of the area of the planet, contain about 1.3×10^9 km^3 of seawater, and have an average depth of 3790 m. A multitude of life forms is known to exist in the oceans and, because the depths are only just beginning to be explored, that number is likely to increase.

The quantity of minerals dissolved in the oceans is vast (Table 20.2). Sodium chloride (sodium and chloride ions) is found in the largest amount, and there are sizable quantities of magnesium ions, calcium ions, potassium ions, and carbonate/bicarbonate ions. Many other elements are present in seawater in concentrations less than one ppm but because of the huge amounts of seawater, the amounts of these elements potentially available in seawater is striking. The lure of obtaining dissolved metals from seawater has tantalized people through the ages. Gold, for example, is present in seawater at a concentration of 10 parts per trillion (10 g in 1 trillion g of water), so the total amount is more than 13 million tons. Although some have tried, no method has been found to extract gold profitably from the oceans.

Table 20.2 Concentrations of Some Cations and Anions in Seawater

ELEMENT	DISSOLVED SPECIES	CONCENTRATIONS (mmol/L)
Chlorine	Cl^-	550
Sodium	Na^+	460
Magnesium	Mg^{2+}	52
Calcium	Ca^{2+}	10
Potassium	K^+	10
Carbon	HCO_3^-, CO_3^{2-}	30
Phosphorus	HPO_4^{2-}	<1

Concerns have been expressed about the effect on sea levels caused by global warming. Melting of ice now stacked on land (such as that in Greenland) would cause an increase in sea level. However, melting of Arctic sea ice, which is occurring, will not raise the sea level because the volume of liquid water formed is smaller than the volume of ice.

Sea Level Rise The U.S. National Research Council reported in June 2012 that the sea level will rise between 8 and 23 cm by 2030 (relative to the 2000 level). "Global mean sea level is rising primarily because global temperatures are rising, causing ocean water to expand and land ice to melt. However, sea-level rise is not uniform; it varies from place to place." (*Sea-Level Rise for the Coasts of California, Oregon, and Washington: Past, Present, and Future.* National Academies Press, 2012.)

Drinking Water

Water is as vital to life as food: You would not last a week if you had no water to drink. Most people in developed countries have clean, safe water supplied to their homes (although curiously many prefer to buy it in small bottles). Sadly, a large number of our fellow humans, generally in less-developed countries, have to make do with whatever water they can find, taking it from a well or even from a river, and then they are at risk of contracting a water-borne disease such as cholera, typhoid, gastroenteritis, or meningitis. More than 5000 people a day are thought to die of diseases contracted from the water they drink.

Water purification began with the ancient Egyptians 3500 years ago. They discovered that, when alum—potassium aluminum sulfate, $KAl(SO_4)_2$—was dissolved

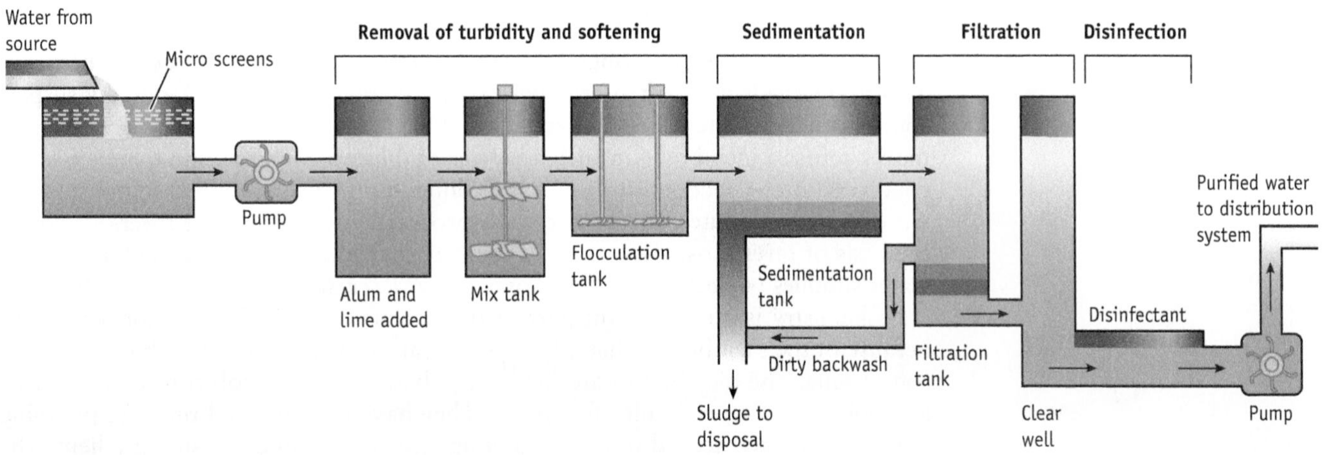

FIGURE 20.8 **A municipal water treatment plant.** The general steps in this process are (1) the removal of turbidity, (2) softening, (3) sedimentation and filtration, and (4) disinfection. The removal of turbidity (by addition of alum) and the disinfection of water are discussed in the text.

in water, visible impurities were removed. In mildly basic conditions, this salt forms a voluminous precipitate of aluminum hydroxide, $Al(OH)_3$, which carries down any cloudiness as it settles. Modern water treatment plants (Figure 20.8) add a small amount of slaked lime ($Ca(OH)_2$) to raise the pH slightly and then a solution of aluminum sulfate or alum to create solid $Al(OH)_3$, which removes many impurities as it settles. The water is then filtered through sand to remove any trace of the aluminum hydroxide.

After treatment with alum and subsequent settling and filtration, water is crystal clear and ready to be disinfected to destroy any pathogens still present. This can be done with a powerful oxidizing agent such as chlorine, sodium hypochlorite (NaClO), or ozone. Chlorine gas and hypochlorite ions have an advantage over ozone in that they are more persistent, meaning that the water will still be fit to drink even when it has been standing in a pipe for a long time. For those areas where the water supply cannot be assumed drinkable, purification tablets are available. These react with the water to form a solution of hypochlorite ions (ClO^-) strong enough to kill off pathogens and make the water safe to drink. Boiling water also makes it potable.

Ozone (O_3) is the most commonly used water supply disinfectant in Europe. It is also currently used in Los Angeles and some smaller communities in the United States. One advantage is that it does not produce toxic trihalomethanes (such as $CHCl_3$), the by-products of chlorine treatment; it is also more effective than chlorine at killing *Cryptosporidium* bacteria and destroying viruses; and it does not leave a residual "chlorine" taste. However, due to its reactivity, ozone must be generated on site and is more expensive. Also, it does not provide residual disinfection in the distribution system.

Ultraviolet (UV) light has been used to disinfect food products, such as milk, for some time and can also be used in water systems. Wavelengths ranging from 200 to 295 nm are used, with maximum disinfection occurring at 253.7 nm (Figure 20.9). UV units are less expensive to install than ozone generators and have the advantage of requiring short contact times for disinfection. In addition, UV radiation disinfection is not pH or temperature dependent, and it leaves no toxic residues. Like ozone, however, UV treatment does not provide residual disinfection.

Glenn Moore/ZUMA Press/Newscom

FIGURE 20.9 **A commercial unit that uses ultraviolet light for water purification in a municipal water system.**

Reverse Osmosis for Water Purification

Potable water can also be obtained from contaminated water by **reverse osmosis**. This technique is most often used with seawater, but waste water from any suspect source can be treated by this technique. Osmosis is the process whereby water moves across a membrane in such a way as to dilute a solution with a higher solute concentration (◀ Section 13-4). If a high enough pressure is applied to the solution with the higher solute concentration, the process of osmosis can be reversed. This is the basis of reverse osmosis, and it is the way that some cities near the sea get their water supplies (◀ Section 13-4 *A Closer Look: Reverse Osmosis for Pure Water*).

Chemistry is an important part of the reverse osmosis desalination apparatus because of the membranes that allow the passage of water molecules but not of dissolved salts. The membranes are made of polymers such as polyvinylidene fluoride and polypropylene with ultrafine pores. They have to withstand the high pumping pressures that are needed to force water against the osmotic pressure gradient. The cost is not excessive, however, and a cubic meter of water (1000 L) produced this way can cost only about \$1. Desalination systems are now a \$1 billion per year industry and growing at a rate of 7% per year.

Water Pollution

Water has been polluted by many things, mainly from activities such as farming, mining, papermaking, inadequate or nonexistent sewage treatment facilities, and waste disposal from the chemical industry. Protecting natural bodies of water is now high on the agenda of most developed societies, and this has been achieved mainly by controlling the handling and use of dangerous chemicals and by installing better sewage treatment facilities.

Phosphates

In the past, phosphate pollution on a massive scale was an environmental problem. One example occurred in Lake Erie, one of the Great Lakes. In the 1960s it appeared Lake Erie was no longer capable of supporting life because of a lack of dissolved oxygen. This was due in part to an excess of nutrients, primarily phosphates, supplied by the rivers that drained into the lake. In this lake and others, these nutrients caused a great increase in the amount of algae present, which in turn used up the dissolved oxygen and made it so that no other life could survive. Where did these phosphates come from? Although sewage treatment plants draining into the rivers removed most pollutants, they were not removing phosphates that had become a major component of household detergents. Phosphate from fertilizers also found its way into surface water (Figure 20.10). Similar problems were experienced in other parts of the world, notably in Europe.

John C. Kotz

FIGURE 20.10 **Algae bloom from excess phosphate in a pond.** In this pond, which borders the fairway of a golf course, algae blooms have occurred because of the phosphate-containing fertilizers used on the course.

Campaigns to control the use of phosphates were successful. These chemicals were taken out of household products, and phosphate was extracted at sewage plants before the waste water was released to rivers. The result was to discourage the growth of algae, and slowly Lake Erie and other lakes began to regenerate. Reduced use of phosphates in fertilizers and improved fertilizer application methods have generally decreased phosphate runoff into waterways.

Heavy Metals

"Heavy metals" are those that have densities substantially greater than about 5 g/cm^3; these include arsenic, cadmium, copper, iron, mercury, lead, and chromium. Many heavy metals are found in our environment and some, such as iron and copper, are essential to life and present in most living organisms. However, even these elements are toxic in sufficient amounts, and many other metals are highly toxic even in very small amounts. Sources of information on heavy metal toxicity tell us that such metals can impair mental and central nervous function and damage lungs, kidneys, liver, and other organs. The effects are best described by the German

A CLOSER LOOK — Chlorination of Water Supplies

Chlorination is the oldest and most commonly used water disinfection method in the United States. Originally, chlorine gas was dissolved in water to yield hypochlorous acid (HClO),

$$Cl_2(g) + H_2O(\ell) \rightarrow HClO(aq) + HCl(aq)$$

which partially ionizes to yield the hypochlorite ion (ClO^-).

$$HClO(aq) + H_2O(\ell) \rightleftharpoons H_3O^+(aq) + ClO^-(aq)$$
$$K_a = 3.5 \times 10^{-8}$$

Two of the chemical species formed by chlorine in water—hypochlorous acid and the hypochlorite ion—are known to environmental engineers as **free available chlorine**, meaning they are available for disinfection. Because chlorine gas is quite toxic and can easily escape from damaged containers, many water treatment facilities have switched to solid hypochlorite salts such as sodium or calcium hypochlorite [NaClO and $Ca(ClO)_2$, respectively].

Hypochlorous acid and hypochlorite ion are effective in killing bacteria. However, they will also oxidize ions such as iron(II), manganese(II), and nitrite ion, as well as organic impurities. These substances are collectively known as the chlorine demand. To be available to kill bacteria, sufficient chlorine must be added to exceed the chlorine demand.

© Cengage Learning/Charles D. Winters

Chlorine tanks in the water treatment plant of a small city.

The advantages of chlorination include its relatively low cost and simple application as well as its ability to maintain residual disinfection throughout the distribution system. However, there are also disadvantages. Chlorine reacts with dissolved, naturally occurring organic compounds in the source water to form carcinogenic compounds such as trihalomethanes (of which chloroform, $CHCl_3$, is one example). Chlorination has also been blamed for causing an unpleasant taste and odor in some drinking water.

In 1998, the Disinfection Byproducts Rule (DBR), which limits the amount of chlorinated organic compounds in water, was implemented in the United States. One way to comply with the DBR is to add ammonia to the water, and about 30% of major U.S. water companies currently use this technique. Ammonia and hypochlorous acid react to form chloramines such as NH_2Cl:

$$HClO(aq) + NH_3(aq) \rightarrow NH_2Cl(aq) + H_2O(\ell)$$

Chloramines are called **combined available chlorine**. Like free available chlorine, combined available chlorine is retained as a disinfectant throughout the water distribution system, but it is a weaker disinfectant overall. Combined available chlorine, however, has the advantage that it is less likely to lead to chlorinated organic compounds.

chemist Walter Stock, who contracted mercury poisoning early in the 20th century. He said "[It] first reveals itself only as an affection of the nerves, causing headaches, numbness, mental lassitude, depression, and the loss of memory; such are very disturbing to one engaged in an intellectual occupation."

Because of the consequences of heavy metals on health, the United States Environmental Protection Agency (EPA) places limits on the amount of many metals allowed in drinking water and in foods. Lead, for example, is a cumulative poison that has been linked to learning disabilities, but it may still be found in the water of older houses due to leaching from lead plumbing and in older paints, which used "white lead" (PbO) as a white pigment. Lead levels in water in the United States are currently required to be no more than 50 μg/L (or 50 ppb).

Knowledge of heavy metal toxicity even made its way to Hollywood in 2000. The movie *Erin Brockovich* is centered around water pollution from chromium(VI) (generally in the form of ions such as CrO_4^{2-} or $Cr_2O_7^{2-}$). For chemists, chromium is a good example of the importance of knowing the oxidation state of an element; chromium(VI) compounds are toxic whereas chromium(III) is an essential trace element that plays a role in human metabolism.

Heavy Metals and ATSDR The federal Agency for Toxic Substances and Disease Registry (ATSDR) lists a number of heavy elements of concern, such as arsenic, cadmium, chromium, lead, mercury, nickel, vanadium, and zinc (among over 15 others). The ATSDR lists four heavy elements in the top 10 on its "Substance Priority List": 1, arsenic; 2, lead; 3, mercury; and 7, cadmium.

Arsenic in Drinking Water

Arsenic is number one on the "Substance Priority List" of the U.S. Agency for Toxic Substances and Disease Registry. Various compounds containing this element are used for wood preservation, in pesticides, and as a component in electronic devices.

Arsenic is also found in several naturally occurring minerals and so can find its way into water supplies.

One well-documented example of arsenic in water supplies is in the West Bengal region of India and the neighboring country of Bangladesh. Unfortunately the contamination went unnoticed for many years. People got their drinking water from tube wells drilled in the 1970s. The wells were installed by the United Nations Children's Fund (UNICEF) to provide safe drinking water for a population that had traditionally taken its water from contaminated streams, rivers, and ponds and which had suffered accordingly from water-borne diseases such as gastroenteritis, typhoid, and cholera. Eventually, 5 million such wells were drilled, and they indeed served the purpose of bringing cholera under control. In its place, however, they unknowingly brought low-level arsenic poisoning to large areas of Bangladesh.

Tube wells are 5 cm in diameter and tap the abundant ground water about 200 meters below the surface. A few had been installed in Bangladesh in the 1930s. Those villages that had installed them showed a decrease in illness, especially among children. UNICEF continued to support the program after Bangladesh independence, and by 1997 it could report that it had already surpassed its goal of providing 80% of the population in those regions with "safe" water. Such had been the success of the program that many villagers installed private wells. Then doctors began to notice a worrying increase in skin cancer and suspected that arsenic was the cause. Analysis of the water from the wells showed that more than 20 million people were drinking water containing arsenic at the 50 ppb level, and as many as 5 million people were drinking water containing 300 ppb arsenic. (The U.S. EPA has set the safe level for arsenic in drinking water at 10 ppb.)

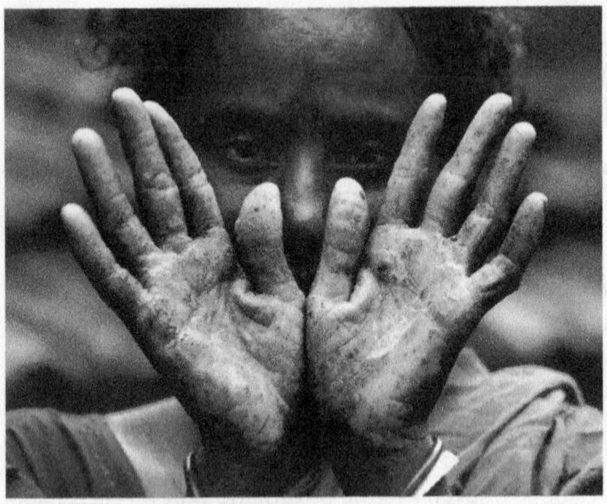

Sucheta Das/Corbis

FIGURE 20.11 **A Bangladesh villager shows his hands affected by arsenic contamination in the water supply.**

In 1997, the Bangladesh government instituted a Rapid Action Program that focused on a group of villages where contamination was most severe. Almost two thirds of the tube wells in these villages were delivering water with arsenic in excess of 100 ppb. A team from the Dhaka Community Hospital visited 18 affected areas and examined 2000 adults and children; they concluded that more than half had skin lesions due to arsenic (Figure 20.11).

So what can the people of this region do? One answer is to dig wells that go deeper than 200 meters or shallower wells that reach down only 20 meters. In this way, the contaminated layer of ground water can be avoided. Once people have access to uncontaminated water, the arsenic in their bodies is quickly lost.

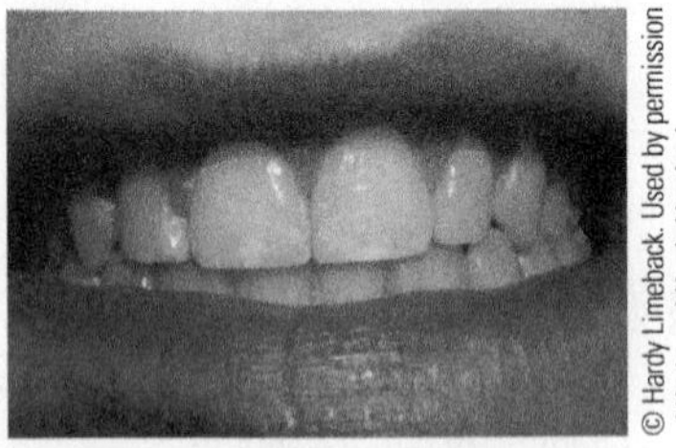

© Hardy Limeback. Used by permission of Kevin and Hardy Limeback

FIGURE 20.12 **Fluorosis.** Here, the teeth have whitish patches, indicating mild fluorosis. Teeth and bones are hydroxyapatite, $Ca_5(OH)(PO_4)_3$. If you drink water with a high F^- ion concentration, the OH^- ion in apatite can be replaced by the F^- ion. This can have the beneficial effect of hardening the surface of teeth. However, when used in excess, fluoride ion can lead to mottling, and in very high concentrations, skeletal deformities can result.

When drinking water is contaminated the problem can be costly to solve. For example, when half a million people in New Mexico were exposed to high arsenic levels in their drinking water, action was taken, but at a cost of $100 million. Taking similar action in Bangladesh would be beyond the ability of that country to pay. Even replacing a shallow well with one that draws water from the lower, safer, water table costs $1000. The alternative is to remove the arsenic from the water. Simple and inexpensive devices have been designed by chemists for doing this, such as passing the water through layers of sand, pieces of iron, and charcoal. The inorganic arsenic, which is present as arsenite ions, AsO_3^{3-}, sticks to the pieces of iron while the organic forms of arsenic are absorbed into the charcoal.

Fluoride in Drinking Water

It is generally acknowledged that a little fluoride in drinking water strengthens tooth enamel and prevents decay, and to this end many public water supplies are fluoridated to a level of 1 ppm. Nevertheless, there are dangers in drinking water that has much higher levels, and in some localities the level of fluoride is naturally high. Humans, as well as animals, can be affected and suffer from *fluorosis* (Figure 20.12), which is a hardening of the bones leading to a deformed skeleton. In certain parts of India, such as the Punjab, the condition is endemic, especially where villagers drink water from wells with high levels of fluoride, up to 15 ppm. About 25 million Indians suffer a mild form of fluorosis, with many thousands showing skeletal deformities.

REVIEW & CHECK FOR SECTION 20-2

1. Various reagents are added to water supplies to kill pathogens and make the water safe to drink. Among the substances listed below, which does not serve that function?

   (a) Cl_2 (b) O_3 (c) $Ca(ClO)_2$ (d) $Al_2(SO_4)_3$

2. Which of the following statements is not correct?

   (a) Phosphates enhance the growth of algae in surface water.

   (b) Melting of the polar ice cap will result in a rise in sea levels.

   (c) Heavy metal toxicity can result from the presence of metal compounds of lead, cadmium, and mercury in water supplies.

   (d) Reverse osmosis is a good way to effect desalination.

20-3 Energy

Look around you—energy is involved in anything that is moving or emitting light, sound, or heat. Heating and lighting your home, propelling your automobile, powering your laptop computer—all are commonplace examples in which energy is used, and all are, at their origin, primarily based on chemical processes. In this section, we examine how chemistry is fundamental to understanding and addressing current energy issues.

Supply and Demand: The Balance Sheet on Energy

We take for granted that energy is available and that it will always be there to use. But will it? Richard Smalley (1943–2005), a chemist and Nobel Prize winner, stated that among the top 10 problems humanity will face over the next 50 years, the energy supply ranks as number one. What is the source of this prediction? Information such as the following is often quoted in the popular press:

- Global demand for energy has almost tripled in the past 40 years and may triple again in the next 50 years. Most of the demand comes from industrialized nations, but most of the increase is coming from developing countries.
- In 2011 fossil fuels accounted for 80% of the total energy used in the United States (Figure 20.13). (Of this total, petroleum accounts for 35%, coal 20%, and natural gas 25%.) Nuclear, biomass, and hydroelectric power contribute about 17% of the total energy budget. The remaining 3% derives from solar, wind, and geothermal energy-generating facilities.
- With only about 5% of the world's population, the United States consumes over 20% of all the energy used in the world. This usage is equivalent to the consumption of 7 gallons of oil or 70 pounds of coal per person per day.

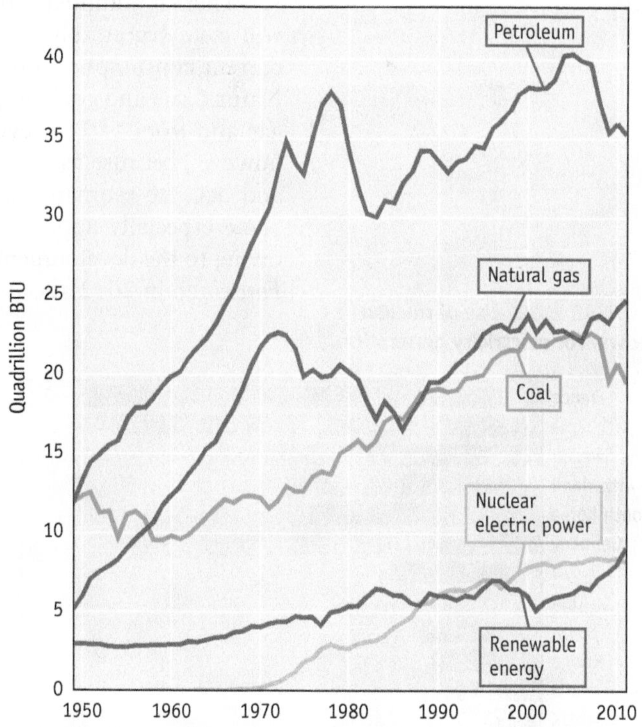

FIGURE 20.13 Changes in U.S. energy usage by source, 1949–2011. The vertical axis is in units of BTU (units of energy called British thermal units). Graph taken from www.eia.gov. The U.S. Energy Information Administration (EIA) is an excellent source of energy information.

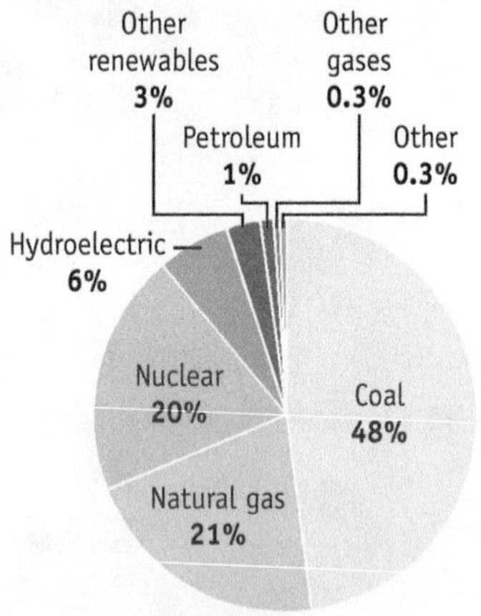

FIGURE 20.14 Fuel used in the electric power industry in the United States, 2008. Source: U.S. Energy Information Administration, *Electric Power Annual* (2010) (www.eia.doe.gov/).

- China and India, growing economic powerhouses, are increasing their energy usage by about 8% per year. In 2007, China passed the United States as the number one emitter of greenhouse gases in the world.

Two basic issues, *energy resources* and *energy usage*, instantly leap out from these statistics and form the basis for this discussion of energy.

Energy Resources

The world is hugely dependent on fossil fuels as a source of energy. Almost 70% of the electricity in the United States is generated using fossil fuels, mostly coal and natural gas (Figure 20.14), and about 80% of the energy consumed for all purposes is derived from fossil fuels.

Why is there such a dominance of fossil fuels on the resource side of the equation? An obvious reason is that energy derived from burning fossil fuels is cheaper than energy from other sources. In addition, societies have made an immense investment in the infrastructure needed to distribute and use this energy. Power plants using coal or natural gas cannot be converted readily to accommodate another fuel. The infrastructure for the distribution of energy—gas pipelines, gasoline dispensing for cars, and the grid distributing electricity to users—is already in place. The system works well.

Because the system using fossil fuels works well, why do we worry about using fossil fuels? One major problem is that fossil fuels are *nonrenewable energy sources*. Nonrenewable sources are those for which the energy source is used and not concurrently replenished. Fossil fuels are the obvious example, and nuclear energy is in this category as well. Conversely, energy sources that involve using the Sun's energy are examples of *renewable resources*. These include solar energy and energy derived from wind, biomass, and moving water. Likewise, geothermal energy is a renewable resource.

There is a limited supply of fossil fuels, so we must ask how long our fossil fuels will last. Regrettably, there is not an exact answer. One estimate suggests that at current consumption rates the world's oil reserves will be depleted in 30–80 years. Natural gas and coal supplies are projected to last longer: 60–200 years for natural gas and from 150 to several hundred years for coal. These numbers are uncertain, however, because assumptions must be made about the future rate of consumption and because estimates are based on guesses regarding reserves. The latter has become especially apparent recently because of the rapid rise in natural gas supply owing to the development of hydraulic fracturing or "fracking" (see *A Closer Look: Fracking*). In 2012 about 1.1 million wells were producing oil and gas in the United States. With the development of hydraulic fracturing, it is estimated that 25,000 new oil and natural gas wells will be drilled in the near future.

FIGURE 20.15 Use of nuclear power for electricity generation.

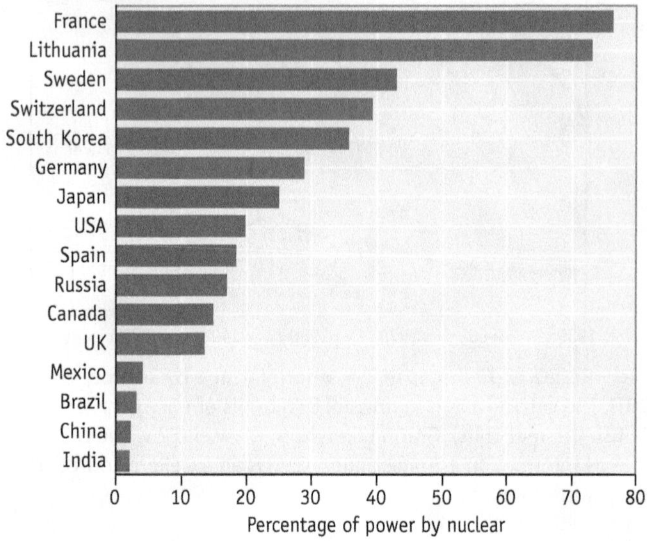

We cannot ignore the fact that a change away from fossil fuels must occur someday. As supply diminishes and demand increases, expansion to other fuel types will inevitably occur. Increased cost of energy based on fossil fuels will encourage these changes. The technologies to facilitate change, and the answers regarding which alternative fuel types will be the most efficient and cost-effective, can be aided by research in chemistry.

One energy source that has been exploited extensively in some countries is nuclear power, and several European countries generate more than 40% of their electricity this way (Figure 20.15). Certain countries (such as Iceland and New Zealand) are also able to exploit geothermal power as an energy source, and Germany and Spain plan on meeting 25% of their electrical energy needs with wind power by the year 2020.

A CLOSER LOOK Fracking

In April 2012 *Chemical & Engineering News* said that "The U.S. is on a natural gas binge. In a mere half-dozen years, natural gas production and prices have been transformed. Thanks to a new unconventional natural gas technology—hydraulic fracturing—the nation has seen natural gas production go from a trickle to a flood."

What is hydraulic fracturing or "fracking" as it is often called? It is a technique to release gas and oil from geological formations that may contain hydrocarbons but that have been previously impervious to standard drilling techniques. In fracking, several million gallons of water and other fluids and sand are forced under pressure into a shale formation. This mixture opens fissures in the formation and allows the oil and gas to escape.

One problem with fracking is that other organic compounds, sulfur dioxide, and other waste materials come to the surface as well. Another is that enormous amounts of water are required. And finally, although methane is usually the desired product, some of it escapes capture and diffuses to the troposphere where it contributes significantly to the greenhouse effect.

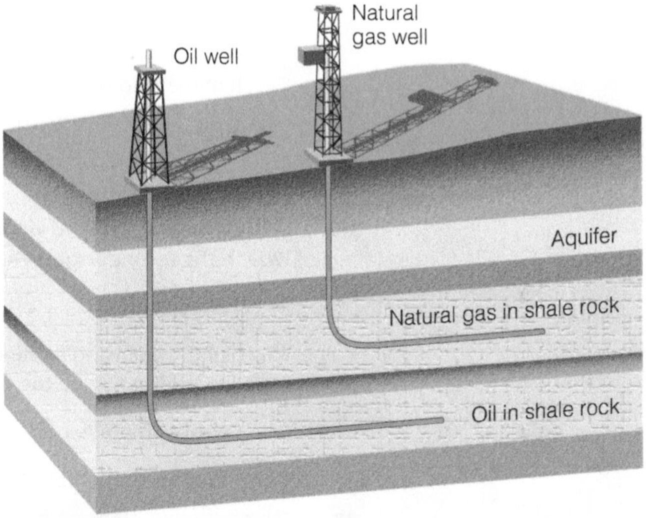

Fracking. A mixture of water, other liquids, and sand is injected into a geological formation that may contain oil and gas (such as gas-rich shale). The fracking mixture opens fissures in the formation and gas and oil are released.

Reference: J. Johnson, "Methane: A New 'Fracking' Fiasco," *Chemical & Engineering News*, April 16, 2012, page 34.

Energy Usage

Energy usage is related to the degree to which a country has industrialized: the more industrialized a country, the more energy is used on a per capita basis (Figure 20.16). This means that, as developing nations become more industrialized, personal energy usage worldwide will surely increase proportionally. There has been rapid growth in energy usage over the past two decades, and it is predicted there will be continued rapid growth in the next half-century.

Conservation is one way to alter energy consumption. This can mean consciously using less energy (such as driving less, turning off lights when not in use, and turning the thermostat down [for heating] or up [for cooling]). It can also mean using energy more efficiently. Some examples of more efficient energy use are:

- Recycling aluminum is now a common practice because it requires only one third of the energy needed to produce the metal from its ore.
- Light-emitting diodes (LEDs) are now used in streetlights, and compact fluorescent lights and LEDs are finding wider use in the home. Both use a fraction of the energy required by incandescent bulbs (in which only 5% of the energy used is delivered in the form of light; the remaining 95% is wasted as heat).
- Hybrid cars offer up to twice the gas mileage as conventional cars.
- Many newer appliances (from refrigerators to air conditioners) are designed to use less energy per delivered output.

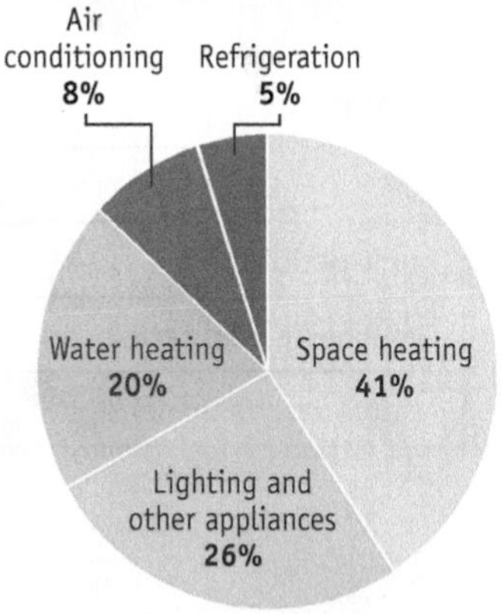

FIGURE 20.16 **Energy use in homes in the United States, 2005.** Source: U.S. Energy Information Administration, *Residential Energy Consumption Survey* (2005) (www.eia.doe.gov/).

One of the exciting areas of current research in chemistry relating to energy conservation focuses on superconductivity. Superconductors are materials that, at temperatures of 30–150 K, offer virtually no resistance to electrical conductivity (◀ Chapter 3, *Applying Chemical Principles*). When an electric current passes through a typical conductor such as a copper wire, some of the energy is lost as heat. As a result, there is substantial energy loss in power transmission lines. Substituting a superconducting wire for copper has the potential to greatly decrease this loss, so the search is on for materials that act as superconductors at moderate temperatures.

REVIEW & CHECK FOR SECTION 20-3

1. Which of the following is a renewable energy resource?
   (a) nuclear fusion
   (b) hydroelectric power
   (c) natural gas
   (d) coal
2. In the United States (and worldwide), fossil fuels provide the larger source of energy. What is the second largest energy source?
   (a) hydroelectric (b) solar (c) nuclear (d) geothermal
3. Which of the following lighting sources is the most energy efficient? (You may need to seek this information on the web.)
   (a) Light-emitting diodes
   (b) Incandescent lightbulbs
   (c) Fluorescent lights
   (d) Candles

20-4 Fossil Fuels

Fossil fuels originate from organic matter that was trapped under the Earth's surface for many millennia. Due to the particular combination of temperature, pressure, and available oxygen, the decomposition of organic matter resulted in the hydrocarbons we extract and use today: coal, crude oil, and natural gas—the solid, liquid, and gaseous forms of fossil fuels, respectively.

Table 20.3 Energy Released by Combustion of Fossil Fuels

SUBSTANCE	ENERGY RELEASED (kJ/g)
Coal	29–37
Crude petroleum	43
Gasoline (refined petroleum)	47
Natural gas (methane)	50

Fossil fuels are simple to use and are relatively inexpensive, compared with the current cost requirements of other sources for the equivalent amount of energy. To use the energy stored in fossil fuels, these materials are burned. The combustion process, when it goes to completion, produces CO_2 and H_2O. The thermal energy is converted to mechanical and sometimes then to electrical energy.

The hydrocarbons of fossil fuels have varying ratios of carbon to hydrogen, and their energy output from burning (Table 20.3) is related to that ratio. You can analyze this relationship using data on enthalpies of formation and by looking at the combustion of a fuel that is 100% carbon and another that is 100% hydrogen. The oxidation of 1.0 mol (12.01 g) of pure carbon produces 393.5 kJ of energy or 32.8 kJ/g.

$$C(s) + O_2(g) \rightarrow CO_2(g)$$

$$\Delta_r H° = -393.5 \text{ kJ/mol-rxn or } -32.8 \text{ kJ/g C}$$

Burning hydrogen to form water is much more exothermic on a per-gram basis, with about 120 kJ evolved per gram of hydrogen consumed.

$$H_2(g) + \tfrac{1}{2} O_2(g) \rightarrow H_2O(g)$$

$$\Delta_r H° = -241.8 \text{ kJ/mol-rxn or } -119.9 \text{ kJ/g } H_2$$

Coal is mostly carbon, so the amount of heat transferred is similar to that of pure carbon. In contrast, methane is 25% hydrogen (by mass), and the higher molecular weight hydrocarbons in petroleum and products refined from petroleum average 16–17% hydrogen content. Therefore, the heat transferred on a per-gram basis is greater than that of pure carbon but less than that of hydrogen itself.

While the basic chemical principles for extracting energy from fossil fuels are simple, complications arise in practice. Let us look at each of these fuels in turn.

Table 20.4 Types of Coal

Type	Consistency	Sulfur Content	Energy Released (kJ/g)
Lignite	Very soft	Very low	28–30
Bituminous coal	Soft	High	29–37
Anthracite	Hard	Low	36–37

Coal

The solid rock-like substance we call *coal* began to form almost 290 million years ago. Decomposition of plant matter occurred to a sufficient extent that the primary component of coal is carbon. Describing coal simply as carbon is a simplification, however, because samples of coal vary considerably in their composition and characteristics. Carbon content may range from 60% to 95%, with variable amounts of hydrogen, oxygen, sulfur, and nitrogen present in various forms.

Sulfur, a common constituent in some coals, was incorporated into the mixture partly from decaying plants and partly from hydrogen sulfide, H_2S, the waste product from certain bacteria. In addition, coal may contain traces of many other elements, including some that are toxic (such as arsenic, mercury, cadmium, and lead) or radioactive (uranium and thorium).

When coal is burned, some of the impurities are dispersed into the air, and some end up in the ash that remains. In the United States, coal-fired power plants are responsible for over 70% of the emissions of SO_2 and 33% of mercury emissions into the environment. (Power plants in the United States emit about 50 tons of mercury per year; worldwide, about 5500 tons are emitted.) Sulfur dioxide reacts with water and oxygen in the atmosphere to form sulfuric acid, which contributes (along with nitric acid) to *acid rain.*

$$2\ SO_2(g) + O_2(g) \rightarrow 2\ SO_3(g)$$

$$SO_3(g) + H_2O(\ell) \rightarrow H_2SO_4(aq)$$

Because these acids are harmful to the environment, legislation limits the extent of sulfur dioxide emissions from coal-fired plants. The combustion gases are passed through a water spray with chemicals such as limestone (calcium carbonate) to form solids that can be removed:

$$2\ SO_2(g) + 2\ CaCO_3(s) + O_2(g) \rightarrow 2\ CaSO_4(s) + 2\ CO_2(g)$$

However, these devices are expensive, and they increase the cost of the energy produced from these facilities.

There are three categories of coal (Table 20.4 and Figure 20.17). *Anthracite,* or hard coal, is the highest-quality coal. Among the forms of coal, anthracite provides the largest amount of energy per gram and has a low sulfur content. Unfortunately, anthracite coal is fairly uncommon, with only 2% of the U.S. coal reserves occurring in this form. *Bituminous coal,* also referred to as *soft coal,* accounts for about 45% of the U.S. coal reserves and is the coal most widely used in electric power generation. Soft coal typically has the highest sulfur content. *Lignite,* also called brown coal because of its paler color, is geologically the "youngest" form of coal. It releases a smaller amount of energy per gram than the other forms of coal, often contains a significant amount of water, and is the least satisfactory as a fuel.

Heating coal in the absence of air converts it to coke, which is almost pure carbon and is an excellent fuel. In the process of coke formation, a variety of organic compounds are driven off. These are used as raw materials in the chemical industry to produce polymers, pharmaceuticals, synthetic fabrics, waxes, tar, and numerous other products.

Technology to convert coal into gaseous fuels (coal gasification) or liquid fuels (liquefaction) is well known,

FIGURE 20.17 **Bituminous coal being extracted from a strip mine in Montana.**

Courtesy of BLM Wyoming

FIGURE 20.18 Automobile powered by natural gas.

but the extent to which these processes are carried out is limited by cost. These processes provide fuels that burn more cleanly than coal, but 30–40% of the available energy is lost in the process. However, as petroleum and natural gas reserves dwindle and the costs of these fuels increase, liquid and gaseous fuels derived from coal are likely to become more important.

Methane/Natural Gas

Natural gas is found deep under the Earth's surface. There is some debate as to how the gas formed, but one major theory is that it was produced by bacteria decomposing organic matter in an anaerobic environment (in which no O_2 is present). The major component of natural gas (70–95%) is methane (CH_4). Lesser quantities of gases such as ethane (C_2H_6), propane (C_3H_8), and butane (C_4H_{10}) may also be present, along with other gases including N_2, He, CO_2, and H_2S. The impurities and higher-molecular-weight components of natural gas are separated out during the refining process, so the gas piped into our homes is primarily methane.

Natural gas emits fewer pollutants when burned and produces relatively more energy than other fossil fuels. For this reason it is gaining increased use in passenger cars and in municipal vehicles such as buses (Figure 20.18). It can be transported by pipelines over land and piped into buildings such as your home, where it is used to heat ambient air, and to heat water for washing, bathing, and cooking. It is also a popular choice for new electrical power plants. Gas-fired power plants emit 40% less carbon dioxide than coal-burning plants and, in contrast to coal-fired power plants, there is no mercury pollution. In addition, the disposal of the solids left from coal combustion (called *fly ash*) is not an issue.

Just as importantly, prices of natural gas are less than half of what they were before 2010, in part because of the discovery of new sources. Among the new processes for obtaining methane is hydraulic fracturing or "fracking" (see *A Closer Look: Fracking*).

Finally, a potential methane source is methane hydrate (see *A Closer Look: Methane Hydrates: Opportunities and Problems*). In 1970, oceanographers drilling into the seabed off the coast of South Carolina pulled up samples of a whitish solid that fizzed and oozed when it was removed from the drill casing. They quickly realized it was methane hydrate. Since this original discovery, methane hydrate has been found in many parts of the oceans as well as under permafrost in the Arctic. It is estimated that 1.5×10^{13} tons of methane hydrate are buried under the sea floor around the world. In fact, the energy available from this source may surpass that of all the other known fossil fuel reserves by as much as a factor of 2! Clearly, this is a potential source of an important fuel in the future.

Petroleum

Petroleum, a complicated mixture of hydrocarbons whose molar masses range from low to very high, is often found in porous rock formations that are bounded by impermeable rock (see *A Closer Look: Petroleum Chemistry*, page 785). The hydrocarbons may have anywhere from one to 20 or more carbon atoms in their structures, and compounds containing sulfur, nitrogen, and oxygen may also be present, usually in small amounts.

Petroleum goes through extensive processing at refineries to separate the various components and convert less valuable compounds into more valuable ones. Nearly

A CLOSER LOOK Methane Hydrates: Opportunities and Problems

Cold water under pressure begins to form complex solid structures at temperatures around 273 K. These are networks of hydrogen-bonded water molecules with large, open cavities. If a small "guest" molecule of the right size is present, however, it can be trapped in the cavities, and the network does not collapse to form the usual ice structure. This phenomenon is most often observed when cold water is saturated with methane, and the result is methane hydrate (Figure A).

Methane hydrates have been known for years, but interest in them has increased because vast deposits were recently discovered deep within sediments on the floor of the oceans and in Arctic permafrost. It is estimated that global methane hydrate deposits contain approximately 10^{13} tons of carbon, or about twice the combined amount in all known reserves of coal, oil, and natural gas. Methane hydrates are also efficient energy storehouses because a cubic meter of hydrate traps about 160 cubic meters of methane gas.

If methane is to be captured from hydrates and used as a fuel, there are difficult problems to solve. Perhaps the greatest is how to bring commercially useful quantities to the surface from deep in the ocean. But, in 2013, the Japanese government announced it had successfully done so. They will doubtless pursue this breakthrough because it is estimated that the waters surrounding Japan harbor enough methane hydrate to serve Japan's energy needs for 100 years. Clearly other countries are making similar efforts. For example, in Alaska's North Slope there are believed to be recoverable deposits of 2400 billion cubic meters of methane, roughly the equivalent of four years of U.S. natural gas production, and there are extensive deposits in other places in the world.

Another problem with exploiting methane hydrate deposits is the possibility of a large, uncontrolled release of the gas (which has been called the "clathrate gun"). As described in this chapter, methane is a very effective greenhouse gas, so the release of a significant quantity into the atmosphere could damage the Earth's climate. (Indeed, some believe a massive release of methane from hydrates about 55 million years ago led to significant global warming.)

In May 2010 methane hydrates may have led to an environmental catastrophe. The Deepwater Horizon rig used for drilling for oil in very deep water in the Gulf of Mexico was destroyed by a fire triggered by a methane explosion. There is a strong suggestion that the ultimate cause may have been the explosive release of the gas from methane hydrates under the sea bed.

A general article on methane hydrates is: E. Suess, G. Bohrmann, J. Greinert, and E. Lausch, *Scientific American*, November 1999, pp. 76–83.

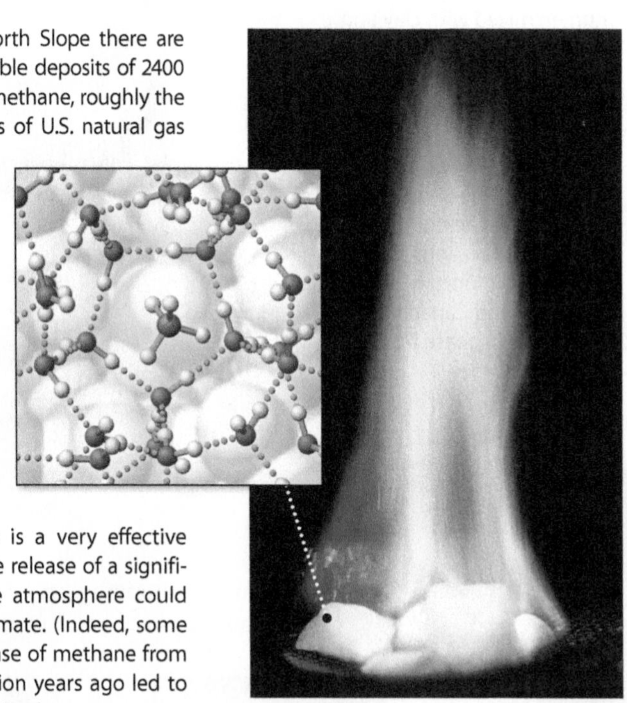

FIGURE A **Methane hydrate.** When a sample is brought to the surface from the depths of the ocean, the methane oozes out of the solid, and the gas readily burns. The structure of the solid methane hydrate consists of methane molecules trapped in a lattice of water molecules. The lattice shown here is a common structural unit of a more complex structure. Each point of the lattice shown here is an O atom of an H_2O molecule. The edges consist of an O—H—O series of atoms connected by a hydrogen bond and covalent bond. (Other, more complex structural units are known.) Such structures are often called "clathrates."

85% of the crude petroleum pumped from the ground ends up being used as a fuel, either for transportation (gasoline and diesel fuel) or for heating (fuel oils).

Another source of fossil fuels is oil from tar sands. **Tar sands** (also called **oil sands**) contain a very viscous organic liquid called *bitumen*. This is chemically similar to the highest-molecular-weight fraction obtained by distillation of crude oil. The largest source of tar sands in the world is in Alberta, Canada (the Athabasca sands, Figure 20.19), followed closely by those in Venezuela. Resources approaching 3.5 trillion barrels of oil—twice the world's known reserves of petroleum—are estimated in these two locations. The United States imports more oil from Canada than any other country (about 1 million barrels per day), and most of this is from the Athabasca oil sands.

Extracting the oil from sands is quite costly. Essentially, the sands must be mined and then mixed with hot water or steam to extract the bitumen. Once extraction is completed, the mined land must be restored (reclaimed), which adds to the cost of the process. Because most of the Canadian oil sands are located in dry

FIGURE 20.19 **Tar sands.** Tar sands are deposits of oil-rich bitumen mixed with clay and sand embedded in rocks often buried beneath the surface. Several tons of top soil must be removed for each barrel of bitumen, and large open-pit mines result. The largest tar sands reserves are in Alberta, Canada. The tar sands are an increasingly important source of petroleum, and Canada is planning a large increase in production.

areas, obtaining an adequate water supply for extraction is a significant constraint on increased production.

REVIEW & CHECK FOR SECTION 20-4

1. Which of the following fuels provides the greatest amount of energy per gram?

   (a) CH_4 (b) C_8H_{18} (c) coal (d) H_2

2. Which of the following statements is not correct?

   (a) Mercury is a common impurity in coal.

   (b) Burning of coal is a source of sulfur dioxide air pollution.

   (c) Oxygen gas is a component in some sources of natural gas.

   (d) Natural gas is preferred over coal for electricity generation.

3. Which of the following is a renewable energy resource?

   (a) biofuels (b) natural gas (c) coal (d) nuclear fission

20-5 Alternative Sources of Energy

At the present time the world economy is built on the use of fossil fuels. However, there will surely be a time when these fuels will become scarce, so chemists and engineers are looking for alternatives.

Fuel Cells

In the United States in 2010, 48% of electricity came from coal-fired power plants and 21% from natural gas units. The heat of combustion from these fuels is used to produce high-pressure steam, which spins a turbine in a generator. Unfortunately, not all of the energy from the combustion can be converted to usable work. Some of the energy stored in the chemical bonds of a fuel is transferred as heat to the surroundings, making this an inherently inefficient process. The efficiency is about 35–40% for a coal-fired steam turbine and 50–55% for the newer natural gas turbines.

A much more efficient process is possible if electrons, the carriers of electricity, could be generated directly from the chemical bonds themselves, rather than going

A CLOSER LOOK Petroleum Chemistry

Much of the world's current technology relies on petroleum. Burning fuels derived from petroleum provides by far the largest amount of energy in the industrial world. Petroleum and natural gas are also the chemical raw materials used in the manufacture of many plastics, pharmaceuticals, and a vast array of other compounds.

The petroleum that is pumped out of the ground is a complex mixture whose composition varies greatly, depending on its source. The primary components of petroleum are always alkanes (hydrocarbons with the formula C_nH_{2n+2}), but, to varying degrees, nitrogen- and sulfur-containing compounds are also present. Aromatic compounds (such as benzene, C_6H_6) are present as well, but more reactive compounds with double and triple carbon–carbon bonds such as alkenes and alkynes are not.

©iStockphoto.com/Olivier Lantzendörffer

A modern petrochemical plant.

An early step in the petroleum refining process is distillation, in which the crude mixture is separated into a series of fractions based on boiling point: first a gaseous fraction (mostly alkanes with one to four carbon atoms; this fraction is often burned off), and then gasoline, kerosene, and fuel oils. After distillation, considerable material, in the form of a semisolid, tar-like residue, remains.

The petrochemical industry seeks to maximize the amounts of the higher-valued fractions of petroleum produced and to make specific compounds for which a particular need exists. This means carrying out chemical reactions involving the raw materials on a huge scale. One process to which petroleum is subjected is known as *cracking*. At very high temperatures, bond breaking or "cracking" can occur, and hydrocarbons with longer carbon chains fragment into smaller molecular units. These reactions are carried out in the presence of a wide array of catalysts, materials that speed up reactions and direct them toward specific products. Among the important products of cracking is ethylene (C_2H_4), which serves as the raw material for the formation of materials such as polyethylene. Cracking also produces other reactive hydrocarbons and gaseous hydrogen, both widely used raw materials.

Other important reactions involving petroleum are run at elevated temperatures and in the presence of specific catalysts. Such reactions include *isomerization* reactions, in which the carbon skeleton of an alkane rearranges to form a new isomeric species, and *reformation* processes, in which alkanes become compounds with carbon rings. Each process is directed toward achieving a specific goal, such as increasing the proportion of branched-chain hydrocarbons in gasoline to obtain higher octane ratings. A great amount of chemical research has gone into developing and understanding these highly specialized processes.

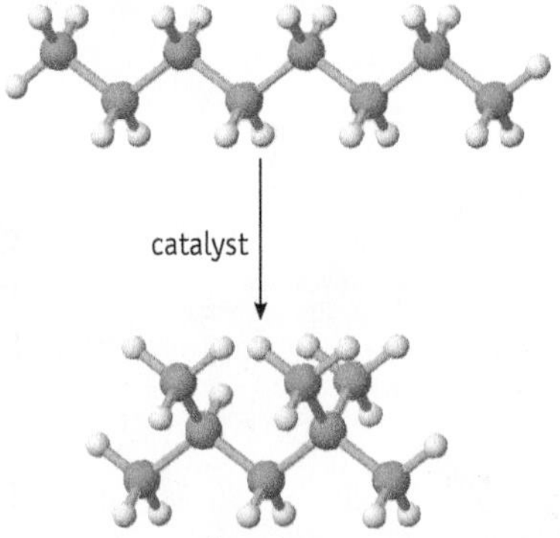

Producing gasoline. Branched hydrocarbons have a higher octane rating in gasoline. Therefore, an important process in producing gasoline is the isomerization of octane to a branched hydrocarbon such as isooctane, 2,2,4-trimethylpentane.

through an energy conversion process from heat to mechanical work to electricity. Fuel cell technology makes this direct conversion to electricity possible.

The electrochemistry of fuel cells was described in Section 19-3, and you saw that they are similar to batteries, except that fuel is supplied from an external source (Figure 20.20). They are more efficient than combustion-based energy production, with up to 60% energy conversion.

The net reaction is the oxidation of the fuel and the consumption of the oxidizing agent. Because the fuel and the oxidant never come directly in contact with each other, there is no combustion and thus minimal loss of energy as heat. The energy evolved in the reaction is converted directly to electricity.

Hydrogen fuel cells have been used on the Space Shuttle and in some prototype automobiles and buses. The overall reaction in these fuel cells is the combination of hydrogen and oxygen to form water. Hydrocarbon-based fuels such as methanol (CH_3OH) are also candidates for use as the fuel in fuel cells, where the net reaction in the cell is

$$CH_3OH(\ell) + {}^3/_2\, O_2(g) \rightarrow CO_2(g) + 2\, H_2O(\ell)$$

$$\Delta_r H° = -727 \text{ kJ/mol-rxn or } -23 \text{ kJ/g } CH_3OH$$

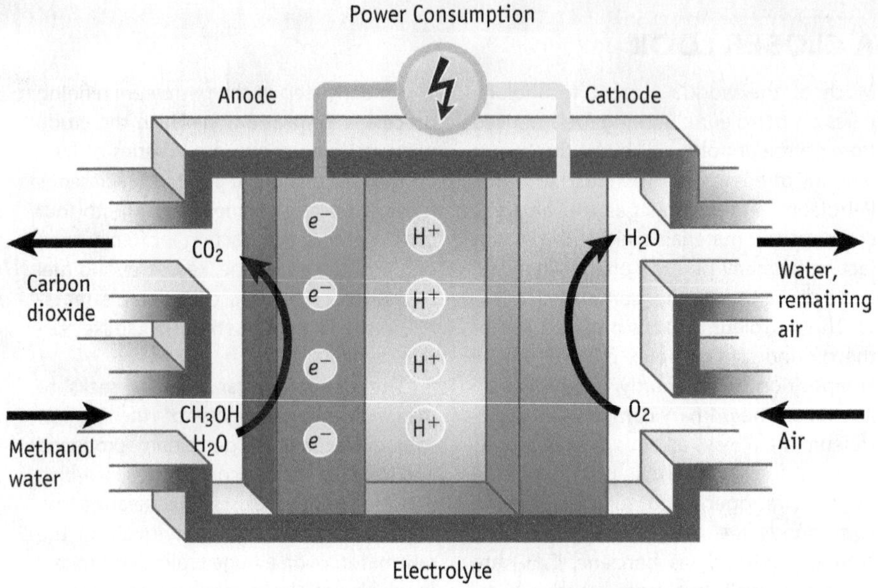

FIGURE 20.20 Fuel cell. This fuel cell uses methanol and oxygen as reactants (see Section 19-3 for the electrochemistry of fuel cells).

Using enthalpies of formation data (◀ Section 5-7), you can confirm that the energy generated from this reaction is 727 kJ/mol-rxn (or 23 kJ/g) of liquid methanol. That is equivalent to 200 watt-hours (W-h) of energy per mole of methanol (1 W =1 J/s), or 5.0 kW-h per liter of methanol.

Hydrogen

Predictions about the diminished supply of fossil fuels have led to speculation about alternative fuels, and hydrogen has been widely suggested as a possible choice. The term *hydrogen economy* has been used to describe the combined processes of producing, storing, and using hydrogen as a fuel. As is the case with fuel cells, the hydrogen economy does not rely on a new energy resource; it merely provides a different way to use existing resources.

There are reasons to consider hydrogen an attractive option. Oxidation of hydrogen yields almost three times as much energy per gram as the oxidation of fossil fuels. Comparing the combustion of hydrogen with that of propane, a fuel used in some cars, you can calculate that H_2 produces about 2.6 times more energy per gram than propane.

$$H_2(g) + \frac{1}{2}\,O_2(g) \rightarrow H_2O(g)$$

$$\Delta_r H° = -241.83 \text{ kJ/mol-rxn or } -119.95 \text{ kJ/g } H_2$$

$$C_3H_8(g) + 5\,O_2(g) \rightarrow 3\,CO_2(g) + 4\,H_2O(g)$$

$$\Delta_r H° = -2043.15 \text{ kJ/mol-rxn or } -46.37 \text{ kJ/g } C_3H_8$$

Another advantage of using hydrogen instead of a hydrocarbon fuel is that the only product of H_2 oxidation is H_2O.

Some have proposed that hydrogen might be able to replace gasoline in automobiles and natural gas to heat homes and even that it could be used as a fuel to generate electricity or to run industrial processes. Before this can happen, however, there are many practical problems to be solved, including the following as-yet-unmet needs:

- An inexpensive method of producing hydrogen
- A practical means of storing hydrogen
- A distribution system (hydrogen refueling stations)

Perhaps the most serious problem is the task of producing hydrogen. Hydrogen is abundant on Earth, but not as the free element. Thus, elemental hydrogen has to be obtained from its compounds. Currently, most hydrogen is produced industrially from the reaction of natural gas and water by *steam reforming* at high temperature (Figure 20.21).

Steam reforming $CH_4(g) + H_2O(g) \rightarrow 3\ H_2(g) + CO(g)$

$$\Delta_r H° = +206.2 \text{ kJ/mol-rxn}$$

Hydrogen can also be obtained from the reaction of coal and water at high temperature (the so-called *water–gas reaction*).

Water–gas reaction $C(s) + H_2O(g) \rightarrow H_2(g) + CO(g)$

$$\Delta_r H° = +131.3 \text{ kJ/mol-rxn}$$

The Linde Group

FIGURE 20.21 An industrial steam reforming plant.

Both steam reforming and the water–gas reaction are highly endothermic, and both rely on use of a fossil fuel as a raw material. This, of course, makes no sense if the overriding goal is to replace fossil fuels. If the hydrogen economy is ever to take hold, the logical source of hydrogen is water.

$$H_2O(\ell) \rightarrow H_2(g) + \tfrac{1}{2}\ O_2(g)$$

$$\Delta_r H° = +285.83 \text{ kJ/mol-rxn}$$

The electrolysis of water provides hydrogen (▶ Section 21-3) but also requires considerable energy. The first law of thermodynamics tells us that we can get no more energy from the oxidation of hydrogen than we expended to obtain H_2 from H_2O. In fact, we cannot even reach this break-even point because some of the energy will inevitably be dispersed (◀ Chapter 18). Hence, the only way to obtain hydrogen from water in amounts that would be needed and in an economically favorable way is to use a cheap and abundant source of energy to drive this process. A logical candidate is solar energy, but, unfortunately, using solar energy in this way has yet to become practical. This is yet another problem for chemists and engineers to solve!

No matter how hydrogen is produced, it has to be delivered to vehicles and homes in a safe and practical manner. Again, many problems remain to be solved. European researchers have found that a tanker truck that can deliver 2400 kg of compressed natural gas (mostly methane) can deliver only 288 kg of H_2 at the same pressure. Although hydrogen oxidation delivers about 2.4 times more energy per gram (119.95 kJ/g) than methane, the tanker can carry about eight times more methane than H_2. That is, it will take more tanker trucks to deliver the hydrogen needed to power the same number of cars or homes running on hydrogen than those running on methane.

Biofuels

Biofuels now supply only about 2% of the fuel used worldwide for transportation, but some people predict that they may contribute much more to U.S. transportation needs by 2030. Biofuels include substances ranging from solids such as wood to bioethanol and biodiesel.

Gasoline sold today often contains ethanol, C_2H_5OH. If the ethanol is derived from fermentation of materials derived from biological sources, then it is sometimes referred to as **bioethanol**. In addition to being a fuel, ethanol improves the burning characteristics of gasoline. Every state in the United States now has available a blend of ethanol and gasoline, the most common being 10% ethanol and 90% petroleum-based fuels. (See *Case Study: The Fuel Controversy—Alcohol and Gasoline,* page 212.)

Ethanol can be made readily by fermentation of sugars derived from renewable resources such as corn, sugar cane, sugar beets, or agricultural residues. Ethanol can also be derived from cellulosic materials such as trees and grasses, but the process is more complicated and not now economically viable.

Brazil has made the production of ethanol from sugar cane a top priority. About 40% of the motor fuel sold in Brazil is ethanol, and most new cars sold in Brazil are "flex-fuel" cars that run on either gasoline or ethanol. The United States and Brazil produce 70% of the world's ethanol.

One significant problem with bioethanol is that the energy content of a liter of ethanol is only about two thirds that of a liter of gasoline (see Study Question 20.21). Unless the ethanol industry is subsidized, the cost of ethanol for transportation would be greater than the cost of using gasoline at current prices.

There are several points to be made about the use of ethanol as a fuel.

- Green plants use the Sun's energy to make biomass from CO_2 and H_2O by photosynthesis. The Sun is a renewable resource and so, in principle, is the ethanol derived from biomass.
- The process recycles CO_2. Plants use CO_2 to create biomass, which in turn is used to make ethanol. In the final step in this cycle, oxidation of ethanol returns CO_2 to the atmosphere.
- One serious issue concerning the use of corn-derived ethanol is the net energy balance. You have to consider the energy expended to run tractors and trucks, harvest corn, and make fertilizer, among other things, versus the energy available in the ethanol produced as the end product. Recent analyses and improvements in corn-to-ethanol technology seem to indicate more energy is available than is used in production, but not by much.

Biodiesel, promoted as an alternative to petroleum-based fuels used in diesel engines, is made from plant and animal oils (Figure 20.22). Chemically, biodiesel is a mixture of esters of long-chain fatty acids prepared from plant and animal fats and oils by *trans-esterification*. This is a reaction between an ester and an alcohol in which the —OR″ on the alcohol exchanges with the OR′ group of the ester (where R′ and R″ are organic groups):

$$\underset{\text{Ester}}{\mathrm{R{-}\overset{\overset{O}{\|}}{C}{-}}}\boxed{\mathrm{O{-}R' + H}}\underset{\text{Alcohol}}{\mathrm{{-}O{-}R''}} \longrightarrow \underset{\text{New ester}}{\mathrm{R{-}\overset{\overset{O}{\|}}{C}{-}O{-}R''}} + \underset{\text{New alcohol}}{\mathrm{R'OH}}$$

FIGURE 20.22 **The biodiesel bus.** Students at Dartmouth College (Hanover, New Hampshire) tour the United States each summer in their "Big Green Bus" to raise awareness of sustainable living and green technology. Their tour is in a bus converted to run on diesel fuel made from waste vegetable oil. When they need more fuel, they stop at fast food restaurants and use waste oil to produce more biodiesel fuel.

Fats and oils are esters, derived from glycerol [$HOCH_2CH(OH)CH_2OH$] and high-molar-mass organic acids with at least 12 carbon atoms in the chain. Common fatty acids found in fats and oils are

lauric acid	$CH_3(CH_2)_{10}CO_2H$
myristic acid	$CH_3(CH_2)_{12}CO_2H$
palmitic acid	$CH_3(CH_2)_{14}CO_2H$
stearic acid	$CH_3(CH_2)_{16}CO_2H$
oleic acid	$CH_3(CH_2)_7CH{=}CH(CH_2)_7CO_2H$

The reaction of fats and oils with methanol (in the presence of a catalyst to speed up the reaction) produces a mixture of the methyl esters of the fatty acids and glycerol.

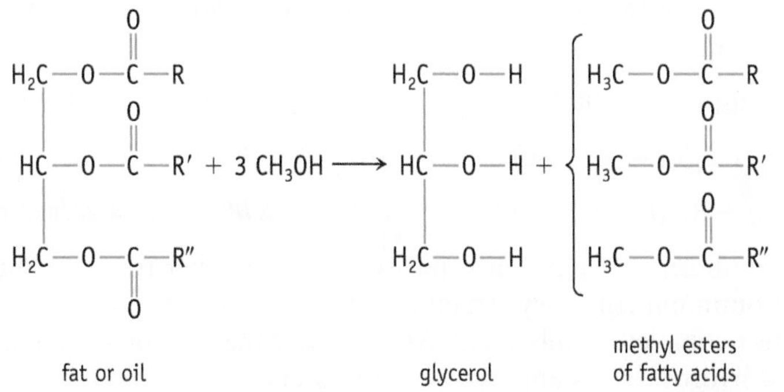

Glycerol, a by-product of the reaction, is a valuable commodity for the health care industry, so it is separated and sold. The mixture of esters that remains can be used directly as a fuel in existing diesel engines, or it can be blended with petroleum products. In the latter case, the fuel mixture is identified by a designation such as B20 (B = biodiesel, 20 refers to 20% by volume). Biodiesel has the advantage of being clean burning with fewer environmental problems associated with exhaust gases than for petroleum-based diesel fuels. In particular, there are no SO_2 emissions, one of the common problems associated with petroleum-based diesel fuels.

MARCEL ANTONISSE/AFP/ Getty Images

Biofuels for the airlines. Airlines have been testing biofuels. This plane uses a fuel that is a blend of 40% algae-based fuel and 60% regular aviation fuel. Source: *Chemical & Engineering News*, June 11, 2012, page 18.

REVIEW & CHECK FOR SECTION 20-5

1. Which of the following is not a limitation for the use of hydrogen as a fuel?
   (a) An inexpensive method of producing hydrogen
   (b) A practical means of storing hydrogen
   (c) Hydrogen is explosive
   (d) A distribution system (hydrogen refueling stations)
2. Which of the following statements is true?
   (a) Fuel cells are widely used in automobiles.
   (b) H_2 is readily available as a transportation fuel.
   (c) Petroleum is a mixture of hydrocarbons.
   (d) Methane hydrate can never be developed as a commercial energy resource.

20-6 Environmental Impact of Fossil Fuels

Learning Objectives: LO 6.8

We are a carbon-based society—about 85% of the energy used in the world today comes from fossil fuels. Because of this, Earth's inhabitants have added gaseous compounds based on carbon, nitrogen, and sulfur to the environment, and, as their energy needs increase, will likely continue to do so. These compounds include mainly CO_2 but also CH_4, NO_x, and SO_2, and it is these gases that have a significant impact on the environment.

Air Pollution

Local and international air pollution is one impact of the use of fossil fuels. The high temperature and pressure used in the combustion process in automobile engines have the unfortunate consequence of also causing a reaction between atmospheric nitrogen and oxygen that results in some NO formation. [The reaction between N_2 and O_2 is strongly disfavored at low temperatures, but it becomes more favorable at the high temperatures in an internal combustion engine (see Reaction type 3 in Table 18.1).] The NO can then react further with oxygen to produce nitrogen dioxide. This poisonous brown gas is further oxidized to form nitric acid, HNO_3, in the presence of water.

$$N_2(g) + O_2(g) \rightarrow 2\ NO(g) \qquad \Delta_r H° = 180.58\ kJ/mol\text{-}rxn$$

$$2\ NO(g) + O_2(g) \rightarrow 2\ NO_2(g) \qquad \Delta_r H° = -114.4\ kJ/mol\text{-}rxn$$

$$3\ NO_2(g) + H_2O(\ell) \rightarrow 2\ HNO_3(aq) + NO(g) \qquad \Delta_r H° = -71.4\ kJ/mol\text{-}rxn$$

Internal combustion engines in vehicles can add further to air pollution if they do not run at optimum efficiency. An engine that "burns lean" is not getting enough oxygen to effect complete combustion. As a result, exhaust emissions may also contain unburned hydrocarbons and carbon monoxide.

To some extent, the amounts of pollutants released can be limited by use of automobile catalytic converters. Catalytic converters are high-surface-area metal grids that are coated with platinum or palladium. These very expensive metals catalyze complete combustion, helping to combine oxygen in the air with unburned hydrocarbons or other by-products in the vehicle exhaust. As a result, the products of incomplete combustion can be converted to water and carbon dioxide (or other oxides). In addition, nitrogen oxides can be decomposed in a catalytic converter to N_2 and O_2. However, some nitric acid and NO_2 inevitably remain in automobile exhaust, and these compounds are major contributors to environmental pollution in the form of acid rain and smog. The brown acidic haze in highly congested cities such as Beijing, Los Angeles, Mexico City, and Houston results largely from automobile emissions. Such pollution problems have led to stricter emission standards for automobiles, and the development of low-emission or emission-free vehicles is a

A CLOSER LOOK

The Clean Air Act

The Clean Air Act was enacted by the U.S. Congress in 1970 and amended twice since then. The act requires the Environmental Protection Agency (EPA) to set standards for air quality (NAAQS, National Ambient Air Quality Standards) for six common pollutants: particulates, ozone (ground level), CO, sulfur oxides, nitrogen oxides, and lead. Standards are set at two levels, a primary standard being health related and a secondary standard pertaining to environmental and property damage. For example:

Lead, primary and secondary, cannot exceed 0.15 $\mu g/m^3$.

Ozone, primary and secondary, 0.075 ppm, annual fourth highest daily maximum 8-hour concentration averaged over 3 years.

The EPA monitors pollutant concentrations at sites throughout the country and determines whether or not the standards are attained. If standards are not met, states are required to develop a general plan to attain and maintain NAAQS.

The Clean Air Act is the law that defines EPA's responsibilities for protecting and improving the nation's air quality and the stratospheric ozone layer. The last major change in the law, the Clean Air Act Amendments, was enacted by Congress in 1990.

See http://www.epa.gov/air/criteria.html. This site provides links to sections of the U.S. Code containing the amended text of the Clean Air Act.

high priority in the automobile industry (motivated in part by emission standards of states such as California).

Greenhouse Effect and Global Warming/Climate Change

The **greenhouse effect** is a name given to the trapping of energy in the Earth's atmosphere by a process very similar to that occurring in glass-enclosed greenhouses in which plants are grown (Figure 20.23). The atmosphere, like window glass, is transparent to incoming solar radiation. This is absorbed by the Earth and re-emitted as infrared radiation. Gases in the atmosphere, like window glass, trap some of these longer infrared rays, keeping the Earth warmer than it would otherwise be.

The greenhouse effect is caused by certain gases in the troposphere. These gases are small molecules whose bonds vibrate with frequencies in the infrared region of the electromagnetic spectrum. Such a gas can trap infrared radiation, thus retaining energy that would otherwise be radiated into space.

Which gases can act as greenhouse gases depends solely on their composition. Gases that are single atoms, like argon, have no chemical bonds and so cannot interact with infrared light. Homonuclear diatomic molecules such as nitrogen (N_2) and oxygen (O_2) also do not absorb infrared radiation. Because these three gases make up 99% of the atmosphere, it is clearly beneficial that they are not greenhouse gases.

On the other hand, diatomic molecules with bonds between different atoms, such as HCl, and any molecules with three or more atoms, such as water (H_2O), carbon dioxide (CO_2), dinitrogen monoxide (N_2O), and methane (CH_4), are greenhouse gases. (Water vapor is the main greenhouse gas and accounts for most of the observed effect.) They allow Earth to warm more than it would based solely on its distance from the Sun. In this respect, these gases are vital. If Earth did not retain some energy supplied by the Sun, the average temperature would be too cold. Life would be impossible.

Atmospheric CO_2 Levels The atmospheric level of CO_2 has risen about 81 ppm in the last 55 years to a current level (397 ppm in March 2013). For more on CO_2 levels and the influence on ocean waters see the section on "Ocean Acidification" below. See also http://co2now.org.

Much of the concern about global warming surrounds the use of fossil fuels and one of their products of the combustion, CO_2. As our society has increased its use of fossil fuels, the concentration of CO_2 in the air has increased. (The increase in CO_2 has been from about 280 ppm prior to the industrial revolution to almost 400 ppm today.) Scientists are concerned that this increased concentration will enhance the natural greenhouse effect, causing the planet's temperature to rise.

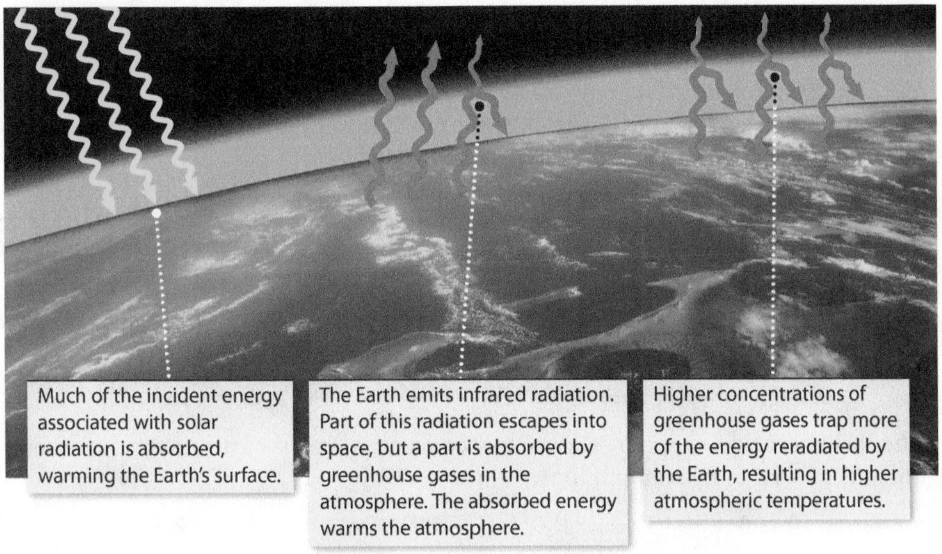

FIGURE 20.23 **The greenhouse effect.**

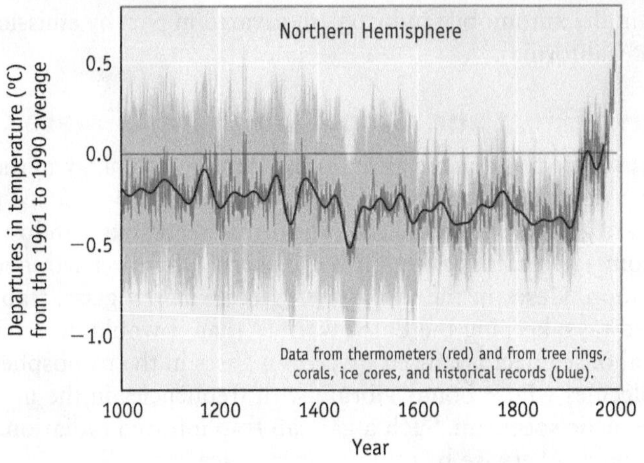

FIGURE 20.24 Variation in global mean surface temperatures for about 1000 years. The plot (known widely as "the hockey stick graph") shows the difference between the average temperature in a given year and the average temperature for the period 1961–1990.

The *Intergovernmental Panel on Climate Change* (IPCC, which is a scientific body under the auspices of the United Nations) has issued four Assessment Reports describing climate change. This term refers to the gradual warming of the surface air and oceans of the Earth and the consequences of that warming. The best estimate is that the surface temperature of the Earth has increased 0.74 ± 0.18 °C during the last century and that it is continuing to increase (Figure 20.24).

Earth began to emerge from a cold period around 150 years ago. Will the natural cycle of temperature change create a warm period like those at the time of the Roman Empire and during the Middle Ages? Or has the increase in human population and the use of fossil fuels, both of which increase the level of CO_2 in the atmosphere, made an additional contribution that will result in a much warmer period than those earlier ages experienced?

In the first three of the IPCC Assessment Reports (1990), the authors warned that human activity might be partly responsible for raising the global temperature. Although some heeded the IPCC warnings, little was done to curtail the use of fossil fuels. However, some effort is now being directed into generating electricity by sustainable means such as wind power and solar panels. In 2007, the *Fourth Assessment Report* from IPCC went further by saying there is now little doubt that the planet is warming and that additions of greenhouse gases to the atmosphere by humans are having a noticeable effect. (For the latest reports, see www.ipcc.ch.)

Other Greenhouse Gases Industry has added new greenhouse gases to the atmosphere such as CFCs (chlorofluorocarbons) and volatile organic compounds (VOCs). Although some VOCs (e.g., isoprene and terpenes) are given off by trees, VOCs are also given off by paints, adhesives, plastics, air fresheners, and cosmetics. The family of CFCs has been replaced by a new generation of hydrofluorocarbon (HFC) compounds such as $F_3C—CH_2F$, also called HFC-134a, a compound now commonly used in air conditioners and refrigerators.

Ocean Acidification

Ocean acidification is a consequence of the increasing atmospheric concentration of CO_2. In 2009 *Chemical & Engineering News* said that "What is known is that the ocean has pulled so much CO_2 from the atmosphere that the resulting levels of carbonic acid could fundamentally change the ocean."

As illustrated in Figure 20.25, the concentration of atmospheric CO_2 has been steadily increasing over the past several decades. In this regard, it is important to recall that the solubility of gases, and specifically CO_2, is directly related to the gas partial pressure (see Section 13-3). An increase in concentration of CO_2 in the atmosphere will lead to a greater concentration of dissolved CO_2 and, because CO_2 is an acidic oxide, to a greater concentration of carbonic acid, H_2CO_3.

$$CO_2(aq) + H_2O(\ell) \rightleftharpoons H_2CO_3(aq) \qquad K = 650$$

The carbonic acid ionizes to produce low concentrations of bicarbonate and carbonate ions as well as hydronium ions.

$$H_2CO_3(aq) + H_2O(\ell) \rightleftharpoons H_3O^+(aq) + HCO_3^-(aq) \qquad K = 4.2 \times 10^{-7}$$

$$HCO_3^-(aq) + H_2O(\ell) \rightleftharpoons H_3O^+(aq) + CO_3^{2-}(aq) \qquad K = 4.8 \times 10^{-11}$$

Reconstruction of Regional and Global Temperature for the Past 11,300 Years S. Marcott, J. D. Shakun, P. U. Clark, and A. C. Mix, *Science*, 2013, 339, 1198-1201. This recent paper showed there was a period from about 11,300 years ago to about 4000 years ago when the climate was warmer than in the period from about 2000 years ago to several hundred years ago. The very rapid, more recent rise in temperature shown in Figure 20.24 was confirmed. The authors state that "Global temperature . . . has risen from near the coldest to the warmest levels of the Holocene within the past century, reversing the long-term cooling trend that began about 5000 [years ago]."

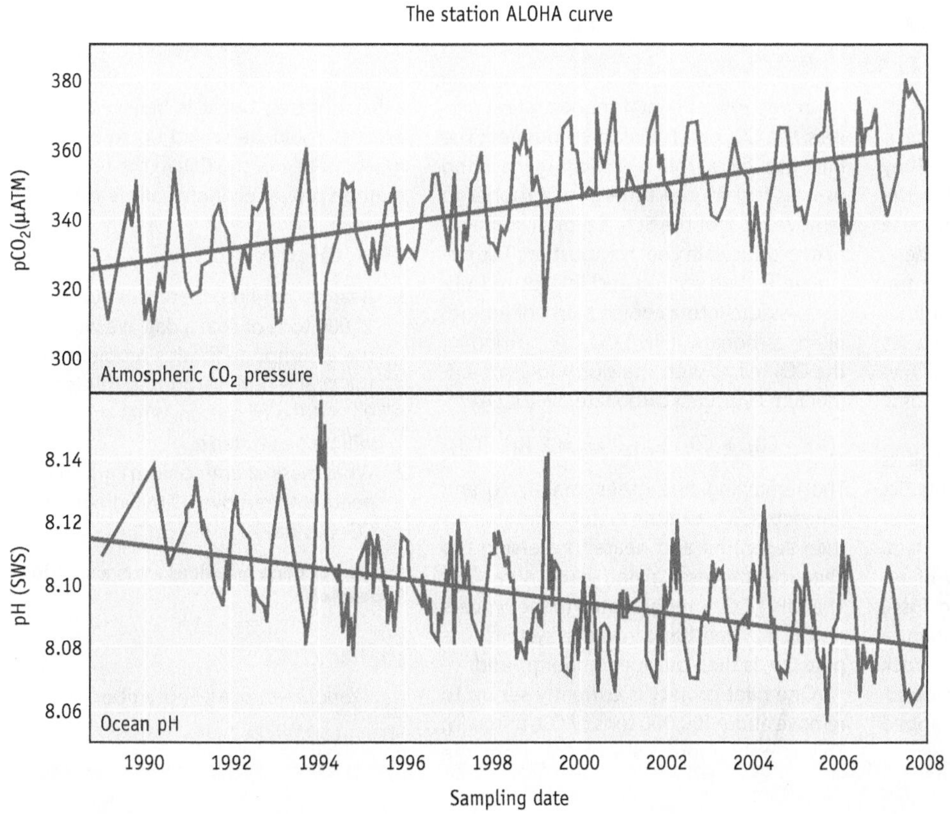

FIGURE 20.25 **Changes in atmospheric and ocean CO_2 concentration and ocean pH at a station in Hawaii.** There are seasonal variations in CO_2 concentration and pH, but the overall trends are clear. http://cmore.soest.hawaii.edu/oceanacidification/index.htm

Most importantly, as Figure 20.26 shows, these equilibria are a function of the pH of the solution. The most obvious effect, and an effect with environmental consequences, is that raising the CO_2 concentration will lead to a lower pH and thus to a decrease in the concentration of carbonate ion.

A result of the absorption of ever increasing amounts of CO_2 has been that the pH of the oceans has declined from about 8.2 in the 18th century to about 8.07 presently. Data obtained in Hawaii since the late 1980s clearly shows the downward trend in pH (Figure 20.25).

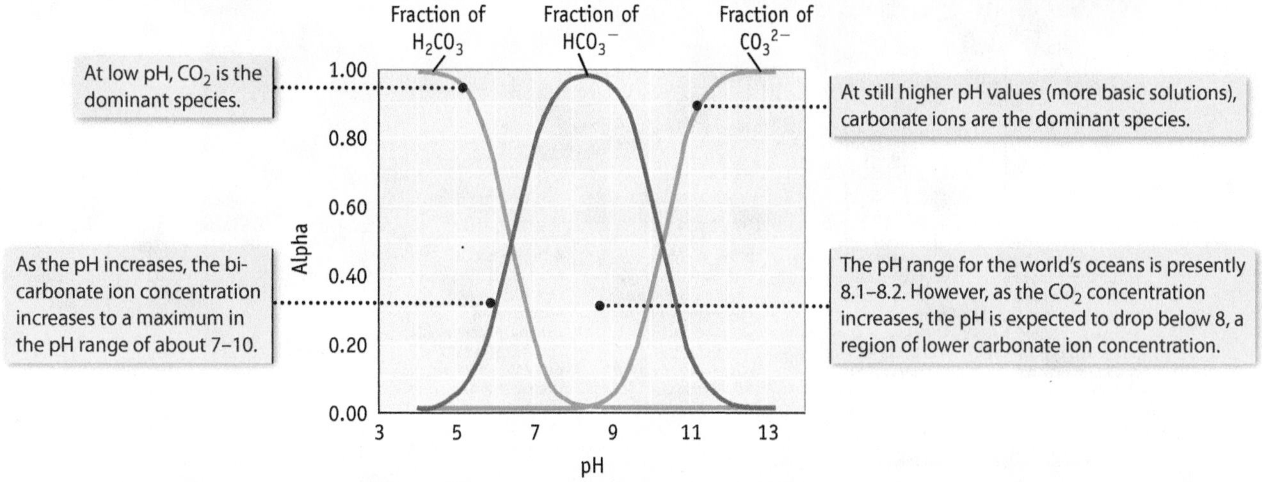

FIGURE 20.26 **Distribution of species for a solution of CO_2 in water.** (The plot shows how the fraction of species in solution [alpha (α)] changes as the pH increases. See Study Questions 17.117 and 17.118 for a description of alpha plots.)

CASE STUDY | What to Do with All of That CO_2? More on Green Chemistry

Most scientists, including the authors of this book, believe that climate change is occurring and that it is a problem. They also believe this increase is related to the increase in the percentage of greenhouse gases, especially CO_2, in the atmosphere. Are there ways to stabilize the concentration of CO_2 at the current level, or at least limit its future increase? This in turn focuses attention on the obvious source of CO_2 in the atmosphere, the combustion of fossil fuels.

The United States obtains almost half its electricity from coal-fired power plants. So, one question is why not capture and dispose of the CO_2 from power plants. In fact, this is being considered. One way of removing CO_2 generated by burning fossil fuels involves geological sequestration, a process in which CO_2 is pumped into rock formations thousands of feet underground. There, it would presumably remain trapped for thousands of years.

In one experimental sequestration process, the CO_2 needs first to be purified. The flue gas from the electricity-generating plant is first routed through a scrubber to remove most of the SO_2, a typical contaminant produced in coal combustion. The gas stream is then cooled and introduced under pressure into a cooled slurry of ammonium carbonate, $(NH_4)_2CO_3$. A portion of the CO_2 reacts with the slurry to form ammonium hydrogen carbonate, NH_4HCO_3:

$$(NH_4)_2CO_3 + CO_2 + H_2O \rightleftharpoons 2\ NH_4HCO_3$$

The remaining flue gases, mainly N_2 and unreacted CO_2, exit the system. The slurry is then separated and heated, reversing the chemical process, giving back pure CO_2. The $(NH_4)_2CO_3$ is regenerated in the process and is recycled back into the system. The pure CO_2 is then pumped underground.

One pilot project is currently set up to remove about 100,000 tons of CO_2 annually. This is only about 1.5% of CO_2 from the exhaust gases, but it is believed that the process could be scaled up to remove as much as 90% of the CO_2 in the future if the method proves economically feasible.

Questions:

1. A large coal-fired plant can burn 10,000 tons of coal a day. We will make the assumption for this problem that the coal is pure carbon, so this is about 9.1×10^9 g of carbon. What mass of CO_2 will be generated?
2. What mass of ammonium carbonate is needed to remove 1.0 million grams of CO_2 per day?

Answers to these questions are available in Appendix N.

Reference:

New York Times, p. A1, September 22, 2009.

Captured, Then Buried

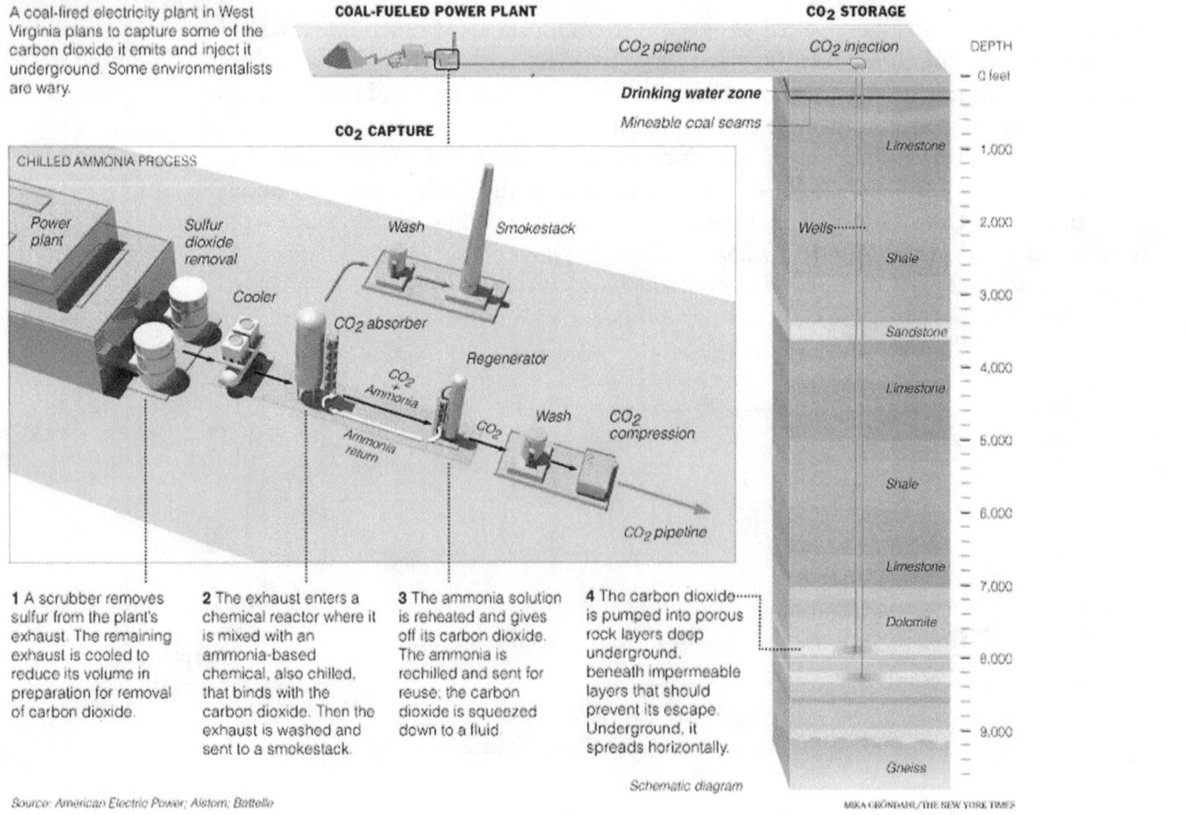

Normal growth at the current CO_2 level in the ocean (400 ppm).

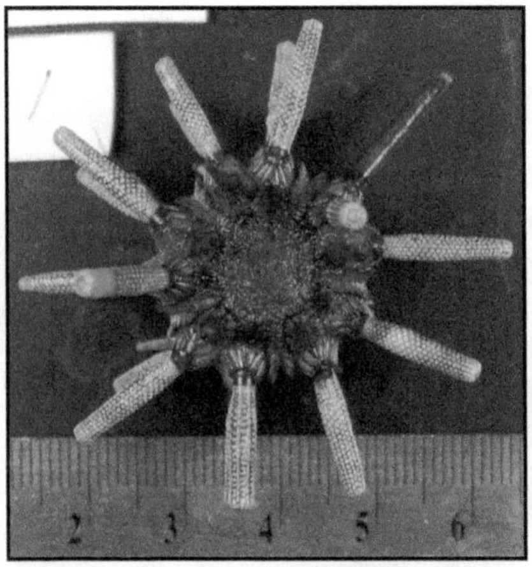

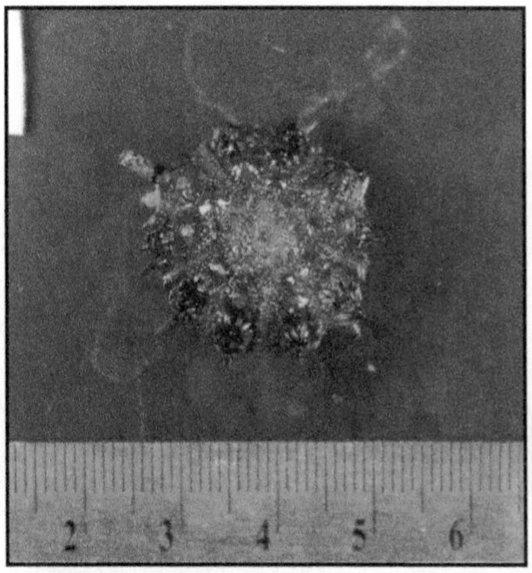

Growth at a level of 2850 ppm (an extreme level used for lab studies).

Photos: Justin B. Ries, Department of Marine Sciences, University of North Carolina at Chapel Hill

FIGURE 20.27 **Sea urchins.** The growth of spines by sea urchins depends on the level of CO_2 in the water.

The trends in CO_2 concentration and pH are clear, and there are at least two major consequences. The first is that sea organisms without shells, such as anemones and jellyfish, will find it particularly difficult to regulate their functions. Many biochemical reactions are dependent on hydronium ion concentration, and, for creatures without shells, their internal pH is that of the surroundings. These organisms evolved over millennia to live in water with a pH of about 8.1–8.2. Because a drop of pH to 7.9 represents a doubling of the hydronium ion concentration, these organisms will surely be affected, likely adversely.

The second major consequence of the trend in CO_2 concentration is that the natural equilibrium involving calcium carbonate is upset.

$$CaCO_3(s) \rightleftharpoons Ca^{2+}(aq) + CO_3^{2-}(aq) \qquad K_{sp} \text{ for calcite} = 3.4 \times 10^{-9}$$

When the pH of sea water drops, excess hydronium ions capture carbonate ions to produce bicarbonate ions,

$$H_3O^+(aq) + CO_3^{2-}(aq) \rightleftharpoons HCO_3^-(aq) + H_2O(aq) \qquad K = 1/4.8 \times 10^{-11} = 2.1 \times 10^{10}$$

thus reducing the carbonate ion concentration. Le Chatelier's principle tells us that additional calcium carbonate will dissolve to compensate for this disturbance. This has serious consequences for corals, which are built of calcium carbonate or for the shells of creatures with calcium carbonate exoskeletons such as oysters, clams, mussels, snails, and a wide variety of seashells (Figure 20.27).

Oceanographers often discuss the potential for calcium carbonate to form in terms of the saturation state, Ω (omega).

$$\Omega = \frac{[Ca^{2+}][CO_3^{2-}]}{K_{sp}}$$

where the product of the ion concentration in a given solution is divided by the solubility product constant, K_{sp}, for the mineral. If Ω is greater than 1, then the shell of an organism will not dissolve. If it is less than 1, then the mineral will dissolve.

It is relevant to this discussion of dissolving calcium carbonate to note that there are two forms of the mineral: aragonite and calcite (Figure 20.28). Their solid-state structures are slightly different and so are their K_{sp} values

$$K_{sp} \text{ for aragonite in sea water} = 8.9 \times 10^{-7}$$

$$K_{sp} \text{ for calcite in sea water} = 6.3 \times 10^{-7}$$

Ocean Acidification "... the rate of ocean acidification is faster than at any time in the past 300 million years." B. Hönisch, *et al.*, *Science*, 2012, **335**, 1058-1063.

Q and *K* This expression for Ω is equivalent to comparing the reaction quotient and equilibrium constant (see Chapters 15–17).

Aragonite and Calcite in Seawater The K_{sp} values for these minerals are more than 100 times larger in seawater than in freshwater. W. Stumm and J. Morgan, *Aquatic Chemistry*, 2nd edition, John Wiley, New York, 1981, page 243.

Aragonite. The primary mineral in sea shells.

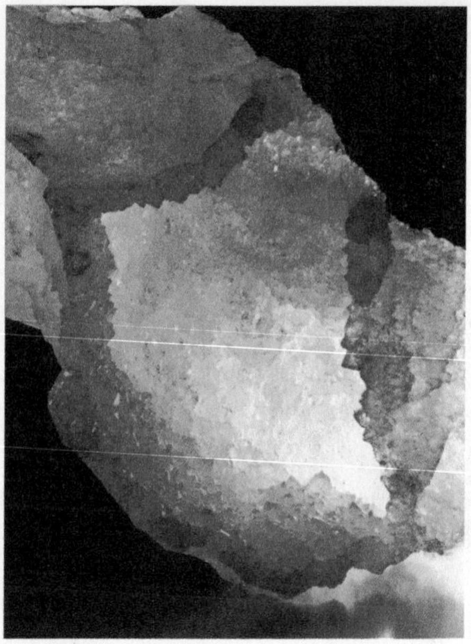

Calcite. The form of $CaCO_3$ found in chalk.

FIGURE 20.28 Forms of calcium carbonate.

Aragonite is slightly more soluble in sea water (at 25 °C) than is calcite. The importance of this is that most shells are made of aragonite, with possibly some parts made of calcite. The result is that organisms that produce aragonite are more vulnerable to changes in sea water pH.

REVIEW & CHECK FOR SECTION 20-6

1. Which of the species listed below is not a greenhouse gas?

   (a) H_2O (b) CO_2 (c) CH_4 (d) O_2

20-7 Green Chemistry and Sustainability

One goal of this book has been to introduce you to the practice of **green chemistry**, which is also called "sustainable chemistry." You first learned about green chemistry in Chapter 1, and you have seen examples of it throughout the book. Now that you are nearing the end of this book, you may better appreciate the complete *Twelve Principles of Green Chemistry* (see *A Closer Look: The Twelve Principles of Green Chemistry*).

If we assume the word "green" means environmentally sound or friendly, how can chemistry be green? People have many different opinions concerning chemistry and chemicals. Some use the word "chemical" as a synonym for a toxic substance. Others believe that all our problems can be solved through research in chemistry and other sciences. Chemists realize that all *matter*, including our food, water, and bodies as well as toxic compounds, is composed of chemicals. The practice of chemistry, like most aspects of life, has created problems at times, but chemistry has also solved many others. Research on two such solutions is described below, and many others are found earlier in this book.

Cleaning up Oil Spills

In April 2010 there was an explosion on the Deepwater Horizon, a platform used to drill for oil in the deep waters of the Gulf of Mexico. The explosion killed 11 men working on the rig and injured many others. It also allowed oil to gush into the

A CLOSER LOOK — The Twelve Principles of Green Chemistry*

Prevention: It is better to prevent waste than to treat or clean up waste after it has been created.

Atom Economy: Synthetic methods should be designed to maximize the incorporation of all materials used in the process into the final product.

Less Hazardous Chemical Syntheses: Wherever practicable, synthetic methods should be designed to use and generate substances that possess little or no toxicity to human health and the environment.

Designing Safer Chemicals: Chemical products should be designed to effect their desired function while minimizing their toxicity.

Safer Solvents and Auxiliaries: The use of auxiliary substances (e.g., solvents, separation agents, etc.) should be made unnecessary wherever possible and innocuous when used.

Design for Energy Efficiency: Energy requirements of chemical processes should be recognized for their environmental and economic impacts and should be minimized. If possible, synthetic methods should be conducted at ambient temperature and pressure.

Use of Renewable Feedstocks: A raw material or feedstock should be renewable rather than depleting whenever technically and economically practicable.

Reduce Derivatives: Unnecessary derivatization (use of blocking groups, protection/deprotection, temporary modification of physical/chemical processes) should be minimized or avoided if possible, because such steps require additional reagents and can generate waste.

Catalysis: Catalytic reagents (as selective as possible) are superior to stoichiometric reagents.

Design for Degradation: Chemical products should be designed so that at the end of their function they break down into innocuous degradation products and do not persist in the environment.

Real-time Analysis for Pollution Prevention: Analytical methodologies need to be further developed to allow for real-time, in-process monitoring and control prior to the formation of hazardous substances.

Inherently Safer Chemistry for Accident Prevention: Substances and the form of a substance used in a chemical process should be chosen to minimize the potential for chemical accidents, including releases, explosions, and fires.

*Anastas, P. T.; Warner, J. C. *Green Chemistry: Theory and Practice*, Oxford University Press: New York, 1998, p. 30. Oxford University Press.

ocean and to spread around the Gulf. An estimated 780,000 cubic meters of oil escaped. The company drilling for oil and governments and environmentalists from states surrounding the Gulf raced to clean it up.

There are at least three methods for cleaning up an oil spill.

- Use a dispersant to form an emulsion with the oil.
- Use a solid sorbent that can absorb the oil.
- Use a solidifier that can form a gel (see Section 13-5) with the oil. These are usually polymeric materials.

There are drawbacks to each of these approaches, but we focus on recent research using a solidifier. This solidifier can selectively form a gel with oil in water at room temperature. It is also easily synthesized at low cost, is environmentally benign, allows oil recovery, and is reusable. A key ingredient for this approach is a readily available sugar, mannitol. Organic groups are attached to the —OH groups at the ends of the molecule to give what is called an *amphiphile*, a molecule that has both polar (the —OH groups) and nonpolar groups (the long chain hydrocarbon ends).

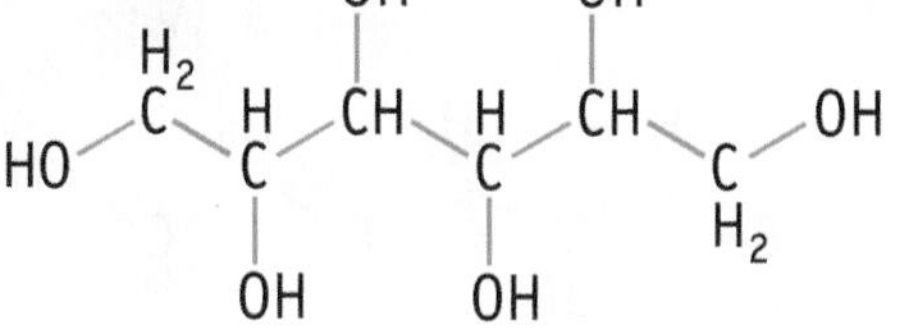

Mannitol, a sugar

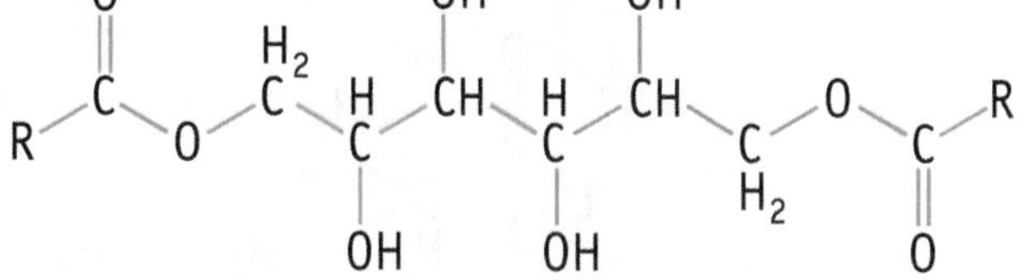

R = C_7H_{15}, a straight chain of 7 carbon atoms

Solidifier for oil recovery, with large hydrocarbon groups attached at the ends of a mannitol molecule.

A solidifier for recovering oil in water. A gel formed from the mannitol derivative and diesel oil in water. The gel can be separated and, when heated, the oil can be recovered.

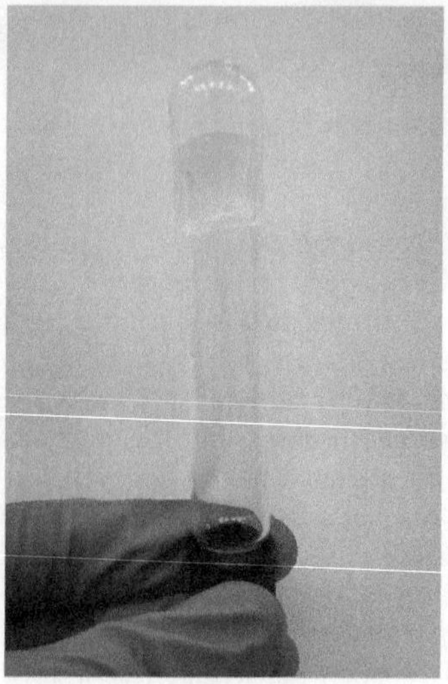

Image courtesy Professor George John

When molecules such as these are added to water with concentrations of 1–5% weight/volume, gels readily form with diesel oil, coconut oil, and many other oils. The gels are easily separated from the water, and, on heating, the oil is recovered and the solidifier can be reused. The reason this system works is that the —OH groups allow the molecules to interact with each other and with water through hydrogen bonding, while the long, nonpolar carbon chains can be immersed in the oil.

Green Chemistry The United States Environmental Protection Agency (EPA) has a Green Chemistry Program, which includes research, education, and outreach efforts as well as the Presidential Green Chemistry Challenge Awards, an annual program recognizing innovations in "cleaner, cheaper, smarter chemistry." The American Chemical Society actively promotes green chemistry, and the Royal Society of Chemistry in England publishes the research journal *Green Chemistry*. Some universities now offer degrees in green chemistry.

Paints That Kill Pathogens

One objective of "green chemistry" is to use readily available, naturally occurring materials and convert them into useful new materials. One example is the production of paints with bactericidal activity.

Commonly used oil paint is derived from vegetable oils, often from linseed or soya. Alkyd paints are based on vegetable-derived drying oils. These are usually esters of glycerol (triglycerides) where the R groups in the structure below are long-chain fatty acids with double bonds (commonly linoleic or linolenic acids) (▶ Section 23-4).

Glycerol

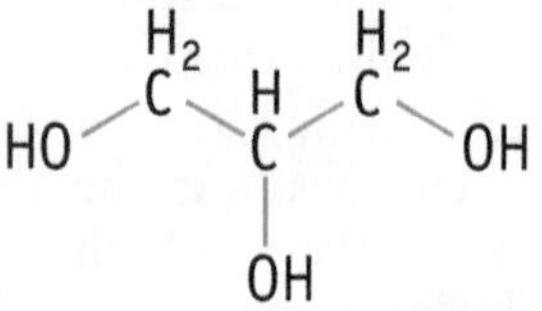

Triglyceride

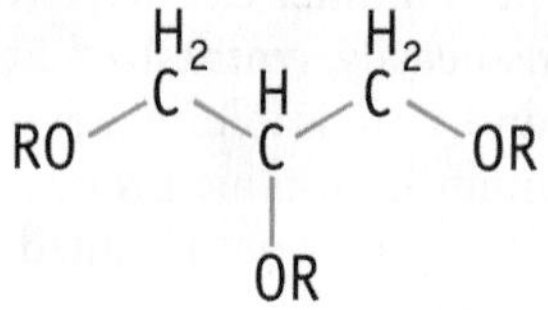

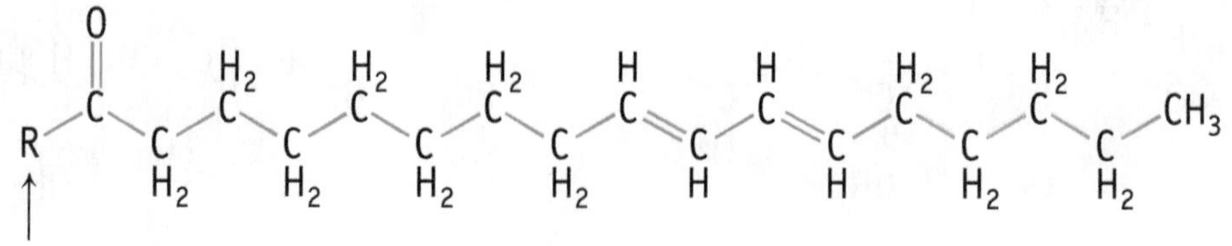

Point of attachment to glycerol

Linoleic acid chain

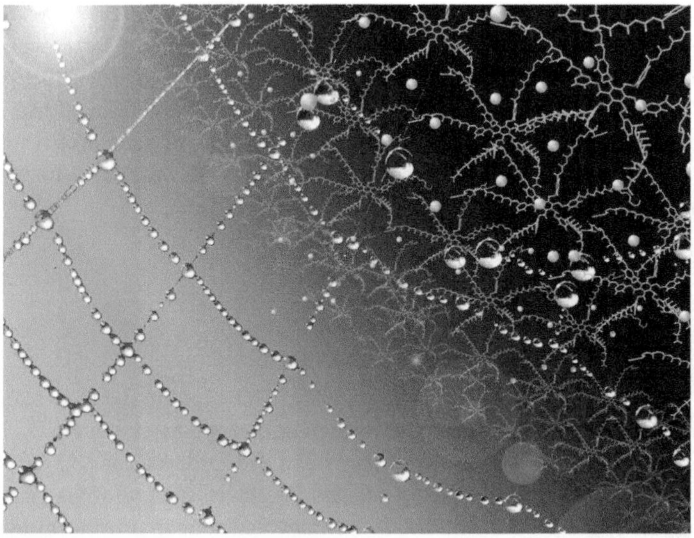

Image courtesy Professor George John. Reproduced from Chemical Communications with permission of The Royal Society of Chemistry (RSC) on behalf of the European Society for Photobiology, the European Photochemistry Association and RSC

FIGURE 20.29 **Paint with silver and gold nanoparticles as imagined by the chemists that developed the material.** Here the organic framework of the paint resembles a spider web with gold (pink) and white (silver) spheres representing the nanoparticles.

When these drying oils are painted on a surface, they "dry" (form a hard surface). Drying involves oxidation (through contact with air), which causes cross-linking between carbon chains.

The drying process of oil-based paints is known to occur by a free-radical process. Further, it is known that the free radicals produced can reduce metal ions. So, chemists recently used this free-radical process to treat alkyd paint with silver(I) and gold(III) salts. The metals ions were reduced to silver and gold nanoparticles that were trapped within the resin (Figure 20.29). When this was painted on surfaces such as glass, wood, or various polymer surfaces, it dried to a hard, scratch-resistant coating. Most importantly, the surfaces were very effective in killing human pathogens (*Staphylococcus aureas*) and bacteria (*Escherichia coli*).

APPLYING CHEMICAL PRINCIPLES

Alkalinity of Water Supplies

The **alkalinity** of a water supply is its capacity to accept hydronium ions. This factor is important to know when assessing water quality, methods of water treatment, and the biology of natural waters because the amount of biomass that can be produced depends on the alkalinity.

Generally, the species most responsible for the alkalinity of a water sample are bicarbonate, carbonate, and hydroxide ions. Other ions, largely the conjugate bases of weak acids (such as phosphate and borate ions), can also be involved. Considering only the carbonate system of ions, alkalinity (Alk) is defined by the equation

$$[Alk] = [HCO_3^-] + 2\,[CO_3^{2-}] + [OH^-]$$

John C. Kotz

Note that the carbonate ion is counted twice because it can react with two hydrogen ions. Alkalinity is often expressed as the number of equivalents per liter, that is, the number of moles of H^+ ions that can be neutralized per liter of water. (Natural water has Alk = 1.00×10^{-3} eq/L.)

The amount of dissolved carbon is important in the growth of aquatic plants. Dissolved carbon (C) is defined by the equation

$$[\text{Dissolved C}] = [H_2CO_3] + [HCO_3^-] + [CO_3^{2-}]$$

and you can show there are about twice as many equivalents of dissolved carbon at pH 7 as at pH 10 (both in solutions with alkalinity = 1.00×10^{-3} eq/L). (See Question 2.)

$$[C]_{pH\ 7} = 1.24 \times 10^{-3}\ \text{mol}$$

$$[C]_{pH\ 10} = 6.8 \times 10^{-4}\ \text{mol}$$

The dissolved carbon is used in photosynthesis to synthesize biomass (algae), represented by the formula $\{CH_2O\}$, according to the general equations

$$CO_2(aq) + H_2O(\ell) + \text{sunlight} \rightarrow \{CH_2O\} + O_2(g)$$

$$HCO_3^-(aq) + H_2O(\ell) + \text{sunlight} \rightarrow \{CH_2O\} + OH^-(aq) + O_2(g)$$

Based on the second equation, you can see that as biomass is produced in an aquatic system from dissolved carbon the system becomes more basic. Further, in going from pH 7 to pH 10 the difference in the amount of dissolved carbon is 0.56×10^{-4} mol, which means that 0.56×10^{-4} mol/L of biomass is produced. Because the biomass $\{CH_2O\}$ has a molar mass of 30 g/mol, this means the system produced about 17 mg of biomass per liter before the water became too alkaline to produce more algae.

QUESTIONS

Use the alpha plot for the H_2CO_2, HCO_3^-, CO_3^{2-} system in Figure 20.26 in working these problems.

1. Assume a solution with a total alkalinity of 1.00×10^{-3} eq/L.
   (a) Define the concentrations of the H_2CO_3, bicarbonate, carbonate, and hydroxide ions at pH 7.00.
   (b) Now define the concentrations of the bicarbonate, carbonate, and hydroxide ions at pH 10.00. (Recall that K_{a2} for the carbonate equilibrium is 4.8×10^{-11}.)

$$HCO_3^-(aq) + H_2O(\ell) \rightleftharpoons CO_3^{2-}(aq) + H_3O^+(aq)$$

2. Using the concentration values at pH 7 and pH 10 from Question 1, show that the dissolved carbon values are those given in the text.

CHAPTER GOALS REVISITED

Now that you have studied this chapter, you should ask whether you have met the chapter goals. In particular, you should be able to

UNDERSTAND

- How human activity contributes to air and water pollution and what is being done to address these problems (Sections 20-2 and 20-6).
- Current energy resources and implications for the future (Section 20-3).
- Efforts by the chemistry community to support green chemistry (Section 20-7).
- Important current issues concerning the environment.

DO

- Calculate enthalpy changes, or use enthalpy changes, associated with burning of fossil fuels or with reactions in the environment. Study Questions: 3b, 16–21, 24, 30, 31, 35.
- Apply the principles of stoichiometry, chemical bonding, gas and solution behavior, chemical equilibria, and kinetics to substances important in the environment. Study Questions: 3, 4, 7, 14, 29, 33, 40, 42.

REMEMBER

- The composition of the atmosphere and the aqua sphere (Sections 20-1 and 20-2). Study Questions: 1, 2, 5, 6.
- The identity of chemical pollutants in air and water and their effects on human life (Sections 20-2, 20-3, and 20-6). Study Questions: 7–10, 35–38, 45, 50, 51.
- The procedures by which water is purified (Section 20-2). Study Question: 46.
- Renewable and nonrenewable energy resources (Sections 20-3–20-6). Study Questions: 25, 29, 30, 43.

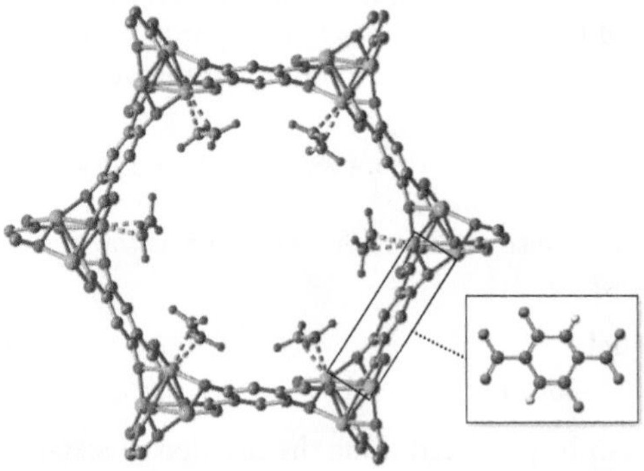

STUDY QUESTIONS

▲ denotes challenging questions.

Blue-numbered questions have answers in Appendix N and fully worked solutions in the *Student Solutions Manual.*

Practicing Skills

The Atmosphere

(See Section 20-1.)

1. In the discussion on the composition of air, mention is made of the fact that water vapor may have a concentration as high as 40,000 ppm. Calculate the partial pressure exerted by water vapor at this concentration. Assume that this represents a situation with 100% humidity. What temperature would be needed to achieve this value? (See Appendix G.)

2. Assume the average CO_2 concentration in the atmosphere is 397 ppm (as of February 2013). The actual concentration of CO_2 at different sites will vary. Speculate on whether the concentration of CO_2 would be expected to be higher, lower, or the same as this average value in a typical large city.

3. A 2011 article in *Science* magazine stated that "Public discussion of climate change . . . is just beginning to reflect an awareness of the important role played by the global nitrogen cycle." (See Figure 20.1.) As part of this cycle it was recently found that nitrite ions in soil can produce nitrous acid, HONO. [M. Kulmala and T. Petaja, *Science*, Vol. 333, pp. 1586–1587, 2011.]
   (a) Draw the Lewis electron dot structure for HONO and indicate the electron-pair geometry around the O and N atoms.
   (b) HONO is a source of hydroxyl radicals, ·OH, in the atmosphere because enough energy is supplied by sunlight to break the N—O bond. Use the bond dissociation enthalpy of the N—O bond (Table 8.8) to calculate the wavelength of light that could cause HONO to dissociate to the radicals ·NO and ·OH.

4. Dinitrogen monoxide, N_2O (commonly called nitrous oxide), is prepared by the careful decomposition of ammonium nitrate and is used as an oxidizing agent in rocket engines as well as a weak general anesthetic (where you may know it as "laughing gas"). However, it is also known to be a powerful greenhouse gas. In a *Science* magazine article, it was stated that "Human activities may be causing an unprecedented rise in the terrestrial N_2O source. Marine N_2O production may also rise substantially as result of eutrophication, warming, and ocean acidification." [L. A. Codispoti, *Science*, Vol. 327, pp. 1339-1340, 2010.]

The powerful greenhouse gas N_2O is used as a propellant in cans of instant whipped cream.

(a) Draw a Lewis electron dot structure for N_2O, and specify the formal charge on each atom and the molecular geometry.
(b) The atom connections are N—N—O. Why is the connection N—O—N not likely?
(c) The highest N_2O concentration observed in the ocean is about 800 nM (nanomolar). At this concentration, what is the mass of N_2O per liter?

5. Suppose you find the CO concentration in your home is 10. ppm by volume at 1.00 atm pressure and 25 °C. What is the CO concentration in mg/L and in ppm by mass. (The average molar mass for dry air is 28.96 g/mol at 1.00 atm pressure and 25 °C.)

6. In 2005, global SO_2 emission was estimated to be 12.83 Gg (gigagrams). According to the EPA, 71% of SO_2 emissions into the atmosphere is from coal-fired power plants. How much coal (in metric tons) must have been burned to produce this much SO_2, assuming that coal is 2.0% sulfur?

The Aqua Sphere

(See Section 20-2.)

7. The carbon content in seawater is 30 mmol/L (Table 20.2). This includes both HCO_3^- and CO_3^{2-} ions. Knowing the pH of seawater is 8.1, what is the ratio of concentrations of these two ions in seawater? (See Figure 20.26.)

8. Using the data in Table 20.2, estimate the minimum mass of solid that would remain after evaporation of 1.0 L of seawater.

9. What mass of NaCl could be obtained by evaporating 1.0 L of seawater? (*Note:* The amount of Na^+ ions in seawater limits the amount of NaCl that can be obtained.)

10. In any solution, there must be a balance between the positive and negative charges of the ions that are present. Use the data in Table 20.2 to determine how close to a balance of charge is achieved for the ions in seawater. (The table lists only the major ions in seawater, and the balance between positive and negative charge will only be approximate.)

11. Although there are a number of magnesium-containing minerals, the commercial source of this metal is seawater. Treatment of seawater with $Ca(OH)_2$ gives insoluble $Mg(OH)_2$. This reacts with HCl to produce $MgCl_2$, which is dried, and the metal is obtained by electrolysis of the molten salt. Write balanced net ionic equations for the three reactions described here.

12. Calculate the mass of Mg that could be obtained by the process described in Question 11 from 1.0 L of seawater. To prepare 100. kg of Mg, what volume of seawater would be needed? (The density of seawater is 1.025 g/cm^3.)

13. A 2010 article in *Science* magazine described "Sewage Treatment with Anammox." [B. Kartal, J. G. Kuenen, and M. C. M. van Loosdrecht, *Science*, Vol. 328, pp. 702-703, 2010.] The authors noted that "Fixed nitrogen such as ammonium and nitrate [ions] must be removed [from sewage] to avoid toxic algal blooms in the environment." One approach to removing ammonium ions is to use ammonium-oxidizing (anammox) bacteria. Two (unbalanced) reactions that are involved are:

$$NH_4^+(aq) + NO_2^-(aq) \rightarrow N_2(g) + H_2O(\ell)$$

$$NH_4^+(aq) + O_2(g) \rightarrow NO_2^-(aq) + H_2O(\ell)$$

Balance these two equations in acid solution.

14. Silver ions have long been known to have biocidal properties. The increasing use of silver for this purpose has led to greater silver concentrations in waste water, and there has been some concern about it. However, recent studies found that the silver was largely put back into the environment as Ag_2S. The solubility of this sulfide is 1.4×10^{-4} g/L.
(a) Estimate the K'_{sp} for Ag_2S. (See Table 18b in Appendix J.)
(b) How does the solubility of Ag_2S change as the pH decreases?

Energy, Fossil Fuels

(See Sections 20-3–20-6.)

15. Hydrogen can be produced using the reaction of steam (H_2O) with various hydrocarbons. Compare the mass of H_2 expected from the reaction of steam with 100. g each of methane, petroleum, and coal. (Assume complete reaction in each case. Use CH_2 and C as the representative formulas for petroleum and coal, respectively.)

16. Use the value for "energy released" in kilojoules per gram from gasoline listed in Table 20.3 to estimate the percentage of carbon, by mass, in gasoline. (*Hint*: Compare the value for gasoline to the $\Delta_rH°$ values for burning pure C and H_2.)

17. Per capita energy consumption in the United States has been equated to the energy obtained by burning 70. lb of coal per day. Use enthalpy of formation data to calculate the energy transferred as heat, in kilojoules, when 70. lb of coal is burned. (Assume the enthalpy of combustion of coal is 33 kJ/g.)

18. The enthalpy of combustion of isooctane (C_8H_{18}), one of the many hydrocarbons in gasoline, is 5.45×10^3 kJ/mol. Calculate the enthalpy change per gram of isooctane and per liter of isooctane (d = 0.688 g/mL).

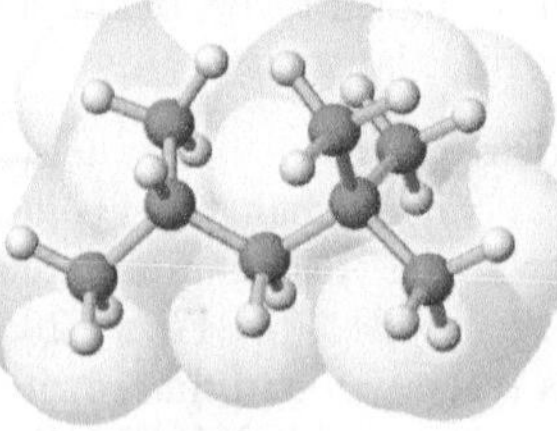

isooctane
C_8H_{18}

19. Energy consumption in the United States amounts to the equivalent of the energy obtained by burning 7.0 gal of oil or 70. lb of coal per day per person. Using data in Table 20.3, carry out calculations to show that the energy evolved from these quantities of oil and coal is approximately equivalent. The density of fuel oil is approximately 0.8 g/mL. (1.00 gal = 3.785 L and 1.00 lb = 454 g)

20. Calculate the energy used, in kilojoules, to power a 100-watt lightbulb continuously over a 24-hour period. How much coal would have to be burned to provide this quantity of energy, assuming that the enthalpy of combustion of coal is 33 kJ/g and the power plant has an efficiency of 35%? [Electrical energy for home use is measured in kilowatt hours (kW-h). One watt is defined as 1 J/s, and 1 kW-h is the quantity of energy transferred when 1000 watt is dispensed over a 1.0-hour period.]

21. Here we want to compare ethanol (C_2H_5OH) and gasoline as fuels. We will use isooctane (C_8H_{18}) as a substitute for gasoline. (Isooctane is one of the many hydrocarbons in gasoline, and its enthalpy of combustion will approximate the energy obtained when gasoline burns. See Question 18.)

(a) Calculate $\Delta_r H°$ for the combustion of 1.00 kg each of liquid ethanol and liquid isooctane. Which fuel releases more energy per kilogram? [$\Delta_f H° = -259.3$ kJ/mol for liquid isooctane at 298 K.] (Assume $H_2O(\ell)$ is one product of combustion.)

(b) Compare the two fuels on the basis of the release of CO_2, a common greenhouse gas. Which fuel produces more CO_2 per kilogram?

(c) On the basis of this simple comparison and neglecting the energy costs involved in producing 1.00 kg each of ethanol and isooctane, which is the better fuel in terms of energy production and greenhouse gases?

22. Major home appliances purchased in the United States are labeled with bright yellow "Energy Guide" tags showing anticipated energy consumption. The tag on a recently purchased washing machine indicated the anticipated energy use would be 940 kW-h per year. Calculate the anticipated annual energy use in kilojoules. (See Question 20 for a definition of kilowatt-hour.) At 8 cents/kW-h, how much would it cost per month to operate this machine?

23. Confirm the statement in the text that oxidation of 1.0 L of methanol to form $CO_2(g)$ and $H_2O(\ell)$ in a fuel cell will provide at least 5.0 kW-h of energy. (The density of liquid methanol is 0.787 g/mL. See Question 20 for definition of kW-h.)

24. List the following substances in order of energy released by combustion per gram: C_8H_{18}, H_2, C(s), CH_4. (See Question 18 for the enthalpy of combustion of isooctane, C_8H_{18}.) Which is the best fuel based on a comparison of kJ/g of fuel?

25. A parking lot in Los Angeles receives an average of 2.6×10^7 J/m² of solar energy per day in the summer.

(a) If the parking lot is 325 m long and 50.0 m wide, what is the total quantity of energy striking the area per day?

(b) What mass of coal would have to be burned to supply the quantity of energy calculated in (a)? (Assume the enthalpy of combustion of coal is 33 kJ/g.)

26. Your home loses energy in the winter through doors, windows, and any poorly insulated walls. A sliding glass door (6 ft × 6.5 ft with 0.5 inch of insulating glass) allows 1.0×10^6 J/h to pass through the glass if the inside temperature is 22 °C (72 °F) and the outside temperature is 0 °C (32 °F). What quantity of energy, expressed in kilojoules, is lost per day? Assume that your house is heated by electricity. How many kilowatt-hours of energy are lost per day through the door? (See Question 20 for the definition of a kilowatt-hour.)

27. Some fuel-efficient hybrid cars are rated at 55.0 miles per gallon of gasoline. Calculate the energy used to drive 1.00 mile if gasoline produces 48.0 kJ/g and the density of gasoline is 0.737 g/cm³. (1.00 gal = 3.785 L)

28. Microwave ovens are highly efficient, compared to other cooking appliances. A 1100-watt microwave oven, running at full power for 90 seconds, will raise the temperature of 1 cup of water (225 mL) from 20 °C to 67 °C. As a rough measure of the efficiency of the microwave oven, compare its energy consumption with the energy required to raise the water temperature.

29. In methane hydrate the methane molecule is trapped in a cage of water molecules. Describe the structure: (a) how many water molecules make up the cage, (b) how many hydrogen bonds are involved, and (c) how many faces does the cage have? (See below and *A Closer Look: Methane Hydrates: Opportunities and Problems.*)

(a) Methane hydrate burns as methane gas escapes from the solid hydrate.

(b) Methane hydrate consists of a lattice of water molecules with methane molecules trapped in the cavity.

30. One cubic meter of methane hydrate has 164 m³ of CH_4 (at STP). If you burn the methane in 1.00 m³ of hydrate [to give $CO_2(g)$ and $H_2O(g)$], how much energy, as heat, can be obtained?

Alternative Fuels

(See Section 20-5.)

31. Methyl myristate, $C_{13}H_{27}CO_2CH_3(\ell)$, can be used as a biofuel.

(a) Write a balanced chemical equation for the reaction that occurs when 1 mol of methyl myristate, $C_{13}H_{27}CO_2CH_3(\ell)$, is burned, forming $CO_2(g)$ and $H_2O(g)$.

(b) Using enthalpy of formation data, calculate the standard enthalpy change for the oxidation of 1.00 mol of methyl myristate ($\Delta_f H° = -771.0$ kJ/mol) to form $CO_2(g)$ and $H_2O(g)$.

(c) Which compound, methyl myristate $[C_{13}H_{27}CO_2CH_3(\ell)]$ or hexadecane ($C_{16}H_{34}$, one of many hydrocarbons in petroleum based diesel fuel), is predicted to provide the greater energy per mole of fuel? Per liter? ($\Delta_f H°$ for $C_{16}H_{34} = -456.1$ kJ/mol) [d(methyl myristate) = 0.86 g/mL, and $d(C_{16}H_{34}) = 0.77$ g/mL].

32. Generating hydrogen gas using the least amount of energy possible is very desirable. One proposed scheme is the catalyzed decomposition of formic acid, HCO_2H. [S. Ott, *Science*, Vol. 333, pp. 1714–1715, 2011.]

$$HCO_2H(g) \rightleftharpoons CO_2(g) + H_2(g)$$

A particularly interesting aspect of this reaction is that it can be run in reverse and so serve as a way of storing hydrogen. Calculate the equilibrium constant (at 298 K) for the decomposition reaction using thermodynamic data. Is the decomposition reaction product-favored at equilibrium at 298 K? (For $HCO_2H(g)$, $\Delta_f H° = -378.6$ kJ/mol and $S° = 248.70$ J/K·mol.)

Green Chemistry

(See Section 20-7.)

33. Acetonitrile, CH_3CN, is an important solvent. The chemical is normally available as a by-product of the manufacture of acrylonitrile, $CH_2{=}CHCN$, the building block of polyacrylonitrile, a widely used polymer. Recently, however, the demand for acrylonitrile dropped, so the supply of acetonitrile diminished to a point where users of the solvent were concerned. For that reason new methods were sought for the synthesis of CH_3CN, and a new "green" method was reported.

Step 1: reaction of ethanol (C_2H_5OH) with ammonia to give ethylamine ($C_2H_5NH_2$) and water.

Step 2: reaction of ethylamine and oxygen (over a ruthenium oxide/aluminum oxide catalyst) to give acetonitrile and water.

(a) Draw Lewis electron dot structures for ethanol, ethylamine, acetonitrile, and acrylonitrile. Specify the molecular geometry around each C atom and, as appropriate, around the O or N atoms.

(b) Write balanced equations for each step in the synthesis of acetonitrile from ethanol.

(c) Calculate the atom economy for the synthesis of acetonitrile from ethanol. (Atom economy is discussed in Chapter 4, *Case Study: Green Chemistry and Atom Economy*.)

34. The refrigerating liquids in air conditioners and refrigerators are largely chlorofluorocarbons (CFCs) and hydrochlorofluorocarbons (HCFCs). Among the latter family of compounds is the refrigerant HCFC-22 ($HCClF_2$). A problem with the use of HCFC-22 is that HFC-23 (trifluoromethane, HCF_3), a gas with high-global-warming potential, is a by-product of its production (and also from the production of the widely used polymer Teflon). Discarding HFC-23 safely can be a problem. However, recently a method has been developed to convert it to the valuable catalyst trifluoromethanesulfonic acid, CF_3SO_3H. Draw an electron dot structure for the acid (which you can think of as sulfuric acid with a CF_3 group in place of one OH group). Indicate the geometry around the C and S atoms. What is the hybridization of these two atoms?

General Questions

These questions are not designated as to type or location in the chapter. They may combine several concepts.

35. Chlorine atoms are formed by photochemical reactions of chlorofluorocarbons in the upper atmosphere. Using the average bond energy of the C—Cl bond in Table 8.8, calculate the wavelength of radiation with sufficient energy to break the C—Cl bond. In what region of the electromagnetic spectrum does this fall?

36. The formation of NO from N_2 and O_2 is unfavorable at 298 K, but it becomes increasingly favored at high temperatures such as those in an automobile cylinder. Using data ($\Delta_f H°$, $S°$ and $\Delta_f G°$) in Appendix L, calculate the equilibrium constant for the reaction ½ $N_2(g)$ + ½ $O_2(g) \rightarrow NO(g)$ at 298 K and at 1000 K.

37. The nitrogen cycle (Figure 20.1) shows the oxidation of NH_4^+, first to NO_2^- and then the subsequent oxidation of NO_2^- to NO_3^-. Write balanced equations for each of these half-reactions (in acid solution).

38. Steps have been taken to limit phosphorus in surface water. However, the amounts of nitrogen-containing species in surface water can also be a problem because they also promote excessive growth of algae and water plants. What are likely sources of this nitrogen? What nitrogen compounds are likely to be present in surface water?

39. The concentration of gold in seawater is 10. ppt (parts per trillion.) How many atoms of gold are contained in 1.00 L of seawater? (The density of seawater is 1.025 g/ml.)

40. Refer to the figure below to answer the following questions regarding the equilibria involved in an aqueous solution of H_2CO_3 (dissolved CO_2) in fresh water at 25 °C. (The plot shows the fraction of species in solution [alpha (α)] as a function of pH. See Study Questions 17.117 and 17.118 for a description of alpha plots.)

(a) At what pH does $[H_2CO_3(aq)] = [HCO_3^-]$?
(b) At what pH does $[HCO_3^-] = [CO_3^{2-}]$?
(c) What is the predominant species in solution when the solution has a pH of 8?
(d) What species are in solution when the solution has a pH of 7?

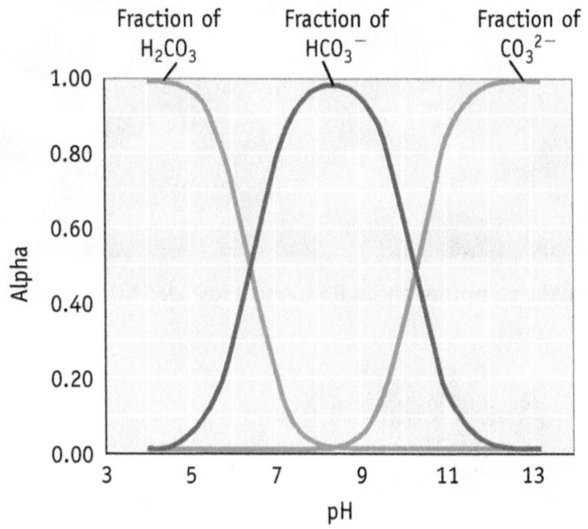

In the Laboratory

41. Imagine the following experiment: You have a large graduated cylinder containing 100. mL of liquid water at 0 °C. You drop an ice cube with a volume of 25 cm³ into the cylinder. Ice has a density of 0.92 g/cm³, less than the density of liquid water, so it floats with 92% being under water.

(a) To what level will the water in the graduated cylinder rise after adding the ice?
(b) Allow the ice to melt. What volume will now be occupied by the liquid water? (One consequence of global warming will be a rise in sea level as ice in the northern and southern regions of the planet melts. However, the effect relates only to melting of ice on land. Melting of floating ice will have no effect on sea levels.)

42. The mineral claudetite contains the element arsenic in the form of arsenic(III) oxide, As_2O_3. The As_2O_3 in a 0.562-g sample of the impure mineral was converted first to H_3AsO_3 and then titrated with a 0.0480 M solution of I_3^-, which reacts with H_3AsO_3 according to the following balanced net ionic equation

$$H_3AsO_3(aq) + 3\ H_2O(\ell) + I_3^-(aq) \rightarrow H_3AsO_4(aq) + 2\ H_3O^+(aq) + 3\ I^-(aq)$$

If the titration required 45.7 mL of the I_3^- solution, what is the percentage of As_2O_3 in the mineral sample?

Summary and Conceptual Questions

The following questions may use concepts from this and previous chapters.

43. Define the terms *renewable* and *nonrenewable* as applied to energy resources. Which of the following energy resources are renewable: solar energy, coal, natural gas, geothermal energy, wind power?

44. What are the three most abundant gases in the atmosphere? Are any of these greenhouse gases?

45. What are the environmental consequences of ozone in the troposphere? In the stratosphere?

46. Compare the advantages and disadvantages of the different methods used to disinfect drinking water.

47. Mercury, lead, and arsenic in the environment are major concerns. Identify the main source or sources of these pollutants.

48. What is the likelihood that hydrogen (H_2) will become a widely used fuel and that the "hydrogen economy" will become a reality? In particular, what are the advantages and disadvantages of H_2 as a fuel? What would be necessary for a significant conversion to a "hydrogen economy"?

49. An understanding of most environmental issues requires one to consider a range of factors—economic, political, sociological, as well as scientific. Bearing this in mind, discuss each of the issues below.

(a) Fracking is now in wide use, allowing us to access large quantities of natural gas. What are the positive factors that argue for continued and expanded use of this technique, and what are the concerns?
(b) Most gasoline now sold contains ethanol. Is production of ethanol for use as a fuel a wise choice? List arguments for and against this policy.
(c) Two types of vehicles, electric cars and cars using natural gas, are in early stages of development in the United States. Should their development be encouraged? What are the advantages and disadvantages to owning these cars now?

50. Refer to Figure 20.6. What is the average rate of increase in atmospheric CO_2 per year? Assuming the rate of increase continues at the same pace, predict the approximate concentration of CO_2 in the atmosphere in 2020.

51. Which sulfur compounds are atmospheric pollutants? What is their origin? Describe steps being taken to prevent sulfur compounds from entering the atmosphere.

A sample of quartz (SiO_2, left) and a large of piece of silicon (right) used to make computer chips. Both are surrounded by dry ice (solid CO_2).

The Chemistry of the Main Group Elements

Chapter Outline

CARBON AND SILICON Carbon and silicon are both significant elements in the Earth's crust. Mendeleev placed them in the same periodic group based on the similarity in stoichiometry of their simple compounds such as their oxides (CO_2 and SiO_2). We know now that carbon is the backbone of millions of organic compounds. As we will see in this chapter, silicon, the second most abundant element in the Earth's crust, is vitally important in the structures of a large number of minerals.

Probe a bit further into silicon chemistry, however, and what emerges are the surprising differences between these elements. We get a hint of this when we compare the two oxides, CO_2, a gas above −78 °C and 1 atm pressure,

Chapter Goals

See Chapter Goals Revisited (page 855) for Study Questions keyed to these goals.

UNDERSTAND

- How the period table can assist in predicting chemical behavior of the elements.
- How principles of bonding, thermodynamics, and electrochemistry can be used when discussing the chemistry of the elements.

DO

- Write chemical equations for common chemical reactions.
- Given reactants in a chemical equation, predict the products.
- Given a formula for a compound, describe its structure and bonding.
- Describe in a general way the chemical behavior of the main group elements.
- Apply the principles of stoichiometry, thermodynamics, and electrochemistry to the chemistry of the main group elements.

REMEMBER

- Where and in what chemical form main group elements occur in nature and how to prepare samples of the pure element from naturally occurring sources.
- Physical and chemical properties of the more common main group elements.
- Applications of main group elements and their compounds in everyday life.

and SiO_2, a rock-hard solid with a very high melting point (about 1600 °C). Another interesting contrast can be made between the reactions of the two simple hydrogen compounds, CH_4 and SiH_4, with water. The reaction of methane with water is endothermic and reactant-favored at equilibrium, whereas silane will explode on contact with water.

In this chapter, we will evaluate and summarize the inorganic chemistry of the main group elements and explore the similarities and differences between elements in each periodic group.

A Study Question related to this story is: 21.111.

The main group or A-Group elements occupy an important place in the world of chemistry. Eight of the 10 most abundant elements on the Earth are in these groups. Likewise, the top 10 chemicals produced by the U.S. chemical industry are all main group elements or their compounds.

Because main group elements and their compounds are economically important—and because they have interesting chemistries—we devote this chapter to a brief survey of these elements.

21-1 Element Abundances

The abundance of the first 18 elements in the solar system is plotted against their atomic numbers in Figure 21.1. Hydrogen and helium are the most abundant by a wide margin because most of the mass of the solar system resides in the Sun, and these elements are the Sun's primary components. Lithium, beryllium, and boron are

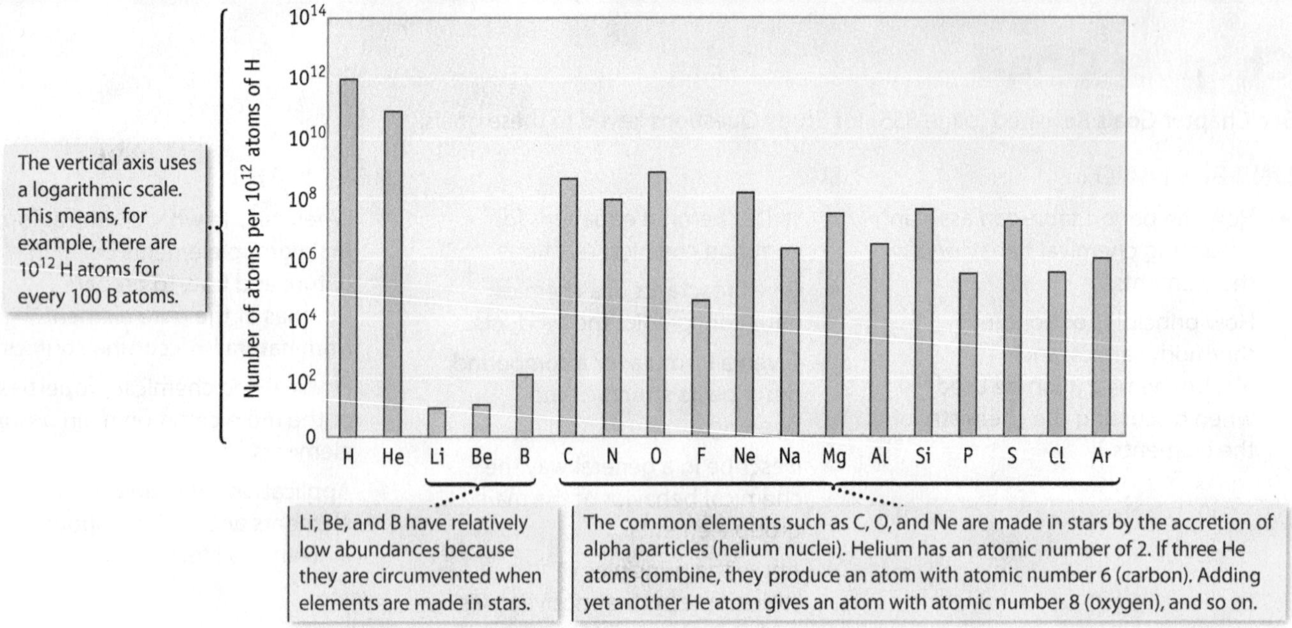

FIGURE 21.1 **Abundance of elements 1–18 in the solar system.**

low in abundance, but carbon's abundance is very high. From this point on, with the exception of iron and nickel, elemental abundances gradually decline as the atomic number increases.

Ten elements account for 99% of the aggregate mass of the Earth's crust (Table 21.1), and oxygen, silicon, and aluminum represent more than 80% of this mass. Oxygen and nitrogen are the primary components of the atmosphere, and oxygen-containing water is highly abundant on the surface, underground, and as a vapor in the atmosphere. Many common minerals also contain these elements, including limestone ($CaCO_3$) and quartz or sand (SiO_2, ◀ Figure 12.18). Aluminum and silicon occur together in many minerals; among the more common ones are feldspar, granite, and clay.

Table 21.1 The 10 Most Abundant Elements in Earth's Crust

RANK	ELEMENT	ABUNDANCE (ppm)*
1	Oxygen	474,000
2	Silicon	277,000
3	Aluminum	82,000
4	Iron	56,300
5	Calcium	41,000
6	Sodium	23,600
7	Magnesium	23,300
8	Potassium	21,000
9	Titanium	5,600
10	Hydrogen	1,520

*ppm = g per 1000 kg. Data taken from J. Emsley: *The Elements*, New York, Oxford University Press, 3rd edition, 1998.

21-2 The Periodic Table: A Guide to the Elements

The similarities in the properties of certain elements guided Mendeleev when he created the first periodic table (◀ Section 2-5). He placed elements in groups based partly on the composition of their common compounds with oxygen and hydrogen (Table 21.2). We now understand that the elements are grouped according to the arrangements of their valence electrons.

Table 21.2 Similarities within Periodic Groups*

GROUP	1A	2A	3A	4A	5A	6A	7A
Common oxide	M_2O	MO	M_2O_3	EO_2	E_4O_{10}	EO_3	E_2O_7
Common hydride	MH	MH_2	MH_3	EH_4	EH_3	EH_2	EH
Highest oxidation state	+1	+2	+3	+4	+5	+6	+7
Common oxoanion			BO_3^{3-}	CO_3^{2-}	NO_3^-	SO_4^{2-}	ClO_4^-
				SiO_4^{4-}	PO_4^{3-}		

*M denotes a metal and E denotes a nonmetal or metalloid.

Recall that the metallic character of the elements declines on moving from left to right in the periodic table. Elements in Group 1A, the alkali metals, are the most metallic elements in the periodic table. Elements on the far right are nonmetals, and in between are the metalloids. Metallic character also increases from the top of a group to the bottom. This is especially well illustrated by Group 4A. Carbon, at the top of the group, is a nonmetal; silicon and germanium are metalloids; and tin and lead are metals (Figure 21.2). The significance of metallic character in a discussion of the chemistry of the elements is readily apparent; metals typically form ionic compounds, whereas compounds composed only of nonmetals are covalent. Typically, ionic compounds are crystalline solids that have high melting points and conduct electricity in the molten state. Covalent compounds, on the other hand, can be gases, liquids, or solids and have low melting and boiling points.

FIGURE 21.2 **Group 4A elements.** A nonmetal, carbon (graphite crucible); a metalloid, silicon (round, lustrous bar); and metals tin (chips of metal) and lead (bullets, a toy, and a sphere).

Valence Electrons

The *ns* and *np* electrons are the valence electrons for main group elements (where *n* is the period in which the element is found) (◀ Section 7-3). The chemical behavior of an element is determined by the valence electrons.

When considering electronic structure, a useful reference point is the noble gases (Group 8A). Helium has an electron configuration of $1s^2$; the other noble gases have ns^2np^6 valence electron configurations. The dominant characteristic of the noble gases is their lack of reactivity. Indeed, the first two elements in the group do not form any compounds that can be isolated. The other four elements are now known to have limited chemistry, however, and the discovery of xenon compounds in the 1960s ranks as one of the most interesting developments in modern chemistry.

Ionic Compounds of Main Group Elements

Ions of main group elements having filled *s* and *p* subshells are common—justifying the often-seen statement that elements react in ways that achieve a "noble gas configuration." The elements in Groups 1A and 2A form 1+ and 2+ ions with electron configurations that are the same as those for the previous noble gases. All common compounds of these elements (e.g., NaCl, $CaCO_3$) are ionic. The metallic elements in Group 3A (aluminum, gallium, indium, and thallium, but not the metalloid boron) form compounds containing 3+ ions.

Elements of Groups 6A and 7A can achieve a noble gas configuration by adding electrons. The Group 7A elements (halogens) form anions with a 1− charge (the halide ions, F^-, Cl^-, Br^-, I^-), and the Group 6A elements form anions with a 2− charge (O^{2-}, S^{2-}, Se^{2-}, Te^{2-}). In Group 5A chemistry, 3− ions with a noble gas configuration (such as the nitride ion, N^{3-}) are also known. The energy required to form highly charged anions is large, however, which means that other types of chemical behavior will usually take precedence.

EXAMPLE 21.1

Reactions of Group 1A–3A Elements

Problem Give the formula and name for the product in each of the following reactions. Write a balanced chemical equation for the reaction.

(a) $Ca(s) + S_8(s)$

(b) $Rb(s) + I_2(s)$

(c) lithium and chlorine

(d) aluminum and oxygen

What Do You Know? The reactions listed are between metals in periodic groups 1A, 2A, and 3A and nonmetals in periodic groups 6A and 7A. The products formed will be ionic compounds made up of cations formed from metals by loss of electrons and anions formed from nonmetals by the gain of electrons.

Strategy Predictions are based on the assumption that ions are formed with the electron configuration of the nearest noble gas. Group 1A elements form 1+ ions; Group 2A elements form 2+ ions; and metals in Group 3A form 3+ ions. In their reactions with metals, halogen atoms typically add a single electron to give anions with a 1− charge; Group 6A elements add two electrons to form anions with a 2− charge. For names of products, refer to the nomenclature discussion in Section 2-7.

Solution

BALANCED EQUATION	PRODUCT NAME
(a) $8\ Ca(s) + S_8(s) \rightarrow 8\ CaS(s)$	Calcium sulfide
(b) $2\ Rb(s) + I_2(s) \rightarrow 2\ RbI(s)$	Rubidium iodide
(c) $2\ Li(s) + Cl_2(g) \rightarrow 2\ LiCl(s)$	Lithium chloride
(d) $4\ Al(s) + 3\ O_2(g) \rightarrow 2\ Al_2O_3(s)$	Aluminum oxide

Think about Your Answer It will be useful to review the formulas and names of common ions in Section 2-7.

Check Your Understanding

Write balanced chemical equations for the reactions forming the following compounds from the elements.

(a) NaBr (b) CaSe (c) PbO (d) $AlCl_3$

FIGURE 21.3 **Boron halides.** Liquid BBr_3 (left) and solid BI_3 (right). Formed from a metalloid and a nonmetal, both are molecular compounds. The two compounds are sealed in glass ampules to prevent them from reacting with H_2O in the air.

Molecular Compounds of Main Group Elements

Many avenues of reactivity are open to nonmetallic main group elements. Reactions with metals generally result in formation of ionic compounds, whereas compounds containing only metalloids and nonmetallic elements are generally molecular in nature.

Molecular compounds are encountered with the Group 3A element boron (Figure 21.3), and the chemistry of carbon in Group 4A is dominated by molecular compounds with covalent bonds (▶ Chapter 23). Similarly, nitrogen chemistry is dominated by molecular compounds. Consider ammonia, NH_3; the various nitrogen oxides (such as "laughing gas," N_2O); and nitric acid, HNO_3. In each of these species, nitrogen bonds covalently to another nonmetallic element. Also in Group 5A, phosphorus reacts with chlorine to produce the molecular compound PCl_3 (◀ Figure 3.1).

The valence electron configuration of an element determines the composition of its molecular compounds. Involving all the valence electrons in the formation of a compound is a frequent occurrence in main group element chemistry. We should not be surprised to discover compounds in which the central element has the highest possible oxidation number (such as P in PF_5). The highest oxidation number is readily predictable: it equals the group number. Thus, the highest (and only) oxidation number of sodium in its compounds is +1; the highest oxidation number of C is +4; and the highest oxidation number of phosphorus is +5 (Tables 21.2 and 21.3).

Table 21.3 Fluorine Compounds Formed by Main Group Elements

GROUP	COMPOUND	BONDING
1A	NaF	Ionic
2A	MgF_2	Ionic
3A	AlF_3	Ionic
4A	SiF_4	Covalent
5A	PF_5	Covalent
6A	SF_6	Covalent
7A	IF_7	Covalent
8A	XeF_4	Covalent

EXAMPLE 21.2

Predicting Formulas for Compounds of Main Group Elements

Problem Predict the formula for each of the following:

(a) The product of the reaction between germanium and excess oxygen

(b) The product of the reaction of arsenic and excess fluorine

(c) A compound formed from phosphorus and excess chlorine

(d) The fully deprotonated anion of selenic acid

What Do You Know? You know the symbol and location of each of the elements in the periodic table.

Strategy You can predict that in each reaction the element bonded to the halogen or oxygen in the product will achieve its most positive oxidation number, a value equal to the number of its periodic group.

Solution

(a) The Group 4A element germanium should have a maximum oxidation number of +4. Thus, its oxide has the formula GeO_2.

(b) Arsenic, in Group 5A, reacts vigorously with fluorine to form AsF_5, in which arsenic has an oxidation number of +5.

(c) PCl_5 is formed when the Group 5A element phosphorus reacts with excess chlorine.

(d) The chemistries of the Group 6A elements S and Se are similar. Sulfur has a maximum oxidation number of +6, so it forms SO_3 and sulfuric acid, H_2SO_4. Selenium has analogous chemistry, forming SeO_3 and selenic acid, H_2SeO_4. The fully deprotonated anion of this acid is the selenate ion, SeO_4^{2-}.

Think about Your Answer Notice that in several questions the use of excess oxidizing agent was specified. This is important because, for some of the nonmetals, several different products were possible. For example, the oxidation of carbon can produce either CO_2 or CO depending on whether there is an excess or a deficiency of oxygen. You will encounter other examples in later sections of this chapter.

Check Your Understanding

Write the formula for each of the following:

(a) hydrogen telluride

(b) sodium arsenate

(c) selenium hexachloride

(d) perbromic acid

There are many similarities among elements in the same periodic table group. This means you can use compounds of more common elements as examples when you encounter compounds of elements with which you are less likely to be familiar. For example, water, H_2O, is the simplest hydrogen compound of oxygen. You can reasonably expect the hydrogen compounds of other Group 6A elements to be H_2S, H_2Se, and H_2Te; all are well known.

EXAMPLE 21.3

Predicting Formulas

Problem Predict the formula for each of the following:

(a) A compound of hydrogen and phosphorus

(b) The hypobromite ion

(c) Germane (the simplest hydrogen compound of germanium)

(d) Two oxides of tellurium

What Do You Know? We expect the elements in a periodic group to behave similarly in their chemistry, in most instances. Thus, we can use known examples from the more common elements found early in the periodic table and extrapolate to predict the behavior of the less common elements found in the same group.

Strategy Recall as examples some of the compounds of lighter elements in a group, and then assume other elements in that group will form analogous compounds.

Solution

(a) Phosphine, PH_3, has a composition analogous to ammonia, NH_3.

(b) Hypobromite ion, BrO^-, is similar to the hypochlorite ion, ClO^-, the anion of hypochlorous acid (HClO).

(c) GeH_4 (germane) is analogous to CH_4 (methane) and SiH_4 (silane), two other Group 4A hydrogen compounds.

(d) Te and S are in Group 6A. TeO_2 and TeO_3 are analogs of the oxides of sulfur, SO_2 and SO_3.

Think about Your Answer Keep in mind there can be differences between elements within a periodic group. One difference is that second-period elements generally obey the octet rule, whereas in the third period and below, compounds with expanded octets can form (see Section 8-5). For example, in reactions with fluorine, nitrogen forms NF_3 whereas phosphorus forms both PF_3 and PF_5.

Check Your Understanding

Identify a compound or ion of a second-period element that has a formula and Lewis structure analogous to each of the following:

(a) PH_4^+ (b) S_2^{2-} (c) P_2H_4 (d) PF_3

EXAMPLE 21.4

Recognizing Incorrect Formulas

Problem One formula is incorrect in each of the following groups. Pick out the incorrect formula, and indicate why it is incorrect.

(a) $CsSO_4$, KCl, $NaNO_3$, Li_2O

(b) MgO, CaI_2, $BaPO_4$, $CaCO_3$

(c) CO, CO_2, CO_3

(d) PF_5, PF_4^+, PF_7, PF_6^-

What Do You Know? One formula in each set is wrong. You can determine which by applying the rules for oxidation states set forth in this section.

Strategy Look for errors such as incorrect charges on ions or an oxidation number exceeding the maximum possible for the periodic group.

Solution

(a) $CsSO_4$. Sulfate ion has a 2− charge, so this formula would require a Cs^{2+} ion. Cesium, in Group 1A, forms only 1+ ions. The formula of cesium sulfate is Cs_2SO_4.

(b) $BaPO_4$. This formula implies a Ba^{3+} ion (because the phosphate anion is PO_4^{3-}). The cation charge does not equal the group number. The formula of barium phosphate is $Ba_3(PO_4)_2$.

(c) CO_3. Given that O has an oxidation number of −2, carbon would have to have an oxidation number of +6. Carbon is in Group 4A, however, and can have a maximum oxidation number of +4.

(d) PF_7. The formula implies P has an oxidation state of +7, whereas +5 is expected for the maximum possible P oxidation state.

Think about Your Answer There are a lot of facts to learn in chemistry. Fortunately, many can be organized in ways that make learning easier. Using the periodic table to predict the chemistry of each element, and recognizing similarities among elements in groups, are an essential aspect of chemistry. This has been the goal of this section of the chapter.

Check Your Understanding

Explain why compounds with the following formulas would not be expected to exist: Na_2Cl, $CaCH_3CO_2$, Mg_2O.

REVIEW & CHECK FOR SECTION 21-2

1. Which of the following formulas is incorrect?

   (a) CaH_2 (b) CaI_2 (c) CaS (d) Ca_2O_3

2. What is the name of the product of the reaction between elemental phosphorus and excess oxygen, P_4O_{10}?

   (a) phosphorus oxide (c) phosphoric acid
   (b) phosphorus decaoxide (d) tetraphosphorus decaoxide

3. Like sulfur, selenium forms compounds in several different oxidation states. Which of the following is not likely to be an oxidation state of selenium in its compounds?

   (a) −2 (b) +3 (c) +6 (d) +4

4. What is the highest oxidation state that antimony can have in its compounds?

   (a) 0 (b) +1 (c) +3 (d) +5

21-3 Hydrogen

Chemical and Physical Properties of Hydrogen

Hydrogen has three isotopes, two of them stable (protium and deuterium) and one radioactive (tritium).

ISOTOPES OF HYDROGEN

ISOTOPE MASS (u)	SYMBOL	NAME
1.0078	^1H (H)	Hydrogen (protium)
2.0141	^2H (D)	Deuterium
3.0160	^3H (T)	Tritium

Of the three isotopes, only H and D are found in nature in significant quantities. Tritium, which is produced by cosmic ray bombardment of nitrogen in the atmosphere, is found to the extent of 1 atom per 10^{18} atoms of ordinary hydrogen. Radioactive tritium has a half-life of 12.26 years.

Under standard conditions, hydrogen is a colorless gas. Its very low boiling point, 20.7 K, reflects its nonpolar character and low molar mass. As the least dense gas known, it is ideal for filling lighter-than-air craft.

A CLOSER LOOK

Hydrogen, Helium, and Balloons

In 1783, Jacques Charles first used hydrogen to fill a balloon large enough to float above the French countryside (◀ page 381). In World War I, hydrogen-filled observation balloons were used. The Graf Zeppelin, a passenger-carrying dirigible built in Germany in 1928, was also filled with hydrogen. It carried more than 13,000 people between Germany and the United States until 1937, when it was replaced by the Hindenburg. The Hindenburg was designed to be filled with helium. At that time, World War II was approaching, and the United States, which has much of the world's supply of helium, would not sell the gas to Germany. As a consequence, the Hindenburg had to use hydrogen. The Hindenburg exploded and burned when landing in Lakehurst, New Jersey, in May 1937. Of the 62 people on board, only about half escaped uninjured. As a result of this disaster, hydrogen has acquired a reputation as being a very dangerous substance. Actually, it is as safe to handle as many other fuels.

Mary Evans Picture Library/Science Source

The Hindenburg. This hydrogen-filled dirigible crashed in Lakehurst, New Jersey, in May 1937. Some have speculated that the aluminum paint coating the skin of the dirigible was involved in sparking the fire.

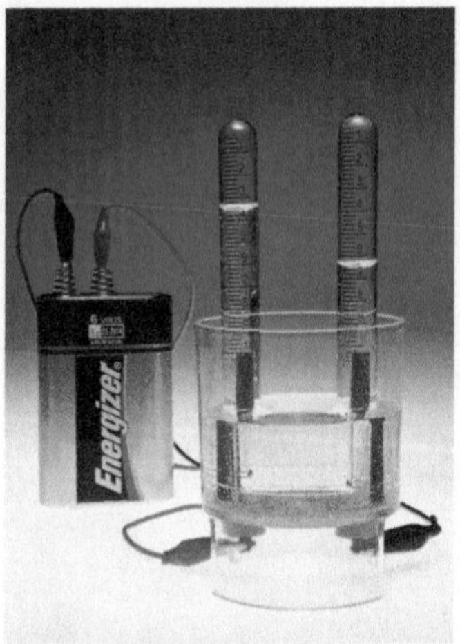

© Cengage Learning/Charles D. Winters

FIGURE 21.4 Electrolysis of water. Electrolysis of water (containing dilute H_2SO_4 as an electrolyte) gives O_2 *(left)* and H_2 *(right)*.

Deuterium compounds have been the subject of much research. One important observation is that, because D has twice the mass of H, reactions involving D atom transfer are slightly slower than those involving H atoms. This knowledge led to a way to obtain D_2O, which is sometimes called "heavy water." Hydrogen can be produced, albeit expensively, by electrolysis of water (Figure 21.4).

$$2\ H_2O(\ell) + \text{electrical energy} \rightarrow 2\ H_2(g) + O_2(g)$$

Any sample of natural water always contains a tiny concentration of D_2O. When electrolyzed, H_2O is electrolyzed more rapidly than D_2O. Thus, as the electrolysis proceeds, the liquid remaining is enriched in D_2O, and repeating the process many times will eventually give pure D_2O. Large amounts of D_2O are now produced because this compound is used as a moderator in some nuclear reactors.

Hydrogen combines chemically with virtually every other element, except the noble gases. There are three different types of binary hydrogen-containing compounds.

Ionic metal hydrides are formed in the reaction of H_2 with a Group 1A or 2A metal.

$$2\ Na(s) + H_2(g) \rightarrow 2\ NaH(s)$$

$$Ca(s) + H_2(g) \rightarrow CaH_2(s)$$

These compounds contain the hydride ion, H^-, in which hydrogen has a -1 oxidation number.

Molecular compounds (such as H_2O, HF, and NH_3) are generally formed by direct combination of hydrogen with nonmetallic elements (Figure 21.5). The oxidation number of the hydrogen atom in these compounds is $+1$; in these compounds, the non-metal and hydrogen are linked by covalent bonds.

$$N_2(g) + 3\ H_2(g) \rightarrow 2\ NH_3(g)$$

$$F_2(g) + H_2(g) \rightarrow 2\ HF(g)$$

Hydrogen is absorbed by many metals to form *interstitial hydrides*, the third general class of hydrogen compounds. This name refers to the structures of these species, in which the hydrogen atoms reside in the spaces between the metal atoms (called *interstices*) in the crystal lattice. Palladium metal, for example, can soak up

1000 times its volume of hydrogen (at STP). Most interstitial hydrides are nonstoichiometric; that is, the ratio of metal and hydrogen is not a whole number. When interstitial metal hydrides are heated, H_2 is driven out. This phenomenon allows these materials to be used to store H_2, just as a sponge can store water. It suggests one way to store hydrogen for use in automobiles.

FIGURE 21.5 **The reaction of H_2 and Br_2.** Hydrogen gas burns in an atmosphere of bromine vapor to give hydrogen bromide.

Preparation of Hydrogen

About 300 billion liters (STP) of hydrogen gas are produced annually worldwide, and virtually all is used immediately in the manufacture of ammonia (▶ Section 21-8), methanol (CH_3OH), or other chemicals.

Some hydrogen is made from coal and steam, a reaction that has been used for more than 100 years.

$$C(s) + H_2O(g) \longrightarrow \underbrace{H_2(g) + CO(g)}_{\text{water gas or synthesis gas}} \qquad \Delta_r H° = +131 \text{ kJ/mol-rxn}$$

The reaction is carried out by injecting water into a bed of red-hot coke. The mixture of gases produced, called *water gas* or *synthesis gas*, was used until about 1950 as a fuel for cooking, heating, and lighting. However, it has serious drawbacks. It produces only about half as much heat as an equal amount of methane does, and the flame is nearly invisible. Moreover, because it contains carbon monoxide, water gas is toxic.

The largest quantity of hydrogen is now produced by the *catalytic steam reformation* of methane in natural gas (Figure 21.6). Methane reacts with steam at high temperature to give H_2 and CO.

$$CH_4(g) + H_2O(g) \rightarrow 3\ H_2(g) + CO(g) \qquad \Delta_r H° = +206 \text{ kJ/mol-rxn}$$

The reaction is rapid at 900–1000 °C and goes nearly to completion. More hydrogen can be obtained in a second step in which the CO formed in the first step reacts with more water. This so-called *water gas shift reaction* is run at 400–500 °C and is slightly exothermic.

$$H_2O(g) + CO(g) \rightarrow H_2(g) + CO_2(g) \qquad \Delta_r H° = -41 \text{ kJ/mol-rxn}$$

The CO_2 formed in the process is removed by reaction with CaO (to give solid $CaCO_3$), leaving fairly pure hydrogen.

Perhaps the cleanest way to make hydrogen on a relatively large scale is the electrolysis of water (see Figure 21.4). This approach provides not only hydrogen gas but also high-purity O_2. Because electricity is quite expensive, however, this method is not generally used commercially.

Table 21.4 and Figure 21.7 give examples of reactions used to produce H_2 gas in the laboratory. The most often used method is the reaction of a metal with an

FIGURE 21.6 **Production of water gas.** Water gas, also called *synthesis gas*, is a mixture of CO and H_2. It is produced by treating coal, coke, or a hydrocarbon like methane with steam at high temperatures in plants such as that pictured here. Methane has the advantage that it gives more total H_2 per gram than other hydrocarbons, and the ratio of the by-product CO_2 to H_2 is lower.

Table 21.4 Methods for Preparing H_2 in the Laboratory

1. Metal + Acid → metal salt + H_2 $Mg(s) + 2\ HCl(aq) \rightarrow MgCl_2(aq) + H_2(g)$
2. Metal + H_2O → metal hydroxide or oxide + H_2 $2\ Na(s) + 2\ H_2O(\ell) \rightarrow 2\ NaOH(aq) + H_2(g)$ $2\ Fe(s) + 3\ H_2O(\ell) \rightarrow Fe_2O_3(s) + 3\ H_2(g)$ $2\ Al(s) + 2\ KOH(aq) + 6\ H_2O(\ell) \rightarrow 2\ K[Al(OH)_4](aq) + 3\ H_2(g)$
3. Metal hydride + H_2O → metal hydroxide + H_2 $CaH_2(s) + 2\ H_2O(\ell) \rightarrow Ca(OH)_2(s) + 2\ H_2(g)$

FIGURE 21.7
Producing hydrogen gas.

(a) The reaction of magnesium and acid. The products are hydrogen gas and a magnesium salt.

(b) The reaction of aluminum and aqueous NaOH. The products of this reaction are hydrogen gas and a solution of $Na[Al(OH)_4]$.

(c) The reaction of CaH_2 and water. The products are hydrogen gas and $Ca(OH)_2$.

acid. Alternatively, the reaction of aluminum with aqueous NaOH (Figure 21.7b) also generates hydrogen. During World War II, this reaction was used to obtain hydrogen to inflate small balloons for weather observation and to raise radio antennas. Metallic aluminum was plentiful at the time because it came from damaged aircraft.

The combination of a metal hydride and water (Figure 21.7c) is an efficient but expensive way to synthesize H_2 in the laboratory. The reaction is commonly used in laboratories to dry organic solvents because the metal hydride reacts with traces of water present in the solvent.

REVIEW & CHECK FOR SECTION 21-3

1. Which of the following elements does not react with hydrogen?

   (a) neon (b) nitrogen (c) potassium (d) fluorine

2. Which of the methods below is the most suitable for the preparation of large quantities of hydrogen (such as the amounts needed as a reagent for the synthesis of compounds such as ammonia)?

   (a) Electrolysis of water

   (b) The reaction of metal hydrides with water

   (c) The high-temperature reaction of methane and water

   (d) The reaction of zinc and hydrochloric acid

21-4 The Alkali Metals, Group 1A

Sodium and potassium are, respectively, the sixth and eighth most abundant elements in the Earth's crust. In contrast, lithium is relatively rare, as are rubidium and cesium. Only traces of radioactive francium occur in nature. Its longest-lived isotope (^{223}Fr) has a half-life of only 22 minutes.

The Group 1A elements are metals, and all are highly reactive with oxygen, water, and other oxidizing agents (◀ Figure 7.12). In all cases, these reactions yield compounds containing the Group 1A metals as a 1+ ion. Because these elements are so reactive, the free metal is never found in nature. Most sodium and potassium compounds are water-soluble (◀ solubility guidelines, Figure 3.10), so it is not surprising that sodium and potassium compounds are found either in the oceans or in underground deposits that are the residue of ancient seas. To a much smaller extent, these elements are also found in minerals, such as Chile saltpeter ($NaNO_3$).

Despite the fact that sodium is only slightly more abundant than potassium on the Earth, seawater contains significantly more sodium than potassium (2.8% NaCl versus 0.8% KCl). Why the great difference? Most compounds of both elements are water-soluble, so why didn't rain dissolve Na- and K-containing minerals over the centuries and carry them down to the sea, so that they appear in the same proportions in the oceans as on land? The answer lies in the fact that potassium is an important factor in plant growth. Most plants contain four to six times as much combined potassium as sodium. Thus, most of the potassium ions in groundwater from dissolved minerals are taken up preferentially by plants, whereas sodium ions continue on to the oceans. (Because plants require potassium, commercial fertilizers usually contain a significant amount of potassium salts.)

Some NaCl is essential in the diet of humans and other animals because many biological functions are controlled by the concentrations of Na^+ and Cl^- ions (Figure 21.8). The fact that salt has long been recognized as important is evident in surprising ways. For example, we are paid a "salary" for work done. This word is derived from the Latin *salarium*, which meant "salt money" because Roman soldiers were paid in salt.

Group **1A** *Alkali metals*
Lithium 3 **Li** 20 ppm
Sodium 11 **Na** 23,600 ppm
Potassium 19 **K** 21,000 ppm
Rubidium 37 **Rb** 90 ppm
Cesium 55 **Cs** 0.0003 ppm
Francium 87 **Fr** trace

Element abundances are in **parts per million** *in the Earth's crust.*

Preparation of Sodium and Potassium

Sodium is produced by reducing sodium ions in sodium salts. However, because few chemical reducing agents are powerful enough to convert sodium ions to sodium metal, the metal is usually prepared by electrolysis.

The English chemist Sir Humphry Davy first isolated sodium in 1807 by the electrolysis of molten sodium carbonate. However, the element remained a laboratory curiosity until 1824 when chemists found sodium could be used to reduce aluminum chloride to aluminum metal. At that time, metallic aluminum was rare and very valuable, so this discovery inspired considerable interest in manufacturing sodium. By 1886, a practical method of sodium production had been devised (the reduction of NaOH with carbon). Unfortunately for sodium producers, in this same year Charles Hall and Paul Heroult invented the electrolytic method for aluminum production (▶ page 823), thereby eliminating this market for sodium.

Sodium is currently produced by the electrolysis of molten NaCl (◀ Section 19-7). The Downs cell for the electrolysis of molten NaCl operates at 7 to 8 V with currents of 25,000 to 40,000 amps (Figure 21.9). The cell is filled with a mixture of dry NaCl, $CaCl_2$, and $BaCl_2$. [Adding other salts to NaCl lowers the melting point from that of pure NaCl (800.7 °C) to about 600 °C. Recall that solutions have lower melting points than pure solvents (◀ Chapter 13).] Sodium is produced at a copper or iron cathode that surrounds a circular graphite anode. Directly over the cathode is an inverted trough in which the low-density, molten sodium (melting point, 97.8 °C) collects. Chlorine, a valuable by-product, collects at the anode.

Potassium can also be made by electrolysis but separation of the metal is difficult because molten potassium is soluble in molten KCl. The preferred method for potassium preparation is the reaction of sodium vapor with molten KCl, with potassium being continually removed from the equilibrium mixture.

$$Na(g) + KCl(\ell) \rightleftharpoons K(g) + NaCl(\ell)$$

FIGURE 21.8 **The importance of salt.** All animals, including humans, need a certain amount of salt in their diet. Sodium ions are important in maintaining electrolyte balance and in regulating osmotic pressure. For an interesting account of the importance of salt in society, culture, history, and economy, see *Salt, A World History*, by M. Kurlansky, New York, Penguin Books, 2003.

Properties of Sodium and Potassium

Sodium and potassium are silvery metals that are soft and easily cut with a knife (◀ Figure 2.6). They are just a bit less dense than water. Their melting points, 97.8 °C for sodium and 63.7 °C for potassium, are quite low.

When exposed to moist air, the surface of an alkali metal quickly becomes coated with a film of oxide or hydroxide. Consequently, the metals must be stored in a way that avoids contact with air, typically by placing them in kerosene or mineral oil.

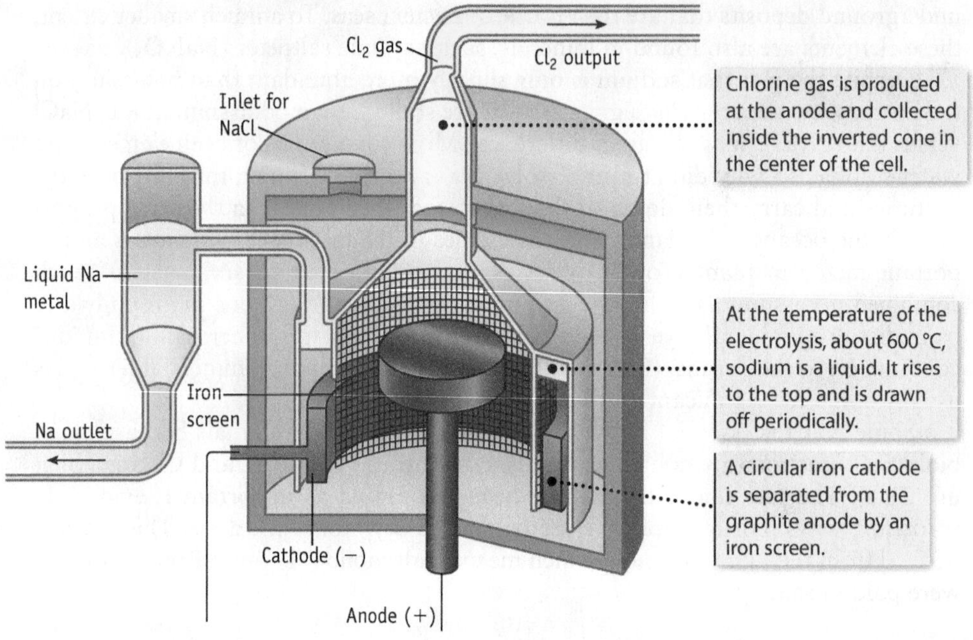

FIGURE 21.9 A Downs cell for preparing sodium.

A CLOSER LOOK The Reducing Ability of the Alkali Metals

The Group 1A or alkali metals (Li, Na, K, Rb, Cs) are readily oxidized. This is often demonstrated in general chemistry classes by their reactions with water. Lithium reacts sluggishly, sodium reacts somewhat more vigorously, and potassium, rubidium, and cesium are still more reactive, exploding on contact with water. The difference in reactivity is sometimes incorrectly ascribed to energetics, to the amount of energy evolved in these reactions. Actually, the differences are due to reaction rates. The lithium reaction is the slowest reaction of the group.

The energy evolved as heat for these reactions can be easily assessed using enthalpy data (see Table); this analysis shows that the reaction of Li with water is the most energetic.

For $M(s) + H_2O(\ell) \rightarrow MOH(aq) + \frac{1}{2} H_2(g)$

$$\Delta_r H° = \Delta_f H°[MOH(aq)] - \Delta_f H°[H_2O(\ell)]$$

M	$\Delta_f H°$ [MOH(aq)] kJ/mol	$\Delta_f H°$ [$H_2O(\ell)$] kJ/mol	$\Delta_r H°$ kJ/mol
Li	−508.48	−285.83	−222.65
Na	−469.15	−285.83	−183.32
K	−482.37	−285.83	−196.54
Rb	−476.1	−285.83	−190.3
Cs	−477.8	−285.83	−192.0

The values of $E°$ reveal that Li is the best reducing agent in the group, whereas Na is the poorest; the remainder of these metals have roughly comparable reducing abilities. This variation in this group matches the variation seen in the enthalpy change in the reaction with water.

Reduction Potential

Element	$E°$ (V)
$Li^+(aq) + e^- \rightarrow Li(s)$	−3.045
$Na^+(aq) + e^- \rightarrow Na(s)$	−2.714
$K^+(aq) + e^- \rightarrow K(s)$	−2.925
$Rb^+(aq) + e^- \rightarrow Rb(s)$	−2.925
$Cs^+(aq) + e^- \rightarrow Cs(s)$	−2.92

To analyze these values further we can break down these half-reactions into three energy terms [formation of metal atoms in the gas phase (atomization), ionization of the metal atoms, and solvation of the gaseous ions] and evaluate the free energy change ($\Delta G°$) for each step. Atomization and ionization both have positive values of $\Delta G°$ while the solvation of the metal cation has a large negative value. When doing this calculation for the various metals, we observe the negative and positive values mostly counterbalance each other and thus there is no clear trend in $\Delta G°$ values for the reaction.

Potassium is a very good reducing agent and reacts vigorously with water.

The high reactivity of Group 1A metals is exemplified by their reaction with water, which generates an aqueous solution of the metal hydroxide and hydrogen gas (see Figure 7.12 and *A Closer Look: The Reducing Ability of the Alkali Metals*),

$$2\ Na(s) + 2\ H_2O(\ell) \rightarrow 2\ Na^+(aq) + 2\ OH^-(aq) + H_2(g)$$

and their reaction with any of the halogens to yield a metal halide (◀ Figure 1.2),

$$2\ Na(s) + Cl_2(g) \rightarrow 2\ NaCl(s)$$

$$2\ K(s) + Br_2(\ell) \rightarrow 2\ KBr(s)$$

Chemistry often produces surprises. Group 1A metal oxides, M_2O, are known, but they are not the principal products of combining Group 1A elements and oxygen. Instead, the primary product of the reaction of sodium and oxygen is sodium *peroxide*, Na_2O_2, whereas the principal product from the reaction of potassium and oxygen is KO_2, potassium *superoxide*.

$$2\ Na(s) + O_2(g) \rightarrow Na_2O_2(s)$$

$$K(s) + O_2(g) \rightarrow KO_2(s)$$

Both Na_2O_2 and KO_2 are ionic compounds where the Group 1A cation is paired with either the peroxide ion (O_2^{2-}) or the superoxide ion (O_2^-). These compounds are not merely laboratory curiosities. They are used in oxygen-generation devices in places where people are confined, such as submarines, aircraft, and spacecraft, or when an emergency supply is needed.

The use of KO_2 in closed-circuit breathing equipment (Figure 21.10) is of particular note. These devices are self-contained, that is, there is no connection to the outside. The device must be able to both consume exhaled CO_2 and provide a continuous supply of oxygen. On average, a person exhales 0.82 L of CO_2 and some water vapor for every 1.0 L of O_2 inhaled. The reaction of KO_2 and exhaled water vapor produces O_2 and KOH, and the latter absorbs exhaled CO_2.

$$4\ KO_2(s) + 2\ H_2O(g) \rightarrow 4\ KOH(aq) + 3\ O_2(g)$$

$$4\ KOH(aq) + 2\ CO_2(g) \rightarrow 2\ K_2CO_3(s) + 2\ H_2O(g)$$

Notice that, for every 4 mol of KO_2, 3 mol O_2 are produced and 2 mol CO_2 is absorbed.

Courtesy Neutronics, Inc.

FIGURE 21.10 A closed-circuit breathing apparatus. Both carbon dioxide and moisture are exhaled by the wearer into a breathing tube. All of the CO_2 exhaled is consumed in the reaction with KO_2. Three moles of oxygen are produced from 2 mol of CO_2, replacing the oxygen consumed in respiration.

Important Lithium, Sodium, and Potassium Compounds

Electrolysis of aqueous sodium chloride (*brine*) is the basis of one of the largest chemical industries in the United States (Figure 21.11).

$$2\ NaCl(aq) + 2\ H_2O(\ell) \rightarrow Cl_2(g) + 2\ NaOH(aq) + H_2(g)$$

Two of the products from this process—chlorine and sodium hydroxide—give the industry its name: the *chlor-alkali industry*. More than 10 billion kilograms of Cl_2 and NaOH is produced annually in the United States.

Sodium carbonate, Na_2CO_3, is another commercially important compound of sodium. It is also known by two common names, *soda ash* and *washing soda*. In the past, it was largely manufactured by combining NaCl, ammonia, and CO_2 in the *Solvay process* (which remains the method of choice in many countries). In the United States, however, sodium carbonate is obtained from naturally occurring deposits of the mineral *trona*, $Na_2CO_3 \cdot NaHCO_3 \cdot 2\ H_2O$ (Figure 21.12).

Sodium bicarbonate, $NaHCO_3$, also known as *baking soda*, is another common compound of sodium. Not only is $NaHCO_3$ used in cooking, but it is also added in small amounts to table salt. NaCl is often contaminated with small amounts of $MgCl_2$. The magnesium salt is hygroscopic; that is, it picks water up from the air

FIGURE 21.11 Producing chlorine and sodium hydroxide in a membrane cell. This is the basis of the chlor-alkali industry. Brine is fed into the anode compartment and dilute sodium hydroxide or water into the cathode compartment. Pipes carry the evolved gases and NaOH away from the chambers of the electrolysis cell.

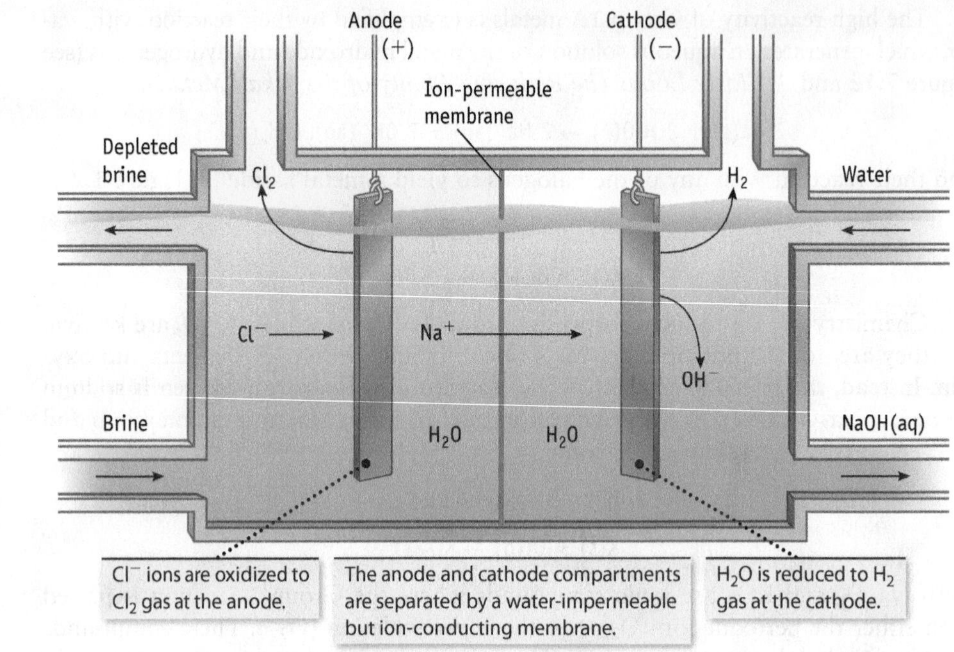

and, in doing so, causes the NaCl to clump. Adding $NaHCO_3$ converts $MgCl_2$ to magnesium carbonate, a nonhygroscopic salt.

$$MgCl_2(s) + 2\ NaHCO_3(s) \rightarrow MgCO_3(s) + 2\ NaCl(s) + H_2O(\ell) + CO_2(g)$$

Sodium nitrate, $NaNO_3$, is another common sodium compound, and large deposits are found in Chile, which explains its common name of "Chile saltpeter." These deposits are thought to have formed by bacterial action on organisms in shallow seas. The initial product was ammonia, which was subsequently oxidized to nitrate ion; combination with sea salt led to sodium nitrate. Because nitrates in general, and alkali metal nitrates in particular, are highly water-soluble, deposits of $NaNO_3$ are found only in areas with very little rainfall.

Sodium nitrate can be converted to potassium nitrate by an exchange reaction.

$$NaNO_3(aq) + KCl(aq) \rightleftharpoons KNO_3(aq) + NaCl(s)$$

Equilibrium favors the products here because, of the four salts involved in this reaction, NaCl is least soluble in hot water. Sodium chloride precipitates, and the KNO_3 that remains in solution can be recovered by evaporating the water.

Potassium nitrate has been used for centuries as the oxidizing agent in gunpowder (page 214). A mixture of KNO_3, charcoal, and sulfur will react when ignited.

$$2\ KNO_3(s) + 4\ C(s) \rightarrow K_2CO_3(s) + 3\ CO(g) + N_2(g)$$

$$2\ KNO_3(s) + 2\ S(s) \rightarrow K_2SO_4(s) + SO_2(g) + N_2(g)$$

FIGURE 21.12 Soda ash. Trona mined in Wyoming and California is processed into soda ash (Na_2CO_3) and other sodium-based chemicals. Soda ash is the ninth most widely used chemical in the United States. Domestically, about half of all soda ash produced is used in making glass. Most of the remainder goes to make chemicals such as sodium silicate, sodium phosphate, and sodium cyanide. Some is also used to make detergents, in the pulp and paper industry, and in water treatment.

Jack Dermid/Science Source

A trona mine in California. The mineral is taken from a mine about 500 m deep.

Notice that both reactions (which are doubtless more complex than described in these equations) produce gases. These gases propel the bullet from a gun or cause a firecracker to explode.

In the past several years lithium has become a significant commodity because of its use in lithium ion batteries (see *Case Study: Lithium and "Green Cars,"* Section 12-1). In fact, there is some concern that shortages of lithium will arise if the use of lithium ion batteries in cars becomes widespread. Currently, most lithium is obtained from concentrated brines in Chile and Bolivia, from which Li_2CO_3 is extracted. There are also ores from which lithium can be obtained. Similar to the other alkali metals, lithium metal is obtained from its compounds by molten salt electrolysis.

Gunpowder Gunpowder was developed well over 1000 years ago by the Chinese. One of the three ingredients is KNO_3, commonly called *saltpeter*. Although there are places in the world where it is prevalent and can be mined, for centuries it was obtained by mixing manure or human waste with wood ashes. Animal and human waste contain ammonia, which is converted by bacterial oxidation to nitrates. Wood ashes contain potash, potassium carbonate, the source of potassium in KNO_3. Sodium nitrate will also work in gunpowder, but it is hygroscopic and the powder is not effective when damp. See *Gunpowder* by J. Kelly, Basic Books, 2004.

REVIEW & CHECK FOR SECTION 21-4

1. Which of the following is not a property of sodium?
   (a) Reacts with Cl_2 to form NaCl
   (b) Has a silvery color
   (c) Has a high melting point (>400 °C)
   (d) Conducts an electric current
2. Which Group 1A metal ion has the most negative enthalpy of hydration?
   (a) Li^+ (b) Na^+ (c) K^+ (d) Cs^+
3. The compound Na_2O_2 consists of
   (a) two Na^+ ions and two O^{2-} ions
   (b) molecules of Na_2O_2
   (c) two Na^+ ions and one O_2^{2-} ion
   (d) Na^{2+} and O^{2-} ions

21-5 The Alkaline Earth Elements, Group 2A

The "earth" part of the name alkaline earth dates back to the days of medieval alchemy. To alchemists, any solid that did not melt and was not changed by fire into another substance was called an "earth." The word "alkaline" applies because compounds of Group 2A elements, such as CaO, are alkaline according to experimental tests conducted by the alchemists: The compounds had a bitter taste and neutralized acids. Finally, with very high melting points, these compounds were unaffected by fire.

Calcium and magnesium rank fifth and eighth, respectively, in abundance on the Earth. Both elements form many commercially important compounds, and we shall focus on these species.

Like the Group 1A elements, Group 2A elements are very reactive, so they are found in nature as compounds. Unlike most of the compounds of the Group 1A metals, however, many compounds of the Group 2A elements have low water-solubility, which explains their occurrence in various minerals (Figure 21.13). Calcium minerals include limestone ($CaCO_3$), gypsum ($CaSO_4 \cdot 2\ H_2O$), and fluorite (CaF_2). Magnesite ($MgCO_3$), talc or soapstone ($3\ MgO \cdot 4\ SiO_2 \cdot H_2O$), and asbestos ($3\ MgO \cdot 4\ SiO_2 \cdot 2\ H_2O$) are common magnesium-containing minerals. The mineral dolomite, $MgCa(CO_3)_2$, contains both magnesium and calcium.

Limestone, a sedimentary rock, is found widely on the Earth's surface. Many of these deposits contain the fossilized remains of marine life. Other forms of calcium carbonate include marble and Icelandic spar, the latter occurring as large, clear crystals with the interesting optical property of birefringence (Figure 21.13).

Group **2A**
Alkaline earths

Element	Atomic number	Symbol	Abundance
Beryllium	4	**Be**	2.6 ppm
Magnesium	12	**Mg**	23,300 ppm
Calcium	20	**Ca**	41,000 ppm
Strontium	38	**Sr**	370 ppm
Barium	56	**Ba**	500 ppm
Radium	88	**Ra**	6×10^{-7} ppm

Element abundances are in ***parts per million*** *in the Earth's crust.*

Properties of Calcium and Magnesium

Calcium and magnesium are fairly high-melting, silvery metals. The chemical properties of these elements present few surprises. They are oxidized by a wide range of oxidizing agents to form ionic compounds that contain the M^{2+} ion. For example, these elements combine with halogens to form MX_2, with oxygen or sulfur to form MO or MS, and with water to form hydrogen and the metal hydroxide, $M(OH)_2$

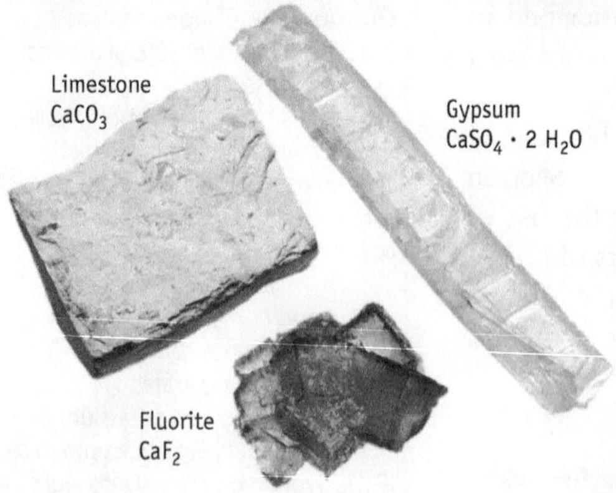

Common minerals of Group 2A elements.

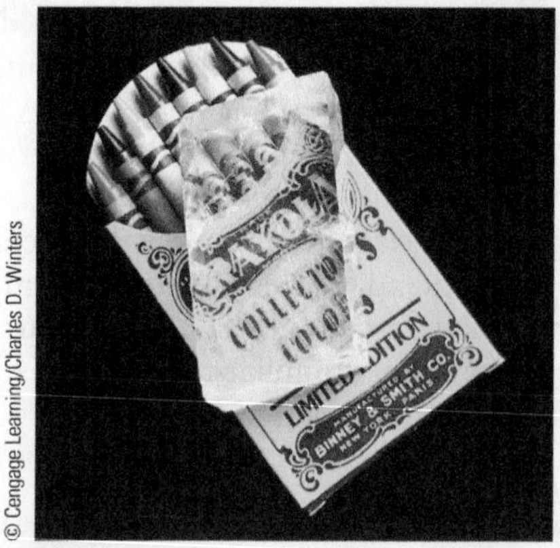

© Cengage Learning/Charles D. Winters

Icelandic spar. This mineral, one of a number of crystalline forms of $CaCO_3$, displays birefringence, a property in which a double image is formed when light passes through the crystal.

© Cengage Learning/Charles D. Winters

James Cowlin

Montezuma Castle National Monument near Sedona, Arizona. The five-story, 20-room cliff dwelling was built around 700 AD and was occupied from about 1125–1400 AD. The building was carved into the limestone cliffs of the Verde River Valley.

FIGURE 21.13 **Various minerals containing calcium.**

© Cengage Learning/Charles D. Winters

FIGURE 21.14 **The reaction of calcium and warm water.** Hydrogen bubbles are seen rising from the metal surface. The other reaction product is $Ca(OH)_2$. The inset is a model of hexagonal close-packed calcium metal (◀ Section 12-1).

(Figure 21.14). With acids, hydrogen is evolved (Figure 21.7), and a salt of the metal cation and the anion of the acid results.

Metallurgy of Magnesium

Several hundred thousand tons of magnesium are produced annually, largely for use in lightweight alloys. (Magnesium has a very low density, 1.74 g/cm^3.) Most aluminum used today contains about 5% magnesium to improve its mechanical properties and to make it more resistant to corrosion. Other alloys having more magnesium than aluminum are used when a high strength-to-weight ratio is needed and when corrosion resistance is important, such as in aircraft and automotive parts and in lightweight tools.

Interestingly, magnesium-containing minerals are not the commercial source of this element. Most magnesium is obtained from seawater, in which Mg^{2+} ion is present in a concentration of about 0.05 M. To obtain magnesium metal, magnesium ions in seawater are first precipitated (Figure 21.15) as the relatively insoluble hydroxide [K_{sp} for $Mg(OH)_2 = 5.6 \times 10^{-12}$]. Calcium hydroxide, the source of OH^- in this reaction, is prepared in a sequence of reactions beginning with $CaCO_3$, which may be in the form of seashells. Heating $CaCO_3$ gives CO_2 and CaO, and addition of water to CaO gives calcium hydroxide. When $Ca(OH)_2$ is added to seawater, $Mg(OH)_2$ precipitates:

$$Mg^{2+}(aq) + Ca(OH)_2(s) \rightleftharpoons Mg(OH)_2(s) + Ca^{2+}(aq)$$

Magnesium hydroxide is isolated by filtration and then converted to magnesium chloride by reaction with hydrochloric acid.

$$Mg(OH)_2(s) + 2\ HCl(aq) \rightarrow MgCl_2(aq) + 2\ H_2O(\ell)$$

After evaporating the water, anhydrous magnesium chloride remains. Solid $MgCl_2$ melts at 714 °C, and the molten salt is electrolyzed to give the metal and chlorine.

$$MgCl_2(\ell) \rightarrow Mg(s) + Cl_2(g)$$

Calcium Minerals and Their Applications

The most common calcium minerals are the fluoride, phosphate, and carbonate salts of the element. Fluorite, CaF_2, and fluoroapatite, $Ca_5F(PO_4)_3$, are important as

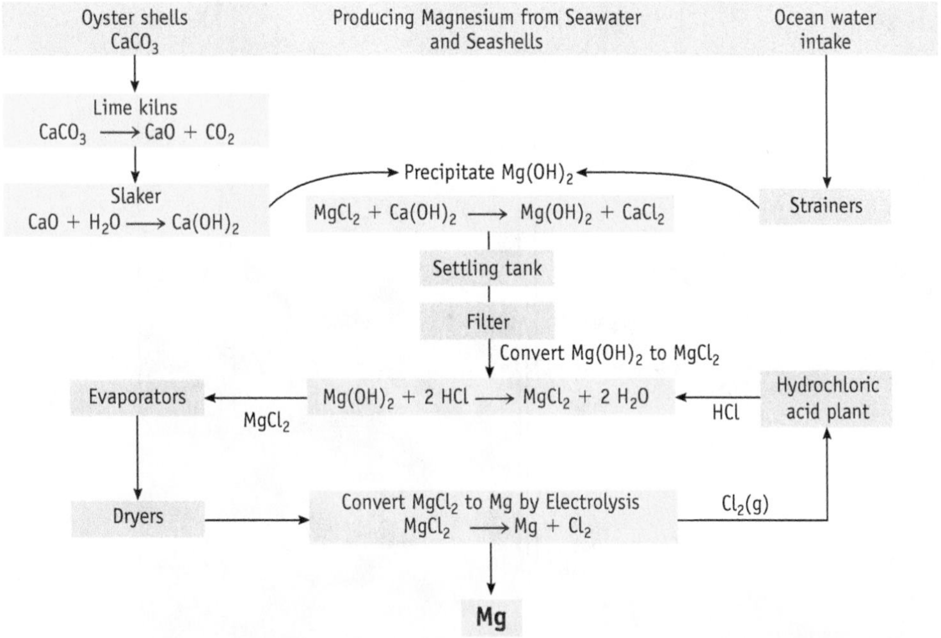

FIGURE 21.15 The process used to produce magnesium metal from the magnesium in seawater.

commercial sources of fluorine. Almost half of the CaF_2 mined is used in the steel industry, where it is added to the mixture of materials that is melted to make crude iron. The CaF_2 acts to remove some impurities and improves the separation of molten metal from silicates and other by-products resulting from the reduction of iron ore to the metal (▶ Chapter 22). A second major use of fluorite is in the manufacture of hydrofluoric acid by a reaction of the mineral with concentrated sulfuric acid.

$$CaF_2(s) + H_2SO_4(\ell) \rightarrow 2\ HF(g) + CaSO_4(s)$$

© Cengage Learning/Charles D. Winters

The mineral fluorite, CaF_2. Calcium fluoride is found in a wide variety of colors, and the crystals are frequently octahedral in shape.

Hydrofluoric acid is used to make cryolite, Na_3AlF_6, a material needed in aluminum production (▶ Section 21-6) and in the manufacture of fluorocarbons such as tetrafluoroethylene, the precursor to Teflon (▶ Table 23.12).

Apatites have the general formula $Ca_5X(PO_4)_3$ (X = F, Cl, OH). More than 100 million tons of apatite is mined annually, with Florida alone accounting for about one third of the world's output. Most of this material is converted to phosphoric acid by reaction with sulfuric acid. Phosphoric acid is needed in the manufacture of a multitude of products, including fertilizers and detergents, baking powder, and various food products (▶ Section 21-8).

Calcium carbonate and calcium oxide (*lime*) are of special interest. The thermal decomposition of $CaCO_3$ to give lime (and CO_2) is one of the oldest chemical reactions known. Lime is one of the top 10 industrial chemicals produced today, with about 20 billion kilograms produced annually.

Louis Goldman/Science Source

The Appian Way in Italy, an early use of lime mortar. The Appian Way in Italy was built as a military road linking Rome to seaports from which soldiers could embark to Greece and other Mediterranean countries. Stretching 560 kilometers (350 miles) from Rome to Brindisi on the Adriatic Sea (at the heel of the Italian "boot"), it took almost 200 years to construct. The Romans used mortar made of lime to "cement" the stones in place.

Limestone, which consists mostly of calcium carbonate, has been used in agriculture for centuries. It is spread on fields to neutralize acidic compounds in the soil and to supply Ca^{2+}, an essential nutrient. Because magnesium carbonate is often present in limestone, "liming" a field also supplies Mg^{2+}, another important nutrient for plants.

For several thousand years, lime has been used in *mortar* (a lime, sand, and water paste) to secure stones to one another in building houses, walls, and roads. The Chinese used it to set stones in the Great Wall. The Romans perfected its use, and the fact that many of their constructions still stand today is testament both to their skill and to the usefulness of lime. The famous Roman road, the Appian Way, used lime mortar between several layers of its stones.

CASE STUDY | Hard Water

No, hard water doesn't refer to ice. It is the name given to water containing high concentrations of Ca^{2+}(aq) and, in some instances, Mg^{2+}(aq) and other divalent metal cations. Accompanying these cations will be various anions, including in particular the hydrogen carbonate anion, HCO_3^-(aq).

Rainwater does not usually contain high concentrations of these ions, and so is not classified as "hard water." In many parts of the country, however, the municipal water supply comes from aquifers deep underground. If rainwater, containing some dissolved CO_2, has to percolate down through layers of limestone ($CaCO_3$) to get into the aquifer, a small amount of the solid will dissolve because of the following equilibrium:

$$CaCO_3(s) + CO_2(aq) + H_2O(\ell) \rightleftharpoons Ca^{2+}(aq) + 2\ HCO_3^-(aq)$$

If hard water containing Ca^{2+}(aq) and HCO_3^-(aq) is heated, or even if it is left to stand in an open vessel, CO_2 will be expelled, and the equilibrium will shift, precipitating $CaCO_3$(s) (◀ Section 15-1). This can be a small problem in a teakettle but a bigger problem in an industrial setting, where the solid $CaCO_3$ can clog pipes. Another consequence of hard water is that scum forms when soap is added. Soap is made by hydrolysis of fats, which produces long chain carboxylic acids. Soap scum is a precipitate of the calcium salt of these acids.

To avoid the problems associated with hard water, chemists and engineers have devised ways to "soften" water, that is, to decrease the concentration of the offending cations. In a water treatment plant for a municipality or a large industrial facility, most of the water hardness will be removed chemically, mainly by treatment with calcium oxide (lime, CaO). If HCO_3^- ions are present along with Ca^{2+} and/or Mg^{2+}, the following reactions occur:

$$Ca^{2+}(aq) + 2\ HCO_3^-(aq) + CaO(s) \rightarrow 2\ CaCO_3(s) + H_2O(\ell)$$

$$Mg^{2+}(aq) + 2\ HCO_3^-(aq) + CaO(s) \rightarrow CaCO_3(s) + MgCO_3(s) + H_2O(\ell)$$

Although it seems odd to add CaO to remove calcium ions, notice that adding one mole of CaO leads to the precipitation of two moles of Ca^{2+} as $CaCO_3$.

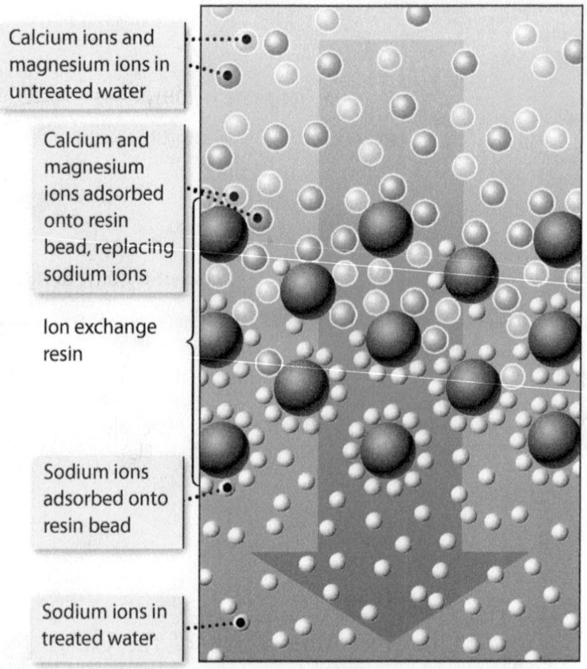

The general operation of an ion-exchange resin. The ion exchange material is usually a polymeric material formed into small beads.

Water softening by ion exchange in the home.

On a smaller scale, most home water purification systems use *ion exchange* to soften water (Figure). This process involves the replacement of an ion adsorbed onto a solid ion exchange resin by an ion in solution. Synthetic organic polymers with negatively charged functional groups (such as carboxylate groups, $—CO_2^-$) are the most commonly used resins for this purpose. Sodium ions, Na^+, are present in the resin to balance the negative charges of the carboxylate groups. The affinity of a surface for multi-charged cations is greater than for monovalent cations. Therefore, when a solution of hard water is passed over the surface of the ion exchange resin, Ca^{2+} and Mg^{2+} (and other divalent ions if present) readily replace Na^+ ions. This process can be illustrated in a general way by the equilibrium

$$2\ NaX + Ca^{2+}(aq) \rightleftharpoons CaX_2 + 2\ Na^+(aq)$$

where X represents an adsorption site on the ion exchange resin. The equilibrium favors adsorption of Ca^{2+} and release of Na^+. However, the equilibrium is reversed if Na^+(aq) ions are present in high concentration, and this allows regeneration of the ion exchange resin. A solution containing a high concentration of Na^+ (usually from salt, NaCl) is passed through the resin to convert the resin back to its initial form.

Questions:

1. Assume that a sample of hard water contains 50. mg/L of Mg^{2+} and 150 mg/L of Ca^{2+}, with HCO_3^- as the accompanying anion. What mass of CaO should be added to 1.0 L of this aqueous solution to cause all of this Mg^{2+} and Ca^{2+} to precipitate as $CaCO_3$ and $MgCO_3$? What is the total mass of the two solids formed?
2. One way to remove the calcium carbonate residue in a teakettle is to add vinegar (a dilute solution of acetic acid). Write a chemical equation to explain this process. What kind of a reaction is this?

Answers to these questions are available in Appendix N.

A CLOSER LOOK Alkaline Earth Metals and Biology

Plants and animals derive energy from the oxidation of a sugar, glucose, with oxygen. Plants are unique, however, in being able to synthesize glucose from CO_2 and H_2O using sunlight as an energy source. This process is initiated by *chlorophyll*, a very large, magnesium-based molecule.

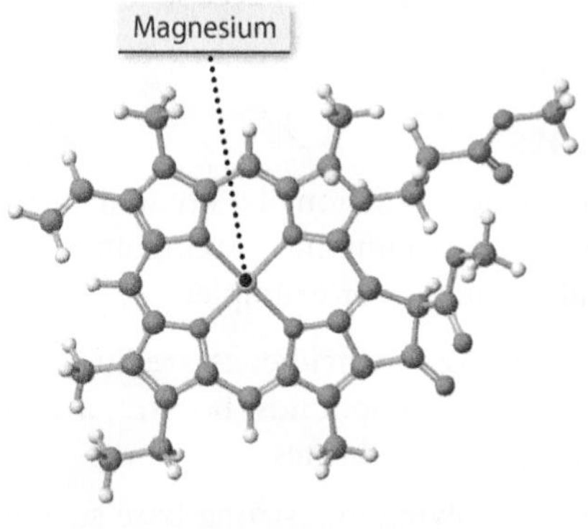

A molecule of chlorophyll. Magnesium is its central element.

In your body, the alkaline earth metal ions Mg^{2+} and Ca^{2+} serve regulatory functions. Although these two metal ions are required by living systems, the other Group 2A elements are toxic. Beryllium compounds are carcinogenic, and soluble barium salts are poisons. You may be concerned if your physician asks you to drink a "barium cocktail" to check the condition of your digestive tract. Don't be afraid, because the "cocktail" contains very insoluble $BaSO_4$ ($K_{sp} = 1.1 \times 10^{-10}$), so it passes through your digestive tract without a significant amount being absorbed. Barium sulfate is opaque to x-rays, so its path through your organs appears on the developed x-ray image.

The calcium-containing compound *hydroxyapatite* is the main component of tooth enamel. Cavities in your teeth form when acids (such as those in soft drinks) decompose the weakly basic hydroxyapatite coating.

$$Ca_5(OH)(PO_4)_3(s) + 4\ H_3O^+(aq) \rightarrow 5\ Ca^{2+}(aq) + 3\ HPO_4^{2-}(aq) + 5\ H_2O(\ell)$$

This reaction can be prevented by converting hydroxyapatite to the much more acid-resistant coating of fluoroapatite.

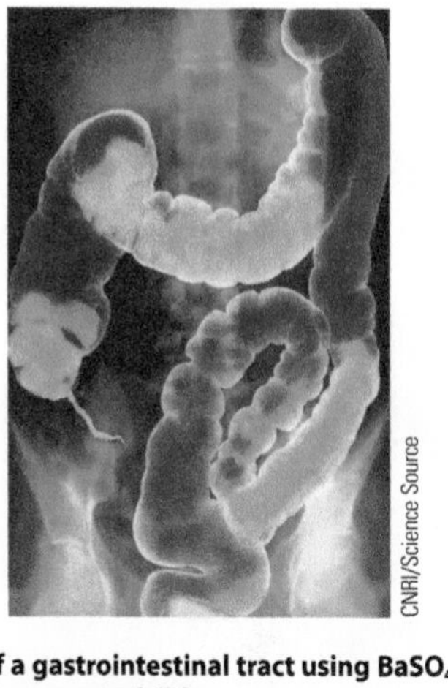

X-ray of a gastrointestinal tract using $BaSO_4$ to make the organs visible.

$$Ca_5(OH)(PO_4)_3(s) + F^-(aq) \rightarrow Ca_5F(PO_4)_3(s) + OH^-(aq)$$

The source of the fluoride ion can be sodium fluoride or sodium monofluorophosphate (Na_2FPO_3, commonly known as MFP) in your toothpaste.

The utility of mortar depends on some simple chemistry. Mortar consists of one part lime to three parts sand, with water added to make a thick paste. The first reaction, referred to as *slaking*, occurs after the solids are mixed with water. This produces a slurry containing calcium hydroxide, which is known as *slaked lime*.

$$CaO(s) + H_2O(\ell) \rightleftharpoons Ca(OH)_2(s)$$

When the wet mortar mix is placed between bricks or stone blocks, it slowly reacts with CO_2 from the air, and the slaked lime is converted to calcium carbonate.

$$Ca(OH)_2(s) + CO_2(g) \rightleftharpoons CaCO_3(s) + H_2O(\ell)$$

The sand grains are bound together by the particles of calcium carbonate.

REVIEW & CHECK FOR SECTION 21-5

1. Which of the following insoluble calcium compounds does not dissolve in hydrochloric acid?

   (a) limestone, $CaCO_3$
   (b) slaked lime, $Ca(OH)_2$
   (c) gypsum, $CaSO_4 \cdot 2\ H_2O$
   (d) hydroxyapatite, $Ca_5(OH)(PO_4)_3$

2. Calcium minerals are the raw materials for a variety of large-scale industrial processes. Which of the following is not an industrial process?

   (a) Converting limestone, $CaCO_3$, to lime
   (b) Converting fluorite, CaF_2, to HF
   (c) Converting slaked lime, $Ca(OH)_2$, to lime
   (d) Converting apatite minerals to phosphate fertilizers

Group 3A

Element	Atomic number	Symbol	Abundance
Boron	5	B	10 ppm
Aluminum	13	Al	82,000 ppm
Gallium	31	Ga	18 ppm
Indium	49	In	0.05 ppm
Thallium	81	Tl	0.6 ppm

Element abundances are in ***parts per million*** *in the Earth's crust.*

21-6 Boron, Aluminum, and the Group 3A Elements

With Group 3A, we see the first evidence of a change from metallic behavior of the elements at the left side of the periodic table to nonmetal behavior on the right side of the table. Boron is a metalloid, whereas all the other elements of Group 3A are metals.

The elements of Group 3A vary widely in their relative abundances on Earth. Aluminum is the third most abundant element in Earth's crust (82,000 ppm), whereas the other elements of the group are relatively rare, and, except for boron, their compounds have limited commercial uses.

Chemistry of the Group 3A Elements

There are chemical similarities between some elements diagonally situated in the periodic table. This diagonal relationship means that lithium and magnesium share some chemical properties, as do Be and Al, and B and Si. For example:

- Boric oxide, B_2O_3, and boric acid, $B(OH)_3$, are weakly acidic, as are SiO_2 and its acid, orthosilicic acid (H_4SiO_4). Boron–oxygen compounds, borates, are often chemically similar to silicon–oxygen compounds, silicates.
- Both $Be(OH)_2$ and $Al(OH)_3$ are amphoteric, dissolving in a strong base such as aqueous NaOH (◀ Figure 16.11).
- Chlorides, bromides, and iodides of boron and silicon (such as BCl_3 and $SiCl_4$) react vigorously with water.
- The hydrides of boron and silicon are simple, molecular species; are volatile and flammable; and react readily with water.
- Beryllium hydride and aluminum hydride are colorless, nonvolatile solids that are extensively polymerized through Be—H—Be and Al—H—Al three-center, two-electron bonds (◀ page 364).

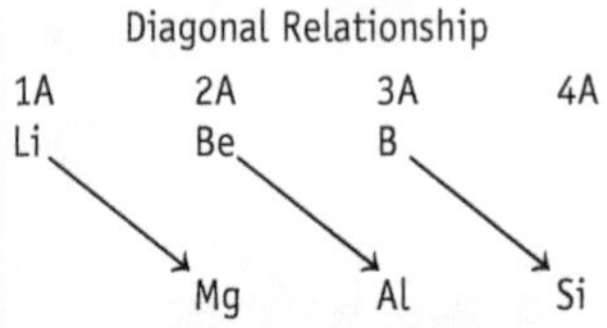

Diagonal Relationship The chemistries of elements diagonally situated in the periodic table are often quite similar.

Finally, the Group 3A elements are characterized by electron configurations of the type ns^2np^1. This means that each may lose three electrons to have a +3 oxidation number, although the heavier elements, especially thallium, also form compounds with an oxidation number of +1.

Boron Minerals and Production of the Element

Although boron has a low abundance on Earth, its minerals are found in concentrated deposits. Large deposits of borax, $Na_2B_4O_7 \cdot 10\ H_2O$, are currently mined in the Mojave Desert near the town of Boron, California.

Isolation of pure, elemental boron from boron-containing minerals is extremely difficult and is done in small quantities. Like most metals and metalloids, boron can be obtained by chemically or electrolytically reducing an oxide or halide. Magnesium has often been used for chemical reductions, but the product of this reaction is a noncrystalline boron of low purity.

$$B_2O_3(s) + 3\ Mg(s) \rightarrow 2\ B(s) + 3\ MgO(s)$$

Boron has several allotropes, all characterized by having an icosahedron of boron atoms as one structural element. Elemental boron is a very hard and refractory (resistant to heat) semiconductor. In this regard, it differs from the other Group 3A elements; Al, Ga, In, and Tl are all relatively low-melting, rather soft metals with high electrical conductivity.

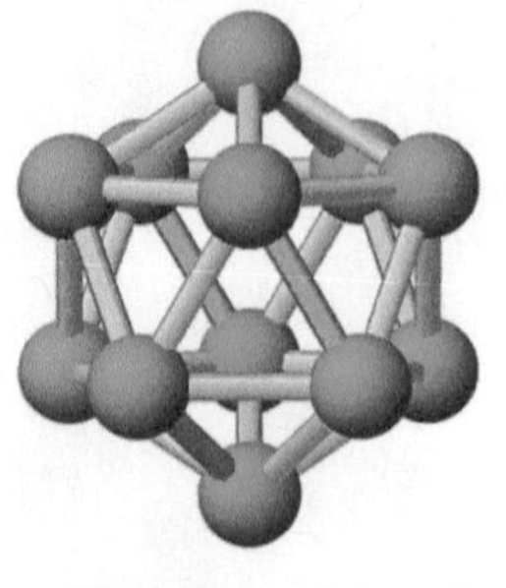
Boron Allotropes. All four allotropes of elemental boron have an icosahedron (a 20-sided polyhedron) of 12 covalently linked boron atoms as a structural element.

Metallic Aluminum and Its Production

The low cost of aluminum and the excellent characteristics of its alloys with other metals (low density, strength, ease of handling in fabrication, and inertness toward

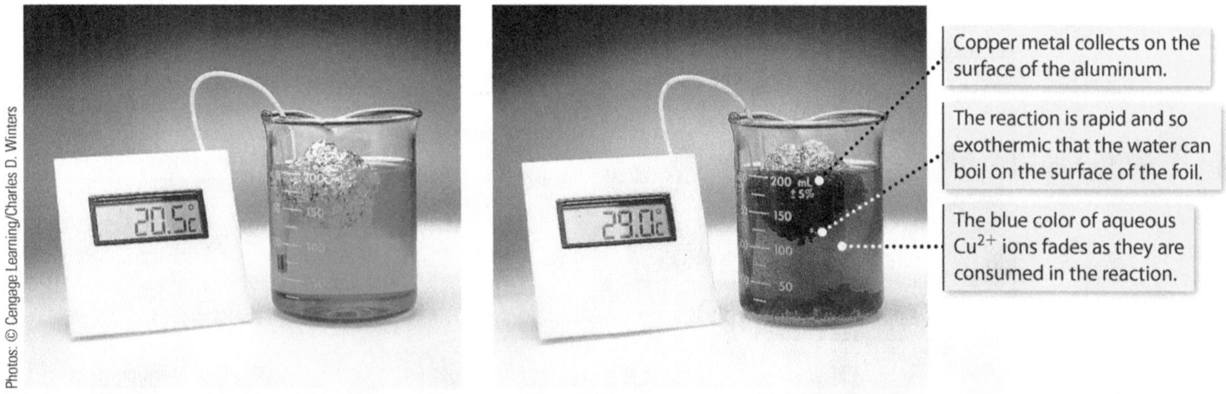

(a) A ball of aluminum foil is added to a solution of copper(II) nitrate and sodium chloride. Normally, the coating of chemically inert Al_2O_3 on the surface of aluminum protects the metal from further oxidation.

(b) In the presence of the Cl^- ion, the coating of Al_2O_3 is breached, and aluminum reduces copper(II) ions to copper metal.

FIGURE 21.16 **Corrosion of aluminum.**

corrosion, among others), have led to its widespread use. You know it best in the form of aluminum foil, aluminum cans, and parts of aircraft.

Pure aluminum is soft and weak; moreover, it loses strength rapidly at temperatures higher than 300 °C. What we call "aluminum" is actually aluminum alloyed with small amounts of other elements to strengthen the metal and improve its properties. A typical alloy may contain about 4% copper with smaller amounts of silicon, magnesium, and manganese. Softer, more corrosion-resistant alloys for window frames, furniture, highway signs, and cooking utensils may include only manganese.

The standard reduction potential of aluminum [$Al^{3+}(aq) + 3\ e^- \rightarrow Al(s)$; $E° = -1.66$ V] tells you that aluminum is easily oxidized. From this, we might expect aluminum to be highly susceptible to corrosion but, in fact, it is quite resistant. Aluminum's corrosion resistance is due to the formation of a thin, tough, and transparent skin of Al_2O_3 that adheres to the metal surface. However, if you penetrate the surface coating by scratching it or using a chemical agent, aluminum on the exposed surface can react immediately with oxygen or other oxidizing agent. In Figure 21.16, the surface is breached by Cl^- ions, and aluminum reacts rapidly with aqueous Cu^{2+} ions.

Charles Martin Hall (1863–1914)
Hall was only 22 years old when he worked out the electrolytic process for extracting aluminum from Al_2O_3 in a woodshed behind the family home in Oberlin, Ohio. He went on to found a company that eventually became ALCOA, the Aluminum Corporation of America.

Aluminum was first prepared by reducing $AlCl_3$ using sodium or potassium. This was a costly process, and, in the 19th century, aluminum was a precious metal. At the 1855 Paris Exposition a sample of aluminum was exhibited along with the crown jewels of France. In 1886, in an interesting coincidence, Frenchman Paul Heroult (1863–1914) and American Charles Martin Hall (1863–1914) simultaneously and independently conceived of the electrochemical method used today. The Hall–Heroult method bears the names of the two discoverers.

Aluminum is found in nature as aluminosilicates, minerals such as clay that are based on aluminum, silicon, and oxygen. As these minerals weather, they break down to various forms of hydrated aluminum oxide, $Al_2O_3 \cdot n\ H_2O$, called *bauxite*. Mined in huge quantities, bauxite is the raw material from which aluminum is obtained. The first step is to purify the ore, separating Al_2O_3 from iron and silicon oxides. This is done by the *Bayer process*, which relies on the amphoteric, basic, or acidic nature of the various oxides. (Silica, SiO_2, is an acidic oxide, whereas Al_2O_3 is amphoteric, and Fe_2O_3 is a basic oxide.) Silica and Al_2O_3 dissolve in a hot concentrated solution of caustic soda (NaOH), leaving insoluble Fe_2O_3 to be filtered out.

$$Al_2O_3(s) + 2\ NaOH(aq) + 3\ H_2O(\ell) \rightarrow 2\ Na[Al(OH)_4](aq)$$

$$SiO_2(s) + 2\ NaOH(aq) + 2\ H_2O(\ell) \rightarrow Na_2[Si(OH)_6](aq)$$

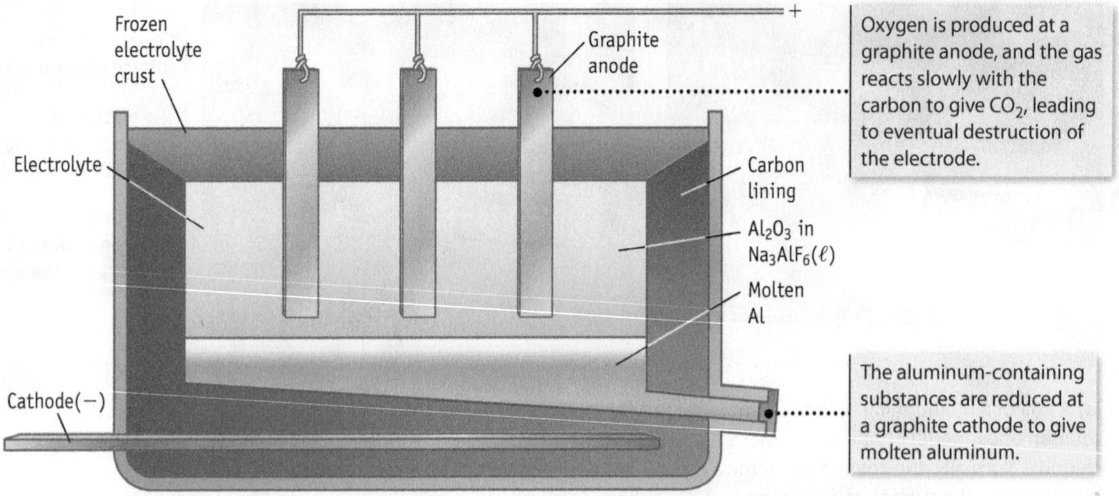

FIGURE 21.17 Industrial production of aluminum. Purified aluminum-containing ore (bauxite) is essentially Al_2O_3. In the Hall–Heroult process this is mixed with cryolite (Na_3AlF_6) and other fluorides such as AlF_3. (The additives serve to lower the melting point of the mixture and increase the conductivity.)

If a solution containing aluminate and silicate anions is treated with CO_2, Al_2O_3 precipitates, and the silicate ion remains in solution. Recall that CO_2 is an acidic oxide that forms the weak acid H_2CO_3 in water, so the Al_2O_3 precipitation in this step is an acid–base reaction.

$$H_2CO_3(aq) + 2\ Na[Al(OH)_4](aq) \rightarrow Na_2CO_3(aq) + Al_2O_3(s) + 5\ H_2O(\ell)$$

Metallic aluminum is obtained from purified bauxite by electrolysis (Figure 21.17). Bauxite is first mixed with cryolite, Na_3AlF_6, to give a lower-melting mixture (melting temperature = 980 °C) that is electrolyzed in a cell with graphite electrodes. The cell operates at a relatively low voltage (4.0–5.5 V) but with an extremely high current (50,000–150,000 A). Aluminum is produced at the cathode and oxygen at the anode. To produce 1 kg of aluminum requires 13 to 16 kilowatt-hours of energy plus the energy required to maintain the high temperature.

Boron Compounds

Borax, $Na_2B_4O_7 \cdot 10\ H_2O$, is the most important boron–oxygen compound and is the form of the element most often found in nature (Figure 21.18). It has been used for centuries in metallurgy because of the ability of molten borax to dissolve other

FIGURE 21.18 Borax, the mineral source of elemental boron.

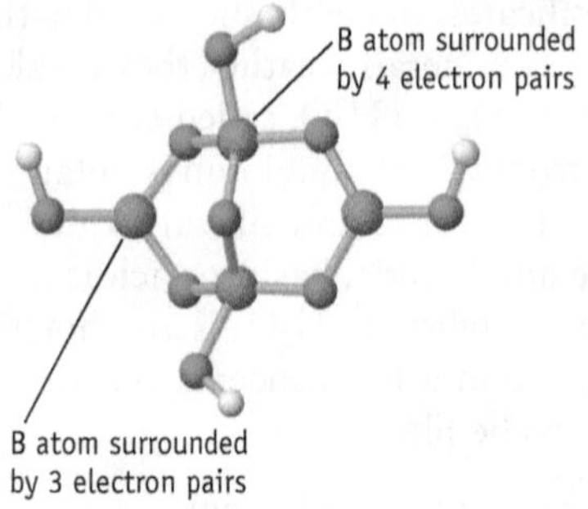

(a) The structure of the ion $[B_4O_5(OH)_4]^{2-}$ found in borax.

(b) The mineral named ulexite, a form of crystalline borax, $Na_2B_4O_7 \cdot 10\ H_2O$.

metal oxides. Because of this, borax is used as a *flux* that cleans the surfaces of metals to be joined and permits a good metal-to-metal contact.

The formula for borax gives little information about its structure. The anion is better described by the formula $[B_4O_5(OH)_4]^{2-}$, the structure of which illustrates two commonly observed structural features in inorganic chemistry. First, many minerals consist of MO_n groups that share O atoms. Second, the sharing of O atoms between two metals or metalloids often leads to MO rings.

After refinement, borax can be treated with sulfuric acid to produce boric acid, $B(OH)_3$.

$$Na_2B_4O_7 \cdot 10\ H_2O(s) + H_2SO_4(aq) \rightarrow 4\ B(OH)_3(aq) + Na_2SO_4(aq) + 5\ H_2O(\ell)$$

The chemistry of boric acid involves both Lewis and Brønsted acid behavior. Hydronium ions are produced by a Lewis acid–base interaction between boric acid and water.

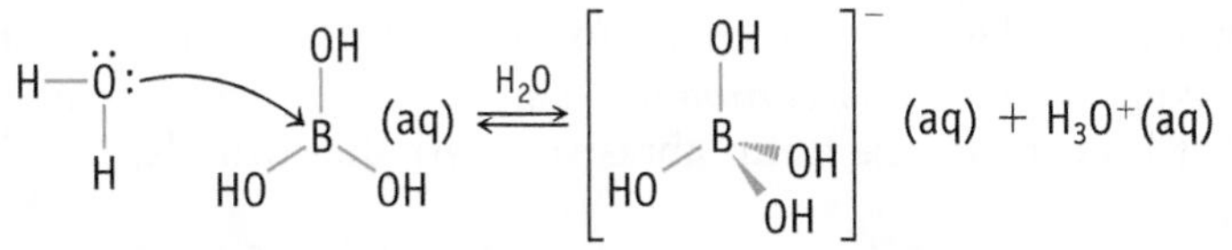

$$K_a = 7.3 \times 10^{-10}$$

Borax in Fire Retardants The second largest use for boric acid and borates is as a flame retardant for cellulose home insulation. Such insulation is often made of scrap paper, which is inexpensive but flammable. To control the flammability, 5%–10% of the weight of the insulation is boric acid.

Because of its weak acid properties and slight biological activity, boric acid has been used for many years as an antiseptic. Furthermore, because boric acid is a weak acid, salts of borate ions, such as the $[B_4O_5(OH)_4]^{2-}$ ion in borax, are weak bases.

Boric acid is dehydrated to boric oxide when strongly heated.

$$2\ B(OH)_3(s) \rightarrow B_2O_3(s) + 3\ H_2O(\ell)$$

By far the largest use for the oxide is in the manufacture of borosilicate glass (the type of glass used in most laboratory glassware). This type of glass is composed of 76% SiO_2, 13% B_2O_3, and much smaller amounts of Al_2O_3 and Na_2O. The presence of boric oxide gives the glass a higher softening temperature, imparts a better resistance to attack by acids, and limits the expansion of the glass on heating. This last property makes borosilicate glass less prone to breakage when heated or cooled.

Borax in Fireworks Barium salts and chlorinated organic compounds are used in fireworks to produce a green color. The problem is, however, that these ingredients are toxic. But a solution was recently found: boron carbide, B_4C, gives off an intense green color when combined with an oxidizing agent such as KNO_3 at high temperatures.

Like its metalloid neighbor silicon, boron forms a series of molecular compounds with hydrogen. Because boron is slightly less electronegative than hydrogen, these compounds are described as hydrides, in which the H atoms bear a partial negative charge. More than 20 neutral boron hydrides, or boranes, with the general formula B_xH_y are known. The simplest of these is diborane, B_2H_6, a colorless, gaseous compound with a boiling point of −92.6 °C. This molecule is described as electron deficient because there are not enough electrons to attach all of the atoms using two-electron bonds. Instead, the description of bonding uses three-center two-electron bonds in the B—H—B bridges (◀ page 364).

Diborane has an endothermic enthalpy of formation ($\Delta_f H° = +41.0$ kJ/mol). For this reason, diborane burns in air to give boric oxide and water vapor in an extremely exothermic reaction. It is not surprising that diborane and other boron hydrides were once considered as possible rocket fuels.

$$B_2H_6(g) + 3\ O_2(g) \rightarrow B_2O_3(s) + 3\ H_2O(g) \qquad \Delta_r H° = -2038\ \text{kJ/mol-rxn}$$

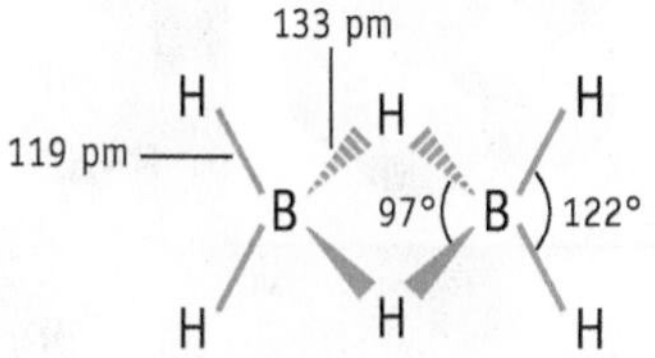

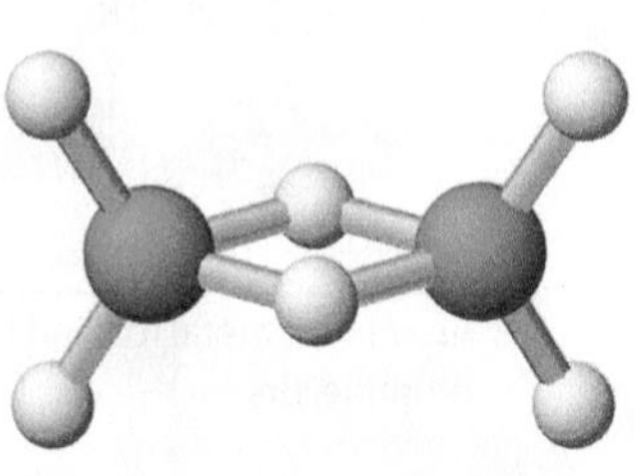

Diborane, B_2H_6, the simplest member of a family of boron hydrides.

Diborane can be synthesized from sodium borohydride, $NaBH_4$, the only B—H compound produced in ton quantities.

$$2\ NaBH_4(s) + I_2(s) \rightarrow B_2H_6(g) + 2\ NaI(s) + H_2(g)$$

Sodium borohydride, $NaBH_4$, a white, crystalline, water-soluble solid, is made from NaH and borate esters such as $B(OCH_3)_3$.

$$4\ NaH(s) + B(OCH_3)_3(g) \rightarrow NaBH_4(s) + 3\ NaOCH_3(s)$$

The main use of $NaBH_4$ is as a reducing agent in organic synthesis (▶ Chapter 23).

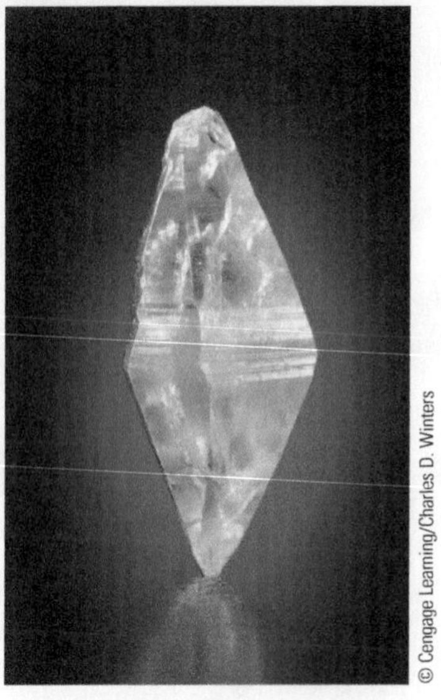

FIGURE 21.19 Corundum, Al_2O_3. Corundum is a crystalline form of aluminum oxide. Both rubies and sapphires are a form of corundum in which a few Al^{3+} ions have been replaced by ions such as Cr^{3+}, Fe^{2+}, or Ti^{4+}.

Aluminum Compounds

Aluminum is an excellent reducing agent, so it reacts readily with hydrochloric acid (forming Al^{3+} ions and H_2). In contrast, it does not react with nitric acid, a stronger oxidizing agent than hydrochloric acid. It turns out that nitric acid oxidizes the surface of aluminum and produces a film of Al_2O_3 that protects the metal from further attack. In fact, this means nitric acid can be shipped in aluminum tanks.

Various salts of aluminum dissolve in water, giving the hydrated $Al^{3+}(aq)$ ion, which is a weak Brønsted acid (◀ Table 16.2).

$$[Al(H_2O)_6]^{3+}(aq) + H_2O(\ell) \rightleftharpoons [Al(H_2O)_5(OH)]^{2+}(aq) + H_3O^+(aq)$$

Adding acid shifts the equilibrium to the left, whereas adding base causes the equilibrium to shift to the right. Addition of sufficient hydroxide ion results ultimately in precipitation of the hydrated oxide $Al_2O_3 \cdot 3\ H_2O$.

Aluminum oxide, Al_2O_3, formed by dehydrating the hydrated oxide, is quite insoluble in water and generally resistant to chemical attack. In the crystalline form, aluminum oxide is known as *corundum*. This material is extraordinarily hard, a property that leads to its use as an abrasive in grinding wheels, "sandpaper," and toothpaste.

Some gems are impure aluminum oxide. Rubies, beautiful red crystals prized for jewelry and used in some lasers, are composed of Al_2O_3 contaminated with a small amount of Cr^{3+} (Figure 21.19). The Cr^{3+} ions replacing some of the Al^{3+} ions in the crystal lattice are the source of the red color. Synthetic rubies were first made in 1902, and the worldwide capacity is now about 200,000 kg/year; much of this production is used for jewel bearings in watches and instruments. Blue sapphires consist of Al_2O_3 with Fe^{2+} and Ti^{4+} impurities in place of Al^{3+} ions.

Boron forms halides such as gaseous BF_3 and BCl_3 that have the expected trigonal planar molecular geometry of halogen atoms surrounding an sp^2 hybridized boron atom. In contrast, the aluminum halides are all solids and have different structures. Aluminum bromide, which is made by the very exothermic reaction of aluminum metal and bromine (Figure 21.20),

$$2\ Al(s) + 3\ Br_2(\ell) \longrightarrow Al_2Br_6(s)$$

has the formula Al_2Br_6. The structure resembles that of diborane in that bridging atoms appear between the two Al atoms. However, Al_2Br_6 is not electron deficient;

Aluminum metal foil and liquid bromine, Br_2.

When the foil is added to the bromine a vigorous reaction occurs.

The reaction produces white solid Al_2Br_6. The heat of the reaction is so high that any aluminum in excess melts.

FIGURE 21.20 Reaction of aluminum metal and bromine to give Al_2Br_6.

the bridge is formed when a Br atom on one $AlBr_3$ uses a lone pair to form a coordinate covalent bond to a neighboring tetrahedral, sp^3-hybridized aluminum atom.

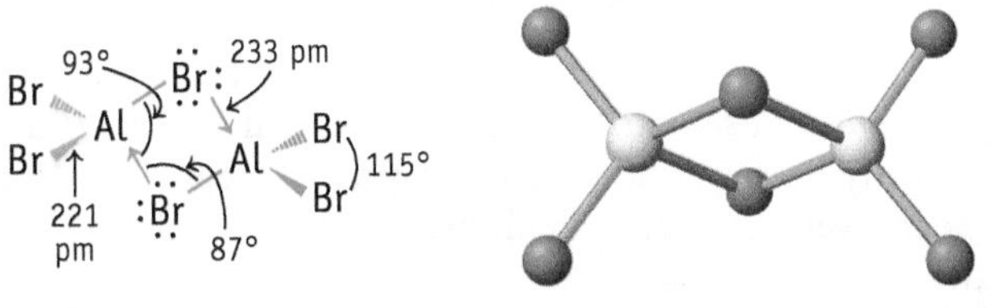

The structure of Al_2Br_6. The bonding in Al_2Br_6 is not unique to the aluminum halides. Metal–halogen–metal bridges are found in many other metal–halogen compounds.

Both aluminum bromide and aluminum iodide have this structure. Aluminum chloride has a different solid state structure, but it exists as dimeric molecules in the vapor state. Aluminum fluoride has an ionic lattice structure, built from Al^{3+} and F^- ions.

Aluminum chloride can react with a chloride ion to form the anion $[AlCl_4]^-$. Aluminum fluoride, in contrast, can accommodate three additional F^- ions to form an octahedral $[AlF_6]^{3-}$ ion. This is the anion found in cryolite, Na_3AlF_6, the compound added to aluminum oxide in the electrolytic production of aluminum metal. Apparently, the Al^{3+} ion can bind to six of the smaller F^- ions, whereas only four of the larger Cl^-, Br^-, or I^- ions can surround an Al^{3+} ion.

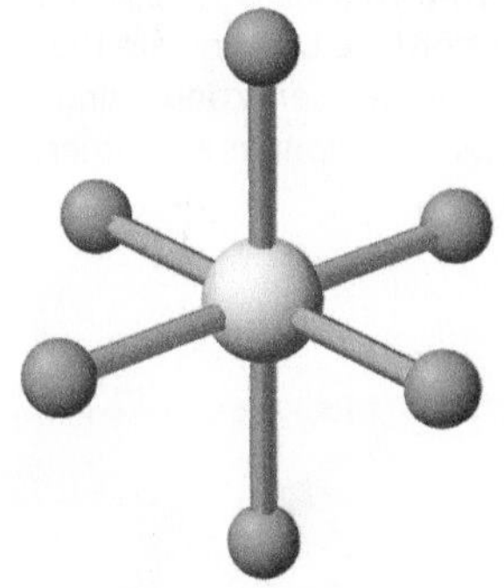

The octahedral $[AlF_6]^{3-}$ anion. This is the anion in the mineral cryolite.

REVIEW & CHECK FOR SECTION 21-6

1. In terms of abundance of the elements in the Earth's crust, aluminum ranks

   (a) first (b) second (c) third (d) fourth

2. The element below aluminum in Group 3A is gallium, and there are numerous similarities in the chemistry of these two elements. For example, the hydroxides of both elements are amphoteric. A consequence of this is that both gallium hydroxide and aluminum hydroxide

   (a) are insoluble in water
   (b) dissolve only in acid
   (c) dissolve only in base
   (d) dissolve in acid and in base

21-7 Silicon and the Group 4A Elements

Carbon is a nonmetal; silicon and germanium are classified as metalloids; and tin and lead are metals. As a result, the elements of Group 4A have a broad range of chemical behavior.

The Group 4A elements are characterized by half-filled valence shells with two electrons in the *ns* orbital and two electrons in *np* orbitals. The bonding in carbon and silicon compounds is largely covalent and involves sharing four electron pairs with neighboring atoms. In germanium compounds, the +4 oxidation state is common (GeO_2 and $GeCl_4$), but some +2 oxidation state compounds exist (GeI_2). Oxidation numbers of both +2 and +4 are common in compounds of tin and lead (such as $SnCl_2$, $SnCl_4$, PbO, and PbO_2). Oxidation numbers two units less than the group number are often encountered for heavier elements in Groups 3A–7A.

Group **4A**

Carbon	6	**C**	480 ppm
Silicon	14	**Si**	277,000 ppm
Germanium	32	**Ge**	1.8 ppm
Tin	50	**Sn**	2.2 ppm
Lead	82	**Pb**	14 ppm

Element abundances are in **parts per million** *in the Earth's crust.*

Silicon

Silicon is second after oxygen in abundance in the Earth's crust, so it is not surprising we are surrounded by silicon-containing materials: bricks, pottery, porcelain, lubricants, sealants, computer chips, and solar cells. The computer revolution is based on the semiconducting properties of silicon.

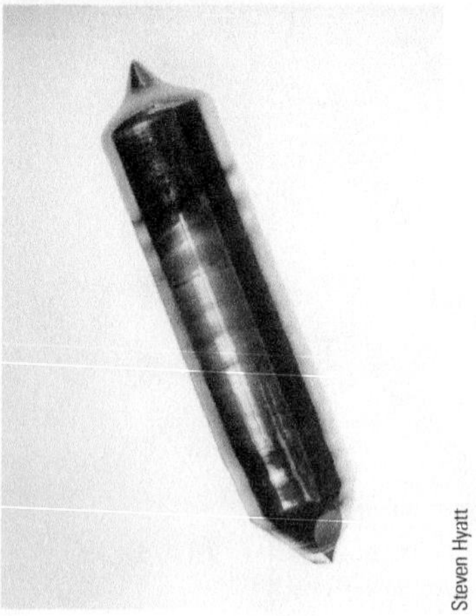

Steven Hyatt

FIGURE 21.21 Bar of pure silicon. Thin wafers of silicon are cut from the bars and are the basis for the semiconducting chips in computers and other devices.

Reasonably pure silicon can be made in large quantities by heating pure silica sand with purified coke to approximately 3000 °C in an electric furnace.

$$SiO_2(s) + 2\ C(s) \rightarrow Si(\ell) + 2\ CO(g)$$

The molten silicon is drawn off the bottom of the furnace and allowed to cool to a shiny blue-gray solid. Because extremely high-purity silicon is needed for the electronics industry, purifying raw silicon requires several steps. First, the silicon in the impure sample is allowed to react with chlorine to convert the silicon to liquid silicon tetrachloride.

$$Si(s) + 2\ Cl_2(g) \rightarrow SiCl_4(\ell)$$

Silicon tetrachloride (boiling point of 57.6 °C) is carefully purified by distillation and then reduced to silicon using magnesium.

$$SiCl_4(g) + 2\ Mg(s) \rightarrow 2\ MgCl_2(s) + Si(s)$$

The magnesium chloride is washed out with water, and the silicon is remelted and cast into bars. A final purification is carried out by zone refining, a process in which a special heating device is used to melt a narrow segment of the silicon rod. The heater is moved slowly down the rod. Impurities contained in the silicon tend to remain in the liquid phase. The silicon that crystallizes above the heated zone is therefore of a higher purity (Figure 21.21).

Silicon Dioxide

The simplest oxide of silicon is SiO_2, commonly called *silica*, a constituent of many rocks such as granite and sandstone. Quartz is a pure crystalline form of silica, but impurities in quartz produce gemstones such as amethyst (Figure 21.22).

Silica and CO_2 are oxides of two elements in the same chemical group, so similarities between them might be expected. In fact, SiO_2 is a high-melting solid (quartz melts at 1610 °C), whereas CO_2 is a gas at room temperature and 1 atm. This great disparity arises from the different structures of the two oxides. Carbon dioxide is a molecular compound, with the carbon atom linked to each oxygen atom by a double bond. In contrast, SiO_2 is a network solid, which is the preferred structure because the bond energy of two Si=O double bonds is much less than the bond energy of four Si—O single bonds. The contrast between SiO_2 and CO_2 is an example of a more general phenomenon. Multiple bonds, often encountered between second-period elements, are rare among elements in the third period and beyond. There are

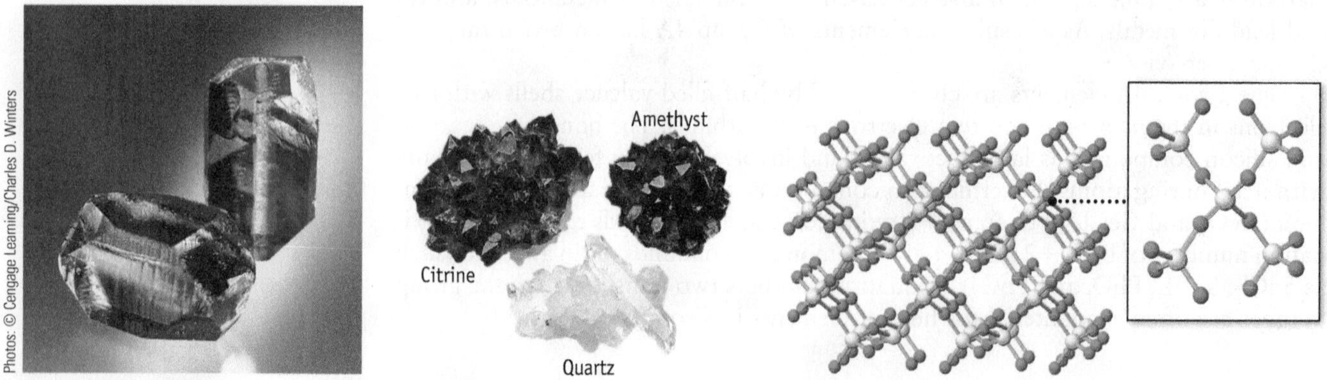

Synthetic quartz. These crystals were grown from silica in sodium hydroxide. The colors come from added Co^{2+} ions (blue) or Fe^{2+} ions (brown).

Natural quartz. Pure quartz is colorless, but impurities add color to produce purple amethyst and brown citrine.

Network solid. Each Si atom is bound tetrahedrally to four O atoms, each linked to another Si atom.

FIGURE 21.22 Various forms of quartz.

many compounds with multiple bonds to carbon but very few compounds featuring multiple bonds to silicon.

Quartz crystals are used to control the frequency of radio and television transmissions. Because these and related applications use so much quartz, there is not enough natural quartz to fulfill demand, and quartz is therefore synthesized. Noncrystalline, or vitreous, quartz, made by melting pure silica sand, is placed in a steel "bomb," and dilute aqueous NaOH is added. A "seed" crystal is placed in the mixture, just as you might use a seed crystal in a hot sugar solution to grow rock candy. When the mixture is heated above the critical temperature of water (above 400 °C and 1700 atm) over a period of days, pure quartz crystallizes.

Silicon dioxide is resistant to attack by all acids except HF, with which it reacts to give SiF_4 and H_2O.

$$SiO_2(s) + 4\ HF(\ell) \rightarrow SiF_4(g) + 2\ H_2O(\ell)$$

Silicon dioxide also dissolves slowly in hot, molten NaOH or Na_2CO_3 to give Na_4SiO_4, sodium silicate.

$$SiO_2(s) + 2\ Na_2CO_3(\ell) \rightarrow Na_4SiO_4(s) + 2\ CO_2(g)$$

After the molten mixture has cooled, hot water is added under pressure. This partially dissolves the material to give a solution of sodium silicate. After filtering off insoluble sand or glass, the solvent is evaporated to leave sodium silicate, called *water glass*. The biggest single use of this material is in household and industrial detergents, in which it is included because a sodium silicate solution maintains pH by its buffering ability. Additionally, sodium silicate is used in various adhesives and binders, especially for gluing corrugated cardboard boxes.

If sodium silicate is treated with acid, a gelatinous precipitate of SiO_2 called *silica gel* is obtained. Washed and dried, silica gel is a highly porous material with many uses. It is a drying agent, readily absorbing up to 40% of its own weight of water. Small packets of silica gel are often placed in packing boxes of merchandise during storage. The material is frequently stained with $(NH_4)_2CoCl_4$, a humidity detector that is pink when hydrated and blue when dry.

Silicate Minerals with Chain and Ribbon Structures

The structure and chemistry of silicate minerals is an enormous topic in geology and chemistry. Although all silicates are built from tetrahedral SiO_4 units, they have different properties and a wide variety of structures because of the way these tetrahedral SiO_4 units link together.

The simplest silicates, *orthosilicates*, contain SiO_4^{4-} anions. The 4− charge of the anion is balanced by four M^+ ions, two M^{2+} ions, or a combination of ions. Olivine, an important mineral in the Earth's mantle, contains Mg^{2+} and Fe^{2+}, with the Fe^{2+} ion giving the mineral its characteristic olive color, and gem-like zircons are $ZrSiO_4$. Calcium orthosilicate, Ca_2SiO_4, is a component of Portland cement, the most common type of cement used in many parts of the world. (Ca_2SiO_4 can be thought of as a mixture of CaO and SiO_2, the main ingredients of cement.)

A group of minerals called *pyroxenes* have as their basic structural unit a chain of SiO_4 tetrahedra.

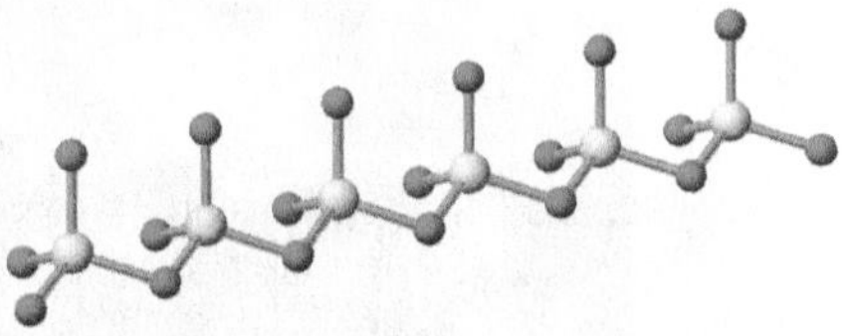

If two such chains are linked together by sharing oxygen atoms, the result is an *amphibole*, of which the asbestos minerals are one example. The molecular chain results in asbestos being a fibrous material.

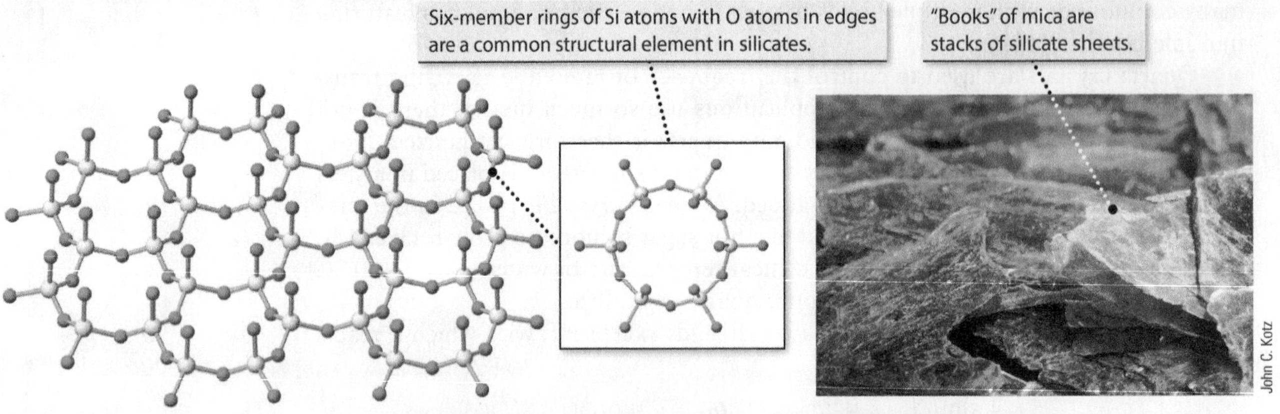

John C. Kotz

FIGURE 21.23 **Mica, a sheet silicate.** The sheet-like molecular structure of mica explains its physical appearance. As in the pyroxenes, each silicon is bonded to four oxygen atoms, but the Si and O atoms form a sheet of six-member rings of Si atoms with O atoms in each edge. The ratio of Si to O in this structure is 1 to 2.5. A formula of $SiO_{2.5}$ requires a positive ion, such as Na^+, to counterbalance the charge. Thus, mica and other sheet silicates, and aluminosilicates such as talc and many clays, have positive ions between the sheets.

Silicates with Sheet Structures and Aluminosilicates

Linking many silicate chains together produces a sheet of SiO_4 tetrahedra (Figure 21.23). This sheet is the basic structural feature of some of Earth's most important minerals, particularly the clay minerals (such as china clay), mica, talc, and the chrysotile form of asbestos. However, these minerals do not contain just silicon and oxygen. Rather, they are often referred to as *aluminosilicates* because they frequently have Al^{3+} ions in place of Si^{4+} (which means that other positive ions such as Na^+, K^+, and Mg^{2+} must also be present in the lattice to balance the net negative and positive charges). In kaolinite clay, for example, the sheet of SiO_4 tetrahedra is bonded to a sheet of AlO_6 octahedra. In addition, some Si^{4+} ions can be replaced by Al^{3+} atoms. Another example is muscovite, a form of mica. Aluminum ions have replaced some Si^{4+} ions, and there are charge-balancing K^+ ions, so it is best represented by the formula $KAl_2(OH)_2(Si_3AlO_{10})$.

There are some interesting uses of clays, one being in medicine (Figure 21.24). In certain cultures, clay is eaten for medicinal purposes. Several remedies for the relief of upset stomach contain highly purified clays that absorb excess stomach acid as well as potentially harmful bacteria and their toxins by exchanging the intersheet cations in the clays for the toxins, which are often organic cations.

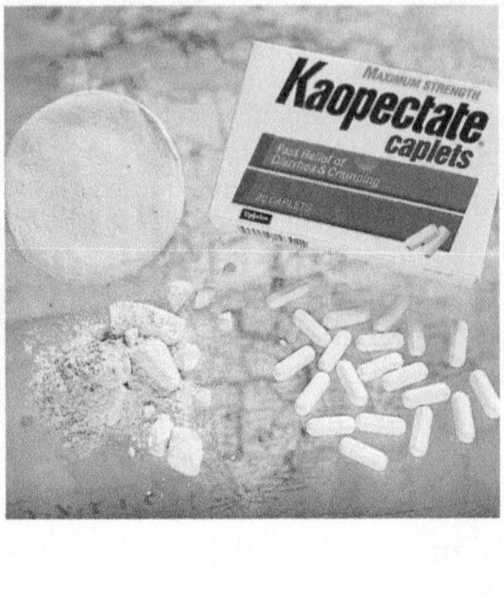

Photos: © Cengage Learning/Charles D. Winters

Remedy for stomach upset. One of the ingredients in Kaopectate is kaolin, one form of clay. The off-white objects are pieces of clay purchased in a market in Ghana, West Africa. It is eaten for an upset stomach, a practice widespread round the world.

Kaolinite clay. The basic structural feature of many clays, and kaolinite in particular, is a sheet of SiO_4 tetrahedra (black and red spheres) bonded to a sheet of AlO_6 octahedra (gray and green spheres).

FIGURE 21.24 **Clay, an aluminosilicate.**

A CLOSER LOOK | Green Cement

Cement is such a commonplace material that we tend to take it for granted. The preparation of cement has origins more the 2000 years ago and was used in Roman roads that still exist today. The current "recipe" for cement was patented in 1824 by a British bricklayer, Joseph Aspdin, and has seen little change since that time. Aspdin called his product Portland cement because it was similar in appearance to Portland stone, from the Isle of Portland in Dorset, England. In 2010, the world production of Portland cement was 3.6 billion tons; this amount is second only to water among substances people use.

The preparation of Portland cement involves heating a mixture of $CaCO_3$, SiO_2, and alumina silicate (clay) at 1450 °C. This produces a solid mass called a *clinker*. Grinding the material with a little $CaSO_4$ gives cement as a fine gray powder; its main components are CaO (60–67 %), SiO_2 (17–25%), Al_2O_3 (3–8%), and Fe_2O_3 (0–6%). Mixing cement with sand and aggregate produces concrete; cement is also the main constituent in mortar, stucco, and some grout. The usefulness of cement in these products comes from the fact that when it is mixed with water a series of not-well-understood reactions ensue to produce a hard, strong, solid product that is ideal for use in construction.

The high temperature required to prepare the clinker makes this process energy intensive. Furthermore, it releases about 900 kg of CO_2 for each 1000 kg of cement, which is estimated to be about 5% of the anthropogenic emissions of CO_2. (About half of the CO_2 comes from decomposition of $CaCO_3$ to form CO_2; the other half is from fuel combustion.) Improving these figures would help address two current environmental concerns, energy consumption and greenhouse gas evolution. Hence, there are a number of ongoing research projects to develop a greener cement.

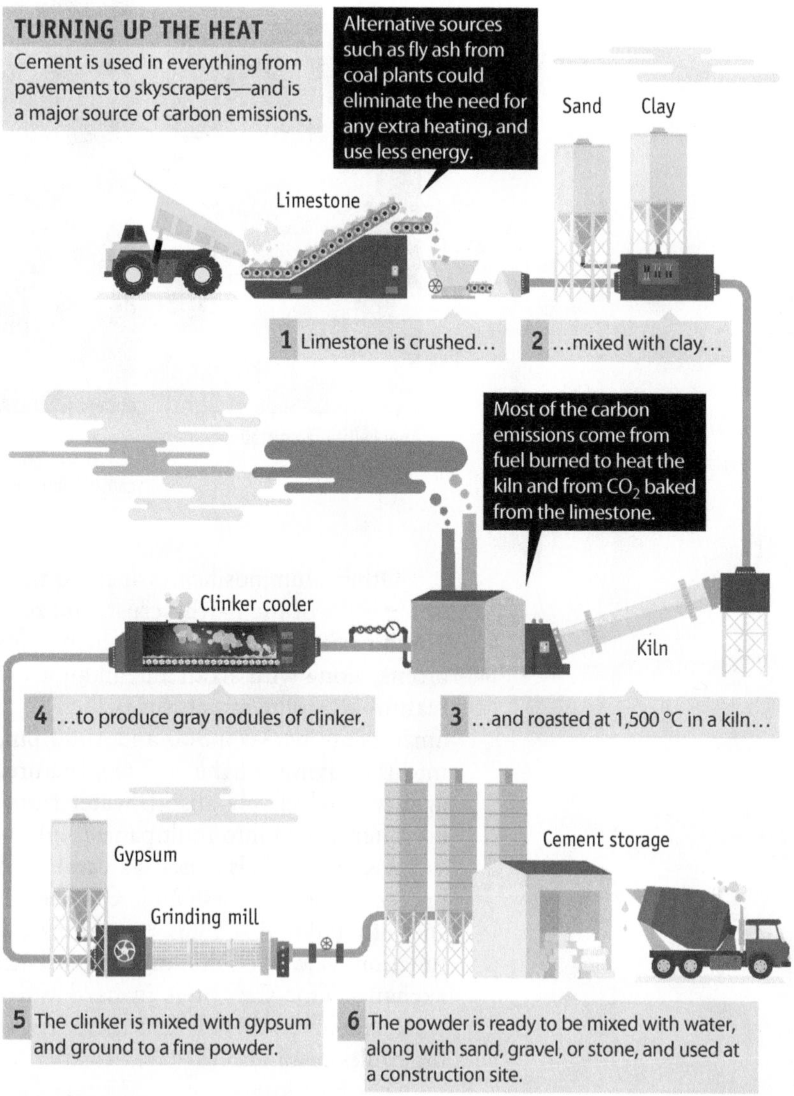

In one of these projects the main interest is in sequestration of CO_2. In this approach CO_2 from power plants is combined with seawater and hard water to create carbonates that can be used in cement manufacture. When these materials are used to make cement, the process ends up being closer to CO_2 neutral, balancing the incorporation and evolution of CO_2 in the overall process.

Novacem, a British company, took a more radical approach. Here, magnesium silicates absorb CO_2 at elevated temperature and pressure to give magnesium oxide and magnesium carbonate, which is then used as a replacement for $CaCO_3$ in cement manufacture. The white solid product had the same characteristics as the calcium based Portland cement. The significant difference is that this process was carbon dioxide positive; overall, the process to make 1000 kg of Novacem cement absorbed 100 kg of CO_2 more than was emitted.

The award-winning Novacem process has unfortunately not been able to compete in the cement industry. The company failed to get the necessary funding to expand and it was liquidated in late 2012 after selling the intellectual property to an Australian company.

Figure from I. Amato, "Green Cement: Concrete Solutions," *Nature*, February 22, 2013.

FIGURE 21.25 Zeolites are aluminosilicates.

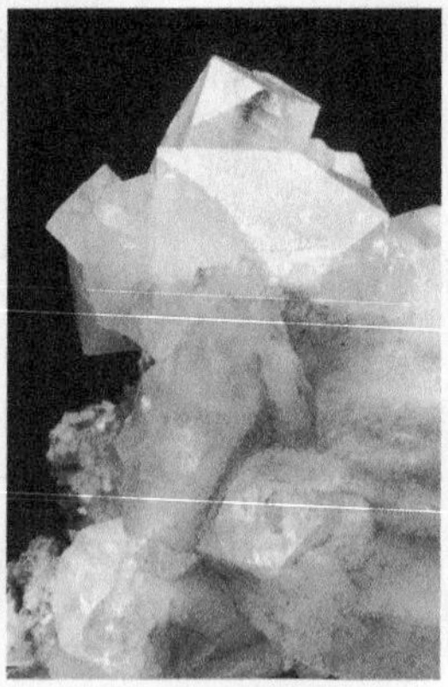

© Cengage Learning/Charles D. Winters

Apophyllite, a crystalline zeolite.

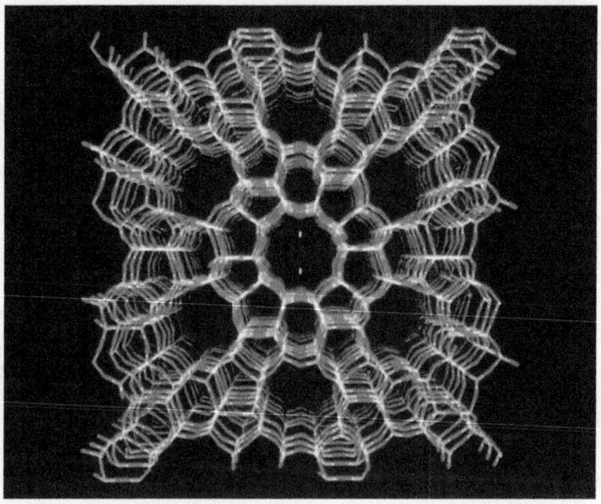

Chemical Design/Science Source

Zeolite structure. Each edge consists of Si—O—Si, Al—O—Si, or Al—O—Al bonds. The channels in the framework can selectively capture ions or small molecules.

Other aluminosilicates include the feldspars, common minerals that make up about 60% of the Earth's crust, and zeolites (Figure 21.25). Both materials are composed of SiO_4 tetrahedra in which some of the Si atoms have been replaced by Al atoms, along with alkali and alkaline earth metal ions for charge balance. The main feature of zeolite structures is their regularly shaped tunnels and cavities. Hole diameters are between 300 and 1000 pm, and small molecules such as water can fit into the cavities of the zeolite structure. As a result, zeolites can be used as drying agents to selectively absorb water from air or a solvent. Small amounts of zeolites are often sealed into multipane windows to keep the air dry between the panes.

Zeolites are also used as catalysts. ExxonMobil, for example, has patented a process in which methanol, CH_3OH, is converted to gasoline in the presence of specially tailored zeolites. In addition, zeolites are added to detergents, where they function as water-softening agents because the sodium ions of the zeolite can be exchanged for Ca^{2+} ions in hard water, effectively removing Ca^{2+} ions from the water. Finally, you will find them in consumer products that remove odor-causing molecules from air.

Silicone Polymers

Silicon and chloromethane (CH_3Cl) react at 300 °C in the presence of a catalyst, Cu powder. The primary product of this reaction is $(CH_3)_2SiCl_2$.

$$Si(s) + 2\ CH_3Cl(g) \rightarrow (CH_3)_2SiCl_2(\ell)$$

Halides of Group 4A elements other than carbon hydrolyze readily. Thus, the reaction of $(CH_3)_2SiCl_2$ with water initially produces $(CH_3)_2Si(OH)_2$. On standing, these molecules combine to form a polymer by eliminating water. The polymer is called polydimethylsiloxane, a member of the *silicone* family of polymers.

$$(CH_3)_2SiCl_2 + 2\ H_2O \rightarrow (CH_3)_2Si(OH)_2 + 2\ HCl$$

$$n\ (CH_3)_2Si(OH)_2 \rightarrow [\text{—}(CH_3)_2SiO\text{—}]_n + n\ H_2O$$

Silicone polymers are nontoxic and have good stability to heat, light, and oxygen; they are chemically inert and have valuable antistick and antifoam properties. They can take the form of oils, greases, and resins. Some have rubber-like properties ("Silly Putty," for example, is a silicone polymer). More than 1 million tons of silicone polymers is made worldwide annually. These materials are used in a wide variety of products: lubricants, peel-off labels, lipstick, suntan lotion, car polish, and building caulk.

CASE STUDY Lead, Beethoven, and a Mystery Solved

Lead anchors the bottom of Group 4A. One of a handful of elements known since ancient times, it has a variety of modern uses. It ranks fifth among metals in usage behind iron, copper, aluminum, and zinc. The major uses of the metal and its compounds are in storage batteries (◀ Section 19-3), pigments, ammunition, solders, plumbing, and bearings.

Unfortunately, lead and its compounds are cumulative poisons, particularly in children. At a blood level as low as 50 ppb (parts per billion), blood pressure is elevated; intelligence is affected at 100 ppb; and blood levels higher than 800 ppb can lead to coma and possible death. Health experts believe more than 200,000 children become ill from lead poisoning annually, a problem caused chiefly by children eating paint containing lead-based pigments. Paint containing "white lead" [2 $PbCO_3 \cdot Pb(OH)_2$] was used until about 40 years ago, when white lead was replaced by TiO_2. Lead salts have a sweet taste, which may contribute to the tendency of children to chew on painted objects.

The symptoms of lead poisoning include nausea, abdominal pain, irritability, headaches, and excess lethargy or hyperactivity. Indeed, these describe some of the symptoms of the illness that affected Ludwig van Beethoven. As a child, he was recognized as a musical prodigy and by the age of 19 he was thought to be the greatest pianist in Europe. But then he fell ill, and,

Erich Lessing/Art Resource, NY

Ludwig van Beethoven (1770–1827).

when he was 29, he wrote to his brother to say he was considering suicide. By the time he died in 1827 at the age of 56, his belly, arms, and legs were swollen, and he complained constantly of pain in his joints and in his big toe. It is said he wandered the streets of Vienna with long, uncombed hair, dressed in a top hat and long coat, and scribbling in a notebook.

An autopsy at the time showed he died of kidney failure. Kidney stones had destroyed his kidneys, stones that presumably came from gout, the buildup of uric acid in his body. (Gout leads to joint pain, among other things.) But why did he have gout?

It was well known in the time of the Roman Empire that lead and its salts are toxic. The Romans drank wine sweetened with a very concentrated grape juice syrup that was prepared by boiling the juice in a lead kettle. The resulting syrup, called *Sapa*, had a very high concentration of lead, and many Romans contracted gout. Thus, if Beethoven enjoyed drinking wine, which was often kept in lead-glass decanters, he could have contracted gout and lead poisoning. One scientist has also noted that he may have been one of a small number of people who had a "metal metabolism disorder," a condition that prevents the excretion of toxic metals like lead.

In 2005, scientists at Argonne National Laboratory examined fragments of Beethoven's hair and skull and found both were extremely high in lead. The hair sample, for example, had 60 ppm lead, about 100 times higher than normal.

The mystery of what caused Beethoven's death has been solved. But what remains a mystery is how he contracted lead poisoning.

Questions:

1. If blood contains 50. ppb lead, how many atoms of lead are there in 1.0 L of blood? (Assume d(blood) = 1.0 g/mL.)
2. Research has found that port wine stored for a year in lead-glass decanters contains 2000 ppm lead. If the decanter contains 750 mL of wine (d = 1.0 g/mL), what mass of lead has been extracted into the wine?

Answers to these questions are available in Appendix N.

REVIEW & CHECK FOR SECTION 21-7

1. Elemental silicon is oxidized by O_2 to give unknown A. Compound A is dissolved in molten Na_2CO_3 giving B. When B was treated with aqueous hydrochloric acid, C is produced. Identify compound C.

   (a) SiH_4 (b) H_4SiO_4 (c) SiO_2 (d) $SiCl_4$

2. Silicon and oxygen form a six-membered ring in the silicate anion $[Si_3O_9]^{6-}$. What is the oxidation state of silicon in this anion? (The rare blue mineral benitoite, the California state gemstone, has the formula $BaTiSi_3O_9$.)

   (a) 0 (b) +2 (c) +4 (d) −4

21-8 Nitrogen, Phosphorus, and the Group 5A Elements

Group 5A elements are characterized by the ns^2np^3 configuration with its half-filled np subshell. In compounds of the Group 5A elements, the primary oxidation numbers are +3 and +5, although common nitrogen compounds display a range of

Group **5A**
Nitrogen 7 **N** 25 ppm
Phosphorus 15 **P** 1000 ppm
Arsenic 33 **As** 1.5 ppm
Antimony 51 **Sb** 0.2 ppm
Bismuth 83 **Bi** 0.048 ppm

Element abundances are in **parts per million** *in the Earth's crust.*

oxidation numbers from −3 to +5. Once again, as in Groups 3A and 4A, the lower oxidation state is more common in the heavier elements than in the lighter ones. In many arsenic, antimony, and bismuth compounds, the element has an oxidation number of +3. Not surprisingly, compounds of these elements with oxidation numbers of +5 are powerful oxidizing agents.

This part of our tour of the main group elements will concentrate on the chemistries of nitrogen and phosphorus. Nitrogen is found primarily as N_2 in the atmosphere, where it constitutes 78.1% by volume (75.5% by weight). In contrast, phosphorus occurs in Earth's crust in solids. More than 200 different phosphorus-containing minerals are known; all contain the tetrahedral phosphate ion, PO_4^{3-}, or a derivative of this ion. By far, the most abundant phosphorus-containing minerals are apatites such as $Ca_5(OH)(PO_4)_3$.

Nitrogen and its compounds play a key role in our economy, with ammonia making a particularly notable contribution. Phosphoric acid is an important commodity chemical, and it finds its greatest use in producing fertilizers.

Both phosphorus and nitrogen are part of every living organism. Phosphorus is contained in nucleic acids and phospholipids, and nitrogen occurs in proteins and nucleic acids (▶ Chapter 24: *Biochemistry*).

Properties of Nitrogen and Phosphorus

Nitrogen (N_2) is a colorless gas that liquefies at 77 K (−196 °C) (◀ Figure 11.1). Its most notable feature is its reluctance to react with other elements or compounds because the N≡N triple bond has a large bond dissociation enthalpy (945 kJ/mol) and because the molecule is nonpolar. Nitrogen does, however, react with hydrogen to give ammonia in the presence of a catalyst (◀ Section 15-6, *Case Study: Applying Equilibrium Concepts—The Haber-Bosch Ammonia Process*) and with a few metals (notably lithium and magnesium) to give metal nitrides, compounds containing the N^{3-} ion.

$$3\,Mg(s) + N_2(g) \longrightarrow \underset{\text{magnesium nitride}}{Mg_3N_2(s)}$$

Elemental nitrogen is a very useful material. Because of its lack of reactivity, it is used to provide a nonoxidizing atmosphere for packaged foods and wine and to pressurize electric cables and telephone wires. Liquid nitrogen is valuable as a coolant in freezing biological samples such as blood and semen, in freeze-drying food, and for other applications that require extremely low temperatures.

Elemental phosphorus was first derived from human waste (see *A Closer Look: Making Phosphorus,* page 841), but it is now produced by the reduction of phosphate minerals in an electric furnace.

$$2\,Ca_3(PO_4)_2(s) + 10\,C(s) + 6\,SiO_2(s) \rightarrow P_4(g) + 6\,CaSiO_3(s) + 10\,CO(g)$$

The phosphorus vapor can then be cooled under water, preventing its spontaneous combustion, and eventually yielding the solid forms of phosphorus present at room temperature. Waxy white phosphorus is the most common allotrope of phosphorus, but paradoxically it is the least stable thermodynamically. Rather than occurring as a diatomic molecule with a triple bond, like its second-period relative nitrogen (N_2), phosphorus is made up of tetrahedral P_4 molecules in which each P atom is joined to three others via single bonds. Red phosphorus is a polymer of P_4 units.

© Cengage Learning/Charles D. Winters

The red and white allotropes of phosphorus.

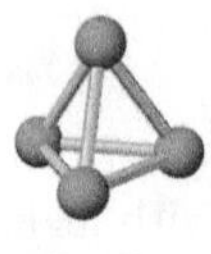

white phosphorus, P_4

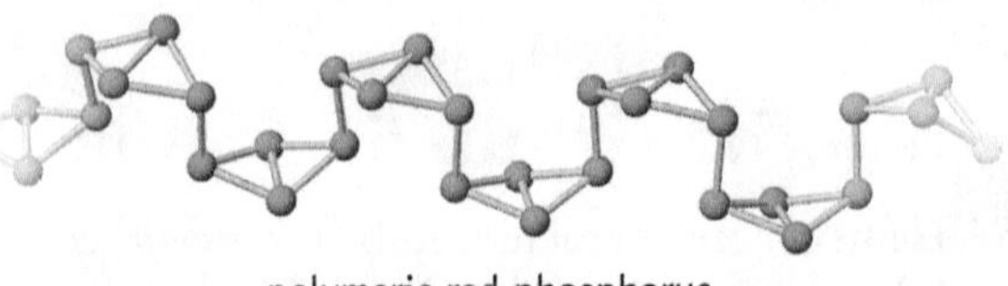

polymeric red phosphorus

Nitrogen Compounds

A notable feature of the chemistry of nitrogen is the wide diversity of its compounds. Compounds are known with nitrogen in all oxidation numbers between −3 and +5 (Figure 21.26).

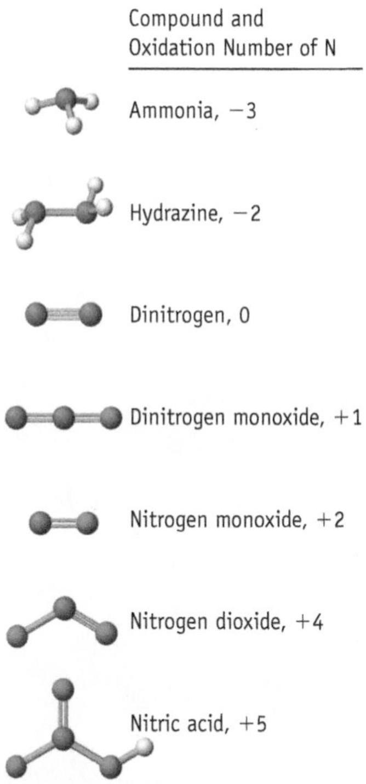

FIGURE 21.26 **Compounds and oxidation numbers for nitrogen.** In its compounds, the N atom can have oxidation states ranging from −3 to +5.

Hydrogen Compounds of Nitrogen: Ammonia and Hydrazine

Ammonia is a gas at room temperature and pressure. It has a very penetrating odor and condenses to a liquid at −33 °C under 1 atm of pressure. Aqueous solutions of ammonia, often referred to as ammonium hydroxide, are basic due to the reaction of ammonia with water (◀ Figure 3.14).

$$NH_3(aq) + H_2O(\ell) \rightleftharpoons NH_4^+(aq) + OH^-(aq) \quad K_b = 1.8 \times 10^{-5} \text{ at } 25\ °C$$

Ammonia is a major industrial chemical and is prepared by the Haber-Bosch process (◀ page 579), largely for use as a fertilizer.

Hydrazine, N_2H_4, is a colorless, fuming liquid with an ammonia-like odor (mp, 2.0 °C; bp, 113.5 °C). Almost 1 million kilograms of hydrazine are produced annually by the Raschig process—the oxidation of ammonia with alkaline sodium hypochlorite in the presence of gelatin (which is added to suppress metal-catalyzed side reactions that lower the yield of hydrazine).

$$2\ NH_3(aq) + NaClO(aq) \rightleftharpoons N_2H_4(aq) + NaCl(aq) + H_2O(\ell)$$

Hydrazine, like ammonia, is a base,

$$N_2H_4(aq) + H_2O(\ell) \rightleftharpoons N_2H_5^+(aq) + OH^-(aq) \qquad K_b = 8.5 \times 10^{-7}$$

and it is a strong reducing agent, as reflected in the reduction potential for the following half-reaction in basic solution:

$$N_2(g) + 4\ H_2O(\ell) + 4\ e^- \rightarrow N_2H_4(aq) + 4\ OH^-(aq) \qquad E° = -1.15\ V$$

Hydrazine's reducing ability is exploited in its use in wastewater treatment for chemical plants. It removes oxidizing ions such as CrO_4^{2-} by reducing them, thus preventing them from entering the environment. A related use is the treatment of water boilers in large electric-generating plants. Oxygen dissolved in the water presents a serious problem in these plants because the dissolved gas can oxidize (corrode) the metal of the boiler and pipes. Hydrazine reduces the amount of dissolved oxygen in water.

$$N_2H_4(aq) + O_2(g) \rightarrow N_2(g) + 2\ H_2O(\ell)$$

Oxides and Oxoacids of Nitrogen

Nitrogen is unique among all elements in the number of binary oxides it forms (Table 21.5). All are thermodynamically unstable with respect to decomposition to N_2 and O_2; that is, all have positive $\Delta_f G°$ values. Most are slow to decompose, however, and so are described as kinetically stable.

Dinitrogen monoxide, N_2O, commonly called *nitrous oxide*, is a nontoxic, odorless, and tasteless gas in which nitrogen has the lowest oxidation number (+1) among the nitrogen oxides. It can be made by the careful decomposition of ammonium nitrate at 250 °C.

$$NH_4NO_3(s) \rightarrow N_2O(g) + 2\ H_2O(g)$$

It is used as an anesthetic in minor surgery and has been called "laughing gas" because of its euphoriant effects. Because it is soluble in vegetable fats, the largest commercial use of N_2O is as a propellant and aerating agent in cans of whipped cream.

Nitrous oxide, N_2O. Not only is this nitrogen oxide used in cans of whipped cream but it is also an anesthetic and considered safe for medical uses. However, significant dangers arise from using it as a recreational drug. Long-term use can induce nerve damage and cause problems such as weakness and loss of feeling.

Nitrogen monoxide, NO, is an odd-electron molecule. It has 11 valence electrons, giving it one unpaired electron and making it a free radical. The compound

Table 21.5 Some Oxides of Nitrogen

Formula	Name	Structure	Nitrogen Oxidation Number	Description
N_2O	Dinitrogen monoxide (nitrous oxide)	:N≡N—Ö: linear	+1	Colorless gas (laughing gas)
NO	Nitrogen monoxide (nitric oxide)	*	+2	Colorless gas; odd-electron molecule (paramagnetic)
N_2O_3	Dinitrogen trioxide	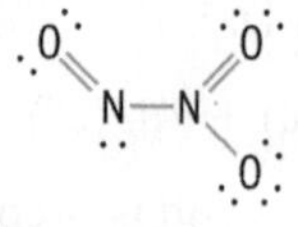 planar	+3	Blue solid (mp, −100.7 °C); reversibly dissociates to NO and NO_2 above its mp.
NO_2	Nitrogen dioxide	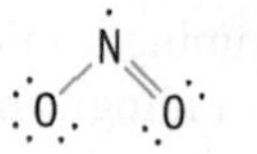	+4	Brown, paramagnetic gas; odd-electron molecule
N_2O_4	Dinitrogen tetraoxide	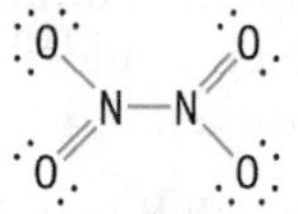 planar	+4	Colorless liquid/gas; dissociates to NO_2 (◀ Figure 15.7).
N_2O_5	Dinitrogen pentaoxide	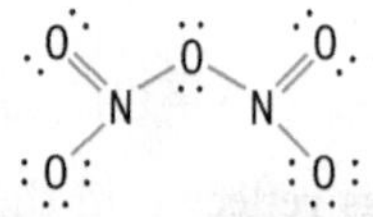	+5	Colorless solid

*It is not possible to draw a Lewis structure that accurately represents the electronic structure of NO (◀ Chapter 8). Also note that only one resonance structure is shown for each structure.

has recently been the subject of intense research because it has been found to be important in a number of biochemical processes.

Nitrogen dioxide, NO_2, is the brown gas you see when a bottle of nitric acid is allowed to stand in the sunlight.

$$2\ HNO_3(aq) \rightarrow 2\ NO_2(g) + H_2O(\ell) + \tfrac{1}{2}\ O_2(g)$$

Nitrogen dioxide is also a culprit in air pollution (◀ Section 20-1). Nitrogen monoxide forms when atmospheric nitrogen and oxygen are heated in internal combustion engines. Released into the atmosphere, NO rapidly reacts with O_2 to form NO_2.

$$2\ NO(g) + O_2(g) \rightarrow 2\ NO_2(g)$$

Nitrogen dioxide has 17 valence electrons, so it is also an odd-electron molecule. Because the odd electron largely resides on the N atom, two NO_2 molecules can combine, forming an N—N bond and producing N_2O_4, *dinitrogen tetraoxide.*

$$\underset{\text{deep brown gas}}{2\ NO_2(g)} \longrightarrow \underset{\text{colorless (mp, −11.2 °C)}}{N_2O_4(g)}$$

Solid N_2O_4 is colorless and consists entirely of N_2O_4 molecules. However, as the solid melts and the temperature increases to the boiling point, the color darkens as N_2O_4 dissociates to form brown NO_2. At the normal boiling point (21.5 °C), the distinctly brown gas consists of 15.9% NO_2 and 84.1% N_2O_4 (see Figure 8.2).

When NO_2 is bubbled into water, nitric acid and nitrous acid form.

$$2\ NO_2(g) + H_2O(\ell) \rightarrow \underset{\text{nitric acid}}{HNO_3(aq)} + \underset{\text{nitrous acid}}{HNO_2(aq)}$$

FIGURE 21.27 The preparation and properties of nitric acid.

(a) Nitric acid is prepared by the reaction of sulfuric acid and sodium nitrate. Pure HNO_3 is colorless, but samples of the acid are often brown because of brown $NO_2(g)$ is formed by decomposition of the acid.

(b) When concentrated nitric acid reacts with copper, the metal is oxidized to copper(II) ions, and NO_2 gas is a reaction product.

Nitric acid has been known for centuries and has become an important compound in our modern economy. The oldest way to make the acid is to treat $NaNO_3$ with sulfuric acid (Figure 21.27).

$$2\ NaNO_3(s) + H_2SO_4(\ell) \rightarrow 2\ HNO_3(\ell) + Na_2SO_4(s)$$

Enormous quantities of nitric acid are now produced industrially by the oxidation of ammonia in the multistep *Ostwald process*. The acid has many applications, but by far the greatest amount is turned into ammonium nitrate (for use as a fertilizer) by the reaction of nitric acid and ammonia.

Nitric acid is a powerful oxidizing agent, as the large, positive $E°$ values for the following half-reactions illustrate:

$$NO_3^-(aq) + 4\ H_3O^+(aq) + 3\ e^- \rightarrow NO(g) + 6\ H_2O(\ell) \qquad E° = +0.96\ V$$

$$NO_3^-(aq) + 2\ H_3O^+(aq) + e^- \rightarrow NO_2(g) + 3\ H_2O(\ell) \qquad E° = +0.80\ V$$

Concentrated nitric acid attacks and oxidizes most metals. (Aluminum is an exception; see Section 21-6.) In this process, the nitrate ion is reduced to one of the nitrogen oxides. Which oxide is formed depends on the metal and on reaction conditions. In the case of copper, for example, either NO or NO_2 is produced, depending on the concentration of the acid (Figure 21.27b).

In dilute acid:

$$3\ Cu(s) + 8\ H_3O^+(aq) + 2\ NO_3^-(aq) \rightarrow 3\ Cu^{2+}(aq) + 12\ H_2O(\ell) + 2\ NO(g)$$

In concentrated acid:

$$Cu(s) + 4\ H_3O^+(aq) + 2\ NO_3^-(aq) \rightarrow Cu^{2+}(aq) + 6\ H_2O(\ell) + 2\ NO_2(g)$$

Four metals (Au, Pt, Rh, and Ir) that are not attacked by nitric acid are often described as the "noble metals." The alchemists of the 14th century, however, knew that if they mixed HNO_3 with HCl in a ratio of about 1:3, this aqua regia, or "kingly water," would attack even gold, the noblest of metals.

$$Au(s) + NO_3^-(aq) + 4\ Cl^-(aq) + 4\ H_3O^+(aq) \rightarrow [AuCl_4]^-(aq) + NO(g) + 6\ H_2O(\ell)$$

CASE STUDY | A Healthy Saltwater Aquarium and the Nitrogen Cycle

by Jeffrey Keaffaber, University of Florida

Steven Hyatt

Large saltwater aquariums like those at Sea World in Florida, the Shedd Aquarium in Chicago, and the new Georgia Aquarium in Atlanta, are a continual source of enjoyment. So are smaller aquariums in your home. Maintaining these facilities is not trivial, however; a healthy environment for its marine inhabitants is essential. For this, chemistry plays an important role.

A key part of aquarium maintenance involves control of the concentrations of various dissolved nitrogen-containing species, including ammonia, nitrite ion, and nitrate ion, all of which are stressful to fish at low concentrations and toxic in higher concentrations. The chemistry that relates to maintaining proper balance among these species is called the *nitrogen cycle*.

Nitrification

The nitrogen cycle begins with the production of ammonia (and, in acid solution, its conjugate acid, the ammonium ion, NH_4^+), a fundamental waste product of protein metabolism in an aquarium habitat. Unless removed, the ammonia concentration will build up over time. To remove it, the aquarium water is cycled through sand filters infused with aerobic, oxygen-loving bacteria. These bacteria utilize enzymes that catalyze the oxidation of ammonia and ammonium ion by O_2 to form first nitrite ion and then nitrate ion. The overall process is called *nitrification*, and the saltwater bacteria that mediate each oxidation step are *Nitrosococcus sp.* and *Nitrococcus sp.*, respectively. Half-reactions representing this chemistry are as follows:

Oxidation half-reactions

$$NH_4^+(aq) + 8\ OH^-(aq) \longrightarrow NO_2^-(aq) + 6\ H_2O(\ell) + 6\ e^-$$

$$NO_2^-(aq) + 2\ OH^-(aq) \longrightarrow NO_3^-(aq) + H_2O(\ell) + 2\ e^-$$

Reduction half-reaction

$$O_2(aq) + 2\ H_2O(\ell) + 4\ e^- \longrightarrow 4\ OH^-(aq)$$

When setting up an aquarium at home, it is appropriate to monitor the concentrations of various nitrogen species. Initially, the NH_3/NH_4^+ concentration rises, but then it begins to fall as oxidation occurs. With time, the nitrite ion concentration builds up, peaks, and then decreases, with an accompanying increase in nitrate ion concentration. To reach a stable situation, as much as 6 weeks may be required.

Denitrification

Nitrate is much less toxic than ammonia and the nitrite ion, but its buildup must also be limited. In a small aquarium, nitrate ion concentration can be controlled by partial exchange of water. However, because of environmental restrictions this is not possible for large aquariums; they must use a closed water treatment process.

To remedy the buildup of the nitrate ion, another biologically catalyzed process is used that reduces the nitrate ion to nitrogen gas, N_2. A reducing agent is required, and early designs of denitrifying filters utilized methanol, CH_3OH, as the reducing agent. Among naturally occurring saltwater bacteria capable of nitrate reduction under low oxygen (anoxic) conditions, *Pseudomonas sp.* is commonly used. The bacteria, utilizing enzymes to catalyze reaction of nitrate and methanol to form N_2 and CO_2, are introduced to sand filters where methanol is added.

A stable pH is also important to the health of aquarium fish. Therefore, the marine environment in a saltwater aquarium is maintained at a relatively constant pH of 8.0–8.2. To aid in this, the CO_2 produced by methanol oxidation remains dissolved in solution, and increases the buffer capacity of the seawater.

Questions:

1. Write a balanced net ionic equation for the oxidation of NH_4^+ by O_2 to produce H_2O and NO_2^-.
2. Write half-reactions for the reduction of NO_3^- to N_2 and for the oxidation of CH_3OH to CO_2 in basic solution. Then, combine these half-reactions to obtain the balanced equation for the reduction of NO_3^- by CH_3OH.
3. Consider the carbon-containing species H_2CO_3, HCO_3^-, and CO_3^{2-}. Which one is present in largest concentration at the pH conditions of the aquarium? Give a short explanation. K_a of $H_2CO_3 = 4.2 \times 10^{-7}$ and K_a of $HCO_3^- = 4.8 \times 10^{-11}$. (See Study Question 17.118.)
4. A large, 2.2×10^7 L, aquarium contains 1.7×10^4 kg of dissolved NO_3^-. Calculate concentrations in mg/L of N and NO_3^-, and the molar concentration of NO_3^-.

Answers to these questions are available in Appendix N.

Hydrogen Compounds of Phosphorus and Other Group 5A Elements

The phosphorus analog of ammonia, phosphine (PH_3), is a poisonous, highly reactive gas with a faint garlic-like odor. Industrially, it is made by the reaction of white phosphorus and aqueous NaOH.

$$P_4(s) + 3\ KOH(aq) + 3\ H_2O(\ell) \rightarrow PH_3(g) + 3\ KH_2PO_2(aq)$$

The hydrides of the heavier Group 5A elements are also toxic and become more unstable as the atomic number of the element increases. Nonetheless, arsine (AsH_3) is used in the semiconductor industry as a starting material in the preparation of gallium arsenide (GaAs) semiconductors.

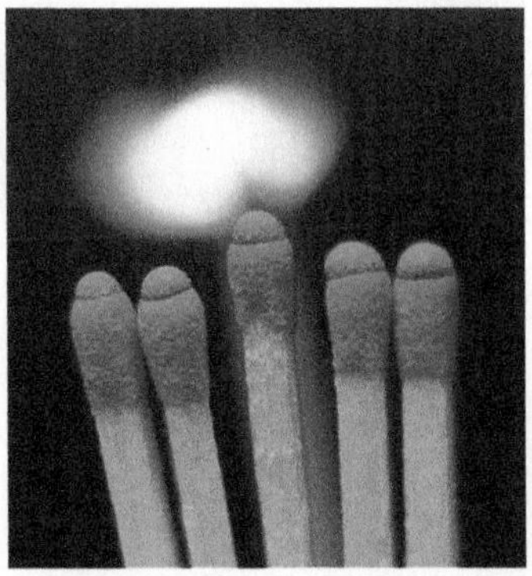

Matches. The head of a "strike anywhere" match contains P_4S_3 and the oxidizing agent $KClO_3$. (Other components are ground glass, Fe_2O_3, ZnO, and glue.) Safety matches have sulfur (3–5%) and $KClO_3$ (45–55%) in the match head and red phosphorus in the striking strip.

Phosphorus Oxides and Sulfides

The most important compounds of phosphorus are those with oxygen, and there are at least six simple binary compounds containing just phosphorus and oxygen. All of them can be thought of as being derived structurally from the P_4 tetrahedron of white phosphorus. For example, if P_4 is carefully oxidized, P_4O_6 is formed; an O atom has been placed into each P—P bond in the tetrahedron (Figure 21.28).

The most common and important phosphorus oxide is tetraphosphorus decaoxide (P_4O_{10}). In P_4O_{10}, each phosphorus atom is surrounded tetrahedrally by O atoms.

Phosphorus also forms a series of compounds with sulfur. Of these, the most important is P_4S_3. In this compound, S atoms are in only three of the P—P bonds. The principal use of P_4S_3 is in "strike anywhere" matches, the kind that light when you rub the head against a rough object. The active ingredients are P_4S_3 and the powerful oxidizing agent potassium chlorate, $KClO_3$. The "safety match" is now more common than the "strike anywhere" match. In safety matches, the head is

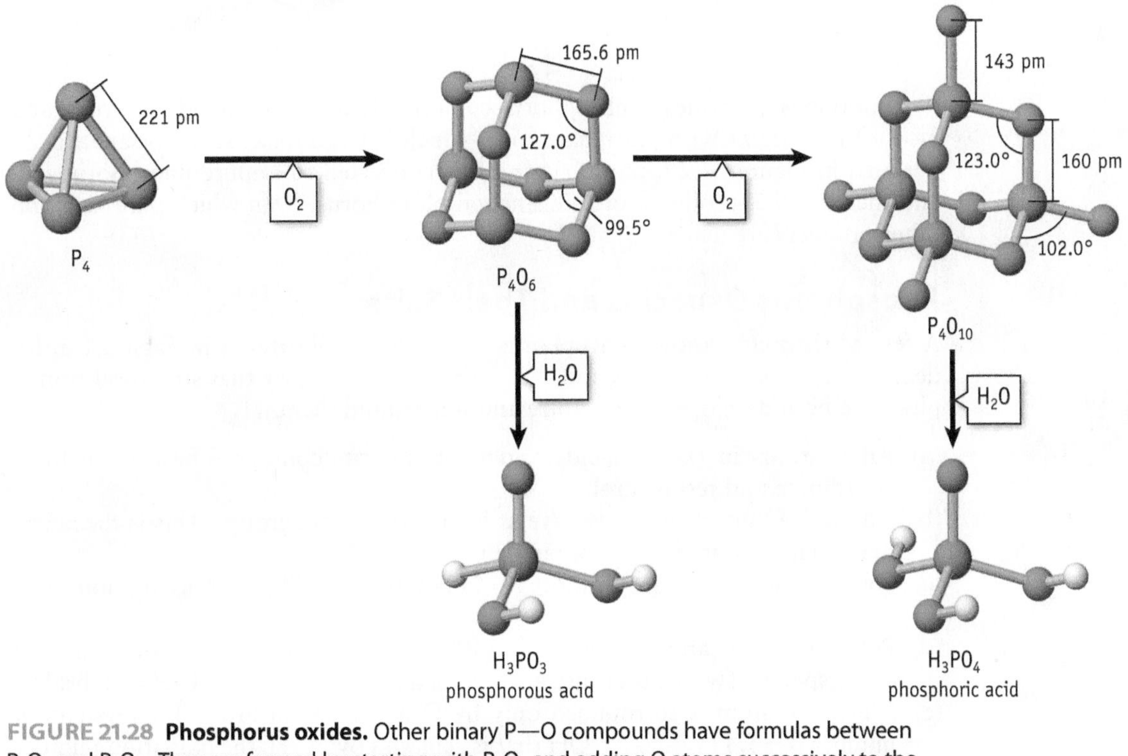

FIGURE 21.28 **Phosphorus oxides.** Other binary P—O compounds have formulas between P_4O_6 and P_4O_{10}. They are formed by starting with P_4O_6 and adding O atoms successively to the P atom vertices.

(a) Mining phosphate rock. Phosphate rock is primarily $Ca_3(PO_4)_2$, and most mined in the United States comes from Florida.

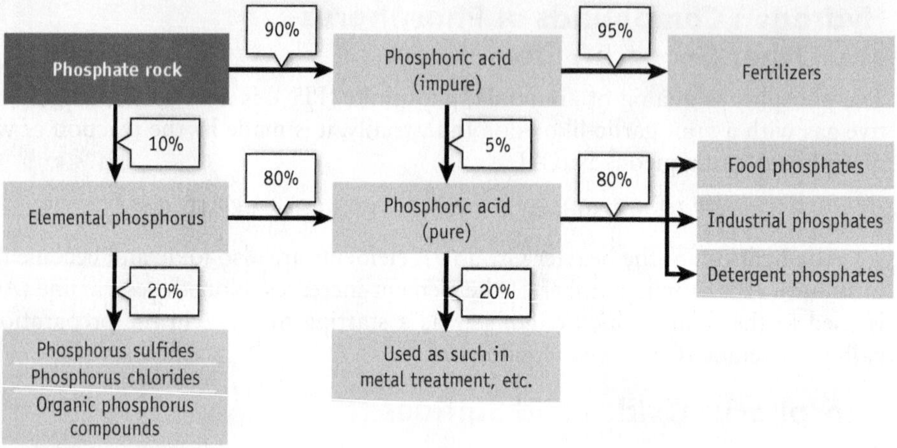

(b) Uses of phosphorus and phosphoric acid.

FIGURE 21.29 **Uses of phosphate rock, phosphorus, and phosphoric acid.**

predominantly $KClO_3$, and the material on the match book is red phosphorus (about 50%), Sb_2S_3, Fe_2O_3, and glue.

$$4\ P(s,\ \text{red allotrope}) + {}^{3}/_{8}\ S_8(s) \longrightarrow$$

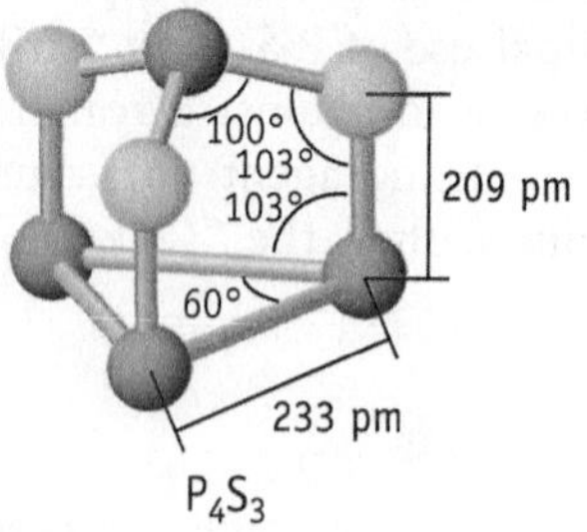

P_4S_3

Enormous quantities of phosphorus compounds are used around the world, and most of this begins with phosphate rock, which is largely $Ca_3(PO_4)_2$ or apatite. As outlined in Figure 21.29, phosphate rock is converted to impure phosphoric acid and then to other products, or to elemental phosphorus, from which pure acid and other products are made.

Phosphorus Oxoacids and Their Salts

A few of the many known phosphorus oxoacids are illustrated in Table 21.6. Indeed, there are so many acids and their salts in this category that structural principles have been developed to organize and understand them.

(a) All P atoms in the oxoacids and their anions (conjugate bases) are four-coordinate and tetrahedral.
(b) All the P atoms in the acids have at least one P—OH group. (This is the acidic hydrogen atom in these compounds.)
(c) Some oxoacids have one or more P—H bonds. These H atoms are not ionizable as H^+.
(d) Polymerization can occur by P—O—P bond formation to give both linear and cyclic species. Two P atoms are never joined by more than one P—O—P bridge.
(e) When a P atom is surrounded only by O atoms (as in H_3PO_4), its oxidation number is +5. For each P—OH that is replaced by P—H, the oxidation number drops by 2. For example, the oxidation number of P in H_3PO_2 is +1.

Orthophosphoric acid, H_3PO_4, and its salts are far more important commercially than other P—O acids. Millions of tons of phosphoric acid are made annually, some

Table 21.6 Phosphorus Oxoacids

Formula	Name	Structure	pK_a
H_3PO_4	Orthophosphoric acid	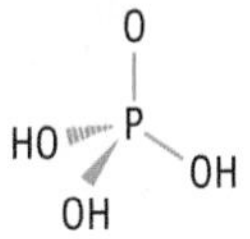	2.21, 7.21, 12.67
$H_4P_2O_7$	Pyrophosphoric acid (diphosphoric acid)	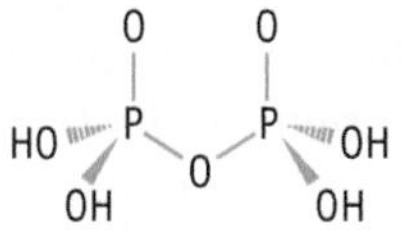	0.85, 1.49, 5.77, 8.22
$(HPO_3)_3$	Metaphosphoric acid	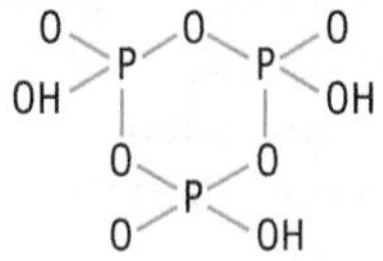	
H_3PO_3	Phosphorous acid (phosphonic acid)	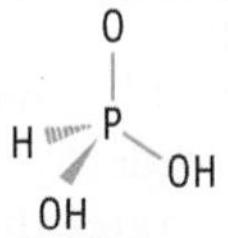	2.00, 6.59
H_3PO_2	Hypophosphorous acid (phosphinic acid)	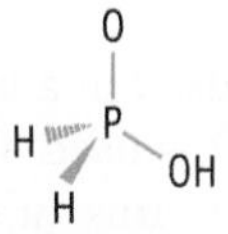	1.24

FIGURE 21.30 **Reaction of P_4O_{10} and water.** The white solid oxide reacts vigorously with water to give orthophosphoric acid, H_3PO_4. (The heat generated vaporizes the water, so steam is visible.)

using white phosphorus as the starting material. The element is burned in oxygen to give P_4O_{10}, and the oxide reacts with water to produce the acid (Figure 21.30).

$$P_4O_{10}(s) + 6\ H_2O(\ell) \rightarrow 4\ H_3PO_4(aq)$$

This approach gives a pure product, so it is used to make phosphoric acid for use in food products in particular. The acid is nontoxic, and it gives the tart or sour taste

A CLOSER LOOK | Making Phosphorus

He stoked his small furnace with more charcoal and pumped the bellows until his retort glowed red hot. Suddenly something strange began to happen. Glowing fumes filled the vessel and from the end of the retort dripped a shining liquid that burst into flames.

J. Emsley: *The 13th Element*, p. 5.
New York, John Wiley, 2000.

John Emsley begins his story of phosphorus, its discovery, and its uses, by imagining what the German alchemist Hennig Brandt must have seen in his laboratory that day in 1669. He was in search of the philosopher's stone, the magic elixir that would turn the crudest substance into gold. (Some may recall that the first Harry Potter novel was titled *Harry Potter and the Philosopher's Stone* when it was published in Great Britain.)

Brandt was experimenting with urine, which had served as the source of useful chemicals since Roman times. It is not surprising that phosphorus could be extracted from this source. Humans consume much more phosphorus, in the form of phosphate, than they require, and the excess phosphorus (about 1.4 g per day) is excreted in the urine. It is nonetheless extraordinary that Brandt was able to isolate the element. According to an 18th-century chemistry book, about 30 g of phosphorus could be obtained from 60 gallons of urine. And the process was not simple. Another 18th century recipe states that "50 or 60 pails full" of urine was to be used. "Let it lie steeping . . . till it putrefy and breed worms." The chemist was then to reduce the whole to a paste and finally to heat the paste very strongly in a retort. After some days, phosphorus distilled from the mixture and was collected in water. (We know now that carbon from the organic compounds in the urine reduces the phosphate to phosphorus.) Phosphorus was made in this manner for more than 100 years.

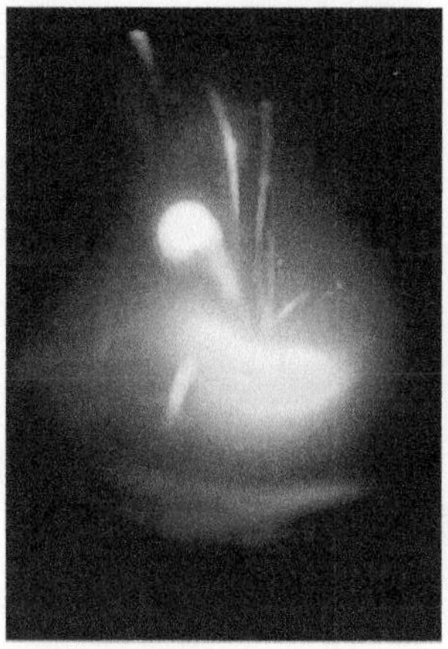

The glow of phosphorus burning in air.

to carbonated "soft drinks," such as various colas (about 0.05% H_3PO_4) or root beer (about 0.01% H_3PO_4).

A major use for phosphoric acid is to impart corrosion resistance to metal objects such as nuts and bolts, tools, and car-engine parts by plunging the object into a hot acid bath. Car bodies are similarly treated with phosphoric acid containing metal ions such as Zn^{2+}, and aluminum trim is "polished" by treating it with the acid.

The reaction of H_3PO_4 with strong bases produces salts such as NaH_2PO_4, Na_2HPO_4, and Na_3PO_4. In industry, the monosodium and disodium salts are produced using Na_2CO_3 as the base, but an excess of the stronger (and more expensive) base NaOH is required to remove the third proton to give Na_3PO_4.

Sodium phosphate (Na_3PO_4) is used in scouring powders and paint strippers because the anion PO_4^{3-} is a relatively strong base in water ($K_b = 2.8 \times 10^{-2}$). Sodium monohydrogen phosphate, Na_2HPO_4, which has a less basic anion than PO_4^{3-}, is widely used in food products. Kraft has patented a process using this compound in the manufacture of pasteurized cheese, for example. Thousands of tons of Na_2HPO_4 are still used for this purpose, even though the function of the salt in this process is not completely understood. In addition, a small amount of Na_2HPO_4 in pudding mixes enables the mix to gel in cold water, and the basic anion raises the pH of cereals to provide "quick-cooking" breakfast cereal. (The OH^- ion from HPO_4^{2-} hydrolysis accelerates the breakdown of the cellulose material in the cereal.)

Calcium phosphates are used in a broad spectrum of products. For example, the weak acid $Ca(H_2PO_4)_2 \cdot H_2O$ is used as the acid leavening agent in baking powder. A typical baking powder contains (along with inert ingredients) 28% $NaHCO_3$, 10.7% $Ca(H_2PO_4)_2 \cdot H_2O$, and 21.4% $NaAl(SO_4)_2$ (also a weak acid). The weak acids react with sodium bicarbonate to produce CO_2 gas. For example,

$$Ca(H_2PO_4)_2 \cdot H_2O(s) + 2\ NaHCO_3(aq) \rightarrow 2\ CO_2(g) + 3\ H_2O(\ell) + Na_2HPO_4(aq) + CaHPO_4(aq)$$

Finally, calcium monohydrogen phosphate, $CaHPO_4$, is used as an abrasive and polishing agent in toothpaste.

REVIEW & CHECK FOR SECTION 21-8

1. Construct Lewis structures for the several resonance forms of N_2O. What is the predicted N—N bond order?

   (a) 1 (b) 2 (c) between 2 and 3 (d) 3

2. Which statement about ammonia is *not correct?*

   (a) Ammonia can be made by a direct reaction of the elements.

   (b) Aqueous solutions of ammonia are acidic.

   (c) Ammonia is a gas at room temperature and atmospheric pressure.

   (d) Ammonia is used as a reactant in the synthesis of nitric acid.

3. What is the oxidation state of phosphorus in phosphorous acid, H_3PO_3?

   (a) 0 (b) +1 (c) +3 (d) +5

21-9 Oxygen, Sulfur, and the Group 6A Elements

Oxygen is by far the most abundant element in Earth's crust, representing slightly less than 50% of it by weight. It is present as elemental oxygen in the atmosphere and is combined with other elements in water and in many minerals. Scientists

Steven Hyatt

FIGURE 21.31 **Sulfide-containing minerals.** Many minerals contain the sulfide ion. A few examples are shown here: *(left)* orpiment, As_2S_3; *(center)* iron pyrite, FeS_2; and *(right)* stibnite, Sb_2S_3.

believe that elemental oxygen did not appear on this planet until about 3.5 billion years ago, when it was formed by plants through the process of photosynthesis.

Sulfur, seventeenth in abundance in the Earth's crust, is also found in its elemental form in nature, but only in certain concentrated deposits. Sulfur-containing compounds occur in natural gas, coal, and oil. In minerals, sulfur occurs as the sulfide ion (Figure 21.31) and as sulfate ion (e.g., in gypsum, $CaSO_4 \cdot 2\ H_2O$). Sulfur oxides (SO_2 and SO_3) also occur in nature, primarily as products of volcanic activity.

In the United States, sulfur—several million tons per year—is obtained from deposits of the element found along the Gulf of Mexico. These deposits occur typically at a depth of 150 to 750 m below the surface in layers about 30 m thick. They are thought to have been formed by anaerobic ("without elemental oxygen") bacteria acting on sedimentary sulfate deposits such as gypsum.

Group **6A**
Oxygen 8 **O** 474,000 ppm
Sulfur 16 **S** 260 ppm
Selenium 34 **Se** 0.5 ppm
Tellurium 52 **Te** 0.005 ppm
Polonium 84 **Po** trace

Element abundances are in **parts per million** *in the Earth's crust.*

Preparation and Properties of the Elements

Pure oxygen is obtained by the fractional distillation of air and is among the top five industrial chemicals produced in the United States. Oxygen can be made in the laboratory by electrolysis of water (see Figure 21.4) and by the catalyzed decomposition of metal chlorates such as $KClO_3$.

$$2\ KClO_3(s) \xrightarrow{\text{catalyst}} 2\ KCl(s) + 3\ O_2(g)$$

At room temperature and pressure, oxygen is a colorless gas, but it is pale blue when condensed to a liquid at −183 °C (◀ Figure 9.13). As described in Section 9-3, diatomic oxygen is paramagnetic because it has two unpaired electrons.

An allotrope of oxygen, ozone (O_3), is a blue, diamagnetic gas with an odor so strong that it can be detected in concentrations as low as 0.05 ppm. Ozone is synthesized by passing O_2 through an electric discharge or by irradiating O_2 with ultraviolet light. It is often in the news because of the realization that the Earth's protective layer of ozone in the stratosphere is being disrupted by chlorofluorocarbons and other chemicals (◀ Section 20-1).

Sulfur has numerous allotropes. The most common and most stable allotrope is the yellow, orthorhombic form, which consists of S_8 molecules with the sulfur atoms arranged in a crown-shaped ring (Figure 21.32a). Less stable allotropes are known that have rings of 6 to 20 sulfur atoms. Another form of sulfur, called plastic sulfur, has a molecular structure with chains of sulfur atoms (Figure 21.32b).

FIGURE 21.32 Sulfur allotropes.

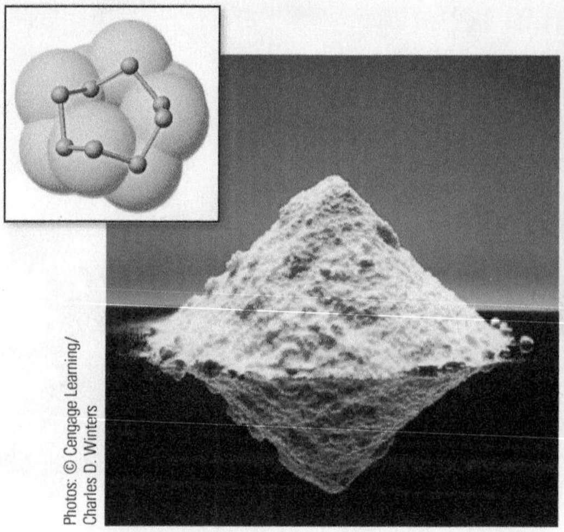

Photos: © Cengage Learning/ Charles D. Winters

(a) At room temperature, sulfur exists as a bright yellow solid composed of S_8 rings.

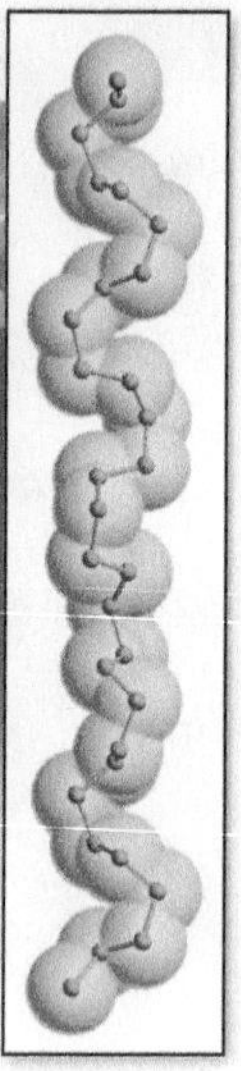

(b) When heated, the rings break open and eventually form chains of S atoms in a material described as "plastic sulfur."

Selenium and tellurium are comparatively rare on Earth, having abundances about the same as those of silver and gold, respectively. Because their chemistry is similar to that of sulfur, they are often found in minerals associated with the sulfides of copper, silver, iron, and arsenic, and they are recovered as by-products of the industries devoted to those elements.

A CLOSER LOOK Snot-tites and Sulfur Chemistry

Sulfur chemistry can be important in cave formation, as a spectacular example in the jungles of southern Mexico amply demonstrates. Toxic hydrogen sulfide gas spews from the Cueva de Villa Luz along with water that is milky white with suspended sulfur particles. The cave can be followed downward to a large underground stream and a maze of actively enlarging cave passages. Water rises into the cave from underlying sulfur-bearing strata, releasing hydrogen sulfide at concentrations up to 150 ppm. Yellow sulfur crystallizes on the cave walls around the inlets. The sulfur and sulfuric acid are produced by the following reactions:

$$2\ H_2S(g) + O_2(g) \longrightarrow 2\ S(s) + 2\ H_2O(\ell)$$

$$2\ S(s) + 2\ H_2O(\ell) + 3\ O_2(g) \longrightarrow 2\ H_2SO_4(aq)$$

The cave atmosphere is poisonous to humans, so gas masks are essential for would-be explorers. But surprisingly, the cave is teeming with life. Several species of bacteria thrive on sulfur compounds in acidic environments. The chemical energy released in their metabolism is used to obtain carbon for their bodies from calcium carbonate and carbon dioxide, both of which are abundant in the cave. One result is that bacterial filaments hang from the walls and ceilings in bundles. Because the filaments look like something coming from a runny nose, cave explorers refer to them as "snot-tites." Other microbes feed on the bacteria, and so on up the food chain—which includes spiders, gnats, and pygmy snails—all the way to sardine-like fish that swim in the cave stream. This entire ecosystem is supported by reactions involving sulfur within the cave.

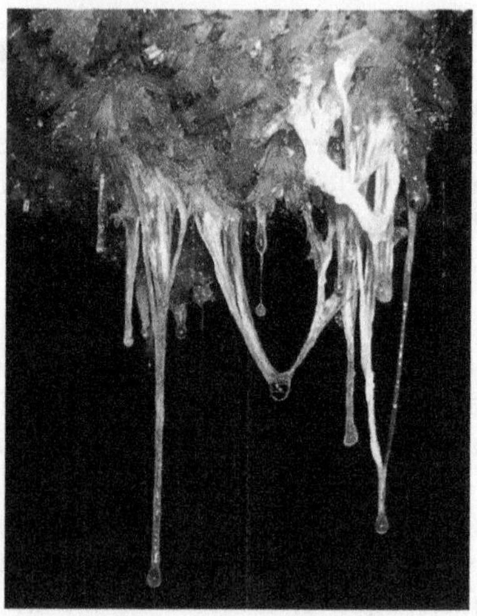

Arthur N. Palmer

Snot-tites. Filaments of sulfur-oxidizing bacteria (dubbed "snot-tites") hang from the ceiling of a Mexican cave containing an atmosphere rich in hydrogen sulfide. The bacteria thrive on the energy released by oxidation of the hydrogen sulfide, forming the base of a complex food chain. Droplets of sulfuric acid on the filaments have an average pH of 1.4, with some as low as zero! Drops that landed on explorers in the cave burned their skin and disintegrated their clothing.

Selenium has a range of uses, including glass making. A cadmium sulfide/selenide mixture is added to glass to give it a brilliant red color. The most familiar use of selenium is in xerography, a word meaning "dry printing" and a process at the heart of the modern copy machine. Most photocopy machines use an aluminum plate or roller coated with selenium. Light coming from the imaging lens selectively discharges a static electric charge on the selenium surface, and the black toner sticks only on the areas that remain charged. A copy is made when the toner is transferred to a sheet of plain paper.

The heaviest element of Group 6A, polonium, is radioactive and found only in trace amounts on Earth. It was discovered in Paris, France, in 1898 by Marie Sklodowska Curie (1867–1934) and her husband Pierre Curie (1859–1906). The Curies painstakingly separated this element from a large quantity of pitchblende, a uranium-containing ore.

© Cengage Learning/Charles D. Winters

Selenium. Glass takes on a brilliant red color when a mixture of cadmium sulfide/selenide (CdS, CdSe) is added to it.

Sulfur Compounds

Hydrogen sulfide, H_2S, has a bent molecular geometry, like water. Unlike water, however, H_2S is a gas under standard conditions (mp, −85.6 °C; bp, −60.3 °C) because its intermolecular forces are weak compared with the strong hydrogen bonding in water (◀ Figure 11.4). Hydrogen sulfide is poisonous, comparable in toxicity to hydrogen cyanide, but fortunately it has a strong odor and is detectable in concentrations as low as 0.02 ppm. You must be careful with H_2S, though. Because it has an anesthetic effect, your nose rapidly loses its ability to detect it. Death occurs at H_2S concentrations of 100 ppm.

Bad Breath Halitosis or "bad breath" is due to three sulfur-containing compounds: H_2S, CH_3SH (methyl mercaptan), and $(CH_3)_2S$ (dimethyl sulfide). All three can be detected in very tiny concentrations. For example, your nose knows if as little as 0.2 microgram of CH_3SH is present per liter of air. The compounds result from bacteria's attack on the sulfur-containing amino acids cysteine and methionine in food particles in the mouth.

Sulfur is often found as the sulfide ion in conjunction with metals and most metal sulfides (except those based on Group 1A metals) are insoluble. The recovery of metals from their sulfide ores usually begins by heating the ore in air.

$$2\ PbS(s) + 3\ O_2(g) \rightarrow 2\ PbO(s) + 2\ SO_2(g)$$

Here, lead(II) sulfide is converted to lead(II) oxide, and this is then reduced to lead using carbon or carbon monoxide in a blast furnace.

$$PbO(s) + CO(g) \rightarrow Pb(\ell) + CO_2(g)$$

Alternatively, the oxide can be reduced to elemental lead by combining it with fresh lead sulfide.

$$2\ PbO(s) + PbS(s) \rightarrow 3\ Pb(s) + SO_2(g)$$

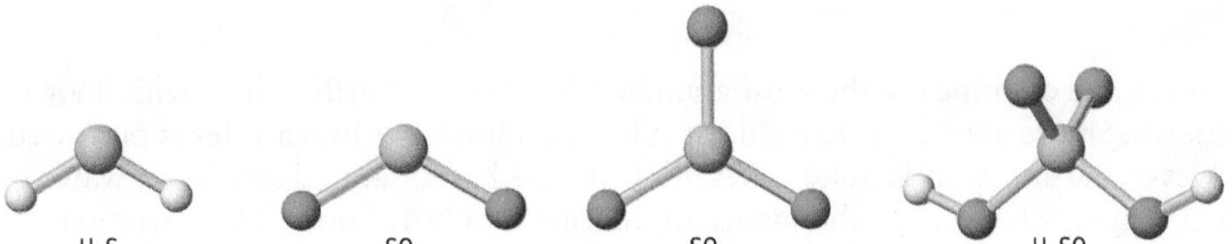

H_2S SO_2 SO_3 H_2SO_4

Models of some common sulfur-containing molecules: H_2S, SO_2, SO_3, and H_2SO_4.

© Cengage Learning/Charles D. Winters

Common household products containing sulfur or sulfur-based compounds.

Sulfur dioxide (SO_2), a colorless, toxic gas with a sharp odor, is produced on an enormous scale by the combustion of sulfur and by roasting sulfide ores in air. The combustion of sulfur in sulfur-containing coal and fuel oil creates particularly large environmental problems. It has been estimated that about 2.0×10^8 tons of sulfur oxides (primarily SO_2) are released into the atmosphere each year by human activities; this is more than half of the total emitted by all other natural sources of sulfur in the environment.

The most important reaction of sulfur dioxide is its oxidation to SO_3.

$$SO_2(g) + \frac{1}{2} O_2(g) \rightarrow SO_3(g) \qquad \Delta_r H° = -98.9 \text{ kJ/mol-rxn}$$

Sulfur trioxide is almost never isolated but is converted directly to sulfuric acid, H_2SO_4, by reaction with water. The acid is the compound manufactured in largest quantity by the chemical industry (◀ Section 3-6). Approximately 40×10^9 kg of acid is produced annually in the United States.

In the United States, roughly 70% of the sulfuric acid is used to manufacture superphosphate fertilizer from phosphate rock. Plants need a soluble form of phosphorus for growth, but calcium phosphate and apatite [$Ca_5X(PO_4)_3$, X = F, OH, Cl] are insoluble. Treating phosphate-containing minerals with sulfuric acid produces a mixture of soluble phosphates. The balanced equation for the reaction of excess sulfuric acid and calcium phosphate, for example, is

$$Ca_3(PO_4)_2(s) + 3\ H_2SO_4(\ell) \rightarrow 2\ H_3PO_4(\ell) + 3\ CaSO_4(s)$$

but it does not tell the whole story. Concentrated superphosphate fertilizer is actually mostly $CaHPO_4$ or $Ca(H_2PO_4)_2$ plus some H_3PO_4 and $CaSO_4$. (Notice that the chemical principle behind this reaction is explained by Brønsted theory: sulfuric acid is a stronger acid than H_3PO_4 (◀ Table 16.2), so the PO_4^{3-} ion is protonated by sulfuric acid.)

Smaller amounts of sulfuric acid are used in the conversion of ilmenite, a titanium-bearing ore, to TiO_2, which is then used as a white pigment in paint, plastics, and paper. The acid is also used to manufacture iron and steel as well as petroleum products, synthetic polymers, and paper.

REVIEW & CHECK FOR SECTION 21-9

1. Which of the following is not a common oxidation number for sulfur in its compounds?

   (a) −2 (b) +6 (c) +3 (d) +4

2. Which statement about oxygen is *not* true?

   (a) Liquid oxygen is attracted to a magnet.

   (b) The allotropes of oxygen are O_2 and O_3.

   (c) Oxygen is the most abundant element in the Earth's crust.

   (d) All electrons in O_2 are paired.

Group **7A**
Halogens

Fluorine	9	**F**	950 ppm
Chlorine	17	**Cl**	130 ppm
Bromine	35	**Br**	0.37 ppm
Iodine	53	**I**	0.14 ppm
Astatine	85	**At**	trace

Element abundances are in **parts per million** *in the Earth's crust.*

21-10 The Halogens, Group 7A

Fluorine and chlorine are the most abundant halogens in Earth's crust, with fluorine somewhat more abundant than chlorine. If their abundance in seawater is measured, however, the situation is quite different. Chlorine has an abundance in seawater of 18,000 ppm, whereas the abundance of fluorine is only 1.3 ppm. This variation is a result of the differences in the solubility of their salts and plays a role in the methods used to obtain the elements themselves.

Preparation of the Elements

Fluorine

The water-insoluble mineral fluorspar or fluorite (calcium fluoride, CaF_2) is one of the many sources of fluorine. Because the mineral was originally used as a flux in metalworking, its name comes from the Latin word meaning "to flow." In the 17th century, it was discovered that solid CaF_2 would emit light when heated, and the phenomenon was called *fluorescence*. In the early 1800s, when it was recognized that a new element was contained in fluorspar, A. M. Ampère (1775–1836) suggested that the element be called fluorine.

Although fluorine was recognized as an element by 1812, it was not until 1886 that it was isolated by the French chemist Henri Moisson (1852–1907) in elemental form as a very pale yellow gas by the electrolysis of KF dissolved in anhydrous HF. Indeed, because F_2 is such a powerful oxidizing agent, chemical oxidation of F^- to F_2 is not feasible, and electrolysis is the only practical way to obtain gaseous F_2 (Figure 21.33).

Fluorine is still prepared by the Moisson method, but the preparation is difficult because F_2 is so reactive. It corrodes the equipment and reacts violently with traces of grease or other contaminants. Furthermore, the products of electrolysis, F_2 and H_2, can recombine explosively, so they must not be allowed to come into contact with each other. (Compare with the reaction of H_2 and Br_2 in Figure 21.5.) Current U.S. production of fluorine is approximately 5000 metric tons per year.

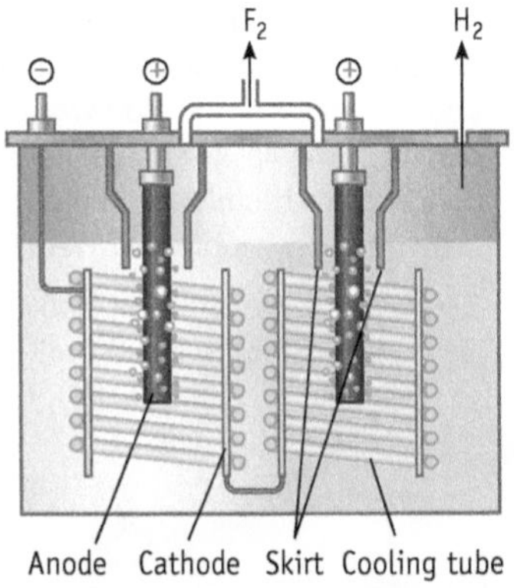

FIGURE 21.33 Schematic of an electrolysis cell for producing fluorine.

Chlorine

Chlorine is a strong oxidizing agent, and to prepare this element from chloride ion by a chemical reaction requires an even stronger oxidizing agent. In the laboratory permanganate ions or dichromate ions in acid solution will serve this purpose (Figure 21.34). Elemental chlorine was first made by the Swedish chemist Karl Wilhelm Scheele (1742–1786) in 1774, by the reaction of sodium chloride with an oxidizing agent (MnO_2) in an acidic solution.

Industrially, chlorine is made by electrolysis of brine (concentrated aqueous NaCl). The other product of the electrolysis, NaOH, is also a valuable industrial chemical. About 80% of the chlorine produced is made using an electrochemical cell similar to the one depicted in Figure 21.11. Oxidation of chloride ion to Cl_2 gas occurs at the anode and reduction of water occurs at the cathode.

Anode reaction (oxidation): $2\ Cl^-(aq) \rightarrow Cl_2(g) + 2\ e^-$

Cathode reaction (reduction): $2\ H_2O(\ell) + 2\ e^- \rightarrow H_2(g) + 2\ OH^-(aq)$

Activated titanium is used for the anode, and stainless steel or nickel is preferred for the cathode. The anode and cathode compartments are separated by a membrane that is not permeable to water but allows Na^+ ions to pass to maintain the charge balance. Thus, the membrane functions as a "salt" bridge between the anode and cathode compartments. The energy consumption of these cells is in the range of 2000–2500 kWh per ton of NaOH produced.

FIGURE 21.34 Chlorine preparation. Chlorine is prepared by oxidation of chloride ion using a strong oxidizing agent. Here, oxidation of NaCl is accomplished using $K_2Cr_2O_7$ in H_2SO_4. (The Cl_2 gas is bubbled into water in a receiving flask.)

Bromine

The standard reduction potentials of the halogens indicate that their strength as oxidizing agents decreases going from F_2 to I_2.

HALF-REACTION	REDUCTION POTENTIAL ($E°$, V)
$F_2(g) + 2\ e^- \rightarrow 2\ F^-(aq)$	2.87
$Cl_2(g) + 2\ e^- \rightarrow 2\ Cl^-(aq)$	1.36
$Br_2(\ell) + 2\ e^- \rightarrow 2\ Br^-(aq)$	1.08
$I_2(s) + 2\ e^- \rightarrow 2\ I^-(aq)$	0.535

This means that Cl_2 will oxidize Br^- ions to Br_2 in aqueous solution, for example.

$$Cl_2(aq) + 2\ Br^-(aq) \rightarrow 2\ Cl^-(aq) + Br_2(aq)$$

$$E°_{net} = E°_{cathode} - E°_{anode} = 1.36\ V - 1.08\ V = +0.28\ V$$

FIGURE 21.35 The preparation of iodine. A mixture of sodium iodide and manganese(IV) oxide was placed in the flask *(left)*. On adding concentrated sulfuric acid *(right)*, brown iodine vapor is evolved.

$$2\ NaI(s) + 2\ H_2SO_4(aq) + MnO_2(s) \rightarrow Na_2SO_4(aq) + MnSO_4(aq) + 2\ H_2O(\ell) + I_2(g)$$

In fact, this is the commercial method of preparing bromine when NaBr is obtained from natural brine wells in Arkansas and Michigan.

Iodine

Iodine is a lustrous, purple-black solid, easily sublimed at room temperature and atmospheric pressure (◀ Figure 12.21). The element was first isolated in 1811 from seaweed and kelp, extracts of which had long been used for treatment of goiter, the enlargement of the thyroid gland. It is now known that the thyroid gland produces a growth-regulating hormone (thyroxine) that contains iodine. Consequently, most table salt in the United States has 0.01% NaI added to provide the necessary iodine in the diet.

A laboratory method for preparing I_2 is illustrated in Figure 21.35. The commercial preparation depends on the source of I^- and its concentration. One method is interesting because it involves some chemistry described earlier in this book. Iodide ions are first precipitated with silver ions to give insoluble AgI.

$$I^-(aq) + Ag^+(aq) \rightarrow AgI(s)$$

This is reduced by clean scrap iron to give iron(II) iodide and metallic silver.

$$2\ AgI(s) + Fe(s) \rightarrow FeI_2(aq) + 2\ Ag(s)$$

The silver is recycled by oxidizing it with nitric acid (forming silver nitrate which is then reused). Finally, iodide ion from water-soluble FeI_2 is oxidized to iodine with chlorine [with iron(III) chloride as a by-product].

$$2\ FeI_2(aq) + 3\ Cl_2(aq) \rightarrow 2\ I_2(s) + 2\ FeCl_3(aq)$$

Fluorine Compounds

Fluorine is the most reactive of all of the elements, forming compounds with every element except He and Ne. In most cases, the elements combine directly, and some reactions can be so vigorous as to be explosive. This can be explained by at least two features of fluorine chemistry: the relatively weak F—F bond compared with chlorine and bromine, and, in particular, the relatively strong bonds formed by fluorine to other elements. This is illustrated by the table of bond dissociation enthalpies in the margin.

Bond Dissociation Enthalpies of Some Halogen Compounds (kJ/mol)

X	X—X	H—X	C—X (in CX_4)
F	155	565	485
Cl	242	432	339
Br	193	366	285
I	151	299	213

In addition to its oxidizing ability, another notable characteristic of fluorine is its small size. These properties lead to the formation of compounds where a number of F atoms can be bonded to a central element in a high oxidation state. Examples include PtF_6, UF_6, IF_7, and XeF_6.

A CLOSER LOOK — Iodine and Your Thyroid Gland

The primary function of the thyroid gland, located in your neck, is the production of thyroxine (3,5,3′,5′-tetraiodothyronine) and 3,5,3′-triiodothyronine. These chemical compounds are hormones that help to regulate the rate of metabolism, a term that refers to all of the chemical reactions that take place in the body. In particular, the thyroid hormones play an important role in the processes that release energy from food.

Abnormally low levels of thyroxine result in a condition known as *hypothyroidism*. Its symptoms include lethargy and feeling cold much of the time. The remedy for this condition is medication, consisting of thyroxine pills. The opposite condition, hyperthyroidism, also occurs in some people. In this condition, the body produces too much of the hormone. Hyperthyroidism is diagnosed by symptoms such as nervousness, heat intolerance, increased appetite, and muscle weakness and fatigue when blood sugar is too rapidly depleted. The standard remedy for hyperthyroidism is to destroy part of the thyroid gland, and one way to do so is to use a compound containing radioactive iodine-123 or iodine-131.

To understand this procedure, you need to know something about iodine in the body. Iodine is an essential element. Some diets provide iodine naturally (seaweed, for example, is a good source of iodine), but in the Western world most iodine taken up by the body comes from iodized salt, NaCl containing about 0.01% of NaI. An adult man or woman of average size should take in about 150 μg (micrograms) of iodine (1 μg = 10^{-6} g) in the daily diet. In the body, iodide ion is transported to the thyroid, where it serves as one of the raw materials in making thyroxine.

The fact that iodine concentrates in the thyroid tissue is essential to the procedure for using radioiodine therapy as a treatment for hyperthyroidism. Typically, an aqueous NaI solution is used in which a small fraction of iodide is the radioactive isotope iodine-131 or iodine-123, and the rest is nonradioactive iodine-127. The radioactivity destroys thyroid tissue, resulting in a decrease in thyroid activity.

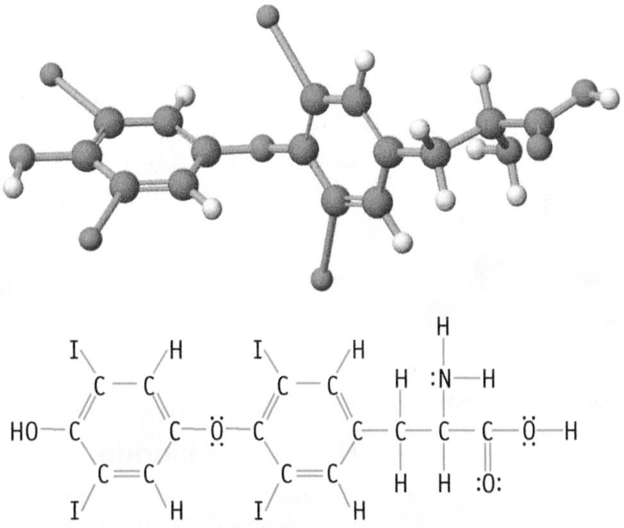

3,5,3′,5′-tetraiodothyronine (thyroxine)

Thyroxine. The hormone 3,5,3′,5′-tetraiodothyronine (thyroxine) exerts a stimulating effect on metabolism.

Hydrogen fluoride is an important industrial chemical. More than 1 million tons of hydrogen fluoride is produced annually worldwide, almost all by the action of concentrated sulfuric acid on fluorspar.

$$CaF_2(s) + H_2SO_4(\ell) \rightarrow CaSO_4(s) + 2\ HF(g)$$

The U.S. capacity for HF production is approximately 210,000 metric tons, but demand often exceeds supply for this chemical. Anhydrous HF is used in a broad range of industries: in the production of refrigerants, herbicides, pharmaceuticals, high-octane gasoline, aluminum, plastics, electrical components, and fluorescent lightbulbs.

The fluorspar used to produce HF must be very pure and free of SiO_2 because HF reacts readily with silicon dioxide.

$$SiO_2(s) + 4\ HF(aq) \rightarrow SiF_4(g) + 2\ H_2O(\ell)$$

$$SiF_4(g) + 2\ HF(aq) \rightarrow H_2SiF_6(aq)$$

This series of reactions explains why HF can be used to etch or frost glass (such as the inside of fluorescent lightbulbs). It also explains why HF is not shipped in glass containers (unlike HCl, for example).

The aluminum industry consumes about 10–40 kg of cryolite, Na_3AlF_6, per metric ton of aluminum produced. The reason is that cryolite is added to aluminum oxide to

Fluorine in Pharmaceuticals *Chemical & Engineering News* reported in 2012 that 3 out of 10 of the best selling drugs contain fluorine, and one fifth of newly approved drugs do so as well. In addition, three common anesthetic agents, sevoflurane, isoflurane, and desflurane, are all more than 50% F by mass.

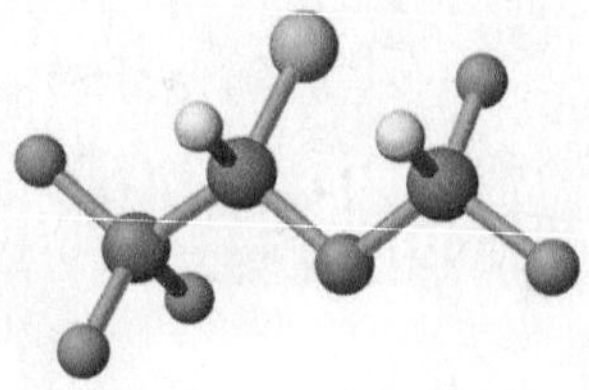

Isoflurane, $CF_3CHClOCHF_2$

produce a lower-melting mixture that can be electrolyzed. Cryolite is found in only small quantities in nature, so it is made in various ways, among them the following reaction:

$$6\ HF(aq) + Al(OH)_3(s) + 3\ NaOH(aq) \rightarrow Na_3AlF_6(s) + 6\ H_2O(\ell)$$

About 3% of the hydrofluoric acid produced is used in uranium fuel production. To separate uranium isotopes in a gas centrifuge (▶ Section 25-6), the uranium must be in the form of a volatile compound. Naturally occurring uranium is processed to give UO_2. This oxide is treated with hydrogen fluoride to give UF_4, which is then reacted with F_2 to produce the volatile solid UF_6.

$$UO_2(s) + 4\ HF(aq) \rightarrow UF_4(s) + 2\ H_2O(\ell)$$

$$UF_4(s) + F_2(g) \rightarrow UF_6(s)$$

This last step consumes 70%–80% of the fluorine produced annually.

Chlorine Compounds

Hydrogen Chloride

Hydrochloric acid, an aqueous solution of hydrogen chloride, is a valuable industrial chemical. Hydrogen chloride gas can be prepared by the reaction of hydrogen and chlorine, but the rapid, exothermic reaction is difficult to control. The classical method of making HCl in the laboratory uses the reaction of NaCl and sulfuric acid, a procedure that takes advantage of the facts that HCl is a gas and that H_2SO_4 will not oxidize the chloride ion.

$$2\ NaCl(s) + H_2SO_4(\ell) \rightarrow Na_2SO_4(s) + 2\ HCl(g)$$

Hydrogen chloride gas has a sharp, irritating odor. Both gaseous and aqueous HCl react with metals and metal oxides to give metal chlorides and, depending on the reactant, hydrogen or water.

$$Mg(s) + 2\ HCl(aq) \rightarrow MgCl_2(aq) + H_2(g)$$

$$ZnO(s) + 2\ HCl(aq) \rightarrow ZnCl_2(aq) + H_2O(\ell)$$

Oxoacids of Chlorine

Oxoacids of chlorine range from HClO, in which chlorine has an oxidation number of +1, to $HClO_4$, in which the oxidation number is equal to the group number, +7. All are strong oxidizing agents.

OXOACIDS OF CHLORINE

ACID	NAME	ANION	NAME
HClO	Hypochlorous	ClO^-	Hypochlorite
$HClO_2$	Chlorous	ClO_2^-	Chlorite
$HClO_3$	Chloric	ClO_3^-	Chlorate
$HClO_4$	Perchloric	ClO_4^-	Perchlorate

Hypochlorous acid, HClO, forms when chlorine dissolves in water. In this reaction, half of the chlorine is oxidized to hypochlorite ion and half is reduced to chloride ion in a **disproportionation reaction.**

Disproportionation A reaction in which an element or compound is simultaneously oxidized and reduced is called a disproportionation reaction. Here, Cl_2 is oxidized to ClO^- and reduced to Cl^-.

$$Cl_2(g) + 2\ H_2O(\ell) \rightleftharpoons H_3O^+(aq) + HClO(aq) + Cl^-(aq)$$

If Cl_2 is dissolved in cold aqueous NaOH instead of in pure water, hypochlorite ion and chloride ion form.

$$Cl_2(g) + 2\ OH^-(aq) \rightleftharpoons ClO^-(aq) + Cl^-(aq) + H_2O(\ell)$$

Under basic conditions, the equilibrium lies far to the right. The resulting alkaline solution is the "liquid bleach" used in home laundries. The bleaching action of this solution is a result of the oxidizing ability of ClO^-. Most dyes are colored organic compounds, and hypochlorite ion oxidizes many dyes to colorless products.

When calcium hydroxide is combined with Cl_2, solid $Ca(ClO)_2$ is the product. This compound is easily handled and is the "chlorine" that is sold for swimming pool disinfection.

When a basic solution of hypochlorite ion is heated, another disproportionation occurs, forming chlorate ion and chloride ion:

$$3\ ClO^-(aq) \rightarrow ClO_3^-(aq) + 2\ Cl^-(aq)$$

Sodium and potassium chlorates are made in large quantities this way. The sodium salt can be reduced to ClO_2, a compound used for bleaching paper pulp. Some $NaClO_3$ is also converted to potassium chlorate, $KClO_3$, an oxidizing agent in fireworks and a component of safety matches.

Perchlorates, salts containing ClO_4^-, are powerful oxidants. Pure perchloric acid, $HClO_4$, is a colorless liquid that explodes if shocked. It explosively oxidizes organic materials and rapidly oxidizes silver and gold. Dilute aqueous solutions of the acid are safe to handle, however.

Perchlorate salts of most metals are usually relatively stable, albeit unpredictable. Great care should be used when handling any perchlorate salt. Ammonium perchlorate, for example, bursts into flame if heated above 200 °C.

$$2\ NH_4ClO_4(s) \rightarrow N_2(g) + Cl_2(g) + 2\ O_2(g) + 4\ H_2O(g)$$

The strong oxidizing ability of the ammonium salt is the reason it has been used as the oxidizer in the solid booster rockets for the Space Shuttle and other space vehicles. The solid propellant in these rockets is largely NH_4ClO_4, the remainder being the reducing agent, powdered aluminum. Each launch requires about 750 tons of ammonium perchlorate, and more than half of the sodium perchlorate currently manufactured is converted to the ammonium salt. The process for making this conversion is an exchange reaction that takes advantage of the fact that ammonium perchlorate is less soluble in water than sodium perchlorate:

$$NaClO_4(aq) + NH_4Cl(aq) \rightleftharpoons NaCl(aq) + NH_4ClO_4(s)$$

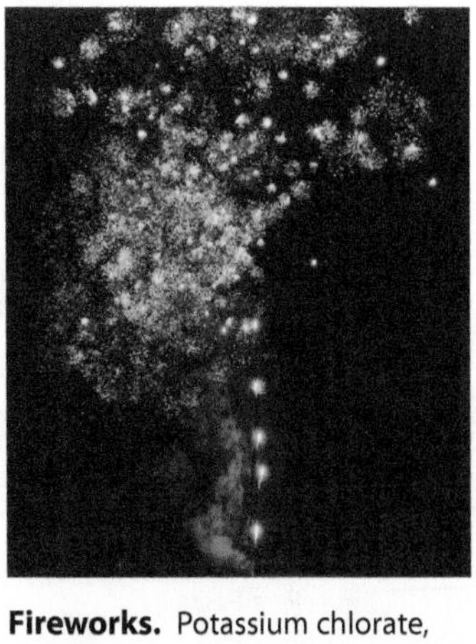

John C. Kotz

Fireworks. Potassium chlorate, $KClO_3$, was commonly used as the oxidizer in fireworks. However, this was the source of numerous accidents because it formed friction-sensitive compounds in contact with sulfur and powdered metals. Now potassium perchlorate, $KClO_4$, is used, even though it is more difficult to ignite.

REVIEW & CHECK FOR SECTION 21-10

1. Which halogen has the highest bond dissociation enthalpy?

   (a) F_2 (b) Cl_2 (c) Br_2 (d) I_2

2. Which of the following statements is *not* correct?

   (a) The ease of oxidation of the halide ions is $F^- < Cl^- < Br^- < I^-$.

   (b) Fluorine is the most abundant halogen in the Earth's crust.

   (c) F_2 is prepared industrially by electrolysis of aqueous NaF.

   (d) HF is used to etch glass.

21-11 The Noble Gases, Group 8A

Helium, neon, argon, krypton, xenon, and radon: These are the noble or rare gases, the elements on the far right of the periodic table. We have already mentioned these elements in various places in this text, most notably their lack of chemical reactivity. At one time these elements were called the "inert gases" but that name was dismissed with the 1962 discovery of compounds of xenon (page 338). Since that time an elaborate chemistry of this element has been developed.

The noble or rare gases. Neon and other gases are used in advertising signs, and xenon gas is found in automobile headlights. Radioactive radon gas occurs naturally in minerals in many parts of the United States and can enter living spaces. You can test your home for radon with a simple kit.

Group **8A**
Rare Gases

Helium 2 **He** 0.008 ppm
Neon 10 **Ne** 7×10^{-5} ppm
Argon 18 **Ar** 1.2 ppm
Krypton 36 **Kr** -1×10^{-5} ppm
Xenon 54 **Xe** 2×10^{-6} ppm
Radon 86 **Rn** trace

Element abundances are in **parts per million** *in the Earth's atmosphere.*

Helium, the first element in this group to be identified, was first detected spectroscopically in the Sun's spectrum in 1868. (The element's name is derived from the Greek word for Sun, *helios.*) In 1895 the pure element was isolated. It is now obtained mostly from natural gas wells where it may be present in amounts up to 7%.

Helium is arguably the most important commercially of these elements, with its main use as a coolant. Part of this use is in chemical instrumentation such as MRIs, which have superconducting magnets that require cooling to liquid helium temperatures (4.2 K) to function. Because of this widespread use, though, there are serious concerns about the supply of helium gas, and labs are encouraged to have helium recovery facilities in place.

Argon is the most abundant of the elements of this group, present in air to the extent of 0.93% by volume. The discovery of argon was an interesting experimental exercise (*Applying Chemical Principles: Argon—An Amazing Discovery;* Chapter 2), requiring highly accurate density measurements. Argon is mainly used to provide an inert atmosphere when required.

Soon after the discovery and characterization of argon in 1895, the other nonradioactive gases neon, krypton, and xenon were found as trace components of air. These gases are best known from their use in lamps: neon for the red color in neon lamps, krypton and xenon for the intense light in lasers, and in xenon headlights for cars. Radioactive radon is found in trace quantities as a product of the decay of uranium minerals (▶ Chapter 25).

An unexpected property of xenon is that it is an inhalation anesthetic. It is more effective than nitrous oxide, but less so than commonly used compounds such as isoflurane ($CF_3CClHOCF_2H$). Xenon is nonpolluting, has analgesic properties and cardiovascular stability, and induces anesthesia rapidly. The problem is its cost (currently about \$1.20/g).

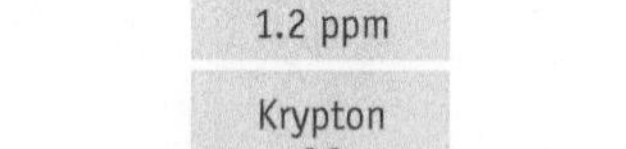

$Xe_2F_3^+$

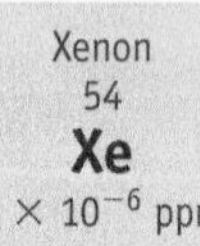

XeO_2F_2

Xenon Compounds

The first evidence that xenon compounds could exist was reported in 1962. Neil Bartlett, then at the University of British Columbia, found that PtF_6, an exceedingly strong oxidizing agent, reacted with molecular oxygen to give $O_2^+PtF_6^-$. Noticing the similarity of the ionization energies of Xe and O_2, Bartlett next carried out a reaction between PtF_6 and Xe, and obtained a mixture of several compounds including $XeF^+PtF_6^-$ and $XeF^+Pt_2F_{11}^-$.

Bartlett's discovery was followed by rapid experimentation that resulted in the identification of a number of new xenon compounds. After chemists had for years predicted that the noble gases would not form compounds, it was particularly notable that XeF_2 (page 338), XeF_4, and XeF_6 could be prepared readily by direct reaction of the elements. The chemistry of these compounds has been further extended, and a number of xenon oxides (such as $XeOF_4$, XeO_2F_2, and XeO_3) as well as ionic species (for example, $Xe_2F_3^+$ and XeF_5^+) are now known.

REVIEW & CHECK FOR SECTION 21-11

1. In which of the following species is Xe in the + 4 oxidation state?

   (a) $XeOF_4$ (b) $Xe_2F_3^+$ (c) XeF_3^+ (d) XeO_6^{4-}

2. Predict the electron pair geometry for the xenon atom in $XeOF_4$.

   (a) linear
   (b) trigonal planar
   (c) tetrahedral
   (d) trigonal bipyramid
   (e) octahedral

A CLOSER LOOK — Predicting the Existence of Xenon Fluorides

Before 1962, most chemists thought that compounds of noble gases could not exist. In fact, few chemists gave this issue much thought, but the data were there to predict that these compounds might exist, had scientists looked for them.

An assessment of bond energy data is the clue to predicting that compounds of xenon should exist. Consider the formation of XeF_2 from Xe and F_2. The enthalpy of this reaction can be related to bond energies (see Section 8-9).

$$Xe(g) + F_2(g) \rightarrow XeF_2(g)$$

$$\Delta_rH = \Delta H(\text{bonds broken}) - \Delta H(\text{bonds formed})$$

$$= \Delta H(\text{F—F}) - 2\,\Delta H(\text{Xe—F})$$

$$= 155\ \text{kJ/mol} - 2\,\Delta H(\text{Xe—F})$$

From these data, one can conclude that if the Xe—F bond energy is 78 kJ/mol or greater this reaction will be exothermic (Δ_rH will be negative).

How might you predict the bond energy of the Xe—F bond? The logical way is to look at trends within the periodic table. In this case, the trend in bond energies in the known compounds TeF_4 and IF_3 allows you to extrapolate a value for Xe—F. The bond dissociation enthalpies of the Te—F bond TeF_4 (BDE = 335 kJ/mol) and the I—F bond in IF_3 (BDE = 272 kJ/mol) are known. Using these numbers, one might predict a bond energy for Xe—F to be substantially more than the value of 78 kJ/mol. This would, in turn, predict the reaction to be exothermic and likely product-favored.

The enthalpy of formation of $XeF_2(g)$ was found by experiment to be −108 kJ/mol. From this the Xe—F bond dissociation enthalpy is calculated to be 132 kJ/mol.

A similar extrapolation predicts that XeF_4 will exist. However, $XeCl_2$, KrF_2, and KrF_4 are all predicted to have positive enthalpies of formation, suggesting that at best these compounds would be unstable and could not formed from direct reactions of the elements.

APPLYING CHEMICAL PRINCIPLES

van Arkel Triangles and Bonding

Two types of bonding, covalent and ionic, involve localized electrons. On one extreme are nonpolar covalent bonds, where electrons are equally shared between two atoms. On the other extreme are ionic bonds, where no sharing of electrons occurs. However, there are many bonds that fall between these extremes, and predictions of the extent of the polarity of a bond can be made using the electronegativity of the individual atoms. And finally, there is a third bonding type: metallic bonding. This raises the question of whether it is possible to develop an integrated picture wherein all three types of bonding, and their variations, can be represented. The answer is that it is possible, at least for binary compounds.

The first efforts in this direction were made by A. E. van Arkel in 1941 and modified later by J. A. A. Ketelaar. They summarized their findings in diagrams such as that shown in the Figure. Referred to now as van Arkel–Ketelaar triangles, the current version of this diagram portrays a wide variety of compounds composed of two different atoms within the boundary of an equilateral triangle. The corners represent the three types of bonding: metallic bonding at the lower left, covalent bonding on the lower right, and ionic bonding at the top. The least electronegative element (Cs), the most electronegative element (F), and the ionic compound formed from these elements are located at the corners of the triangle. All other binary compounds can be positioned inside the triangle.

Different versions of the van Arkel triangle have been developed, each using different scales on the axes. The one chosen for the Figure uses electronegativity values. Here, the *x*-axis is defined as the average of the electronegativities of the two atoms; as such, the x-axis is a measure of the localization of bonding electrons. The bonding electrons are completely delocalized in cesium, whereas the bonding electrons are completely localized in fluorine. The *y*-axis is defined as the difference in electronegativities. The greater the value in the *y*-axis, the greater the ionic character of the compound. With these parameters, the position of each binary compound can be assigned, associating the bond between elements with the degree of ionic/covalent/metallic character.

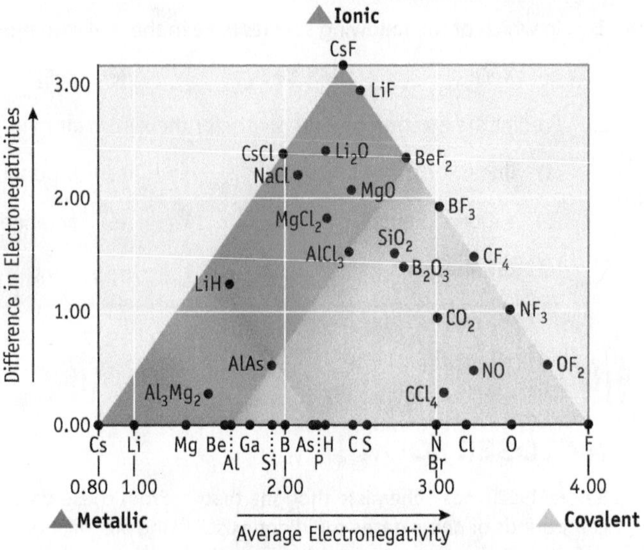

FIGURE A van Arkel–Ketelaar diagram. The four regions of this triangle represent the locations of metallic (blue), semiconducting (green), ionic (red), and covalent (orange) compounds

QUESTIONS:

1. Use electronegativity values (◀ Figure 8.10) to place the compounds GaAs, SBr_2, Mg_3N_2, BP, C_3N_4, CuZn, and $SrBr_2$ on the van Arkel diagram and use the results to answer the following questions:
   (a) Which of the compounds are metallic?
   (b) Which of the compounds are semiconductors? Are either (or both) element(s) in these compounds metalloid(s)?
   (c) Which of the compounds are ionic? Are the compounds composed of a metal and a nonmetal?
   (d) Carbon nitride (C_3N_4) is predicted to be harder than diamond (which is currently the hardest known substance), but too little has been synthesized to enable a comparison. What type of bonding is predicted for C_3N_4?
   (e) Which of the compounds are covalent? Are both elements in these compounds nonmetallic?
2. High boiling points are one characteristic of ionic compounds. For example, magnesium chloride boils at 1412 °C. Beryllium chloride, on the other hand, vaporizes at 520 °C. The boiling point of $BeCl_2$ is far lower than expected for an ionic compound, yet large for a covalent one. Determine where $BeCl_2$ lies on the van Arkel diagram.

REFERENCE:

W. B. Jensen, *Journal of Chemical Education*, Vol. 72, pp. 395–398, 1995.

CHAPTER GOALS REVISITED

Now that you have studied this chapter, you should ask whether you have met the chapter goals. In particular, you should be able to:

UNDERSTAND

- How the period table can assist in predicting chemical behavior of the elements.
- How principles of bonding, thermodynamics, and electrochemistry can be used when discussing the chemistry of the elements.

DO

- Write chemical equations for common chemical reactions.
- Given reactants in a chemical equation, predict the products.
  a. Predict several chemical reactions of the Group A elements (Section 21-2). Study Questions: 13, 14, 71.
  b. Know which reactions produce ionic compounds, and predict formulas for common ions and common ionic compounds based on electron configurations (Section 21-2). Study Questions: 5, 6, 16.
  c. Write formulas based on general principles governing electron configurations (Section 21-2). Study Questions: 13, 14, 68, 69, 72.
- Given a formula for a compound, describe its structure and bonding. Study Questions: 43, 44, 51, 52, 56, 62, 78, 84, 89, 106.
- Describe in a general way the chemical behavior of the main group elements.
  a. Identify the most abundant elements, know how they are obtained, and list some of their common chemical and physical properties.
  b. Be able to summarize briefly a series of facts about the most common compounds of main group elements (ionic or covalent bonding, color, solubility, simple reaction chemistry) (Sections 21-3–21-10).
  c. Identify uses of common elements and compounds, and understand the chemistry that relates to their usage (Sections 21-3–21-10).
- Apply the principles of stoichiometry, thermodynamics, and electrochemistry to the chemistry of the main group elements. Study Questions: 18, 24, 29, 32, 34, 43, 48, 50, 54, 58, 61, 79, 96, 98.

REMEMBER

- Where and in what chemical form main group elements occur in nature and how to prepare samples of the pure element from naturally occurring sources.
- Physical and chemical properties of the more common main group elements.
- Applications of main group elements and their compounds in everyday life.

© Cengage Learning/Charles D. Winters

STUDY QUESTIONS

▲ denotes challenging questions.

Blue-numbered questions have answers in Appendix N and fully worked solutions in the *Student Solutions Manual.*

Practicing Skills

Properties of the Elements

(See Sections 21-1 and 21-2.)

1. Give examples of two basic oxides. Write equations illustrating the formation of each oxide from its component elements. Write another chemical equation that illustrates the basic character of each oxide.

2. Give examples of two acidic oxides. Write equations illustrating the formation of each oxide from its component elements. Write another chemical equation that illustrates the acidic character of each oxide.

3. Give the name and symbol of each element having the valence configuration [noble gas] ns^2np^1.

4. Give symbols and names for four monatomic ions that have the same electron configuration as argon.

5. Select one of the alkali metals, and write a balanced chemical equation for its reaction with chlorine. Is the reaction likely to be exothermic or endothermic? Is the product ionic or molecular?

6. Select one of the alkaline earth metals and write a balanced chemical equation for its reaction with oxygen. Is the reaction likely to be exothermic or endothermic? Is the product ionic or molecular?

7. For the product of the reaction you selected in Study Question 5, predict the following physical properties: color, state of matter (s, ℓ, or g), solubility in water.

8. For the product of the reaction you selected in Study Question 6, predict the following physical properties: color, state of matter (s, ℓ, or g), solubility in water.

9. Would you expect to find calcium occurring naturally in the Earth's crust as a free element? Why or why not?

10. Which of the first 10 elements in the periodic table are found as free elements in the Earth's crust? Which elements in this group occur in the Earth's crust only as part of a chemical compound?

11. Place the following oxides in order of increasing basicity: CO_2, SiO_2, SnO_2.

12. Place the following oxides in order of increasing basicity: Na_2O, Al_2O_3, SiO_2, SO_3.

13. Complete and balance the equations for the following reactions. [Assume an excess of oxygen for (d).]
    (a) $Na(s) + Br_2(\ell) \rightarrow$
    (b) $Mg(s) + O_2(g) \rightarrow$
    (c) $Al(s) + F_2(g) \rightarrow$
    (d) $C(s) + O_2(g) \rightarrow$

14. Complete and balance the equations for the following reactions:
    (a) $K(s) + I_2(g) \rightarrow$
    (b) $Ba(s) + O_2(g) \rightarrow$
    (c) $Al(s) + S_8(s) \rightarrow$
    (d) $Si(s) + Cl_2(g) \rightarrow$

Hydrogen

(See Section 21-3.)

15. Write balanced chemical equations for the reaction of hydrogen gas with oxygen, chlorine, and nitrogen.

16. Write an equation for the reaction of potassium and hydrogen. Name the product. Is it ionic or covalent? Predict one physical property and one chemical property of this compound.

17. Write a balanced chemical equation for the preparation of H_2 (and CO) by the reaction of CH_4 and water. Using data in Appendix L, calculate $\Delta_rH°$, $\Delta_rG°$, and $\Delta_rS°$ for this reaction at 298 K.

18. Using data in Appendix L, calculate $\Delta_rH°$, $\Delta_rG°$, and $\Delta_rS°$ for the reaction of carbon and water to give CO and H_2 at 298 K.

19. A method recently suggested for the preparation of hydrogen (and oxygen) from water proceeds as follows:
    (a) Sulfuric acid and hydrogen iodide are formed from sulfur dioxide, water, and iodine.
    (b) The sulfuric acid from the first step is decomposed by heat to water, sulfur dioxide, and oxygen.
    (c) The hydrogen iodide from the first step is decomposed with heat to hydrogen and iodine.

    Write a balanced equation for each of these steps, and show that their sum is the decomposition of water to form hydrogen and oxygen.

20. Compare the mass of H_2 expected from the reaction of steam (H_2O) per mole of methane, petroleum, and coal. (Assume complete reaction in each case. Use CH_2 and CH as representative formulas for petroleum and coal, respectively.)

Alkali Metals

(See Section 21-4.)

21. Write equations for the reaction of sodium with each of the halogens. Predict at least two physical properties that are common to all of the alkali metal halides.

22. Write balanced equations for the reaction of lithium, sodium, and potassium with O_2. Specify which metal

forms an oxide, which forms a peroxide, and which forms a superoxide.

23. The electrolysis of aqueous NaCl gives NaOH, Cl_2, and H_2.
   (a) Write a balanced equation for the process.
   (b) In the United States, 1.19×10^{10} kg of NaOH and 1.14×10^{10} kg of Cl_2 were produced in a recent year. Does the ratio of masses of NaOH and Cl_2 produced agree with the ratio of masses expected from the balanced equation? If not, what does this tell you about the way in which NaOH and Cl_2 are actually produced? Is the electrolysis of aqueous NaCl the only source of these chemicals?

24. (a) Write equations for the half-reactions that occur at the cathode and the anode when an aqueous solution of KCl is electrolyzed. Which chemical species is oxidized, and which chemical species is reduced in this reaction?
   (b) Predict the products formed when an aqueous solution of CsI is electrolyzed.

Alkaline Earth Elements

(See Section 21-5.)

25. When magnesium burns in air, it forms both an oxide and a nitride. Write balanced equations for the formation of both compounds.

26. Calcium reacts with hydrogen gas at 300–400 °C to form a hydride. This compound reacts readily with water, so it is an excellent drying agent for organic solvents.
   (a) Write a balanced equation showing the formation of calcium hydride from Ca and H_2.
   (b) Write a balanced equation for the reaction of calcium hydride with water (Figure 21.7).

27. Name three uses of limestone. Write a balanced equation for the reaction of limestone with CO_2 in water.

28. Explain what is meant by "hard water." What causes hard water, and what problems are associated with it?

29. Calcium oxide, CaO, is used to remove SO_2 from power plant exhaust. These two compounds react to give solid $CaSO_3$. What mass of SO_2 can be removed using 1.2×10^3 kg of CaO?

30. $Ca(OH)_2$ has a K_{sp} of 5.5×10^{-5}, whereas K_{sp} for $Mg(OH)_2$ is 5.6×10^{-12}. Calculate the equilibrium constant for the reaction

$$Ca(OH)_2(s) + Mg^{2+}(aq) \rightleftharpoons Ca^{2+}(aq) + Mg(OH)_2(s)$$

Explain why this reaction can be used in the commercial isolation of magnesium from seawater.

Boron and Aluminum

(See Section 21-6.)

31. Draw a possible structure for the cyclic anion in the salt $K_3B_3O_6$ and the anion in $Ca_2B_2O_5$.

32. The boron trihalides (except BF_3) hydrolyze completely to boric acid and the acid HX.
   (a) Write a balanced equation for the reaction of BCl_3 with water.
   (b) Calculate $\Delta_r H°$ for the hydrolysis of BCl_3 using data in Appendix L and the following information: $\Delta_f H°$ [BCl_3(g)] = −403 kJ/mol; $\Delta_f H°$ [$B(OH)_3$(s)] = −1094 kJ/mol.

33. When boron hydrides burn in air, the reactions are very exothermic.
   (a) Write a balanced equation for the combustion of B_5H_9(g) in air to give B_2O_3(s) and H_2O(g). Calculate the enthalpy of combustion for B_5H_9(g) ($\Delta_f H°$ = 73.2 kJ/mol), and compare it with the enthalpy of combustion of B_2H_6 (−2038 kJ/mol). (The enthalpy of formation of B_2O_3(s) is −1271.9 kJ/mol.)
   (b) Compare the enthalpy of combustion of C_2H_6(g) with that of B_2H_6(g). Which transfers more energy as heat per gram?

34. Diborane can be prepared by the reaction of $NaBH_4$ and I_2. Which substance is oxidized, and which is reduced?

35. Write balanced equations for the reactions of aluminum with HCl(aq), Cl_2, and O_2.

36. (a) Write a balanced equation for the reaction of Al and $H_2O(\ell)$ to produce H_2 and Al_2O_3.
   (b) Using thermodynamic data in Appendix L, calculate $\Delta_r H°$, $\Delta_r S°$, and $\Delta_r G°$ for this reaction. Do these data indicate that the reaction should favor the products at equilibrium?
   (c) Why is aluminum metal unaffected by water?

37. Aluminum dissolves readily in hot aqueous NaOH to give the aluminate ion, $[Al(OH)_4]^-$, and H_2. Write a balanced equation for this reaction. If you begin with 13.2 g of Al, what volume (in liters) of H_2 gas is produced when the gas is measured at 22.5 °C and a pressure of 735 mm Hg?

38. Alumina, Al_2O_3, is amphoteric. Among examples of its amphoteric character are the reactions that occur when Al_2O_3 is heated strongly or "fused" with acidic oxides and basic oxides.
   (a) Write a balanced equation for the reaction of alumina with silica, an acidic oxide, to give aluminum metasilicate, $Al_2(SiO_3)_3$.
   (b) Write a balanced equation for the reaction of alumina with the basic oxide CaO to give calcium aluminate, $Ca(AlO_2)_2$.

39. Aluminum sulfate is the most commercially important aluminum compound, after aluminum oxide and aluminum hydroxide. It is produced from the reaction of aluminum oxide and sulfuric acid. What masses (in kilograms) of aluminum oxide and sulfuric acid must be used to manufacture 1.00 kg of aluminum sulfate?

40. "Aerated" concrete bricks are widely used building materials. They are obtained by mixing gas-forming additives with a moist mixture of lime, cement, and possibly sand. Industrially, the following reaction is important:

$$2\ Al(s) + 3\ Ca(OH)_2(s) + 6\ H_2O(\ell) \rightarrow 3\ CaO \cdot Al_2O_3 \cdot 6\ H_2O(s) + 3\ H_2(g)$$

Assume the mixture of reactants contains 0.56 g of Al (as well as excess calcium hydroxide and water) for each brick. What volume of hydrogen gas do you expect at 26 °C and a pressure of 745 mm Hg?

Silicon

(See Section 21-7.)

41. Describe the structure of pyroxenes (see page 829). What is the ratio of silicon to oxygen in this type of silicate?

42. Describe how ultrapure silicon can be produced from sand.

43. Silicate structures: Draw a structure, and give the charge for a cyclic silicate anion with the formula $[Si_6O_{18}]^{n-}$.

44. Silicates often have chain, ribbon, cyclic, or sheet structures. One of the simpler ribbon structures is $[Si_2O_5^{2-}]_n$. Draw a structure for this anionic material.

Nitrogen and Phosphorus

(See Section 21-8.)

45. Consult the data in Appendix L. Are any of the nitrogen oxides listed there stable with respect to decomposition to N_2 and O_2?

46. Use data in Appendix L to calculate the enthalpy and free energy change for the reaction

$$2\ NO_2(g) \rightarrow N_2O_4(g)$$

Is this reaction exothermic or endothermic? Is the reaction product- or reactant-favored at equilibrium?

47. Use data in Appendix L to calculate the enthalpy and free energy change for the reaction

$$2\ NO(g) + O_2(g) \rightarrow 2\ NO_2(g)$$

Is this reaction exothermic or endothermic? Is the reaction product- or reactant-favored at equilibrium?

48. The overall reaction involved in the industrial synthesis of nitric acid is

$$NH_3(g) + 2\ O_2(g) \rightarrow HNO_3(aq) + H_2O(\ell)$$

Calculate $\Delta_r G°$ for this reaction and its equilibrium constant at 25 °C.

49. A major use of hydrazine, N_2H_4, is in steam boilers in power plants.
   (a) The reaction of hydrazine with O_2 dissolved in water gives N_2 and water. Write a balanced equation for this reaction.
   (b) O_2 dissolves in water to the extent of 0.0044 g in 100. mL of water at 20 °C. What mass of N_2H_4 is needed to consume all of the dissolved O_2 in 3.00×10^4 L of water (enough to fill a small swimming pool)?

50. Before hydrazine came into use to remove dissolved oxygen in the water in steam boilers, Na_2SO_3 was commonly used for this purpose:

$$2\ Na_2SO_3(aq) + O_2(aq) \rightarrow 2\ Na_2SO_4(aq)$$

What mass of Na_2SO_3 is required to remove O_2 from 3.00×10^4 L of water as outlined in Study Question 49?

51. Review the structure of phosphorous acid in Table 21.6.
   (a) What is the oxidation number of the phosphorus atom in this acid?
   (b) Draw the structure of diphosphorous acid, $H_4P_2O_5$. What is the maximum number of ionizable protons in a molecule of this acid?

52. Unlike carbon, which can form extended chains of atoms, nitrogen can form chains of very limited length. Draw the Lewis electron dot structure of the azide ion, N_3^-. Is the ion linear or bent?

Oxygen and Sulfur

(See Section 21-9.)

53. In the "contact process" for making sulfuric acid, sulfur is first burned to SO_2. Environmental restrictions allow no more than 0.30% of this SO_2 to be vented to the atmosphere.
   (a) If enough sulfur is burned in a plant to produce 1.80×10^6 kg of pure, anhydrous H_2SO_4 per day, what is the maximum amount of SO_2 that is allowed to be exhausted to the atmosphere?
   (b) One way to prevent any SO_2 from reaching the atmosphere is to "scrub" the exhaust gases with slaked lime, $Ca(OH)_2$:

$$Ca(OH)_2(s) + SO_2(g) \rightarrow CaSO_3(s) + H_2O(\ell)$$

$$2\ CaSO_3(s) + O_2(g) \rightarrow 2\ CaSO_4(s)$$

   What mass of $Ca(OH)_2$ (in kilograms) is needed to remove the SO_2 calculated in part (a)?

54. A sulfuric acid plant produces an enormous amount of heat. To keep costs as low as possible, much of this heat is used to make steam to generate electricity. Some of the electricity is used to run the plant, and the excess is sold to the local electrical utility. Three reactions are important in sulfuric acid production: (1) burning S to SO_2; (2) oxidation of SO_2 to SO_3; and (3) reaction of SO_3 with H_2O:

$$SO_3(g) + H_2O\ (\text{in } 98\%\ H_2SO_4) \rightarrow H_2SO_4(\ell)$$

The enthalpy change of the third reaction is −130 kJ/mol. Estimate the enthalpy change when 1.00 mol of S is used to produce 1.00 mol of H_2SO_4. How much energy is produced per metric ton (1.00×10^3 kg) of H_2SO_4?

55. Sulfur forms anionic chains of S atoms called polysulfides. Draw a Lewis electron dot structure for the S_2^{2-} ion. The S_2^{2-} ion is the disulfide ion, an analogue of the peroxide ion. It occurs in iron pyrites, FeS_2.

56. Sulfur forms a range of compounds with fluorine. Draw Lewis electron dot structures for S_2F_2 (connectivity is FSSF), SF_2, SF_4, SF_6, and S_2F_{10}. What is the oxidation number of sulfur in each of these compounds?

The Halogens

(See Section 21-10.)

57. The halogen oxides and oxoanions are good oxidizing agents. For example, the reduction of bromate ion has an $E°$ value of 1.44 V in acid solution:

$$2\ BrO_3^-(aq) + 12\ H^+(aq) + 10\ e^- \rightarrow Br_2(aq) + 6\ H_2O(\ell)$$

Is it possible to oxidize aqueous 1.0 M Mn^{2+} to aqueous MnO_4^- with 1.0 M bromate ion?

58. The hypohalite ions, XO^-, are the anions of weak acids. Calculate the pH of a 0.10 M solution of NaClO. What is the concentration of HClO in this solution?

59. Bromine is obtained from brine wells. The process involves treating water containing bromide ion with Cl_2 and extracting the Br_2 from the solution using an organic solvent. Write a balanced equation for the reaction of Cl_2 and Br^-. What are the oxidizing and reducing agents in this reaction? Using the table of standard reduction potentials (Appendix M), verify that this is a product-favored reaction at equilibrium.

60. To prepare chlorine from chloride ion a strong oxidizing agent is required. The dichromate ion, $Cr_2O_7^{2-}$, is one example (Figure 21.34). Consult the table of standard reduction potentials (Appendix M), and identify several other oxidizing agents that may be suitable. Write balanced equations for the reactions of these substances with chloride ion.

61. If an electrolytic cell for producing F_2 (Figure 21.33) operates at 5.00×10^3 A (at 10.0 V), what mass of F_2 can be produced per 24-hour day? Assume the conversion of F^- to F_2 is 100%.

62. Halogens combine with one another to produce *interhalogens* such as BrF_3. Sketch a possible molecular structure for this molecule, and decide if the F—Br—F bond angles will be less than or greater than ideal.

The Noble Gases

(See Section 21-11.)

63. The standard enthalpy of formation of XeF_4 is −218 kJ/mol. Use this value and the enthalpy of dissociation of the F—F bond to calculate the Xe—F bond dissociation enthalpy.

64. Draw the Lewis electron dot structure for XeO_3F_2. What is its electron-pair geometry and its molecular geometry?

65. Argon is present in dry air to the extent of 0.93% by volume. What quantity of argon is present in 1.00 L of air? If you wanted to isolate 1.00 mol of argon, what volume of air would you need at 1.00 atm pressure and 25 °C?

66. The reaction of XeF_6 with water gives a yellow solution from which solid xenon trioxide, XeO_3, can be isolated (using extreme caution).

(a) Write a balanced equation for this reaction.
(b) What is the molecular geometry of XeO_3?
(c) Xenon trioxide is described as treacherous, exploding with little provocation. Even so, it has been possible to determine the enthalpy of formation, +402 kJ/mol, for this compound. Use this value, and the value of the O=O bond energy, to determine the bond energy of the Xe−O bond.

General Questions

The questions are not designated as to type or location in the chapter. They may combine several concepts.

67. For each of the third-period elements (Na through Ar), identify the following:

(a) whether the element is a metal, nonmetal, or metalloid
(b) the color and appearance of the element
(c) the state of the element (s, ℓ, or g) under standard conditions

68. Consider the chemistries of C, Si, Ge, and Sn.

(a) Write a balanced chemical equation to depict the reaction of each element with elemental chlorine.
(b) Describe the bonding in each of the products of the reactions with chlorine as ionic or covalent.
(c) Compare the reactions, if any, of some Group 4A chlorides —CCl_4, $SiCl_4$, and $SnCl_4$— with water.

69. Consider the chemistries of the elements potassium, calcium, gallium, germanium, and arsenic.

(a) Write a balanced chemical equation depicting the reaction of each element with elemental chlorine.
(b) Describe the bonding in each of the products of the reactions with chlorine as ionic or covalent.
(c) Draw Lewis electron dot structures for the products of the reactions of gallium and arsenic with chlorine. What are their electron-pair and molecular geometries?

70. When BCl_3 gas is passed through an electric discharge, small amounts of the reactive molecule B_2Cl_4 are produced. (The molecule has a B—B covalent bond.)

(a) Draw a Lewis electron dot structure for B_2Cl_4.
(b) Describe the hybridization of the B atoms in the molecule and the geometry around each B atom.

71. Complete and balance the following equations.

(a) $KClO_3$ + heat →
(b) $H_2S(g) + O_2(g) \rightarrow$
(c) $Na(s) + O_2(g) \rightarrow$
(d) $P_4(s) + KOH(aq) + H_2O(\ell) \rightarrow$
(e) $NH_4NO_3(s)$ + heat →
(f) $In(s) + Br_2(\ell) \rightarrow$
(g) $SnCl_4(\ell) + H_2O(\ell) \rightarrow$

72. (a) Heating barium oxide in pure oxygen gives barium peroxide. Write a balanced equation for this reaction.
(b) Barium peroxide is an excellent oxidizing agent. Write a balanced equation for the reaction of iron with barium peroxide to give iron(III) oxide and barium oxide.

73. Worldwide production of silicon carbide, SiC, is several hundred thousand tons annually. If you want to produce 1.0×10^5 metric tons of SiC, what mass (metric tons) of silicon sand (SiO_2) will you use if 70% of the sand is converted to SiC? (A metric ton is exactly 1000 kg.)

74. To store 2.88 kg of gasoline with an energy equivalence of 1.43×10^8 J requires a volume of 4.1 L. In comparison, 1.0 kg of H_2 has the same energy equivalence. What volume is required if this quantity of H_2 is to be stored at 25 °C and 1.0 atm of pressure?

75. Using data in Appendix L, calculate $\Delta_r G°$ values for the decomposition of MCO_3 to MO and CO_2 where M = Mg, Ca, Ba. What is the relative tendency of these carbonates to decompose?

76. Ammonium perchlorate is used as the oxidizer in solid-fuel rockets. Assume that one launch requires 700. tons (6.35×10^5 kg) of the salt, and the salt decomposes according to the equation on page 851.

(a) What mass of water is produced? What mass of O_2 is produced?

(b) If all the O_2 produced is assumed to react with the powdered aluminum present in the rocket engine, what mass of aluminum is required to use up all of the O_2?

(c) What mass of Al_2O_3 is produced?

77. ▲ Metals react with hydrogen halides (such as HCl) to give the metal halide and hydrogen:

$$M(s) + n\ HX(g) \rightarrow MX_n(s) + \tfrac{1}{2}n\ H_2(g)$$

The free energy change for the reaction is $\Delta_r G° = \Delta_f G°(MX_n) - n\ \Delta_f G°[HX(g)]$.

(a) $\Delta_f G°$ for HCl(g) is −95.1 kJ/mol. What must be the value for $\Delta_f G°$ for MX_n for the reaction to be product-favored at equilibrium?

(b) Which of the following metals is (are) predicted to have product-favored reactions with HCl(g): Ba, Pb, Hg, Ti?

78. Halogens form polyhalide ions. Sketch Lewis electron dot structures and molecular structures for the following ions:

(a) I_3^-

(b) $BrCl_2^-$

(c) ClF_2^+

(d) An iodide ion and two iodine molecules form the I_5^- ion. Here, the ion has five I atoms in a row, but the ion is not linear. Draw the Lewis dot structure for the ion, and propose a structure for the ion.

79. The standard enthalpy of formation of OF_2 gas is +24.5 kJ/mol. Calculate the average O—F bond enthalpy.

80. Calcium fluoride can be used in the fluoridation of municipal water supplies. If you want to achieve a fluoride ion concentration of 2.0×10^{-5} M, what mass of CaF_2 must you use for 1.0×10^6 L of water? (K_{sp} for CaF_2 is 5.3×10^{-11}.)

81. The steering rockets in space vehicles use N_2O_4 and a derivative of hydrazine, 1,1-dimethylhydrazine (Study Question 5.86). This mixture is called a *hypergolic fuel* because it ignites when the reactants come into contact:

$$H_2NN(CH_3)_2(\ell) + 2\ N_2O_4(\ell) \rightarrow 3\ N_2(g) + 4\ H_2O(g) + 2\ CO_2(g)$$

(a) Identify the oxidizing agent and the reducing agent in this reaction.

(b) The same propulsion system was used by the Lunar Lander on moon missions in the 1970s. If the Lander used 4100 kg of $H_2NN(CH_3)_2$, what mass (in kilograms) of N_2O_4 was required to react with it? What mass (in kilograms) of each of the reaction products was generated?

82. ▲ Liquid HCN is dangerously unstable with respect to trimer formation—that is, formation of $(HCN)_3$ with a cyclic structure.

(a) Propose a structure for this cyclic trimer.

(b) Estimate the energy of the trimerization reaction using bond dissociation enthalpies (◀ Table 8.8).

83. Use $\Delta_f H°$ data in Appendix L to calculate the enthalpy change of the reaction

$$2\ N_2(g) + 5\ O_2(g) + 2\ H_2O(\ell) \rightarrow 4\ HNO_3(aq)$$

Speculate on whether such a reaction could be used to "fix" nitrogen. Would research to find ways to accomplish this reaction be a useful endeavor?

84. ▲ Phosphorus forms an extensive series of oxoanions.

(a) Draw a structure, and give the charge for an oxophosphate anion with the formula $[P_4O_{13}]^{n-}$. How many ionizable H atoms should the completely protonated acid have?

(b) Draw a structure, and give the charge for a cyclic oxophosphate anion with the formula $[P_4O_{12}]^{n-}$. How many ionizable H atoms should the completely protonated acid have?

85. ▲ Boron and hydrogen form an extensive family of compounds, and the diagram below shows how they are related by reaction.

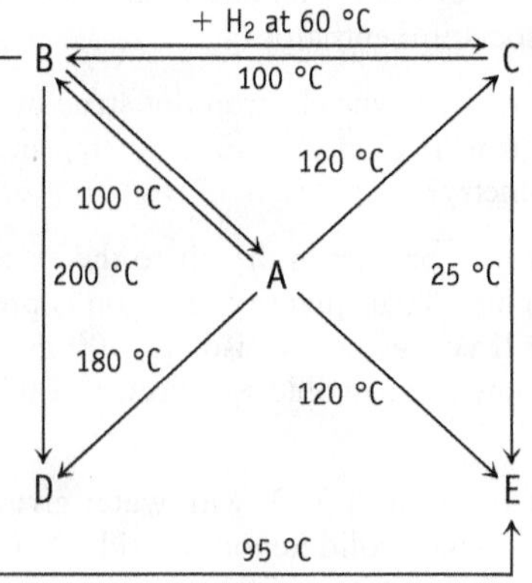

The following table gives the weight percent of boron in each of the compounds. Derive the empirical and molecular formulas of compounds A–E.

Substance	State (at STP)	Mass Percent B	Molar Mass (g/mol)
A	Gas	78.3	27.7
B	Gas	81.2	53.3
C	Liquid	83.1	65.1
D	Liquid	85.7	63.1
E	Solid	88.5	122.2

86. ▲ In 1774, C. Scheele obtained a gas by reacting pyrolusite (MnO_2) with sulfuric acid. The gas, which had been obtained that same year by Joseph Priestley by a different method, was an element, A.

(a) What is the element isolated by Scheele and Priestley?

(b) Element **A** combines with almost all other elements. For example, with cesium it gives a compound in which the mass percent of **A** is 19.39%. The element combines with hydrogen to give a compound with a mass percent of element **A** of 94.12%. Determine the formulas of the cesium and hydrogen compounds.

(c) The compounds of cesium and hydrogen with element **A** react with one another. Write a balanced equation for the reaction.

87. What current must be used in a Downs cell operating at 7.0 V to produce 1.00 metric ton (exactly 1000 kg) of sodium per day? Assume 100% efficiency.

88. The chemistry of gallium:

(a) Gallium hydroxide, like aluminum hydroxide, is amphoteric. Write a balanced equation to show how this hydroxide can dissolve in both HCl(aq) and NaOH(aq).

(b) Gallium ion in water, Ga^{3+}(aq), has a K_a value of 1.2×10^{-3}. Is this ion a stronger or a weaker acid than Al^{3+}(aq)?

89. Silicon-oxygen rings are a common structural feature in silicate chemistry. Draw the structure for the anion $[Si_3O_9]^{6-}$, which is found in minerals such as benitoite. Is the ring expected to be planar?

90. Using enthalpy of formation data in Appendix L, determine whether the decomposition of NH_4NO_3(s) to give N_2O(g) and H_2O(g) is endothermic or exothermic.

91. Metal sulfides roasted in air produce metal oxides.

$$2\ ZnS(s) + 3\ O_2(g) \rightarrow 2\ ZnO(s) + 2\ SO_2(g)$$

Use thermodynamics to decide if the reaction is product- or reactant-favored at equilibrium at 298 K. Will the reaction be more or less product-favored at a high temperature?

92. Metals generally react with hydrogen halides to give the metal halide and hydrogen. Determine whether this is true for silver by calculating $\Delta_rG°$ for the reaction with each of the hydrogen halides.

$$Ag(s) + HX(g) \rightarrow AgX(s) + \tfrac{1}{2}\ H_2(g)$$

The required free energies of formation are:

HX	$-\Delta_fG°$(kJ/mol)	AgX	$-\Delta_fG°$(kJ/mol)
HF	273.2	AgF	193.8
HCl	95.09	AgCl	109.76
HBr	53.45	AgBr	96.90
HI	1.56	AgI	66.19

In the Laboratory

93. One material needed to make silicones is dichlorodimethylsilane, $(CH_3)_2SiCl_2$. It is made by treating silicon powder at about 300 °C with CH_3Cl in the presence of a copper-containing catalyst.

(a) Write a balanced equation for the reaction.

(b) Assume you carry out the reaction on a small scale with 2.65 g of silicon. To measure the CH_3Cl gas, you fill a 5.60-L flask at 24.5 °C. What pressure of CH_3Cl gas must you have in the flask to have the stoichiometrically correct amount of the compound?

(c) What mass of $(CH_3)_2SiCl_2$ can be produced from 2.65 g of Si and excess CH_3Cl?

94. Sodium borohydride, $NaBH_4$, reduces many metal ions to the metal.

(a) Write a balanced equation for the reaction of $NaBH_4$ with $AgNO_3$ in water to give silver metal, H_2 gas, boric acid, and sodium nitrate. (The chemistry of $NaBH_4$ is described in Section 21-6.)

(b) What mass of silver can be produced from 575 mL of 0.011 M $AgNO_3$ and 13.0 g of $NaBH_4$?

95. A common analytical method for hydrazine involves its oxidation with iodate ion, IO_3^-, in acid solution. In the process, hydrazine acts as a four-electron reducing agent.

$$N_2(g) + 5\ H_3O^+(aq) + 4\ e^- \rightarrow N_2H_5^+(aq) + 5\ H_2O(\ell) \qquad E° = -0.23\ V$$

Write the balanced equation for the reaction of hydrazine in acid solution ($N_2H_5^+$) with IO_3^-(aq) to give N_2 and I_2. Calculate $E°$ for this reaction.

96. When 1.00 g of a white solid **A** is strongly heated, you obtain another white solid, **B**, and a gas. An experiment is carried out on the gas, showing that it exerts a pressure of 209 mm Hg in a 450-mL flask at 25 °C. Bubbling the gas into a solution of $Ca(OH)_2$ gives another white solid, **C**. If the white solid **B** is added to water, the resulting solution turns red litmus paper blue.

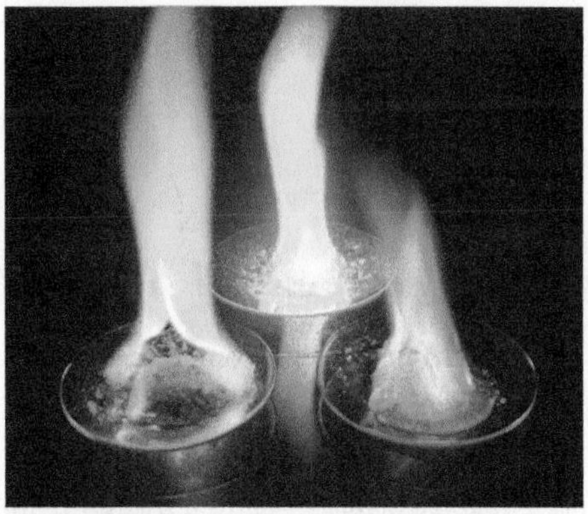
© Cengage Learning/Charles D. Winters

The salts $CaCl_2$, $SrCl_2$, and $BaCl_2$ were suspended in methanol. When the methanol is set ablaze, the heat of combustion causes the salts to emit light of characteristic wavelengths: Calcium salts are yellow; strontium salts are red; and barium salts are green-yellow.

Addition of aqueous HCl to the solution of **B** and evaporation of the resulting solution to dryness yield 1.055 g of a white solid **D**. When **D** is placed in a Bunsen burner flame, it colors the flame green. Finally, if the aqueous solution of **B** is treated with sulfuric acid, a white precipitate, **E**, forms. Identify the lettered compounds in the reaction scheme.

97. ▲ In 1937, R. Schwartz and M. Schmiesser prepared a yellow-orange bromine oxide (BrO_2) by treating Br_2 with ozone in a fluorocarbon solvent. Many years later, J. Pascal found that, on heating, this oxide decomposed to two other oxides, a less volatile golden yellow oxide (**A**) and a more volatile deep brown oxide (**B**). Oxide **B** was later identified as Br_2O. To determine the formula for oxide **A**, a sample was treated with sodium iodide. The reaction liberated iodine, which was titrated to an equivalence point with 17.7 mL of 0.065 M sodium thiosulfate.

$$I_2(aq) + 2\ S_2O_3^{2-}(aq) \rightarrow 2\ I^-(aq) + S_4O_6^{2-}(aq)$$

Compound **A** was also treated with $AgNO_3$, and 14.4 mL of 0.020 M $AgNO_3$ was required to completely precipitate the bromine from the sample.

(a) What is the formula of the unknown bromine oxide **A**?

(b) Draw Lewis structures for **A** and Br_2O. Speculate on their molecular geometry.

98. A mixture of PCl_5 (12.41 g) and excess NH_4Cl was heated at 145 °C for 6 hours. The two reacted in equimolar amounts and evolved 5.14 L of HCl (at STP). Three substances (**A**, **B**, and **C**) were isolated from the reaction mixture. The three substances had the same elemental composition but differed in their molar mass. Substance **A** had a molar mass of 347.7 g/mol and **B** had a molar mass of 463.5 g/mol. Give the empirical and molecular formulas for **A** and **B** and draw a reasonable Lewis structure for **A**.

Summary and Conceptual Questions

The following questions may use concepts from this and previous chapters.

99. Dinitrogen trioxide, N_2O_3, has the structure shown here.

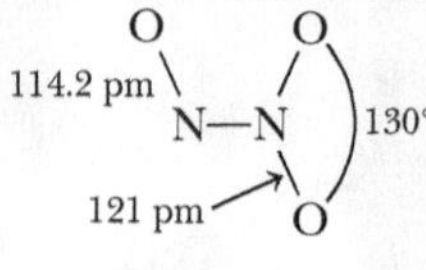

The oxide is unstable, decomposing to NO and NO_2 in the gas phase at 25 °C.

$$N_2O_3(g) \rightarrow NO(g) + NO_2(g)$$

(a) Draw resonance structures for N_2O_3 and explain why one N—O bond distance is 114.2 pm, whereas the other two bonds are longer (121 pm) and nearly equal to each other.

(b) For the decomposition reaction, $\Delta_rH°$ = +40.5 kJ/mol and $\Delta_rG°$ = −1.59 kJ/mol. Calculate $\Delta S°$ and K for the reaction at 298 K.

(c) Calculate $\Delta_fH°$ for $N_2O_3(g)$.

100. ▲ The density of lead is 11.350 g/cm³, and the metal crystallizes in a face-centered cubic unit cell. Estimate the radius of a lead atom.

101. You have a 1.0-L flask that contains a mixture of argon and hydrogen. The pressure inside the flask is 745 mm Hg, and the temperature is 22 °C. Describe an experiment that you could use to determine the percentage of hydrogen in this mixture.

102. The boron atom in boric acid, $B(OH)_3$, is bonded to three —OH groups. In the solid state, the —OH groups are in turn hydrogen-bonded to —OH groups in neighboring molecules.

(a) Draw the Lewis structure for boric acid.

(b) What is the hybridization of the boron atom in the acid?

(c) Sketch a picture showing how hydrogen bonding can occur between neighboring molecules.

103. How would you extinguish a sodium fire in the laboratory? What is the worst thing you could do?

104. Tin(IV) oxide, cassiterite, is the main ore of tin. It crystallizes in a rutile-like unit cell with tin(IV) ions taking the place of Ti^{4+} ions (Study Question 12.4). (The O^{2-} ions marked x are wholly within the unit cell.)

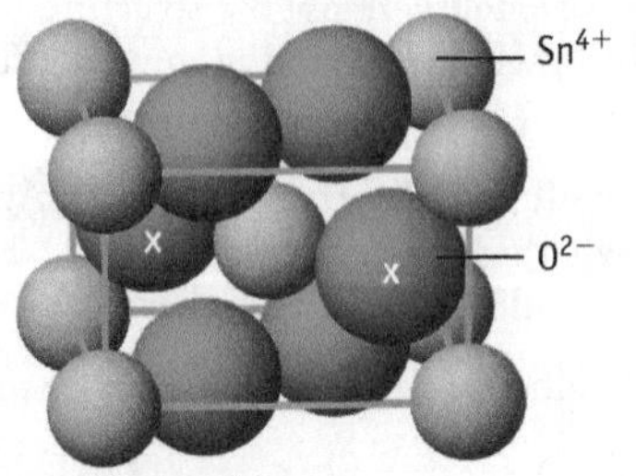

(a) How many tin(IV) ions and oxide ions are there per unit cell of this oxide?

(b) Is it thermodynamically feasible to transform solid SnO_2 into liquid $SnCl_4$ by reaction of the oxide with gaseous HCl? What is the equilibrium constant for this reaction at 25 °C?

105. You are given a stoppered flask that contains hydrogen, nitrogen, or oxygen. Suggest an experiment you could do to identify the gas.

106. The structure of nitric acid is illustrated on page 835.

(a) Why are the N—O bonds the same length, and why are both shorter than the N—OH bond length?

(b) Rationalize the bond angles in the molecule.

(c) What is the hybridization of the central N atom? Which orbitals overlap to form the N—O π bond?

107. Assume an electrolysis cell that produces chlorine from aqueous sodium chloride operates at 4.6 V (with a current of 3.0 × 10⁵ A). Calculate the number of kilowatt-hours of energy required to produce 1.00 kg of chlorine (1 kWh = 1 kilowatt-hour = 3.6 × 10⁶ J).

108. Sodium metal is produced by electrolysis of molten sodium chloride. The cell operates at 7.0 V with a current of 25×10^3 A.

(a) What mass of sodium can be produced in 1 hour?
(b) How many kilowatt-hours of electricity are used to produce 1.00 kg of sodium metal (1 kWh = 3.6×10^6 J)?

109. The reduction potentials for the Group 3A metals, $E°$, are given below. What trend or trends do you observe in these data? What can you learn about the chemistry of the Group 3A elements from these data?

Half-Reaction	Reduction Potential ($E°$, V)
$Al^{3+}(aq) + 3\,e^- \longrightarrow Al(s)$	−1.66
$Ga^{3+}(aq) + 3\,e^- \longrightarrow Ga(s)$	−0.53
$In^{3+}(aq) + 3\,e^- \longrightarrow In(s)$	−0.338
$Tl^{3+}(aq) + 3\,e^- \longrightarrow Tl(s)$	+0.72

110. (a) Magnesium is obtained from seawater. If the concentration of Mg^{2+} in seawater is 0.050 M, what volume of seawater (in liters) must be treated to obtain 1.00 kg of magnesium metal? What mass of lime (CaO; in kilograms) must be used to precipitate the magnesium in this volume of seawater?
(b) When 1.2×10^3 kg of molten $MgCl_2$ is electrolyzed to produce magnesium, what mass (in kilograms) of metal is produced at the cathode? What is produced at the anode? What is the mass of this product? What is the total number of Faradays of electricity used in the process?
(c) One industrial process has an energy consumption of 18.5 kWh/kg of Mg. How many joules are required per mole (1 kWh = 1 kilowatt-hour = 3.6×10^6 J)? How does this energy compare with the energy of the following process?

$$MgCl_2(s) \rightarrow Mg(s) + Cl_2(g)$$

111. Comparing the chemistry of carbon and silicon.

(a) Write balanced chemical equations for the reactions of $H_2O(\ell)$ with CH_4 (forming CO_2 and H_2) and SiH_4 (forming SiO_2 and H_2).
(b) Using thermodynamic data, calculate the standard free energy change for the reactions in (a). Is either reaction product-favored at equilibrium?
(c) Look up the electronegativities of carbon, silicon, and hydrogen. What conclusion can you draw concerning the polarity of C—H and Si—H bonds?
(d) Carbon and silicon compounds with the formulas $(CH_3)_2CO$ (acetone) and $[(CH_3)_2SiO]_n$ (a silicone polymer) also have quite different structures. Draw Lewis structures for these species. This difference, along with the difference between structures of CO_2 and SiO_2, suggests a general observation about silicon compounds. Based on that observation, do you expect that a silicon compound with a structure similar to ethene (C_2H_4) exists?

112. ▲ Boron nitride, BN, has the same solid state structure as ZnS (see Figure 12.10).

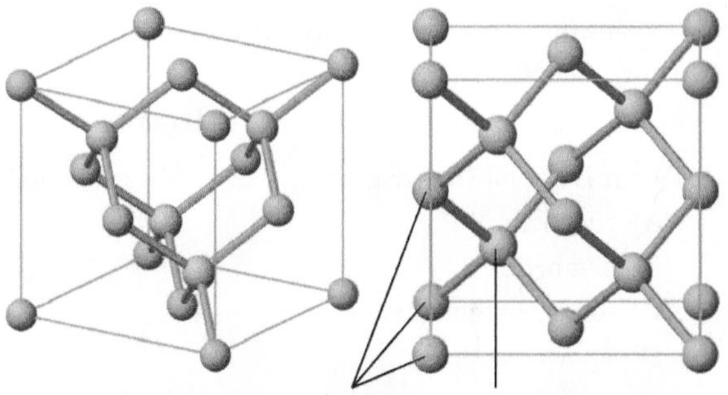

You can consider it a face-centered cube of nitrogen atoms with boron atoms in one half of the tetrahedral holes of the lattice. If the density of this form of BN is 3.45 g/cm³, what is the B−N bond length?

113. ▲ Xenon trioxide, XeO_3, reacts with aqueous base to form the xenate anion, $HXeO_4^-$. This ion reacts further with OH^- to form the perxenate anion, XeO_6^{4-}, in the following reaction:

$$2\,HXeO_4^-(aq) + 2\,OH^-(aq) \rightarrow XeO_6^{4-}(aq) + Xe(g) + O_2(g) + 2\,H_2O(\ell)$$

Identify the elements that are oxidized and reduced in this reaction. You will note that the equation is balanced with respect to the number of atoms on either side. Verify that the redox part of this equation is also balanced, that is, that the extents of oxidation and reduction are also equal.

AP Multiple-Choice Review Questions

Questions 1–4 refer to the following information:

The noble gas xenon was not discovered until 1898. It is obtained in very small quantities by distillation of the oxygen in air. Initially thought to be completely inert, the first xenon compound was made in 1962. Many different compounds have since been made from xenon, as well as from argon, krypton, and radon.

Xenon tetrafluoride was one of the first compounds synthesized from xenon by the following reaction:

$$Xe(g) + 2\ F_2(g) \rightarrow XeF_4(s) \qquad \Delta H = -251\ \text{kJ/mol}$$

Xenon tetrafluoride reacts readily with water according to the following reaction:

$$XeF4(s) + 2H_2O(\ell) \rightarrow Xe(g) + 4HF(aq) + O_2(g)$$

1. What is the molecular geometry of xenon tetrafluoride?
(A) tetrahedral
(B) octahedral
(C) square pyramidal
(D) square planar

2. What conditions would maximize the yield in the reaction for the formation of xenon tetrafluoride?
(A) high temperature, high pressure
(B) high temperature, low pressure
(C) low temperature, high pressure
(D) low temperature, low pressure

3. If 103.5 g of XeF_4 is reacted with excess water, how many moles of hydrofluoric acid are produced? Molar mass of XeF_4 = 207 g/mol.
(A) 0.125 mol
(B) 0.500 mol
(C) 1.00 mol
(D) 2.00 mol

4. The boiling points of the noble gases are shown in the table below. What is the best explanation as to why the boiling point of xenon is the highest in its group?

Element	Helium	Neon	Argon	Krypton	Xenon
Boiling Point	−269 °C	−246 °C	−186 °C	−153 °C	−107 °C

(A) Xe atoms are polar, whereas other noble gases are nonpolar.
(B) Xe has the highest atomic mass in the group; thus it has a lower velocity.
(C) Xe has more electrons than the others, making it more polarizable.
(D) Xe is at the bottom of its group; boiling point always increases going down a group.

5. Milk of Magnesia contains magnesium hydroxide and is often used as an antacid. Estimate the pH of a 1.0×10^{-3} *M* solution of $Mg(OH)_2$.
(A) 2.70
(B) 3.00
(C) 11.00
(D) 11.30

6. The K_{sp} of magnesium hydroxide is 8.9×10^{-12}. If 0.010 mole of $Mg(OH)_2$ is added to 1.00 L of water, will it all dissolve?
(A) Yes, it will all dissolve because *Q* is less than *K*.
(B) Yes, it will dissolve because *Q* is greater than *K*.
(C) No, it will not all dissolve because *Q* is less than *K*.
(D) No, it will not all dissolve because *Q* is greater than *K*.

7. The reduction potentials of three alkali metals are given in the table below, along with the reduction potential of water. Given that reactions with more positive cell potentials are more thermodynamically favorable, what is the best explanation for the fact that the reaction of lithium with water occurs more slowly than the reaction of either sodium or potassium with water?

Alkali Metal	Reaction	$\mathcal{E}^\circ_{red}$
Li	$Li \rightarrow Li^+ + e^-$	−3.05 V
Na	$Na \rightarrow Na^+ + e^-$	−2.71 V
K	$K \rightarrow K^+ + e^-$	−2.92 V
$2H_2O + 2e^- \rightarrow H_2 + 2OH^-$		−0.83 V

(A) Even though the reaction of lithium with water is thermodynamically favorable, it is kinetically slow.
(B) The reaction of lithium with water requires a catalyst, whereas the reactions of potassium and sodium do not.
(C) Reactivity increases going down a group of the periodic table. Lithium is above sodium and potassium in Group I.
(D) The reactions of sodium and potassium with water produce hydrogen gas, whereas the reaction of lithium with water does not.

8. Which of these compounds is most likely to consist of ionic bonds?
(A) ClF_3
(B) Rb_2O
(C) PH_3
(D) $SnCl_4$

9. Sodium reacts in a 1:1 ratio with bromine to form NaBr, whereas magnesium reacts in a 1:2 ratio with fluorine to form MgF_2 and aluminum reacts in a 1:3 ratio with chlorine to form $AlCl_3$. What compound is formed when barium reacts with iodine?
(A) BaI
(B) BaI_2
(C) BaI_3
(D) BaI_4

10. The alkali metals are not found free in nature, only chemically combined with other elements in compounds. Why is this true?
(A) Alkali metals have a full valence shell of electrons and are quite stable.
(B) Alkali metals are extremely reactive because of their low ionization energies.
(C) Alkali metals all have a large size in comparison to other elements in their period.
(D) Alkali metals have very positive reduction potentials and are thus easily reduced.

11. Atomic size generally ____ across a row and generally ____ down a column for representative elements on the periodic table.
(A) increases; increases
(B) increases; decreases
(C) decreases; increases
(D) decreases; decreases

12. How many of the following are covalent hydrides?

NH_3 CH_4 H_2O LiH

(A) 1
(B) 2
(C) 3
(D) 4

13. Which of the following alkaline earth metals has the highest ionization energy?
(A) beryllium
(B) barium
(C) magnesium
(D) strontium

14. Which group on the periodic table forms hydrides of the general formula H_2X?
(A) Group 6A
(B) Group 5A
(C) Group 4A
(D) Group 2A

Steven Hyatt

Copper-fittings in the Ronald McDonald House, a home for seriously ill children and their families in Charleston, SC.

The Chemistry of the Transition Elements

Chapter Outline

LIFE-SAVING COPPER If you are admitted to a hospital in the United States, there is a 1 in 20 chance you will develop an infection. And if you do become infected, there is a 1 in 20 chance you will die from that infection. The U.S. Centers for Disease Control and Prevention (CDC) estimates that hospital-acquired infections kill about 100,000 people in the United States and cost almost $50 billion annually. Clearly it is in our interest to prevent these infections, and recent clinical trials point the way to simple and low-cost ways to do so.

Dr. Michael Schmidt of the Medical University of South Carolina said that "Bacteria present on ICU room surfaces are probably responsible for 35–80 percent of patient infections, demonstrating how critical it is to keep hospitals clean." Therefore, in addition to following normal cleaning processes, the hospital carried out a study in which they covered bed rails, tray tables, chair arms, call

Chapter Goals

See Chapter Goals Revisited (page 894) for Study Questions keyed to these goals.

UNDERSTAND

- Ligand field theory description of metal-ligand bonding in coordination compounds.
- Isomerism and its occurrence in coordination chemistry.
- How color and magnetism are related to the electronic structure of a complex.
- How spectroscopy and magnetism can be used to identify high- and low-spin complexes.

DO

- Given the formula for a coordination complex, identify the metal and its oxidation state, the ligands, the coordination number and coordination geometry, and the overall charge on the complex.
- Given the molecular formula of a complex, determine whether isomers are possible, and draw their structures.
- Given a formula, name a complex; given a name of a complex, write its formula.
- Draw an energy level diagram representing splitting of the metal *d* orbitals by the ligand field.
- Apply the principles of stoichiometry, thermodynamics, and equilibrium to transition metal compounds.

REMEMBER

- General chemical and physical properties of common transition metal elements.
- The terminology of coordination chemistry: coordination number and coordination geometry, ligand, chelate, bidentate.
- The terminology of ligand field theory: low spin and high spin, ligand field splitting.
- The names and formulas for common ligands.

buttons, and IV poles with various copper alloys. (The alloys varied from 75% to 99% copper.) In all they covered 282 objects in copper alloys in 32 rooms and compared the results with 288 noncovered items in 27 rooms. (Similar trials were done in two other large hospitals.) Copper coatings reduced the "microbial burden" (MB) of pathogens by 99% on bed rails and call buttons and by 38% on chair arms. Copper was found to be effective against the following bacteria, among others:

(a) *Staphylococcus aureus*, a bacterium commonly found in hospitals.

(b) Methicillin-resistant *Staphylococcus aureus* (MRSA). This is a virulent strain of antibiotic-resistant bacteria and a common cause of hospital infections.

(c) Vancomycin-resistant *Enterococcus* (VRE), the second leading cause of hospital-acquired infections.

The research team noted that "although MRSA and VRE were frequently isolated from non-copper objects, they were never isolated from copper objects over the study period." Now, because of the apparent effectiveness of using copper on surfaces where the most human contact occurs, hospitals and other medical facilities are expanding their use of copper alloys.

But why did we not recognize this before? Hippocrates (460–370 BC), the father of medicine, recommended the use of copper to treat leg ulcers related to varicose veins. In Roman times, Pliny used copper oxide and honey to treat intestinal worms. More recently scientists from Britain and India investigated a long-held belief among people in India that storing water in brass pitchers can ward off illness. (Brass is an alloy of copper and zinc.) They filled brass pitchers with previously sterile water to which they had added *E. coli* (a bacterium that lives in the lower intestine of many warm-blooded animals and consequently is found in their feces). Other brass pitchers were filled with contaminated river water from India. In both cases, they found fecal bacteria counts dropped from as high as 1,000,000 bacteria per milliliter to zero in 2 days. In contrast, bacteria levels stayed high in plastic or earthenware pots.

The underlying mechanism by which bacteria are destroyed by copper ions is not yet well understood, but there is research activity on this question in academic laboratories around the world.

Study Questions related to this story on copper compounds are: 22.58 and 22.59.

The transition elements are the large block of elements in the central portion of the periodic table, bridging the *s*-block elements at the left and the *p*-block elements on the right (Figure 22.1). The transition elements are often divided into two groups, depending on the valence electrons involved in their chemistry. The first group are the ***d*-block elements**, because their occurrence in the periodic table coincides with the filling of the *d* orbitals. The second group are the ***f*-block elements**, characterized by filling of the *f* orbitals. Contained within this group of elements are two subgroups: the *lanthanides,* elements that occur between La and Hf, and the *actinides,* elements that occur between Ac and Rf.

This chapter focuses primarily on the *d*-block elements, and within this group we concentrate mainly on the elements in the fourth period, that is, the elements of the first transition series, scandium to zinc.

22-1 Properties of the Transition Elements

The *d*-block metals include elements with a wide range of properties. They encompass the most common metal used in construction and manufacturing (iron), metals valued for their beauty (gold, silver, and platinum), and metals used in coins (nickel, copper, and zinc). There are metals used in modern technology (titanium) and metals known and used in early civilizations (copper, silver, gold, and iron). The *d*-block contains the

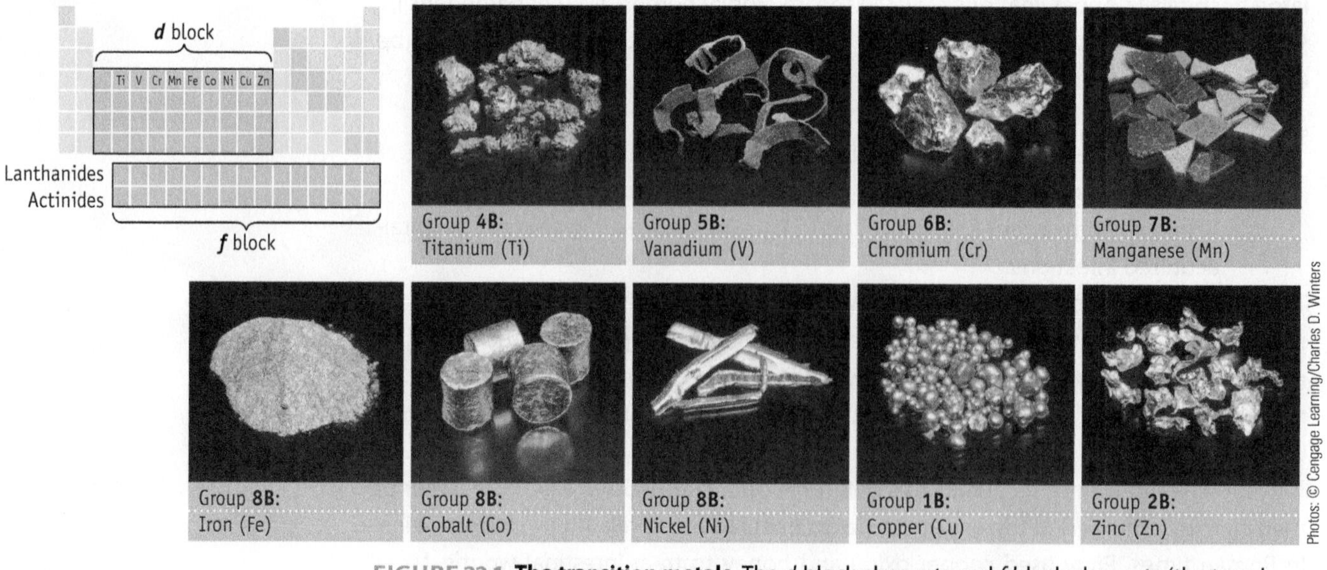

FIGURE 22.1 **The transition metals.** The *d*-block elements and *f*-block elements (the transition elements) are highlighted in a darker shade of blue.

(a) Paint pigments: yellow, CdS; green, Cr_2O_3; white, TiO_2 and ZnO; purple, $Mn_3(PO_4)_2$; blue, Co_2O_3 and Al_2O_3; ochre, Fe_2O_3.

(b) Small amounts of transition metal compounds are used to color glass: blue, Co_2O_3; green, copper or chromium oxides; purple, nickel or cobalt oxides; red, copper oxide; iridescent green, uranium oxide.

(c) Traces of transition metal ions are responsible for the colors of green jade (iron), red corundum (chromium), blue azurite, blue-green turquoise (copper), and purple amethyst (iron).

FIGURE 22.2 **Colorful chemistry.** Transition metal compounds have a wide variety of colors.

densest elements (osmium, $d = 22.49$ g/cm^3, and iridium, $d = 22.41$ g/cm^3), the metals with the highest and lowest melting points (tungsten, mp = 3410 °C, and mercury, mp = −38.9 °C), and one of just two elements with atomic numbers less than 83 that have only radioactive isotopes [technetium (Tc), atomic number 43; promethium (Pm), atomic number 61, in the *f*-block].

With the exception of mercury, the transition elements are solids. They have a metallic sheen and conduct electricity and heat. They react with various oxidizing agents to give ionic compounds, although there is considerable variation in such reactions among the elements. Because silver, gold, and platinum resist oxidation, for example, they are used for jewelry and decorative items.

Certain *d*-block elements are important in living organisms. Cobalt is the crucial element in vitamin B_{12}, which is part of a catalyst essential for several biochemical reactions. Hemoglobin and myoglobin, oxygen-carrying and storage proteins, contain iron. Molybdenum and iron, together with sulfur, form the reactive portion of nitrogenase, a biological catalyst used by nitrogen-fixing organisms to convert atmospheric nitrogen into ammonia.

Many transition metal compounds are highly colored, which makes them useful as pigments in paints and dyes (Figure 22.2). Prussian blue, $Fe_4[Fe(CN)_6]_3 \cdot 14\ H_2O$, is a "bluing agent" used in engineering blueprints and in the laundry to brighten yellowed white cloth. A common pigment used by artists (cadmium yellow) contains cadmium sulfide, CdS, and the white in most white paints is titanium(IV) oxide, TiO_2.

The presence of transition metal ions in crystalline silicates or alumina transforms these common materials into gemstones. Iron(II) ions produce the yellow color in citrine, and chromium(III) ions produce the red color of a ruby. Transition metal compounds in small quantities add color to glass. Blue glass contains a small amount of a cobalt(III) oxide, and addition of chromium(III) oxide to glass gives a green color. Old window panes sometimes take on a purple color over time as a consequence of oxidation of traces of manganese(II) ion present in the glass to permanganate ion (MnO_4^-).

In the next few pages, we will examine the properties of the transition elements, concentrating on the underlying principles that govern these properties.

Prussian blue. The deep blue compound called Prussian blue has the formula $Fe_4[Fe(CN)_6]_3 \cdot 14\ H_2O$. The color arises from electron transfer between Fe(II) and Fe(III) ions in the compound.

Electron Configurations

Because chemical behavior is related to electron structure, it is important to know the electron configurations of the *d*-block elements (Table 22.1) and their common ions (◀ Sections 7-3 and 7-4). Recall that the configuration of these metals has the

Table 22.1 Electron Configurations of the Fourth-Period Transition Elements

	spdf Configuration	Box Notation 3*d*	4*s*
Sc	$[\text{Ar}]3d^{1}4s^{2}$	[↑][ ][ ][ ][ ]	[↑↓]
Ti	$[\text{Ar}]3d^{2}4s^{2}$	[↑][↑][ ][ ][ ]	[↑↓]
V	$[\text{Ar}]3d^{3}4s^{2}$	[↑][↑][↑][ ][ ]	[↑↓]
Cr	$[\text{Ar}]3d^{5}4s^{1}$	[↑][↑][↑][↑][↑]	[↑]
Mn	$[\text{Ar}]3d^{5}4s^{2}$	[↑][↑][↑][↑][↑]	[↑↓]
Fe	$[\text{Ar}]3d^{6}4s^{2}$	[↑↓][↑][↑][↑][↑]	[↑↓]
Co	$[\text{Ar}]3d^{7}4s^{2}$	[↑↓][↑↓][↑][↑][↑]	[↑↓]
Ni	$[\text{Ar}]3d^{8}4s^{2}$	[↑↓][↑↓][↑↓][↑][↑]	[↑↓]
Cu	$[\text{Ar}]3d^{10}4s^{1}$	[↑↓][↑↓][↑↓][↑↓][↑↓]	[↑]
Zn	$[\text{Ar}]3d^{10}4s^{2}$	[↑↓][↑↓][↑↓][↑↓][↑↓]	[↑↓]

Table 22.2 Products from Reactions of the Elements in the First Transition Series with O_2, Cl_2, or Aqueous HCl

Element	Reaction with O_2*	Reaction with Cl_2	Reaction with Aqueous HCl
Scandium	Sc_2O_3	$ScCl_3$	Sc^{3+}(aq)
Titanium	TiO_2	$TiCl_4$	Ti^{3+}(aq)
Vanadium	V_2O_5	VCl_4	NR†
Chromium	Cr_2O_3	$CrCl_3$	Cr^{2+}(aq)
Manganese	MnO_2	$MnCl_2$	Mn^{2+}(aq)
Iron	Fe_2O_3	$FeCl_3$	Fe^{2+}(aq)
Cobalt	Co_2O_3	$CoCl_2$	Co^{2+}(aq)
Nickel	NiO	$NiCl_2$	Ni^{2+}(aq)
Copper	CuO	$CuCl_2$	NR†
Zinc	ZnO	$ZnCl_2$	Zn^{2+}(aq)

*Product obtained with excess oxygen.
†NR = no reaction.

general form [noble gas core]$(n-1)d^{b}ns^{a}$; that is, valence electrons for the transition elements reside in the *ns* and $(n-1)d$ subshells.

Oxidation and Reduction

A characteristic chemical property of all metals is that they undergo oxidation by a wide range of oxidizing agents such as oxygen, the halogens, and aqueous acids. Standard reduction potentials for the elements of the first transition series can be used to predict which elements will be oxidized by a given oxidizing agent in aqueous solution. For example, all of these metals except vanadium and copper are oxidized by aqueous HCl (Table 22.2). Oxidation, which dominates the chemistry of these elements, is sometimes highly undesirable (see *A Closer Look: Corrosion of Iron,* page 863).

When a transition metal is oxidized, the outermost *s* electrons are removed, followed by one or more *d* electrons. With a few exceptions, transition metal ions have the electron configuration [noble gas core]$(n-1)d^{x}$. In contrast to ions formed by main group elements, transition metal cations often possess unpaired electrons, resulting in paramagnetism (◀ Section 7-5). They are frequently colored as well, due to the absorption of light in the visible region of the electromagnetic spectrum. Color and magnetism figure prominently in a discussion of the properties and bonding of these elements, as you shall see shortly.

In the first transition series, the most commonly encountered metal ions have oxidation numbers of +2 and +3 (Table 22.2). With iron, for example, oxidation converts Fe($[\text{Ar}]3d^{6}4s^{2}$) to either Fe^{2+}($[\text{Ar}]3d^{6}$) or Fe^{3+}($[\text{Ar}]3d^{5}$). Iron reacts with chlorine to give $FeCl_3$, and it reacts with aqueous acids to produce Fe^{2+}(aq) and H_2 (Figure 22.3). Despite the preponderance of 2+ and 3+ ions in compounds of the first transition metal series, the range of possible oxidation states for these compounds is broad (Figure 22.4). Earlier in this text, we encountered chromium with a +6 oxidation number (CrO_4^{2-}, $Cr_2O_7^{2-}$), manganese with an oxidation number of +7 (MnO_4^-), silver and copper as 1+ ions, and vanadium oxidation numbers that can range from +5 to +2 (◀ Figure 19.3).

(a) Steel wool reacts with O_2. (b) Steel wool reacts with chlorine gas, Cl_2. (c) Iron chips react with aqueous HCl.

FIGURE 22.3 **Typical reactions of transition metals.** These metals react with oxygen, with halogens, and with acids under appropriate conditions.

Higher oxidation numbers are more common in compounds of the elements in the second and third transition series. For example, the naturally occurring sources of molybdenum and tungsten are the ores molybdenite (MoS_2) and wolframite (WO_3). This general trend is carried over in the *f*-block. The lanthanides form primarily 3+ ions. In contrast, actinide elements usually have higher oxidation numbers in their compounds; +4 and even +6 are typical. For example, UO_3 is a common oxide of uranium, and UF_6 is a compound important in processing uranium fuel for nuclear reactors (▶ Section 25-6).

Periodic Trends in the *d* Block: Size, Density, Melting Point

Let us look at three important physical properties of the transition elements that vary periodically: atomic radii, density, and melting point.

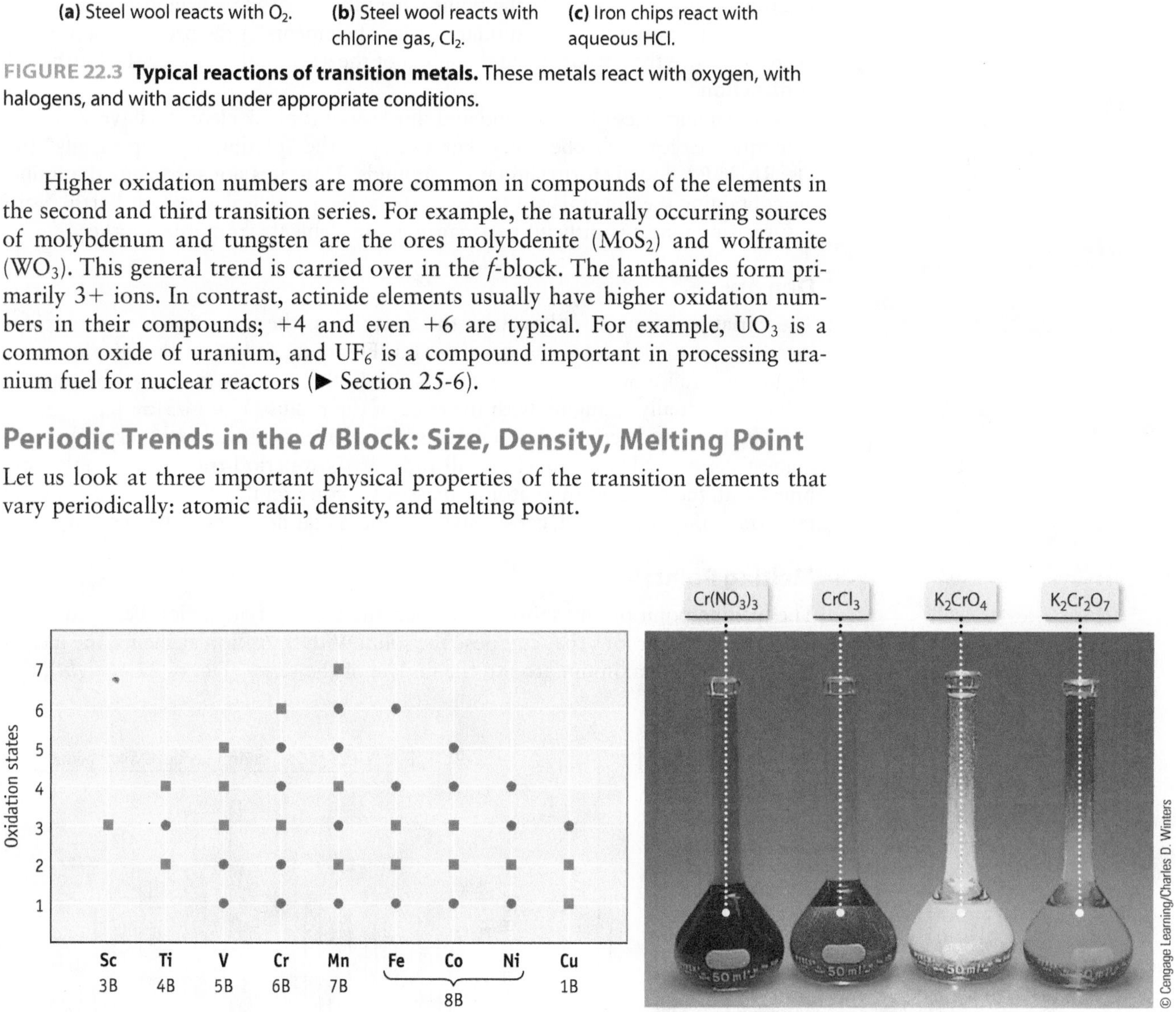

(a) The most common oxidation states are indicated with *red squares;* less common oxidation states are indicated with *blue dots.*

(b) Aqueous solutions of chromium compounds with two different oxidation numbers: +3 in $Cr(NO_3)_3$ (violet) and $CrCl_3$ (green), and +6 in K_2CrO_4 (yellow) and $K_2Cr_2O_7$ (orange). The two Cr(III) species have different colors in solution because there are different complex ions in solution. The complex ion in the purple solution is $[Cr(H_2O)_6]^{3+}$; the complex ion in the green solution is $[Cr(H_2O)_4Cl_2]^+$.

FIGURE 22.4 **Oxidation states of the transition elements in the first transition series.**

Metal Atom Radii

The radii of the transition elements vary over a fairly narrow range, with a small decrease to a minimum being observed around the middle of this group of elements (◀ Figure 7.8). This similarity of radii can be understood based on electron configurations. Atom size is determined by the electrons in the outermost orbital, which for these elements is the *ns* orbital ($n = 4, 5,$ or 6). Progressing from left to right in the periodic table, the size decline expected from increasing the number of protons in the nucleus is mostly canceled out by an opposing effect, repulsion from additional electrons in the $(n - 1)d$ orbitals.

The radii of the *d*-block elements in the fifth and sixth periods in each group are almost identical. The reason is that the lanthanide elements immediately precede the third series of *d*-block elements. The filling of 4*f* orbitals is accompanied by a steady contraction in size, consistent with the general trend of decreasing size from left to right in the periodic table. At the point where the 5*d* orbitals begin to fill again, the radii have decreased to a size similar to that of elements in the previous period. The decrease in size that results from the filling of the 4*f* orbitals is called the **lanthanide contraction.**

The similar sizes of the second and third series *d*-block elements have significant consequences for their chemistry. For example, the "platinum group metals" (Ru, Os, Rh, Ir, Pd, and Pt) form similar compounds. Thus, it is not surprising that minerals containing these metals are found in the same geological zones on Earth. Nor is it surprising that it is difficult to separate these elements from one another.

Density

The variation in metal radii causes the densities of the transition elements to first increase and then decrease across a period (Figure 22.5, *left*). Although the overall change in radii among these elements is small, the effect is magnified because the volume is actually changing with the cube of the radius [$V = (4/3)\pi r^3$].

The lanthanide contraction explains why elements in the sixth period have the highest densities. The relatively small radii of sixth-period transition metals, combined with the fact that their atomic masses are considerably larger than their counterparts in the fifth period, causes sixth-period metal densities to be very large.

Melting Point

The melting point of any substance reflects the forces of attraction between the atoms, molecules, or ions that compose the solid. With transition elements, the melting points rise to a maximum around the middle of the series (Figure 22.5, *right*), then

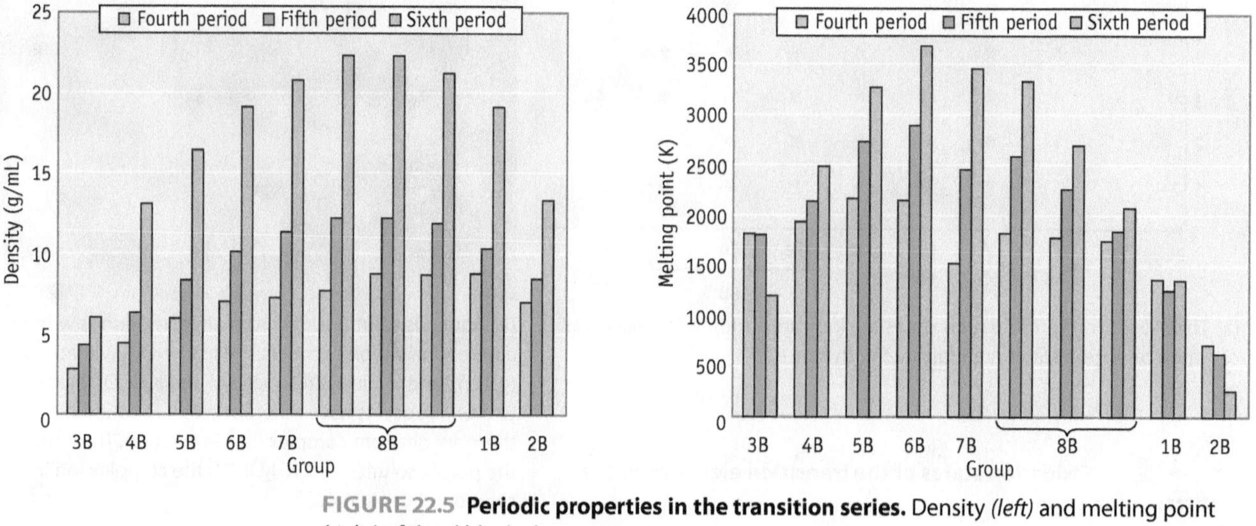

FIGURE 22.5 **Periodic properties in the transition series.** Density *(left)* and melting point *(right)* of the *d*-block elements.

A CLOSER LOOK — Corrosion of Iron

It is hard not to be aware of corrosion. Those of us who live in the northern part of the United States are well aware of the problems of rust on our automobiles. It is estimated that 20% of iron production each year goes solely to replace iron that has rusted away.

Qualitatively, we describe corrosion as the deterioration of metals by a product-favored oxidation reaction. The corrosion of iron, for example, converts iron metal to red-brown rust, which is hydrated iron(III) oxide, $Fe_2O_3 \cdot H_2O$. This process requires both air and water, and it is enhanced if the water contains dissolved ions and if the metal is stressed (e.g., if it has dents, cuts, and scrapes on the surface).

The corrosion process occurs in what is essentially a small electrochemical cell. There is an anode and a cathode, an electrical connection between the two (the metal itself), and an electrolyte in contact with both anode and cathode. When a metal corrodes, the metal is oxidized on anodic areas of the metal surface.

Anode, oxidation $\quad M(s) \longrightarrow M^{n+} + n\,e^-$

The electrons are consumed by several possible half-reactions in cathodic areas.

Cathode, reduction

$$2\,H_3O^+(aq) + 2\,e^- \longrightarrow H_2(g) + 2\,H_2O(\ell)$$

$$2\,H_2O(\ell) + 2\,e^- \longrightarrow H_2(g) + 2\,OH^-(aq)$$

$$O_2(g) + 2\,H_2O(\ell) + 4\,e^- \longrightarrow 4\,OH^-(aq)$$

The rate of iron corrosion is controlled by the rate of the cathodic process. Of the three possible cathodic reactions, the one that is fastest is determined by acidity and the amount of oxygen present. If little or no oxygen is present—as when a piece of iron is buried in soil such as moist clay—hydronium ions or water are reduced, and $H_2(g)$ and hydroxide ions are the products. Iron(II) hydroxide is relatively insoluble and will precipitate on the metal surface, inhibiting the further formation of Fe^{2+}.

Anode	$Fe(s) \longrightarrow Fe^{2+}(aq) + 2\,e^-$
Cathode	$2\,H_2O(\ell) + 2\,e^- \longrightarrow H_2(g) + 2\,OH^-(aq)$
Precipitation	$Fe^{2+}(aq) + 2\,OH^-(aq) \longrightarrow Fe(OH)_2(s)$
Net reaction	$Fe(s) + 2\,H_2O(\ell) \longrightarrow H_2(g) + Fe(OH)_2(s)$

If both water and O_2 are present, the chemistry of iron corrosion is somewhat different, and the corrosion reaction is about 100 times faster than without oxygen.

Anode	$2\,Fe(s) \longrightarrow 2\,Fe^{2+}(aq) + 4\,e^-$
Cathode	$O_2(g) + 2\,H_2O(\ell) + 4\,e^- \longrightarrow 4\,OH^-(aq)$
Precipitation	$2\,Fe^{2+}(aq) + 4\,OH^-(aq) \longrightarrow 2\,Fe(OH)_2(s)$
Net reaction	$2\,Fe(s) + 2\,H_2O(\ell) + O_2(g) \longrightarrow 2\,Fe(OH)_2(s)$

If oxygen is present but not in excess, further oxidation of the iron(II) hydroxide leads to the formation of magnetic iron oxide Fe_3O_4, (which can be thought of as a mixed oxide of Fe_2O_3 and FeO).

$$6\,Fe(OH)_2(s) + O_2(g) \longrightarrow \underset{\text{green hydrated magnetite}}{2\,Fe_3O_4 \cdot H_2O(s)} + 4\,H_2O(\ell)$$

$$Fe_3O_4 \cdot H_2O(s) \longrightarrow H_2O(\ell) + \underset{\text{black magnetite}}{Fe_3O_4(s)}$$

It is the black magnetite that you find coating an iron object that has corroded by resting in moist soil.

If the iron object has free access to oxygen and water, as in the open or in flowing water, red-brown iron(III) oxide will form.

$$4\,Fe(OH)_2(s) + O_2(g) \longrightarrow \underset{\text{red-brown}}{2\,Fe_2O_3 \cdot H_2O(s)} + 2\,H_2O(\ell)$$

This is the familiar rust you see on cars and buildings and the substance that colors the water red in some mountain streams or in your home.

© Cengage Learning/Charles D. Winters

The corrosion or rusting of iron results in major economic loss.

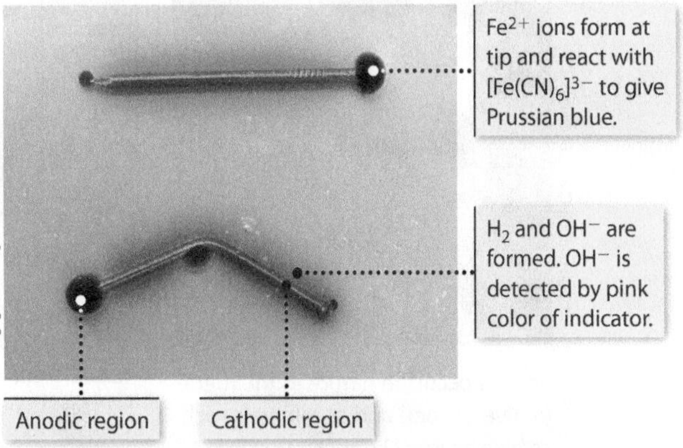

© Cengage Learning/Charles D. Winters

Anode and cathode reactions in iron corrosion. Two iron nails were placed in an agar gel that contains phenolphthalein and $K_3[Fe(CN)_6]$. In this electrochemical cell, regions of stress—the ends and the bent region of the nail—act as anodes, and the remainder of the surface serves as the cathode.

descend. Again, the element electron configurations provide us with an explanation. The variation in melting points indicates that the strongest metallic bonds occur when the *d* subshell is about half filled. This is also the point at which the largest number of electrons occupy the bonding molecular orbitals in the metal. (See the discussion of bonding in metals in Section 12-4.)

REVIEW & CHECK FOR SECTION 22-1

1. What is the maximum oxidation number that manganese can exhibit in its compounds?

   (a) +3 (b) +4 (c) +5 (d) +6 (e) +7

2. The "lanthanide contraction" is often given as an explanation for the fact that the sixth period transition elements have

   (a) densities smaller than that of the fifth period transition elements.

   (b) atomic radii that are similar to the fifth period transition elements.

   (c) melting points that are lower than the fifth period transition elements.

22-2 Metallurgy

Most metals are found in nature as oxides, sulfides, halides, carbonates, or other ionic compounds (Figure 22.6), but some such as copper, silver, and gold can occur uncombined. Some metal-containing mineral deposits have little economic value, either because the concentration of the metal is too low or because the metal is difficult to separate from impurities. The relatively few minerals from which elements can be obtained profitably are called *ores*. **Metallurgy** is the general name given to the process of obtaining metals from their ores.

Very few ores are chemically pure substances. Instead, the desired mineral is usually mixed with large quantities of impurities such as sand and clay, called **gangue** (pronounced "gang"). Generally, the first step in a metallurgical process is to separate the mineral from the gangue. Then the ore is converted to the metal, a reduction process. Pyrometallurgy and hydrometallurgy are two methods of recovering metals from their ores. As the names imply, **pyrometallurgy** involves high temperatures and **hydrometallurgy** uses aqueous solutions (and thus is limited to

© Cengage Learning/Charles D. Winters

Copper occurs in nature as the metal (native copper) and as minerals such as blue azurite [$2\ CuCO_3 \cdot Cu(OH)_2$] and green malachite [$CuCO_3 \cdot Cu(OH)_2$].

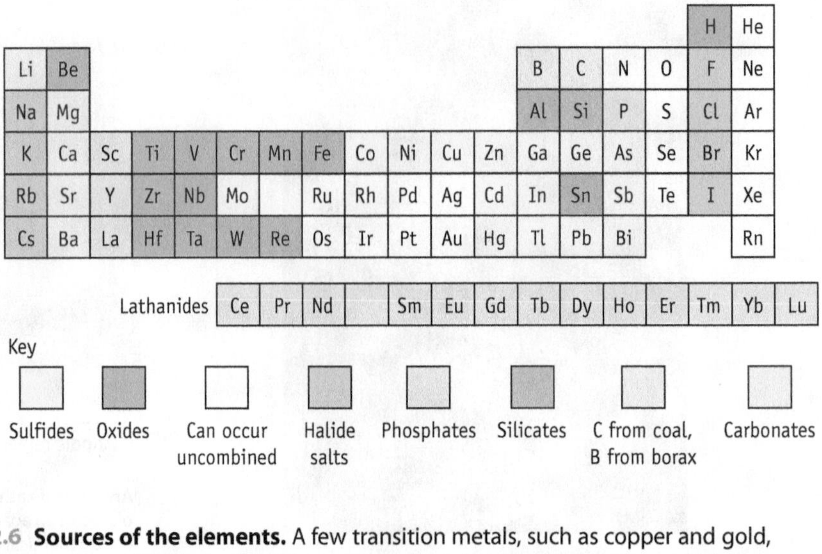

FIGURE 22.6 **Sources of the elements.** A few transition metals, such as copper and gold, occur in nature as the metal. Most other elements are found naturally as oxides, sulfides, or other salts.

the relatively low temperatures at which water is a liquid). Iron and copper metallurgy illustrate these two methods of metal production.

Pyrometallurgy: Iron Production

The production of iron from its ores is carried out in a blast furnace (Figure 22.7). The furnace is charged with a mixture of ore (usually hematite, Fe_2O_3), coke (which is primarily carbon), and limestone ($CaCO_3$). A blast of hot air forced in at the bottom of the furnace causes the coke to burn with such an intense heat that the temperature at the bottom is almost 1500 °C. The quantity of air input is controlled so that carbon monoxide is the primary product. Both carbon and carbon monoxide participate in the reduction of iron(III) oxide to give impure metal.

Coke: A Reducing Agent Coke is made by heating coal in a tall, narrow oven that is sealed to keep out oxygen. Heating drives off volatile chemicals, including benzene and ammonia. What remains is nearly pure carbon.

$$Fe_2O_3(s) + 3\ C(s) \longrightarrow 2\ Fe(\ell) + 3\ CO(g)$$

$$Fe_2O_3(s) + 3\ CO(g) \longrightarrow 2\ Fe(\ell) + 3\ CO_2(g)$$

Much of the carbon dioxide formed in the reduction process (and from heating limestone) is reduced on contact with unburned coke and produces carbon monoxide, which can then function as a reducing agent.

$$CO_2(g) + C(s) \longrightarrow 2\ CO(g)$$

The molten iron flows down through the furnace and collects at the bottom, where it is tapped off through an opening in the side. This impure iron is called *cast iron* or *pig iron*. Usually, the impure metal is either brittle or soft (undesirable properties for most uses) due to the presence of impurities such as elemental carbon, phosphorus, and sulfur.

Iron ores generally contain silicate minerals and silicon dioxide. Lime (CaO), formed when limestone is heated, reacts with these materials to give calcium silicate.

$$SiO_2(s) + CaO(s) \longrightarrow CaSiO_3(\ell)$$

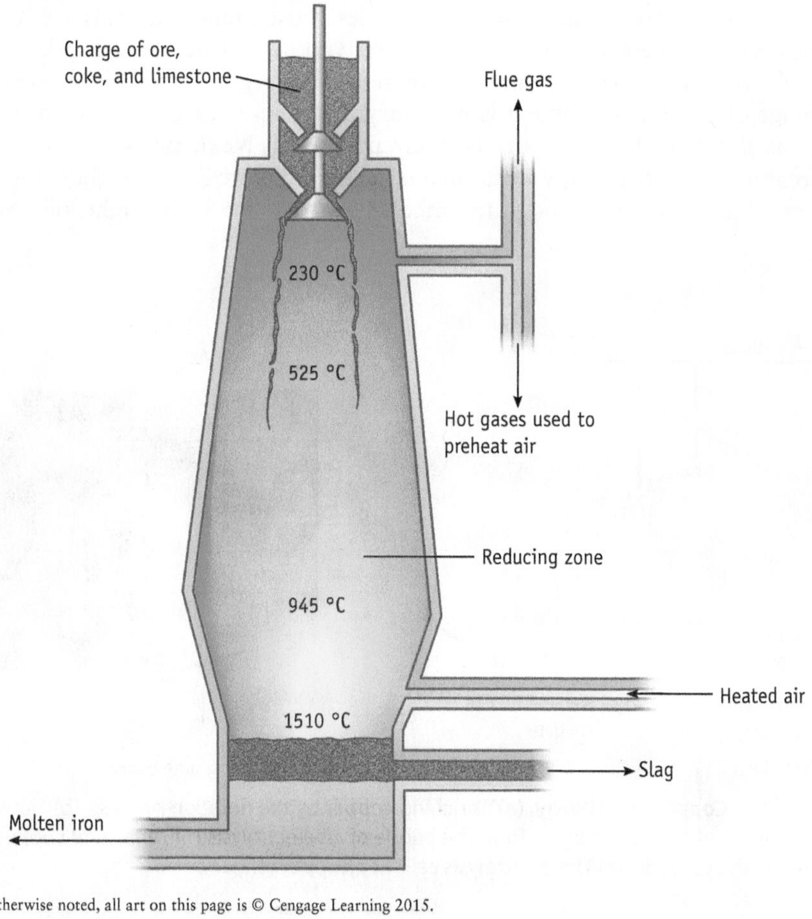

FIGURE 22.7 **A blast furnace.** The largest modern furnaces have hearths 14 meters in diameter. They can produce as much as 10,000 tons of iron per day.

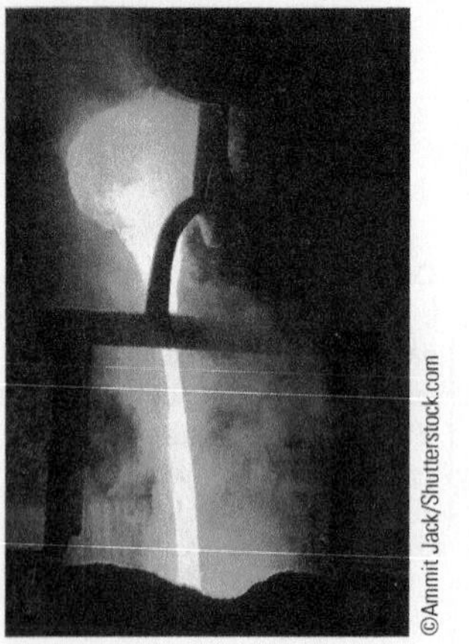

©Ammit Jack/Shutterstock.com

FIGURE 22.8 Molten iron being poured from a basic oxygen furnace.

(This is an acid–base reaction because CaO is a basic oxide and SiO_2 is an acidic oxide.) The calcium silicate, molten at the temperature of the blast furnace and less dense than molten iron, floats on the iron. Other nonmetal oxides dissolve in this layer and the mixture, called *slag*, is easily removed.

Pig iron from the blast furnace may contain as much as 4.5% carbon, 0.3% phosphorus, 0.04% sulfur, 1.5% silicon, and some other elements as well. The impure iron must be purified to remove these nonmetal components. Several processes are available to accomplish this task, but the most important uses the *basic oxygen furnace* (Figure 22.8). The process in the furnace removes much of the carbon and all of the phosphorus, sulfur, and silicon. Pure oxygen is blown into the molten pig iron and oxidizes phosphorus to P_4O_{10}, sulfur to SO_2, and carbon to CO_2. These nonmetal oxides either escape as gases or react with basic oxides such as CaO that are added or are used to line the furnace. For example,

$$P_4O_{10}(g) + 6\ CaO(s) \longrightarrow 2\ Ca_3(PO_4)_2(\ell)$$

The result is ordinary *carbon steel*. Almost any degree of flexibility, hardness, strength, and malleability can be achieved in carbon steel by reheating and cooling in a process called *tempering* (see *Case Study: High-Strength Steel*). The resulting material can then be used in a wide variety of applications. The major disadvantages of carbon steel are that it corrodes easily and that it loses its properties when heated strongly.

Other transition metals, such as chromium, manganese, and nickel, can be added during the steel-making process, giving *alloys* (solids made up of two or more metals) that have specific physical, chemical, and mechanical properties. One well-known alloy is stainless steel, which contains 18% to 20% Cr and 8% to 12% Ni. Stainless steel is much more resistant to corrosion than carbon steel. Another alloy of iron is alnico V. Used in loudspeaker magnets because of its permanent magnetism, it contains five elements: Al (8%), Ni (14%), Co (24%), Cu (3%), and Fe (51%).

Hydrometallurgy: Copper Production

In contrast to iron ores, which are mostly oxides, most copper minerals are sulfides. Copper-bearing minerals include chalcopyrite ($CuFeS_2$), chalcocite (Cu_2S), and covellite (CuS). Because ores containing these minerals generally have a very low percentage of copper, enrichment is necessary. This step is carried out by a process known as *flotation*. First, the ore is finely powdered. Next, oil is added and the mixture is agitated with soapy water in a large tank (Figure 22.9). At the same time, compressed air is forced through the mixture, so that the lightweight, oil-covered

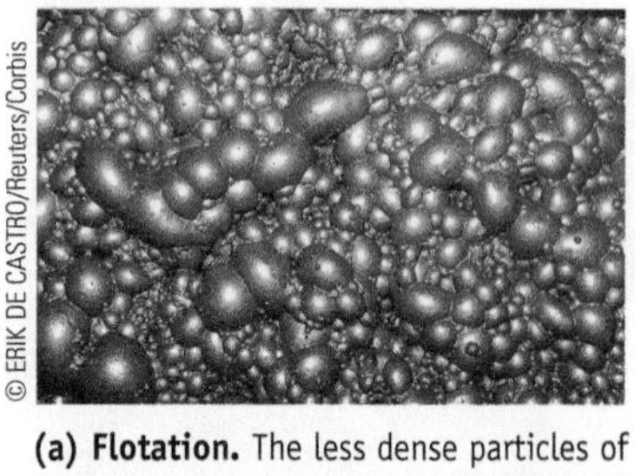

© ERIK DE CASTRO/Reuters/Corbis

(a) Flotation. The less dense particles of Cu_2S are trapped in the soap bubbles and float. The denser gangue settles to the bottom.

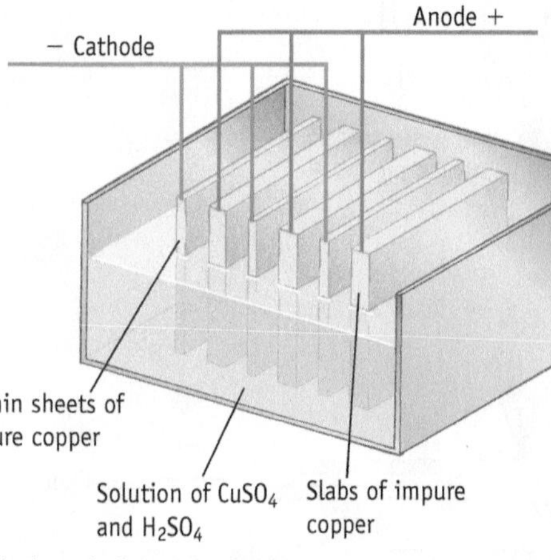

(b) Electrolysis

Simon Fraser/Northumbria Circuits/Science Photo Library/Science Source

(c) Producing pure copper

FIGURE 22.9 Copper metallurgy. (a) Enriching copper by the flotation process. **(b)** Slabs of impure copper, called *blister copper*, form the anode of an electrolysis cell, and pure copper is deposited at the cathode. **(c)** The electrolysis cells at a copper refinery.

CASE STUDY High-Strength Steel

A few decades ago if you rolled a car over or suffered a front end or side collision, you were likely to be seriously injured or killed. In recent years, though, the use of seat belts and air bags has greatly increased survivability. However, there is an additional factor—the steels used in cars have improved greatly and have led to both stronger frames and energy-absorbing front ends. At the same time cars are lighter and, partly as a result, more fuel-efficient. Much of this is due to the "design" of better steel.

Bill Pugliano/Getty Images

FIGURE A Modern high-strength steels can save the lives of passengers in serious accidents such as rollovers.

Iron and steel are still made the same way they have always been. Iron ore is reduced with carbon to produce raw iron, and this is then heated in a "basic oxygen furnace" to remove impurities. Stronger steels were traditionally produced by adding very small amounts of other metals at this point to produce alloys that have very specific properties, but this can be expensive. So, the steel industry has developed new methods for producing steels that are less expensive.

When steel is produced, it is not a single, large crystal of iron atoms neatly arranged in a lattice. Rather, it consists of grains or crystallites of iron in various forms as well as carbon. The characteristics of this material can be changed by rolling a slab at room temperature, by annealing, or by quenching. Quenching refers to a process in which the steel slab is rolled at room temperature, heated to a high temperature, and then rapidly cooled or "quenched" in cold water.

Pure iron (ferrite) has a unit cell consisting only of iron atoms (Figure B); it is ferromagnetic. Only a small amount of carbon can dissolve in ferrite, but, on heating, ferrite undergoes a phase transition and can now incorporate carbon. This new form with an embedded carbon atom is the *austenite form*. When the steel is then quenched, another rearrangement occurs, this time to the martensite form, still with an embedded carbon atom.

Steel that has gone through this process will consist of crystallites of ferrite, austenite, and martensite. Depending on the precise conditions used, the proportion of these can vary, and so can the strength of the steel. For example, steel with a high proportion of martensite is very strong and is used in car bumpers.

Some steels may have added boron, which gives an ultra-high-strength steel that can be used in door pillars and beams. The lives of passengers can be saved in the event of a rollover.

Questions:

1. What is the unit cell of ferrite?
2. Describe the unit cell of austenite.
3. What change has occurred on going from the austenite form to the martensite form?

Answers to these questions are available in Appendix N.

Reference:

New York Times, September 25, 2009, page D1.

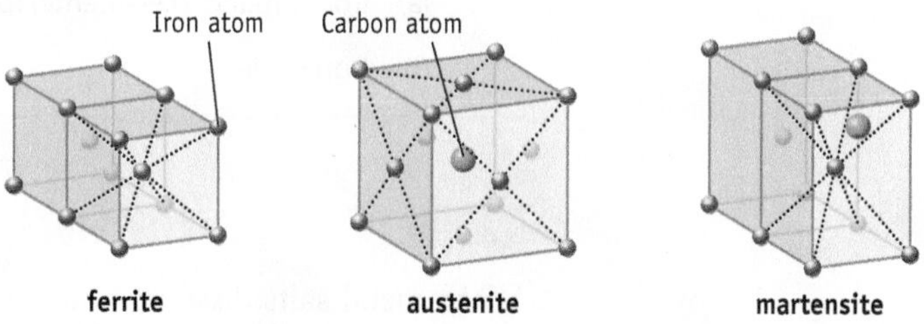

FIGURE B **The structures of various iron species.**

copper sulfide particles are carried to the top as a frothy mixture. The heavier gangue settles to the bottom of the tank, and the copper-laden froth is skimmed off.

Hydrometallurgy can be used to obtain copper from an enriched ore. In one method, enriched chalcopyrite ore is treated with a solution of copper(II) chloride. A reaction ensues that leaves copper in the form of solid, insoluble CuCl, which is easily separated from the iron that remains in solution as aqueous $FeCl_2$.

$$CuFeS_2(s) + 3\ CuCl_2(aq) \longrightarrow 4\ CuCl(s) + FeCl_2(aq) + 2\ S(s)$$

Aqueous NaCl is then added, and CuCl dissolves upon formation of the soluble complex ion $[CuCl_2]^-$.

$$CuCl(s) + Cl^-(aq) \longrightarrow [CuCl_2]^-(aq)$$

Copper(I) compounds in solution are unstable with respect to Cu(0) and Cu(II). Thus, $[CuCl_2]^-$ disproportionates to the metal and $CuCl_2$, and the latter is used to treat further ore.

$$2\ [CuCl_2]^-(aq) \longrightarrow Cu(s) + Cu^{2+}(aq) + 4\ Cl^-(aq)$$

Approximately 10% of the copper produced in the United States is obtained with the aid of bacteria. Acidified water is sprayed onto copper-mining wastes that contain low levels of copper. As the water trickles down through the crushed rock, the bacterium *Thiobacillus ferrooxidans* breaks down the iron sulfides in the rock and converts iron(II) to iron(III). Iron(III) ions oxidize the sulfide ion of copper sulfide to sulfate ions, leaving copper(II) ions in solution. Then the copper(II) ion is reduced to metallic copper by reaction with iron.

$$Cu^{2+}(aq) + Fe(s) \longrightarrow Cu(s) + Fe^{2+}(aq)$$

The purity of the copper obtained via these metallurgical processes is about 99%, but this is not acceptable because even traces of impurities greatly diminish the electrical conductivity of the metal. Consequently, a further purification step is needed—one involving electrolysis (Figure 22.9). Thin sheets of pure copper metal and slabs of impure copper are immersed in a solution containing $CuSO_4$ and H_2SO_4. The pure copper sheets serve as the cathode of an electrolysis cell, and the impure slabs are the anode. Copper in the impure sample is oxidized to copper(II) ions at the anode, and copper(II) ions in solution are reduced to pure copper at the cathode.

REVIEW & CHECK FOR SECTION 22-2

1. In the reaction between $CuFeS_2(s)$ and $CuCl_2(aq)$, what element is reduced and what element is oxidized?
   (a) Sulfur is reduced, iron is oxidized.
   (b) Copper is reduced, sulfur is oxidized.
   (c) Sulfur is reduced, copper is oxidized.
   (d) This is not a redox reaction.

2. What is the most common form in which iron is found in the Earth's crust?
   (a) Iron is found in elemental form
   (b) Iron oxide
   (c) Iron sulfide
   (d) Iron silicate

22-3 Coordination Compounds

When metal salts dissolve, water molecules cluster around the ions (◀ Figure 3.7). The negative end of each polar water molecule is attracted to the positively charged metal ion, and the positive end of the water molecule is attracted to the anion. As noted earlier (◀ Section 11-2), the energy of the ion–solvent interaction (solvation energy) is an important aspect of the solution process. But there is much more to this story.

Complexes and Ligands

A green solution formed by dissolving nickel(II) chloride in water contains $Ni^{2+}(aq)$ and $Cl^-(aq)$ ions (Figure 22.10). If the solvent is removed, a green crystalline solid is obtained. The formula of this solid is often written as $NiCl_2 \cdot 6\ H_2O$, and the compound is called nickel(II) chloride hexahydrate. Addition of ammonia to the aqueous nickel(II) chloride solution gives a lilac-colored solution from which another compound, $NiCl_2 \cdot 6\ NH_3$, can be isolated. This formula looks very similar to the formula for the hydrate, with ammonia substituted for water.

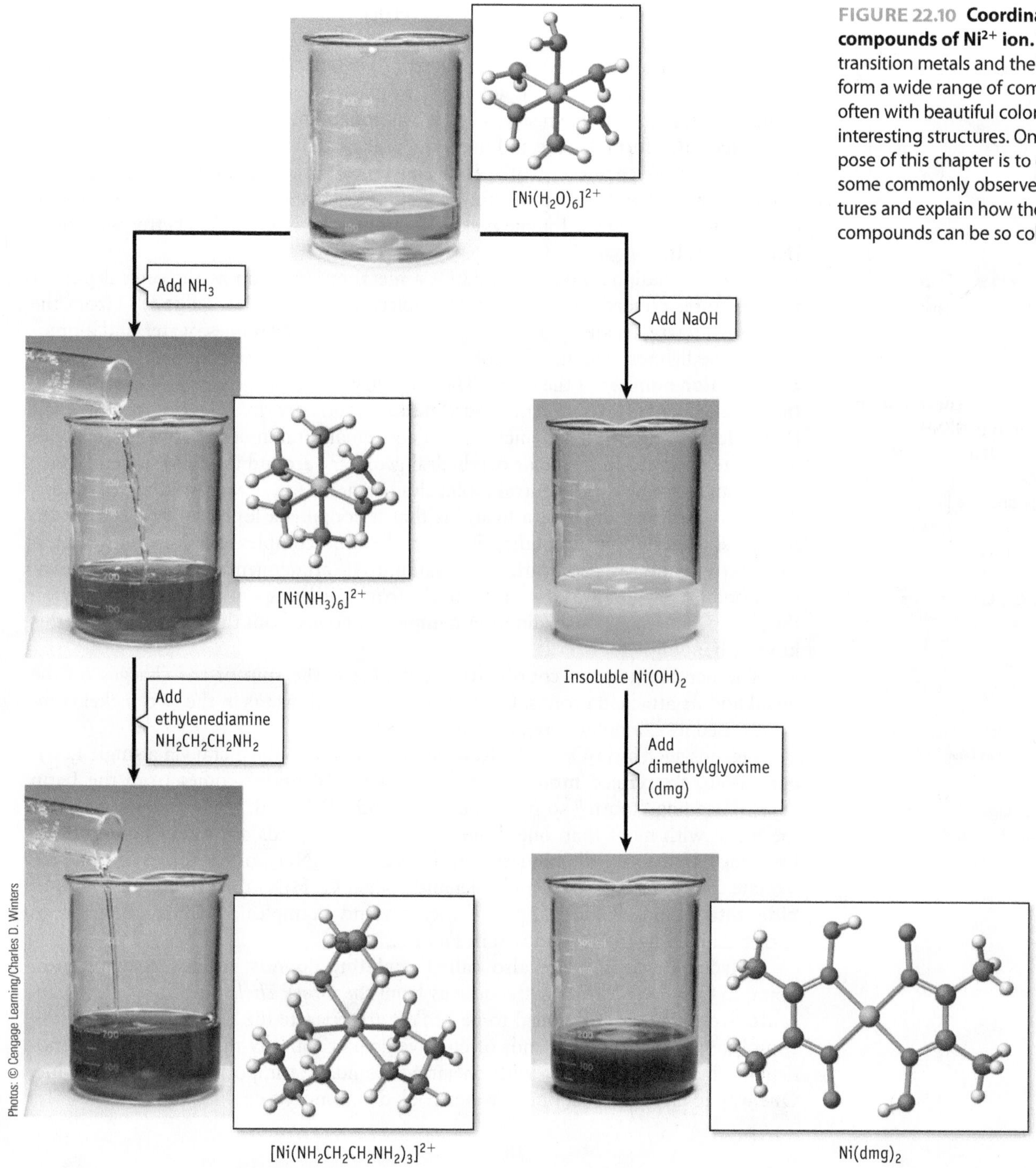

FIGURE 22.10 **Coordination compounds of Ni^{2+} ion.** The transition metals and their ions form a wide range of compounds, often with beautiful colors and interesting structures. One purpose of this chapter is to explore some commonly observed structures and explain how these compounds can be so colorful.

What are these two nickel species? The formulas identify the compositions of the compounds but fail to give information about their structures. Because properties of compounds derive from their structures, we need to evaluate the structures in more detail. Typically, metal compounds are ionic, and solid ionic compounds have structures with cations and anions arranged in a regular array. The structure of hydrated nickel(II) chloride contains cations with the formula $[Ni(H_2O)_6]^{2+}$ and chloride anions. The structure of the ammonia-containing compound is similar to the hydrate; it is made up of $[Ni(NH_3)_6]^{2+}$ cations and chloride anions.

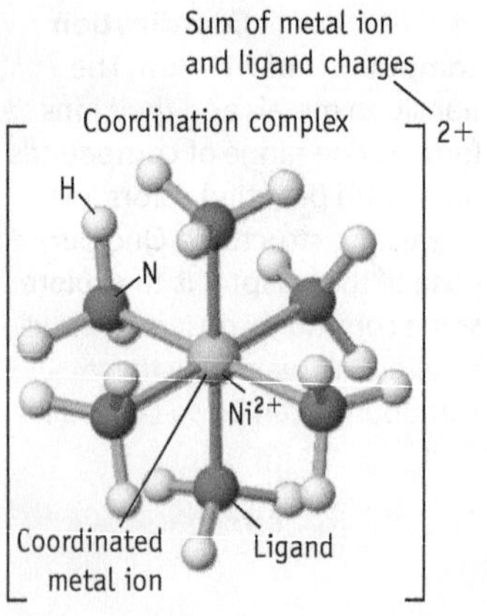

FIGURE 22.11 **A coordination complex.** In the $[Ni(NH_3)_6]^{2+}$ ion, the ligands are NH_3 molecules. Because the metal has a 2+ charge and the ligands have no charge, the charge on the complex ion is 2+.

Ligands Are Lewis Bases Ligands are Lewis bases because they furnish the electron pair; the metal ion is a Lewis acid because it accepts electron pairs (◀ Section 16-10). Thus, the coordinate covalent bond between ligand and metal can be viewed as a Lewis acid–Lewis base interaction.

Bidentate Ligands All common bidentate ligands bind to *adjacent* sites on the metal.

Ions such as $[Ni(H_2O)_6]^{2+}$ and $[Ni(NH_3)_6]^{2+}$, in which a metal ion and either water or ammonia molecules compose a single structural unit, are examples of **coordination complexes**, also known as **complex ions** (Figure 22.11). Compounds containing a coordination complex as part of the structure are called **coordination compounds**, and their chemistry is known as **coordination chemistry**. Although the older "hydrate" formulas are still used, the preferred method of writing the formula for coordination compounds places the metal atom or ion and the molecules or anions directly bonded to it within brackets to show that it is a single structural entity. Thus, the formula for the nickel(II)–ammonia compound is better written as $[Ni(NH_3)_6]Cl_2$.

All coordination complexes contain a metal atom or ion as the central part of the structure. Bonded to the metal are molecules or ions called **ligands** (from the Latin verb *ligare*, meaning "to bind"). In the preceding examples, water and ammonia are the ligands. The number of ligand atoms attached to the metal defines the **coordination number** of the metal. The geometry around the metal and described by the attached ligands is called the **coordination geometry.** In the nickel complex ion $[Ni(NH_3)_6]^{2+}$ (Figure 22.11), nickel has a coordination number of six and the six ligands are arranged in a regular octahedral geometry around the central metal ion.

Ligands can be either neutral molecules or anions (or, in rare instances, cations). The characteristic feature of a ligand is that it contains a lone pair of electrons. In the classic description of bonding in a coordination complex, the lone pair of electrons on a ligand is shared with the metal ion. The attachment is a coordinate covalent bond (◀ Section 8-5), because the electron pair being shared was originally on the ligand. The name "coordination complex" derives from the name given to this kind of bonding.

The net charge on a coordination complex is the sum of the charges on the metal and its attached groups. Complexes can be cations (as in the two nickel complexes used as examples here), anions, or uncharged.

Ligands such as H_2O and NH_3, which coordinate to the metal via a single Lewis base atom, are termed **monodentate**. The word "dentate" comes from the Latin *dentis*, meaning "tooth," so NH_3 is a "one-toothed" ligand. Some ligands attach to the metal with more than one donor atom. These ligands are called **polydentate.** Ethylenediamine (1,2-diaminoethane), $H_2NCH_2CH_2NH_2$, often abbreviated as en; oxalate ion, $C_2O_4^{2-}$ (ox^{2-}); and phenanthroline, $C_{12}H_8N_2$ (phen), are examples of **bidentate** ligands (Figure 22.12). Structures and examples of some complex ions with bidentate ligands are shown in Figure 22.13.

Polydentate ligands are also called **chelating ligands**, or just *chelates* (pronounced "key-lates"). The name derives from the Greek *chele*, meaning "claw." Because two or more bonds need to be broken to separate the ligand from the metal, complexes with chelated ligands often have greater stability than those with monodentate ligands. Complexes with chelating ligands are important in everyday life. One way to clean the rust out of water-cooled automobile engines and steam boilers

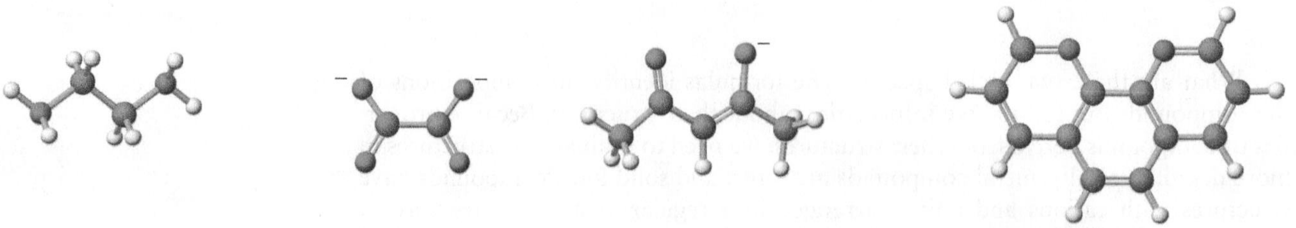

(a) $H_2NCH_2CH_2NH_2$, en ethylenediamine

(b) $C_2O_4^{2-}$, ox oxalate ion

(c) $CH_3COCHCOCH_3^-$, acac$^-$ acetylacetonate ion

(d) $C_{12}H_8N_2$, phen phenanthroline

FIGURE 22.12 **Common bidentate ligands.** Coordination of these bidentate ligands to a transition metal ion results in five- or six-member metal-containing rings and no ring strain. (Only one resonance structure each of the acetylacetonate ion and phenanthroline molecule are shown.)

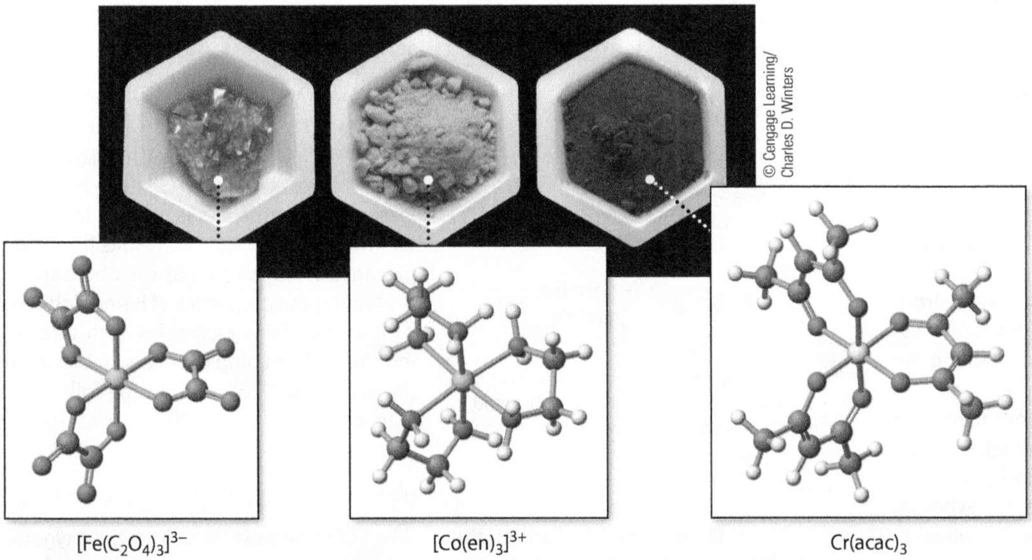

FIGURE 22.13 **Complex ions with bidentate ligands.** The three ligands shown are the oxalate anion ($C_2O_4^{2-}$), ethylenediamine (en), and the acetylacetonate anion (acac) (see Figure 22.12).

is to add a solution of oxalic acid. Iron(III) oxide reacts with oxalic acid to give a water-soluble iron oxalate complex ion:

$$3\ H_2O(\ell) + Fe_2O_3(s) + 6\ H_2C_2O_4(aq) \longrightarrow 2\ [Fe(C_2O_4)_3]^{3-}(aq) + 6\ H_3O^+(aq)$$

Ethylenediaminetetraacetate ion ($EDTA^{4-}$), a hexadentate ligand, is an excellent chelating ligand (Figure 22.14). It can wrap around a metal ion, encapsulating it. Salts of this anion are often added to commercial salad dressings to remove traces of free metal ions from solution; otherwise, these metal ions can act as catalysts for the oxidation of the oils in the dressing. Without $EDTA^{4-}$, the dressing would quickly become rancid. Another use is in bathroom cleansers. The $EDTA^{4-}$ ion removes deposits of $CaCO_3$ and $MgCO_3$ left by hard water by coordinating to Ca^{2+} or Mg^{2+} to create soluble complex ions.

Complexes with polydentate ligands play particularly important roles in biochemistry, one example of which is described in *A Closer Look: Hemoglobin: A Molecule with a Tetradentate Ligand* (page 872).

Formulas of Coordination Compounds

It is useful to be able to predict the formula of a coordination complex, given the metal ion and ligands, and to derive the oxidation number of the coordinated metal ion, given the formula of a coordination compound. The following examples explore these issues.

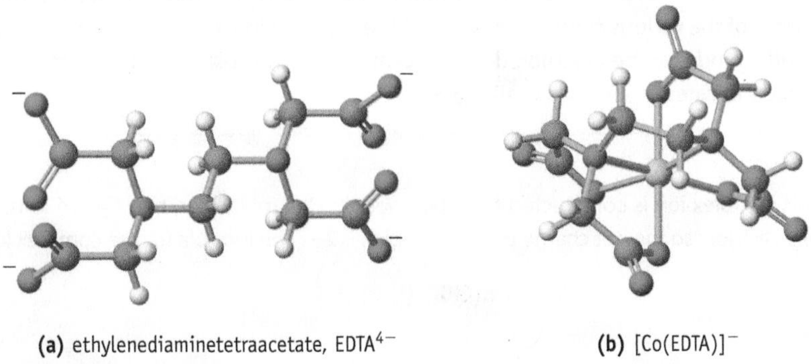

FIGURE 22.14 **$EDTA^{4-}$, a hexadentate ligand. (a)** Ethylenediaminetetraacetate, $EDTA^{4-}$. **(b)** $[Co(EDTA)]^-$. Notice the five-member rings created when this ligand bonds to the metal.

A CLOSER LOOK — Hemoglobin: A Molecule with a Tetradentate Ligand

Metal-containing coordination compounds figure prominently in many biochemical reactions. Perhaps the best-known example is hemoglobin, the molecule responsible for O_2 transport in the blood. It is also one of the most thoroughly studied bioinorganic compounds.

Hemoglobin (Hb) is a large iron-containing protein. It includes four polypeptide segments, each containing an iron(II) ion locked inside a porphyrin ring system and coordinated to a nitrogen atom from another part of the protein. A sixth site is available to attach to oxygen.

Hemoglobin functions by reversibly adding oxygen to the sixth coordination position of each iron, giving a complex called *oxyhemoglobin.*

Because hemoglobin features four iron centers, a maximum of four molecules of oxygen can bind to the molecule. The binding to oxygen is cooperative; that is, binding one O_2 molecule enhances the tendency to bind the second, third, and fourth O_2 molecules. Formation of the oxygenated complex is favored, but not too highly, because oxygen must also be released by the molecule to body tissues. Interestingly, an increase in acidity leads to a decrease in the stability of the oxygenated complex. This phenomenon is known as the *Bohr effect*, named for Christian Bohr, the father of Niels Bohr (Section 6-3). Release of oxygen in tissues is facilitated by an increase in acidity that results from the presence of CO_2 formed by metabolism.

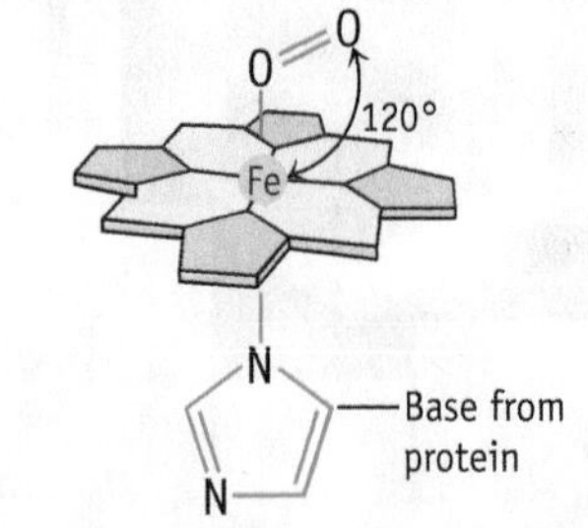

FIGURE **Oxygen binding.** Oxygen binds to the iron of the heme group in oxyhemoglobin (and in myoglobin). Interestingly, the Fe—O—O angle is bent.

Among the properties of hemoglobin is its ability to form a complex with carbon monoxide. This complex is very stable, with the equilibrium constant for the following reaction being about 200 (where Hb is hemoglobin):

$$HbO_2(aq) + CO(g) \rightleftharpoons HbCO(aq) + O_2(g)$$

When CO complexes with iron, the oxygen-carrying capacity of hemoglobin is lost. Consequently, CO (and the isoelectronic CN^- ion) is highly toxic to humans. Exposure to even small amounts greatly reduces the capacity of the blood to transport oxygen.

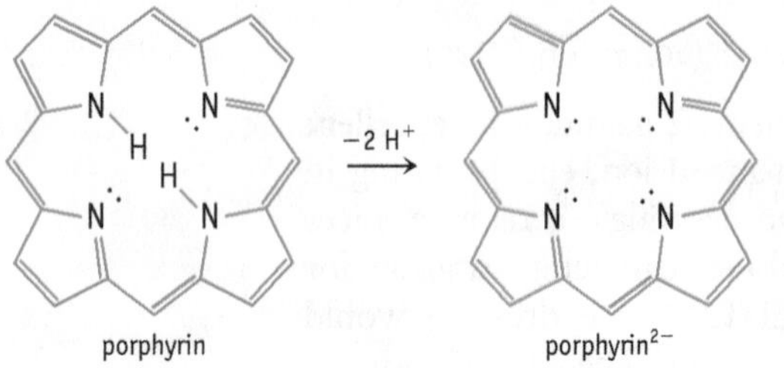

FIGURE **Porphyrin ring of the heme group.** The tetradentate ligand surrounding the iron(II) ion in hemoglobin is a dianion of a molecule called a *porphyrin*. Because of the double bonds in this structure, all of the carbon and nitrogen atoms in the dianion of the porphyrin lie in a plane. In addition, the nitrogen lone pairs are directed toward the center of the ion, and the molecular dimensions are such that a metal ion may fit nicely into the cavity.

EXAMPLE 22.1

Formulas of Coordination Complexes

Problem Give the formulas of the following coordination complexes:

(a) A Ni^{2+} ion is bound to two water molecules and two bidentate oxalate ions.

(b) A Co^{3+} ion is bound to one Cl^- ion, one ammonia molecule, and two bidentate ethylenediamine (en) molecules.

What Do You Know? The composition of the coordination complex is given for each part of the question.

Strategy The problem requires determining the net charge, which equals the sum of the charges of the various component parts of the complex ion. With that information, the metal and ligands can be assembled in the formula, which is placed in brackets, and the net charge indicated.

Solution

(a) This complex ion is constructed from two neutral H_2O molecules, two $C_2O_4^{2-}$ ions, and one Ni^{2+} ion, so the net charge on the complex is 2−. The formula for the complex ion is

$$[Ni(C_2O_4)_2(H_2O)_2]^{2-}$$

(b) This cobalt(III) complex ion combines two en molecules and one NH_3 molecule, none having a charge, as well as one Cl^- ion and a Co^{3+} ion. Thus, the net charge is 2+. The formula for this complex (writing out the entire formula for ethylenediamine) is

$$[Co(H_2NCH_2CH_2NH_2)_2(NH_3)Cl]^{2+}$$

Think about Your Answer Enclosing the formula of a complex in brackets is done to designate that this is a single unit. Species outside the brackets are counterions (when shown).

Check Your Understanding

(a) What is the formula of a complex ion composed of one Co^{3+} ion, three ammonia molecules, and three Cl^- ions?

(b) What is the formula for the coordination complex of an Fe^{2+} ion having two ethylenediamine ligands and two bromide ion ligands?

EXAMPLE 22.2

Coordination Compounds

Problem In each of the following coordination complexes, determine the metal's oxidation number and coordination number.

(a) $[Co(en)_2(NO_2)_2]Cl$

(b) $Pt(NH_3)_2(C_2O_4)$

(c) $Pt(NH_3)_2Cl_4$

(d) $[Co(NH_3)_5Cl]SO_4$

What Do You Know? The oxidation number is the charge that must be present on the metal ion. The coordination number is the number of ligand attachments to the metal. Remember that bidentate ligands coordinate to two adjacent positions.

Strategy Each formula consists of a complex ion or molecule made up of the metal ion, neutral, and anionic ligands. Counterions (shown outside the square brackets) may also be present. The oxidation number of the metal is the charge necessary to balance the sum of the negative charges associated with any anionic ligands and counterions. The coordination number is the number of donor atoms in the ligands that are bonded to the metal. Remember that the bidentate ligands in these examples (en, oxalate ion) attach to the metal at two sites and that any counterions present are not part of the complex ion—that is, they are not ligands.

Solution

(a)

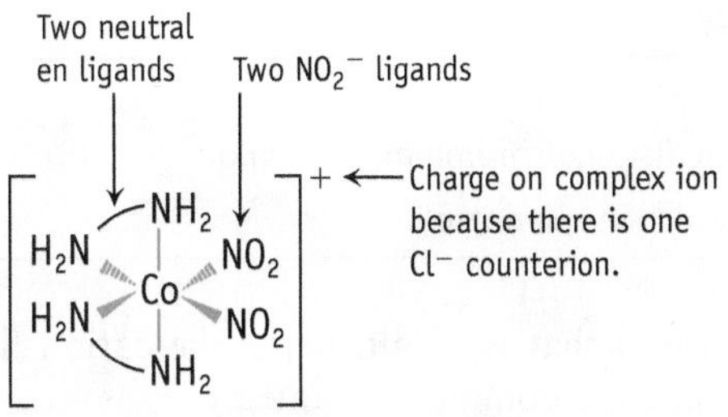

The central cobalt ion has a 3+ charge and the coordination number is 6.

(b)

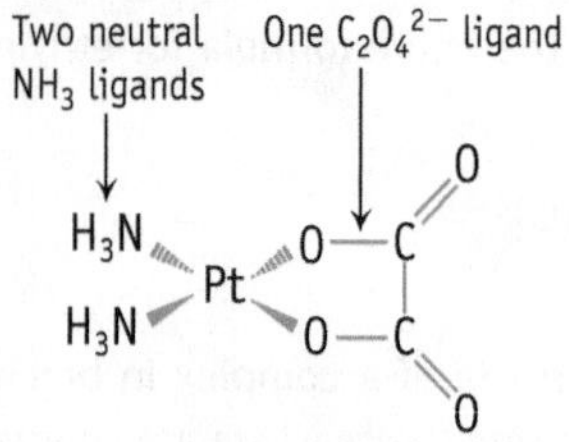

The central platinum ion has a 2+ charge and the coordination number is 4.

(c)

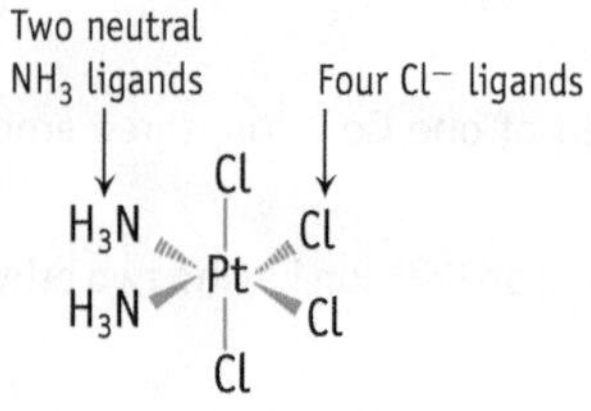

The central platinum ion has a 4+ charge and the coordination number is 6.

(d)

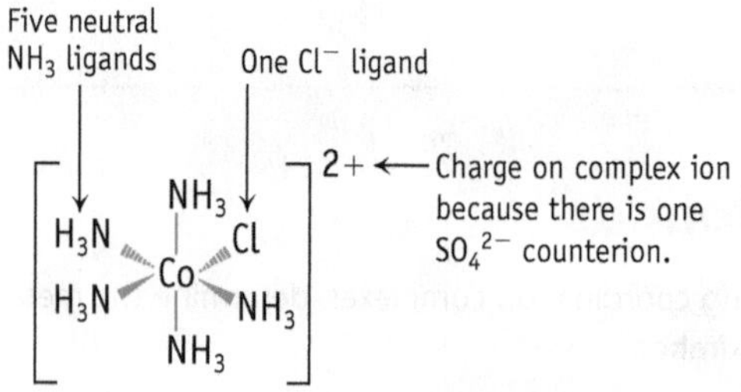

The central cobalt ion has a 3+ charge and the coordination number is 6.

Think about Your Answer Knowing the oxidation state of the metal in a coordination compound is important. From this, you can determine the electron configuration of the metal. As we shall see in Section 22-5, this information will be needed to determine important properties of a complex such as magnetism and color.

Check Your Understanding

(a) Determine the metal's oxidation number and coordination number in (i) $K_3[Co(NO_2)_6]$ and in (ii) $Mn(NH_3)_4Cl_2$.

(b) Determine the oxidation number and coordination number of cobalt in the complex $NH_4[Co(EDTA)]$.

Common Monodentate Ligands and Their Names

Ligand	Name
F^-	fluoro
Cl^-	chloro
Br^-	bromo
I^-	iodo
H_2O	aqua
NH_3	ammine
CO	carbonyl
CN^-	cyano
OH^-	hydroxo
$—NO_2^-$	nitro

Naming Coordination Compounds

Coordination compounds are named according to an established system. The three compounds below are named according to the rules that follow.

COMPOUND	SYSTEMATIC NAME
$[Ni(H_2O)_6]SO_4$	Hexaaquanickel(II) sulfate
$[Cr(en)_2(CN)_2]Cl$	Dicyanobis(ethylenediamine)chromium(III) chloride
$K[Pt(NH_3)Cl_3]$	Potassium amminetrichloroplatinate(II)

1. In naming a coordination compound that is a salt, name the cation first and then the anion. (This is how all salts are commonly named.)

2. When giving the name of the complex ion or molecule, name the ligands first, in alphabetical order, followed by the name of the metal. (When determining alphabetical order of the ligands, ignore any prefix.)
3. Ligands and their names:
   (a) If a ligand is an anion whose name ends in *-ite* or *-ate*, the final *e* is changed to *o* (sulfate ⟶ sulfato or nitrite ⟶ nitrito).
   (b) If the ligand is an anion whose name ends in *-ide*, the ending is changed to *o* (chloride ⟶ chloro, cyanide ⟶ cyano).
   (c) If the ligand is a neutral molecule, its common name is usually used with several important exceptions: Water as a ligand is referred to as *aqua;* ammonia is called *ammine;* and CO is called *carbonyl.*
   (d) When there is more than one of a particular monodentate ligand with a simple name, the number of ligands is designated by the appropriate prefix: *di, tri, tetra, penta,* or *hexa.* If the ligand name is complicated, the prefix changes to *bis, tris, tetrakis, pentakis,* or *hexakis,* followed by the ligand name in parentheses.
4. If the coordination complex is an anion, the suffix *-ate* is added to the metal name.
5. Following the name of the metal, the oxidation number of the metal is given in Roman numerals.

EXAMPLE 22.3

Naming Coordination Compounds

Problem Name the following compounds:

(a) $[Cu(NH_3)_4]SO_4$

(b) $K_2[CoCl_4]$

(c) $Co(phen)_2Cl_2$

(d) $[Co(en)_2(H_2O)Cl]Cl_2$

What Do You Know? The formula of each compound is given.

Strategy Apply the rules for nomenclature given above.

Solution

(a) The complex ion (in square brackets) is composed of four NH_3 molecules (named *ammine* in a complex) and the copper ion. To balance the 2− charge on the sulfate counterion and account for four NH_3 ligands with no charge, copper must have a 2+ charge. The compound's name is

tetraamminecopper(II) sulfate

(b) The complex ion $[CoCl_4]^{2-}$ has a 2− charge to balance two K^+ counterions. With four Cl^- ligands, the cobalt ion must have a 2+ charge, so the sum of charges is 2−. The name of the compound is

potassium tetrachlorocobaltate(II)

(c) This is a neutral coordination compound. The ligands include two Cl^- ions and two neutral bidentate *phen* (phenanthroline) ligands (page 870). The metal ion must therefore have a 2+ charge (Co^{2+}). The name, listing ligands in alphabetical order, is

dichlorobis(phenanthroline)cobalt(II)

(d) The complex ion has a 2+ charge because it is paired with two uncoordinated Cl^- ions. The cobalt ion is Co^{3+} because it is bonded to two neutral en ligands, one neutral water, and one Cl^-. The name is

aquachlorobis(ethylenediamine)cobalt(III) chloride

Think about Your Answer The earliest studies of coordination compounds created a colorful array of names, and a few of these are still used (Prussian Blue, mentioned earlier, and Zeise's salt, $K[Pt(C_2H_4)Cl_3]$, are two examples). However, as the depth and breadth of coordination chemistry expands, a systematic nomenclature is essential to communication among scientists working in the area. The rules of nomenclature make it possible for any scientist to derive a formula from the name, or to name a compound given its formula.

Check Your Understanding

Name the following coordination compounds.

(a) $[Ni(H_2O)_6]SO_4$ (b) $[Cr(en)_2(CN)_2]Cl$ (c) $K[Pt(NH_3)Cl_3]$ (d) $K[CuCl_2]$

REVIEW & CHECK FOR SECTION 22-3

1. What is the coordination number for the metal in the compound tetraaquaoxalatoiron(III) chloride?

   (a) 4 (b) 6 (c) 7 (d) 2

2. What is the oxidation number of the metal in $(NH_4)_3[Fe(CN)_6]$?

   (a) 0 (b) +1 (c) +2 (d) +3

3. Which of the following is a complex ion based on an iron(II) ion?

   (a) $[Fe(H_2O)_4Cl_2]ClO_4$ (c) $Fe(acac)_3$

   (b) $Na_4[Fe(C_2O_4)_3]$ (d) $[Fe(NH_3)_5Cl]SO_4$

4. In which of the following complexes is the metal 6-coordinate?

   (a) lithium tetrachlorocobaltate(II)

   (b) pentaamminehydroxochromium(III) chloride

   (c) bis(ethylenediamine)silver(I) chloride

   (d) diamminedichlorozinc(II)

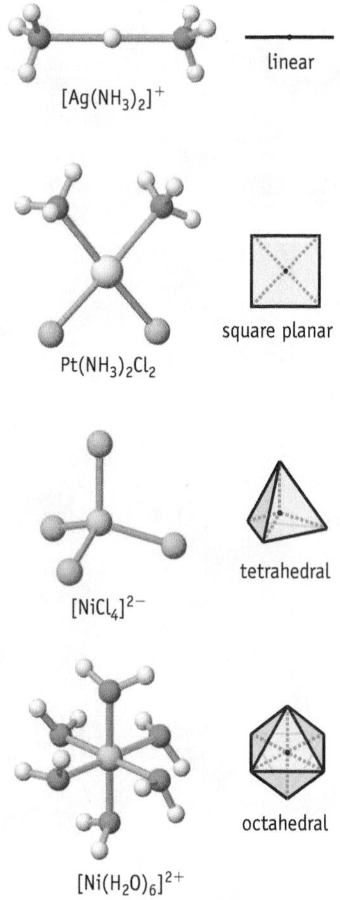

Common Coordination Geometries

22-4 Structures of Coordination Compounds

Common Coordination Geometries

The geometry of a coordination complex is defined by the arrangement of donor atoms of the ligands around the central metal ion. Metal ions in coordination compounds can have coordination numbers ranging from 2 to 12. Only complexes with coordination numbers of 2, 4, and 6 are common, however, so we will concentrate on species such as $[ML_2]^{n\pm}$, $[ML_4]^{n\pm}$, and $[ML_6]^{n\pm}$, where M is the metal ion and L is a *monodentate* ligand. For complexes having these stoichiometries, the following geometries are encountered:

- All $[ML_2]^{n\pm}$ complexes are linear. The two ligands are on opposite sides of the metal, and the L—M—L bond angle is 180°. Common examples include $[Ag(NH_3)_2]^+$ and $[CuCl_2]^-$.
- Tetrahedral geometry occurs in many $[ML_4]^{n\pm}$ complexes. Examples include $TiCl_4$, $[CoCl_4]^{2-}$, $[NiCl_4]^{2-}$, and $[Zn(NH_3)_4]^{2+}$.

- Some $[ML_4]^{n\pm}$ complexes have square planar geometry. It is most often found for metal ions that have eight *d* electrons. Examples include $Pt(NH_3)_2Cl_2$, $[Ni(CN)_4]^{2-}$, and the nickel complex with the dimethylglyoximate (dmg^-) ligand in Figure 22.10.
- Octahedral geometry is found in complexes with the stoichiometry $[ML_6]^{n\pm}$ (Figure 22.10).

Isomerism

Isomers are compounds with the same molecular formulas but different arrangements of atoms. There are several forms of isomerism and some are key to the chemical behavior of the compounds.

- *Structural isomers* have the same molecular formula but different bonding arrangements of atoms.
- *Stereoisomers* have the same atom-to-atom bonding sequence, but the atoms differ in their arrangement in space. There are two types of stereoisomerism: *geometric isomerism* and *optical isomerism*.

All three types of isomerism—structural, geometric, and optical—are encountered in coordination chemistry.

Structural Isomerism

The two most important types of structural isomerism in coordination chemistry are coordination isomerism and linkage isomerism. **Coordination isomerism** occurs when it is possible to exchange a coordinated ligand and the uncoordinated counterion. For example, dark violet $[Co(NH_3)_5Br]SO_4$ and red $[Co(NH_3)_5SO_4]Br$ are coordination isomers. In the first compound, bromide ion is a ligand and sulfate is a counterion; in the second, sulfate is a ligand and bromide is the counterion. A diagnostic test for this kind of isomer is often made based on chemical reactions. For example, these two compounds can be distinguished by precipitation reactions. Addition of Ba^{2+}(aq) to a solution of $[Co(NH_3)_5Br]SO_4$ gives a precipitate of $BaSO_4$, indicating the presence of sulfate ion in solution. In contrast, no reaction occurs if Ba^{2+}(aq) is added to a solution of $[Co(NH_3)_5SO_4]Br$. In this complex, sulfate ion is attached to Co^{3+} and is not a free ion in solution.

$$[Co(NH_3)_5Br]SO_4 + Ba^{2+}(aq) \longrightarrow BaSO_4(s) + [Co(NH_3)_5Br]^{2+}(aq)$$

$$[Co(NH_3)_5SO_4]Br + Ba^{2+}(aq) \longrightarrow \text{no reaction}$$

Linkage isomerism occurs when it is possible to attach a ligand to the metal through different atoms. The two most common ligands with which linkage isomerism arises are thiocyanate, SCN^-, and nitrite, NO_2^-. The Lewis structure of the thiocyanate ion shows that there are lone pairs of electrons on sulfur and nitrogen. The ligand can attach to a metal either through sulfur (called *S-bonded thiocyanate)* or through nitrogen (called *N-bonded thiocyanate*). Nitrite ion can attach either at oxygen or at nitrogen. The former are called nitrito complexes; the latter are nitro complexes (Figure 22.15).

Ligands forming linkage isomers

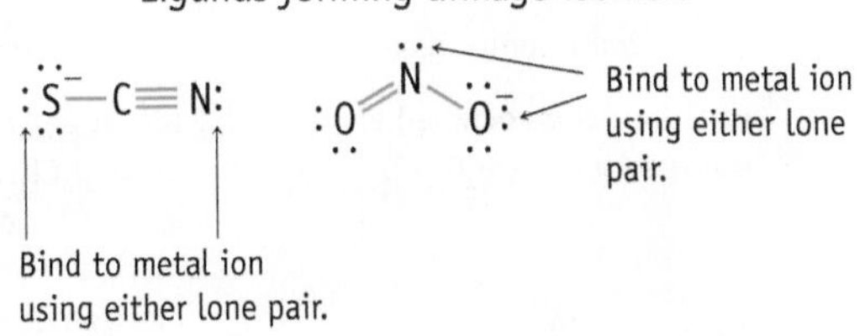

© Cengage Learning/Charles D. Winters

FIGURE 22.15 **Linkage isomers, $[Co(NH_3)_5ONO]^{2+}$ and $[Co(NH_3)_5NO_2]^{2+}$.** These complex ions, whose systematic names are pentaamminenitritocobalt(III) and pentaamminenitrocobalt(III), respectively, were the first known examples of this type of isomerism. (The compounds shown in this figure have two chloride ions as counterions.)

Geometric Isomerism

Cis–Trans Isomerism *Cis–trans* isomerism is not possible for tetrahedral complexes. All L—M—L angles are 109.5°, and all positions are equivalent in this three-dimensional structure.

Geometric isomerism results when the atoms bonded directly to the metal have a different spatial arrangement. The simplest example of geometric isomerism in coordination chemistry is *cis–trans* isomerism, which occurs in both square-planar and octahedral complexes. An example of *cis–trans* isomerism is seen in the square-planar complex $Pt(NH_3)_2Cl_2$ (Figure 22.16a). In this complex, the two Cl^- ions can be either adjacent to each other (*cis*) or on opposite sides of the metal (*trans*). The *cis* isomer is effective in the treatment of testicular, ovarian, bladder, and osteogenic sarcoma cancers, but the *trans* isomer has no effect on these diseases.

Cis–trans isomerism occurs in octahedral complexes with the formula MA_4B_2. In the complex $[Co(NH_3)_4Cl_2]^+$ the two Cl^- ions can occupy positions that are either adjacent (Cl—Co—Cl angle = 90°) or on opposite sides of the metal (Cl—Co—Cl angle = 180°) (Figure 22.16b).

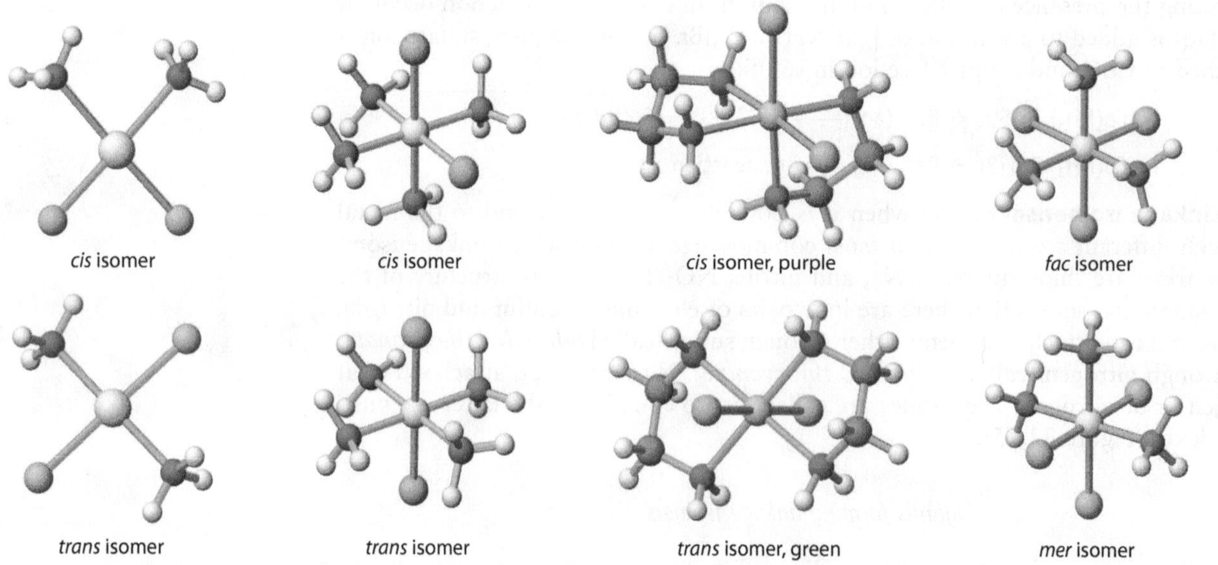

(a) The square-planar complex $Pt(NH_3)_2Cl_2$ can exist in two geometries, *cis* and *trans*.

(b) *Cis* and *trans* octahedral isomers for $[Co(NH_3)_4Cl_2]^+$.

(c) *Cis* and *trans* octahedral isomers for $[Co(en)_2Cl_2]^+$.

(d) *Fac* and *mer* isomers of $Cr(NH_3)_3Cl_3$: *fac* isomer, the three identical ligands are arranged at the corners of a triangular face. In the *mer* isomer, the three similar ligands follow a meridian.

FIGURE 22.16 **Geometric isomers.**

Cis–trans isomerism in an octahedral complex with two bidentate ethylenediamine ligands is illustrated by $[Co(H_2NCH_2CH_2NH_2)_2Cl_2]^+$. The two Cl^- ions occupy positions that are either adjacent (the purple *cis* isomer) or opposite (the green *trans* isomer) (Figure 22.16c).

Another common type of geometric isomerism occurs for octahedral complexes with the general formula MA_3B_3. A *fac* isomer has three identical ligands lying at the corners of a triangular face of an octahedron defined by the ligands (*fac* = facial), whereas the ligands follow a meridian in the *mer* isomer (*mer* = meridional). *Fac* and *mer* isomers of $Cr(NH_3)_3Cl_3$ are shown in Figure 22.16d.

Optical Isomerism

Optical isomerism is a second type of stereoisomerism. Optical isomers are molecules that have nonsuperimposable mirror images. Molecules that have nonsuperimposable mirror images are termed **chiral.** Pairs of nonsuperimposable, mirror-image molecules are called **enantiomers.**

In chemistry the usual model for chirality is a carbon-based compound with four different groups attached to the C atom (Figure 22.17). One enantiomer is a mirror image of the other, and one cannot be superimposed on the other. (Chirality occurs widely in organic and biochemistry chemistry and will be discussed in Chapters 23 and 24.)

There are many examples of chirality in non-chemical contexts. Seashells, for example, may spiral in different directions, giving left-handed and right-handed shells (Figure 22.17). Bolts and screws can also have left-handed or right-handed threads. Although they appear similar, they cannot be interchanged in use.

Pure samples of enantiomers have the same physical properties, such as melting point, boiling point, density, and solubility in common solvents, but they differ in a significant way: When a beam of plane-polarized light passes through a solution of a pure enantiomer, the plane of polarization rotates (Figure 22.18). The two enantiomers rotate polarized light to an equal extent, but do so in opposite directions. The term optical isomerism is used because this effect involves light.

Optical isomerism (chirality) occurs for octahedral complexes when the metal ion coordinates to three bidentate ligands or when the metal ion coordinates to two bidentate ligands and two monodentate ligands in a *cis* position. The complexes $[Co(en)_3]^{3+}$ and *cis*-$[Co(en)_2Cl_2]^+$, illustrated in Figure 22.19, are examples of chiral

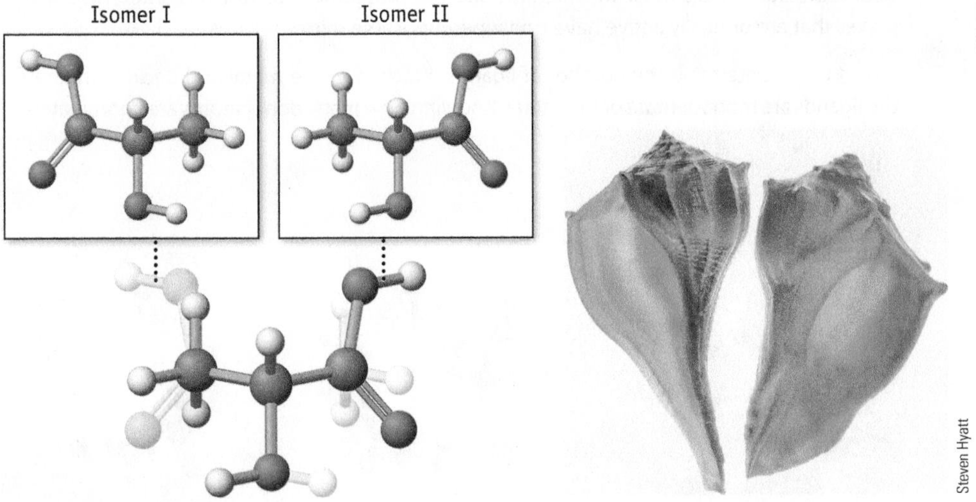

Lactic acid enantiomers are nonsuperimposable, just as your right hand is not superimposable on your left.

Left- and right-handed seashells (of different species)

FIGURE 22.17 **Stereoisomerism in chemistry and nature.**

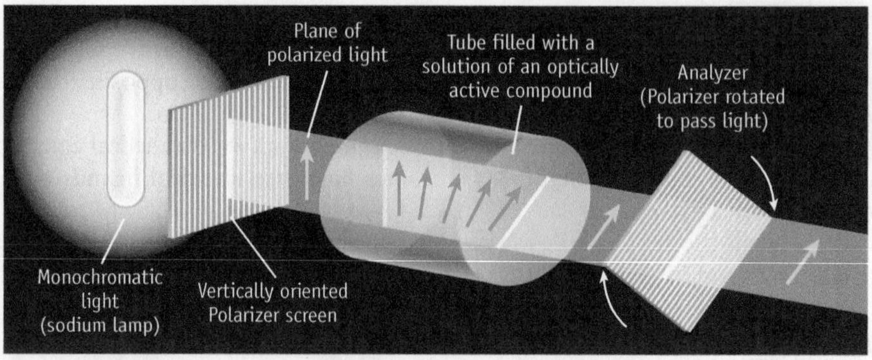

FIGURE 22.18 **Rotation of plane polarized light by an optical isomer.** Monochromatic light (light of only one wavelength) is produced by a sodium lamp. After it passes through a polarizing filter, the light vibrates in only one direction—it is polarized. A solution of an optical isomer placed between the first and second polarizing filters causes rotation of the plane of polarized light. The second filter is rotated to a point where a maximum of light is transmitted and the angle of rotation is calculated. The magnitude and direction of rotation are unique physical properties of the optical isomer being tested.

complexes. The diagnostic test for chirality is met with both species: Mirror images of these molecules are not superimposable on one another, and solutions of the optical isomers rotate plane-polarized light in opposite directions.

EXAMPLE 22.4

Isomerism in Coordination Chemistry

Problem For which of the following compounds or complex ions do isomers exist? If isomers are possible, identify the type of isomerism (structural, geometric, or optical).

(a) $[Co(NH_3)_4Cl_2]^+$ (d) $K_3[Fe(C_2O_4)_3]$

(b) $Pt(NH_3)_2(CN)_2$ (square-planar) (e) $Zn(NH_3)_2Cl_2$ (tetrahedral)

(c) $Co(NH_3)_3Cl_3$ (f) $[Co(NH_3)_5SCN]^{2+}$

What Do You Know? You can infer coordination number and geometry from the formulas. Structural isomers are those for which there are different attachments of atoms; geometric isomers are those in which the spatial arrangement of atoms is different. Complexes that are optically active have nonsuperimposable mirror images.

Strategy Determine the number of ligands attached to the metal and decide whether the ligands are monodentate or bidentate. Knowing how many donor atoms are coordinated

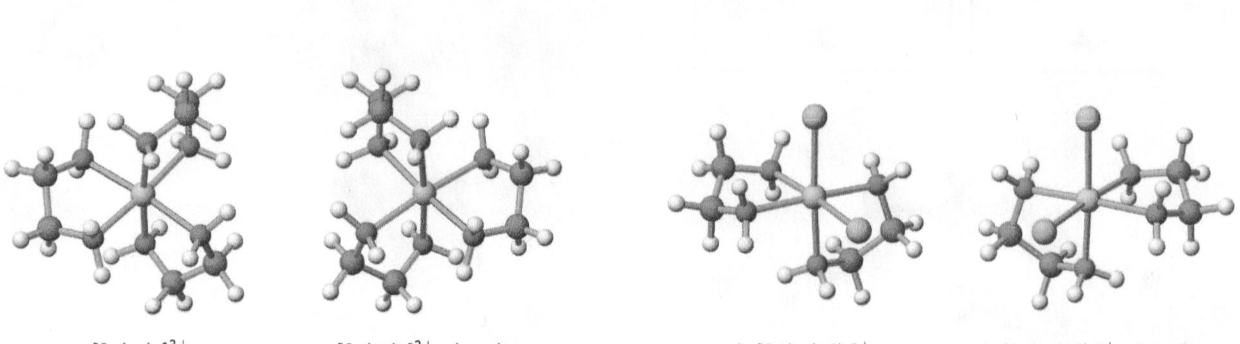

$[Co(en)_3]^{3+}$ $[Co(en)_3]^{3+}$ mirror image *cis*-$[Co(en)_2Cl_2]^+$ *cis*-$[Co(en)_2Cl_2]^+$ mirror image

FIGURE 22.19 **Chiral metal complexes.** Both $[Co(en)_3]^{3+}$ and *cis*-$[Co(en)_2Cl_2]^+$ are chiral. Notice that the image of a compound is not superimposable on its mirror image.

to the metal (the coordination number) will allow you to establish the metal geometry. The only stereoisomerism possible for square-planar complexes is geometric (*cis* and *trans*). Tetrahedral coordination complexes do not have geometric or optical isomers. Six-coordinate complexes of the formula MA_4B_2 can be either *cis* or *trans*. *Mer* and *fac* isomers are possible with a stoichiometry of MA_3B_3. Optical activity arises for metal complexes of the formula *cis*-M(bidentate)$_2$X$_2$ and M(bidentate)$_3$. Drawing pictures of the molecules will help you visualize the isomers.

Solution

(a) Two geometric isomers can be drawn for octahedral complexes with a formula of MA_4B_2. One isomer has two Cl^- ions in *cis* positions (adjacent positions, at a 90° angle), and the other isomer has the Cl^- ligands in *trans* positions (with a 180° angle between the ligands). Optical isomers are not possible.

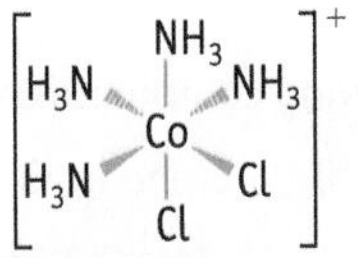

cis isomer

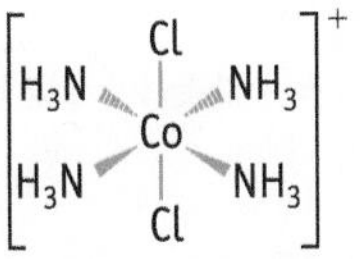

trans isomer

(b) In this square-planar complex, the two NH_3 ligands (and the two CN^- ligands) can be either *cis* or *trans*. These are geometric isomers. Optical isomers are not possible.

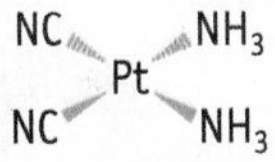

cis isomer

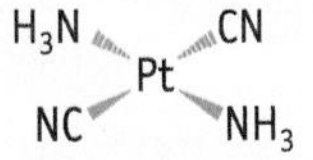

trans isomer

(c) Two geometric isomers of this octahedral complex, with chloride ligands either *fac* or *mer*, are possible. In the *fac* isomer, the three Cl^- ligands are all at 90° to each other; in the *mer* isomer, two Cl^- ligands are at 180°, and the third is 90° from the other two. Optical isomers are not possible.

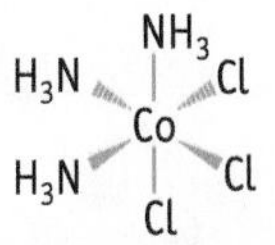

fac isomer

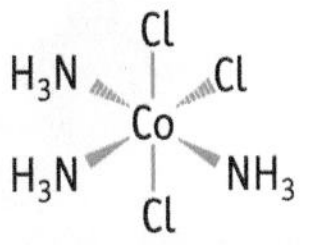

mer isomer

(d) Ignore the counterions, K^+. The anion is an octahedral complex. Remember that the bidentate oxalate ion occupies two adjacent coordination sites of the metal, and that three oxalate ligands means that the metal has a coordination number of 6. Mirror images of complexes of the stoichiometry M(bidentate)$_3$ are not superimposable; therefore, two optical isomers are possible. (Here the ligands, $C_2O_4^{2-}$, are drawn abbreviated as O—O.)

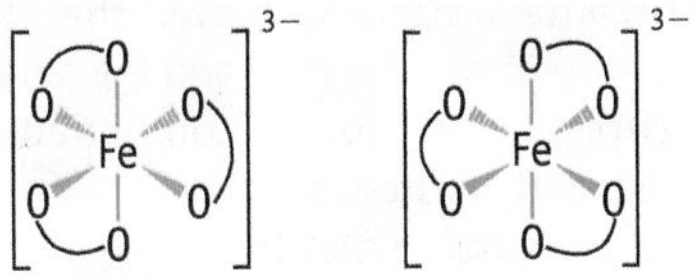

nonsuperimposable mirror images of $[Fe(ox)_3]^{3-}$

(e) Only a single structure is possible for tetrahedral complexes such as $Zn(NH_3)_2Cl_2$.

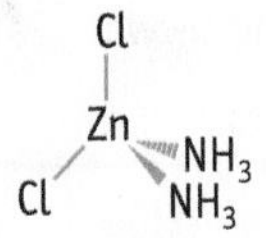

Optical Isomerism Square-planar complexes are incapable of optical isomerism based at the metal center; mirror images are always superimposable. Chiral tetrahedral complexes are possible, but examples of complexes with a metal bonded tetrahedrally to four different monodentate ligands are extremely rare.

(f) Only linkage isomerism (structural isomerism) is possible for this octahedral cobalt complex. Either the sulfur or the nitrogen of the SCN^- anion can be attached to the cobalt(III) ion in this complex.

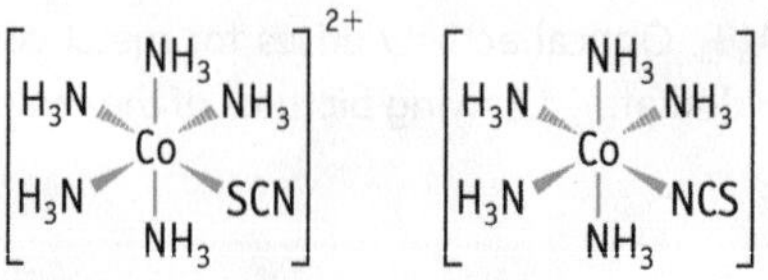

S-bonded SCN^- N-bonded SCN^-

Think about Your Answer More complex situations occur when a complex has three or more different ligands. In those instances it is important to be able to visualize the three-dimensional molecule and to organize your approach.

Check Your Understanding

What types of isomers are possible for the following compounds or complex ions?

(a) $K[Co(NH_3)_2Cl_4]$

(b) $Pt(en)Cl_2$ (square-planar)

(c) $[Co(NH_3)_5Cl]^{2+}$

(d) $[Ru(phen)_3]Cl_3$

(e) $Na_2[MnCl_4]$ (tetrahedral)

(f) $[Co(NH_3)_5NO_2]^{2+}$

CASE STUDY Cisplatin: Accidental Discovery of a Chemotherapy Agent

$$Pt(NH_3)_2Cl_2(aq) + H_2O(\ell) \longrightarrow [Pt(NH_3)_2(H_2O)Cl]^+(aq) + Cl^-(aq)$$

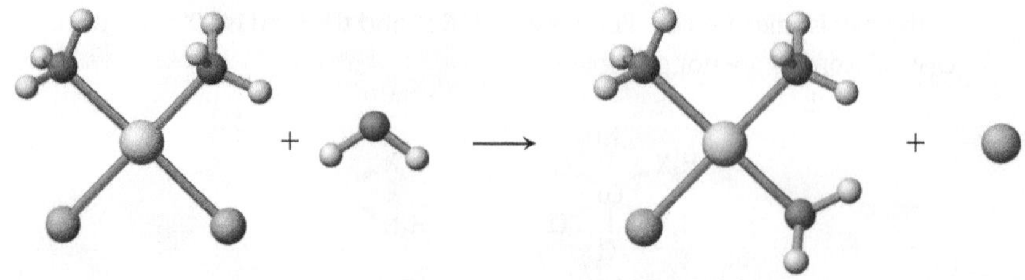

There are many naturally occurring metal-based molecules such as heme, vitamin B_{12}, and the enzyme involved in fixing nitrogen (nitrogenase). Chemists have also synthesized various metal-based compounds for medical purposes. One of these, cisplatin $[PtCl_2(NH_3)_2]$, was known for many years, but it was discovered serendipitously to be effective in treatment of certain kinds of cancers.

In 1965, Barnett Rosenberg, a biophysicist at Michigan State University, set out to study the effect of electric fields on living cells, but the results of his experiments were very different from his expectations. He and his students had placed an aqueous suspension of live *Escherichia coli* bacteria in an electric field between supposedly inert platinum electrodes. Much to their surprise, they found that cell growth was significantly affected. After careful experimentation, the effect on cell division was found to be due to a trace of a complex of platinum, ammonia, and chloride ion formed by an electrolytic process involving the platinum electrode in the presence of ammonia in the growth medium.

To follow up on this interesting discovery, Rosenberg and his students tested the effect of *cis*- and *trans*-$PtCl_2(NH_3)_2$ on cell growth and found that only the *cis* isomer was effective. This led Rosenberg and others to study the effect of so-called cisplatin on cancer cell growth, and the result is that *cisplatin* and similar compounds are now used to treat genitourinary tumors. In fact, testicular cancer in particular is now considered largely curable because of cisplatin chemotherapy.

The chemistry of cisplatin has now been thoroughly studied and illustrates many of the principles of transition metal coordination chemistry. It has been found that *cisplatin* has a half-life of 2.5 hours for the replacement of a Cl^- ligand by water at 310 K (in a first-order reaction) and that the replacement of a second Cl^- ligand by water is slightly faster.

The aqua species are acidic and damaging to the kidneys, so cisplatin is generally used in a saline solution to prevent the hydrolysis reactions. It has been found that, in blood plasma at pH 7.4 and with a Cl^- ion concentration of about 1.04×10^{-5} M, $PtCl_2(NH_3)_2$ and $PtCl(OH)(NH_3)_2$ are the dominant species. In the cell nucleus, however, the Cl^- ion concentration is lower, and the aqua species are present in higher concentration.

Question:

If a patient is given 10.0 mg of cisplatin, what quantity remains as cisplatin at 24 hours?

The answer to this question is available in Appendix N.

REVIEW & CHECK FOR SECTION 22-4

1. Which of the following complexes cannot exist as *cis–trans* isomers?

   (a) $Fe(NH_3)_4Cl_2$
   (b) $Ni(H_2O)_4(C_2O_4)$ ($C_2O_4^{2-}$ = oxalate)
   (c) Square-planar $[PtCl_2(CN)_2]^{2-}$
   (d) $Mn(en)_2Cl_2$ (en = ethylenediamine)

2. Which of the following complexes can exist as optical isomers?

   (a) Square-planar $Pt(NH_3)(H_2O)(CN)Cl$
   (b) $Fe(en)_2(CN)_2$ (en = ethylenediamine)
   (c) $Fe(NH_3)_4Cl_2$
   (d) $Cr(NH_3)_3Cl_3$

3. Which statement best describes the isomers for the complex $Fe(en)_2Cl_2$? (en = ethylenediamine)

   (a) Only a single structure can be drawn.
   (b) There are two geometric isomers, one of which has an optical isomer.
   (c) The compound exists as a pair of optical isomers.
   (d) This compound exists as two structural isomers.

4. How many geometric isomers are possible for $Fe(en)(NH_3)_2Cl_2$? (To answer this question, try to draw out possible structures in an organized manner. Start by placing the bidentate ethylenediamine ligand in two coordination sites, then add chloride and ammonia ligands into the remaining positions in various ways.)

   (a) 0 (b) 1 (c) 2 (d) 3

22-5 Bonding in Coordination Compounds

Metal–ligand bonding in a coordination complex was described earlier in this chapter as being covalent, resulting from the sharing of an electron pair between the metal and the ligand donor atom. Although frequently used, this description is not capable of explaining the color and magnetic behavior of these complexes. As a consequence, the covalent bonding picture has now largely been superseded by two other bonding models: molecular orbital theory and ligand field theory.

The bonding model based on molecular orbital theory assumes that the metal and the ligand bond through the molecular orbitals formed by atomic orbital overlap between metal and ligand. The **ligand field model**, in contrast, focuses on repulsion (and destabilization) of electrons in the metal coordination sphere. The ligand field model also assumes that the positive metal ion and the negative ligand lone pair are attracted electrostatically; that is, the bond results from the attraction between a positively charged metal ion and a negative ion or the negative end of a polar molecule. For the most part, the molecular orbital and ligand field models predict similar, qualitative results regarding color and magnetic behavior. Here, we will focus on the ligand field approach and illustrate how it explains color and magnetism of transition metal complexes.

The *d* Orbitals: Ligand Field Theory

To understand ligand field theory, it is necessary to look at the *d* orbitals, specifically with regard to their orientation relative to the positions of ligands in a metal complex.

In an isolated atom or ion, the five *d* orbitals have the same energy. For a metal atom or ion in a coordination complex, however, the *d* orbitals have different energies. According to the ligand field model, repulsion between *d* electrons on the metal and electron pairs of the ligands destabilizes electrons that reside in the *d* orbitals;

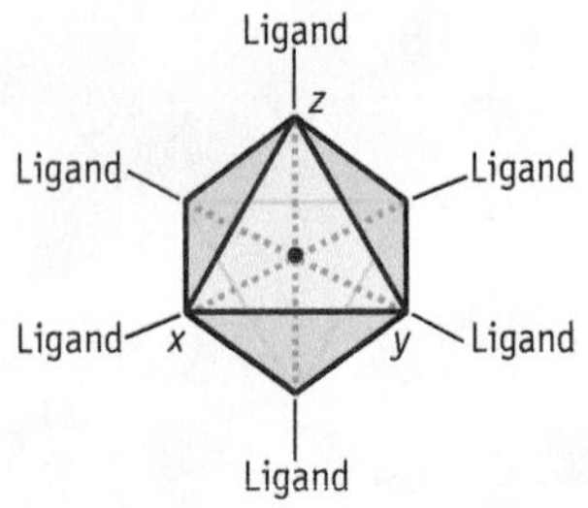

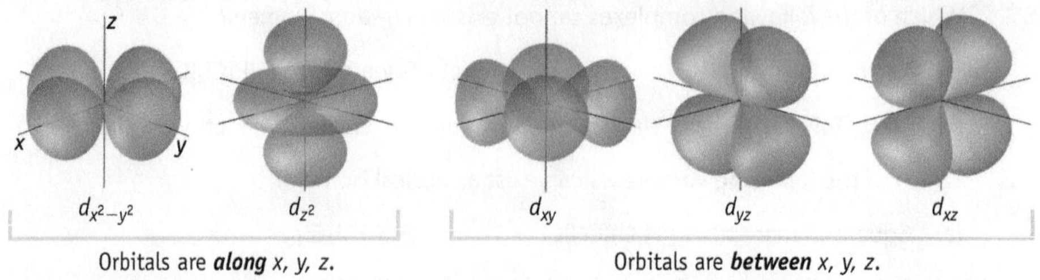

FIGURE 22.20 **The *d* orbitals.** The five *d* orbitals and their spatial relation to the ligands on the *x*-, *y*-, and *z*-axes.

that is, it causes their energy to increase. Electrons in the various *d* orbitals are not affected equally, however, because of their different orientations in space relative to the position of the ligand lone pairs.

We look first at octahedral complexes. Assume the ligands in an octahedral complex lie along the *x*-, *y*-, and *z*-axes. This results in the five *d* orbitals being subdivided into two sets: the $d_{x^2-y^2}$ and d_{z^2} orbitals in one set and the d_{xy}, d_{xz}, and d_{yz} orbitals in the second (Figure 22.20). The $d_{x^2-y^2}$ and d_{z^2} orbitals are directed along the *x*-, *y*-, and *z*-axes, whereas the orbitals of the second group are aligned between these axes. Electrons in the $d_{x^2-y^2}$ and d_{z^2} orbitals experience a larger repulsion because these orbitals point directly at the ligand electron pairs. A smaller repulsive effect is experienced by electrons in the d_{xy}, d_{xz}, and d_{yz} orbitals. The difference in degree of repulsion means that an energy difference exists between the two sets of orbitals in an octahedral complex (Figure 22.21). This difference, called the **ligand field splitting** and denoted by the symbol Δ_O, is a function of the metal and the ligands and varies predictably from one complex to another.

A different splitting pattern is encountered with square-planar complexes (Figure 22.22). Assume that the four ligands are along the *x*- and *y*-axes. The $d_{x^2-y^2}$ orbital also points along these axes, so it has the highest energy. The d_{xy} orbital (which also lies in the *xy*-plane, but does not point at the ligands) is next highest in energy, followed by the d_{z^2} orbital. The d_{xz} and d_{yz} orbitals, both of which partially point in the *z*-direction, have the lowest energy.

The *d*-orbital splitting pattern for a tetrahedral complex is the reverse of the pattern observed for octahedral complexes. Three orbitals (d_{xz}, d_{xy}, d_{yz}) are higher in energy, whereas the $d_{x^2-y^2}$ and d_{z^2} orbitals are below them in energy (Figure 22.22).

FIGURE 22.21 **Ligand field splitting for an octahedral complex.** The *d*-orbital energies increase as the ligands approach the metal along the *x*-, *y*-, and *z*-axes. The d_{xy}, d_{xz}, and d_{yz} orbitals, not pointed toward the ligands, are less destabilized than the $d_{x^2-y^2}$ and d_{z^2} orbitals. Thus, the d_{xy}, d_{xz}, and d_{yz} orbitals are at lower energy. (Δ_O stands for the splitting in an octahedral ligand field.)

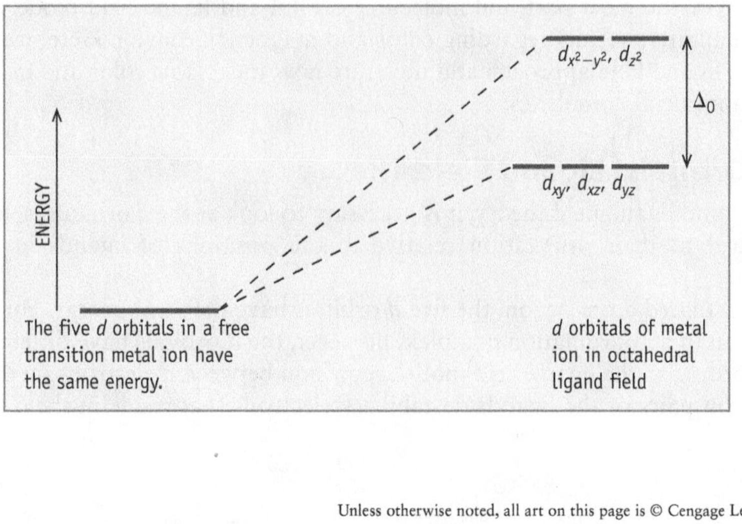

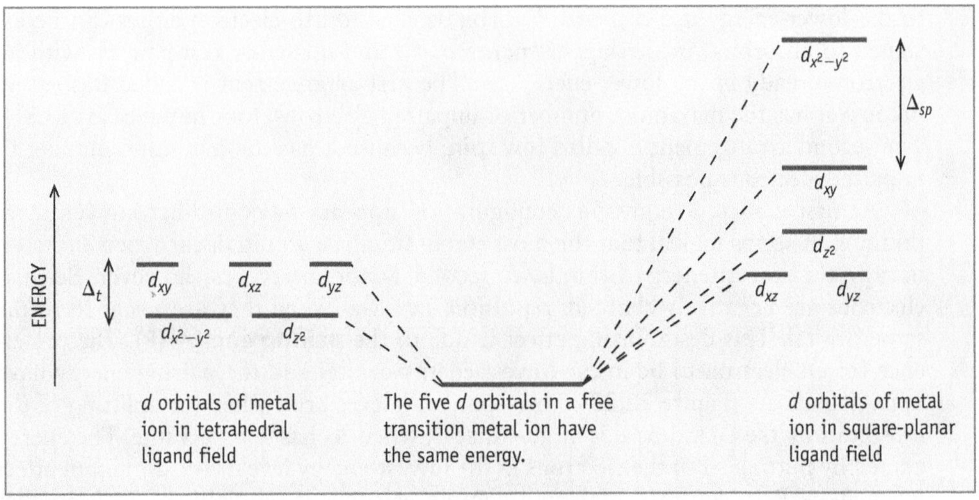

FIGURE 22.22 **Splitting of the *d* orbitals in *(left)* tetrahedral and *(right)* square-planar geometries.** (Δ_t and Δ_{sp} are, respectively, the splitting in tetrahedral and square-planar ligand fields.)

Electron Configurations and Magnetic Properties

The *d*-orbital splitting in coordination complexes provides an explanation of both the magnetic behavior and the color of these complexes. To understand this explanation, however, we must first understand how to assign electrons to the various orbitals in each geometry.

A gaseous Cr^{2+} ion has the electron configuration [Ar]$3d^4$. The term *gaseous* in this context is used to denote a single, isolated atom or ion with all other particles located an infinite distance away. In this situation, the five $3d$ orbitals have the same energy. The four electrons reside singly in different *d* orbitals, according to Hund's rule, and the Cr^{2+} ion has four unpaired electrons.

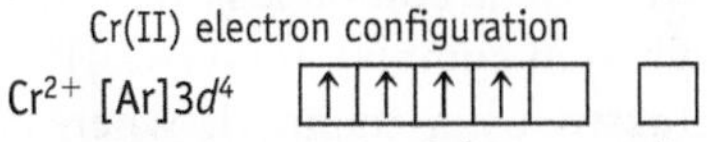

When the Cr^{2+} ion is part of an octahedral complex, the five *d* orbitals do not have identical energies. As illustrated in Figure 22.21, these orbitals divide into two sets, with the d_{xy}, d_{xz}, and d_{yz} orbitals having a lower energy than the $d_{x^2-y^2}$ and d_{z^2} orbitals. Having two sets of orbitals means that two different electron configurations are possible (Figure 22.23). Three of the four *d* electrons in Cr^{2+} are assigned

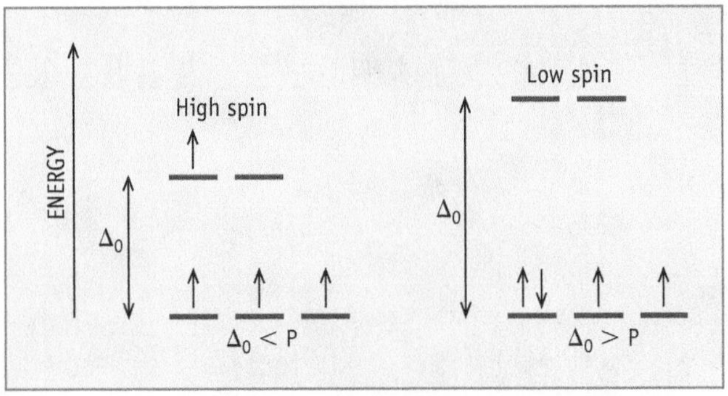

FIGURE 22.23 **High- and low-spin cases for an octahedral chromium(II) complex.** *(left, high spin)* If the ligand field splitting (Δ_O) is smaller than the pairing energy (P), the electrons are placed in different orbitals, and the complex has four unpaired electrons. *(right, low spin)* If the splitting is larger than the pairing energy, all four electrons will be in the lower-energy orbital set. This requires pairing two electrons in one of the orbitals, so the complex will have two unpaired electrons.

to the lower-energy d_{xy}, d_{xz}, and d_{yz} orbitals. The fourth electron either can be assigned to an orbital in the higher-energy $d_{x^2-y^2}$ and d_{z^2} set or can pair up with an electron already in the lower-energy set. The first arrangement is called **high spin**, because it has the maximum number of unpaired electrons, four in the case of Cr^{2+}. The second arrangement is called **low spin**, because it has the minimum number of unpaired electrons possible.

At first glance, a high-spin configuration appears to contradict conventional thinking. It seems logical that the most stable situation would occur when electrons occupy the lowest-energy orbitals. A second factor intervenes, however. Because electrons are negatively charged, repulsion increases when they are assigned to the same orbital. This destabilizing effect is due to the **pairing energy (P)**. The preference for an electron to be in the lowest-energy orbital and the pairing energy have opposing effects (Figure 22.23). Low-spin complexes arise when the splitting of the d orbitals by the ligand field is large—that is, when Δ_O has a large value. The energy gained by putting all of the electrons in the lowest-energy level is the dominant effect when $\Delta_O > P$. In contrast, high-spin complexes occur if the value of Δ_O is smaller than the energy required to pair electrons ($\Delta_O < P$).

For octahedral complexes, high- and low-spin complexes are possible only for configurations d^4 through d^7 (Figure 22.24). Complexes of the d^6 metal ion, Fe^{2+}, for example, can have either high spin or low spin. The complex formed when the Fe^{2+} ion is placed in water, $[Fe(H_2O)_6]^{2+}$, is high spin, whereas the $[Fe(CN)_6]^{4-}$ complex ion is low spin.

Electron configuration for Fe^{2+} in an octahedral complex

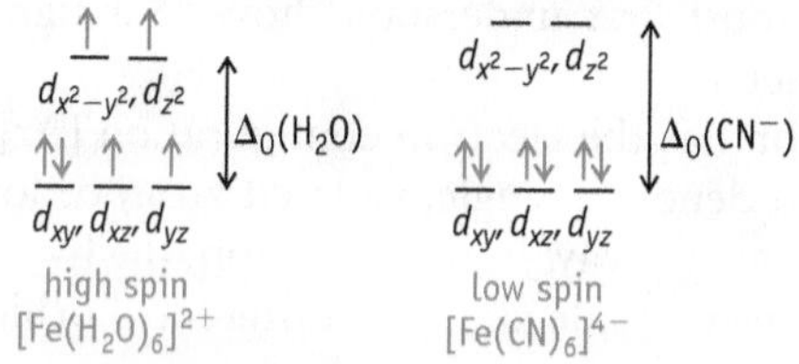

It is possible to tell whether a complex is high or low spin by examining its magnetic behavior. The high-spin complex $[Fe(H_2O)_6]^{2+}$ has four unpaired electrons and is *paramagnetic* (attracted by a magnet), whereas the low-spin $[Fe(CN)_6]^{4-}$ complex has no unpaired electrons and is *diamagnetic* (repelled by a magnet) (◀ Section 7-4).

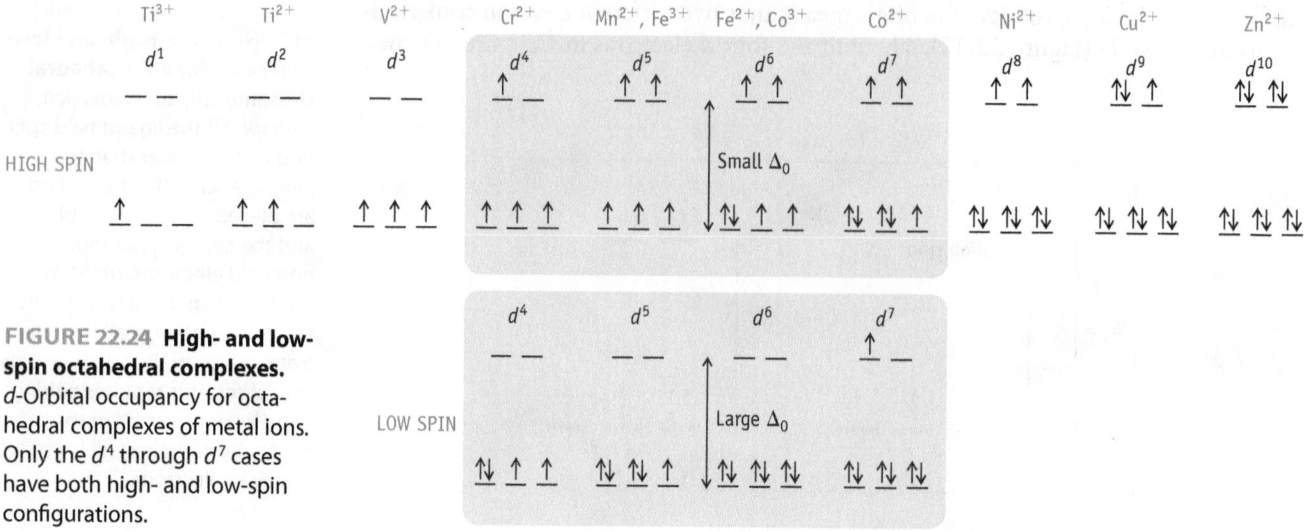

FIGURE 22.24 High- and low-spin octahedral complexes. d-Orbital occupancy for octahedral complexes of metal ions. Only the d^4 through d^7 cases have both high- and low-spin configurations.

PROBLEM SOLVING TIP 22.1

Ligand Field Theory

This summary of the concepts of ligand field theory may help you to keep the broader picture in mind.

- Ligand–metal bonding results from the electrostatic attraction between a metal cation and either an anion or a polar molecule.
- The ligands define a coordination geometry. Common geometries are linear (coordination number = 2), tetrahedral and square-planar (coordination number = 4), and octahedral (coordination number = 6).
- The placement of the ligands around the metal causes the *d* orbitals on the metal to have different energies. In an octahedral complex, for example, the *d* orbitals divide into two groups: a higher-energy group ($d_{x^2-y^2}$ and d_{z^2}) and a lower-energy group (d_{xy}, d_{xz}, and d_{yz}).
- Electrons are assigned to metal *d* orbitals in a manner that leads to the lowest total energy. Two competing features determine the placement: the relative energy of the sets of orbitals and the electron pairing energy.
- For the electron configurations of d^4, d^5, d^6, and d^7 in octahedral complexes, two electron configurations are possible: high spin, which occurs when the orbital splitting is small, and low spin, which occurs with a large orbital splitting. To determine whether a complex is high spin or low spin, its magnetism can be measured to determine the number of unpaired electrons.
- The *d*-orbital splitting (the energy difference between the metal *d*-orbital energies) often corresponds to the energy associated with visible light. As a consequence, many metal complexes absorb visible light and thus are colored.

Most complexes of Pd^{2+} and Pt^{2+} ions are square-planar, the electron configuration of these metals being [noble gas]$(n-1)d^8$. In a square-planar complex, there are four sets of orbitals (see Figure 22.22). For square-planar d^8 complexes, all except the highest-energy orbital are filled, and all electrons are paired, resulting in diamagnetic (low-spin) complexes.

Nickel, which is found above palladium in the periodic table, forms both square-planar and tetrahedral complexes (as well as octahedral complexes). For example, the complex ion $[Ni(CN)_4]^{2-}$ is square-planar, whereas the $[NiCl_4]^{2-}$ ion is tetrahedral. Magnetism allows us to differentiate between these two geometries. Based on the ligand field splitting pattern, the cyanide complex is expected to be diamagnetic, whereas the chloride complex is paramagnetic with two unpaired electrons.

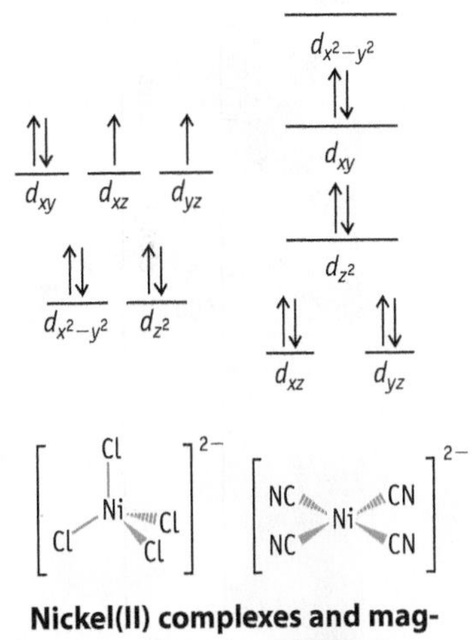

Nickel(II) complexes and magnetism. The anion $[NiCl_4]^{2-}$ is a paramagnetic tetrahedral complex. In contrast, $[Ni(CN)_4]^{2-}$ is a diamagnetic square-planar complex.

EXAMPLE 22.5

High- and Low-Spin Complexes and Magnetism

Problem Give the electron configuration for the metal ion in each of the following complexes. How many unpaired electrons are present in each? Are the complexes paramagnetic or diamagnetic?

(a) Low-spin $[Co(NH_3)_6]^{3+}$ (b) High-spin $[CoF_6]^{3-}$

What Do You Know? From their formulas, we know that these have six ligands and we can presume that they have octahedral geometry. Both are complexes of cobalt(III), a metal ion with a d^6 configuration. One complex is low spin, the other high spin.

Strategy Set up an energy-level diagram for an octahedral complex. In low-spin complexes, the electrons are added preferentially to the lower-energy set of orbitals. In high-spin complexes, the first five electrons are added singly to each of the five orbitals, then additional electrons are paired with electrons in orbitals in the lower-energy set.

Solution

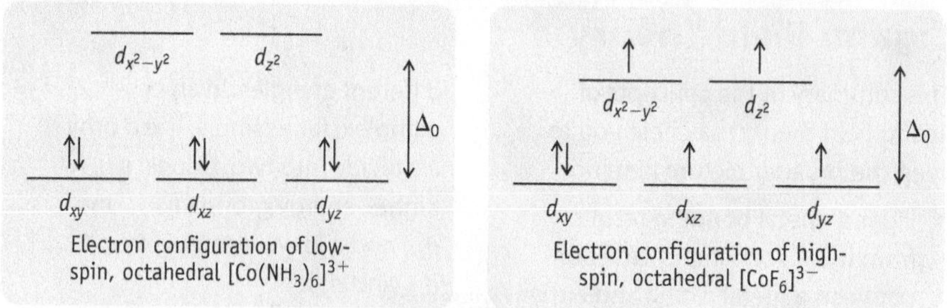

(a) (b)

(a) The six electrons of the Co^{3+} ion fill the lower-energy set of orbitals entirely. This d^6 complex ion has no unpaired electrons and is diamagnetic.

(b) To obtain the electron configuration in high-spin $[CoF_6]^{3-}$, place one electron in each of the five *d* orbitals, and then place the sixth electron in one of the lower-energy orbitals. The complex has four unpaired electrons and is paramagnetic.

Think about Your Answer The two complexes have different magnetic properties; low-spin $[Co(NH_3)_6]^{3+}$ is diamagnetic and high-spin $[CoF_6]^{3-}$ is paramagnetic.

Check Your Understanding

For each of the following complex ions, give the oxidation number of the metal, depict possible low- and high-spin configurations, give the number of unpaired electrons in each configuration, and tell whether each is paramagnetic or diamagnetic.

(a) $[Ru(H_2O)_6]^{2+}$ (b) $[Ni(NH_3)_6]^{2+}$

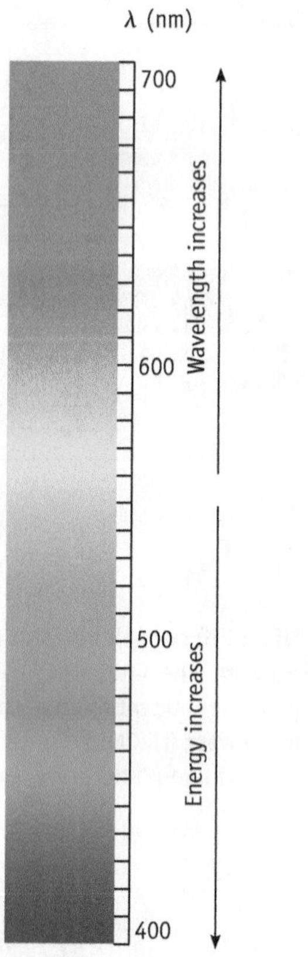

The ROY G BIV spectrum of colors of visible light. The colors used in printing this book are cyan, magenta, yellow, and black. The blue in ROY G BIV is actually cyan, according to color industry standards. Magenta doesn't have its own wavelength region. Rather, it is a mixture of blue and red.

REVIEW & CHECK FOR SECTION 22-5

1. Which of the following complexes has the greatest number of unpaired electrons?
   (a) Low-spin $[Fe(CN)_6]^{4-}$
   (b) High-spin $[Mn(NH_3)_6]^{2+}$
   (c) $[V(H_2O)_6]^{3+}$
   (d) $[Ni(en)_3]^{2+}$ (en = ethylenediamine)
2. Which of the following complexes is diamagnetic?
   (a) Square-planar $[PtCl_4]^{2-}$
   (b) Tetrahedral $[NiCl_4]^{2-}$
   (c) $[Fe(H_2O)_6]^{3+}$
   (d) High-spin $[CoF_6]^{3-}$

22-6 Colors of Coordination Compounds

The range of colors observed for compounds of the transition elements is one of their most interesting features (Figures 22.2 and 22.25), and the underlying reason for this is *d*-orbital splitting due to the ligands surrounding the metal atom or ion. Before discussing how *d*-orbital splitting is involved, however, let us look more closely at what we mean by color.

Color

Visible light, consists of radiation with wavelengths from 400 to 700 nm (◀ Section 6-1). Within this region are all the colors you see when white light passes through a prism: red, orange, yellow, green, blue, indigo, and violet (ROY G BIV). Each color is identified with a portion of the wavelength range.

Isaac Newton did experiments with light and established that the mind's perception of color requires only three colors! When we see white light, we are seeing a

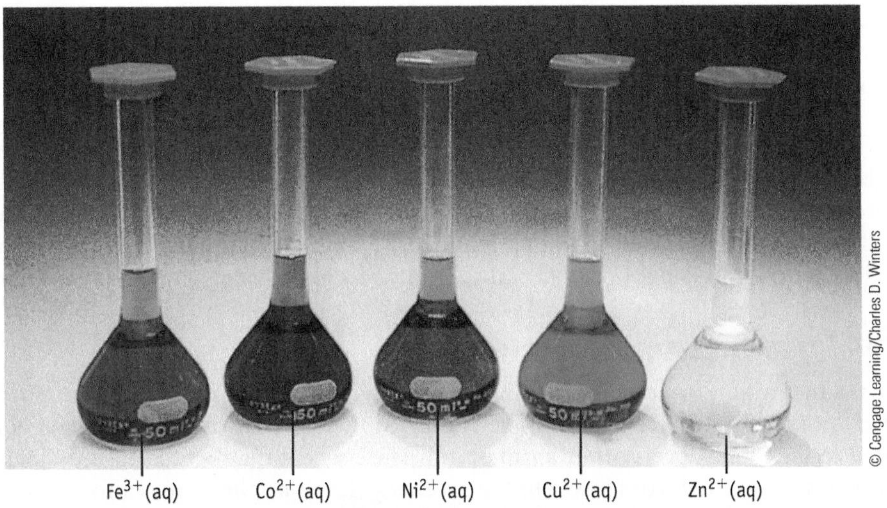

FIGURE 22.25 **Aqueous solutions of some transition metal ions.** Compounds of transition metal elements are often colored, whereas those of main group metals are usually colorless. Pictured here, from *left* to *right*, are solutions of the nitrate salts of Fe^{3+}, Co^{2+}, Ni^{2+}, Cu^{2+}, and Zn^{2+}.

mixture of all of the colors—in other words, the superposition of red, green, and blue. If one or more of these colors is absent, the light of the other colors that reaches your eyes is interpreted by your mind as color.

Figure 22.26 will help you in analyzing perceived colors. The three primary colors—red, green, and blue—are shown as overlapping disks arranged in a triangle. The secondary colors—cyan, magenta, and yellow—appear where two disks overlap. The overlap of all three disks in the center produces white light.

The colors we perceive are determined as follows:

- Light of a single primary color is perceived as that color: Red light is perceived as red, green light as green, blue light as blue.
- Light made up of two primary colors is perceived as the color shown where the disks in Figure 22.26 overlap: Red and green light together appear yellow, green and blue light together are perceived as cyan; and red and blue light are perceived as magenta.
- Light made up of the three primary colors is white (colorless).

In discussing the color of a substance such as a coordination complex *in solution,* we are interested in the light that is absorbed.

- Red color is the result of the absorption of green and blue light by the solution.
- Green color results if red and blue light are absorbed.
- Blue color results if red and green light are absorbed.

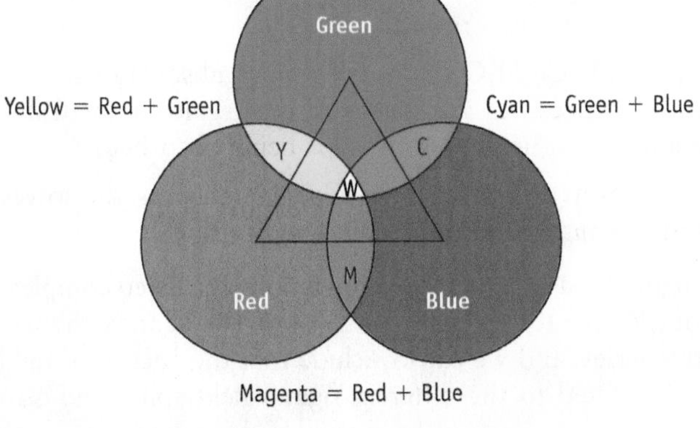

FIGURE 22.26 **Using color disks to analyze colors.** The three primary colors are red, green, and blue. Adding light of two primary colors gives the secondary colors yellow (= red + green), cyan (= green + blue), and magenta (= red + blue). Adding all three primary colors results in white light.

FIGURE 22.27 Light absorption and color. The color of a solution is due to the color of the light *not* absorbed by the solution. Here, a solution of Ni^{2+} ion in water absorbs red and blue light and so appears green (see also Figures 4.13–4.15).

Green jade. This photo shows the entire piece of jade that is featured on the cover of this book. The rich green color comes from iron(II) and iron(III) ions in the mineral. It is likely that the iron ions within the mineral are surrounded by oxide ions at the corners of an octahedron.

The secondary colors are rationalized similarly. Absorption of blue light gives yellow (the color across from it in Figure 22.26); absorption of red light results in cyan; and absorption of green light results in magenta.

Now we can apply these ideas to explain colors in transition metal complexes. Focus on what kind of light is *absorbed*. A solution of $[Ni(H_2O)_6]^{2+}$ is green. Green light is the result of removing red and blue light from white light. As white light passes through an aqueous solution of Ni^{2+}, red and blue light are absorbed, and green light is allowed to pass (Figure 22.27). Similarly, the $[Co(NH_3)_6]^{3+}$ ion is yellow because blue light has been absorbed and red and green light pass through.

The Spectrochemical Series

Recall that atomic spectra are obtained when electrons are excited from one energy level to another (◀ Section 6-3). The energy of the light absorbed or emitted is related to the energy levels of the atom or ion. The concept that light is absorbed when electrons are excited from lower to higher energy levels applies not just to atoms but also to ions and molecules of all types, including transition metal complexes.

In coordination complexes, the splitting between *d* orbitals often corresponds to the energy of visible light, so light in the visible region of the spectrum is absorbed when electrons move from a lower-energy *d* orbital to a higher-energy *d* orbital. This change, as an electron moves between two orbitals having different energies in a complex, is called a ***d*-to-*d* transition.** Qualitatively, such a transition for $[Co(NH_3)_6]^{3+}$ might be represented using an energy-level diagram such as that shown here.

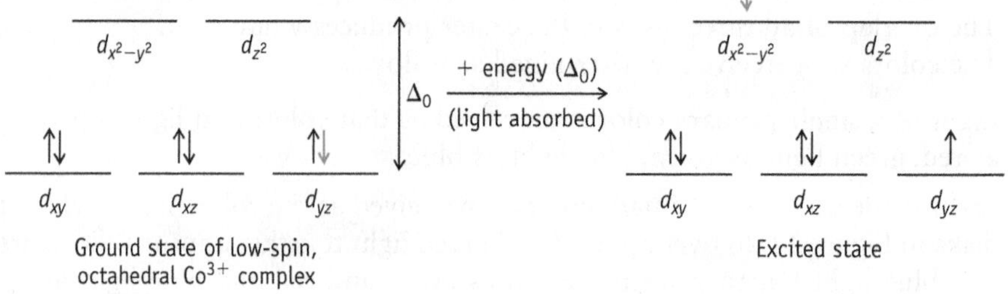

Experiments with coordination complexes reveal that, for a given metal ion, some ligands cause a small energy separation of the *d* orbitals, whereas others cause a large separation. In other words, some ligands create a small ligand field, and others create a large one. An example is seen in the spectroscopic data for several cobalt(III) complexes presented in Table 22.3.

- Both $[Co(NH_3)_6]^{3+}$ and $[Co(en)_3]^{3+}$ are yellow-orange, because they absorb light in the blue portion of the visible spectrum. These compounds have very similar spectra, to be expected because in both the metal is coordinated to six N donor atoms.
- Although $[Co(CN)_6]^{3-}$ does not have an absorption band whose maximum falls in the visible region, it is pale yellow. The peak of the absorption band occurs in the ultraviolet region, but the absorption band is broad and extends minimally into the visible (blue) region.
- $[Co(C_2O_4)_3]^{3-}$ and $[Co(H_2O)_6]^{3+}$ have similar absorptions, in the yellow and violet regions. Their colors are shades of green with a small difference due to the relative amount of light of each color being absorbed.
- Of the complex ions in Table 22.3, $[CoF_6]^{3-}$ absorbs the lowest energy light (red) and so transmits the highest energy light (blue).

The wavelength of maximum absorption among the listed complexes ranges from 700 nm for $[CoF_6]^{3-}$ to 310 nm for $[Co(CN)_6]^{3-}$. The ligands change from member to member of this series, and we can conclude that the energy of the light absorbed by the complex is related to the different ligand field splittings, Δ_o, caused by the

Table 22.3 The Colors of Some Co^{3+} Complexes*

Complex Ion	Wavelength of Light Absorbed (nm)	Color of Light Absorbed	Color of Complex
$[CoF_6]^{3-}$	700	Red	Blue
$[Co(C_2O_4)_3]^{3-}$	600, 420	Yellow, violet	Dark green
$[Co(H_2O)_6]^{3+}$	600, 400	Yellow, violet	Blue-green
$[Co(NH_3)_6]^{3+}$	475, 340	Blue, ultraviolet	Yellow-orange
$[Co(en)_3]^{3+}$	470, 340	Blue, ultraviolet	Yellow-orange
$[Co(CN)_6]^{3-}$	310	Ultraviolet	Pale yellow

*The complex with fluoride ion, $[CoF_6]^{3-}$, is high spin and has one absorption band. The other complexes are low spin and have two absorption bands. In all but one case, one of these absorptions occurs in the visible region of the spectrum. The wavelengths are measured at the top of that absorption band.

CASE STUDY The Rare Earths

The lanthanide elements are often referred to as "rare earth elements." But what elements are really included in the list and why are they called "rare"? And what are they used for?

In this book we include the 14 elements from Ce (cerium) through Lu (lutetium) in the list of rare earths, but it is common to also include La, lanthanum. In addition, if you read about rare earth chemistry, the Group 3B elements Sc (scandium) and Y (yttrium) are often added to the list.

Why are they called "rare earth elements" and are they in fact "rare"? In 1803 German and Swedish chemists isolated a new oxide (an "earth") from a mineral found in Sweden. At first this was thought to be an oxide of a new element, cerium, but several decades later it was discovered that the "earth" was a mixture of cerium oxide and oxides of other lanthanides. The term "rare" has been attached to the elements because it is difficult to find them in concentrations great enough for commercial purposes and because they are difficult to separate one from another. But they are in fact rather abundant. Cerium, for example, is 26th most abundant in Earth's crust, about half as abundant as chlorine and 5 times as abundant as lead.

The elements were slow to find commercial uses, but some are now crucially important in our modern economy. Cerium(IV) oxide is used in catalysts and in the coatings of self-cleaning ovens. Neodymium (Nd) and samarium (Sm) are both used to make powerful magnets. Europium (Eu) is used in the phosphors inside compact fluorescent lightbulbs. (This coating is what allows the bulb to emit a very bright light.) Other uses are in batteries and wind turbines.

One consequence of the growing importance of the rare earths is that they are becoming scarce. China presently produces about 97% of the metals and oxides, and companies in the United States and elsewhere are opening old mines or seeking new sources.

© Cengage Learning/Charles D. Winters

Compact fluorescent bulbs. They have an inside coating of a phosphorescent europium compound.

Argonne National Laboratory

Cerium-based catalyst. A chemist at Argonne National Laboratory holds a beaker of Cu-ZSM-5 catalyst used to remove harmful nitrogen oxides from diesel exhaust. The catalyst is a zeolite that contains copper ions in the lattice and is coated with cerium(IV) oxide.

Questions:

1. What are the electron configurations for Nd and Eu?
2. The lanthanide elements form ionic compounds, with the 3+ oxidation state dominating. What are the electron configurations for Ce^{3+} and Nd^{3+}?
3. The compound $(NH_4)_2Ce(NO_3)_6$ is a widely used oxidizing agent in redox titrations. A 0.181 g sample of pure iron is dissolved in acid, reduced to Fe^{2+}, and then titrated with 31.33 mL of $(NH_4)_2Ce(NO_3)_6$ (to give Ce^{3+} and Fe^{3+}). Calculate the concentration of the cerium salt.
4. Cerium(IV) oxide is used in catalytic converters in the oxidation of CO (to give cerium(III) oxide and CO_2). The cerium(III) oxide is converted back to cerium(IV) oxide by atmospheric oxygen. Balance equations for these reactions.

The answers to these questions are found in Appendix N.

different ligands. Fluoride ion causes the smallest splitting of the *d* orbitals among the complexes listed in Table 22.3, whereas cyanide causes the largest splitting.

Spectra of complexes of other metals provide similar results. Based on this information, ligands can be listed in order of their ability to split the *d* orbitals. This list is called the **spectrochemical series** because it was determined by spectroscopy. A short list, with some of the more common ligands, follows:

$$F^-, Cl^-, Br^-, I^- < C_2O_4^{2-} < H_2O < NH_3 = en < phen < CN^-$$

small *d* orbital splitting — large *d* orbital splitting

small Δ_o — large Δ_o

The spectrochemical series is applicable to a wide range of metal complexes. Indeed, the ability of ligand field theory to explain the differences in the colors of the transition metal complexes is one of the strengths of this theory.

Based on the relative position of a ligand in the series, predictions can be made about a compound's magnetic behavior. Recall that d^4, d^5, d^6, and d^7 complexes can be high or low spin, depending on the ligand field splitting, Δ_O. Complexes formed with ligands near the left end of the spectrochemical series are expected to have small Δ_O values and, therefore, are likely to be high spin. In contrast, complexes with ligands near the right end are expected to have large Δ_O values and low-spin configurations. The complex $[CoF_6]^{3-}$ is high spin, whereas $[Co(NH_3)_6]^{3+}$ and the other complexes in Table 22.3 are low spin.

EXAMPLE 22.6

Spectrochemical Series

Problem An aqueous solution of $[Fe(H_2O)_6]^{2+}$ is light blue-green. Do you expect the d^6 Fe^{2+} ion in this complex to have a high- or low-spin configuration? How could you test your prediction experimentally?

What Do You Know? This is an octahedral complex of Fe^{2+}, an ion with a d^6 configuration. The blue-green color is the result of the absorption of visible light due to a *d*-to-*d* transition. The complex could be either low spin (no unpaired electrons) or high spin (four unpaired electrons).

Strategy Use the color wheel in Figure 22.26 to determine what color light is transmitted and therefore what color of light has been absorbed. Based on the energy of the light absorbed, determine if Δ_O is high or low. If it is low, then the complex is high spin. If it is high, then the complex is low spin.

Solution In this case, the blue-green color of the solution indicates that blue and green light is transmitted. This implies that red light was absorbed. The low energy of the light absorbed suggests that Δ_O is small and so $[Fe(H_2O)_6]^{2+}$ is likely to be a high-spin complex. If the complex is high spin, it will have four unpaired electrons and be paramagnetic; if, contrary to our prediction, it is low spin, it will have no unpaired electrons and be diamagnetic. Thus, identifying the presence of four unpaired electrons by measuring the compound's magnetism can be used to verify the high-spin configuration experimentally.

Think about Your Answer The spectrochemical series was generated by measuring the absorptions for a series of complexes of a given metal, varying the ligands. As in the example here, the spectrochemical series is useful because it allows you to predict whether a complex is likely to be high or low spin. The more definitive evidence for high or low spin comes from information on the magnetism of the complex.

Check Your Understanding

1. The complex $[Co(NH_3)_5OH]^{2+}$ has an absorption maximum at 500 nm. What color of light is absorbed and what color is the complex?
2. Figure 22.15 shows a sample of yellow $[Co(NH_3)_5NO_2]^{2+}$. What color of light is absorbed by this complex? Predict whether this is a high-spin or low-spin complex.

REVIEW & CHECK FOR SECTION 22-6

1. Solutions of each of the following complexes absorb light in the visible region of the spectrum. Predict which complex will absorb light of the longest wavelength.

   (a) $[Cr(H_2O)_6]^{3+}$ (b) $[Cr(NH_3)_6]^{3+}$ (c) $[CrF_6]^{3-}$ (d) $[Cr(CN)_6]^{3-}$

APPLYING CHEMICAL PRINCIPLES

Green Catalysts

You were introduced to "green chemistry" in Chapter 1 and have seen several instances of it throughout the book. The important objective of this field is that a process that creates a useful product must have a negligible impact on the environment. Thus, important goals of green chemistry include eliminating the use of toxic substances as reactants and reducing the quantity of unwanted reaction by-products.

Catalysts can play an important role in green chemistry processes. Catalysts increase reaction rates sufficiently so that reactions can often be run at lower temperatures, thereby reducing energy usage. Catalysts may also improve the reaction specificity, yielding higher percentages of products, often in fewer synthetic steps. A specific area where green catalytic alternatives are needed is in oxidation reactions. At present these are often carried out by environmentally unfriendly compounds such as chlorine or chlorine dioxide.

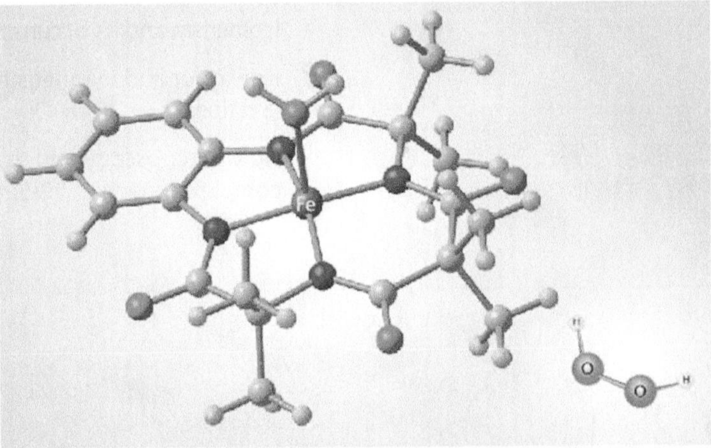

Courtesy of Professor Terry Collins, The Institute for Green Science, Carnegie Mellon University

The prototype TAML activator. A model of hydrogen peroxide is also shown. The central iron cation is coordinated to four nitrogen atoms and a water molecule. The geometry around the central iron atom is square pyramidal. (Model from the Institute for Green Science: www.chem.cmu .edu/groups/collins.)

Terry Collins, Professor of Chemistry at the Carnegie Mellon Institute for Green Chemistry, has designed a family of iron-based coordination complexes that are promising oxidation catalysts. Named Fe-TAML® (where TAML stands for tetraamidomacrocyclic ligand), these complexes catalyze reactions using hydrogen peroxide as an oxidizing agent. Hydrogen peroxide is an environmentally friendly oxidizing agent. However, when used without a suitable catalyst, H_2O_2 decomposes it tends to produce hydroxyl radicals that indiscriminately attack organic molecules.

Recently, this catalyst has shown positive results in the treatment of waste water from wood pulp treatment plants. Wood pulp consists of two naturally occurring polymers, cellulose and lignin. Cellulose is used for making white paper, whereas lignin is a dark colored polymer that must be removed. Current practice is to oxidize the lignin with chlorine dioxide before releasing it into waste water. However, all the lignin is destroyed in this process, and the remaining lignin darkens the water and affects the quantity of light absorbed by aquatic life. Low concentrations of Fe-TAML (500 nanomolar) combined with small amounts of hydrogen peroxide have been shown to destroy the majority of lignin quickly at room temperature.

QUESTIONS:

Answer the following questions concerning the Fe-TAML catalyst in the Figure.

1. What is the coordination number of the metal in the Fe-TAML catalyst?
2. Fe-TAML, as pictured here, is a complex ion of a macrocyclic ligand (with a charge of 4−), a water molecule, and an iron(III) ion. What is the overall charge on the Fe-TAML complex ion?
3. TAML is a tetra________ macrocyclic ligand, meaning it has four "teeth" that can bond to the metal.
4. Can this metal–ligand complex have any isomers?
5. What is the geometry of the coordinating atoms around the Fe^{3+} ion in the Fe-TAML complex ion if the water is removed: tetrahedral, square-planar, square-pyramidal, or octahedral?

REFERENCES AND NOTES:

1. Professor Terry Collins, whose research group developed the Fe-TAML catalyst, received the 1999 Presidential Green Chemistry Challenge Award.
2. See an outline of the Twelve Principles of green chemistry in Section 20-7. See also the U. S. Environmental Protection Agency website: www.epa.gov/greenchemistry/pubs/principles.html.

CHAPTER GOALS REVISITED

Now that you have studied this chapter, you should ask whether you have met the chapter goals. In particular, you should be able to:

UNDERSTAND

- Ligand field theory description of metal-ligand bonding in coordination compounds (Section 22-5).
- Isomerism and its occurrence in coordination chemistry (Sections 22-3 and 22-4).
- How color and magnetism are related to the electronic structure of a complex (Section 22-6). Study Questions: 23–30, 34, 35, 42, 43, 50, 53, 54, 58, 61.
- How spectroscopy and magnetism can be used to identify high- and low-spin complexes (Section 22-5). Study Questions: 29, 30, 54.

DO

- Given the formula for a coordination complex, identify the metal and its oxidation state, the ligands, the coordination number and coordination geometry, and the overall charge on the complex (Section 22-3 and 22-4). Study Questions: 9–12, 46, 47.
- Given the molecular formula of a complex, determine whether isomers are possible, and draw their structures (Section 22-4). Study Questions: 39, 42, 43, 45, 46.
- Given a formula, name a complex; given a name of a complex, write its formula (Section 22-4). Study Questions: 13–18.
- Draw an energy level diagram representing splitting of the metal *d* orbitals by the ligand field (Section 22-5). Study Question: 40.
- Apply the principles of stoichiometry, thermodynamics, and equilibrium to transition metal compounds. Study Questions: 62, 70.

REMEMBER

- General chemical and physical properties of common transition metal elements.
  - **a.** Identify the general classes of transition elements (Section 22-1).
  - **b.** Identify the transition metals from their symbols and positions in the periodic table, and recall some physical and chemical properties (Section 22-1).
  - **c.** Understand the electrochemical nature of corrosion (Section 22-1).
  - **d.** Describe the metallurgy of iron and copper (Section 22-2).
- The terminology of coordination chemistry: coordination number and coordination geometry, ligand, chelate, bidentate (Sections 22-3 and 22-4).
- The terminology of ligand field theory: low spin and high spin, ligand field splitting (Section 22-5).
- The names and formulas for common ligands (Sections 22-3 and 22-4).

Steven Hyatt

STUDY QUESTIONS

▲ denotes challenging questions.

Blue-numbered questions have answers in Appendix N and fully worked solutions in the *Student Solutions Manual.*

Practicing Skills

Properties of Transition Elements

(See Section 22-1 and Examples 7.3 and 7.4.)

1. Give the electron configuration for each of the following ions, and tell whether each is paramagnetic or diamagnetic.
(a) Cr^{3+} (b) V^{2+} (c) Ni^{2+} (d) Cu^{+}

2. Identify two transition metal cations with each of the following electron configurations.
(a) $[Ar]3d^6$ (b) $[Ar]3d^{10}$ (c) $[Ar]3d^5$ (d) $[Ar]3d^8$

3. Identify a cation of a first series transition metal that is isoelectronic with each of the following.
(a) Fe^{3+} (b) Zn^{2+} (c) Fe^{2+} (d) Cr^{3+}

4. Match up the isoelectronic ions on the following list.
Cu^{+} Mn^{2+} Fe^{2+} Co^{3+} Fe^{3+} Zn^{2+} Ti^{2+} V^{3+}

5. The following equations represent various ways of obtaining transition metals from their compounds. Balance each equation.
(a) $Cr_2O_3(s) + Al(s) \longrightarrow Al_2O_3(s) + Cr(s)$
(b) $TiCl_4(\ell) + Mg(s) \longrightarrow Ti(s) + MgCl_2(s)$
(c) $[Ag(CN)_2]^-(aq) + Zn(s) \longrightarrow Ag(s) + [Zn(CN)_4]^{2-}(aq)$
(d) $Mn_3O_4(s) + Al(s) \longrightarrow Mn(s) + Al_2O_3(s)$

6. Identify the products of each reaction, and balance the equation.
(a) $CuSO_4(aq) + Zn(s) \longrightarrow$
(b) $Zn(s) + HCl(aq) \longrightarrow$
(c) $Fe(s) + Cl_2(g) \longrightarrow$
(d) $V(s) + O_2(g) \longrightarrow$

Formulas of Coordination Compounds

(See Examples 22.1 and 22.2.)

7. Which of the following ligands is expected to be monodentate, and which might be polydentate?
(a) CH_3NH_2 (b) CH_3CN (c) N_3^- (d) en (e) Br^- (f) phen

8. One of the following nitrogen compounds or ions is not capable of serving as a ligand: NH_4^+, NH_3, NH_2^-. Identify this species, and explain your answer.

9. Give the oxidation number of the metal ion in each of the following compounds.
(a) $[Mn(NH_3)_6]SO_4$ (b) $K_3[Co(CN)_6]$ (c) $[Co(NH_3)_4Cl_2]Cl$ (d) $Cr(en)_2Cl_2$

10. Give the oxidation number of the metal ion in each of the following complexes.
(a) $[Fe(NH_3)_6]^{2+}$ (b) $[Zn(CN)_4]^{2-}$ (c) $[Co(NH_3)_5(NO_2)]^+$ (d) $[Cu(en)_2]^{2+}$

11. Give the formula of a complex constructed from one Ni^{2+} ion, one ethylenediamine ligand, three ammonia molecules, and one water molecule. Is the complex neutral or is it charged? If charged, give the charge.

12. Give the formula of a complex constructed from one Cr^{3+} ion, two ethylenediamine ligands, and two ammonia molecules. Is the complex neutral or is it charged? If charged, give the charge.

Naming Coordination Compounds

(See Example 22.3.)

13. Write formulas for the following ions or compounds.
(a) dichlorobis(ethylenediamine)nickel(II)
(b) potassium tetrachloroplatinate(II)
(c) potassium dicyanocuprate(I)
(d) tetraamminediaquairon(II)

14. Write formulas for the following ions or compounds.
(a) diamminetriaquahydroxochromium(II) nitrate
(b) hexaammineiron(III) nitrate
(c) pentacarbonyliron(0) (where the ligand is CO)
(d) ammonium tetrachlorocuprate(II)

15. Name the following ions or compounds.
(a) $[Ni(C_2O_4)_2(H_2O)_2]^{2-}$ (b) $[Co(en)_2Br_2]^+$ (c) $[Co(en)_2(NH_3)Cl]^{2+}$ (d) $Pt(NH_3)_2(C_2O_4)$

16. Name the following ions or compounds.
(a) $[Co(H_2O)_4Cl_2]^+$ (b) $Co(H_2O)_3F_3$ (c) $[Pt(NH_3)Br_3]^-$ (d) $[Co(en)(NH_3)_3Cl]^{2+}$

17. Give the name or formula for each ion or compound, as appropriate.
(a) pentaaquahydroxoiron(III) ion
(b) $K_2[Ni(CN)_4]$
(c) $K[Cr(C_2O_4)_2(H_2O)_2]$
(d) ammonium tetrachloroplatinate(II)

18. Give the name or formula for each ion or compound, as appropriate.
    (a) tetraaquadichlorochromium(III) chloride
    (b) $[Cr(NH_3)_5SO_4]Cl$
    (c) sodium tetrachlorocobaltate(II)
    (d) $[Fe(C_2O_4)_3]^{3-}$

Isomerism

(See Example 22.4.)

19. Draw all possible geometric isomers for each of the following ions or molecules.
    (a) $Fe(NH_3)_4Cl_2$
    (b) $Pt(NH_3)_2(SCN)(Br)$ (SCN^- is bonded to Pt^{2+} through S)
    (c) $Co(NH_3)_3(NO_2)_3$ (NO_2^- is bonded to Co^{3+} through N)
    (d) $[Co(en)Cl_4]^-$

20. In which of the following complexes are geometric isomers possible? If isomers are possible, draw their structures and label them as *cis* or *trans,* or as *fac* or *mer.*
    (a) $[Co(H_2O)_4Cl_2]^+$
    (b) $Co(NH_3)_3F_3$
    (c) $[Pt(NH_3)Br_3]^-$
    (d) $[Co(en)_2(NH_3)Cl]^{2+}$

21. Determine whether the following complexes have a chiral metal center.
    (a) $[Fe(en)_3]^{2+}$
    (b) *trans*-$[Co(en)_2Br_2]^+$
    (c) *fac*-$[Co(en)(H_2O)Cl_3]$
    (d) square-planar $Pt(NH_3)(H_2O)(Cl)(NO_2)$

22. Four geometric isomers are possible for $[Co(en)(NH_3)_2(H_2O)Cl]^+$. Draw the structures of all four. (Two of the isomers are chiral, meaning that each has a non-superimposable mirror image.)

Magnetic Properties of Complexes

(See Example 22.5.)

23. The following are low-spin complexes. Use the ligand field model to find the electron configuration of the central metal ion in each ion. Determine which are diamagnetic. Give the number of unpaired electrons for the paramagnetic complexes.
    (a) $[Mn(CN)_6]^{4-}$
    (b) $[Co(NH_3)_6]Cl_3$
    (c) $[Fe(H_2O)_6]^{3+}$
    (d) $[Cr(en)_3]SO_4$

24. The following are high-spin complexes. Use the ligand field model to find the electron configuration of the central metal ion in each ion. Determine the number of unpaired electrons, if any, in each.
    (a) $K_4[FeF_6]$
    (b) $[MnF_6]^{4-}$
    (c) $[Cr(H_2O)_6]^{2+}$
    (d) $(NH_4)_3[FeF_6]$

25. Determine the number of unpaired electrons in the following tetrahedral complexes. All tetrahedral complexes are high spin.
    (a) $[FeCl_4]^{2-}$
    (b) $Na_2[CoCl_4]$
    (c) $[MnCl_4]^{2-}$
    (d) $(NH_4)_2[ZnCl_4]$

26. Determine the number of unpaired electrons in the following tetrahedral complexes. All tetrahedral complexes are high spin.
    (a) $[Zn(H_2O)_4]^{2+}$
    (b) $VOCl_3$
    (c) $Mn(NH_3)_2Cl_2$
    (d) $[Cu(en)_2]^{2+}$

27. For the high-spin complex $[Fe(H_2O)_6]SO_4$, identify the following:
    (a) the coordination number of iron
    (b) the coordination geometry for iron
    (c) the oxidation number of iron
    (d) the number of unpaired electrons
    (e) whether the complex is diamagnetic or paramagnetic

28. For the low-spin complex $[Co(en)(NH_3)_2Cl_2]ClO_4$, identify the following:
    (a) the coordination number of cobalt
    (b) the coordination geometry for cobalt
    (c) the oxidation number of cobalt
    (d) the number of unpaired electrons
    (e) whether the complex is diamagnetic or paramagnetic
    (f) Draw any geometric isomers.

29. The anion $[NiCl_4]^{2-}$ is paramagnetic, but when CN^- ions are added, the product, $[Ni(CN)_4]^{2-}$, is diamagnetic. Explain this observation.

$$\underset{\text{paramagnetic}}{[NiCl_4]^{2-}(aq)} + 4\ CN^-(aq) \longrightarrow \underset{\text{diamagnetic}}{[Ni(CN)_4]^{2-}(aq)} + 4\ Cl^-(aq)$$

30. An aqueous solution of iron(II) sulfate is paramagnetic. If NH_3 is added, the solution becomes diamagnetic. Why does the magnetism change?

Spectroscopy of Complexes

(See Example 22.6.)

31. In water, the titanium(III) ion, $[Ti(H_2O)_6]^{3+}$, has a broad absorption band centered at about 500 nm. What color light is absorbed by the ion?

32. In water, the chromium(II) ion, $[Cr(H_2O)_6]^{2+}$, absorbs light with a wavelength of about 700 nm. What color is the solution?

General Questions

These questions are not designated as to type or location in the chapter. They may contain several concepts.

33. Describe an experiment that would determine whether nickel in $K_2[NiCl_4]$ is square-planar or tetrahedral.

34. Which of the following high-spin complexes has the greatest number of unpaired electrons?
    (a) $[Cr(H_2O)_6]^{3+}$
    (b) $[Mn(H_2O)_6]^{2+}$
    (c) $[Fe(H_2O)_6]^{2+}$
    (d) $[Ni(H_2O)_6]^{2+}$

35. How many unpaired electrons are expected for high-spin and low-spin complexes of Fe^{2+}?

36. Excess silver nitrate is added to a solution containing 1.0 mol of $[Co(NH_3)_4Cl_2]Cl$. What amount of AgCl (in moles) will precipitate?

37. Which of the following complex ions is (are) square-planar?

(a) $[Ti(CN)_4]^{2-}$
(b) $[Ni(CN)_4]^{2-}$
(c) $[Zn(CN)_4]^{2-}$
(d) $[Pt(CN)_4]^{2-}$

38. Which of the following complex ions containing the oxalate ion is (are) chiral?

(a) $[Fe(C_2O_4)Cl_4]^{2-}$
(b) *cis*-$[Fe(C_2O_4)_2Cl_2]^{2-}$
(c) *trans*-$[Fe(C_2O_4)_2Cl_2]^{2-}$

39. How many geometric isomers are possible for the square-planar complex ion $[Pt(NH_3)(CN)Cl_2]^-$?

40. For a tetrahedral complex of a metal in the first transition series, which of the following statements concerning energies of the 3*d* orbitals is correct?

(a) The five *d* orbitals have the same energy.
(b) The $d_{x^2-y^2}$ and d_{z^2} orbitals are higher in energy than the d_{xz}, d_{yz}, and d_{xy} orbitals.
(c) The d_{xz}, d_{yz}, and d_{xy} orbitals are higher in energy than the $d_{x^2-y^2}$ and d_{z^2} orbitals.

41. A transition metal coordination compound absorbs 425-nm light. What is its color?

(a) red
(b) green
(c) yellow
(d) blue

42. For the low-spin coordination compound $[Fe(en)_2Cl_2]Cl$, identify the following.

(a) the oxidation number of iron
(b) the coordination number for iron
(c) the coordination geometry for iron
(d) the number of unpaired electrons per metal atom
(e) whether the complex is diamagnetic or paramagnetic
(f) the number of geometric isomers

43. For the high-spin coordination compound $Mn(NH_3)_4Cl_2$, identify the following.

(a) the oxidation number of manganese
(b) the coordination number for manganese
(c) the coordination geometry for manganese
(d) the number of unpaired electrons per metal atom
(e) whether the complex is diamagnetic or paramagnetic
(f) the number of geometric isomers

44. A platinum-containing compound, known as Magnus's green salt, has the formula $[Pt(NH_3)_4][PtCl_4]$ (in which both platinum ions are Pt^{2+}). Name the cation and the anion.

45. Early in the 20th century, coordination compounds sometimes were given names based on their colors. Two compounds with the formula $CoCl_3 \cdot 4\ NH_3$ were named praseo-cobalt chloride (*praseo* = green) and violio-cobalt chloride (violet color). We now know that these compounds are octahedral cobalt complexes and that they are *cis* and *trans* isomers. Draw the structures of these two compounds, and name them using systematic nomenclature.

46. Give the formula and name of a square-planar complex of Pt^{2+} with one nitrite ion (NO_2^-, which binds to Pt^{2+} through N), one chloride ion, and two ammonia molecules as ligands. Are isomers possible? If so, draw the structure of each isomer, and tell what type of isomerism is observed.

47. Give the formula of the coordination complex formed from one Co^{3+} ion, two ethylenediamine molecules, one water molecule, and one chloride ion. Is the complex neutral or charged? If charged, give the net charge on the ion.

48. ▲ How many geometric isomers of the complex ion $[Cr(dmen)_3]^{3+}$ can exist? (dmen is the bidentate ligand 1,1-dimethylethylenediamine.)

$(CH_3)_2\ddot{N}CH_2CH_2\ddot{N}H_2$

1,1-Dimethylethylenediamine, dmen

49. ▲ Diethylenetriamine (dien) is capable of serving as a tridentate ligand.

$H_2\ddot{N}CH_2CH_2—\ddot{N}(H)—CH_2CH_2\ddot{N}H_2$

Diethylenetriamine, dien

(a) Draw the structures of *fac*-$Cr(dien)Cl_3$ and *mer*-$Cr(dien)Cl_3$.
(b) Two different geometric isomers of *mer*-$Cr(dien)Cl_2Br$ are possible. Draw the structure for each.
(c) Three different geometric isomers are possible for $[Cr(dien)_2]^{3+}$. Two have the dien ligand in a *fac* configuration, and one has the ligand in a *mer* orientation. Draw the structure of each isomer.

50. From experiment, we know that $[CoF_6]^{3-}$ is paramagnetic and $[Co(NH_3)_6]^{3+}$ is diamagnetic. Using the ligand field model, depict the electron configuration for each ion, and use this model to explain the magnetic property. What can you conclude about the effect of these ligands on the magnitude of Δ_O?

51. Three geometric isomers are possible for $[Co(en)(NH_3)_2(H_2O)_2]^{3+}$. One of the three is chiral; that is, it has a nonsuperimposable mirror image. Draw the structures of the three isomers. Which one is chiral?

52. The square-planar complex $Pt(en)Cl_2$ has chloride ligands in a *cis* configuration. No *trans* isomer is known. Based on the bond lengths and bond angles of carbon and nitrogen in the ethylenediamine ligand, explain why the *trans* compound is not possible.

53. The complex $[Mn(H_2O)_6]^{2+}$ has five unpaired electrons, whereas $[Mn(CN)_6]^{4-}$ has only one. Using the ligand field model, depict the electron configuration for each ion. What can you conclude about the effects of the different ligands on the magnitude of Δ_O?

54. Experiments show that $K_4[Cr(CN)_6]$ is paramagnetic and has two unpaired electrons. The related complex $K_4[Cr(SCN)_6]$ is paramagnetic and has four unpaired electrons. Account for the magnetism of each compound using the ligand field model. Predict where the SCN^- ion occurs in the spectrochemical series relative to CN^-.

55. Give a systematic name or the formula for the following:

(a) $(NH_4)_2[CuCl_4]$
(b) tetraaquadichlorochromium(III) chloride
(c) aquabis(ethylenediamine)thiocyanatocobalt(III) nitrate

56. When $CrCl_3$ dissolves in water, three different species can be obtained.

(a) $[Cr(H_2O)_6]Cl_3$, violet
(b) $[Cr(H_2O)_5Cl]Cl_2$, pale green
(c) $[Cr(H_2O)_4Cl_2]Cl$, dark green

If diethyl ether is added, a fourth complex can be obtained: $Cr(H_2O)_3Cl_3$ (brown). Describe an experiment that will allow you to differentiate these complexes.

57. ▲ The complex ion $[Co(CO_3)_3]^{3-}$, an octahedral complex with bidentate carbonate ions as ligands, has one absorption in the visible region of the spectrum at 640 nm. From this information,

(a) Predict the color of this complex and explain your reasoning.
(b) Is the carbonate ion a weak- or strong-field ligand?
(c) Predict whether $[Co(CO_3)_3]^{3-}$ will be paramagnetic or diamagnetic.

58. The glycinate ion, $H_2NCH_2CO_2^-$, formed by deprotonation of the amino acid glycine, can function as a bidentate ligand, coordinating to a metal through the nitrogen of the amino group and one of the oxygen atoms.

Glycinate ion, a bidentate ligand

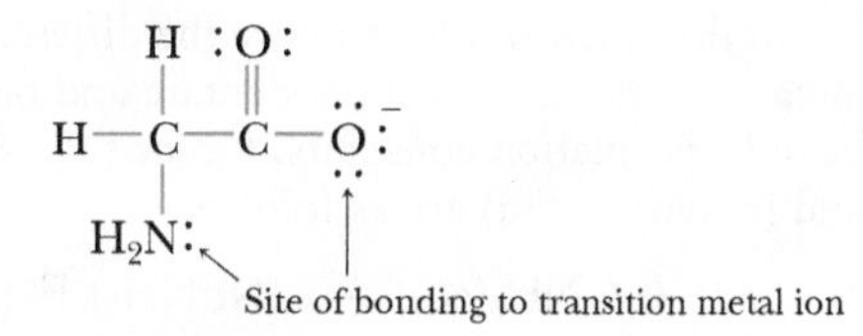

A copper complex of this ligand has the formula $Cu(H_2NCH_2CO_2)_2(H_2O)_2$. For this complex, determine the following:

(a) the oxidation state of copper
(b) the coordination number of copper
(c) the number of unpaired electrons
(d) whether the complex is diamagnetic or paramagnetic

59. ▲ Draw structures for the five possible geometric isomers of $Cu(H_2NCH_2CO_2)_2(H_2O)_2$. Are any of these species chiral? (See the structure of the ligand in Study Question 58.)

60. A manganese compound has the formula $Mn(CO)_x(CH_3)_y$. To find the empirical formula of the compound, you burn 0.225 g of the solid in oxygen and isolate 0.283 g of CO_2 and 0.0290 g of H_2O. What is the empirical formula for the compound? That is, what are the values of x and y?

61. Nickel and palladium both form complexes of the general formula $M(PR_3)_2Cl_2$. (The ligand PR_3 is a phosphine such as $P(C_6H_5)_3$, triphenylphosphine. It is Lewis base.) The nickel(II) compound is paramagnetic whereas the palladium(II) compound is diamagnetic.

(a) Explain the magnetic properties of these compounds.
(b) How many isomers of each compound are expected?

62. ▲ The transition metals form a class of compounds called metal carbonyls, an example of which is the tetrahedral complex $Ni(CO)_4$. Given the following thermodynamic data (at 298 K):

	$\Delta_f H°$ (kJ/mol)	$S°$ (J/K · mol)
Ni(s)	0	29.87
CO(g)	−110.525	+197.674
$Ni(CO)_4$(g)	−602.9	+410.6

(a) Calculate the equilibrium constant for the formation of $Ni(CO)_4$(g) from nickel metal and CO gas.
(b) Is the reaction of Ni(s) and CO(g) product- or reactant-favored at equilibrium?
(c) Is the reaction more or less product-favored at higher temperatures? How could this reaction be used in the purification of nickel metal?

63. Cerium, as noted in *Case Study: The Rare Earths* (page 891), is a relatively abundant lanthanide element that has some important uses. Cerium(IV) oxide, CeO_2, is widely used as a polishing agent for glass. Cerium(III) sulfide, Ce_2S_3, is becoming more widely used as a red pigment to replace cadmium pigments, which are environmentally less desirable.

(a) Give the electron configurations (using the noble gas notation) for Ce, Ce^{3+}, and Ce^{4+}.
(b) Is either Ce^{3+} or Ce^{4+} paramagnetic? If so, how many unpaired electrons does each have?
(c) The solid state structure for CeO_2 is shown below. Describe the unit cell of the compound. How is this structure related to the formula?

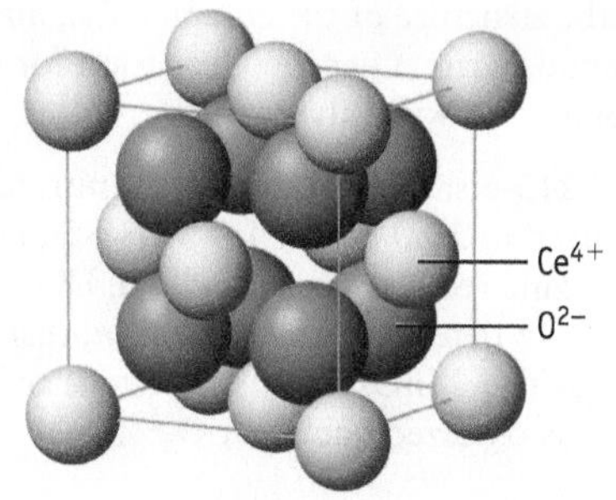

CeO_2

64. Neodymium is a component of powerful magnets.

(a) Neodymium is different than most lanthanides in that it has three common oxidation states: +2, +3, and +4. Give the electron configurations for Nd and its three positive oxidation states.

(b) Are any of the common Nd ions paramagnetic?

(c) Neodymium magnets, which are composed of Nd, Fe, and B, were developed because samarium-based magnets (SmCo) were very costly. What is the empirical formula for the neodymium-based magnet material if it is 26.68% Nd, 72.32% Fe, and the remainder B?

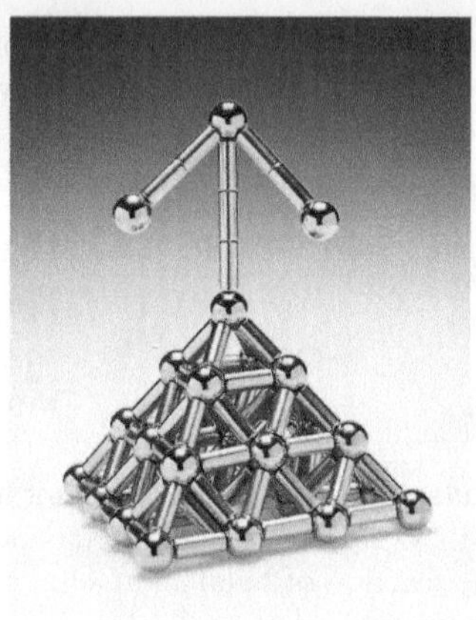
© Cengage Learning/Charles D. Winters

Neodymium magnets

In the Laboratory

65. Two different coordination compounds containing one cobalt(III) ion, five ammonia molecules, one bromide ion, and one sulfate ion exist. The dark violet form (A) gives a precipitate upon addition of aqueous $BaCl_2$. No reaction is seen upon addition of aqueous $BaCl_2$ to the violet-red form (B). Suggest structures for these two compounds, and write a chemical equation for the reaction of (A) with aqueous $BaCl_2$.

66. Three different compounds of chromium(III) with water and chloride ion have the same composition: 19.51% Cr, 39.92% Cl, and 40.57% H_2O. One of the compounds is violet and dissolves in water to give a complex ion with a 3+ charge and three chloride ions. All three chloride ions precipitate immediately as AgCl on adding $AgNO_3$. Draw the structure of the complex ion, and name the compound. Write a net ionic equation for the reaction of this compound with silver nitrate.

67. ▲ A 0.213-g sample of uranyl(VI) nitrate, $UO_2(NO_3)_2$, is dissolved in 20.0 mL of 1.0 M H_2SO_4 and shaken with Zn. The zinc reduces the uranyl ion, UO_2^{2+}, to a uranium ion, U^{n+}. To determine the value of n, this solution is titrated with $KMnO_4$. Permanganate is reduced to Mn^{2+} and U^{n+} is oxidized back to UO_2^{2+}.

(a) In the titration, 12.47 mL of 0.0173 M $KMnO_4$ was required to reach the equivalence point. Use this information to determine the charge on the ion U^{n+}.

(b) With the identity of U^{n+} now established, write a balanced net ionic equation for the reduction of UO_2^{2+} by zinc (assume acidic conditions).

(c) Write a balanced net ionic equation for the oxidation of U^{n+} to UO_2^{2+} by MnO_4^- in acid.

68. Fireworks contain $KClO_3$. To analyze a sample for the amount of $KClO_3$ a chemist first reacts the sample with excess iron(II),

$$ClO_3^-(aq) + 6\ Fe^{2+}(aq) + 6\ H_3O^+(aq) \longrightarrow Cl^-(aq) + 9\ H_2O(\ell) + 6\ Fe^{3+}(aq)$$

and then titrates the resulting solution with Ce^{4+} [in the form of $(NH_4)_2Ce(NO_3)_6$]

$$Fe^{2+}(aq) + Ce^{4+}(aq) \longrightarrow Fe^{3+}(aq) + Ce^{3+}(aq)$$

to determine the quantity of iron(II) that did not react with ClO_3^-. (This is referred to as a "back titration.") Suppose a 0.1342-g sample of a firework was treated with 50.00 mL of 0.0960 M Fe^{2+}. The unreacted Fe^{2+} ions then required 12.99 mL of 0.08362 M Ce^{4+}. What is the weight percent of $KClO_3$ in the original sample?

Summary and Conceptual Questions

The following questions may use concepts from this and previous chapters.

69. The stability of analogous complexes $[ML_6]^{n+}$ (relative to ligand dissociation) is in the general order $Mn^{2+} < Fe^{2+} < Co^{2+} < Ni^{2+} < Cu^{2+} > Zn^{2+}$. This order of ions is called the Irving–Williams series. Look up the values of the formation constants for the ammonia complexes of Co^{2+}, Ni^{2+}, Cu^{2+}, and Zn^{2+} in Appendix K, and verify this statement.

70. ▲ In this question, we explore the differences between metal coordination by monodentate and bidentate ligands. Formation constants, K_f, for $[Ni(NH_3)_6]^{2+}(aq)$ and $[Ni(en)_3]^{2+}(aq)$ are as follows:

$$Ni^{2+}(aq) + 6\ NH_3(aq) \longrightarrow [Ni(NH_3)_6]^{2+}(aq) \qquad K_f = 10^8$$

$$Ni^{2+}(aq) + 3\ en(aq) \longrightarrow [Ni(en)_3]^{2+}(aq) \qquad K_f = 10^{18}$$

The difference in K_f between these complexes indicates a higher thermodynamic stability for the chelated complex, caused by the *chelate effect*. Recall that K is related to the standard free energy of the reaction by $\Delta_rG° = -RT \ln K$ and $\Delta_rG° = \Delta_rH° - T\Delta_rS°$. We know from experiment that $\Delta_rH°$ for the NH_3 reaction is −109 kJ/mol-rxn, and $\Delta_rH°$ for the ethylenediamine reaction is −117 kJ/mol-rxn. Is the difference in $\Delta_rH°$ sufficient to account for the 10^{10} difference in K_f? Comment on the role of entropy in the second reaction.

71. Nitinol, a nickel-titanium alloy, is used in eyeglass frames or orthodontics. If you bend a pair of eyeglass frames out of shape, they snap back to the proper fit. That is the reason nitinol is often called "memory metal."

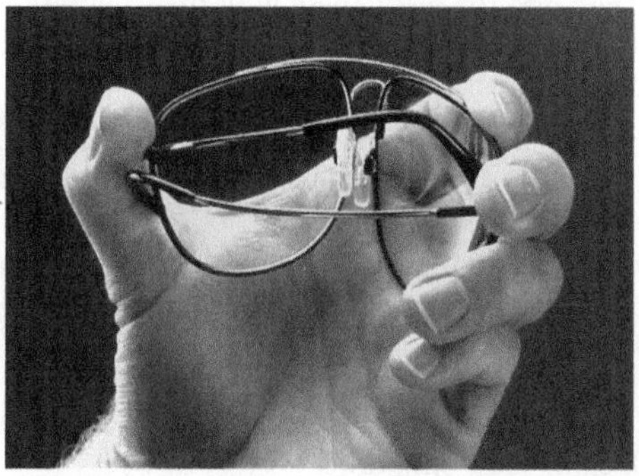

Memory metal is an alloy with roughly the same number of Ni and Ti atoms. When the atoms are arranged in the highly symmetrical austenite phase, the alloy is relatively rigid. In this phase a specific shape is established that will be "remembered." If the alloy is cooled below its "phase transition temperature," it enters a less symmetrical but flexible phase (martensite). Below this transition temperature, the metal is fairly soft and may be bent and twisted out of shape. When warmed above the phase transition temperature, nitinol returns to its original shape. The temperature at which the change in shape occurs varies with small differences in the nickel-to-titanium ratio.

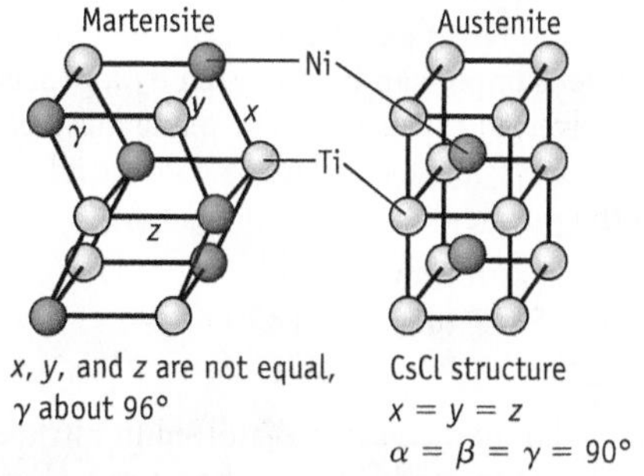

Two phases of nitinol. The austenite form has a structure like CsCl.

(a) What are the dimensions of the austenite unit cell? Assume the Ti and Ni atoms are just touching along the unit cell diagonal. (Atom radii: Ti = 145 pm; Ni = 125 pm.)

(b) Calculate the density of nitinol based on the austenite unit cell parameters. Does the calculated density of the austenite unit cell agree with the reported density of 6.5 g/cm^3?

(c) Are Ti and Ni atoms paramagnetic or diamagnetic?

AP Multiple-Choice Review Questions

Questions 1–5 refer to the following information:

Manganese is added to all steel in small quantities to increase the strength and hardness of the steel. The amount of manganese in a steel sample can be analyzed by a process where the steel is dissolved in nitric acid. The manganese present is then oxidized by potassium periodate to convert all of the manganese into the purple-colored permanganate ion.

The reaction is as follows:

$$2Mn^{2+}(aq) + 5IO_4^-(aq) + 3H_2O(\ell) \rightleftharpoons 2MnO_4^-(aq) + 5IO_3^-(aq) + 6H^+(aq)$$

1. When solid manganese is dissolved in nitric acid, the Mn^{2+} ion is formed. Choose the correct electron configuration for the Mn^{2+} ion.

(A) $[Ar]3d^5$
(B) $[Ar]4s^23d^3$
(C) $[Ar]4s^23d^5$
(D) $[Ar]4s^23d^7$

2. Which element is reduced in the reaction shown above?

(A) hydrogen
(B) iodine
(C) manganese
(D) oxygen

3. If 20.00 mL of 0.100 *M* potassium periodate were needed to react completely with a sample containing Mn^{2+}, how many moles of MnO_4^- would be produced?

(A) 1.00×10^{-4} mole
(B) 2.00×10^{-4} mole
(C) 5.00×10^{-4} mole
(D) 8.00×10^{-4} mole

4. The solution containing the permanganate ion can be analyzed spectrophotometrically to determine the concentration of permanganate.

The colorimeter to be used has only four available wavelengths. Which wavelength should be chosen to get the maximum absorbance of light in the permanganate sample?

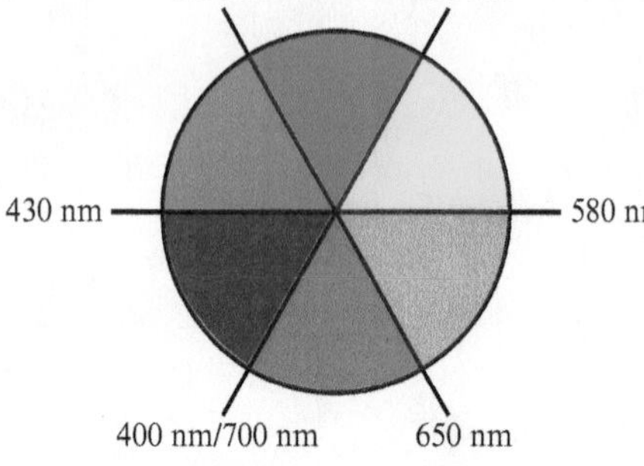

(A) 430 nm
(B) 470 nm
(C) 565 nm
(D) 635 nm

5. Steel is an alloy of iron and other elements. It always contains carbon and manganese and can contain other elements depending on the desired qualities of the steel.

Which correctly lists the type of alloy formed by the carbon and the manganese with the iron in the steel?

	Type of Alloy with Carbon	Type of Alloy with Manganese
(A)	Substitutional	Substitutional
(B)	Substitutional	Interstitial
(C)	Interstitial	Substitutional
(D)	Interstitial	Interstitial

6. A visible light spectrophotometer would best be used in which of these situations?

(A) to determine the isotopic composition of a sample of carbon
(B) to determine the concentration of a solution of copper(II) nitrate
(C) to determine the electron configuration of a sample of nickel
(D) to determine the bonding present in an organic compound

7. Which of these sets of elements show the most similar first ionization energies?

(A) C, N, O, F
(B) F, Cl, Br, I
(C) Fe, Co, Ni, Cu
(D) He, Ne, Ar, Kr

8. The atomic radii of the transition metals do not vary much across a period. How can this best be explained?

(A) Electrons in a transition metal all experience the same nuclear charge.
(B) Electrons are being added to new energy levels, further from the nucleus.
(C) Electrons are added to the same energy level as the number of protons increases.
(D) Electrons are being added to inner *d* orbitals rather than to outer energy levels.

9. Solid platinum is often used to increase the rate of a chemical reaction. How would Pt(*s*) most likely accomplish this?

(A) The solid acts as an enzyme to catalyze biological reactions.
(B) The metal directly participates in the reaction mechanism but is not a reactant or product.
(C) It acts as a site for the reactants to temporarily bind to during the reaction process.
(D) It provides extra energy for the reaction, resulting in more particles having the activation energy.

10. The oxygen in blood is carried by a large iron-containing protein called hemoglobin (Hb). Carbon monoxide also reacts with hemoglobin. The equilibrium constant for the reaction of carbon monoxide with hemoglobin is approximately 200 times larger than that for the reaction of oxygen with hemoglobin. From one to all four of the oxygen molecules can be replaced with a carbon monoxide molecule. The following reaction shows only one oxygen molecule replaced with carbon monoxide.

$$Hb(O_2)_4(aq) + CO(g) \rightleftharpoons Hb(O_2)_3(CO)(aq) + O_2(g)$$

Using this information, which of the following treatments might be highly effective for carbon monoxide poisoning, if started immediately?

(A) Have the patient breathe pure oxygen.
(B) Add additional iron to the patient's diet.
(C) Remove 250 mL of blood from the patient.
(D) Decrease the pressure of the air that the patient is breathing.

Top: John C. Kotz; bottom: © Cengage Learning/Charles D. Winters

Cacao pods on a tree in an island in the Caribbean and the ultimate product.

Carbon: Not Just Another Element

Chapter Outline

THE FOOD OF THE GODS There is a tree that grows in the tropics called *Theobroma cacao,* a name given to it in 1735 by the Swedish biologist Linnæus. The root of the name comes from the Greek language, meaning "food of the gods."

What could be the "food of the gods"? Chocolate, of course.

The history of chocolate can be traced back to Central America. When the Spanish came to the New World, they discovered cocoa beans were highly prized by the natives—100 beans would purchase a slave in 1500 AD—and that a drink made from the beans was quite delicious. The Spanish explorers first took cocoa to Spain in the late 1500s, and by the 17th century chocolate was popular with the Spanish court.

The appeal of chocolate soon spread to the rest of Europe, and, in the late 1800s two Swiss, Henri Nestlé and Daniel Peter, added dried milk to produce the first milk chocolate.

Chapter Goals

See Chapter Goals Revisited (page 942) for Study Questions keyed to these goals.

UNDERSTAND

- General principles of structure and bonding applied to organic compounds.
- Why carbon forms a vast array of diverse chemical compounds.

DO

- Classify organic compounds based on formula and structure.
- Recognize and draw structures of structural isomers and stereo-isomers for carbon compounds.
- Draw structures of molecules, given the name and/or the formula, and name organic compounds using standard nomenclature rules.
- Predict the products of common organic reactions.
- Identify common polymers.
- Relate properties to molecular structure.

REMEMBER

- Common chemical and physical properties of organic compounds.
- Names, structures, and properties of common organic polymers.

This chapter is about organic chemistry, the branch of chemistry that studies molecules based on carbon. Carbon compounds are the basis of all living species on this planet. Chocolate certainly fits into a chapter on organic chemistry, as there are almost 400 organic compounds in chocolate.

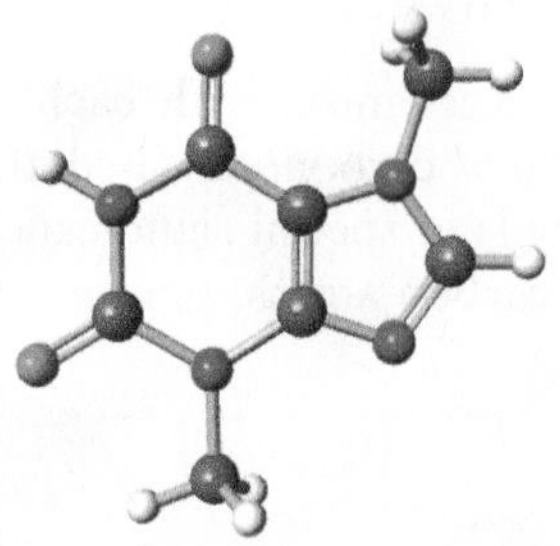

Theobromine, $C_7H_8N_4O_2$, one of many molecules in chocolate and a smooth muscle stimulator.

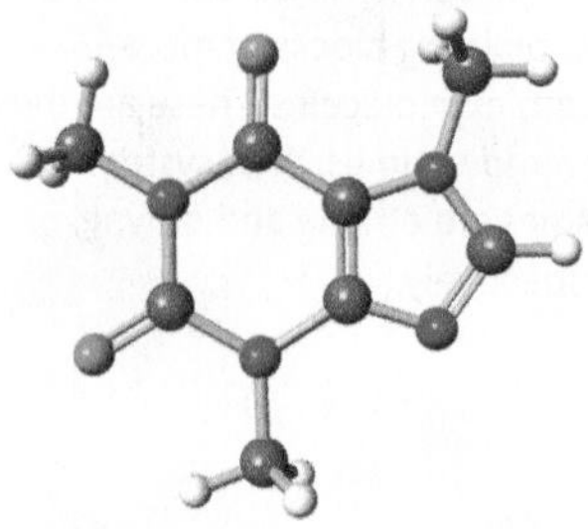

Caffeine, $C_8H_{10}N_4O_2$, like theobromine is a member of a class of compounds called *xanthines.*

A key compound in chocolate is the organic compound theobromine, a bitter alkaloid from the cocoa plant. In spite of the name, there is no bromine in the molecule; its name is derived from the genus of the cocoa plant, *Theobroma*. In medicine, theobromine can be used as a vasodilator, a diuretic, and a heart stimulator. It has even been reputed to be an aphrodisiac! But it can also cause restlessness, tremors, sleeplessness, and anxiety.

Chocolate products usually contain only a few milligrams of theobromine per gram and are quite safe to consume. However, chocolate can be toxic to dogs, and they should not be given chocolate even if they have a sweet tooth.

Theobromine is one of a class of molecules called *xanthines*, a class that includes caffeine. In fact, caffeine is metabolized in the body to theobromine, among other xanthine derivatives.

A Study Question related to this story is: 23.93.

The vast majority of the millions of chemical compounds currently known are organic; that is, they are compounds built on a carbon framework. Organic compounds vary greatly in size and complexity, from the simplest hydrocarbon, methane (CH_4), to molecules made up of many thousands of atoms. As you read this chapter, you will see why the range of possible compounds is huge and why they are so interesting and very often useful.

23-1 Why Carbon?

We begin this discussion of organic chemistry with a question: What features of carbon lead to both the abundance and the complexity of organic compounds? The answers to this question revolve around two main issues: structural diversity and stability.

Structural Diversity

With four electrons in its outer shell, carbon will form four bonds to reach an octet configuration. In contrast, the elements boron and nitrogen generally form three bonds in molecular compounds; oxygen forms two bonds; and hydrogen and the halogens form one bond. With a larger number of bonds comes the opportunity to create more complex structures. This will become increasingly evident in this brief tour of organic chemistry.

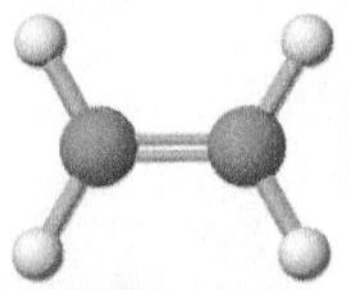

ethene (ethylene), $H_2C{=}CH_2$

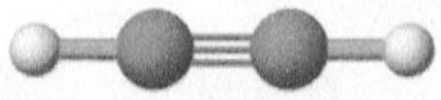

ethyne (acetylene), $HC{\equiv}CH$

Ethylene and acetylene. These two-carbon hydrocarbons can be the building blocks of more complex molecules. These are their common names; their systematic names are ethene and ethyne, respectively.

A carbon atom can reach an octet of electrons in various ways (Figure 23.1):

- *By forming four single bonds.* A carbon atom can bond to four other atoms, which can be either atoms of other elements (often H, N, or O) or other carbon atoms.
- *By forming a double bond and two single bonds.* The carbon atoms in ethylene, $H_2C{=}CH_2$, are linked in this way.
- *By forming two double bonds,* as in carbon dioxide ($O{=}C{=}O$).
- *By forming a triple bond and a single bond*, an arrangement seen in acetylene, $HC{\equiv}CH$.

Recognize, with each of these arrangements, the various possible geometries around carbon: tetrahedral, trigonal-planar, and linear. Carbon's tetrahedral geometry is of special significance because it leads to three-dimensional chains and rings of carbon atoms, as in propane and cyclopentane.

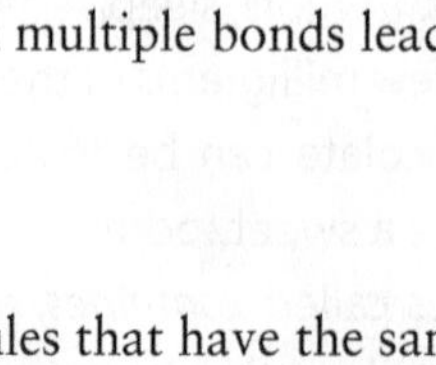

propane, C_3H_8

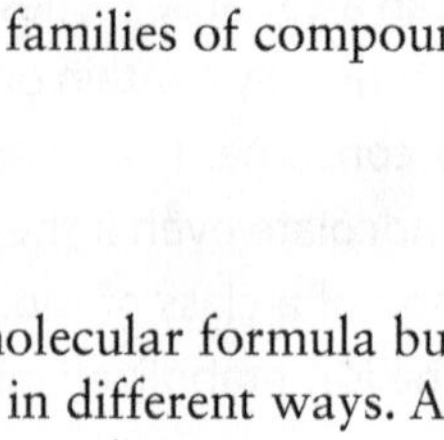

cyclopentane, C_5H_{10}

The ability to form multiple bonds leads to families of compounds with double and triple bonds.

Isomers

Isomers are molecules that have the same molecular formula but that have different atom-to-atom connections or that fill space in different ways. A hallmark of carbon chemistry is that there is a remarkable array of isomers, two major groups being structural isomers and stereoisomers.

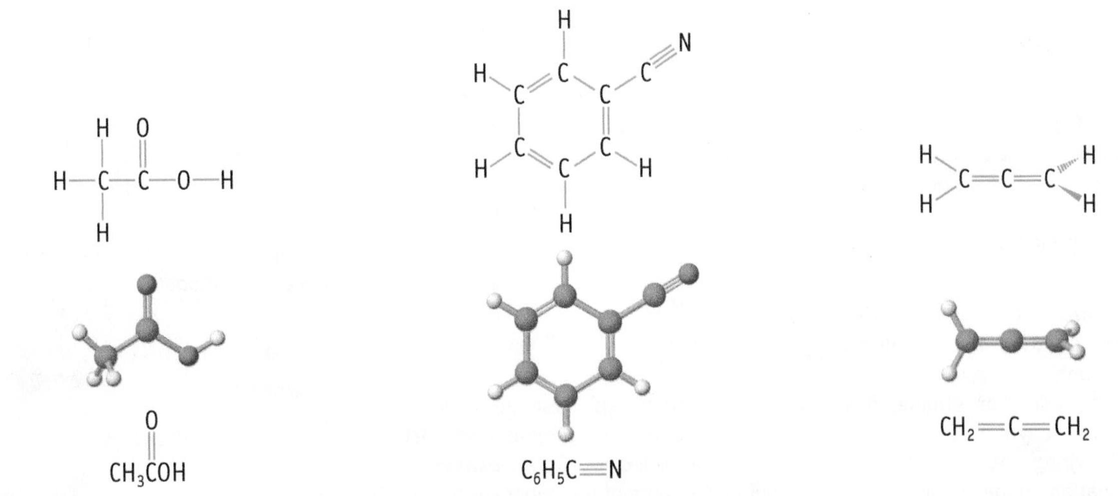

(a) Acetic acid. One carbon atom in this compound is attached to four other atoms by single bonds and has tetrahedral geometry. The second carbon atom, connected by a double bond to one oxygen and by single bonds to the other oxygen and to the first carbon, has trigonal-planar geometry.

(b) Benzonitrile. Six trigonal-planar carbon atoms make up the benzene ring. The seventh C atom, bonded by a single bond to carbon and a triple bond to nitrogen, has a linear geometry.

(c) Carbon is linked by double bonds to two other carbon atoms in C_3H_4, a linear molecule commonly called allene.

FIGURE 23.1 **Ways that carbon atoms bond.**

Structural isomers are species with the same elemental composition but the atoms are linked together in different ways. For example, ethanol and dimethyl ether are structural isomers, as are 1-butene and 2-methylpropene.

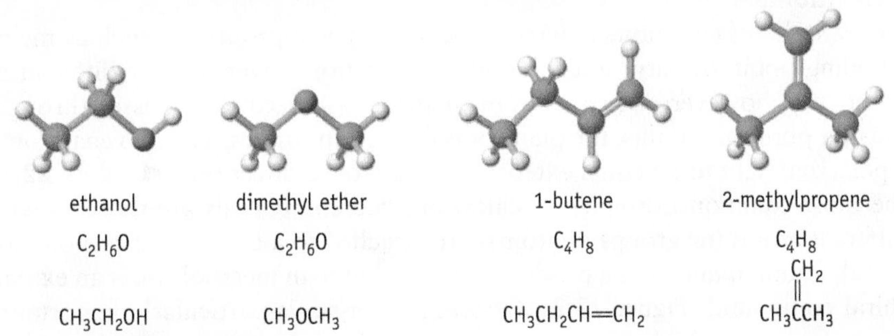

Stereoisomers are compounds with the same attachment of atoms but different orientation in space. There are two types of stereoisomers: geometric isomers and optical isomers.

Cis- and *trans-*2-butene are **geometric isomers**. Geometric isomerism in these compounds occurs as a result of the C=C double bond. *Recall that the carbon atom and the attached groups cannot rotate around a double bond* (page 352). Thus, the geometry around the C=C double bond is fixed in space. *Cis–trans* isomerism occurs if each carbon atom involved in the double bond has two different groups attached. If, on the adjacent carbons, it turns out that identical groups are on the same side of the double bond, then it is a *cis* isomer. If those groups appear on opposite sides, a *trans* isomer is produced.

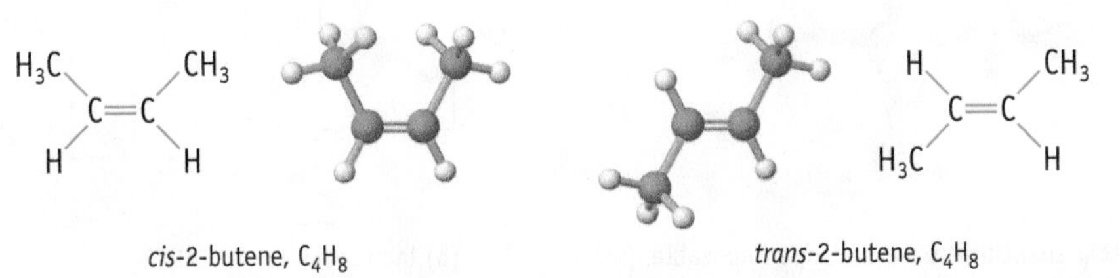

cis-2-butene, C_4H_8 *trans*-2-butene, C_4H_8

A CLOSER LOOK Writing Formulas and Drawing Structures

In Chapter 2, you learned that there are various ways of presenting structures (page 65). It is appropriate to return to this topic as we look at organic compounds. Consider methane and ethane, for example. We can represent these molecules in several ways:

1. *Molecular formula:* CH_4 or C_2H_6. This type of formula gives information on composition only.
2. *Condensed formula:* For ethane, this would typically be written CH_3CH_3. This method of writing the formula gives some information on the way atoms are connected.
3. *Structural formula:* You will recognize this formula as the Lewis structure. An elaboration on the condensed formula in (2), this representation defines more clearly how the atoms are connected, but it fails to describe the shapes of molecules.

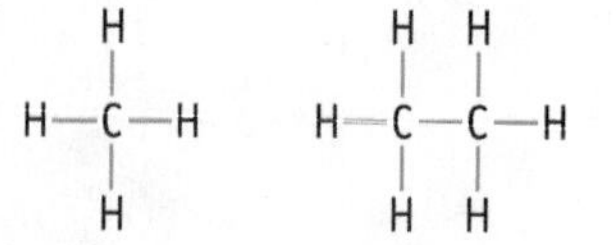

methane, CH_4 ethane, C_2H_6

4. *Perspective drawings:* These drawings are used to convey the three-dimensional nature of molecules. Bonds extending out of the plane of the paper are drawn with wedges, and bonds behind the plane of the paper are represented as dashed wedges (page 65). Using these guidelines, the structures of methane and ethane could be drawn as follows:

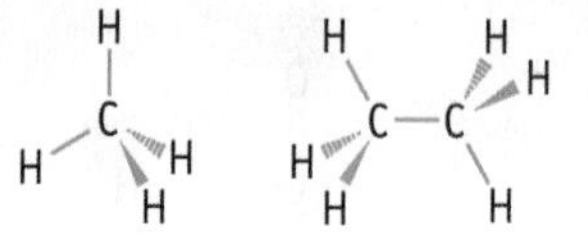

5. *Computer-drawn ball-and-stick and space-filling models.*

ball-and-stick

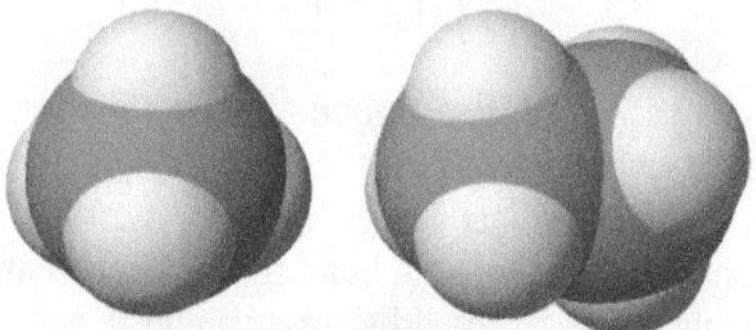

space-filling

Optical isomers are molecules that have nonsuperimposable mirror images (Figure 23.2). Molecules (and other objects) that have nonsuperimposable mirror images are termed **chiral**. Pairs of nonsuperimposable, mirror-image molecules are called **enantiomers**.

Pure samples of enantiomers have the same physical properties, such as melting point, boiling point, density, and solubility in common solvents. They differ in one significant way, however: When a beam of plane-polarized light passes through a solution of a pure enantiomer, the plane of polarization rotates. The two enantiomers rotate polarized light to an equal extent, but in opposite directions (◀ Figure 22.18).

The most common examples of chiral organic compounds are those in which four different atoms (or groups of atoms) are attached to a tetrahedral carbon atom. Lactic acid, found in milk and a product of normal human metabolism, is an example of a chiral compound (Figure 23.2). Optical isomerism is particularly important in

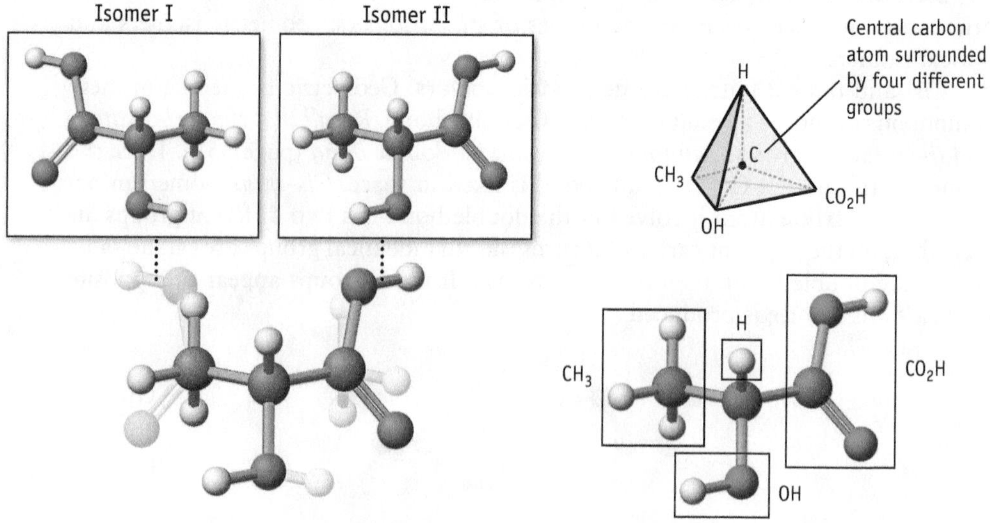

(a) Lactic acid enantiomers are nonsuperimposable, just as your right hand is not superimposable on your left hand.

(b) lactic acid, $CH_3CH(OH)CO_2H$

FIGURE 23.2 Optical isomers. Lactic acid, $CH_3CH(OH)CO_2H$, is produced when milk is fermented to make cheese. It is also found in other sour foods such as sauerkraut and is a preservative in pickled foods such as onions and olives. In our bodies, it is produced by muscle activity and normal metabolism.

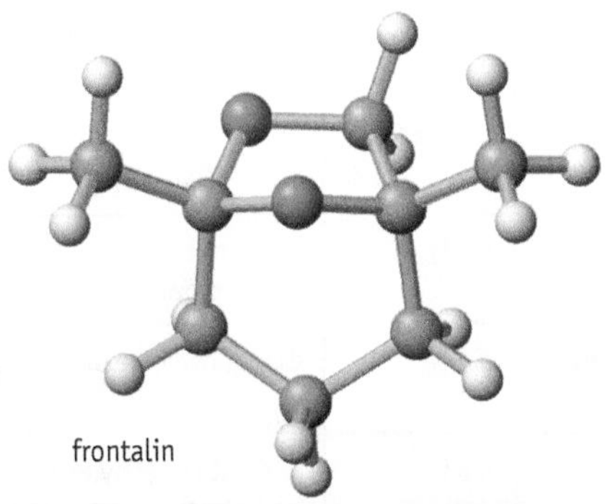

One enantiomer of frontalin.

John C. Kotz

An African elephant. Fluid containing the enantiomers of frontalin flows from a gland between the elephant's eye and ear.

FIGURE 23.3 **Chirality and elephants.** During musth, a time of heightened sexual activity, male elephants produce a secretion containing the enantiomers of frontalin, $C_8H_{14}O_2$. Young males produce more of one enantiomer than the other, whereas older elephants produce a more balanced and more concentrated mixture. The secretion from older elephants repels other males while attracting ovulating female elephants.

amino acids and other biologically important molecules. Among the many interesting examples of optically active compounds is frontalin, produced naturally by male elephants (Figure 23.3).

Chirality and Death Virtually all naturally occurring amino acids, the basis of proteins, are left-handed (see Chapter 24), but right-handed amino acids exist. One such right-handed amino acid has been found to be the toxin in a strain of mushrooms in southern China, and the venom from a bite by a duck-billed platypus is based on a right-handed amino acid. See S. Everts, *Scientific American*, May 2013, pages 78–81.

Stability of Carbon Compounds

Carbon compounds are notable for their resistance to chemical change. This resistance is a result of two things: strong bonds and slow reactions.

Strong bonds are needed for molecules to survive in their environment. Energetic collisions between molecules in gases, liquids, and solutions can provide enough energy to break some bonds, and bonds can be broken if the energy associated with photons of visible and ultraviolet light exceeds the bond energy. Carbon–carbon bonds are relatively strong, however, as are the bonds between carbon and most other atoms. The average C—C bond energy is 346 kJ/mol; the C—H bond energy is 413 kJ/mol; and carbon–carbon double and triple bond energies are even higher (◀ Section 8-9). Contrast these values with bond energies for the Si—Si bond (222 kJ/mol) and the Si—H bond (328 kJ/mol). The consequence of high bond energies for bonds to carbon is that, for the most part, organic compounds do not decompose thermally under normal conditions.

Oxidation of most organic compounds is strongly product-favored, but most organic compounds survive continual and prolonged contact with O_2. The reason is that reactions of most organic compounds with oxygen are very slow. Typically, organic compounds burn only if their combustion is initiated by heat or by a spark. As a consequence, oxidative degradation is not a barrier to the existence of organic compounds.

REVIEW & CHECK FOR SECTION 23-1

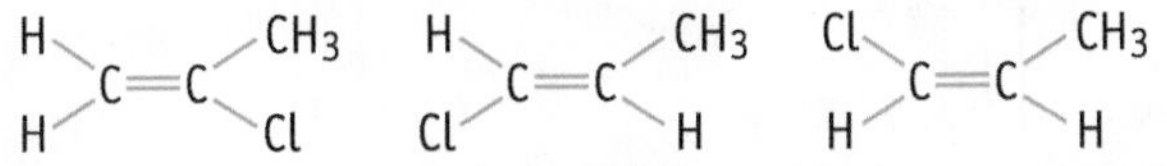

(a) (b) (c)

1. Which pair of the three compounds pictured above are stereoisomers?

   (a) a and b (b) a and c (c) b and c

2. Which pair of compounds are structural isomers?

   (a) a and b (b) b and c

3. How many chiral carbon atoms are there in frontalin (Figure 23.3)?

   (a) 0 (b) 1 (c) 2 (d) 3

Table 23.1 Some Types of Hydrocarbons

Type of Hydrocarbon	Characteristic Features	General Formula	Example
Alkanes	C—C single bonds and all C atoms have four single bonds	C_nH_{2n+2}	CH_4, methane C_2H_6, ethane
Cycloalkanes	C—C single bonds, C atoms arranged in a ring	C_nH_{2n}	C_6H_{12}, cyclohexane
Alkenes	C═C double bond	C_nH_{2n}	$H_2C{=}CH_2$, ethylene
Alkynes	C≡C triple bond	C_nH_{2n-2}	HC≡CH, acetylene
Aromatics	Rings with π bonding extending over several C atoms	—	Benzene, C_6H_6

23-2 Hydrocarbons

Hydrocarbons, compounds made only of carbon and hydrogen, are divided into several subgroups: alkanes, cycloalkanes, alkenes, alkynes, and aromatic compounds (Table 23.1). We begin our discussion by considering alkanes and cycloalkanes, compounds in which each carbon atom is linked with four single bonds to other carbon atoms or to hydrogen.

Alkanes

Petroleum Petroleum is a mixture of alkanes and other hydrocarbons. The petroleum industry is described briefly in Section 20-4.

Alkanes have the general formula C_nH_{2n+2}, with n having integer values (Table 23.2). Formulas of specific compounds can be generated from this formula, the first four of which are CH_4 (methane), C_2H_6 (ethane), C_3H_8 (propane), and C_4H_{10} (butane) (Figure 23.4). Methane has four hydrogen atoms arranged tetrahedrally around a single carbon atom. Replacing a hydrogen atom in methane by a —CH_3 group gives ethane. If an H atom of ethane is replaced by yet another —CH_3 group, propane results. Butane is derived from propane by replacing an H atom of one of the chain-ending carbon atoms with a —CH_3 group. In all of these compounds, each C atom is attached to four other atoms, either C or H, so alkanes are often called **saturated compounds.**

Table 23.2 Selected Hydrocarbons of the Alkane Family, C_nH_{2n+2}*

Name	Molecular Formula	State at Room Temperature
Methane Ethane Propane Butane	CH_4 C_2H_6 C_3H_8 C_4H_{10}	Gas
Pentane Hexane Heptane Octane Nonane Decane	C_5H_{12} (pent- = 5) C_6H_{14} (hex- = 6) C_7H_{16} (hept- = 7) C_8H_{18} (oct- = 8) C_9H_{20} (non- = 9) $C_{10}H_{22}$ (dec- = 10)	Liquid
Octadecane Eicosane	$C_{18}H_{38}$ (octadec- = 18) $C_{20}H_{42}$ (eicos- = 20)	Solid

*This table lists only selected alkanes. At 25 °C straight-chain alkanes with 11–17 C atoms are liquid. Those with more than 17 C atoms are solid.

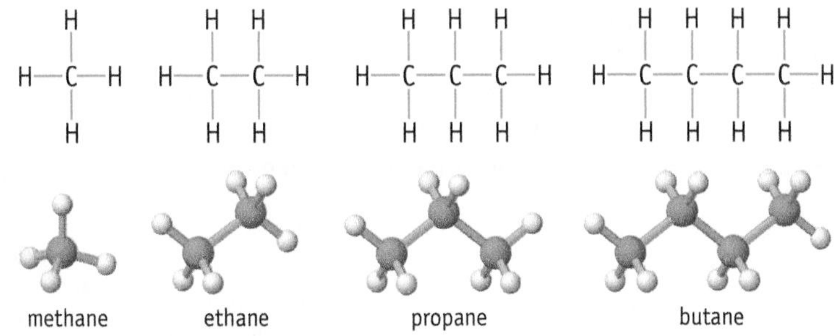

FIGURE 23.4 **Alkanes.** The lowest-molar-mass alkanes, all gases under normal conditions, are methane, ethane, propane, and butane.

Structural Isomers

Structural isomers are possible for all alkanes larger than propane. For example, there are two structural isomers for C_4H_{10} and three for C_5H_{12}. As the number of carbon atoms in an alkane increases, the number of possible structural isomers greatly increases; there are five isomers possible for C_6H_{14}, nine isomers for C_7H_{16}, 18 for C_8H_{18}, 75 for $C_{10}H_{22}$, and 1858 for $C_{14}H_{30}$.

To recognize the isomers corresponding to a given formula, keep in mind the following points:

- Each alkane has a framework of tetrahedral carbon atoms, and each carbon has four single bonds.
- An effective approach to deriving isomer structures is to create a framework of carbon atoms and then fill the remaining positions around carbon with H atoms so that each C atom has four bonds.
- Nearly free rotation occurs around carbon–carbon single bonds. Therefore, when atoms are assembled to form the skeleton of an alkane, the emphasis is on how carbon atoms are attached to one another and not on how they might lie relative to one another in the plane of the paper.

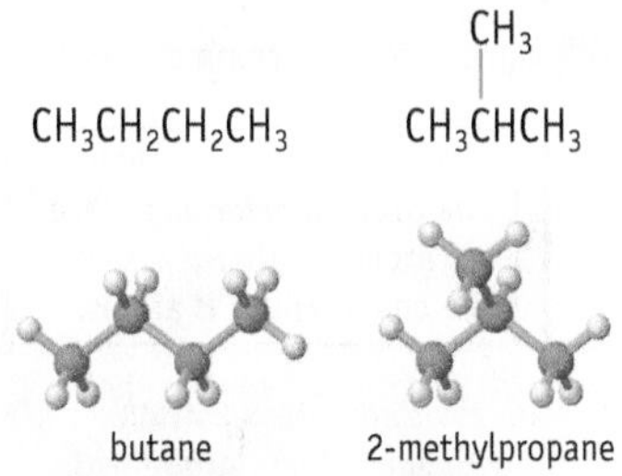

Structural isomers of butane, C_4H_{10}

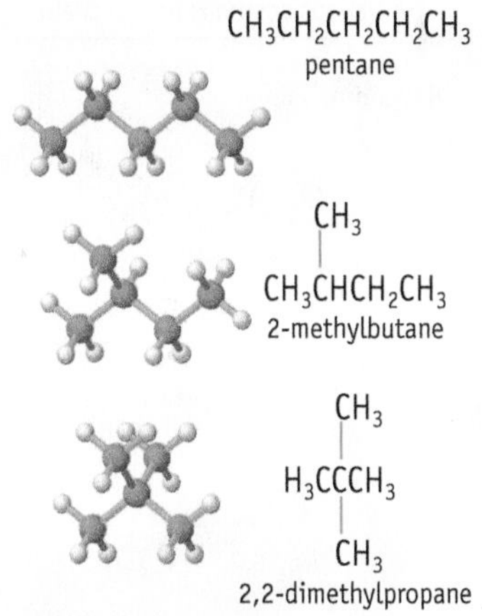

Structural isomers of pentane, C_5H_{12}

EXAMPLE 23.1

Drawing Structural Isomers of Alkanes

Problem Draw structures of the five isomers of C_6H_{14}. Are any of these isomers chiral?

What Do You Know? Each structure must have six carbon and 14 hydrogen atoms. There must be four single bonds to each carbon atom, and each hydrogen will form one bond.

Strategy Focus first on the different frameworks that can be built from six carbon atoms. Having created a carbon framework, fill hydrogen atoms into the structure so that each carbon has four bonds.

Solution

Step 1. Placing six carbon atoms in a chain gives the framework for the first isomer. Now fill in hydrogen atoms: three on the carbons on the ends of the chain and two on each of the carbons in the middle. You have created the first isomer, hexane.

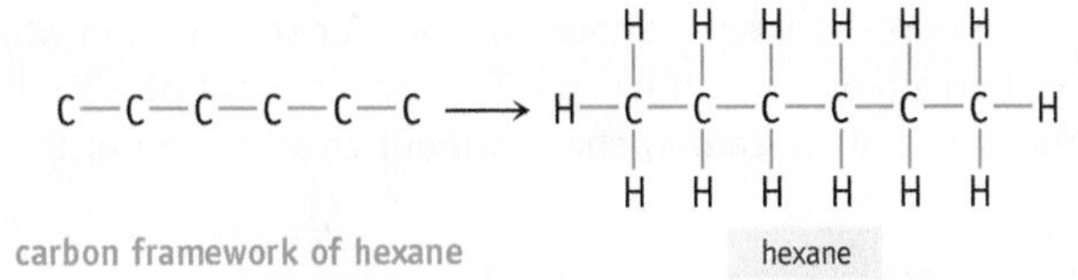

Strategy Map 23.1

PROBLEM

Draw ***structural isomers*** of an **alkane.**

↓

DATA/INFORMATION

- The **formula** is known, so the *longest possible* **C atom chain** is known.

STEP 1. Draw the ***longest*** **C atom chain** possible.

↓

Simplest **straight-chain alkane**

STEP 2. Draw C atom chain ***one atom shorter*** and place a C atom at other places on the chain. Fill in **H** atoms.

↓

Alkane with **one less C atom** but with ***substituent group*** with **one C atom**

STEP 3. Draw ***shorter chains*** and place remaining C atoms at various positions on the chain.

↓

Remaining isomers

Step 2. Draw a chain of five carbon atoms, then add the sixth carbon atom to one of the carbon atoms in the middle of this chain. (Adding it to a carbon at the end of the chain gives a six-carbon chain, the same framework drawn in Step 1.) Two different carbon frameworks can be built from the five-carbon chain, depending on whether the sixth carbon is linked to the 2 or 3 position. For each of these frameworks, fill in the hydrogens.

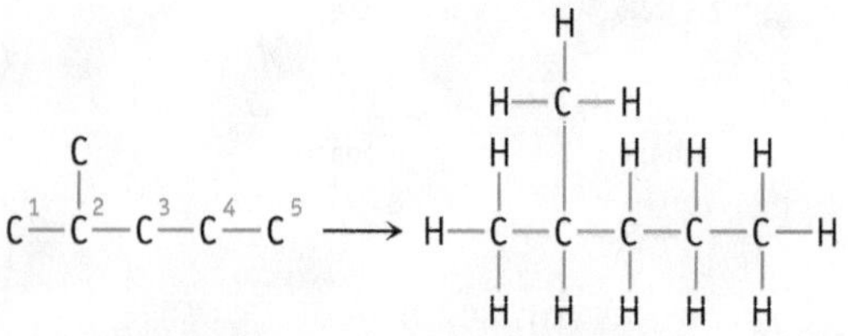

carbon framework of methylpentane isomers

2-methylpentane

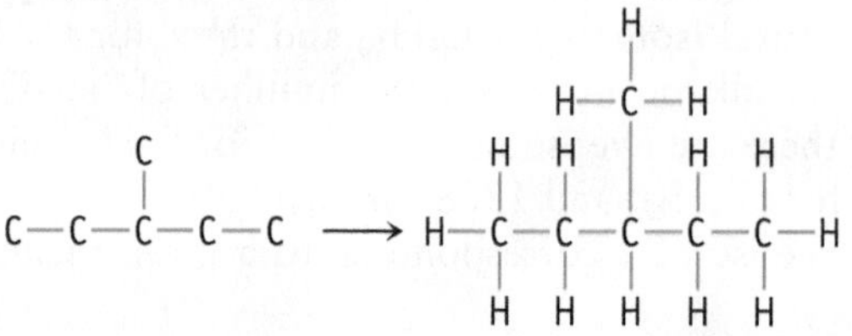

3-methylpentane

Step 3. Draw a chain of four carbon atoms. Add in the two remaining carbons, again being careful not to extend the chain length. Two different structures are possible: one with the remaining carbon atoms in the 2 and 3 positions, and another with both extra carbon atoms attached at the 2 position. Fill in the 14 hydrogens. You have now drawn the fourth and fifth isomers.

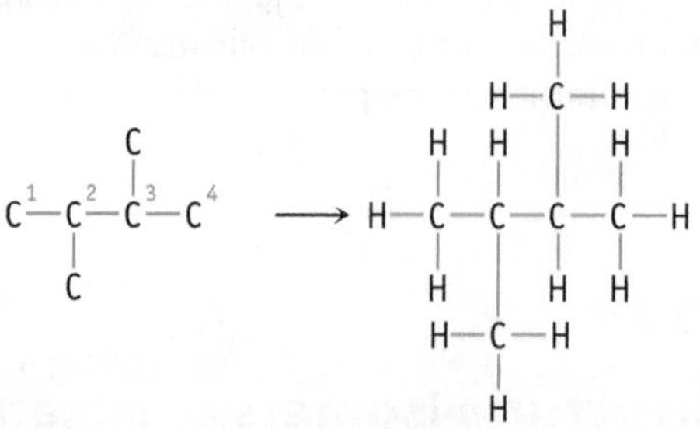

carbon atom frameworks for dimethylbutane isomers

2,3-dimethylbutane

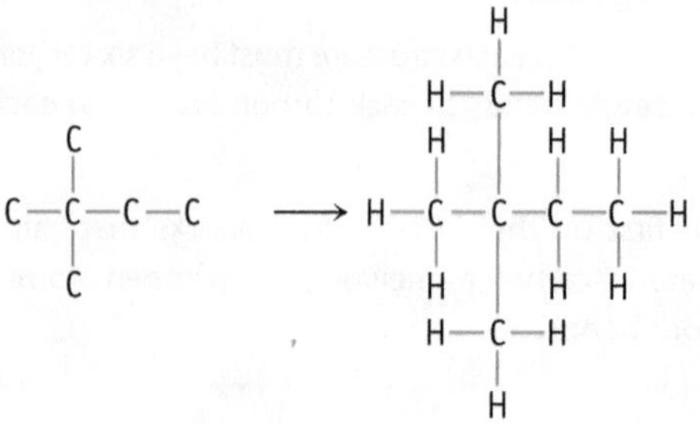

2,2-dimethylbutane

None of the isomers of C_6H_{14} is chiral. *To be chiral, a compound must have at least one C atom with four different groups attached.* This condition is not met in any of these isomers.

Think about Your Answer Should we look for structures in which the longest chain is three carbon atoms? Try it, but you will see that it is not possible to add the three remaining carbons to a three-carbon chain without creating one of the carbon chains

Naming Guidelines For more details on naming organic compounds, see Appendix E.

already drawn in a previous step. Thus, we have completed the analysis, with five isomers of this compound being identified.

Names have been given to each of these compounds. See the text that follows this Example, and see Appendix E for guidelines on nomenclature.

Check Your Understanding

(a) Draw the nine isomers having the formula C_7H_{16}. (*Hint:* There is one structure with a seven-carbon chain, two structures with six-carbon chains, five structures with a five-carbon chain [one is illustrated in the margin], and one structure with a four-carbon chain.)

(b) Identify the isomers of C_7H_{16} that are chiral.

Chirality in Alkanes To be chiral, *a compound must have at least one C atom attached to four* ***different*** *groups.* Thus, the C_7H_{16} isomer here is chiral.

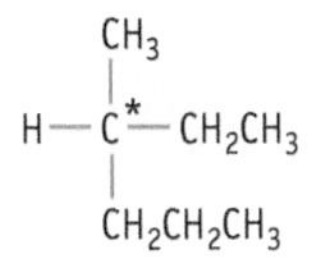

The center of chirality is often indicated with an asterisk.

Naming Alkanes

With so many possible isomers for a given alkane, chemists need a systematic way of naming them. The guidelines for naming alkanes and their derivatives follow:

- The names of alkanes end in "-ane."
- When naming a specific alkane, the root of the name corresponds to the longest carbon chain in the compound. (The names of alkanes with chains of 1 to 10 carbon atoms are given in Table 23.2. After the first four compounds, the names are derived from Greek and Latin numbers—pentane, hexane, heptane, octane, nonane, decane—and this regular naming continues for higher alkanes.)
- Substituent groups on a hydrocarbon chain are identified by a name and the position of substitution in the carbon chain; this information precedes the root of the name. The position is indicated by a number that refers to the carbon atom to which the substituent is attached. Numbering of the carbon atoms in a chain should begin at the end of the carbon chain that allows the first substituent encountered to have the lowest possible number. (If there is no distinction at this point, then number the carbon atoms so that the second substituent group has the lowest number.)
- Names of hydrocarbon substituents, called **alkyl groups**, are derived from the name of the hydrocarbon. The group $—CH_3$, derived by taking a hydrogen from methane, is called the *methyl* group; the $—C_2H_5$ group is the *ethyl* group.
- If two or more of the same substituent groups are present in the molecule, the prefixes di-, tri-, and tetra- are added. When different substituent groups are present, they are generally listed in alphabetical order.

Systematic and Common Names The IUPAC (International Union of Pure and Applied Chemistry) has formulated rules for systematic names, which are generally used in this book (see Appendix). However, many organic compounds are known by common names. For example, 2,2-dimethylpropane is also called neopentane.

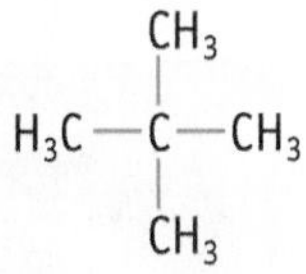

2,2-dimethylpropane

This isomer of C_5H_{12} has a three-carbon chain with two $—CH_3$ groups on the second C atom of the chain. Thus, its name is based on propane, and both $—CH_3$ groups are located at the 2 position.

PROBLEM SOLVING TIP 23.1
Drawing Structural Formulas

An error students sometimes make is to suggest that the three carbon skeletons drawn here are different. They are, in fact, the same. All are five-carbon chains with another C atom in the 2 position.

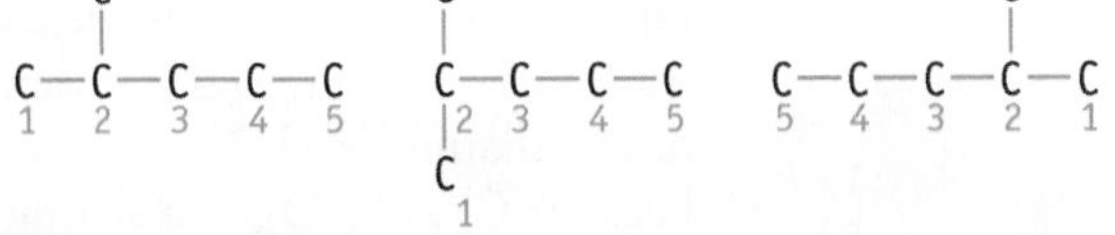

Remember that Lewis structures do not indicate the geometry of molecules.

EXAMPLE 23.2

Naming Alkanes

Problem Give the systematic name for

```
CH3         CH2CH3
 |           |
CH3CHCH2CH2CHCH2CH3
```

What Do You Know? You know the condensed formula and can recognize that the compound is an alkane. You also know the rules for naming alkanes.

Strategy (a) Identify the longest carbon chain and base the name of the compound on that alkane. (b) Identify the substituent groups on the chain and their locations. (c) When there are two or more substituents (the groups attached to the chain), number the parent chain from the end that gives the lower number to the substituent encountered first. (d) If the substituents are different, list them in alphabetical order.

Solution Here, the longest chain has seven C atoms, so the root of the name is *heptane.* There is a methyl group (—CH_3) on C-2 and an ethyl group (—C_2H_5) on C-5. Giving the substituents in alphabetical order and numbering the chain from the end having the methyl group, the systematic name is 5-ethyl-2-methylheptane.

Think about Your Answer Notice that the carbon atoms in the longest chain are numbered so that the lower number is given to the substituent encountered first.

Check Your Understanding

Name the nine isomers of C_7H_{16} in "Check Your Understanding" in Example 23.1.

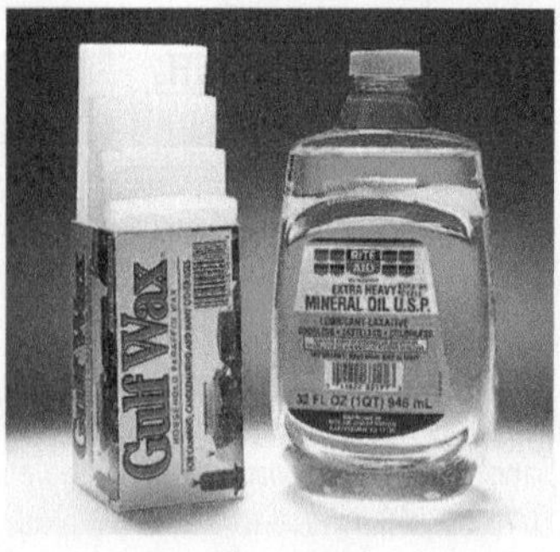

©Cengage Learning/Charles D. Winters

FIGURE 23.5 Paraffin wax and mineral oil. These common consumer products are mixtures of alkanes.

Properties of Alkanes

Methane, ethane, propane, and butane are gases at room temperature and pressure, whereas the higher-molar-mass compounds are liquids or solids (see Table 23.2). An increase in melting point and boiling point with molar mass in a series of similar compounds is a general observation (◀ Sections 11-4 and 11-6).

You already know about alkanes in a nonscientific context because several are common fuels. Natural gas, gasoline, kerosene, fuel oils, and lubricating oils are all mixtures of various alkanes. White mineral oil is also a mixture of alkanes, as is paraffin wax (Figure 23.5).

Pure alkanes are colorless and odorless. All are insoluble in water, a property typical of nonpolar compounds. Low polarity is expected for alkanes because the electronegativities of carbon ($\chi = 2.5$) and hydrogen ($\chi = 2.2$) are not greatly different (◀ Section 8-8).

All alkanes burn readily in air to give CO_2 and H_2O in very exothermic reactions. This is, of course, the reason they are widely used as fuels.

$$CH_4(g) + 2\ O_2(g) \rightarrow CO_2(g) + 2\ H_2O(\ell) \qquad \Delta_rH° = -890.3\ \text{kJ/mol-rxn}$$

Other than in combustion reactions, alkanes exhibit relatively low chemical reactivity. One reaction that does occur, however, is the replacement of the hydrogen atoms of an alkane by chlorine atoms on reaction with Cl_2. It is formally an oxidation because Cl_2, like O_2, is a strong oxidizing agent. These reactions, which can be initiated by ultraviolet radiation, are free radical reactions (◀ Section 14-6). Highly reactive Cl atoms are formed from Cl_2 under ultraviolet (UV) radiation. Reaction of methane with Cl_2 under these conditions proceeds in a series of steps, eventually yielding CCl_4, commonly known as carbon tetrachloride. (HCl is the other product of these reactions.)

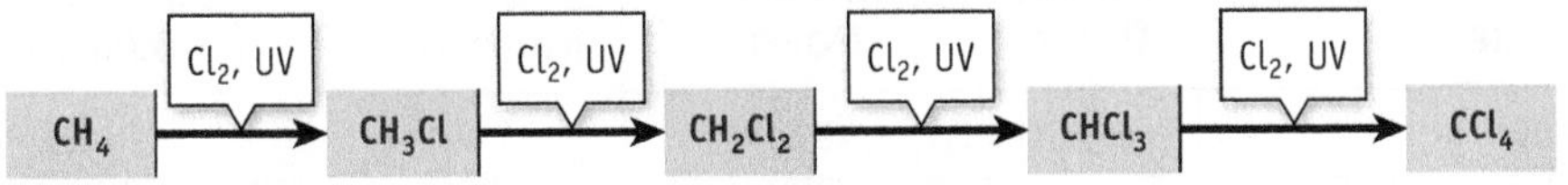

Systematic name:	chloromethane	dichloromethane	trichloromethane	tetrachloromethane
Common name:	methyl chloride	methylene chloride	chloroform	carbon tetrachloride

The last three compounds are used as solvents, albeit infrequently because of their toxicity.

Cycloalkanes, C_nH_{2n}

Cycloalkanes are constructed with tetrahedral carbon atoms joined together to form a ring. Cyclopropane and cyclobutane are the simplest cycloalkanes, although the bond angles in these species are much less than 109.5°. Chemists refer to these compounds as *strained hydrocarbons* because an unfavorable geometry is imposed around carbon. One of the features of strained hydrocarbons is that the C—C bonds are weaker and the molecules readily undergo ring-opening reactions that relieve the bond angle strain.

The most common cycloalkane is cyclohexane, C_6H_{12}, which has a nonplanar ring with six —CH_2 groups. If the carbon atoms in this compound were in the form of a regular hexagon with all carbon atoms in one plane, the C—C—C bond angles would be 120°. To have tetrahedral bond angles of 109.5° around each C atom, the ring has to pucker. The C_6 ring is flexible and exists in two interconverting forms (see *A Closer Look: Flexible Molecules*).

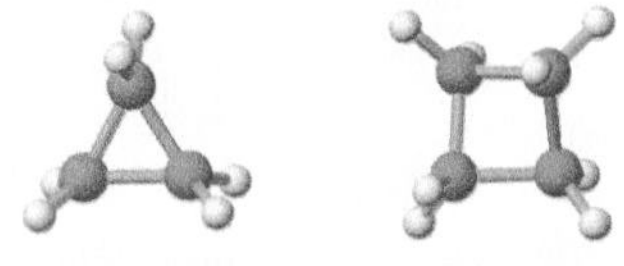

cyclopropane, C_3H_6 cyclobutane, C_4H_8

Cyclopropane and cyclobutane. Cyclopropane was at one time used as a general anesthetic in surgery. However, its explosive nature when mixed with oxygen soon eliminated this application.

Alkenes and Alkynes

The diversity seen for alkanes is repeated with **alkenes**, hydrocarbons with one or more C=C double bonds. The presence of a double bond adds two features missing in alkanes: the possibility of geometric isomerism and a higher degree of reactivity.

A CLOSER LOOK | Flexible Molecules

Most organic molecules are flexible; that is, they can twist and bend in various ways. Few molecules better illustrate this behavior than cyclohexane. Two structures are possible: "chair" and "boat" forms, which can interconvert by partial rotation of several bonds.

The more stable structure is the chair form, which allows the hydrogen atoms to remain as far apart as possible. A side view of this form of cyclohexane reveals two sets of hydrogen atoms in this molecule. Six hydrogen atoms, called the *equatorial hydrogens*, lie in a plane around the carbon ring. The other six hydrogens are positioned above and below the plane and are called *axial hydrogens*. Flexing the ring (a rotation around the C—C single bonds) moves the hydrogen atoms between axial and equatorial environments.

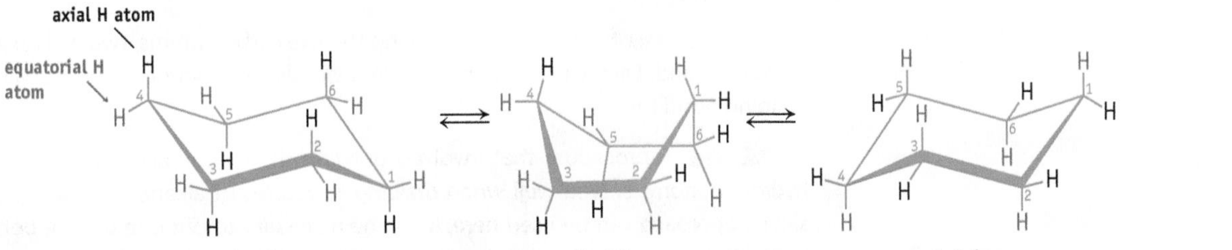

Table 23.3 Properties of Butene Isomers

NAME	BOILING POINT	MELTING POINT	DIPOLE MOMENT (D)	$\Delta_f H°$ (GAS) (kJ/mol)
1-Butene	−6.26 °C	−185.4 °C	—	−0.63
2-Methylpropene	−6.95 °C	−140.4 °C	0.503	−17.9
Cis-2-butene	3.71 °C	−138.9 °C	0.253	−7.7
Trans-2-butene	0.88 °C	−105.5 °C	0	−10.8

The general formula for alkenes with one double bond is C_nH_{2n}. The first two members of the series are ethene, C_2H_4 (common name, ethylene), and propene, C_3H_6 (common name, propylene). Only a single structure can be drawn for these compounds. As with alkanes, the occurrence of isomers begins with species containing four carbon atoms. Four alkene isomers have the formula C_4H_8, and each has distinct chemical and physical properties (Table 23.3). There are three structural isomers, one of which (2-butene, $CH_3CH{=}CHCH_3$) exists as stereoisomers.

C_2H_4
Systematic name: ethene
Common name: ethylene

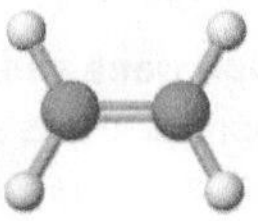

C_3H_6
Systematic name: propene
Common name: propylene

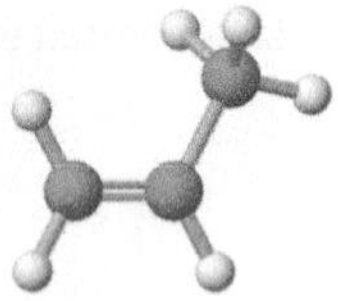

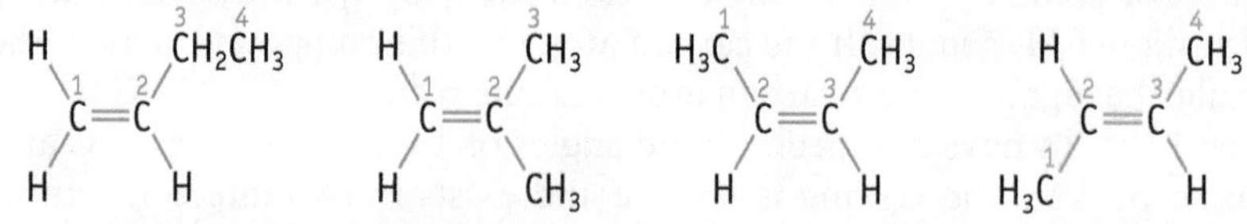

1-butene   2-methylpropene   *cis*-2-butene   *trans*-2-butene

Alkene names end in "-ene." As with alkanes, the root for the name of an alkene is determined by the longest carbon chain that contains the double bond. The position of the double bond is indicated with a number, and, when appropriate, the prefix *cis* or *trans* is added.

Three of the C_4H_8 isomers have four-carbon chains and so are butenes. One has a three-carbon chain and is a propene. Notice that the carbon chain is numbered from the end that gives the double bond the lowest number. In the first isomer at the left, the double bond is between C atoms 1 and 2, so the name is 1-butene and not 3-butene.

EXAMPLE 23.3

Determining Isomers of Alkenes from a Formula

Problem Draw structures for the six possible alkene isomers with the formula C_5H_{10}. Give the systematic name of each.

What Do You Know? When linking the five carbon atoms, two will be joined with a double bond. Each carbon must have four bonds, and hydrogen atoms will fill the remaining positions.

Strategy A procedure that involved drawing the carbon skeleton and then adding hydrogen atoms served well when drawing structures of alkanes (Example 23.1), and a similar approach can be used here. It will be necessary to put one double bond into the framework and to be alert for *cis-trans* isomerism.

Solution

Step 1. A five-carbon chain with one double bond can be constructed in two ways. *Cis–trans* isomers are possible for 2-pentene.

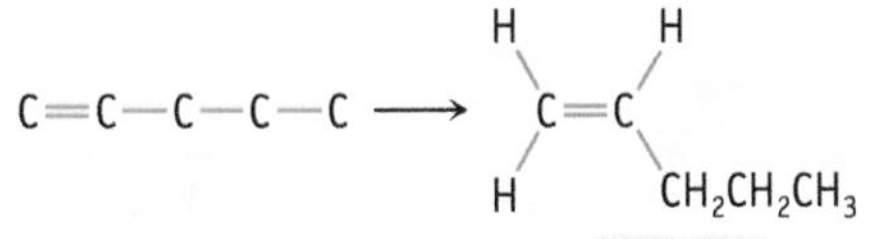

1-pentene

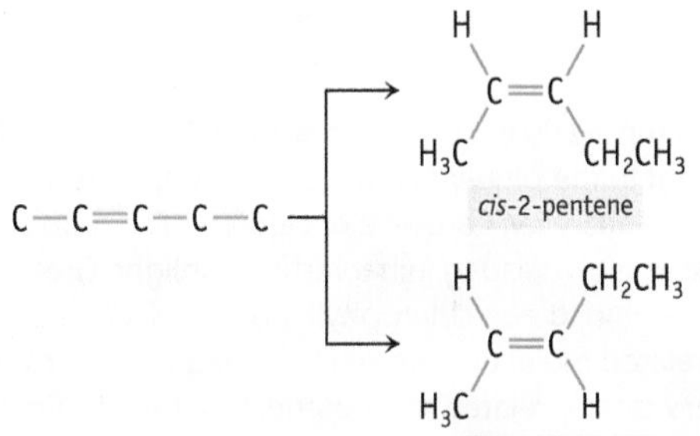

cis-2-pentene

trans-2-pentene

Step 2. Draw the possible four-carbon chains containing a double bond. Add the fifth carbon atom to either the 2 or 3 position. When all the possible combinations are found, fill in the hydrogen atoms. This results in three more structures:

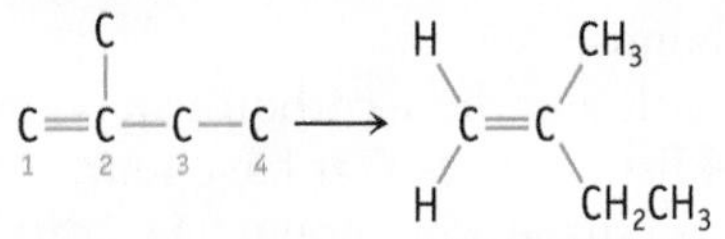

2-methyl-1-butene

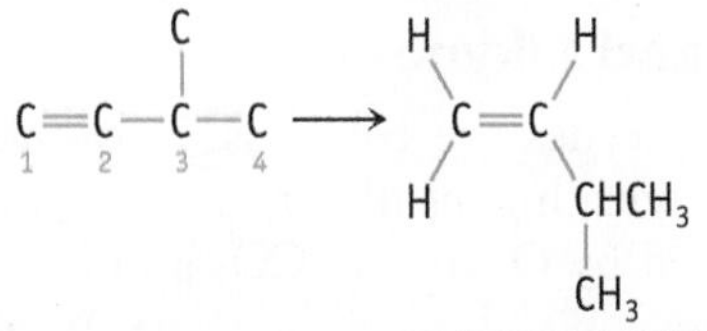

3-methyl-1-butene

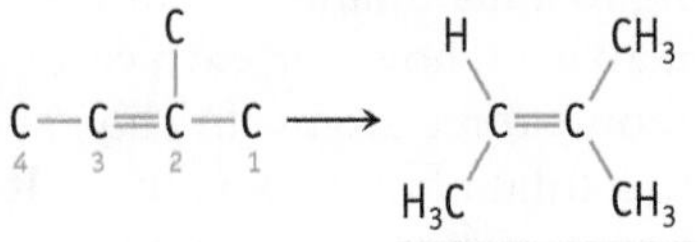

2-methyl-2-butene

Think about Your Answer It is important to be very organized in your approach when drawing isomers. You should look carefully to see that each structure is unique, that is, that no two are the same.

Check Your Understanding

There are 17 possible alkene isomers with the formula C_6H_{12}. Draw structures of the five isomers in which the longest chain has six carbon atoms, and give the name of each. Are any of these isomers chiral? (There are also eight isomers in which the longest chain has five carbon atoms, and four isomers in which the longest chain has four carbon atoms. How many can you find?)

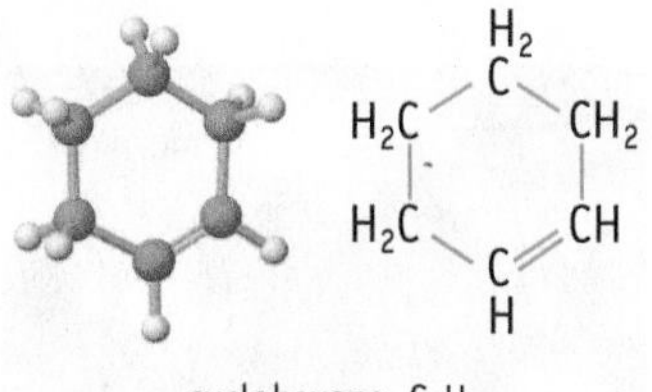

cyclohexene, C_6H_{10}

$H_2C{=}CHCH{=}CH_2$

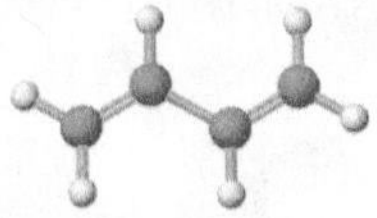

1,3-butadiene, C_4H_6

Cycloalkenes and dienes. Cyclohexene, C_6H_{10} (*top*) and 1,3-butadiene (C_4H_6) (*bottom*).

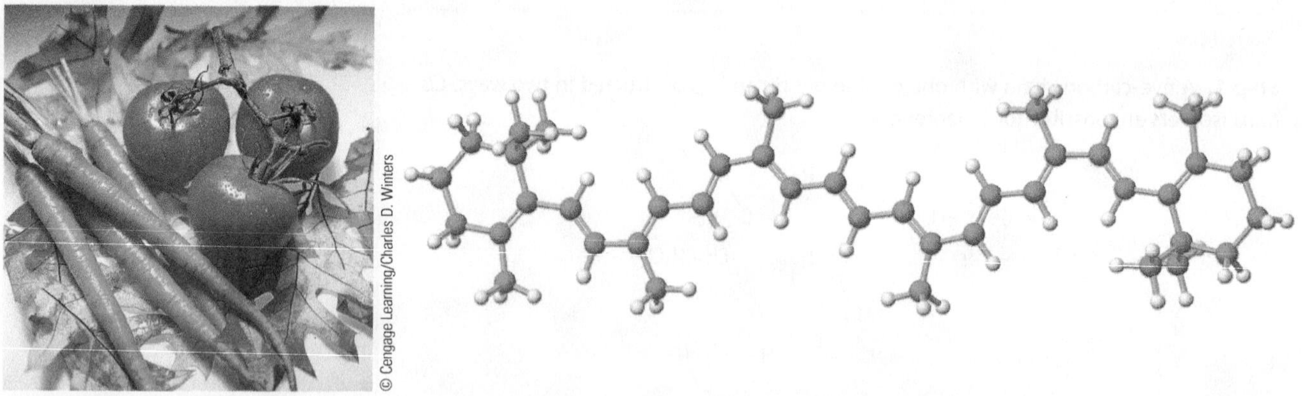

FIGURE 23.6 **Carotene, a naturally occurring compound with 11 C=C bonds.** The π electrons can be excited by visible light in the blue-violet region of the spectrum. As a result, carotene appears orange-yellow to the observer. Carotene or carotene-like molecules are partnered with chlorophyll in nature in the role of assisting in harvesting sunlight. Green leaves have a high concentration of carotene. In autumn, green chlorophyll molecules are destroyed, and the yellows and reds of carotene and related molecules are seen. The red color of tomatoes, for example, comes from a molecule very closely related to carotene. As a tomato ripens, its chlorophyll disintegrates, and the green color is replaced by the red of the carotene-like molecule.

Hydrocarbons exist that have two or more double bonds. Butadiene, for example, has two double bonds and is known as a *diene*. Many natural products have numerous double bonds (Figure 23.6). There are also cyclic hydrocarbons, such as cyclohexene, with double bonds.

Alkynes, compounds with a carbon–carbon triple bond, have the general formula (C_nH_{2n-2}). Table 23.4 lists alkynes that have four or fewer carbon atoms. The first member of this family is ethyne (common name, acetylene), a gas used as a fuel in metal cutting torches.

An oxy-acetylene torch. The reaction of ethyne (acetylene) with oxygen produces a very high temperature. Oxy-acetylene torches, used in welding, take advantage of this fact.

Properties of Alkenes and Alkynes

Like alkanes, alkenes and alkynes are colorless. Low–molar-mass compounds are gases, whereas compounds with higher molar masses are liquids or solids. Alkenes and alkynes are also oxidized by O_2 to give CO_2 and H_2O.

Alkenes and alkynes have an elaborate chemistry. We get some insight into their chemical behavior by knowing they are called **unsaturated compounds**. Carbon atoms are capable of bonding to a maximum of four other atoms, and they do so in alkanes and cycloalkanes. In alkenes, however, each carbon atom linked by a double bond is bonded to a total of only three atoms. In alkynes, each carbon atom linked by a triple bond is bonded to a total of only two atoms. It is possible to increase the number of groups attached to a carbon atom in an alkene or alkyne by **addition reactions**, in which molecules with the general formula X—Y (such as hydrogen, halogens, hydrogen halides, and water) add across the carbon–carbon double or

Table 23.4 Some Simple Alkynes C_nH_{2n-2}

STRUCTURE	SYSTEMATIC NAME	COMMON NAME	BP (°C)
HC≡CH	ethyne	acetylene	−85
$CH_3C{\equiv}CH$	propyne	methylacetylene	−23
$CH_3CH_2C{\equiv}CH$	1-butyne	ethylacetylene	9
$CH_3C{\equiv}CCH_3$	2-butyne	dimethylacetylene	27

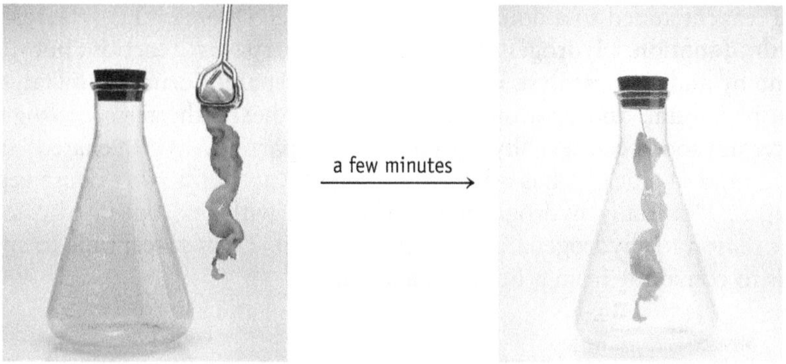

Photos: © Cengage Learning/Charles D. Winters

FIGURE 23.7 Bacon fat and addition reactions. The fat in bacon is partially unsaturated. Like other unsaturated compounds, bacon fat reacts with Br_2 in an addition reaction. Here, you see the color of Br_2 vapor fade when a strip of bacon is introduced.

triple bond (Figure 23.7). For an alkene the result is a compound with four groups bonded to each carbon.

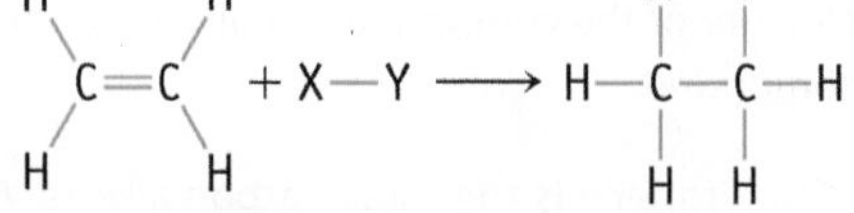

X—Y = H_2, Cl_2, Br_2; H—Cl, H—Br, H—OH, HO—Cl

The products of some addition reactions are substituted alkanes. For example, the addition of bromine to ethene (ethylene) forms 1,2-dibromoethane.

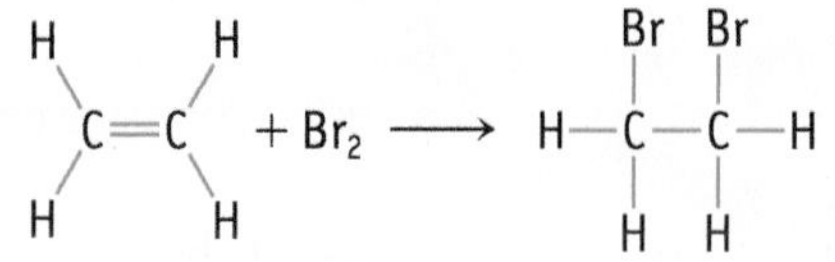

1,2-dibromoethane

The addition of 2 mol of chlorine to ethyne (acetylene) gives 1,1,2,2-tetrachloroethane.

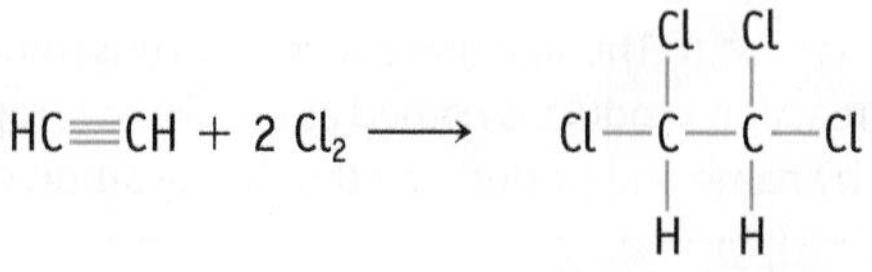

1,1,2,2-tetrachloroethane

Nomenclature of Substituted Alkanes The substituent groups in substituted alkanes are identified by the name and position of the substituent on the alkane chain.

During the 1860s, the Russian chemist Vladimir Markovnikov examined a large number of alkene addition reactions. In cases in which two isomeric products were possible, he found that one was more likely to predominate. Based on these results, Markovnikov formulated a rule (now called *Markovnikov's rule*) stating that, when a reagent HX adds to an unsymmetrical alkene, the hydrogen atom in the reagent becomes attached to the carbon that already has the largest number of hydrogens. An example of Markovnikov's rule is the reaction of 2-methylpropene with HCl that results in formation of 2-chloro-2-methylpropane rather than 1-chloro-2-methylpropane.

Remembering Markovnikov's Rule One of the authors of this book was taught the sentence "Hydrogen goes where hydrogen is." For example, in the reaction of 2-methylpropene, H attaches to the carbon of the $=CH_2$ group.

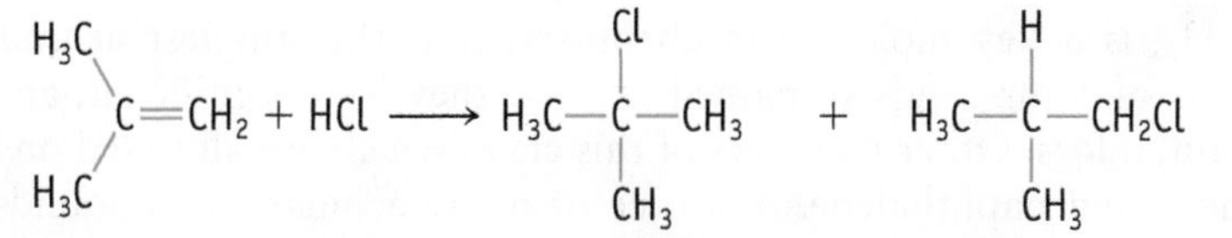

2-methylpropene | 2-chloro-2-methylpropane sole product | 1-chloro-2-methylpropane *not* formed

Catalysts A catalyst is a substance that causes a reaction to occur at a faster rate without itself being permanently changed in the reaction (see Section 14-5).

If the reagent added to a double bond is hydrogen (X—Y = H_2), the reaction is called **hydrogenation.** Hydrogenation is usually a very slow reaction, but it can be speeded up by adding a catalyst, often a specially prepared form of a metal, such as platinum, palladium, and rhodium. You may have heard the term *hydrogenation* because certain foods contain "hydrogenated" or "partially hydrogenated" ingredients. One brand of crackers has a label that says, "Made with 100% pure vegetable shortening . . . (partially hydrogenated soybean oil with hydrogenated cottonseed oil)." One reason for hydrogenating an oil is to make it less susceptible to spoilage; another is to convert it from a liquid to a solid.

EXAMPLE 23.4

Reaction of an Alkene

Problem Draw the structure of the compound obtained from the reaction of Br_2 with propene, and name the compound.

What Do You Know? Propene is the three-carbon alkene. Addition reactions are among the most common reactions of alkenes, and bromine is one of several common reagents that adds to double bonds.

Strategy Bromine adds across the C=C double bond (Figure 23.7). The name of the product is based on the name of the carbon chain and indicates the positions of the Br atoms.

Solution

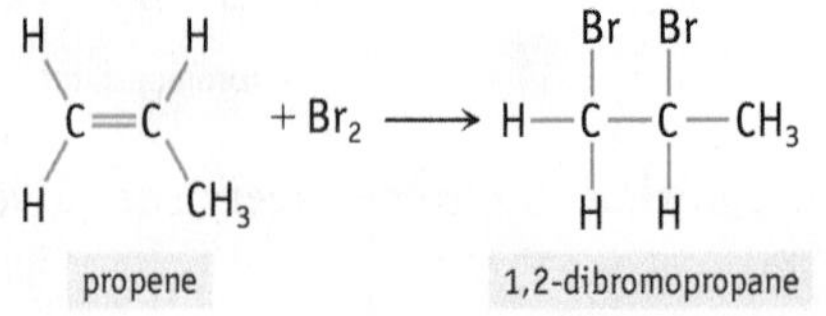

Think about Your Answer This reaction converts an unsaturated hydrocarbon to a substituted alkane. The reaction product is named as an alkane (propane) with substituents (Br atoms) identified by name and position on the three-carbon chain.

Check Your Understanding

(a) Draw the structure of the compound obtained from the reaction of HBr with ethylene, and name the compound.

(b) Draw the structure of the product of the reaction of Br_2 with *cis*-2-butene, and name this compound.

Aromatic Compounds

Benzene, C_6H_6, is a key molecule in chemistry. It is the simplest **aromatic compound,** a class of compounds so named because they have significant, and usually not unpleasant, odors. Other members of this class, which are all based on benzene, include toluene and naphthalene. A source of many aromatic compounds is coal.

Table 23.5 Some Aromatic Compounds from Coal Tar

Common Name	Formula	Boiling Point (°C)	Melting Point (°C)
Benzene	C_6H_6	80	+6
Toluene	$C_6H_5CH_3$	111	−95
o-Xylene	1,2-$C_6H_4(CH_3)_2$	144	−25
m-Xylene	1,3-$C_6H_4(CH_3)_2$	139	−48
p-Xylene	1,4-$C_6H_4(CH_3)_2$	138	+13
Naphthalene	$C_{10}H_8$	218	+80

These compounds, along with other volatile substances, are released when coal is heated to a high temperature in the absence of air (Table 23.5).

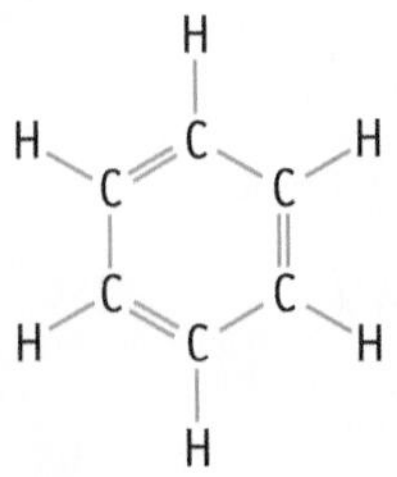
benzene

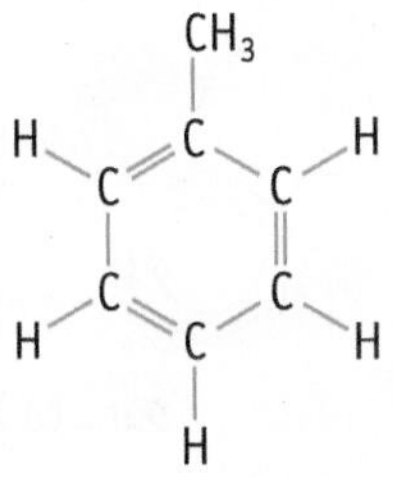
toluene

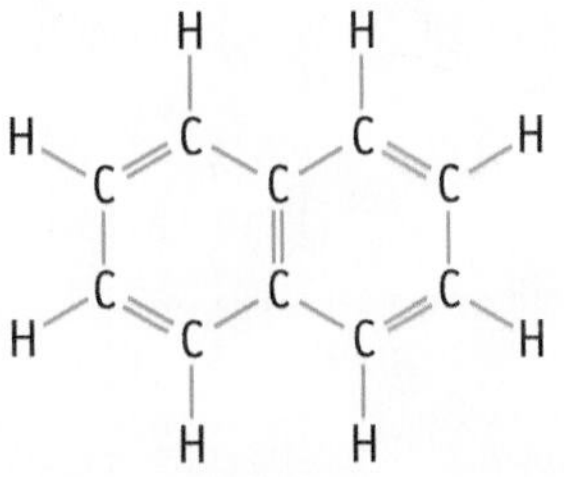
naphthalene

Benzene occupies a pivotal place in the history and practice of chemistry. Michael Faraday discovered this compound in 1825 as a by-product in the formation of illuminating gas, a fuel produced by heating coal. Today, benzene is an important industrial chemical, usually ranking among the top 25 chemicals in production annually in the United States. It is used as a solvent and is also the starting point for making thousands of different compounds by replacing the H atoms of the ring.

Toluene was originally obtained from tolu balsam, the pleasant-smelling gum of a South American tree, *Toluifera balsamum*. This balsam has been used in cough syrups and perfumes. Naphthalene is an ingredient in "moth balls," although 1,4-dichlorobenzene is now more commonly used. Aspartame and another artificial sweetener, saccharin, are also benzene derivatives.

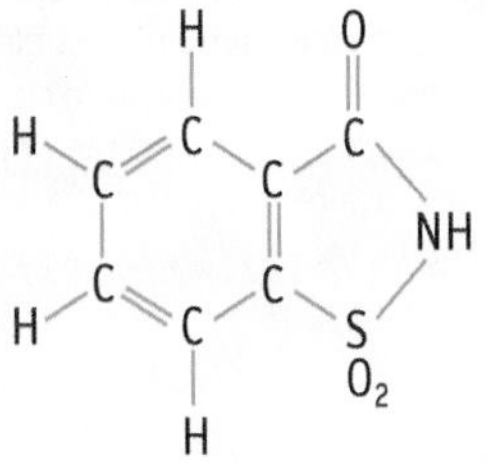

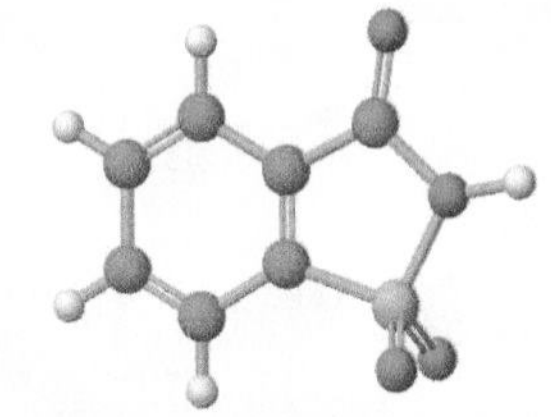

Saccharin ($C_7H_5NO_3S$). This compound, an artificial sweetener, contains an aromatic ring.

The Structure of Benzene

The formula of benzene suggested to 19th-century chemists that this compound should be unsaturated, but, if viewed this way, its chemistry was perplexing. Whereas alkenes readily undergo addition reactions, benzene does not do so under similar conditions. We now recognize that benzene's different reactivity relates to its structure and bonding, both of which are quite different from the structure and bonding in alkenes. Benzene has six equivalent carbon–carbon bonds, 139 pm in length, intermediate between a C—C single bond (154 pm) and a C=C double bond (134 pm). The π bonds are formed by the continuous overlap of the p orbitals on the six carbon atoms (◀ Section 9-2). Using valence bond terminology, the structure is represented by two resonance structures.

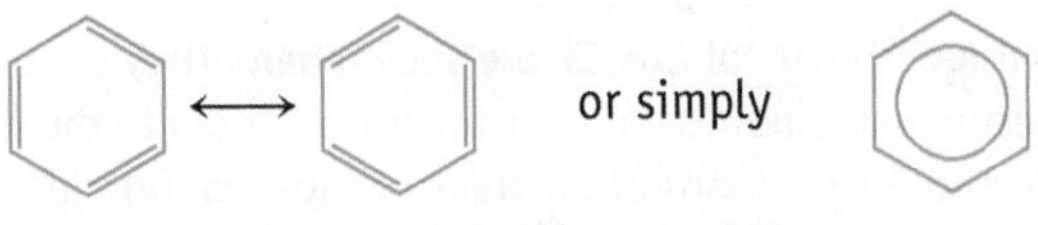

representations of benzene, C_6H_6

Drawing Aromatic Rings When drawing benzene rings chemists often allow the vertices of the hexagon to represent the carbon atoms and do not show the H atoms attached to those carbon atoms. The circle inside the ring indicates the two resonance structures.

August Kekulé and the Structure of Benzene The structural question was solved by August Kekulé (1829–1896). Kekulé, one of the most prominent organic chemists in Europe in the late 19th century, argued for the ring structure with alternating double bonds based on the number of isomers possible for the structure. The legend in chemistry is that Kekulé proposed the ring structure after dreaming of a snake biting its tail.

Benzene Derivatives

Toluene, chlorobenzene, benzoic acid, aniline, styrene, and phenol are common examples of benzene derivatives.

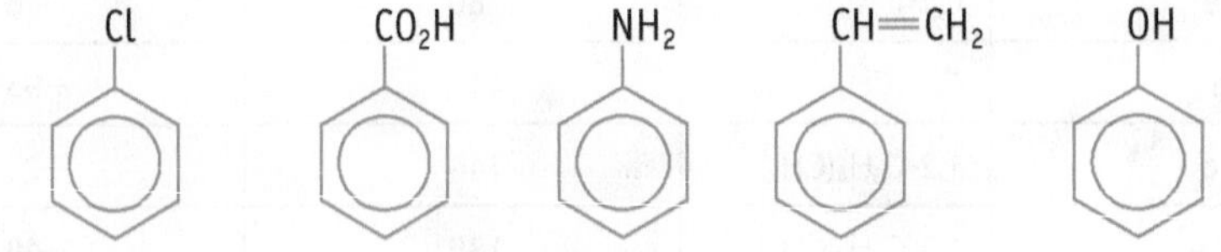

chlorobenzene   benzoic acid   aniline   styrene   phenol

The systematic nomenclature for benzene derivatives with two or more substituent groups involves naming these groups and identifying their positions on the ring by numbering the six carbon atoms (▶ Appendix E). Some common names, which are based on an older naming scheme, are also used. This scheme identified isomers of disubstituted benzenes with the prefixes *ortho* (*o*-, substituent groups on adjacent carbons in the benzene ring), *meta* (*m*-, substituents separated by one carbon atom), and *para* (*p*-, substituent groups on carbons on opposite sides of the ring).

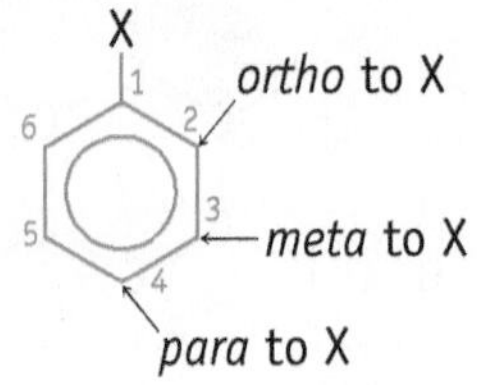

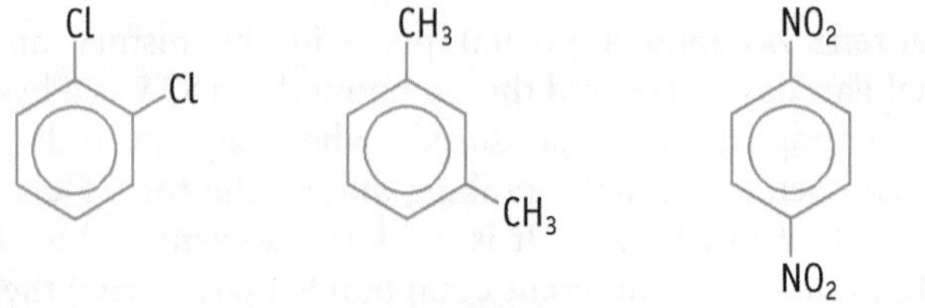

Systematic name:	1,2-dichlorobenzene	1,3-dimethylbenzene	1,4-dinitrobenzene
Common name:	*o*-dichlorobenzene	*m*-xylene	*p*-dinitrobenzene

EXAMPLE 23.5

Isomers of Substituted Benzenes

Problem Draw and name the isomers of $C_6H_3Cl_3$.

What Do You Know? From the formula you can infer that $C_6H_3Cl_3$ is a substituted benzene with three hydrogen atoms replaced by chlorine atoms.

Strategy Begin by drawing the carbon framework of benzene, and attach a chlorine atom to one of the carbon atoms. Place a second Cl atom on the ring in the *ortho, meta,* and *para* positions. Add the third Cl in one of the remaining positions, being careful not to repeat a structure already drawn.

Solution The three isomers of $C_6H_3Cl_3$ are shown here. They are named as derivatives of benzene by specifying the number of substituent groups with the prefix "tri-," the name of the substituent, and the positions of the three groups around the six-member ring.

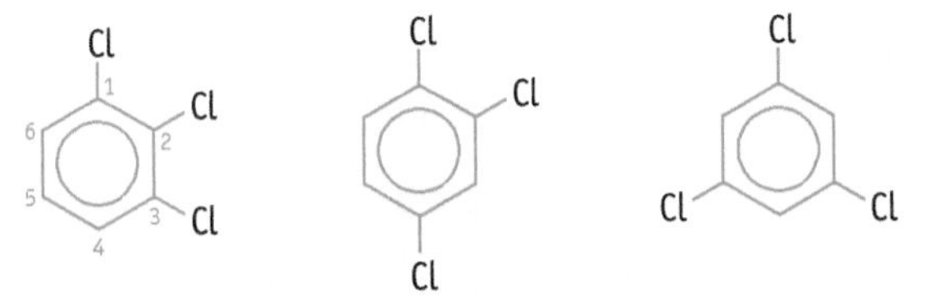

1,2,3-trichlorobenzene   1,2,4-trichlorobenzene   1,3,5-trichlorobenzene

Think about Your Answer Are there other possibilities? Try moving the chlorine atoms around in each isomer. In every case, you will find that moving one Cl atom to a different position generates one of these three isomers. For example, in the first structure, moving the Cl atom at position 1 to either position 5 or 6 leads to the second structure.

Check Your Understanding

Aniline, $C_6H_5NH_2$, is the common name for aminobenzene. Draw a structure for *p*-diaminobenzene, a compound used in dye manufacture. What is the systematic name for *p*-diaminobenzene?

Properties of Aromatic Compounds

Benzene is a colorless liquid, and simple substituted benzenes are liquids or solids under normal conditions. The properties of aromatic hydrocarbons are typical of hydrocarbons in general: They are insoluble in water, soluble in nonpolar solvents, and are oxidized by O_2 to form CO_2 and H_2O.

One of the most important properties of benzene and other aromatic compounds is an unusual stability that is associated with the unique π bonding in this molecule (◀ Section 9-2 and Figure 9.12). Because the π bonding in benzene is typically described using resonance structures, the extra stability is termed **resonance stabilization.** The extent of resonance stabilization in benzene is evaluated by comparing the energy evolved in the hydrogenation of benzene to form cyclohexane

$$C_6H_6(\ell) + 3\ H_2(g) \xrightarrow{\text{catalyst}} C_6H_{12}(\ell) \qquad \Delta_rH° = -206.7\ \text{kJ/mol-rxn}$$

with the energy evolved in hydrogenation of three isolated double bonds.

$$3\ H_2C{=}CH_2(g) + 3\ H_2(g) \rightarrow 3\ C_2H_6(g) \qquad \Delta_rH° = -410.8\ \text{kJ/mol-rxn}$$

The hydrogenation of benzene is about 200 kJ/mol less exothermic than the hydrogenation of three moles of ethene, a difference attributable to the added stability associated with π bonding in benzene.

Although aromatic compounds are unsaturated hydrocarbons, they do not undergo the addition reactions typical of alkenes and alkynes. Instead, *substitution reactions* occur, in which one or more hydrogen atoms are replaced by other groups. Such reactions require higher temperatures and a strong Brønsted acid such as H_2SO_4 or a Lewis acid such as $AlCl_3$ or $FeBr_3$.

Nitration: $C_6H_6(\ell) + HNO_3(\ell) \xrightarrow{H_2SO_4} C_6H_5NO_2(\ell) + H_2O(\ell)$

Alkylation: $C_6H_6(\ell) + CH_3Cl(\ell) \xrightarrow{AlCl_3} C_6H_5CH_3(\ell) + HCl(g)$

Halogenation: $C_6H_6(\ell) + Br_2(\ell) \xrightarrow{FeBr_3} C_6H_5Br(\ell) + HBr(g)$

Lewis Acids G. N. Lewis (page 285) defined an acid as an electron-pair acceptor (such as $AlCl_3$ and BF_3) (see Section 16-10).

REVIEW & CHECK FOR SECTION 23-2

1. What is the systematic name for this alkane?

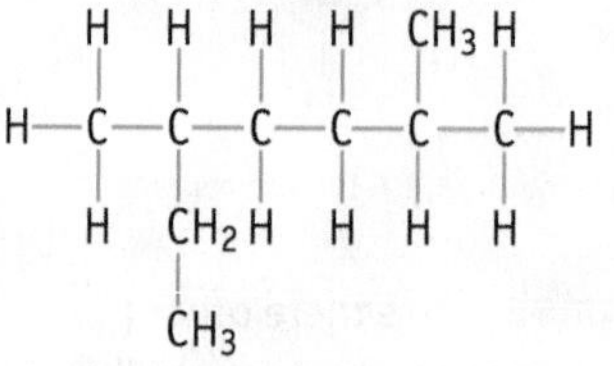

(a) nonane
(b) 2-ethyl-5-methylhexane
(c) 2, 5-dimethylheptane
(d) dimethyloctane

2. Which statement below correctly describes the following compound?

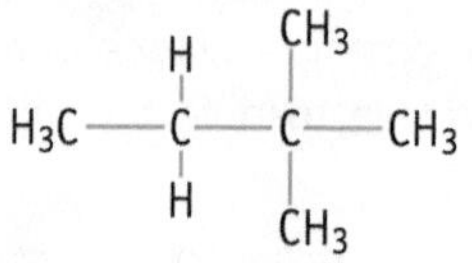

(a) The compound is an isomer of pentane, is chiral, and is named 2,3-dimethylbutane.

(b) The compound is an isomer of octane, is not chiral, and is named 2,2-dimethylbutane.

(c) The compound is an isomer of hexane, is not chiral, and is named 2,2-dimethylbutane.

(d) The compound is an isomer of hexane, is not chiral, and is named 3,3-dimethylbutane.

3. Consider the following list of compounds:

1. C_2H_4 2. C_5H_{10} 3. $C_{14}H_{30}$ 4. C_7H_8

(i) Which compound or compounds in the list can be an (non-cyclic) alkane?

(a) only 1 (b) 2 and 3 (c) only 3 (d) 3 and 4

(ii) Which compound or compounds in the list can be an alkene?

(a) only 1 (b) only 2 (c) 1 and 2 (d) 3 and 4

4. What is the product of the following reaction?

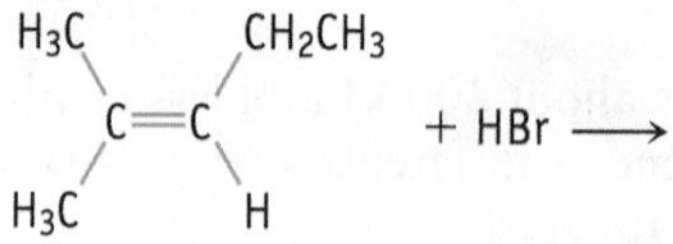

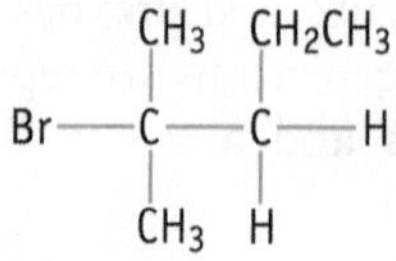

(a)

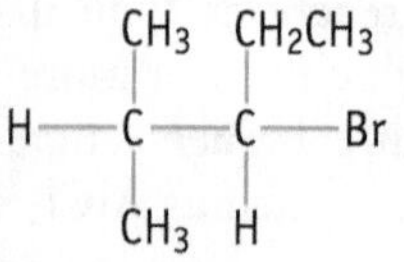

(b)

5. How many isomers are possible for $C_6H_4(CH_3)Cl$, a benzene derivative?

(a) 1 (b) 2 (c) 3

Table 23.6 Common Functional Groups and Derivatives of Alkanes

Functional Group*	General Formula*	Class of Compound	Examples
F, Cl, Br, I	RF, RCl, RBr, RI	Haloalkane	CH_3CH_2Cl, chloroethane
OH	ROH	Alcohol	CH_3CH_2OH, ethanol
OR′	ROR′	Ether	$(CH_3CH_2)_2O$, diethyl ether
NH_2†	RNH_2	(Primary) Amine	$CH_3CH_2NH_2$, ethylamine
$-\overset{O}{\overset{\Vert}{C}}H$	RCHO	Aldehyde	CH_3CHO, ethanal (acetaldehyde)
$-\overset{O}{\overset{\Vert}{C}}-R'$	RCOR′	Ketone	CH_3COCH_3, propanone (acetone)
$-\overset{O}{\overset{\Vert}{C}}-OH$	RCO_2H	Carboxylic acid	CH_3CO_2H, ethanoic acid (acetic acid)
$-\overset{O}{\overset{\Vert}{C}}-OR'$	RCO_2R'	Ester	$CH_3CO_2CH_3$, methyl acetate
$-\overset{O}{\overset{\Vert}{C}}-NH_2$	$RCONH_2$	Amide	CH_3CONH_2, acetamide

*R and R′ can be the same or different hydrocarbon groups.
†Secondary amines (R_2NH) and tertiary amines (R_3N) are also possible, see discussion in the text.

23-3 Alcohols, Ethers, and Amines

Learning Objectives: LO 2.1

Organic compounds often contain other elements in addition to carbon and hydrogen. Two elements in particular, oxygen and nitrogen, add a rich dimension to carbon chemistry.

Organic chemistry organizes compounds containing elements other than carbon and hydrogen as derivatives of hydrocarbons. Formulas (and structures) are represented by substituting one or more hydrogens in a hydrocarbon molecule by a **functional group**. A functional group is an atom or group of atoms attached to a carbon atom in the hydrocarbon. Formulas of hydrocarbon derivatives are then written as R—X, in which R is a hydrocarbon lacking a hydrogen atom, and X is the functional group (such as —OH, $—NH_2$, a halogen atom, or $—CO_2H$) that has replaced the hydrogen. The chemical and physical properties of the hydrocarbon derivatives are a blend of the properties associated with hydrocarbons and the group that has been substituted for hydrogen.

Table 23.6 identifies some common functional groups and the families of organic compounds resulting from their attachment to a hydrocarbon.

Alcohols and Ethers

If one of the hydrogen atoms of an alkane is replaced by a hydroxyl (—OH) group, the result is an **alcohol**, ROH. Methanol, CH_3OH, and ethanol, CH_3CH_2OH, are the most important alcohols, but others are also commercially important (Table 23.7). Notice that several have more than one OH functional group.

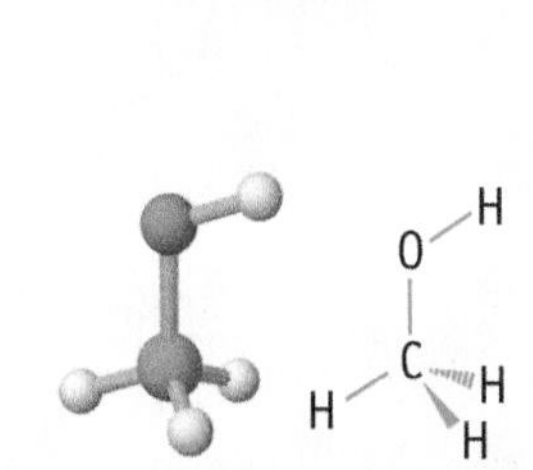

Methanol, CH_3OH, the simplest alcohol. Methanol is often called *wood alcohol* because it was originally produced by heating wood in the absence of air.

More than 5×10^8 kg of methanol is produced in the United States annually. Most of this is used to make formaldehyde (CH_2O) and acetic acid (CH_3CO_2H), both important chemicals in their own right. Methanol is also used as a solvent, as a de-icer in gasoline, and as a fuel in high-powered racing cars. It is found in low concentration in new wine, where it contributes to the odor, or "bouquet." Like

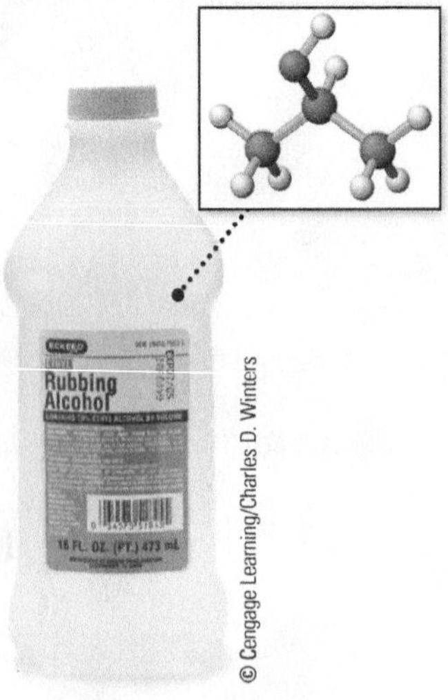

Rubbing alcohol. Common rubbing alcohol is 2-propanol, also called *isopropyl alcohol.*

Table 23.7 Some Important Alcohols

Condensed Formula	BP (°C)	Systematic Name	Common Name	Use
CH_3OH	65.0	Methanol	Methyl alcohol	Fuel, gasoline additive, making formaldehyde
CH_3CH_2OH	78.5	Ethanol	Ethyl alcohol	Beverages, gasoline additive, solvent
$CH_3CH_2CH_2OH$	97.4	1-Propanol	Propyl alcohol	Industrial solvent
$CH_3CH(OH)CH_3$	82.4	2-Propanol	Isopropyl alcohol	Rubbing alcohol
$HOCH_2CH_2OH$	198	1,2-Ethanediol	Ethylene glycol	Antifreeze
$HOCH_2CH(OH)CH_2OH$	290	1,2,3-Propanetriol	Glycerol (glycerin)	Moisturizer in consumer products

ethanol, methanol causes intoxication, but methanol differs in being more poisonous, largely because the human body converts it to formic acid (HCO_2H) and formaldehyde (CH_2O). These compounds attack the cells of the retina in the eye, leading to permanent blindness.

Ethanol is the "alcohol" of alcoholic beverages, in which it is formed by the anaerobic (without air) fermentation of sugar. On a much larger scale, ethanol for use as a fuel is made by fermentation of corn and other plant materials. Some ethanol (about 5%) is made from petroleum, by the reaction of ethylene and water.

Naming Alcohols Substitute "-ol" for the final "-e" in the name of the hydrocarbon, and designate the position of the —OH group by the number of the carbon atom. For example, $CH_3CH_2CHOHCH_3$ is named as a derivative of butane. The —OH group is attached to the second carbon, so the name is 2-butanol.

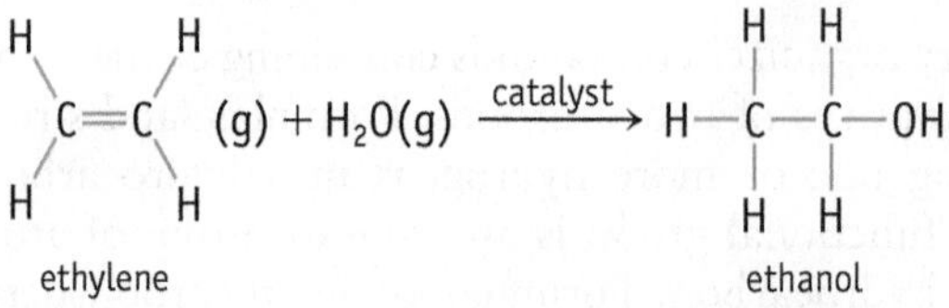

Beginning with three-carbon alcohols, structural isomers are possible. For example, 1-propanol and 2-propanol (common names, propyl alcohol and isopropyl alcohol) are different compounds (Table 23.7).

Ethylene glycol and glycerol are common alcohols having two and three —OH groups, respectively. Ethylene glycol is used as antifreeze in automobiles. Glycerol's most common use is as a softener in soaps and lotions. It is also a raw material for the preparation of nitroglycerin (Figure 23.8).

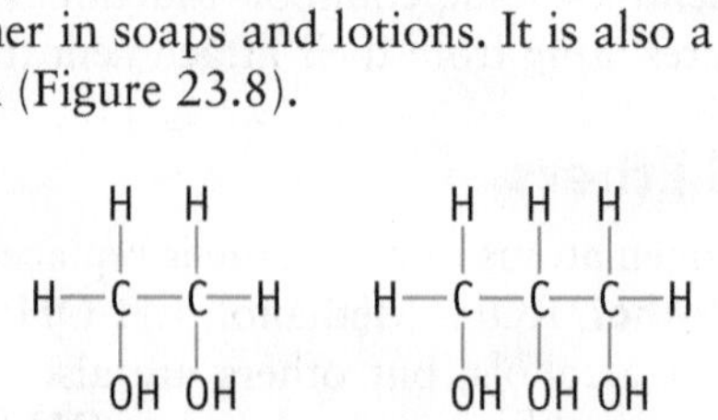

Systematic name:	1,2-ethanediol	1,2,3-propanetriol
Common name:	ethylene glycol	glycerol or glycerin

Ethers have the general formula ROR′. The best-known ether is diethyl ether, $CH_3CH_2OCH_2CH_3$. Lacking an —OH group, the properties of ethers are in sharp contrast to those of alcohols. Diethyl ether, for example, has a lower boiling point (34.5 °C) than ethanol, CH_3CH_2OH (78.3 °C), and is only slightly soluble in water.

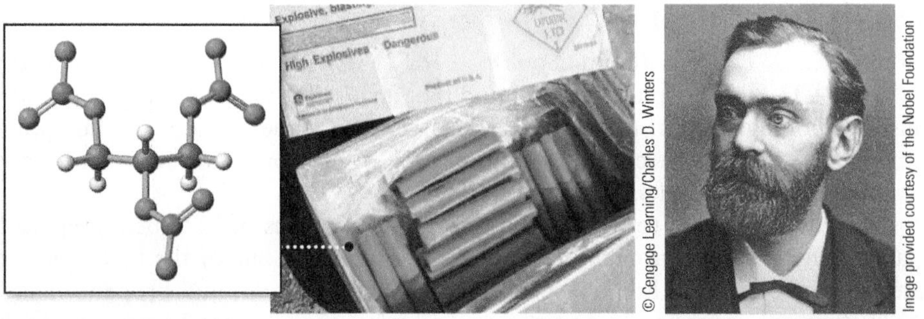

(a) (b) (c)

Concentrated nitric acid and glycerin react to form an oily, highly unstable compound called *nitroglycerin,* $C_3H_5(ONO_2)_3$. It is more stable if absorbed onto an inert solid, a combination called *dynamite.*

The fortune of Alfred Nobel (1833–1896), built on the manufacture of dynamite, now funds the Nobel Prizes.

FIGURE 23.8 **Nitroglycerin, dynamite, and Nobel.**

EXAMPLE 23.6

Structural Isomers of Alcohols

Problem How many different alcohols with one —OH group are derivatives of pentane? Draw their structures, and name each alcohol.

What Do You Know? The formula for pentane is C_5H_{12}. In an alcohol an —OH group will replace one H atom.

Strategy Pentane, C_5H_{12}, has a five-carbon chain. An —OH group can replace a hydrogen atom on one of the carbon atoms. Alcohols are named as derivatives of the alkane (pentane) by replacing the "-e" at the end with "-ol" and indicating the position of the —OH group by a numerical prefix (Appendix E).

Solution Three different alcohols are possible, depending on whether the —OH group is placed on the first, second, or third carbon atom in the chain. (The fourth and fifth positions are identical to the second and first positions in the chain, respectively.)

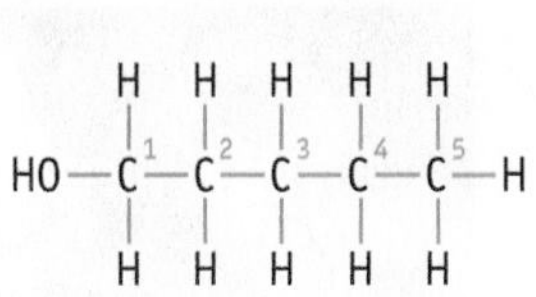

1-pentanol

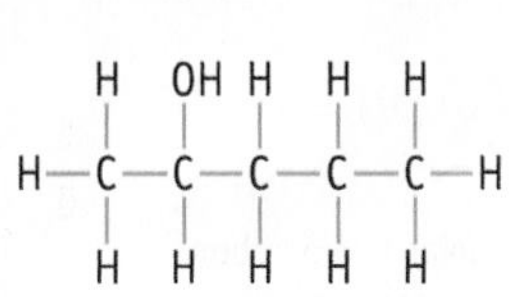

2-pentanol

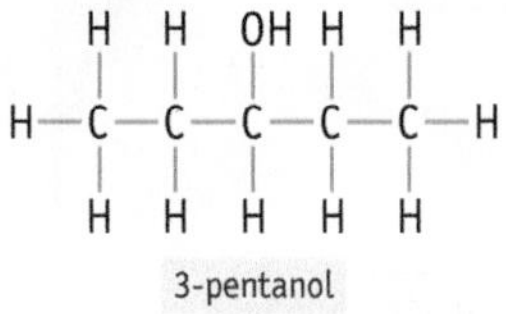

3-pentanol

Think about Your Answer Additional structural isomers with the formula $C_5H_{11}OH$ are possible in which the longest carbon chain has three C atoms (one isomer) or four C atoms (four isomers).

Check Your Understanding

Draw the structure of 1-butanol and alcohols that are structural isomers of the compound.

Properties of Alcohols

Methane, CH_4, is a gas (boiling point, −161 °C) with low solubility in water. Methanol, CH_3OH, by contrast, is a liquid that is *miscible* with water in all proportions. The boiling point of methanol, 65 °C, is 226 °C higher than the boiling point of methane. What a difference the addition of a single atom into the structure can make in the properties of simple molecules!

Alcohols are related to water, with one of the H atoms of H_2O being replaced by an organic group. If a methyl group is substituted for one of the hydrogens of water, methanol results. Ethanol has a —C_2H_5 (ethyl) group, and propanol has a —C_3H_7 (propyl) group in place of one of the hydrogens of water. Viewing alcohols as related to water also helps in understanding their properties.

The two parts of methanol, the —CH_3 group and the —OH group, contribute to its properties. For example, methanol will burn, a property associated with hydrocarbons. On the other hand, its boiling point is more like that of water. The temperature at which a substance boils is related to the forces of attraction between molecules, called *intermolecular forces:* The stronger the attractive, intermolecular forces in a sample, the higher the boiling point (◀ Section 11-3). These forces are particularly strong in water, a result of the polarity of the —OH group in this molecule (◀ Section 8-8). Methanol is also a polar molecule, and it is the polar —OH group that leads to a high boiling point. In contrast, methane is nonpolar and its low boiling point is the result of weak intermolecular forces.

It is also possible to explain the differences in the solubility of methane, methanol, and other alcohols in water (Figure 23.9). The solubility of methanol and ethylene glycol is conferred by the polar —OH portion of the molecule. Methane, which is nonpolar, has low water solubility.

As the size of the alkyl group in an alcohol increases, the alcohol boiling point rises, a general trend seen in families of similar compounds and related to molar mass (see Table 23.7). The solubility in water in this series decreases. Methanol and ethanol are completely miscible in water, whereas 1-propanol is moderately water soluble; 1-butanol is less soluble than 1-propanol. With an increase in the size of the hydrocarbon group, the organic group (the nonpolar part of the molecule) has become a larger fraction of the molecule, and properties associated with nonpolarity begin to dominate. Space-filling models show that in methanol, the polar and

Methanol is often added to automobile gasoline tanks in the winter to prevent water in the fuel lines from freezing. It is soluble in water and lowers the water's freezing point.

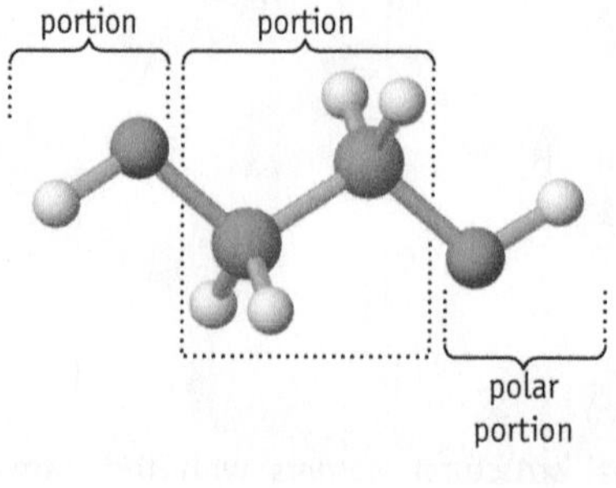

Ethylene glycol is used in automobile radiators. It is soluble in water, and lowers the freezing point and raises the boiling point of the water in the cooling system. (▶ Section 14-4.)

Ethylene glycol, a major component of automobile antifreeze, is completely miscible with water.

FIGURE 23.9 **Properties and uses of two alcohols, methanol and ethylene glycol.**

nonpolar parts of the molecule are approximately similar in size, but in 1-butanol the —OH group is less than 20% of the molecule. The molecule is less like water and more "organic." Electrostatic potential surfaces amplify this point.

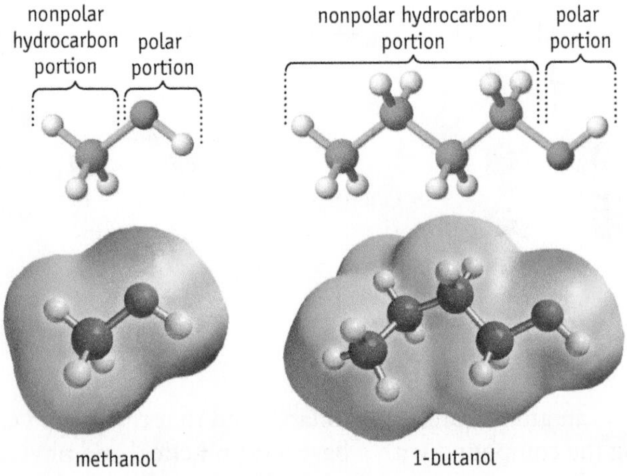

Amines

It is often convenient to think about water and ammonia as being similar molecules: They are the simplest hydrogen compounds of adjacent second-period elements. Both are polar and exhibit some similar chemistry, such as protonation (to give H_3O^+ and NH_4^+) and deprotonation (to give OH^- and NH_2^-).

This comparison of water and ammonia can be extended to alcohols and amines. Alcohols have formulas related to water in which one hydrogen in H_2O is replaced with an organic group (R—OH). In organic **amines,** one or more hydrogen atoms of NH_3 are replaced with an organic group. Amine structures are similar to ammonia's structure; that is, the geometry about the N atom is trigonal pyramidal.

Amines are categorized based on the number of organic substituents as *primary* (one organic group), *secondary* (two organic groups), or *tertiary* (three organic groups). As examples, consider the three amines with methyl groups: CH_3NH_2, $(CH_3)_2NH$, and $(CH_3)_3N$.

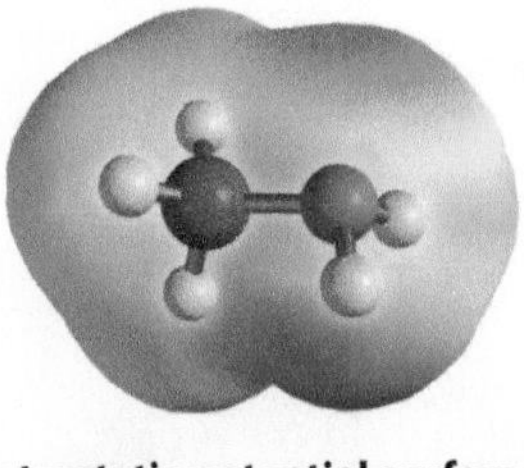

Electrostatic potential surface for methylamine. The surface for methyl-amine shows that this water-soluble amine is polar with the partial negative charge on the N atom.

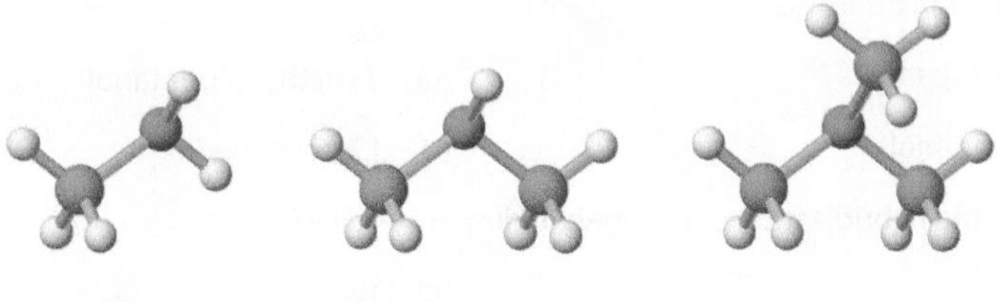

CH_3NH_2	$(CH_3)_2NH$	$(CH_3)_3N$
primary amine	secondary amine	tertiary amine
methylamine	dimethylamine	trimethylamine

Properties of Amines

Amines usually have offensive odors. You know what the odor is if you have ever smelled decaying fish. Two appropriately named amines, putrescine and cadaverine, add to the odor of urine, rotten meat, and bad breath.

$H_2NCH_2CH_2CH_2CH_2NH_2$	$H_2NCH_2CH_2CH_2CH_2CH_2NH_2$
putrescine	cadaverine
1,4-butanediamine	1,5-pentanediamine

The smallest amines are water soluble, but most amines are not. All amines are bases, however, and they react with acids to give salts, many of which are water

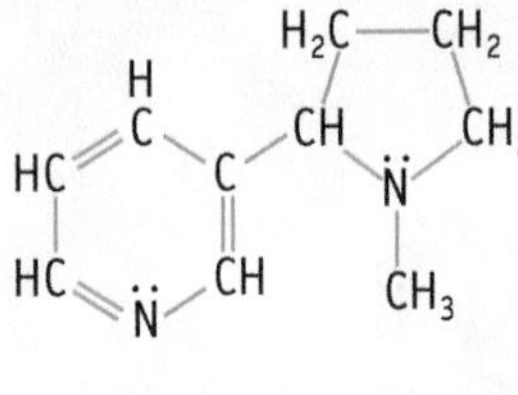

nicotine

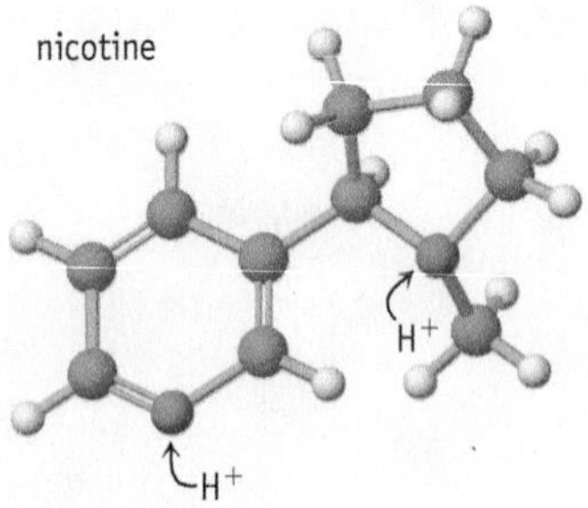

Nicotine, an amine. Two nitrogen atoms in the nicotine molecule can be protonated, which is the form in which nicotine is normally found. The protons can be removed, by treating it with a base. This "free-base" form is much more poisonous and addictive.

soluble. As with ammonia, the reactions involve adding H^+ to the lone pair of electrons on the N atom. This is illustrated by the reaction of aniline (aminobenzene) with H_2SO_4 to give anilinium hydrogen sulfate.

$$C_6H_5NH_2(aq) + H_2SO_4(aq) \longrightarrow C_6H_5NH_3^+(aq) + HSO_4^-(aq)$$

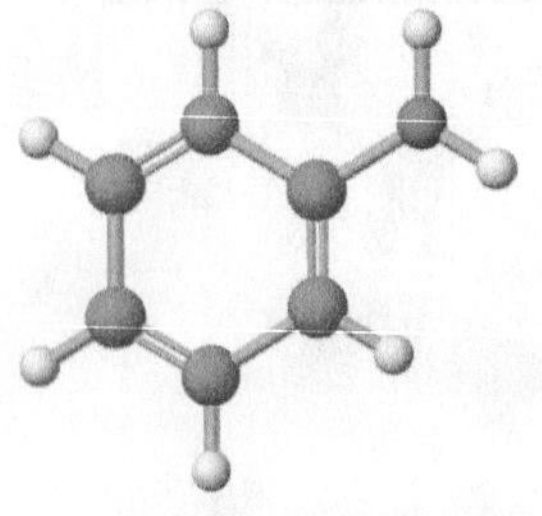

aniline

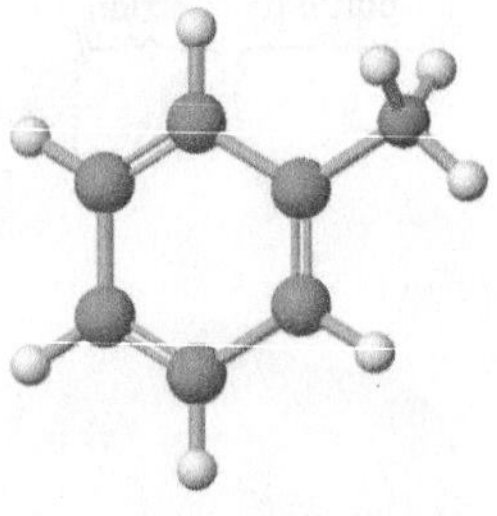

anilinium ion

The facts that an amine can be protonated and that the proton can be removed again by treating the compound with a base have practical and physiological importance. Nicotine in cigarettes is normally found in the protonated form. (This water-soluble form is also used often in insecticides.) Adding a base such as ammonia removes the H^+ ion to leave nicotine in its "free-base" form.

$$NicH_2^{2+}(aq) + 2\ NH_3(aq) \rightarrow Nic(aq) + 2\ NH_4^+(aq)$$

In this form, nicotine is much more readily absorbed by the skin and mucous membranes, so the compound is a much more potent poison.

REVIEW & CHECK FOR SECTION 23-3

1. How many different compounds (alcohols and ethers) exist with the molecular formula $C_4H_{10}O$?

   (a) 2 (b) 3 (c) 4 (d) more than 4

2. Which of the following compounds is not chiral, that is, which does not possess a carbon atom attached to four different groups?

   (a) 2-propanol (c) 2-methyl-3-pentanol
   (b) 2-butanol (d) 1,2-propanediol

3. What is the hybridization of nitrogen in dimethylamine?

   (a) sp^3 (c) sp
   (b) sp^2 (d) nitrogen is not hybridized

4. What chemical reagent will react with the ethylammonium ion $[CH_3CH_2NH_3]^+$ to form ethylamine?

   (a) O_2 (b) N_2 (c) H_2SO_4 (d) NaOH

23-4 Compounds with a Carbonyl Group

Formaldehyde, acetic acid, and acetone are among the most important organic compounds, and they share a common structural feature: Each contains a trigonal-planar carbon atom doubly bonded to an oxygen. The C=O group is called the

CASE STUDY An Awakening with L-DOPA

From about 1917 to 1928, millions of people worldwide were affected by a condition known as *encephalitis lethargica*, a form of sleeping sickness. Those who suffered from the condition were in a state of semi-consciousness that lasted for decades. In his book *Awakenings*, Oliver Sacks wrote about treating a patient with the compound L-DOPA, which "was started in early March 1969 and raised by degrees to 5.0 g a day. Little effect was seen for two weeks, and then a sudden 'conversion' took place. . . . Mr. L enjoyed a mobility, a health, and a happiness which he had not known in thirty years. Everything about him filled with delight: he was like a man who had awoken from a nightmare or a serious illness. . . ."

COLUMBIA/THE KOBAL COLLECTION/ GOLDMAN, LOUIS

Robert DeNiro as Leonard Lowe and Robin Williams as Malcolm Sayer, a fictionalized portrayal of Oliver Sacks, in the movie version of *Awakenings*.

If you have read the book or have seen the movie of the same name, you know that Mr. L eventually could not tolerate the treatment, but that Sacks treated many others who benefitted from it. L-DOPA is now widely used in the treatment of another condition, Parkinson's disease, a degenerative disorder of the central nervous system.

L-DOPA or L-dopamine (L-3,4-dihydroxy–phenylalanine) is chiral. The symbol L stands for "levo," which means a solution of the compound rotates polarized light to the left. The compound is also a derivative of phenylalanine, one of many naturally occurring alpha-amino acids that play such an important role in protein formation and other natural processes.

L-DOPA also illustrates why chiral molecules are so interesting to chemists: Only the "levo" enantiomer is physiologically active. The enantiomer that rotates polarized light in the opposite direction has no biological function.

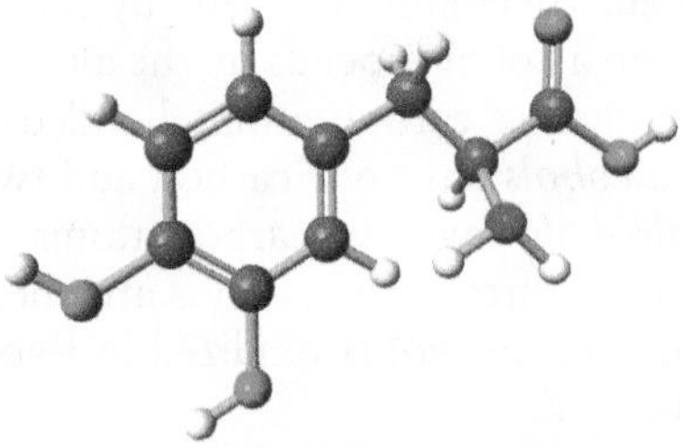

L-DOPA, $C_9H_{11}NO_4$, a treatment for Parkinson's disease

When L-DOPA is ingested, it is metabolized to dopamine in a process that removes the carboxylic acid group, —CO_2H, and it is dopamine that is physiologically active. Dopamine is a neurotransmitter that occurs in a wide variety of animals.

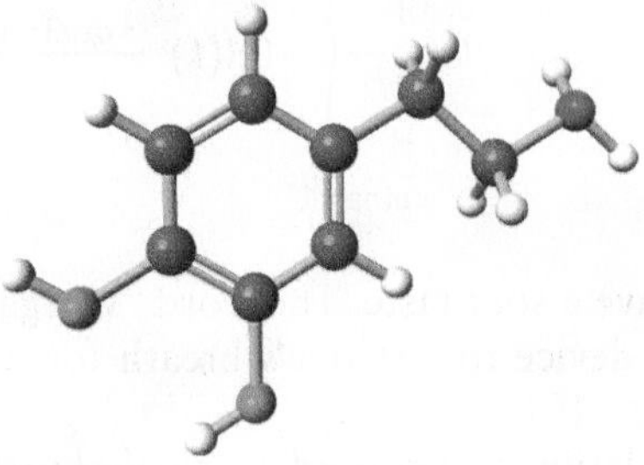

dopamine, $C_8H_{11}NO_2$, a neurotransmitter

Interestingly, both L-DOPA and dopamine are closely related to another amine, epinephrine. This is sometimes referred to as adrenaline, the hormone that is released from the adrenal glands when there is an emergency or danger threatens.

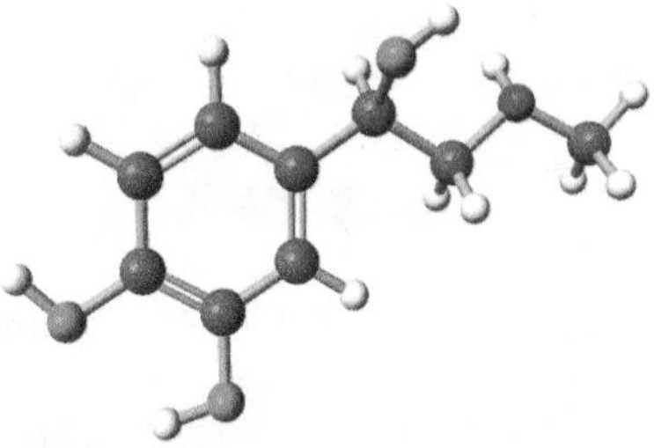

epinephrine or adrenaline, $C_9H_{13}NO_3$

Questions:

1. L-DOPA is chiral. What is the center of chirality in the molecule?
2. Is either dopamine or epinephrine chiral? If so, what is the center of chirality?
3. If you are treated with 5.0 g of L-DOPA, what amount (in moles) is this?

Answers to these questions are available in Appendix N.

References:

1. Oliver Sacks, *Awakenings*, Vintage Books, New York, 1999.
2. N. Angier, "A Molecule of Motivation, Dopamine Excels at Its Task," *New York Times*, October 27, 2009.

carbonyl group, and these compounds are members of a large class of compounds called **carbonyl compounds.**

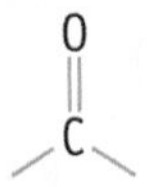

carbonyl group

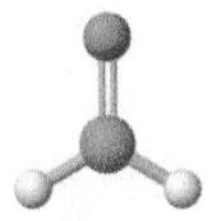

formaldehyde
CH_2O
aldehyde

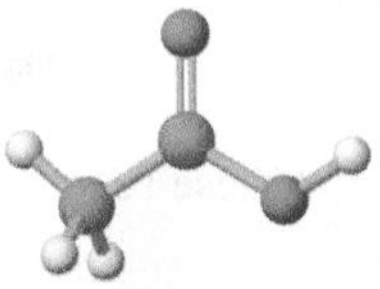

acetic acid
CH_3CO_2H
carboxylic acid

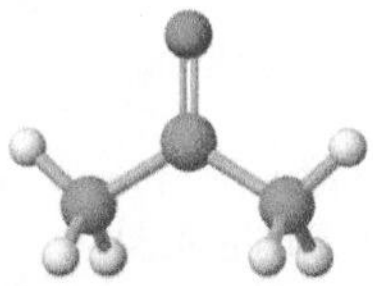

acetone
CH_3COCH_3
ketone

Primary alcohol: ethanol

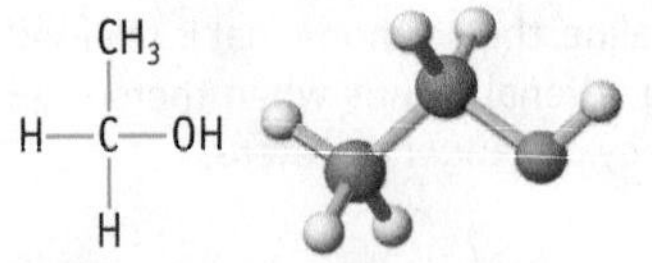

Secondary alcohol: 2-propanol

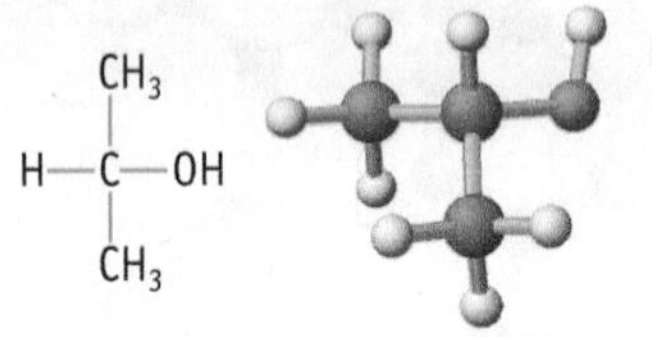

Tertiary alcohol: 2-methyl-2-propanol

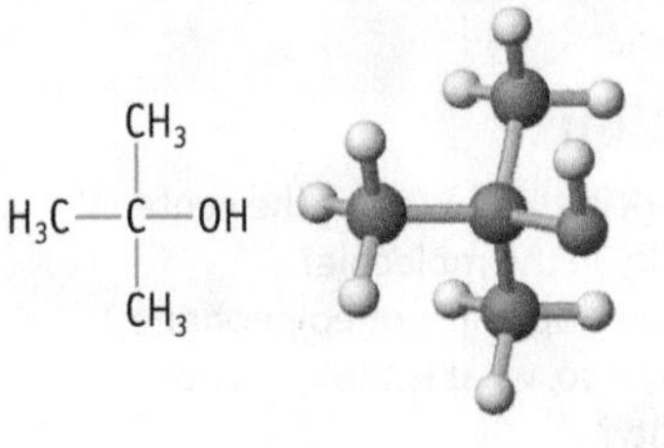

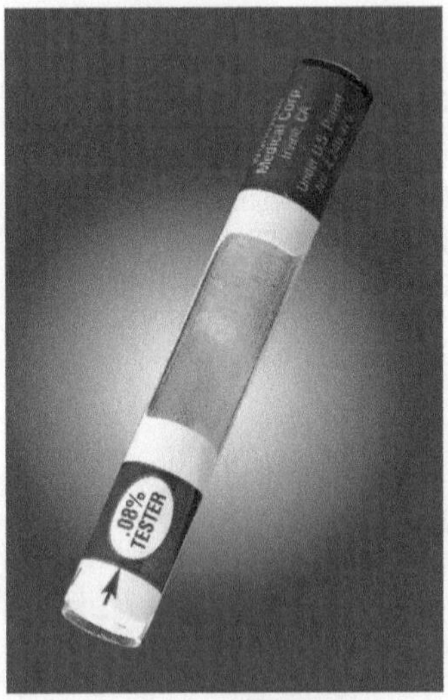

© Cengage Learning/Charles D. Winters

FIGURE 23.10 Alcohol tester. This device for testing a person's breath for the presence of ethanol relies on the oxidation of the alcohol. If present, ethanol is oxidized by potassium dichromate, $K_2Cr_2O_7$, to acetaldehyde and then to acetic acid. The yellow-orange dichromate ion is reduced to green $Cr^{3+}(aq)$, with the color change indicating that ethanol was present.

In this section, we will examine five groups of carbonyl compounds (see Table 23.6):

- *Aldehydes* (RCHO) have an organic group (—R) and an H atom attached to a carbonyl group.
- *Ketones* (RCOR′) have two —R groups attached to the carbonyl carbon; they may be the same groups, as in acetone, or different groups.
- *Carboxylic acids* (RCO_2H) have an —R group and an —OH group attached to the carbonyl carbon.
- *Esters* (RCO_2R') have —R and —OR′ groups attached to the carbonyl carbon.
- *Amides* ($RCONR_2'$, RCONHR′, and $RCONH_2$) have an —R group and an amino group (—NH_2, —NHR, —NR_2) bonded to the carbonyl carbon.

Aldehydes, ketones, and carboxylic acids are oxidation products of alcohols and, indeed, are commonly made by this route. The product obtained through oxidation of an alcohol depends on the alcohol's structure, which is classified according to the number of carbon atoms bonded to the C atom bearing the —OH group. *Primary alcohols* have one carbon and two hydrogen atoms attached, whereas *secondary alcohols* have two carbon atoms and one hydrogen atom attached. *Tertiary alcohols* have three carbon atoms attached to the C atom bearing the —OH group.

A *primary alcohol* is oxidized in two steps, first to an aldehyde and then to a carboxylic acid:

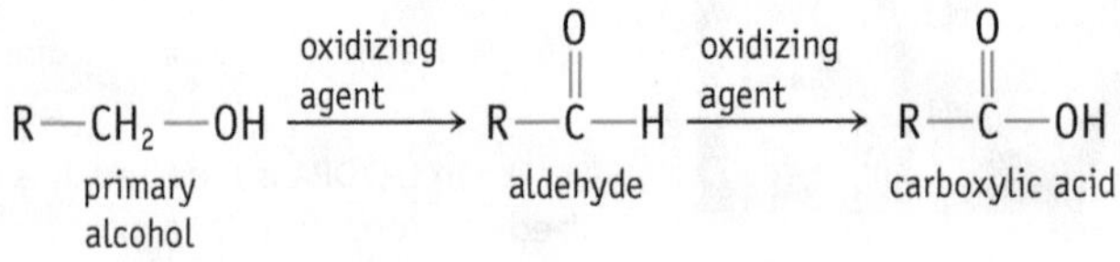

For example, the air oxidation of ethanol in wine produces wine vinegar, the most important ingredient of which is acetic acid.

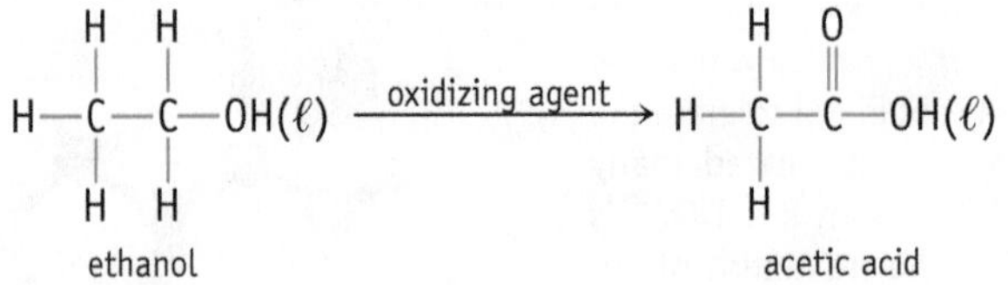

Acids have a sour taste. The word "vinegar" (from the French *vin aigre*) means sour wine. A device to test one's breath for alcohol relies on the oxidation of ethanol (Figure 23.10).

Oxidation of a *secondary alcohol* produces a ketone:

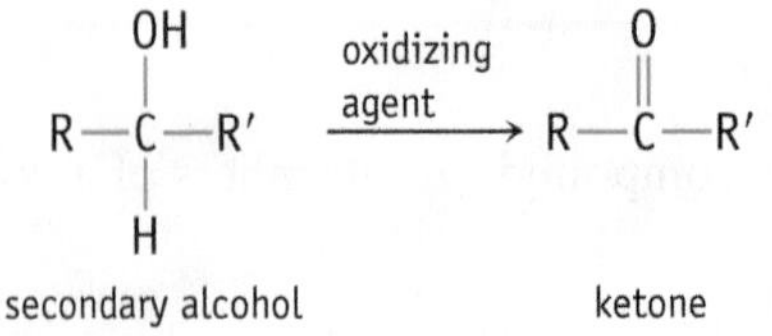

(—R and —R′ are organic groups. They may be the same or different.)

Common oxidizing agents used for these reactions are reagents such as $KMnO_4$ and $K_2Cr_2O_7$ (◀ Table 3.3).

Finally, tertiary alcohols do *not* react with the usual oxidizing agents.

$$(CH_3)_3COH \xrightarrow{\text{oxidizing agent}} \text{no reaction}$$

Aldehydes and Ketones

Aldehydes and **ketones** can have pleasant odors and are often used in fragrances. Benzaldehyde is responsible for the odor of almonds and cherries; cinnamaldehyde is found in the bark of the cinnamon tree; and the ketone 4-(*p*-hydroxyphenyl)-2-butanone is responsible for the odor of ripe raspberries (a favorite of the authors of this book). Table 23.8 lists several simple aldehydes and ketones.

Aldehydes and odors. The odors of almonds and cinnamon are due to aldehydes, whereas the odor of fresh raspberries comes from a ketone.

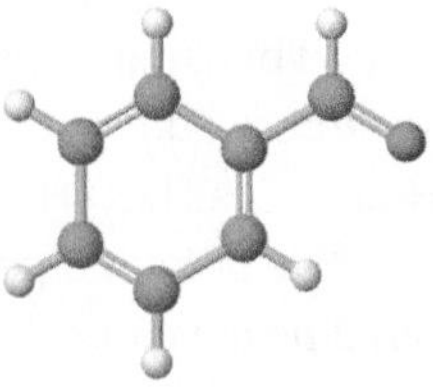

benzaldehyde, C_6H_5CHO

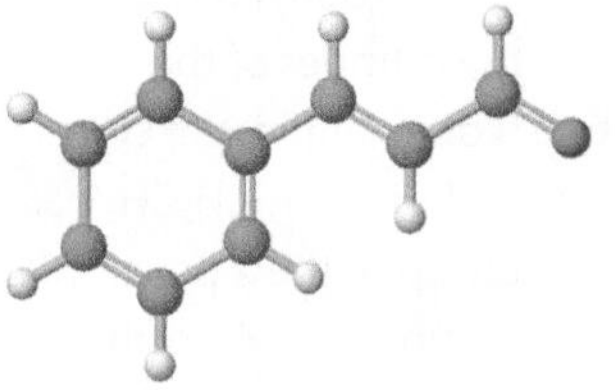

trans-cinnamaldehyde, $C_6H_5CH{=}CHCHO$

Aldehydes and ketones are the oxidation products of primary and secondary alcohols, respectively. The reverse reactions—reduction of aldehydes to primary alcohols and reduction of ketones to secondary alcohols—are also known. Commonly used reagents for such reductions are $NaBH_4$ and $LiAlH_4$, although H_2 is used on an industrial scale.

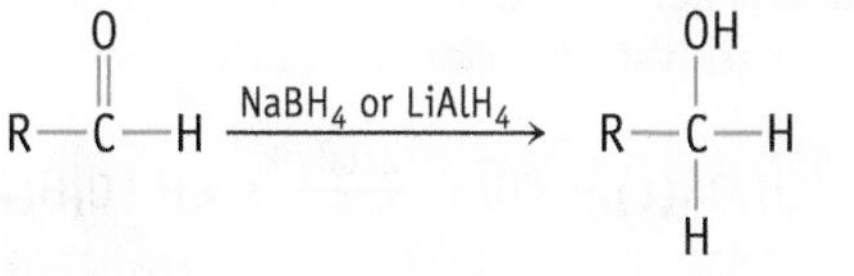

aldehyde → primary alcohol

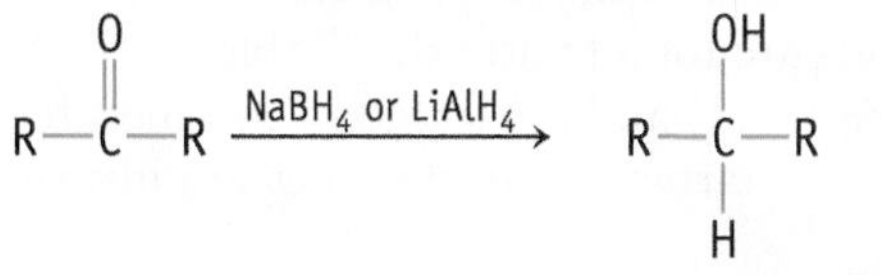

ketone → secondary alcohol

Table 23.8 Simple Aldehydes and Ketones

Structure	Common Name	Systematic Name	BP (°C)
$\mathrm{H\overset{O}{\overset{\|}{C}}H}$	Formaldehyde	Methanal	−19
$\mathrm{CH_3\overset{O}{\overset{\|}{C}}H}$	Acetaldehyde	Ethanal	20
$\mathrm{CH_3\overset{O}{\overset{\|}{C}}CH_3}$	Acetone	Propanone	56
$\mathrm{CH_3\overset{O}{\overset{\|}{C}}CH_2CH_3}$	Methyl ethyl ketone	Butanone	80
$\mathrm{CH_3CH_2\overset{O}{\overset{\|}{C}}CH_2CH_3}$	Diethyl ketone	3-Pentanone	102

PROBLEM SOLVING TIP 23.2
Naming Aldehydes, Ketones, and Carboxylic Acids

Aldehydes: Substitute "-al" for the final "-e" in the name of the hydrocarbon. The carbon atom of an aldehyde is, by definition, carbon-1 in the hydrocarbon chain. For example, the compound $CH_3CH(CH_3)CH_2CH_2CHO$ contains a 5-carbon chain with the aldehyde functional group being carbon-1 and the $-CH_3$ group at position 4; thus, the name is *4-methylpentanal.*

Ketones: Substitute "-one" for the final "-e" in the name of the hydrocarbon. The position of the ketone functional group (the carbonyl group) is indicated by the number of the carbon atom. For example, the compound $CH_3COCH_2CH(C_2H_5)CH_2CH_3$ has the carbonyl group at the 2 position and an ethyl group at the 4 position of a 6-carbon chain; its name is *4-ethyl-2-hexanone.*

Carboxylic acids (organic acids): Substitute "-oic" for the final "-e" in the name of the hydrocarbon. The carbon atoms in the longest chain are counted beginning with the carboxylic carbon atom. For example, *trans*-$CH_3CH{=}CHCH_2CO_2H$ is named as a derivative of *trans*-3-pentene, that is, *trans-3-pentenoic acid.*

Carboxylic Acids

Acetic acid is the most common and most important **carboxylic acid.** For many years, acetic acid was made by oxidizing ethanol produced by fermentation. Now, however, most of the acetic acid is made by combining carbon monoxide and methanol in the presence of a catalyst:

$$\underset{\text{methanol}}{CH_3OH(\ell)} + CO(g) \xrightarrow{\text{catalyst}} \underset{\text{acetic acid}}{CH_3CO_2H(\ell)}$$

About 1 billion kilograms of acetic acid are produced annually in the United States for use in plastics, synthetic fibers, and fungicides.

Many organic acids are found naturally (Table 23.9). Acids are recognizable by their sour taste (Figure 23.11) and are found in common foods: Citric acid in fruits, acetic acid in vinegar, and tartaric acid in grapes are just three examples.

FIGURE 23.11 **Acetic acid in bread.** Acetic acid is produced in bread leavened with the yeast *Saccharomyces exiguus*. Another group of bacteria, *Lactobacillus sanfrancisco*, contributes to the flavor of sourdough bread. These bacteria metabolize the sugar maltose, excreting acetic acid and lactic acid, $CH_3CH(OH)CO_2H$, thereby giving the bread its unique sour taste.

Table 23.9 Some Naturally Occurring Carboxylic Acids

Name	Structure	Natural Source
Benzoic acid	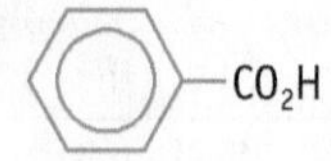	Berries
Citric acid	$HO_2C—CH_2—C(OH)(CO_2H)—CH_2—CO_2H$	Citrus fruits
Lactic acid	$H_3C—CH(OH)—CO_2H$	Sour milk
Malic acid	$HO_2C—CH_2—CH(OH)—CO_2H$	Apples
Oleic acid	$CH_3(CH_2)_7—CH{=}CH—(CH_2)_7—CO_2H$	Vegetable oils
Oxalic acid	$HO_2C—CO_2H$	Rhubarb, spinach, cabbage, tomatoes
Stearic acid	$CH_3(CH_2)_{16}—CO_2H$	Animal fats
Tartaric acid	$HO_2C—CH(OH)—CH(OH)—CO_2H$	Grape juice, wine

Table 23.10 Some Simple Carboxylic Acids

Structure	Common Name	Systematic Name	BP (°C)
$H\overset{\overset{O}{\|}}{C}OH$	Formic acid	Methanoic acid	101
$CH_3\overset{\overset{O}{\|}}{C}OH$	Acetic acid	Ethanoic acid	118
$CH_3CH_2\overset{\overset{O}{\|}}{C}OH$	Propionic acid	Propanoic acid	141
$CH_3(CH_2)_2\overset{\overset{O}{\|}}{C}OH$	Butyric acid	Butanoic acid	163
$CH_3(CH_2)_3\overset{\overset{O}{\|}}{C}OH$	Valeric acid	Pentanoic acid	187

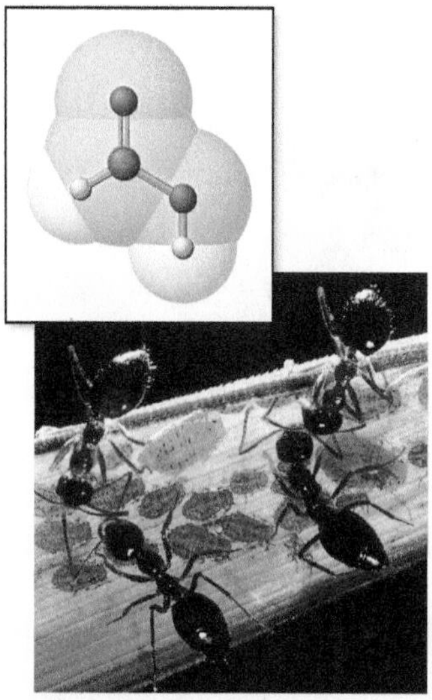

Formic acid, HCO_2H. This acid puts the sting in ant bites.

Some carboxylic acids have common names derived from the source of the acid (Tables 23.9 and 23.10). Because formic acid is found in ants, its name comes from the Latin word for ant (*formica*). Butyric acid gives rancid butter its unpleasant odor, and the name is related to the Latin word for butter (*butyrum*). The systematic names of acids (Table 23.10) are formed by dropping the "-e" on the name of the corresponding alkane and adding "-oic" (and the word "acid").

Because of the substantial electronegativity of oxygen, the two O atoms of the carboxylic acid group are slightly negatively charged, and the H atom of the —OH group is partially positively charged. This charge distribution has several important implications:

- The polar acetic acid molecule dissolves readily in water, which you already know because vinegar is an aqueous solution of acetic acid. (Acids with larger organic groups are less soluble, however.)
- The hydrogen of the —OH group is the acidic hydrogen. As noted in Table 3.1, acetic acid is a weak acid in water, as are most other organic acids.

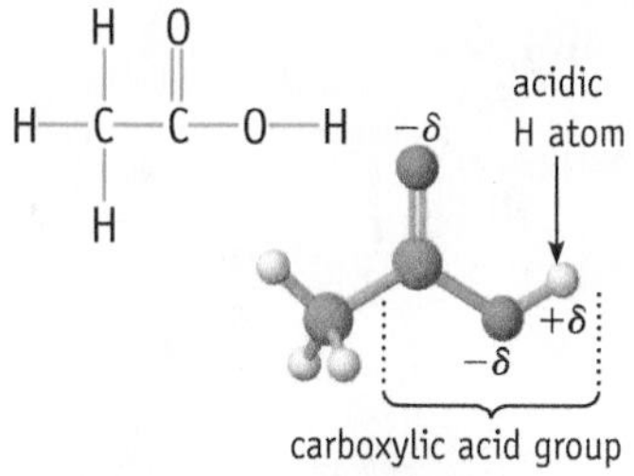

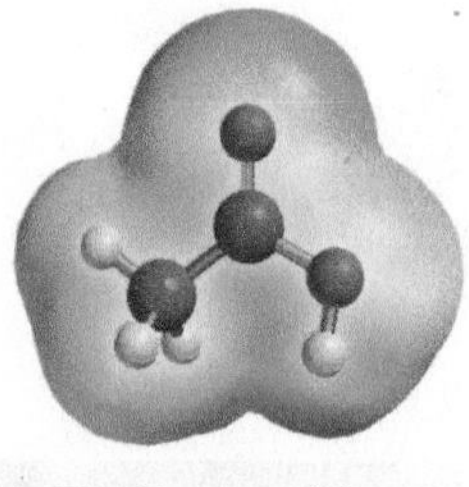
Acetic acid. The H atom of the carboxylic acid group (—CO_2H) is the acidic proton of this and other carboxylic acids.

Carboxylic acids undergo a number of reactions. Among these is the reduction of the acid (with reagents such as $LiAlH_4$ or $NaBH_4$) first to an aldehyde and then to an alcohol. For example, acetic acid is reduced first to acetaldehyde and then to ethanol.

$$\underset{\text{acetic acid}}{CH_3CO_2H} \xrightarrow{LiAlH_4} \underset{\text{acetaldehyde}}{CH_3CHO} \xrightarrow{LiAlH_4} \underset{\text{ethanol}}{CH_3CH_2OH}$$

Yet another important aspect of carboxylic acid chemistry is the reaction with bases to give carboxylate anions. For example, acetic acid reacts with hydroxide ions to give acetate ions and water.

$$CH_3CO_2H(aq) + OH^-(aq) \rightarrow CH_3CO_2^-(aq) + H_2O(\ell)$$

Esters

Esters are the product of the reaction of an acid with an alcohol. Such reactions, called **esterification** reactions, are usually carried out with an acid catalyst (such as HCl). These reactions do not go to completion, however; instead, they proceed to form an equilibrium mixture of the reactants and products. To obtain the ester in good yield, the reaction can be forced to completion. One way to do this is to remove

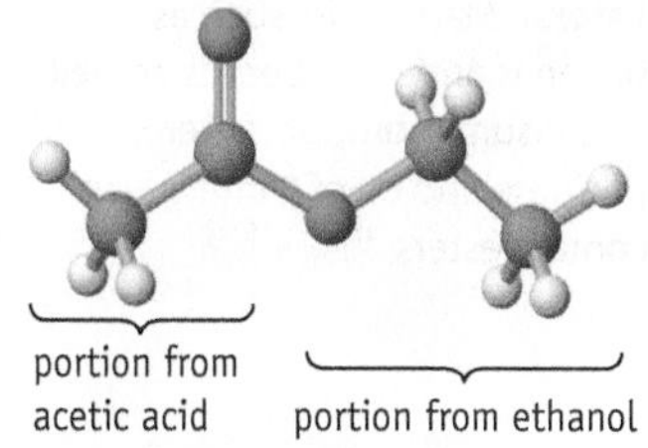

ethyl acetate, an ester
$CH_3CO_2CH_2CH_3$

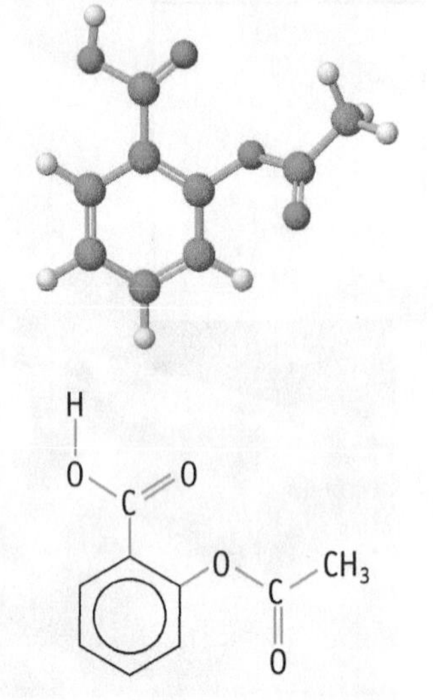

Aspirin, a commonly used analgesic. It is based on benzoic acid with an acetate group, $—O_2CCH_3$, in the *ortho* position. Aspirin has both carboxylic acid and ester functional groups.

water from the system (for example, by distilling it from the reaction mixture); this causes the equilibrium to shift to the right, thus forming more of the ester.

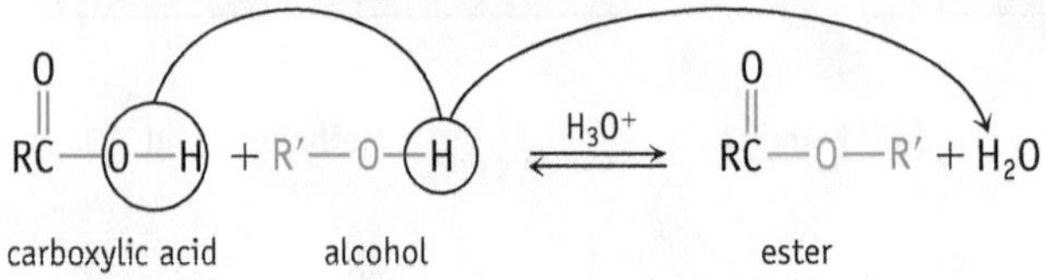

$$\underset{\text{acetic acid}}{CH_3\overset{O}{\overset{\|}{C}}OH} + \underset{\text{ethanol}}{CH_3CH_2OH} \underset{}{\overset{H_3O^+}{\rightleftharpoons}} \underset{\text{ethyl acetate}}{CH_3\overset{O}{\overset{\|}{C}}OCH_2CH_3} + H_2O$$

In these reactions the O atom of the alcohol ends up as part of the ester. This is known from isotope labeling experiments. If the reaction is run using an alcohol in which the alcohol oxygen is ^{18}O, all of the ^{18}O ends up in the ester molecule.

Table 23.11 lists a few common esters and the acid and alcohol from which they are formed. The two-part name of an ester is given by (1) the name of the hydrocarbon group from the alcohol and (2) the name of the carboxylate group derived from the acid name by replacing "-ic" with "-ate." For example, ethanol (commonly called ethyl alcohol) and acetic acid combine to give the ester ethyl acetate.

An important reaction of esters is *hydrolysis* (literally, reaction with water), a reaction that is the reverse of the reaction forming the ester. In a neutral solution, this reaction also gives an equilibrium mixture of acid and ester. In order for this reaction to reach completion, however, it is carried out in a basic solution. The base, NaOH for example, reacts with the acid, thus shifting the equilibrium toward the product.

$$\underset{\text{ester}}{R\overset{O}{\overset{\|}{C}}OR'} + NaOH \xrightarrow[\text{in water}]{\text{heat}} \underset{\text{carboxylate salt}}{R\overset{O}{\overset{\|}{C}}O^-Na^+} + \underset{\text{alcohol}}{R'OH}$$

$$\underset{\text{ethyl acetate}}{CH_3\overset{O}{\overset{\|}{C}}OCH_2CH_3} + NaOH \xrightarrow[\text{in water}]{\text{heat}} \underset{\text{sodium acetate}}{CH_3\overset{O}{\overset{\|}{C}}O^-Na^+} + \underset{\text{ethanol}}{CH_3CH_2OH}$$

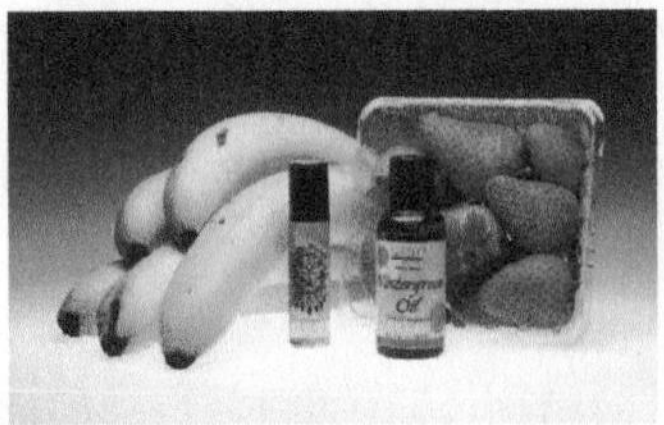

Esters. Many fruits such as bananas and strawberries as well as consumer products (here, perfume and oil of wintergreen) contain esters.

Table 23.11 Some Acids, Alcohols, and Their Esters

Acid	Alcohol	Ester	Odor of Ester
CH_3CO_2H acetic acid	$CH_3\overset{CH_3}{\overset{\vert}{C}}HCH_2CH_2OH$ 3-methyl-1-butanol	$CH_3\overset{O}{\overset{\|}{C}}OCH_2CH_2\overset{CH_3}{\overset{\vert}{C}}HCH_3$ 3-methylbutyl acetate	Banana
$CH_3CH_2CH_2CO_2H$ butanoic acid	$CH_3CH_2CH_2CH_2OH$ 1-butanol	$CH_3CH_2CH_2\overset{O}{\overset{\|}{C}}OCH_2CH_2CH_2CH_3$ butyl butanoate	Pineapple
$CH_3CH_2CH_2CO_2H$ butanoic acid	$C_6H_5—CH_2OH$ benzyl alcohol	$CH_3CH_2CH_2\overset{O}{\overset{\|}{C}}OCH_2—C_6H_5$ benzyl butanoate	Rose

The carboxylic acid can be recovered if the sodium salt is treated with a strong acid such as HCl:

$$\underset{\text{sodium acetate}}{CH_3\overset{\overset{\displaystyle O}{\|}}{C}O^-Na^+(aq)} + HCl(aq) \longrightarrow \underset{\text{acetic acid}}{CH_3\overset{\overset{\displaystyle O}{\|}}{C}OH(aq)} + NaCl(aq)$$

Unlike the acids from which they are derived, esters often have pleasant odors (Table 23.11). Typical examples are methyl salicylate, or "oil of wintergreen," and benzyl acetate. Methyl salicylate is derived from salicylic acid, the parent compound of aspirin.

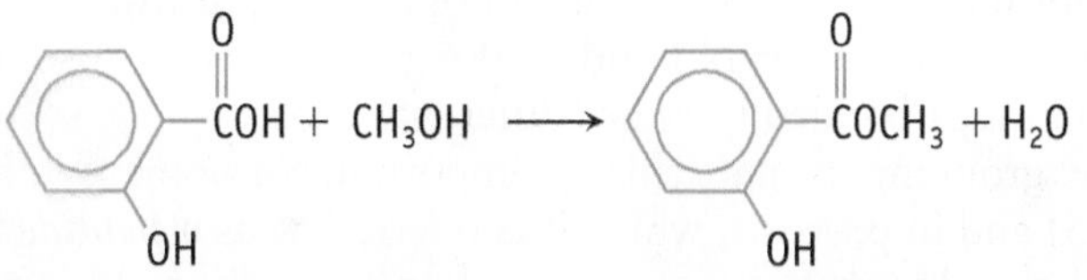

salicylic acid methanol methyl salicylate, oil of wintergreen

Benzyl acetate, the active component of "oil of jasmine," is formed from benzyl alcohol ($C_6H_5CH_2OH$) and acetic acid. The chemicals are inexpensive, so synthetic jasmine is used as a fragrance in less-expensive perfumes and toiletries.

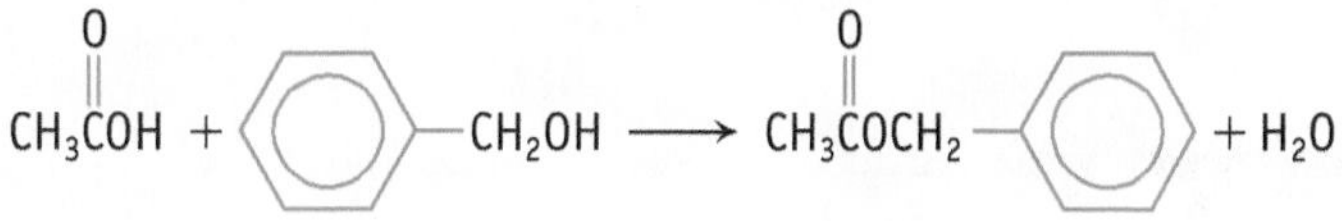

acetic acid benzyl alcohol benzyl acetate oil of jasmine

Amides

A carboxylic acid and an alcohol react by loss of water to form an ester. In a similar manner, another class of organic compounds—amides—form when a carboxylic acid reacts with an amine, again with loss of water.

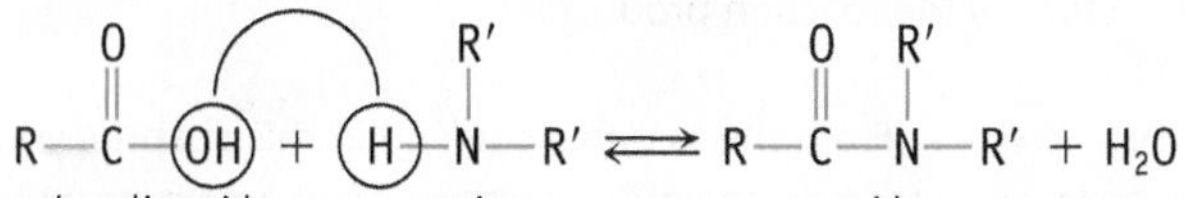

carboxylic acid amine amide

Amides have an organic group and an amino group ($—NH_2$, $—NHR'$, or $—NR'R$) attached to the carbonyl group.

The C atom involved in the amide bond has three bonded groups and no lone pairs around it. We would predict it should be sp^2 hybridized with trigonal-planar geometry and bond angles of approximately 120°—and this is what is found. However, the structure of the amide group offers a surprise. The N atom is also observed to have trigonal-planar geometry with bonds to three attached atoms at 120°. Because the amide nitrogen is surrounded by four pairs of electrons, we would have predicted the N atom would have sp^3 hybridization and bond angles of about 109°.

Based on the observed geometry of the amide N atom, the atom is assigned sp^2 hybridization. To rationalize the observed angle and sp^2 hybridization, we can introduce a second resonance form of the amide.

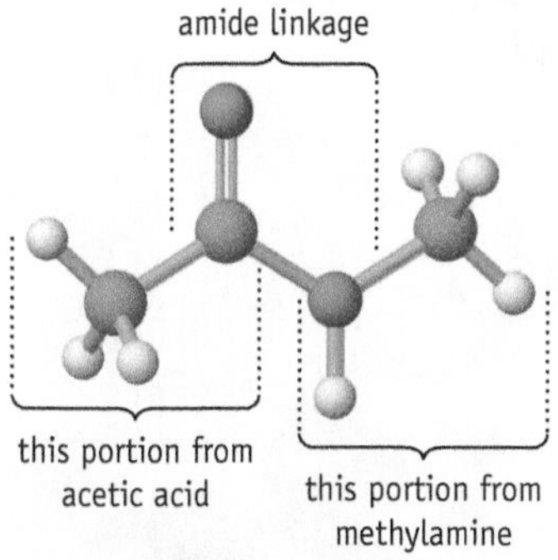

An amide, *N*-methylacetamide. The *N*-methyl portion of the name derives from the amine portion of the molecule, where the *N* indicates that the methyl group is attached to the nitrogen atom. The "-acet" portion of the name indicates the acid on which the amide is based. The electrostatic potential surface and model show the polarity and planarity of the amide linkage.

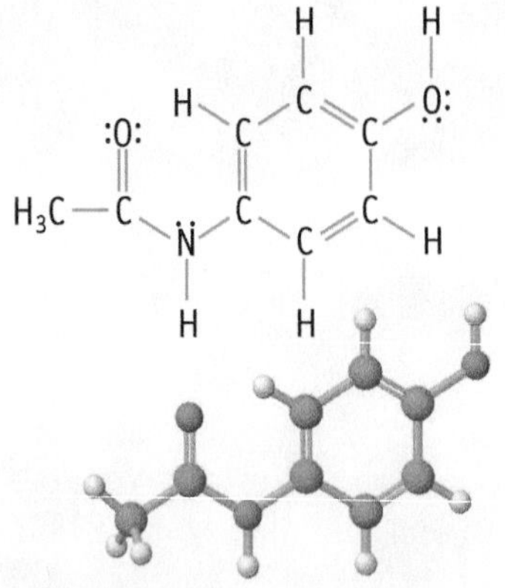

Acetaminophen, *N*-acetyl-*p*-aminophenol. This analgesic is an amide. It is used in over-the-counter painkillers such as Tylenol.

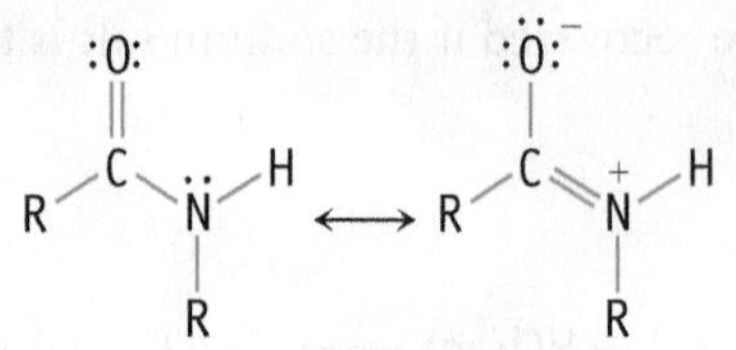

(A) (B)

Form B contains a C=N double bond, and the O and N atoms have negative and positive charges, respectively. The N atom can be assigned sp^2 hybridization, and the π bond in B arises from overlap of p orbitals on C and N.

The second resonance structure for an amide link also explains why the carbon–nitrogen bond is relatively short, about 132 pm, a value between that of a C—N single bond (149 pm) and a C=N double bond (127 pm). In addition, restricted rotation occurs around the C=N bond, making it possible for isomeric species to exist if the two groups bonded to N are different.

The amide grouping is particularly important in some synthetic polymers (▶ Section 23-5) and in proteins, where it is referred to as a *peptide* link. The compound *N*-acetyl-*p*-aminophenol, an analgesic known by the generic name acetaminophen, is another amide. Use of this compound as an analgesic was apparently discovered by accident when a common organic compound called acetanilide (like acetaminophen but without the —OH group) was mistakenly put into a prescription for a patient. Acetanilide acts as an analgesic, but it can be toxic. An —OH group *para* to the amide group makes the compound nontoxic, an interesting example of how a seemingly small structural difference affects chemical function.

EXAMPLE 23.7

Functional Group Chemistry

Problem

(a) Draw the structure of the product of the reaction between propanoic acid and 1-propanol. What is the systematic name of the reaction product, and what functional group does it contain?

(b) What is the result of reacting 2-butanol with an oxidizing agent? Give the name, and draw the structure of the reaction product.

What Do You Know? From the material covered in this chapter, you should know the names, structures, and common chemical reactions of organic compounds mentioned in this question.

Strategy Determine the products of these reactions, based on the discussion in the text. Propanoic acid is a carboxylic acid, and 1-propanol and 2-butanol are both alcohols.

Solution

(a) Carboxylic acids such as propanoic acid react with alcohols to give esters.

$$\underset{\text{propanoic acid}}{CH_3CH_2\overset{\overset{O}{\|}}{C}OH} + \underset{\text{1-propanol}}{CH_3CH_2CH_2OH} \longrightarrow \underset{\text{propyl propanoate, an ester}}{CH_3CH_2\overset{\overset{O}{\|}}{C}OCH_2CH_2CH_3} + H_2O$$

(b) 2-Butanol is a secondary alcohol. Such alcohols are oxidized to ketones.

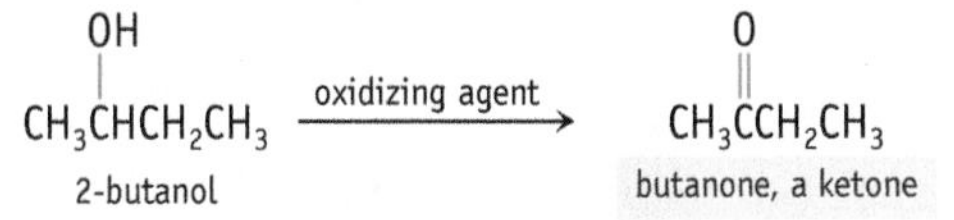

Think about Your Answer Students sometimes find themselves overwhelmed by the large amount of information presented in organic chemistry. Your study of this material will be more successful if you carefully organize information based on the type of compound.

Check Your Understanding

(a) Name each of the following compounds and its functional group.

(1) $CH_3CH_2CH_2OH$ (2) $CH_3C(=O)OH$ (3) $CH_3CH_2NH_2$

(b) Name the product from the reaction of compounds 1 and 2 above.

(c) What is the name and structure of the product from the oxidation of 1 with an excess of oxidizing agent?

(d) Give the name and structure of the compound that results from combining 2 and 3.

(e) What is the result of adding an acid (say HCl) to compound 3?

REVIEW & CHECK FOR SECTION 23-4

1. How many aldehydes and ketones are possible that have the formula $C_5H_{10}O$ and that have a five-carbon chain?

(a) 2 aldehydes and 1 ketone

(b) 1 aldehyde and 3 ketones

(c) 1 aldehyde and 1 ketone

(d) 1 aldehyde and 2 ketones

A CLOSER LOOK Omega-3-Fatty Acids

There is considerable interest today in incorporating omega-3-fatty acids in the diet. Although potential health benefits are not fully defined, proponents say there is some evidence that they lower blood pressure and reduce the chances of heart attacks and strokes. Sources of omega-3-fatty acids include fish and plant oils.

These compounds are polyunsaturated, long-chain carboxylic acids, and there are a number of different, naturally occurring compounds in this class.

The word "omega" in the name refers to the last carbon atom in the carbon chain of the acid, and the number 3 indicates that there is a double bond between carbon atoms 3 and 4 when counted from that end of the molecule.

An example of an omega-3-fatty acid is all-*cis*-7,10,13-hexadecatrienoic acid, whose structure is shown here. Naming large complicated molecules is challenging, but it is possible to decipher the structure from the name. *Hexadeca* identifies this as a 16-carbon atom compound, *triene* tells us there are 3 double bonds (all with *cis* geometry), and the *oic* ending defines it as a carboxylic acid. The numbers 7, 10, and 13 indicate the positions of the double bonds relative to the carboxylic carbon atom.

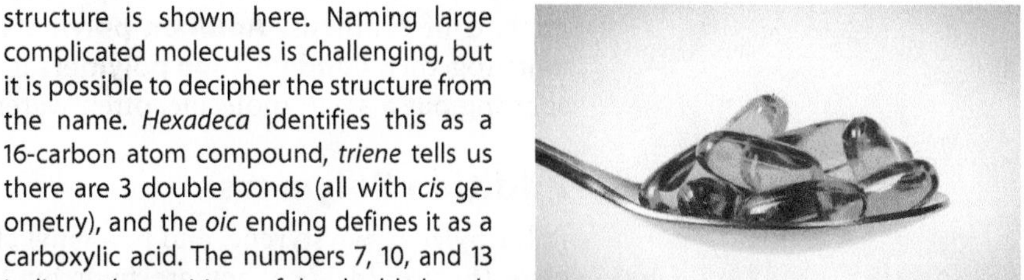

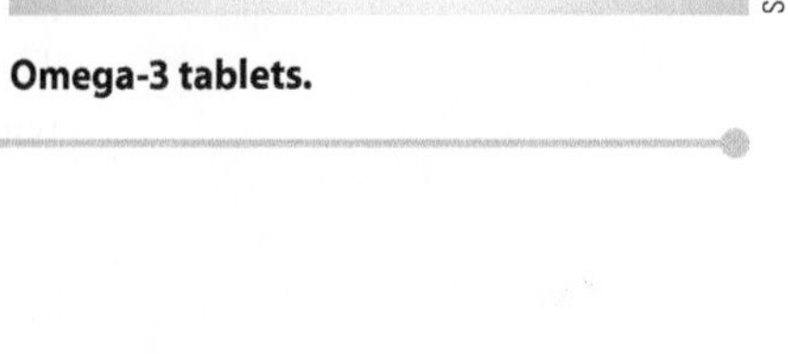

Omega-3 tablets.

2. Addition of water to 2-butene gives a single product. Oxidation of this product with $K_2Cr_2O_7$ gives a single compound. What is its name?

(a) butanal (c) 2-butanol

(b) 2-butanone (d) butane

3. What is the bond angle of the O—C—O group of atoms in benzoic acid and what is the hybridization of the carbonyl carbon atom?

(a) 90°, not hybridized (c) 180°, *sp* hybridized

(b) 109.5°, sp^3 hybridized (d) 120°, sp^2 hybridized

4. A sample of ethanol is divided into two portions. One portion is oxidized with excess oxidizing agent to give an acid. The acid and the remaining alcohol react to give an ester. What is the name of the ester?

(a) ethyl propanoate (c) ethyl ethanoate

(b) ethanoic acid (d) methyl propanoate

Learning Objectives: LO 5.11

23-5 Polymers

We turn now to the very large molecules known as *polymers*. These can be either synthetic materials or naturally occurring substances such as proteins or nucleic acids. Although many different types of polymers are known and they have widely different compositions and structures, their properties are understandable, based on the principles developed for small molecules.

Classifying Polymers

The word *polymer* means "many parts" (from the Greek, *poly* and *meros*). Thus, **polymers** are giant molecules made by chemically joining many small molecules called **monomers.** Polymer molar masses can range from thousands to millions.

Extensive use of synthetic polymers is a fairly recent development. A few synthetic polymers (Bakelite, rayon, and celluloid) were made early in the 20th century, but most of the products with which you are likely to be familiar originated in the last 75 years. By 1976, synthetic polymers outstripped steel as the most widely used materials in the United States. The average production of synthetic polymers in the United States is now 150 kg or more per person annually.

The polymer industry classifies polymers in several different ways. One is their response to heating. **Thermoplastics** (such as polyethylene) soften and flow when they are heated and harden when they are cooled. **Thermosetting plastics** (such as Formica) are initially soft but set to a solid when heated and cannot be resoftened. Another classification scheme depends on the end use of the polymer—for example, plastics, fibers, elastomers, coatings, and adhesives.

A more chemically oriented approach to polymer classification is based on the method of synthesis. **Addition polymers** are made by directly adding monomer units together. **Condensation polymers** are made by combining monomer units and splitting out a small molecule, often water.

Addition Polymers

Polyethylene, polystyrene, and polyvinyl chloride (PVC) are common addition polymers (Figure 23.12). They are built by "adding together" simple alkenes such as ethylene ($CH_2{=}CH_2$), styrene ($C_6H_5CH{=}CH_2$), and vinyl chloride ($CH_2{=}CHCl$). These and other addition polymers (Table 23.12), all derived from alkenes, have widely varying properties and uses.

(a) High-density polyethylene.

(b) Polystyrene.

(c) Polyvinyl chloride.

FIGURE 23.12 **Common polymer-based consumer products.** Recycling information is provided on most plastics (often molded into the bottom of bottles). High-density polyethylene is designated with a "2" inside a triangular symbol and the letters "HDPE." Polystyrene is designated by "6" with the symbol PS, and polyvinyl chloride, PVC, is designated with a "3" inside a triangular symbol with the symbol "V" or "PVC" below.

Table 23.12 Ethylene Derivatives That Undergo Addition

Formula	Monomer Common Name	Polymer Name (Trade Names)	Uses
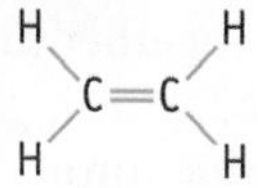	Ethylene	Polyethylene (polythene)	Squeeze bottles, bags, films, toys and molded objects, electric insulation
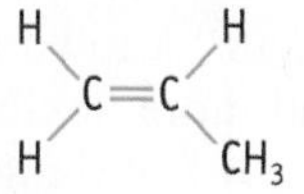	Propylene	Polypropylene (Vectra, Herculon)	Bottles, films, indoor-outdoor carpets
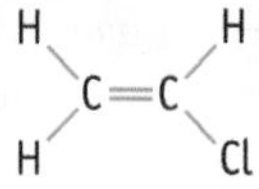	Vinyl chloride	Polyvinyl chloride (PVC)	Floor tile, raincoats, pipe
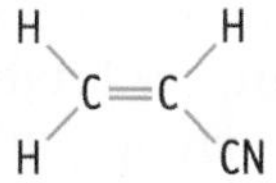	Acrylonitrile	Polyacrylonitrile (Orlon, Acrilan)	Rugs, fabrics
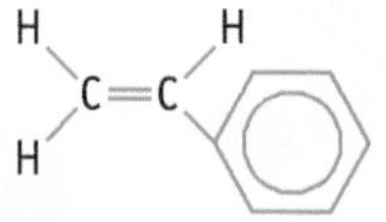	Styrene	Polystyrene (Styrofoam, Styron)	Food and drink coolers, building material, insulation
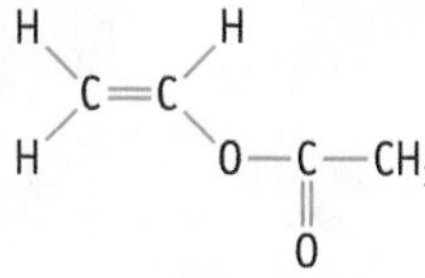	Vinyl acetate	Polyvinyl acetate (PVA)	Latex paint, adhesives, textile coatings
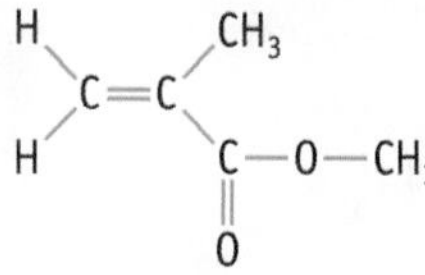	Methyl methacrylate	Polymethyl methacrylate (Plexiglas, Lucite)	High-quality transparent objects, latex paints, contact lenses
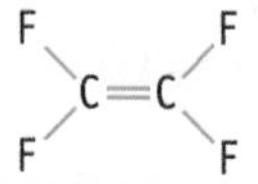	Tetrafluoroethylene	Polytetrafluoroethylene (Teflon)	Gaskets, insulation, bearings, pan coatings

James Holmes/Zedcor/Science Source

Polyethylene film. The polymer film is produced by extruding the molten plastic through a ring-like gap and inflating the film like a balloon.

Polyethylene and Other Polyolefins

Polyethylene is by far the leader in amount of polymer produced. Ethylene (C_2H_4), the monomer from which polyethylene is made, is a product of petroleum refining and one of the top five chemicals produced in the United States. When ethylene is heated to between 100 and 250 °C at a pressure of 1000 to 3000 atm in the presence of a catalyst, polymers with molar masses up to several million are formed. The reaction can be expressed as the chemical equation:

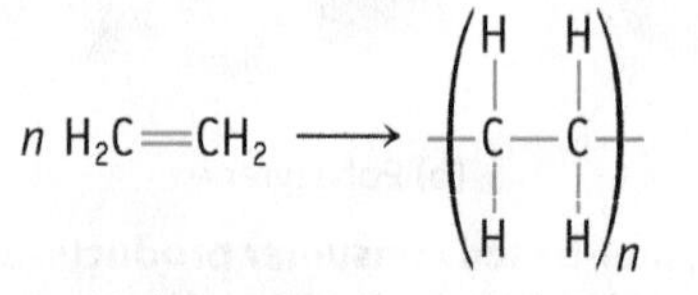

ethylene polyethylene

The abbreviated formula of the reaction product, $-\!\!(CH_2CH_2)\!\!-_n$, shows that polyethylene is a chain of carbon atoms, each bearing two hydrogens. The chain length for polyethylene can be very long. A polymer with a molar mass of 1 million would contain almost 36,000 ethylene molecules linked together.

Samples of polyethylene formed under various pressures and catalytic conditions have different properties, as a result of different molecular structures. For example, when chromium(III) oxide is used as a catalyst, the product is almost exclusively a linear chain (Figure 23.13a). If ethylene is heated to 230 °C at high pressure, however, irregular branching occurs (Figure 23.13b). Still other conditions lead to cross-linked polyethylene, in which different chains are linked together (Figure 23.13c).

The high molar mass chains of linear polyethylene pack closely together and result in a material with a density of 0.97 g/cm^3. This material, referred to as high-density polyethylene (HDPE), is hard and tough, which makes it suitable for items such as milk bottles. If the polyethylene chain contains branches, however, the chains cannot pack as closely, and a lower-density material (0.92 g/cm^3) known as low-density polyethylene (LDPE) results. This material is softer and more flexible than HDPE. It is used in plastic wrap and sandwich bags, among other things. Linking up the polymer chains in cross-linked polyethylene (CLPE) causes the material to be even more rigid and inflexible. Plastic bottle caps are often made of CLPE.

Polymers formed from substituted ethylenes ($CH_2{=}CHX$) have a range of properties and uses (see Table 23.12). Sometimes, the properties are predictable based on the molecule's structure. Polymers without polar substituent groups, such

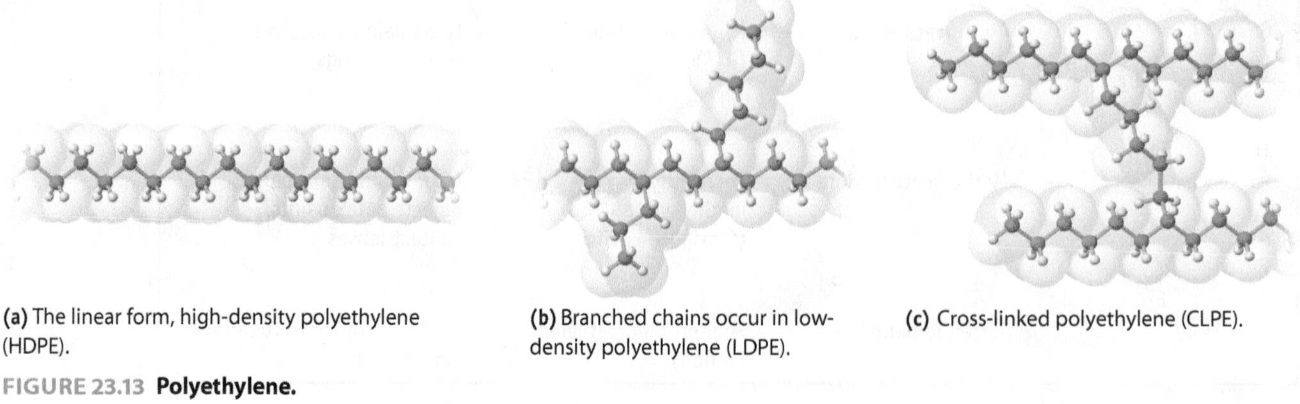

(a) The linear form, high-density polyethylene (HDPE).

(b) Branched chains occur in low-density polyethylene (LDPE).

(c) Cross-linked polyethylene (CLPE).

FIGURE 23.13 **Polyethylene.**

as polystyrene, often dissolve in organic solvents, a property useful for some types of fabrication.

polymers based on substituted ethylenes, $H_2C{=}CHX$

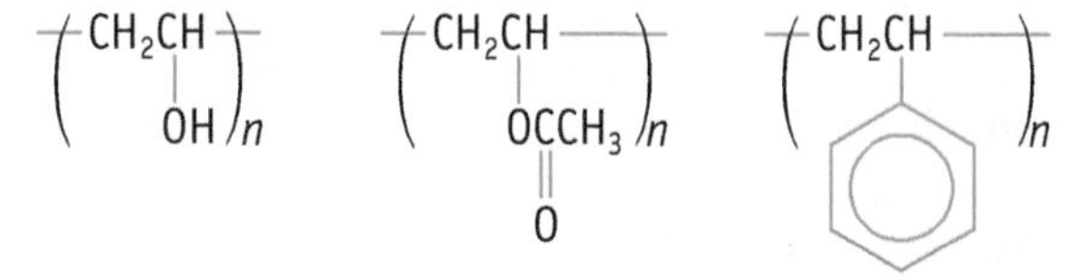

polyvinyl alcohol polyvinyl acetate polystyrene

Polyvinyl alcohol is a polymer with little affinity for nonpolar solvents but an affinity for water, which is not surprising, based on the large number of polar OH groups (Figure 23.14). Vinyl alcohol ($CH_2{=}CHOH$) is not a stable compound (it isomerizes to acetaldehyde CH_3CHO), so polyvinyl alcohol cannot be made from this compound. Instead, it is made by hydrolyzing the ester groups in polyvinyl acetate.

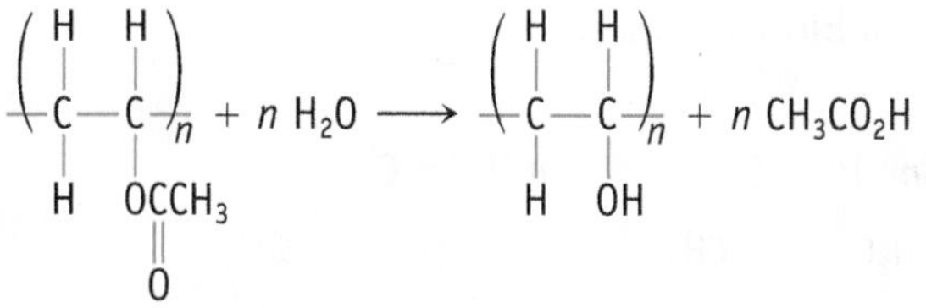

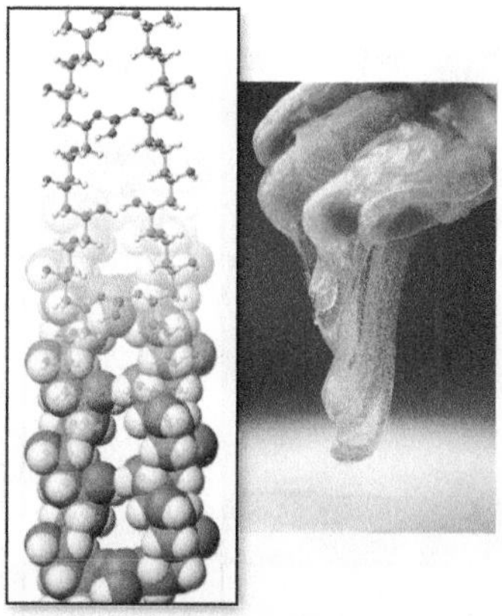

© Cengage Learning/Charles D. Winters

FIGURE 23.14 Slime from polyvinyl alcohol. When boric acid, $B(OH)_3$, is added to an aqueous suspension of polyvinyl alcohol, $(CH_2CHOH)_n$, the mixture becomes very viscous because boric acid reacts with the —OH groups on the polymer chain, causing cross-linking to occur. (The model shows an idealized structure of a portion of the polymer.)

Solubility in water or organic solvents can be a liability for polymers. The many uses of polytetrafluoroethylene [Teflon, $\left(-CF_2CF_2-\right)_n$] stem from the fact that it does not interact with water or organic solvents.

Polystyrene, with $n = 5700$, is a clear, hard, colorless solid that can be molded easily at 250 °C. However, you are probably more familiar with the very light, foam-like material known as Styrofoam that is used widely for food and beverage containers and for home insulation (see Figure 23.12). Styrofoam is produced by a process called "expansion molding." Polystyrene beads containing 4% to 7% of a low-boiling liquid like pentane are placed in a mold and heated with steam or hot air. Heat causes the solvent to vaporize, creating a foam in the molten polymer that expands to fill the shape of the mold.

Natural and Synthetic Rubber

Natural rubber was first introduced in Europe in 1740, but it remained a curiosity until 1823, when Charles Macintosh invented a way of using it to waterproof cotton cloth. The macintosh, as rain coats are still sometimes called, became popular despite major problems: Natural rubber is notably weak and is soft and tacky when warm, but it is brittle at low temperatures. In 1839, after 5 years of research on natural rubber, the American inventor Charles Goodyear (1800–1860) discovered that heating gum rubber with sulfur produces a material that is elastic, water-repellent, resilient, and no longer sticky.

Rubber is a naturally occurring polymer, the monomers of which are molecules of 2-methyl-1,3-butadiene, commonly called *isoprene*. In natural rubber, isoprene monomers are linked together through carbon atoms 1 and 4—that is, through the end carbon atoms of the C_4 chain (Figure 23.15). This leaves a double bond between carbon atoms 2 and 3. In natural rubber, these double bonds have a *cis* configuration.

In vulcanized rubber, the material that Goodyear discovered, the polymer chains of natural rubber are cross-linked by short chains of sulfur atoms. Cross-linking helps to align the polymer chains, so the material does not undergo a permanent change when stretched and it springs back when the stress is removed. Substances that behave this way are called **elastomers**.

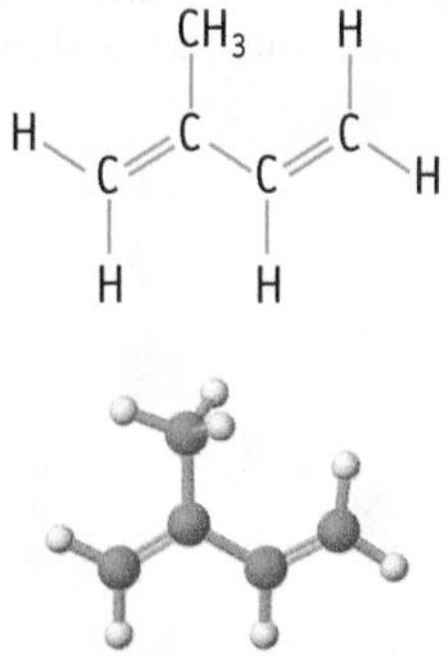

isoprene, 2-methyl-1,3-butadiene

FIGURE 23.15 Natural rubber. The sap that comes from the rubber tree is a natural polymer of isoprene. All the linkages in the carbon chain are *cis*. When natural rubber is heated strongly in the absence of air, it smells of isoprene. This observation provided a clue that rubber is composed of this building block.

With a knowledge of the composition and structure of natural rubber, chemists began searching for ways to make synthetic rubber. When they first tried to make the polymer by linking isoprene monomers together, however, what they made was sticky and useless. The problem was that synthesis procedures gave a mixture of *cis*- and *trans*-polyisoprene. In 1955, however, chemists at the Goodyear and Firestone companies discovered special catalysts to prepare the all-*cis* polymer. This synthetic material, which was structurally identical to natural rubber, is now manufactured cheaply. In fact, more than 8.0×10^8 kg of synthetic polyisoprene is produced annually in the United States. Other kinds of polymers have further expanded the repertoire of elastomeric materials now available. Polybutadiene, for example, is currently used in the production of tires, hoses, and belts.

Some elastomers, called **copolymers**, are formed by polymerization of two (or more) different monomers. A copolymer of butadiene and styrene, made with a 3:1 ratio of these raw materials, is the most important synthetic rubber now made; more than 1 billion kilograms of styrene-butadiene rubber (SBR) is produced each year in the United States for making tires. And a little is left over each year to make bubble gum. The stretchiness of bubble gum once came from natural rubber, but SBR is now used to help you blow bubbles.

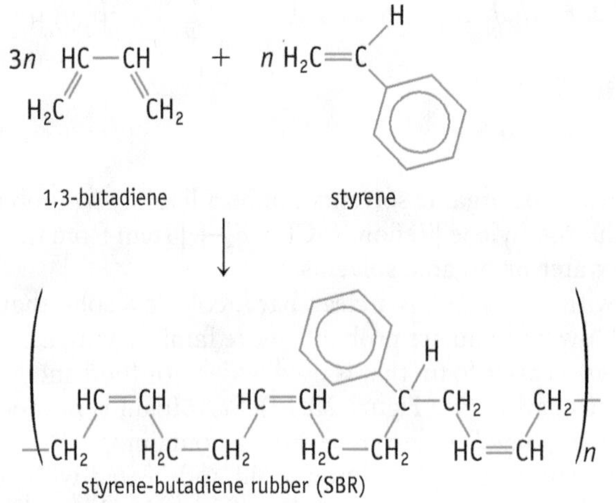

1,3-butadiene styrene

styrene-butadiene rubber (SBR)

A CLOSER LOOK Copolymers and Engineering Plastics for Lego Bricks and Tattoos

Many commonly used products are not made of a single monomer but are copolymers or a combination of polymers. One example is ABS plastic. This is a copolymer of acrylonitrile (A) and styrene (S), which is made in the presence of polybutadiene (B).

The result is a thermoplastic that holds color well and has a shiny, impervious surface. It is used to make many consumer items: toys (such as Lego bricks), automobile body parts, and pressure tubing for water and other fluids. There is evidence that some tattoo inks with vivid colors also contain ABS plastic.

When acrylonitrile and styrene are polymerized in the presence of polybutadiene, short chains of the acrylonitrile-styrene polymer are mingled with longer polybutadiene chains. The polar —CN groups from neighboring ABS chains interact with each other and bind the chains together. The result is a stronger plastic than polystyrene.

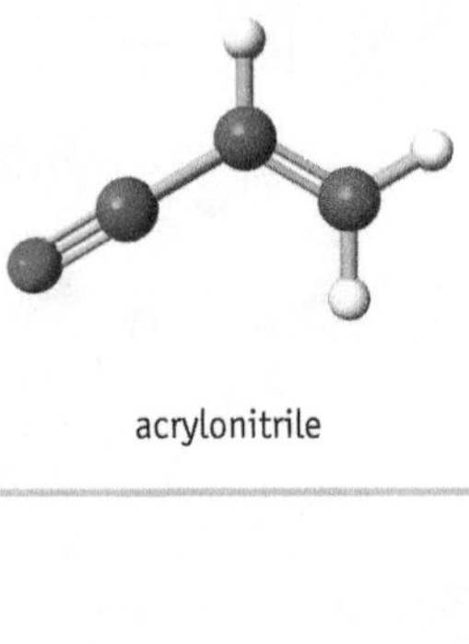
acrylonitrile

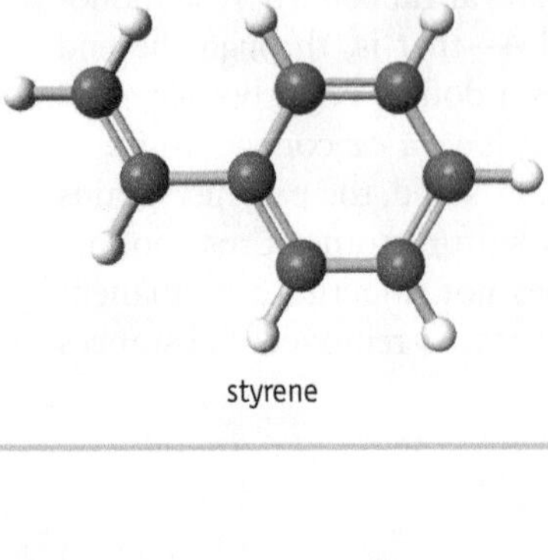
styrene

Condensation Polymers

A chemical reaction in which two molecules react by splitting out, or eliminating, a small molecule is called a **condensation reaction**. The reaction of an alcohol with a carboxylic acid to give an ester is an example of a condensation reaction. One way to form a condensation polymer uses *two* different reactant molecules, each containing *two* functional groups. Another route uses a single molecule with two different functional groups. Commercial polyesters are made using both types of reactions.

Polyesters

Terephthalic acid contains two carboxylic acid groups, and ethylene glycol contains two alcohol groups. When mixed, the acid and alcohol functional groups at both ends of these molecules can react to form ester linkages, splitting out water. The result is a condensation polymer called polyethylene terephthalate (PET). The multiple ester linkages make this substance a **polyester** (Figure 23.16).

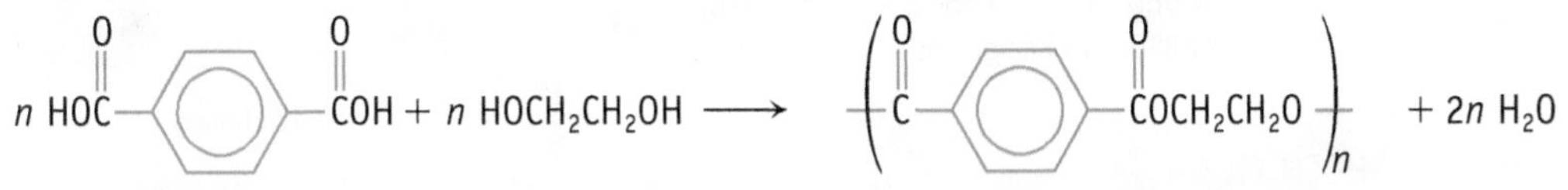

terephthalic acid — ethylene glycol — polyethylene terephthalate (PET), a polyester

PET is also made by a reaction between methyl terephthalate and ethylene glycol, a reaction called **transesterification**. In this reaction one ester is converted to another, and removal of methanol by distillation allows the reaction to reach completion.

$$n\ CH_3O_2CC_6H_4CO_2CH_3 + n\ HOCH_2CH_2OH \rightleftharpoons -(O_2CC_6H_4CO_2CH_2CH_2)_n- + 2n\ CH_3OH$$

Polyester textile fibers made from PET are marketed as Dacron and Terylene. The inert, nontoxic, nonflammable, and non-blood-clotting properties of Dacron polymers make Dacron tubing an excellent substitute for human blood vessels in heart bypass operations, and Dacron sheets are sometimes used as temporary skin for burn victims. A polyester film, Mylar, has unusual strength and can be rolled into sheets one-thirtieth the thickness of a human hair.

There is considerable interest in another polyester, polylactic acid (PLA). Lactic acid contains both carboxylic acid and alcohol functional groups, so condensation between molecules of this monomer gives a polymer.

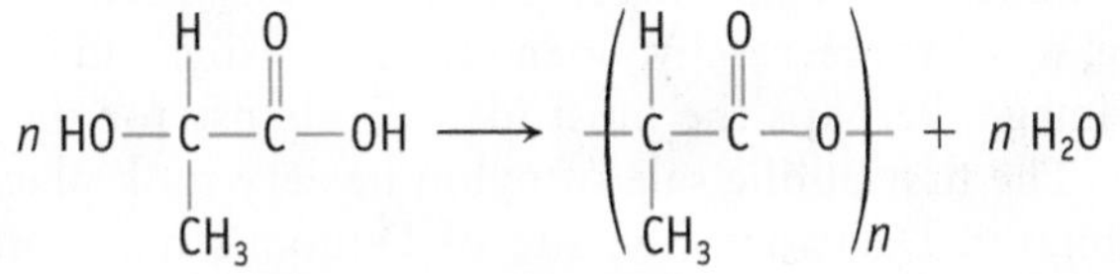

The interest in polylactic acid arises because it is "green" for several reasons. First, the monomer used to make this polymer is obtained by biological fermentation of plant materials. As a result, formation of this polymer is carbon-neutral. All of the carbon in this polymer came from CO_2 in the atmosphere, and degradation at some future time will return the same quantity of CO_2 to the environment. In addition, this polymer, which is currently being used in packaging material, is biodegradable, which has the potential to alleviate landfill disposal problems.

© Cengage Learning/Charles D. Winters

FIGURE 23.16 Polyesters. Polyethylene terephthalate is used to make clothing, soda bottles, car parts, and many other consumer products.

Polyamides

In 1928, the DuPont Company embarked on a basic research program headed by Wallace Carothers (1896–1937). Carothers was interested in high molar mass compounds, such as rubbers, proteins, and resins. In 1935, his research yielded nylon-6,6

A CLOSER LOOK — Green Chemistry: Recycling PET

In 2009, the world production of polyethylene terephthalate amounted to 49.2 billion kg. Most of this was used to produce fibers and packaging materials; the remainder was used for automobile parts, luggage, filters, and much more. Currently, much of the PET used to make beverage containers is recycled.

The recycling process uses some familiar chemistry. Scrap PET is dissolved at over 220 °C in dimethyl phthalate (DMT) and then treated with methanol at 260–300 °C and 340–650 kPa. In this process, the methanol reacts with the polymer to break down the chains forming more DMT and ethylene glycol. DMT and ethylene glycol are separated, purified, and used to make more PET.

The recovery of DMT and ethylene glycol means that increasingly scarce petroleum is not needed to make the starting materials for the manufacture of billions of kilograms of new PET!

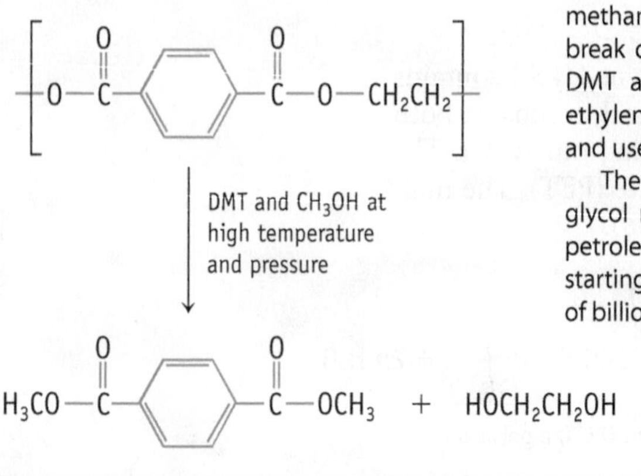

Clothing made of recycled polyester.

FIGURE 23.17 **Nylon-6,6.** Hexamethylenediamine is dissolved in water *(bottom layer),* and adipoyl chloride (a derivative of adipic acid) is dissolved in hexane *(top layer).* The two compounds react at the interface between the layers to form nylon-6,6, which is being wound onto a stirring rod.

(Figure 23.17), a **polyamide** prepared from adipoyl chloride, a derivative of adipic acid (a diacid) and hexamethylenediamine (a diamine):

$$n\ \mathrm{ClC(=O)(CH_2)_4C(=O)Cl} + n\ \mathrm{H_2N(CH_2)_6NH_2} \longrightarrow \left(\!-\mathrm{C(=O)(CH_2)_4C(=O)}\!-\!\mathrm{N(H)(CH_2)_6N(H)}-\right)_n + 2n\ \mathrm{HCl}$$

adipoyl chloride — hexamethylenediamine — amide link in nylon-6,6, a polyamide

Nylon can be extruded easily into fibers that are stronger than natural fibers and chemically more inert, and this fact jolted the American textile industry at a critical time. Natural fibers were not meeting 20th-century needs. Silk was expensive and not durable, wool was scratchy, linen crushed easily, and cotton did not have a high-fashion image. Perhaps the most identifiable use for the new fiber was in nylon stockings. The first public sale of nylon hosiery took place on October 24, 1939, in Wilmington, Delaware (the site of DuPont's main office). This use of nylon in commercial products ended shortly thereafter, however, with the start of World War II. All nylon was diverted to making parachutes and other military gear. It was not until about 1952 that nylon reappeared in the consumer marketplace.

Figure 23.18 illustrates why nylon makes such a good fiber. To have good tensile strength (the ability to resist tearing), the polymer chains should be able to attract one another, albeit not so strongly that the plastic cannot be drawn into fibers. Ordinary covalent bonds between the chains (cross-linking) would be too strong. Instead, cross-linking occurs by the somewhat weaker intermolecular force called *hydrogen bonding* (◀ Section 11-3) between the hydrogens of N—H groups on one chain and the carbonyl oxygens on another chain. The polarities of the $N^{\delta-}$—$H^{\delta+}$ group and the $C^{\delta+}{=}O^{\delta-}$ group lead to attractive forces between the polymer chains of the desired magnitude.

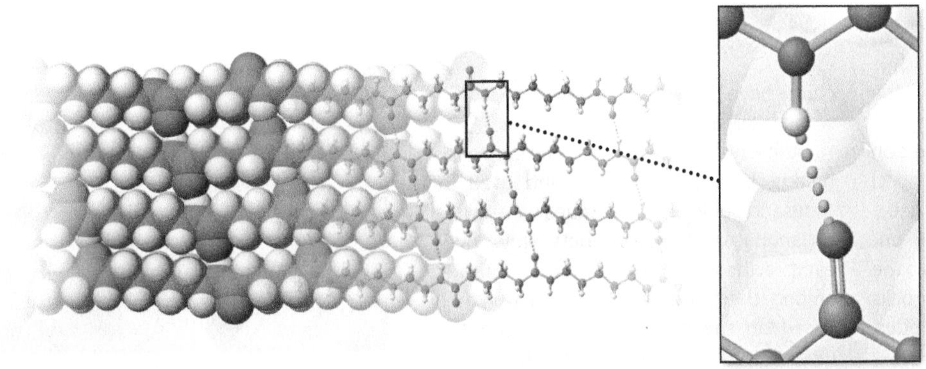

FIGURE 23.18 **Hydrogen bonding between polyamide chains.** Carbonyl oxygen atoms with a partial negative charge on one chain interact with an amine hydrogen with a partial positive charge on a neighboring chain. (Hydrogen bonding is described in more detail in Section 11-3.)

EXAMPLE 23.8

Condensation Polymers

Problem What is the repeating unit of the condensation polymer obtained by combining $HO_2CCH_2CH_2CO_2H$ (succinic acid) and $H_2NCH_2CH_2NH_2$ (1,2-ethylenediamine)?

What Do You Know? Carboxylic acids and amines react to form amides, splitting out water. Here we have a diacid and diamine that will react. The repeating unit will be the shortest sequence that when repeated gives a long polymer chain.

Strategy Recognize that the polymer will link the two monomer units through the amide linkage. The smallest repeating unit of the chain will contain two parts, one from the diacid and the other from the diamine.

Solution The repeating unit of this polyamide is

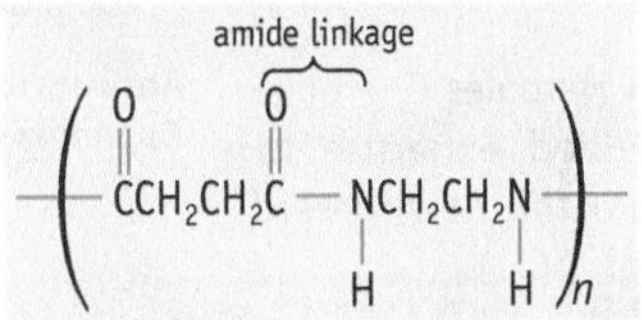

Think about Your Answer Alternating fragments of the diacid and diamine appear in the polymer chain. The fragments are linked by amide bonds making this a polyamide.

Check Your Understanding

Kevlar is a well-known polymer that is now used to make sports equipment and bulletproof vests. The basic structure of the polymer is shown below. Is this a condensation polymer or an addition polymer? What chemicals could be used to make this polymer? Write a balanced equation for the formation of Kevlar.

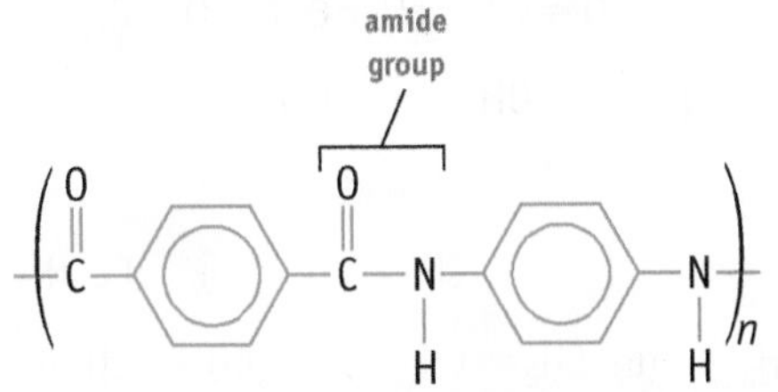

CASE STUDY Green Adhesives

Chemist Kaichang Li was trained in the chemistry of wood and is now doing research at Oregon State University. Oregon has a beautiful and rugged coast, and Li went there in search of mussels to make a special dish. As the waves pounded onshore, he was struck by the fact that the mussels could cling stubbornly to the rocks in spite of the force of the waves and tides. What glue enabled them to do this?

Back in his lab Li found that the strands of glue were largely protein-based. Proteins are simply polymers of amino acids with an amide link between units (see Chapter 24). Li realized that such polymers could have enormous application in the wood industry.

Adhesives, or glues in common terminology, have been known and used for thousands of years. Early glues were based on animal or plant products. Now, however, adhesives are largely synthetic, among them are condensation polymers based on the combination of phenol or urea with formaldehyde. These have been used for well over a half-century in the manufacture of plywood and particle board, and your home or dormitory likely contains a significant amount of these building materials. Unfortunately, they have a disadvantage. In their manufacture and use, formaldehyde, a suspected carcinogen, can be released into the air.

Li's work with mussels eventually led to a new, safer adhesive that could be used in these same wood products. His first problem was how to make a protein-based adhesive in the laboratory. The idea came to him one day at lunch when he was eating tofu, a soy-based food very high in protein. Why not modify soy protein to make a new adhesive? Using mussels as his model, Li did exactly that, and, as he said, "We turned soy proteins into mussel adhesive proteins."

Scientists at Hercules Chemical Company provided expertise to cure (or harden) the new "green" adhesive, and the Columbia Forest Products Company adopted the environmentally friendly adhesive for use in plywood and particle board.

In 2007 Li and his coworkers, as well as Columbia Forest Products and Hercules, shared a Presidential Green Chemistry Challenge Award.

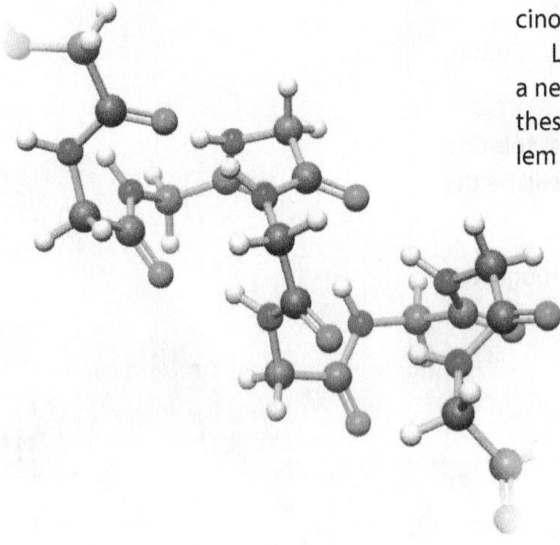

FIGURE A **A portion of a protein chain made of repeating glycine molecules ($H_2NCH_2CO_2H$).**

Courtesy of Oregon State University

Professor K. Li, a discoverer of "green" adhesives.

Questions:

1. Draw structures of phenol, urea, and formaldehyde.
2. Describe the bonding in formaldehyde.
3. It has been said that nylon is similar to a protein. Compare and contrast the structures of nylon-6,6 and a protein (for more information on the structure of proteins, see Chapter 24).

Answers to these questions are available in Appendix N.

REVIEW & CHECK FOR SECTION 23-5

1. Polyacrylic acid, shown below, is made from which of the following monomers? (The sodium salt of this polymer, sodium polyacrylate, and cellulose are the important ingredients in disposable baby diapers.)

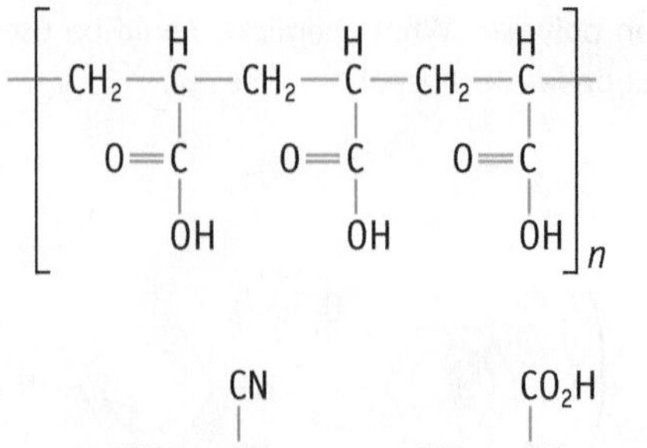

(a) $CH_2{=}CH_2$ (b) $CH_2{=}CH(CN)$ (c) $CH_2{=}CH(CO_2H)$ (d) $CH_2{=}CH(OH)$

APPLYING CHEMICAL PRINCIPLES

Bisphenol A (BPA)

Bisphenol A (BPA) is an organic compound consisting of two phenol groups linked through a carbon atom. It was first synthesized around 1900 but only recently has it become commercially important. And even more recently it has been very much in the news because of its much-debated possible toxicity.

Bisphenol A is a white solid, slightly water soluble (300 mg/L), and a weak acid (pK_a of 9.9). In 2011 the total world demand for BPA was about 5.4×10^9 kg.

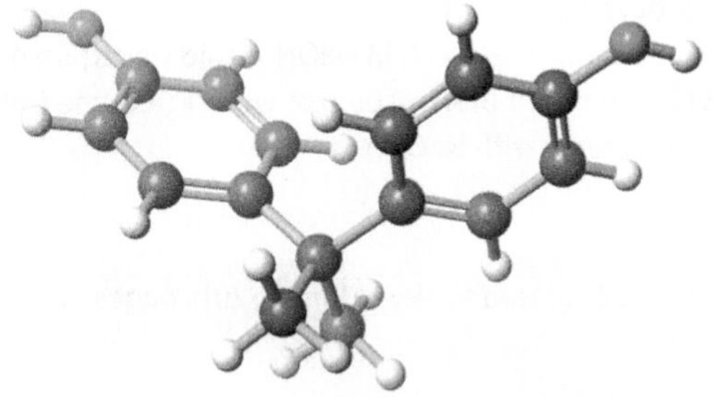

bisphenol-A

If BPA is treated with phosgene (Cl_2CO), the product is the polymer polycarbonate, and approximately 74% of the BPA is used to make this polymer. Because polycarbonate is lightweight, durable, clear, and nearly shatterproof, it is used to make, among other things, bottles, eyeglass lenses, football helmets, and CDs and DVDs.

Another 20% of BPA is converted into epoxy resins by reacting BPA with epichlorohydrin. Until recently epoxy resins were used to coat the inside of some food cans, but they still find use in paints and coatings, adhesives, and composite materials.

Some of the remaining 6% of BPA is used in thermal paper. When you get a cash register receipt in a restaurant or store, the coating on the paper may contain BPA.

BPA is such a useful material. What could go wrong? The problem is that BPA has estrogenic activity, the ability to simulate the activity of primary female sex hormones. But this is also true for some compounds found naturally in beans, olive oil, and some fruits and vegetables. Nonetheless, there has been a vigorous debate on the biological effects of BPA and its polymers.

Because of this debate the use of BPA polymers has been virtually eliminated in making bottles (especially baby bottles) and for coating food cans. Substitutes are also being found for BPA in cash register receipts.

The Environmental Protection Agency (EPA) currently states that it is safe to ingest up to 50 μg per kilogram of body weight per day. However, many scientists believe the safe limit should be much lower, or that BPA should be eliminated entirely. To put this in context, some studies have indicated that infants fed from polycarbonate bottles may ingest up to 13 μg/kg/day. A normal adult may take in about 1.5 μg/kg/day.

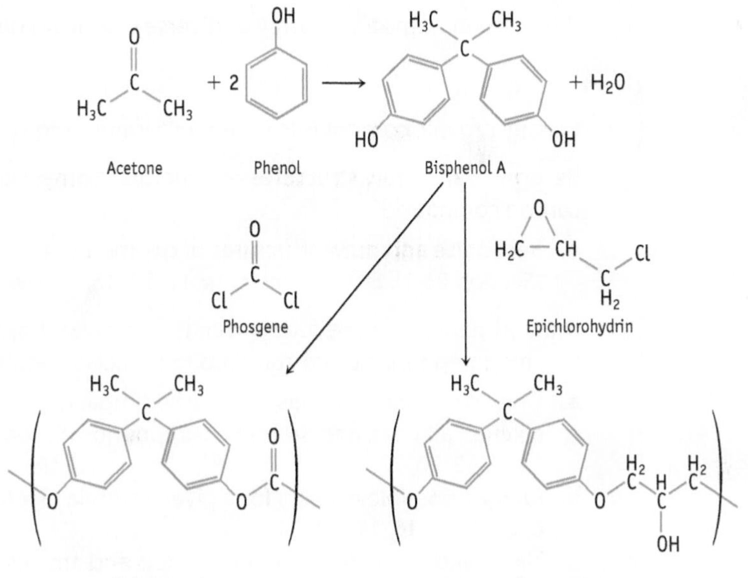

Synthesis of BPA and polycarbonate and epoxy resin from BPA

Most drinking bottles are no longer made of BPA-based polymers.

In a series of articles on BPA and its effects in *Chemical & Engineering News*, the authors wrote, "Given mounting knowledge of BPA's estrogen-mimicking properties and possible toxic effects, decisions have to be made on whether it should continue to be freely used, restricted for some uses, or banned completely. There are no simple answers."

QUESTIONS:

1. What is the atom economy for the reaction of acetone with phenol to make BPA? (See page 150; *Case Study: Green Chemistry and Atom Economy.*)
2. Are polycarbonate and epoxy resins addition polymers or condensation polymers?
3. Does an infant, who weighs about 15 lb, ingest over 50 μg per day? (1.00 lb = 454 g)
4. Assume you weigh 156 lb. How much BPA do you ingest per day?
5. What quantity of 0.050 M NaOH would be required to react with 300 mg of BPA in 1.00 L of water? (Assume both —OH groups react with NaOH.)

REFERENCE:

Chemical & Engineering News, June 6, 2011, pages 13–22.

CHAPTER GOALS REVISITED

Now that you have studied this chapter, you should ask whether you have met the chapter goals. In particular, you should be able to:

UNDERSTAND

- General principles of structure and bonding applied to organic compounds.
- Why carbon forms a vast array of diverse chemical compounds.

DO

- Classify organic compounds based on formula and structure.
- Recognize and draw structures of structural isomers and stereoisomers for carbon compounds.
  - **a.** Recognize and draw structures of geometric isomers and optical isomers (Section 23-1). Study Questions: 11, 12, 15, 19, 69.
- Draw structures of molecules, given the name and/or the formula, and name organic compounds using standard nomenclature rules.
  - **a.** Draw structural formulas, and name simple hydrocarbons, including alkanes, alkenes, alkynes, and aromatic compounds (Section 23-2). Study Questions: 1–16, 69, 70, 77.
  - **b.** Identify possible isomers for a given formula (Section 23-2). Study Questions: 6, 8, 11, 15, 16, 19–22, 28.
  - **c.** Name and draw structures of alcohols and amines (Section 23-3). Study Questions: 37–42.
  - **d.** Name and draw structures of carbonyl compounds—aldehydes, ketones, acids, esters, and amides (Section 23-4). Study Questions: 47–50.

- Predict the products of common organic reactions.
  a. Predict the products of the reactions of alkenes, aromatic compounds, alcohols, amines, aldehydes and ketones, and carboxylic acids. Study Questions: 23–26, 29, 30, 33–36, 43–46, 51–56, 59, 62, 71–74, 89, 91, 95.
- Identify common polymers.
  a. Write equations for the formation of addition polymers and condensation polymers, and describe their structures (Section 23-5). Study Questions: 63–66.
  b. Relate properties of polymers to their structures (Section 23-5). Study Question: 109.
- Relate properties to molecular structure.
  a. Describe the physical and chemical properties of the various classes of hydrocarbon compounds (Section 23-2). Study Question: 17.
  b. Recognize the connection between the structures and the properties of alcohols (Section 23-3). Study Questions: 45, 46, 72.
  c. Know the structures and properties of some natural products (Section 23-4). Study Questions: 57, 58, 83, 84, 87.

REMEMBER

- Common chemical and physical properties of organic compounds.
- Names, structures, and properties of common organic polymers.

Top: John C. Kotz; bottom: © Cengage Learning/ Charles D. Winters

▲ denotes challenging questions.

Blue-numbered questions have answers in Appendix N and fully worked solutions in the *Student Solutions Manual.*

Practicing Skills

Alkanes and Cycloalkanes

(See Section 23-2 and Examples 23.1 and 23.2.)

1. What is the name of the straight (unbranched) chain alkane with the formula C_7H_{16}?

2. What is the molecular formula for an alkane with 12 carbon atoms?

3. Which of the following compounds can be an alkane?
   (a) C_2H_4
   (b) C_5H_{12}
   (c) $C_{14}H_{30}$
   (d) C_7H_8

4. Which of the following compounds can be a cyclo-alkane?
   (a) C_3H_5
   (b) C_5H_{10}
   (c) $C_{14}H_{30}$
   (d) C_8H_8

5. One of the structural isomers with the formula C_9H_{20} has the name 3-ethyl-2-methylhexane. Draw its structure. Draw and name another structural isomer of C_9H_{20} in which there is a five-carbon chain.

6. Isooctane, 2,2,4-trimethylpentane, is one of the possible structural isomers with the formula C_8H_{18}. Draw the structure of this isomer, and draw and name structures of two other isomers of C_8H_{18} in which the longest carbon chain is five atoms.

7. Give the systematic name for the following alkane:

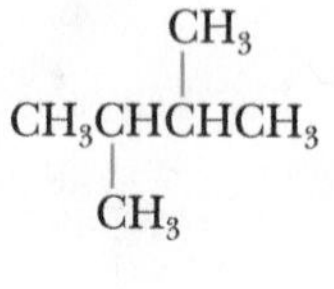

8. Give the systematic name for the following alkane. Draw a structural isomer of the compound, and give its name.

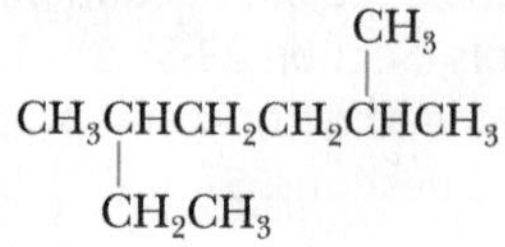

9. Draw the structure of each of the following compounds:
   (a) 2,3-dimethylhexane
   (b) 2,3-dimethyloctane
   (c) 3-ethylheptane
   (d) 3-ethyl-2-methylhexane

10. Draw structures for the following compounds.
    (a) 3-ethylpentane
    (b) 2,3-dimethylpentane
    (c) 2,4-dimethylpentane
    (d) 2,2-dimethylpentane

11. Draw Lewis structures and name all possible alkanes that have a seven-carbon chain with one methyl substituent group. Which of these isomers has a chiral carbon center?

12. Four (of six possible) dimethylhexanes are named below. Draw the structures of each, and determine which of these isomers has a chiral carbon center.
    (a) 2,2-dimethylhexane
    (b) 2,3-dimethylhexane
    (c) 2,4-dimethylhexane
    (d) 2,5-dimethylhexane

13. Draw the structure of the chair form of cyclohexane. Identify the axial and equatorial hydrogen atoms in this drawing.

14. Draw a structure for cycloheptane. Is the seven-member ring planar? Explain your answer.

15. There are two ethylheptanes (compounds with a seven-carbon chain and one ethyl substituent). Draw the structures, and name these compounds. Is either isomer chiral?

16. Among the 18 structural isomers with the formula C_8H_{18} are two with a five-carbon chain having one ethyl and one methyl substituent group. Draw their structures, and name these two isomers.

17. List several typical physical properties of C_4H_{10}. Predict the following physical properties of dodecane, $C_{12}H_{26}$: color, state (s, ℓ, g), solubility in water, solubility in a nonpolar solvent.

18. Write balanced equations for the following reactions of alkanes.

(a) The reaction of methane with excess chlorine.
(b) Complete combustion of cyclohexane, C_6H_{12}, with excess oxygen.

Alkenes and Alkynes

(See Section 23-2 and Examples 23.3 and 23.4.)

19. Draw structures for the *cis* and *trans* isomers of 4-methyl-2-hexene.

20. What structural requirement is necessary for an alkene to have *cis* and *trans* isomers? Can *cis* and *trans* isomers exist for an alkane? For an alkyne?

21. A hydrocarbon with the formula C_5H_{10} can be either an alkene or a cycloalkane.

(a) Draw a structure for each of the six isomers possible for C_5H_{10}, assuming it is an alkene. Give the systematic name of each isomer.
(b) Draw a structure for a cycloalkane having the formula C_5H_{10}.

22. Five alkenes have the formula C_7H_{14} and a seven-carbon chain. Draw their structures and name them.

23. Draw the structure and give the systematic name for the products of the following reactions:

(a) $CH_3CH{=}CH_2 + Br_2 \rightarrow$
(b) $CH_3CH_2CH{=}CHCH_3 + H_2 \rightarrow$

24. Draw the structure and give the systematic name for the products of the following reactions:

(a) 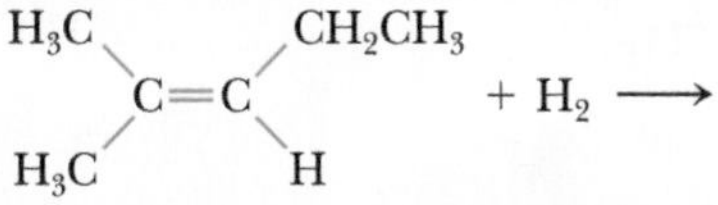

(b) $CH_3C{\equiv}CCH_2CH_3 + 2\,Br_2 \longrightarrow$

25. The compound 2-bromobutane is a product of addition of HBr to three different alkenes. Identify the alkenes and write an equation for the reaction of HBr with one of the alkenes.

26. The compound 2,3-dibromo-2-methylhexane is formed by addition of Br_2 to an alkene. Identify the alkene, and write an equation for this reaction.

27. Draw structures for the four alkenes that have the formula C_3H_5Cl, and name each compound. (These are derivatives of propene in which a chlorine atom replaces one hydrogen atom.)

28. There are seven possible dichloropropene isomers (molecular formula $C_3H_4Cl_2$). Draw their structures and name each isomer. (Hint: Don't overlook *cis-trans* isomers.)

29. Hydrogenation is an important chemical reaction of compounds that contain double bonds. Write a chemical equation for the hydrogenation of 1-hexene. Hydrogenation reactions are used extensively in the food industry. Describe this reaction and explain its use and importance.

30. Elemental analysis of a colorless liquid has given its formula as C_5H_{10}. You recognize that this could be either a cycloalkane or an alkene. A chemical test to determine the class to which this compound belongs involves adding bromine. Explain how this would allow you to distinguish between the two classes.

Aromatic Compounds

(See Section 23-2 and Example 23.5.)

31. Draw structural formulas for the following compounds:

(a) 1,3-dichlorobenzene (alternatively called *m*-dichlorobenzene)
(b) 1-bromo-4-methylbenzene (alternatively called *p*-bromotoluene)

32. Give the systematic name for each of the following compounds:

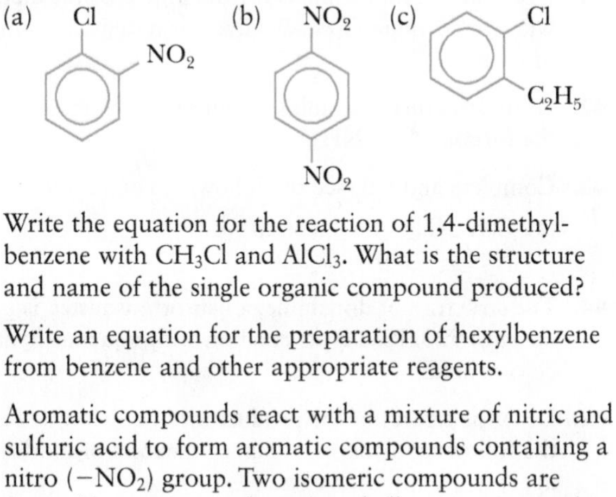

33. Write the equation for the reaction of 1,4-dimethylbenzene with CH_3Cl and $AlCl_3$. What is the structure and name of the single organic compound produced?

34. Write an equation for the preparation of hexylbenzene from benzene and other appropriate reagents.

35. Aromatic compounds react with a mixture of nitric and sulfuric acid to form aromatic compounds containing a nitro ($-NO_2$) group. Two isomeric compounds are formed by nitration of 1,2-dimethylbenzene. Draw the structures and name these compounds.

36. Nitration of toluene gives a mixture of two products, one with the nitro group ($-NO_2$) in the *ortho* position and one with the nitro group in the *para* position. Draw structures of the two products.

Alcohols, Ethers, and Amines

(See Section 23-3 and Example 23.6.)

37. Give the systematic name for each of the following alcohols, and tell if each is a primary, secondary, or tertiary alcohol:

(a) $CH_3CH_2CH_2OH$
(b) $CH_3CH_2CH_2CH_2OH$
(c) 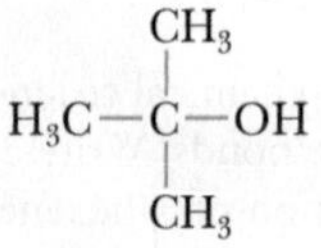
(d) 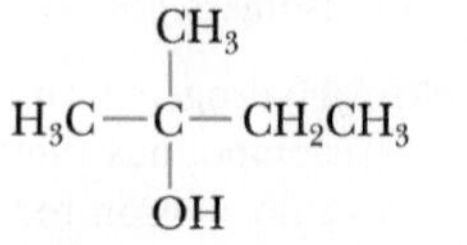

38. Draw structural formulas for the following alcohols, and tell if each is primary, secondary, or tertiary:

(a) 1-butanol
(b) 2-butanol
(c) 3,3-dimethyl-2-butanol
(d) 3,3-dimethyl-1-butanol

39. Write the formula, and draw the structure, for each of the following amines:

(a) ethylamine
(b) dipropylamine
(c) butyldimethylamine
(d) triethylamine

40. Name the following amines:

(a) $CH_3CH_2CH_2NH_2$
(b) $(CH_3)_3N$
(c) $(CH_3)(C_2H_5)NH$
(d) $C_6H_{13}NH_2$

41. Draw structural formulas for the four possible alcohols with the formula $C_4H_{10}O$. Give the systematic name of each.

42. Draw structural formulas for all primary amines with the formula $C_4H_9NH_2$.

43. Complete and balance the following equations:

(a) $C_6H_5NH_2(\ell) + HCl(aq) \rightarrow$
(b) $(CH_3)_3N(aq) + H_2SO_4(aq) \rightarrow$

44. The structure of dopamine, a neurotransmitter, is given on page 923. Predict its reaction with aqueous hydrochloric acid.

45. Draw structures of the product formed by oxidation of the following alcohols. Assume an excess of oxidizing agent is used in each case.

(a) 2-methyl-1-pentanol
(b) 3-methyl-2-pentanol
(c) $HOCH_2CH_2CH_2CH_2OH$
(d) $H_2NCH_2CH_2CH_2OH$

46. Aldehydes and carboxylic acids are formed by oxidation of primary alcohols, and ketones are formed when secondary alcohols are oxidized. Give the name and formula for the alcohol that, when oxidized, gives the following products:

(a) $CH_3CH_2CH_2CHO$
(b) 2-hexanone

Compounds with a Carbonyl Group

(See Section 23-4 and Example 23.7.)

47. Draw structural formulas for (a) 2-pentanone, (b) hexanal, and (c) pentanoic acid.

48. Draw structural formulas for the following acids and esters:

(a) 2-methylhexanoic acid
(b) pentyl butanoate (which has the odor of apricots)
(c) octyl acetate (which has the odor of oranges)

49. Identify the class of each of the following compounds, and give the systematic name for each:

(a) $CH_3CH_2CH(CH_3)CH_2CO_2H$ (the CH_3 drawn above the CH)
(b) $CH_3CH_2C(=O)OCH_3$
(c) $CH_3C(=O)OCH_2CH_2CH_2CH_3$
(d) 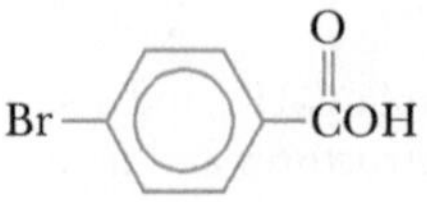

50. Identify the class of each of the following compounds, and give the systematic name for each:

(a) $CH_3C(=O)CH_3$
(b) $CH_3CH_2CH_2CH(=O)$
(c) $CH_3C(=O)CH_2CH_2CH_3$

51. Give the structural formula and systematic name for the organic product, if any, from each of the following reactions:

(a) pentanal and $KMnO_4$
(b) 2-octanone and $LiAlH_4$

52. Give the structural formula and name for the organic product from the following reactions.

(a) $CH_3CH_2CH_2CH_2CHO + LiAlH_4$
(b) $CH_3CH_2CH_2CH_2OH + KMnO_4$

53. Describe how to prepare propyl propanoate beginning with 1-propanol as the only carbon-containing reagent.

54. Give the name and structure of the product of the reaction of benzoic acid and 2-propanol.

55. Draw structural formulas and give the names for the products of the following reaction:

$$CH_3\overset{\overset{O}{\|}}{C}OCH_2CH_2CH_2CH_3 + NaOH$$

56. Draw structural formulas, and give the names for the products of the following reaction:

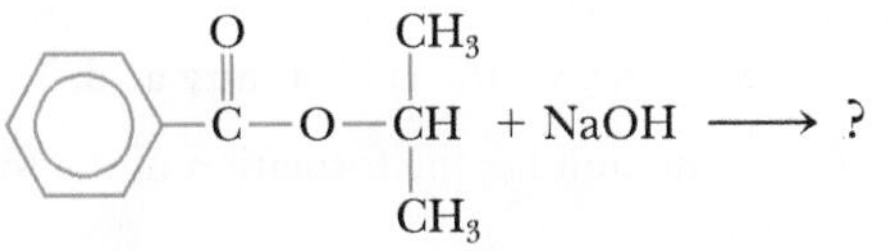

57. The structure of phenylalanine, one of the 20 amino acids that make up proteins, is drawn below (without lone pairs of electrons). The carbon atoms are numbered for the purpose of this question.

(a) What is the geometry of C_3?
(b) What is the O—C—O bond angle?
(c) Is this molecule chiral? If so, which carbon atom is chiral?
(d) Which hydrogen atom in this compound is acidic?

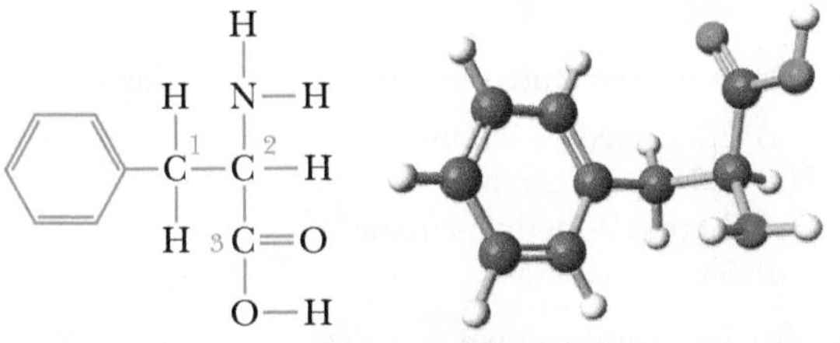

58. The structure of vitamin C, whose chemical name is ascorbic acid, is drawn below (without lone pairs of electrons).

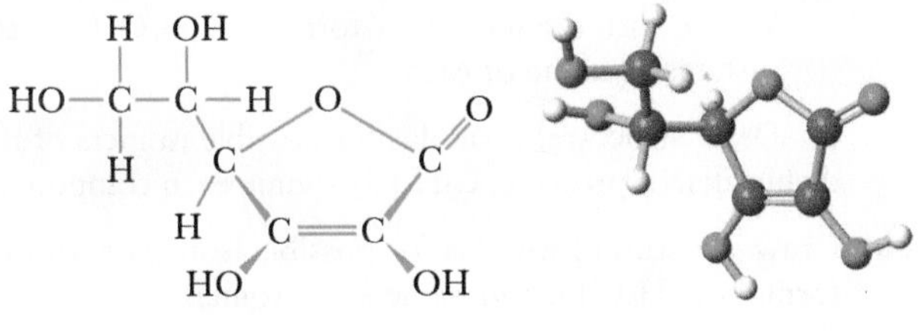

(a) What is the approximate value for the O—C—O bond angle in the five-member ring?
(b) There are four OH groups in this structure. Estimate the C—O—H bond angles for these groups. Will they be the same value (more or less), or should there be significant differences in these bond angles?
(c) Is the molecule chiral? How many chiral carbon atoms can be identified in this structure?
(d) Identify the shortest bond in this molecule.
(e) What are the functional groups of the molecule?

59. What is the structure of the product from the reaction of butanoic acid and methylamine? To what class of compounds does this belong? Write a balanced chemical equation for the reaction.

60. The structure of acetaminophen is shown on page 930. Using structural formulas, write an equation for the reaction of an acid and an amine to form this compound.

Functional Groups

(See Section 23-4 and Example 23.7.)

61. Identify the functional groups in the following molecules.

(a) $CH_3CH_2CH_2OH$
(b) $H_3C\overset{\overset{O}{\|}}{C}NHCH_3$
(c) $CH_3CH_2\overset{\overset{O}{\|}}{C}OH$
(d) $CH_3CH_2\overset{\overset{O}{\|}}{C}OCH_3$

62. Consider the following molecules:

(1) $CH_3CH_2\overset{\overset{O}{\|}}{C}CH_3$
(2) $CH_3CH_2\overset{\overset{O}{\|}}{C}OH$
(3) $H_2C{=}CHCH_2OH$
(4) $CH_3CH_2\overset{\overset{OH}{|}}{C}HCH_3$

(a) What is the result of treating compound 1 with $NaBH_4$? What is the functional group in the product? Name the product.
(b) Draw the structure of the reaction product from compounds 2 and 4. What is the functional group in the product?
(c) What compound results from adding H_2 to compound 3? Name the reaction product.
(d) What compound results from adding NaOH to compound 2?

Polymers

(See Section 23-5 and Example 23.8.)

63. Polyvinyl acetate is the binder in water-based paints.
   (a) Write an equation for its formation from vinyl acetate.
   (b) Show a portion of this polymer with three monomer units.
   (c) Describe how to make polyvinyl alcohol from polyvinyl acetate.

64. Neoprene (polychloroprene, a kind of rubber) is a polymer formed from the chlorinated butadiene $H_2C{=}CHCCl{=}CH_2$.
   (a) Write an equation showing the formation of polychloroprene from the monomer.
   (b) Show a portion of this polymer with three monomer units.

65. Polyacrylonitrile is a polymer of acrylonitrile, $CH_2{=}CHCN$. Write an equation for the synthesis of this polymer.

66. The structure of methyl methacrylate is given in Table 23.12. Draw the structure of a polymethyl methacrylate (PMMA) polymer that has four monomer units. (PMMA has excellent optical properties and is used to make hard contact lenses.)

General Questions

These questions are not designated as to type or location in the chapter. They may combine several concepts.

67. Three different compounds with the formula $C_2H_2Cl_2$ are known.
   (a) Two of these compounds are geometric isomers. Draw their structures.
   (b) The third compound is a structural isomer of the other two. Draw its structure.

68. Draw the structure of 2-butanol. Identify the chiral carbon atom in this compound. Draw the mirror image of the structure you first drew. Are the two molecules superimposable?

69. An alkene having the formula C_6H_{12} is known to have a six-carbon chain. How many isomeric species can be drawn based on this description? List the names of these species.

70. Draw structures and name the four alkenes that have the formula C_4H_8.

71. Write equations for the reactions of *cis*-2-butene with the following reagents, representing the reactants and products using structural formulas.
   (a) H_2O
   (b) HBr
   (c) Cl_2

72. Draw the structure and name the product formed if the following alcohols are oxidized. Assume an excess of the oxidizing agent is used. If the alcohol is not expected to react with a chemical oxidizing agent, write NR (no reaction).
   (a) $CH_3CH_2CH_2CH_2OH$
   (b) 2-butanol
   (c) 2-methyl-2-propanol
   (d) 2-methyl-1-propanol

73. Write equations for the following reactions, representing the reactants and products using structural formulas.
   (a) The reaction of acetic acid and sodium hydroxide
   (b) The reaction of methylamine with HCl

74. Write equations for the following reactions, representing the reactants and products using structural formulas.
   (a) The formation of ethyl acetate from acetic acid and ethanol
   (b) The hydrolysis of glyceryl tristearate (the triester of glycerol with stearic acid, a fatty acid; Table 23.9)

75. Write an equation for the formation of the following polymers.
   (a) Polystyrene, from styrene ($C_6H_5CH{=}CH_2$)
   (b) PET (polyethylene terephthalate), from ethylene glycol and terephthalic acid

76. Write equations for the following reactions, representing the reactants and products using structural formulas.
   (a) The hydrolysis of the amide $C_6H_5CONHCH_3$ to form benzoic acid and methylamine
   (b) The hydrolysis of $\text{+}CO(CH_2)_4CONH(CH_2)_6NH\text{+}_n$, (nylon-6,6, a polyamide) to give a carboxylic acid and an amine

77. Draw the structure of each of the following compounds:
   (a) 2,2-dimethylpentane
   (b) 3,3-diethylpentane
   (c) 3-ethyl-2-methylpentane
   (d) 3-ethylhexane

78. ▲ Structural isomers.
   (a) Draw all of the isomers possible for C_3H_8O. Give the systematic name of each, and tell into which class of compound it fits.
   (b) Draw the structural formulas for an aldehyde and a ketone with the molecular formula C_4H_8O. Give the systematic name of each.

79. ▲ Draw structural formulas for possible isomers of the dichlorinated propane, $C_3H_6Cl_2$. Name each compound.

80. Draw structural formulas for possible isomers with the formula C_3H_6ClBr, and name each isomer.

81. Give structural formulas and systematic names for the three structural isomers of trimethylbenzene, $C_6H_3(CH_3)_3$.

82. Give structural formulas and systematic names for possible isomers of dichlorobenzene, $C_6H_4Cl_2$.

83. Voodoo lilies depend on carrion beetles for pollination. Carrion beetles are attracted to dead animals, and because dead and putrefying animals give off the horrible-smelling amine cadaverine, the lily likewise releases cadaverine (and the closely related compound putrescine, page 921). A biological catalyst, an enzyme, converts the naturally occurring amino acid lysine to cadaverine.

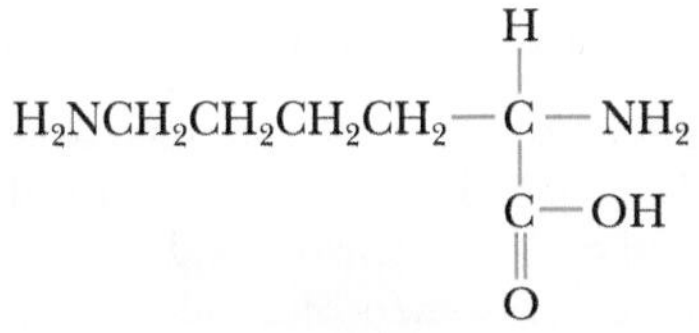

Lysine

What group of atoms must be replaced in lysine to make cadaverine? (Lysine is essential to human nutrition but is not synthesized in the human body.)

84. Benzoic acid occurs in many berries. When humans eat berries, benzoic acid is converted to hippuric acid in the body by reaction with the amino acid glycine $H_2NCH_2CO_2H$. Draw the structure of hippuric acid, knowing it is an amide formed by reaction of the carboxylic acid group of benzoic acid and the amino group of glycine. Why is hippuric acid referred to as an acid?

85. Consider the reaction of *cis*-2-butene with H_2 (in the presence of a catalyst).

(a) Draw the structure, and give the name of the reaction product. Is this reaction product chiral?
(b) Draw an isomer of the reaction product.

86. Give the name of each compound below, and name the functional group involved.

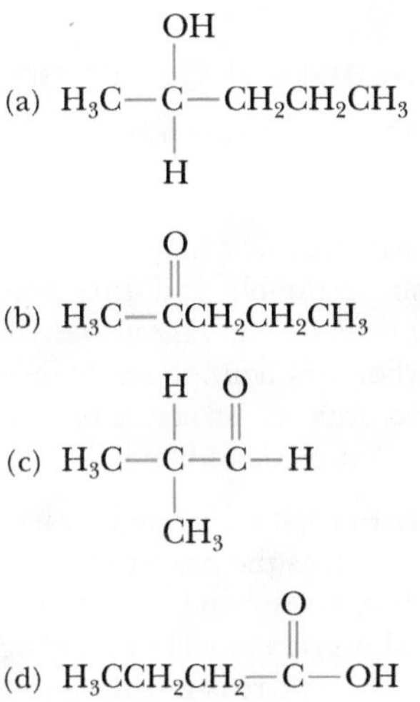

87. Draw the structure of glyceryl trilaurate, a fat. Lauric acid (page 789) has the formula $C_{11}H_{23}CO_2H$.

(a) Write an equation for the base hydrolysis of glyceryl trilaurate.
(b) Write an equation for the reaction that could be used to prepare biodiesel fuel from this fat.

88. A well-known company sells outdoor clothing made of recycled polyethylene terephthalate (PET), the principal material in many soft drink bottles. Another company makes PET fibers by treating recycled bottles with methanol to give the diester dimethyl terephthalate and ethylene glycol and then repolymerizes these compounds to give new PET. Write a chemical equation to show how the reaction of PET with methanol can give dimethyl terephthalate and ethylene glycol.

89. Identify the reaction products, and write an equation for the following reactions of $CH_2{=}CHCH_2OH$.

(a) H_2 (hydrogenation, in the presence of a catalyst)
(b) Oxidation (excess oxidizing agent)
(c) Addition polymerization
(d) Ester formation, using acetic acid

90. Write a chemical equation describing the reaction between glycerol and stearic acid (Table 23.9) to give glyceryl tristearate.

91. The product of an addition reaction of an alkene is often predicted by Markovnikov's rule.

(a) Draw the structure of the product of adding HBr to propene, and give the name of the product.
(b) Draw the structure and give the name of the compound that results from adding H_2O to 2-methyl-1-butene.
(c) If you add H_2O to 2-methyl-2-butene, is the product the same or different than the product from the reaction in part (b)?

92. There are three ethers with the formula $C_4H_{10}O$. Draw their structures.

93. Review the introductory story about chocolate and then answer the following questions.

(a) How do theobromine and caffeine differ structurally?
(b) A 5.00-g sample of Hershey's cocoa contains 2.16% theobromine. What is the mass of the compound in the sample?

94. Nylon-6 is a polyamide formed by polymerizing $H_2NCH_2CH_2CH_2CH_2CH_2CO_2H$. Write an equation for this reaction.

In the Laboratory

95. Which of the following compounds produces acetic acid when treated with an oxidizing agent such as $KMnO_4$?

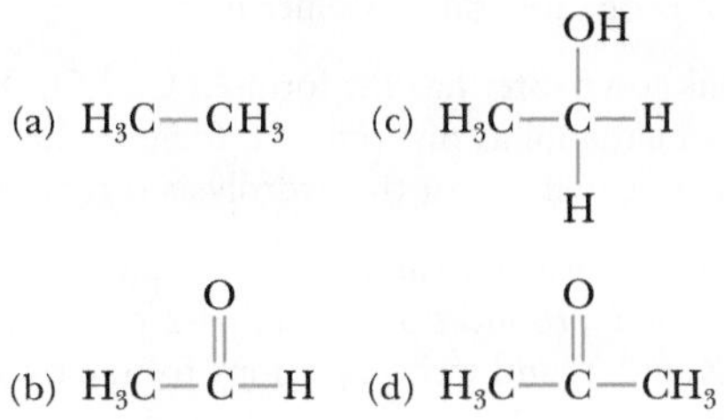

96. Consider the reactions of C_3H_7OH.

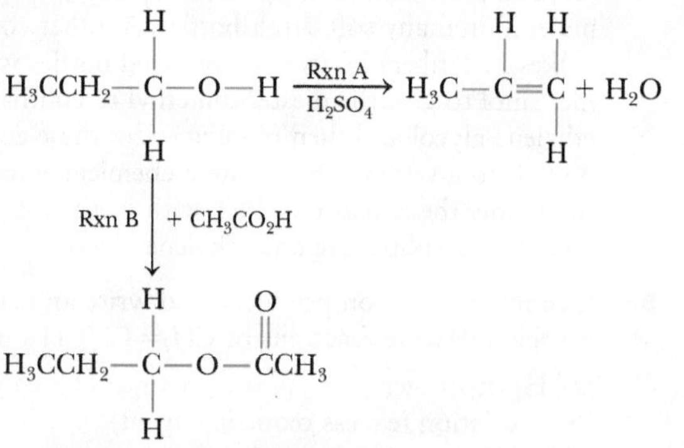

(a) Name the reactant C_3H_7OH.
(b) Draw a structural isomer of the reactant, and give its name.
(c) Name the product of reaction A.
(d) Name the product of reaction B.

97. You have a liquid that is either cyclohexene or benzene. When the liquid is exposed to dark-red bromine vapor, the vapor is immediately decolorized. What is the identity of the liquid? Write an equation for the chemical reaction that has occurred.

98. ▲ Hydrolysis of an unknown ester of butanoic acid, $CH_3CH_2CH_2CO_2R$, produces an alcohol A and butanoic acid. Oxidation of alcohol A forms an acid B that is a structural isomer of butanoic acid. Give the names and structures for alcohol A and acid B.

99. ▲ You are asked to identify an unknown colorless, liquid carbonyl compound. Analysis has determined that the formula for this unknown is C_3H_6O. Only two compounds match this formula.

(a) Draw structures for the two possible compounds.
(b) To decide which of the two structures is correct, you react the compound with an oxidizing agent and isolate from that reaction a compound that is found to give an acidic solution in water. Use this result to identify the structure of the unknown.
(c) Name the compound formed by oxidation of the unknown.

100. Describe a simple chemical test to tell the difference between $CH_3CH_2CH_2CH{=}CH_2$ and its isomer cyclopentane.

101. Describe a simple chemical test to tell the difference between 2-propanol and its isomer methyl ethyl ether.

102. ▲ An unknown ester has the formula $C_4H_8O_2$. Hydrolysis gives methanol as one product. Identify the ester, and write an equation for the hydrolysis reaction.

103. ▲ Addition of water to alkene X gives an alcohol Y. Oxidation of Y produces 3,3-dimethyl-2-pentanone. Identify X and Y, and write equations for the two reactions.

104. 2-Iodobenzoic acid, a tan, crystalline solid, can be prepared from 2-aminobenzoic acid. Other required reagents are $NaNO_2$ and KI (as well as HCl).

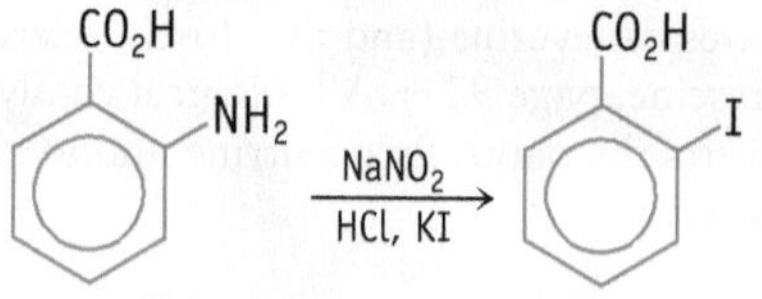

2-aminobenzoic acid 2-iodobenzoic acid

(a) If you use 4.0 g of 2-aminobenzoic acid, 2.2 g of $NaNO_2$, and 5.3 g of KI, what is the theoretical yield of 2-iodobenzoic acid?
(b) Are other isomers of 2-iodobenzoic acid possible?
(c) You titrate the product in a mixture of water and ethanol. If you use 15.62 mL of 0.101 M NaOH to titrate 0.399 g of the product, what is its molar mass? Is it in reasonable agreement with the theoretical molar mass?

105. The transestification reaction between PET and CH_3OH forms dimethyl terephthalate and ethylene glycol. If the methanol used in this reaction is labeled with oxygen-18 (^{18}O) in which of the products will the label be found?

106. Vitamin B-5, pantothenic acid, has the structure shown below. Base hydrolysis of this compound followed by acidification gives two compounds. Draw their structures.

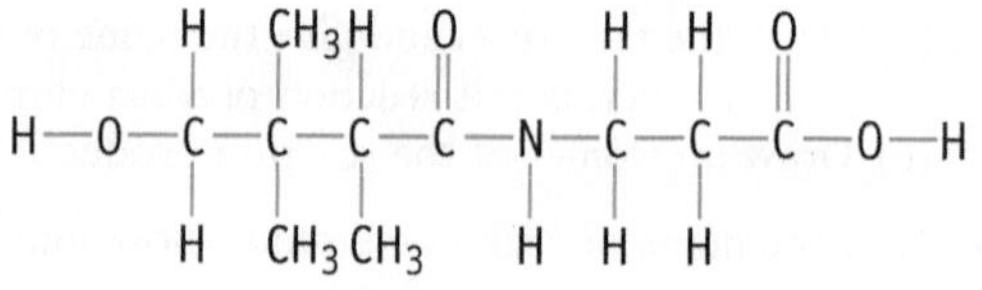

Vitamin B-5, pantothenic acid

Summary and Conceptual Questions

The following questions may use concepts from this and previous chapters.

107. Carbon atoms appear in organic compounds in several different ways with single, double, and triple bonds combining to give an octet configuration. Describe the various ways that carbon can bond to reach an octet, and give the name and draw the structure of a compound that illustrates that mode of bonding.

108. There is a high barrier to rotation around a carbon–carbon double bond, whereas the barrier to rotation around a carbon–carbon single bond is considerably smaller. Use the orbital overlap model of bonding (Chapter 9) to explain why there is restricted rotation around a double bond.

109. What important properties do the following characteristics impart to a polymer?

(a) Cross-linking in polyethylene
(b) The OH groups in polyvinyl alcohol
(c) Hydrogen bonding in a polyamide like nylon

110. One of the resonance structures for pyridine (C_5H_5N) is illustrated here. Draw another resonance structure for the molecule. Comment on the similarity between this compound and benzene.

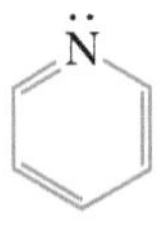

Pyridine

111. Write balanced equations for the combustion of ethane gas and liquid ethanol (to give gaseous products).

(a) Calculate the enthalpy of combustion of each compound. Which has the more negative enthalpy change for combustion per gram?
(b) If ethanol is assumed to be partially oxidized ethane, what effect does this have on the enthalpy of combustion?

112. Plastics make up about 20% of the volume of landfills. There is, therefore, considerable interest in reusing or recycling these materials. To identify common plastics, a set of universal symbols is now used, five of which are illustrated here. They symbolize low- and high-density polyethylene, polyvinyl chloride, polypropylene, and polyethylene terephthalate.

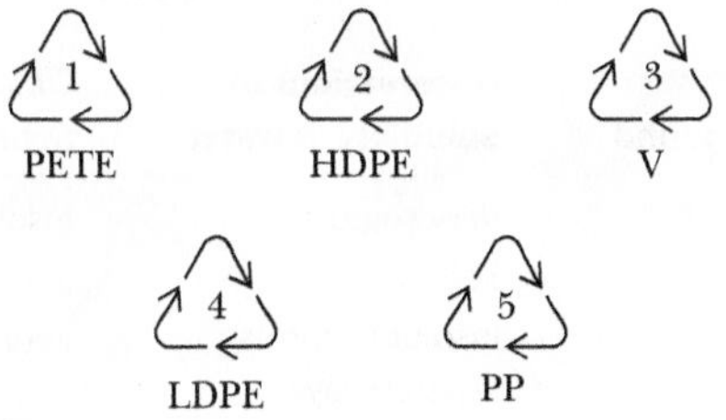

(a) Tell which symbol belongs to which type of plastic.
(b) Find an item in the grocery or drug store made from each of these plastics.
(c) Properties of several plastics are listed in the table. Based on this information, describe how to separate samples of these plastics from one another.

Plastic	Density (g/cm^3)	Melting Point (°C)
Polypropylene	0.92	170
High-density polyethylene	0.97	135
Polyethylene terephthalate	1.34–1.39	245

113. ▲ Maleic acid is prepared by the catalytic oxidation of benzene. It is a dicarboxylic acid; that is, it has two carboxylic acid groups.

(a) Combustion of 0.125 g of the acid gives 0.190 g of CO_2 and 0.0388 g of H_2O. Calculate the empirical formula of the acid.
(b) A 0.261-g sample of the acid requires 34.60 mL of 0.130 M NaOH for complete titration (so that the H ions from both carboxylic acid groups are used). What is the molecular formula of the acid?
(c) Draw a Lewis structure for the acid.
(d) Describe the hybridization used by the C atoms.
(e) What are the bond angles around each C atom?

AP Multiple-Choice Review Questions

1. An aqueous solution of which of these compounds would have a pH of greater than 8.0?

(A) CH_3NH_2

(B) CH_3COOH

(C) CH_3CH_2OH

(D) $CH_3-\overset{\overset{\large O}{\|}}{C}-CH_3$

2. The boiling points of four different organic compounds whose structures are shown were determined and are given in the table below. Which boiling point is most likely that of ethanol?

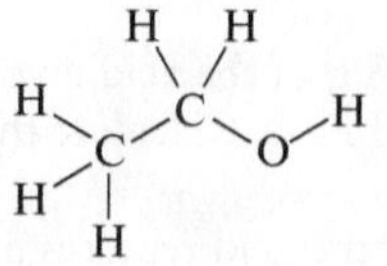

ethanol

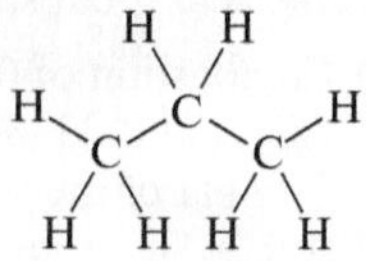

propane

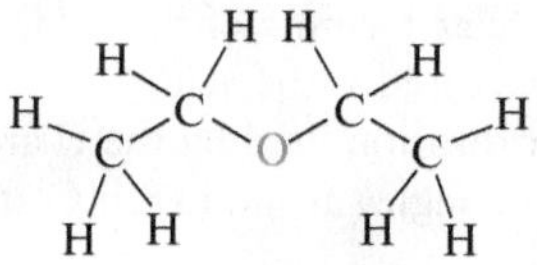

diethyl ether

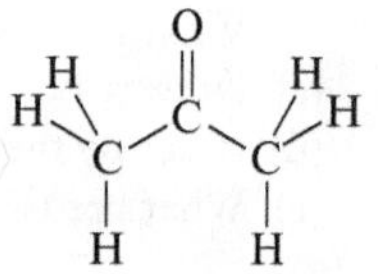

acetone

Compound	Boiling Point
(A)	−42 °C
(B)	35 °C
(C)	56 °C
(D)	78 °C

Questions 3 and 4 refer to the following acetic acid molecule:

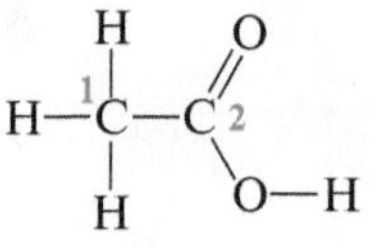

3. Predict the approximate bond angle around the carbon labeled 1 in the acetic acid molecule.

(A) 90°

(B) 109.5°

(C) 120°

(D) 180°

4. What is the expected hybridization of the carbon labeled 2 in the acetic acid molecule?

(A) *sp*

(B) s^2p

(C) sp^2

(D) sp^3

5.

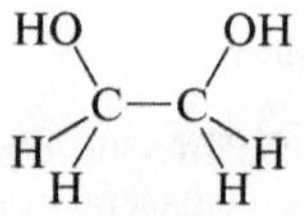

#1

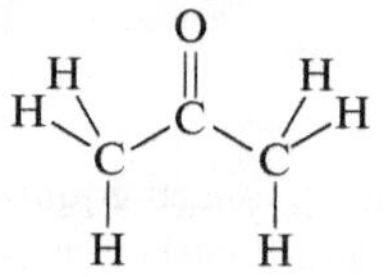

#2

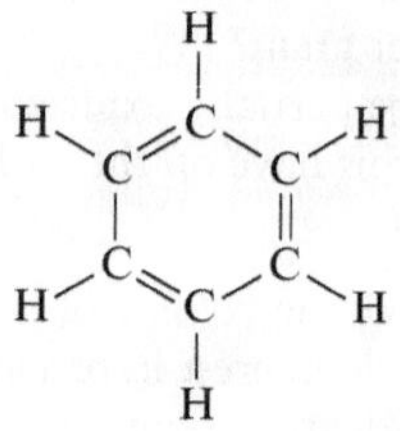

#3

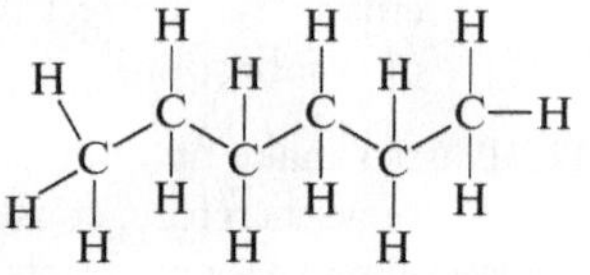

hexane

The first three organic compounds shown above were tested for their solubility both in water and also in hexane. The results are shown in the table below. Which of these conclusions could be predicted from these data?

Compound	Observations of Solubility in Water	Observations of Solubility in Hexane
#1	Very soluble	Insoluble
#2	Soluble	Soluble
#3	Insoluble, forms separate layer	Very soluble

(A) Compound 1 = benzene, compound 2 = acetone, compound 3 = ethylene glycol

(B) Compound 1 = ethylene glycol, compound 2 = acetone, compound 3 = benzene

(C) Compound 1 = acetone, compound 2 = benzene, compound 3 = ethylene glycol

(D) Compound 1 = benzene, compound 2 = ethylene glycol, compound 3 = acetone

6. Which of these compounds would you predict to have the highest boiling point?

(A) CO_2

(B) CH_4

(C) CCl_4

(D) CBr_4

7. 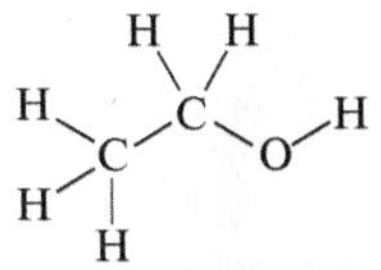

ethanol

A 25-mL sample of ethanol is slowly heated to 80 °C using a hot plate. The volume of ethanol in the beaker gradually decreases to 10 mL. What is the best conclusion for what is occurring to the ethanol?

(A) A chemical change is occurring because the covalent bonds are being broken.
(B) A chemical change is occurring because the hydrogen bonds are being broken.
(C) A physical change is occurring because the covalent bonds are being broken.
(D) A physical change is occurring because the hydrogen bonds are being broken.

8. The four compounds shown all exhibit *intermolecular* hydrogen bonding. Which one of these compounds can also form *intramolecular* hydrogen bonds?

(A) 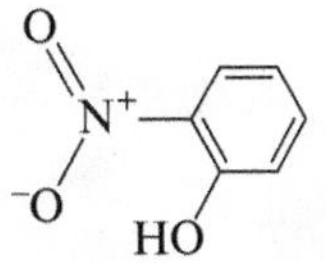

(B) 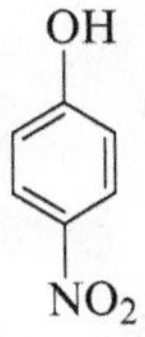

(C) 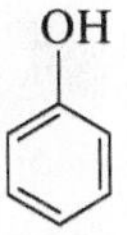

(D) 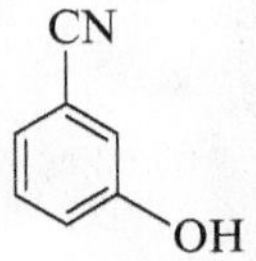

Najlah Feanny-Hicks/Corbis

Dolly the Sheep, the first cloned mammal.

Biochemistry

Chapter Outline

ANIMAL CLONING The world was startled when it was announced that on July 5, 1996, a sheep named Dolly was born at the Roslin Institute at the University of Edinburgh in Scotland. What made Dolly so special was that she was not born in the normal way. Instead, she was the first clone, a genetically exact duplicate, of an adult mammal.

The process began when scientists led by Professor Ian Wilmut of the Roslin Institute took a mammary cell from a donor sheep and prepared its DNA so that it could be accepted by an egg from another sheep. The scientists then removed the DNA from the egg of the other sheep and replaced it with the DNA they had prepared. The egg developed and grew into an embryo. The embryo was then implanted into an adult female sheep who eventually gave birth to a normal lamb—Dolly. She went on to live a normal life, giving birth to lambs of her own. After living for six years, she eventually contracted a lung infection and had to be euthanized to prevent her from suffering further from this infection.

Chapter Goals

See Chapter Goals Revisited (page 973) for Study Questions keyed to these goals.

UNDERSTAND

- Structure determines the function of biological molecules.
- The process of protein synthesis.
- The RNA World hypothesis for the origin of life.
- The construction of a phospholipid bilayer and transport of materials across such a membrane.
- Coupling of ATP hydrolysis with a reactant-favored reaction can lead to a product-favored reaction.

DO

- Draw the structural formulas of common biochemical molecules.
- Predict the sequence of nucleotides complementary to a given strand of DNA.
- Predict the amino acid selected by a given sequence of three nucleotides in mRNA.

REMEMBER

- Proteins are condensation polymers of amino acids.
- The active site of an enzyme is the cleft or cavity where the substrate binds and the catalyzed chemical reaction takes place.
- DNA and RNA are condensation polymers of nucleotides.
- RNA undergoes hydrolysis much more quickly than DNA.
- The identity of some lipids.
- NAD^+ and NADH are involved in biochemical redox reactions.

Biotechnology has certainly progressed far since Watson and Crick first determined the structure of DNA in 1953. Though much remains to be discovered, we can now do things, such as cloning, that were only dreamed of in science fiction in the past. Such power, however, also brings with it ethical dilemmas. Even though it is currently banned by most countries, should cloning be expanded to humans? Unlike human cloning, animal cloning is permitted in the United States and the European Union as well as in many other countries in the world. Would farmers want clones of an animal well suited for food? Might researchers introduce a mutation into an animal so that it produces a particular compound in its blood or milk that could be used as a drug to treat a human illness and then clone the animal to get large quantities of the drug? Though currently unlikely due to practical limitations of present cloning technology, could we reintroduce a species that is extinct? Answering all of these questions and others will take the combined efforts of scientists, ethicists, politicians, and a well-informed populace.

This chapter will introduce you to the science behind some of the most important biological compounds and to some processes that occur in cells. This knowledge is essential to being able to understand the great strides being made in biotechnology today.

You are a marvelously complex biological organism, and so is every other living thing on Earth. What molecules are present in you, and what are their properties? How is genetic information passed from generation to generation? How does your body carry out the numerous reactions that are needed for life?

These questions and many others fall into the realm of biochemistry, a rapidly expanding area of science. As the name implies, biochemistry exists at the interface of two scientific disciplines: biology and chemistry.

What separates a biochemist's perspective of biological phenomena from a biologist's perspective? The difference is becoming less distinct, but biochemists tend to concentrate on the specific molecules involved in biological processes and on how chemical reactions occur in an organism (Figure 24.1). They use the strategies of chemistry to understand processes in living things.

The goal of this chapter is to consider how chemistry is involved in answering important biological questions. To do so, we will examine four major classes of biological compounds: proteins, carbohydrates, nucleic acids, and lipids. We will also discuss chemical reactions that occur in living things, including some reactions involved in obtaining energy from food.

Learning Objectives: LO 4.9

24-1 Proteins

Your body contains thousands of different proteins, and about 50% of the dry weight of your body consists of proteins. Proteins provide structural support (muscle, collagen), help organisms move (muscle), store and transport chemicals from one area to another (hemoglobin), regulate when certain chemical reactions will occur (hormones), and catalyze a host of chemical reactions (enzymes). All of these different functions and others are accomplished using this one class of compounds.

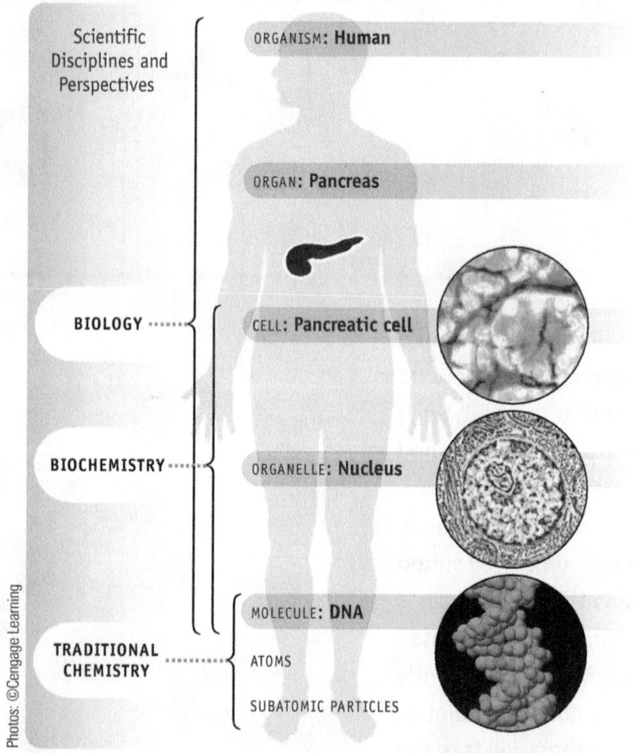

FIGURE 24.1 The human body with areas of interest to biologists, biochemists, and chemists.

Amino Acids Are the Building Blocks of Proteins

Proteins are condensation polymers (◀ Section 23-5) formed from amino acids. **Amino acids** are organic compounds that contain an amino group (—NH_2) and a carboxylic acid group (—CO_2H)

Almost all amino acids that make up proteins are α-amino acids. In an α-amino acid, the amino group is at one end of the molecule, and the acid group is at the other end. In between these two groups, a single carbon atom (the α-carbon) has attached to it a hydrogen atom and either another hydrogen atom or an organic group, denoted R. Naturally occurring proteins are predominantly built using 20 amino acids, which differ only in the identity of the organic group, R. These organic groups can be nonpolar (groups derived from alkanes or aromatic hydrocarbons) or polar (with alcohol, acidic, basic, or other polar functional groups) (Figure 24.2). Depending on which amino acids are present, a region in a protein may be nonpolar, very polar, or anything in between.

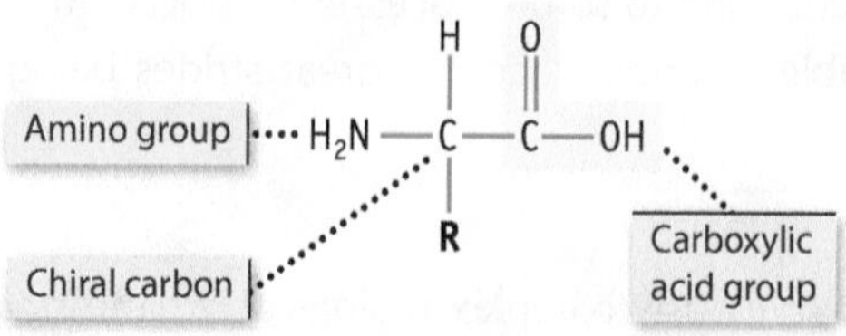

All α-amino acids, except glycine, have four different groups attached to the α-carbon. The α-carbon is thus a chiral center (◀ Section 23-1), and two enantiomers exist. Interestingly, all of these amino acids occur in nature in a single

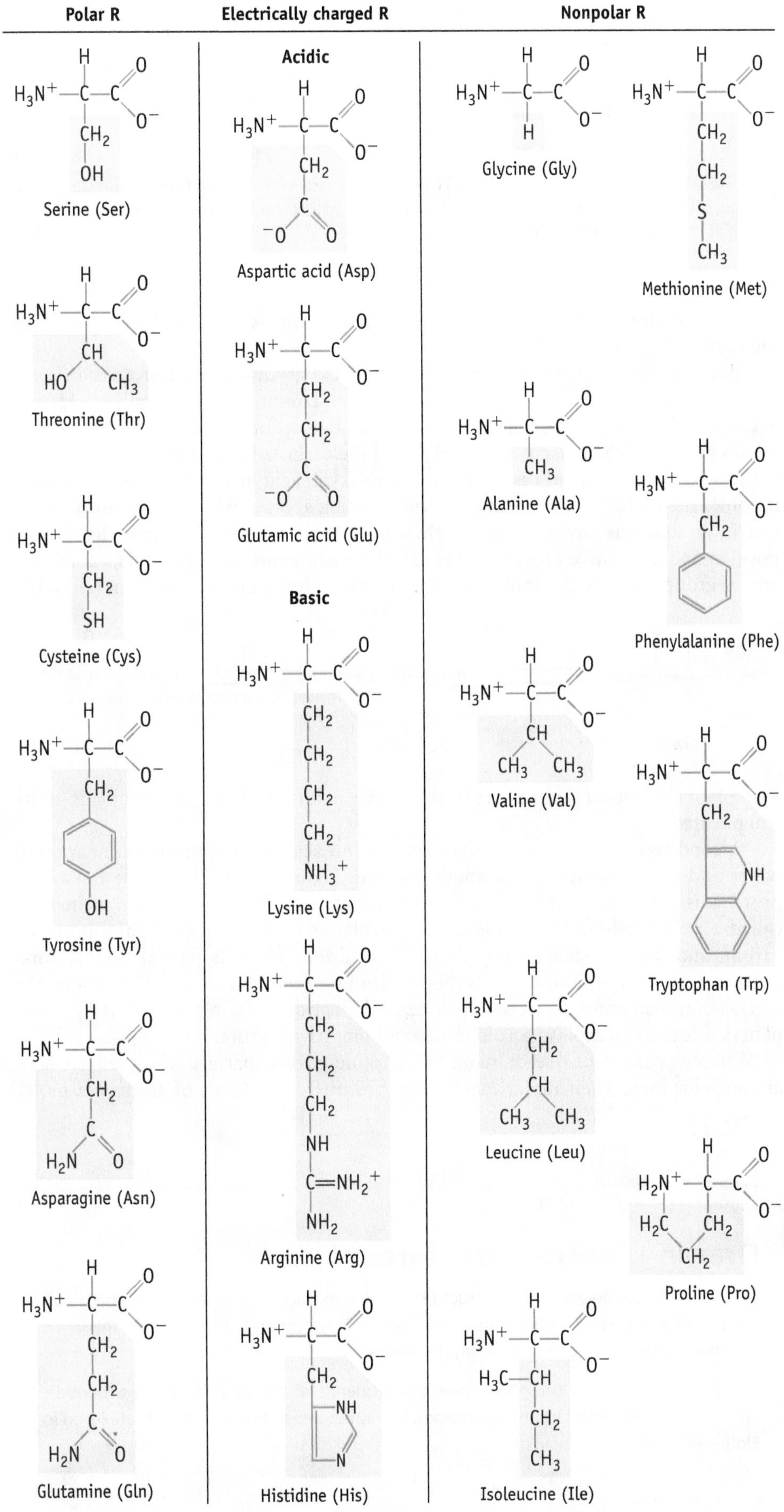

FIGURE 24.2 The 20 most common amino acids. The amino acids are shown in the form most common at a pH of about 7, physiological pH. (Histidine is shown in the electrically charged column because the unprotonated N in the organic group can easily be protonated.)

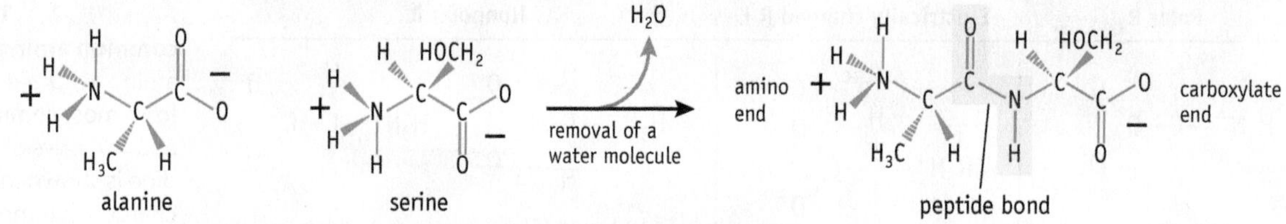

FIGURE 24.3 Formation of a peptide. Two α-amino acids condense to form an amide linkage, often called a *peptide bond*. Proteins are polypeptides, polymers consisting of many amino acid units linked through peptide bonds.

enantiomeric form—the form with the L-configuration (◀ *Case Study—An Awakening with L-DOPA*, p. 923).

Both the amino group and the carboxylic acid group can exist in two different states: an ionized form (—NH_3^+ and —CO_2^-) and an un-ionized form (—NH_2 and —CO_2H). At low pH, both groups will be in their protonated forms, that is, the amino group will be present as —NH_3^+ and the carboxylic acid group will be present as —CO_2H. As the pH is raised, the carboxylic acid group loses its proton and becomes the ionized form (—CO_2^-). The resulting species, which is the form prevalent in an aqueous environment at physiological pH (about 7.4), contains both a positive and a negative charge and is called a **zwitterion**. At higher pH values, the amino group loses its ionizable proton and becomes the un-ionized form (—NH_2).

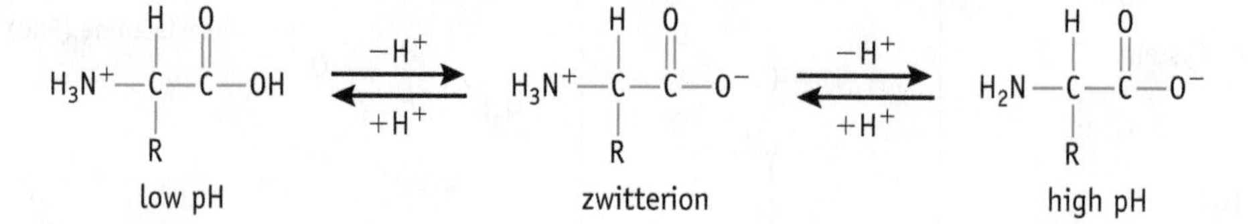

The pH behavior of amino acids that have acidic or basic *R* groups is more complicated.

A condensation reaction between two amino acids results in the elimination of water and the formation of an amide linkage (Figure 24.3). The amide linkage in proteins is often referred to as a **peptide bond**, and the polymer (the protein) is called a **polypeptide**. The amide linkage is planar (◀ Section 23-4), and both the carbon and the nitrogen atoms are sp^2 hybridized. There is partial double-bond character in the C—O and C—N bonds, leading to restricted rotation about the carbon–nitrogen bond. As a consequence, each peptide bond in a protein is rigid and planar, a feature that plays a role in determining its structure.

Proteins consist of one or more polypeptide chains that are often hundreds of amino acids long. Their molar masses are thus often thousands of grams per mole.

EXAMPLE 24.1

Drawing Peptide Structures

Problem Peptide and protein structures are drawn starting with the free amino group on the left and ending with the free carboxylic acid group on the right. Draw the Lewis structure for the tripeptide alanine-glycine-serine.

What Do You Know? You know the sequence of amino acids in the tripeptide, and that they are joined by amide linkages. The structures of the amino acids are listed in Figure 24.2.

Strategy Begin with the amino group of alanine on the left. Connect it via an amide linkage to glycine and then connect glycine to serine by another amide linkage.

Solution The Lewis structure for this tripeptide is

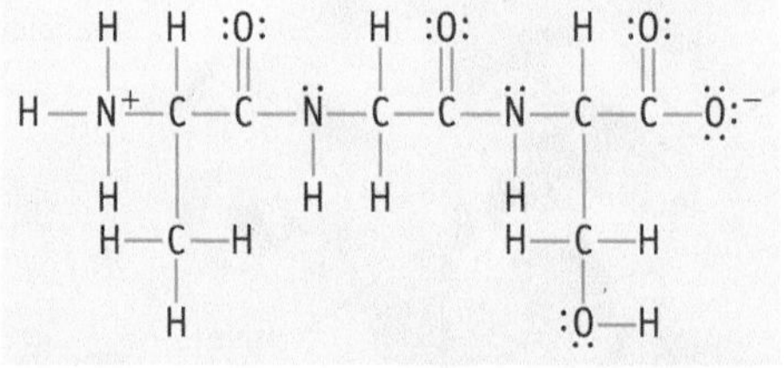

Think about Your Answer A tripeptide contains three amino acids and two peptide bonds. The zwitterionic form of the tripeptide was shown as this is the form present at physiological pH.

Check Your Understanding

Draw the Lewis structure for the tripeptide glycine-phenylalanine-valine.

Protein Structure and Hemoglobin

With this basic understanding of amino acids and peptide bonds, let us examine some larger issues related to protein structure. One of the central tenets of biochemistry is that "structure determines function." In other words, what a molecule can do is determined by which atoms or groups of atoms are present and how they are arranged in space. It is not surprising, therefore, that much effort has been devoted to determining the structures of proteins.

To simplify their discussions, biochemists describe proteins as having different structural levels. Each level of structure can be illustrated using hemoglobin.

Hemoglobin is the molecule in red blood cells that carries oxygen from the lungs to all of the body's other cells. It is a large iron-containing protein, made up of more than 10,000 atoms and having a molar mass of 64,500 g/mol. Hemoglobin consists of four polypeptide segments: two identical segments called the α subunits containing 141 amino acids each and two other segments called the β subunits containing 146 amino acids each. The β subunits are identical to each other but different from the α subunits. Each subunit contains an iron(II) ion locked inside an organic ion called a **heme** unit (Figure 24.4). The oxygen molecules transported by hemoglobin bind to these iron(II) ions.

Let us focus on the polypeptide part of hemoglobin (Figure 24.5). The first step in describing a structure is to identify how the atoms are covalently linked together. This is called the **primary structure** of a protein, which is simply the sequence of amino acids linked together by peptide bonds. For example, a glycine unit can be followed by an alanine, followed by a valine, and so on.

The remaining levels of structure all deal with noncovalent (nonbonding) interactions—that is, intermolecular forces—between amino acids in the protein. The **secondary structure** of a protein refers to hydrogen bonding networks formed between amide linkages in the protein backbone (◀ Figure 23.18 for an example of interchain hydrogen bonding). Specifically, the carbonyl group of one amide linkage interacts with the amino hydrogen of another amide. Some regular patterns, such as helices, sheets, and turns, often emerge as a result of hydrogen bonding. In hemoglobin, the amino acids in large portions of the polypeptide chains arrange themselves into many helical regions.

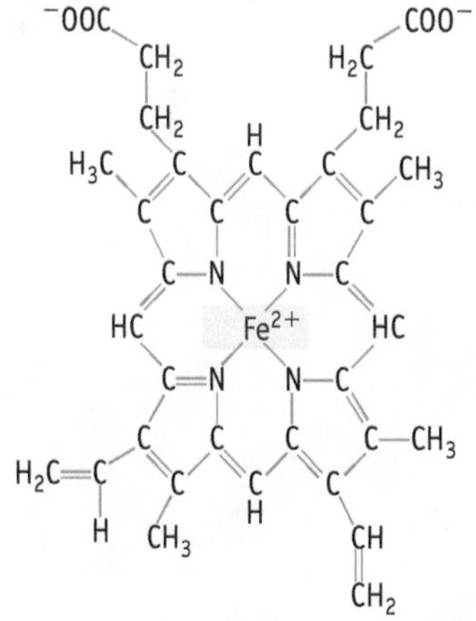

heme
(Fe-protoporphyrin IX)

FIGURE 24.4 **Heme.** The heme unit in hemoglobin (and in myoglobin, a related protein) consists of an iron ion in the center of a porphyrin ring system. (For more information about the iron-containing heme group, see *A Closer Look: Hemoglobin: A Molecule with a Tetradentate Ligand,* on page 872.)

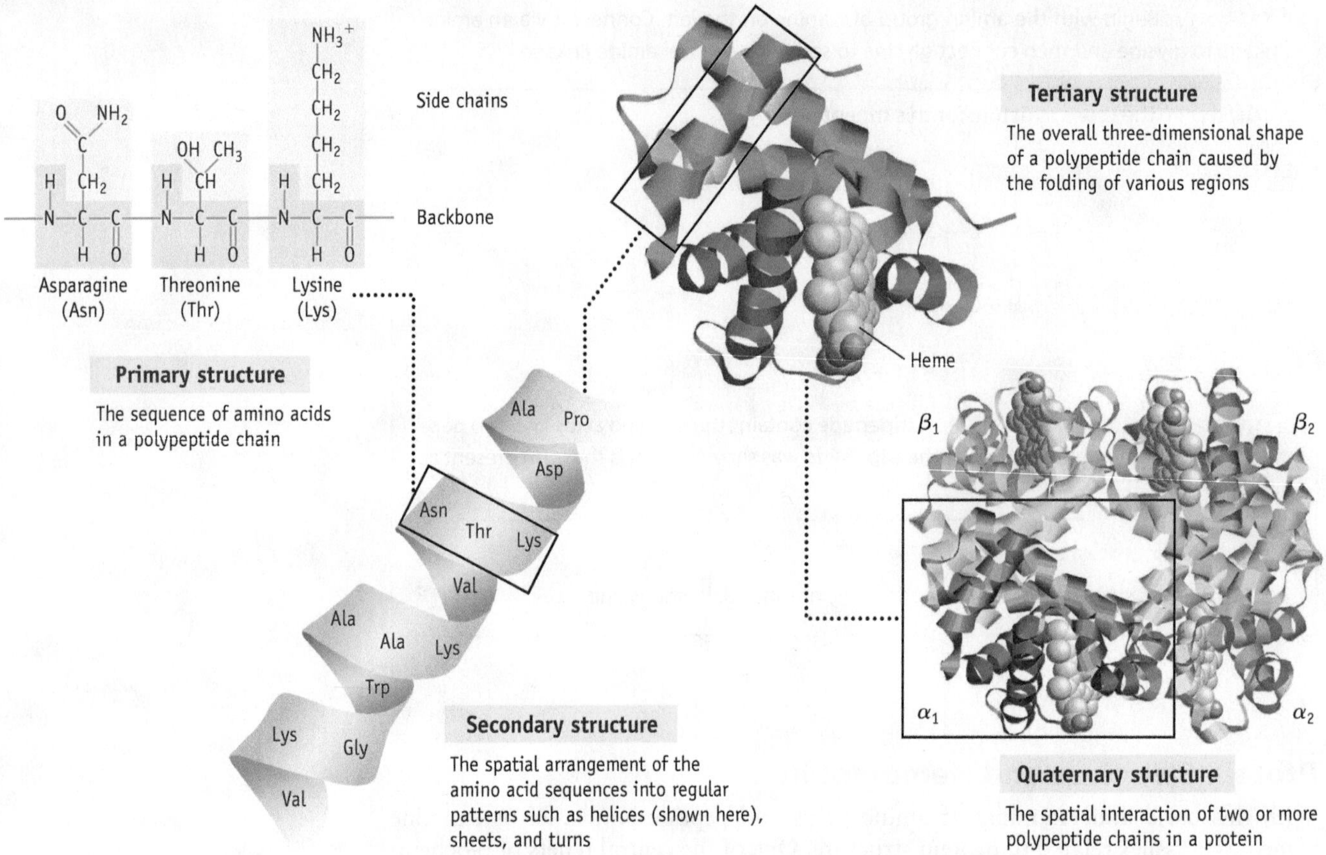

FIGURE 24.5 **The primary, secondary, tertiary, and quaternary structures of hemoglobin.**

The **tertiary structure** of a protein refers to how the chain is folded, including how amino acids far apart in the sequence interact with each other. In other words, this structure deals with how the regions of the polypeptide chain fold into the overall three-dimensional structure.

For proteins consisting of only one chain, the tertiary structure is the highest level of structure present. In proteins consisting of more than one polypeptide chain, such as hemoglobin, there is a fourth level of structure, called the **quaternary structure.** It is concerned with how the different chains interact. The quaternary structure of hemoglobin shows how the four subunits are related to one another in the overall protein.

The subtleties of sequence, structure, and function are dramatically illustrated in the case of hemoglobin. Seemingly small changes in the amino acid sequence of hemoglobin and other molecules can be important in determining function, as is illustrated by the disease called *sickle cell anemia*. This disease, which is sometimes fatal, affects some individuals of African descent. Persons affected by this disease are anemic; that is, they have low red blood cell counts. In addition, many of their red blood cells are elongated and curved like a sickle instead of being round disks (Figure 24.6a). These elongated red blood cells are more fragile than normal blood cells and thus often break, leading to the anemia that is observed. The elongated cells also do not fit through the capillaries properly and so block the flow of blood, thereby decreasing the amount of oxygen that the individual's cells receive.

The cause of sickle cell anemia has been traced to a small structural difference in hemoglobin. In the β subunits of the hemoglobin in individuals carrying the sickle cell trait, a valine has been substituted for a glutamic acid. An amino acid in this position ends up on the surface of the protein, where it is exposed to the aqueous environment of the cell. Glutamic acid and valine are quite different from each other. The side chain in glutamic acid is ionic, whereas that in valine is nonpolar. The nonpolar

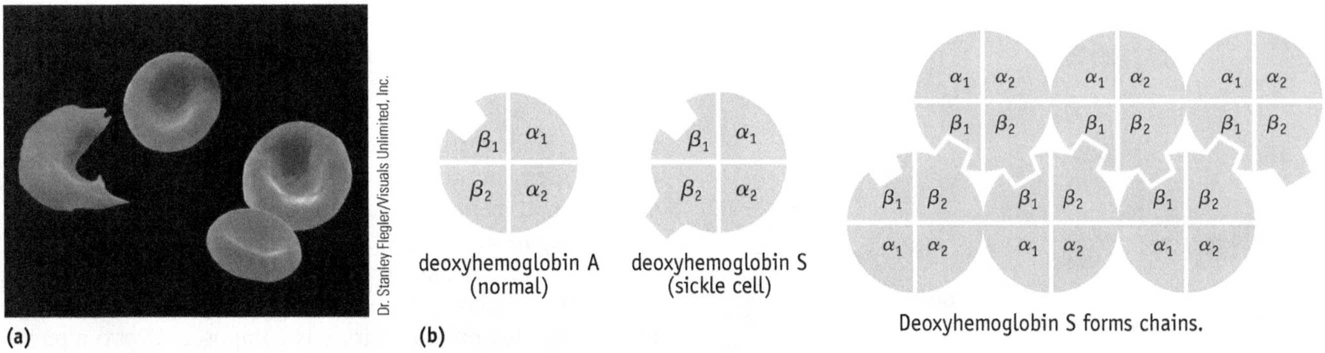

FIGURE 24.6 **Normal and sickled red blood cells. (a)** Red blood cells are normally rounded in shape, but people afflicted with sickle cell anemia have cells with a characteristic "sickle" shape. **(b)** Sickle cell hemoglobin has a nonpolar region that can fit into a nonpolar cavity on another hemoglobin. Sickle cell hemoglobins can link together to form long chainlike structures.

side chain on valine causes a nonpolar region to stick out from the molecule. When hemoglobin (normal or sickle cell) is in the deoxygenated state, it has a nonpolar cavity in another region. The nonpolar region around the valine on one sickle cell hemoglobin molecule fits nicely into this nonpolar cavity on another hemoglobin. The sickle cell hemoglobins thus link together, forming long chainlike structures (Figure 24.6b) that lead to the symptoms described.

Just one amino acid substitution in each β subunit causes sickle cell anemia! While other amino acid substitutions may not lead to such severe consequences, sequence, structure, and function are intimately linked and of crucial importance throughout biochemistry.

Enzymes, Active Sites, and Lysozyme

Many reactions necessary for life occur too slowly on their own, so organisms speed them up to the appropriate level using biological catalysts called **enzymes.** Almost every metabolic reaction in a living organism requires an enzyme, and most of these enzymes are proteins. Enzymes are often able to speed up reaction rates tremendously, typically 10^7 to 10^{14} times faster than uncatalyzed rates.

Enzyme Catalysis For more information about enzymes, see *Case Study: Enzymes—Nature's Catalysts* on p. 540.

For an enzyme to catalyze a reaction, several key steps must occur:

1. A reactant (often called the **substrate**) must bind to the enzyme.
2. The chemical reaction must take place.
3. The product(s) of the reaction must leave the enzyme so that more substrate can bind and the process can be repeated.

Typically, enzymes are very specific; that is, only a limited number of compounds (often only one) serve as substrates for a given enzyme, and the enzyme catalyzes only one type of reaction. The place in the enzyme where the substrate binds and the reaction occurs is called the **active site.** The active site often consists of a cavity or cleft in the structure of the enzyme into which the substrate or part of the substrate can fit. The R groups of amino acids or the presence of metal ions in an active site are often important factors in binding a substrate and catalyzing a reaction.

Lysozyme is an enzyme that can be obtained from human mucus and tears and from other sources, such as egg whites. Alexander Fleming (1881–1955) (who later discovered penicillin) is said to have discovered its presence in mucus when he had a cold. He purposely allowed some of the mucus from his nose to drip onto a dish containing a bacteria culture and found that some of the bacteria died. The chemical in the mucus responsible for this effect was a protein. Fleming called it *lysozyme* because it is an enzyme that causes some bacteria to undergo lysis (rupture).

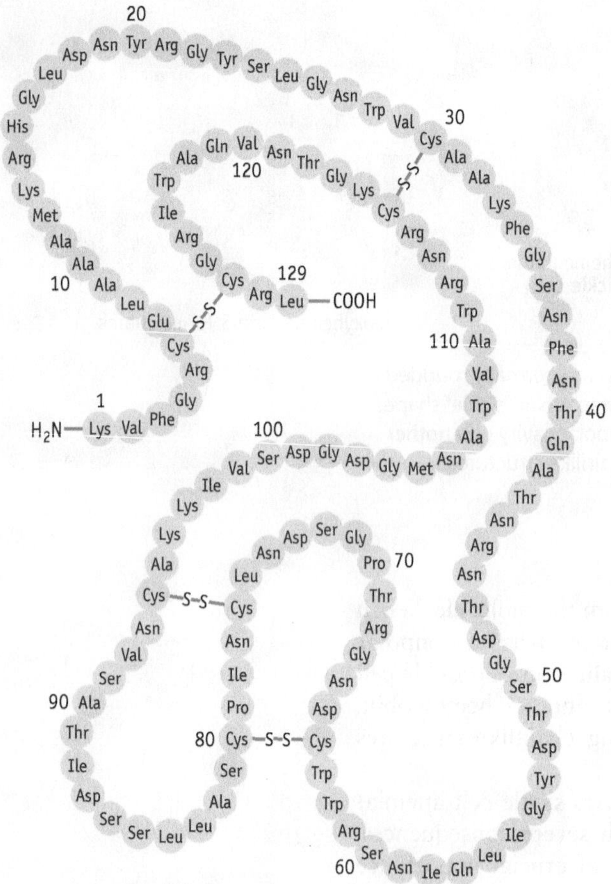

FIGURE 24.7 **The primary structure of lysozyme.** The cross-chain disulfide links (—S—S—) are links between cysteine amino acid residues.

Lysozyme is a protein containing 129 amino acids linked together in a single polypeptide chain (Figure 24.7). Its molar mass is 14,000 g/mol. As was true in the determination of the double-helical structure of DNA (◀ pages 332–333), x-ray crystallography and model building were key techniques used in determining lysozyme's three-dimensional structure and method of action.

Lysozyme's antibiotic activity results from its catalysis of a reaction that breaks down the cell walls of some bacteria. These cell walls contain a **polysaccharide**, a polymer of sugar molecules. This polysaccharide is composed of two alternating sugars: *N*-acetylmuramic acid (NAM) and *N*-acetylglucosamine (NAG). Lysozyme speeds up the reaction that breaks the bond between carbon-1 of NAM and carbon-4 of NAG (Figure 24.8), thereby breaking down the cell wall.

Lysozyme also catalyzes the breakdown of polysaccharides containing only NAG, but it is not very effective in cleaving molecules consisting of only two or three NAG units [$(NAG)_3$]. In fact, these molecules act as inhibitors of the enzyme. Researchers surmised that the inhibition resulted from these small molecules binding to but not completely filling the active site in the enzyme. X-ray crystallography of crystals of lysozyme that had been treated with $(NAG)_3$ revealed that $(NAG)_3$ binds to a cleft in lysozyme (Figure 24.9).

This cleft has room for a total of six NAG units. Molecular models of the enzyme and $(NAG)_6$ showed that five of the six sugars fit nicely into the cleft but that the fourth sugar in the sequence did not fit well. To get this fourth sugar into the active site, its structure has to be distorted. Assuming that the bond cleaved is the one connecting this fourth sugar to the fifth sugar, this distortion is advantageous because it deforms the molecule to more closely resemble the transition state of the cleavage reaction, thus speeding up this reaction. Amino acids immediately around this location can also assist in the cleavage reaction. In addition, models showed that if an alternating sequence of NAM and NAG binds to the enzyme in this cleft, NAM must bind to this fourth sugar location in the active site because it cannot fit into the third sugar-binding site, whereas NAG can. Cleavage must therefore occur only between carbon-1 of NAM and carbon-4 of the following NAG, not the other way around—and this is exactly what occurs.

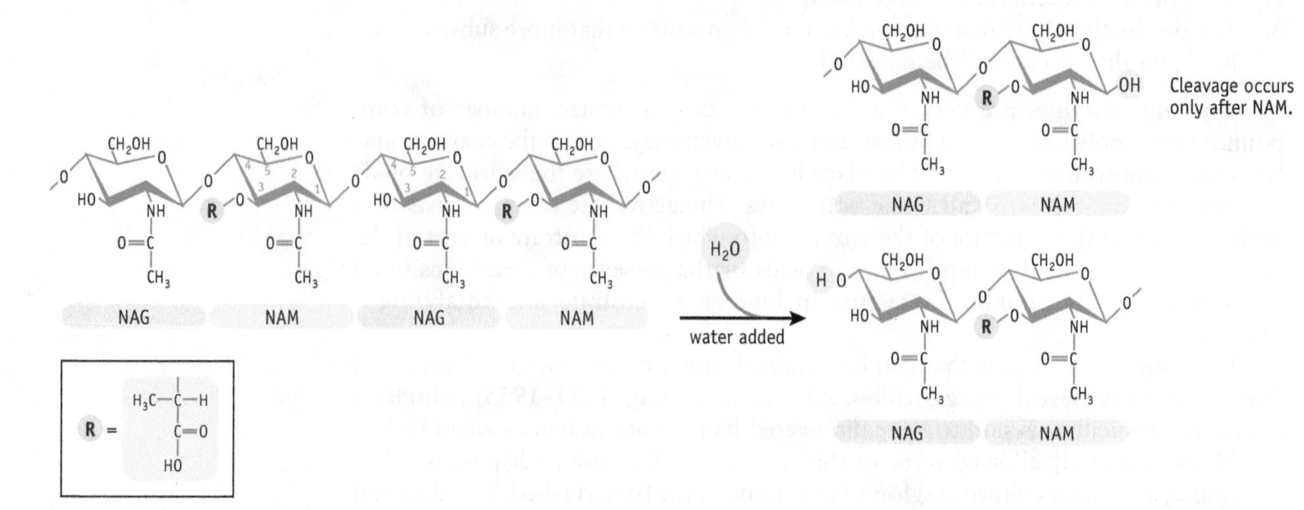

FIGURE 24.8 **Cleavage of a bond between *N*-acetylmuramic acid (NAM) and *N*-acetylglucosamine (NAG).** This reaction is accelerated by the enzyme lysozyme.

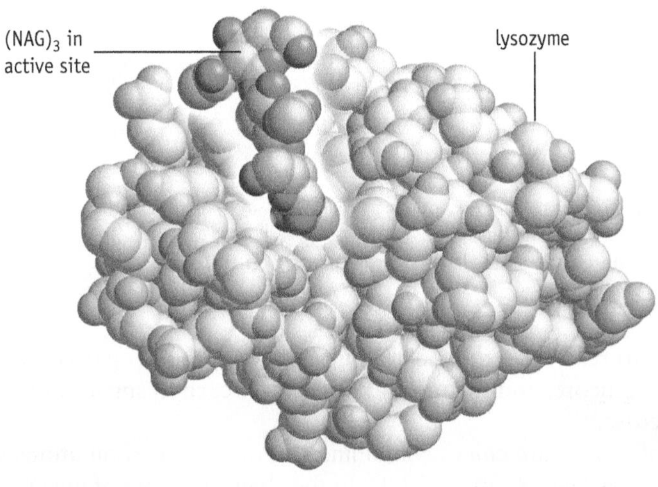

FIGURE 24.9 **Lysozyme with (NAG)$_3$ binds to the active site in lysozyme by means of intermolecular forces of attraction.**

REVIEW & CHECK FOR SECTION 24-1

1. Proteins are made out of
   (a) amino acids
   (b) carbohydrates
   (c) nucleic acids
   (d) polyprotic acids
2. Under physiological conditions, amino acids are
   (a) fully protonated
   (b) fully deprotonated
   (c) zwitterionic
3. The secondary structure of a protein refers to
   (a) the sequence of amino acids in the protein
   (b) structures built from the hydrogen bonding network of the amide linkages in the protein's backbone
   (c) the overall three-dimensional structure of the protein
   (d) the arrangement of the different polypeptide strands in the protein

24-2 Carbohydrates

Carbohydrates, or sugars, constitute another major class of compounds found in living things. They serve as our fuel for life's many activities. Ribose and deoxyribose, two sugars, are components of the nucleic acids (► Section 24-3) that store and translate the genetic information in our cells. Polymers of sugars, polysaccharides, serve as structural molecules in plants and bacteria. Finally, sugar molecules linked to other biomolecules are involved in cell-cell interactions.

Monosaccharides

Carbohydrates are polyhydroxy aldehydes or ketones. The open-chain structures of glucose, a polyhydroxy aldehyde or *aldose*, and of fructose, a polyhydroxy ketone or *ketose*, are shown in Figure 24.10. Both glucose and fructose are examples of **monosaccharides**, which are the simplest sugars. Monosaccharides usually have the general formula $C_x(H_2O)_x$, and it is from this formula that this class of compounds derives its name of carbohydrate, a combination of carbon and water. Thus, the formula of glucose, $C_6H_{12}O_6$, is equivalent to $C_6(H_2O)_6$.

The most abundant sugars in nature contain five or six carbon atoms and are referred to as *pentoses* and *hexoses*, respectively. Ribose and deoxyribose (► Section 24-3), found in the nucleic acids RNA and DNA, are the most abundant

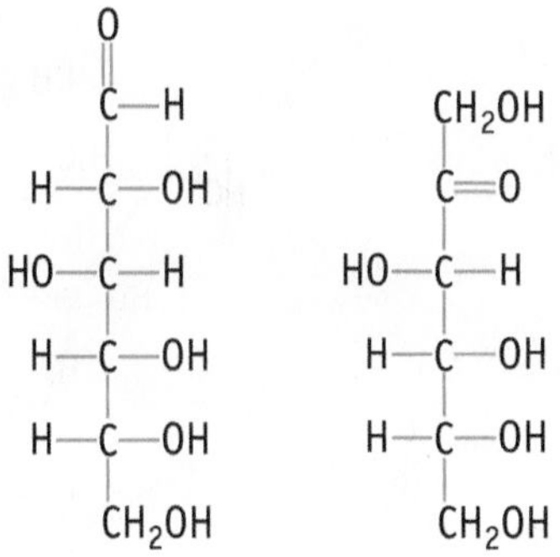

D-glucose D-fructose

FIGURE 24.10 **D-glucose and D-fructose.** D-Glucose (an aldehyde) and D-fructose (a ketone) both have the molecular formula $C_6H_{12}O_6$.

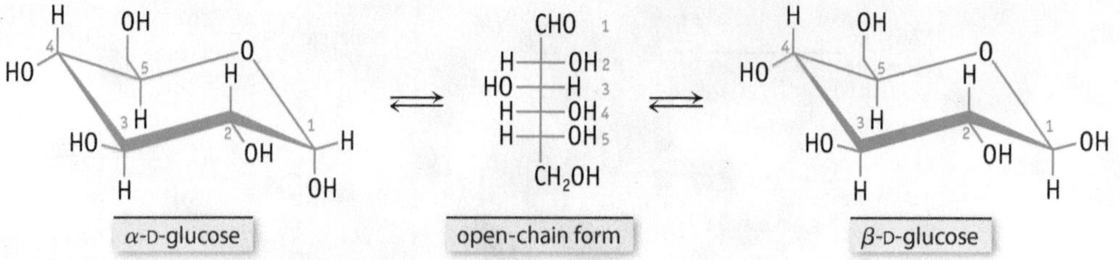

FIGURE 24.11 The straight-chain and ring forms of D-glucose.

pentoses in nature. By far, the most abundant six-carbon sugar containing an aldehyde group is glucose, and the most abundant six-carbon sugar containing a ketone group is fructose.

Almost all sugars are chiral, containing one or more carbon atoms with four different groups attached (◀ Section 23-1). In the chain structure of glucose, for example, four of the carbon atoms are bonded to four different groups. In nature, glucose occurs in just one of its enantiomeric forms; thus a solution of glucose rotates polarized light. The structures shown in Figure 24.10 are the D-isomers of glucose and fructose.

D-glucose exists in three different isomeric forms in aqueous solutions. Two of the isomers contain six-member rings, and the third is the open chain structure (Figure 24.11). Notice that the two ring structures differ by the orientation of the hydroxyl group and hydrogen atom at C-1. In α-D-glucose, the hydroxyl group is pointing down, whereas in β-D-glucose, it is pointing up. In aqueous solution, the three different forms of glucose rapidly interconvert, but the three different forms are not present in equal amounts. The straight chain isomer makes up less than 1% of the molecules with the cyclic forms predominating and present in a 63%:37% ratio of β-D-glucose to α-D-glucose. The predominant structures of most monosaccharides in aqueous solution contain rings.

Knowing the structure of glucose allows one to predict some of its properties. With five polar —OH groups in the molecule, glucose is, not surprisingly, soluble in water. The aldehyde group is susceptible to chemical oxidation to form a carboxylic acid, and detection of glucose (in urine or blood) takes advantage of this fact. Diagnostic tests for glucose involve oxidation with subsequent detection of the products.

Disaccharides

When two sugar molecules join together to form a **disaccharide**, they do so by means of a condensation reaction, in which a water molecule is lost. The two sugars end up connected to each other by a bridging oxygen atom; this type of bond between two sugar molecules is called a **glycosidic bond**. Table sugar, sucrose (Figure 24.12a), is

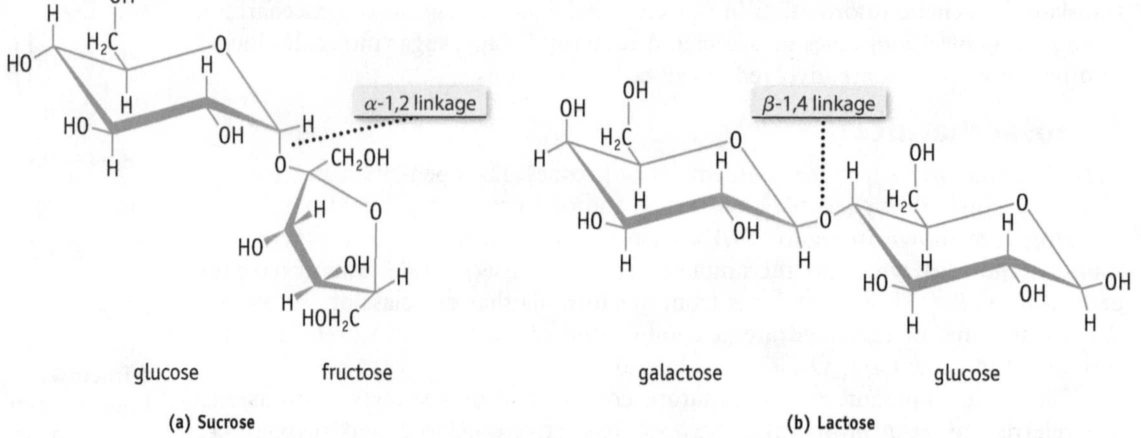

FIGURE 24.12 The disaccharides sucrose and lactose.

a disaccharide formed by the reaction of the hydroxyl group at position 1 in α-D-glucose with the hydroxyl group at position 2 of β-D-fructose. Because the hydroxyl group used in the first sugar (the glucose molecule) was in the α configuration, this type of linkage is referred to as an α-1,2 glycosidic bond.

Another common disaccharide is lactose (Figure 24.12b), a sugar found in milk. This sugar contains another hexose called β-D-galactose, which is combined with α-D-glucose by means of a β-1,4 linkage. When milk is consumed, lactose is broken down into its monosaccharides by utilizing an enzyme called lactase. As many humans grow older, their ability to produce lactase and thus digest lactose decreases; they are said to become lactose intolerant. In such individuals, the lactose is instead fermented by bacteria in the digestive tract into lactic acid, producing methane gas and hydrogen gas in the process. These gases can cause discomfort and lead to flatulence. In addition, the lactic acid and any undigested lactose can sometimes lead to diarrhea. These symptoms can certainly be avoided if the affected person abstains from dairy products, but they can also be avoided if a supplement containing the enzyme lactase is consumed along with the dairy products.

Polysaccharides

Long polymers of sugars, or **polysaccharides**, result when a large number of sugar molecules are joined by glycosidic bonds. In animal cells, excess glucose is stored as the polysaccharide called *glycogen* (Figure 24.13). The basic structure of glycogen is a branched chain of glucose molecules. Within a chain, the linkages are all α-1,4 glycosidic bonds. Branch points to the chain occur by means of α-1,6 glycosidic bonds. Branch points occur around every 10 or so glucose units in a chain.

Plant cells often store glucose in the form of starch. The chain lengths in starch are variable, ranging in size from molar masses of thousands to half a million g/mol. There are two main types of starch: *amylose starch* and *amylopectin starch*. Amylose starch contains linear chains of glucose molecules connected by means of α-1,4 glycosidic bonds. Amylopectin starch, like glycogen, is a branched chain of glucose molecules. The key difference is that the α-1,6 branch points in amylopectin occur less often than in glycogen, only every 30 or so glucose units.

Finally, the major structural molecule in plants, *cellulose*, is also a polysaccharide with chain lengths ranging from hundreds to many thousands of glucose units. The linkage between glucose molecules in cellulose is β-1,4 rather than α-1,4. This seemingly small change has a tremendous effect. Humans have enzymes that break down the α-1,4 linkages in starch but do not have an enzyme that breaks down the β-1,4 linkages between glucose molecules in cellulose. We can thus digest starch but cannot digest cellulose, and, when ingested, it passes through our systems unchanged as insoluble dietary fiber.

REVIEW & CHECK FOR SECTION 24-2

1. Glyceraldehyde is a monosaccharide with three carbon atoms. Its molecular formula is
   (a) $C_3H_3O_3$
   (b) $C_3H_4O_2$
   (c) $C_3H_6O_3$
   (d) $C_3H_6O_6$
2. The monomers of sucrose are
   (a) galactose and fructose
   (b) glucose and fructose
   (c) two molecules of fructose
   (d) two molecules of glucose
3. Which of the following cannot be digested by humans?
   (a) amylose starch
   (b) amylopectin starch
   (c) cellulose
   (d) sucrose

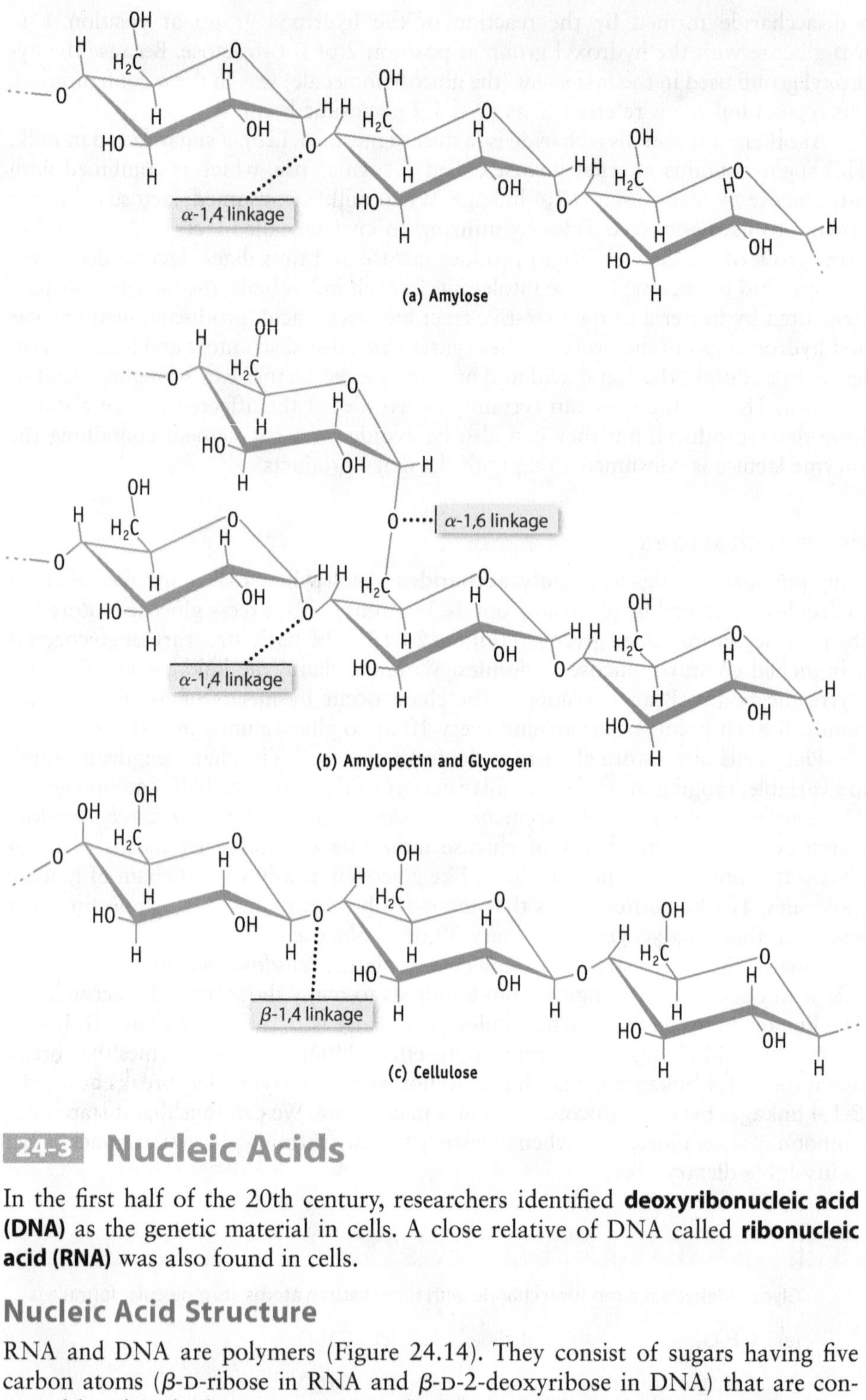

FIGURE 24.13 Polysaccharides.

24-3 Nucleic Acids

In the first half of the 20th century, researchers identified **deoxyribonucleic acid (DNA)** as the genetic material in cells. A close relative of DNA called **ribonucleic acid (RNA)** was also found in cells.

Nucleic Acid Structure

RNA and DNA are polymers (Figure 24.14). They consist of sugars having five carbon atoms (β-D-ribose in RNA and β-D-2-deoxyribose in DNA) that are connected by phosphodiester groups. At physiological pH, these phosphodiester linkages are in their ionized states with a net 1− charge per linkage. Thus, there is also a 1+ cation present per phosphodiester linkage (not shown in Figure 24.14). A phosphodiester group links the 3′ (pronounced "three prime") position of one sugar to the 5′ position of the next sugar. Attached at the 1′ position of each sugar is a nitrogen-containing (nitrogenous) base. The bases in DNA are adenine (A), cytosine (C), guanine (G), and thymine (T); in RNA, the nitrogenous bases are the same as in DNA, except that uracil (U) is used rather than thymine. A single sugar with a nitrogenous base attached is called a **nucleoside**. If a phosphate group is also attached, then the combination is called a **nucleotide** (Figure 24.15).

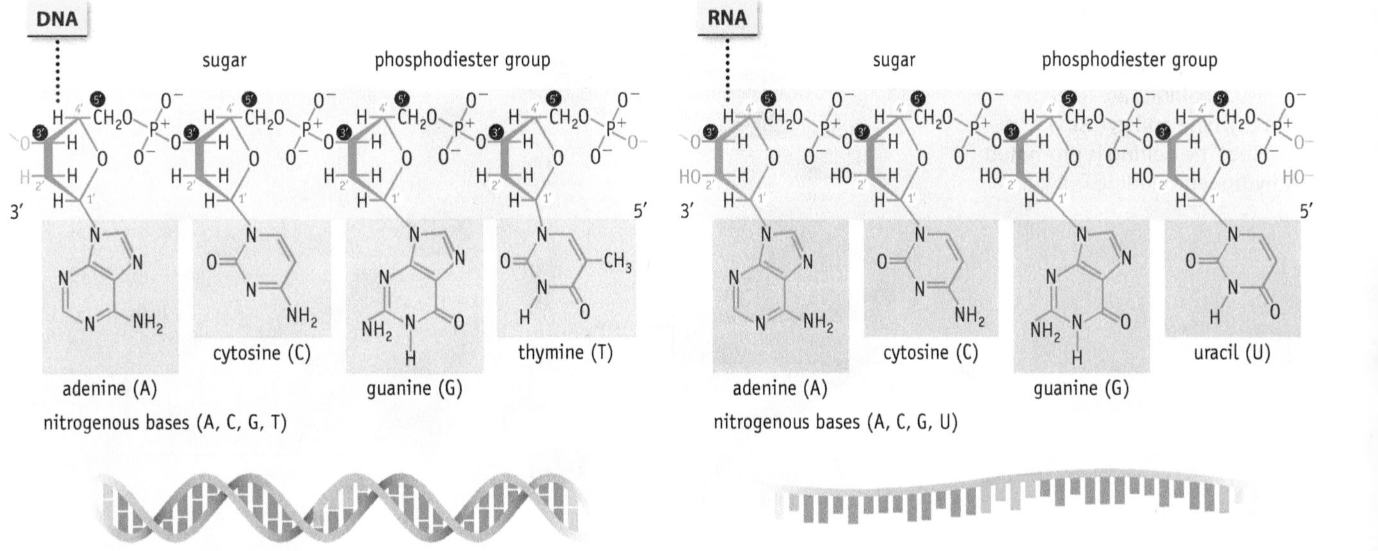

FIGURE 24.14 **DNA and RNA.**

The principal chemical difference between RNA and DNA is the identity of the sugar.

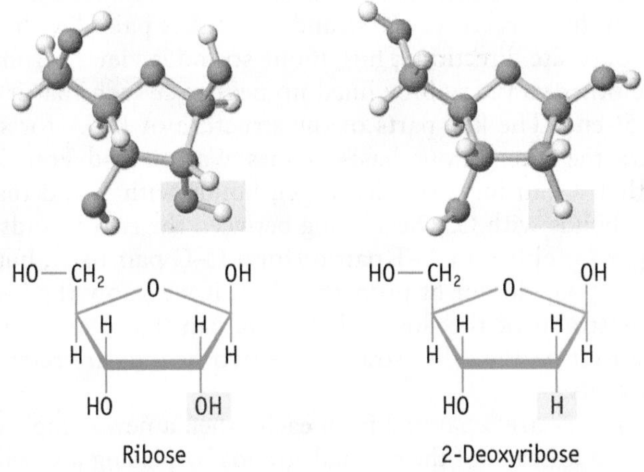

Ribose has a hydroxyl group (—OH) at the 2 position, whereas 2-deoxyribose has only a hydrogen atom at this position. This seemingly small difference turns out to have profound effects. The polymer chain of RNA is cleaved many times faster than

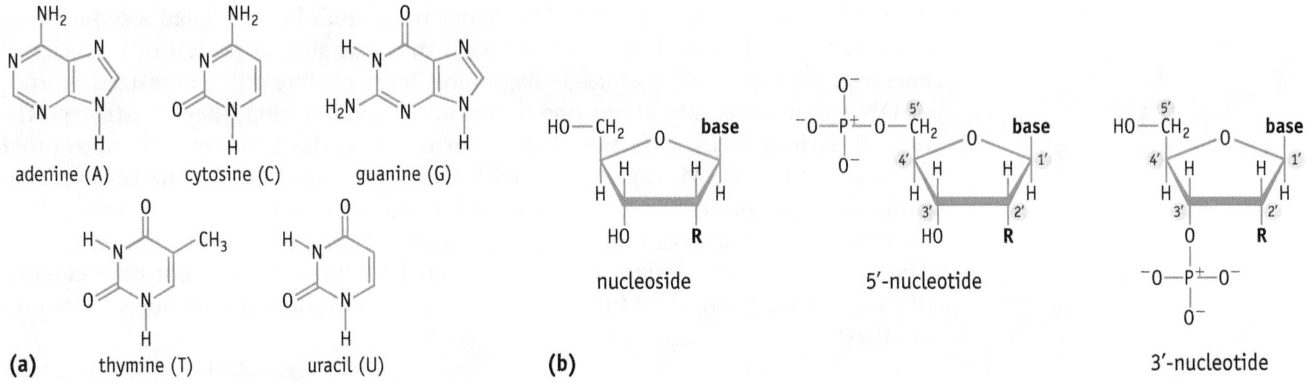

FIGURE 24.15 **Bases, nucleosides, and nucleotides.**

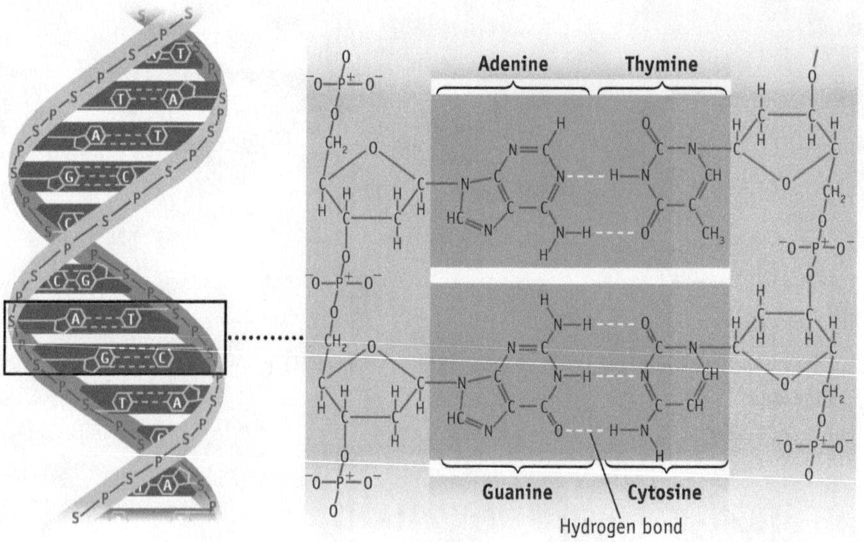

FIGURE 24.16 Base pairs and complementary strands in DNA. With the four bases in DNA, the usual pairings are adenine with thymine and cytosine with guanine. The pairing is promoted by hydrogen bonding.

a corresponding chain of DNA under similar conditions due to the involvement of this hydroxyl group in the cleavage reaction. The greater stability of DNA contributes to it being a better repository for genetic information.

How does DNA store genetic information? DNA consists of a double helix (Figure 24.16). In this structure, one strand of DNA is paired with another strand running in the opposite direction. Thus, if one strand is viewed from the 5′-end to the 3′-end, the other strand will be lined up next to it such that it runs from the 3′-end to the 5′-end. The key parts of the structure of DNA for storing genetic information are the nitrogenous bases. James Watson and Francis Crick (page 333) noticed that A can form two hydrogen bonds with T and that C can form three hydrogen bonds with G. The spacing between the two strands of the double helix is just right for either an A–T pair or for a C–G pair to fit, but other combinations (such as A–G) do not fit properly. Thus, if we know the identity of a nucleotide on one strand of the double helix, we can figure out which nucleotide must be bound to it on the other strand. The two strands are referred to as **complementary strands.**

The Structure of DNA For more information about the structure of DNA, see *Chemical Bonding in DNA* on p. 282, *Section 8-10: DNA, Revisited* on pp. 332–333, and *A Closer Look: Hydrogen Bonding in Biochemistry* on p. 414.

If the two strands are separated from each other, a new complementary strand can be constructed for each of the original strands by placing a G wherever there is a C, a T wherever there is an A, and so forth. Through this process, called **replication**, the cell ends up with two identical double-stranded DNA molecules for each molecule of DNA initially present. When the cell divides, each of the two resulting cells gets one copy of each DNA molecule (Figure 24.17). In this way, genetic information is passed along from one generation to the next.

The power of DNA was demonstrated further in 2010 in an experiment conducted by researchers at the J. Craig Venter Institute. They designed a sequence of DNA with a little over 1 million base pairs that was similar to that of a species of bacteria, *Mycoplasma mycoides*. Beginning with chemically synthesized strands of DNA that were only about one thousand base pairs long, they constructed the overall desired DNA sequence. They then replaced the DNA in cells of another species of bacteria, *M. capricolum,* with this synthesized DNA. The resulting organisms could perform cell division and grew into colonies of bacteria. These bacteria had characteristics not of *M. capricolum* but of the modified *M. mycoides*. The synthetic DNA, designed and constructed by humans, was not only capable of carrying out the normal functions of DNA but had transformed one species into another!

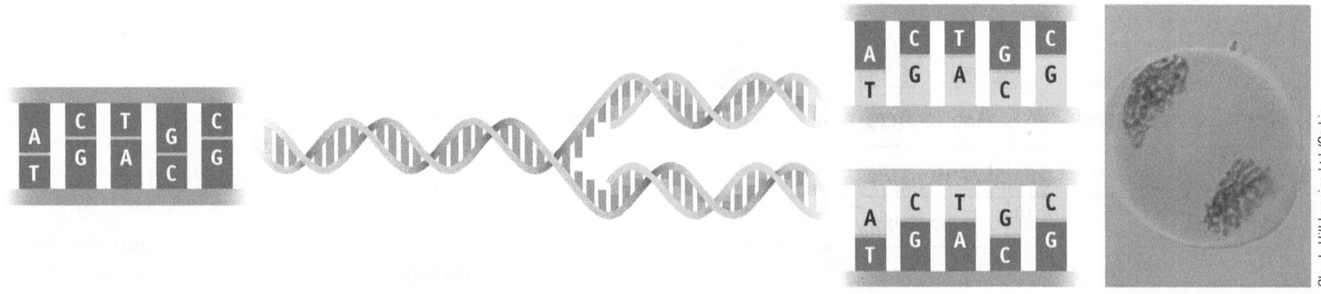

Two strands of DNA. Each base is paired with its partner: adenine (A) with thymine (T), guanine (G) with cytosine (C).

The two DNA strands are separated from each other.

Two new complementary strands are built using the original strands.

Replication results in two identical double-stranded DNA molecules.

At this stage during cell division, the chromosomes containing the DNA have been duplicated, and the two sets have been separated.

FIGURE 24.17 **The main steps in DNA replication.** The products of this replication are two identical double-helical DNA molecules. When a cell divides, each resulting cell gets one set.

EXAMPLE 24.2

Complementary Strands of DNA

Problem Nucleic acid sequences are usually written starting with the nucleotide on the 5′-end and proceeding to the 3′-end. A particular segment of a strand of DNA has the sequence AGTCCTCATG. What is the sequence of the complementary strand?

What Do You Know? You know the sequence of a segment of DNA and that in the complementary strand A will base pair with T, and C will base pair with G.

Strategy Write the sequence of DNA that is complementary to the given sequence by completing the base pairs (A with T and G with C). Make sure that in your final answer you list the sequence from the 5′-end to the 3′-end.

Solution The given sequence and it complement are as follows

Given sequence: 5′-AGTCCTCATG-3′

Complementary sequence: 3′-TCAGGAGTAC-5′

In order from the 5′-end to the 3′-end, this sequence is CATGAGGACT.

Think about Your Answer Knowing the sequence of one strand of DNA allows us to predict the sequence of DNA on the complementary strand.

Check Your Understanding

What is the sequence of the strand of DNA complementary to CGATACGTAC.

Protein Synthesis

The sequence of nucleotides in a cell's DNA contains the instructions to make the proteins the cell needs. DNA is the information storage molecule. To use this information, the cell first makes a complementary copy of the required portion of the DNA using RNA. This step is called **transcription**. The molecule of RNA that results is called **messenger RNA (mRNA)** because it takes this message to where

Table 24.1 Examples of the 64 Codons in the Genetic Code

CODON BASE SEQUENCE*	AMINO ACID TO BE ADDED
AAA	Lysine
AAC	Asparagine
AUG	Start
CAA	Glutamine
CAU	Histidine
GAA	Glutamic acid
GCA	Alanine
UAA	Stop
UAC	Tyrosine

*A = Adenine, C = cytosine, G = guanine, U = uracil.

protein synthesis occurs in the cell. The cell uses the more rapidly cleaved RNA rather than DNA to carry out this function.

It makes sense to use DNA, the more stable molecule, to store the genetic information because the cell wants this information to be passed from generation to generation intact. Conversely, it makes sense to use RNA to send the message to make a particular protein. By using the less-stable RNA, the message will not be permanent but rather will be destroyed after a certain time, thus allowing the cell to turn off the synthesis of the protein.

Protein synthesis occurs in **ribosomes**, complex bodies in a cell consisting of a mixture of proteins and RNA. The new protein is made as the ribosome moves along the strand of mRNA. The sequence of nucleotides in mRNA contains information about the order of amino acids in the desired protein. Following the signal in mRNA to start protein synthesis, every sequence of three nucleotides provides the code for an amino acid in the protein until the ribosome reaches the signal to stop (Table 24.1). These three-nucleotide sequences in mRNA are referred to as **codons**, and the correspondence between each codon and its message (start, add a particular amino acid, or stop) is referred to as the **genetic code**.

How is the genetic code used to make a protein? In the ribosome–mRNA complex, there are two neighboring binding sites, called the P site and the A site. (The ribosomes of eukaryotic cells, cells that contain nuclei, also have a third binding site, called the E site.) Each cycle that adds an amino acid to a growing protein begins with that part of the protein already constructed being located in the P site. The A site is where the next amino acid is brought in, and yet another type of RNA becomes involved at this point. This **transfer RNA (tRNA)** consists of a strand of RNA to which an amino acid can be attached (Figure 24.18). A strand of tRNA has a particular region that contains a sequence of three nucleotides that can attempt to form base pairs to a codon in the mRNA at the ribosome's A site. This three-nucleotide sequence in the tRNA is called the **anticodon**. Only if the base pairing between the codon and anticodon is complementary (for example, A with U) will the tRNA be

FIGURE 24.18 **tRNA structure.**

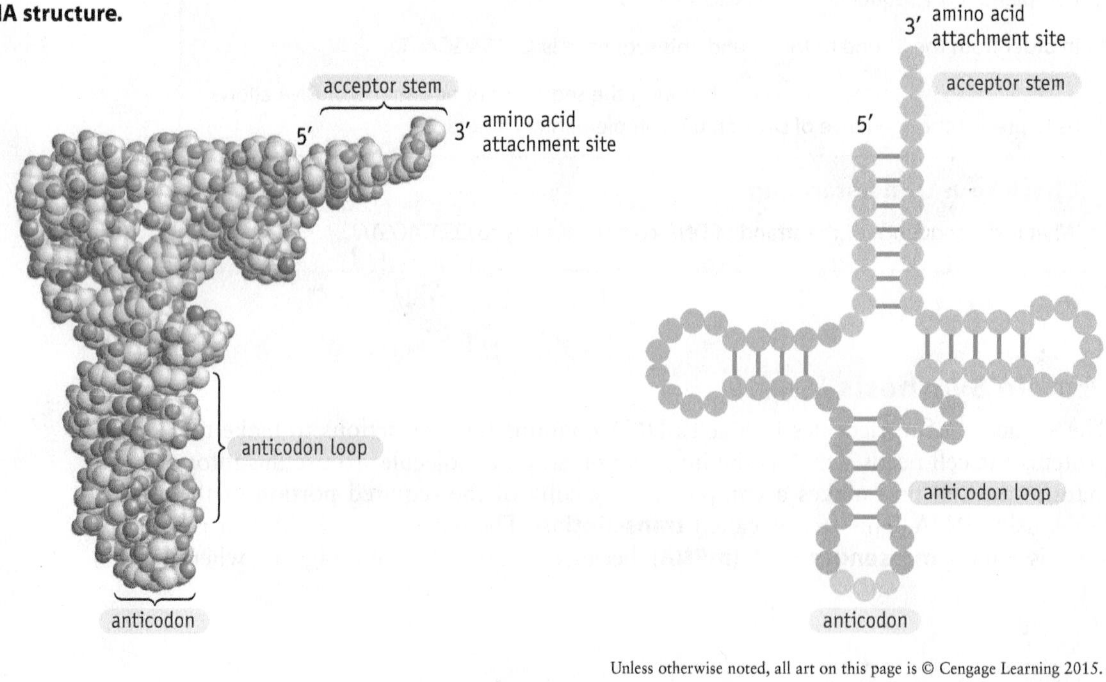

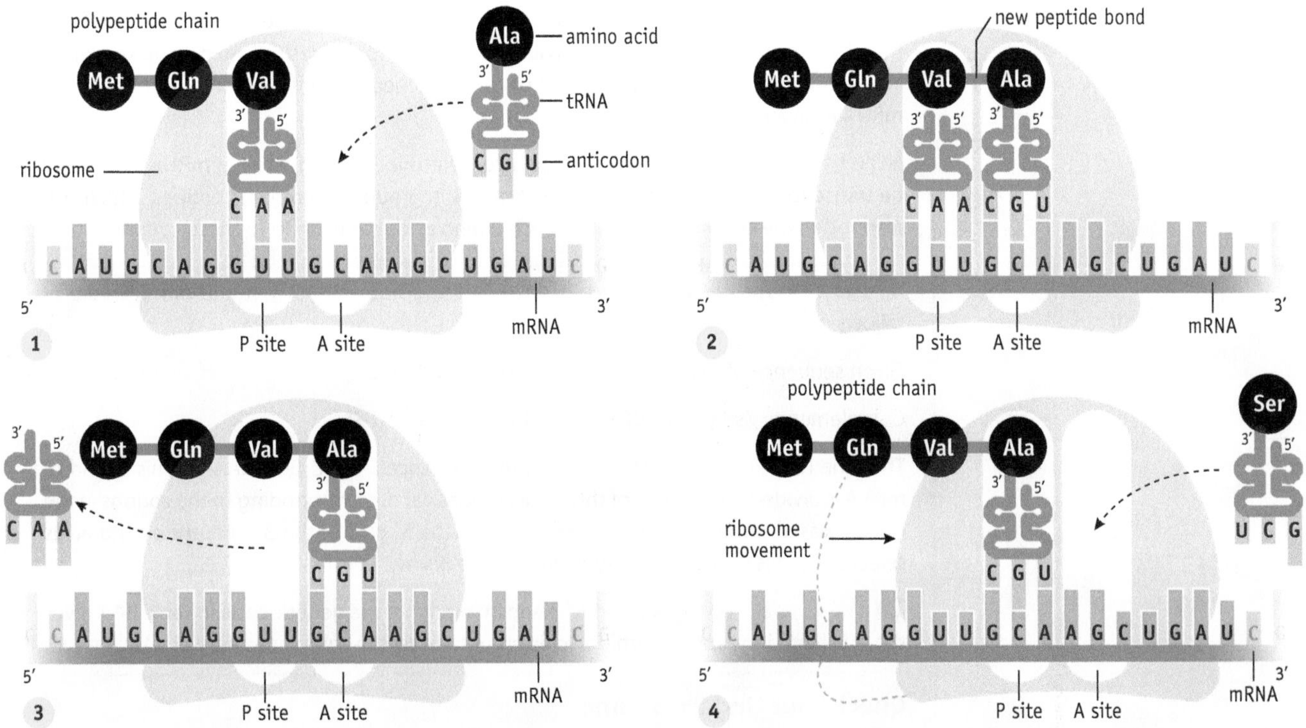

FIGURE 24.19 **Protein synthesis.** The tRNA with an anticodon complementary to the mRNA codon exposed in the A site of the ribosome brings the next amino acid to be added to the growing protein chain. After the new peptide bond is formed, the ribosome moves down the mRNA, exposing a new codon in the A site and transferring the previous tRNA and the protein chain to the P site.

able to bind to the mRNA–ribosome complex. Not only does the anticodon determine to which codon a particular strand of tRNA can bind, but it also determines which amino acid will be attached to the end of the tRNA molecule. Thus, a codon in the mRNA is complementary to a particular tRNA anticodon, which in turn specifies the correct amino acid.

The growing protein chain in the P site (Figure 24.19) reacts with the amino acid in the A site, resulting in the protein chain being elongated by one amino acid and moving the chain into the A site. The ribosome then moves down the mRNA chain, moving the tRNA along with the protein strand from the A site into the P site and exposing a new codon in the A site. The tRNA that had been in the P site and that no longer has an amino acid attached either leaves the ribosome directly or, if there is an E site present, moves into the E site before exiting from the ribosome. The process is then repeated.

Converting the information from a nucleotide sequence in mRNA into an amino acid sequence in a protein is called **translation.** Protein synthesis thus consists of two main processes: transcription of the DNA's information into RNA, followed by translation of the RNA's message into the amino acid sequence of the protein. There is more involved, but the processes of transcription and translation as discussed here provide a basic introduction to this important topic.

EXAMPLE 24.3

Protein Synthesis

Problem A strand of DNA that codes for three amino acids in a protein has the following sequence: TTT TGC GTA. What is the sequence of amino acids that will result from this sequence?

What Do You Know? The sequence of DNA is given. The information in DNA is transcribed into mRNA and then translated by tRNA into the desired amino acid sequence. You know the rules for forming base pairs. The genetic code for some of the codons in mRNA is given in Table 24.1.

Strategy From the given DNA sequence, determine the sequence of mRNA that would be transcribed. Look at the sequence of mRNA in groups of three nucleotides, which correspond to the codons. Determine which amino acids correspond to these codons.

Solution The given sequence of DNA and its complementary strand of mRNA are as follows:

Given sequence of DNA: 5′-TTT TGC GTA-3′

Complementary sequence of mRNA: 3′-AAA ACG CAU-5′

Thus the resulting strand of mRNA has the sequence 5′-UAC GCA AAA-3′. This strand of mRNA is divided into groups of three nucleotides each, corresponding to the codons in the mRNA. Based on Table 24.1 and reading from the 5′ end to the 3′ end, the amino acids selected by this sequence are tyrosine-alanine-lysine.

Think about Your Answer Keep in mind that the genetic code in Table 24.1 gives the mRNA codons and the amino acids brought in by the complementary tRNAs.

Check Your Understanding

What is the sequence of amino acids encoded by the DNA sequence TTG TGC TTT?

The RNA World and the Origin of Life

One of the most fascinating and persistent questions scientists pursue is how life arose on Earth. Plaguing those trying to answer this question is a molecular chicken-and-egg problem: Which came first, DNA or proteins? DNA is good at storing genetic information, but it is not good at catalyzing reactions. Proteins are good at catalyzing reactions, but they are not good at storing genetic information. In trying to picture an early self-replicating molecule, deciding whether it should be based on DNA or proteins seemed hopeless. Ultimately, both functions are important. These problems have caused some scientists to turn away from considering either DNA or proteins as candidates for the first molecule of life. One hypothesis that has gained support in recent years suggests that the first life on Earth may have been based on RNA instead.

Like DNA, RNA is a nucleic acid and can serve as a genetic storage molecule. We have already seen how it serves as an information molecule in the process of protein synthesis. In addition, scientists have discovered that retroviruses, like the human immunodeficiency virus (HIV) that causes AIDS, use RNA as the repository of genetic information instead of DNA. Perhaps the first organisms on Earth also used RNA to store genetic information.

In the 1980s, researchers discovered that particular strands of RNA catalyze some reactions involving cutting and joining together strands of RNA. Thomas Cech, a professor at the University of Colorado, Boulder, and Sidney Altman, a professor at Yale University, shared the 1989 Nobel Prize in Chemistry for their independent discoveries of systems that utilize "catalytic RNA." One might imagine that an organism could use RNA both as the genetic material and as a catalyst. Information and action are thus combined in this one molecule.

According to proponents of the "RNA World" hypothesis, the first organisms may have used RNA for both information and catalysis. At some later date, DNA

A CLOSER LOOK — HIV and Reverse Transcriptase

One of the major health crises in modern times is the epidemic associated with the disease called *acquired immune deficiency syndrome* (AIDS). A person develops AIDS in the final stages of infection with the *human immunodeficiency virus* (HIV). At the time of this writing, an estimated 34 million people worldwide are infected with HIV, a retrovirus. Unlike all organisms and most viruses, a retrovirus uses single-stranded RNA rather than DNA as its genetic material.

During the course of infection, the viral RNA is transcribed into DNA by means of an enzyme called *reverse transcriptase*. It is so named because the direction of information flow is in the opposite direction (RNA → DNA) than that usually found in cells. The resulting DNA is inserted into the cell's DNA. The infected cell then produces the proteins and RNA to make new virus particles.

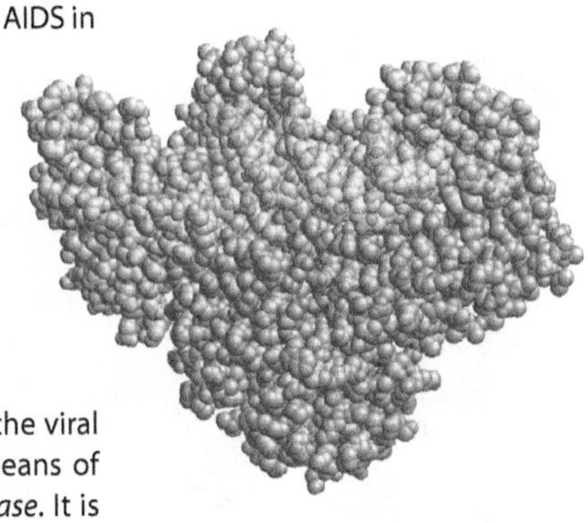

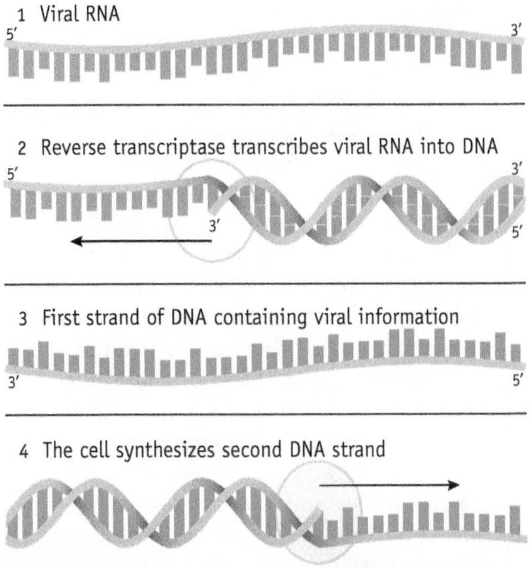

Reverse transcriptase. The reverse transcriptase enzyme consists of two subunits (shown in red and purple). Reverse transcriptase catalyzes the transcription of viral RNA into DNA. The cell then constructs a complementary strand of DNA. The resulting double-stranded DNA is inserted into the cell's DNA.

Reverse transcriptase consists of two subunits (see Figure). One subunit has a molar mass of approximately 6.6×10^4 g/mol, and the other has a molar mass of roughly 5.1×10^4 g/mol. Reverse transcriptase is not a very accurate enzyme, however. It makes an error in transcription for every 2000 to 4000 nucleotides copied. This is a much larger error rate than that for most cellular enzymes that copy DNA, which typically make one error for every 10^9 to 10^{10} nucleotides copied. The high error rate for reverse transcriptase contributes to the challenge scientists face in trying to combat HIV because these reverse transcription errors in the resulting DNA lead to frequent mutations in the virus. That is, the virus keeps changing, which means that developing a treatment that works and will continue to work is very difficult. Some treatments have been successful in significantly delaying the onset of AIDS, but none has yet proven to be a cure. More research is needed to combat this deadly disease.

evolved and had better information storage capabilities, so it took over the genetic information storage functions from RNA. Likewise, proteins eventually evolved and proved better at catalysis than RNA, so they took over this role for most reactions in a cell. RNA still plays a central role in the flow of genetic information, however. Genetic information does not go directly from DNA to proteins; it must pass through RNA along the way. Those favoring the RNA World hypothesis also point out that many enzyme cofactors, molecules that must be present for an enzyme to work, are RNA nucleotides or are based on RNA nucleotides. As we shall see, one of the most important molecules in metabolism is an RNA nucleotide, adenosine 5′-triphosphate (ATP). The importance of these nucleotides might date back to an earlier time when organisms were based on RNA alone.

REVIEW & CHECK FOR SECTION 24-3

1. Which breaks down more quickly in an aqueous solution?

   (a) DNA (b) RNA

2. What sequence of RNA is complementary to the DNA sequence AUG?

   (a) 5′-AUG-3′ (c) 5′-CAU-3′
   (b) 5′-CAT-3′ (d) 5′-TAC-3′

CASE STUDY Antisense Therapy

Much traditional research in finding new drugs focuses on discovering compounds that bind to proteins involved in a disease. A different approach is followed by what is called "antisense" therapy. Rather than proteins, antisense therapy focuses on nucleic acids, specifically the mRNA or even the DNA coding for the protein in the first place. A compound is introduced that is complementary to this strand and that will therefore bind to it, thus tying up the strand of nucleic acid so that it will not deliver its message to the ribosome in the case of mRNA or will not be transcribed in the case of DNA. The sequence of the targeted nucleic acid is referred to as the "sense" strand and the complementary strand, the drug, is referred to as the antisense strand.

In 2013, a drug produced by Isis Pharmaceuticals became the second antisense compound approved by the Food and Drug Administration for human use in the United States. The drug, called Kynamro, targets the mRNA for a protein involved in a rare condition that leads to very high levels of cholesterol called *homozygous familial hypercholesterolemia*. (The first compound ever approved was produced by Isis in the late 1990s but was not commercially successful.)

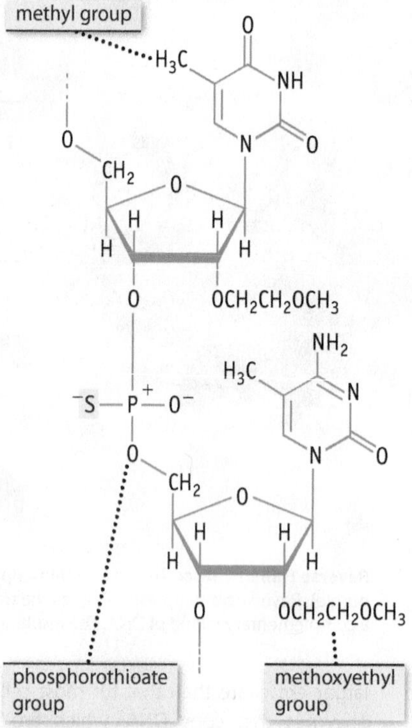

Part of the sequence of the antisense drug, Kynamro.

Nucleic acid strands with natural phosphodiester linkages are very susceptible to enzyme breakdown in the body and thus do not make good drug candidates. Kynamro uses a backbone that contains phosphorothioate groups (Figure) in which an oxygen attached to phosphorus is replaced by a sulfur atom. In addition, the drug uses deoxyribose sugars in some locations and modified ribose sugars in other locations. In these ribose sugars, the 2′-OH group has been replaced by a methoxyethyl group. Yet another modification is that a methyl group has been added to each of the cytosine and uracil bases in the compound.

Kynamro may be just the beginning of what is likely to be many more antisense treatments; at the time of this writing, there were over 50 clinical drug studies under way for compounds from a variety of companies that utilize some form of gene silencing technology.

Questions:

1. Kynamro has the hydrogen bonding sequence: GCCUCAGTCTGCTTCGCACC. What is the sequence of nucleotides in the targeted mRNA?
2. The formula of Kynamro is $C_{230}H_{305}N_{67}O_{122}P_{19}S_{19}Na_{19}$. What is the molar mass of this compound?
3. What is the molecular geometry around the phosphorus atom in the phosphorothioate group?

Answers to these questions are available in Appendix N.

3. Which amino acid is selected by the mRNA codon GAA?
   (a) alanine
   (b) glutamic acid
   (c) histidine
   (d) tyrosine

24-4 Lipids and Cell Membranes

Lipids are another important type of compound found in organisms. Among other things, they are the principal components of cell membranes and a repository of chemical energy in the form of fat. In addition, some of the chemical messengers called **hormones** are lipids.

Lipids include a wide range of compounds because classification of a compound as a lipid is based on its solubility rather than on a particular chemical functional group. A lipid is a compound that is at best slightly soluble in water but is soluble in organic solvents.

Polar compounds tend to be soluble in a polar solvent such as water. Nonpolar compounds are soluble in nonpolar solvents but they tend not to be soluble in polar solvents. This tendency is sometimes referred to as "like dissolves like"

(◄ Section 13-2). Compounds in biological organisms that are nonpolar, or at least substantially nonpolar, have limited solubility in water and are therefore lipids.

A major category of lipids consists of molecules that have a polar end and a nonpolar end. The polar end provides the slight water affinity necessary for it to be compatible with being in the aqueous environment of the cell, but the nonpolar end greatly limits the solubility. Many of these compounds are fats, oils, fatty acids, or related to these compounds.

Fats and **oils** serve many functions in the body, a primary one being the storage of energy. Fats (solids) and oils (liquids) are triesters formed from glycerol (1,2,3-propanetriol) and three carboxylic acids that can be the same or different. Because they are triesters of glycerol, they are sometimes referred to as **triglycerides**.

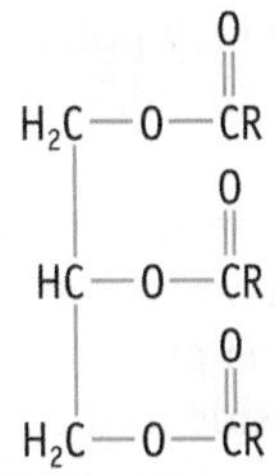

Triglyceride. R = long chain fatty acid (Table 24.2)

The carboxylic acids in fats and oils are known as **fatty acids** and have a lengthy carbon chain, usually between 12 and 18 carbon atoms (Table 24.2). Fatty acids and triglycerides are lipids of the type where one end of the molecule is polar and the other end is nonpolar. The polar end in fatty acids is a carboxylic acid group, and the nonpolar end is a long hydrocarbon chain.

The hydrocarbon chains can be saturated (◄ Section 23-2) or may include one or more double bonds. Saturated compounds are more common in animal products while unsaturated fats and oils are more common in plants. In general, triglycerides containing saturated fatty acids are solids, and those containing unsaturated fatty acids are liquids at room temperature. The difference in melting point relates to the molecular structure. With only single bonds linking carbon atoms in saturated fatty acids, the hydrocarbon group is flexible, allowing the molecules to pack more closely together. This greater contact between the molecules leads to greater London dispersion forces between the molecules and thus to higher melting points. The double bonds in unsaturated triglycerides, on the other hand, introduce kinks that make the hydrocarbon group less flexible; consequently, the molecules pack less tightly together, leading to smaller London dispersion forces and lower melting points.

Table 24.2 Common Fatty Acids

NAME	NUMBER OF C ATOMS	FORMULA
Saturated Acids		
Lauric	C_{12}	$CH_3(CH_2)_{10}CO_2H$
Myristic	C_{14}	$CH_3(CH_2)_{12}CO_2H$
Palmitic	C_{16}	$CH_3(CH_2)_{14}CO_2H$
Stearic	C_{18}	$CH_3(CH_2)_{16}CO_2H$
Unsaturated Acid		
Oleic	C_{18}	$CH_3(CH_2)_7CH{=}CH(CH_2)_7CO_2H$

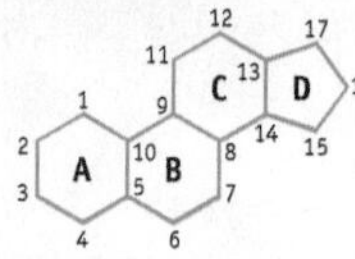

The ring structure present in all steroids three six member rings (A, B, and C) and one five-member ring (D).

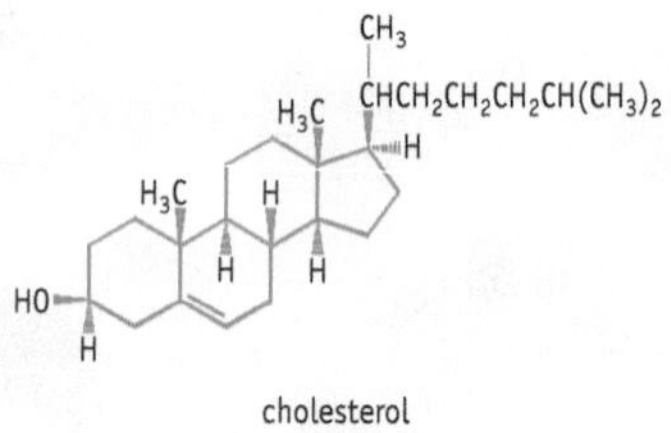

cholesterol

FIGURE 24.20 **Steroids.**

Steroids are another category of lipids. Steroid molecules consist of four hydrocarbon rings joined together (Figure 24.20). Three of the rings contain six carbon atoms, and one contains five carbon atoms. Examples of steroids are the sex hormones testosterone, estradiol, and progesterone. Cholesterol (Figure 24.20) is also an important steroid. You may have heard of cholesterol because of its correlation with heart disease. While some cholesterol is necessary for humans, excess cholesterol can deposit in blood vessels, thus partially blocking them and causing the heart to work harder than it should.

The most prevalent molecules in most cell membranes are **phospholipids** (Figure 24.21a). These are similar to triglycerides in that they are based on glycerol. Two of the alcohol groups in glycerol are esterified to long-chain fatty acids. The third alcohol group is bonded to a phosphate that has another hydrocarbon chain attached to it. Phosphate groups are very polar. In phospholipid molecules, the phosphate end is sometimes called the "head," and the nonpolar hydrocarbon chains comprise the "tail."

When phospholipids are placed in water, they typically arrange themselves in a **bilayer structure** (Figure 24.21b). This is exactly the arrangement that phospholipids have in a cell membrane. Water is present on both the inside and the outside of the bilayer, corresponding to the inside and outside of the cell. In the outside layer of the membrane, the phospholipids line up alongside each other such that their polar heads face the aqueous environment outside the cell. Moving inward, next come the tails of these lipids. The phospholipids in the second layer align themselves so that their nonpolar tails are in contact with the outer layer's nonpolar tails. Finally, the polar heads of the second layer face the aqueous environment inside the cell. The phospholipid bilayer nicely encloses the cell and provides a good barrier between the inside and the outside of the cell, due to the different solubility characteristics of the nonpolar region in the middle of the bilayer.

There are other molecules present in cell membranes. Cholesterol is an important part of animal cell membranes, helping to give the membranes greater rigidity. Some proteins in the cell membrane allow select materials to cross from one side of the membrane to the other (*transport proteins*). Others accept chemical signals from other cells or respond to materials in the cell's environment (*receptor proteins*). Finally, some enzymes are also associated with the membrane.

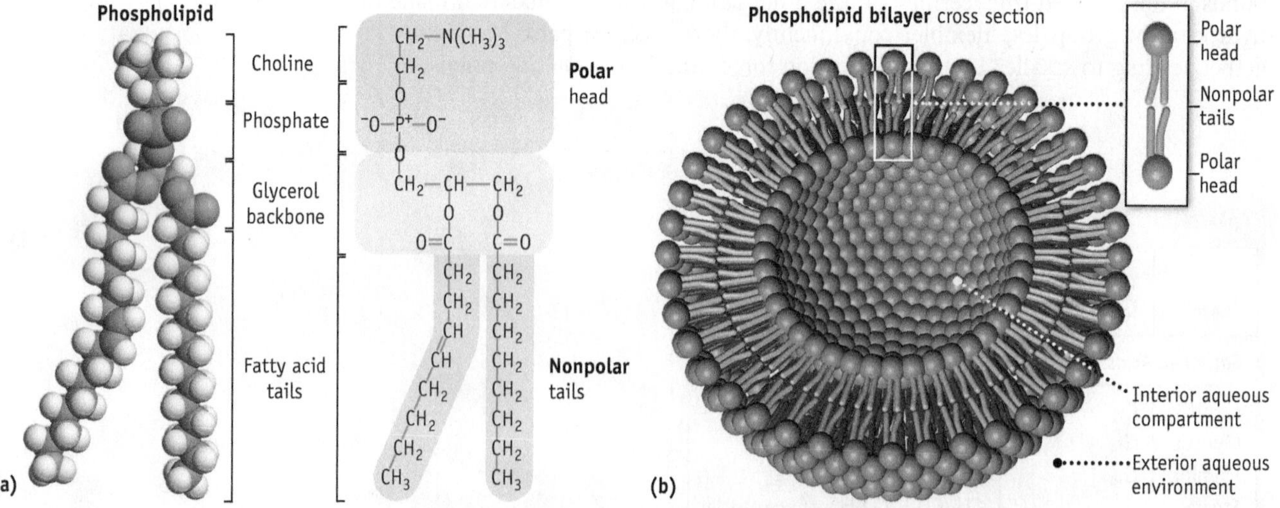

FIGURE 24.21 **Phospholipids. (a)** The structure of a phospholipid. **(b)** A cross-section of a phospholipid bilayer. The polar heads of the phospholipids are exposed to water, whereas the nonpolar tails are located in the interior of the bilayer.

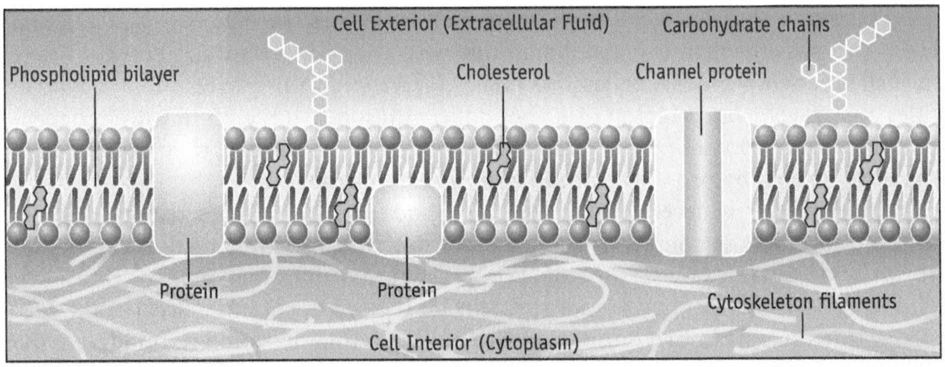

FIGURE 24.22 **The fluid-mosaic model of cell membranes.** A cell membrane is made up primarily of a phospholipid bilayer in which are embedded cholesterol, other lipids, and proteins. Movement within a layer occurs, but movement from one side of the bilayer to the other is rare.

The overall model for a cell membrane is called the **fluid-mosaic model** (Figure 24.22). In this model, the membrane's structure is largely that of a phospholipid bilayer. Embedded in this bilayer are molecules such as cholesterol and proteins. Movement of all of these components within each layer of the bilayer occurs readily; the membrane is thus fluid to a certain extent. On the other hand, there is little movement of components, such as phospholipids, from one side of the membrane to the other. The "like dissolves like" observation provides the reason for this lack of exchange between layers. The head of a phospholipid in the outer layer, for example, would not be compatible with the very nonpolar region within the bilayer that the phospholipid would need to pass through in order to traverse from one side of the bilayer to the other.

A cell membrane serves as the boundary between the cell and the rest of the universe, but exchange of some materials between the cell and the outside world needs to occur. There are different mechanisms by which this happens (Figure 24.23). The simplest is *passive diffusion.* In this process, a molecule moves through the phospholipid bilayer from a region of higher concentration to a region of lower concentration, the natural direction of flow. Because the bilayer provides such a

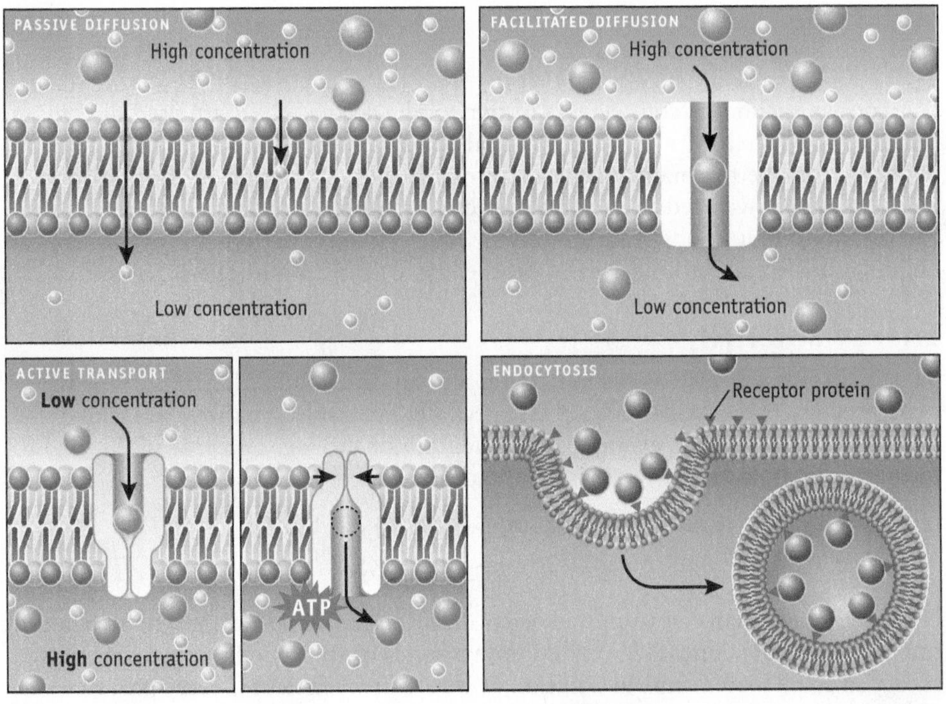

FIGURE 24.23 **Transport of materials across a cell membrane.**

good barrier, only a few very small uncharged molecules (such as N_2, O_2, CO_2, and H_2O) can pass through the membrane this way. Many more species enter or leave the cell through a process called *facilitated diffusion*. In this process, ions or molecules still travel from a region of higher concentration to a region of lower concentration, but they do not pass directly through the bilayer. Instead, they pass through channels formed by proteins embedded in the cell membrane.

Sometimes, it is necessary for the cell to move species from a region of lower concentration to a region of higher concentration, the opposite direction that would normally occur on its own. The cell accomplishes this by means of *active transport*. This is again mediated by transport proteins in the cell membrane. Because the species of interest must move in the opposite direction than it would normally go, the cell must expend energy in order to make this occur.

Finally, cells sometimes transport materials into themselves by means of *endocytosis*. This process is usually mediated by a receptor protein. The species of interest (called the *substrate*) binds to the receptor protein. A portion of the cell membrane surrounds the receptor–substrate complex. This portion of the cell membrane is then broken off, bringing the complex into the cell.

REVIEW & CHECK FOR SECTION 24-4

1. Which of the following is not an example of a lipid?
   (a) cholesterol
   (b) ethanol
   (c) a fat
   (d) an oil
2. In the fluid-mosaic model of the cell membrane, the phospholipids arrange themselves so as to have
   (a) polar heads pointing to the extracellular fluid
   (b) polar heads pointing to the intracellular fluid
   (c) polar heads pointing to both the extracellular fluid and the intracellular fluid
   (d) polar heads pointing to each other in the middle of the membrane

Learning Objectives: LO 5.15, LO 5.16

24-5 Metabolism

Why do we eat? Some components of our food, such as water, are used directly in our bodies. We break down other chemicals to obtain the molecular building blocks we need to make the many chemicals in our bodies. Oxidation of foods also provides the energy we need to perform the activities of life. The many different chemical reactions that foods undergo in the body to provide energy and chemical building blocks fall into the area of biochemistry called **metabolism**.

Energy and ATP

Substances in food, such as carbohydrates and fats, are oxidized in part of the metabolic process. These oxidations are energetically favorable reactions, releasing large quantities of energy. For example, the oxidation of the sugar glucose ($C_6H_{12}O_6$) to form carbon dioxide and water is very exothermic.

$$C_6H_{12}O_6(s) + 6\ O_2(g) \rightarrow 6\ CO_2(g) + 6\ H_2O(\ell)$$

$$\Delta_r H^\circ = -2803\ \text{kJ/mol-rxn}$$

However, rather than carry out this reaction in one rapid and exothermic step, a cell carries out a more controlled oxidation in a series of steps so that it can obtain the energy in small increments. In addition, it would be inefficient if every part of a cell needed to have all the mechanisms necessary to carry out the oxidation of every type

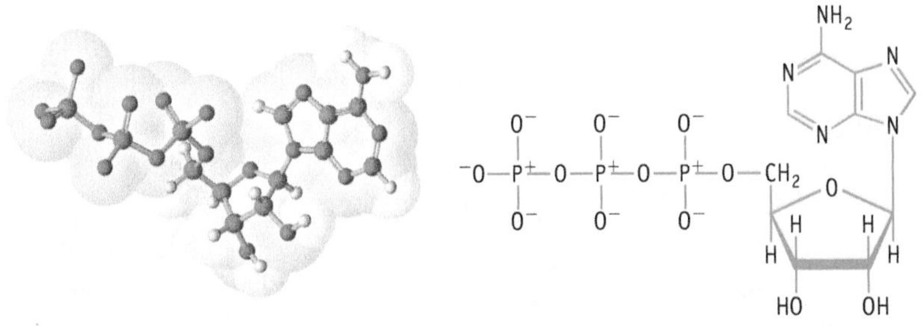

FIGURE 24.24 **Adenosine-5′-triphosphate (ATP).**

of molecule used for energy. Instead, it carries out the oxidation of compounds such as glucose in one location and stores the energy in a small set of compounds that can be used almost anywhere in the cell.

The principal compound used to perform this storage and transport of energy function is **adenosine 5′-triphosphate** (ATP). This ribonucleotide consists of a ribose molecule to which the nitrogenous base adenine is connected at the 1′ position and a triphosphate group is connected at the 5′ position (Figure 24.24). In aerobic respiration, the equivalent of 30–32 mol of ATP is typically produced per mole of glucose oxidized. Based on the ΔH values for the processes, a greater production of ATP might be expected, but the process is not completely efficient.

The hydrolysis of ATP to adenosine 5′-diphosphate (ADP) and inorganic phosphate (P_i) is an exothermic process that is product-favored at equilibrium (Figure 24.25).

$$\text{ATP} + H_2O \rightarrow \text{ADP} + P_i \qquad \Delta_r H° \approx -24 \text{ kJ/mol-rxn } (\Delta_r G°' = -30.5 \text{ kJ/mol-rxn})$$

ΔG°′ For the definition of $\Delta G°'$, see *Case Study: Thermodynamics and Living Things* on p. 706.

Why is this reaction exothermic? In this reaction, we must break two bonds, a P—O bond in ATP and an H—O bond in water. But we also form two new bonds: a P—O bond connecting the phosphate group being cleaved off the ATP with the OH of the original water and an H—O bond connecting the hydrogen from the water with the portion of the ATP that forms ADP. In this overall process, more energy is released in forming these new bonds in the products than is required to break the necessary bonds in the reactants.

In cells, many chemical processes that would be reactant-favored on their own are linked with the hydrolysis of ATP. The combination of an energetically unfavorable process with the energetically favorable hydrolysis of ATP can yield a process that is energetically favorable and product-favored at equilibrium. For example, most cells have a greater concentration of potassium ions and a smaller concentration of sodium ions inside them than are present outside them. The natural tendency, therefore, is for sodium ions to flow into the cell and for potassium ions to flow out. To maintain the correct concentrations, the cell must counteract this movement and

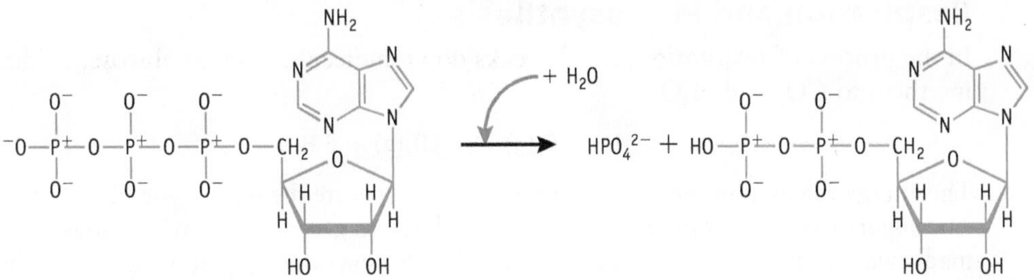

ATP
adenosine-5′-triphosphate

ADP
adenosine-5′-diphosphate

FIGURE 24.25 **The exothermic conversion of adenosine-5′-triphosphate (ATP) to adenosine-5′-diphosphate (ADP).**

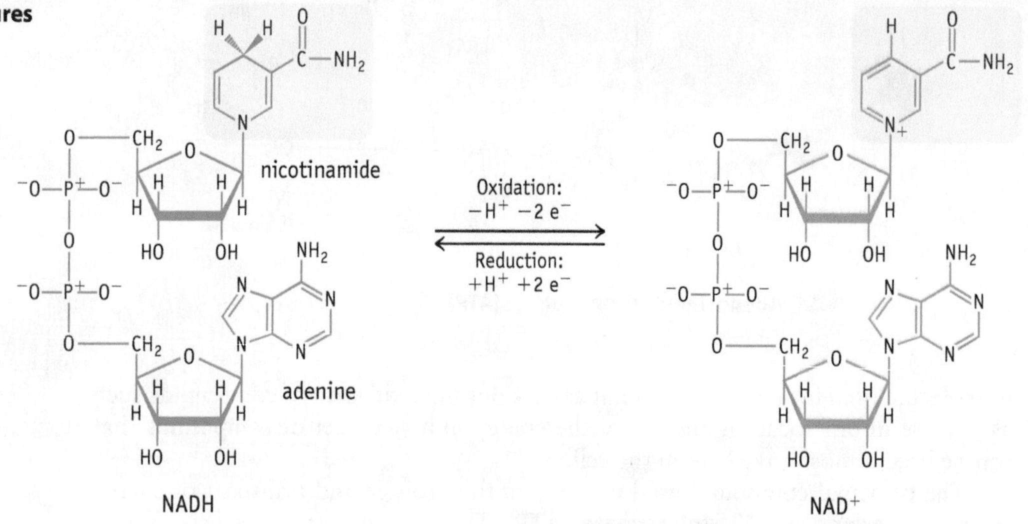

FIGURE 24.26 The structures of NADH and NAD$^+$.

pump sodium ions out of the cell and potassium ions into the cell. This requires energy. To accomplish this feat, the cell links this pumping process to the hydrolysis of ATP to ADP. The energy released from the hydrolysis reaction provides the energy to run a molecular pump (a transport protein) that moves the ions in the direction the cell needs.

Oxidation–Reduction and NADH

Cells also need compounds that can be used to carry out oxidation–reduction reactions. Just as ATP is a compound used in many biochemical reactions when energy is needed, so nature uses another small set of compounds to run many redox reactions. An important example is **nicotinamide adenine dinucleotide (NADH)**. This compound consists of two ribonucleotides joined at their 5′ positions via a diphosphate linkage. One of the nucleotides has adenine as its nitrogenous base, whereas the other has a nicotinamide ring (Figure 24.26). When NADH is oxidized, changes occur in the nicotinamide ring, such that the equivalent of a hydride ion (H^-) is lost. Because this hydride ion has two electrons associated with it, the nicotinamide ring loses two electrons in the process. The resulting species, referred to as NAD$^+$, is shown on the right in Figure 24.26.

In many biochemical reactions, when a particular species needs to be reduced, it reacts with NADH. The NADH is oxidized to NAD$^+$, losing two electrons in the process, and the species of interest is reduced by gaining these electrons. If a species must be oxidized, the opposite process often occurs; that is, it reacts with NAD$^+$. The NAD$^+$ is reduced to NADH, and the species of interest is oxidized.

Respiration and Photosynthesis

In the process of **respiration**, a cell breaks down molecules such as glucose, oxidizing them to CO_2 and H_2O.

$$C_6H_{12}O_6(s) + 6\ O_2(g) \rightarrow 6\ CO_2(g) + 6\ H_2O(\ell)$$

The energy released in these reactions is used to generate the ATP needed by the cell. The sugars used in this process can be traced back to green plants, where sugars are made via the process of **photosynthesis**. In photosynthesis, plants carry out the reverse of glucose oxidation—that is, the synthesis of glucose from CO_2 and H_2O.

$$6\ CO_2(g) + 6\ H_2O(\ell) \rightarrow C_6H_{12}O_6(s) + 6\ O_2(g)$$

Green plants have found a way to use light to provide the energy needed to run this endothermic reaction.

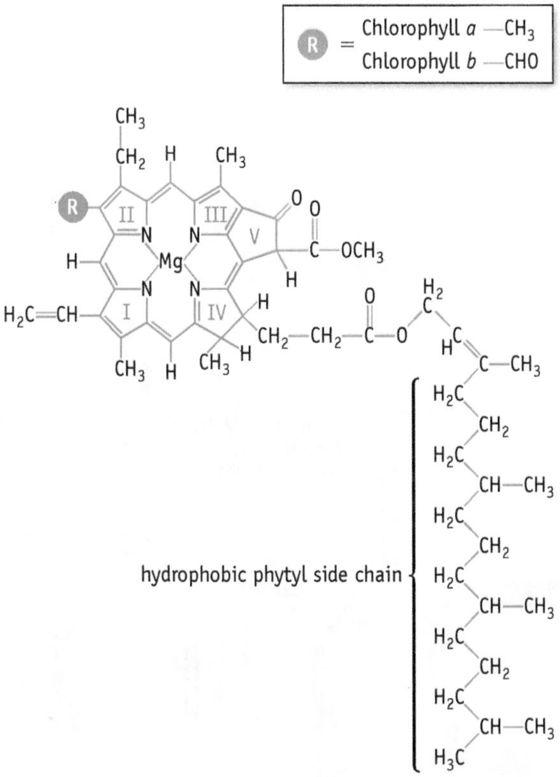

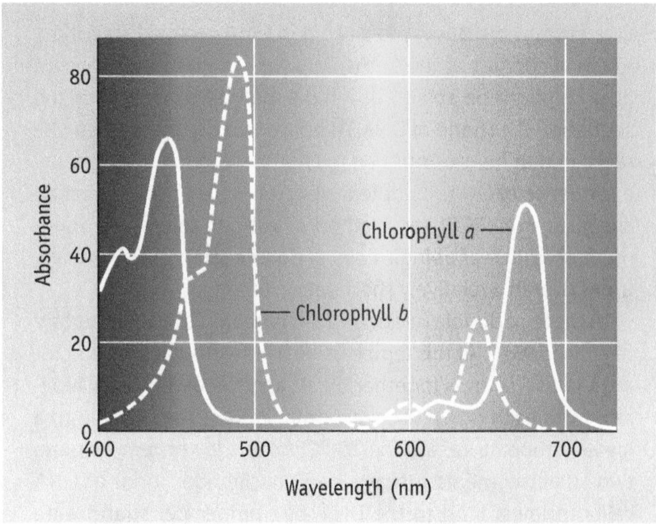

FIGURE 24.27 **The structure of chlorophyll and the visible absorbance spectra of chlorophylls a and b.**

The key molecule involved in trapping the energy from light in photosynthesis is chlorophyll. Green plants contain two types of chlorophyll: chlorophyll *a* and chlorophyll *b* (Figure 24.27). The absorbance spectra of chlorophyll *a* and chlorophyll *b* are also shown in Figure 24.27. Notice that these molecules absorb best in the blue-violet and red-orange regions of the visible spectrum. Not much light is absorbed in the green region. When white light shines on chlorophyll, red-orange and blue-violet light are absorbed by the chlorophyll; green light is reflected. We see the reflected light, so plants appear green to us. The light energy absorbed by the chlorophyll is used to drive the process of photosynthesis.

REVIEW & CHECK FOR SECTION 24-5

1. The hydrolysis of ATP is
   (a) endothermic and product-favored at equilibrium
   (b) endothermic and reactant-favored at equilibrium
   (c) exothermic and product-favored at equilibrium
   (d) exothermic and reactant-favored at equilibrium
2. The reduced form of nicotinamide adenine dinucleotide is
   (a) ADP
   (b) NAD^+
   (c) ATP
   (d) NADH

APPLYING CHEMICAL PRINCIPLES

Polymerase Chain Reaction

One night while driving to a cabin in Northern California, Kary Mullis, a chemist at the Cetus Corporation, was musing about how he might be able to develop a method to determine the sequence of a strand of DNA. As he worked on this problem, he realized that his musings had led him instead to a way to copy a sequence of DNA multiple times. Now called the *polymerase chain reaction* (PCR), the method allows one to amplify a segment of as little as a single copy of double-stranded DNA many times over in a relatively short period of time.

A piece of double-stranded DNA is heated to a temperature of around 95 °C. At this temperature, the hydrogen bonds holding the two strands together break, and the two strands separate from each other. The reaction mixture is then cooled to a lower temperature, around 55 °C. At this lower temperature, two small segments (usually 18–30 nucleotides long) of DNA called primers bind to the DNA, one primer per strand. One primer is complementary to the 3′-region of DNA to be amplified on one strand, and the other primer is complementary to the 3′-region of DNA to be amplified on the other strand. The temperature is then raised to around 72 °C where an enzyme called *Taq* polymerase becomes active. This polymerase, from a species of bacteria that lives at high temperature called *Thermus aquaticus (Taq)*, takes DNA nucleotide triphosphates (dATP, dGTP, dCTP, and dTTP) from the solution and adds them to the primers in the proper order so that new strands of DNA complementary to the original strands are produced. The process began with one double-stranded DNA, but two are now present at the end of the first cycle of PCR. The temperature is then raised again to 95 °C, and a new cycle is begun. After this second cycle, there will be four double-stranded DNAs present. After three cycles, the number will be eight, and so on with the amount of DNA growing exponentially. In this way, millions of copies of the original DNA can be made fairly quickly.

PCR has become commonplace in forensic science where it is used to amplify DNA found at a crime scene so that it can be tested against a suspect's DNA. It has also been used in tests for HIV infection, paternity tests, and for determining the DNA of organisms long extinct, as well as many other uses. Kary Mullis shared the Nobel Prize in Chemistry in 1983 for his work in developing this technique.

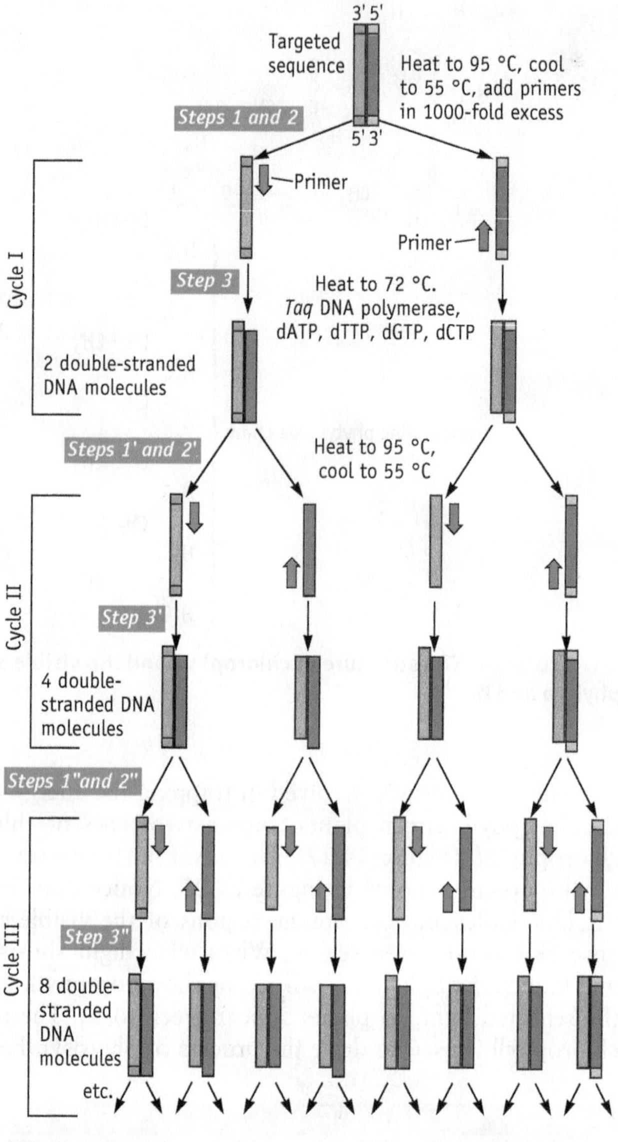

PCR. Note that at the end of three cycles of PCR, eight copies of the segment of DNA exist.

QUESTIONS:

1. Theoretically, how many copies of double-stranded DNA could be present after 20 cycles of PCR?
2. How does the fact that DNA molecules separate at 95 °C give evidence that the forces holding together DNA molecules are not covalent bonds?
3. Care must be exercised in selecting good primers to use in PCR.
   (a) Why are primers often chosen that have a high number of cytosines and guanines in their sequences?
   (b) Why would a primer sequence of CCCCCCCCCCGGGGGGGGGG not be a good choice?
   (c) Why is a vast excess of primer used for the amount of DNA to be amplified?

CHAPTER GOALS REVISITED

Now that you have studied this chapter, you should ask whether you have met the chapter goals. In particular, you should be able to:

UNDERSTAND

- Structure determines the function of biological molecules.
  - **a.** Understand the different levels of protein structure (primary, secondary, tertiary, and quaternary) (Section 24-1). Study Questions: 9, 10.
  - **b.** Recognize that one amino acid substitution in the structure of hemoglobin leads to sickle cell anemia (Section 24-1).
  - **c.** Understand that the structure of DNA leads to a method for replication of genetic information (Section 24-3).
- The process of protein synthesis (Section 24-3).
- The RNA World hypothesis for the origin of life (Section 24-3).
- The construction of a phospholipid bilayer and transport of materials across such a membrane (Section 24-4). Study Question: 19.
- Coupling of ATP hydrolysis with a reactant-favored reaction can lead to a product-favored reaction (Section 24-5). Study Question: 34.

DO

- Draw the structural formulas of common biochemical molecules.
  - **a.** Draw the Lewis structures for the most prevalent naturally-occurring amino acids (Section 24-1). Study Questions: 1–4.
  - **b.** Understand that under physiological conditions, amino acids exist as zwitterions in aqueous solution (Section 24-1). Study Questions: 1, 2.
  - **c.** Draw the Lewis structures for short polypeptides (Section 24-1). Study Questions: 5–8.
  - **d.** Draw the Lewis structures for commonly occurring mono-, di-, and polysaccharides (Section 24-2). Study Questions: 11, 12.
  - **e.** Recognize that amylose starch contains glucose molecules linked by α-1,4 glycosidic bonds, amylopectin starch and glycogen contain glucose molecules linked in chains containing α-1,4 glycosidic bonds with branch points made of α-1,6 glycosidic bonds, and cellulose contains chains of glucose linked by β-1,4 glycosidic bonds. (Section 24-2).
  - **f.** Draw the Lewis structures for short strands of DNA or RNA (Section 24-3). Study Questions: 15, 16.
- Predict the sequence of nucleotides complementary to a given strand of DNA (Section 24-3). Study Questions: 17, 18.
- Predict the amino acid selected by a given sequence of three nucleotides in mRNA (Section 24-3). Study Questions: 17, 18.

REMEMBER

- Proteins are condensation polymers of amino acids (Section 24-1).
- The active site of an enzyme is the cleft or cavity where the substrate binds and the catalyzed chemical reaction takes place (Section 24-1).
- DNA and RNA are condensation polymers of nucleotides (Section 24-3).
- RNA undergoes hydrolysis much more quickly than DNA (Section 24-3).
- The identity of some lipids (Section 24-4).
- NAD^+ and NADH are involved in biochemical redox reactions (Section 24-5).

Najlah Feanny-Hicks/Corbis

STUDY QUESTIONS

▲ denotes challenging questions.

Blue-numbered questions have answers in Appendix N and fully worked solutions in the *Student Solutions Manual.*

Practicing Skills

Proteins

(See Section 24-1 and Example 24.1.)

1. (a) Draw the Lewis structure for the amino acid valine, showing the amino group and the carboxylic acid group in their un-ionized forms.
   (b) Draw the Lewis structure for the zwitterionic form of valine.
   (c) Which of these structures will be the predominant form at physiological pH?

2. (a) Draw the Lewis structure for the amino acid phenylalanine, showing the amino group and the carboxylic group in their un-ionized forms.
   (b) Draw the Lewis structure for the zwitterionic form of phenylalanine.
   (c) Which of these structures will be the predominant form at physiological pH?

3. Consider the amino acids alanine, leucine, serine, phenylalanine, lysine, and aspartic acid. Which have polar R groups, and which have nonpolar R groups?

4. Consider the amino acids arginine, cysteine, glutamine, isoleucine, threonine, and tryptophan. Which have polar R groups, and which have nonpolar R groups?

5. Draw Lewis structures for the two dipeptides that contain both alanine and glycine.

6. Do the amino acid sequences: valine-asparagine and asparagine-valine represent the same compound? Explain.

7. Draw the Lewis structure for the tripeptide serine-leucine-valine.

8. Draw the Lewis structure for the tripeptide tyrosine-histidine-glycine.

9. Identify the type of structure (primary, secondary, tertiary, or quaternary) that corresponds to the following statements.
   (a) This type of structure is the amino acid sequence in the protein.
   (b) This type of structure indicates how different peptide chains in the overall protein are arranged with respect to one another.
   (c) This type of structure refers to how the polypeptide chain is folded, including how amino acids that are far apart in the sequence end up in the overall molecule.
   (d) This type of structure deals with structures that arise from hydrogen bonding between amide groups in the protein's backbone.

10. The β-pleated sheet is a structure that commonly arises in proteins. Part of a β-pleated sheet is shown in the following figure. This type of structure is an example of which level of protein structure: primary, secondary, tertiary, or quaternary?

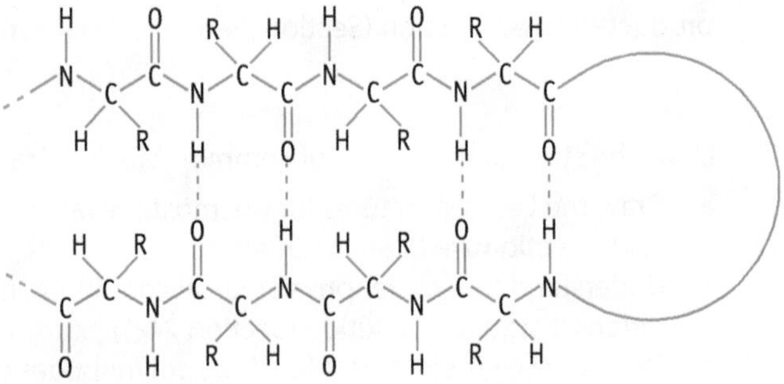

Carbohydrates

(See Section 24-2.)

11. Draw the structural formulas for α-D-glucose and β-D-glucose.

12. Draw the structural formula for two glucose molecules joined by a β-1,4 linkage.

Nucleic Acids

(See Section 24-3 and Examples 24.2 and 24.3.)

13. (a) Draw the structural formula for the sugar β-D-ribose.
    (b) Draw the structural formula for the nucleoside adenosine (it consists of β-D-ribose and adenine).
    (c) Draw the structural formula for the nucleotide adenosine 5′-monophosphate.

14. (a) Draw the structural formula for the sugar β-D-2-deoxyribose.
    (b) Draw the structural formula for the nucleoside deoxyadenosine (it consists of β-D-2-deoxyribose and adenine).
    (c) Draw the structural formula for the nucleotide deoxyadenosine 5′-monophosphate.

15. Draw the structural formula for the tetranucleotide AUGC.

16. Draw the structural formula for the tetradeoxynucleotide CGTA.

17. Given the following nucleotide sequence in DNA: 5′—ACGCGATTC—3′:
   (a) Determine the sequence of the complementary strand of DNA. Report this sequence by writing it from its 5′ end to its 3′ end.
   (b) Write the sequence (5′–3′) for the strand of mRNA that would be complementary to the original strand of DNA.
   (c) Assuming that this sequence is part of the coding sequence for a protein and that it is properly lined up so that the first codon of this sequence begins with the 5′ nucleotide of the mRNA, write the sequences for the three anticodons that would be complementary to this strand of mRNA.
   (d) What sequence of amino acids is selected by this mRNA? (The complete genetic code is listed in several sites on the Internet.)

18. Given the following nucleotide sequence in DNA: 5′—TCGTAGGAT—3′:
   (a) Determine the sequence of the complementary strand of DNA. Report this sequence by writing it from its 5′ end to its 3′ end.
   (b) Write the sequence (5′–3′) for the strand of mRNA that would be complementary to the original strand of DNA.
   (c) Assuming that this sequence is part of the coding sequence for a protein and that it is properly lined up so that the first codon of this sequence begins with the 5′ nucleotide of the mRNA, write the sequences for the three anticodons that would be complementary to this strand of mRNA.
   (d) What sequence of amino acids is selected by this mRNA? (The complete genetic code is listed in several sites on the Internet.)

Lipids and Cell Membranes

(See Section 24-4.)

19. Sketch a section of a phospholipid bilayer in which you let a circle represent the polar head group and curvy lines represent the hydrocarbon tails. Label the regions of the bilayer as being polar or nonpolar.

20. If a drop of oleic acid is added to a dish of water, the oleic acid will spread out and form a layer that is one molecule thick on top of the water.
   (a) Draw the Lewis structure for oleic acid.
   (b) Label the region of the oleic acid molecule that is polar and the region that is nonpolar.
   (c) In the layer of oleic acid that forms, which part of the oleic acid molecule points down into the water and which part points out of the water?

21. What structure do all steroids have in common?

22. The structures of the sex hormones testosterone (a male sex hormone) and estrogen (a female sex hormone) are shown below.

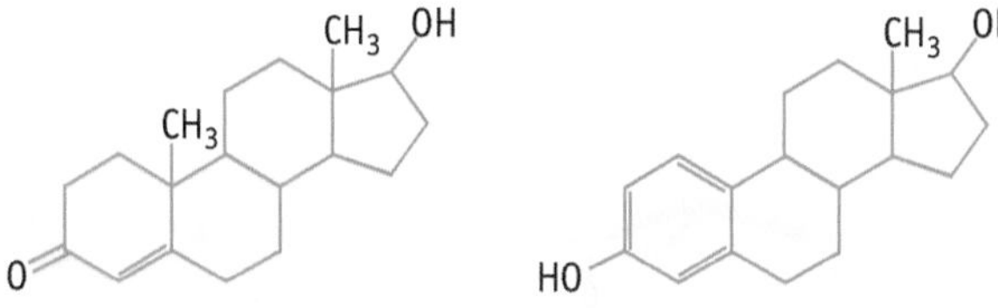

   (a) Compare these two structures.
   (b) Are these molecules steroids? Explain.

Metabolism

(See Section 24-5.)

23. The section about metabolism provided a value for $\Delta_r H°$ for the oxidation of one mole of glucose (−2803 kJ/mol-rxn). Using $\Delta_f H°$ values at 25 °C, verify that this is the correct value for the equation

$$C_6H_{12}O_6(s) + 6\ O_2(g) \rightarrow 6\ CO_2(g) + 6\ H_2O(\ell)$$

$$\Delta_f H°[C_6H_{12}O_6(s)] = -1273.3\ \text{kJ/mol}$$

24. The chemical equation for the fermentation of glucose into ethanol is

$$C_6H_{12}O_6(s) \rightarrow 2\ C_2H_5OH(\ell) + 2\ CO_2(g)$$

Using $\Delta_f H°$ values at 25 °C, calculate $\Delta_r H°$ for this reaction. (See Question 23 for $\Delta_f H°$ for glucose.)

25. Consider the following reaction:

$$NADH + H^+ + \tfrac{1}{2}\ O_2 \rightarrow NAD^+ + H_2O$$

   (a) Which species (NADH, H^+, or O_2) undergoes oxidation?
   (b) Which species undergoes reduction?
   (c) Which species is the oxidizing agent?
   (d) Which species is the reducing agent?

26. The body processes ethanol by first converting it to acetaldehyde in a reaction catalyzed by the enzyme alcohol dehydrogenase.

$$CH_3CH_2OH + NAD^+ \xrightarrow{\text{alcohol dehydrogenase}} CH_3CHO + NADH + H^+$$

In the body, acetaldehyde can cause headaches and nausea and is one of the causes of hangovers. Eventually, the acetaldehyde is oxidized to the acetate ion and then converted to carbon dioxide and water. In the reaction of ethanol with NAD^+, which species (ethanol or NAD^+) undergoes oxidation? Which species undergoes reduction?

General Questions

These questions are not designated as to type or location in the chapter. They may combine several concepts.

27. Draw two Lewis structures for the dipeptide alanine-isoleucine that show the resonance structures of the amide linkage.

28. What is the equilibrium constant for the conversion of α-D-glucose to β-D-glucose in water at room temperature (assume that there is no glucose present in the open-chain structure)?

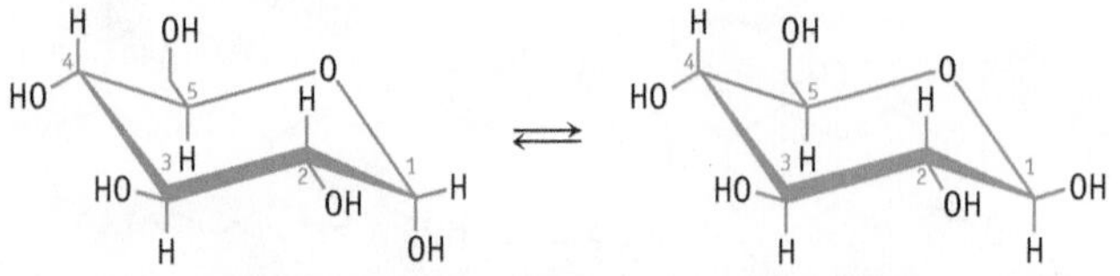

α-D-glucose 37%   β-D-glucose 63%

29. (a) Calculate the enthalpy change for the production of one mole of glucose by the process of photosynthesis at 25 °C. $\Delta_f H°$ [glucose(s)] = −1273.3 kJ/mol

$$6\ CO_2(g) + 6\ H_2O(\ell) \rightarrow C_6H_{12}O_6(s) + 6\ O_2(g)$$

(b) What is the enthalpy change involved in producing one molecule of glucose by this process?

(c) Chlorophyll molecules absorb light of various wavelengths. One wavelength absorbed is 650 nm. Calculate the energy of a photon of light having this wavelength.

(d) Assuming that all of this energy goes toward providing the energy required for the photosynthetic reaction, can the absorption of one photon at 650 nm lead to the production of one molecule of glucose, or must multiple photons be absorbed?

30. (a) According to the genetic code in Table 24.1, which amino acid is selected by the mRNA codon GAA?

(b) What is the sequence in the original DNA that led to this codon being present in the mRNA?

(c) If a mutation occurs in the DNA in which a G is substituted for the nucleotide at the second position of this coding region in the DNA, which amino acid will now be selected?

31. How many codons are possible? All of these codons are used in molecules of mRNA and there are only 20 amino acids normally encoded (plus start codons and stop codons). Is there exactly one codon per amino acid, must some codons select for more than one amino acid, or must there be some amino acids for which there is more than one codon?

32. There are $4^1 = 4$ mononucleotides of DNA, there are $4^2 = 16$ possible dinucleotides, and so on. If a segment of DNA were completely random, how many nucleotides long would it need to be in order to have one possible sequence for each person on Earth (currently about 7 billion people)?

33. In the process of respiration

$$C_6H_{12}O_6(s) + 6\ O_2(g) \rightarrow 6\ CO_2(g) + 6\ H_2O(\ell)$$

which molecule undergoes oxidation? Which molecule undergoes reduction?

34. The first step of the metabolic process known as glycolysis is the conversion of glucose to glucose-6-phosphate This process has a positive value for $\Delta_r G°'$.

$$\text{Glucose} + P_i \rightarrow \text{Glucose-6-phosphate} + H_2O$$
$$\Delta_r G°' = +13.8\ \text{kJ/mol-rxn}$$

This reaction is coupled to the hydrolysis of ATP

$$ATP + H_2O \rightarrow ADP + P_i$$
$$\Delta_r G°' = -30.5\ \text{kJ/mol-rxn}$$

What is the sum of these two equations and the value of $\Delta_r G°'$ for the coupled reaction? Is the coupled reaction product-favored at equilibrium?

In the Laboratory

35. The enzyme lipase catalyzes the hydrolysis of esters of fatty acids. The hydrolysis of *p*-nitrophenyloctanoate was followed by measuring the appearance of *p*-nitrophenol in the reaction mixture:

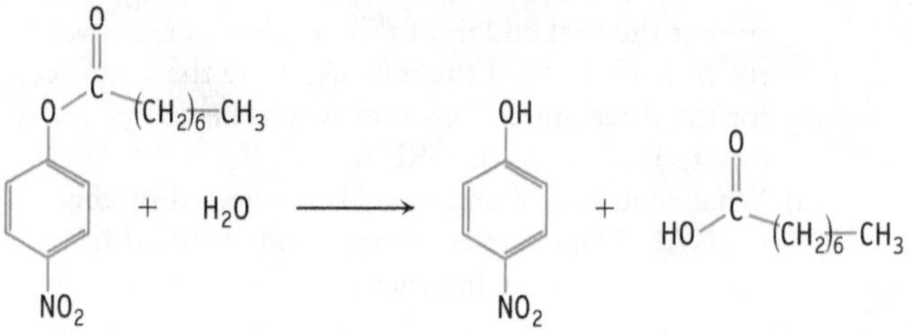

p-nitrophenol

The following data were obtained at 30 °C:

Substrate Concentration (mol/L)	Reaction Rate (mol/L · min)
1.0×10^{-5}	6.3×10^{-6}
1.4×10^{-5}	8.8×10^{-6}
2.0×10^{-5}	1.2×10^{-5}
5.0×10^{-5}	2.6×10^{-5}
6.7×10^{-5}	3.1×10^{-5}

This reaction obeys Michaelis-Menten kinetics (*Case Study: Enzymes—Nature's Catalysts*, p. 540). Determine the value of $Rate_{max}$ for this reaction using the method described in Question 2 of that Case Study.

36. Insulin is a protein important in the metabolism of sugar. Its molar mass can be determined by means of an osmotic pressure experiment. A 50.0-mg sample of insulin was dissolved in enough water to make 100. mL of solution. This solution was determined to have an osmotic pressure of 21.8 mm H_2O. What is the molar mass of insulin? (Hint: The density of mercury is 13.6 g/mL.)

Summary and Conceptual Questions

The following questions may use concepts from this and previous chapters.

37. Which of the amino acids listed in Figure 24.2 is not chiral?

38. (a) What type of interaction holds DNA's double-helical strands together?

(b) Why would it not be good for DNA's double-helical strands to be held together by covalent bonds?

39. Do the DNA sequences ATGC and CGTA represent the same compound? Explain.

40. For many chemical reactions in the laboratory, a percent yield of the correct product of 95% is considered very good. Many biochemical reactions, however, require a much greater percent yield of the correct product.

(a) Assume that there is a process that replicates DNA with only 95% accuracy for each nucleotide added and that we wish to make complementary copies of identical strands of DNA 10 nucleotides long. What fraction of the molecules produced would have the correct sequence of nucleotides?

(b) Many naturally occurring DNA polymerases, enzymes that catalyze the replication of DNA, have an accuracy much greater, often being 99.999999% accurate. If an enzyme with this accuracy constructed a 10-nucleotide sequence of DNA, what fraction of the molecules would have the correct sequence?

41. (a) Describe what occurs in the process of transcription.
(b) Describe what occurs in the process of translation.

42. Which of the following statements is/are true?

(a) Breaking the P—O bond in ATP is an exothermic process.

(b) Making a new bond between the phosphorus atom in the phosphate group being cleaved off ATP and the OH group of water is an exothermic process.

(c) Breaking bonds is an endothermic process.

(d) The energy released in the hydrolysis of ATP may be used to run endothermic reactions in a cell.

AP Multiple-Choice Review Questions

1. Which of these amino acids would you expect to exhibit the most hydrophilic behavior?

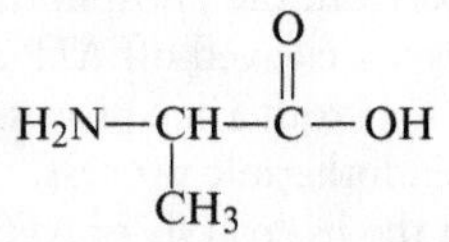

Alanine

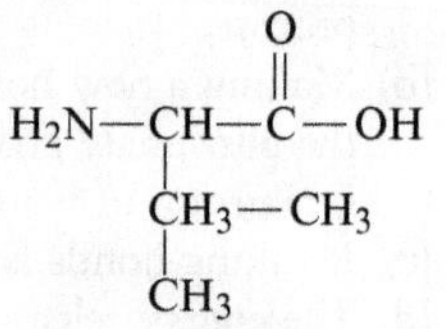

Valine

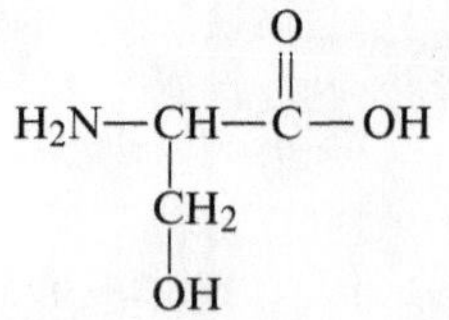

Serine

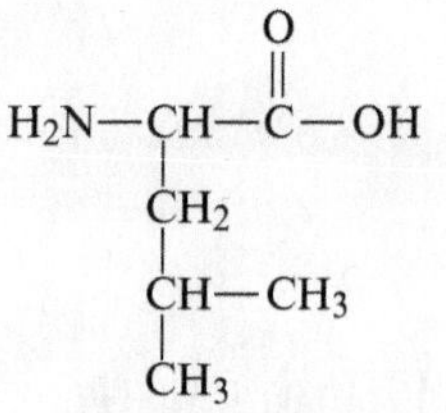

Leucine

(A) alanine
(B) valine
(C) serine
(D) leucine

2. There are two possible types of secondary structures in proteins: an α-helix and a pleated sheet. In the case of an α-helix, the polypeptide twists into a helix. What enables the formation and stability of the α-helix secondary structures?

(A) Hydrogen bonds form between adjacent proteins.

(B) Covalent bonds form between adjacent proteins.

(C) Hydrogen bonds form between amino acids in the same protein.

(D) Covalent bonds form between amino acids in the same protein.

The natural nuclear reactor in Oklo, Gabon (West Africa). Nearly 2 billion years ago, a natural formation containing uranium oxide (the yellow material) underwent fission that started and stopped over a period of a million years.

Nuclear Chemistry

Chapter Outline

A PRIMORDIAL NUCLEAR REACTOR

The natural nuclear reactors in West Africa have been called "one of the greatest natural phenomena that ever occurred." In 1972, a French scientist noticed that the uranium taken from a mine in Oklo, Gabon, was strangely deficient in ^{235}U. Uranium exists in nature as two principal isotopes, ^{238}U (99.275% abundant) and ^{235}U (0.72% abundant). It is ^{235}U that most readily undergoes nuclear fission and is used to fuel nuclear power plants around the world. But the uranium found in the Oklo mines had an isotope ratio like that of the spent fuel that comes from modern reactors. Based on this and other evidence, scientists concluded that ^{235}U at the Oklo mine was once about 3% of the total and that a "natural" fission process occurred in the bed of uranium ore nearly 2 billion years ago.

But intriguing questions remained: Why could fission occur to a significant extent in this natural deposit of uranium and why didn't the "reactor" explode? Apparently,

Chapter Goals

See Chapter Goals Revisited (page 1006) for Study Questions keyed to these goals.

UNDERSTAND

- The criteria for nuclear stability and the processes by which unstable nuclides decay.
- The methods used to synthesize new isotopes of the elements.
- The plot showing numbers of protons and neutrons in stable and unstable nuclides.
- The graph showing binding energy per nucleon versus atomic number.
- Issues of safety and health with respect to radioactivity.
- Uses of radioactive isotopes in science and medicine.

DO

- Write equations for the decay of radioactive elements and the synthesis of new isotopes.
- Predict possible modes of decomposition of unstable nuclei based on n/p ratios.
- Calculate the binding energy and binding energy per nucleon for a particular isotope.
- Carry out calculations based on equations for the first-order rate of decomposition of unstable isotopes.

REMEMBER

- Nuclear decay series and their implications.
- Types of radiation.
- The processes of fission and fusion.

there must have been a moderator of neutron energy and a regulation mechanism. In a modern nuclear power reactor, control rods slow down the neutrons from nuclear fission so that they can induce fission in other ^{235}U nuclei; that is, they moderate the neutron energy. Without a moderator, the neutrons just fly off. In the Oklo reactors, water seeping into the bed of uranium ore could have acted as a moderator.

The reason the Oklo reactor did not explode is that water could have also been the regulator. As the fission process heated the water, it boiled off as steam. This caused the fission to stop, but it began again when more water seeped in. Scientists now believe this natural reactor would turn on for about 30 minutes and then shut down for several hours before turning on again. There is evidence this natural reactor functioned intermittently for about 1 million years, until the concentration of uranium isotopes was too low to keep the reaction going.

A Study Question related to this story is: 25.54.

History of science scholars cite areas of study out of which modern chemistry arose: technology, medicine, and alchemy. The third of these pillars, alchemy, was pursued in many cultures on three continents for well over 1000 years. Simply stated, the goal of the ancient alchemists was to turn less valuable materials into gold. We now recognize the futility of these efforts, because this goal is not reachable by chemical processes. But we now also know that their dream of transmuting one element into another can be achieved by means of nuclear reactions. This

Table 25.1 Characteristics of α, β, and γ Radiation

NAME	SYMBOLS	CHARGE	MASS (g/particle)
Alpha	${}^{4}_{2}He$, ${}^{4}_{2}\alpha$	2+	6.65×10^{-24}
Beta	${}^{0}_{-1}e$, ${}^{0}_{-1}\beta$	1−	9.11×10^{-28}
Gamma	γ	0	0

happens naturally in the decomposition of uranium and other radioactive elements, and scientists can intentionally carry out such reactions in the laboratory. The goal is no longer to make gold, however. Far more important and valuable products of nuclear reactions are possible.

Nuclear chemistry encompasses a wide range of topics that share one thing in common: they involve changes in the atom's nucleus. While nuclear "chemistry" is a major focus in this chapter, this subject cuts across many areas of science and modern society. Radioactive isotopes are used in medicine. Nuclear power provides a sizable fraction of energy for modern society. And then, there are nuclear weapons. . . .

25-1 Natural Radioactivity

Discovery of Radioactivity The discovery of radioactivity by Henri Becquerel and the isolation of radium and polonium from pitchblende, a uranium ore, by Marie Curie were described in *Key Experiments: How Do We Know the Nature of the Atom and Its Components*, Chapter 2.

Common Symbols: α and β Symbols used to represent alpha and beta particles do not include a plus or minus superscript, respectively, to show that they have a charge.

In the late 19th century, while studying radiation emanating from uranium and thorium, Ernest Rutherford (1871–1937) stated, "There are present at least two distinct types of radiation—one that is readily absorbed, which will be termed for convenience **α (alpha) radiation**, and the other of a more penetrative character, which will be termed **β (beta) radiation**." Subsequently, charge-to-mass ratio measurements showed that α radiation is composed of helium nuclei (He^{2+}) and β radiation is composed of electrons (e^-) (Table 25.1).

Rutherford hedged his bet when he said at least two types of radiation existed. A third type was later discovered by the French scientist Paul Villard (1860–1934); he named it **γ (gamma) radiation**, using the third letter in the Greek alphabet in keeping with Rutherford's scheme. Unlike α and β radiation, γ radiation is not affected by electric and magnetic fields. Rather, it is a form of electromagnetic radiation like x-rays but even more energetic.

Early studies measured the penetrating power of the three types of radiation (Figure 25.1). Alpha radiation is the least penetrating; it can be stopped by several sheets of ordinary paper or clothing. Beta particles can penetrate several millimeters of living bone or tissue, but about 0.5 cm of lead will stop the particles. Gamma radiation is the most penetrating. Thick layers of lead or concrete are required to

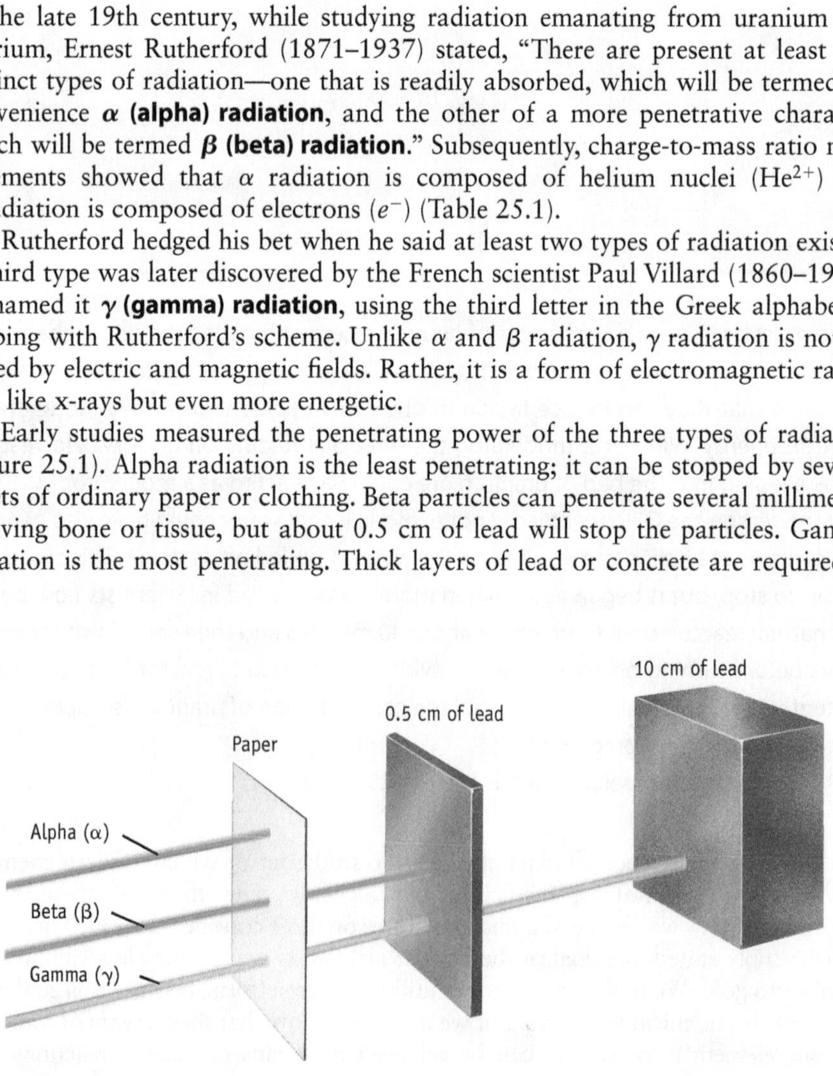

FIGURE 25.1 **The relative penetrating ability of α, β, and γ radiation.** Highly charged α particles interact strongly with matter and are stopped by a piece of paper. Beta particles, with less mass and a lower charge, interact to a lesser extent with matter and thus can penetrate farther. Gamma radiation is the most penetrating.

shield the body from this radiation, and γ rays can pass completely through the human body.

Alpha and β particles typically possess high kinetic energies. The energy of γ radiation is similarly very high. When α and β particles are stopped by a material, or when γ radiation is absorbed, the energy associated with the radiation is transferred to the material. This fact is important because the damage caused by radiation is related to the energy absorbed (▶ Section 25-8).

25-2 Nuclear Reactions and Radioactive Decay

Equations for Nuclear Reactions

In 1903, Rutherford and Frederick Soddy (1877–1956) proposed that radioactivity is the result of a natural change of an isotope of one element into an isotope of a different element. Such processes are called **nuclear reactions.**

Consider a reaction in which radium-226 (the isotope of radium with mass number 226) emits an α particle to form radon-222. The equation for this reaction is

Symbols Used in Nuclear Equations The mass number is included as a superscript, and the atomic number is included as a subscript preceding the symbols for reactants and products. This is done to facilitate balancing these equations.

$$^{226}_{88}\text{Ra} \rightarrow ^{4}_{2}\alpha + ^{222}_{86}\text{Rn}$$

In a nuclear reaction, the sum of the mass numbers of reacting particles must equal the sum of the mass numbers of products. Furthermore, to maintain nuclear charge balance, the sum of the atomic numbers of the products must equal the sum of the atomic numbers of the reactants. These principles are illustrated using the preceding nuclear equation:

	$^{226}_{88}\text{Ra}$	$\rightarrow$	$^{4}_{2}\alpha$	+	$^{222}_{86}\text{Rn}$
	RADIUM-226	$\rightarrow$	α PARTICLE	+	RADON-222
Mass number: (protons + neutrons)	226	=	4	+	222
Atomic number: (protons)	88	=	2	+	86

Alpha-particle emission causes a decrease of two units in atomic number and four units in the mass number.

Similarly, nuclear mass and nuclear charge balance accompany β-particle emission, as illustrated by the decomposition of uranium-239:

	$^{239}_{92}\text{U}$	$\rightarrow$	$^{0}_{-1}\beta$	+	$^{239}_{93}\text{Np}$
	URANIUM-239	$\rightarrow$	β PARTICLE	+	NEPTUNIUM-239
Mass number: (protons + neutrons)	239	=	0	+	239
Atomic number: (protons)	92	=	−1	+	93

The β particle has a charge of 1−. Charge balance requires that the atomic number of the product be one unit greater than the atomic number of the reacting nucleus. The mass number does not change in this process.

How does a nucleus, composed of protons and neutrons, eject an electron? It is a complex process, but the net result is the conversion within the nucleus of a neutron to a proton and an electron.

$$\underset{\text{neutron}}{^{1}_{0}\text{n}} \longrightarrow \underset{\text{electron}}{^{0}_{-1}\text{e}} + \underset{\text{proton}}{^{1}_{1}\text{p}}$$

Notice that the mass and charge numbers balance in this equation.

What is the origin of the γ radiation that accompanies many nuclear reactions? Recall that a photon of visible light is emitted when an atom undergoes a transition from an excited electronic state to a lower energy state (◀ Section 6-3). Gamma radiation originates from transitions between nuclear energy levels. Nuclear reactions often result in the formation of a product nucleus in an excited nuclear state. One option is to return to the ground state by emitting a photon. The energy of γ radiation is a measure of the large energy difference between the energy levels in the nucleus.

Radioactive Decay Series

Several naturally occurring radioactive isotopes decay to form a product that is also radioactive. When this happens, the initial nuclear reaction is followed by a second nuclear reaction; if the situation is repeated, a third and a fourth nuclear reaction occur; and so on. Eventually, a nonradioactive isotope is formed to end the series. Such a sequence of nuclear reactions is called a **radioactive decay series.** In each step of this sequence, the reactant nucleus is called the *parent,* and the product is called the *daughter.*

Uranium-238, the most abundant of three naturally occurring uranium isotopes, heads one of four radioactive decay series. This series begins with the loss of an α particle from $^{238}_{92}U$ to form radioactive $^{234}_{90}Th$. Thorium-234 then decomposes by β emission to $^{234}_{91}Pa$, which emits a β particle to give $^{234}_{92}U$. Uranium-234 is an α emitter, forming $^{230}_{90}Th$. Further α and β emissions follow, until the series ends with formation of the stable, nonradioactive isotope, $^{206}_{82}Pb$. In all, this radioactive decay series converting $^{238}_{92}U$ to $^{206}_{82}Pb$ is made up of 14 decays, with eight α and six β particles being emitted. The series is portrayed graphically by plotting atomic number versus mass number (Figure 25.2). An equation can be written for each step in the sequence. Equations for the first four steps in the uranium-238 radioactive decay series are as follows:

Step 1. $^{238}_{92}U \rightarrow {}^{234}_{90}Th + {}^{4}_{2}\alpha$

Step 2. $^{234}_{90}Th \rightarrow {}^{234}_{91}Pa + {}^{0}_{-1}\beta$

Step 3. $^{234}_{91}Pa \rightarrow {}^{234}_{92}U + {}^{0}_{-1}\beta$

Step 4. $^{234}_{92}U \rightarrow {}^{230}_{90}Th + {}^{4}_{2}\alpha$

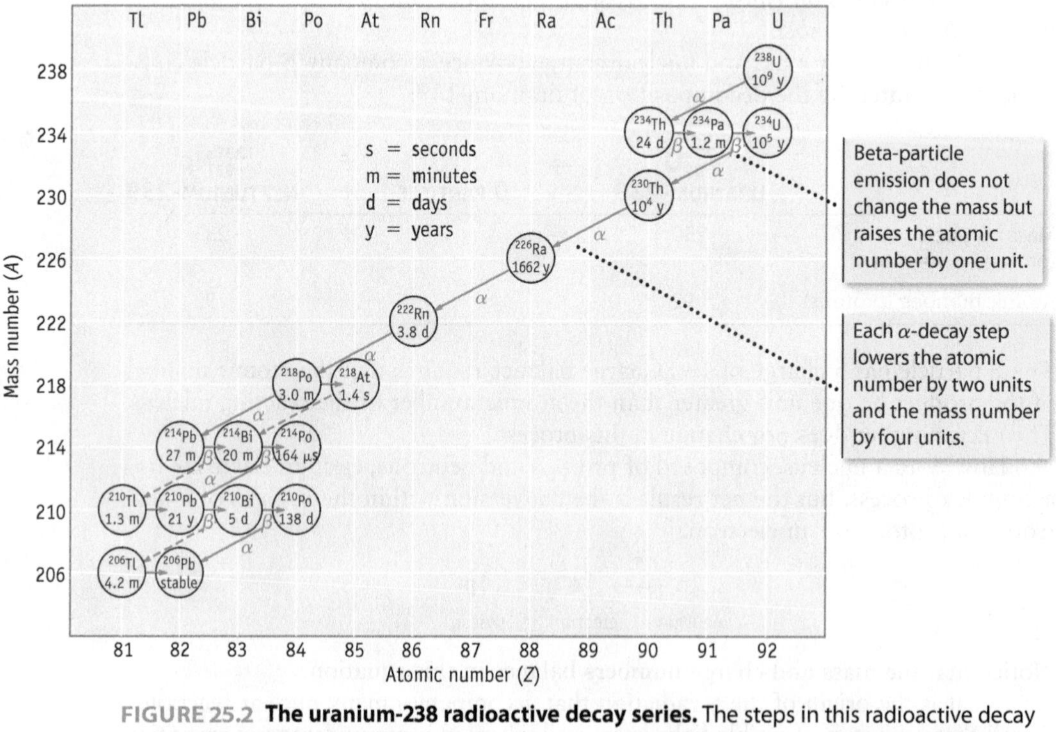

FIGURE 25.2 **The uranium-238 radioactive decay series.** The steps in this radioactive decay series are shown graphically in this plot of mass number versus atomic number. Half-lives of the isotopes are included on the chart. Notice that several of the isotopes in this series decompose by two different pathways.

Uranium ore contains trace quantities of the radioactive elements formed in the radioactive decay series. A significant development in nuclear chemistry was Marie Curie's discovery in 1898 of radium and polonium as trace components of pitchblende, a uranium ore. The amount of each of these elements is small because their isotopes have short half-lives. Consequently, Marie Curie was able to isolate only a single gram of radium from 7 tons of ore. It is a credit to her skills as a chemist that she extracted sufficient amounts of radium and polonium from uranium ore to identify these elements.

The uranium-238 radioactive decay series is also the source of the environmental hazard radon. Trace quantities of uranium are often present naturally in soil and rocks, and radon-222 is being continuously formed. Because radon is chemically inert, it is not trapped by chemical processes in soil or water and is free to seep into mines or into homes through pores in cement block walls, through cracks in the basement floor or walls, or around pipes. Because it is more dense than air, radon tends to collect in low spots, and its concentration can build up in a basement if steps are not taken to remove it.

The major health hazard from radon, when it is inhaled by humans, arises not from radon itself but from its decomposition product, polonium.

$$^{222}_{86}\text{Rn} \rightarrow {}^{218}_{84}\text{Po} + {}^{4}_{2}\alpha \qquad t_{1/2} = 3.82 \text{ days}$$

$$^{218}_{84}\text{Po} \rightarrow {}^{214}_{82}\text{Pb} + {}^{4}_{2}\alpha \qquad t_{1/2} = 3.04 \text{ minutes}$$

Radon does not undergo chemical reactions or form compounds that can be taken up in the body. Polonium, however, is not chemically inert. Polonium-218 can lodge in body tissues, where it undergoes α decay to give lead-214, another radioactive isotope. The range of an α particle in body tissue is quite small, perhaps 0.7 mm. This is approximately the thickness of the epithelial cells of the lungs, however, so α-particle radiation can cause serious damage to lung tissues.

Virtually every home in the United States has some level of radon, and kits can be purchased to test for the presence of this gas. If a significant amount of radon gas is detected in your home, you should take corrective actions such as sealing cracks around the foundation and in the basement. It may be reassuring to know that the health risks associated with radon are low. The likelihood of getting lung cancer from exposure to radon is about the same as the likelihood of dying in an accident in your home.

© Cengage Learning/Charles D. Winters

Radon detector. This kit is intended for use in the home to detect radon gas. The small device is placed in the home's basement for a given time period and is then sent to a laboratory to measure the amount of radon that might be present.

EXAMPLE 25.1

Radioactive Decay Series

Problem Another radioactive decay series begins with $^{235}_{92}\text{U}$ and ends with $^{207}_{82}\text{Pb}$.

(a) How many α and β particles are emitted in this series?

(b) The first three steps of this series are (in order) α, β, and α emission. Write an equation for each of these steps.

What Do You Know? You are given the starting (long-lived radioactive) isotope and the final (stable) isotope. A series of α and β reactions is the link between these two species.

Strategy First, find the total change in atomic number and mass number. A combination of α and β particles is required that will decrease the total nuclear mass by 28 (235 − 207) and at the same time decrease the atomic number by 10 (92 − 82). Each equation must give symbols for the parent and daughter nuclei and the emitted particle. In the equations, the sums of the atomic numbers and mass numbers for reactants and products must be equal.

Solution

(a) Mass declines by 28 mass units (235 − 207). Because a decrease of 4 mass units occurs with each α emission, 7 α particles must be emitted. Also, for each α emission, the atomic number decreases by 2. Emission of 7 α particles would cause the atomic number to decrease by 14, but the actual decrease in atomic number is 10 (92 − 82). This means that 4 β particles must also have been emitted because each β emission increases the atomic number of the product by one unit. Thus, the radioactive decay sequence involves emission of 7 α and 4 β particles.

(b) Step 1. $^{235}_{92}U \rightarrow ^{231}_{90}Th + ^{4}_{2}\alpha$

Step 2. $^{231}_{90}Th \rightarrow ^{231}_{91}Pa + ^{0}_{-1}\beta$

Step 3. $^{231}_{91}Pa \rightarrow ^{227}_{89}Ac + ^{4}_{2}\alpha$

Think about Your Answer Because the mass number changes in these series only when an α particle is lost, all of the mass numbers in a given decay series are some multiple of four less than the first isotope in the series. For the series beginning with U-238, the mass numbers are in the series 238, 234, 230, . . . , 206. This series is sometimes called the *$4n + 2$ series* because each mass number (M) fits the equation $4n + 2 = M$, where n is an integer (n is 59 for the first member of this series and 51 for the last member). For the series headed by $^{235}_{92}U$, the mass numbers are 235, 231, 227, . . . , 207; this is the *$4n + 3$ series.*

Two other decay series are possible. One, called the *$4n$ series* and beginning with ^{232}Th, is found in nature. The other, the $4n + 1$ series, is not found because no member of the series has a very long half-life. During the 4.5 billion years since this planet was formed, all radioactive members of the $4n + 1$ series have completely decayed to the end product, ^{209}Bi.

Check Your Understanding

(a) Six α and four β particles are emitted in the thorium-232 radioactive decay series before a stable isotope is reached. What is the final product in this series?

(b) The first three steps in the thorium-232 decay series (in order) are α, β, and β emission. Write an equation for each step.

Other Types of Radioactive Decay

Positrons Positrons were discovered by Carl Anderson (1905–1991) in 1932. The positron is one of a group of particles known as *antimatter.* If matter and antimatter particles collide, mutual annihilation occurs, with energy being emitted.

Most naturally occurring radioactive elements decay by emission of α, β, and γ radiation. Other nuclear decay processes became known, however, when new radioactive elements were synthesized by artificial means. These include **positron** ($^{0}_{+1}\beta$) **emission** and **electron capture**.

Positrons ($^{0}_{+1}\beta$) and electrons have the same mass but opposite charge. The positron is the antimatter analog to an electron. *Positron emission* by polonium-207, for example, results in the formation of bismuth-207.

	$^{207}_{84}Po$	$\rightarrow$	$^{0}_{+1}\beta$	+	$^{207}_{83}Bi$
	POLONIUM-207	$\rightarrow$	POSITRON	+	BISMUTH-207
Mass number: (protons + neutrons)	207	=	0	+	207
Atomic number: (protons)	84	=	1	+	83

To retain charge balance, *positron decay results in a decrease in the atomic number.*

In *electron capture,* an extranuclear electron is captured by the nucleus. The mass number is unchanged, and *the atomic number is reduced by 1.* (In an old nomenclature, the innermost electron shell was called the *K shell,* and electron capture was called *K capture.*)

	$^{7}_{4}\text{Be}$	+	$^{0}_{-1}e$	→	$^{7}_{3}\text{Li}$
	BERYLLIUM-7	+	ELECTRON	→	LITHIUM-7
Mass number: (protons + neutrons)	7	+	0	=	7
Atomic number: (protons)	4	+	−1	=	3

In summary, most unstable nuclei decay by one of four paths: α or β decay, positron emission, or electron capture. Gamma radiation often accompanies these processes. Section 25-6 introduces a fifth way that nuclei decompose, *fission.*

Neutrinos and Antineutrinos
Beta particles having a wide range of energies are emitted. To balance the energy and momentum associated with β decay, it is necessary to postulate the concurrent emission of another particle, the *antineutrino*. Similarly, neutrino emission accompanies positron emission. Much study has gone into detecting neutrinos and antineutrinos. These particles do not have a charge. They are believed to have mass, but their mass is so small it has not been possible to measure it. Neutrinos and antineutrinos are not included when writing nuclear equations.

EXAMPLE 25.2

Nuclear Reactions

Problem Complete the following equations. Give the symbol, mass number, and atomic number of the product species.

(a) $^{37}_{18}\text{Ar} + ^{0}_{-1}\text{e} \rightarrow ?$

(b) $^{11}_{6}\text{C} \rightarrow ^{11}_{5}\text{B} + ?$

(c) $^{35}_{16}\text{S} \rightarrow ^{35}_{17}\text{Cl} + ?$

(d) $^{30}_{15}\text{P} \rightarrow ^{0}_{+1}\beta + ?$

What Do You Know? You are given the reactant and one of two products formed in these nuclear reactions. You know that both the masses and charges must balance in a balanced nuclear equation.

Strategy The missing product in each reaction can be determined by recognizing that the sums of mass numbers and atomic numbers for products and reactants must be equal. When you know the nuclear mass and nuclear charge of the product, you can identify it with the appropriate symbol.

Solution

(a) This is an electron capture reaction. The product has a mass number of 37 + 0 = 37 and an atomic number of 18 − 1 = 17. Therefore, the symbol for the product is $^{37}_{17}\text{Cl}$.

(b) This missing particle has a mass of zero and a charge of 1+; these are the characteristics of a positron, $^{0}_{+1}\beta$. If this particle is included in the equation, the sums of the atomic numbers (6 = 5 + 1) and the mass numbers (11) on both sides of the equation are equal.

(c) A β particle, $^{0}_{-1}\beta$, is required to balance the mass numbers (35) and atomic numbers (16 = 17 − 1) in the equation.

(d) The product nucleus has mass number 30 and atomic number 14. This identifies the unknown as $^{30}_{14}\text{Si}$.

Think about Your Answer The product in each reaction is a stable isotope. As discussed in the next section, there is a narrow range of neutron-to-proton ratios for stable isotopes. Spontaneous nuclear reactions always occur in a way that moves either into or closer to the narrow range of stable isotopes.

Check Your Understanding

Indicate the symbol, the mass number, and the atomic number of the missing product in each of the following nuclear reactions.

(a) $^{13}_{7}\text{N} \rightarrow ^{13}_{6}\text{C} + ?$

(b) $^{41}_{20}\text{Ca} + ^{0}_{-1}\text{e} \rightarrow ?$

(c) $^{90}_{38}\text{Sr} \rightarrow ^{90}_{39}\text{Y} + ?$

(d) $^{22}_{11}\text{Na} \rightarrow ? + ^{0}_{+1}\beta$

REVIEW & CHECK FOR SECTION 25-2

1. Identify the type of radiation associated with a nuclear reaction converting radon-222 to polonium-218.

   (a) alpha radiation (c) positron emission

   (b) beta radiation (d) fission

2. The uranium-235 radioactive decay series ends with the formation of ^{207}Pb. How many alpha (α) and beta (β) particles are emitted in this series?

   (a) 8 α and 4 β (c) 7 α and 6 β

   (b) 7 α and 4 β (d) 6 α and 4 β

3. Which of the following reactions involves emission of a beta particle?

   (a) $^{13}_{7}N \rightarrow {}^{13}_{6}C + ?$ (c) $^{90}_{38}Sr \rightarrow {}^{90}_{39}Y + ?$

   (b) $^{41}_{20}Ca + {}^{0}_{-1}e \rightarrow ?$ (d) $^{232}_{90}Th \rightarrow {}^{228}_{88}Ra + ?$

25-3 Stability of Atomic Nuclei

We can learn something about nuclear stability from Figure 25.3, a plot of the composition of the known isotopes of the elements. The horizontal axis represents the number of protons, and the vertical axis gives the number of neutrons. Each circle represents an isotope identified by the number of neutrons and protons contained in its nucleus. The black circles represent stable (nonradioactive) isotopes, 254 in number, and the red circles represent some of the known radioactive isotopes. For example, the three isotopes of hydrogen are $^{1}_{1}H$ and $^{2}_{1}H$ (neither is radioactive) and

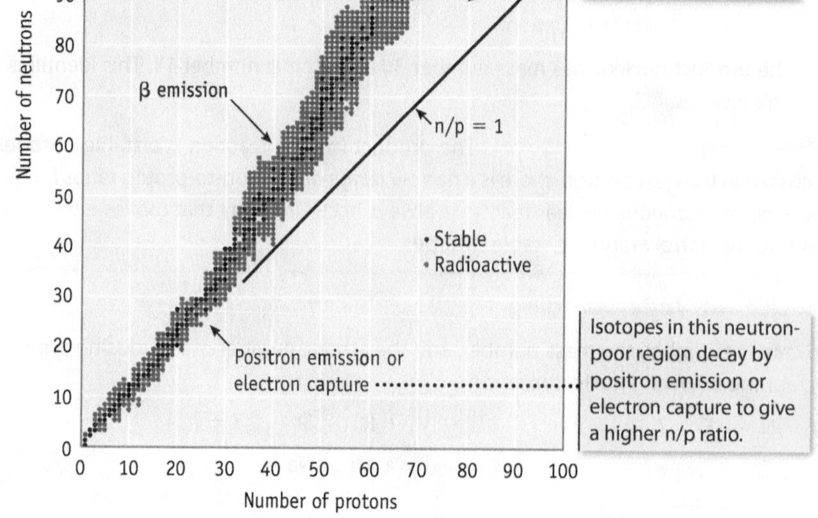

FIGURE 25.3 Stable and unstable isotopes. A graph of the number of neutrons (n) versus the number of protons (p) for stable (*black circles*) and radioactive (*red circles*) isotopes from hydrogen to bismuth. This graph is used to assess criteria for nuclear stability and to predict modes of decay for unstable nuclei.

$^{3}_{1}H$ (tritium, radioactive). For lithium, the third element, isotopes are known with mass numbers 4, 5, 6, and 7. The isotopes with masses of 6 and 7 (shown in black) are stable, whereas the other two isotopes (in red) are radioactive.

Figure 25.3 gives us the following information about nuclear stability:

- Stable isotopes fall in a very narrow range called the **band of stability**. It is remarkable how few isotopes are stable.
- Only two stable isotopes ($^{1}_{1}H$ and $^{3}_{2}He$) have more protons than neutrons.
- Up to calcium ($Z = 20$), stable isotopes often have equal numbers of protons and neutrons or only one or two more neutrons than protons.
- Beyond calcium, the neutron-to-proton ratio is always greater than 1. As the mass increases, the band of stable isotopes deviates more and more from a 1:1 neutron-to-proton ratio (the line in Figure 25.3 for which n/p = 1).
- Beyond bismuth (83 protons and 126 neutrons), all isotopes are unstable and radioactive. There is apparently no nuclear "superglue" strong enough to hold heavy nuclei together.
- Isotopes that fall farther from the band of stability tend to have shorter half-lives than do unstable isotopes nearer to the band of stability.
- Isotope stability is associated with even atomic numbers and even atomic weights. Among the stable isotopes, 148 have an even number of protons and neutrons, 53 have an even number of protons and an odd number of neutrons, and 48 have an odd number of protons and an even number of neutrons. Only five stable isotopes ($^{2}_{1}H$, $^{6}_{3}Li$, $^{10}_{5}B$, $^{14}_{7}N$, and $^{180}_{73}Ta$) have odd numbers of both protons and neutrons.

The Band of Stability and Radioactive Decay

Besides being a criterion for stability, the neutron-to-proton ratio can assist in predicting what type of radioactive decay will be observed. Unstable nuclei decay in a manner that brings them toward a stable neutron-to-proton ratio—that is, toward the band of stability.

- All elements beyond bismuth ($Z = 83$) are unstable. For an element beyond this atomic number, a process that decreases the atomic number is needed to reach the band of stability. Alpha emission is an effective way to do this because each emission decreases the atomic number by 2. For example, americium, the radioactive element used in smoke detectors, decays by α emission:

$$^{243}_{95}\text{Am} \rightarrow {}^{4}_{2}\alpha + {}^{239}_{93}\text{Np}$$

- Beta emission occurs for isotopes that have a high neutron-to-proton ratio—that is, isotopes above the band of stability. With β decay, the atomic number increases by 1, and the mass number remains constant, resulting in a lower neutron-to-proton ratio:

$$^{60}_{27}\text{Co} \rightarrow {}^{0}_{-1}\beta + {}^{60}_{28}\text{Ni}$$

- Isotopes with a low neutron-to-proton ratio, below the band of stability, decay by positron emission or by electron capture. Both processes lead to product nuclei with a lower atomic number and the same mass number and move the product closer to the band of stability:

$$^{13}_{7}\text{N} \rightarrow {}^{0}_{+1}\beta + {}^{13}_{6}\text{C}$$

$$^{41}_{20}\text{Ca} + {}^{0}_{-1}\text{e} \rightarrow {}^{41}_{19}\text{K}$$

EXAMPLE 25.3

Predicting Modes of Radioactive Decay

Problem Identify probable mode(s) of decay for each isotope and write an equation for the decay process.

(a) oxygen-15, $^{15}_{8}O$

(b) uranium-234, $^{234}_{92}U$

(c) fluorine-20, $^{20}_{9}F$

(d) manganese-56, $^{56}_{25}Mn$

What Do You Know? You are given the formulas for four radioactive isotopes. The possible modes of decomposition are α, β, or positron emission and electron capture. The preferred mode will give a more stable isotope and create a nucleus that is closer to the band of stability.

Strategy There are two main ideas to look at. First, if Z is greater than 83, then α decay is likely. Second, consider the n/p ratio. If the ratio is much greater than 1, then β decay is probable. If the ratio is less than 1, then positron emission or electron capture is the more likely process. It is not possible to choose between the latter two modes of decay without further information.

Solution

(a) Oxygen-15 has 7 neutrons and 8 protons, so the neutron-to-proton (n/p) ratio is less than 1—too low for ^{15}O to be stable. Nuclei with too few neutrons are expected to decay by either positron emission or electron capture. In this instance, the process is $^{0}_{+1}\beta$ emission, and the equation is $^{15}_{8}O \rightarrow ^{0}_{+1}\beta + ^{15}_{7}N$.

(b) Alpha emission is a common mode of decay for isotopes of elements with atomic numbers higher than 83. The decay of uranium-234 is one example:

$$^{234}_{92}U \rightarrow ^{230}_{90}Th + ^{4}_{2}\alpha$$

(c) Fluorine-20 has 11 neutrons and 9 protons, a high n/p ratio. The ratio is lowered by β emission:

$$^{20}_{9}F \rightarrow ^{0}_{-1}\beta + ^{20}_{10}Ne$$

(d) The mass number of ^{56}Mn is higher than the atomic weight of the element (54.85). This suggests that this radioactive isotope has an excess of neutrons (giving a high n/p ratio), in which case it would be expected to decay by β emission:

$$^{56}_{25}Mn \rightarrow ^{0}_{-1}\beta + ^{56}_{26}Fe$$

Think about Your Answer Decomposition can occur by four possible paths, α and β emission, positron emission, and electron capture. Whether the decay follows beta emission or positron emission (or electron capture) is predicted by the neutron/proton ratio, relative to the n/p ratio in stable isotopes.

Check Your Understanding

Write an equation for the probable mode of decay for each of the following unstable isotopes, and write an equation for that nuclear reaction.

(a) silicon-32, $^{32}_{14}Si$

(b) titanium-45, $^{45}_{22}Ti$

(c) plutonium-239, $^{239}_{94}Pu$

(d) potassium-42, $^{42}_{19}K$

Nuclear Binding Energy

An atomic nucleus can contain as many as 83 protons and still be stable. For stability, nuclear binding (attractive) forces must be greater than the electrostatic repulsive forces between the closely packed protons in the nucleus. **Nuclear binding energy,**

E_b, is defined as the energy required to separate the nucleus of an atom into protons and neutrons. For example, the nuclear binding energy for deuterium is the energy required to convert one mole of deuterium (^2_1H) nuclei into one mole of protons and one mole of neutrons.

$$^2_1H \rightarrow {}^1_1p + {}^1_0n \qquad E_b = +2.15 \times 10^8 \text{ kJ/mol}$$

The positive sign for E_b indicates that energy is required for this process. A deuterium nucleus is more stable than an isolated proton and an isolated neutron, just as the H_2 molecule is more stable than two isolated H atoms. Recall, however, that the H—H bond energy is only 436 kJ/mol. The energy holding a proton and a neutron together in a deuterium nucleus, 2.15×10^8 kJ/mol, is about 500,000 times larger than the typical covalent bond energies.

To further understand nuclear binding energy, we turn to an experimental observation and a theory. The experimental observation is that the mass of a nucleus is *always* less than the sum of the masses of its constituent protons and neutrons. The theory is that the "missing mass," called the **mass defect**, is equated with the energy that holds the nuclear particles together.

The mass defect for deuterium is the difference between the mass of a deuterium nucleus and the sum of the masses of a proton and a neutron. Mass spectrometric measurements (◀ Section 2-3) give the masses of these particles to a high level of accuracy, providing the numbers needed to carry out calculations of mass defects.

Masses of atomic nuclei are not generally listed in reference tables, but masses of atoms are. Calculation of the mass defect can be carried out using masses of atoms instead of masses of nuclei. By using atomic masses, we are including in this calculation the masses of extranuclear electrons in the reactants and the products. However, because the same number of extranuclear electrons appears in products and reactants, this does not affect the result. Thus, for one mole of deuterium nuclei, the mass defect is found as follows:

$$\begin{array}{ccccc} ^2_1H & \rightarrow & ^1_1H & + & ^1_0n \\ 2.01410 \text{ g/mol} & & 1.007825 \text{ g/mol} & & 1.008665 \text{ g/mol} \end{array}$$

$$\begin{aligned} \text{Mass defect} = \Delta m &= \text{mass of products} - \text{mass of reactants} \\ &= [1.007825 \text{ g/mol} + 1.008665 \text{ g/mol}] - 2.01410 \text{ g/mol} \\ &= 0.00239 \text{ g/mol} \end{aligned}$$

The relationship between mass and energy is contained in Albert Einstein's 1905 theory of special relativity, which holds that mass and energy are different manifestations of the same quantity. Einstein defined the energy–mass relationship: Energy is equivalent to mass times the square of the speed of light; that is, $E = mc^2$. In the case of atomic nuclei, it is assumed that the missing mass (the mass defect, Δm) is equated with the binding energy holding the nucleus together.

$$E_b = (\Delta m)c^2 \qquad \textbf{(25.1)}$$

If Δm is given in kilograms and the speed of light is given in meters per second, E_b will have units of joules (because $1 \text{ J} = 1 \text{ kg} \cdot \text{m}^2/\text{s}^2$). For the decomposition of one mole of deuterium nuclei to one mole of protons and one mole of neutrons, we have

$$\begin{aligned} E_b &= (2.39 \times 10^{-6} \text{ kg/mol})(2.998 \times 10^8 \text{ m/s})^2 \\ &= 2.15 \times 10^{11} \text{ J/mol of } ^2_1\text{H nuclei } (= 2.15 \times 10^8 \text{ kJ/mol of } ^2_1\text{H nuclei}) \end{aligned}$$

The nuclear stabilities of different elements are compared using the **binding energy per mole of nucleons.** (**Nucleon** is the general name given to nuclear particles—that is, protons and neutrons.) A deuterium nucleus contains two

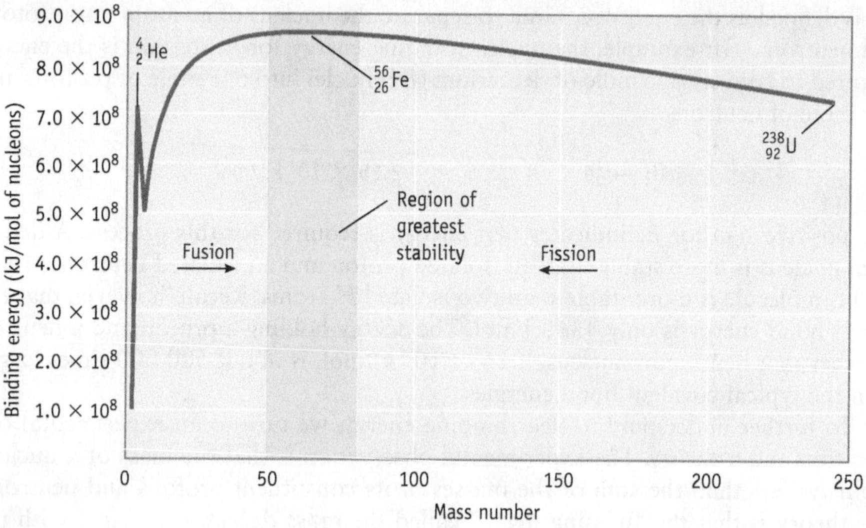

FIGURE 25.4 Relative stability of nuclei. Binding energy per nucleon for the most stable isotope of elements between hydrogen and uranium is plotted as a function of mass number. (Fission and fusion are discussed in Sections 25-6 and 25-7.)

nucleons, so the binding energy per mole of nucleons, E_b/n, is 2.15×10^8 kJ/mol divided by 2, or 1.08×10^8 kJ/mol nucleon.

$$E_b/n = \left(\frac{2.15 \times 10^8 \text{ kJ}}{\text{mol } {}^2_1\text{H nuclei}}\right)\left(\frac{1 \text{ mol } {}^2_1\text{H nuclei}}{2 \text{ mol nucleons}}\right)$$

$$E_b/n = 1.08 \times 10^8 \text{ kJ/mol nucleons}$$

The binding energy per nucleon can be calculated for any atom whose mass is known. Then, to compare nuclear stabilities, we can plot binding energies per nucleon as a function of mass number (Figure 25.4). The greater the binding energy per nucleon, the greater the stability of the nucleus. From the graph in Figure 25.4, the point of maximum nuclear stability occurs at a mass of 56 (that is, at iron in the periodic table).

EXAMPLE 25.4

Nuclear Binding Energy

Problem Calculate the binding energy per mole of nucleons, E_b (in kJ/mol), and the binding energy per nucleon, E_b/n (in kJ/mol nucleon), for carbon-12.

What Do You Know? The mass of carbon-12 is, by definition, exactly 12 g/mol. You will need the molar masses of hydrogen atoms (${}^1_1$H) and neutrons (1.007825 g/mol and 1.008665 g/mol, respectively, to determine the mass defect.

Strategy The mass defect is the difference between the mass of carbon-12 and the masses of 6 protons, 6 neutrons, and 6 electrons. The mass of 1 mol of protons and 1 mol of electrons can be taken into account by using the molar mass of ${}^1_1$H. Use the values given to calculate the mass defect (in g/mol). The binding energy is calculated from the mass defect using Equation 25.1.

Solution The mass of ${}^1_1$H is 1.007825 g/mol, and the mass of ${}^1_0$n is 1.008665 g/mol. Carbon-12, ${}^{12}_6$C, is the standard for the atomic masses in the periodic table, and its mass is defined as exactly 12 g/mol

$$\Delta m = [(6 \times \text{mass } {}^1_1\text{H}) + (6 \times \text{mass } {}^1_0\text{n})] - \text{mass } {}^{12}_6\text{C}$$

$$= [(6 \times 1.007825 \text{ g/mol}) + (6 \times 1.008665 \text{ g/mol})] - 12.000000 \text{ g/mol}$$

$$= 9.8940 \times 10^{-2} \text{ g/mol}$$

The binding energy is calculated using Equation 25.1. Using the mass in kilograms and the speed of light in meters per second gives the binding energy in joules:

$$E_b = (\Delta m)c^2$$
$$= (9.8940 \times 10^{-5}\ \text{kg/mol})(2.99792 \times 10^8\ \text{m/s})^2$$
$$= 8.8923 \times 10^{12}\ \text{J/mol}\ (= 8.8923 \times 10^9\ \text{kJ/mol})$$

The binding energy per nucleon, E_b/n, is determined by dividing the binding energy by 12 (the number of nucleons).

$$\frac{E_b}{n} = \frac{8.8923 \times 10^9\ \text{kJ/mol}}{12\ \text{mol nucleons/mol}}$$
$$= 7.4102 \times 10^8\ \text{kJ/mol nucleons}$$

Think about Your Answer The binding energy is a very large quantity of energy compared to those of ordinary chemical reactions. Compare binding energy to the very exothermic reaction of hydrogen and oxygen to form water vapor, for which $\Delta_r H°$ is only −242 kJ per mol of water vapor formed at 25 °C.

Check Your Understanding

Calculate the binding energy per nucleon, in kilojoules per mole, for lithium-6. The molar mass of $^{6}_{3}Li$ is 6.015125 g/mol.

REVIEW & CHECK FOR SECTION 25-3

1. Among the listed species, which has the highest binding energy per nucleon?

(a) $^{2}_{1}D$ (b) $^{20}_{10}Ne$ (c) $^{56}_{26}Fe$ (d) $^{238}_{92}U$

25-4 Rates of Nuclear Decay

Learning Objectives: LO 4.3

Half-Life

When a new radioactive isotope is identified, its *half-life* is usually determined. Half-life ($t_{1/2}$) is used in nuclear chemistry in the same way it is used when discussing the kinetics of first-order chemical reactions (◀ Section 14-4): It is the time required for half of a sample to decay to products (Figure 25.5). Recall that for first-order kinetics the half-life is independent of the amount of sample.

Half-lives for radioactive isotopes cover a wide range of values. Uranium-238 has one of the longer half-lives, 4.47×10^9 years, a length of time close to the age of

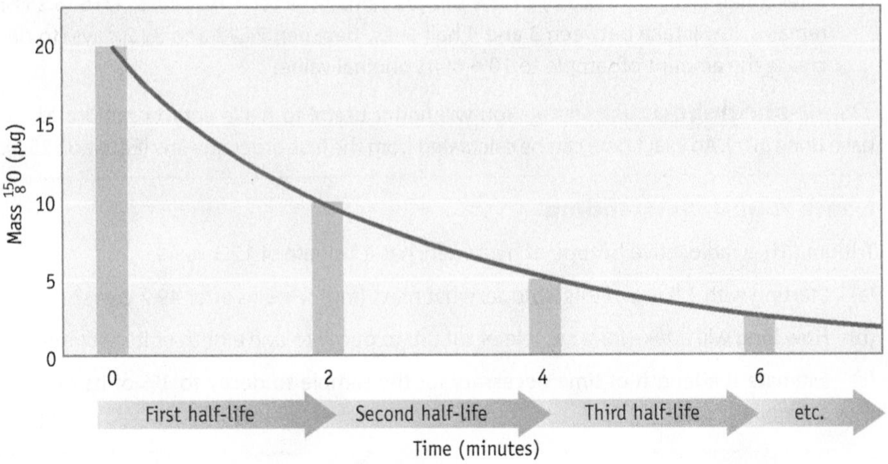

FIGURE 25.5 Decay of 20.0 µg of oxygen-15. After each half-life period of 2.0 minutes, the mass of oxygen-15 decreases by one half. (Oxygen-15 decays by positron emission.)

the Earth (estimated at 4.5–4.6 × 10^9 years). Thus, roughly half of the uranium-238 present when the planet was formed is still around. At the other end of the range of half-lives are isotopes such as the 277 isotope of element 112 (recently named copernicium, ^{277}Cn), which has a half-life of 240 microseconds (1 μs = 1 × 10^{-6} s).

Half-life provides an easy way to estimate the time required before a radioactive element is no longer a health hazard. Strontium-90, for example, is a β emitter with a half-life of 29.1 years. Significant quantities of strontium-90 were dispersed into the environment during atmospheric nuclear bomb tests in the 1950s and 1960s, and, from the half-life, we know that about one-fourth is still around. The health problems associated with strontium-90 arise because calcium and strontium have similar chemical properties. Strontium-90 is taken into the body and deposited in bone, taking the place of calcium. Radiation damage by strontium-90 (a β emitter) in bone has been directly linked to bone-related cancers.

EXAMPLE 25.5

Using Half-Life

Problem Radioactive iodine-131, used to treat hyperthyroidism, has a half-life of 8.04 days.

(a) If you have 8.8 μg (micrograms) of this isotope, what mass remains after 32.2 days?

(b) How long will it take for a sample of iodine-131 to decay to one eighth of its activity?

(c) Estimate the length of time necessary for the sample to decay to 10% of its original activity.

What Do You Know? The half-life of ^{131}I, 8.04 days, is given in the problem.

Strategy This problem asks you to use half-life to qualitatively assess the rate of decay. After one half-life, half of the sample remains. After another half-life, the amount of sample is again decreased by half to one fourth of its original value. To answer these questions, assess the number of half-lives that have elapsed and use this information to determine the amount of sample remaining.

Solution

(a) The time elapsed, 32.2 days, is 4 half-lives (32.2/8.04 = 4). The amount of iodine-131 has decreased to 1/16 of the original amount [1/2 × 1/2 × 1/2 × 1/2 = $(1/2)^4$ = 1/16]. The amount of iodine remaining is 8.8 μg × $(1/2)^4$ or 0.55 μg.

(b) After 3 half-lives (24.12 days), the amount of iodine-131 remaining is 1/8 [= $(1/2)^3$] of the original amount. The amount remaining is 8.8 μg × $(1/2)^3$ = 1.1 μg.

(c) After 3 half-lives, 1/8 (12.5%) of the sample remains; after 4 half-lives, 1/16 (6.25%) remains. It will take between 3 and 4 half-lives, between 24.12 and 32.2 days, to decrease the amount of sample to 10% of its original value.

Think about Your Answer You will find it useful to make approximations as we have done in (c). An exact time can be calculated from the first-order rate law (Equation 25.5).

Check Your Understanding

Tritium (^3_1H), a radioactive isotope of hydrogen, has a half-life of 12.3 years.

(a) Starting with 1.5 mg of this isotope, what mass (mg) remains after 49.2 years?

(b) How long will it take for a sample of tritium to decay to one eighth of its activity?

(c) Estimate the length of time necessary for the sample to decay to 1% of its original activity.

Kinetics of Nuclear Decay

The rate of nuclear decay is determined from measurements of the **activity** (A) of a sample. Activity refers to the number of disintegrations observed per unit of time, a quantity that can be measured readily with devices such as a Geiger–Müller counter (Figure 25.6). *Activity is proportional to the number of radioactive atoms present (N).*

$$A \propto N \quad (25.2)$$

If the number of radioactive nuclei N is reduced by half, the activity of the sample will be half as large. Doubling N will double the activity. This relationship indicates that the rate of decomposition is first order with respect to N. Consequently, the equations describing rates of radioactive decay are the same as those used to describe the kinetics of first-order chemical reactions; the change in the number of radioactive atoms N per unit of time is proportional to N (◀ Section 14-4)

$$\frac{\Delta N}{\Delta t} = -kN \quad (25.3)$$

The integrated rate equation can be written in two ways depending on the data used:

$$\ln\left(\frac{N}{N_0}\right) = -kt \quad (25.4)$$

or

$$\ln\left(\frac{A}{A_0}\right) = -kt \quad (25.5)$$

Here, N_0 and A_0 are the number of atoms and the initial activity of the sample, respectively, and N and A are the number of atoms and the activity of the sample after time t, respectively. Thus, N/N_0 is the fraction of atoms remaining after a given time (t), and A/A_0 is the fraction of the activity remaining after the same period. In these equations, k is the rate constant (decay constant) for the isotope in question. The relationship between half-life and the first-order rate constant is the same as seen with chemical kinetics (◀ Equation 14.4):

$$t_{1/2} = \frac{0.693}{k} \quad (25.6)$$

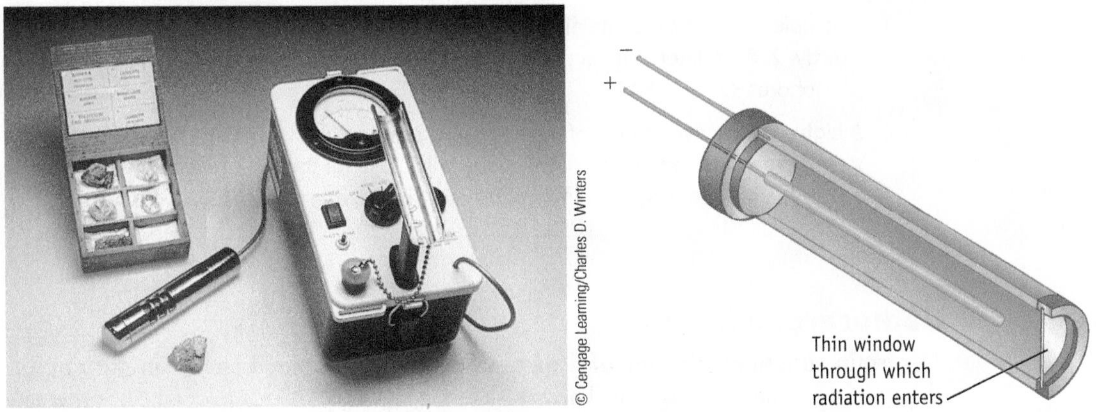

FIGURE 25.6 **A Geiger–Müller counter.** A charged particle (an α or β particle) enters the gas-filled tube (diagram at the *right*) and ionizes the gas. The gaseous ions migrate to electrically charged electrodes and are recorded as a pulse of electric current. The current is amplified and used to operate a counter. A sample of carnotite, a mineral containing uranium oxide, is also shown in the photograph.

Equations 25.3–25.6 are useful in several ways:

- If the activity (A) or the number of radioactive nuclei (N) is measured in the laboratory over some period t, k can be calculated. The decay constant k can then be used to determine the half-life of the sample.
- If k is known, the fraction of a radioactive sample (N/N_0) still present after some time t has elapsed can be calculated.
- If k is known, the time required for that isotope to decay to a fraction of the original activity (A/A_0) can be calculated.

EXAMPLE 25.6

Kinetics of Radioactive Decay

Problem A sample of radon-222 has an initial α-particle activity (A_0) of 7.0×10^4 dps (disintegrations per second). After 6.6 days, its activity (A) is 2.1×10^4 dps. What is the half-life of radon-222?

What Do You Know? You are given the initial and final activities of the sample of ^{222}Rn and the time elapsed.

Strategy Values for A, A_0, and t are given. The problem can be solved using Equation 25.5 with k as the unknown. Once k is found, the half-life can be calculated using Equation 25.6.

Solution

$$\ln(2.1 \times 10^4 \text{ dps}/7.0 \times 10^4 \text{ dps}) = -k\ (6.6 \text{ day})$$

$$\ln(0.30) = -k(6.6 \text{ day})$$

$$k = 0.18 \text{ days}^{-1}$$

From k we obtain $t_{1/2}$:

$$t_{1/2} = 0.693/0.18 \text{ days}^{-1} = 3.8 \text{ days}$$

Think about Your Answer Notice that the activity decreased to between one half and one fourth of its original value. The 6.6 days of elapsed time represents one full half-life and part of another half-life.

Check Your Understanding

(a) A sample of $Ca_3(PO_4)_2$ containing phosphorus-32 has an activity of 3.35×10^3 dpm. Exactly 2 days later, the activity is 3.18×10^3 dpm. Calculate the half-life of phosphorus-32.

(b) A highly radioactive sample of nuclear waste products with a half-life of 200. years is stored in an underground tank. How long will it take for the activity to diminish from an initial activity of 6.50×10^{12} dpm to a fairly harmless activity of 3.00×10^3 dpm?

Radiocarbon Dating

In certain situations, the age of a material can be determined based on the rate of decay of a radioactive isotope. The best-known example of this procedure is the use of carbon-14 to date historical artifacts.

Naturally occurring carbon is primarily carbon-12 and carbon-13 with isotopic abundances of 98.9% and 1.1%, respectively. In addition, traces of a third isotope, carbon-14, are present to the extent of about 1 in 10^{12} atoms in atmospheric CO_2 and in living materials. Carbon-14 is a β emitter with a half-life of 5730 years. A

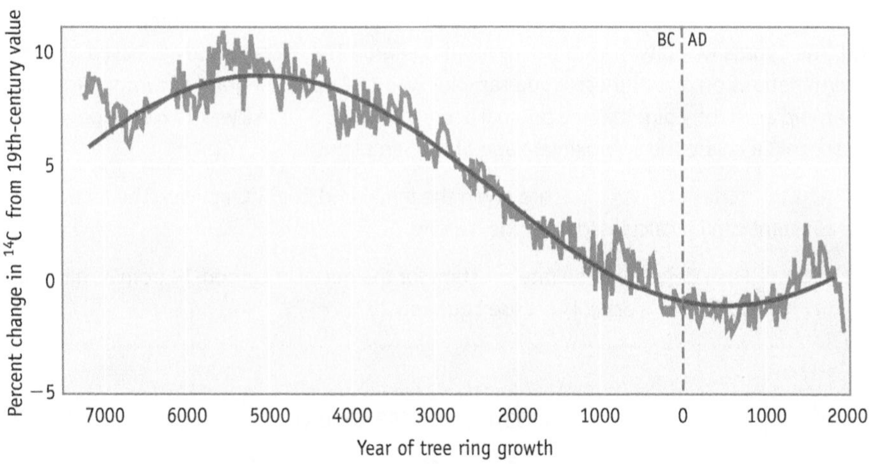

Source: Hans E. Suess, La Jolla Radiocarbon Laboratory

FIGURE 25.7 **Variation of atmospheric carbon-14 activity.** The amount of carbon-14 has changed with the variation in cosmic ray activity. To obtain the data for the pre-1990 part of the curve shown in this graph, scientists carried out carbon-14 dating of artifacts for which the age was accurately known (often through written records). Data for this figure were obtained using carbon-14 dating of tree rings.

1-gram sample of carbon from living material will show about 14 disintegrations per minute, not a lot of radioactivity but nevertheless detectable by modern methods.

Carbon-14 is formed in the upper atmosphere by nuclear reactions initiated by neutrons in cosmic radiation:

$$^{14}_{7}N + ^{1}_{0}n \rightarrow ^{14}_{6}C + ^{1}_{1}H$$

Once formed, carbon-14 is oxidized to $^{14}CO_2$. This product enters the carbon cycle, circulating through the atmosphere, oceans, and biosphere.

The usefulness of carbon-14 for dating comes about in the following way. Plants absorb CO_2 and convert it to organic compounds, thereby incorporating carbon-14 into living tissue. As long as a plant remains alive, this process will continue, and the percentage of carbon that is carbon-14 in the plant will equal the percentage in the atmosphere. When the plant dies, carbon-14 will no longer be taken up. Radioactive decay continues, however, with the carbon-14 activity decreasing over time. After 5730 years, the activity will be 7 dpm/g; after 11,460 years, it will be 3.5 dpm/g; and so on. By measuring the activity of a sample, and knowing the half-life of carbon-14, it is possible to calculate when a plant (or a plant-eating animal) died.

As with all experimental procedures, carbon-14 dating has limitations. Although the procedure assumes that the amount of carbon-14 in the atmosphere hundreds or thousands of years ago was the same as it is now, in fact the percentage has varied by as much as 10% (Figure 25.7). Furthermore, it is not possible to use carbon-14 to date an object less than about 100 years old; the radiation level from carbon-14 will not change enough in this short time period to permit accurate detection of a difference from the initial value. In most instances, the accuracy of the measurement is, in fact, only about ±100 years. Finally, it is not possible to determine ages of objects much older than about 60,000 years. By then, after more than 10 half-lives, the ^{14}C radioactivity will have decreased virtually to zero. But for the span of time between 100 and 60,000 years, this technique has provided important information (Figure 25.8).

Oesper Collection in the History of Chemistry, University of Cincinnati

Willard Libby (1908–1980) Libby received the 1960 Nobel Prize in Chemistry for developing carbon-14 dating techniques. Carbon-14 dating is widely used in fields such as anthropology.

PHOTOPQR/LA DEPECHE DU MIDI/Newscom

FIGURE 25.8 **The Iceman.** The world's oldest preserved human remains were discovered in the ice of a glacier high in the Alps. Carbon-14 dating techniques allowed scientists to determine that he lived about 5300 years ago. See pages 2 and 53 for more information on the Iceman.

EXAMPLE 25.7

Radiochemical Dating

Problem To test the concept of carbon-14 dating, J. R. Arnold and W. F. Libby applied this technique to analyze samples of acacia and cyprus wood whose ages were already known. (The acacia wood, which was supplied by the Metropolitan Museum of Art in New

York, came from the tomb of Zoser, the first Egyptian pharaoh to be entombed in a pyramid. The cyprus wood was from the tomb of Sneferu.) The average activity based on five determinations on one of these wood samples was 7.04 dpm per gram of carbon. Assume (as Arnold and Libby did) that the original activity of carbon-14, A_0, was 12.6 dpm per gram of carbon. Calculate the approximate age of the sample.

What Do You Know? You are given the initial and final ^{14}C activity. The first-order rate constant can be calculated from the half-life.

Strategy First, determine the rate constant for the decay of carbon-14 from its half-life ($t_{1/2}$ for ^{14}C is 5.73×10^3 years). Then, use Equation 25.5.

Solution

$$k = 0.693/t_{1/2} = 0.693/5730 \text{ yr}$$
$$= 1.21 \times 10^{-4} \text{ yr}^{-1}$$
$$\ln(A/A_0) = -kt$$
$$\ln\left(\frac{7.04 \text{ dpm/g}}{12.6 \text{ dpm/g}}\right) = (-1.21 \times 10^{-4} \text{ yr}^{-1})t$$
$$t = 4.8 \times 10^3 \text{ yr}$$

The wood is about 4800 years old.

Think about Your Answer This problem uses real data from an early research paper in which the carbon-14 dating method was being tested. The age of the wood was known to be 4750 ± 250 years. (See J. R. Arnold and W. F. Libby: *Science,* Vol. 110, p. 678, 1949.)

Check Your Understanding

A sample of the inner part of a redwood tree felled in 1874 was shown to have ^{14}C activity of 9.32 dpm/g. Calculate the approximate age of the tree when it was cut down. Compare this age with that obtained from tree ring data, which estimated that the tree began to grow in 979 ± 52 BC. Use 13.4 dpm/g for the value of A_0.

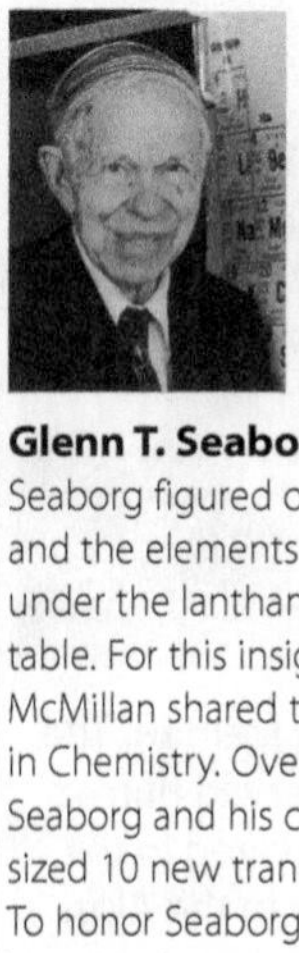

Lawrence Berkeley Laboratory

Glenn T. Seaborg (1912–1999) Seaborg figured out that thorium and the elements that followed it fit under the lanthanides in the periodic table. For this insight, he and Edwin McMillan shared the 1951 Nobel Prize in Chemistry. Over a 21-year period, Seaborg and his colleagues synthesized 10 new transuranium elements. To honor Seaborg's scientific contributions, the name "seaborgium" was assigned to element 106 in 1997. It marked the first time an element was named for a living person.

REVIEW & CHECK FOR SECTION 25-4

1. The age of the Earth is thought to be 4.5 billion years. Approximately what percentage of ^{232}Th has decomposed during this period of time? The half-life of ^{232}Th is 1.4×10^{10} years.

   (a) 20% (b) 40% (c) 60% (d) 80%

2. The half-life of ^{32}P is 14.3 days. How much ^{32}P in a sample will remain after 71.5 days have elapsed?

   (a) 1/4 (b) 1/8 (c) 1/16 (d) 1/32

25-5 Artificial Nuclear Reactions

How many different isotopes are found on Earth? All of the stable isotopes occur naturally as well as a few unstable (radioactive) isotopes that have long half-lives; the best-known examples of the latter type are uranium-235, uranium-238, and thorium-232. Trace quantities of other radioactive isotopes with short half-lives are also present because they are being formed continuously by nuclear reactions. These include isotopes of radium, polonium, and radon, along with other elements

A CLOSER LOOK The Search for New Elements

By 1936, guided first by Mendeleev's predictions and later by atomic theory, chemists had identified all but two of the elements with atomic numbers between 1 and 92. From this point onward, all new elements to be discovered came from artificial nuclear reactions. Two gaps in the periodic table were filled when radioactive technetium and promethium, the last two elements with atomic numbers less than 92, were identified in 1937 and 1942, respectively. The first success in the search for elements with atomic numbers higher than 92 came with the 1940 discovery of neptunium and plutonium.

Since 1950, laboratories in the United States (Lawrence Berkeley National Laboratory), Russia (Joint Institute for Nuclear Research at Dubna, near Moscow), and Europe (Institute for Heavy Ion Research at Darmstadt, Germany) have competed to make new elements. Syntheses of new transuranium elements use a standard methodology. An element of fairly high atomic number is bombarded with a beam of high-energy particles. Initially, neutrons were used; later, helium nuclei and then larger nuclei such as ^{11}B and ^{12}C were used; and, more recently, highly charged ions of elements such as calcium, chromium, cobalt, and zinc have been chosen. The bombarding particle fuses with the nucleus of the target atom, forming a new nucleus that lasts for a short time before decomposing. New elements are detected by their decomposition products, a signature of particles with specific masses and energies.

By using bigger particles and higher energies, the list of known elements reached 106 by the end of the 1970s. To further extend the search, Russian scientists used a new idea, precisely matching the energy of the bombarding particle with the energy required to fuse the nuclei. This technique enabled the synthesis of elements 107, 108, and 109 in Darmstadt in the early 1980s, and the synthesis of elements 110, 111, and 112 in the following decade. Lifetimes of these elements were in the millisecond range; copernicium-277, $^{277}_{112}Cn$, for example, has a half-life of 240 μs.

Yet another breakthrough was needed to extend the list further. Scientists have long known that isotopes with specific so-called *magic numbers* of neutrons and protons are more stable. Elements with 2, 8, 20, 50, and 82 protons are members of this category, as are elements with 126 neutrons. The magic numbers correspond to filled shells in the nucleus. Their significance is analogous to the significance of filled shells for electronic structure. Theory had predicted that the next magic numbers would be 114 protons and 184 neutrons. Using this information, researchers discovered element 114 in early 1999. The Dubna group reporting this discovery found that the mass 289 isotope had an exceptionally long half-life, about 20 seconds. The element was recently named flerovium, Fl, after the name of the laboratory in Dubna, Russia.

Element 116 was discovered in 1999 and is now named livermorium, Lv, for the laboratory in Berkeley, California. About 35 atoms of Lv have been obtained with the longest-lived isotope, Lv-293, having a half-life of about 60 ms.

The discovery of element 117, Uus, was announced in April 2010 by an international team at the Flerov Laboratories in Dubna, Russia. They obtained 6 atoms of the element by bombarding ^{249}Bk with ^{48}Ca atoms.

Finally, several atoms of element 118, *which completes row 7 of the periodic table,* were discovered in 2006 by bombarding atoms of californium-249 with atoms of calcium-48.

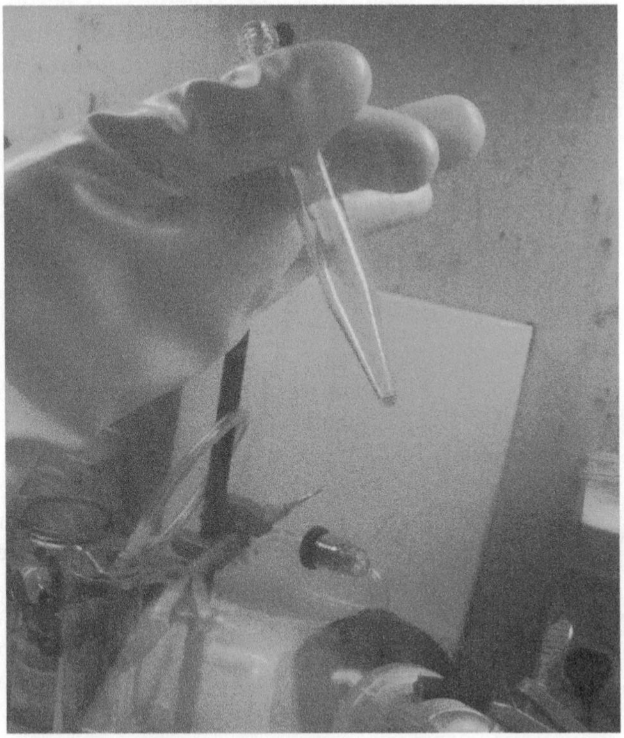

Jim Roberto/Department of Energy/ORNL

Discovery of element 117, Fl, flerovium. Scientists at the Flerov Laboratories in Dubna, Russia, used radioactive berkelium-249 as the starting material to make two isotopes of element 117. Berkelium-249 is contained in the greenish fluid in the tip of the vial. It was made in the research reactor at Oak Ridge National Laboratory.

produced in various radioactive decay series, and carbon-14, formed in a nuclear reaction initiated by cosmic radiation.

Naturally occurring isotopes account for only a very small fraction of the currently known radioactive isotopes, however. The rest—several thousand—have been synthesized via artificial nuclear reactions, sometimes referred to as *transmutation.*

The first artificial nuclear reaction was identified by Rutherford about 90 years ago. Recall the classic experiment that led to the nuclear model of the atom (◀ *Key Experiments—How Do We Know the Nature of the Atom and its Components,* Chapter 2) in which gold foil was bombarded with α particles. In the years following that experiment, Rutherford and his coworkers bombarded many other elements with α particles. In 1919, one of these experiments led to an unexpected result: When nitrogen atoms were bombarded with α particles, protons were detected among the products. Rutherford correctly concluded that a nuclear reaction had occurred. Nitrogen had undergone a *transmutation* to oxygen:

$$^{4}_{2}\text{He} + ^{14}_{7}\text{N} \rightarrow ^{17}_{8}\text{O} + ^{1}_{1}\text{H}$$

During the next decade, other nuclear reactions were discovered by bombarding other elements with α particles. Progress was slow, however, because in most cases α particles are simply scattered by target nuclei. The bombarding particles cannot get close enough to the nucleus to react because of the strong repulsive forces between the positively charged α particle and the positively charged atomic nucleus.

Discovery of Neutrons Neutrons had been predicted to exist for more than a decade before they were identified in 1932 by James Chadwick (1891–1974). Chadwick produced neutrons in a nuclear reaction between α particles and beryllium: $^{4}_{2}\alpha + ^{9}_{4}\text{Be} \rightarrow ^{12}_{6}\text{C} + ^{1}_{0}\text{n}$.

Two advances were made in 1932 that greatly extended nuclear reaction chemistry. The first involved the use of particle accelerators to create high-energy particles as projectiles. The second was the use of neutrons as the bombarding particles.

The α particles used in the early studies on nuclear reactions came from naturally radioactive materials such as uranium and had relatively low energies. Particles with higher energy were needed, so J. D. Cockcroft (1897–1967) and E. T. S. Walton (1903–1995), working in Rutherford's laboratory in Cambridge, England, turned to protons. Protons are formed when hydrogen atoms ionize in a cathode-ray tube, and it was known that they could be accelerated to higher energy by applying a high voltage. Cockcroft and Walton found that when energetic protons struck a lithium target, the following reaction occurs:

$$^{7}_{3}\text{Li} + ^{1}_{1}\text{p} \rightarrow 2\ ^{4}_{2}\text{He}$$

This was the first example of a reaction initiated by a particle that had been artificially accelerated to high energy. Since this experiment was done, the technique has been developed much further, and the use of particle accelerators in nuclear chemistry is now commonplace. Particle accelerators operate on the principle that a charged particle placed between charged plates will be accelerated to a high speed and high energy. Modern examples of this process are seen in the synthesis of the transuranium elements, several of which are described in more detail in *A Closer Look: The Search for New Elements*, on the previous page.

Transuranium Elements in Nature Neptunium, plutonium, and americium were unknown prior to their preparation via these nuclear reactions. Later, these elements were found to be present in trace quantities in uranium ores.

Experiments using neutrons as bombarding particles were first carried out in both the United States and Great Britain in 1932. Nitrogen, oxygen, fluorine, and neon were bombarded with energetic neutrons, and α particles were detected among the products. Using neutrons made sense: Because neutrons have no charge, it was reasoned that these particles would not be repelled by the positively charged nuclear particles. Thus, neutrons did not need high energies to react.

In 1934, Enrico Fermi (1901–1954) and his coworkers showed that nuclear reactions using neutrons are more favorable if the neutrons have low energy. A low-energy neutron is simply captured by the nucleus, giving a product in which the mass number is increased by one unit. Because of the low energy of the bombarding particle, the product nucleus does not have sufficient energy to fragment in these reactions. The new nucleus is produced in an excited state, however; when the nucleus returns to the ground state, a γ ray is emitted. Reactions in which a neutron is captured and a γ ray is emitted are called **(n, γ) reactions.**

The (n, γ) reactions are the source of many of the radioisotopes used in medicine and chemistry. An example is radioactive phosphorus, $^{32}_{15}\text{P}$, which is used in chemical studies such as tracing the uptake of phosphorus in the body.

$$^{31}_{15}\text{P} + ^{1}_{0}\text{n} \rightarrow ^{32}_{15}\text{P} + \gamma$$

Transuranium elements, elements with an atomic number greater than 92, were first made in a nuclear reaction sequence beginning with an (n, γ) reaction. Scientists at the University of California at Berkeley bombarded uranium-238 with neutrons. Among the products identified were neptunium-239 and plutonium-239. These new elements were formed when ^{239}U decayed by β radiation.

$$^{238}_{92}U + ^{1}_{0}n \rightarrow ^{239}_{92}U$$

$$^{239}_{92}U \rightarrow ^{239}_{93}Np + ^{0}_{-1}\beta$$

$$^{239}_{93}Np \rightarrow ^{239}_{94}Pu + ^{0}_{-1}\beta$$

Four years later, a similar reaction sequence was used to make americium-241. Plutonium-239 was found to add two neutrons to form plutonium-241, which decays by β emission to give americium-241.

EXAMPLE 25.8

Nuclear Reactions

Problem Write equations for the nuclear reactions described below.

(a) Fluorine-19 undergoes an (n, γ) reaction to give a radioactive product that decays by β emission. (Write equations for both nuclear reactions.)

(b) When an atom of beryllium-9 (the only stable isotope of beryllium) reacts with an α particle emitted by a plutonium-239 atom, a neutron is ejected.

What Do You Know? Reactants and one of two products are given for each reaction.

Strategy The equations are written so that both mass and charge are balanced.

Solution

(a) $^{19}_{9}F + ^{1}_{0}n \rightarrow ^{20}_{9}F + \gamma$

$^{20}_{9}F \rightarrow ^{20}_{10}Ne + ^{0}_{-1}\beta$

(b) $^{239}_{94}Pu \rightarrow ^{235}_{92}U + ^{4}_{2}\alpha$

$^{4}_{2}\alpha + ^{9}_{4}Be \rightarrow ^{12}_{6}C + ^{1}_{0}n$

Think about Your Answer Both answers deal with neutrons. The equation given for part (a), an (n, γ) reaction, illustrates a process that is easy to carry out. In a lab, the neutrons might be produced in a small device called a *Pu-Be neutron source.* The answer to part (b) of this question describes the nuclear reactions in such a device.

Check Your Understanding

Technetium is one of the two elements with atomic numbers less than 83 for which there is no stable isotope (promethium, element 61, is the other). Nevertheless, technetium is a very important element because of its extensive use in medical imaging (page 1002). It is produced in a two-step process. First, ^{98}Mo undergoes an (n, γ) reaction; then, the resulting unstable isotope decomposes to ^{99}Tc. Write equations for these two reactions.

REVIEW & CHECK FOR SECTION 25-5

1. Which of the following is seldom used as a bombarding particle to initiate a nuclear reaction?

(a) protons (b) neutrons (c) electrons (d) alpha particles

25-6 Nuclear Fission

The Atomic Bomb In an atomic bomb, each nuclear fission step produces 3 neutrons, which leads to about 3 more fissions and 9 more neutrons, which leads to 9 more fission steps and 27 more neutrons, and so on. The rate of fission depends on the number of neutrons, so the nuclear reaction occurs faster and faster as more and more neutrons are formed, leading to an enormous output of energy in a short time span.

In 1938, two chemists, Otto Hahn (1879–1968) and Fritz Strassman (1902–1980), isolated and identified barium in a sample of uranium that had been bombarded with neutrons. How was barium formed? The answer—that the uranium nucleus had split into smaller pieces in a process we now call **nuclear fission**—was one of the most significant scientific discoveries of the 20th century.

The details of nuclear fission were unraveled through the work of a number of scientists. They determined that a uranium-235 nucleus initially captured a neutron to form uranium-236. This isotope then underwent nuclear fission to produce two new nuclei, one with a mass around 140 and the other with a mass around 90, along with several neutrons (Figure 25.9). The nuclear reactions that led to formation of barium when a sample of ^{235}U was bombarded with neutrons are

$$^{235}_{92}U + ^{1}_{0}n \rightarrow ^{236}_{92}U$$

$$^{236}_{92}U \rightarrow ^{141}_{56}Ba + ^{92}_{36}Kr + 3\ ^{1}_{0}n$$

An important aspect of fission reactions is that they produce more neutrons than are used to initiate the process. Under the right circumstances, these neutrons then serve to continue the reaction. If one or more of these neutrons are captured by another ^{235}U nucleus, then a further reaction can occur, releasing still more neutrons. This sequence repeats over and over. Such a mechanism, in which each step generates a reactant to continue the reaction, is called a **chain reaction.**

Lise Meitner (1878–1968)
Meitner's greatest contribution to 20th-century science was her explanation of the process of nuclear fission. She and her nephew, Otto Frisch, also a physicist, published a paper in 1939 that was the first to use the term *nuclear fission.* Element number 109 is named *meitnerium* to honor Meitner's contributions. The leader of the team that discovered this element said that "She should be honored as the most significant woman scientist of [the 20th] century."

A nuclear fission chain reaction has three general steps:

1. *Initiation.* The reaction of a single atom is needed to start the chain. Fission of ^{235}U is initiated by the absorption of a neutron.
2. *Propagation.* This part of the process repeats itself over and over, with each step yielding more product. The fission of ^{236}U releases neutrons that initiate the fission of other uranium atoms.
3. *Termination.* Eventually, the chain will end. Termination could occur if the reactant (^{235}U) is used up, or if the neutrons that continue the chain escape from the sample without being captured by ^{235}U.

To harness the energy produced in a nuclear reaction, it is necessary to control the rate at which a fission reaction occurs. This is managed by balancing the propagation and termination steps by limiting the number of neutrons available. In a nuclear reactor, this balance is accomplished by using cadmium rods to absorb neutrons. By withdrawing or inserting the rods, the number of neutrons available to propagate the chain can be changed, and the rate of the fission reaction (and the rate of energy production) can be increased or decreased.

Uranium-235 and plutonium-239 are the fissionable isotopes most commonly used in power reactors. Natural uranium contains only 0.72% of uranium-235; more

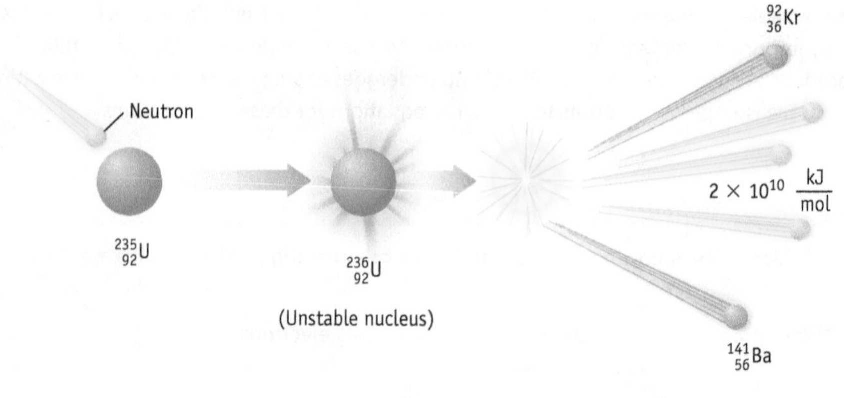

FIGURE 25.9 **Nuclear fission.** Neutron capture by $^{235}_{92}U$ produces $^{236}_{92}U$. This isotope undergoes fission, which yields several fragments along with several neutrons. These neutrons initiate further nuclear reactions by adding to other $^{235}_{92}U$ nuclei. The process is highly exothermic, producing about 2×10^{10} kJ/mol.

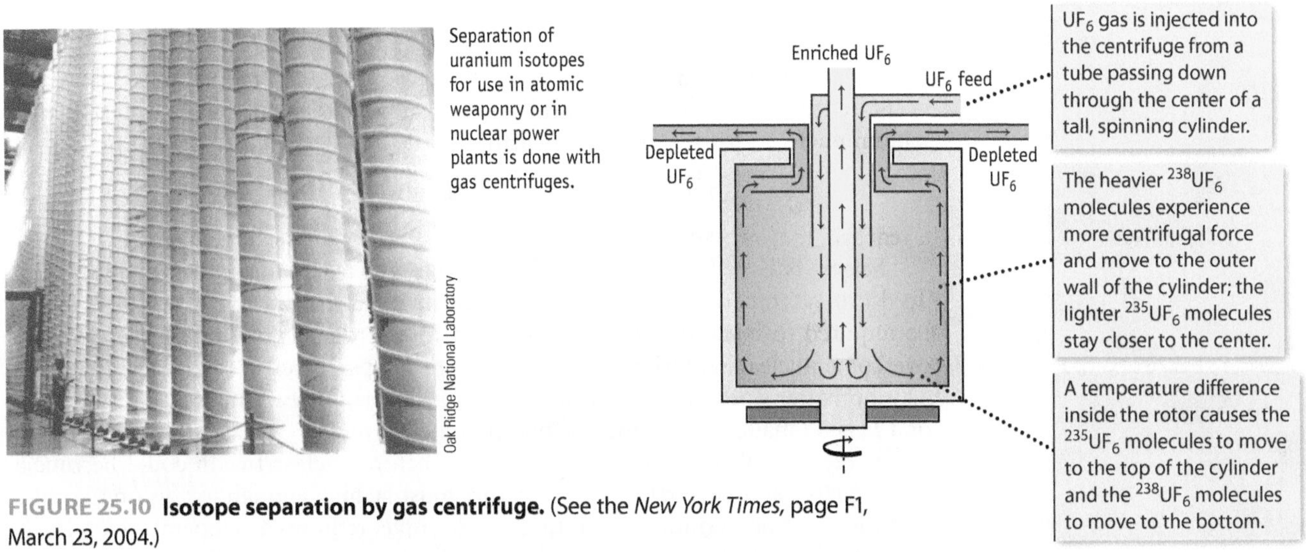

FIGURE 25.10 **Isotope separation by gas centrifuge.** (See the *New York Times,* page F1, March 23, 2004.)

than 99% of the natural element is uranium-238. The percentage of uranium-235 in natural uranium is too small to sustain a chain reaction, however, so the uranium used for nuclear fuel must be enriched in this isotope. One way to do so is by gaseous centrifugation (Figure 25.10). Plutonium, on the other hand, occurs naturally in only trace quantities and so must be made by a nuclear reaction. The raw material for this nuclear synthesis is the more abundant uranium isotope, ^{238}U. Addition of a neutron to ^{238}U gives ^{239}U, which, as noted earlier, undergoes two β emissions to form ^{239}Pu.

Currently, there are over 100 operating nuclear power plants in the United States and more than 400 worldwide. About 20% of this country's electricity (and 17% of the world's energy) comes from nuclear power (◀ Chapter 20). Although one might imagine that nuclear energy would be called upon to meet the ever-increasing needs of society, only three new nuclear power plants are under construction in the United States. Among other things, the disasters at Chernobyl (in the former Soviet Union) in 1986, Three Mile Island (in Pennsylvania) in 1979, and the Fukushima power plant in Japan (which was damaged by a tsunami in 2011) have sensitized the public to the issue of safety. The cost to construct a nuclear power plant (measured in terms of dollars per kilowatt-hour of power) is considerably more than the cost for a natural gas–powered facility, and there are severe regulatory restrictions for nuclear power. Disposal of highly radioactive nuclear waste is another thorny problem, with 20 metric tons of waste being generated per year at each reactor.

In addition to technical problems, nuclear energy production brings with it significant geopolitical security concerns. The process for enriching uranium for use in a reactor is the same process used for generating weapons-grade uranium. Also, some nuclear reactors are designed so that one by-product of their operation is the isotope plutonium-239, which can be removed and used in a nuclear weapon. Despite these problems, nuclear fission is an important part of the energy profile in a number of countries. For example, about 75% of power production in France and 25% in Japan is nuclear generated.

REVIEW & CHECK FOR SECTION 25-6

1. Identify the other element generated in this fission reaction: $^{235}_{92}U + ^{1}_{0}n \rightarrow ^{141}_{55}Cs + ? + 2^{1}_{0}n$

   (a) $^{93}_{37}Rb$ (b) $^{141}_{56}Ba$ (c) $^{92}_{36}Kr$

25-7 Nuclear Fusion

In a **nuclear fusion** reaction, several small nuclei react to form a larger nucleus and generate tremendous amounts of energy. An example is the fusion of deuterium and tritium nuclei to form $^{4}_{2}He$ and a neutron:

$$^{2}_{1}H + ^{3}_{1}H \rightarrow ^{4}_{2}He + ^{1}_{0}n \qquad \Delta E = -1.7 \times 10^9 \text{ kJ/mol}$$

a reaction that provides the energy of our Sun and other stars.

Scientists have long dreamed of being able to harness fusion to provide power. To do so, a temperature of 10^6 to 10^7 K, like that in the interior of the Sun, would be required to bring the positively charged nuclei together with enough energy to overcome nuclear repulsions. At the very high temperatures needed for a fusion reaction, matter does not exist as atoms or molecules; instead, matter is in the form of a *plasma* made up of unbound nuclei and electrons.

Three critical requirements must be met before nuclear fusion could become a viable energy source. First, the temperature must be high enough for fusion to occur. The fusion of deuterium and tritium, for example, requires a temperature of 10^7 K or more. Second, the plasma must be confined long enough to release a net output of energy. Third, the energy must be recovered in some usable form.

Harnessing a nuclear fusion reaction for a peaceful use has not yet been achieved. Nevertheless, many attractive features encourage continuing research in this field. The hydrogen used as "fuel" is cheap and available in almost unlimited amounts. As a further benefit, most radioisotopes produced by fusion have short half-lives, so they remain a radiation hazard for only a short time.

25-8 Radiation Health and Safety

Units for Measuring Radiation

Several units of measurement are used to describe levels and doses of radioactivity. In the United States, the degree of radioactivity is often measured in **curies** (Ci). Less commonly used in the United States is the SI unit, the **becquerel** (Bq). Both units measure the number of disintegrations per second; 1 Ci is 3.7×10^{10} dps (disintegrations per second), while 1 Bq represents 1 dps. The curie and the becquerel are used to report the amount of radioactivity when multiple kinds of unstable nuclei are decaying and to report amounts necessary for medical purposes.

By itself, the amount of radioactivity does not provide a good measure of the amount of energy in the radiation or the amount of damage that the radiation can cause to living tissue. Two additional kinds of information are necessary. The first is the amount of energy absorbed; the second is the effectiveness of the particular kind of radiation in causing tissue damage. The amount of energy absorbed by living tissue is measured in **rads.** *Rad* is an acronym for "radiation absorbed dose." One rad represents 0.01 J of energy absorbed per kilogram of tissue. Its SI equivalent is the **gray** (Gy); 1 Gy denotes the absorption of 1 J per kilogram of tissue.

Units of Radiation The roentgen (R) is an older unit of radiation exposure. It is defined as the amount of x-rays or γ radiation that will produce 2.08×10^9 ions in 1 cm^3 of dry air. The roentgen and the rad are similar in size. Wilhelm Roentgen (1845–1923) first produced and detected x radiation. Element 111 has been named roentgenium in his honor. The curie is named for Marie Curie (1867–1934, page 54), who is also honored by the name given element 96. The becquerel is named for Henri Becquerel (1852–1908), and the sievert is named for a Swedish physicist, Rolf Sievert (1896–1966).

Different forms of radiation cause different amounts of biological damage. The amount of damage depends on how strongly a form of radiation interacts with matter. Alpha particles cannot penetrate the body any farther than the outer layer of skin. If α particles are emitted within the body, however, they will cause between 10 and 20 times the amount of damage done by γ rays, which can go entirely through a human body without being stopped. In determining the amount of biological damage to living tissue, differences in damaging power are accounted for using a "quality factor." This quality factor has been set at 1 for β and γ radiation, 5 for low-energy protons and neutrons, and 20 for α particles or high-energy protons and neutrons.

Biological damage is quantified in a unit called the **rem** (an acronym for "roentgen equivalent man"). A dose of radiation in rem is determined by multiplying the energy absorbed in rads by the quality factor for that kind of radiation. The rad and the rem are very large in comparison to normal exposures to radiation, so it is more common to express exposures in millirems (mrem). The SI equivalent of the rem is the **sievert** (Sv), determined by multiplying the dose in grays by the quality factor.

Radiation: Doses and Effects

Exposure to a small amount of radiation is unavoidable. Earth is constantly being bombarded with radioactive particles from outer space. There is also some exposure to radioactive elements that occur naturally on Earth, including ^{14}C, ^{40}K (a radioactive isotope that occurs naturally in 0.0117% abundance), ^{238}U, and ^{232}Th. Radioactive elements in the environment that were created artificially (in the fallout from nuclear bomb tests, for example) also contribute to this exposure. For some people, medical procedures using radioisotopes are a major contributor.

The average dose of background radioactivity to which a person in the United States is exposed is about 200 mrem per year (Table 25.2). Well over half of that amount comes from natural sources over which we have no control. Of the 60–70 mrem per year exposure that comes from artificial sources, nearly 90% is delivered in medical procedures such as x-ray examinations and radiation therapy. Considering the controversy surrounding nuclear power, it is interesting to note that less than 0.5% of the total annual background dose of radiation the average person receives can be attributed to the nuclear power industry.

Table 25.2 Radiation Exposure of an Individual for One Year from Natural and Artificial Sources

	Millirem/Year	Percentage
Natural Sources		
Cosmic radiation	50.0	25.8
The Earth	47.0	24.2
Building materials	3.0	1.5
Inhaled from the air	5.0	2.6
Elements found naturally in human tissue	21.0	10.8
Subtotal	**126.0**	**64.9**
Medical Sources		
Diagnostic x-rays	50.0	25.8
Radiotherapy	10.0	5.2
Internal diagnosis	1.0	0.5
Subtotal	**61.0**	**31.5**
Other Artificial Sources		
Nuclear power industry	0.85	0.4
Luminous watch dials, TV tubes	2.0	1.0
Fallout from nuclear tests	4.0	2.1
Subtotal	**6.9**	**3.5**
Total	**193.9**	**99.9**

A CLOSER LOOK What Is a Safe Exposure?

Is the exposure to natural background radiation totally without effect? Can you equate the effect of a single dose and the effect of cumulative, smaller doses that are spread out over a long period of time? The assumption generally made is that no "safe maximum dose," or level below which absolutely no damage will occur, exists. However, the accuracy of this assumption has come into question. These issues are not testable with human subjects, and tests based on animal studies are not completely reliable because of the uncertainty of species-to-species variations.

The model used by government regulators to set exposure limits assumes that the relationship between exposure to radiation and incidence of radiation-induced problems, such as cancer, anemia, and immune system problems, is linear. Under this assumption, if a dose of $2x$ rem causes damage in 20% of the population, then a dose of x rem will cause damage in 10% of the population. But is this true? Cells do possess mechanisms for repairing damage. Many scientists believe that this self-repair mechanism renders the human body less susceptible to damage from smaller doses of radiation, because the damage will be repaired as part of the normal course of events. They argue that, at extremely low doses of radiation, the self-repair response results in less damage.

The bottom line is that much still remains to be learned in this area. And the stakes are significant.

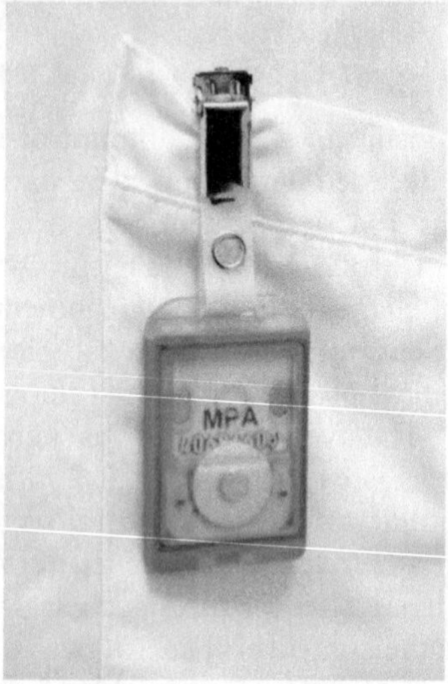

© Jurgen Schulzki/Alamy

The film badge. These badges, worn by scientists using radioactive materials, are used to monitor cumulative exposure to radiation.

Describing the biological effects of a dose of radiation precisely is not a simple matter. The amount of damage done depends not only on the kind of radiation and the amount of energy absorbed, but also on the particular tissues exposed and the rate at which the dose builds up. A great deal has been learned about the effects of radiation on the human body by studying the survivors of the bombs dropped over Japan in World War II and the workers exposed to radiation from the reactor disaster at Chernobyl. From studies of the health of these survivors, we have learned that the effects of radiation are not generally observable below a single dose of 25 rem. At the other extreme, a single dose of >200 rem will be fatal to about half the population (Table 25.3).

Our information is more accurate when dealing with single, large doses than it is for the effects of chronic, smaller doses of radiation. One current issue of debate in the scientific community is how to judge the effects of multiple smaller doses or long-term exposure.

Table 25.3 Effects of a Single Dose of Radiation

Dose (rem)	Effect
0–25	No effect observed
26–50	Small decrease in white blood cell count
51–100	Significant decrease in white blood cell count, lesions
101–200	Loss of hair, nausea
201–500	Hemorrhaging, ulcers, death in 50% of population
500	Death

25-9 Applications of Nuclear Chemistry

We tend to think about nuclear chemistry in terms of power plants and bombs. In truth, radioactive elements are now used in many areas of science and medicine, and they are of ever-increasing importance to our lives. Because describing all of their uses would take several books, we have selected just a few examples to illustrate the diversity of applications of radioactivity.

Nuclear Medicine: Medical Imaging

Diagnostic procedures using nuclear chemistry are essential in medical imaging, which entails the creation of images of specific parts of the body. There are three principal components to constructing a radioisotope-based image:

- A radioactive isotope, administered as the element or incorporated into a compound that concentrates the radioactive isotope in the tissue to be imaged
- A method of detecting the type of radiation involved
- A computer to assemble the information from the detector into a meaningful image

The choice of a radioisotope and the manner in which it is administered are determined by the tissue in question. A compound containing the isotope must be absorbed more by the target tissue than by the rest of the body. Table 25.4 lists radioisotopes that are commonly used in nuclear imaging processes, their half-lives, and the tissues they are used to image. All the isotopes in Table 25.4 are γ emitters because γ radiation is preferred for imaging; it is less damaging to the body in small doses than either α or β radiation.

Technetium-99m is used in more than 85% of the diagnostic scans done in hospitals each year (see *Case Study: Technetium-99m and Medical Imaging*). The "m" stands for *metastable,* a term used to identify an excited state that exists for a finite period of time. Recall that atoms in excited electronic states emit visible, infrared, and ultraviolet radiation (◀ Chapter 6). Similarly, a nucleus in an excited state gives up its excess energy, but in this case a much higher energy is involved, and the emission occurs as γ radiation.

Another medical imaging technique based on nuclear chemistry is *positron emission tomography* (PET). In PET, an isotope that decays by positron emission is incorporated into a carrier compound and given to the patient. The emitted positron travels no more than a few millimeters before undergoing matter–antimatter annihilation.

$$^{0}_{+1}\beta + ^{0}_{-1}e \rightarrow 2\gamma$$

Table 25.4 Radioisotopes Used in Medical Diagnostic Procedures

Radioisotope	Half-Life (h)	Imaging
^{99m}Tc	6.0	Thyroid, brain, kidneys
^{201}Tl	73.0	Heart
^{123}I	13.2	Thyroid
^{67}Ga	78.2	Various tumors and abscesses
^{18}F	1.8	Brain, sites of metabolic activity

CASE STUDY Technetium-99m and Medical Imaging

Technetium was the first new element to be made artificially. One might think that this would make the element a chemical rarity, but this is not so. Technetium is the product of nuclear reactions that can be done in a laboratory. As a consequence it has been readily available and even inexpensive (about $60 per gram). This has also led to widespread use in medical diagnosis, and it is now used all over the world in evaluations of the thyroid gland, the heart, kidneys, and lungs.

Technetium-99m is formed when molybdenum-99 decays by β emission. Technetium-99m (^{99m}Tc) then decays to its ground state (forming ^{99}Tc) with a half-life of 6.01 hours, giving off a 140-KeV γ ray in the process. (Technetium-99 is also radioactive, decaying to stable ^{99}Ru with a half-life of 2.1×10^5 years.)

Molydenum-99 is not a component of naturally occurring molybdenum. It is made in an (n, γ) reaction from molybdenum-98 (23.8% abundant in naturally occurring samples of the element). Nuclear power reactors utilizing U-235 provide the source of neutrons for this synthesis. But there was a problem with this route beginning about 2010 when the main reactors producing the molybdenum (in Canada and The Netherlands) had to be closed for some months for repairs. Because technetium is so important worldwide for medical procedures, scientists immediately began looking for new sources.

Technetium-99m is produced in hospitals using a molybdenum–technetium generator. Shielded in lead, the generator contains the isotope ^{99}Mo in the form of the molybdate ion, MoO_4^{2-}, adsorbed on a column of alumina, Al_2O_3. The MoO_4^{2-} ion is continually converted into the pertechnetate ion, $^{99m}TcO_4^-$ by β emission. When it is needed, the $^{99m}TcO_4^-$ is washed from the column using a saline solution. Technetium-99m may be used directly as the pertechnetate ion (as $NaTcO_4$) or converted into other compounds. The pertechnetate ion or radiopharmaceuticals made from it are administered intravenously to the patient. Such small quantities are needed that 1 μg (microgram) of technetium-99m is sufficient for the average hospital's daily imaging needs.

One use of ^{99m}Tc is for imaging the thyroid gland. Because $I^-(aq)$ and $TcO_4^-(aq)$ ions have very similar sizes, the thyroid will (mistakenly) take up $TcO_4^-(aq)$ along with iodide ion. This uptake concentrates ^{99m}Tc in the thyroid and allows a physician to obtain images such as the one shown here.

Questions:

1. Write an equation for the β decay of ^{99}Mo to ^{99}Tc.
2. What is the oxidation number of Tc in the pertechnetate ion? What is the electron configuration of a Tc^{n+} ion with a charge equal to this oxidation number? Should the TcO_4^- ion be paramagnetic or diamagnetic?
3. What amount of $NaTcO_4$ is there in 1.0 μg of the salt? What mass of Tc?
4. If you have 1.0 μg of Tc, what mass remains at the end of 24 hours?
5. ^{99}Tc decays to ^{99}Ru. What particle is produced in this decay?
6. Speculate on the reason the TcO_4^- ion is held less strongly to a column of Al_2O_3 than in the MoO_4^{2-} ion.

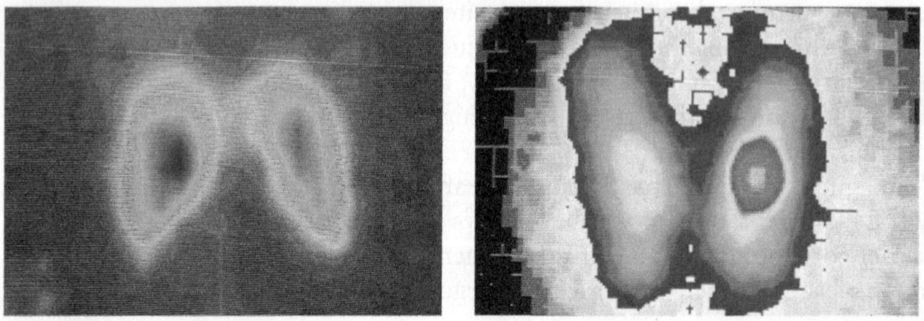

(a) Healthy human thyroid gland. (b) Thyroid gland showing effect of hyperthyroidism.

Thyroid imaging with technetium-99m. The radioactive isotope ^{99m}Tc concentrates in sites of high activity. Images of this gland, which is located at the base of the neck, were obtained by recording γ-ray emission after the patient was given radioactive technetium-99m. Current technology creates a computer color-enhanced scan.

The two emitted γ rays travel in opposite directions. By determining where high numbers of γ rays are being emitted, one can construct a map showing where the positron emitter is located in the body.

An isotope often used in PET is ^{15}O. A patient is given gaseous O_2 that contains ^{15}O. This isotope travels throughout the body in the bloodstream, allowing images of the brain and bloodstream to be obtained (Figure 25.11). Because positron emitters are typically very short-lived, PET facilities must be located near a cyclotron where the radioactive nuclei are prepared and then immediately incorporated into a carrier compound.

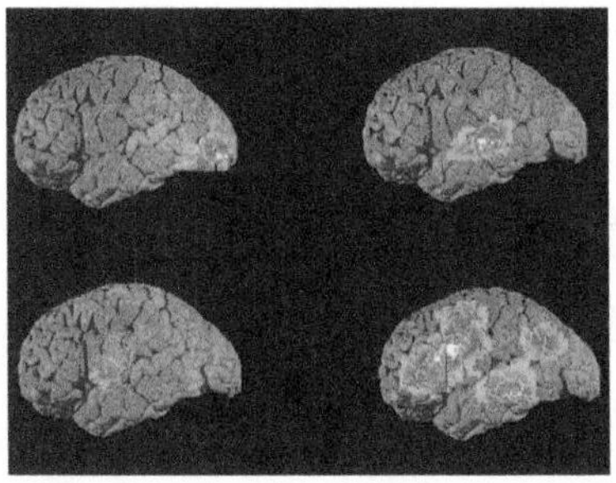

FIGURE 25.11 **PET scans of the brain.** These scans show the left side of the brain; *red* indicates an area of highest activity. *(upper left) Sight* activates the visual area in the occipital cortex at the back of the brain. *(upper right) Hearing* activates the auditory area in the superior temporal cortex of the brain. *(lower left) Speaking* activates the speech centers in the insula and motor cortex. *(lower right) Thinking* about verbs, and speaking them, generates high activity, including in the hearing, speaking, temporal, and parietal areas.

Nuclear Medicine: Radiation Therapy

To treat most cancers, it is necessary to use radiation that can penetrate the body to the location of the tumor. Gamma radiation from a cobalt-60 source is commonly used. Unfortunately, the penetrating ability of γ rays makes it virtually impossible to destroy diseased tissue without also damaging healthy tissue in the process. Nevertheless, this technique is a regularly sanctioned procedure, and its successes are well known.

Analytical Methods: The Use of Radioactive Isotopes as Tracers

Radioactive isotopes can be used to help determine the fate of compounds in the body or in the environment. In biology, for example, scientists can use radioactive isotopes to measure the uptake of nutrients. Plants take up phosphorus-containing compounds from the soil through their roots. By adding a small amount of radioactive ^{32}P, a β emitter with a half-life of 14.3 days, to fertilizer and then measuring the rate at which the radioactivity appears in the leaves, plant biologists can determine the rate at which phosphorus is taken up. The outcome can assist scientists in identifying hybrid strains of plants that can absorb phosphorus quickly, resulting in faster-maturing crops, better yields per acre, and more food or fiber at less expense.

To measure pesticide levels, a pesticide can be tagged with a radioisotope and then applied to a test field. By counting the disintegrations of the radioactive tracer, information can be obtained about how much pesticide accumulates in the soil, is taken up by the plant, and is carried off in runoff surface water. After these tests are completed, the radioactive isotope decays to harmless levels in a few days or a few weeks because of the short half-lives of the isotopes used.

Boron Neutron Capture Therapy (BNCT) To avoid the side effects associated with more traditional forms of radiation therapy, BNCT is an experimental treatment that has been explored in the last 10 to 15 years. BNCT is unusual in that boron-10, the isotope of boron used as part of the treatment, is not radioactive. This isotope is highly effective in capturing neutrons, however: 2500 times better than boron-11 and eight times better than uranium-235. When the nucleus of a boron-10 atom captures a neutron, the resulting boron-11 nucleus has so much energy that it fragments to form an α particle and a lithium-7 atom. Although the α particles do a great deal of damage, because their penetrating power is so low, the damage remains confined to an area not much larger than one or two cells in diameter.

Analytical Methods: Isotope Dilution

Imagine, for the moment, that you wanted to estimate the volume of blood in an animal subject. How might you do this? Obviously, draining the blood and measuring its volume in volumetric glassware is not a desirable option.

One technique uses a method called *isotope dilution.* In this process, a small amount of radioactive isotope is injected into the bloodstream. After a period of time to allow the isotope to become distributed throughout the body, a blood sample is taken and its radioactivity measured. The calculation used to determine the total blood volume is illustrated in the next example.

EXAMPLE 25.9

Analysis Using Radioisotopes

Problem A 1.00-mL solution containing 0.240 μCi of tritium is injected into a dog's bloodstream. After a period of time to allow the isotope to be dispersed, a 1.00-mL sample of blood is drawn. The radioactivity of this sample is found to be 4.3×10^{-4} μCi/mL. What is the total volume of blood in the dog?

What Do You Know? You know the concentration (activity) and volume of a concentrated solution and you then measure the concentration of the dilute solution. The unknown is the volume of the dilute solution.

Strategy In this problem, we relate the activity of the sample (in Ci) to the amount of the radioisotope present. The total amount of solute is 0.240 μCi, and the concentration (measured on the small sample of blood) is 4.3×10^{-4} μCi/mL. The unknown is the total volume of blood, *V*.

Solution The blood contains a total of 0.240 μCi of radioactive material. Exactly 1.00 mL containing this amount was injected. After dilution in the bloodstream, 1.00 mL of blood, representative of the total volume *V*, is found to have an activity of 4.3×10^{-4} μCi/mL.

$$(0.240\ \mu\text{Ci/mL})(1.00\ \text{mL}) = (4.3 \times 10^{-4}\ \mu\text{Ci/mL})(V)$$

$$V = 560\ \text{mL}$$

Think about Your Answer This is solved as a classic dilution problem, by equating $C_{dil} \times V_{dil} = C_{conc} \times V_{conc}$

Check Your Understanding

To measure the solubility for $PbCrO_4$ you mix a small amount of a lead(II) salt having radioactive ^{212}Pb with a lead salt containing 0.0100 g of lead. To this mixture you add enough K_2CrO_4 to completely precipitate the lead(II) ions as $PbCrO_4$. The supernatant solution still contains a trace of lead, of course, and when you evaporate 10.00 mL of this solution to solid $PbCrO_4$, you find a radioactivity that is 4.17×10^{-5} of what it is for the pure ^{212}Pb salt. Calculate the solubility of $PbCrO_4$ in mol/L. (Adapted from C. E. Housecraft and A. G. Sharpe, *Inorganic Chemistry*, Pearson, 3rd edition, 2008, p. 84.)

Space Science: Neutron Activation Analysis and the Moon Rocks

The first manned space mission to the moon brought back a number of samples of soil and rock—a treasure trove for scientists. One of their first tasks was to analyze these samples to determine their identity and composition. Most analytical methods require chemical reactions using at least a small amount of material; however, this was not a desirable option, considering that the moon rocks were at the time the most valuable rocks on Earth.

A few scientists got a chance to work on this unique project, and one of the analytical tools they used was **neutron activation analysis.** In this nondestructive process, a sample is irradiated with neutrons. Most isotopes add a neutron to form a new isotope that is one mass unit higher and in an excited nuclear state. When the nucleus decays to its ground state, it emits a γ ray. The energy of the γ ray identifies the element, and the number of γ rays can be counted to determine the amount of the element in the sample. Using neutron activation analysis, it is possible to analyze for a number of elements in a single experiment (Table 25.5).

Neutron activation analysis has many other uses. This analytical procedure yields a kind of fingerprint that can be used to identify a substance. For example, this technique has been applied in determining whether an art work is real or fraudulent. Analysis of the pigments in paints on a painting can be carried out without damaging the painting to determine whether the composition resembles modern paints or paints used hundreds of years ago.

Table 25.5 Rare Earth Analysis of Moon Rock Sample 10022 (Fine-Grain Igneous Rock)

Element	Concentration (ppm)
La	26.4
Ce	68
Nd	66
Sm	21.2
Eu	2.04
Gd	25
Tb	4.7
Dy	31.2
Ho	5.5
Er	16
Yb	17.7
Lu	2.55

Source: L. A. Haskin, P. A, Helmke, and R. O. Allen: *Science*, Vol. 167, p. 487, 1970. The concentrations of rare earths in moon rocks were quite similar to the values in terrestrial rocks except that the europium concentration is much depleted. The January 30, 1970, issue of *Science* was devoted to analysis of moon rocks.

Food Science: Food Irradiation

Refrigeration, canning, and chemical additives provide significant protection in terms of food preservation, but in some parts of the world these procedures are unavailable, and stored-food spoilage may claim as much as 50% of the food crop. Irradiation with γ rays from sources such as ^{60}Co and ^{137}Cs is an option for prolonging the shelf life of foods. Relatively low levels of radiation may retard the growth of organisms, such as bacteria, molds, and yeasts, that can cause food spoilage. After irradiation, milk in a sealed container has a minimum shelf life of 3 months without refrigeration. Chicken normally has a 3-day refrigerated shelf life; after irradiation, it may have a 3-week refrigerated shelf life.

Higher levels of radiation, in the 1- to 5-Mrad (1 Mrad = 1×10^6 rad) range, will kill every living organism. Foods irradiated at these levels will keep indefinitely when sealed in plastic or aluminum-foil packages. Ham, beef, turkey, and corned beef sterilized by radiation have been used on many Space Shuttle flights, for example. An astronaut said, "The beautiful thing was that it didn't disturb the taste, which made the meals much better than the freeze-dried and other types of foods we had."

"Radura". This international symbol called the "radura" should appear on the packaging of produce (fruits, vegetables, meat) that has been irradiated. See the EPA website for more information: www.epa.gov/radiation/sources/food_irrad.html.

These procedures are not without their opponents, and the public has not fully embraced irradiation of foods. An interesting argument favoring this technique is that radiation is less harmful than other methodologies for food preservation. This type of sterilization offers greater safety to food workers because it lessens chances of exposure to harmful chemicals, and it protects the environment by avoiding contamination of water supplies with toxic chemicals.

Food irradiation is commonly used in European countries, Canada, and Mexico. Its use in the United States is currently regulated by the U.S. Food and Drug Administration (FDA) and Department of Agriculture (USDA). In 1997, the FDA approved the irradiation of refrigerated and frozen uncooked meat to control pathogens and extend shelf-life, and in 2000 the USDA approved the irradiation of eggs to control *Salmonella* infection.

APPLYING CHEMICAL PRINCIPLES

The Age of Meteorites

Meteorites have a significant value for collectors, but they are also of scientific interest. Meteorites are generally regarded as some of the oldest materials in the solar system. And this raises the obvious question: How is the age of a meteorite determined? By age, we are referring to the time since the meteor condensed to a solid, locking the components into a solid matrix so they cannot escape. There are a number of methods to measure the age of a meteor, all involving the decay of long-lived radioactive elements.

One dating procedure involves vaporizing samples of the material and measuring the amounts of ^{86}Sr, ^{87}Sr, and ^{87}Rb by mass spectrometry. Both ^{86}Sr and ^{87}Sr are stable isotopes. The rubidium isotope, which decays to ^{87}Sr, has a half-life of 4.88×10^{10} years. The amount of ^{87}Sr measured includes the

© Denis Scott/CORBIS

Meteorites. Meteorites are materials that originate in outer space and survive the fall to the Earth's surface. They can be large or small, but as they enter Earth's atmosphere they are warmed to a high temperature by friction in the atmosphere and emit light, forming a fireball. There are three general categories: stony meteorites, which are silicate minerals; iron meteorites, largely composed of iron and nickel; and stony-iron meteorites. (See the photo of an iron meteorite, Figure 7.6.)

amount of ^{87}Sr initially present ($^{87}Sr_0$) when the meteorite was formed plus the amount formed by decay of ^{87}Rb. The ^{86}Sr remains constant and is used as a check on the original amounts of the other isotopes. The three measured amounts are related by an equation (which can be derived from the first-order rate law):

$$[^{87}Sr/^{86}Sr] = (e^{kt} - 1)\ [^{87}Rb/^{86}Sr] + [^{87}Sr_0/^{86}Sr]$$

The equation has the form of the equation of a straight line, $y = mx + b$. Multiple samples are analyzed from each meteorite. The amounts of each isotope may vary between samples, but a graph of $[^{87}Sr/^{86}Sr]$ versus $[^{87}Rb/^{86}Sr]$ will give a straight line with a slope $m = (e^{kt} - 1)$ and a y-intercept of $[^{87}Sr_0/^{86}Sr]$. The symbol k refers to the rate constant for the radioactive decomposition. This method is called *isochron dating*.

QUESTIONS:

1. Write a balanced equation for the radioactive decomposition of ^{87}Rb.
2. The decomposition of ^{87}Rb occurs by which of the following processes?
   (a) alpha emission
   (b) beta emission
   (c) gamma emission
   (d) electron capture
   (e) positron emission
3. Determine the rate constant for the radioactive decay of ^{87}Rb.
4. The oldest dated meteorites have ages of about 4.5 billion years. What fraction of the initial ^{87}Rb has decayed?
5. The relative abundances of ^{86}Sr, ^{87}Sr, and ^{87}Rb were measured for four samples of a meteorite; the results were tabulated below. Make a strontium-rubidium isochron plot of these data, then use the slope of the line to determine the age of the meteorite.

RELATIVE ABUNDANCE

SAMPLE #	^{86}Sr	^{87}Sr	^{87}Rb
1	1.000	0.819	0.839
2	1.063	0.855	0.506
3	0.950	0.824	1.929
4	1.011	0.809	0.379

6. Derive the equation given above for $[^{87}Sr/^{86}Sr]$. (*Hint:* Start with the rate equation in the form $[^{87}Rb_0] = [^{87}Rb]\ e^{kt}$.)

CHAPTER GOALS REVISITED

Now that you have studied this chapter, you should ask whether you have met the chapter goals. In particular, you should be able to:

UNDERSTAND

- The criteria for nuclear stability and the processes by which unstable nuclides decay (Figure 25.3 and Section 25-3). Study Questions: 4, 17–22.
- The methods used to synthesize new isotopes of the elements (Section 25-5). Study Questions: 5, 39–43, 48.
- The plot showing numbers of protons and neutrons in stable and unstable nuclides (Section 25-3 and Figure 25.3). Study Question: 4.
- The graph showing binding energy per nucleon versus atomic number (Section 25-3 and Figure 25.4). Study Question: 3.
- Issues of safety and health with respect to radioactivity (Section 25-8). Study Question: 10.
- Uses of radioactive isotopes in science and medicine (Section 25-9).

DO

- Write equations for the decay of radioactive elements and the synthesis of new isotopes (Section 25-2). Study Questions: 11–16, 32, 41.
- Predict possible modes of decomposition of unstable nuclei based on n/p ratios (Sections 25-2 and 25-3). Study Questions: 17–22.
- Calculate the binding energy and binding energy per nucleon for a particular isotope (Section 25-3). Study Questions: 23–28, 52.
- Carry out calculations based on equations for the first-order rate of decomposition of unstable isotopes (Section 25-4). Study Questions: 29–38, 47, 50, 54, 58.

REMEMBER

- Nuclear decay series and their implications (Section 25-2). Study Questions: 9, 15, 16.
- Types of radiation (Sections 25-1 and 25-2).
- The processes of fission and fusion (Sections 25-6 and 25-7).

KEY EQUATIONS

Equation 25.1 (page 985): The equation relating interconversion of mass (m) and energy (E). This equation is applied in the calculation of binding energy (E_b) for nuclei.

$$E_b = (\Delta m)c^2$$

Equation 25.2 (page 989): The activity of a radioactive sample (A) is proportional to the number of radioactive atoms (N).

$$A \propto N$$

Equation 25.3 (page 989): The change in the number of radioactive elements with time is equal to the product of the rate constant (k, decay constant) and number of atoms present (N).

$$\Delta N/\Delta t = -kN$$

Equation 25.4 (page 989): The rate law for nuclear decay based on number of radioactive atoms initially present (N_0) and the number N after time t.

$$\ln(N/N_0) = -kt$$

Equation 25.5 (page 989): The rate law for nuclear decay based on the measured activity of a sample (A).

$$\ln(A/A_0) = -kt$$

Equation 25.6 (page 989): The relationship between the half-life and the rate constant for a nuclear decay process.

$$t_{1/2} = 0.693/k$$

Courtesy of Francois Gauthier-Lafaye

STUDY QUESTIONS

▲ denotes challenging questions.

Blue-numbered questions have answers in Appendix N and fully worked solutions in the *Student Solutions Manual.*

Practicing Skills

Important Concepts

1. Some important discoveries in scientific history that contributed to the development of nuclear chemistry are listed below. Briefly, describe each discovery, identify prominent scientists who contributed to it, and comment on the significance of the discovery to the development of this field.
   (a) 1896, the discovery of radioactivity
   (b) 1898, the identification of radium and polonium
   (c) 1919, the first artificial nuclear reaction
   (d) 1932, (n, γ) reactions
   (e) 1939, fission reactions

2. In Chapter 3, the law of conservation of mass was introduced as an important principle in chemistry. The discovery of nuclear reactions forced scientists to modify this law. Explain why, and give an example illustrating that mass is not conserved in a nuclear reaction.

3. A graph of binding energy per nucleon is shown in Figure 25.4. Explain how the data used to construct this graph were obtained.

4. How is Figure 25.3 used to predict the type of decomposition for unstable (radioactive) isotopes?

5. Outline how nuclear reactions are carried out in the laboratory. Describe the artificial nuclear reactions used to make an element with an atomic number greater than 92.

6. What mathematical equations define the rates of decay for radioactive elements?

7. Explain how carbon-14 is used to estimate the ages of archeological artifacts. What are the limitations for use of this technique?

8. Describe how the concept of half-life for nuclear decay is used.

9. What is a radioactive decay series? Explain why radium and polonium are found in uranium ores.

10. The interaction of radiation with matter has both positive and negative consequences. Discuss briefly the hazards of radiation and the way that radiation can be used in medicine.

Nuclear Reactions

(See Section 25-2 and Examples 25.1 and 25.2.)

11. Complete the following nuclear equations. Write the mass number and atomic number for the remaining particle, as well as its symbol.
    (a) ${}^{54}_{26}\text{Fe} + {}^{4}_{2}\text{He} \longrightarrow 2\,{}^{1}_{0}\text{n} + ?$
    (b) ${}^{27}_{13}\text{Al} + {}^{4}_{2}\text{He} \longrightarrow {}^{30}_{15}\text{P} + ?$
    (c) ${}^{32}_{16}\text{S} + {}^{1}_{0}\text{n} \longrightarrow {}^{1}_{1}\text{H} + ?$
    (d) ${}^{96}_{42}\text{Mo} + {}^{2}_{1}\text{H} \longrightarrow {}^{1}_{0}\text{n} + ?$
    (e) ${}^{98}_{42}\text{Mo} + {}^{1}_{0}\text{n} \longrightarrow {}^{99}_{43}\text{Tc} + ?$
    (f) ${}^{18}_{9}\text{F} \longrightarrow {}^{18}_{8}\text{O} + ?$

12. Complete the following nuclear equations. Write the mass number, atomic number, and symbol for the remaining particle.
    (a) ${}^{9}_{4}\text{Be} + ? \longrightarrow {}^{6}_{3}\text{Li} + {}^{4}_{2}\text{He}$
    (b) $? + {}^{1}_{0}\text{n} \longrightarrow {}^{24}_{11}\text{Na} + {}^{4}_{2}\text{He}$
    (c) ${}^{40}_{20}\text{Ca} + ? \longrightarrow {}^{40}_{19}\text{K} + {}^{1}_{1}\text{H}$
    (d) ${}^{241}_{95}\text{Am} + {}^{4}_{2}\text{He} \longrightarrow {}^{243}_{97}\text{Bk} + ?$
    (e) ${}^{246}_{96}\text{Cm} + {}^{12}_{6}\text{C} \longrightarrow 4\,{}^{1}_{0}\text{n} + ?$
    (f) ${}^{238}_{92}\text{U} + ? \longrightarrow {}^{249}_{100}\text{Fm} + 5\,{}^{1}_{0}\text{n}$

13. Complete the following nuclear equations. Write the mass number, atomic number, and symbol for the remaining particle.
    (a) ${}^{111}_{47}\text{Ag} \longrightarrow {}^{111}_{48}\text{Cd} + ?$
    (b) ${}^{87}_{36}\text{Kr} \longrightarrow {}^{0}_{-1}\beta + ?$
    (c) ${}^{231}_{91}\text{Pa} \longrightarrow {}^{227}_{89}\text{Ac} + ?$
    (d) ${}^{230}_{90}\text{Th} \longrightarrow {}^{4}_{2}\text{He} + ?$
    (e) ${}^{82}_{35}\text{Br} \longrightarrow {}^{82}_{36}\text{Kr} + ?$
    (f) $? \longrightarrow {}^{24}_{12}\text{Mg} + {}^{0}_{-1}\beta$

14. Complete the following nuclear equations. Write the mass number, atomic number, and symbol for the remaining particle.

(a) $^{19}_{10}Ne \longrightarrow {}^{0}_{+1}\beta + ?$
(b) $^{59}_{26}Fe \longrightarrow {}^{0}_{-1}\beta + ?$
(c) $^{40}_{19}K \longrightarrow {}^{0}_{-1}\beta + ?$
(d) $^{37}_{18}Ar + {}^{0}_{-1}e$ (electron capture) $\longrightarrow ?$
(e) $^{55}_{26}Fe + {}^{0}_{-1}e$ (electron capture) $\longrightarrow ?$
(f) $^{26}_{13}Al \longrightarrow {}^{25}_{12}Mg + ?$

15. The uranium-235 radioactive decay series, beginning with $^{235}_{92}U$ and ending with $^{207}_{82}Pb$, occurs in the following sequence: α, β, α, β, α, α, α, α, β, β, α. Write an equation for each step in this series.

16. The thorium-232 radioactive decay series, beginning with $^{232}_{90}Th$ and ending with $^{208}_{82}Pb$, occurs in the following sequence: α, β, β, α, α, α, α, β, β, α. Write an equation for each step in this series.

Nuclear Stability and Nuclear Decay

(See Section 25-3 and Examples 25.3 and 25.4.)

17. What particle is emitted in the following nuclear reactions? Write an equation for each reaction.

(a) Gold-198 decays to mercury-198.
(b) Radon-222 decays to polonium-218.
(c) Cesium-137 decays to barium-137.
(d) Indium-110 decays to cadmium-110.

18. What is the product of the following nuclear decay processes? Write an equation for each process.

(a) Gallium-67 decays by electron capture.
(b) Potassium-38 decays with positron emission.
(c) Technetium-99m decays with γ emission.
(d) Manganese-56 decays by β emission.

19. Predict the probable mode of decay for each of the following radioactive isotopes, and write an equation to show the products of decay.

(a) bromine-80
(b) californium-240
(c) cobalt-61
(d) carbon-11

20. Predict the probable mode of decay for each of the following radioactive isotopes, and write an equation to show the products of decay.

(a) manganese-54
(b) americium-241
(c) silver-110
(d) mercury-197m

21. (a) Which of the following nuclei decay by ${}^{0}_{-1}\beta$ decay?

^{3}H ^{16}O ^{20}F ^{13}N

(b) Which of the following nuclei decays by ${}^{0}_{+1}\beta$ decay?

^{238}U ^{19}F ^{22}Na ^{24}Na

22. (a) Which of the following nuclei decay by ${}^{0}_{-1}\beta$ decay?

^{1}H ^{23}Mg ^{32}P ^{20}Ne

(b) Which of the following nuclei decay by ${}^{0}_{+1}\beta$ decay?

^{235}U ^{35}Cl ^{38}K ^{24}Na

23. Boron has two stable isotopes, ^{10}B and ^{11}B. Calculate the binding energies per mole of nucleons of these two nuclei. The required masses (in g/mol) are $^{1}_{1}H = 1.00783$, $^{1}_{0}n = 1.00867$, $^{10}_{5}B = 10.01294$, and $^{11}_{5}B = 11.00931$.

24. Calculate the binding energy in kilojoules per mole of nucleons of P for the formation of ^{30}P and ^{31}P. The required masses (in g/mol) are $^{1}_{1}H = 1.00783$, $^{1}_{0}n = 1.00867$, $^{30}_{15}P = 29.97832$, and $^{31}_{15}P = 30.97376$.

25. Calculate the binding energy per mole of nucleons for calcium-40, and compare your result with the value in Figure 25.4. Masses needed for this calculation are (in g/mol) $^{1}_{1}H = 1.00783$, $^{1}_{0}n = 1.00867$, and $^{40}_{20}Ca = 39.96259$.

26. Calculate the binding energy per mole of nucleons for iron-56. Masses needed for this calculation (in g/mol) are $^{1}_{1}H = 1.00783$, $^{1}_{0}n = 1.00867$, and $^{56}_{26}Fe = 55.9349$. Compare the result of your calculation to the value for iron-56 in the graph in Figure 25.4.

27. Calculate the binding energy per mole of nucleons for $^{16}_{8}O$. Masses needed for this calculation are $^{1}_{1}H = 1.00783$, $^{1}_{0}n = 1.00867$, and $^{16}_{8}O = 15.99492$.

28. Calculate the binding energy per mole of nucleons for nitrogen-14. The mass of nitrogen-14 is 14.003074.

Rates of Radioactive Decay

(See Section 25-4 and Examples 25.5–25.7.)

29. Copper(II) acetate containing ^{64}Cu is used to study brain tumors. This isotope has a half-life of 12.7 hours. If you begin with 25.0 μg of ^{64}Cu, what mass remains after 63.5 hours?

30. Gold-198 is used in the diagnosis of liver problems. The half-life of ^{198}Au is 2.69 days. If you begin with 2.8 μg of this gold isotope, what mass remains after 10.8 days?

31. Iodine-131 is used to treat thyroid cancer.

(a) The isotope decays by β-particle emission. Write a balanced equation for this process.
(b) Iodine-131 has a half-life of 8.04 days. If you begin with 2.4 μg of radioactive ^{131}I, what mass remains after 40.2 days?

32. Phosphorus-32 is used in the form of Na_2HPO_4 in the treatment of chronic myeloid leukemia, among other things.
   (a) The isotope decays by β-particle emission. Write a balanced equation for this process.
   (b) The half-life of ^{32}P is 14.3 days. If you begin with 4.8 μg of radioactive ^{32}P in the form of Na_2HPO_4, what mass remains after 28.6 days (about 1 month)?

33. Gallium-67 ($t_{1/2}$ = 78.25 hours) is used in the medical diagnosis of certain kinds of tumors. If you ingest a compound containing 0.015 mg of this isotope, what mass (in milligrams) remains in your body after 13 days? (Assume none is excreted.)

34. Iodine-131 ($t_{1/2}$ = 8.04 days), a β emitter, is used to treat thyroid cancer.
   (a) Write an equation for the decomposition of ^{131}I.
   (b) If you ingest a sample of NaI containing ^{131}I, how much time is required for the activity to decrease to 35.0% of its original value?

35. Radon has been the focus of much attention recently because it is often found in homes. Radon-222 emits α particles and has a half-life of 3.82 days.
   (a) Write a balanced equation to show this process.
   (b) How long does it take for a sample of ^{222}Rn to decrease to 20.0% of its original activity?

36. Strontium-90 is a hazardous radioactive isotope that resulted from atmospheric testing of nuclear weapons. A sample of strontium carbonate containing ^{90}Sr is found to have an activity of 1.0×10^3 dpm. One year later, the activity of this sample is 975 dpm.
   (a) Calculate the half-life of strontium-90 from this information.
   (b) How long will it take for the activity of this sample to drop to 1.0% of the initial value?

37. Radioactive cobalt-60 is used extensively in nuclear medicine as a γ-ray source. It is made by a neutron capture reaction from cobalt-59 and is a β emitter; β emission is accompanied by strong γ radiation. The half-life of cobalt-60 is 5.27 years.
   (a) How long will it take for a cobalt-60 source to decrease to one eighth of its original activity?
   (b) What fraction of the activity of a cobalt-60 source remains after 1.0 year?

38. Scandium occurs in nature as a single isotope, scandium-45. Neutron irradiation produces scandium-46, a β emitter with a half-life of 83.8 days. If the initial activity is 7.0×10^4 dpm, draw a graph showing disintegrations per minute as a function of time during a period of 1 year.

Nuclear Reactions

(See Section 25-5 and Example 25.9.)

39. Americium-240 is made by bombarding plutonium-239 with α particles. In addition to ^{240}Am, the products are a proton and two neutrons. Write a balanced equation for this process.

40. There are two isotopes of americium, both with half-lives sufficiently long to allow the handling of large quantities. Americium-241, with a half-life of 432 years, is an α emitter used in smoke detectors. The isotope is formed from ^{239}Pu by absorption of two neutrons followed by emission of a β particle. Write a balanced equation for this process.

41. The superheavy element ^{287}Fl (element 114) was made by firing a beam of ^{48}Ca ions at ^{242}Pu. Three neutrons were ejected in the reaction. Write a balanced nuclear equation for the synthesis of ^{287}Fl.

42. To synthesize the heavier transuranium elements, a nucleus must be bombarded with a relatively large particle. If you know the products are californium-246 and four neutrons, with what particle would you bombard uranium-238 atoms?

43. Deuterium nuclei (^2_1H) are particularly effective as bombarding particles to carry out nuclear reactions. Complete the following equations:
   (a) $^{114}_{48}Cd + ^2_1H \longrightarrow ? + ^1_1H$
   (b) $^6_3Li + ^2_1H \longrightarrow ? + ^1_0n$
   (c) $^{40}_{20}Ca + ^2_1H \longrightarrow ^{38}_{19}K + ?$
   (d) $? + ^2_1H \longrightarrow ^{65}_{30}Zn + \gamma$

44. Element $^{287}_{114}Fl$ decays by α emission with a half-life of about 5 seconds. Write an equation for this process.

45. Boron is an effective absorber of neutrons. When boron-10 is bombarded by neutrons, an α particle is emitted. Write an equation for this nuclear reaction.

46. Some of the reactions explored by Ernest Rutherford (pages 55 and 994) and others are listed below. Identify the unknown species in each reaction.
   (a) $^{14}_7N + ^4_2He \longrightarrow ^{17}_8O + ?$
   (b) $^9_4Be + ^4_2He \longrightarrow ? + ^1_0n$
   (c) $? + ^4_2He \longrightarrow ^{30}_{15}P + ^1_0n$
   (d) $^{239}_{94}Pu + ^4_2He \longrightarrow ? + ^1_0n$

General Questions

These questions are not designated as to type or location in the chapter. They may combine several concepts.

47. ▲ A technique to date geological samples uses rubidium-87, a long-lived radioactive isotope of rubidium ($t_{1/2} = 4.8 \times 10^{10}$ years). Rubidium-87 decays by

β emission to strontium-87. If rubidium-87 is part of a rock or mineral, then strontium-87 will remain trapped within the crystalline structure of the rock. The age of the rock dates back to the time when the rock solidified. Chemical analysis of the rock gives the amounts of ^{87}Rb and ^{87}Sr. From these data, the fraction of ^{87}Rb that remains can be calculated. Suppose analysis of a stony meteorite determined that 1.8 mmol of ^{87}Rb and 1.6 mmol of ^{87}Sr (the portion of ^{87}Sr formed by decomposition of ^{87}Rb) were present. Estimate the age of the meteorite. (*Hint:* The amount of ^{87}Rb at t_0 is moles ^{87}Rb + moles ^{87}Sr.)

48. Tritium, ^3_1H, is one of the nuclei used in fusion reactions. This isotope is radioactive, with a half-life of 12.3 years. Like carbon-14, tritium is formed in the upper atmosphere from cosmic radiation, and it is found in trace amounts on Earth. To obtain the amounts required for a fusion reaction, however, it must be made via a nuclear reaction. The reaction of ^6_3Li with a neutron produces tritium and an α particle. Write an equation for this nuclear reaction.

49. Phosphorus occurs in nature as a single isotope, phosphorus-31. Neutron irradiation of phosphorus-31 produces phosphorus-32, a β emitter with a half-life of 14.28 days. Assume you have a sample containing phosphorus-32 that has a rate of decay of 3.2×10^6 dpm. Draw a graph showing disintegrations per minute as a function of time during a period of 1 year.

50. In June 1972, natural fission reactors, which operated billions of years ago, were discovered in Oklo, Gabon (page 974). At present, natural uranium contains 0.72% ^{235}U. How many years ago did natural uranium contain 3.0% ^{235}U, the amount needed to sustain a natural reactor? ($t_{1/2}$ for ^{235}U is 7.04×10^8 years.)

51. If a shortage in worldwide supplies of fissionable uranium arose, it would be possible to use other fissionable nuclei. Plutonium, one such fuel, can be made in "breeder" reactors that manufacture more fuel than they consume. The sequence of reactions by which plutonium is made is as follows:

(a) A ^{238}U nucleus undergoes an (n, γ) reaction to produce ^{239}U.
(b) ^{239}U decays by β emission ($t_{1/2}$ = 23.5 min) to give an isotope of neptunium.
(c) This neptunium isotope decays by β emission to give a plutonium isotope.
(d) The plutonium isotope is fissionable. On collision of one of these plutonium isotopes with a neutron, fission occurs, with at least two neutrons and two other nuclei as products.

Write an equation for each of the nuclear reactions.

52. When a neutron is captured by an atomic nucleus, energy is released as γ radiation. This energy can be calculated based on the change in mass in converting reactants to products.

For the nuclear reaction $^6_3Li + ^1_0n \longrightarrow ^7_3Li + \gamma$:

(a) Calculate the energy evolved in this reaction (per atom). Masses needed (in g/mol) are ^6_3Li = 6.01512, ^1_0n = 1.00867, and ^7_3Li = 7.01600.
(b) Use the answer in part (a) to calculate the wavelength of the γ rays emitted in the reaction.

53. The synthesis of livermorium:

(a) Lv-296 is made from the collision of a relatively light atom with curium-248. What is the lighter particle?
(b) Lv-296 is not stable, decaying to Lv-293. What particles are emitted in this process?

54. Although plutonium does not occur naturally on Earth now, it is thought to have been produced in the Oklo reactor (and then decayed). Write balanced nuclear equations for:

(a) the reaction of ^{238}U and a neutron to give ^{239}U
(b) the decay of ^{239}U to ^{239}Np and then to ^{239}Pu by β emission
(c) the decay of ^{239}Pu to ^{235}U by α emission

In the Laboratory

55. A piece of charred bone found in the ruins of a Native American village has a $^{14}C/^{12}C$ ratio that is 72% of the ratio found in living organisms. Calculate the age of the bone fragment. ($t_{1/2}$ for ^{14}C is 5.73×10^3 years.)

56. A sample of wood from a Thracian chariot found in an excavation in Bulgaria has a ^{14}C activity of 11.2 dpm/g. Estimate the age of the chariot and the year it was made. ($t_{1/2}$ for ^{14}C is 5.73×10^3 years, and the activity of ^{14}C in living material is 14.0 dpm/g.)

57. The isotope of polonium that was most likely isolated by Marie Curie in her pioneering studies is polonium-210. A sample of this element was prepared in a nuclear reaction. Initially, its activity (α emission) was 7840 dpm. Measuring radioactivity over time produced the data below. Determine the half-life of polonium-210.

Activity (dpm)	Time (days)
7840	0
7570	7
7300	14
5920	56
5470	72

58. Sodium-23 (in a sample of NaCl) is subjected to neutron bombardment in a nuclear reactor to produce ^{24}Na. When removed from the reactor, the sample is radioactive, with β activity of 2.54×10^4 dpm. The decrease in radioactivity over time was studied, producing the following data:

Activity (dpm)	Time (hours)
2.54×10^4	0
2.42×10^4	1
2.31×10^4	2
2.00×10^4	5
1.60×10^4	10
1.01×10^4	20

(a) Write equations for the neutron capture reaction and for the reaction in which the product of this reaction decays by β emission.
(b) Determine the half-life of sodium-24.

59. The age of minerals can sometimes be determined by measuring the amounts of ^{206}Pb and ^{238}U in a sample. This determination assumes that all of the ^{206}Pb in the sample comes from the decay of ^{238}U. The date obtained identifies when the rock solidified. Assume that the ratio of ^{206}Pb to ^{238}U in an igneous rock sample is 0.33. Calculate the age of the rock. ($t_{1/2}$ for ^{238}U is 4.5×10^9 years.)

60. To measure the volume of the blood system of an animal, the following experiment was done. A 1.0-mL sample of an aqueous solution containing tritium, with an activity of 2.0×10^6 dps, was injected into the animal's bloodstream. After time was allowed for complete circulatory mixing, a 1.0-mL blood sample was withdrawn and found to have an activity of 1.5×10^4 dps. What was the volume of the circulatory system? (The half-life of tritium is 12.3 years, so this experiment assumes that only a negligible amount of tritium has decayed in the time of the experiment.)

Summary and Conceptual Questions

The following questions may use concepts from this and previous chapters.

61. The average energy output of a good grade of coal is 2.6×10^7 kJ/ton. Fission of 1 mol of ^{235}U releases 2.1×10^{10} kJ. Find the number of tons of coal needed to produce the same energy as 1 lb of ^{235}U. (See Appendix C for conversion factors.)

62. Collision of an electron and a positron results in formation of two γ rays. In the process, their masses are converted completely into energy.
(a) Calculate the energy evolved from the annihilation of an electron and a positron, in kilojoules per mole.
(b) Using Planck's equation (Equation 6.2), determine the frequency of the γ rays emitted in this process.

63. The principle underlying the isotope dilution method of analysis can be applied to many kinds of problems. Suppose that you, a marine biologist, want to estimate the number of fish in a lake. You release 1000 tagged fish, and after allowing an adequate amount of time for the fish to disperse evenly in the lake, you catch 5250 fish and find that 27 of them have tags. How many fish are in the lake?

64. ▲ Radioactive isotopes are often used as "tracers" to follow an atom through a chemical reaction. The following is an example of this process: Acetic acid reacts with methanol, CH_3OH, by eliminating a molecule of H_2O to form methyl acetate, $CH_3CO_2CH_3$. Explain how you would use the radioactive isotope ^{15}O to show whether the oxygen atom in the water product comes from the —OH of the acid or the —OH of the alcohol.

65. ▲ Radioactive decay series begin with a very long-lived isotope. For example, the half-life of ^{238}U is 4.5×10^9 years. Each series is identified by the name of the long-lived parent isotope of highest mass.
(a) The uranium-238 radioactive decay series is sometimes referred to as the $4n + 2$ series because the masses of all 13 members of this series can be expressed by the equation $M = 4n + 2$, where M is the mass number and n is an integer. Explain why the masses are correlated in this way.
(b) Two other radioactive decay series identified in minerals in the Earth's crust are the thorium-232 series and the uranium-235 series. Do the masses of the isotopes in these series conform to a simple mathematical equation? If so, identify the equation.
(c) Identify the radioactive decay series to which each of the following isotopes belongs: $^{226}_{88}Ra$, $^{215}_{86}At$, $^{228}_{90}Th$, $^{210}_{83}Bi$.
(d) Evaluation reveals that one series of elements, the $4n + 1$ series, is not present in the Earth's crust. Speculate why.

66. ▲ The thorium decay series includes the isotope $^{228}_{90}Th$. Determine the sequence of nuclei on going from $^{232}_{90}Th$ to $^{228}_{90}Th$.

67. ▲ The last unknown element between bismuth and uranium was discovered by Lise Meitner (1878–1968) and Otto Hahn (1879–1968) in 1918. They obtained ^{231}Pa by chemical extraction of pitchblende, in which its concentration is about 1 ppm (part per million). This isotope, an α emitter, has a half-life of 3.27×10^4 years.
(a) Which radioactive decay series (the uranium-235, uranium-238, or thorium-232 series) contains ^{231}Pa as a member?
(b) Suggest a possible sequence of nuclear reactions starting with the long-lived isotope that eventually forms this isotope.
(c) What quantity of ore would be required to isolate 1.0 g of ^{231}Pa, assuming 100% yield?
(d) Write an equation for the radioactive decay process for ^{231}Pa.

68. ▲ You might wonder how it is possible to determine the half-life of long-lived radioactive isotopes such as ^{238}U. With a half-life of more than 10^9 years, the radioactivity of a sample of uranium will not measurably change in your lifetime. In fact, you can calculate the half-life using the mathematics governing first-order reactions.

It can be shown that a 1.0-mg sample of ^{238}U decays at the rate of 12 α emissions per second. Set up a mathematical equation for the rate of decay, $\Delta N/\Delta t = -kN$, where N is the number of nuclei in the 1.0-mg sample and $\Delta N/\Delta t$ is 12 dps. Solve this equation for the rate constant for this process, and then relate the rate constant to the half-life of the reaction. Carry out this calculation, and compare your result with the literature value, 4.5×10^9 years.

69. ▲ Marie and Pierre Curie isolated radium and polonium from uranium ore (pitchblende, which contains ^{238}U and ^{235}U). Which of the following isotopes of radium and polonium can be found in the uranium ore? (*Hint:* Consider both the isotope half-lives and the decay series starting with ^{238}U and ^{235}U.)

Isotope	Half-Life
^{226}Ra	1620 y
^{225}Ra	14.8 d
^{228}Ra	6.7 y
^{216}Po	0.15 s
^{210}Po	138.4 d

AP Multiple-Choice Review Questions

1. ^{87}Sr is a radiotracer used in studying bones. It decays by a first-order process and has a half-life of almost 3 hours. Approximately what percentage of radioactive material remains after a day?
(A) 0.3%
(B) 1%
(C) 3%
(D) 10%

2. The observed first-order rate of decay of carbon-14 in living material is 13.6 counts per minute per gram of carbon. An old wooden cup was discovered and found to give 10.9 counts per minute per gram of carbon. Approximately how old is the cup? For ^{14}C, $t_{1/2} = 5730$ years.
(A) 1800 years
(B) 4900 years
(C) 5700 years
(D) 11,000 years

3. The mass spectrum of a sample of radioactive plutonium recovered from a nuclear reactor is shown below.

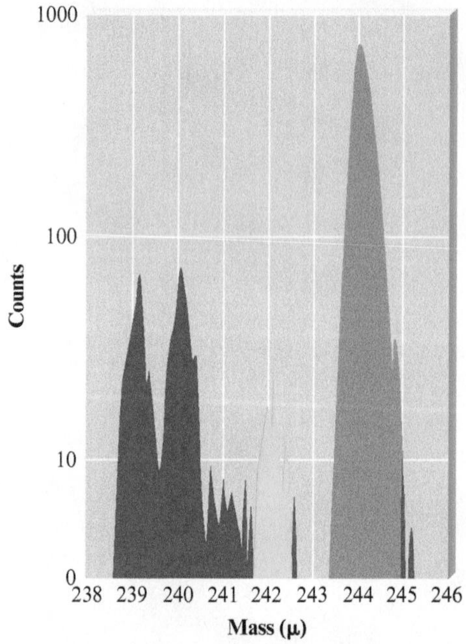

Using the graph, determine the number of neutrons in the isotope of plutonium having the greatest abundance in this sample.
(A) 94
(B) 150
(C) 242
(D) 244

4. Plutonium-243 decays into americium-243 by first-order kinetics. The half-life of ^{243}Pu is 5 hours. If the white spheres represent atoms of ^{243}Pu and the gray spheres represent ^{243}Am, which diagram would show the ratio of atoms of ^{243}Pu to ^{243}Am after 10 hours?

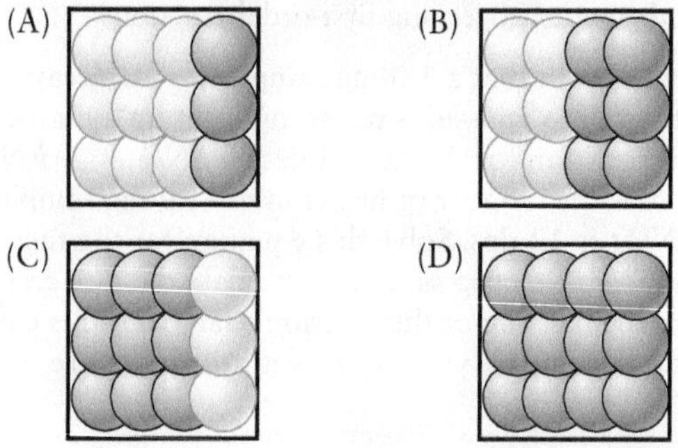

5. Bismuth-214 is a radioactive isotope that may decay into polonium-214 or into thallium-210. Which isotope would have the most similar *chemical* reactivity to bismuth-214?
(A) lead-214
(B) polonium-214
(C) thallium-210
(D) bismuth-210

6. Gold-198 is a radioactive isotope that is used to treat several types of cancer. Its first-order decay has a half-life of 2.7 days. How many grams must a physician order for a treatment that will begin in 11 days, if approximately 15 grams of gold-198 are needed for the treatment?
(A) 15 g
(B) 30 g
(C) 60 g
(D) 240 g

7. The half-life for the first-order nuclear decay of a 10.0-g sample of strontium-90 is 28 years. What is the half-life of a 5.0-g sample of strontium-90?
(A) 7 years
(B) 14 years
(C) 28 years
(D) 56 years

8. Cesium-137 is a common radioactive product of fission that has many uses in industry and medicine. The half-life of this decay is 30. years. Determine the specific rate constant for this first-order decay.
(A) 0.023 yr^{-1}
(B) 30. yr^{-1}
(C) 43 yr^{-1}
(D) 140 yr^{-1}

9. Minerals containing uranium can be dated to determine their approximate age by analyzing the isotopes of lead found in the sample. Uranium-236 decays to lead-206. Lead-206 is not a common isotope of lead, so any lead-206 found in a mineral must come from the decay of uranium-236. A mineral was analyzed, and its mass spectrum is shown below.

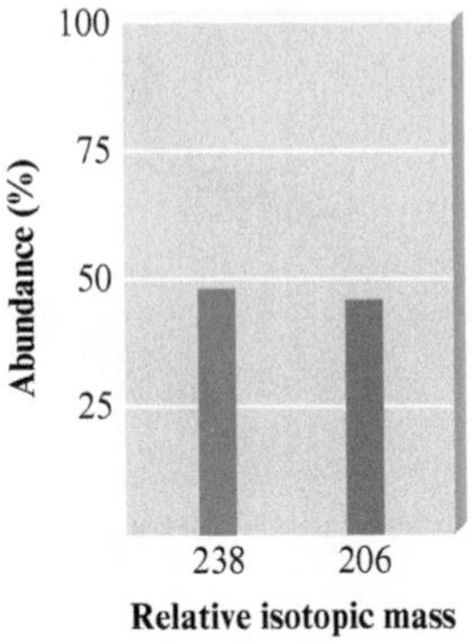

If the radioactive decay of uranium-236 is first order with a half-life of 4.5 billion years, estimate the age of the sample.

(A) 2.3 billion years

(B) 4.5 billion years

(C) 6.8 billion years

(D) 9.0 billion years

10. Radioactive decay displays first-order kinetics. If the decay of iodine-131 is measured over time, which of these graphs will show a straight line?

(A) mass of ^{131}I versus time

(B) natural logarithm of mass of ^{131}I versus time

(C) reciprocal of mass of ^{131}I versus time

(D) mass of ^{131}I versus reciprocal time

List of Appendices

Using Logarithms and Solving Quadratic Equations

An introductory chemistry course requires basic algebra plus a knowledge of (1) exponential (or scientific) notation, (2) logarithms, and (3) quadratic equations. The use of exponential notation was reviewed on pages 32–33, and this appendix reviews the last two topics.

A-1 Logarithms

Two types of logarithms are used in this text: (1) common logarithms (abbreviated log) whose base is 10 and (2) natural logarithms (abbreviated ln) whose base is *e* (= 2.71828):

$$\log x = n, \text{ where } x = 10^n$$
$$\ln x = m, \text{ where } x = e^m$$

Most equations in chemistry and physics were developed in natural, or base *e*, logarithms, and we follow this practice in this text. The relation between log and ln is

$$\ln x = 2.303 \log x$$

Despite the different bases of the two logarithms, they are used in the same manner. What follows is largely a description of the use of common logarithms.

A common logarithm is the power to which you must raise 10 to obtain the number. For example, the log of 100 is 2, since you must raise 10 to the second power to obtain 100. Other examples are

$$\log 1000 = \log (10^3) = 3$$
$$\log 10 = \log (10^1) = 1$$
$$\log 1 = \log (10^0) = 0$$
$$\log 0.1 = \log (10^{-1}) = -1$$
$$\log 0.0001 = \log (10^{-4}) = -4$$

To obtain the common logarithm of a number other than a simple power of 10, you must resort to a log table or an electronic calculator. For example,

$$\log 2.10 = 0.322, \text{ which means that } 10^{0.322} = 2.10$$
$$\log 5.16 = 0.713, \text{ which means that } 10^{0.713} = 5.16$$
$$\log 3.125 = 0.4949, \text{ which means that } 10^{0.4949} = 3.125$$

To check this on many calculators, enter the number, and then press the "log" key. You should make sure that you understand how to use your particular calculator.

To obtain the natural logarithm ln of the numbers shown here, use a calculator having this function. Enter each number, and press "ln:"

$$\ln 2.10 = 0.742, \text{ which means that } e^{0.742} = 2.10$$
$$\ln 5.16 = 1.641, \text{ which means that } e^{1.641} = 5.16$$

To find the common logarithm of a number greater than 10 or less than 1 with a log table, first express the number in scientific notation. Then find the log of each part of the number and add the logs. For example,

$$\begin{aligned}\log 241 &= \log (2.41 \times 10^2) = \log 2.41 + \log 10^2\\ &= 0.382 + 2 = 2.382\\ \log 0.00573 &= \log (5.73 \times 10^{-3}) = \log 5.73 + \log 10^{-3}\\ &= 0.758 + (-3) = -2.242\end{aligned}$$

Significant Figures and Logarithms

Notice that the mantissa has as many significant figures as the number whose log was found.

Logarithms and Nomenclature
The number to the left of the decimal in a logarithm is called the **characteristic**, and the number to the right of the decimal is the **mantissa**.

Obtaining Antilogarithms

If you are given the logarithm of a number and find the number from it, you have obtained the "antilogarithm," or "antilog," of the number. Two common procedures used by electronic calculators to do this are as follows:

PROCEDURE A	PROCEDURE B
1. Enter the value of the log or ln.	1. Enter value of the log or ln.
2. Press 2ndF.	2. Press INV.
3. Press 10^x or e^x.	3. Press log or ln x.

Make sure you can properly perform this operation on your calculator by working the following examples:

1. Find the number whose log is 5.234:
   Recall that $\log x = n$, where $x = 10^n$. In this case, $n = 5.234$. Find the value of 10^n, the antilog. In this case,

   $$10^{5.234} = 10^{0.234} \times 10^5 = 1.71 \times 10^5$$

   Notice that the characteristic (5) sets the decimal point; it is the power of 10 in the exponential form. The mantissa (0.234) gives the value of the number x, 1.71 in this case.
2. Find the number whose log is −3.456:

   $$10^{-3.456} = 10^{0.544} \times 10^{-4} = 3.50 \times 10^{-4}$$

   Notice here that −3.456 is expressed as the sum of −4 and +0.544.

Mathematical Operations Using Logarithms

Because logarithms are exponents, operations involving them follow the same rules used for exponents. Thus, multiplying two numbers can be done by adding logarithms:

$$\log xy = \log x + \log y$$

For example, we multiply 563 by 125 by adding their logarithms and finding the antilogarithm of the result:

$$\begin{aligned}\log 563 &= 2.751\\ \log 125 &= \underline{2.097}\\ \log xy &= 4.848\\ xy &= 10^{4.848} = 10^{0.848} \times 10^4 = 7.05 \times 10^4\end{aligned}$$

One number (x) can be divided by another (y) by subtraction of their logarithms:

$$\log \frac{x}{y} = \log x - \log y$$

For example, to divide 125 by 742,

$$\begin{aligned} \log 125 &= 2.097 \\ -\log 742 &= \underline{2.870} \\ \log \frac{x}{y} &= -0.773 \end{aligned}$$

$$\frac{x}{y} = 10^{-0.773} = 10^{0.227} \times 10^{-1} = 1.68 \times 10^{-1}$$

Similarly, powers and roots of numbers can be found using logarithms.

$$\log x^y = y(\log x)$$

$$\log \sqrt[y]{x} = \log x^{1/y} = \frac{1}{y} \log x$$

As an example, find the fourth power of 5.23. We first find the log of 5.23 and then multiply it by 4. The result, 2.874, is the log of the answer. Therefore, we find the antilog of 2.874:

$$\begin{aligned} (5.23)^4 &= ? \\ \log (5.23)^4 &= 4 \log 5.23 = 4(0.719) = 2.874 \\ (5.23)^4 &= 10^{2.874} = 748 \end{aligned}$$

As another example, find the fifth root of 1.89×10^{-9}:

$$\sqrt[5]{1.89 \times 10^{-9}} = (1.89 \times 10^{-9})^{1/5} = ?$$

$$\log (1.89 \times 10^{-9})^{1/5} = \frac{1}{5} \log(1.89 \times 10^{-9}) = \frac{1}{5}(-8.724) = -1.745$$

The answer is the antilog of -1.745:

$$(1.89 \times 10^{-9})^{1/5} = 10^{-1.745} = 1.80 \times 10^{-2}$$

A-2 Quadratic Equations

Algebraic equations of the form $ax^2 + bx + c = 0$ are called **quadratic equations.** The coefficients a, b, and c may be either positive or negative. The two roots of the equation may be found using the *quadratic formula:*

$$x = \frac{-b \pm \sqrt{b^2 - 4ac}}{2a}$$

As an example, solve the equation $5x^2 - 3x - 2 = 0$. Here $a = 5$, $b = -3$, and $c = -2$. Therefore,

$$\begin{aligned} x &= \frac{3 \pm \sqrt{(-3)^2 - 4(5)(-2)}}{2(5)} \\ &= \frac{3 \pm \sqrt{9 - (-40)}}{10} = \frac{3 \pm \sqrt{49}}{10} = \frac{3 \pm 7}{10} \\ &= 1 \text{ and } -0.4 \end{aligned}$$

How do you know which of the two roots is the correct answer? Mathematically, both roots are possible, but in chemistry problems you have to decide in each case which root has physical significance. It is *usually* true in this course, however, that negative values are not significant.

When you have solved a quadratic expression, you should always check your values by substitution into the original equation. In the previous example, we find that $5(1)^2 - 3(1) - 2 = 0$ and that $5(-0.4)^2 - 3(-0.4) - 2 = 0$.

The most likely place you will encounter quadratic equations is in the chapters on chemical equilibria, particularly in Chapters 15 through 17. Here, you will often be faced with solving an equation such as

$$1.8 \times 10^{-4} = \frac{x^2}{0.0010 - x}$$

This equation can certainly be solved using the quadratic formula (to give $x = 3.4 \times 10^{-4}$). You may find the **method of successive approximations** to be especially convenient, however. Here we begin by making a reasonable approximation of x. This approximate value is substituted into the original equation, which is then solved to give what is hoped to be a more correct value of x. This process is repeated until the answer converges on a particular value of x—that is, until the value of x derived from two successive approximations is the same.

Step 1: First, assume that x is so small that $(0.0010 - x) \approx 0.0010$. This means that

$$x^2 = 1.8 \times 10^{-4}\ (0.0010)$$
$$x = 4.2 \times 10^{-4} \text{ (to 2 significant figures)}$$

Step 2: Substitute the value of x from Step 1 into the denominator of the original equation, and again solve for x:

$$x^2 = 1.8 \times 10^{-4}(0.0010 - 0.00042)$$
$$x = 3.2 \times 10^{-4}$$

Step 3: Repeat Step 2 using the value of x found in that step:

$$x = \sqrt{1.8 \times 10^{-4}(0.0010 - 0.00032)} = 3.5 \times 10^{-4}$$

Step 4: Continue repeating the calculation, using the value of x found in the previous step:

$$x = \sqrt{1.8 \times 10^{-4}(0.0010 - 0.00035)} = 3.4 \times 10^{-4}$$

Step 5: $$x = \sqrt{1.8 \times 10^{-4}(0.0010 - 0.00034)} = 3.4 \times 10^{-4}$$

Here, we find that iterations after the fourth step give the same value for x, indicating that we have arrived at a valid answer (and the same one obtained from the quadratic formula).

Here are some final thoughts on using the method of successive approximations. First, in some cases the method does not work. Successive steps may give answers that are random or that diverge from the correct value. In Chapters 15 through 17, you confront quadratic equations of the form $K = x^2/(C - x)$. The method of successive approximations works as long as $K < 4C$ (assuming one begins with $x = 0$ as the first guess, that is, $K \approx x^2/C$). This is always going to be true for weak acids and bases (the topic of Chapters 16 and 17), but it may *not* be the case for problems involving gas phase equilibria (Chapter 15), where K can be quite large.

Second, values of K in the equation $K = x^2/(C - x)$ are usually known only to two significant figures. We are therefore justified in carrying out successive steps until two answers are the same to two significant figures.

Finally, we highly recommend this method of solving quadratic equations, especially those in Chapters 16 and 17. If your calculator has a memory function, successive approximations can be carried out easily and rapidly.

Some Important Physical Concepts

B-1 Matter

The tendency to maintain a constant velocity is called *inertia*. Thus, unless acted on by an unbalanced force, a body at rest remains at rest, and a body in motion remains in motion with uniform velocity. Matter is anything that exhibits inertia; the quantity of matter is its mass.

B-2 Motion

Motion is the change of position or location in space. Objects can have the following classes of motion:

- Translation occurs when the center of mass of an object changes its location. Example: a car moving on the highway.
- Rotation occurs when each point of a moving object moves in a circle about an axis through the center of mass. Examples: a spinning top, a rotating molecule.
- Vibration is a periodic distortion and then recovery of original shape. Examples: a struck tuning fork, a vibrating molecule.

B-3 Force and Weight

Force is that which changes the velocity of a body; it is defined as

$$\text{Force} = \text{mass} \times \text{acceleration}$$

The SI unit of force is the **newton**, N, whose dimensions are kilograms times meter per second squared ($kg \cdot m/s^2$). A newton is therefore the force needed to change the velocity of a mass of 1 kilogram by 1 meter per second in a time of 1 second.

Because the Earth's gravity is not the same everywhere, the weight (a force) corresponding to a given mass is not a constant. At any given spot on Earth, gravity is constant, however, and therefore weight is proportional to mass. When a balance tells us that a given sample (the "unknown") has the same weight as another sample (the "weights," as given by a scale reading or by a total of counterweights), it also tells us that the two masses are equal. The balance is therefore a valid instrument for measuring the mass of an object independently of slight variations in the force of gravity.

*Adapted from F. Brescia, J. Arents, H. Meislich, et al.: *General Chemistry*, 5th ed. Philadelphia: Harcourt Brace, 1988.

Table 1 Pressure Conversions

FROM	TO	MULTIPLY BY
atmosphere	mm Hg	760 mm Hg/atm (exactly)
atmosphere	lb/in^2	14.6960 $lb/(in^2 \cdot atm)$
atmosphere	kPa	101.325 kPa/atm
bar	Pa	10^5 Pa/bar (exactly)
bar	lb/in^2	14.5038 $lb/(in^2 \cdot bar)$
mm Hg	torr	1 torr/mm Hg (exactly)

B-4 Pressure†

Pressure is force per unit area. The SI unit, called the *pascal,* Pa, is

$$1 \text{ pascal} = \frac{1 \text{ newton}}{\text{m}^2} = \frac{1 \text{ kg} \cdot \text{m/s}^2}{\text{m}^2} = \frac{1 \text{ kg}}{\text{m} \cdot \text{s}^2}$$

The International System of Units also recognizes the bar, which is 10^5 Pa and which is close to standard atmospheric pressure (Table 1).

Chemists also express pressure in terms of the heights of liquid columns, especially water and mercury. This usage is not completely satisfactory because the pressure exerted by a given column of a given liquid is not a constant but depends on the temperature (which influences the density of the liquid) and the location (which influences the magnitude of the force exerted by gravity). Such units are therefore not part of the SI, and their use is now discouraged. The older units are still used in books and journals, however, and chemists must be familiar with them.

The pressure of a liquid or a gas depends only on the depth (or height) and is exerted equally in all directions. At sea level, the pressure exerted by the Earth's atmosphere supports a column of mercury about 0.76 m (76 cm, or 760 mm) high.

One **standard atmosphere** (atm) is the pressure exerted by exactly 76 cm of mercury at 0 °C (density, 13.5951 g/cm^3) and at standard gravity, 9.80665 m/s^2. The **bar** is equivalent to 0.9869 atm. One **torr** is the pressure exerted by exactly 1 mm of mercury at 0 °C and standard gravity.

B-5 Energy and Power

The SI unit of energy is the product of the units of force and distance, or kilograms times meter per second squared ($kg \cdot m/s^2$) times meters ($\times$ m), which is $kg \cdot m^2/s^2$; this unit is called the **joule,** J. The joule is thus the work done when a force of 1 newton acts through a distance of 1 meter.

Work may also be done by moving an electric charge in an electric field. When the charge being moved is 1 coulomb (C) and the potential difference between its initial and final positions is 1 volt (V), the work is 1 joule. Thus,

$$1 \text{ joule} = 1 \text{ coulomb volt (CV)}$$

Another unit of electric work that is not part of the International System of Units but is still in use is the **electron volt,** eV, which is the work required to move an electron against a potential difference of 1 volt. (It is also the kinetic energy acquired

†See Section 10-1.

by an electron when it is accelerated by a potential difference of 1 volt.) Because the charge on an electron is 1.602×10^{-19} C, we have

$$1\ \text{eV} = 1.602 \times 10^{-19}\ \text{CV} \times \frac{1\ \text{J}}{1\ \text{CV}} = 1.602 \times 10^{-19}\ \text{J}$$

If this value is multiplied by Avogadro's number, we obtain the energy involved in moving 1 mol of electron charges (1 faraday) in a field produced by a potential difference of 1 volt:

$$1\ \frac{\text{eV}}{\text{particle}} = \frac{1.602 \times 10^{-19}\ \text{J}}{\text{particle}} \times \frac{6.022 \times 10^{23}\ \text{particles}}{\text{mol}} \cdot \frac{1\ \text{kJ}}{1000\ \text{J}} = 96.49\ \text{kJ/mol}$$

Power is the amount of energy delivered per unit time. The SI unit is the watt, W, which is 1 joule per second. One kilowatt, kW, is 1000 W. Watt-hours and kilowatt-hours are therefore units of energy (Table 2). For example, 1000 watt-hours, or 1 kilowatt-hour, is

$$1.0 \times 10^{3}\ \text{W} \cdot \text{h} \times \frac{1\ \text{J}}{1\ \text{W} \cdot \text{s}} \times \frac{3.6 \times 10^{3}\ \text{s}}{1\ \text{h}} = 3.6 \times 10^{6}\ \text{J}$$

Table 2 Energy Conversions

FROM	TO	MULTIPLY BY
calorie (cal)	joule	4.184 J/cal (exactly)
kilocalorie (kcal)	cal	10^3 cal/kcal (exactly)
kilocalorie	joule	4.184×10^3 J/kcal (exactly)
liter atmosphere (L · atm)	joule	101.325 J/L · atm
electron volt (eV)	joule	1.60218×10^{-19} J/eV
electron volt per particle	kilojoules per mole	96.485 kJ · particle/eV · mol
coulomb volt (CV)	joule	1 CV/J (exactly)
kilowatt-hour (kW-h)	kcal	860.4 kcal/kW-h
kilowatt-hour	joule	3.6×10^6 J/kW-h (exactly)
British thermal unit (BTU)	calorie	252 cal/BTU

Abbreviations and Useful Conversion Factors

Table 3 Some Common Abbreviations and Standard Symbols

Term	Abbreviation	Term	Abbreviation
Activation energy	E_a	Entropy	S
Ampere	A	Standard entropy	$S°$
Aqueous solution	aq	Entropy change for reaction	$\Delta_r S°$
Atmosphere, unit of pressure	atm	Equilibrium constant	K
Atomic mass unit	u	Concentration basis	K_c
Avogadro's constant	N	Pressure basis	K_p
Bar, unit of pressure	bar	Ionization weak acid	K_a
Body-centered cubic	bcc	Ionization weak base	K_b
Bohr radius	a_0	Solubility product	K_{sp}
Boiling point	bp	Formation constant	K_f
Celsius temperature	°C	Ethylenediamine	en
Charge number of an ion	z	Face-centered cubic	fcc
Coulomb, electric charge	C	Faraday constant	F
Curie, radioactivity	Ci	Gas constant	R
Cycles per second, hertz	Hz	Gibbs free energy	G
Debye, unit of electric dipole	D	Standard free energy	$G°$
Electron	e^-	Standard free energy of formation	$\Delta_f G°$
Electron volt	eV	Standard free energy change for reaction	$\Delta_r G°$
Electronegativity	χ	Half-life	$t_{1/2}$
Energy	E	Heat	q
Enthalpy	H	Hertz	Hz
Standard enthalpy	$H°$	Hour	h
Standard enthalpy of formation	$\Delta_f H°$	Joule	J
Standard enthalpy of reaction	$\Delta_r H°$	Kelvin	K

(continued)

Table 3 Some Common Abbreviations and Standard Symbols (continued)

TERM	ABBREVIATION	TERM	ABBREVIATION
Kilocalorie	kcal	Planck's constant	*h*
Liquid	ℓ	Pound	lb
Logarithm, base 10	log	Primitive cubic (unit cell)	pc
Logarithm, base *e*	ln	Pressure	*P*
Millimeters of mercury, unit of pressure	mm Hg	Proton number	*Z*
Minute	min	Rate constant	*k*
Molar	M	Standard temperature and pressure	STP
Molar mass	*M*	Temperature	*T*
Mole	mol	Volt	V
Osmotic pressure	Π	Watt	W
Pascal, unit of pressure	Pa	Wavelength	λ

C-1 Fundamental Units of the SI System

The metric system was begun by the French National Assembly in 1790 and has undergone many modifications. The International System of Units or *Système International* (SI), which represents an extension of the metric system, was adopted by the 11th General Conference of Weights and Measures in 1960. It is constructed from seven base units, each of which represents a particular physical quantity (Table 4).

Table 4 SI Fundamental Units

PHYSICAL QUANTITY	NAME OF UNIT	SYMBOL
Length	meter	m
Mass	kilogram	kg
Time	second	s
Temperature	kelvin	K
Amount of substance	mole	mol
Electric current	ampere	A
Luminous intensity	candela	cd

The first five units listed in Table 4 are particularly useful in general chemistry and are defined as follows:

1. The *meter* was redefined in 1960 to be equal to 1,650,763.73 wavelengths of a certain line in the emission spectrum of krypton-86.
2. The *kilogram* represents the mass of a platinum–iridium block kept at the International Bureau of Weights and Measures at Sèvres, France.
3. The *second* was redefined in 1967 as the duration of 9,192,631,770 periods of a certain line in the microwave spectrum of cesium-133.

4. The *kelvin* is 1/273.16 of the temperature interval between absolute zero and the triple point of water.
5. The *mole* is the amount of substance that contains as many entities as there are atoms in exactly 0.012 kg of carbon-12 (12 g of ^{12}C atoms).

C-2 Prefixes Used with Traditional Metric Units and SI Units

Decimal fractions and multiples of metric and SI units are designated by using the prefixes listed in Table 5. Those most commonly used in general chemistry appear in italics.

Table 5 Traditional Metric and SI Prefixes

FACTOR	PREFIX	SYMBOL	FACTOR	PREFIX	SYMBOL
10^{12}	tera	T	10^{-1}	*deci*	d
10^{9}	giga	G	10^{-2}	*centi*	c
10^{6}	mega	M	10^{-3}	*milli*	m
10^{3}	*kilo*	k	10^{-6}	micro	μ
10^{2}	hecto	h	10^{-9}	*nano*	n
10^{1}	deka	da	10^{-12}	*pico*	p
			10^{-15}	femto	f
			10^{-18}	atto	a

C-3 Derived SI Units

In the International System of Units, all physical quantities are represented by appropriate combinations of the base units listed in Table 4. A list of the derived units frequently used in general chemistry is given in Table 6.

Table 6 Derived SI Units

PHYSICAL QUANTITY	NAME OF UNIT	SYMBOL	DEFINITION
Area	square meter	m^2	
Volume	cubic meter	m^3	
Density	kilogram per cubic meter	kg/m^3	
Force	newton	N	$kg \cdot m/s^2$
Pressure	pascal	Pa	N/m^2
Energy	joule	J	$kg \cdot m^2/s^2$
Electric charge	coulomb	C	$A \cdot s$
Electric potential difference	volt	V	$J/(A \cdot s)$

Table 7 Common Units of Mass and Weight

1 POUND = 453.39 GRAMS
1 kilogram = 1000 grams = 2.205 pounds
1 gram = 1000 milligrams
1 gram = 6.022×10^{23} atomic mass units
1 atomic mass unit = 1.6605×10^{-24} gram
1 short ton = 2000 pounds = 907.2 kilograms
1 long ton = 2240 pounds
1 metric tonne = 1000 kilograms = 2205 pounds

Table 8 Common Units of Length

1 INCH = 2.54 CENTIMETERS (EXACTLY)
1 mile = 5280 feet = 1.609 kilometers
1 yard = 36 inches = 0.9144 meter
1 meter = 100 centimeters = 39.37 inches = 3.281 feet = 1.094 yards
1 kilometer = 1000 meters = 1094 yards = 0.6215 mile
1 Ångstrom = 1.0×10^{-8} centimeter = 0.10 nanometer = 100 picometers = 1.0×10^{-10} meter = 3.937×10^{-9} inch

Table 9 Common Units of Volume

1 QUART = 0.9463 LITER **1 LITER = 1.0567 QUARTS**
1 liter = 1 cubic decimeter = 1000 cubic centimeters = 0.001 cubic meter
1 milliliter = 1 cubic centimeter = 0.001 liter = 1.056×10^{-3} quart
1 cubic foot = 28.316 liters = 29.924 quarts = 7.481 gallons

Physical Constants

Table 10 Physical Constants

QUANTITY	SYMBOL	TRADITIONAL UNITS	SI UNITS
Acceleration of gravity	g	980.6 cm/s^2	9.806 m/s^2
Atomic mass unit (1/12 the mass of ^{12}C atom)	u	1.6605×10^{-24} g	1.6605×10^{-27} kg
Avogadro's number	N	$6.02214129 \times 10^{23}$ particles/mol	$6.02214129 \times 10^{23}$ particles/mol
Bohr radius	a_0	0.052918 nm 5.2918×10^{-9} cm	5.2918×10^{-11} m
Boltzmann constant	k	1.3807×10^{-16} erg/K	1.3807×10^{-23} J/K
Charge-to-mass ratio of electron	e/m	1.7588×10^{8} C/g	1.7588×10^{11} C/kg
Electron rest mass	m_e	9.1094×10^{-28} g 0.00054858 u	9.1094×10^{-31} kg
Electronic charge	e	1.6022×10^{-19} C 4.8033×10^{-10} esu	1.6022×10^{-19} C
Faraday constant	F	96,485 C/mol e$^-$ 23.06 kcal/V · mol e$^-$	96,485 C/mol e$^-$ 96,485 J/V · mol e$^-$
Gas constant	R	$0.082057 \dfrac{\text{L} \cdot \text{atm}}{\text{mol} \cdot \text{K}}$ $1.987 \dfrac{\text{cal}}{\text{mol} \cdot \text{K}}$	$8.3145 \dfrac{\text{Pa} \cdot \text{dm}^3}{\text{mol} \cdot \text{K}}$ 8.3145 J/mol · K
Molar volume (STP)	V_m	22.414 L/mol	22.414×10^{-3} m^3/mol 22.414 dm^3/mol
Neutron rest mass	m_n	1.67493×10^{-24} g 1.008665 u	1.67493×10^{-27} kg
Planck's constant	h	6.6261×10^{-27} erg · s	$6.6260693 \times 10^{-34}$ J · s
Proton rest mass	m_p	1.6726×10^{-24} g 1.007276 u	1.6726×10^{-27} kg
Rydberg constant	R Rhc	—	1.0974×10^{7} m^{-1} 2.1799×10^{-18} J
Velocity of light (in a vacuum)	c	2.9979×10^{10} cm/s (186,282 miles/s)	2.9979×10^{8} m/s
$\pi = 3.1416$			
$e = 2.7183$			
$\ln X = 2.303 \log X$			

Table 11 Specific Heats and Heat Capacities for Some Common Substances at 25 °C

Substance	Specific Heat (J/g · K)	Molar Heat Capacity (J/mol · K)
Al(s)	0.897	24.2
Ca(s)	0.646	25.9
Cu(s)	0.385	24.5
Fe(s)	0.449	25.1
Hg(ℓ)	0.140	28.0
H_2O(s), ice	2.06	37.1
H_2O(ℓ), water	4.184	75.4
H_2O(g), steam	1.86	33.6
C_6H_6(ℓ), benzene	1.74	136
C_6H_6(g), benzene	1.06	82.4
C_2H_5OH(ℓ), ethanol	2.44	112.3
C_2H_5OH(g), ethanol	1.41	65.4
$(C_2H_5)_2O$(ℓ), diethyl ether	2.33	172.6
$(C_2H_5)_2O$(g), diethyl ether	1.61	119.5

Table 12 Heats of Transformation and Transformation Temperatures of Several Substances

		Heat of Fusion			Heat of Vaporization	
Substance	MP (°C)	J/g	kJ/mol	BP (°C)	J/g	kJ/mol
Elements*						
Al	660	395	10.7	2518	12083	294
Ca	842	212	8.5	1484	3767	155
Cu	1085	209	13.3	2567	4720	300
Fe	1535	267	13.8	2861	6088	340
Hg	−38.8	11	2.29	357	295	59.1
Compounds						
H_2O	0.00	333	6.01	100.0	2260	40.7
CH_4	−182.5	58.6	0.94	−161.5	511	8.2
C_2H_5OH	−114	109	5.02	78.3	838	38.6
C_6H_6	5.48	127.4	9.95	80.0	393	30.7
$(C_2H_5)_2O$	−116.3	98.1	7.27	34.6	357	26.5

*Data for the elements are taken from J. A. Dean: *Lange's Handbook of Chemistry,* 15th ed. New York: McGraw-Hill Publishers, 1999.

A Brief Guide to Naming Organic Compounds

It seems a daunting task to devise a systematic procedure that gives each organic compound a unique name, but that is what has been done. A set of rules was developed to name organic compounds by the International Union of Pure and Applied Chemistry (IUPAC). The IUPAC nomenclature allows chemists to write a name for any compound based on its structure or to identify the formula and structure for a compound from its name. In this book, we have generally used the IUPAC nomenclature scheme when naming compounds.

In addition to the systematic names, many compounds have common names. The common names came into existence before the nomenclature rules were developed, and they have continued in use. For some compounds, these names are so well entrenched that they are used most of the time. One such compound is acetic acid, which is almost always referred to by that name and not by its systematic name, ethanoic acid.

The general procedure for systematic naming of organic compounds begins with the nomenclature for hydrocarbons. Other organic compounds are then named as derivatives of hydrocarbons. Nomenclature rules for simple organic compounds are given in the following section.

E-1 Hydrocarbons

Alkanes

The names of alkanes end in "-ane." When naming a specific alkane, the root of the name identifies the longest carbon chain in the compound. Specific substituent groups attached to this carbon chain are identified by name and position.

Alkanes with chains of one to ten carbon atoms are given in Table 23.2. After the first four compounds, the names derive from Greek and Latin numbers—pentane, hexane, heptane, octane, nonane, decane—and this regular naming continues for higher alkanes. For substituted alkanes, the substituent groups on a hydrocarbon chain must be identified both by a name and by the position of substitution; this information precedes the root of the name. The position is indicated by a number that refers to the carbon atom to which the substituent is attached. (Numbering of the carbon atoms in a chain should begin at the end of the carbon chain that allows the substituent groups to have the lowest numbers.)

Names of hydrocarbon substituents are derived from the name of the hydrocarbon. The group $—CH_3$, derived by taking a hydrogen from methane, is called the *methyl group;* the $—C_2H_5$ group is the *ethyl group.* The nomenclature scheme is easily extended to derivatives of hydrocarbons with other substituent groups such as —Cl (chloro), $—NO_2$ (nitro), —CN (cyano), —D (deuterio), and so on (Table 13). If two or more of the same substituent groups occur, the prefixes "di-," "tri-," and "tetra-" are added. When different substituent groups are present, they are generally listed in alphabetical order.

Table 13 Names of Common Substituent Groups

FORMULA	NAME	FORMULA	NAME
$-CH_3$	methyl	$-D$	deuterio
$-C_2H_5$	ethyl	$-Cl$	chloro
$-CH_2CH_2CH_3$	propyl (*n*-propyl)	$-Br$	bromo
$-CH(CH_3)_2$	1-methylethyl (isopropyl)	$-F$	fluoro
$-CH{=}CH_2$	ethenyl (vinyl)	$-CN$	cyano
$-C_6H_5$	phenyl	$-NO_2$	nitro
$-OH$	hydroxo		
$-NH_2$	amino		

Example:

$$CH_3CH_2\underset{}{\overset{\overset{\displaystyle CH_3}{|}}{C}}HCH_2\overset{\overset{\displaystyle C_2H_5}{|}}{C}HCH_2CH_3$$

STEP	INFORMATION TO INCLUDE	CONTRIBUTION TO NAME
1	An alkane	Name will end in "-ane"
2	Longest chain is 7 carbons	Name as a *heptane*
3	$-CH_3$ group at carbon 3	*3-methyl*
4	$-C_2H_5$ group at carbon 5	*5-ethyl*
Name:		5-ethyl-3-methylheptane

Cycloalkanes are named based on the ring size and by adding the prefix "cyclo"; for example, the cycloalkane with a six-member ring of carbons is called *cyclohexane.*

Alkenes

Alkenes have names ending in "-ene." The name of an alkene must specify the length of the carbon chain and the position of the double bond (and when appropriate, the configuration, either *cis* or *trans*). As with alkanes, both identity and position of substituent groups must be given. The carbon chain is numbered from the end that gives the double bond the lowest number.

Compounds with two double bonds are called *dienes,* and they are named similarly—specifying the positions of the double bonds and the name and position of any substituent groups.

For example, the compound $H_2C{=}C(CH_3)CH(CH_3)CH_2CH_3$ has a five-carbon chain with a double bond between carbon atoms 1 and 2 and methyl groups on carbon atoms 2 and 3. Its name using IUPAC nomenclature is **2,3-dimethyl-1-pentene.** The compound $CH_3CH{=}CHCCl_3$ with a *cis* configuration around the double bond is named **1,1,1-trichloro-*cis*-2-butene.** The compound $H_2C{=}C(Cl)CH{=}CH_2$ is **2-chloro-1,3-butadiene.**

Alkynes

The naming of alkynes is similar to the naming of alkenes, except that *cis–trans* isomerism isn't a factor. The ending "-yne" on a name identifies a compound as an alkyne.

Benzene Derivatives

The carbon atoms in the six-member ring are numbered 1 through 6, and the name and position of substituent groups are given. The two examples shown here are **1-ethyl-3-methylbenzene** and **1,4-diaminobenzene.**

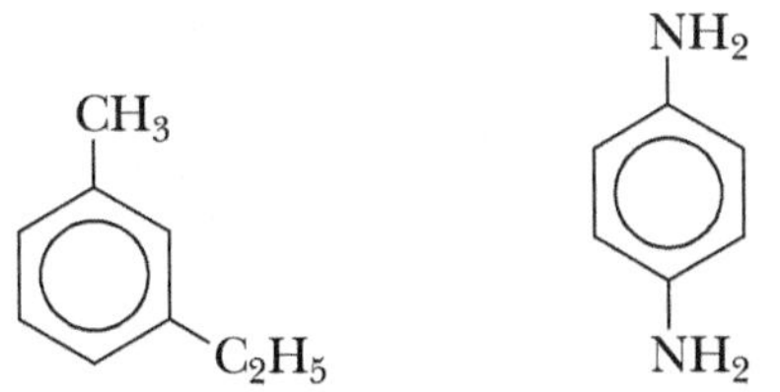

1-ethyl-3-methylbenzene 1,4-diaminobenzene

E-2 Derivatives of Hydrocarbons

The names for alcohols, aldehydes, ketones, and acids are based on the name of the hydrocarbon with an appropriate suffix to denote the class of compound, as follows:

- **Alcohols:** Substitute "-ol" for the final "-e" in the name of the hydrocarbon, and designate the position of the —OH group by the number of the carbon atom. For example, $CH_3CH_2CHOHCH_3$ is named as a derivative of the 4-carbon hydrocarbon butane. The —OH group is attached to the second carbon, so the name is **2-butanol.**
- **Aldehydes:** Substitute "-al" for the final "-e" in the name of the hydrocarbon. The carbon atom of an aldehyde is, by definition, carbon-1 in the hydrocarbon chain. For example, the compound $CH_3CH(CH_3)CH_2CH_2CHO$ contains a 5-carbon chain with the aldehyde functional group being carbon-1 and the $—CH_3$ group at position 4; thus, the name is **4-methylpentanal.**
- **Ketones:** Substitute "-one" for the final "-e" in the name of the hydrocarbon. The position of the ketone functional group (the carbonyl group) is indicated by the number of the carbon atom. For example, the compound $CH_3COCH_2CH(C_2H_5)CH_2CH_3$ has the carbonyl group at the 2 position and an ethyl group at the 4 position of a 6-carbon chain; its name is **4-ethyl-2-hexanone.**
- **Carboxylic acids (organic acids):** Substitute "-oic" for the final "-e" in the name of the hydrocarbon. The carbon atoms in the longest chain are counted beginning with the carboxylic carbon atom. For example, *trans*-$CH_3CH{=}CHCH_2CO_2H$ is named as a derivative of *trans*-3-pentene—that is, ***trans*-3-pentenoic acid.**

An **ester** is named as a derivative of the alcohol and acid from which it is made. The name of an ester is obtained by splitting the formula RCO_2R' into two parts, the $RCO_2—$ portion and the $—R'$ portion. The $—R'$ portion comes from the alcohol and is identified by the hydrocarbon group name; derivatives of ethanol, for example, are called *ethyl* esters. The acid part of the compound is named by dropping the "-oic" ending for the acid and replacing it by "-oate." The compound $CH_3CH_2CO_2CH_3$ is named **methyl propanoate.**

Notice that an anion derived from a carboxylic acid by loss of the acidic proton is named the same way. Thus, $CH_3CH_2CO_2^-$ is the **propanoate anion,** and the sodium salt of this anion, $Na(CH_3CH_2CO_2)$, is **sodium propanoate.**

Values for the Ionization Energies and Electron Attachment Enthalpies of the Elements

First Ionization Energies for Some Elements (kJ/mol)

1A (1)	2A (2)	3B (3)	4B (4)	5B (5)	6B (6)	7B (7)	8B (8,9,10)			1B (11)	2B (12)	3A (13)	4A (14)	5A (15)	6A (16)	7A (17)	8 (18)
H 1312																	He 2371
Li 520	Be 899											B 801	C 1086	N 1402	O 1314	F 1681	Ne 2081
Na 496	Mg 738											Al 578	Si 786	P 1012	S 1000	Cl 1251	Ar 1521
K 419	Ca 599	Sc 631	Ti 658	V 650	Cr 652	Mn 717	Fe 759	Co 758	Ni 757	Cu 745	Zn 906	Ga 579	Ge 762	As 947	Se 941	Br 1140	Kr 1351
Rb 403	Sr 550	Y 617	Zr 661	Nb 664	Mo 685	Tc 702	Ru 711	Rh 720	Pd 804	Ag 731	Cd 868	In 558	Sn 709	Sb 834	Te 869	I 1008	Xe 1170
Cs 377	Ba 503	La 538	Hf 681	Ta 761	W 770	Re 760	Os 840	Ir 880	Pt 870	Au 890	Hg 1007	Tl 589	Pb 715	Bi 703	Po 812	At 890	Rn 1037

Table 14 Electron Attachment Enthalpy Values for Some Elements (kJ/mol)*

H −72.77						
Li −59.63	Be 0†	B −26.7	C −121.85	N 0	O −140.98	F −328.0
Na −52.87	Mg 0	Al −42.6	Si −133.6	P −72.07	S −200.41	Cl −349.0
K −48.39	Ca 0	Ga −30	Ge −120	As −78	Se −194.97	Br −324.7
Rb −46.89	Sr 0	In −30	Sn −120	Sb −103	Te −190.16	I −295.16
Cs −45.51	Ba 0	Tl −20	Pb −35.1	Bi −91.3	Po −180	At −270

*Derived from data taken from H. Hotop and W. C. Lineberger: *Journal of Physical Chemistry, Reference Data*, Vol. 14, p. 731, 1985. (This paper also includes data for the transition metals.) Some values are known to more than two decimal places. See also: http://en.wikipedia.org/wiki/Electron_affinity_(data_page)
†Elements with an electron attachment enthalpy of zero indicate that a stable anion A^- of the element does not exist in the gas phase.

Vapor Pressure of Water at Various Temperatures

Table 15 Vapor Pressure of Water at Various Temperatures

Temperature (°C)	Vapor Pressure (torr)	Temperature (°C)	Vapor Pressure (torr)	Temperature (°C)	Vapor Pressure (torr)	Temperature (°C)	Vapor Pressure (torr)
−10	2.1	21	18.7	51	97.2	81	369.7
−9	2.3	22	19.8	52	102.1	82	384.9
−8	2.5	23	21.1	53	107.2	83	400.6
−7	2.7	24	22.4	54	112.5	84	416.8
−6	2.9	25	23.8	55	118.0	85	433.6
−5	3.2	26	25.2	56	123.8	86	450.9
−4	3.4	27	26.7	57	129.8	87	468.7
−3	3.7	28	28.3	58	136.1	88	487.1
−2	4.0	29	30.0	59	142.6	89	506.1
−1	4.3	30	31.8	60	149.4	90	525.8
0	4.6	31	33.7	61	156.4	91	546.1
1	4.9	32	35.7	62	163.8	92	567.0
2	5.3	33	37.7	63	171.4	93	588.6
3	5.7	34	39.9	64	179.3	94	610.9
4	6.1	35	42.2	65	187.5	95	633.9
5	6.5	36	44.6	66	196.1	96	657.6
6	7.0	37	47.1	67	205.0	97	682.1
7	7.5	38	49.7	68	214.2	98	707.3
8	8.0	39	52.4	69	223.7	99	733.2
9	8.6	40	55.3	70	233.7	100	760.0
10	9.2	41	58.3	71	243.9	101	787.6
11	9.8	42	61.5	72	254.6	102	815.9
12	10.5	43	64.8	73	265.7	103	845.1
13	11.2	44	68.3	74	277.2	104	875.1
14	12.0	45	71.9	75	289.1	105	906.1
15	12.8	46	75.7	76	301.4	106	937.9
16	13.6	47	79.6	77	314.1	107	970.6
17	14.5	48	83.7	78	327.3	108	1004.4
18	15.5	49	88.0	79	341.0	109	1038.9
19	16.5	50	92.5	80	355.1	110	1074.6
20	17.5						

Ionization Constants for Aqueous Weak Acids at 25 °C

Table 16 Ionization Constants for Aqueous Weak Acids at 25 °C

ACID	FORMULA AND IONIZATION EQUATION	K_a
Acetic	$CH_3CO_2H \rightleftharpoons H^+ + CH_3CO_2^-$	1.8×10^{-5}
Arsenic	$H_3AsO_4 \rightleftharpoons H^+ + H_2AsO_4^-$ $H_2AsO_4^- \rightleftharpoons H^+ + HAsO_4^{2-}$ $HAsO_4^{2-} \rightleftharpoons H^+ + AsO_4^{3-}$	$K_1 = 5.8 \times 10^{-3}$ $K_2 = 1.1 \times 10^{-7}$ $K_3 = 3.2 \times 10^{-12}$
Arsenous	$H_3AsO_3 \rightleftharpoons H^+ + H_2AsO_3^-$ $H_2AsO_3^- \rightleftharpoons H^+ + HAsO_3^{2-}$	$K_1 = 6.0 \times 10^{-10}$ $K_2 = 3.0 \times 10^{-14}$
Benzoic	$C_6H_5CO_2H \rightleftharpoons H^+ + C_6H_5CO_2^-$	6.3×10^{-5}
Boric	$H_3BO_3 \rightleftharpoons H^+ + H_2BO_3^-$ $H_2BO_3^- \rightleftharpoons H^+ + HBO_3^{2-}$ $HBO_3^{2-} \rightleftharpoons H^+ + BO_3^{3-}$	$K_1 = 7.3 \times 10^{-10}$ $K_2 = 1.8 \times 10^{-13}$ $K_3 = 1.6 \times 10^{-14}$
Carbonic	$H_2CO_3 \rightleftharpoons H^+ + HCO_3^-$ $HCO_3^- \rightleftharpoons H^+ + CO_3^{2-}$	$K_1 = 4.2 \times 10^{-7}$ $K_2 = 4.8 \times 10^{-11}$
Citric	$H_3C_6H_5O_7 \rightleftharpoons H^+ + H_2C_6H_5O_7^-$ $H_2C_6H_5O_7^- \rightleftharpoons H^+ + HC_6H_5O_7^{2-}$ $HC_6H_5O_7^{2-} \rightleftharpoons H^+ + C_6H_5O_7^{3-}$	$K_1 = 7.4 \times 10^{-3}$ $K_2 = 1.7 \times 10^{-5}$ $K_3 = 4.0 \times 10^{-7}$
Cyanic	$HOCN \rightleftharpoons H^+ + OCN^-$	3.5×10^{-4}
Formic	$HCO_2H \rightleftharpoons H^+ + HCO_2^-$	1.8×10^{-4}
Hydrazoic	$HN_3 \rightleftharpoons H^+ + N_3^-$	1.9×10^{-5}
Hydrocyanic	$HCN \rightleftharpoons H^+ + CN^-$	4.0×10^{-10}
Hydrofluoric	$HF \rightleftharpoons H^+ + F^-$	7.2×10^{-4}
Hydrogen peroxide	$H_2O_2 \rightleftharpoons H^+ + HO_2^-$	2.4×10^{-12}
Hydrosulfuric	$H_2S \rightleftharpoons H^+ + HS^-$ $HS^- \rightleftharpoons H^+ + S^{2-}$	$K_1 = 1 \times 10^{-7}$ $K_2 = 1 \times 10^{-19}$
Hypobromous	$HOBr \rightleftharpoons H^+ + OBr^-$	2.5×10^{-9}
Hypochlorous	$HOCl \rightleftharpoons H^+ + OCl^-$	3.5×10^{-8}
Nitrous	$HNO_2 \rightleftharpoons H^+ + NO_2^-$	4.5×10^{-4}
Oxalic	$H_2C_2O_4 \rightleftharpoons H^+ + HC_2O_4^-$ $HC_2O_4^- \rightleftharpoons H^+ + C_2O_4^{2-}$	$K_1 = 5.9 \times 10^{-2}$ $K_2 = 6.4 \times 10^{-5}$

(continued)

Table 16 Ionization Constants for Aqueous Weak Acids at 25 °C (continued)

Acid	Formula and Ionization Equation	K_a
Phenol	$C_6H_5OH \rightleftharpoons H^+ + C_6H_5O^-$	1.3×10^{-10}
Phosphoric	$H_3PO_4 \rightleftharpoons H^+ + H_2PO_4^-$ $H_2PO_4^- \rightleftharpoons H^+ + HPO_4^{2-}$ $HPO_4^{2-} \rightleftharpoons H^+ + PO_4^{3-}$	$K_1 = 7.5 \times 10^{-3}$ $K_2 = 6.2 \times 10^{-8}$ $K_3 = 3.6 \times 10^{-13}$
Phosphorous	$H_3PO_3 \rightleftharpoons H^+ + H_2PO_3^-$ $H_2PO_3^- \rightleftharpoons H^+ + HPO_3^{2-}$	$K_1 = 1.6 \times 10^{-2}$ $K_2 = 7.0 \times 10^{-7}$
Selenic	$H_2SeO_4 \rightleftharpoons H^+ + HSeO_4^-$ $HSeO_4^- \rightleftharpoons H^+ + SeO_4^{2-}$	K_1 = very large $K_2 = 1.2 \times 10^{-2}$
Selenous	$H_2SeO_3 \rightleftharpoons H^+ + HSeO_3^-$ $HSeO_3^- \rightleftharpoons H^+ + SeO_3^{2-}$	$K_1 = 2.7 \times 10^{-3}$ $K_2 = 2.5 \times 10^{-7}$
Sulfuric	$H_2SO_4 \rightleftharpoons H^+ + HSO_4^-$ $HSO_4^- \rightleftharpoons H^+ + SO_4^{2-}$	K_1 = very large $K_2 = 1.2 \times 10^{-2}$
Sulfurous	$H_2SO_3 \rightleftharpoons H^+ + HSO_3^-$ $HSO_3^- \rightleftharpoons H^+ + SO_3^{2-}$	$K_1 = 1.2 \times 10^{-2}$ $K_2 = 6.2 \times 10^{-8}$
Tellurous	$H_2TeO_3 \rightleftharpoons H^+ + HTeO_3^-$ $HTeO_3^- \rightleftharpoons H^+ + TeO_3^{2-}$	$K_1 = 2 \times 10^{-3}$ $K_2 = 1 \times 10^{-8}$

Ionization Constants for Aqueous Weak Bases at 25 °C

Table 17 Ionization Constants for Aqueous Weak Bases at 25 °C

Base	Formula and Ionization Equation	K_b
Ammonia	$NH_3 + H_2O \rightleftharpoons NH_4^+ + OH^-$	1.8×10^{-5}
Aniline	$C_6H_5NH_2 + H_2O \rightleftharpoons C_6H_5NH_3^+ + OH^-$	4.0×10^{-10}
Dimethylamine	$(CH_3)_2NH + H_2O \rightleftharpoons (CH_3)_2NH_2^+ + OH^-$	7.4×10^{-4}
Ethylamine	$C_2H_5NH_2 + H_2O \rightleftharpoons C_2H_5NH_3^+ + OH^-$	4.3×10^{-4}
Ethylenediamine	$H_2NCH_2CH_2NH_2 + H_2O \rightleftharpoons H_2NCH_2CH_2NH_3^+ + OH^-$ $H_2NCH_2CH_2NH_3^+ + H_2O \rightleftharpoons H_3NCH_2CH_2NH_3^{2+} + OH^-$	$K_1 = 8.5 \times 10^{-5}$ $K_2 = 2.7 \times 10^{-8}$
Hydrazine	$N_2H_4 + H_2O \rightleftharpoons N_2H_5^+ + OH^-$ $N_2H_5^+ + H_2O \rightleftharpoons N_2H_6^{2+} + OH^-$	$K_1 = 8.5 \times 10^{-7}$ $K_2 = 8.9 \times 10^{-16}$
Hydroxylamine	$NH_2OH + H_2O \rightleftharpoons NH_3OH^+ + OH^-$	6.6×10^{-9}
Methylamine	$CH_3NH_2 + H_2O \rightleftharpoons CH_3NH_3^+ + OH^-$	5.0×10^{-4}
Pyridine	$C_5H_5N + H_2O \rightleftharpoons C_5H_5NH^+ + OH^-$	1.5×10^{-9}
Trimethylamine	$(CH_3)_3N + H_2O \rightleftharpoons (CH_3)_3NH^+ + OH^-$	7.4×10^{-5}

Solubility Product Constants for Some Inorganic Compounds at 25 °C

Table 18A Solubility Product Constants at 25 °C

CATION	COMPOUND	K_{sp}
Ba^{2+}	*$BaCrO_4$	1.2×10^{-10}
	$BaCO_3$	2.6×10^{-9}
	BaF_2	1.8×10^{-7}
	*$BaSO_4$	1.1×10^{-10}
Ca^{2+}	$CaCO_3$ (calcite)	3.4×10^{-9}
	*CaF_2	5.3×10^{-11}
	*$Ca(OH)_2$	5.5×10^{-5}
	$CaSO_4$	4.9×10^{-5}
Cu^{+}, Cu^{2+}	CuBr	6.3×10^{-9}
	CuI	1.3×10^{-12}
	$Cu(OH)_2$	2.2×10^{-20}
	CuSCN	1.8×10^{-13}
Au^{+}	AuCl	2.0×10^{-13}
Fe^{2+}	$FeCO_3$	3.1×10^{-11}
	$Fe(OH)_2$	4.9×10^{-17}
Pb^{2+}	$PbBr_2$	6.6×10^{-6}
	$PbCO_3$	7.4×10^{-14}
	$PbCl_2$	1.7×10^{-5}
	$PbCrO_4$	2.8×10^{-13}
	PbF_2	3.3×10^{-8}
	PbI_2	9.8×10^{-9}
	$Pb(OH)_2$	1.4×10^{-15}
	$PbSO_4$	2.5×10^{-8}
Mg^{2+}	$MgCO_3$	6.8×10^{-6}
	MgF_2	5.2×10^{-11}
	$Mg(OH)_2$	5.6×10^{-12}
Mn^{2+}	$MnCO_3$	2.3×10^{-11}
	*$Mn(OH)_2$	1.9×10^{-13}
Hg_2^{2+}	*Hg_2Br_2	6.4×10^{-23}
	Hg_2Cl_2	1.4×10^{-18}
	*Hg_2I_2	2.9×10^{-29}
	Hg_2SO_4	6.5×10^{-7}
Ni^{2+}	$NiCO_3$	1.4×10^{-7}
	$Ni(OH)_2$	5.5×10^{-16}
Ag^{+}	*AgBr	5.4×10^{-13}
	*$AgBrO_3$	5.4×10^{-5}
	$AgCH_3CO_2$	1.9×10^{-3}
	AgCN	6.0×10^{-17}
	Ag_2CO_3	8.5×10^{-12}
	*$Ag_2C_2O_4$	5.4×10^{-12}
	*AgCl	1.8×10^{-10}
	Ag_2CrO_4	1.1×10^{-12}
	*AgI	8.5×10^{-17}
	AgSCN	1.0×10^{-12}
	*Ag_2SO_4	1.2×10^{-5}
Sr^{2+}	$SrCO_3$	5.6×10^{-10}
	SrF_2	4.3×10^{-9}
	$SrSO_4$	3.4×10^{-7}
Tl^{+}	TlBr	3.7×10^{-6}
	TlCl	1.9×10^{-4}
	TlI	5.5×10^{-8}
Zn^{2+}	$Zn(OH)_2$	3×10^{-17}
	$Zn(CN)_2$	8.0×10^{-12}

The values reported in this table were taken from J. A. Dean: *Lange's Handbook of Chemistry,* 15th ed. New York: McGraw-Hill Publishers, 1999. Values have been rounded off to two significant figures.

*Calculated solubility from these K_{sp} values will match experimental solubility for this compound within a factor of 2. Experimental values for solubilities are given in R. W. Clark and J. M. Bonicamp: *Journal of Chemical Education,* Vol. 75, p. 1182, 1998.

Table 18B Modified K'_{sp} Values* for Some Metal Sulfides at 25 °C

SUBSTANCE	K_{spa}
HgS (red)	4×10^{-54}
HgS (black)	2×10^{-53}
CuS	6×10^{-37}
PbS	3×10^{-28}
CdS	8×10^{-28}
SnS	1×10^{-26}
FeS	6×10^{-19}

*The equilibrium constant values for these metal sulfides refers to the equilibrium $MS(s) + H_2O(\ell) \rightleftharpoons M^{2+}(aq) + OH^-(aq) + HS^-(aq)$; see R. J. Myers, *Journal of Chemical Education*, Vol. 63, p. 687, 1986.

Formation Constants for Some Complex Ions in Aqueous Solution at 25 °C

Table 19 Formation Constants for Some Complex Ions in Aqueous Solution at 25 °C*

FORMATION EQUILIBRIUM	*K*
$Ag^+ + 2\ Br^- \rightleftharpoons [AgBr_2]^-$	2.1×10^7
$Ag^+ + 2\ Cl^- \rightleftharpoons [AgCl_2]^-$	1.1×10^5
$Ag^+ + 2\ CN^- \rightleftharpoons [Ag(CN)_2]^-$	1.3×10^{21}
$Ag^+ + 2\ S_2O_3^{2-} \rightleftharpoons [Ag(S_2O_3)_2]^{3-}$	2.9×10^{13}
$Ag^+ + 2\ NH_3 \rightleftharpoons [Ag(NH_3)_2]^+$	1.1×10^7
$Al^{3+} + 6\ F^- \rightleftharpoons [AlF_6]^{3-}$	6.9×10^{19}
$Al^{3+} + 4\ OH^- \rightleftharpoons [Al(OH)_4]^-$	1.1×10^{33}
$Au^+ + 2\ CN^- \rightleftharpoons [Au(CN)_2]^-$	2.0×10^{38}
$Cd^{2+} + 4\ CN^- \rightleftharpoons [Cd(CN)_4]^{2-}$	6.0×10^{18}
$Cd^{2+} + 4\ NH_3 \rightleftharpoons [Cd(NH_3)_4]^{2+}$	1.3×10^7
$Co^{2+} + 6\ NH_3 \rightleftharpoons [Co(NH_3)_6]^{2+}$	1.3×10^5
$Cu^+ + 2\ CN^- \rightleftharpoons [Cu(CN)_2]^-$	1.0×10^{24}
$Cu^+ + 2\ Cl^- \rightleftharpoons [CuCl_2]^-$	3.2×10^5
$Cu^{2+} + 4\ NH_3 \rightleftharpoons [Cu(NH_3)_4]^{2+}$	2.1×10^{13}
$Fe^{2+} + 6\ CN^- \rightleftharpoons [Fe(CN)_6]^{4-}$	1.0×10^{35}
$Hg^{2+} + 4\ Cl^- \rightleftharpoons [HgCl_4]^{2-}$	1.2×10^{15}
$Ni^{2+} + 4\ CN^- \rightleftharpoons [Ni(CN)_4]^{2-}$	2.0×10^{31}
$Ni^{2+} + 6\ NH_3 \rightleftharpoons [Ni(NH_3)_6]^{2+}$	5.5×10^8
$Zn^{2+} + 4\ OH^- \rightleftharpoons [Zn(OH)_4]^{2-}$	4.6×10^{17}
$Zn^{2+} + 4\ NH_3 \rightleftharpoons [Zn(NH_3)_4]^{2+}$	2.9×10^9

*Data reported in this table are taken from J. A. Dean: *Lange's Handbook of Chemistry*, 15th ed. New York: McGraw-Hill Publishers, 1999.

Selected Thermodynamic Values

Table 20 Selected Thermodynamic Values*

SPECIES	$\Delta_f H°$ (298.15 K) (kJ/mol)	$S°$ (298.15 K) (J/K · mol)	$\Delta_f G°$ (298.15 K) (kJ/mol)
Aluminum			
Al(s)	0	28.3	0
$AlCl_3$(s)	−705.63	109.29	−630.0
Al_2O_3(s)	−1675.7	50.92	−1582.3
Barium			
$BaCl_2$(s)	−858.6	123.68	−810.4
$BaCO_3$(s)	−1213	112.1	−1134.41
BaO(s)	−548.1	72.05	−520.38
$BaSO_4$(s)	−1473.2	132.2	−1362.2
Beryllium			
Be(s)	0	9.5	0
$Be(OH)_2$(s)	−902.5	51.9	−815.0
Boron			
BCl_3(g)	−402.96	290.17	−387.95
Bromine			
Br(g)	111.884	175.022	82.396
$Br_2(\ell)$	0	152.2	0
Br_2(g)	30.91	245.47	3.12
BrF_3(g)	−255.60	292.53	−229.43
HBr(g)	−36.29	198.70	−53.45

*Most thermodynamic data are taken from the NIST Chemistry WebBook at http://webbook.nist.gov.

(continued)

Table 20 Selected Thermodynamic Values (continued)

Species	$\Delta_f H°$ (298.15 K) (kJ/mol)	$S°$ (298.15 K) (J/K · mol)	$\Delta_f G°$ (298.15 K) (kJ/mol)
Calcium			
Ca(s)	0	41.59	0
Ca(g)	178.2	158.884	144.3
Ca^{2+}(g)	1925.90	—	—
CaC_2(s)	−59.8	70.	−64.93
$CaCO_3$(s, calcite)	−1207.6	91.7	−1129.16
$CaCl_2$(s)	−795.8	104.6	−748.1
CaF_2(s)	−1219.6	68.87	−1167.3
CaH_2(s)	−186.2	42	−147.2
CaO(s)	−635.09	38.2	−603.42
CaS(s)	−482.4	56.5	−477.4
$Ca(OH)_2$(s)	−986.09	83.39	−898.43
$Ca(OH)_2$(aq)	−1002.82	—	−868.07
$CaSO_4$(s)	−1434.52	106.5	−1322.02
Carbon			
C(s, graphite)	0	5.6	0
C(s, diamond)	1.8	2.377	2.900
C(g)	716.67	158.1	671.2
CCl_4(ℓ)	−128.4	214.39	−57.63
CCl_4(g)	−95.98	309.65	−53.61
$CHCl_3$(ℓ)	−134.47	201.7	−73.66
$CHCl_3$(g)	−103.18	295.61	−70.4
CH_4(g, methane)	−74.87	186.26	−50.8
C_2H_2(g, ethyne)	226.73	200.94	209.20
C_2H_4(g, ethene)	52.47	219.36	68.35
C_2H_6(g, ethane)	−83.85	229.2	−31.89
C_3H_8(g, propane)	−104.7	270.3	−24.4
C_6H_6(ℓ, benzene)	48.95	173.26	124.21
CH_3OH(ℓ, methanol)	−238.4	127.19	−166.14
CH_3OH(g, methanol)	−201.0	239.7	−162.5
C_2H_5OH(ℓ, ethanol)	−277.0	160.7	−174.7
C_2H_5OH(g, ethanol)	−235.3	282.70	−168.49

(continued)

Table 20 Selected Thermodynamic Values (continued)

SPECIES	$\Delta_f H°$ (298.15 K) (kJ/mol)	$S°$ (298.15 K) (J/K · mol)	$\Delta_f G°$ (298.15 K) (kJ/mol)
Carbon (continued)			
CO(g)	−110.525	197.674	−137.168
CO_2(g)	−393.509	213.74	−394.359
$CS_2(\ell)$	89.41	151	65.2
CS_2(g)	116.7	237.8	66.61
$COCl_2$(g)	−218.8	283.53	−204.6
Cesium			
Cs(s)	0	85.23	0
Cs^+(g)	457.964	—	—
CsCl(s)	−443.04	101.17	−414.53
Chlorine			
Cl(g)	121.3	165.19	105.3
Cl^-(g)	−233.13	—	—
Cl_2(g)	0	223.08	0
HCl(g)	−92.31	186.2	−95.09
HCl(aq)	−167.159	56.5	−131.26
Chromium			
Cr(s)	0	23.62	0
Cr_2O_3(s)	−1134.7	80.65	−1052.95
$CrCl_3$(s)	−556.5	123.0	−486.1
Copper			
Cu(s)	0	33.17	0
CuO(s)	−156.06	42.59	−128.3
$CuCl_2$(s)	−220.1	108.07	−175.7
$CuSO_4$(s)	−769.98	109.05	−660.75
Fluorine			
F_2(g)	0	202.8	0
F(g)	78.99	158.754	61.91
F^-(g)	−255.39	—	—
F^-(aq)	−332.63	—	−278.79
HF(g)	−273.3	173.779	−273.2
HF(aq)	−332.63	88.7	−278.79

(continued)

Table 20 Selected Thermodynamic Values (continued)

Species	$\Delta_f H°$ (298.15 K) (kJ/mol)	$S°$ (298.15 K) (J/K · mol)	$\Delta_f G°$ (298.15 K) (kJ/mol)
Hydrogen			
H_2(g)	0	130.7	0
H(g)	217.965	114.713	203.247
H^+(g)	1536.202	—	—
$H_2O(\ell)$	−285.83	69.95	−237.15
H_2O(g)	−241.83	188.84	−228.59
$H_2O_2(\ell)$	−187.78	109.6	−120.35
Iodine			
I_2(s)	0	116.135	0
I_2(g)	62.438	260.69	19.327
I(g)	106.838	180.791	70.250
I^-(g)	−197	—	—
ICl(g)	17.51	247.56	−5.73
Iron			
Fe(s)	0	27.78	0
FeO(s)	−272	—	—
Fe_2O_3(s, hematite)	−825.5	87.40	−742.2
Fe_3O_4(s, magnetite)	−1118.4	146.4	−1015.4
$FeCl_2$(s)	−341.79	117.95	−302.30
$FeCl_3$(s)	−399.49	142.3	−344.00
FeS_2(s, pyrite)	−178.2	52.93	−166.9
$Fe(CO)_5(\ell)$	−774.0	338.1	−705.3
Lead			
Pb(s)	0	64.81	0
$PbCl_2$(s)	−359.41	136.0	−314.10
PbO(s, yellow)	−219	66.5	−196
PbO_2(s)	−277.4	68.6	−217.39
PbS(s)	−100.4	91.2	−98.7
Lithium			
Li(s)	0	29.12	0
Li^+(g)	685.783	—	—
LiOH(s)	−484.93	42.81	−438.96

(continued)

Table 20 Selected Thermodynamic Values (continued)

Species	$\Delta_f H°$ (298.15 K) (kJ/mol)	$S°$ (298.15 K) (J/K · mol)	$\Delta_f G°$ (298.15 K) (kJ/mol)
Lithium (continued)			
$LiOH(aq)$	−508.48	2.80	−450.58
$LiCl(s)$	−408.701	59.33	−384.37
Magnesium			
$Mg(s)$	0	32.67	0
$MgCl_2(s)$	−641.62	89.62	−592.09
$MgCO_3(s)$	−1111.69	65.84	−1028.2
$MgO(s)$	−601.24	26.85	−568.93
$Mg(OH)_2(s)$	−924.54	63.18	−833.51
$MgS(s)$	−346.0	50.33	−341.8
Mercury			
$Hg(\ell)$	0	76.02	0
$HgCl_2(s)$	−224.3	146.0	−178.6
HgO(s, red)	−90.83	70.29	−58.539
HgS(s, red)	−58.2	82.4	−50.6
Nickel			
$Ni(s)$	0	29.87	0
$NiO(s)$	−239.7	37.99	−211.7
$NiCl_2(s)$	−305.332	97.65	−259.032
Nitrogen			
$N_2(g)$	0	191.56	0
$N(g)$	472.704	153.298	455.563
$NH_3(g)$	−45.90	192.77	−16.37
$N_2H_4(\ell)$	50.63	121.52	149.45
$NH_4Cl(s)$	−314.55	94.85	−203.08
$NH_4Cl(aq)$	−299.66	169.9	−210.57
$NH_4NO_3(s)$	−365.56	151.08	−183.84
$NH_4NO_3(aq)$	−339.87	259.8	−190.57
$NO(g)$	90.29	210.76	86.58
$NO_2(g)$	33.1	240.04	51.23
$N_2O(g)$	82.05	219.85	104.20
$N_2O_4(g)$	9.08	304.38	97.73

(continued)

Table 20 Selected Thermodynamic Values (continued)

Species	$\Delta_f H°$ (298.15 K) (kJ/mol)	$S°$ (298.15 K) (J/K · mol)	$\Delta_f G°$ (298.15 K) (kJ/mol)
Nitrogen (continued)			
NOCl(g)	51.71	261.8	66.08
$HNO_3(\ell)$	−174.10	155.60	−80.71
HNO_3(g)	−135.06	266.38	−74.72
HNO_3(aq)	−207.36	146.4	−111.25
Oxygen			
O_2(g)	0	205.07	0
O(g)	249.170	161.055	231.731
O_3(g)	142.67	238.92	163.2
Phosphorus			
P_4(s, white)	0	41.1	0
P_4(s, red)	−17.6	22.80	−12.1
P(g)	314.64	163.193	278.25
PH_3(g)	5.47	210.24	6.64
PCl_3(g)	−287.0	311.78	−267.8
P_4O_{10}(s)	−2984.0	228.86	−2697.7
$H_3PO_4(\ell)$	−1279.0	110.5	−1119.1
Potassium			
K(s)	0	64.63	0
KCl(s)	−436.68	82.56	−408.77
$KClO_3$(s)	−397.73	143.1	−296.25
KI(s)	−327.90	106.32	−324.892
KOH(s)	−424.72	78.9	−378.92
KOH(aq)	−482.37	91.6	−440.50
Silicon			
Si(s)	0	18.82	0
$SiBr_4(\ell)$	−457.3	277.8	−443.9
SiC(s)	−65.3	16.61	−62.8
$SiCl_4$(g)	−662.75	330.86	−622.76
SiH_4(g)	34.31	204.65	56.84
SiF_4(g)	−1614.94	282.49	−1572.65
SiO_2(s, quartz)	−910.86	41.46	−856.97

(continued)

Table 20 Selected Thermodynamic Values (continued)

Species	$\Delta_f H°$ (298.15 K) (kJ/mol)	$S°$ (298.15 K) (J/K · mol)	$\Delta_f G°$ (298.15 K) (kJ/mol)
Silver			
Ag(s)	0	42.55	0
Ag_2O(s)	−31.1	121.3	−11.32
AgCl(s)	−127.01	96.25	−109.76
$AgNO_3$(s)	−124.39	140.92	−33.41
Sodium			
Na(s)	0	51.21	0
Na(g)	107.3	153.765	76.83
Na^+(g)	609.358	—	—
NaBr(s)	−361.02	86.82	−348.983
NaCl(s)	−411.12	72.11	−384.04
NaCl(g)	−181.42	229.79	−201.33
NaCl(aq)	−407.27	115.5	−393.133
NaOH(s)	−425.93	64.46	−379.75
NaOH(aq)	−469.15	48.1	−418.09
Na_2CO_3(s)	−1130.77	134.79	−1048.08
Sulfur			
S(s, rhombic)	0	32.1	0
S(g)	278.98	167.83	236.51
S_2Cl_2(g)	−18.4	331.5	−31.8
SF_6(g)	−1209	291.82	−1105.3
H_2S(g)	−20.63	205.79	−33.56
SO_2(g)	−296.84	248.21	−300.13
SO_3(g)	−395.77	256.77	−371.04
$SOCl_2$(g)	−212.5	309.77	−198.3
H_2SO_4(ℓ)	−814	156.9	−689.96
H_2SO_4(aq)	−909.27	20.1	−744.53
Tin			
Sn(s, white)	0	51.08	0
Sn(s, gray)	−2.09	44.14	0.13
$SnCl_4$(ℓ)	−511.3	258.6	−440.15
$SnCl_4$(g)	−471.5	365.8	−432.31
SnO_2(s)	−577.63	49.04	−515.88

(continued)

Table 20 Selected Thermodynamic Values (continued)

Species	$\Delta_f H°$ (298.15 K) (kJ/mol)	$S°$ (298.15 K) (J/K · mol)	$\Delta_f G°$ (298.15 K) (kJ/mol)
Titanium			
Ti(s)	0	30.72	0
$TiCl_4(\ell)$	−804.2	252.34	−737.2
$TiCl_4(g)$	−763.16	354.84	−726.7
$TiO_2(s)$	−939.7	49.92	−884.5
Zinc			
Zn(s)	0	41.63	0
$ZnCl_2(s)$	−415.05	111.46	−369.398
ZnO(s)	−348.28	43.64	−318.30
ZnS(s, sphalerite)	−205.98	57.7	−201.29

Standard Reduction Potentials in Aqueous Solution at 25 °C

Table 21 Standard Reduction Potentials in Aqueous Solution at 25 °C

Acidic Solution	Standard Reduction Potential $E°$ (volts)
$F_2(g) + 2e^- \longrightarrow 2F^-(aq)$	2.87
$Co^{3+}(aq) + e^- \longrightarrow Co^{2+}(aq)$	1.82
$Pb^{4+}(aq) + 2e^- \longrightarrow Pb^{2+}(aq)$	1.8
$H_2O_2(aq) + 2H^+(aq) + 2e^- \longrightarrow 2H_2O$	1.77
$NiO_2(s) + 4H^+(aq) + 2e^- \longrightarrow Ni^{2+}(aq) + 2H_2O$	1.7
$PbO_2(s) + SO_4^{2-}(aq) + 4H^+(aq) + 2e^- \longrightarrow PbSO_4(s) + 2H_2O$	1.685
$Au^+(aq) + e^- \longrightarrow Au(s)$	1.68
$2HClO(aq) + 2H^+(aq) + 2e^- \longrightarrow Cl_2(g) + 2H_2O$	1.63
$Ce^{4+}(aq) + e^- \longrightarrow Ce^{3+}(aq)$	1.61
$NaBiO_3(s) + 6H^+(aq) + 2e^- \longrightarrow Bi^{3+}(aq) + Na^+(aq) + 3H_2O$	≈1.6
$MnO_4^-(aq) + 8H^+(aq) + 5e^- \longrightarrow Mn^{2+}(aq) + 4H_2O$	1.51
$Au^{3+}(aq) + 3e^- \longrightarrow Au(s)$	1.50
$ClO_3^-(aq) + 6H^+(aq) + 5e^- \longrightarrow \frac{1}{2}Cl_2(g) + 3H_2O$	1.47
$BrO_3^-(aq) + 6H^+(aq) + 6e^- \longrightarrow Br^-(aq) + 3H_2O$	1.44
$Cl_2(g) + 2e^- \longrightarrow 2Cl^-(aq)$	1.36
$Cr_2O_7^{2-}(aq) + 14H^+(aq) + 6e^- \longrightarrow 2Cr^{3+}(aq) + 7H_2O$	1.33
$N_2H_5^+(aq) + 3H^+(aq) + 2e^- \longrightarrow 2NH_4^+(aq)$	1.24
$MnO_2(s) + 4H^+(aq) + 2e^- \longrightarrow Mn^{2+}(aq) + 2H_2O$	1.23
$O_2(g) + 4H^+(aq) + 4e^- \longrightarrow 2H_2O$	1.229
$Pt^{2+}(aq) + 2e^- \longrightarrow Pt(s)$	1.2
$IO_3^-(aq) + 6H^+(aq) + 5e^- \longrightarrow \frac{1}{2}I_2(aq) + 3H_2O$	1.195
$ClO_4^-(aq) + 2H^+(aq) + 2e^- \longrightarrow ClO_3^-(aq) + H_2O$	1.19
$Br_2(\ell) + 2e^- \longrightarrow 2Br^-(aq)$	1.08

(continued)

Table 21 Standard Reduction Potentials in Aqueous Solution at 25 °C (continued)

Acidic Solution	Standard Reduction Potential $E°$ (volts)
$AuCl_4^-(aq) + 3\,e^- \longrightarrow Au(s) + 4\,Cl^-(aq)$	1.00
$Pd^{2+}(aq) + 2\,e^- \longrightarrow Pd(s)$	0.987
$NO_3^-(aq) + 4\,H^+(aq) + 3\,e^- \longrightarrow NO(g) + 2\,H_2O$	0.96
$NO_3^-(aq) + 3\,H^+(aq) + 2\,e^- \longrightarrow HNO_2(aq) + H_2O$	0.94
$2\,Hg^{2+}(aq) + 2\,e^- \longrightarrow Hg_2^{2+}(aq)$	0.920
$Hg^{2+}(aq) + 2\,e^- \longrightarrow Hg(\ell)$	0.855
$Ag^+(aq) + e^- \longrightarrow Ag(s)$	0.7994
$Hg_2^{2+}(aq) + 2\,e^- \longrightarrow 2\,Hg(\ell)$	0.789
$Fe^{3+}(aq) + e^- \longrightarrow Fe^{2+}(aq)$	0.771
$SbCl_6^-(aq) + 2\,e^- \longrightarrow SbCl_4^-(aq) + 2\,Cl^-(aq)$	0.75
$[PtCl_4]^{2-}(aq) + 2\,e^- \longrightarrow Pt(s) + 4\,Cl^-(aq)$	0.73
$O_2(g) + 2\,H^+(aq) + 2\,e^- \longrightarrow H_2O_2(aq)$	0.682
$[PtCl_6]^{2-}(aq) + 2\,e^- \longrightarrow [PtCl_4]^{2-}(aq) + 2\,Cl^-(aq)$	0.68
$I_2(aq) + 2\,e^- \longrightarrow 2\,I^-(aq)$	0.621
$H_3AsO_4(aq) + 2\,H^+(aq) + 2\,e^- \longrightarrow H_3AsO_3(aq) + H_2O$	0.58
$I_2(s) + 2\,e^- \longrightarrow 2\,I^-(aq)$	0.535
$TeO_2(s) + 4\,H^+(aq) + 4\,e^- \longrightarrow Te(s) + 2\,H_2O$	0.529
$Cu^+(aq) + e^- \longrightarrow Cu(s)$	0.521
$[RhCl_6]^{3-}(aq) + 3\,e^- \longrightarrow Rh(s) + 6\,Cl^-(aq)$	0.44
$Cu^{2+}(aq) + 2\,e^- \longrightarrow Cu(s)$	0.337
$Hg_2Cl_2(s) + 2\,e^- \longrightarrow 2\,Hg(\ell) + 2\,Cl^-(aq)$	0.27
$AgCl(s) + e^- \longrightarrow Ag(s) + Cl^-(aq)$	0.222
$SO_4^{2-}(aq) + 4\,H^+(aq) + 2\,e^- \longrightarrow SO_2(g) + 2\,H_2O$	0.20
$SO_4^{2-}(aq) + 4\,H^+(aq) + 2\,e^- \longrightarrow H_2SO_3(aq) + H_2O$	0.17
$Cu^{2+}(aq) + e^- \longrightarrow Cu^+(aq)$	0.153
$Sn^{4+}(aq) + 2\,e^- \longrightarrow Sn^{2+}(aq)$	0.15
$S(s) + 2\,H^+ + 2\,e^- \longrightarrow H_2S(aq)$	0.14
$AgBr(s) + e^- \longrightarrow Ag(s) + Br^-(aq)$	0.0713
$2\,H^+(aq) + 2\,e^- \longrightarrow H_2(g)$(reference electrode)	0.0000
$N_2O(g) + 6\,H^+(aq) + H_2O + 4\,e^- \longrightarrow 2\,NH_3OH^+(aq)$	−0.05
$Pb^{2+}(aq) + 2\,e^- \longrightarrow Pb(s)$	−0.126
$Sn^{2+}(aq) + 2\,e^- \longrightarrow Sn(s)$	−0.14

(continued)

Table 21 Standard Reduction Potentials in Aqueous Solution at 25 °C (continued)

ACIDIC SOLUTION	STANDARD REDUCTION POTENTIAL $E°$ (VOLTS)
$AgI(s) + e^- \longrightarrow Ag(s) + I^-(aq)$	−0.15
$[SnF_6]^{2-}(aq) + 4\ e^- \longrightarrow Sn(s) + 6\ F^-(aq)$	−0.25
$Ni^{2+}(aq) + 2\ e^- \longrightarrow Ni(s)$	−0.25
$Co^{2+}(aq) + 2\ e^- \longrightarrow Co(s)$	−0.28
$Tl^+(aq) + e^- \longrightarrow Tl(s)$	−0.34
$PbSO_4(s) + 2\ e^- \longrightarrow Pb(s) + SO_4^{2-}(aq)$	−0.356
$Se(s) + 2\ H^+(aq) + 2\ e^- \longrightarrow H_2Se(aq)$	−0.40
$Cd^{2+}(aq) + 2\ e^- \longrightarrow Cd(s)$	−0.403
$Cr^{3+}(aq) + e^- \longrightarrow Cr^{2+}(aq)$	−0.41
$Fe^{2+}(aq) + 2\ e^- \longrightarrow Fe(s)$	−0.44
$2\ CO_2(g) + 2\ H^+(aq) + 2\ e^- \longrightarrow H_2C_2O_4(aq)$	−0.49
$Ga^{3+}(aq) + 3\ e^- \longrightarrow Ga(s)$	−0.53
$HgS(s) + 2\ H^+(aq) + 2\ e^- \longrightarrow Hg(\ell) + H_2S(g)$	−0.72
$Cr^{3+}(aq) + 3\ e^- \longrightarrow Cr(s)$	−0.74
$Zn^{2+}(aq) + 2\ e^- \longrightarrow Zn(s)$	−0.763
$Cr^{2+}(aq) + 2\ e^- \longrightarrow Cr(s)$	−0.91
$FeS(s) + 2\ e^- \longrightarrow Fe(s) + S^{2-}(aq)$	−1.01
$Mn^{2+}(aq) + 2\ e^- \longrightarrow Mn(s)$	−1.18
$V^{2+}(aq) + 2\ e^- \longrightarrow V(s)$	−1.18
$CdS(s) + 2\ e^- \longrightarrow Cd(s) + S^{2-}(aq)$	−1.21
$ZnS(s) + 2\ e^- \longrightarrow Zn(s) + S^{2-}(aq)$	−1.44
$Zr^{4+}(aq) + 4\ e^- \longrightarrow Zr(s)$	−1.53
$Al^{3+}(aq) + 3\ e^- \longrightarrow Al(s)$	−1.66
$Mg^{2+}(aq) + 2\ e^- \longrightarrow Mg(s)$	−2.37
$Na^+(aq) + e^- \longrightarrow Na(s)$	−2.714
$Ca^{2+}(aq) + 2\ e^- \longrightarrow Ca(s)$	−2.87
$Sr^{2+}(aq) + 2\ e^- \longrightarrow Sr(s)$	−2.89
$Ba^{2+}(aq) + 2\ e^- \longrightarrow Ba(s)$	−2.90
$Rb^+(aq) + e^- \longrightarrow Rb(s)$	−2.925
$K^+(aq) + e^- \longrightarrow K(s)$	−2.925
$Li^+(aq) + e^- \longrightarrow Li(s)$	−3.045

(continued)

Table 21 Standard Reduction Potentials in Aqueous Solution at 25 °C (continued)

Basic Solution	Standard Reduction Potential $E°$ (volts)
$ClO^-(aq) + H_2O + 2\,e^- \longrightarrow Cl^-(aq) + 2\,OH^-(aq)$	0.89
$OOH^-(aq) + H_2O + 2\,e^- \longrightarrow 3\,OH^-(aq)$	0.88
$2\,NH_2OH(aq) + 2\,e^- \longrightarrow N_2H_4(aq) + 2\,OH^-(aq)$	0.74
$ClO_3^-(aq) + 3\,H_2O + 6\,e^- \longrightarrow Cl^-(aq) + 6\,OH^-(aq)$	0.62
$MnO_4^-(aq) + 2\,H_2O + 3\,e^- \longrightarrow MnO_2(s) + 4\,OH^-(aq)$	0.588
$MnO_4^-(aq) + e^- \longrightarrow MnO_4^{2-}(aq)$	0.564
$NiO_2(s) + 2\,H_2O + 2\,e^- \longrightarrow Ni(OH)_2(s) + 2\,OH^-(aq)$	0.49
$Ag_2CrO_4(s) + 2\,e^- \longrightarrow 2\,Ag(s) + CrO_4^{2-}(aq)$	0.446
$O_2(g) + 2\,H_2O + 4\,e^- \longrightarrow 4\,OH^-(aq)$	0.40
$ClO_4^-(aq) + H_2O + 2\,e^- \longrightarrow ClO_3^-(aq) + 2\,OH^-(aq)$	0.36
$Ag_2O(s) + H_2O + 2\,e^- \longrightarrow 2\,Ag(s) + 2\,OH^-(aq)$	0.34
$2\,NO_2^-(aq) + 3\,H_2O + 4\,e^- \longrightarrow N_2O(g) + 6\,OH^-(aq)$	0.15
$N_2H_4(aq) + 2\,H_2O + 2\,e^- \longrightarrow 2\,NH_3(aq) + 2\,OH^-(aq)$	0.10
$[Co(NH_3)_6]^{3+}(aq) + e^- \longrightarrow [Co(NH_3)_6]^{2+}(aq)$	0.10
$HgO(s) + H_2O + 2\,e^- \longrightarrow Hg(\ell) + 2\,OH^-(aq)$	0.0984
$O_2(g) + H_2O + 2\,e^- \longrightarrow OOH^-(aq) + OH^-(aq)$	0.076
$NO_3^-(aq) + H_2O + 2\,e^- \longrightarrow NO_2^-(aq) + 2\,OH^-(aq)$	0.01
$MnO_2(s) + 2\,H_2O + 2\,e^- \longrightarrow Mn(OH)_2(s) + 2\,OH^-(aq)$	−0.05
$CrO_4^{2-}(aq) + 4\,H_2O + 3\,e^- \longrightarrow Cr(OH)_3(s) + 5\,OH^-(aq)$	−0.12
$Cu(OH)_2(s) + 2\,e^- \longrightarrow Cu(s) + 2\,OH^-(aq)$	−0.36
$S(s) + 2\,e^- \longrightarrow S^{2-}(aq)$	−0.48
$Fe(OH)_3(s) + e^- \longrightarrow Fe(OH)_2(s) + OH^-(aq)$	−0.56
$2\,H_2O + 2\,e^- \longrightarrow H_2(g) + 2\,OH^-(aq)$	−0.8277
$2\,NO_3^-(aq) + 2\,H_2O + 2\,e^- \longrightarrow N_2O_4(g) + 4\,OH^-(aq)$	−0.85
$Fe(OH)_2(s) + 2\,e^- \longrightarrow Fe(s) + 2\,OH^-(aq)$	−0.877
$SO_4^{2-}(aq) + H_2O + 2\,e^- \longrightarrow SO_3^{2-}(aq) + 2\,OH^-(aq)$	−0.93
$N_2(g) + 4\,H_2O + 4\,e^- \longrightarrow N_2H_4(aq) + 4\,OH^-(aq)$	−1.15
$[Zn(OH)_4]^{2-}(aq) + 2\,e^- \longrightarrow Zn(s) + 4\,OH^-(aq)$	−1.22
$Zn(OH)_2(s) + 2\,e^- \longrightarrow Zn(s) + 2\,OH^-(aq)$	−1.245
$[Zn(CN)_4]^{2-}(aq) + 2\,e^- \longrightarrow Zn(s) + 4\,CN^-(aq)$	−1.26
$Cr(OH)_3(s) + 3\,e^- \longrightarrow Cr(s) + 3\,OH^-(aq)$	−1.30
$SiO_3^{2-}(aq) + 3\,H_2O + 4\,e^- \longrightarrow Si(s) + 6\,OH^-(aq)$	−1.70

Answers to Study Questions, Review & Check, Check Your Understanding, and Case Study Questions

Chapter 1 and Chapter 1-LR

Case Study

CO_2 in the Oceans

1. Carbon dioxide
2. Calcium: Ca; copper: Cu; manganese: Mn; iron: Fe
3. Most dense: copper, least dense: calcium
4. Elements: calcium, carbon, oxygen
   Compound name: calcium carbonate

Review & Check

Section 1-3

1. (a) dry ice (solid CO_2)
2. (c) Can be separated into two other pure substances by physical means.

Section 1-4

1. (b) Na
2. (d) silicon

Section 1-5

1. (d) water
2. (c) potassium

Section 1-6

1. (c) gasoline burns in air
2. (b) polypropylene < water < soda bottle plastic
3. (d) volume = 13.6 cm^3

Section 1-7

1. (b) The campfire wood burns.

Section 1-8

1. (d) 1.0 g of water vapor at 100 °C
2. (a) A mixture of H_2 and O_2 has lower chemical potential energy than H_2O.

Study Questions

1.1 (a) C, carbon
(b) K, potassium
(c) Cl, chlorine
(d) P, phosphorus
(e) Mg, magnesium
(f) Ni, nickel

1.3 (a) Ba, barium
(b) Ti, titanium
(c) Cr, chromium
(d) Pb, lead
(e) As, arsenic
(f) Zn, zinc

1.5 (a) Na (element) and NaCl (compound)
(b) Sugar (compound) and carbon (element)
(c) Gold (element) and gold chloride (compound)

1.7 (a) Physical property
(b) Chemical property
(c) Chemical property
(d) Physical property
(e) Physical property
(f) Physical property

1.9 (a) Physical (colorless liquid) and chemical (burns in air)
(b) Physical (shiny metal, orange-red) and chemical (reacts with bromine)

1.11 Mechanical energy is used to move the lever, which in turn moves gears. The device produces electrical energy and radiant energy.

1.13 (a) Kinetic energy
(b) Potential energy
(c) Potential energy
(d) Potential energy

1.15 (a) Qualitative: blue-green color, solid physical state
Quantitative: density = 2.65 g/cm^3 and mass = 2.5 g
(b) Density, physical state, and color are intensive properties, whereas mass is an extensive property.
(c) Volume = 0.94 cm^3

1.17 Observation c is a chemical property.

1.19 Calcium, Ca; fluorine, F

The crystals are cubic in shape because the atoms are arranged in cubic structures.

1.21 The water can be removed by boiling the solution until all of the water evaporates. The solid that remains is salt, NaCl.

1.23 Physical changes: a, b, d
Chemical changes: c

1.25 The macroscopic view is the photograph of NaCl, and the particulate view is the drawing of the ions in a cubic arrangement. The structure of the compound at the particulate level determines the properties that are observed at the macroscopic level.

1.27 The density of the plastic is less than that of CCl_4, so the plastic will float on the liquid CCl_4. Aluminum is more dense than CCl_4, so aluminum will sink when placed in CCl_4.

1.29 (a) Mixture
(b) Mixture
(c) Element
(d) Compound

1.31

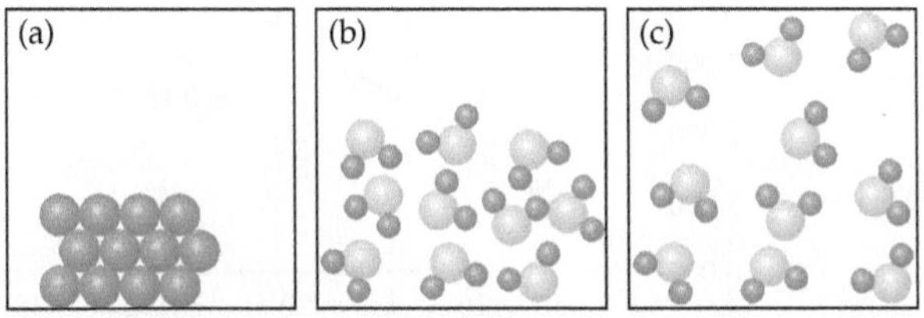

1.33 The three liquids will form three separate layers with hexane on the top, water in the middle, and perfluorohexane on the bottom. The HDPE will float at the interface of the hexane and water layers. The PVC will float at the interface of the water and perfluorohexane layers. The Teflon will sink to the bottom of the cylinder.

1.35 HDPE will float in ethylene glycol, water, acetic acid, and glycerol.

1.37 Milk is mostly water. When water freezes its density decreases, so for a given mass of water, the volume increases considerably. The increased volume means that the frozen water expands out of the bottle.

1.39 If too much sugar is excreted, the density of the urine would be higher than normal. If too much water is excreted, the density would be lower than normal.

1.41 (a) Solid potassium metal reacts with liquid water to produce gaseous hydrogen and a homogeneous mixture (solution) of potassium hydroxide in liquid water.
(b) The reaction is a chemical change.
(c) The reactants are potassium and water. The products are hydrogen gas and a water (aqueous) solution of potassium hydroxide. Heat and light are also evolved.
(d) Among the qualitative observations are (i) the reaction is violent, and (ii) heat and light (a purple flame) are produced.

1.43 The balloons containing helium and neon will float in air.

1.45 Physical change

1.47 (a) Gold = Au, silver = Ag, and copper = Cu
(b) T (K) = (1 K/1 °C)(1064 °C + 273 °C) = 1337 K
(c) No, gold is not the most dense element. Iridium Ir, is slightly more dense (22.65 g/cm^3).
(d) Mass gold = 0.75 × 5.58 g = 4.2 g
(e) Mass loss = (6.15 mg/ring)(1 g/1000 mg)(5.6 × 10^7 rings) = 3.4 × 10^5 g
Value lost = (3.4 × 10^5 g)(1 troy oz/31.1 g)($1620/1 troy oz) = $1.8 × 10^7 (or 18 million dollars)

Case Study

Out of Gas!

1. Fuel density in kg/L: (1.77 lb/L)(0.4536 kg/lb) = 0.803 kg/L
2. Mass of fuel already in tank: 7682 L (0.803 kg/L) = 6170 kg

   Mass of fuel needed: 22,300 kg − 6,170 kg = 16,100 kg (answer to three significant figures)

   Volume of fuel needed: 16,130 kg (1 L/0.803 kg) = 20,100 L

Check Your Understanding

LR-1. 0.154 nm (1 m/10^9 nm)(10^{12} pm/1 m) = 154 pm

0.154 nm (1 m/10^9 nm)(100 cm/1 m) = 1.54 × 10^{-8} cm

LR-2. Student A: average = 5.4 °C;
percent error = [0.1/278.65] × 100% = 0.04%

Student B: average = 5.51 °C;
percent error = [0.01/278.65] × 100% = 0.004%

Student B has the smaller error.

LR-3. x = 3.9 × 10^5. The difference between 110.7 and 64 is 47. Dividing 47 by 0.056 and 0.00216 gives an answer with two significant figures.

LR-4. (19,320 kg/m^3)(10^3 g/1 kg)(1 m^3/10^6 cm^3) = 19.32 g/cm^3

LR-5. Change all dimensions to centimeters: 7.6 m = 760 cm; 2.74 m = 274 cm; 0.13 mm = 0.013 cm.

Volume of paint = (760 cm)(274 cm)(0.013 cm) = 2.7×10^3 cm^3

Volume (L) = (2.7×10^3 cm^3)(1 L/10^3 cm^3) = 2.7 L

Mass = (2.7×10^3 cm^3)(0.914 g/cm^3) = 2.5×10^3 g

Review & Check

Section 1

1. (b) −196 °C
2. (c) 0.16 cm^3
3. (a) 0.750 L
4. (c) 1.9 L
5. (a) 5.59×10^3 mg
6. (d) 2×10^{-8} g/L
7. (c) 1050 kJ

Section 2

1. (c) 0.03 g
2. (b) Student B

Section 3

1. (c) 3
2. (a) 1
3. (b) 10.32 g
4. (c) 0.65 cm^2

Section 4

1. (a) 23.3 km^2

Section 5

1. (a) 2.4
2. (d) 78 g

Section 6

1. (c) 130 m

Study Questions

1. 298 K

3. (a) 289 K
(b) 97 °C
(c) 310 K (3.1×10^2 K)

5. 42,195 m; 26.219 miles

7. 5.3 cm^2; 5.3×10^{-4} m^2

9. 250. cm^3; 0.250 L, 2.50×10^{-4} m^3; 0.250 dm^3

11. 2.52×10^3 g

13. 555 g

15. (c) zinc

17. 5.0×10^6 J

19. 170 kcal is equivalent to 710 kJ, which is considerably greater than 280 kJ.

21. (a) Method A with all data included:
average = 2.4 g/cm^3

Method B with all data included:
average = 3.480 g/cm^3

For B, the 5.811 g/cm^3 data point can be excluded because it is more than twice as large as all other points for Method B. Using only the first three points, average = 2.703 g/cm^3

(b) Method A: error = 0.3 g/cm^3 or about 10%

Method B: error = 0.001 g/cm^3 or about 0.04%

(c) Method A: standard deviation = 0.2 g/cm^3

Method B (including all data points):
standard deviation = 1.554 g/cm^3

Method B (excluding the 5.811 g/cm^3 data point):
standard deviation = 0.002 g/cm^3

(d) Method B's average value is both more precise and more accurate so long as the 5.811 g/cm^3 data point is excluded.

23. (a) 5.4×10^{-2} g, two significant figures
(b) 5.462×10^3 g, four significant figures
(c) 7.92×10^{-4} g, three significant figures
(d) 1.6×10^3 mL, two significant figures

25. (a) 9.44×10^{-3}
(b) 5694
(c) 11.9
(d) 0.122

27.

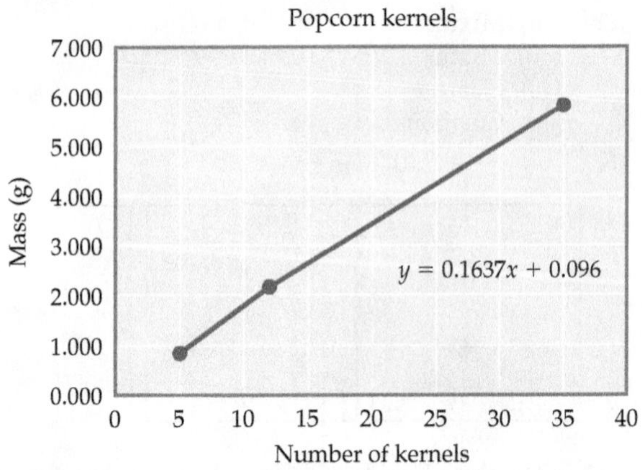

Slope: 0.1637 g/kernel

The slope represents the average mass of a popcorn kernel.

Mass of 20 popcorn kernels = 3.370 g

There are 127 kernels in a sample with a mass of 20.88 g.

29. (a) y = −4.00x + 20.00
(b) y = −4.00

31. C = 0.0823

33. T = 295

35. 0.197 nm; 197 pm

37. (a) 7.5×10^{-6} m; (b) 7.5×10^{3} nm; (c) 7.5×10^{6} pm

39. 50. mg procaine hydrochloride

41. The volume of the marbles is 99 mL − 61 mL = 38 mL. This yields a density of 2.5 g/cm^3.

43. (a) 0.178 nm^3; 1.78×10^{-22} cm^3
(b) 3.87×10^{-22} g
(c) 9.68×10^{-23} g

45. Your normal body temperature (about 98.6 °F) is 37 °C. As this is higher than gallium's melting point, the metal will melt in your hand.

47. (a) 15%
(b) 3.63×10^{3} kernels

49. 8.0×10^{4} kg of sodium fluoride per year

51. 245 g sulfuric acid

53. (a) 272 mL ice
(b) The ice cannot be contained in the can.

55. 7.99 g/cm^3

57. (a) 8.7 g/cm^3
(b) The metal is probably cadmium, but the calculated density is close to that of cobalt, nickel, and copper. Further testing should be done on the metal.

59. 0.0927 cm

61. (a) 1.143×10^{21} atoms; 76.4% of the lattice is filled with atoms; 23.6% of the lattice is open space.

Atoms are spheres. When spheres are packed together, they touch only at certain points, therefore leaving spaces in the structure.

(b) Four atoms

63. Al, aluminum

65.

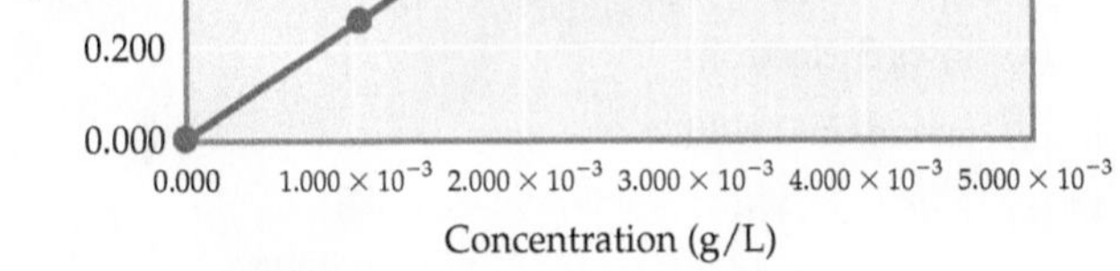

When absorbance = 0.635, concentration = 2.55×10^{-3} g/L = 2.55×10^{-3} mg/mL

67. Average = 5.24%, standard deviation = 0.05%

Seven of the ten values fall within the region $5.19 \leq x \leq 5.29$

Chapter 2

Case Studies

Using Isotopes: Ötzi, the Iceman of the Alps

1. ^{18}O: 18 − 8 = 10 neutrons
^{204}Pb: 204 − 82 = 122 neutrons
^{206}Pb: 206 − 82 = 124 neutrons

2. 15.9993 u

Arsenic, Medicine, and the Formula of Compound 606

1. Amount As: 19.024 g As × (1 mol As/74.9216 g As) = 0.25392 mol As

Amount Cu: 48.407 g Cu × (1 mol Cu/63.546 g Cu) = 0.76176 mol Cu

Amount S: 32.569 g S × (1 mol S/32.066 g S) = 1.0157 mol S

Mole ratio Cu/As: 0.76176 mol Cu/0.25392 mol As = 3.0000 mol Cu/1 mol As

Mole ratio S/As: 1.0157 mol S/0.25392 mol As = 4.0001 mol S/1 mol As

Empirical formula: Cu_3AsS_4

2. Amount C: 39.37 g C × (1 mol C/12.011 g C) = 3.278 mol C

Amount H: 3.304 g H × (1 mol H/1.0079 g H) = 3.278 mol H

Amount O: 8.741 g O × (1 mol O/15.999 g O) = 0.5463 mol O

Amount N: 7.652 g N × (1 mol N/14.007 g N) = 0.5463 mol N

Amount As: 40.932 g As × (1 mol As/74.9216 g As) = 0.54633 mol As

Mole ratio C/O and H/O: 3.278 mol C/0.5463 mol O = 6.000 mol C/1 mol O. A similar calculation yields 6.000 mol H/1 mol O.

Mole ratio N/O and As/O: 0.5463 mol N/0.5463 mol O = 1.000 mol N/1 mol O. A similar calculation yields 1.000 mol As/1 mol O.

Empirical formula: C_6H_6AsNO

Molar mass of C_6H_6AsNO: 183.0 g/mol

Compound 1: 549/183.0 = 3.00; therefore, the molecular formula is $C_{18}H_{18}As_3N_3O_3$.

Compound 2: 915/183.0 = 5.00; therefore, the molecular formula is $C_{30}H_{30}As_5N_5O_5$.

Check Your Understanding

2.1 (1) Mass number with 26 protons and 30 neutrons is 56
(2) (59.930788 u)(1.661×10^{-24} g/u) = 9.955×10^{-23} g
(3) ^{64}Zn has 30 protons, 30 electrons, and (64 − 30) = 34 neutrons.

2.2 Use Equation 2.2 for the calculation.

Atomic mass = (34.96885)(75.77/100) + (36.96590)(24.23/100) = 35.45. (Accuracy is limited by the value of the percent abundance to four significant figures.)

2.3 Use Equation 2.2 for the calculation. Let x = percent abundance of ^{20}Ne and y = percent abundance of ^{22}Ne.

20.1797 u = (x/100)(19.992435 u) + (0.27/100)(20.993843 u) + (y/100)(21.991383 u)

Because all the percent abundances must sum to 100%, $y = 100 - x - 0.27 = 99.73 - x$.

20.1797 u = (x/100)(19.992435 u) + 0.27/100)(20.993843 u) + [(99.73 − x)/100](21.991383 u)

x = 90.5; therefore the percent abundance of ^{20}Ne = 90.5% and the percent abundance of ^{22}Ne = 9.2%.

2.4 (a) (1) NaF: 1 Na^+ and 1 F^- ion. (2) $Cu(NO_3)_2$: 1 Cu^{2+} and 2 NO_3^- ions. (3) $NaCH_3CO_2$: 1 Na^+ and 1 $CH_3CO_2^-$ ion.

2.5 (a) Na_2S, Na_3PO_4, BaS, $Ba_3(PO_4)_2$
(b) $FeCl_2$, $FeCl_3$

2.6 (2.6 × 10^{24} atoms)(1 mol/6.022 × 10^{23} atoms)(197.0 g Au/1 mol) = 850 g Au

Volume = (850 g Au)(1.00 cm^3/19.32 g) = 44 cm^3

2.7 Molar mass $H_3C_6H_5O_7$ = 8(1.01) + 6(12.01) + 7(16.00) = 192.14 g/mol

(454 g $H_3C_6H_5O_7$)(1 mol $H_3C_6H_5O_7$/192.14 g $H_3C_6H_5O_7$) = 2.36 mol $H_3C_6H_5O_7$

(2.36 mol $H_3C_6H_5O_7$)(6.022 × 10^{23} molecules/1 mol) = 1.42 × 10^{24} molecules $H_3C_6H_5O_7$

(1.42 × 10^{24} molecules $H_3C_6H_5O_7$)(6 atoms C/1 molecule $H_3C_6H_5O_7$) = 8.54 × 10^{24} atoms C

2.8 (1) 1.00 mol $(NH_4)_2CO_3$ (molar mass 96.09 g/mol) has 28.0 g of N (29.1%), 8.06 g of H (8.39%), 12.0 g of C (12.5%), and 48.0 g of O (50.0%)
(2) 454 g C_8H_{18} (1 mol C_8H_{18}/114.2 g)(8 mol C/1 mol C_8H_{18})(12.01 g C/1 mol C) = 382 g C

2.9 (1) C_5H_4
(2) $C_2H_4O_2$
(3) (88.17 g C)(1 mol C/12.011 g C) = 7.341 mol C

(11.83 g H)(1 mol H/1.008 g H) = 11.74 mol H

11.74 mol H/7.341 mol C = 1.6 mol H/1 mol C = (8/5); (mol H/1 mol C) = 8 mol H/5 mol C

The empirical formula is C_5H_8. The molar mass, 68.11 g/mol, closely matches this formula, so C_5H_8 is also the molecular formula.

(4) (78.90 g C)(1 mol C/12.011 g C) = 6.569 mol C

(10.59 g H)(1 mol H/1.008 g H) = 10.51 mol H

(10.51 g O)(1 mol O/16.00 g O) = 0.6569 mol O

10.51 mol H/0.6569 mol O = 16 mol H/1 mol O

6.569 mol C/0.6569 mol O = 10 mol C/1 mol O

The empirical formula is $C_{10}H_{16}O$.

2.10 (1.25 g Ga)(1 mol Ga/69.72 g Ga) = 0.0179 mol Ga

1.68 g product − 1.25 g Ga = 0.43 g O

(0.43 g O)(1 mol O/16.00 g O) = 0.027 mol O

Mole ratio = 0.027 mol O/0.0179 mol Ga = 1.5 mol O/1.0 mol Ga = 3.0 mol O/2.0 mol Ga

Empirical formula = Ga_2O_3

2.11 Mass of water lost on heating is 0.235 g − 0.128 g = 0.107 g; 0.128 g $NiCl_2$ remain

(0.107 g H_2O)(1 mol H_2O/18.016 g H_2O) = 0.00594 mol H_2O

(0.128 g $NiCl_2$)(1 mol $NiCl_2$/129.6 g $NiCl_2$) = 0.000988 mol $NiCl_2$

Mole ratio = 0.00594 mol H_2O/0.000988 mol $NiCl_2$ = 6.01: Therefore x = 6

The formula for the hydrate is $NiCl_2 \cdot 6\,H_2O$.

Review & Check

Section 2-2

1. (b) 30 neutrons
2. (c) Na

Section 2-3

1. (d) $^{109}_{47}$Ag, 48.161%
2. (a) 99.60%

Section 2-4

1. (a) ^{63}Cu
2. (b) 40%
3. (b) Pb

Section 2-5

1. (a) Ge
2. (a) Si
3. (c) O
4. (c) allotropes

Section 2-6

1. (b) $C_3H_7NO_2S$

Section 2-7

1. (b) 2+
2. (a) loses 3 electrons
3. (b) ammonium sulfide
4. (a) $Ba(CH_3CO_2)_2$
5. (a) vanadium(III) oxide
6. (a) MgO

Section 2-8

1. (a) O_2F_2
2. (b) nitrogen pentaoxide, N_2O_5
3. (c) dinitrogen tetrafluoride
4. (b) tetraphosphorus decaoxide

Section 2-9

1. (c) 164.09 g/mol
2. (b) 4.0 g H_2
3. (c) 0.40 mol Ca
4. (d) 30 g HF
5. (a) 6.0×10^{23} atoms O

Section 2-10

1. (d) butane, C_4H_{10}
2. (b) $C_6H_{12}O_6$
3. (b) C_5H_6O, $C_{10}H_{12}O_2$
4. (d) $MgSO_4 \cdot 3\ H_2O$

Applying Chemical Principles: Argon—An Amazing Discovery

1. 162.18 cm^3

3. % Abundance ^{40}Ar = 99.600%
Atomic mass of ^{40}Ar = 39.963 u

Study Questions

2.1 Atoms contain the following fundamental particles: protons (+1 charge), neutrons (zero charge), and electrons (−1 charge). Protons and neutrons are in the nucleus of an atom. Electrons are the least massive of the three particles.

2.3 The electron cloud would extend around 1×10^{-13} cm = 1 fm.

2.5 (a) $^{27}_{12}Mg$
(b) $^{48}_{22}Ti$
(c) $^{62}_{30}Zn$

2.7

Element	Electrons	Protons	Neutrons
^{24}Mg	12	12	12
^{119}Sn	50	50	69
^{232}Th	90	90	142
^{13}C	6	6	7
^{63}Cu	29	29	34
^{205}Bi	83	83	122

2.9 mass p/mass e = 1.672622×10^{-24} g/9.109383×10^{-28} g = 1836.15. The proton is more than 1800 times heavier than the electron. Thomson's estimate was off by a factor of 2.

2.11 Gamma rays (γ) have no charge and so are unaffected by the electric field. Alpha particles (α) are positively charged and attracted to the negative plate, and beta particles (β) are negatively charged and attracted to the positive plate. Beta particles are more affected by the electric field because they are lighter than alpha particles. (Alpha particles are He^+ ions, whereas beta particles are electrons.)

2.13 $^{16}O/^{12}C = 1.3329$

2.15 $^{57}_{27}Co$, $^{58}_{27}Co$, $^{60}_{27}Co$

2.17 Protium: one proton, one electron
Deuterium: one proton, one neutron, one electron
Tritium: one proton, two neutrons, one electron

2.19 ^{205}Tl is more abundant than ^{203}Tl. The atomic mass of thallium is closer to 205 than to 203.

2.21 $(0.0750)(6.015121) + (0.9250)(7.016003) = 6.94$

2.23 ^{69}Ga, 60.12%; ^{71}Ga, 39.88%

2.25

	Symbol	Atomic No.	Atomic Mass	Group	Period	
Titanium	Ti	22	47.867	4B(IUPAC 4)	4	Metal
Thallium	Tl	81	204.3833	3A(IUPAC 13)	6	Metal

2.27 Eight elements: periods 2 and 3. 18 elements: periods 4 and 5. 32 elements: periods 6 and 7.

2.29 (a) Nonmetals: C, Cl
(b) Main group elements: C, Ca, Cl, Cs
(c) Lanthanides: Ce
(d) Transition elements: Cr, Co, Cd, Ce, Cm, Cu, Cf
(e) Actinides: Cm, Cf
(f) Gases: Cl

2.31 Metals: Na, Ni, Np
Metalloids: None in this list
Nonmetals: N, Ne

2.33 Molecular formula: HNO_3.
Structural formula:

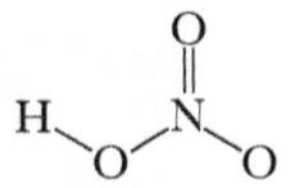

The structure around the N atom is flat. The O atoms are arranged around the N atoms at the corners of a triangle. The hydrogen atom is connected to one of the oxygen atoms.

2.35 (a) Mg^{2+}
(b) Zn^{2+}
(c) Ni^{2+}
(d) Ga^{3+}

2.37 (a) Ba^{2+}
(b) Ti^{4+}
(c) PO_4^{3-}
(d) HCO_3^-
(e) S^{2-}
(f) ClO_4^-
(g) Co^{2+}
(h) SO_4^{2-}

2.39 K loses one electron per atom to form a K^+ ion. It has the same number of electrons as an Ar atom.

2.41 Ba^{2+} and Br^- ions. The compound's formula is $BaBr_2$.

2.43 (a) Two K^+ ions and one S^{2-} ion
(b) One Co^{2+} ion and one SO_4^{2-} ion
(c) One K^+ ion and one MnO_4^- ion
(d) Three NH_4^+ ions and one PO_4^{3-} ion
(e) One Ca^{2+} ion and two ClO^- ions
(f) One Na^+ ion and one $CH_3CO_2^-$ ion

2.45 Co^{2+} gives CoO and Co^{3+} gives Co_2O_3.

2.47 (a) $AlCl_2$ should be $AlCl_3$ (based on an Al^{3+} ion and three Cl^- ions).
(b) KF_2 should be KF (based on a K^+ ion and an F^- ion).
(c) Ga_2O_3 is correct.
(d) MgS is correct.

2.49 (a) Potassium sulfide
(b) Cobalt(II) sulfate
(c) Ammonium phosphate
(d) Calcium hypochlorite

2.51 (a) $(NH_4)_2CO_3$
(b) CaI_2
(c) $CuBr_2$
(d) $AlPO_4$
(e) $AgCH_3CO_2$

2.53 Compounds with Na^+: Na_2CO_3 (sodium carbonate) and NaI (sodium iodide). Compounds with Ba^{2+}: $BaCO_3$ (barium carbonate) and BaI_2 (barium iodide).

2.55 The force of attraction is stronger in NaF than in NaI because the distance between ion centers is smaller in NaF (235 pm) than in NaI (322 pm).

2.57 (a) Nitrogen trifluoride
(b) Hydrogen iodide
(c) Boron triiodide
(d) Phosphorus pentafluoride

2.59 (a) SCl_2
(b) N_2O_5
(c) $SiCl_4$
(d) B_2O_3

2.61 (a) 67 g Al
(b) 0.0698 g Fe
(c) 0.60 g Ca
(d) 1.32×10^4 g Ne

2.63 (a) 1.9998 mol Cu
(b) 0.0017 mol Li
(c) 2.1×10^{-5} mol Am
(d) 0.250 mol Al

2.65 Of these elements, He has the smallest molar mass, and Fe has the largest molar mass. Therefore, 1.0 g of He has the largest number of atoms in these samples, and 1.0 g of Fe has the smallest number of atoms.

2.67 0.020 mol H $<$ 0.0597 mol P $<$ 0.0996 mol Ca $<$ 0.259 mol O

2.69 (a) 159.7 g/mol
(b) 117.2 g/mol
(c) 176.1 g/mol

2.71 (a) 290.8 g/mol
(b) 249.7 g/mol

2.73 (a) 1.53 g
(b) 4.60 g
(c) 4.60 g
(d) 1.48 g

2.75 Amount of SO_3 = 12.5 mol
Number of molecules = 7.52×10^{24} molecules
Number of S atoms = 7.52×10^{24} atoms
Number of O atoms = 2.26×10^{25} atoms

2.77 4×10^{21} molecules

2.79 (a) 86.60% Pb and 13.40% S
(b) 81.71% C and 18.29% H
(c) 79.96% C, 9.394% H, and 10.65% O

2.81 66.46% copper in CuS. 15.0 g of CuS is needed to obtain 10.0 g of Cu.

2.83 $C_4H_6O_4$

2.85 (a) CH, 26.0 g/mol; C_2H_2
(b) CHO, 116.1 g/mol; $C_4H_4O_4$
(c) CH_2, 112.2 g/mol, C_8H_{16}

2.87 Empirical formula, CH; molecular formula, C_2H_2

2.89 Empirical formula, C_3H_4; molecular formula, C_9H_{12}

2.91 Empirical and molecular formulas are both $C_8H_8O_3$

2.93 XeF_2

2.95 $MgSO_4 \cdot 2\ H_2O$

2.97

Symbol	^{58}Ni	^{33}S	^{20}Ne	^{55}Mn
Protons	28	16	10	25
Neutrons	30	17	10	30
Electrons	28	16	10	25
Name	Nickel	Sulfur	Neon	Manganese

2.99

S	N
B	I

2.101 (a) 1.0552×10^{-22} g for 1 Cu atom
(b) 6.3×10^{-22} dollars for 1 Cu atom

2.103 (a) Strontium
(b) Zirconium
(c) Carbon
(d) Arsenic
(e) Iodine
(f) Magnesium
(g) Krypton
(h) Sulfur
(i) Germanium or arsenic

2.105 (a) 0.25 mol U
(b) 0.50 mol Na
(c) 10 atoms of Fe

2.107 40.157 g H_2 (b) $<$ 103.0 g C (c) $<$ 182 g Al (f) $<$ 210 g Si (d) $<$ 212.0 g Na (e) $<$ 351 g Fe (a) $<$ 650 g Cl_2 (g)

2.109 (a) Atomic mass of O = 15.873 u; Avogadro's number = 5.9802×10^{23} particles per mole
(b) Atomic mass of H = 1.00798 u; Avogadro's number = 6.0279×10^{23} particles per mole

2.111 $(NH_4)_2CO_3$, $(NH_4)_2SO_4$, $NiCO_3$, $NiSO_4$

2.113 All of these compounds have one atom of some element plus three Cl atoms. The highest mass percent of chlorine will occur in the compound having the lightest central element. Here, that element is B, so BCl_3 should have the highest mass percent of Cl (90.77%).

2.115 The molar mass of adenine ($C_5H_5N_5$) is 135.13 g/mol. 3.0×10^{23} molecules represents 67 g. Thus, 3.0×10^{23} molecules of adenine has a larger mass than 40.0 g of the compound.

2.117 1.7×10^{21} molecules of water

2.119 245.75 g/mol. Mass percent: 25.86% Cu, 22.80% N, 5.742% H, 13.05% S, and 32.55% O. In 10.5 g of compound there are 2.72 g Cu and 0.770 g H_2O.

2.121 Empirical formula of malic acid: $C_4H_6O_5$

2.123 $Fe_2(CO)_9$

2.125 (a) $C_7H_5NO_3S$

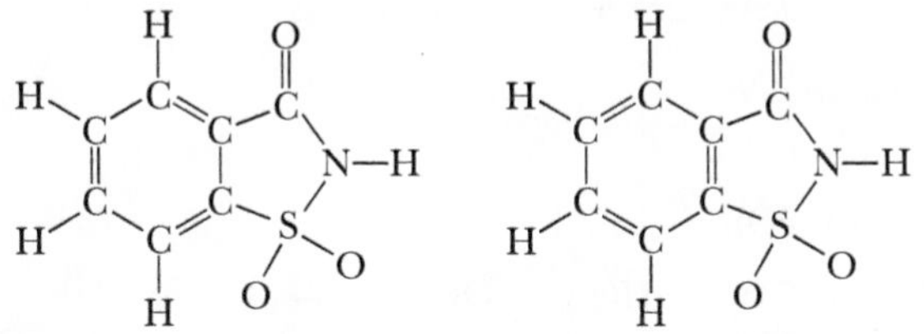

(b) 6.82×10^{-4} mol saccharin
(c) 21.9 mg S

2.127 (a) NaClO, ionic
(b) BI_3
(c) $Al(ClO_4)_3$, ionic
(d) $Ca(CH_3CO_2)_2$, ionic
(e) $KMnO_4$, ionic
(f) $(NH_4)_2SO_3$, ionic
(g) KH_2PO_4, ionic
(h) S_2Cl_2
(i) ClF_3
(j) PF_3

2.129 (a) Empirical formula = molecular formula = CF_2O_2
(b) Empirical formula = C_5H_4; molecular formula = $C_{10}H_8$

2.131 Empirical formula and molecular formula = $C_5H_{14}N_2$

2.133 $C_9H_7MnO_3$

2.135 68.42% Cr; 1.2×10^3 kg Cr_2O_3

2.137 Empirical formula = ICl_3; molecular formula = I_2Cl_6

2.139 7.35 kg of iron

2.141 (d) Na_2MoO_4

2.143 5.52×10^{-4} mol $C_{21}H_{15}Bi_3O_{12}$; 0.346 g Bi

2.145 The molar mass of the compound is 154 g/mol. The unknown element is carbon.

2.147 $n = 2.19 \times 10^3$

2.149 (a) 2.3×10^{14} g/cm^3
(b) 3.34×10^{-3} g/cm^3
(c) The nucleus is much more dense than the space occupied by the electrons.

2.151 (a) 0.0130 mol Ni
(b) NiF_2
(c) Nickel(II) fluoride

2.153 Volume = 3.0 cm^3; length of side = 1.4 cm

2.155 (a) $m/Z = 50$ is $^{12}C^1H_3{}^{35}Cl^+$; $m/Z = 52$ is $^{12}C^1H_3{}^{37}Cl^+$
The height of the line at $m/Z = 52$ is about 1/3 the height of the line at $m/Z = 50$ because the abundance of ^{37}Cl is about 1/3 that of ^{35}Cl.
(b) $^{13}C^1H_3{}^{35}Cl^+$ (a small portion of this peak is also due to $^{12}C^2H^1H_2{}^{35}Cl^+$)

2.157 Formula is $MgSO_4 \cdot 7\ H_2O$

2.159 SnI_4

2.161 (c) The calculated mole ratio is 0.78 mol H_2O per mol $CaCl_2$. The student should heat the crucible again and then reweigh it. More water might be driven off.

2.163 Required data: density of iron (d), molar mass of iron (b), Avogadro's number (c)

$$1.00\ \text{cm}^3\left(\frac{7.87\ \text{g}}{1\ \text{cm}^3}\right)\left(\frac{1\ \text{mol}}{55.85\ \text{g}}\right)\left(\frac{6.022 \times 10^{23}\ \text{atoms}}{1\ \text{mol}}\right) = 8.49 \times 10^{22}\ \text{atoms Fe}$$

2.165 (a) Barium would be more reactive than calcium, so a more vigorous evolution of hydrogen should occur.
(b) Reactivity generally increases on descending the periodic table, at least for Groups 1A and 2A.

Chapter 3

Case Study

Killing Bacteria with Silver

1. 100×10^{15} Ag^+ ions (1 mol/6.022×10^{23} ions) = 2×10^{-7} mol Ag^+
2. 2×10^{-7} mol Ag^+ (107.9 g Ag^+/1 mol Ag^+) = 2×10^{-5} g Ag^+ ions

Check Your Understanding

3.1 (a) $2\ C_4H_{10}(g) + 13\ O_2(g) \rightarrow 8\ CO_2(g) + 10\ H_2O(g)$
(b) $2\ C_3H_7BO_3(\ell) + 8\ O_2(g) \rightarrow 6\ CO_2(g) + 7\ H_2O(g) + B_2O_3(s)$

3.2 (a) $LiNO_3$ is soluble and gives $Li^+(aq)$ and $NO_3^-(aq)$ ions.
(b) $CaCl_2$ is soluble and gives $Ca^{2+}(aq)$ and $Cl^-(aq)$ ions.
(c) CuO is not water soluble.
(d) $NaCH_3CO_2$ is soluble and gives $Na^+(aq)$ and $CH_3CO_2^-(aq)$ ions.

3.3 (a) $Na_2CO_3(aq) + CuCl_2(aq) \rightarrow 2\ NaCl(aq) + CuCO_3(s)$
(b) No reaction; no insoluble compound is produced.
(c) $NiCl_2(aq) + 2\ KOH(aq) \rightarrow Ni(OH)_2(s) + 2\ KCl(aq)$

3.4 (a) $3\ CaCl_2(aq) + 2\ Na_3PO_4(aq) \rightarrow Ca_3(PO_4)_2(s) + 6\ NaCl(aq)$
$3\ Ca^{2+}(aq) + 2\ PO_4^{3-}(aq) \rightarrow Ca_3(PO_4)_2(s)$
(b) $FeCl_3(aq) + 3\ KOH(aq) \rightarrow Fe(OH)_3(s) + 3\ KCl(aq)$
$Fe^{3+}(aq) + 3\ OH^-(aq) \rightarrow Fe(OH)_3(s)$
(c) $Pb(NO_3)_2(aq) + 2\ KCl(aq) \rightarrow PbCl_2(s) + 2\ KNO_3(aq)$
$Pb^{2+}(aq) + 2\ Cl^-(aq) \rightarrow PbCl_2(s)$

3.5 (a) $H_3PO_4(aq) + H_2O(\ell) \rightarrow H_3O^+(aq) + H_2PO_4^-(aq)$
(b) Acting as an acid:
$H_2PO_4^-(aq) + H_2O(\ell) \rightleftharpoons HPO_4^{2-}(aq) + H_3O^+(\ell)$
Acting as a base:
$H_2PO_4^-(aq) + H_2O(\ell) \rightleftharpoons H_3PO_4(aq) + OH^-(aq)$
Because $H_2PO_4^-(aq)$ can react as a Brønsted acid and as a base, it is said to be amphiprotic.

3.6 $Mg(OH)_2(s) + 2\ HCl(aq) \rightarrow MgCl_2(aq) + 2\ H_2O(\ell)$
Net ionic equation:
$Mg(OH)_2(s) + 2\ H_3O^+(aq) \rightarrow Mg^{2+}(aq) + 4\ H_2O(\ell)$

3.7 $BaCO_3(s) + 2\ HNO_3(aq) \rightarrow Ba(NO_3)_2(aq) + CO_2(g) + H_2O(\ell)$
Barium carbonate and nitric acid produce barium nitrate, carbon dioxide, and water.

3.8 (a) Fe in Fe_2O_3, +3; (b) S in H_2SO_4, +6; (c) C in CO_3^{2-}, +4; (d) N in NO_2^+, +5

3.9 Dichromate ion is the oxidizing agent and is reduced. (Cr with a +6 oxidation number is reduced to Cr^{3+} with a +3 oxidation number.) Ethanol is the reducing agent and is oxidized. (The C atoms in ethanol have an oxidation number of −2. The oxidation number is 0 in acetic acid.)

3.10 (a) Gas-forming reaction:
$CuCO_3(s) + H_2SO_4(aq) \rightarrow CuSO_4(aq) + H_2O(\ell) + CO_2(g)$
Net ionic equation:
$CuCO_3(s) + 2\ H_3O^+(aq) \rightarrow Cu^{2+}(aq) + 3\ H_2O(\ell) + CO_2(g)$
(b) Oxidation–reduction:
$4\ Ga(s) + 3\ O_2(g) \rightarrow 2\ Ga_2O_3(s)$
(c) Acid–base reaction:
$Ba(OH)_2(aq) + 2\ HNO_3(aq) \rightarrow Ba(NO_3)_2(aq) + 2\ H_2O(\ell)$
Net ionic equation:
$OH^-(aq) + H_3O^+(aq) \rightarrow 2\ H_2O(\ell)$
(d) Precipitation reaction:
$CuCl_2(aq) + (NH_4)_2S(aq) \rightarrow CuS(s) + 2\ NH_4Cl(aq)$
Net ionic equation:
$Cu^{2+}(aq) + S^{2-}(aq) \rightarrow CuS(s)$

Review & Check

Section 3-1

1. (b) 2, 3, 1
2. (c) 12,000

Section 3-2

1. (b) 9 O_2, 8 H_2O

Section 3-3

1. (d) All chemical reactions are product-favored at equilibrium.

Section 3-4

1. (a) $Ba(NO_3)_2$
2. (b) Ca^{2+} and 2 NO_3^-
3. (b) acetic acid

Section 3-5

1. (d) 1, 2, 3, and 4
2. (c) $2\ Ag^+(aq) + CO_3^{2-}(aq) \rightarrow Ag_2CO_3(s)$

Section 3-6

1. (d) H_2SO_4
2. (d) PO_4^{3-}
3. (c) $CH_3CO_2H(aq) + OH^-(aq) \rightarrow H_2O(\ell) + CH_3CO_2^-(aq)$
4. (b) BaO

Section 3-7

1. (b) Na_2CO_3

Section 3-8

1. (c) +6
2. (c) 2 and 4
3. (c) $KMnO_4$

Section 3-9

1. (c) acid–base and precipitation

Applying Chemical Principles: Superconductors

1. In this case, because you know that Cu has an implied subscript of 1, divide the number of moles of each element determined by the number of moles of Cu.
   $x = 0.15$; Formula = $La_{1.85}Ba_{0.15}CuO_4$
3. One formula unit of the compound contains two Cu^{2+} ions and one Cu^{3+} ion.
5. 0.011 g O_2

Study Questions

3.1 (a) $2\ Al(s) + Fe_2O_3(s) \rightarrow 2\ Fe(\ell) + Al_2O_3(s)$
So much energy is released as heat in this reaction that the iron formed is in the liquid state.

(b) $C(s) + H_2O(g) \rightarrow CO(g) + H_2(g)$
(c) $SiCl_4(\ell) + 2\ Mg(s) \rightarrow Si(s) + 2\ MgCl_2(s)$

3.3 (a) $4\ Cr(s) + 3\ O_2(g) \rightarrow 2\ Cr_2O_3(s)$
(b) $Cu_2S(s) + O_2(g) \rightarrow 2\ Cu(s) + SO_2(g)$
(c) $C_6H_5CH_3(\ell) + 9\ O_2(g) \rightarrow 4\ H_2O(\ell) + 7\ CO_2(g)$

3.5 (a) $Fe_2O_3(s) + 3\ Mg(s) \rightarrow 3\ MgO(s) + 2\ Fe(s)$
Reactants = iron(III) oxide, magnesium
Products = magnesium oxide, iron
(b) $AlCl_3(s) + 3\ NaOH(aq) \rightarrow Al(OH)_3(s) + 3\ NaCl(aq)$
Reactants = aluminum chloride, sodium hydroxide
Products = aluminum hydroxide, sodium chloride
(c) $2\ NaNO_3(s) + H_2SO_4(aq) \rightarrow Na_2SO_4(s) + 2\ HNO_3(aq)$
Reactants = sodium nitrate, sulfuric acid
Products = sodium sulfate, nitric acid
(d) $NiCO_3(s) + 2\ HNO_3(aq) \rightarrow Ni(NO_3)_2(aq) + CO_2(g) + H_2O(\ell)$
Reactants = nickel(II) carbonate, nitric acid
Products = nickel(II) nitrate, carbon dioxide, water

3.7 The reaction involving HCl is more product-favored at equilibrium.

3.9 Electrolytes are compounds whose aqueous solutions conduct electricity. Given an aqueous solution containing a strong electrolyte and another aqueous solution containing a weak electrolyte at the same concentration, the solution containing the strong electrolyte (such as NaCl) will conduct electricity much better than the one containing the weak electrolyte (such as acetic acid).

3.11 (a) $CuCl_2$
(b) $AgNO_3$
(c) All are water-soluble.

3.13 (a) K^+ and OH^- ions
(b) K^+ and SO_4^{2-} ions
(c) Li^+ and NO_3^- ions
(d) NH_4^+ and SO_4^{2-} ions

3.15 (a) Soluble, Na^+ and CO_3^{2-} ions
(b) Soluble, Cu^{2+} and SO_4^{2-} ions
(c) Insoluble
(d) Soluble, Ba^{2+} and Br^- ions

3.17 $CdCl_2(aq) + 2\ NaOH(aq) \rightarrow Cd(OH)_2(s) + 2\ NaCl(aq)$
$Cd^{2+}(aq) + 2\ OH^-(aq) \rightarrow Cd(OH)_2(s)$

3.19 (a) $NiCl_2(aq) + (NH_4)_2S(aq) \rightarrow NiS(s) + 2\ NH_4Cl(aq)$
$Ni^{2+}(aq) + S^{2-}(aq) \rightarrow NiS(s)$
(b) $3\ Mn(NO_3)_2(aq) + 2\ Na_3PO_4(aq) \rightarrow Mn_3(PO_4)_2(s) + 6\ NaNO_3(aq)$
$3\ Mn^{2+}(aq) + 2\ PO_4^{3-}(aq) \rightarrow Mn_3(PO_4)_2(s)$

3.21 $HNO_3(aq) + H_2O(\ell) \rightarrow H_3O^+(aq) + NO_3^-(aq)$

3.23 $H_2C_2O_4(aq) + H_2O(\ell) \rightarrow H_3O^+(aq) + HC_2O_4^-(aq)$
$HC_2O_4^-(aq) + H_2O(\ell) \rightarrow H_3O^+(aq) + C_2O_4^{2-}(aq)$

3.25 $MgO(s) + H_2O(\ell) \rightarrow Mg(OH)_2(s)$

3.27 (a) Acetic acid reacts with magnesium hydroxide to give magnesium acetate and water.
$2\ CH_3CO_2H(aq) + Mg(OH)_2(s) \rightarrow Mg(CH_3CO_2)_2(aq) + 2\ H_2O(\ell)$
(b) Perchloric acid reacts with ammonia to give ammonium perchlorate
$HClO_4(aq) + NH_3(aq) \rightarrow NH_4ClO_4(aq)$

3.29 $Ba(OH)_2(aq) + 2\ HNO_3(aq) \rightarrow Ba(NO_3)_2(aq) + 2\ H_2O(\ell)$

3.31 $HNO_3(aq) + H_2O(\ell) \rightleftharpoons H_3O^+(aq) + NO_3^-(aq)$
Brønsted acids: $HNO_3(aq)$ and $H_3O^+(aq)$
Brønsted bases: $H_2O(\ell)$ and $NO_3^-(aq)$
HNO_3 is a strong acid; therefore, this reaction is product-favored at equilibrium.

3.33 $H_2O(\ell) + HBr(aq) \rightleftharpoons H_3O^+(aq) + Br^-(aq)$
Water accepts H^+ from HBr(aq)
$H_2O(\ell) + NH_3(aq) \rightleftharpoons OH^-(aq) + NH_4^+(aq)$
Water donates H^+ to $NH_3(aq)$

3.35 (a) $(NH_4)_2CO_3(aq) + Cu(NO_3)_2(aq) \rightarrow CuCO_3(s) + 2\ NH_4NO_3(aq)$
$CO_3^{2-}(aq) + Cu^{2+}(aq) \rightarrow CuCO_3(s)$
(b) $Pb(OH)_2(s) + 2\ HCl(aq) \rightarrow PbCl_2(s) + 2\ H_2O(\ell)$
$Pb(OH)_2(s) + 2\ H_3O^+(aq) + 2\ Cl^-(aq) \rightarrow PbCl_2(s) + 4\ H_2O(\ell)$
(c) $BaCO_3(s) + 2\ HCl(aq) \rightarrow BaCl_2(aq) + H_2O(\ell) + CO_2(g)$
$BaCO_3(s) + 2\ H_3O^+(aq) \rightarrow Ba^{2+}(aq) + 3\ H_2O(\ell) + CO_2(g)$
(d) $2\ CH_3CO_2H(aq) + Ni(OH)_2(s) \rightarrow Ni(CH_3CO_2)_2(aq) + 2\ H_2O(\ell)$
$2\ CH_3CO_2H(aq) + Ni(OH)_2(s) \rightarrow Ni^{2+}(aq) + 2\ CH_3CO_2^-(aq) + 2\ H_2O(\ell)$

3.37 (a) $AgNO_3(aq) + KI(aq) \rightarrow AgI(s) + KNO_3(aq)$
$Ag^+(aq) + I^-(aq) \rightarrow AgI(s)$
(b) $Ba(OH)_2(aq) + 2\ HNO_3(aq) \rightarrow Ba(NO_3)_2(aq) + 2\ H_2O(\ell)$
$OH^-(aq) + H_3O^+(aq) \rightarrow 2\ H_2O(\ell)$
(c) $2\ Na_3PO_4(aq) + 3\ Ni(NO_3)_2(aq) \rightarrow Ni_3(PO_4)_2(s) + 6\ NaNO_3(aq)$
$2\ PO_4^{3-}(aq) + 3\ Ni^{2+}(aq) \rightarrow Ni_3(PO_4)_2(s)$

3.39 (a) $HNO_2(aq) + OH^-(aq) \rightarrow NO_2^-(aq) + H_2O(\ell)$
(b) $Ca(OH)_2(s) + 2\ H_3O^+(aq) \rightarrow Ca^{2+}(aq) + 4\ H_2O(\ell)$

3.41 $FeCO_3(s) + 2\ HNO_3(aq) \rightarrow Fe(NO_3)_2(aq) + CO_2(g) + H_2O(\ell)$
Iron(II) carbonate reacts with nitric acid to give iron(II) nitrate, carbon dioxide, and water.

3.43 $(NH_4)_2S(aq) + 2\ HBr(aq) \rightarrow 2\ NH_4Br(aq) + H_2S(g)$
Ammonium sulfide reacts with hydrobromic acid to give ammonium bromide and hydrogen sulfide.

3.45 (a) Br = +5 and O = −2
(b) C = +3 each and O = −2
(c) F = −1
(d) Ca = +2 and H = −1
(e) H = +1, Si = +4, and O = −2
(f) H = +1, S = +6, and O = −2

3.47 (a) Oxidation–reduction
Zn is oxidized from 0 to +2, and N in NO_3^- is reduced from +5 to +4 in NO_2.
(b) Acid–base reaction
(c) Oxidation–reduction
Calcium is oxidized from 0 to +2 in $Ca(OH)_2$, and H is reduced from +1 in H_2O to 0 in H_2.

3.49 (a) O_2 is the oxidizing agent (as it always is), so C_2H_4 is the reducing agent. In this process, C_2H_4 is oxidized, and O_2 is reduced.
(b) Si is oxidized from 0 in Si to +4 in $SiCl_4$. Cl_2 is reduced from 0 in Cl_2 to −1 in Cl^-. Si is the reducing agent, and Cl_2 is the oxidizing agent.

3.51 (a) Acid–base
$Ba(OH)_2(aq) + 2\ HCl(aq) \rightarrow BaCl_2(aq) + 2\ H_2O(\ell)$
(b) Gas-forming
$2\ HNO_3(aq) + CoCO_3(s) \rightarrow Co(NO_3)_2(aq) + H_2O(\ell) + CO_2(g)$
(c) Precipitation
$2\ Na_3PO_4(aq) + 3\ Cu(NO_3)_2(aq) \rightarrow Cu_3(PO_4)_2(s) + 6\ NaNO_3(aq)$

3.53 (a) Precipitation
$MnCl_2(aq) + Na_2S(aq) \rightarrow MnS(s) + 2\ NaCl(aq)$
$Mn^{2+}(aq) + S^{2-}(aq) \rightarrow MnS(s)$
(b) Precipitation
$K_2CO_3(aq) + ZnCl_2(aq) \rightarrow ZnCO_3(s) + 2\ KCl(aq)$
$CO_3^{2-}(aq) + Zn^{2+}(aq) \rightarrow ZnCO_3(s)$

3.55 (a) $CuCl_2(aq) + H_2S(aq) \rightarrow CuS(s) + 2\ HCl(aq)$; precipitation
(b) $H_3PO_4(aq) + 3\ KOH(aq) \rightarrow 3\ H_2O(\ell) + K_3PO_4(aq)$
acid–base
(c) $Ca(s) + 2\ HBr(aq) \rightarrow H_2(g) + CaBr_2(aq)$
oxidation–reduction and gas-forming
(d) $MgCl_2(aq) + 2\ NaOH(aq) \rightarrow Mg(OH)_2(s) + 2\ NaCl(aq)$
precipitation

3.57 (a) $Ca(OH)_2(s) + 2\ HBr(aq) \rightarrow 2\ H_2O(\ell) + CaBr_2(aq)$
(b) $MgCO_3(s) + 2\ HNO_3(aq) \rightarrow Mg(NO_3)_2(aq) + CO_2(g) + H_2O(\ell)$
(c) $BaCl_2(aq) + Na_2SO_4(aq) \rightarrow BaSO_4(s) + 2\ NaCl(aq)$
(d) $NH_3(g) + H_2O(\ell) \rightarrow NH_4^+(aq) + OH^-(aq)$

3.59 (a) $CO_2(g) + 2\ NH_3(g) \rightarrow NH_2CONH_2(s) + H_2O(\ell)$
(b) $UO_2(s) + 4\ HF(aq) \rightarrow UF_4(s) + 2\ H_2O(\ell)$
$UF_4(s) + F_2(g) \rightarrow UF_6(s)$
(c) $TiO_2(s) + 2\ Cl_2(g) + 2\ C(s) \rightarrow TiCl_4(\ell) + 2\ CO(g)$
$TiCl_4(\ell) + 2\ Mg(s) \rightarrow Ti(s) + 2\ MgCl_2(s)$

3.61 (a) NaBr, KBr, or other alkali metal bromides; Group 2A bromides; other metal bromides except AgBr, Hg_2Br_2, and $PbBr_2$
(b) $Al(OH)_3$ and transition metal hydroxides
(c) Alkaline earth carbonates ($CaCO_3$) or transition metal carbonates ($NiCO_3$)
(d) Metal nitrates are generally water-soluble [e.g., $NaNO_3$, $Ni(NO_3)_2$].
(e) CH_3CO_2H, other acids containing the $—CO_2H$ group

3.63 Water soluble: $Cu(NO_3)_2$, $CuCl_2$. Water insoluble: $CuCO_3$, $Cu_3(PO_4)_2$

3.65 $2\ H_3O^+(aq) + Mg(OH)_2(s) \rightarrow 4\ H_2O(\ell) + Mg^{2+}(aq)$
Spectator ion, NO_3^-. Acid–base reaction.

3.67 (a) Cl_2 is reduced (to Cl^-) and Br^- is oxidized (to Br_2).
(b) Cl_2 is the oxidizing agent and Br^- is the reducing agent.

3.69 (a) $MgCO_3(s) + 2\ H_3O^+(aq) \rightarrow CO_2(g) + Mg^{2+}(aq) + 3\ H_2O(\ell)$
Chloride ion (Cl^-) is the spectator ion.
(b) Gas-forming reaction

3.71 (a) H_2O, NH_3, NH_4^+, and OH^- (and a trace of H_3O^+)
weak Brønsted base
(b) H_2O, CH_3CO_2H, $CH_3CO_2^-$, and H_3O^+ (and a trace of OH^-)
weak Brønsted acid
(c) H_2O, Na^+, and OH^- (and a trace of H_3O^+)
strong Brønsted base
(d) H_2O, H_3O^+, and Br^- (and a trace of OH^-)
strong Brønsted acid

3.73 (a) $K_2CO_3(aq) + 2\ HClO_4(aq) \rightarrow 2\ KClO_4(aq) + CO_2(g) + H_2O(\ell)$
gas-forming
Potassium carbonate and perchloric acid react to form potassium perchlorate, carbon dioxide, and water.
$CO_3^{2-}(aq) + 2\ H_3O^+(aq) \rightarrow CO_2(g) + 3\ H_2O(\ell)$
(b) $FeCl_2(aq) + (NH_4)_2S(aq) \rightarrow FeS(s) + 2\ NH_4Cl(aq)$
precipitation
Iron(II) chloride and ammonium sulfide react to form iron(II) sulfide and ammonium chloride.
$Fe^{2+}(aq) + S^{2-}(aq) \rightarrow FeS(s)$
(c) $Fe(NO_3)_2(aq) + Na_2CO_3(aq) \rightarrow FeCO_3(s) + 2\ NaNO_3(aq)$
precipitation
Iron(II) nitrate and sodium carbonate react to form iron(II) carbonate and sodium nitrate
$Fe^{2+}(aq) + CO_3^{2-}(aq) \rightarrow FeCO_3(s)$
(d) $3\ NaOH(aq) + FeCl_3(aq) \rightarrow 3\ NaCl(aq) + Fe(OH)_3(s)$
precipitation
Sodium hydroxide and iron(III) chloride react to form sodium chloride and iron(III) hydroxide.
$3\ OH^-(aq) + Fe^{3+}(aq) \rightarrow Fe(OH)_3(s)$

3.75 (a) NaOH
(b) $MgCl_2$
(c) KI
(d) NH_4Cl

3.77 (a) NH_3
(b) CH_3CO_2H, HF

3.79 $2\ H_3O^+(aq) + S^{2-}(aq) \rightarrow H_2S(g) + 2\ H_2O(\ell)$
$H_2S(g) + Pb^{2+}(aq) + 2\ H_2O(\ell) \rightarrow PbS(s) + 2\ H_3O^+(aq)$

3.81 (a) Reactants: Na(+1), I(−1), H(+1), S(+6), O(−2), Mn(+4)
Products: Na(+1), S(+6), O(−2), Mn(+2), I(0), H(+1)
(b) The oxidizing agent is MnO_2, and NaI is oxidized. The reducing agent is NaI, and MnO_2 is reduced.
(c) Based on the picture, the reaction is product-favored.
(d) Sodium iodide, sulfuric acid, and manganese(IV) oxide react to form sodium sulfate, manganese(II) sulfate, iodine, and water.

3.83 Among the reactions that could be used are the following:
$MgCO_3(s) + 2\ HCl(aq) \rightarrow MgCl_2(aq) + CO_2(g) + H_2O(\ell)$
$MgS(s) + 2\ HCl(aq) \rightarrow MgCl_2(aq) + H_2S(g)$
$MgSO_3(s) + 2\ HCl(aq) \rightarrow MgCl_2(aq) + SO_2(g) + H_2O(\ell)$
In each case, the resulting solution could be evaporated to obtain the desired magnesium chloride.

3.85 The Ag^+ was reduced (to silver metal), and the glucose was oxidized (to $C_6H_{12}O_7$). The Ag^+ is the oxidizing agent, and the glucose is the reducing agent.

3.87 Weak electrolyte test: Compare the conductivity of a solution of lactic acid and that of an equal concentration of a strong acid. The conductivity of the lactic acid solution should be significantly less.
Reversible reaction: The fact that lactic acid is an electrolyte indicates that the reaction proceeds in the forward direction. To test whether the ionization is reversible, one could prepare a solution containing as much lactic acid as it will hold and then add a strong acid (to provide H_3O^+). If the reaction proceeds in the reverse direction, this will cause some lactic acid to precipitate.

3.89 (a) Several precipitation reactions are possible:
i. $BaCl_2(aq) + H_2SO_4(aq) \rightarrow BaSO_4(s) + 2\ HCl(aq)$
ii. $BaCl_2(aq) + Na_2SO_4(aq) \rightarrow BaSO_4(s) + 2\ NaCl(aq)$
iii. $Ba(OH)_2(aq) + H_2SO_4(aq) \rightarrow BaSO_4(s) + 2\ H_2O(\ell)$
(b) Gas-forming reaction:
$BaCO_3(s) + H_2SO_4(aq) \rightarrow BaSO_4(s) + CO_2(g) + H_2O(\ell)$

3.91 $NiC_8H_{14}N_4O_4$

3.93 (a) Reactants: As: +3; S: −2; N: +5
Products: As: +5; S: 0; N: +2
(b) Ag_3AsO_4

Chapter 4

Case Studies

Green Chemistry and Atom Economy

Reactant molecules contain 5 C, 10 H, 3 O. Combined molar mass = 118.1 g/mol

Desired product (methyl methacrylate) contains 5 C, 8 H, 2 O. Molar mass = 100.1 g/mol

% Atom economy = (100.1/118.1) × 100 = 84.75%

How Much Salt Is There in Seawater?

1. Step 1: Calculate the amount of Cl^- in the diluted solution from titration data.

Mol Cl^- in 50 mL of dilute solution = mol Ag^+ = (0.100 mol/L)(0.02625 L) = 2.63×10^{-3} mol Cl^-

Step 2: Calculate the concentration of Cl^- in the dilute solution.

Concentration of Cl^- in dilute solution = 2.63×10^{-3} mol/0.0500 L = 5.25×10^{-2} M

Step 3: Calculate the concentration of Cl^- in seawater.

Seawater was initially diluted to one hundredth its original concentration. Thus, the concentration of Cl^- in seawater (undiluted) = 5.25 M

Forensic Chemistry: Titrations and Food Tampering

1. Step 1: Calculate the amount of I_2 in solution from titration data.

Amount I_2 = (0.0425 mol $S_2O_3^{2-}$/L)(0.0253 L)(1 mol I_2/2 mol $S_2O_3^{2-}$) = 5.38×10^{-4} mol I_2

Step 2: Calculate the amount of NaClO present based on the amount of I_2 formed, and from that value calculate the mass of NaClO.

Mass NaClO = 5.38×10^{-4} mol I_2 (1 mol HClO/1 mol I_2)(1 mol NaClO/1 mol HClO)(74.44 g NaClO/1 mol NaClO) = 0.0400 g NaClO

Check Your Understanding

4.1 (454 g C_3H_8)(1 mol C_3H_8/44.10 g C_3H_8) = 10.3 mol C_3H_8

10.3 mol C_3H_8 (5 mol O_2/1 mol C_3H_8)(32.00 g O_2/1 mol O_2) = 1650 g O_2

(10.3 mol C_3H_8)(3 mol CO_2/1 mol C_3H_8)(44.01 g CO_2/1 mol CO_2) = 1360 g CO_2

(10.3 mol C_3H_8)(4 mol H_2O/1 mol C_3H_8)(18.02 g H_2O/1 mol H_2O) = 742 g H_2O

4.2 (a) Amount Al = (50.0 g Al)(1 mol Al/26.98 g Al) = 1.85 mol Al

Amount Fe_2O_3 = (50.0 g Fe_2O_3)(1 mol Fe_2O_3/159.7 g Fe_2O_3) = 0.313 mol Fe_2O_3

Mol Al/mol Fe_2O_3 = 1.85/0.313 = 5.92

This is more than the 2:1 ratio required, so the limiting reactant is Fe_2O_3.

(b) Mass Fe = (0.313 mol Fe_2O_3)(2 mol Fe/1 mol Fe_2O_3) (55.85 g Fe/1 mol Fe) = 35.0 g Fe

4.3 (0.143 g O_2)(1 mol O_2/32.00 g O_2)(3 mol TiO_2/3 mol O_2)(79.87 g TiO_2/1 mol TiO_2) = 0.357 g TiO_2

Percent TiO_2 in sample = (0.357 g/2.367 g)(100%) = 15.1%

4.4 (1.612 g CO_2)(1 mol CO_2/44.010 g CO_2)(1 mol C/1 mol CO_2) = 0.03663 mol C

(0.7425 g H_2O)(1 mol H_2O/18.015 g H_2O)(2 mol H/1 mol H_2O) = 0.08243 mol H

0.08243 mol H/0.03663 mol = 2.250 H/1 C = 9 H/4 C

The empirical formula is C_4H_9, which has a molar mass of 57 g/mol. This is one half of the measured value of molar mass, so the molecular formula is C_8H_{18}.

4.5 (0.240 g CO_2)(1 mol CO_2/44.01 g CO_2) (1 mol C/1 mol CO_2)(12.01 g C/1 mol C) = 0.06549 g C

(0.0982 g H_2O)(1 mol H_2O/18.02 g H_2O)(2 mol H/1 mol H_2O)(1.008 g H/1 mol H) = 0.01099 g H

Mass O (by difference) = 0.1342 g − 0.06549 g − 0.01099 g = 0.0577 g

Amount C = 0.06549 g(1 mol C/12.01 g C) = 0.00545 mol C

Amount H = 0.01099 g H(1 mol H/1.008 g H) = 0.01090 mol H

Amount O = 0.0577 g O(1 mol O/16.00 g O) = 0.00361 mol O

To find a whole-number ratio, divide each value by 0.00361; this gives 1.51 mol C:3.02 mol H:1 mol O. Multiply each value by 2, and round off to 3 mol C: 6 mol H:2 mol O. The empirical formula is $C_3H_6O_2$; given the molar mass of 74.1, this is also the molecular formula.

4.6 (26.3 g)(1 mol $NaHCO_3$/84.01 g $NaHCO_3$) = 0.313 mol $NaHCO_3$

0.313 mol $NaHCO_3$/0.200 L = 1.57 M

Ion concentrations: $[Na^+] = [HCO_3^-]$ = 1.57 M

4.7 (2.00 M)(V_{conc}) = (1.00 M)(0.250 L); V_{conc} = 0.125 L

To prepare the solution, measure accurately 125 mL of 2.00 M NaOH into a 250-mL volumetric flask, and add water to give a total volume of 250 mL.

4.8 (a) pH = −log (2.6 × 10^{-2}) = 1.59

(b) −log $[H^+]$ = 3.80; $[H^+]$ = 1.6 × 10^{-4} M

4.9 HCl is the limiting reagent.

(0.350 mol HCl/1 L)(0.0750 L)(1 mol CO_2/2 mol HCl)(44.01 g CO_2/1 mol CO_2) = 0.578 g CO_2

4.10 (0.953 mol NaOH/1 L)(0.02833 L NaOH) = 0.0270 mol NaOH

(0.0270 mol NaOH)(1 mol CH_3CO_2H/1 mol NaOH) = 0.0270 mol CH_3CO_2H

(0.0270 mol CH_3CO_2H)(60.05 g/mol) = 1.62 g CH_3CO_2H

0.0270 mol CH_3CO_2H/0.0250 L = 1.08 M

4.11 (0.100 mol HCl/1 L)(0.02967 L) = 0.00297 mol HCl

(0.00297 mol HCl)(1 mol NaOH/1 mol HCl) = 0.00297 mol NaOH

0.00297 mol NaOH/0.02500 L = 0.119 M NaOH

4.12 Moles acid = moles base = (0.323 mol/L)(0.03008 L) = 9.716 × 10^{-3} mol

Molar mass = 0.856 g acid/9.716 × 10^{-3} mol acid = 88.1 g/mol

4.13 (0.196 mol $Na_2S_2O_3$/1 L)(0.02030 L) = 0.00398 mol $Na_2S_2O_3$

(0.00398 mol $Na_2S_2O_3$)(1 mol I_2/2 mol $Na_2S_2O_3$) = 0.00199 mol I_2

0.00199 mol I_2 is in excess and was not used in the reaction with ascorbic acid.

I_2 originally added = (0.0520 mol I_2/1 L)(0.05000 L) = 0.00260 mol I_2

I_2 used in reaction with ascorbic acid = 0.00260 mol − 0.00199 mol = 6.1 × 10^{-4} mol I_2

(6.1 × 10^{-4} mol I_2)(1 mol $C_6H_8O_6$/1 mol I_2)(176.1 g/1 mol) = 0.11 g $C_6H_8O_6$

4.14 A Beer's Law plot of the calibration data was constructed by plotting concentration of Cu^{2+} along the x-axis and the absorbance along the y-axis. The equation for the best-fit line is $y = 13.0x + 0.011$.

Substituting the absorbance for the solution of unknown concentration yields

$$0.418 = 13.0x + 0.011$$

$$x = 0.0315$$

Thus the concentration of Cu^{2+} in the solution of unknown concentration is 0.0315 M

Review & Check

Section 4-1

1. (b) 0.60 moles Cl_2
2. (a) 0.60 g Mg

Section 4-2

1. (b) O_2

Section 4-3

1. (c) 41.8 g
2. (c) 32.5%

Section 4-4

1. (c) C_4H_4O

Section 4-5

1. (c) 0.080 M
2. (b) 0.010 M
3. (c) 12.7 mL

Section 4-6

1. (a) 0.10 M HCl

2. (c) 1.301

3. (a) 2.9×10^{-11} M

Section 4-7

1. (a) acidic

2. (a) 80.0 mL

Section 4-8

1. (b) A is reduced to half the original value.

2. (a) 0.169 M

Applying Chemical Principles: Antacids

1. $NaHCO_3$, $KHCO_3$, and $CaCO_3$

3. (a) $Mg(OH)_2(s) + 2\ HCl(aq) \rightarrow MgCl_2(aq) + 2\ H_2O(\ell)$
(b) 110. mg $Mg(OH)_2$

5. Rolaids neutralizes the greatest quantity of acid.

Study Questions

4.1 6.0 mol Al and 335 g Fe

4.3 22.7 g Br_2; 25.3 g Al_2Br_6

4.5 (a) CO_2, carbon dioxide, and H_2O, water
(b) $CH_4(g) + 2\ O_2(g) \rightarrow CO_2(g) + 2\ H_2O(\ell)$
(c) 102 g O_2
(d) 128 g products

4.7

Equation	2 PbS(s)	+ 3 O_2(g)	→ 2 PbO(s)	+ 2 SO_2(g)
Initial (mol)	2.50	3.75	0	0
Change (mol)	−2.50	−3/2(2.50) = −3.75	+2/2(2.50) = +2.50	+2/2(2.50) = +2.50
Final (mol)	0	0	2.50	2.50

The amounts table shows that 2.50 mol of PbS requires $\frac{3}{2}(2.50) = 3.75$ mol of O_2 and produces 2.50 mol of PbO and 2.50 mol of SO_2.

4.9 (a) Balanced equation: $4\ Cr(s) + 3\ O_2(g) \rightarrow 2\ Cr_2O_3(s)$
(b) 0.175 g of Cr is equivalent to 0.00337 mol

Equation	4 Cr(s)	+ 3 O_2(g)	→ 2 Cr_2O_3(s)
Initial (mol)	0.00337	0.00252 mol	0
Change (mol)	−0.00337	−3/4(0.00337) = −0.00252	2/4(0.00337) = +0.00168
Final (mol)	0	0	0.00168

The 0.00168 mol Cr_2O_3 produced corresponds to 0.256 g Cr_2O_3.
(c) 0.081 g O_2

4.11 0.11 mol of Na_2SO_4 and 0.62 mol of C are mixed. Sodium sulfate is the limiting reactant. Therefore, 0.11 mol of Na_2S is formed, or 8.2 g.

4.13 (a) F_2 is the limiting reactant.
(b) 12 mol SF_6

4.15 (a) CH_4 is the limiting reactant.
(b) 375 g H_2
(c) Excess H_2O = 1390 g

4.17 (a) Fe_2O_3 is the limiting reactant.
(b) 6.99 g Fe produced
(c) 16.6 g of aluminum remains
(d) Amounts table

Equation	Fe_2O_3(s)	+ 2 Al(s)	→ 2 Fe(ℓ)	+ Al_2O_3(g)
Initial (mol)	0.0626	0.741	0	0
Change (mol)	−0.0626	−0.125	+0.125	+0.0626
Final (mol)	0	0.616	0.125	0.0626

4.19 (332 g CH_3OH/407 g)100% = 81.6%

4.21 (a) 14.3 g $Cu(NH_3)_4SO_4$
(b) 88.3% yield

4.23 110 g CH_4 required

4.25 91.9% $CuSO_4 \cdot 5\ H_2O$

4.27 84.3% $CaCO_3$

4.29 13.8% NiS

4.31 Empirical formula = CH

4.33 Empirical formula = C_5H_4; molecular formula = $C_{10}H_8$

4.35 (a) CH_3O (b) $C_2H_6O_2$

4.37 $Ni(CO)_4$

4.39 $[Na_2CO_3] = 0.254$ M; $[Na^+] = 0.508$ M; $[CO_3^{2-}] = 0.254$ M

4.41 0.494 g $KMnO_4$

4.43 5.08×10^3 mL

4.45 (a) 0.50 M NH_4^+ and 0.25 M SO_4^{2-}
(b) 0.246 M Na^+ and 0.123 M CO_3^{2-}
(c) 0.056 M H_3O^+ and 0.056 M NO_3^-

4.47 A mass of 1.06 g of Na_2CO_3 is required. After weighing out this quantity of Na_2CO_3, transfer it to a 500.-mL volumetric flask. Rinse any solid from the neck of the flask while filling the flask with distilled water. Dissolve the solute in water. Add water until the bottom of the meniscus of the water is at the top of the scribed mark on the neck of the flask. Thoroughly mix the solution.

4.49 0.0750 M

4.51 Method (a) is correct. Method (b) gives an acid concentration of 0.15 M.

4.53 0.00340 M

4.55 $[H_3O^+] = 10^{-pH} = 4.0 \times 10^{-4}$ M; the solution is acidic.

4.57 HNO_3 is a strong acid, so $[H_3O^+] = 0.0013$ M. pH = 2.89.

4.59

	pH	$[H_3O^+]$	Acidic/Basic
(a)	1.00	0.10 M	Acidic
(b)	10.50	3.2×10^{-11} M	Basic
(c)	4.89	1.3×10^{-5} M	Acidic
(d)	7.64	2.3×10^{-8} M	Basic

4.61 268 mL

4.63 210 g NaOH and 190 g Cl_2

4.65 174 mL of $Na_2S_2O_3$ solution

4.67 1.50×10^3 mL of $Pb(NO_3)_2$ solution

4.69 44.6 mL

4.71 1.052 M HCl

4.73 104 g/mol

4.75 12.8% Fe

4.77

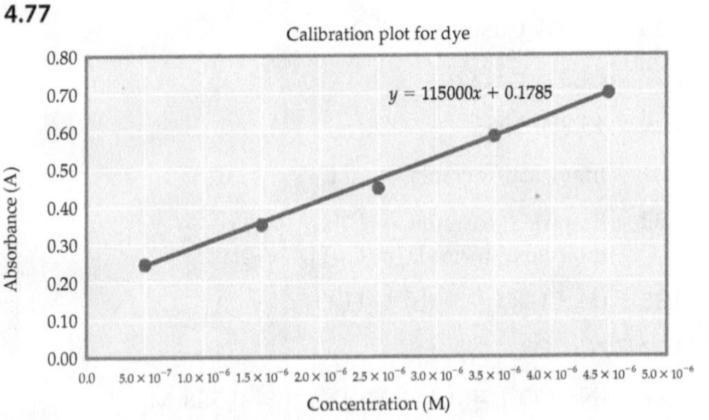

(a) Slope = 1.2×10^5 M^{-1}; y-intercept = 0.18 M
(b) 3.0×10^{-6} M

4.79 (a) Products = $CO_2(g)$ and $H_2O(g)$
(b) $2\ C_6H_6(\ell) + 15\ O_2(g) \rightarrow 12\ CO_2(g) + 6\ H_2O(g)$
(c) 49.28 g O_2
(d) 65.32 g products (= sum of C_6H_6 mass and O_2 mass)

4.81 0.28 g arginine, 0.21 g ornithine

4.83 (a) Titanium(IV) chloride, water, titanium(IV) oxide, hydrogen chloride
(b) 4.60 g H_2O
(c) 10.2 TiO_2, 18.6 g HCl

4.85 85.33 g NaN_3

4.87 Mass percent saccharin = 75.92%

4.89 SiH_4

4.91 C_3H_2O

4.93 1.85 kg H_2SO_4

4.95 The calculated molar mass of the metal is 1.2×10^2 g/mol. The metal is probably tin (118.67 g/mol).

4.97 479 kg Cl_2

4.99 66.5 kg CaO

4.101 1.27 g C_4H_8 (44.4%) and 1.59 g C_4H_{10} (55.6%)

4.103 62.2% Cu_2S and 26.8% CuS

4.105 15.0 g of $NaHCO_3$ require 1190 mL of 0.15 M acetic acid. Therefore, acetic acid is the limiting reactant. (Conversely, 125 mL of 0.15 M acetic acid requires only 1.58 g of $NaHCO_3$.) 1.54 g of $NaCH_3CO_2$ produced.

4.107 3.13 g $Na_2S_2O_3$, 96.8%

4.109 (a) pH = 0.979
(b) $[H_3O^+]$ = 0.0028 M; the solution is acidic.
(c) $H_3O^+]$ = 2.1×10^{-10} M; the solution is basic.
(d) The new solution's concentration is 0.102 M HCl; the pH = 0.990

4.111 The concentration of hydrochloric acid is 2.92 M; the pH is −0.465

4.113 1.56 g of $CaCO_3$ required; 1.00 g $CaCO_3$ remain; 1.73 g $CaCl_2$ produced.

4.115 Volume of water in the pool = 7.6×10^4 L

4.117 (a) Au, gold, has been oxidized and is the reducing agent.
O_2, oxygen, has been reduced and is the oxidizing agent.
(b) 26 L NaCN solution

4.119 % Atom economy = 49.81%

4.121 The concentration of Na_2CO_3 in the first solution prepared is 0.0275 M, in the second solution prepared the concentration of Na_2CO_3 is 0.00110 M.

4.123 (a) $Ag^+(aq) + Cl^-(aq) \rightarrow AgCl(s)$
(b) Balanced equation:
$2\ AgNO_3(aq) + K_2CrO_4(aq) \rightarrow 2\ KNO_3(aq) + Ag_2CrO_4(s)$
Net ionic equation:
$2\ Ag^+(aq) + CrO_4^{2-}(aq) \rightarrow Ag_2CrO_4(s)$
(c) $[Cl^-] = 5.30 \times 10^{-4}$ mol/L = 18.8 mg/L

4.125 (a) First reaction: oxidizing agent = Cu^{2+} and reducing agent = I^-. Second reaction: oxidizing agent = I_3^- and reducing agent = $S_2O_3^{2-}$.
(b) 67.3% copper

4.127 $x = 6$; $Cr(NH_3)_6Cl_3$.

4.129 11.48% 2,4-D

4.131 3.3 mol H_2O/mol $CaCl_2$

4.133 (a) Slope = 2.06×10^5; y-intercept = 0.024
(b) 1.20×10^{-4} g/L
(c) 0.413 mg PO_4^{3-}

4.135 The total mass of the beakers and products after reaction is equal to the total mass before the reaction (167.170 g) because no gases were produced in the reaction and there is conservation of mass in chemical reactions.

4.137 The balanced chemical equation indicates that the stoichiometric ratio of HCl to Zn is 2 mol HCl/1 mol Zn. In each reaction, there is 0.100 mol of HCl present. In reaction 1, there is 0.107 mol of Zn present. This gives a 0.93 mol HCl/mol Zn ratio, indicating that HCl is the limiting reactant. In reaction 2, there is 0.050 mol of Zn, giving a 2.0 mol HCl/mol Zn ratio. This indicates that the two reactants are present in exactly the correct stoichiometric ratio. In reaction 3, there is 0.020 mol of Zn, giving a 5.0 mol HCl/mol Zn ratio. This indicates that the HCl is present in excess and that the zinc is the limiting reactant.

4.139 If both students base their calculations on the amount of HCl solution pipeted into the flask (20 mL), then the second student's result will be (e), the same as the first student's. However, if the HCl concentration is calculated using the diluted solution volume, student 1 will use a volume of 40 mL, and student 2 will use a volume of 80 mL in the calculation. The second student's result will be (c), half that of the first student's.

4.141 (a) % Atom economy = 44.15%

(b) Theoretical yield of maleic anhydride = 1.26×10^3 g; % yield = 77.4%

The theoretical yield of carbon dioxide from 1.00 kg of benzene is 1.13 kg.

Chapter 5

Case Study

The Fuel Controversy—Alcohol and Gasoline

In the following, we assume water vapor, $H_2O(g)$, is formed upon oxidation.

1. Burning ethanol: $C_2H_5OH(\ell) + 3\ O_2(g) \rightarrow 2\ CO_2(g) + 3\ H_2O(g)$

$\Delta_rH° =$ (2 mol CO_2/mol-rxn)[$\Delta_fH°(CO_2)$] + (3 mol H_2O/mol-rxn)[$\Delta_fH°(H_2O)$] − (1 mol C_2H_5OH/mol-rxn)[$\Delta_fH°(C_2H_5OH)$]

$\Delta_rH° =$ (2 mol CO_2/mol-rxn)[−393.5 kJ/mol O_2] + (3 mol H_2O/mol-rxn)[−241.8 kJ/mol H_2O] − (1 mol C_2H_5OH/mol-rxn)[−277.0 kJ/mol C_2H_5OH)] = −1235.4 kJ/mol-rxn

1 mol ethanol per 1 mol-rxn; therefore, q per mol is −1235.4 kJ/mol

q per gram: (−1235.4 kJ/mol)(1 mol C_2H_5OH/46.07 g C_2H_5OH) = −26.82 kJ/g C_2H_5OH

Burning octane: $C_8H_{18}(\ell) + 12.5\ O_2(g) \rightarrow 8\ CO_2(g) + 9\ H_2O(g)$

$\Delta_rH° =$ (8 mol CO_2/mol-rxn)[$\Delta_fH°(CO_2)$] + (9 mol H_2O/mol-rxn)[$\Delta_fH°(H_2O)$] − (1 mol C_8H_{18}/mol-rxn)[$\Delta_fH°(C_8H_{18})$]

$\Delta_rH° =$ (8 mol CO_2/mol-rxn)[−393.5 kJ/mol CO_2] + (9 mol H_2O/mol-rxn)[−241.8 kJ/mol H_2O] − (1 mol C_8H_{18}/mol-rxn)[−250.1 kJ/mol C_8H_{18})] = −5074.1 kJ/mol-rxn

1 mol octane per mol-rxn; therefore, q per mol octane is −5074.1 kJ/mol

q per gram: −5074.1 kJ/1 mol C_8H_{18} (1 mol C_8H_{18}/114.2 g C_8H_{18}) = −44.43 kJ/g C_8H_{18}

Octane provides more energy per gram than ethanol.

2. For ethanol, per liter: q = (−26.82 kJ/g)(785 g/L) = -2.11×10^4 kJ/L

For octane, per liter: q = (−44.43 kJ/g)(699 g/L) = $-\ 3.11 \times 10^4$ kJ/L

Octane produces almost 50% more energy per liter of fuel.

3. Mass of CO_2 per liter of ethanol = 1.000 L (785 g C_2H_5OH/L)(1 mol C_2H_5OH/46.07 g C_2H_5OH) (2 mol CO_2/1 mol C_2H_5OH)(44.01 g CO_2/1 mol CO_2) = 1.50×10^3 g CO_2

Mass of CO_2 per liter of octane = 1.000 L (699 g C_8H_{18}/L)(1 mol C_8H_{18} /114.2 g C_8H_{18}) (8 mol CO_2/1 mol C_8H_{18})(44.01 g CO_2/1 mol CO_2) = 2.16×10^3 g CO_2

4. Volume of ethanol needed to obtain 3.11×10^4 kJ of energy from oxidation: (2.11×10^4 kJ/L C_2H_5OH)(x) = 3.11×10^4 kJ (where x is volume of ethanol)

Volume of ethanol = x = 1.47 L

Mass of CO_2 produced by burning 1.47 L of ethanol = (1.50×10^3 g CO_2/L C_2H_5OH)(1.47 L C_2H_5OH) = 2.22×10^3 g CO_2

To obtain the same amount of energy, slightly more CO_2 is produced by burning ethanol than by burning octane.

5. Your car will travel about 50% farther on a liter of octane, and it will produce slightly less CO_2 emissions, than if you burned 1.0 L of ethanol.

Check Your Understanding

5.1 C = 59.8 J/[(25.0 g)(1.00 K)] = 2.39 J/g · K

5.2 (15.5 g)(C_{metal})(18.9 °C − 100.0 °C) + (55.5 g)(4.184 J/g · K)(18.9 °C − 16.5 °C) = 0

C_{metal} = 0.44 J/g · K

5.3 1.00 L (1000 mL/1 L)(0.7849 g/cm3) = 785 g

Heat liquid from 25.0 °C to 78.3 °C.

ΔT = 78.3 °C − 25.0 °C = 53.3 °C = 53.3 K

q = (2.44 J/g · K)(785 g)(53.3 K) = 1.02×10^5 J = 102 kJ

Boil the liquid.

q = 38.56 kJ/mol (785 g)(1 mol/46.08 g) = 657 kJ

Total = 102 kJ + 657 kJ = 759 kJ

5.4 Energy transferred as heat from tea + energy as heat expended to melt ice = 0.

(250 g)(4.2 J/g · K)(273.2 K − 291.4 K) + x g (333 J/g) = 0

x = 57 g

57 g of ice melts with energy supplied by cooling 250 g of tea from 18.2 °C (291.4 K) to 0 °C (273.2 K).

Mass of ice remaining = mass of ice initially − mass of ice melted

Mass of ice remaining = 75 g − 57 g = 18 g

5.5 The volume change is $(-0.65\ \text{L})(1\ \text{m}^3/1000\ \text{L}) = -6.5 \times 10^{-4}\ \text{m}^3$. Work, $w_p = -P\Delta V = -(1.01 \times 10^5\ \text{kg/m}\cdot\text{s}^2)(-6.5 \times 10^{-4}\ \text{m}^3) = 66\ \text{J}$ (work done on the system by the surroundings).

Heat (485 J) is transferred from system; q_p for system = −485 J.

$\Delta U = q_p + w_p = -485\ \text{J} + 66\ \text{J} = -419\ \text{J}$

5.6 $(15.0\ \text{g}\ C_2H_6)(1\ \text{mol}\ C_2H_6/30.07\ \text{g}\ C_2H_6) = 0.499\ \text{mol}\ C_2H_6$

$\Delta H° = 0.499\ \text{mol}\ C_2H_6(1\ \text{mol-rxn}/2\ \text{mol}\ C_2H_6)(-2857.3\ \text{kJ/mol-rxn}) = -713\ \text{kJ}$

5.7 Mass of final solution = 400. g

$\Delta T = 27.78\ °C - 25.10\ °C = 2.68\ °C = 2.68\ K$

Amount of HCl used = amount of NaOH used = $C \times V = (0.400\ \text{mol/L}) \times 0.200\ \text{L} = 0.0800\ \text{mol}$

Energy transferred as heat by acid−base reaction + energy gained as heat to warm solution = 0

$q_{rxn} + (4.20\ \text{J/g}\cdot\text{K})(400.\ \text{g})(2.68\ \text{K}) = 0$

$q_{rxn} = -4.50 \times 10^3\ \text{J}$

This represents the energy transferred as heat in the reaction of 0.0800 mol HCl.

Energy transferred as heat per mole = $\Delta_r H$ = −4.50 kJ/0.0800 mol HCl = −56.3 kJ/mol HCl

5.8 (a) Energy evolved as heat in reaction + energy as heat absorbed by H_2O + energy as heat absorbed by bomb = 0

$q_{rxn} + (1.50 \times 10^3\ \text{g})(4.20\ \text{J/g}\cdot\text{K})(27.32\ °C - 25.00\ °C) + (837\ \text{J/K})(27.32\ °C - 25.00\ °C) = 0$

$q_{rxn} = -16{,}600\ \text{J}$ (energy as heat evolved in burning 1.0 g sucrose)

(b) Energy evolved as heat per mole = (−16.6 kJ/g sucrose)(342.3 g sucrose/1 mol sucrose) = −5670 kJ/mol sucrose

5.9 $C(s) + O_2(g) \rightarrow CO_2(g)$ $\quad \Delta_r H_1° = -393.5\ \text{kJ}$

$2\ [S(s) + O_2(g) \rightarrow SO_2(g)]$

$\Delta_r H° = 2\ \Delta_r H_2° = 2(-296.8) = -593.6\ \text{kJ}$

$CO_2(g) + 2\ SO_2(g) \rightarrow CS_2(g) + 3\ O_2(g)$

$\Delta_r H° = -\Delta_r H_3° = +1103.9\ \text{kJ}$

Net: $C(s) + 2\ S(s) \rightarrow CS_2(g)$

$\Delta_r H°_{net} = -393.5\ \text{kJ} + (-593.6\ \text{kJ}) + 1103.9\ \text{kJ} = +116.8\ \text{kJ}$

5.10 $\Delta_r H° = (6\ \text{mol}\ CO_2/\text{mol-rxn})\Delta_f H°[CO_2(g)] + (3\ \text{mol}\ H_2O/\text{mol-rxn})\Delta_f H°[H_2O(\ell)] - \{(1\ \text{mol}\ C_6H_6/1\ \text{mol-rxn})\Delta_f H°[C_6H_6(\ell)] + (15/2\ \text{mol}\ O_2/\text{mol-rxn})\Delta_f H°[O_2(g)]\}$

$= (6\ \text{mol/mol-rxn})(-393.5\ \text{kJ/mol}) + (3\ \text{mol/mol-rxn})(-285.8\ \text{J/mol}) - (1\ \text{mol/mol-rxn})(+49.0\ \text{kJ/mol}) - 0$

$= -3267.4\ \text{kJ/mol-rxn}$

Review & Check

Section 5-1

1. (a) melting of ice at 0 °C
2. (b) $q < 0$

Section 5-2

1. (a) warming 2.0 g of copper by 10 °C
2. (c) 20 g of water at 20 °C + 10 g of water at 30 °C

Section 5-3

1. (a) Raising the temperature of 100 g of water by 1.0 °C
2. (b) All of the ice melts; liquid water is at a temperature between 0 °C and 10 °C.

Section 5-4

1. (b) 2 and 4
2. (c) $2\ C(s) + O_2(g) \rightarrow 2\ CO(g)$

Section 5-5

1. (c) 90.8 kJ
2. (b) −425 kJ

Section 5-6

1. (b) endothermic
2. (b) The calculated value of $\Delta_{solution}H°$ will be too small.

Section 5-7

1. (d) $Al(s) + 3/2\ Cl_2(g) \rightarrow AlCl_3(s)$
2. (c) $1/2\ \Delta_r H_1° - \Delta_r H_2° + 1/2\ \Delta_r H_3°$

Applying Chemical Principles: Gunpowder

1. (a) $\Delta_r H° = -567.9$ kJ/mol-rxn
   (b) $\Delta H° = -2.10$ kJ
3. (a) $4\ C_3H_5N_3O_9(\ell) \rightarrow 12\ CO_2(g) + 6\ N_2(g) + 10\ H_2O(g) + O_2(g)$
   (b) $\Delta_f H° = -3.70 \times 10^2$ kJ/mol

Study Questions

5.1 The system is the part of the universe being studied. The surroundings are everything else in the universe that can exchange matter and/or energy with the system. A system and its surroundings are said to be in thermal equilibrium if they can exchange energy with each other but are at the same temperature; therefore, there is no net transfer of energy as heat from one to the other.

5.3 (a) Exothermic
(b) Endothermic
(c) Endothermic
(d) Endothermic

5.5 0.140 J/g · K

5.7 2.44 kJ

5.9 32.8 °C

5.11 20.7 °C

5.13 $T_{initial} = 37.4$ °C

5.15 0.40 J/g · K

5.17 330 kJ

5.19 49.3 kJ

5.21 273 J

5.23 9.97×10^5 J

5.25 $w = P\Delta V = 126$ J

5.27 $\Delta V = 4.42$ L

5.29 $\Delta U = 433$ J

5.31 $V_{final} = 2.6$ L

5.33 Reaction is exothermic because $\Delta_r H°$ is negative. The heat evolved is 2.38 kJ.

5.35 -3.3×10^4 kJ

5.37 $\Delta H = -56$ kJ/mol CsOH

5.39 0.52 J/g · K

5.41 $\Delta_r H = +23$ kJ/mol-rxn

5.43 -297 kJ/mol SO_2

5.45 -3.09×10^3 kJ/mol $C_6H_5CO_2H$

5.47 0.236 J/g · K

5.49 (a) $\Delta_r H° = -126$ kJ/mol-rxn
(b)

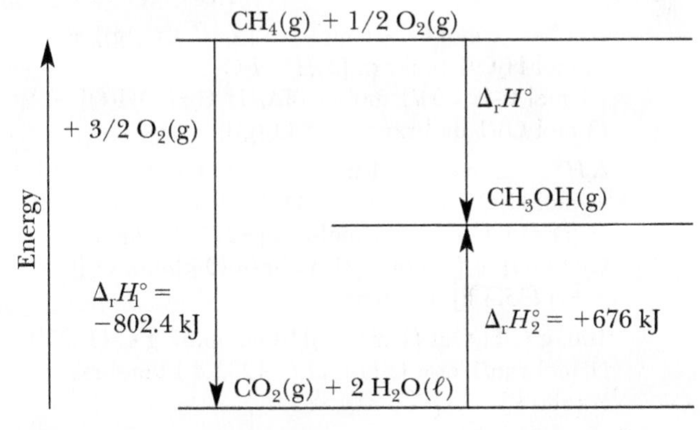

5.51 $\Delta_r H° = +90.3$ kJ/mol-rxn

5.53 $C(s) + 2\ H_2(g) + 1/2\ O_2(g) \rightarrow CH_3OH(\ell)$
$\Delta_f H° = -238.4$ kJ/mol

5.55 (a) $2\ Cr(s) + 3/2\ O_2(g) \rightarrow Cr_2O_3(s)$
$\Delta_f H° = -1134.7$ kJ/mol
(b) 2.4 g is equivalent to 0.046 mol of Cr. This will produce 26 kJ of energy transferred as heat.

5.57 (a) $\Delta H° = -24$ kJ for 1.0 g of phosphorus
(b) $\Delta H° = -18$ kJ for 0.20 mol NO
(c) $\Delta H° = -16.9$ kJ for the formation of 2.40 g of NaCl(s)
(d) $\Delta H° = -1.8 \times 10^3$ kJ for the oxidation of 250 g of iron

5.59 (a) $\Delta_r H° = -906.2$ kJ
(b) The heat evolved is 133 kJ for the oxidation of 10.0 g of NH_3

5.61 (a) $\Delta_r H° = +161.6$ kJ/mol-rxn; the reaction is endothermic.
(b)

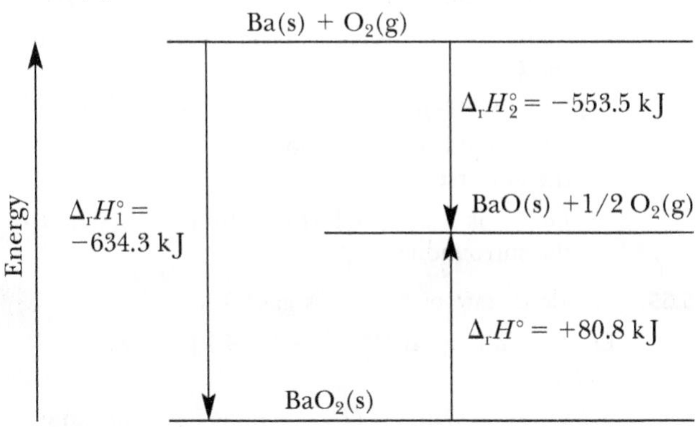

5.63 $\Delta_f H° = +77.7$ kJ/mol for naphthalene

5.65 (a) Exothermic: a process in which energy is transferred as heat from a system to its surroundings. (The combustion of methane is exothermic.)

Endothermic: a process in which energy is transferred as heat from the surroundings to the system. (Ice melting is endothermic.)

(b) System: the object or collection of objects being studied. (A chemical reaction—the system—taking place inside a calorimeter—the surroundings.)

Surroundings: everything outside the system that can exchange mass or energy with the system. (The calorimeter and everything outside the calorimeter comprise the surroundings.)

(c) Specific heat capacity: the quantity of energy that must be transferred as heat to raise the temperature of 1 gram of a substance 1 kelvin. (The specific heat capacity of water is 4.184 J/g · K.)

(d) State function: a quantity that is characterized by changes that do not depend on the path chosen to go from the initial state to the final state. (Enthalpy and internal energy are state functions.)

(e) Standard state: the most stable form of a substance in the physical state that exists at a pressure of 1 bar and at a specified temperature. (The standard state of carbon at 25 °C is graphite.)

(f) Enthalpy change, ΔH: the energy transferred as heat at constant pressure. (The enthalpy change for melting ice at 0 °C is 6.00 kJ/mol.)

(g) Standard enthalpy of formation: the enthalpy change for the formation of 1 mol of a compound in its standard state directly from the component elements in their standard states. ($\Delta_f H°$ for liquid water is -285.83 kJ/mol.)

5.67 (a) System: reaction between methane and oxygen

Surroundings: the furnace and the rest of the universe. Energy is transferred as heat from the system to the surroundings.

(b) System: water drops
Surroundings: skin and the rest of the universe
Energy is transferred as heat from the surroundings to the system
(c) System: water
Surroundings: freezer and the rest of the universe
Energy is transferred as heat from the system to the surroundings
(d) System: reaction of aluminum and iron(III) oxide
Surroundings: flask, laboratory bench, and rest of the universe
Energy is transferred as heat from the system to the surroundings.

5.69 Standard state of oxygen is gas, $O_2(g)$.
$O_2(g) \rightarrow 2\ O(g)$, $\Delta_r H° = +498.34$ kJ/mol-rxn, endothermic
$3/2\ O_2(g) \rightarrow O_3(g)$, $\Delta_r H° = +142.67$ kJ/mol-rxn

5.71 (a) Energy is transferred as heat from the surroundings to the system and as work done by the system.
(b) Energy is transferred as heat from the surroundings to the system and as work done by the system.

5.73 $\Delta H° = -0.627$ kJ

5.75 $C_{Ag} = 0.24$ J/g · K

5.77 Mass of ice melted = 75.4 g

5.79 Final temperature = 278 K (5 °C)

5.81 (a) When summed, the following equations give the balanced equation for the formation of $B_2H_6(g)$ from the elements.

$2\ B(s) + 3/2\ O_2(g) \rightarrow B_2O_3(s)$	$\Delta_r H° = -1271.9$ kJ
$3\ H_2(g) + 3/2\ O_2(g) \rightarrow 3\ H_2O(g)$	$\Delta_r H° = -725.4$ kJ
$B_2O_3(s) + 3\ H_2O(g) \rightarrow B_2H_6(g) + 3\ O_2(g)$	$\Delta_r H° = +2032.9$ kJ
$2\ B(s) + 3\ H_2(g) \rightarrow B_2H_6(g)$	$\Delta_r H° = +35.6$ kJ

(b) The enthalpy of formation of $B_2H_6(g)$ is +35.6 kJ/mol.
(c)

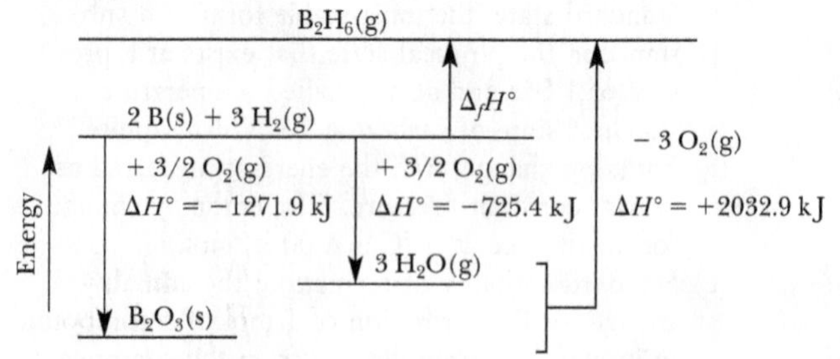

(d) The formation of $B_2H_6(g)$ is endothermic.

5.83 (a) $\Delta_r H° = +131.31$ kJ
(b) Endothermic
(c) 1.0932×10^7 kJ

5.85 Assuming $CO_2(g)$ and $H_2O(\ell)$ are the products of combustion:
$\Delta_r H°$ for isooctane is −5461.3 kJ/mol or −47.81 kJ per gram.
$\Delta_r H°$ for liquid methanol is −726.77 kJ/mol or −22.682 kJ per gram.

5.87 (a) Adding the equations as they are given in the question results in the desired equation for the formation of $SrCO_3(s)$. The calculated $\Delta_r H° = -1220.$ kJ/mol.
(b)

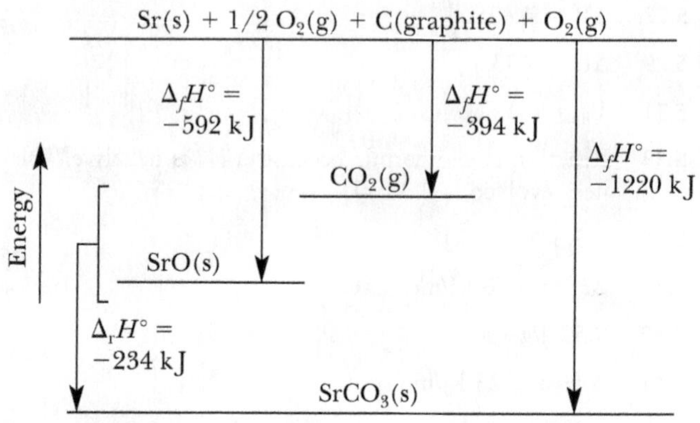

5.89 $\Delta_r H° = -305.3$ kJ

5.91 This calculation assumes water vapor, $H_2O(g)$, is formed upon oxidation.
Balanced Equation: $C_2H_5OH(\ell) + 3\ O_2(g) \rightarrow 2\ CO_2(g) + 3\ H_2O(g)$
$\Delta_r H°$ = (2 mol CO_2/1 mol-rxn)[$\Delta_f H°$ $CO_2(g)$] + (3 mol H_2O/1 mol-rxn)[$\Delta_f H°$ $H_2O(g)$] − {(1 mol C_2H_5OH/1 mol-rxn)[$\Delta_f H°$ $C_2H_5OH(\ell)$] + (3 mol O_2/1 mol-rxn)[$\Delta_f H°$ $O_2(g)$]}
$\Delta_r H°$ = (2 mol CO_2/1 mol-rxn)[−393.5 kJ/mol CO_2] + (3 mol H_2O/1 mol-rxn)[−241.8 kJ/mol H_2O] − {(1 mol C_2H_5OH/1 mol-rxn)[−277.0 kJ/mol C_2H_5OH] + (3 mol O_2/1 mol-rxn)[0 kJ/mol O_2]}
= −1235.4 kJ/mol-rxn
100. g C_2H_5OH (1 mol C_2H_5OH/46.07 g C_2H_5OH)(1 mol-rxn/1 mol C_2H_5OH)(−1235.4 kJ/mol-rxn) = −2680 kJ

5.93 $C_{Pb} = 0.121$ J/g · K

5.95 $\Delta_r H = -69$ kJ/mol AgCl

5.97 36.0 kJ evolved per mol of NH_4NO_3

5.99 The standard enthalpy change, $\Delta_r H°$, is −352.88 kJ. The quantity of magnesium needed is 0.43 g.

5.101 (a) Exothermic
(b) Exothermic

5.103 The enthalpy change for each of the following three reactions is known or can be measured by calorimetry. The three equations sum to give the enthalpy of formation of $CaSO_4(s)$.

Ca(s)	+ 1/2 O_2(g)	→ CaO(s)	$\Delta_rH° = \Delta_fH° = -635.09$ kJ
1/8 S_8(s)	+ 3/2 O_2(g)	→ SO_3(g)	$\Delta_rH° = \Delta_fH° = -395.77$ kJ
CaO(s)	+ SO_3(g)	→ $CaSO_4$(s)	$\Delta_rH° = -402.7$ kJ
Ca(s)	+ 1/8 S_8(s) + 2 O_2(g)	→ $CaSO_4$(s)	$\Delta_rH° = \Delta_fH° = -1433.6$ kJ

5.105

Metal	Molar Heat Capacity (J/mol · K)
Al	24.2
Fe	25.1
Cu	24.5
Au	25.4

All the metals have a molar heat capacity of 24.8 ± 0.5 J/mol · K. Therefore, assuming the molar heat capacity of Ag is 24.8 J/mol · K, its specific heat capacity is 0.230 J/g · K. This is very close to the experimental value of 0.236 J/g · K.

5.107 120 g of CH_4 required (assuming H_2O(g) as product)

5.109 1.6×10^{11} kJ released to the surroundings. This is equivalent to 3.8×10^4 tons of dynamite.

5.111 (a)

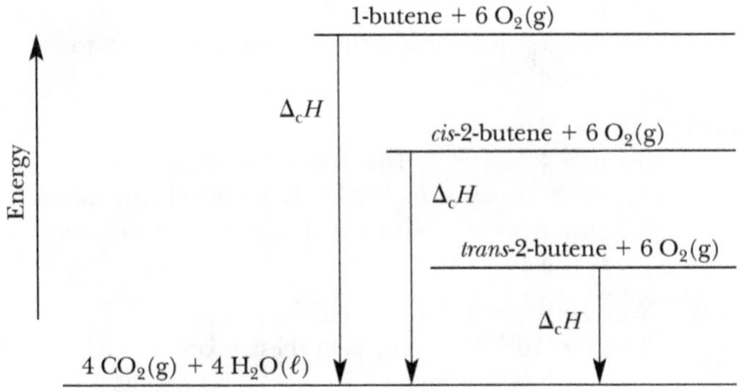

(b) *cis*-2-butene: $\Delta_fH° = -7.6$ kJ/mol
trans-2-butene: $\Delta_fH° = -10.8$ kJ/mol
1-butene: $\Delta_fH° = -0.6$ kJ/mol

(c)

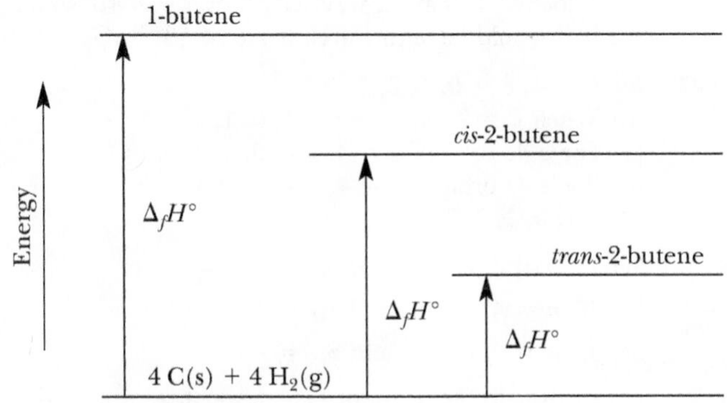

(d) −3.4 kJ/mol-rxn

5.113 (a) −726 kJ/mol Mg
(b) 25.0 °C

5.115 (a) Methane
(b) Methane
(c) −279 kJ
(d) CH_4(g) + 1/2 O_2(g) → CH_3OH(ℓ)

5.117 (a) Metal heated = 100.0 g of Al; metal cooled = 50.0 g of Au; final temperature = 26 °C
(b) Metal heated = 50.0 g of Zn; metal cooled = 50.0 g of Al; final temperature = 21 °C

5.119 $w = -(1.0 \text{ L} \cdot \text{atm})(0.36 \text{ L} - 0 \text{ L}) = -0.36 \text{ L atm} = -36 \text{ J}$

Thus, 36 J of work is done by the system on the surroundings.

Chapter 6

Case Study

What Makes the Colors in Fireworks?

1. Yellow light is from the 589 and 590 nm emissions.
2. Primary emission for Sr is red. This has a longer wavelength than yellow light.
3. 4 Mg(s) + $KClO_4$(s) → KCl(s) + 4 MgO(s)

Check Your Understanding

6.1 (a) Highest frequency, violet; lowest frequency, red
(b) The wavelength of radiation in a microwave oven is shorter than the FM radio wavelength.
(c) The wavelength of x-rays is shorter than the wavelength of ultraviolet light.
(d) $\lambda = 5.10 \times 10^{-7}$ m
$\nu = c/\lambda = (2.998 \times 10^8 \text{ m/s}^{-1})/(5.10 \times 10^{-7} \text{ m}) = 5.88 \times 10^{14} \text{ s}^{-1}$

6.2 $\nu = c/\lambda = (2.998 \times 10^8 \text{ m/s})/(4.05 \times 10^{-7} \text{ m}) = 7.40 \times 10^{14} \text{ s}^{-1}$
$E = N_Ah\nu = (6.022 \times 10^{23} \text{ photons/mole})(6.626 \times 10^{-34} \text{ J s/photon})(7.40 \times 10^{14} \text{ s}^{-1})$
$E = 295{,}000$ J/mol (= 295 kJ/mol)

6.3 (a) E (per atom) $= -Rhc/n^2$
$= (-2.179 \times 10^{-18})/(3^2)$ J/atom
$= -2.421 \times 10^{-19}$ J/atom
(b) E (per mol) $= (-2.421 \times 10^{-19} \text{ J/atom})(6.022 \times 10^{23} \text{ atoms/mol})(1 \text{ kJ}/10^3 \text{ J})$
$= -145.8$ kJ/mol

6.4 The least energetic line is from the electron transition from $n = 2$ to $n = 1$.
$\Delta E = -Rhc[1/1^2 - 1/2^2]$
$= -(2.179 \times 10^{-18} \text{ J/atom})(3/4)$
$= -1.634 \times 10^{-18}$ J/atom
The photon emitted thus has $E_{photon} = 1.634 \times 10^{-18}$ J
$\nu = E_{photon}/h$
$= (1.634 \times 10^{-18} \text{ J})/(6.626 \times 10^{-34} \text{ J} \cdot \text{s})$
$= 2.466 \times 10^{15} \text{ s}^{-1}$
$\lambda = c/\nu = (2.998 \times 10^8 \text{ m/s}^{-1})/(2.466 \times 10^{15} \text{ s}^{-1})$
$= 1.216 \times 10^{-7}$ m (or 121.6 nm)

6.5 First, calculate the velocity of the neutron:

$v = [2E/m]^{1/2} = [2(6.21 \times 10^{-21}\ \text{kg} \cdot \text{m}^2\ \text{s}^{-2})/(1.675 \times 10^{-27}\ \text{kg})]^{1/2}$
$= 2720\ \text{m} \cdot \text{s}^{-1}$

Use this value in the de Broglie equation:

$\lambda = h/mv = (6.626 \times 10^{-34}\ \text{kg} \cdot \text{m}^2\ \text{s}^{-2} \cdot \text{s})/(1.675 \times 10^{-27}\ \text{kg})\ (2720\ \text{m s}^{-1})$
$= 1.45 \times 10^{-10}\ \text{m} = 0.145\ \text{nm}$

Review & Check

Section 6-1

1. (d) microwaves from a microwave oven
2. (c) 3.27 m

Section 6-2

1. (a) 3.9×10^5 J/mol
2. (a) UVB

Section 6-3

1. (d) from $n = 6$ to $n = 2$
2. (b) from $n = 4$ to $n = 2$

Section 6-4

1. (b) Wavelength will be shorter.

Section 6-5

1. (b) $4p$
2. (d) 16
3. (c) n and ℓ

Section 6-6

1. (d) $3f$
2. (b) $n = 4, \ell = 1, m_\ell = 0$
3. (c) 2

Section 6-7

1. (d) $n = 1, \ell = 0, m_\ell = 0, m_s = -1/2$

Applying Chemical Principles: Chemistry of the Sun

1. $\nu = 5.102 \times 10^{14}\ \text{s}^{-1}$

3. For $\lambda = 589.00$ nm, $E = 3.3726 \times 10^{-19}$ J
For $\lambda = 589.59$ nm, $E = 3.3692 \times 10^{-19}$ J
$\Delta E = 3.4 \times 10^{-22}$ J

5. Line F corresponds to a wavelength of 486 nm. Based on Figure 6.10, this line arises from the electron in hydrogen moving from $n = 4$ to $n = 2$.

Study Questions

6.1 (a) Microwaves
(b) Red light
(c) Infrared

6.3 (a) Green light has a higher frequency than amber light
(b) $5.04 \times 10^{14}\ \text{s}^{-1}$

6.5 Frequency = $6.0 \times 10^{14}\ \text{s}^{-1}$; energy per photon = 4.0×10^{-19} J; energy per mol of photons = 2.4×10^5 J

6.7 Frequency = $7.5676 \times 10^{14}\ \text{s}^{-1}$; energy per photon = 5.0144×10^{-19} J; 301.97 kJ/mol of photons

6.9 In order of increasing energy: FM station < microwaves < yellow light < x-rays

6.11 Light with a wavelength as long as 600 nm would be sufficient. This is in the visible region.

6.13 (a) The light of shortest wavelength has a wavelength of 253.652 nm.
(b) Frequency = $1.18190 \times 10^{15}\ \text{s}^{-1}$. Energy per photon = 7.83139×10^{-19} J/photon.
(c) The lines at 404 nm (violet) and 436 nm (blue) are in the visible region of the spectrum.

6.15 The color is violet. $n_{\text{initial}} = 6$ and $n_{\text{final}} = 2$

6.17 (a) 10 lines possible
(b) Highest frequency (highest energy), $n = 5$ to $n = 1$
(c) Longest wavelength (lowest energy), $n = 5$ to $n = 4$

6.19 (a) $n = 3$ to $n = 2$
(b) $n = 4$ to $n = 1$. The energy levels are progressively closer at higher levels, so the energy difference from $n = 4$ to $n = 1$ is greater than from $n = 5$ to $n = 2$.

6.21 Wavelength = 102.6 nm and frequency = $2.923 \times 10^{15}\ \text{s}^{-1}$. Light with these properties is in the ultraviolet region.

6.23 Wavelength = 0.29 nm

6.25 The wavelength is 4.8×10^{-25} nm. (Calculated from $\lambda = h/m \cdot v$, where m is the ball's mass in kg and v is the velocity.) To have a wavelength of 5.6×10^{-3} nm, the ball would have to travel at 2.6×10^{-21} m/s.

6.27 (a) $n = 4, \ell = 0, 1, 2, 3$
(b) When $\ell = 2, m_\ell = -2, -1, 0, 1, 2$
(c) For a $4s$ orbital, $n = 4, \ell = 0$, and $m_\ell = 0$
(d) For a $4f$ orbital, $n = 4, \ell = 3$, and $m_\ell = -3, -2, -1, 0, 1, 2, 3$

6.29 Set 1: $n = 4, \ell = 1$, and $m_\ell = -1$
Set 2: $n = 4, \ell = 1$, and $m_\ell = 0$
Set 3: $n = 4, \ell = 1$, and $m_\ell = +1$

6.31 Four subshells. (The number of subshells in a shell is always equal to n.)

6.33 (a) ℓ must have a value no greater than $n - 1$.
(b) When $\ell = 0$, m_ℓ can only equal 0.
(c) When $\ell = 0$, m_ℓ can only equal 0.

6.35 (a) None. The quantum number set is not possible. When $\ell = 0$, m_ℓ can only equal 0.
(b) 3 orbitals
(c) 11 orbitals
(d) 1 orbital

6.37 (a) $m_s = 0$ is not possible. m_s may only have values of $\pm 1/2$.
One possible set of quantum numbers: $n = 4$, $\ell = 2$, $m_\ell = 0$, $m_s = +1/2$
(b) m_ℓ cannot equal -3 in this case. If $\ell = 1$, m_ℓ can only be -1, 0, or 1.
One possible set of quantum numbers: $n = 3$, $\ell = 1$, $m_\ell = -1$, $m_s = -1/2$
(c) $\ell = 3$ is not possible in this case. The maximum value of ℓ is $n - 1$.
One possible set of quantum numbers: $n = 3$, $\ell = 2$, $m_\ell = -1$, $m_s = +1/2$

6.39 2*d* and 3*f* orbitals cannot exist. The $n = 2$ shell consists only of *s* and *p* subshells. The $n = 3$ shell consists only of *s*, *p*, and *d* subshells.

6.41 (a) For 2*p*: $n = 2$, $\ell = 1$, and $m_\ell = -1, 0,$ or $+1$
(b) For 3*d*: $n = 3$, $\ell = 2$, and $m_\ell = -2, -1, 0, +1,$ or $+2$
(c) For 4*f*: $n = 4$, $\ell = 3$, and $m_\ell = -3, -2, -1, 0, +1, +2,$ or $+3$

6.43 4*d*

6.45 (a) 2*s* has 0 nodal surfaces that pass through the nucleus ($\ell = 0$).
(b) 5*d* has 2 nodal surfaces that pass through the nucleus ($\ell = 2$).
(c) 5*f* has three nodal surfaces that pass through the nucleus ($\ell = 3$).

6.47 (a) Correct
(b) Incorrect. The intensity of a light beam is independent of frequency and is related to the number of photons of light with a certain energy.
(c) Correct

6.49 Considering only angular nodes (nodal surfaces that pass through the nucleus):
s orbital — 0 nodal surfaces through the nucleus
p orbitals — 1 nodal surface or plane passing through the nucleus
d orbitals — 2 nodal surfaces or planes passing through the nucleus
f orbitals — 3 nodal surfaces or planes passing through the nucleus

6.51

ℓ Value	Orbital Type
3	*f*
0	*s*
1	*p*
2	*d*

6.53 Considering only angular nodes (nodal surfaces that pass through the nucleus):

Orbital Type	Number of Orbitals in a Given Subshell	Number of Nodal Surfaces
s	1	0
p	3	1
d	5	2
f	7	3

6.55 (a) Green light
(b) Red light has a wavelength of 680 nm, and green light has a wavelength of 500 nm.
(c) Green light has a higher frequency than red light.

6.57 (a) Wavelength = 0.35 m
(b) Energy = 0.34 J/mol
(c) Violet light (with $\lambda = 420$ nm) has an energy of 280 kJ/mol of photons.
(d) Violet light has an energy (per mol of photons) that is 840,000 times greater than a mole of photons from a cell phone.

6.59 The ionization energy for He^+ is 5248 kJ/mol. This is four times the ionization energy for the H atom.

6.61 $1s < 2s = 2p < 3s = 3p = 3d < 4s$
In the H atom orbitals in the same shell (e.g., 2*s* and 2*p*) have the same energy.

6.63 Frequency = 2.836×10^{20} s^{-1} and wavelength = 1.057×10^{-12} m

6.65 260 s or 4.3 min

6.67 (a) Size and energy
(b) ℓ
(c) More
(d) 7 (when $\ell = 3$ these are *f* orbitals)
(e) One orbital
(f) (Left to right) *d*, *s*, and *p*
(g) $\ell = 0, 1, 2, 3, 4$
(h) 16 orbitals (1 *s* orbital, 3 *p* orbitals, 5 *d* orbitals, and 7 *f* orbitals) ($= n^2$)

6.69 Energy = 4.576×10^{-19} J
Frequency = 6.906×10^{14} s^{-1}
Wavelength = 434.1 nm

6.71 The pickle glows because it was made by soaking a cucumber in brine, a concentrated solution of NaCl. The sodium atoms in the pickle are excited by the electric current and release energy as yellow light as they return to the ground state. Excited sodium atoms are the source of the yellow light you see in fireworks and in certain kinds of street lighting.

6.73 (a) $\lambda = 0.0005$ cm $= 5$ μm
(b) The left side is the higher energy side, and the right side is the lower energy side.
(c) The interaction with O—H requires more energy.

6.75 (c)

6.77 An experiment can be done that shows that the electron can behave as a particle, and another experiment can be done to show that it has wave properties. (However, no single experiment shows both properties of the electron.) The modern view of atomic structure is based on the wave properties of the electron.

6.79 (a) and (b)

6.81 Radiation with a wavelength of 93.8 nm is sufficient to raise the electron to the $n = 6$ quantum level (see Figure 6.10). There should be 15 emission lines involving transitions from $n = 6$ to lower energy levels. (There are five lines for transitions from $n = 6$ to lower levels, four lines for $n = 5$ to lower levels, three for $n = 4$ to lower levels, two lines for $n = 3$ to lower levels, and one line for $n = 2$ to $n = 1$.) Wavelengths for many of the lines are given in Figure 6.10. For example, there will be an emission involving an electron moving from $n = 6$ to $n = 2$ with a wavelength of 410.2 nm.

6.83 (a) Group 7B (IUPAC Group 7); Period 5
(b) $n = 5$, $\ell = 0$, $m_\ell = 0$, $m_s = +1/2$
(c) $\lambda = 8.79 \times 10^{-12}$ m; $\nu = 3.41 \times 10^{19}$ s^{-1}
(d) (i) $HTcO_4(aq) + NaOH(aq) \rightarrow H_2O(\ell) + NaTcO_4(aq)$
(ii) 8.5×10^{-3} g $NaTcO_4$ produced; 1.8×10^{-3} g NaOH needed
(e) 0.28 mg $NaTcO_4$; 0.00015 M

Chapter 7

Case Study

Metals in Biochemistry and Medicine

1. Fe: $[Ar]3d^64s^2$; Fe^{2+}: $[Ar]3d^6$; Fe^{3+}: $[Ar]3d^5$
2. Both iron ions are paramagnetic.
3. The slightly larger size of Cu compared to Fe is related to greater electron–electron repulsions.
4. Fe^{2+} is larger than Fe^{3+} and will fit less well into the structure. As a result, some distortion of the ring structure from planarity occurs.

Check Your Understanding

7.1 (a) chlorine (Cl)
(b) $1s^22s^22p^63s^23p^3$

3s 3p
[Ne] [↑↓] [↑][↑][↑]

7.2 Calcium has two valence electrons in the 4s subshell. Quantum numbers for these two electrons are $n = 4$, $\ell = 0$, $m_\ell = 0$, and $m_s = \pm 1/2$

7.3 Obtain the answers from Table 7.3.

7.4

V^{2+} [Ar] 3d: [↑][↑][↑][ ][ ] 4s: [ ]

V^{3+} [Ar] 3d: [↑][↑][ ][ ][ ] 4s: [ ]

Co^{3+} [Ar] 3d: [↑↓][↑][↑][↑][↑] 4s: [ ]

All three ions are paramagnetic with three, two, and four unpaired electrons, respectively.

7.5 (a) Increasing atomic radius: C < B < Al
(b) Increasing ionization energy: Al < B < C
(c) Carbon is predicted to have the more negative electron attachment enthalpy.

Review & Check

Section 7-1

1. (d) 98
2. (b) $n = 3$, $\ell = 2$, $m_\ell = -1$, and $m_s = -1/2$

Section 7-2

1. (a) the 4s orbital fills before the 4p orbitals

Section 7-3

1. (c) $3d^{10}4s^24p^4$
2. (c) Ni

Section 7-4

1. (d) Fe^{2+}
2. (c) Co^{3+}
3. (a) Cr

Section 7-5

1. (d) $S^{2-} > Cl^- > K^+$
2. (c) N highest, Si lowest

Section 7-6

1. (a) MgCl
2. (d) S^{3-}

Applying Chemical Principles: The Not-So-Rare Earths

1. (a) Sm^{3+}: $[Xe]4f^5$
(b) $4\ Sm(s) + 3\ O_2(g) \rightarrow 2\ Sm_2O_3(s)$

3. (a) [Xe] 4f: [↑][↑][↑][↑][↑][↑][↑] 5d: [↑][ ][ ][ ][ ] 6s: [↑↓]

(b) The most common oxidation state is +3, corresponding to the loss of the two 6s and one 5d electrons. The electron configuration of Gd^{3+} is $[Xe]4f^7$.

5. $\nu = 4.90 \times 10^{14}$ s^{-1}; $E = 3.25 \times 10^{-19}$ J/photon

Study Questions

7.1 (a) Phosphorus: $1s^22s^22p^63s^23p^3$

[↑↓] [↑↓] [↑↓|↑↓|↑↓] [↑↓] [↑|↑|↑]
1s 2s 2p 3s 3p

The element is in the third period in Group 5A. Therefore, it has five electrons in the third shell.

(b) Chlorine: $1s^22s^22p^63s^23p^5$

[↑↓] [↑↓] [↑↓|↑↓|↑↓] [↑↓] [↑↓|↑↓|↑]
1s 2s 2p 3s 3p

The element is in the third period and in Group 7A. Therefore, it has seven electrons in the third shell.

7.3 (a) Chromium: $1s^22s^22p^63s^23p^63d^54s^1$
(b) Iron: $1s^22s^22p^63s^23p^63d^64s^2$

7.5 (a) Arsenic: $1s^22s^22p^63s^23p^63d^{10}4s^24p^3$; $[Ar]3d^{10}4s^24p^3$
(b) Krypton: $1s^22s^22p^63s^23p^63d^{10}4s^24p^6$; $[Ar]3d^{10}4s^24p^6 = [Kr]$

7.7 (a) Tantalum: This is the third element in the transition series in the sixth period. Therefore, it has a core equivalent to Xe plus two 6*s* electrons, 14 4*f* electrons, and three electrons in 5*d*: $[Xe]4f^{14}5d^36s^2$
(b) Platinum: This is the eighth element in the transition series in the sixth period. Therefore, it is predicted to have a core equivalent to Xe plus two 6*s* electrons, 14 4*f* electrons, and eight electrons in 5*d*: $[Xe]4f^{14}5d^86s^2$. In reality, its actual configuration (Table 7.3) is $[Xe]4f^{14}5d^96s^1$.

7.9 Americium: $[Rn]5f^77s^2$ (see Table 7.3)

7.11 (a) 2
(b) 1
(c) None (because ℓ cannot equal n)

7.13 Magnesium: $1s^22s^22p^63s^2$

[Ne] [↑↓]
3s

Quantum numbers for the two electrons in the 3*s* orbital:

$n = 3, \ell = 0, m_\ell = 0$, and $m_s = +1/2$

$n = 3, \ell = 0, m_\ell = 0$, and $m_s = -1/2$

7.15 Gallium: $1s^22s^22p^63s^23p^63d^{10}4s^24p^1$

[Ar] [↑↓|↑↓|↑↓|↑↓|↑↓] [↑↓] [↑| |]
3d 4s 4p

Quantum numbers for the 4*p* electron:

$n = 4, \ell = 1, m_\ell = -1, 0$, or $+1$, and $m_s = +½$ or $-½$

7.17 (a) Mg^{2+} ion

[↑↓] [↑↓] [↑↓|↑↓|↑↓]
1s 2s 2p

(b) K^+ ion

[↑↓] [↑↓] [↑↓|↑↓|↑↓] [↑↓] [↑↓|↑↓|↑↓]
1s 2s 2p 3s 3p

(c) Cl^- ion (Note that both Cl^- and K^+ have the same configuration; both are equivalent to Ar.)

[↑↓] [↑↓] [↑↓|↑↓|↑↓] [↑↓] [↑↓|↑↓|↑↓]
1s 2s 2p 3s 3p

(d) O^{2-} ion

[↑↓] [↑↓] [↑↓|↑↓|↑↓]
1s 2s 2p

7.19 (a) V (paramagnetic; three unpaired electrons)

[Ar] [↑|↑|↑| |] [↑↓]
3d 4s

(b) V^{2+} ion (paramagnetic, three unpaired electrons)

[Ar] [↑|↑|↑| |] [ ]
3d 4s

(c) V^{5+} ion. This ion has an electron configuration equivalent to argon, [Ar]. It is diamagnetic with no unpaired electrons.

7.21 (a) Manganese

[Ar] [↑|↑|↑|↑|↑] [↑↓]
3d 4s

(b) Mn^{4+}

[Ar] [↑|↑|↑| |] [ ]
3d 4s

(c) The 4+ ion is paramagnetic to the extent of three unpaired electrons.
(d) 3

7.23 Increasing size: C < B < Al < Na < K

7.25 (a) Cl^-
(b) Al
(c) In

7.27 (c)

7.29 (a) Largest radius, Na
(b) Most negative electron attachment enthalpy: O
(c) Ionization energy: Na < Mg < P < O

7.31 (a) Increasing ionization energy: S < O < F. S is less than O because the IE decreases down a group. F is greater than O because IE generally increases across a period.
(b) Largest IE: O. IE decreases down a group.
(c) Most negative electron attachment enthalpy: Cl. Electron attachment enthalpy generally becomes more negative across the periodic table and on ascending a group.
(d) Largest size: O^{2-}. Negative ions are larger than their corresponding neutral atoms. F^- is thus larger than F. O^{2-} and F^- are isoelectronic, but the O^{2-} ion has only eight protons in its nucleus to attract the 10 electrons, whereas the F^- has nine protons, making the O^{2-} ion larger.

7.33 (a) Li (b) K (c) Sc

7.35 Identify orbitals that contain electrons: In H and He only the 1*s* orbital is occupied; in Li electrons are present in the 1*s* and 2*s* orbitals. The intensities of peaks in the Li PES are 1 (for the 2*s* electron) and 2 (for the 1*s* electrons).

7.37 (a) Cr configuration: $[Ar]3d^5 4s^1$
Cr^{3+} configuration: $[Ar]3d^3$
(b) Both Cr^{2+} and Cr^{3+} are paramagnetic
(c) The radii are similar (radius for Al^{3+} = 57 nm), which is the reason that Cr^{3+} ions are sometimes found in solid Al_2O_3 in place of Al^{3+}.

7.39 Uranium configuration: $[Rn]5f^3 6d^1 7s^2$

[Rn] [↑|↑|↑| | | |] [↑| | | |] [↑↓]
5*f* 6*d* 7*s*

Uranium(IV) ion, U^{4+}: $[Rn]5f^2$

[Rn] [↑|↑| | | | |] [| | | |] [ ]
5*f* 6*d* 7*s*

Both U and U^{4+} are paramagnetic.

7.41 (a) Atomic number = 20
(b) Total number of *s* electrons = 8
(c) Total number of *p* electrons = 12
(d) Total number of *d* electrons = 0
(e) The element is Ca, calcium, a metal.

7.43 (a) Valid. Possible elements are Li and Be.
(b) Not valid. The maximum value of ℓ is $(n - 1)$.
(c) Valid. Possible elements are B through Ne.
(d) Valid. Possible elements are Y through Cd.

7.45 (a) Neodymium, Nd: $[Xe]4f^4 6s^2$ (Table 7.3)

[Xe] [↑|↑|↑|↑| | |] [| | | |] [↑↓]
4*f* 5*d* 6*s*

Iron, Fe: $[Ar]3d^6 4s^2$

[Ar] [↑↓|↑|↑|↑|↑] [↑↓]
3*d* 4*s*

Boron, B: $[He]2s^2 2p^1$

[He] [↑↓] [↑| |]
2*s* 2*p*

(b) All three elements have unpaired electrons and so should be paramagnetic.
(c) Neodymium(III) ion, Nd^{3+}: $[Xe]4f^3$

[Xe] [↑|↑|↑| | | |] [| | | |] [ ]
4*f* 5*d* 6*s*

Iron(III) ion, Fe^{3+}: $[Ar]3d^5$

[Ar] [↑|↑|↑|↑|↑] [ ]
3*d* 4*s*

Both neodymium(III) and iron(III) have unpaired electrons and are paramagnetic.

7.47 K < Ca < Si < P

7.49 (a) Metal
(b) B
(c) A
(d) A
(e) Rb_2Se

7.51 In^{4+}: Indium has three outer shell electrons and so is unlikely to form a 4^+ ion.
Fe^{6+}: Although iron has eight electrons in its 3*d* and 4*s* orbitals, ions with a 6^+ charge are highly unlikely. The ionization energy is too large.
Sn^{5+}: Tin has four outer shell electrons and so is unlikely to form a 5^+ ion.

7.53 (a) Se
(b) Br^-
(c) Na
(d) N
(e) N^{3-}

7.55 (a) Na
(b) C
(c) Na < Al < B < C

7.57 (a) Cobalt
(b) Paramagnetic
(c) Four unpaired electrons

7.59 (a) metal
(b) B
(c) A
(d) B
(e) A
(f) AB_2 or SrI_2

7.61 (a) 0.421 g
(b) Paramagnetic; two unpaired electrons
(c) 99.8 mg; the nickel powder is paramagnetic and will stick to a magnet.

7.63 Li has three electrons ($1s^2 2s^1$) and Li^+ has only two electrons ($1s^2$). The ion is smaller than the atom because there are only two electrons to be held by three protons in the ion. Also, an electron in a larger orbital has been removed. Fluorine atoms have nine electrons and nine protons ($1s^2 2s^2 2p^5$). The anion, F^-, has one additional electron, which means that 10 electrons must be held by only nine protons, and so the ion is larger than the atom.

7.65 (a) The electron removed from Al is in the 3*p* orbital, which has a less negative energy than the 3*s* orbital from which the electron is removed in Mg. See the plot of orbital energies in *A Closer Look: Orbital Energies, Z*, and Electron Configurations*, page 262.
(b) The electron removed from S is one of a pair. Electron-electron repulsion lowers the energy required to remove the electron. (The 3*p* electrons of P are not paired.)

7.67 The most stable configuration is (d) (parallel spins in different orbitals, according to Hund's rule.) Configuration (b) is less stable than (c) due to repulsion of the two electrons in the same orbital. Configuration (a) is not an acceptable possibility; two electrons cannot have the same set of quantum numbers.

7.69 K $(1s^22s^22p^63s^23p^64s^1) \rightarrow K^+(1s^22s^22p^63s^23p^6)$

K^+ $(1s^22s^22p^63s^23p^6) \rightarrow K^{2+}(1s^22s^22p^63s^23p^5)$

The first ionization is for the removal of an electron from the valence shell of electrons. The second electron, however, is removed from the 3*p* subshell. This subshell is significantly lower in energy than the 4*s* subshell, and considerably more energy is required to remove this second electron.

7.71 (a) In going from one element to the next across the period, the effective nuclear charge increases slightly and the attraction between the nucleus and the electrons increases.
(b) The size of fourth period transition elements, for example, is a reflection of the size of the 4*s* orbital. As *d* electrons are added across the series, protons are added to the nucleus. Adding protons should lead to a decreased atom size, but the effect of the protons is balanced by repulsions of the 3*d* electrons and 4*s* electrons, and the atom size is changed little.

7.73 Among the arguments for a compound composed of Mg^{2+} and O^{2-} are the following:
(a) Chemical experience suggests that all Group 2A elements form 2^+ cations, and that oxygen is typically the O^{2-} ion in its compounds.
(b) Other alkaline earth elements form oxides such as BeO, CaO, and BaO.

A possible experiment is to measure the melting point of the compound. An ionic compound such as NaF (with ions having 1^+ and 1^- charges) melts at 990 °C, whereas a compound analogous to MgO, CaO, melts at a much higher temperature (2580 °C).

7.75 (a) The effective nuclear charge increases, causing the valence orbital energies to become more negative on moving across the period.
(b) As the valence orbital energies become more negative, it is increasingly difficult to remove an electron from the atom, and the IE increases. Toward the end of the period, the orbital energies have become so negative that removing an electron requires significant energy. Instead, the effective nuclear charge has reached the point that the atom forms a negative ion, in line with the more negative electron attachment enthalpy for elements on the right side of the periodic table.
(c) The valence orbital energies are in the order:

Li (−520.0 kJ) < Be (−899.3 kJ) >
B (−800.8 kJ) < C (−1029 kJ)

This means it is more difficult to remove an electron from Be than from either Li or B. The energy is more negative for C than for B, so it is more difficult to remove an electron from C than from B.

7.77 The size declines across this series of elements while their mass increases. Thus, the mass per volume, the density, increases.

7.79 (a) Element 113: $[Rn]5f^{14}6d^{10}7s^27p^1$
Element 115: $[Rn]5f^{14}6d^{10}7s^27p^3$
(b) Element 113 is in Group 3A (with elements such as boron and aluminum), and element 115 is in Group 5A (with elements such as nitrogen and phosphorus).
(c) Americium ($Z = 95$) + argon ($Z = 18$) = element 113

7.81 (a) Sulfur electron configuration

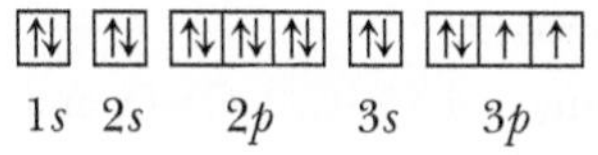

(b) One possible set of quantum numbers for a 3*p* electron is:
$n = 3$, $\ell = 1$, $m_\ell = 1$, and $m_s = +1/2$
(c) S has the smallest ionization energy and O has the smallest radius.
(d) S is smaller than the S^{2-} ion.
(e) 584 g SCl_2
(f) 10.0 g of SCl_2 is the limiting reactant, and 11.6 g of $SOCl_2$ can be produced.
(g) $\Delta_f H°[SCl_2(g)] = -17.6$ kJ/mol

7.83 (a) Z* for F is 5.20; Z* for Ne is 5.85. The effective nuclear charge increases from O to F to Ne. As the effective nuclear charge increases, the atomic radius decreases, and the first ionization energy increases.
(b) Z* for a 3*d* electron in Mn is 5.6; for a 4*s* electron it is only 3.6. The effective nuclear charge experienced by a 4*s* electron is much smaller than that experienced by a 3*d* electron. A 4*s* electron in Mn is thus more easily removed.

Chapter 8

Case Studies

Free Radicals, Atmospheric Chemistry, and Hair Dyes

1. 18 valence electrons

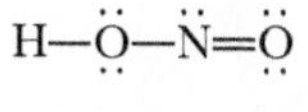

All atoms have a formal charge of zero. There are no equivalent resonance structures.

2. 30 valence electrons

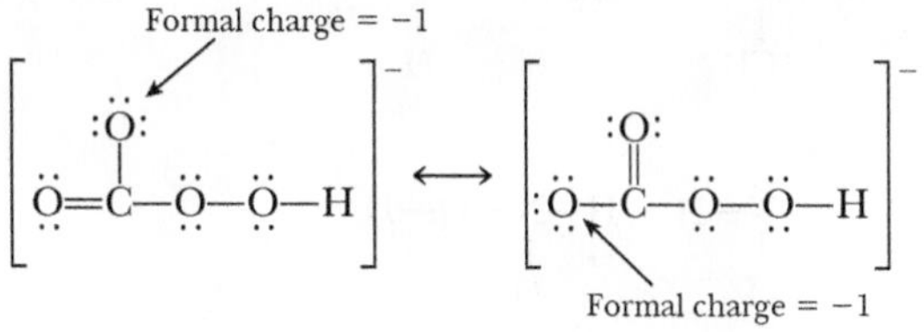

All atoms have zero formal charge except for those indicated.

Ibuprofen, a Study in Green Chemistry

1. The Lewis structures for the key portions of the molecules where the reaction takes place are the following:

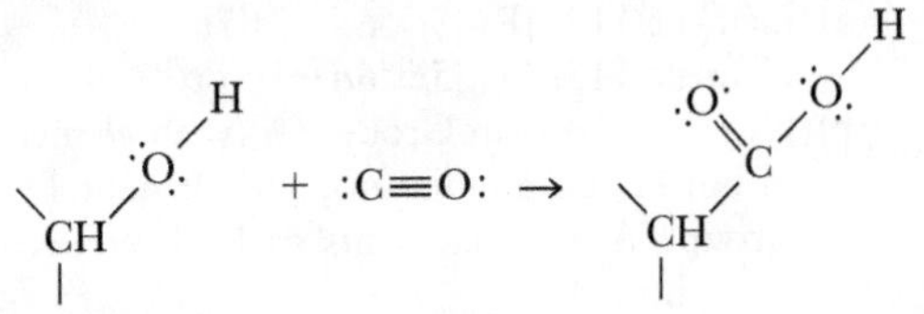

Bonds broken: 1 C—O and 1 C≡O

(1 mol C—O/1 mol-rxn)(358 kJ/mol C—O) + (1 mol C≡O/1 mol-rxn)(1046 kJ/mol C≡O) = 1404 kJ/mol-rxn

Bonds formed: 1 C—C, 1 C=O, and 1 C—O

(1 mol C—C/1 mol-rxn)(346 kJ/mol C—C) + (1 mol C=O/1 mol-rxn)(745 kJ/mol C=O) + (1 mol C—O/1 mol-rxn)(358 kJ/mol C—O) = 1449 kJ/mol-rxn

$\Delta_r H° \approx$ 1404 kJ/mol-rxn − 1449 kJ/mol-rxn = −45 kJ/mol-rxn

The reaction is thus predicted to be exothermic.

2. All of the atoms in ibuprofen have a formal charge of zero.
3. The most polar bond in the molecule is the O—H bond.
4. The molecule is not symmetrical and so is polar.
5. The shortest bond in the molecule is the O—H bond.
6. The C=O bond has the highest bond order. The C=C bonds in the ring have an order of 1.5.
7. Yes, there are 120° bond angles present: the bond angles around the C atoms in the ring and those around the C atom in the —CO_2H group are all 120°. There are no 180° angles in this molecule.
8. There is one acid group in ibuprofen (—CO_2H), therefore 1 mol of ibuprofen will react with 1 mol of NaOH.

   200. mg ibuprofen (1 g/1000 mg)(1 mol ibuprofen/206.3 g ibuprofen)(1 mol NaOH/1 mol ibuprofen)(1 L/0.0259 mol NaOH)(1000 mL/1 L) = 37.4 mL

   Therefore 37.4 mL of the NaOH solution would be required.

Check Your Understanding

8.1

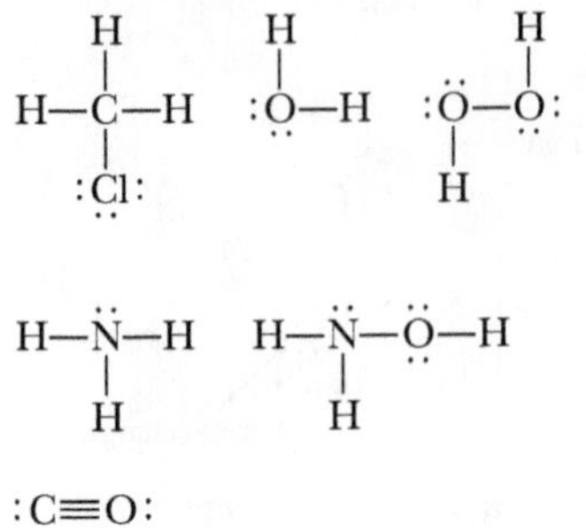

8.2 :C≡O:

8.3

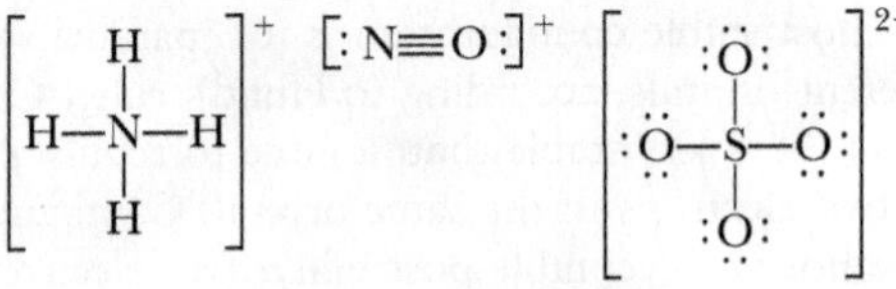

8.4

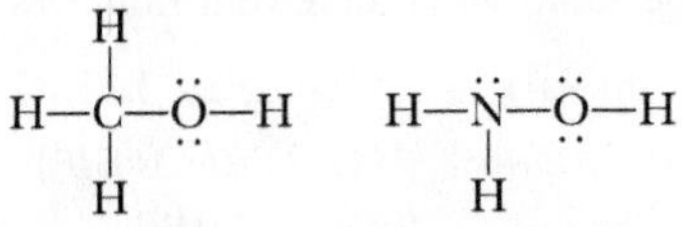

methanol hydroxylamine

8.5 (a) CN^- : formal charge on C is −1; formal charge on N is 0.
(b) SO_3^{2-}: formal charge on S is +1; formal charge on each O is −1.

8.6 Resonance structures for the HCO_3^- ion:

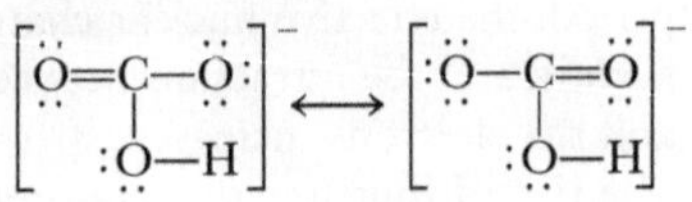

(a) No. Three resonance structures are needed in the description of CO_3^{2-}; only two are needed to describe HCO_3^-.
(b) In each resonance structure: carbon's formal charge is 0; the oxygen of the —OH group and the double-bonded oxygen have a formal charge of zero; the singly bonded oxygen has a formal charge of −1. The average formal charge on the latter two oxygen atoms is −½. In the carbonate ion, each of the three oxygen atoms has an average formal charge of −⅔.
(c) H^+ would be expected to add to one of the oxygens with a negative formal charge; that is, one of the oxygens with formal charge of −½ in this structure.

8.7 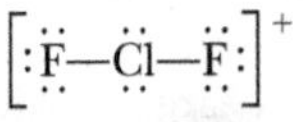 ClF_2^+, 2 bond pairs and 2 lone pairs.

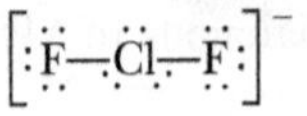 ClF_2^-, 2 bond pairs and 3 lone pairs.

8.8 Tetrahedral geometry around carbon. The Cl—C—Cl bond angle will be close to 109.5°.

8.9 For each species, the electron-pair geometry and the molecular shape are the same. BF_3: trigonal-planar; BF_4^-: tetrahedral. Adding F^- to BF_3 adds an electron pair to the central atom and changes the shape.

8.10 The electron-pair geometry around I is trigonal-bipyramidal. The molecular geometry of the ion is linear.

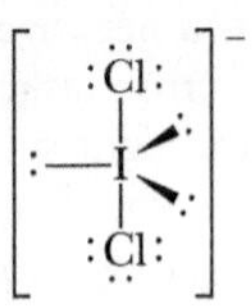

8.11 (a) In PO_4^{3-}, there is tetrahedral electron-pair geometry. The molecular geometry is also tetrahedral.

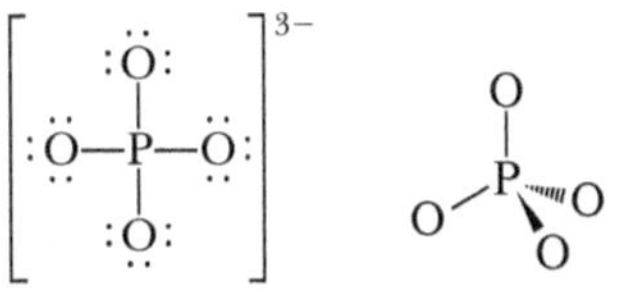

(b) In SO_3^{2-}, there is tetrahedral electron-pair geometry. The molecular geometry is trigonal-pyramidal.

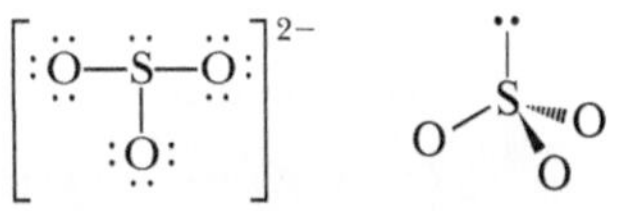

(c) In IF_5, there is octahedral electron-pair geometry. The molecular geometry is square-pyramidal.

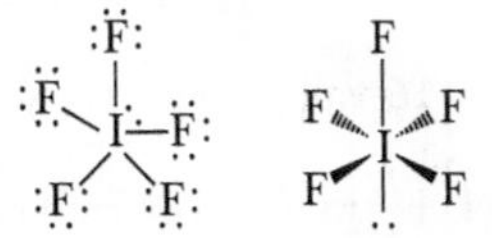

8.12 (a) The H atom is the positive pole in each case. H—F ($\Delta\chi = 1.8$) is more polar than H—I ($\Delta\chi = 0.5$).

(b) The B atom is the positive pole in each case. B—F ($\Delta\chi = 2.0$) is more polar than B—C ($\Delta\chi = 0.5$).

(c) C—Si ($\Delta\chi = 0.6$) is more polar than C—S ($\Delta\chi = 0.1$). In C—Si, C is the negative pole, and Si is the positive pole. In C—S, S is the negative pole, and C the positive pole.

8.13 16 valence electrons

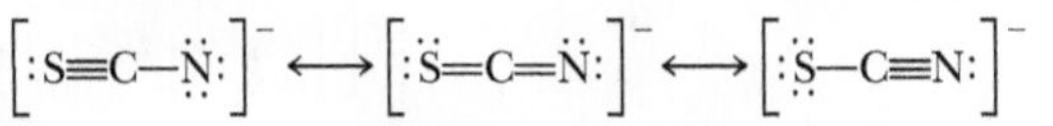

Formal charges +1 0 2−   0 0 −1   −1 0 0

Formal charge considerations favor the middle structure because it has less formal charge than the left structure and, unlike the right structure, it has the negative formal charge on the most electronegative atom in the ion.

Bond polarity: For the C—N bond, $\Delta\chi = 0.5$, so this bond is polar and should have a partially positive C and a partially negative N. For the C—S bond, $\Delta\chi = 0.1$, so this bond should be only slightly polar with a partially positive C and a partially negative S.

Comparison of formal charge and bond polarity: The bonding in SCN^- will be closest to the middle resonance structure with a smaller contribution of the resonance structure on the right. From this we conclude that both N and S will have a negative formal charge, with N having the more negative value. The polarities of the C—N and C—S bonds match this description, with N and S being the negative end of each polar bond.

8.14 (a) $BFCl_2$, polar, negative side is the F atom because F is the most electronegative atom in the molecule.

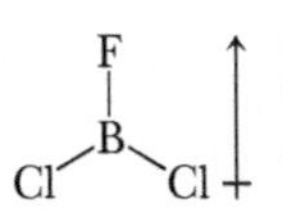

(b) NH_2Cl, polar, negative side is the Cl atom.

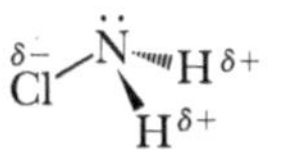

(c) SCl_2, polar, Cl atoms are on the negative side.

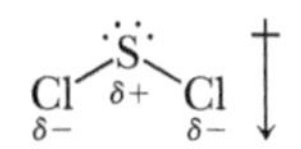

8.15 (a)

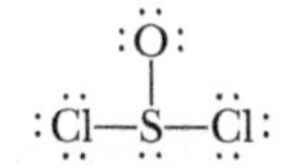

Formal charges: S = +1, O = −1, Cl = 0

(b) Geometry: trigonal-pyramidal. The molecule is polar. The positive charge is on sulfur, the negative charge on oxygen.

8.16 $CH_4(g) + 2\ O_2(g) \rightarrow CO_2(g) + 2\ H_2O(g)$

Break 4 C—H bonds and 2 O=O bonds:
(4 mol)(413 kJ/mol) + (2 mol)(498 kJ/mol) = 2648 kJ

Make 2 C=O bonds and 4 H—O bonds:
(2 mol)(803 kJ/mol) + (4 mol)(463 kJ/mol) = 3458 kJ

$\Delta_r H° = 2648\ \text{kJ} - 3458\ \text{kJ} = -810\ \text{kJ/mol-rxn}$
(value calculated using enthalpies of formation = −802 kJ/mol-rxn)

Review & Check

Section 8-2

1. (a) Sulfur has three single bonds to oxygen and a lone pair.
2. (c) O_3
3. (b) OCN^-
4. (b) Lewis structure shown has 5 bonds to each C atom.

Section 8-3

1. (c) +1

Section 8-4

1. (c) NO_2^+
2. (b) Formal charge on N is +1, formal charge on each oxygen is 0.

Section 8-5

1. (b) SF_4, SF_5^+, SF_6
2. (d) 3

Section 8-6

1. (a) PCl_3
2. (c) square pyramidal
3. (c) 120°
4. (a) linear, 180° angle

Section 8-7

1. (d) Al—Cl
2. (c) The I—Cl bond is polar with I being the positive end.
3. (a) :N≡N—Ö:

Section 8-8

1. (a) HF
2. (a) BCl_3

Section 8-9

1. (d) H_2NOH
2. (a) CN^-
3. (b) −206 kJ/mol-rxn

Applying Chemical Principles: Linus Pauling and Electronegativity

1. Using average bond dissociation enthalpies: $\chi_{Cl} - \chi_H = 0.98$
   According to Figure 8.10, $\chi_{Cl} - \chi_H = 1.0$
3. $\chi_S = 2.55$

Study Questions

8.1. (a) Group 6A, six valence electrons
(b) Group 3A, three valence electrons
(c) Group 1A, one valence electron
(d) Group 2A, two valence electrons
(e) Group 7A, seven valence electrons
(f) Group 6A, six valence electrons

8.3 Group 4A, four bonds
Group 5A, three bonds (for a neutral compound)
Group 6A, two bonds (for a neutral compound)
Group 7A, one (for a neutral compound)

8.5 (a) NF_3, 26 valence electrons

(b) ClO_3^-, 26 valence electrons

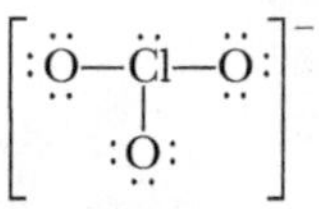

(c) HOBr, 14 valence electrons

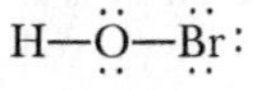

(d) SO_3^{2-}, 26 valence electrons

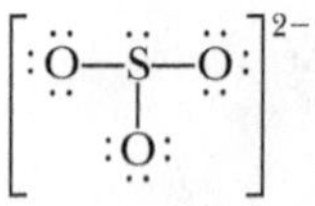

8.7 (a) $CHClF_2$, 26 valence electrons

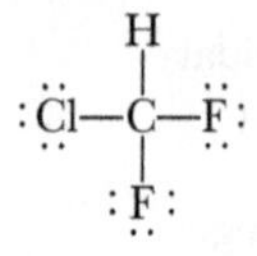

(b) CH_3CO_2H, 24 valence electrons

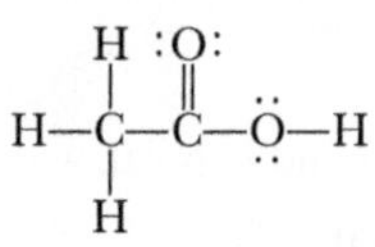

(c) CH_3CN, 16 valence electrons

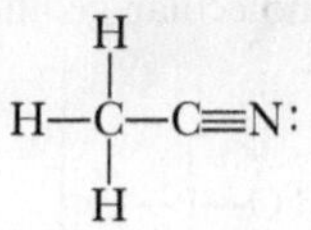

(d) H_2CCCH_2, 16 valence electrons

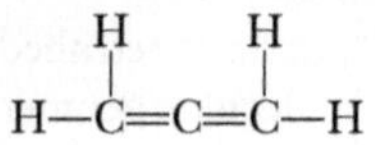

8.9 (a) SO_2, 18 valence electrons

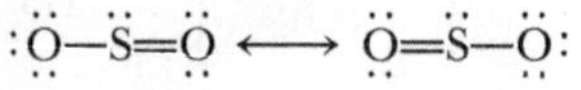

(b) HNO_2, 18 valence electrons

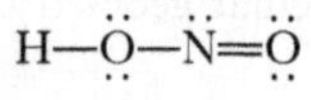

(c) SCN^-, 16 valence electrons

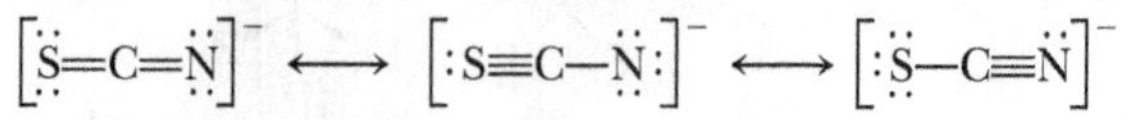

8.11 (a) BrF_3, 28 valence electrons

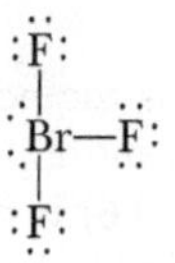

(b) I_3^-, 22 valence electrons

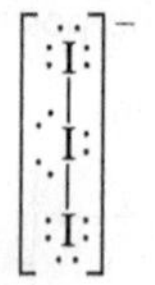

(c) XeO_2F_2, 34 valence electrons

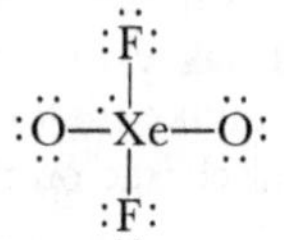

(d) XeF_3^+, 28 valence electrons

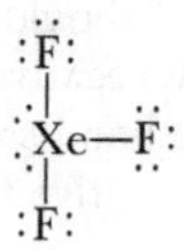

8.13 (a) N = 0; H = 0
(b) P = +1; O = −1
(c) B = −1; H = 0
(d) All are zero.

8.15 (a) N = +1; O = 0
(b) The central N is 0. The singly bonded O atom is −1, and the doubly bonded O atom is 0.

(c) N and F are both 0.

(d) The central N atom is +1, one of the O atoms is −1, and the other two O atoms and the H atom are all 0.

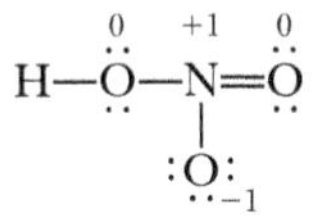

8.17 (a) Electron-pair geometry around N is tetrahedral. Molecular geometry is trigonal-pyramidal.

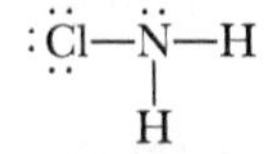

(b) Electron-pair geometry around O is tetrahedral. Molecular geometry is bent.

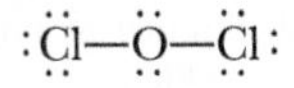

(c) Electron-pair geometry around C is linear. Molecular geometry is linear.

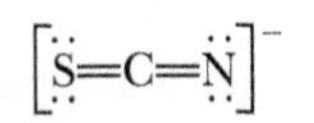

(d) Electron-pair geometry around O is tetrahedral. The molecular geometry is bent.

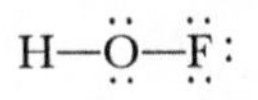

8.19 (a) Electron-pair geometry around C is linear. Molecular geometry is linear.

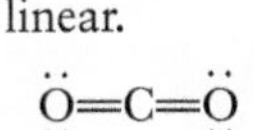

(b) Electron-pair geometry around N is trigonal-planar. Molecular geometry is bent.

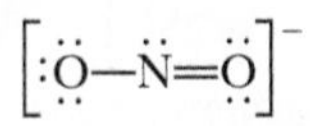

(c) Electron-pair geometry around O is trigonal-planar. Molecular geometry is bent.

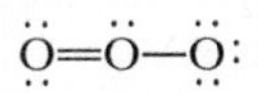

(d) Electron-pair geometry around Cl atom is tetrahedral. Molecular geometry is bent.

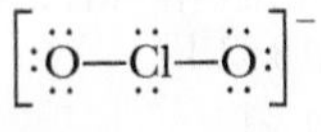

All have two atoms attached to the central atom. As the bond and lone pairs vary, the electron-pair geometries vary from linear to tetrahedral, and the molecular geometries vary from linear to bent.

8.21 (a) Electron-pair geometry around Cl is trigonal-bipyramidal. Molecular geometry is linear.

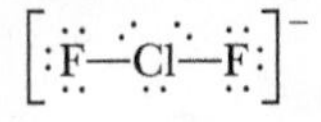

(b) Electron-pair geometry around Cl is trigonal-bipyramidal. Molecular geometry is T-shaped.

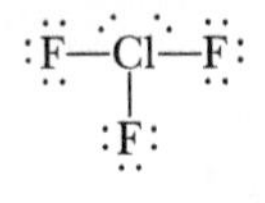

(c) Electron-pair geometry around Cl is octahedral. Molecular geometry is square-planar.

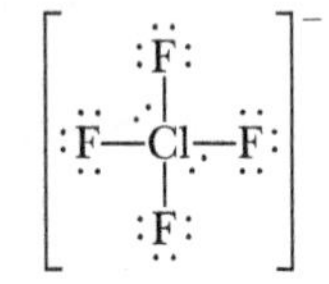

(d) Electron-pair geometry around Cl is octahedral. Molecular geometry is a square-pyramidal.

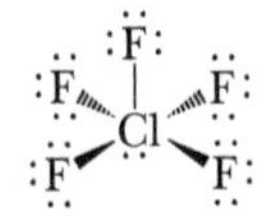

8.23 (a) Ideal O—S—O angle = 120°
(b) 120°
(c) 120°
(d) H—C—H = 109° and C—C—N angle = 180°

8.25 1 = 120°; 2 = 109°; 3 = 120°; 4 = 109°; 5 = 109°

The chain cannot be linear because the first two carbon atoms in the chain have bond angles of 109° and the final one has a bond angle of 120°. These bond angles do not lead to a linear chain.

8.27

$\overrightarrow{\text{C—O}}$ (+δ −δ) $\overrightarrow{\text{C—N}}$ (+δ −δ)

CO is more polar

$\overrightarrow{\text{P—Cl}}$ (+δ −δ) $\overrightarrow{\text{P—Br}}$ (+δ −δ)

PCl is more polar

$\overrightarrow{\text{B—O}}$ (+δ −δ) $\overrightarrow{\text{B—S}}$ (+δ −δ)

BO is more polar

$\overrightarrow{\text{B—F}}$ (+δ −δ) $\overrightarrow{\text{B—I}}$ (+δ −δ)

BF is more polar

8.29 (a) CH and CO bonds are polar.
(b) The CO bond is most polar, and O is the most negative atom.

8.31 (a) OH^-: The formal charge on O is −1 and on H it is 0.
(b) BH_4^-: Even though the formal charge on B is −1 and on H is 0, H is slightly more electronegative than B. The four H atoms are therefore more likely to bear the −1 charge of the ion. The BH bonds are polar with the H atom the negative end.
(c) The CH and CO bonds are all polar (but the C—C bond is not). The negative charge in the CO bonds lies on the O atoms.

8.33 Structure C is most reasonable. The charges are as small as possible, and the negative charge resides on the more electronegative atom.

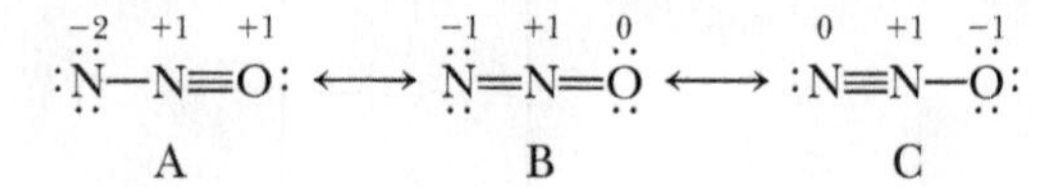

A B C

8.35 Lewis structures:

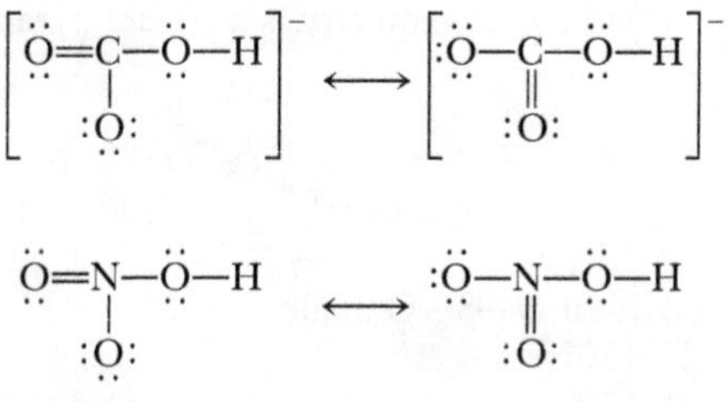

(a) These species are isoelectronic.
(b) Each has two major resonance structures.
(c) In HCO_3^-, the H, C, and O attached to the H all have a formal charge of 0. Each of the other oxygen atoms has a formal charge of −1/2.

In HNO_3, the same formal charges are present as in HCO_3^- except that the central N has a formal charge of +1.

(d) HNO_3 is much more acidic than HCO_3^-. This is due, in part, to simple electrostatics. It is much easier to remove a positively charge species (H^+) from a neutral species (HNO_3) than from a negatively charged one (HCO_3^-).

8.37 (a)

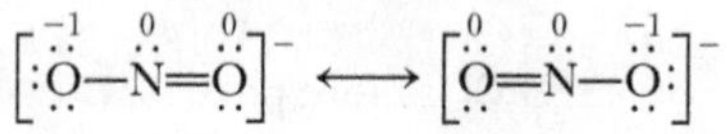

(b) If an H^+ ion were to attack NO_2^-, it would attach to an O atom because the O atoms bear the negative charge in this ion.

(c) H—Ö—N̈=Ö: ⟷ :Ö—N̈=Ö—H

The structure on the left is strongly favored because all of the atoms have zero formal charge, whereas the structure on the right has a −1 formal charge on one oxygen (*left*) and a +1 formal charge on the other (*right*).

8.39 (i) The most polar bonds are in H_2O (because O and H have the largest difference in electronegativity).
(ii) Not polar: CO_2 and CCl_4
(iii) The F atom is more negatively charged.

8.41 (a) $BeCl_2$, nonpolar linear molecule
(b) HBF_2, polar trigonal-planar molecule with F atoms on the negative end of the dipole and the H atom on the positive end.
(c) CH_3Cl, polar tetrahedral molecule. The Cl atom is on the negative end of the dipole and the three H atoms are on the positive side of the molecule.
(d) SO_3, a nonpolar trigonal-planar molecule

8.43 (a) Two C—H bonds, bond order is 1; 1 C=O bond, bond order is 2.
(b) Three S—O single bonds, bond order is 1.
(c) Two nitrogen–oxygen double bonds, bond order is 2.
(d) One N=O double bond, bond order is 2; one N—Cl bond, bond order is 1.

8.45 (a) B—Cl
(b) C—O
(c) P—O
(d) C=O

8.47 NO bond orders: 2 in NO_2^+, 1.5 in NO_2^-; 1.33 in NO_3^-. The NO bond is longest in NO_3^- and shortest in NO_2^+.

8.49 The CO bond in carbon monoxide is a triple bond, so it is both shorter and stronger than the CO double bond in H_2CO.

8.51 Using bond dissociation enthalpy data, $\Delta_r H° \approx -44$ kJ/mol-rxn. Using $\Delta_f H°$ data, $\Delta_r H° = -45.9$ kJ/mol-rxn.

8.53 $\Delta_r H = -126$ kJ

8.55 O—F bond dissociation energy = 192 kJ/mol

8.57

Element	Number of Valence Electrons
Li	1
Ti	4
Zn	2
Si	4
Cl	7

8.59 SeF_4, BrF_4^-, XeF_4

8.61

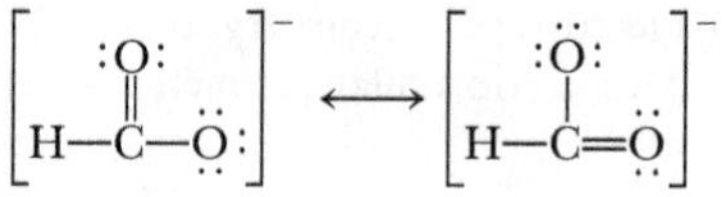

Bond order = 3/2

8.63 To estimate the enthalpy change, we need bond dissociation enthalpies for the following bonds: O=O, H—H, and H—O.

ΔH to break bonds ≈ 498 kJ (for O=O) + 2 × 436 kJ (for H—H) = +1370 kJ

ΔH evolved when bonds are made ≈ 4 × 463 kJ (for O—H) = −1852 kJ

$\Delta_r H \approx -482$ kJ

8.65 All the species in the series have 16 valence electrons and all are linear.

(a) Ö=C=Ö ⟷ :Ö—C≡O: ⟷ :O≡C—Ö:

(b)

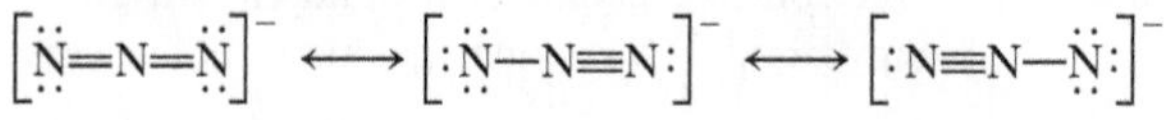

(c)

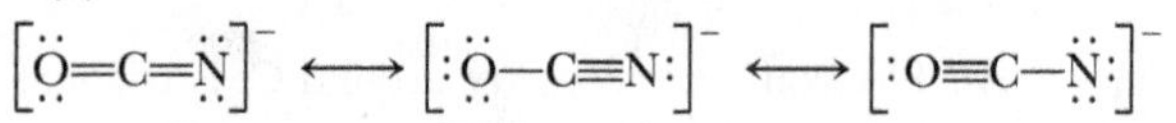

8.67 The N—O bonds in NO_2^- have a bond order of 1.5, whereas in NO_2^+ the bond order is 2. The shorter bonds (110 pm) are the NO bonds with the higher bond order (in NO_2^+), whereas the longer bonds (124 pm) in NO_2^- have a lower bond order.

8.69 The F—Cl—F bond angle in ClF_2^+, which has a tetrahedral electron-pair geometry, is approximately 109°.

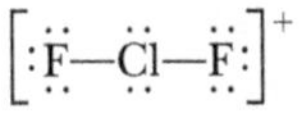

The ClF_2^- ion has a trigonal-bipyramidal electron-pair geometry with F atoms in the axial positions and the lone pairs in the equatorial positions. Therefore, the F—C—F angle is 180°.

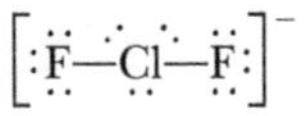

The anion ClF_2^- has the greater bond angle.

8.71 An H^+ ion will attach to an O atom of SO_3^{2-} and not to the S atom. The O atoms each have a formal charge of −1, whereas the S atom formal charge is +1.

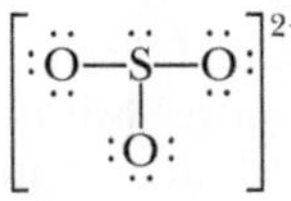

8.73 (a) Calculation from bond dissociation enthalpies: $\Delta_r H° = -1070$ kJ/mol-rxn; $\Delta H° = -535$ kJ/mol CH_3OH
(b) Calculation from thermochemical data: $\Delta_r H° = -1352.3$ kJ/mol-rxn; $\Delta H° = -676$ kJ/mol CH_3OH

8.75 (a)

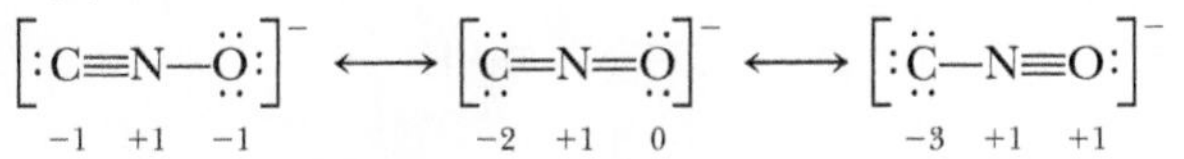

(b) The first resonance structure is the most reasonable because oxygen, the most electronegative atom, has a negative formal charge, and the unfavorable negative charge on the least electronegative atom, carbon, is smallest.
(c) This species is so unstable because carbon, the least electronegative element in the ion, has a negative formal charge. In addition, all three resonance structures have an unfavorable charge distribution.

8.77

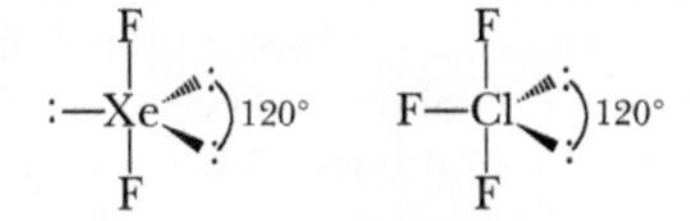

(a) XeF_2 has three lone pairs around the Xe atom. The electron-pair geometry is trigonal-bipyramidal. Because lone pairs require more space than bond pairs, it is better to place the lone pairs in the equator of the bipyramid where the angles between them are 120°.
(b) Like XeF_2, ClF_3 has a trigonal-bipyramidal electron-pair geometry, but with only two lone pairs around the Cl. These are again placed in the equatorial plane where the angle between them is 120°.

8.79 (a) Angle 1 = 109°; angle 2 = 120°; angle 3 = 109°; angle 4 = 109°; and angle 5 = 109°
(b) The O—H bond is the most polar bond.

8.81 $\Delta_r H = +146 \text{ kJ} = 2\,(\Delta H_{C-N}) + \Delta H_{C=O} - [\Delta H_{N-N} + \Delta H_{C\equiv O}]$

8.83 (a) Two C—H bonds and one O═O are broken and two O—C bonds and two H—O bonds are made in the reaction. $\Delta_r H = -318$ kJ. The reaction is exothermic.
(b) Both hydroxyacetone and acetone are polar.
(c) The O—H hydrogen atoms are the most positive in dihydroxyacetone.

8.85 (a) The C═C bond is stronger than the C—C bond.
(b) The C—C single bond is longer than the C═C double bond.
(c) Ethylene is nonpolar, whereas acrolein is polar.
(d) The reaction is exothermic ($\Delta_r H = -45$ kJ).

8.87 $\Delta_r H = -211$ kJ

8.89 Methanol is a polar solvent. Methanol contains two bonds of significant polarity, the C—O bond and the O—H bond. The C—O—H atoms are in a bent configuration, leading to a polar molecule. Toluene contains only carbon and hydrogen atoms, which have similar electronegativites and which are arranged in tetrahedral or trigonal planar geometries, leading to a molecule that is largely nonpolar.

8.91 (a)

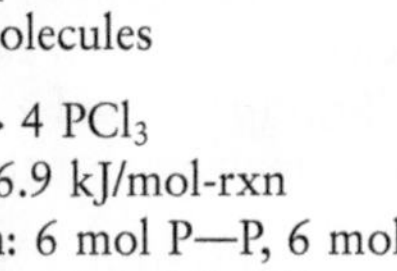

The bond angles are all approximately 109°.
(b) The sulfur atom should have a slight partial negative charge, and the carbons should have slight partial positive charges. The molecule has a bent shape and is polar.
(c) 1.6×10^{18} molecules

8.93 (a) $P_4 + 6\,Cl_2 \rightarrow 4\,PCl_3$
(b) $\Delta_r H = -1206.9$ kJ/mol-rxn
(c) Bonds broken: 6 mol P—P, 6 mol Cl—Cl
Bonds formed: 12 mol P—Cl
$\Delta H_{P-Cl} = 322$ kJ/mol; the value in Table 8.9 is 326 kJ/mol

8.95 (a) Odd electron molecules: BrO (13 electrons)
(b) $Br_2(g) \rightarrow 2\,Br(g)$ $\quad \Delta_r H = +193$ kJ
$2\,Br(g) + O_2(g) \rightarrow 2\,BrO(g)$ $\quad \Delta_r H = +96$ kJ
$BrO(g) + H_2O(g) \rightarrow HOBr(g) + OH(g)$ $\quad \Delta_r H = 0$ kJ
(c) $\Delta_f H\,[HOBr(g)] = -101$ kJ/mol
(d) The reactions in part (b) are endothermic (or thermal-neutral for the third reaction), and the enthalpy of formation in part (c) is exothermic.

Chapter 9

Case Study

Green Chemistry, Safe Dyes, and Molecular Orbitals

1. C_8H_4BrNO
2. The energy per photon is inversely proportional to wavelength. The light absorbed by butter yellow has a smaller wavelength than that absorbed by nitrated butter yellow; therefore, butter yellow absorbs higher energy light than does nitrated butter yellow.
3. Tyrian purple: 9
   Nitrated butter yellow: 8

Check Your Understanding

9.1 The carbon and nitrogen atoms in CH_3NH_2 are sp^3 hybridized. The C—H bonds arise from overlap of carbon sp^3 orbitals and hydrogen 1*s* orbitals. The bond between C and N is formed by overlap of sp^3 orbitals from these atoms. Overlap of nitrogen sp^3 and hydrogen 1*s* orbitals gives the two N—H bonds, and there is a lone pair in the remaining sp^3 orbital on nitrogen.

9.2 (a) sp^3
(b) (from left to right) sp^2, sp^2, sp^3
(c) sp^2

9.3 The two CH_3 carbon atoms are sp^3 hybridized, and the center carbon atom is sp^2 hybridized. For each of the carbon atoms in the methyl groups, the sp^3 orbitals overlap with hydrogen 1*s* orbitals to form the three C—H bonds, and the fourth sp^3 orbital overlaps with an sp^2 orbital on the central carbon atom, forming a carbon–carbon sigma bond. Overlap of an sp^2 orbital on the central carbon and an oxygen sp^2 orbital gives the sigma bond between these elements. The π bond between carbon and oxygen arises by overlap of a *p* orbital from each element.

9.4 H_2^+: $(\sigma_{1s})^1$ The ion has a bond order of ½ and is expected to exist. A bond order of ½ is predicted for He_2^+ and H_2^-, both of which are predicted to have electron configurations $(\sigma_{1s})^2(\sigma^*_{1s})^1$.

9.5 Li_2^- is predicted to have an electron configuration $(\sigma_{1s})^2(\sigma^*_{1s})^2(\sigma_{2s})^2(\sigma^*_{2s})^1$ and a bond order of ½, the positive value implying that the ion might exist.

9.6 O_2^+: [core electrons] $(\sigma_{2s})^2(\sigma^*_{2s})^2(\sigma_{2p})^2(\pi_{2p})^4(\pi^*_{2p})^1$. The bond order is 2.5. The ion is paramagnetic with one unpaired electron.

Review & Check

Section 9-2

1. (c) sp^3
2. (c) N is sp^2 in NO_2^-
3. (d) *p* on atom A with *p* on atom B
4. (b) The nitrogens are attached by one σ and two π bonds.

Section 9-3

1. (b) 2.5
2. (b) π^*_{2p}
3. (c) C_2
4. (a) O_2^+

Applying Chemical Principles: Probing Molecules with Photoelectron Spectroscopy

1. Metal
3. σ_{2p}
5. The 15.6 eV and 16.7 eV ejected electrons came from bonding orbitals. Removing an electron from a bonding orbital weakens the bond and thus results in a longer bond length. The 18.6 eV ejected electron comes from an antibonding orbital.

Study Questions

9.1 The electron-pair and molecular geometry of $CHCl_3$ are both tetrahedral. Each C—Cl bond is formed by the overlap of an sp^3 hybrid orbital on the C atom with a 3*p* orbital on a Cl atom to form a sigma bond. A C—H sigma bond is formed by the overlap of an sp^3 hybrid orbital on the C atom with an H atom 1*s* orbital.

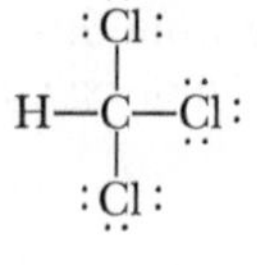

9.3

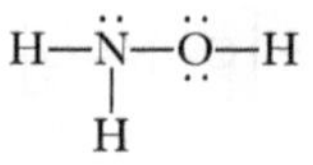

Both the N and the O are sp^3 hybridized. One of the sp^3 orbitals on the N overlaps with one of the sp^3 hybrid orbitals on the O.

9.5

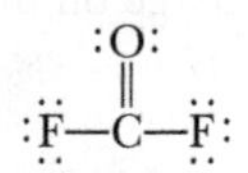

The electron-pair and molecular geometries are both trigonal-planar. The carbon atom is sp^2 hybridized. The σ bond between the C and O is formed by the overlap of an sp^2 hybrid orbital on C with an sp^2 hybrid orbital on O. The π bond is formed by the overlap of a 2*p* orbital on C with a 2*p* orbital on O.

9.7

	Electron-Pair Geometry	Molecular Geometry	Hybrid Orbital Set
(a)	Trigonal-planar	Trigonal-planar	sp^2
(b)	Linear	Linear	sp
(c)	Tetrahedral	Tetrahedral	sp^3
(d)	Trigonal-planar	Trigonal-planar	sp^2

9.9 (a) C, sp^3; O, sp^3
(b) CH_3, sp^3; middle C, sp^2; CH_2, sp^2
(c) CH_2, sp^3; CO_2H, sp^2; N, sp^3

9.11 There are 32 valence electrons in both HPO_2F_2 and its anion. Both have a tetrahedral molecular geometry, so the P atom in both is sp^3 hybridized.

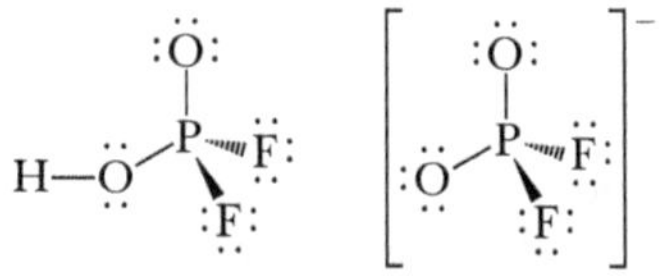

9.13 The C atom is sp^2 hybridized. Two of the sp^2 hybrid orbitals are used to form C—Cl σ bonds, and the third is used to form the C—O σ bond. The p orbital not used in the C atom hybrid orbitals is used to form the CO pi bond.

9.15 The electron-pair geometry around S is tetrahedral, and the molecular geometry is trigonal-pyramidal. The S atom is sp^3 hybridized.

9.17

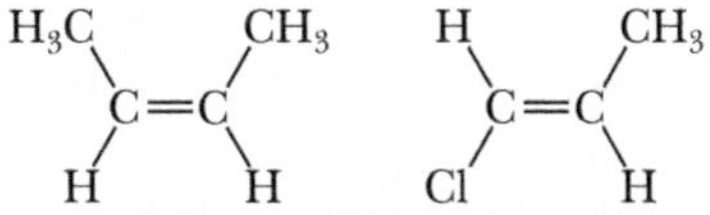

cis isomer — *trans* isomer

9.19 H_2^+ ion: $(\sigma_{1s})^1$. Bond order is 0.5. The bond in H_2^+ is weaker than in H_2 (bond order = 1).

9.21 MO diagram for C_2^{2-} ion

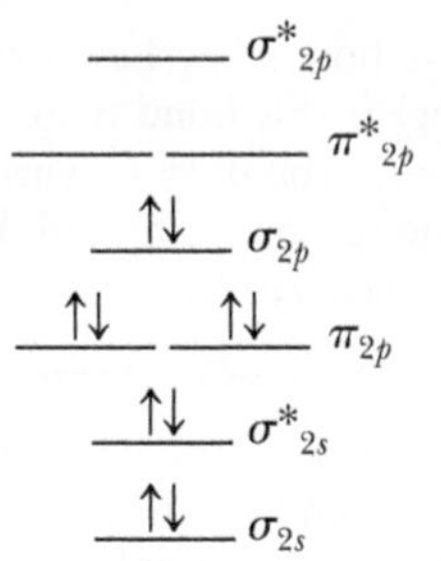

The ion has 10 valence electrons (isoelectronic with N_2). There are one net σ bond and two net π bonds, for a bond order of 3. The bond order increases by 1 on going from C_2 to C_2^{2-}. The ion is not paramagnetic.

9.23 O_2: (core electrons)$(\sigma_{2s})^2(\sigma^*_{2s})^2(\sigma_{2p})^2(\pi_{2p})^4(\pi^*_{2p})^2$
O_2^{2-}: (core electrons)$(\sigma_{2s})^2(\sigma^*_{2s})^2(\sigma_{2p})^2(\pi_{2p})^4(\pi^*_{2p})^4$
(a) O_2 is paramagnetic; O_2^{2-} is diamagnetic.
(b) O_2 has one net σ bond and one net π bond. O_2^{2-} has one net σ bond.
(c) O_2 bond order = 2; O_2^{2-} bond order = 1
(d) The bond length in O_2 is shorter than that in O_2^{2-}.

9.25 Shortest, N_2; longest, Li_2

9.27 (a) ClO has 13 valence electrons

$$[\text{core}](\sigma_s)^2(\sigma^*_s)^2(\pi_p)^4(\sigma_p)^2(\pi^*_p)^3$$

(b) π^*_p
(c) Paramagnetic
(d) There are net 1 σ bond and 0.5 π bonds; bond order is 1.5.

9.29

The electron pair and molecular geometries are both tetrahedral. The Al atom is sp^3 hybridized, so the Al—F bonds are formed by overlap of an Al sp^3 orbital with a p orbital on each F atom. The formal charge on each of the fluorines is 0, and that on the Al is −1. This is not a reasonable charge distribution because the less electronegative atom, aluminum, has the negative charge.

9.31

The electron-pair geometry is trigonal-planar. The molecular geometry is bent (or angular). The O—N—O angle will be about 120°, the average N—O bond order is 3/2, and the N atom is sp^2 hybridized.

9.33 The resonance structures of N_2O, with formal charges, are shown here.

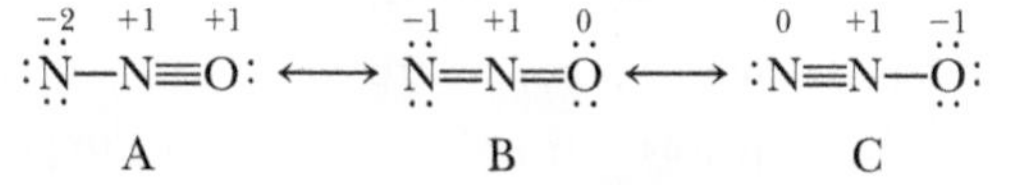

The central N atom is sp hybridized in all structures. The two sp hybrid orbitals on the central N atom are used to form N—N and N—O σ bonds. The two p orbitals not used in the N atom hybridization are used to form the required π bonds.

9.35 (a) All three have the formula C_2H_4O. (These are isomers because they have the same formula. However, they have different structures.)
(b) *Ethylene oxide:* Both C atoms are sp^3 hybridized.
Acetaldehyde: The CH_3 carbon atom has sp^3 hybridization, and the other C atom is sp^2 hybridized.
Vinyl alcohol: Both C atoms are sp^2 hybridized.
(c) *Ethylene oxide:* 109°
Acetaldehyde: 109°
Vinyl alcohol: 120°
(d) All are polar.
(e) Acetaldehyde has the strongest CO bond, and vinyl alcohol has the strongest C—C bond.

9.37 (a) CH_3 carbon atom: sp^3
C═N carbon atom: sp^2
N atom: sp^2
(b) C—N—O bond angle = 120°

9.39 (a) C(1) = sp^2; O(2) = sp^3; N(3) = sp^3; C(4) = sp^3; P(5) = sp^3
(b) Angle A = 120°; angle B = 109°; angle C = 109°; angle D = 109°
(c) The P—O and O—H bonds are most polar ($\Delta\chi$ = 1.3).

9.41 (a) C═O bond is most polar.
(b) 18 σ bonds and five π bonds
(c)

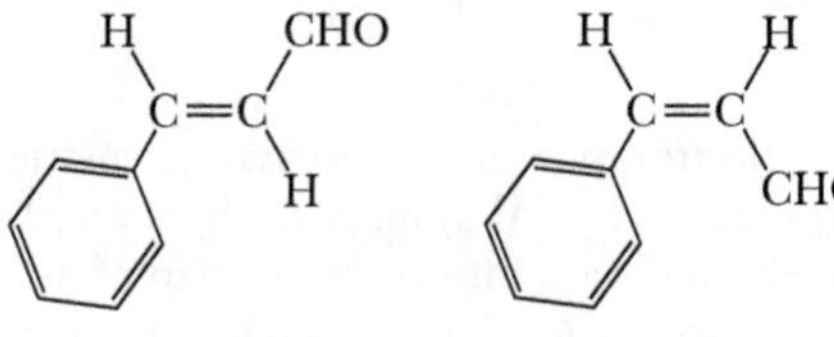

trans isomer *cis* isomer

(d) All C atoms are sp^2 hybridized.
(e) All bond angles are 120°.

9.43 (a) The peroxide ion has a bond order of 1.

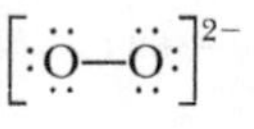

(b) [Core electrons]$(\sigma_{2s})^2(\sigma^*_{2s})^2(\sigma_{2p})^2(\pi_{2p})^4(\pi^*_{2p})^4$
This configuration also leads to a bond order of 1.
(c) Both theories lead to a diamagnetic ion with a bond order of 1.

9.45 Paramagnetic diatomic molecules: B_2 and O_2
Bond order of 1: Li_2, B_2, F_2; bond order of 2: C_2 and O_2; highest bond order: N_2

9.47 CN has nine valence electrons.

$$[\text{core electrons}](\sigma_{2s})^2(\sigma^*_{2s})^2(\pi_{2p})^4(\sigma_{2p})^1$$

(a) HOMO, σ_{2p}
(b, c) Bond order = 2.5 (0.5 σ bond and 2 π bonds)
(d) Paramagnetic

9.49 (a) All C atoms are sp^3 hybridized.
(b) About 109°
(c) Polar
(d) The six-membered ring cannot be planar, owing to the tetrahedral C atoms of the ring. The bond angles are all 109°.

9.51 (a) The geometry about the boron atom is trigonal-planar in BF_3 but tetrahedral in $H_3N—BF_3$.
(b) Boron is sp^2 hybridized in BF_3 but sp^3 hybridized in $H_3N—BF_3$.
(c) The ammonia molecule is polar with the N atom partially negative. While the BF_3 molecule is nonpolar overall, each of the B—F bonds is polarized such that the B has a partial positive charge. The partially negative N in NH_3 is attracted to the partially positive B in BF_3.
(d) One of the lone pairs on the oxygen of H_2O can form a coordinate covalent bond with the B in BF_3. The resulting compound would be (the lone pairs on the F's not shown):

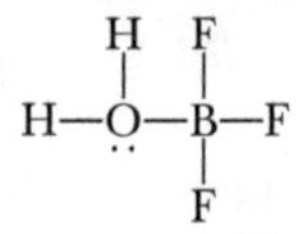

9.53 (a) NH_2^-: electron-pair geometry = tetrahedral, molecular geometry = bent, hybridization of N = sp^3
SO_3: electron-pair geometry = molecular geometry = trigonal-planar, hybridization of S = sp^2
(b)

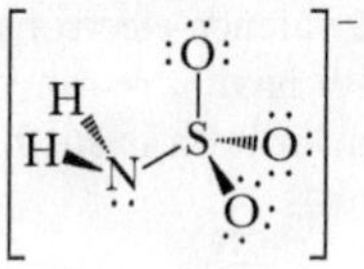

The bond angles around the N and the S are all approximately 109°.
(c) The N does not undergo any change in its hybridization; the S changes from sp^2 to sp^3.
(d) The SO_3 is the acceptor of an electron pair in this reaction. The electrostatic potential map confirms this to be reasonable because the sulfur has a partial positive charge.

9.55

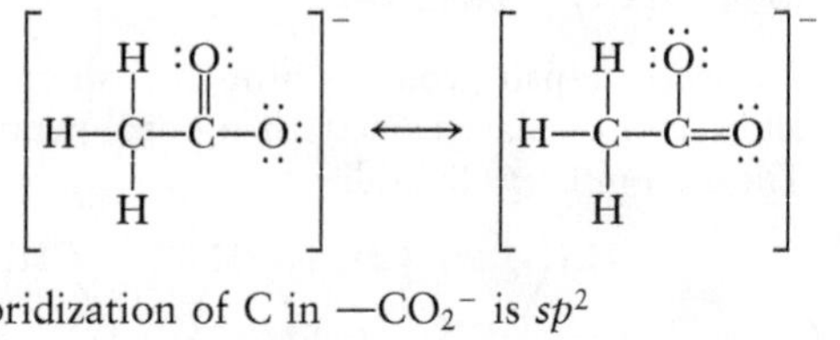

Hybridization of C in $—CO_2^-$ is sp^2

C—C bond: overlap of sp^2 hybrid orbital on the carbon of $—CO_2^-$ with sp^3 hybrid orbital on the other C.

C—O σ bond of C═O double bond: overlap of sp^2 hybrid orbital on C with sp^2 hybrid orbital on O

C—O π bond of C═O double bond: overlap of *p* orbital on C with *p* orbital on O

C—O single bond: The Lewis structure by itself would make it appear this bond is formed by the overlap of an sp^2 hybrid orbital on C with an sp^3 hybrid orbital on O. In the resonance hybrid, however, this oxygen would also have sp^2 hybridization.

9.57

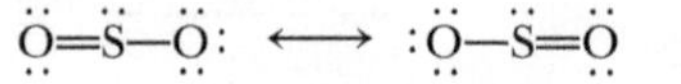

MO theory pictures one net σ bond for each S—O linkage plus a contribution from π bonding. The π bonding in this molecule will be similar to that in O_3 discussed in the text. There will be two electrons in a π bonding MO and two electrons in a π nonbonding MO. This gives an overall bond order of 1 for the π bonding in the entire molecule and therefore a net π bond order of 0.5 for each S—O linkage. The total bond order for each S—O linkage is therefore 1.5 (1 from σ bonding, 0.5 from π bonding).

9.59 A C atom may form, at most, four hybrid orbitals (sp^3). The minimum number is two, for example, the *sp* hybrid orbitals used by carbon in CO. Carbon has only four valence orbitals, so it cannot form more than four hybrid orbitals.

9.61 (a) C, sp^2; N (predicted based on Lewis structure), sp^3
(b) The amide or peptide link has two resonance structures (shown here with formal charges on the O and N atoms). Structure B is less favorable, owing to the separation of charge.

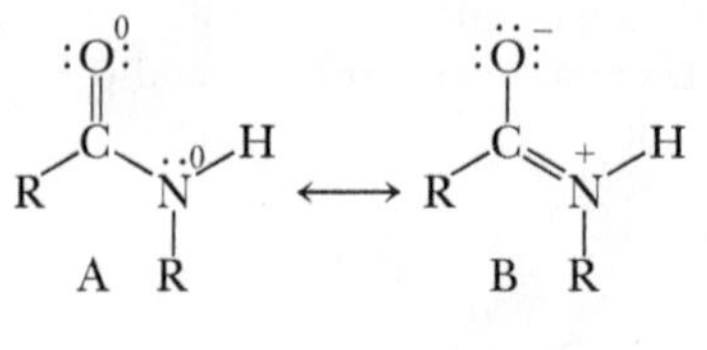

(c) The fact that the amide link is planar indicates that structure B has some importance and that the N of the peptide linkage is sp^2 hybridized.

The principal sites of positive charge are the nitrogen in the amide linkage and the hydrogen of the —O—H group. The principal regions of negative charge are oxygen atoms and the nitrogen of the free $—NH_2$ group.

9.63 MO theory is better to use when explaining or understanding the effect of adding energy to molecules. A molecule can absorb energy and an electron can thus be promoted to a higher level. Using MO theory, one can see how this can occur. Additionally, MO theory is a better model to use to predict whether a molecule is paramagnetic.

9.65 Lowest energy = orbital C < orbital B < orbital A = highest energy

9.67 B surrounded by three electron pairs: electron-pair geometry = molecular geometry = trigonal planar; hybridization = sp^2; formal charge = 0

B surrounded by four electron pairs; electron-pair geometry = molecular geometry = tetrahedral; hybridization = sp^3; formal charge = −1

9.69 HF has a bond order of 1. HF_2^- has a bond order of 1 for the entire three-center-four-electron bond and thus a 0.5 bond order per H—F linkage. It should therefore be easier to break the bond in HF_2^-, leading to a smaller bond enthalpy for HF_2^- than for HF.

9.71 (a) empirical formula = Br_2O

:B̤̈r—Ö̤—B̤̈r:

The O should have sp^3 hybrid orbitals.

(b) 13 valence electrons; $(\sigma_s)^2(\sigma^*_s)^2(\pi_p)^4(\sigma_p)^2(\pi^*_p)^3$

HOMO = π^*_p

9.73 (a) Bonds broken: two N—H bonds, one N—H bond in each N in urea; two C—O bonds in malonic acid (at each end of the molecule). Bonds made: two N—C bond in barbituric acid; two O—H bonds, one in each molecule of H_2O (the other product of this reaction). Estimated enthalpy change calculated from average bond energies: 38 kJ evolved, exothermic.

(b) $H_2NCONH_2 + HO_2CCH_2CO_2H \rightarrow C_4H_4N_2O_3 + 2\ H_2O$

(c) 109.5° angles in bonds to C in the CH_2 group; all other angles will be close to 120°

(d) The C and N atoms in the ring are sp^2 hybridized except for the C atom of the CH_2 group where the C atom is sp^3 hybridized.

(e) C=O group, as the difference in electronegativity is greatest between C and O.

(f) yes, it is polar.

Chapter 10

Case Study

The Methane Mystery

1. Ratio $[CO_2]/[CH_4]$ = 390 ppm/0.1774 ppm = 2.2×10^3
2. Both C and P have tetrahedral geometry and sp^3 hybridization.
3. Oxidation number of P is +5
4. (a) mole fraction of CH_4 in air = 1.774×10^{-7} mol (There is 1.774×10^{-7} mol of CH_4 in 1 mol of air.)

   Vol of air = $(1.00\ km^3)(10^9\ m^3/km^3)(10^6\ cm^3/m^3)(1L/10^3\ cm) = 1.00 \times 10^{12}$ L

   Moles gases in 1 km³ of air: $n = PV/RT$ = (1.00 atm) $(1.00 \times 10^{12}\ L)/[(0.08205\ L\ atm/mol\ K)(298\ K)] = 4.09 \times 10^{10}$ mol gases

   Amt CH_4 = $(1.774 \times 10^{-7}\ mol\ CH_4/mol)(4.09 \times 10^{10}\ mol) = 7.26 \times 10^3\ mol\ CH_4/km^3$

   Molecules CH_4 in 1 km³ of air = $(7.26 \times 10^3\ mol\ CH_4)(6.022 \times 10^{23}\ molecules/mol) = 4.37 \times 10^{27}$ molecules CH_4

   (b) $(7.26 \times 10^3\ mol\ CH_3PO_3H^-)(95.0\ g/mol) = 6.90 \times 10^5$ g

Check Your Understanding

10.1 0.29 atm(760 mm Hg/1 atm) = 220 mm Hg
0.29 atm(1.01325 bar/1 atm) = 0.29 bar
0.29 bar(10^5 Pa/1 bar)(1 kPa/10^3 Pa) = 29 kPa

10.2 $V_2 = P_1V_1/P_2$ = (745 mm Hg)(65.0 L)/[0.70(745 mm Hg)] = 93 L

10.3 V_1 = 45 L and T_1 = 298 K; V_2 = ? and T_2 = 263 K

$V_2 = V_1(T_2/T_1)$ = (45 L)(263 K/298 K) = 40. L

10.4 $V_2 = V_1(P_1/P_2)(T_2/T_1)$ = (22 L)(150 atm/0.993 atm)(295 K/304 K) = 3200 L

At 5.0 L per balloon, there is sufficient He to fill 640 balloons.

10.5 44.8 L of O_2(g) is required; 44.8 L of H_2O(g) and 22.4 L of CO_2(g) are produced.

10.6 $PV = nRT$

(750/760 atm)(V) = (1300 mol)(0.08206 L · atm/mol · K)(296 K)

$V = 3.2 \times 10^4$ L

10.7 According to Equation 10.5, density is inversely proportional to T (K).

d (at 55° C) = (1.18 g/L)(298 K/328 K) = 1.07 g/L

10.8 $PV = (m/M)RT$; $M = mRT/PV$

M = (0.105 g)(0.08206 L · atm/mol · K)(296.2 K)/[(561/760) atm (0.125 L)] = 27.8 g/mol

10.9 $2\ Na(s) + 2\ H_2O(\ell) \rightarrow 2\ NaOH(aq) + H_2(g)$

Amount H_2 = (15.0 g Na)(1 mol Na/22.99 g Na)(1 mol H_2/2 mol Na) = 0.326 mol

Volume of $H_2 = V = nRT/P$ = (0.326 mol)(0.08206 L atm/mol K)(298.2 K)/1.10 atm = 7.25 L

10.10 $P_{halothane}$ (5.00 L) = (0.0760 mol)(0.08206 L · atm/mol · K) (298.2 K)

$P_{halothane}$ = 0.372 atm (or 283 mm Hg)

P_{oxygen} (5.00 L) = (0.734 mol)(0.08206 L · atm/mol · K)(298.2 K)

P_{oxygen} = 3.59 atm (or 2730 mm Hg)

$P_{total} = P_{halothane} + P_{oxygen}$ = 283 mm Hg + 2730 mm Hg = 3010 mm Hg

10.11 For He: Use Equation 10.9, with $M = 4.00 \times 10^{-3}$ kg/mol, T = 298 K, and R = 8.314 J/mol · K to calculate the rms speed of 1360 m/s. A similar calculation for N_2, with $M = 28.01 \times 10^{-3}$ kg/mol, gives an rms speed of 515 m/s.

10.12 The molar mass of CH_4 is 16.0 g/mol.

$$\frac{\text{Rate for } CH_4}{\text{Rate for unknown}} = \frac{n \text{ molecules}/1.50 \text{ min}}{n \text{ molecules}/4.73 \text{ min}} = \sqrt{\frac{M_{unknown}}{16.0}}$$

$M_{unknown}$ = 159 g/mol

Review & Check

Section 10-1

1. (b) 16 kPa
2. (b) 7.8 m

Section 10-2

1. (b) 463 mL
2. (d) 120. °C
3. (d) none of the above (pressure = 0.458 atm)

Section 10-3

1. (e) Xe
2. (b) B
3. (b) D

Section 10-4

1. (d) 0.88 g
2. (a) 0.18 mol

Section 10-5

1. (c) 40. mm Hg C_2H_2 and 100. mm Hg O_2

Section 10-6

1. (d) 329 m/s
2. (a) A = Xe, B = O_2, C = Ne, D = He

Section 10-7

1. (c) rms for HCl/rms for NH_3 = 0.68

Section 10-8

1. (a) 18.0 atm

Applying Chemical Principles: The Goodyear Blimp

1. 0.164 g/L

3. Mass of passengers + ballast = 5.75×10^5 g = 575 kg

Study Questions

10.1 (a) 0.58 atm
(b) 0.59 bar
(c) 59 kPa

10.3 (a) 0.754 bar
(b) 650 kPa
(c) 934 kPa

10.5 2.70×10^2 mm Hg

10.7 3.7 L

10.9 250 mm Hg

10.11 3.2×10^2 mm Hg

10.13 9.72 atm

10.15 (a) 75 mL O_2
(b) 150 mL NO_2

10.17 0.919 atm

10.19 V = 2.9 L

10.21 1.9×10^6 g He

10.23 3.7×10^{-4} g/L

10.25 34.0 g/mol

10.27 57.5 g/mol

10.29 Molar mass = 74.9 g/mol; B_6H_{10}

10.31 0.039 mol H_2; 0.096 atm; 73 mm Hg

10.33 170 g NaN_3

10.35 1.7 atm O_2

10.37 4.1 atm H_2; 1.6 atm Ar; total pressure = 5.7 atm

10.39 (a) 0.30 mol halothane/1 mol O_2
(b) 3.0×10^2 g halothane

10.41 (a) CO_2 has the higher kinetic energy.
(b) The root mean square speed of the H_2 molecules is greater than the root mean square speed of the CO_2 molecules.
(c) The number of CO_2 molecules is greater than the number of H_2 molecules [$n(CO_2) = 1.8n(H_2)$].
(d) The mass of CO_2 is greater than the mass of H_2.

10.43 Average speed of CO_2 molecules = 3.65×10^4 cm/s

10.45 Average speed increases (and molar mass decreases) in the order CH_2F_2 < Ar < N_2 < CH_4.

10.47 (a) F_2 (38 g/mol) effuses faster than CO_2 (44 g/mol).
(b) N_2 (28 g/mol) effuses faster than O_2 (32 g/mol).
(c) C_2H_4 (28.1 g/mol) effuses faster than C_2H_6 (30.1 g/mol).
(d) $CFCl_3$ (137 g/mol) effuses faster than $C_2Cl_2F_4$ (171 g/mol).

10.49 36 g/mol

10.51 (c) High pressure and low temperature (T near condensation point)

10.53 P from the van der Waals equation = 26.0 atm

P from the ideal gas law = 30.6 atm

10.55 (a) As an ideal gas, P = 162 atm. Using the van der Waals equation, P = 111.10 atm.
(b) $a(n/V^2)$

10.57 (a) Standard atmosphere: 1 atm; 760 mm Hg; 101.325 kPa; 1.013 bar
(b) N_2 partial pressure: 0.780 atm; 593 mm Hg; 79.1 kPa; 0.791 bar
(c) H_2 pressure: 131 atm; 9.98×10^4 mm Hg; 1.33×10^4 kPa; 133 bar
(d) Air: 0.333 atm; 253 mm Hg; 33.7 kPa; 0.337 bar

10.59 T = 290. K or 17 °C

10.61 $2\ C_4H_9SH(g) + 15\ O_2(g) \rightarrow 8\ CO_2(g) + 10\ H_2O(g) + 2\ SO_2(g)$

Total pressure = 37.3 mm Hg. Partial pressures: CO_2 = 14.9 mm Hg, H_2O = 18.6 mm Hg, and SO_2 = 3.73 mm Hg.

10.63 4 mol

10.65 V = 44.8 L O_2

10.67 Ni is the limiting reactant; 1.31 g $Ni(CO)_4$

10.69 (a, b) Sample 4 (He) has the largest number of molecules and sample 3 (H_2 at 27 °C and 760 mm Hg) has the fewest number of molecules.
(c) Sample 2 (Ar)

10.71 8.54 g $Fe(CO)_5$

10.73 S_2F_{10}

10.75 (a) 28.7 g/mol ≃ 29 g/mol
(b) X of O_2 = 0.17 and X of N_2 = 0.83

10.77 Molar mass = 86.4 g/mol. The gas is probably ClO_2F.

10.79 Calculate molar mass (44 g/mol). Gas is probably CO_2.

10.81 (d) is not correct. The rate of effusion is really inversely proportional to the square root of a gas's molar mass.

10.83 1.3×10^2 g/mol

10.85 n(He) = 0.0128 mol

10.87 Weight percent $KClO_3$ = 69.1%

10.89 (a) $NO_2 < O_2 < NO$
(b) $P(O_2)$ = 75 mm Hg
(c) $P(NO_2)$ = 150 mm Hg

10.91 $P(NH_3)$ = 69 mm Hg and $P(F_2)$ = 51 mm Hg

Pressure after reaction = 17 mm Hg

10.93 At 20 °C, there is 7.8×10^{-3} g H_2O/L. At 0 °C, there is 4.6×10^{-3} g H_2O/L.

10.95 The mixture contains 0.22 g CO_2 and 0.77 g CO.

$P(CO_2)$ = 0.22 atm; $P(O_2)$ = 0.12 atm; P(CO) = 1.22 atm

10.97 The formula of the iron compound is $Fe(CO)_5$.

10.99 (a) $P(B_2H_6)$ = 0.0160 atm
(b) $P(H_2)$ = 0.0320 atm, so P_{total} = 0.0480 atm

10.101 Amount of Na_2CO_3 = 0.00424 mol
Amount of $NaHCO_3$ = 0.00951 mol
Amount of CO_2 produced = 0.0138 mol
Volume of CO_2 produced = 0.343 L

10.103 Decomposition of 1 mol of $Cu(NO_3)_2$ should give 2 mol NO_2 and ½ mol of O_2. Total actual amount = 4.72×10^{-3} mol of gas.
(a) Average molar mass = 41.3 g/mol
(b) Mole fractions: $X(NO_2)$ = 0.666 and $X(O_2)$ = 0.334
(c) Amount of each gas: 3.13×10^{-3} mol NO_2 and 1.57×10^{-3} mol O_2. The ratio of these amounts is 1.99 mol NO_2/mol O_2. This is different from the 4 mol NO_2/mol O_2 ratio expected from the reaction.
(d) If some NO_2 molecules combine to form N_2O_4, the apparent mole fraction of NO_2 would be smaller than expected (= 0.8). As this is the case, it is apparent that some N_2O_4 has been formed (as is observed in the experiment).

10.105 (a) M = 138 g/mol; the unknown compound is P_2F_4.
(b) $M = 1.4 \times 10^2$ g/mol; this is consistent with the result obtained in part (a).

10.107 (a) 10.0 g of O_2 represents more molecules than 10.0 g of CO_2. Therefore, O_2 has the greater partial pressure.
(b) The average speed of the O_2 molecules is greater than the average speed of the CO_2 molecules.
(c) The gases are at the same temperature and so have the same average kinetic energy.

10.109 (a) $P(C_2H_2) > P(CO)$
(b) There are more molecules in the C_2H_2 container than in the CO container.

10.111 (a) Not a gas. A gas would expand to an infinite volume.
(b) Not a gas. A density of 8.2 g/mL is typical of a solid.
(c) Insufficient information
(d) Gas

10.113 (a) There are more molecules of H_2 than atoms of He.
(b) The mass of He is greater than the mass of H_2.

10.115 The speed of gas molecules is related to the square root of the absolute temperature, so a doubling of the temperature will lead to an increase of about $(2)^{1/2}$ or 1.4.

Chapter 11

Case Study

A Pet Food Catastrophe

1. % N in melamine = 84/126 × 100 = 67%

   % N in cyanuric acid = 42/129 × 100 = 33%

   Both of these compounds have a greater percentage of nitrogen than the average protein.

2. 454 g sample (0.14 g melamine/1,000,000 g sample) = 6.4×10^{-5} g melamine = 0.064 mg melamine = 64 μg melamine

Check Your Understanding

11.1 Because F^- is the smaller ion, water molecules can approach more closely and interact more strongly. Thus, F^- should have the more negative enthalpy of hydration.

11.2

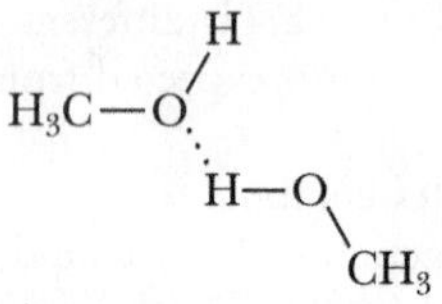

Hydrogen bonding in methanol entails the attraction of the hydrogen atom bearing a partial positive charge (δ^+) on one molecule to the oxygen atom bearing a partial negative charge (δ^-) on a second molecule. The strong attractive force of hydrogen bonding will cause the boiling point and the enthalpy of vaporization of methanol to be quite high.

11.3 Water is a polar solvent, while hexane and CCl_4 are nonpolar. London dispersion forces are the primary forces of attraction between all pairs of dissimilar solvents. For mixtures of water with the other solvents, dipole–induced dipole forces will also be important.

11.4 (a) O_2: induced dipole–induced dipole forces only.
(b) CH_3OH: strong hydrogen bonding (dipole–dipole forces) as well as induced dipole–induced dipole forces.
(c) Forces between water molecules: strong hydrogen bonding and induced dipole–induced dipole forces. Between N_2 and H_2O: dipole-induced dipole forces and induced dipole–induced dipole forces.

11.5 $(1.00 \times 10^3 \text{ g})(1 \text{ mol}/32.04 \text{ g})(35.2 \text{ kJ/mol}) = 1.10 \times 10^3$ kJ

11.6 (a) At 40 °C, the vapor pressure of ethanol is about 120 mm Hg.
(b) The equilibrium vapor pressure of ethanol at 60 °C is about 320 mm Hg. At 60 °C and 600 mm Hg, ethanol is a liquid. If vapor is present, it will condense to a liquid.

Review & Check

Section 11-2

1. (b) $AlCl_3$

Section 11-3

1. (b) CH_3OH
2. (a) H_2O

Section 11-4

1. (d) I_2
2. (d) octane, C_8H_{18}

Section 11-5

1. (a) dispersion

Section 11-6

1. (b) All the water evaporates.
2. (a) 29.0 kJ/mol
3. (d) shorter, higher

Applying Chemical Principles: Chromatography

1. (a) The 1,5-pentanediol is most attracted to the mobile phase. The primary attractive force is hydrogen bonding. Dipole–dipole forces and dispersion forces are also present.
   (b) The propyl ethyl ether is most attracted to the stationary phase by dispersion forces but there are also some dipole–induced dipole interactions.
   (c) The molecules will elute in the following order (first to last): 1,5-pentanediol, 1-pentanol, and propyl ethyl ether.

Study Questions

11.1 (a) Dipole–dipole interactions (and hydrogen bonds)
(b) Induced dipole–induced dipole forces
(c) Dipole–dipole interactions (and hydrogen bonds)

11.3 (a) Induced dipole–induced dipole forces
(b) Induced dipole–induced dipole forces
(c) Dipole–dipole forces
(d) Dipole–dipole forces (and hydrogen bonding)

11.5 (a), (b), and (c). The boiling points of these liquids are: Ne, (−246 °C), CO (−192 °C), CH_4 (−162 °C), and CCl_4 (77 °C).

11.7 (c) HF; (d) acetic acid; (f) CH_3OH

11.9 (a) LiCl. The Li^+ ion is smaller than Cs^+ (Figure 7.12), which makes the ion–ion forces of attraction stronger in LiCl.
(b) $Mg(NO_3)_2$. The Mg^{2+} ion is smaller than the Na^+ ion (Figure 7.11), and the magnesium ion has a 2+ charge (as opposed to 1+ for sodium). Both of these effects lead to stronger ion–ion forces of attraction in magnesium nitrate.
(c) $NiCl_2$. The nickel(II) ion has a larger charge than Rb^+ and is considerably smaller. Both effects mean that there are stronger ion–ion forces of attraction in nickel(II) chloride.

11.11 $q = +90.1$ kJ

11.13 (a) Water vapor pressure is about 150 mm Hg at 60 °C. (Appendix G gives a value of 149.4 mm Hg at 60 °C.)
(b) 600 mm Hg at about 93 °C
(c) At 70 °C, ethanol has a vapor pressure of about 520 mm Hg, whereas that of water is about 225 mm Hg.

11.15 At 30 °C, the vapor pressure of ether is about 590 mm Hg. (This pressure requires 0.23 g of ether in the vapor phase at the given conditions, so there is sufficient ether in the flask.) At 0 °C, the vapor pressure is about 160 mm Hg, so some ether condenses when the temperature declines.

11.17 (a) O_2 (−183 °C) (bp of N_2 = −196 °C)
(b) SO_2 (−10 °C) (CO_2 sublimes at −78 °C)
(c) HF (+19.7 °C) (HI, −35.6 °C)
(d) GeH_4 (−90.0 °C) (SiH_4, −111.8 °C)

11.19 (a) CS_2, about 620 mm Hg; CH_3NO_2, about 80 mm Hg
(b) CS_2, induced dipole–induced dipole forces; CH_3NO_2, dipole–dipole forces
(c) CS_2, about 46 °C; CH_3NO_2, about 100 °C
(d) About 39 °C
(e) About 95 °C

11.21 (a) 80.1 °C
(b) At about 48 °C, the liquid has a vapor pressure of 250 mm Hg. The vapor pressure is 650 mm Hg at 75 °C.
(c) 33.5 kJ/mol (from slope of plot)

11.23 No, CO cannot be liquefied at room temperature because the critical temperature is lower than room temperature.

11.25 The layer of molecules on the surface of a liquid is harder to break through than the bulk liquid. The energy needed to break through this skin is the surface tension. An application of surface tension is that it is possible to float a paperclip on the surface of water, but if the paperclip breaks through the surface, it will sink. Surface tension results from intermolecular forces because molecules in the interior of a liquid interact through intermolecular forces with molecules all around them, but molecules on the surface have intermolecular forces only with molecules at or below the surface layer and thus feel a net inward force of attraction.

11.27 This phenomenon results from capillary action. The water is attracted to —OH groups in the paper. As a result of these adhesive forces, some water molecules begin to move up the paper. Other water molecules remain in contact with these water molecules by means of cohesive forces. A stream of water molecules thus moves up the paper.

11.29 (a) Induced dipole-induced dipole
(b) Induced dipole-induced dipole, dipole-dipole
(c) Induced dipole-induced dipole, dipole-dipole, hydrogen bonding.

11.31 Li^+ ions are smaller than Cs^+ ions (78 pm and 165 pm, respectively; see Figure 7.11). Thus, there will be a stronger attractive force between Li^+ ion and water molecules than between Cs^+ ions and water molecules.

11.33 (a) 350 mm Hg
(b) Ethanol (lower vapor pressure at every temperature)
(c) 84 °C
(d) CS_2, 46 °C; C_2H_5OH, 78 °C; C_7H_{16}, 99 °C
(e) CS_2, gas; C_2H_5OH, gas; C_7H_{16}, liquid

11.35 Molar enthalpy of vaporization increases with increasing intermolecular forces: C_2H_6 (14.69 kJ/mol; induced dipole) < HCl (16.15 kJ/mol; dipole) < CH_3OH (35.21 kJ/mol, hydrogen bonds). (The molar enthalpies of vaporization here are given at the boiling point of the liquid.)

11.37 5.49×10^{19} atoms/m^3

11.39 (a) 70.3 °C
(b)

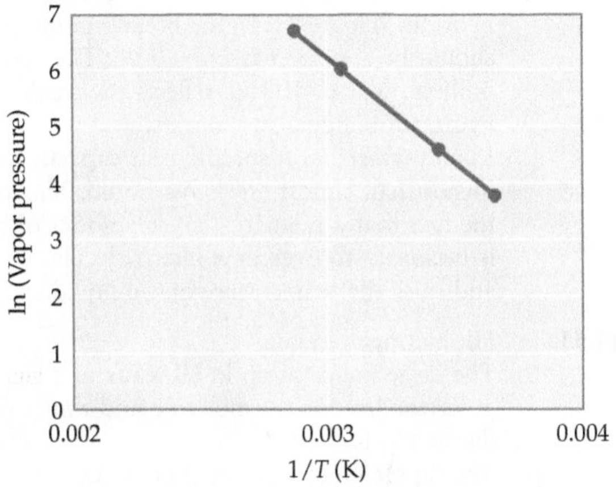

Using the equation for the straight line in the plot
$\ln P = -3885\,(1/T) + 17.949$
we calculate that T = 311.6 K (39.5 °C) when P = 250 mm Hg. When P = 650 mm Hg, T = 338.7 K (65.5 °C).
(c) Calculated $\Delta_{vap}H$ = 32.3 kJ/mol

11.41 (a) When the can is inverted in cold water, the water vapor pressure in the can, which was approximately 760 mm Hg, drops rapidly—say, to 9 mm Hg at 10 °C. This creates a partial vacuum in the can, and the can is crushed because of the difference in pressure inside the can and the pressure of the atmosphere pressing down on the outside of the can.
(b)

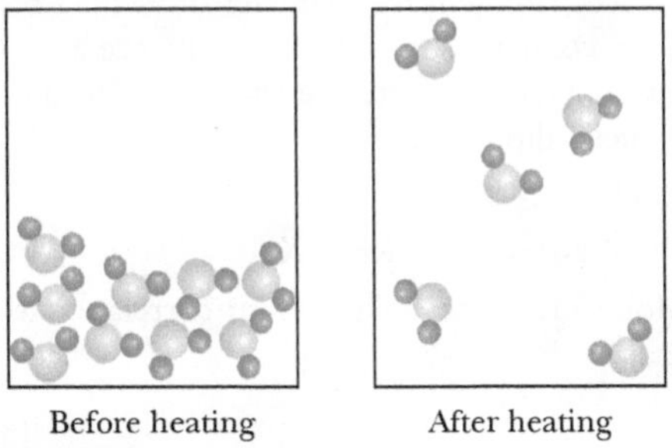

11.43 Acetone and water can interact by hydrogen bonding.

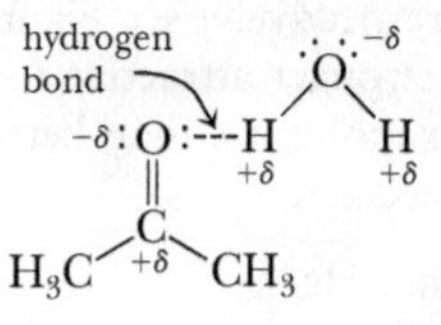

11.45 Ethylene glycol's viscosity will be greater than ethanol's, owing to the greater hydrogen-bonding capacity of glycol.

11.47 (a) Water has two OH bonds and two lone pairs, whereas the O atom of ethanol has only one OH bond (and two lone pairs). More extensive hydrogen bonding is likely for water.
(b) Water and ethanol interact extensively through hydrogen bonding, so the volume is expected to be slightly smaller than the sum of the two volumes.

11.49 Two pieces of evidence for $H_2O(\ell)$ having considerable intermolecular attractive forces:
(a) Based on the boiling points of the Group 6A hydrides (Figure 11.4), the boiling point of water should be approximately −80 °C. The actual boiling point of 100 °C reflects the significant hydrogen bonding that occurs.
(b) Liquid water has a specific heat capacity that is higher than almost any other liquid. This reflects the fact that a relatively larger amount of energy is necessary to overcome intermolecular forces and raise the temperature of the liquid.

11.51 (a) HI, hydrogen iodide
(b) The large iodine atom in HI leads to a significant polarizability for the molecule and thus to a large dispersion force.
(c) The dipole moment of HCl (1.07 D, Table 8.6) is larger than for HI (0.38 D).
(d) HI. See part (b).

11.53 A gas can be liquefied at or below its critical temperature. The critical temperature for CF_4 (−45.7 °C) is below room temperature (25 °C), so it cannot be liquefied at room temperature.

11.55 Hydrogen bonding is most likely at the O—H group at the "right" end of the molecule, and at the C═O and N—H groups in the amide group (—NH—CO—).

11.57 Boiling point, enthalpy of vaporization, volatility, surface tension

11.59 The more branching in the hydrocarbons, the lower the boiling point. This implies weaker induced dipole–induced dipole forces. Greater branching results in a more compact shape with less surface area available for contact and therefore smaller induced dipole–induced dipole forces.

11.61 $F_2 < Cl_2 < Br_2 < I_2$
He < Ne < Ar < Kr < Xe
Molar mass and boiling point correlate with these orders.

11.63 The boiling point of the water in the pressure cooker is 121 °C.

11.65 Using the equation of the line from Question 11.64, $P = 9.8$ atm.

11.67 (a) There will be water in the tube in equilibrium with its vapor, but almost all of the water will be present as liquid water.
(b) 760. mm Hg
(c) 10.4 cm^3
(d) 0.0233 g H_2O

Chapter 12

Case Studies

Lithium and "Green Cars"

1. 73,000,000 metric tons Li_2CO_3 (13.88 metric tons Li/73.89 metric tons Li_2CO_3) = 1.4×10^7 metric tons Li (= 14 million metric tons Li)
2. The unit cell for lithium metal is body-centered cubic. (There are atoms at each of the corners of a cube and one atom embedded in the middle of the cube.)
3. 351 pm (1 m/10^{12} pm)(100 cm/1 m) = 3.51×10^{-8} cm
   V of unit cell = $(3.51 \times 10^{-8}\ cm)^3 = 4.32 \times 10^{-23}\ cm^3$
   Mass of unit cell = 6.941 g Li/mol (1 mol/6.022×10^{23} atoms)(2 atoms/unit cell) = 2.305×10^{-23} g/unit cell
   Density = mass/volume = 2.305×10^{-23} g/4.32×10^{-23} cm^3 = 0.533 g/cm^3
4. One method is to carry out the following gas-forming reaction:
   $$Li_2CO_3(aq) + 2\ HCl(aq) \rightarrow 2\ LiCl(aq) + H_2O(\ell) + CO_2(g)$$

Nanotubes and Graphene—The Hottest New Network Solids

1. We want to know the distance x in the diagram of the hexagon. You know the interior angles in a hexagon are all 120°. To find x, we can find the distance y in the figure and then double it ($x = 2y$). The angle bounded by the side of the hexagon and y is 30°, and, from geometry, cos 30° = y/(hexagon side) so y = (cos 30°)(139 pm) = (0.866)(139 pm) = 120. pm. Finally, x = 241 pm.

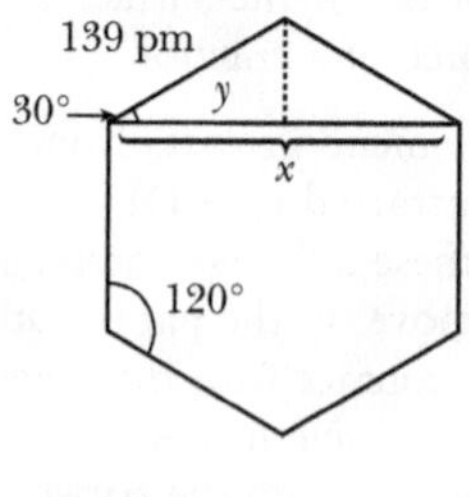

2. 1.0 μm (1 m/10^6 μm)(10^{12} pm/1 m)(1 C_6-ring/241 pm) = 4.1×10^3 C_6-rings
3. The thickness would be approximately 150 pm. This corresponds to the diameter of a carbon atom, found by multiplying the radius of a carbon atom (given in Figure 7.7) by 2 and rounding off to two significant figures.

Check Your Understanding

12.1 (a) The strategy to solve this problem is given in Example 12.1.

Step 1. Mass of the unit cell
= (197.0 g/mol)(1 mol/6.022 × 10^{23} atom) (4 atoms/unit cell)
= 1.309 × 10^{-21} g/unit cell

Step 2. Volume of unit cell
= (1.309 × 10^{-21} g/unit cell)(1 cm^3/19.32 g)
= 6.773 × 10^{-23} cm^3/unit cell

Step 3. Length of side of unit cell
= [6.773 × 10^{-23} cm^3/unit cell]$^{1/3}$
= 4.076 × 10^{-8} cm

Step 4. Calculate the radius from the edge dimension.

Diagonal distance = 4.076 × 10^{-8} cm ($2^{½}$) = 4 (r_{Au})

r_{Au} = 1.441 × 10^{-8} cm (= 144.1 pm)

(b) To verify a body-centered cubic structure, calculate the mass contained in the unit cell. If the structure is bcc, then the mass will be the mass of 2 Fe atoms. (Other possibilities: fcc – mass of 4 Fe; primitive cubic – mass of 1 Fe atom.) This calculation uses the four steps from the previous exercise in reverse order.

Step 1. Use radius of Fe to calculate cell dimensions. In a body-centered cube, atoms touch across the diagonal of the cube.

Diagonal distance = side dimension ($\sqrt{3}$) = 4 r_{Fe}

Side dimension of cube =
4 (1.26 × 10^{-8} cm)/($\sqrt{3}$) = 2.910 × 10^{-8} cm

Step 2. Calculate unit cell volume

Unit cell volume = (2.910 × 10^{-8} cm)^3 = 2.464 × 10^{-23} cm^3

Step 3. Combine unit cell volume and density to find the mass of the unit cell.

Mass of unit cell = 2.464 × 10^{-23} cm^3 (7.8740 g/cm^3) = 1.940 × 10^{-22} g

Step 4. Calculate the mass of 2 Fe atoms, and compare this to the answer from step 3.

Mass of 2 Fe atoms =
55.85 g/mol (1 mol/6.022 × 10^{23} atoms)(2 atoms)
= 1.85 × 10^{-22} g.

This is a fairly good match, and clearly much better than the two other possibilities, primitive and fcc.

12.2 M_2X. In a face-centered cubic unit cell, there are four anions and eight tetrahedral holes in which to place metal ions. All of the tetrahedral holes are inside the unit cell, so the ratio of atoms in the unit cell is 2:1.

12.3 We need to calculate the mass and volume of the unit cell from the information given. The density of KCl will then be mass/volume. Select units so the density is calculated as g/cm^3.

Step 1. Mass: The unit cell contains 4 K^+ ions and 4 Cl^- ions

Unit cell mass = (39.10 g/mol)(1 mol/6.022 × 10^{23} K^+ ions)(4 K^+ ions) + (35.45 g/mol)(1 mol/6.022 × 10^{23} Cl^- ions)(4 Cl^- ions) = 2.597 × 10^{-22} g + 2.355 × 10^{-22} g = 4.952 × 10^{-22} g

Step 2. Volume: Assuming K^+ and Cl^- ions touch along one edge of the cube, the side dimension = 2 r_{K^+} + 2 r_{Cl^-}. The volume of the cube is the cube of this value. (Convert the ionic radius from pm to cm.)

V = [2(1.33 × 10^{-8} cm) + 2(1.81 × 10^{-8} cm)]^3 = 2.477 × 10^{-22} cm^3

Step 3. Density = mass/volume =
4.952 ×10^{-22} g/2.477 × 10^{-22} cm^3) = 2.00 g/cm^3

Review & Check

Section 12-1

1. (b) body-centered cubic
2. (a) 0.858 g/cm^3

Section 12-2

1. (c) face-centered cubic
2. (c) 3.21 g/cm^3

Section 12-3

1. (d) NaF
2. (c) $Na^+(g) + Cl^-(g) \rightarrow NaCl(s)$
3. (c) −702 kJ/mol

Section 12-4

1. (a) 1800 nm, infrared

Section 12-5

1. (c) buckyballs (C_{60})
2. (b) an amorphous solid

Section 12-6

1. (a) NaCl
2. (b) 15 g

Section 12-7

1. (d) Supercritical CO_2 can be obtained at 25 °C if a high enough pressure is applied.

Applying Chemical Principles: Tin Disease

1. β-Tin has four atoms in the unit cell. α-Tin has eight atoms in the unit cell.

3. The length of each side is 649.0 pm.

Study Questions

12.1 Two possible unit cells are illustrated here. The simplest formula is AB_8.

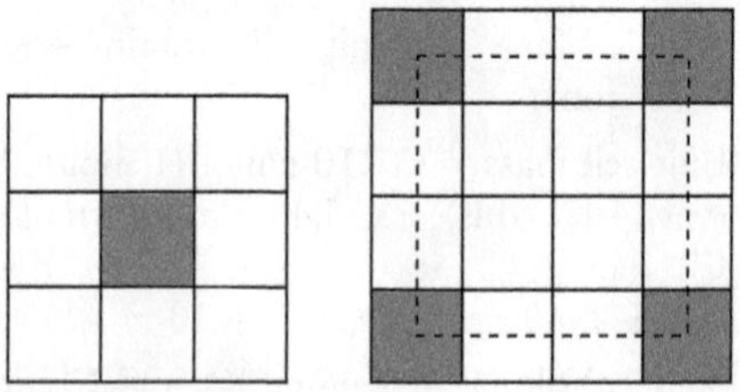

12.3 Ca^{2+} ions at eight corners = 1 net Ca^{2+} ion

O^{2-} ions in six faces = 3 net O^{2-} ions

Ti^{4+} ion in center of unit cell = 1 net Ti^{4+} ion

Formula = $CaTiO_3$

12.5 (a) There are eight O^{2-} ions at the corners and one in the center for a net of two O^{2-} ions per unit cell. There are four Cu ions in the interior in tetrahedral holes. The ratio of ions is Cu_2O.
(b) The oxidation number of copper must be +1.

12.7 Calcium atom radius = 197 pm

12.9 There are three ways the edge dimensions can be calculated:
(a) Calculate mass of unit cell (= 1.103×10^{-21} g/uc)

Calculate volume of unit cell from mass (= 3.53×10^{-22} cm^3/uc)

Calculate edge length from volume (= 707 pm)
(b) Assume I^- ions touch along the cell diagonal (◀ Check Your Understanding 12.1) and use I^- radius to find the edge length. Radius I^- = 220 pm

Edge = $4(220 \text{ pm})/2^{1/2}$ = 622 pm
(c) Assume the I^- and K^+ ions touch along the cell edge (page 449)

Edge = 2 × I^- radius + 2 × K^+ radius = 706 pm

Methods (a) and (c) agree. It is apparent that the sizes of the ions are such that the I^- ions cannot touch along the cell diagonal.

12.11 Increasing lattice energy: RbI < LiI < LiF < CaO

12.13 As the ion–ion distance decreases, the force of attraction between ions increases. This should make the lattice more stable, and more energy should be required to melt the compound.

12.15 $\Delta_f H° = -607$ kJ/mol

12.17 The 1000 2*s* orbitals will combine to form 1000 molecular orbitals. In the lowest energy state, 500 of these will be populated by pairs of electrons, and 500 will be empty.

12.19 In metals, thermal energy causes some electrons to occupy higher-energy orbitals in the band of molecular orbitals. For each electron promoted, two singly occupied levels result: a negative electron above the Fermi level and a positive hole below the Fermi level. Electrical conductivity results because in the presence of an electric field, these negative electrons will move toward the positive side of the field and the positive holes will move toward the negative side.

12.21 In carbon the band gap is too large for electrons to move up in energy from the valence band to the conduction band, whereas in silicon the band gap is small enough to permit this.

12.23 An intrinsic semiconductor (such as Si or Ge) is one that naturally can have electrons move across the band gap, whereas an extrinsic semiconductor (such as Ge with added As) requires the addition of dopants in order for it to conduct.

12.25 (a) Eight C atoms per unit cell. There are eight corners (= 1 net C atom), six faces (= 3 net C atoms), and four internal C atoms
(b) Face-centered cubic (fcc) with C atoms in the tetrahedral holes

12.27 Type of solid: particles, forces of attraction
(a) Metallic: metal atoms, metallic bonding
(b) Ionic: ions, ion–ion interactions
(c) Molecular: molecules, covalent bonds within the molecules and intermolecular forces between the molecules
(d) Network: extended network of covalently bonded atoms, covalent bonds
(e) Amorphous: covalently bonded networks with no long-range regularity, covalent bonds

12.29 Substance: type of solid, particles, forces, property
(a) Gallium arsenide: network, covalently bonded atoms, covalent bonds, semiconductor
(b) Polystyrene: amorphous, covalent bonds within the polymer molecules and dispersion forces between the polymer molecules, thermal insulator
(c) Silicon carbide: network, covalently bonded atoms, covalent bonds, very hard material
(d) Perovskite: ionic, Ca^{2+} and TiO_3^{2-} ions, ion–ion interactions, high melting point

12.31 q (for fusion) = −1.97 kJ; q (for melting) = +1.97 kJ

12.33 (a) The density of liquid CO_2 is less than that of solid CO_2.
(b) CO_2 is a gas at 5 atm and 0 °C.
(c) Critical temperature = 31 °C, so CO_2 cannot be liquefied at 45 °C.

12.35 q (to heat the liquid) = 9.4×10^2 kJ

q (to vaporize NH_3) = 1.6×10^4 kJ

q (to heat the vapor) = 8.8×10^2 kJ

$q_{total} = 1.8 \times 10^4$ kJ

12.37 O_2 phase diagram. (i) Note the slight positive slope of the solid–liquid equilibrium line. It indicates that the density of solid O_2 is greater than that of liquid O_2. (ii) Using the diagram here, the vapor pressure of O_2 at 77 K is between 150 and 200 mm Hg.

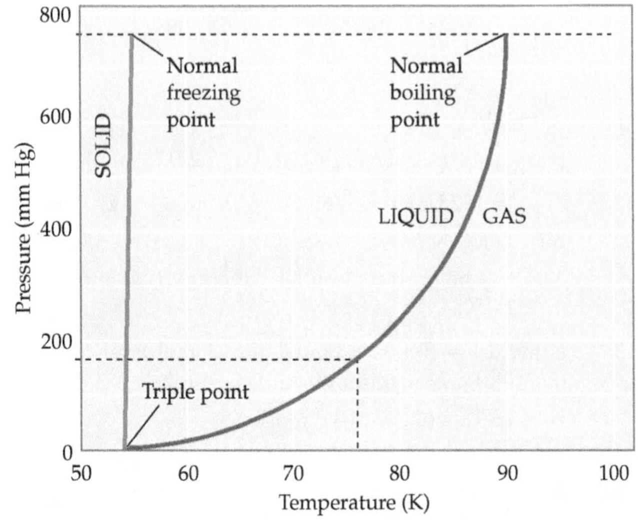

12.39 Radius of silver = 145 pm

12.41 1.356×10^{-8} cm (literature value is 1.357×10^{-8} cm)

12.43 Mass of 1 CaF_2 unit calculated from crystal data = 1.2963×10^{-22} g. Divide molar mass of CaF_2 (78.077 g/mol) by mass of 1 CaF_2 to obtain Avogadro's number. Calculated value = 6.0230×10^{23} CaF_2/mol.

12.45 Diagram A leads to a surface coverage of 78.5%. Diagram B leads to 90.7% coverage.

12.47 (a) The lattice can be described as an fcc lattice of Si atoms.
(b) Si atoms are located in one half of the tetrahedral holes.
(c) There are eight Si atoms in the unit cell.
(d) Mass of unit cell = 3.731×10^{-22} g

Volume of unit cell = 1.602×10^{-22} cm^3

Density = 2.329 g/cm^3 (which is the same as the literature value)

(e) In the Si unit cell we cannot assume the atoms touch along the edge or along the face diagonal. Instead, we know that the Si atoms in the tetrahedral holes are bonded to the Si atoms at the corner.

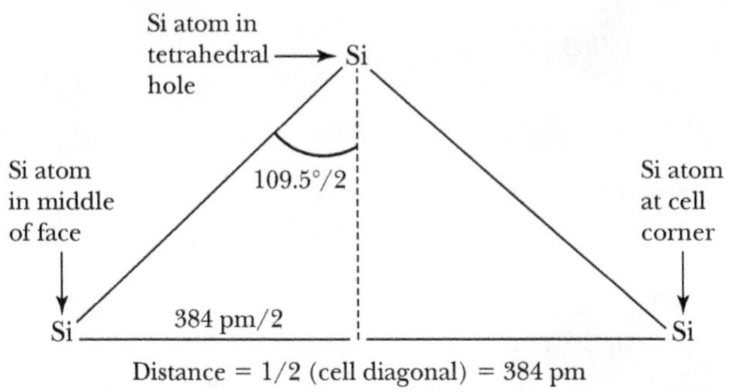

Distance across cell face diagonal = 768 pm

Sin (109.5°/2) = 0.817 = (384 pm/2)/(Si-Si distance)

Distance from Si in tetrahedral hole to face or corner Si = 235 pm

Si radius = 118 pm

Figure 7.5 gives Si radius as 117 pm

12.49 (a) Mg^{2+} ions are in ⅛ of the eight possible tetrahedral holes, and Al^{3+} ions are in ½ of the four available octahedral holes.
(b) Fe^{2+} ions are in ⅛ of the eight possible tetrahedral holes, and Cr^{3+} ions are in ½ of the four available octahedral holes.

12.51 8.5×10^2 nm

12.53 Germanium has a smaller band gap, so it has a higher conductivity.

12.55 Because boron is electron deficient in comparison to carbon, this is a p-type semiconductor.

12.57 Lead sulfide has the same structure as sodium chloride, not the same structure as ZnS. There are four Pb^{2+} ions and four S^{2-} ions per unit cell, a 1:1 ratio that matches the compound formula.

12.59 4 formula units/unit cell; mass of unit cell = 7.904×10^{-22} g

Dimension of one side of unit cell = $2r(K^+) + 2r(Br^-) = 6.58 \times 10^{-8}$ cm; so volume of the unit cell = side^3 = 2.85×10^{-22} cm^3

Density = 7.902×10^{-22} g/2.85×10^{-22} cm^3 = 2.77 g/cm^3

12.61 (a) $BBr_3(g) + PBr_3(g) + 3\ H_2(g) \rightarrow BP(s) + 6\ HBr(g)$
(b) If B atoms are in an fcc lattice, then the P atoms must be in ½ of the tetrahedral holes. (In this way it resembles Si in Question 12.47.)
(c) Unit cell volume = 1.092×10^{-22} cm^3
Unit cell mass = 2.775×10^{-22} g
Density = 2.54 g/cm^3
(d) The solution to this problem is identical to Question 12.47. In the BP lattice, the cell face diagonal is 676 pm. Therefore, the calculated BP distance is 207 pm.

12.63 Assuming the spheres are packed in an identical way, the water levels are the same. A face-centered cubic lattice, for example, uses 74% of the available space, regardless of the sphere size.

12.65 Step 1. There are four atoms within a ccp unit cell. Calculate the volume of these four atoms (V of a sphere = $(4/3)\pi r^3$).

Step 2. Calculate the total volume of the unit cell (V_{cell} = side^3).

Step 3. Percent occupancy = $(V_{atoms}/V_{cell})100\%$

12.67 (a) Two triple points. One with diamond, graphite and liquid C; the second with liquid C, graphite, and carbon vapor.
(b) no

(c) diamond
(d) Graphite is the stable form of carbon at room temperature and 1 atmosphere of pressure.

Chapter 13

Case Study

Henry's Law and Exploding Lakes

1. $PV = nRT$

   $4.0\ \text{atm}(0.025\ \text{L}) = n(0.08206\ \text{L} \cdot \text{atm/mol} \cdot \text{K})(298\ \text{K})$; $n = 4.1 \times 10^{-3}$ mol

2. $P_1V_1 = P_2V_2$

   $4.0\ \text{atm}(0.025\ \text{L}) = 3.7 \times 10^{-4}\ \text{atm}\ (V_2)$; $V_2 = 270$ L

   The gas expanded by a factor of 11,000 (= 270 L/0.025 L).

3. Solubility of $CO_2 = k_HP_g = 0.034$ mol/kg · bar $(3.7 \times 10^{-4}\ \text{bar}) = 1.3 \times 10^{-5}$ mol/kg

4. Before opening: Solubility of CO_2 before opening = $k_HP_g = 0.034$ mol/kg · bar (4.0 bar) = 0.14 mol/kg

   Assume the density of the solution is 1.0 g/cm^3, therefore 1.0 L corresponds to 1.0 kg. The amount of CO_2 dissolved is 0.14 mol.

   After opening: Solubility of $CO_2 = 1.3 \times 10^{-5}$ mol/kg as calculated in part 3 above. The amount of CO_2 in 1.0 kg is 1.3×10^{-5} mol.

   Mass of CO_2 released = (0.14 mol CO_2 − 1.3×10^{-5} mol CO_2)(44.01 g CO_2/1 mol CO_2) = 6.0 g CO_2

Check Your Understanding

13.1 (a) 10.0 g sucrose = 0.0292 mol; 250. g H_2O = 13.9 mol

$X_{sucrose}$ = (0.0292 mol)/(0.0292 mol + 13.9 mol) = 0.00210

$c_{sucrose}$ = (0.0292 mol sucrose)/(0.250 kg solvent) = 0.117 m

Weight % sucrose = (10.0 g sucrose/260 g soln)(100%) = 3.85%

(b) 1.08×10^4 ppm = 1.08×10^4 mg Na^+ per 1000 g soln = (1.08×10^4 mg Na^+/1000 g soln)(1050 g soln/1 L) = 1.13×10^4 mg Na^+/L = 11.3 g Na^+/L

(11.3 g Na^+/L)(58.44 g NaCl/23.0 g Na^+) = 28.8 g NaCl/L

13.2 $\Delta_{soln}H° = \Delta_fH°[\text{NaOH(aq)}] - \Delta_fH°[\text{NaOH(s)}]$
= −469.2 kJ/mol − (−425.9 kJ/mol)
= −43.3 kJ/mol

13.3 Solubility of $CO_2 = k_HP_g = 0.034$ mol/kg · bar × 0.33 bar = 1.1×10^{-2} mol/kg

13.4 The solution contains sucrose [(10.0 g)(1 mol/342.3 g) = 0.0292 mol] in water [(225 g)(1 mol/18.02 g) = 12.5 mol].

X_{water} = (12.5 mol H_2O)/(12.5 mol + 0.0292 mol) = 0.998

$P_{water} = X_{water}P°_{water}$ = 0.998(149.4 mm Hg) = 149 mm Hg

13.5 $c_{glycol} = \Delta T_{bp}/K_{bp}$ = 1.0 °C/(0.512 °C/m) = 2.0 m = 2.0 mol/kg

mass$_{glycol}$ = (2.0 mol/kg)(0.125 kg)(62.07 g/mol) = 15 g

13.6 c_{glycol} = (525 g)(1 mol/62.07 g)/(3.00 kg) = 2.82 m

$\Delta T_{fp} = K_{fp} \times m$ = (−1.86 °C/m)(2.82 m) = −5.24 °C

You will be protected only to about −5 °C and not to −25 °C.

13.7 c (mol/L) = (0.033 g bradykinin)(1 mol bradykinin/1060 g bradykinin)/0.0500 L = 6.2×10^{-4} M

$\Pi = cRT$ = (6.2×10^{-4} mol/L)(0.082057 L · atm/mol · K)(293 K) = 0.015 atm

13.8 ΔT_{fp} = 5.265 °C − 5.50 °C = −0.24 °C

$\Delta T_{fp} = K_{fp} \times m_{solute}$

m_{solute} = −0.24 °C/−5.12 °C/m = 0.046 mol/kg

m_{solute} = (0.046 mol solute/kg benzene)(0.02346 kg benzene) = 0.0011 mol solute

M = 0.448 g/0.0011 mol = 4.2×10^2 g/mol

M(compound)/M(empirical formula) = 4.2×10^2 g/mol/104.1 g/mol = 4.0

Molecular formula = $(C_2H_5)_8Al_4F_4$

13.9 c (mol/L) = Π/RT = [(1.86 mm Hg)(1 atm/760 mm Hg)]/[(0.08206 L · atm/mol · K)(298 K)] = 1.00×10^{-4} M

(1.00×10^{-4} mol/L)(0.100 L) = 1.00×10^{-5} mol

Molar mass = 1.40 g/1.00×10^{-5} mol = 1.4×10^5 g/mol

(Assuming the polymer is composed of CH_2 units, the polymer is about 10,000 units long.)

13.10 c_{NaCl} = (25.0 g NaCl)(1 mol/58.44 g)/(0.525 kg) = 0.815 m

$\Delta T_{fp} = K_{fp} \times m \times i$ = (−1.86 °C/m)(0.815 m)(1.85) = −2.80 °C

Review & Check

Section 13-1

1. (b) 0.063
   (b) 3.7
2. (b) 0.88 mol/kg

Section 13-2

1. (c) −23.55 kJ/mol

Section 13-3

1. (b) 0.097 mol

Section 13-4

1. (b) Na_2SO_4 < sugar < KBr < $C_2H_4(OH)_2$
2. (d) naphthalene, $C_{10}H_8$
3. (c) 1.0 g propylene glycol, $C_3H_6(OH)_2$
4. (c) 122 g/mol

Section 13-5

1. (b) 40 million atoms.

Applying Chemical Principles: Distillation

1. X(hexane) = 0.59
3. Mass percent (hexane) = 18%

Study Questions

13.1 (a) Concentration (m) = 0.0434 m
(b) Mole fraction of acid = 0.000781
(c) Weight percent of acid = 0.509%

13.3 NaI: 0.15 m; 2.2%; $X = 2.7 \times 10^{-3}$
CH_3CH_2OH: 1.1 m; 5.0%; $X = 0.020$
$C_{12}H_{22}O_{11}$: 0.15 m; 4.9%; $X = 2.7 \times 10^{-3}$

13.5 2.65 g Na_2CO_3; $X(Na_2CO_3) = 3.59 \times 10^{-3}$

13.7 220 g glycerol; 5.7 m

13.9 16.2 m; 37.1%

13.11 Molality = 2.6×10^{-5} m (assuming that 1 kg of seawater is equivalent to 1 kg of solvent)

13.13 (b) and (c)

13.15 $\Delta_{soln}H°$ for LiCl = −36.9 kJ/mol. This is an exothermic enthalpy of solution, as compared with the very slightly endothermic value for NaCl.

13.17 Above about 40 °C the solubility increases with temperature; therefore, add more NaCl and raise the temperature.

13.19 2×10^{-3} g O_2

13.21 1100 mm Hg or 1.5 bar

13.23 (a) $S = 2.0 \times 10^{-3}$ mol/kg
(b) Raising the pressure to 1.7 atm will result in an increased concentration of dissolved O_2; lowering the pressure to 1.0 atm will lead to a lower concentration of dissolved O_2.

13.25 35.0 mm Hg

13.27 $X(H_2O)$ = 0.869; 16.7 mol glycol; 1040 g glycol

13.29 Calculated boiling point = 84.2 °C

13.31 ΔT_{bp} = 0.808 °C; solution boiling point = 62.51 °C

13.33 Molality = 8.60 m; 28.4%

13.35 Molality = 0.195 m; ΔT_{fp} = fp = −0.362 °C

13.37 (a) ΔT_{fp} = −0.348 °C; fp = −0.348 °C
(b) ΔT_{bp} = +0.0959 °C; bp = 100.0959 °C
(c) Π = 4.58 atm
The osmotic pressure is large and can be measured with a small experimental error.

13.39 Molar mass = 6.0×10^3 g/mol

13.41 Molar mass = 360 g/mol; $C_{20}H_{16}Fe_2$

13.43 Molar mass = 150 g/mol

13.45 Molar mass = 170 g/mol

13.47 Freezing point = −24.6 °C

13.49 0.08 m $CaCl_2$ < 0.1 m NaCl < 0.04 m Na_2SO_4 < 0.1 sugar

13.51 (a) $BaCl_2(aq) + Na_2SO_4(aq) \rightarrow BaSO_4(s) + 2\ NaCl(aq)$
(b) Initially, the $BaSO_4$ particles form a colloidal suspension.
(c) Over time, the particles of $BaSO_4(s)$ grow and precipitate.

13.53 Molar mass = 110 g/mol

13.55 (a) Increase in vapor pressure of water
0.20 m Na_2SO_4 < 0.50 m sugar < 0.20 m KBr < 0.35 m ethylene glycol
(b) Increase in boiling point
0.35 m ethylene glycol < 0.20 m KBr < 0.50 m sugar < 0.20 m Na_2SO_4

13.57 (a) 0.456 mol DMG and 11.4 mol ethanol; X(DMG) = 0.0385
(b) 0.869 m
(c) VP ethanol over the solution at 78.4 °C = 730.7 mm Hg
(d) bp = 79.5 °C

13.59 For ammonia: 23 m; $X(NH_3)$ = 0.29; 28%

13.61 0.592 g Na_2SO_4

13.63 (a) 0.20 m KBr; (b) 0.10 m Na_2CO_3

13.65 Freezing point = −11 °C

13.67 4.0×10^2 g/mol

13.69 4.7×10^{-4} mol/kg

13.71 (a) Molar mass = 4.9×10^4 g/mol
(b) $\Delta T_{fp} = -3.8 \times 10^{-4}$ °C

13.73 $\Delta_{soln}H°$ [Li_2SO_4] = −28.0 kJ/mol
$\Delta_{soln}H°$ [LiCl] = −36.9 kJ/mol
$\Delta_{soln}H°$ [K_2SO_4] = +23.7 kJ/mol
$\Delta_{soln}H°$ [KCl] = +17.2 kJ/mol
Both lithium compounds have exothermic enthalpies of solution, whereas both potassium compounds have endothermic values. Consistent with this is the fact that lithium salts (LiCl) are often more water-soluble than potassium salts (KCl) (see Figure 13.11).

13.75 X(benzene in solution) = 0.67 and X(toluene in solution) = 0.33

$$P_{total} = P_{toluene} + P_{benzene} = 7.3 \text{ mm Hg} + 50. \text{ mm Hg} = 57 \text{ mm Hg}$$

$$X(\text{toluene in vapor}) = \frac{7.3 \text{ mm Hg}}{57 \text{ mm Hg}} = 0.13$$

$$X(\text{benzene in vapor}) = \frac{50. \text{ mm Hg}}{57 \text{ mm Hg}} = 0.87$$

13.77 $i = 1.7$. That is, there is 1.7 mol of ions in solution per mole of compound.

13.79 (a) Calculate the number of moles of ions in 10^6 g H_2O: 550. mol Cl^-; 470. mol Na^+; 53.1 mol Mg^{2+}; 9.42 mol SO_4^{2-}; 10.3 mol Ca^{2+}; 9.72 mol K^+; 0.84 mol Br^-. Total moles of ions = 1.103×10^3 per 10^6 g water. This gives ΔT_{fp} of −2.05 °C.
(b) Π = 27.0 atm. This means that a minimum pressure of 27 atm would have to be used in a reverse osmosis device.

13.81 (a) $i = 2.06$
(b) There are approximately two particles in solution, so $H^+ + HSO_4^-$ best represents H_2SO_4 in aqueous solution.

13.83 Mass of N_2O = 0.53 g; concentration = 1.1×10^3 ppm

13.85 The best method would be to shine a laser through the liquid and look for the Tyndall effect. Some other properties of colloids that could be utilized are that the dispersed material in a colloid will either not crystallize or crystallize only with difficulty and will either not diffuse across a membrane or do so much more slowly than a true solute.

13.87 The calculated molality at the freezing point of benzene is 0.47 m, whereas it is 0.99 m at the boiling point. A higher molality at the higher temperature indicates more molecules are dissolved. Therefore, assuming benzoic acid forms dimers like acetic acid (page 413), dimer formation is more prevalent at the lower temperature. In this process two molecules become one entity, lowering the number of separate species in solution and lowering the molality.

13.89 Molar mass in benzene = 1.20×10^2 g/mol; molar mass in water = 62.4 g/mol. The actual molar mass of acetic acid is 60.1 g/mol. In benzene, the molecules of acetic acid form "dimers." That is, two molecules form a single unit through hydrogen bonding (see page 413).

13.91 The empirical formula, calculated from the percent composition data, is $C_7H_6N_2$. The calculated molar mass of the compound is 118 g/mol, which agrees with the molar mass calculated from the vapor pressure data.

13.93 The strength of the interactions is related to the size of the ion. Thus, Be^{2+} is most strongly hydrated, and Ca^{2+} is least strongly hydrated.

13.95 Colligative properties depend on the number of ions or molecules in solution. Each mole of $CaCl_2$ provides 1.5 times as many ions as each mole of NaCl.

13.97 Benzene is a nonpolar solvent. Thus, ionic substances such as $NaNO_3$ and NH_4Cl will certainly not dissolve. However, naphthalene is also nonpolar and resembles benzene in its structure; it should dissolve very well. (A chemical handbook gives a solubility of 33 g naphthalene per 100 g benzene.) Diethyl ether is weakly polar but is miscible to some extent with benzene.

Water is a polar solvent. The ionic compounds, $NaNO_3$ and NH_4Cl, are both soluble in water ($NaNO_3$ solubility (at 25 °C) = 91 g per 100 g water; NH_4Cl solubility (at 25 °C) = 40 g per 100 g water. The slightly polar compound diethyl ether is soluble to a small extent in water (about 6 g per 100 g water at 25 °C). Nonpolar naphthalene is not soluble in water (solubility at 25 °C = 0.003 g per 100 g water).

13.99 The C—C and C—H bonds in hydrocarbons are nonpolar or weakly polar and tend to make such dispersions hydrophobic (water-hating). The C—O and O—H bonds in starch present opportunities for hydrogen bonding with water. Hence, starch is expected to be more hydrophilic.

13.101 [NaCl] = 1.0 M and [KNO_3] = 0.88 M. The KNO_3 solution has a higher solvent concentration, so solvent will flow from the KNO_3 solution to the NaCl solution.

13.103 (a) $X(C_2H_5OH) = 0.051$; $X(H_2O) = 0.949$
(b) $P(C_2H_5OH)$ over mixture = 38 mm Hg; $P°(H_2O)$ calculated by linear interpolation using the vapor pressures at 78 °C and 79 °C = 334.2 mm Hg; $P(H_2O)$ over mixture = 317 mm Hg
(c) $X(C_2H_5OH) = 0.11$; $X(H_2O) = 0.89$
(d) The mole fraction of ethanol increased from 0.051 to 0.11, a factor of 2.2 times.

Weight percent of C_2H_5OH = 24%

13.105 The molality of the 5.00% NaCl solution is 0.901 m. Assuming no dissociation, this leads to ΔT_{fp}(calculated) = −1.68 °C and i = 1.82. The molality of the 5.00% Na_2SO_4 solution is 0.371 m, ΔT_{fp}(calculated) = −0.689 °C, and i = 1.97. These values are consistent with the trends seen in Table 13.4. As the concentration of the ionic solute increases, the value of i continues to decrease for both solutes, and rate of decrease is falling for both solutes. In the case of NaCl, this value is leveling off quite a bit. In the case of Na_2SO_4, it is continuing to decrease by significant amounts. Interestingly, the value of i for Na_2SO_4 has now fallen below 2 and is getting closer to that for NaCl.

13.107 This does not lend credence to this story. The reported lowest temperature for a NaCl solution corresponds to a temperature of 2.372 °F. The temperature of 0 °F is still below this.

Chapter 14

Case Study

Enzymes—Nature's Catalysts

1. To decompose an equivalent amount of H_2O_2 catalytically would take 1.0×10^{-7} years; this is equivalent to 3.2 seconds.

2.

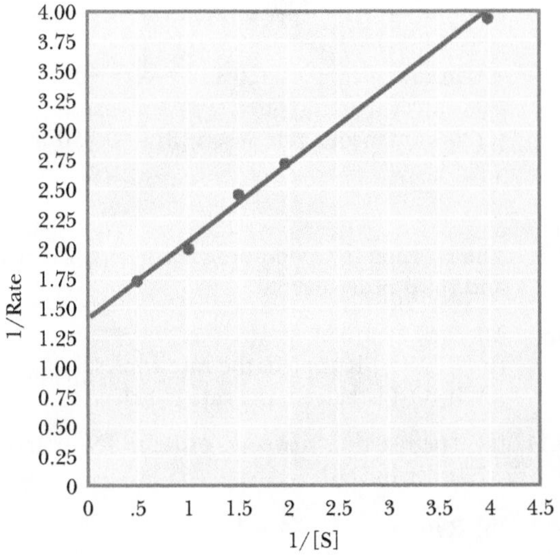

[S]	1/[S]	Rate	1/Rate
2.50	0.400	0.588	1.70
1.00	1.00	0.500	2.00
0.714	1.40	0.417	2.40
0.526	1.90	0.370	2.70
0.250	4.00	0.256	3.91

From the graph, we obtain a value of 1/Rate = 1.47 when 1/[S] = 0. From this, R_{max} = 0.68 mmol/min.

Check Your Understanding

14.1 For the first 2 hours:

$-\Delta[\text{sucrose}]/\Delta t = -[(0.033 - 0.050)\text{ mol/L}]/(2.0\text{ h}) = 0.0085\text{ mol/L}\cdot\text{h}$

For the last 2 hours:

$-\Delta[\text{sucrose}]/\Delta t = -[(0.010 - 0.015)\text{ mol/L}]/(2.0\text{ h}) = 0.003\text{ mol/L}\cdot\text{h}$

Instantaneous rate at 4 hours = 0.0045 mol/L · h. (Calculated from the slope of a line tangent to the curve at the defined concentration.)

14.2 $-\frac{1}{2}(\Delta[\text{NOCl}]/\Delta t) = \frac{1}{2}(\Delta[\text{NO}]/\Delta t) = \Delta[\text{Cl}_2]/\Delta t$

14.3 Compare experiments 1 and 2: Doubling $[O_2]$ causes the rate to double, so the rate is first order in $[O_2]$. Compare experiments 2 and 4: Doubling [NO] causes the rate to increase by a factor of 4, so the rate is second order in [NO]. Thus, the rate law is

$\text{Rate} = -(\Delta[\text{NO}]/\Delta t) = k[\text{NO}]^2[\text{O}_2]$

Using the data in experiment 1 to determine k:

$0.028\text{ mol/L}\cdot\text{s} = k[0.020\text{ mol/L}]^2[0.010\text{ mol/L}]$

$k = 7.0 \times 10^3\text{ L}^2/\text{mol}^2\cdot\text{s}$

14.4 $\text{Rate} = k[\text{Pt(NH}_3)_2\text{Cl}_2] = (0.27\text{ h}^{-1})(0.020\text{ mol/L})$
$= 0.0054\text{ mol/L}\cdot\text{h}$

14.5 $\ln([\text{sucrose}]/[\text{sucrose}]_o) = -kt$

$\ln([\text{sucrose}]/[0.010]) = -(0.21\text{ h}^{-1})(5.0\text{ h})$

$[\text{sucrose}] = 0.0035\text{ mol/L}$

14.6 (a) The fraction remaining is $[CH_3N_2CH_3]/[CH_3N_2CH_3]_o$.

$\ln([CH_3N_2CH_3]/[CH_3N_2CH_3]_o) = -(3.6 \times 10^{-4}\text{ s}^{-1})(150\text{ s})$

$[CH_3N_2CH_3]/[CH_3N_2CH_3]_o = 0.95$

(b) After the reaction is 99% complete $[CH_3N_2CH_3]/[CH_3N_2CH_3]_o = 0.010$

$\ln(0.010) = -(3.6 \times 10^{-4}\text{ s}^{-1})(t)$

$t = 1.3 \times 10^4\text{ s}$ (210 min)

14.7 $1/[\text{HI}] - 1/[\text{HI}]_o = kt$

$1/[\text{HI}] - 1/[0.010\text{ M}] = (30.\text{ L/mol}\cdot\text{min})(12\text{ min})$

$[\text{HI}] = 0.0022\text{ M}$

14.8 (0.060 M/0.24 M) = 0.25; thus ¼ of the original material remains and two half-lives have transpired. $t_{1/2}$ = 141 min.

$k = \ln 2/t_{1/2} = (\ln 2)/141\text{ min} = 4.92 \times 10^{-3}\text{ min}^{-1}$

Initial rate = $k[H_2O_2]_0$ = $4.92 \times 10^{-3}\text{ min}^{-1}$ (0.24 mol/L) = 1.2×10^{-3} mol/L · min

14.9 (a) For ^{241}Am, $t_{1/2} = 0.693/k = 0.693/(0.0016\text{ y}^{-1}) = 430\text{ y}$

For ^{125}I, $t_{1/2} = 0.693/(0.011\text{ d}^{-1}) = 63\text{ d}$

(b) ^{125}I decays much faster.

(c) $\ln[(n)/(1.6 \times 10^{15}\text{ atoms})] = -(0.011\text{ d}^{-1})(2.0\text{ d})$

$n/1.6 \times 10^{15}\text{ atoms} = 0.978$;

$n = 1.57 \times 10^{15}$ atoms

Since the answer should have two significant figures, we should round this off to 1.6×10^{15} atoms. The approximately 2% that has decayed is not discernable within the limits of accuracy of the data presented.

14.10 An Arrhenius plot was constructed by plotting ln k on the y-axis and $1/T$ on the x-axis. Using Microsoft Excel, the equation of the best-fit line is $y = -22336x + 27.304$.

$E_a = -R\cdot(\text{slope}) = -(0.0083145\text{ kJ/mol}\cdot\text{K})(-22336\text{ K}) = 1.9 \times 10^2\text{ kJ/mol}$

14.11 $\ln(k_2/k_1) = (-E_a/R)(1/T_2 - 1/T_1)$

$\ln[(1.00 \times 10^4)/(4.5 \times 10^3)] = -(E_a/8.3145 \times 10^{-3}\text{ kJ/mol}\cdot\text{K})(1/283\text{ K} - 1/274\text{ K})$

$E_a = 57$ kJ/mol

14.12 All three steps are bimolecular.

For step 3: Rate = $k[N_2O][H_2]$.

There are two intermediates, N_2O_2(g) and N_2O(g).

When the three equations are added, N_2O_2 (a product in the first step and a reactant in the second step) and N_2O (a product in the second step and a reactant in the third step) cancel, leaving the net equation:

$2\text{ NO(g)} + 2\text{ H}_2\text{(g)} \rightarrow \text{N}_2\text{(g)} + 2\text{ H}_2\text{O(g)}$.

14.13 (a) $2\ NH_3(aq) + OCl^-(aq) \rightarrow N_2H_4(aq) + Cl^-(aq) + H_2O(\ell)$
(b) The second step is the rate-determining step.
(c) Rate = $k[NH_2Cl][NH_3]$
(d) NH_2Cl, $N_2H_5^+$, and OH^- are intermediates.

14.14 Overall reaction: $2\ NO_2Cl(g) \rightarrow 2\ NO_2(g) + Cl_2(g)$
Rate = $k'[NO_2Cl]^2/[NO_2]$ (where $k' = k_1k_2/k_{-1}$)
Increasing $[NO_2]$ causes the reaction rate to decrease.

Review & Check

Section 14-1

1. (b) The rate of disappearance of NO(g) is twice the rate of disappearance of $O_2(g)$.
2. (c) 0.6×10^{-5} mol/L · min

Section 14-2

1. (b) decreasing the concentration of one of the reactants.

Section 14-3

1. (b) 1.24×10^{-5} mol/L · s

Section 14-4

1. (b) between 6 and 7
2. (d) A graph of $\ln[SO_2Cl_2]$ vs. time gives a straight line.
3. (b) second order

Section 14-5

1. (c) $\ln k$ vs. $1/T$
2. (b) A higher proportion of reactant molecules exceeds the activation energy.

Section 14-6

1. (b) This reaction might occur in a single elementary step.
2. (c) Rate = $k[A]^2[B]$

Applying Chemical Principles: Kinetics and Mechanisms: A 70-Year-Old Mystery Solved

1. (a) 207 kJ/mol photons
(b) 792 nm

3. The probability of three particles colliding simultaneously with the correct geometry for a successful reaction is low.

Study Questions

14.1 (a) $-\frac{1}{2}\frac{\Delta[O_3]}{\Delta t} = \frac{1}{3}\frac{\Delta[O_2]}{\Delta t}$

(b) $-\frac{1}{2}\frac{\Delta[HOF]}{\Delta t} = \frac{1}{2}\frac{\Delta[HF]}{\Delta t} = \frac{\Delta[O_2]}{\Delta t}$

14.3 $\frac{1}{3}\frac{\Delta[O_2]}{\Delta t} = -\frac{1}{2}\frac{\Delta[O_3]}{\Delta t}$ or $\frac{\Delta[O_3]}{\Delta t} = -\frac{2}{3}\frac{\Delta[O_2]}{\Delta t}$

so $\Delta[O_3]/\Delta t = -1.0 \times 10^{-3}$ mol/L · s.

14.5 (a) The graph of [B] (product concentration) versus time shows [B] increasing from zero. The line is curved, indicating the rate changes with time; thus the rate depends on concentration. Rates for the four 10–s intervals are as follows: 0–10 s, 0.0326 mol/L · s; from 10–20 s, 0.0246 mol/L · s; 20–30 s, 0.0178 mol/L · s; 30–40 s, 0.0140 mol/L · s.

(b) $-\frac{\Delta[A]}{\Delta t} = \frac{1}{2}\frac{\Delta[B]}{\Delta t}$ throughout the reaction

In the interval 10–20 s, $\frac{\Delta[A]}{\Delta t} = -0.0123 \frac{mol}{L \cdot s}$

(c) Instantaneous rate when [B] = 0.750 mol/L = $\frac{\Delta[B]}{\Delta t} = 0.0163 \frac{mol}{L \cdot s}$

14.7 The reaction is second order in A, first order in B, and third order overall.

14.9 (a) Rate = $k[NO_2][O_3]$
(b) If $[NO_2]$ is tripled, the rate triples.
(c) If $[O_3]$ is halved, the rate is halved.

14.11 (a) The reaction is second order in [NO] and first order in $[O_2]$.
(b) Rate = $\frac{-\Delta[NO]}{\Delta t} = k[NO]^2[O_2]$
(c) $k = 25\ L^2/mol^2 \cdot s$
(d) Rate = 2.8×10^{-5} mol/L · s
(e) When $-\Delta[NO]/\Delta t = 1.0 \times 10^{-4}$ mol/L · s, $\Delta[O_2]/\Delta t = 5.0 \times 10^{-5}$ mol/L · s and $\Delta[NO_2]/\Delta t = 1.0 \times 10^{-4}$ mol/L · s.

14.13 (a) Rate = $-\Delta[NO]/\Delta t = k[NO]^2[O_2]$
(b) 50. $L^2/mol^2 \cdot h$
(c) Rate = 8.4×10^{-9} mol/L · h

14.15 $k = 3.73 \times 10^{-3}\ min^{-1}$

14.17 5.0×10^2 min

14.19 (a) 153 min
(b) 1790 min

14.21 140 s

14.23 6.3 s

14.25 (a) $t_{1/2} = 1.0 \times 10^4$ s (b) 34,000 s

14.27 1.0×10^3 min

14.29 Fraction of ^{64}Cu remaining = 0.030

14.31 The straight line obtained in a graph of $\ln[N_2O]$ versus time indicates a first-order reaction.
k = (−slope) = 0.0128 min^{-1}
The rate when $[N_2O]$ = 0.035 mol/L is 4.5×10^{-4} mol/L · min.

14.33 The graph of $1/[NO_2]$ versus time gives a straight line, indicating the reaction is second order with respect to $[NO_2]$ (see Table 14.1 on page 524). The slope of the line is k, so k = 1.1 L/mol · s.

14.35 $-\Delta[C_2F_4]/\Delta t = k[C_2F_4]^2 = (0.04\ L/mol \cdot s)[C_2F_4]^2$

14.37 Activation energy = 102 kJ/mol

14.39 k = 0.3 s^{-1}

14.41

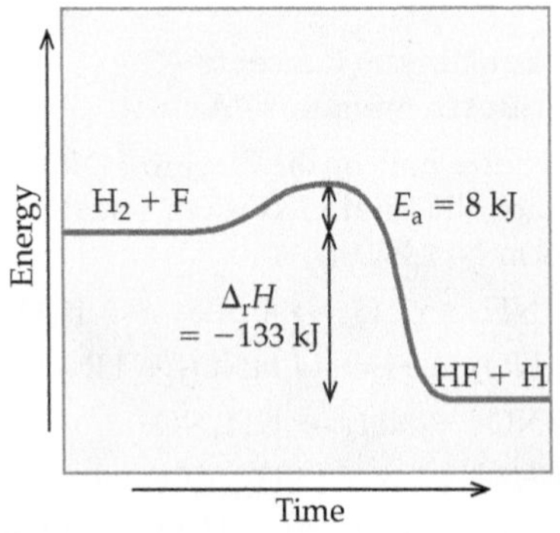

14.43 (a) Rate = $k[NO_3][NO]$
(b) Rate = $k[Cl][H_2]$
(c) Rate = $k[(CH_3)_3CBr]$

14.45 (a) The second step; (b) Rate = $k[O_3][O]$

14.47 (a) NO_2 is a reactant in the first step and a product in the second step. CO is a reactant in the second step. NO_3 is an intermediate, and CO_2 is a product. NO is a product.
(b) Reaction coordinate diagram

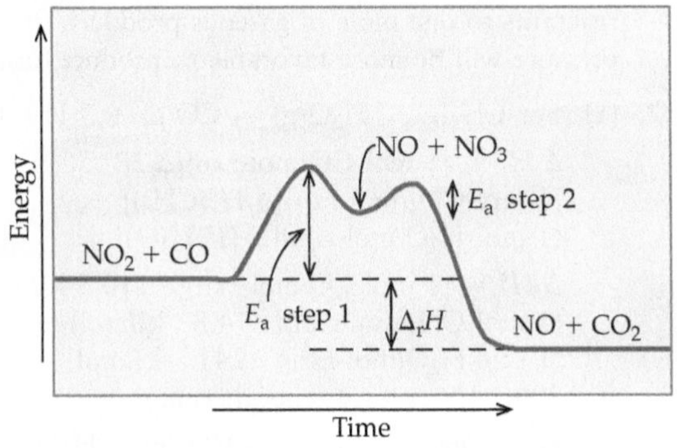

14.49 Doubling the concentration of A will increase the rate by a factor of 4 because the concentration of A appears in the rate law as $[A]^2$. Halving the concentration of B will halve the rate The net result is that the rate of the reaction will double.

14.51 After measuring pH as a function of time, one could then calculate pOH and then $[OH^-]$. Finally, a plot of $1/[OH^-]$ versus time would give a straight line with a slope equal to k.

14.53 72 s represents two half-lives, so $t_{1/2}$ = 36 s.

14.55 (a) A plot of $1/[C_2F_4]$ versus time indicates the reaction is second order with respect to $[C_2F_4]$. The rate law is Rate = $k[C_2F_4]^2$.
(b) The rate constant (= slope of the line) is about 0.045 L/mol · s. (The graph does not allow a very accurate calculation.)
(c) Using k = 0.045 L/mol · s, the concentration after 600 s is 0.03 M (to one significant figure).
(d) Time = 2000 s [using k from part (b)].

14.57 (a) A plot of $1/[NH_4NCO]$ versus time is linear, so the reaction is second order with respect to NH_4NCO.
(b) Slope = k = 0.0109 L/mol · min.
(c) $t_{1/2}$ = 200. min
(d) $[NH_4NCO]$ = 0.0997 mol/L

14.59 Mechanism 2

14.61 k = 0.0176 h^{-1} and $t_{1/2}$ = 39.3 h

14.63 (a) After 125 min, 0.250 g remains. After 145, 0.144 g remains.
(b) Time = 43.9 min
(c) Fraction remaining = 0.016

14.65 Plotting 1/concentration versus the time gives a reasonably good linear correlation. The reaction is second order.

14.67 The rate equation for the slow step is Rate = $k[O_3][O]$. The equilibrium constant, K, for step 1 is $K = [O_2][O]/[O_3]$. Solving this for [O], we have $[O] = K[O_3]/[O_2]$. Substituting the expression for [O] into the rate equation we find

Rate = $k[O_3]\{K[O_3]/[O_2]\} = kK[O_3]^2/[O_2]$

14.69 The slope of the ln k versus $1/T$ plot is −6370. From slope = $-E_a/R$, we derive E_a = 53.0 kJ/mol.

14.71 Step 2 is the rate-determining step, and N_2O_2 is an intermediate.

Rate = $-\frac{1}{2}\ \Delta[NO]/\Delta t = k[NO]^2[O_2]$

14.73 (a) k = 3.41 L/mol · min
(b) The rate constant (k') for the rewritten equation is ½ the value of the rate constant, k, for the original equation. The rate equation for the original equation is $-\Delta[NO_2]/\Delta t = k[NO_2]$. For the rewritten equation the rate equation is $-(\frac{1}{2})\Delta[NO_2]/\Delta t = k'[NO_2]$ or $-\Delta[NO_2]/\Delta t = 2k'[NO_2]$. Therefore, $k = 2k'$ or $k' = (\frac{1}{2})k$.

14.75 Estimated time at 90 °C = 4.76 min

14.77 After 30 min (one half-life), P_{HOF} = 50.0 mm Hg and P_{total} = 125.0 mm Hg. After 45 min, P_{HOF} = 35.4 mm Hg and P_{total} = 132 mm Hg.

14.79 (a) Reaction is first order in NO_2NH_2 and −1 for H_3O^+. In a buffered solution, $[H_3O]^+$ is constant, so the reaction has an apparent order of 1.
(b, c) Mechanism 3

In step 1, $K = k_4/k_4' = [NO_2NH^-][H_3O^+]/[NO_2NH_2]$

Rearrange this and substitute into the rate law for the slow step.

Rate = $k_5[NO_2NH^-] = k_5K[NO_2NH_2]/[H_3O^+]$

This is the same as the experimental rate law, where the overall rate constant $k = k_5K$.
(d) Addition of OH^- ions will shift the equilibrium in step 1 (by reacting with H_3O^+) to produce a larger concentration of NO_2NH^-, the reactant in the rate-determining step, thus the reaction rate will increase.

14.81 (a) Average rate for $t = 0$ to $t = 15$ is about 4.7×10^{-5} M/s. For $t = 100$ s to 125 s, the average rate is about 1.6×10^{-5} M/s. The rate slows because the rate of the reaction is dependent on the concentration of reactant and this concentration is declining with time.
(b) Instantaneous rate at 50 s is about 2.7×10^{-5} M/s.
(c) A plot of ln (concentration) versus time is a straight line with an equation of $y = -0.010x - 5.30$. This indicates the reaction is a first-order reaction; Rate = k[phenolphthalein]. The slope, which is equal to $-k$, is -0.010, so $k = 0.010\ s^{-1}$.
(d) From the data the half-life is 69.3 s, and the same value comes from the relation $t_{1/2} = \ln 2/k$.

14.83 A plot of 1/Rate versus 1/[S] gives the equation
1/Rate = 94 (1/[S]) + 7.6×10^4
so $Rate_{max} = 1/(7.6 \times 10^4) = 1.3 \times 10^{-5}$ M min^{-1}.

14.85 (a) The reaction is first order in $[ClO^-]$ (experiments 1 and 3), first order in $[I^-]$ (experiments 2 and 3), and -1 order in $[OH^-]$ (experiments 3 and 4). Therefore, Rate = $k[ClO^-][I^-]/[OH^-]$
(b) Step 2 is the rate determining step. For this step, rate = $k[I^-][HOCl]$. From the first step, $K_{eq} = [HOCl][OH^-]/[ClO^-]$, so $[HOCl] = K_{eq}[ClO^-]/[OH^-]$; substituting for [HOCl] in the rate equation for the second step gives the observed rate law.

14.87 The finely divided rhodium metal will have a significantly greater surface area than the small block of metal. This leads to a large increase in the number of reaction sites and vastly increases the reaction rate.

14.89 (a) False. The reaction may occur in a single step but this does not have to be true.
(b) True
(c) False. Raising the temperature increases the value of k.
(d) False. Temperature has no effect on the value of E_a.
(e) False. If the concentrations of both reactants are doubled, the rate will increase by a factor of 4.
(f) True

14.91 (a) True
(b) True
(c) False. As a reaction proceeds, the reactant concentration decreases and the rate decreases.
(d) False. It is possible to have a one-step mechanism for a third-order reaction if the slow, rate-determining step is termolecular.

14.93 (a) Decrease (d) No change
(b) Increase (e) No change
(c) No change (f) No change

14.95 (a) There are three mechanistic steps.
(b) The overall reaction is exothermic.

Chapter 15

Case Study

Applying Equilibrium Concepts—The Haber-Bosch Ammonia Process

1. (a) Oxidize part of the NH_3 to HNO_3, then react NH_3 and HNO_3 (an acid–base reaction) to form NH_4NO_3.

$4\ NH_3 + 7\ O_2 \rightarrow 4\ NO_2 + 6\ H_2O$

$2\ NO_2 + H_2O \rightarrow HNO_3 + HNO_2$

$HNO_3 + NH_3 \rightarrow NH_4NO_3$

(b) $\Delta_rH° = (1 \text{ mol } (NH_2)_2CO/\text{mol-rxn})[\Delta_fH°\{(NH_2)_2CO\}] + (1 \text{ mol } H_2O/\text{mol-rxn})[\Delta_fH°(H_2O)] - (2 \text{ mol } NH_3/\text{mol-rxn})[\Delta_fH°(NH_3)] - (1 \text{ mol } CO_2/\text{mol-rxn})[\Delta_fH°(CO_2)]$

$\Delta_rH° = (1 \text{ mol } (NH_2)_2CO/\text{mol-rxn})(-333.1 \text{ kJ/mol}) + (1 \text{ mol } H_2O/\text{mol-rxn})(-241.8 \text{ kJ/mol}) - (2 \text{ mol } NH_3/\text{mol-rxn})(-45.90 \text{ kJ/mol}) - (1 \text{ mol } CO_2/\text{mol-rxn})(-393.5 \text{ kJ/mol})$

$\Delta_rH° = -89.6$ kJ/mol-rxn.

The reaction as written is exothermic, so the equilibrium will be more favorable for product formation at a low temperature. The reaction converts three moles of gaseous reactants to one mole of gaseous products; thus, high pressure will be more favorable to product formation.

2. (a) For $CH_4(g) + H_2O(g) \rightarrow CO(g) + 3\ H_2(g)$

$\Delta_rH° = (1 \text{ mol CO/mol-rxn})[\Delta_fH°(CO)] - (1 \text{ mol } CH_4/\text{mol-rxn})[\Delta_fH°(CH_4)] - (1 \text{ mol } H_2O/\text{mol-rxn})[\Delta_fH°(H_2O)]$

$\Delta_rH° = (1 \text{ mol CO/mol-rxn})(-110.5 \text{ kJ/mol}) - (1 \text{ mol } CH_4/\text{mol-rxn})(-74.87 \text{ kJ/mol}) - (1 \text{ mol } H_2O/\text{mol-rxn})(-241.8 \text{ kJ/mol}) = 206.2$ kJ/mol-rxn (endothermic)

For $CO(g) + H_2O(g) \rightarrow CO_2(g) + H_2(g)$

$\Delta_rH° = (1 \text{ mol } CO_2/\text{mol-rxn})[\Delta_fH°(CO_2)] - (1 \text{ mol CO/mol-rxn})[\Delta_fH°(CO)] - (1 \text{ mol } H_2O/\text{mol-rxn})[\Delta_fH°(H_2O)]$

$\Delta_rH° = (1 \text{ mol } CO_2/\text{mol-rxn})(-393.5 \text{ kJ/mol}) - (1 \text{ mol CO/mol-rxn})(-110.5 \text{ kJ/mol}) - (1 \text{ mol } H_2O/\text{mol-rxn})(-241.8 \text{ kJ/mol}) = -41.2$ kJ/mol-rxn (exothermic)

(b) (15 billion kg = 1.5×10^{13} g)

Add the two equations:
$CH_4(g) + 2\ H_2O(g) \rightarrow CO_2(g) + 4\ H_2(g)$

CH_4 required = $(1.5 \times 10^{13} \text{ g } NH_3)(1 \text{ mol } NH_3/17.03 \text{ g } NH_3)(3 \text{ mol } H_2/2 \text{ mol } NH_3)(1 \text{ mol } CH_4/4 \text{ mol } H_2)(16.04 \text{ g } CH_4/1 \text{ mol } CH_4) = 5.3 \times 10^{12} \text{ g } CH_4$

CO_2 formed = $(1.5 \times 10^{13} \text{ g } NH_3)(1 \text{ mol } NH_3/17.03 \text{ g } NH_3)(3 \text{ mol } H_2/2 \text{ mol } NH_3)(1 \text{ mol } CO_2/4 \text{ mol } H_2)(44.01 \text{ g } CO_2/1 \text{ mol } CO_2) = 1.5 \times 10^{13} \text{ g } CO_2$

Check Your Understanding

15.1 (a) $K = [CO]^2/[CO_2]$
(b) $K = [Cu^{2+}][NH_3]^4/[Cu(NH_3)_4{}^{2+}]$
(c) $K = [H_3O^+][CH_3CO_2{}^-]/[CH_3CO_2H]$

15.2 (a) $Q = 0.00218/0.00097 = 2.2$. The system is not at equilibrium; $Q < K$. To reach equilibrium, [isobutane] will increase and [butane] will decrease.
(b) $Q = 0.00260/0.00075 = 3.5$. The system is not at equilibrium; $Q > K$. To reach equilibrium, [butane] will increase and [isobutane] will decrease.

15.3 (a)

Equation	$C_6H_{10}I_2$ ⇌	C_6H_{10} +	I_2
Initial (M)	0.050	0	0
Change (M)	−0.035	+0.035	+0.035
Equilibrium (M)	0.015	0.035	0.035

(b) $K = (0.035)\ (0.035)/(0.015) = 0.082$

15.4

Equation	H_2 +	I_2 ⇌	2 HI
Initial (M)	6.00×10^{-3}	6.00×10^{-3}	0
Change (M)	$-x$	$-x$	$+2x$
Equilibrium (M)	$0.00600 - x$	$0.00600 - x$	$+2x$

$$K_c = 33 = \frac{(2x)^2}{(0.00600 - x)^2}$$

$x = 0.0045$ M, so $[H_2] = [I_2] = 0.0015$ M and [HI] = 0.0090 M.

15.5

Equation	$PCl_5(g)$ ⇌	$PCl_3(g)$ +	$Cl_{2(g)}$
Initial (M)	0.1000	0	0
Change (M)	$-x$	$+x$	$+x$
Equilibrium (M)	$0.1000 - x$	x	x

$K_c = [PCl_3][Cl_2]/[PCl_5]$

$33.3 = x^2/0.1000 - x$

We cannot use the simplifying assumption in this case (K is > 1 and $100 \cdot K > 0.1000$), so we must solve using the quadratic formula.

$x^2 + 33.3x - 3.33 = 0$

Using the quadratic formula, $x = 0.0997$ (the other root, $x = -33.4$, is not possible because it leads to negative concentrations).

$[PCl_3] = [Cl_2] = 0.0997$ M

$[PCl_5] = 0.1000\text{ M} - 0.0997\text{ M} = 0.0003$ M

15.6 (a) $K' = K^2 = (2.5 \times 10^{-29})^2 = 6.3 \times 10^{-58}$
(b) $K'' = 1/K^2 = 1/(6.3 \times 10^{-58}) = 1.6 \times 10^{57}$

15.7

Equation	Butane ⇌	Isobutane
Initial (M)	0.020	0.050
After adding more isobutane (M)	0.020	0.050 + 0.020
Change (M)	$+x$	$-x$
Equilibrium (M)	$0.020 + x$	$0.070 - x$

$K = (0.070 - x)/(0.020 + x)$

Solving for x gives $x = 0.0057$ M. Therefore, [isobutane] = 0.070 − 0.0057 = 0.064 M and [butane] = 0.020 + 0.0057 = 0.026 M.

Review & Check

Section 15-1

1. (c) The forward and reverse reactions occur at an equal rate.

Section 15-2

1. (b) $K = [SO_2]^2[O_2]/[SO_3]^2$

2. (b) No, it is not at equilibrium, and the reaction proceeds further to the right.

Section 15-3

1. (b) 6.1×10^{-4}

Section 15-4

1. (b) 0.011 M

Section 15-5

1. (c) $K_p = 2.7 \times 10^{33}$

Section 15-6

1. (b) shift right

2. (a) shift left

3. (a) exothermic

Applying Chemical Principles: Trivalent Carbon

1. (a) Concentration (molality) = −0.542 °C/−5.12 °C/*m* = 0.106 mol dimer/kg benzene

Amount dimer = (0.106 mol dimer/kg benzene) (0.0100 kg benzene) = 1.06×10^{-3} mol dimer

Molar mass of dimer = 0.503 g/1.06×10^{-3} mol = 475 g/mol

(b) Each molecule of the dimer that decomposes produces two monomer particles, increasing the total number of moles of particles in solution. When the mass of the dimer is divided by the moles of particles, the calculated molar mass is too low.

3. [Monomer] = 0.0045 M, [dimer] = 0.0503 M

5. (b) Triphenylmethyl radical

Study Questions

15.1 (a) $K_c = \dfrac{[H_2O]^2[O_2]}{[H_2O_2]^2}$

(b) $K_c = \dfrac{[CO_2]}{[CO][O_2]^{1/2}}$

(c) $K_c = \dfrac{[CO]^2}{[CO_2]}$

(d) $K_c = \dfrac{[CO_2]}{[CO]}$

15.3 $Q = (2.0 \times 10^{-8})^2/(0.020) = 2.0 \times 10^{-14}$
$Q < K_c$, so the reaction proceeds to the right.

15.5 $Q = 1.0 \times 10^3$, so $Q > K_c$ and the reaction is not at equilibrium. It proceeds to the left to convert products to reactants.

15.7 $K_c = 1.2$

15.9 (a) $K_c = 0.025$
(b) $K_c = 0.025$
(c) The amount of solid does not affect the equilibrium.

15.11 (a) $[COCl_2] = 0.00308$ M; $[CO] = 0.0071$ M
(b) $K_c = 140$

15.13 [isobutane] = 0.024 M; [butane] = 0.010 M

15.15 $[I_2] = 6.14 \times 10^{-3}$ M; $[I] = 4.79 \times 10^{-3}$ M

15.17 $[COBr_2] = 0.0026$ M; $[CO] = [Br_2] = 0.0224$ M
89.6% of the $COBr_2$ has decomposed.

15.19 (b)

15.21 (e) $K_2 = 1/(K_1)^2$

15.23 $K_c = 13.7$

15.25 (a) $K_c = K_p/(RT)^{\Delta n} = 0.16/[(0.08205)(298)] = 6.5 \times 10^{-3}$
(b) $\Delta n = 0$, therefore $K_c = K_p = 1.05$

15.27 (a) Equilibrium shifts to the right
(b) Equilibrium shifts to the left
(c) Equilibrium shifts to the right
(d) Equilibrium shifts to the left

15.29 Equilibrium concentrations are the same under both circumstances: [butane] = 1.1 M and [isobutane] = 2.9 M.

15.31 $K = 3.9 \times 10^{-4}$

15.33 For decomposition of $COCl_2$, $K_c = 1/(K_c$ for $COCl_2$ formation$) = 1/(6.5 \times 10^{11}) = 1.5 \times 10^{-12}$

15.35 $K_c = 3.9$

15.37 Q is less than K_c, so the system shifts to form more isobutane.

At equilibrium, [butane] = 0.86 M and [isobutane] = 2.14 M.

15.39 The second equation has been reversed and multiplied by 2.
(c) $K_2 = 1/K_1^2$

15.41 (a) No change (d) Shifts right
(b) Shifts left (e) Shifts right
(c) No change

15.43 (a) The equilibrium will shift to the left on adding more Cl_2.
(b) K_c is calculated (from the quantities of reactants and products at equilibrium) to be 0.00470. After Cl_2 is added, the concentrations are: $[PCl_5] = 0.00199$ M, $[PCl_3] = 0.00231$ M, and $[Cl_2] = 0.00403$ M.

15.45 $K_p = 0.215$

15.47 (a) Fraction dissociated = 0.15
(b) Fraction dissociated = 0.189. If the pressure decreases, the equilibrium shifts to the right, increasing the fraction of N_2O_4 dissociated.

15.49 $[NH_3] = 0.67$ M; $[N_2] = 0.57$ M; $[H_2] = 1.7$ M; $P_{total} = 180$ atm

15.51 (a) $[NH_3] = [H_2S] = 0.013$ M
(b) $[NH_3] = 0.027$ M and $[H_2S] = 0.0067$ M

15.53 $P(NO_2) = 0.066$ atm and $P(N_2O_4) = 0.066$ atm; $P(\text{total}) = 0.16$ atm

15.55 (a) $K_p = K_c = 56$. Because 2 mol of reactant gases gives 2 mol of product gases, Δn does not change and $K_p = K_c$ (◀ page 560).
(b) Total pressure before reaction is 0.52 atm. After reaction the total pressure is the same because the amount of gas present has not changed.
(c) After reaction, at equilibrium, $P(H_2) = P(I_2) = 0.052$ atm and $P(HI) = 0.42$ atm.

15.57 $P(CO) = 0.0010$ atm

15.59 3.9×10^{17} O atoms

15.61 Glycerin concentration should be 1.7 M

15.63 (a) $K_p = 0.20$
(b) When initial $[N_2O_4] = 1.00$ atm, the equilibrium pressures are $[N_2O_4] = 0.80$ atm and $[NO_2] = 0.40$ atm. When initial $[N_2O_4] = 0.10$ atm, the equilibrium pressures are $[N_2O_4] = 0.050$ atm and $[NO_2] = 0.10$ atm. The percent dissociation is now 50.%. This is in accord with Le Chatelier's principle: If the initial pressure of the reactant is smaller, the equilibrium shifts to the right, increasing the fraction of the reactant dissociated. [This might be clearer if you imagine beginning with the equilibrium system in the case when the initial pressure of N_2O_4 was 1.00 atm and then increasing the volume tenfold (obtaining the same equilibrium system as starting with 0.10 atm N_2O_4). Le Chatelier's principle predicts a shift in the direction that has a greater number of gas molecules. See also Question 15.45.]

15.65 (a) The flask containing $(H_3N)B(CH_3)_3$ will have the largest partial pressure of $B(CH_3)_3$.
(b) $P[B(CH_3)_3] = P(NH_3) = 0.23$ and $P[(H_3N)B(CH_3)_3] = 0.012$ atm
$P_{total} = 0.48$ atm
Percent dissociation = 95%

15.67 (a) As more KSCN is added, Le Chatelier's principle predicts more of the red complex ion $[Fe(H_2O)_5(SCN)]^+$ will form.
(b) Adding Ag^+ ions leads to a precipitate of AgSCN, thus removing SCN^- ions from solution. The equilibrium shifts left, dropping the concentration of the red complex ion.

15.69 (a) False. The magnitude of K is always dependent on temperature.
(b) True
(c) False. The equilibrium constant for a reaction is the reciprocal of the value of K for its reverse.
(d) True
(e) False. $\Delta n = 1$, so $K_p = K_c(RT)$

15.71 (a) Product-favored, $K >> 1$
(b) Reactant-favored, $K << 1$
(c) Product-favored, $K >> 1$

15.73 Begin with an equilibrium system containing $^{14}N_2$, H_2, and $^{14}NH_3$. Introduce some $^{15}N_2$ and allow the system to equilibrate. The presence of $^{15}NH_3$ indicates that the forward reaction has occurred. In addition, the presence of $^{15}N^{14}N$ indicates that the reverse reaction has occurred. Further evidence of the reverse reaction occurring could be obtained by carrying out another trial in which $^{15}NH_3$ is added to the initial equilibrium mixture. The presence of $^{15}N^{14}N$ or $^{15}N_2$ indicates that the reverse reaction is occurring. (A similar set of experiments could be run using ^2H instead of ^{15}N.)

15.75 $K_p = 3.2 \times 10^{-7}$

Chapter 16

Case Study

Would You Like Some Belladonna Juice in Your Drink?

1. (100. mg $C_{17}H_{23}NO_3$)(1 g/1000 mg)(1 mol $C_{17}H_{23}NO_3$/289.4 g $C_{17}H_{23}NO_3$) = 3.46×10^{-4} mol $C_{17}H_{23}NO_3$
2. The proton will attach to the N.
3. The pK_a of protonated atropine (4.35) is less than that of the ammonium (pK_a = 9.26), methylammonium (pK_a = 10.70), and anilinium (pK_a = 4.60) ions.

Check Your Understanding

16.1 $[H_3O^+] = 4.0 \times 10^{-3}$ M; $[OH^-] = K_w/[H_3O^+] = 2.5 \times 10^{-12}$ M

16.2 (a) pH = 7
(b) pH < 7 (NH_4^+ is an acid)
(c) pH < 7 $[Al(H_2O)_6]^{3+}$ is an acid
(d) pH > 7 (HPO_4^{2-} is a stronger base than it is an acid)

16.3 (a) NH_4^+ is a stronger acid than HCO_3^-. CO_3^{2-}, the conjugate base of HCO_3^-, is a stronger base than NH_3, the conjugate base of NH_4^+.
(b) Reactant-favored; the reactants are the weaker acid and base.
(c) Reactant-favored; the reactants are the weaker acid and base, so reaction lies to the left.

16.4 From the pH, we can calculate $[H_3O^+] = 1.9 \times 10^{-3}$ M. Also, [butanoate$^-$] = $[H_3O^+] = 1.9 \times 10^{-3}$ M. Use these values along with [butanoic acid] to calculate K_a.

$K_a = [1.9 \times 10^{-3}]\,[1.9 \times 10^{-3}]/(0.055 - 1.9 \times 10^{-3}) = 6.8 \times 10^{-5}$

16.5 $K_a = 1.8 \times 10^{-5} = [x][x]/(0.10 - x)$
$x = [H_3O^+] = [CH_3CO_2^-] = 1.3 \times 10^{-3}$ M; $[CH_3CO_2H] = 0.099$ M; pH = 2.87

16.6 $HF(aq) + H_2O(\ell) \rightleftharpoons H_3O^+(aq) + F^-(aq)$
$K_a = 7.2 \times 10^{-4} = [x][x]/(0.00150 - x)$

The x in the denominator cannot be dropped. This equation must be solved with the quadratic formula or by successive approximations. Because this problem follows the section dealing with the method of successive approximations, that method will be used here.

$7.2 \times 10^{-4} = x^2/(0.00150)$; $x = 1.0 \times 10^{-3}$

$7.2 \times 10^{-4} = x^2/(0.00150 - 1.0 \times 10^{-3})$; $x = 6.0 \times 10^{-4}$

$7.2 \times 10^{-4} = x^2/(0.00150 - 6.0 \times 10^{-4})$; $x = 8.0 \times 10^{-4}$

$7.2 \times 10^{-4} = x^2/(0.00150 - 8.0 \times 10^{-4})$; $x = 7.1 \times 10^{-4}$

$7.2 \times 10^{-4} = x^2/(0.00150 - 7.1 \times 10^{-4})$; $x = 7.5 \times 10^{-4}$

$7.2 \times 10^{-4} = x^2/(0.00150 - 7.5 \times 10^{-4})$; $x = 7.3 \times 10^{-4}$

$7.2 \times 10^{-4} = x^2/(0.00150 - 7.3 \times 10^{-4})$; $x = 7.4 \times 10^{-4}$

$7.2 \times 10^{-4} = x^2/(0.00150 - 7.4 \times 10^{-4})$; $x = 7.4 \times 10^{-4}$

The result has converged to two significant figures.

$[H_3O^+] = [F^-] = 7.4 \times 10^{-4}$ M

$[HF] = 0.00150$ M $- 7.4\ 10^{-4}$ M $= 7.6 \times 10^{-4}$ M

pH = 3.13

16.7 $OCl^-(aq) + H_2O(\ell) \rightleftharpoons HOCl(aq) + OH^-(aq)$
$K_b = 2.9 \times 10^{-7} = [x][x]/(0.015 - x)$
$x = [OH^-] = [HOCl] = 6.6 \times 10^{-5}$ M
pOH = 4.18; pH = 9.82

16.8 Equivalent amounts of acid and base react to form water, $CH_3CO_2^-$ and Na^+. Acetate ion hydrolyzes to a small extent, giving CH_3CO_2H and OH^-. We need to determine $[CH_3CO_2^-]$ and then solve a weak base equilibrium problem to determine $[OH^-]$.

Amount $CH_3CO_2^-$ = moles base = 0.12 mol/L × 0.015 L = 1.8×10^{-3} mol

Total volume = 0.030 L, so $[CH_3CO_2^-] = (1.8 \times 10^{-3}\ \text{mol})/0.030\ \text{L} = 0.060$ M

$CH_3CO_2^-(aq) + H_2O(\ell) \rightleftharpoons CH_3CO_2H(aq) + OH^-(aq)$

$K_b = 5.6 \times 10^{-10} = [x][x]/(0.060 - x)$

$x = [OH^-] = [CH_3CO_2H] = 5.8 \times 10^{-6}$ M

pOH = 5.24; pH = 8.76

16.9 $H_2C_2O_4(aq) + H_2O(\ell) \rightleftharpoons H_3O^+(aq) + HC_2O_4^-(aq)$
$K_{a1} = 5.9 \times 10^{-2} = [x][x]/(0.10 - x)$

The x in the denominator cannot be dropped. This equation must be solved with the quadratic formula or by successive approximations.

$x = [H_3O^+] = [HC_2O_4^-] = 5.3 \times 10^{-2}$ M

pH = 1.28

$K_{a2} = [H_3O^+][C_2O_4^{2-}]/[HC_2O_4^-]$; because $[H_3O^+] = [HC_2O_4^-]$

$[C_2O_4^{2-}] = K_{a2} = 6.4 \times 10^{-5}$ M

Review & Check

Section 16-1

1. (c) amphiprotic
2. (b) base
3. (b) acid = HNO_3 and conjugate base = NO_3^-
   (a) base = NH_3 and conjugate acid = NH_4^+
4. (c) HF/F^- and $CH_3CO_2H/CH_3CO_2^-$

Section 16-2

1. (b) 11.08
2. (a) 4.8×10^{-5} M
3. (d) 1.4×10^{-4} M

Section 16-3

1. (a) HF
2. (c) HCN
3. (a) $C_6H_5CO_2H$
4. (b) 9.25
5. (c) 10.15

Section 16-4

1. (b) decrease
2. (a) increase

Section 16-5

1. (b) product-favored
2. (b) right

Section 16-6

1. (a) acidic
2. (a) acidic
3. (b) basic

Section 16-7

1. (b) 6.3×10^{-6} M
2. (a) 2.3×10^{-5}
3. (b) pH = 8.37, $[Na^+]$ = 0.10 M, $[CHO_2^-]$ = 0.10 M, $[OH^-] = 2.4 \times 10^{-6}$ M
4. (c) greater than 7

Section 16-8

1. (c) 10.16

Section 16-9

1. (a) H_2SeO_4
2. (b) $[Fe(H_2O)_6]^{3+}$
3. (a) HOCl

Section 16-10

1. (b) BCl_3
2. (c) Brønsted base and (d) Lewis base

Applying Chemical Principles: The Leveling Effect, Nonaqueous Solvents, and Superacids

1. $HClO_4$ ($K = 5 \times 10^{-6}$) > H_2SO_4 ($K = 2 \times 10^{-7}$) > HCl ($K = 2 \times 10^{-9}$)

3. $NH_2^-(aq) + H_2O(\ell) \rightleftharpoons NH_3(aq) + OH^-(aq)$
   The reaction is product-favored at equilibrium.

5. (a) $2\,NH_3 \rightleftharpoons NH_4^+ + NH_2^-$
   (b) The strongest acid is NH_4^+; the strongest base is NH_2^-.
   (c) HCl is a stronger acid than NH_4^+, so HCl will be completely ionized. The solution will be a strong conductor.
   (d) $O^{2-} + NH_3 \rightleftharpoons OH^- + NH_2^-$
   The reaction is product-favored at equilibrium.

Study Questions

16.1 (a) CN^-, cyanide ion
(b) SO_4^{2-}, sulfate ion
(c) F^-, fluoride ion

16.3 (a) $H_3O^+(aq) + NO_3^-(aq)$; $H_3O^+(aq)$ is the conjugate acid of H_2O, and $NO_3^-(aq)$ is the conjugate base of HNO_3.
(b) $H_3O^+(aq) + SO_4^{2-}(aq)$; $H_3O^+(aq)$ is the conjugate acid of H_2O, and $SO_4^{2-}(aq)$ is the conjugate base of HSO_4^-.
(c) H_2O + HF; H_2O is the conjugate base of H_3O^+, and HF is the conjugate acid of F^-.

16.5 Brønsted acid: $HC_2O_4^-(aq) + H_2O(\ell) \rightleftharpoons H_3O^+(aq) + C_2O_4^{2-}(aq)$

Brønsted base: $HC_2O_4^-(aq) + H_2O(\ell) \rightleftharpoons H_2C_2O_4(aq) + OH^-(aq)$

16.7

	Acid (A)	Base (B)	Conjugate Base of A	Conjugate Acid of B
(a)	HCO_2H	H_2O	HCO_2^-	H_3O^+
(b)	H_2S	NH_3	HS^-	NH_4^+
(c)	HSO_4^-	OH^-	SO_4^{2-}	H_2O

16.9 $[H_3O^+] = 1.8 \times 10^{-4}$ M; acidic

16.11 HCl is a strong acid, so $[H_3O^+]$ = concentration of the acid. $[H_3O^+]$ = 0.0075 M and $[OH^-] = 1.3 \times 10^{-12}$ M. pH = 2.12.

16.13 $Ba(OH)_2$ is a strong base, so $[OH^-] = 2 \times$ concentration of the base.

$[OH^-] = 3.0 \times 10^{-3}$ M; pOH = 2.52; and pH = 11.48

16.15 (a) The strongest acid is HCO_2H (largest K_a) and the weakest acid is C_6H_5OH (smallest K_a).
(b) The strongest acid (HCO_2H) has the weakest conjugate base.
(c) The weakest acid (C_6H_5OH) has the strongest conjugate base.

16.17 (c) HClO, the weakest acid in this list (Table 16.2), has the strongest conjugate base.

16.19 (a) HCO_3^-. Decide based on the base strength (Table 16.2). The strongest base of the three listed examples has the weakest conjugate acid.

16.21 $CO_3^{2-}(aq) + H_2O(\ell) \rightleftharpoons HCO_3^-(aq) + OH^-(aq)$

16.23 Highest pH, Na_2S; lowest pH, $AlCl_3$ (which gives the weak acid $[Al(H_2O)_6]^{3+}$ in solution)

16.25 $pK_a = 4.19$

16.27 $K_a = 3.0 \times 10^{-10}$; in Table 16.2, this acid falls between hexaaquairon(II) ion and the hydrogen carbonate ion.

16.29 2-Chlorobenzoic acid is the stronger acid; it has the smaller pK_a value.

16.31 $K_b = 7.1 \times 10^{-12}$

16.33 $K_b = 6.3 \times 10^{-5}$

16.35 $CH_3CO_2H(aq) + HCO_3^-(aq) \rightleftharpoons CH_3CO_2^-(aq) + H_2CO_3(aq)$

Equilibrium lies predominantly to the right because CH_3CO_2H is a stronger acid than H_2CO_3.

16.37 (a) Left; NH_3 and HBr are the stronger base and acid, respectively.
(b) Left; PO_4^{3-} and CH_3CO_2H are the stronger base and acid, respectively.
(c) Right; $[Fe(H_2O)_6]^{3+}$ and HCO_3^- are the stronger acid and base, respectively.

16.39 (a) $OH^-(aq) + HPO_4^{2-}(aq) \rightleftharpoons H_2O(\ell) + PO_4^{3-}(aq)$
(b) OH^- is a stronger base than PO_4^{3-}, so the equilibrium will lie to the right.

16.41 (a) $CH_3CO_2H(aq) + HPO_4^{2-}(aq) \rightleftharpoons CH_3CO_2^-(aq) + H_2PO_4^-(aq)$
(b) CH_3CO_2H is a stronger acid than $H_2PO_4^-$, so the equilibrium will lie to the right.

16.43 (a) 2.1×10^{-3} M; (b) $K_a = 3.5 \times 10^{-4}$

16.45 $K_b = 6.6 \times 10^{-9}$

16.47 (a) $[H_3O^+] = 1.6 \times 10^{-4}$ M
(b) Moderately weak; $K_a = 1.1 \times 10^{-5}$

16.49 $[CH_3CO_2^-] = [H_3O^+] = 1.9 \times 10^{-3}$ M and $[CH_3CO_2H] = 0.20$ M

16.51 $[H_3O^+] = [CN^-] = 3.2 \times 10^{-6}$ M; [HCN] = 0.025 M; pH = 5.50

16.53 $[NH_4^+] = [OH^-] = 1.6 \times 10^{-3}$ M; $[NH_3]$ = 0.15 M; pH = 11.22

16.55 $[OH^-] = 0.010$ M; pH = 12.01; pOH = 1.99

16.57 pH = 3.25

16.59 $[H_3O^+] = 1.1 \times 10^{-5}$ M; pH = 4.98

16.61 $[HCN] = [OH^-] = 3.3 \times 10^{-3}$ M; $[H_3O^+] = 3.0 \times 10^{-12}$ M; $[Na^+] = 0.441$ M

16.63 $[H_3O^+] = 1.5 \times 10^{-9}$ M; pH = 8.81

16.65 (a) The reaction produces acetate ion, the conjugate base of acetic acid. The solution is weakly basic. pH is greater than 7.
(b) The reaction produces NH_4^+, the conjugate acid of NH_3. The solution is weakly acidic. pH is less than 7.
(c) The reaction mixes equal molar amounts of strong base and strong acid. The solution will be neutral. pH will be 7.

16.67 $H_2C_2O_4(aq) + H_2O(\ell) \rightleftharpoons HC_2O_4^-(aq) + H_3O^+(aq)$

$HC_2O_4^-(aq) + H_2O(\ell) \rightleftharpoons C_2O_4^{2-}(aq) + H_3O^+(aq)$

16.69 $H_2C_2O_4(aq) + H_2O(\ell) \rightleftharpoons HC_2O_4^-(aq) + H_3O^+(aq)$ $\quad K_{a1} = 5.2 \times 10^{-2}$

$HC_2O_4^-(aq) + H_2O(\ell) \rightleftharpoons H_2C_2O_4(aq) + OH^-(aq)$ $\quad K_{b2} = 1.9 \times 10^{-13}$

Sum: $2\ H_2O(\ell) \rightleftharpoons H_3O^+(aq) + OH^-(aq)$ $\quad K_w = K_{a1} \times K_{b2} = 1.0 \times 10^{-14}$

16.71 (a) pH = 1.17; (b) $[SO_3^{2-}] = 6.2 \times 10^{-8}$ M

16.73 (a) $[OH^-] = [N_2H_5^+] = 9.2 \times 10^{-5}$ M; $[N_2H_6^{2+}] = 8.9 \times 10^{-16}$ M
(b) pH = 9.96

16.75 HOCN should be a stronger acid than HCN because the H atom in HOCN is attached to the more electronegative O atom. The electron attachment enthalpy of OCN is thus more negative than that of CN, which stabilizes the conjugate base that forms and makes the ionization of HOCN more product-favored.

16.77 The S atom is surrounded by four highly electronegative O atoms. These help stabilize the conjugate base that needs to form so that the negative charge is more readily accepted.

16.79 (a) Lewis base
(b) Lewis acid
(c) Lewis base (owing to lone pair of electrons on the N atom)

16.81 CO is a Lewis base in its reactions with transition metal atoms. It donates a lone pair of electrons on the C atom.

16.83 pH = 2.671

16.85 Both $Ba(OH)_2$ and $Sr(OH)_2$ dissolve completely in water to provide M^{2+} and OH^- ions. 2.50 g $Sr(OH)_2$ in 1.00 L of water gives $[Sr^{2+}] = 0.021$ M and $[OH^-] = 0.041$ M. The concentration of OH^- is reflected in a pH of 12.61.

16.87 $H_2S(aq) + CH_3CO_2^-(aq) \rightleftharpoons CH_3CO_2H(aq) + HS^-(aq)$

The equilibrium lies to the left and favors the reactants.

16.89 $[X^-] = [H_3O^+] = 3.0 \times 10^{-3}$ M; $[HX] = 0.007$ M; pH = 2.52

16.91 $K_a = 1.4 \times 10^{-5}$; $pK_a = 4.86$

16.93 pH = 5.84

16.95 (a) Ethylamine is a stronger base than ethanolamine. (b) For ethylamine, the pH of the solution is 11.82.

16.97 pH = 7.66

16.99 Acidic: $NaHSO_4$, NH_4Br, $FeCl_3$
Neutral: $KClO_4$, $NaNO_3$, LiBr
Basic: Na_2CO_3, $(NH_4)_2S$, Na_2HPO_4
Highest pH: $(NH_4)_2S$, lowest pH: $NaHSO_4$

16.101 $K_{net} = K_{a1} \times K_{a2} = 3.8 \times 10^{-6}$

16.103 For the reaction $HCO_2H(aq) + OH^-(aq) \rightarrow H_2O(\ell) + HCO_2^-(aq)$, $K_{net} = K_a$ (for HCO_2H) $\times [1/K_w] = 1.8 \times 10^{10}$

16.105 To double the percent ionization, you must dilute 100 mL of solution to 400 mL.

16.107 $H_2O > H_2C_2O_4 > HC_2O_4^- = H_3O^+ > C_2O_4^{2-} > OH^-$

16.109 Measure the pH of 0.1 M solutions of the three bases. The solution containing the strongest base will have the highest pH. The solution having the weakest base will have the lowest pH.

16.111 The possible cation–anion combinations are NaCl (neutral), NaOH (basic), NH_4Cl (acidic), NH_4OH (basic), HCl (acidic), and H_2O (neutral).
A = H^+ solution; B = NH_4^+ solution; C = Na^+ solution; Y = Cl^- solution; Z = OH^- solution

16.113 $K_a = 3.0 \times 10^{-5}$

16.115 (a) Aniline is both a Brønsted and a Lewis base. As a proton acceptor it gives $C_6H_5NH_3^+$. The N atom can also donate an electron pair to give a Lewis acid–base adduct, $F_3B \leftarrow NH_2C_6H_5$.
(b) pH = 7.97

16.117 Water can both accept a proton (a Brønsted base) and donate a lone pair (a Lewis base). Water can also donate a proton (Brønsted acid), but it cannot accept a pair of electrons (and act as a Lewis acid).

16.119 (a) HOCl is the strongest acid (smallest pK_a and largest K_a), and HOI is the weakest acid.
(b) Cl is more electronegative than Br or I, so the OCl^- anion is more stable than the other two oxoanions.

16.121 (a) $HClO_4 + H_2SO_4 \rightleftharpoons ClO_4^- + H_3SO_4^+$
(b) The O atoms on sulfuric acid have lone pairs of electrons that can be used to bind to an H^+ ion.

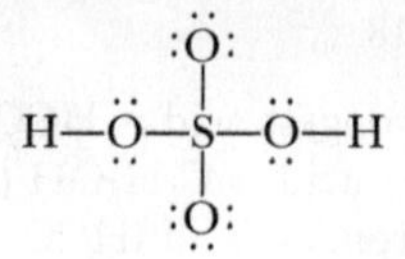

16.123 (a) 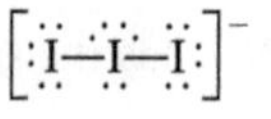

(b) $I^-(aq)$ [Lewis base] + $I_2(aq)$ [Lewis acid] $\rightarrow I_3^-(aq)$

16.125 (a) For the weak acid HA, the concentrations at equilibrium are $[HA] = C_0 - \alpha C_0$, $[H_3O^+] = [A^-] = \alpha C_0$. Putting these into the usual expression for K_a we have $K_a = \alpha^2 C_0/(1-\alpha)$.
(b) For 0.10 M NH_4^+, $\alpha = 7.5 \times 10^{-5}$ (reflecting the fact that NH_4^+ is a much weaker acid than acetic acid).

16.127 (a) Add the three equations.

$$NH_4^+(aq) + H_2O(\ell) \rightleftharpoons NH_3(aq) + H_3O^+(aq) \quad K_1 = K_w/K_b$$

$$CN^-(aq) + H_2O(\ell) \rightleftharpoons HCN(aq) + OH^-(aq) \quad K_2 = K_w/K_a$$

$$H_3O^+(aq) + OH^-(aq) \rightleftharpoons 2\,H_2O(\ell) \quad K_3 = 1/K_w$$

$$NH_4^+(aq) + CN^-(aq) \rightleftharpoons NH_3(aq) + HCN(aq) \quad K_{net} = K_1K_2K_3 = K_w/K_aK_b$$

(b) The salts NH_4CN, $NH_4CH_3CO_2$, and NH_4F have K_{net} values of 1.4, 3.1×10^{-5}, and 7.7×10^{-7}, respectively. Only in the case of NH_4CN is the base (the cyanide ion) strong enough to remove a proton from the ammonium ion and produce a significant concentration of products.
(c) NH_4CN: basic, K_b of $CN^- > K_a$ of NH_4^+
$NH_4CH_3CO_2$: neutral, K_b of $CH_3CO_2^- = K_a$ of NH_4^+
NH_4F: acidic, K_b of F^- is less than K_a of NH_4^+

Chapter 17

Case Study

Take a Deep Breath

1. pH = pK_a + log$[HPO_4^{2-}]/[H_2PO_4^-]$
7.4 = 7.20 + log$[HPO_4^{2-}]/[H_2PO_4^-]$
$[HPO_4^{2-}]/[H_2PO_4^-] = 1.6$
2. Assign $x = [HPO_4^{2-}]$, then $[H_2PO_4^-] = (0.020 - x)$
$1.6 = x/(0.020 - x)$; $x = 0.012$
$[HPO_4^{2-}] = x = 0.012$ mol/L
$[H_2PO_4^-] = 0.020 - x = 0.008$ mol/L

Check Your Understanding

17.1 pH of 0.30 M HCO_2H:

$K_a = [H_3O^+][HCO_2^-]/[HCO_2H]$

$1.8 \times 10^{-4} = [x][x]/[0.30 - x]$

$x = 7.3 \times 10^{-3}$ M; pH = 2.13

pH of 0.30 M formic acid + 0.10 M $NaHCO_2$

$K_a = [H_3O^+][HCO_2^-]/[HCO_2H]$

$1.8 \times 10^{-4} = [x][0.10 + x]/(0.30 - x)$

$x = 5.4 \times 10^{-4}$ M; pH = 3.27

17.2

Equation	$HCO_2H + H_2O \rightleftharpoons$	H_3O^+ +	HCO_2^-
Initial (M)	0.50	0	0.70
Change (M)	$-x$	$+x$	$+x$
Equilibrium (M)	$0.50 - x$	x	$0.70 + x$

$K_a = 1.8 \times 10^{-4} = (x)(0.70 + x)/(0.50 - x)$

The value of x will be insignificant compared to 0.50 M and 0.70 M.

$1.8 \times 10^{-4} = (x)(0.70)/(0.50)$

$x = [H_3O^+] = 1.3 \times 10^{-4}$ M

$pH = -\log[H_3O^+] = 3.89$

17.3 (15.0 g $NaHCO_3$)(1 mol/84.01 g) = 0.179 mol $NaHCO_3$, and (18.0 g Na_2CO_3)(1 mol/106.0 g) = 0.170 mol Na_2CO_3

$pH = pK_a + \log \{[base]/[acid]\}$

$pH = -\log (4.8 \times 10^{-11}) + \log \{[0.170]/[0.179]\}$

pH = 10.32 − 0.02 = 10.30

17.4 $pH = pK_a + \log \{[base]/[acid]\}$

$5.00 = -\log (1.8 \times 10^{-5}) + \log \{[base]/[acid]\}$

$5.00 = 4.74 + \log \{[base]/[acid]\}$

[base]/[acid] = 1.8

To prepare this buffer solution, the ratio [base]/[acid] must equal 1.8. For example, you can dissolve 1.8 mol (148 g) of $NaCH_3CO_2$ and 1.0 mol (60.05 g) of CH_3CO_2H in some amount of water.

17.5 Initial pH (before adding acid):

$pH = pK_a + \log \{[base]/[acid]\}$
$= -\log (1.8 \times 10^{-4}) + \log \{[0.70]/[0.50]\}$
$= 3.74 + 0.15 = 3.89$

After adding acid, the added HCl will react with the weak base (formate ion) and form more formic acid. The net effect is to change the ratio of [base]/[acid] in the buffer solution.

Initial amount HCO_2H = 0.50 mol/L × 0.500 L = 0.25 mol

Initial amount HCO_2^- = 0.70 mol/L × 0.50 L = 0.35 mol

Amount HCl added = 1.0 mol/L × 0.010 L = 0.010 mol

Amount HCO_2H after HCl addition = 0.25 mol + 0.010 mol = 0.26 mol

Amount HCO_2^- after HCl addition = 0.35 mol − 0.010 mol = 0.34 mol

$pH = pK_a + \log \{[base]/[acid]\}$

$pH = -\log (1.8 \times 10^{-4}) + \log \{[0.34]/[0.26]\}$

pH = 3.74 + 0.12 = 3.86

17.6 35.0 mL base will partially neutralize the acid.

Initial amount CH_3CO_2H = (0.100 mol/L)(0.1000 L) = 0.0100 mol

Amount NaOH added = (0.100 mol/L)(0.0350 L) = 0.00350 mol

Amount CH_3CO_2H after reaction = 0.0100 − 0.00350 = 0.0065 mol

Amount $CH_3CO_2^-$ after reaction = 0.00350 mol

$[CH_3CO_2H]$ after reaction = 0.0065 mol/0.1350 L = 0.048 M

$[CH_3CO_2^-]$ after reaction = 0.00350 mol/0.1350 L = 0.0259 M

$K_a = [H_3O^+][CH_3CO_2^-]/[CH_3CO_2H]$

$1.8 \times 10^{-5} = [x][0.0259 + x]/[0.048 - x]$

$x = [H_3O^+] = 3.3 \times 10^{-5}$ M; pH = 4.48

17.7 75.0 mL acid will partially neutralize the base.

Initial amount NH_3 = (0.100 mol/L)(0.1000 L) = 0.0100 mol

Amount HCl added = (0.100 mol/L)(0.0750 L) = 0.00750 mol

Amount NH_3 after reaction = 0.0100 − 0.00750 = 0.0025 mol

Amount NH_4^+ after reaction = 0.00750 mol

Solve using the Henderson–Hasselbalch equation; use K_a for the weak acid NH_4^+:

$pH = pK_a + \log \{[base]/[acid]\}$

$pH = -\log (5.6 \times 10^{-10}) + \log \{[0.0025]/[0.00750]\}$

pH = 9.25 − 0.48 = 8.77

17.8 $BaF_2(s) \rightleftharpoons Ba^{2+}(aq) + 2\ F^-(aq)$

$[F^-] = 2[Ba^{2+}] = 2(3.6 \times 10^{-3}\ M) = 7.2 \times 10^{-3}$ M

$K_{sp} = [Ba^{2+}][F^-]^2 = (3.6 \times 10^{-3})(7.2 \times 10^{-3})^2 = 1.9 \times 10^{-7}$

17.9 $AgCN(s) \rightleftharpoons Ag^+(aq) + CN^-(aq)$

$K_{sp} = [Ag^+][CN^-]$

Let x = solubility of AgCN in mol/L

$6.0 \times 10^{-17} = x^2$

$x = 7.7 \times 10^{-9}$ mol/L

(7.7×10^{-9} mol AgCN/L)(133.9 g AgCN/1 mol AgCN) = 1.0×10^{-6} g/L

17.10 $Ca(OH)_2(s) \rightleftharpoons Ca^{2+}(aq) + 2\ OH^-(aq)$

$K_{sp} = [Ca^{2+}][OH^-]^2$; $K_{sp} = 5.5 \times 10^{-5}$

$5.5 \times 10^{-5} = [x][2x]^2$ (where x = solubility in mol/L)

$x = 2.4 \times 10^{-2}$ mol/L

Solubility in g/L = (2.4×10^{-2} mol/L)(74.1 g/mol) = 1.8 g/L

17.11 (a) In pure water:
$K_{sp} = [Ba^{2+}][SO_4^{2-}]$; $1.1 \times 10^{-10} = [x][x]$;
$x = 1.0 \times 10^{-5}$ mol/L
(b) In 0.010 M $Ba(NO_3)_2$, which furnishes 0.010 M Ba^{2+} in solution:
$K_{sp} = [Ba^{2+}][SO_4^{2-}]$
$1.1 \times 10^{-10} = [0.010 + x][x]$
$x = 1.1 \times 10^{-8}$ mol/L

17.12 (a) In pure water:
$K_{sp} = [Zn^{2+}][CN^-]^2$; $8.0 \times 10^{-12} = [x][2x]^2 = 4x^3$
Solubility $= x = 1.3 \times 10^{-4}$ mol/L
(b) In 0.10 M $Zn(NO_3)_2$, which furnishes 0.10 M Zn^{2+} in solution:
$K_{sp} = [Zn^{2+}][CN^-]^2$; $8.0 \times 10^{-12} = [0.10 + x][2x]^2$
Solubility $= x = 4.5 \times 10^{-6}$ mol/L

17.13 When $[Pb^{2+}] = 1.1 \times 10^{-3}$ M, $[I^-] = 2.2 \times 10^{-3}$ M.
$Q = [Pb^{2+}][I^-]^2 = [1.1 \times 10^{-3}][2.2 \times 10^{-3}]^2 = 5.3 \times 10^{-9}$
This value is less than K_{sp}, which means that the system has not yet reached equilibrium and more PbI_2 will dissolve.

17.14 $K_{sp} = [Pb^{2+}][I^-]^2$. Let x be the concentration of I^- required at equilibrium.
$9.8 \times 10^{-9} = [0.050][x]^2$
$x = [I^-] = 4.4 \times 10^{-4}$ mol/L. A concentration greater than this value will result in precipitation of PbI_2.
Let x be the concentration of Pb^{2+} in solution, in equilibrium with 0.0015 M I^-.
$9.8 \times 10^{-9} = [x][1.5 \times 10^{-3}]^2$
$x = [Pb^{2+}] = 4.4 \times 10^{-3}$ M

17.15 First, determine the concentrations of Ag^+ and Cl^-; then calculate Q, and see whether it is greater than or less than K_{sp}. Concentrations are calculated using the final volume, 105.0 mL, in the equation $C_{dil} \times V_{dil} = C_{conc} \times V_{conc}$.
$[Ag^+](0.1050 \text{ L}) = (0.0010 \text{ mol/L})(0.1000 \text{ L})$
$[Ag^+] = 9.5 \times 10^{-4}$ M
$[Cl^-](0.1050 \text{ L}) = (0.025 \text{ M})(0.0050 \text{ L})$
$[Cl^-] = 1.2 \times 10^{-3}$ M
$Q = [Ag^+][Cl^-] = [9.5 \times 10^{-4}][1.2 \times 10^{-3}] = 1.1 \times 10^{-6}$
Because $Q > K_{sp}$, precipitation occurs.

17.16

Equation	$[Ag(NH_3)_2]^+ \rightleftharpoons$	Ag^+	$+ 2\ NH_3$
Initial (M)	0.0050	0	$1.00 - 2(0.0050)$
Change	$-x$	$+x$	$+2x$
Equilibrium (M)	$0.0050 - x$	x	$0.99 + 2x$

$K = 1/K_f = 1/1.1 \times 10^7 = [x][0.99]^2/0.0050$
$x = [Ag^+] = 4.6 \times 10^{-10}$ mol/L

17.17 $Cu(OH)_2(s) \rightleftharpoons Cu^{2+}(aq) + 2\ OH^-(aq)$
$K_{sp} = [Cu^{2+}][OH^-]^2$
$Cu^{2+}(aq) + 4\ NH_3(aq) \rightleftharpoons [Cu(NH_3)_4]^{2+}(aq)$
$K_{form} = [Cu(NH_3)_4{}^{2+}]/[Cu^{2+}][NH_3]^4$
Net: $Cu(OH)_2(s) + 4\ NH_3(aq) \rightleftharpoons Cu(NH_3)_4{}^{2+}(aq) + 2\ OH^-(aq)$
$K_{net} = K_{sp} \times K_f = (2.2 \times 10^{-20})(2.1 \times 10^{13}) = 4.6 \times 10^{-7}$

Review & Check

Section 17-1

1. (b) 5.05

Section 17-2

1. (a) 0.20 M KCH_3CO_2 and 0.10 M CH_3CO_2H
2. (d) 18 mL
3. (b) 9.25
4. (c) 1/1.8

Section 17-3

1. (b) 1.48
2. (d) 11.29
3. (c) methyl red

Section 17-4

1. (b) $K_{sp} = [Ag^+]^2[CO_3^{2-}]$
2. (a) AgCl
(b) $Ca(OH)_2$
(c) $Ca(OH)_2$
3. (b) 1.6×10^{-4} M
4. (a) 1.0×10^{-7} M
5. (a) $FeCO_3$

Section 17-5

1. (b) no

Section 17-6

1. (b) 1.9×10^{-36} M

Section 17-7

1. (c) 1.1×10^5

Applying Chemical Principles: Everything That Glitters . . .

1. 2.9×10^2 mL
3. $[Au^+] = 1.1 \times 10^{-38}$ M. Yes, the conclusion is reasonable; less than one free Au^+ ion is present per liter of solution.
5. $2\ NaAu(CN)_2(aq) + Zn(s) \rightarrow 2\ Au(s) + Na_2Zn(CN)_4(aq)$

Study Questions

17.1 (a) Decrease pH; (b) increase pH; (c) no change in pH

17.3 pH = 9.25

17.5 pH = 4.38

17.7 pH = 9.12; pH of buffer is lower than the pH of the original solution of NH_3 (pH = 11.17).

17.9 4.7 g

17.11 pH = 4.92

17.13 $[CH_3CO_2H]/[CH_3CO_2^-] = 0.56$

17.15 (a) pH = 3.59; (b) $[HCO_2H]/[HCO_2^-] = 0.45$

17.17 (b) $NH_3 + NH_4Cl$

17.19 The buffer must have a ratio of 0.51 mol NaH_2PO_4 to 1 mol Na_2HPO_4. For example, dissolve 0.51 mol NaH_2PO_4 (61 g) and 1.0 mol Na_2HPO_4 (140 g) in some amount of water.

17.21 46 mL of 1.0 M NaOH

17.23 (a) pH = 4.95; (b) pH = 5.05

17.25 (a) pH = 9.55; (b) pH = 9.50

17.27 (a) Original pH = 5.62
(b) $[Na^+] = 0.0323$ M, $[OH^-] = 1.5 \times 10^{-3}$ M, $[H_3O^+] = 6.5 \times 10^{-12}$ M, and $[C_6H_5O^-] = 0.0308$ M
(c) pH = 11.19

17.29 (a) Original NH_3 concentration = 0.0154 M
(b) At the equivalence point $[H_3O^+] = 1.9 \times 10^{-6}$ M, $[OH^-] = 5.3 \times 10^{-9}$ M, $[NH_4^+] = 6.25 \times 10^{-3}$ M.
(c) pH at equivalence point = 5.73

17.31 The titration curve begins at pH = 13.00 and drops slowly as HCl is added. Just before the equivalence point (when 30.0 mL of acid has been added), the curve falls steeply. The pH at the equivalence point is exactly 7. Just after the equivalence point, the curve flattens again and begins to approach the final pH of just over 1.0. The total volume at the equivalence point is 60.0 mL.

17.33 (a) Starting pH = 11.12
(b) pH at equivalence point = 5.28
(c) pH at midpoint (half-neutralization point) = 9.25
(d) Methyl red, bromcresol green
(e)

Acid (mL)	Added pH
5.00	9.85
15.0	9.08
20.0	8.65
22.0	8.39
30.0	2.04

17.35 See Figure 17.10 on page 655.
(a) Thymol blue or bromphenol blue
(b) Phenolphthalein
(c) Methyl red; thymol blue

17.37 (a) Silver chloride, AgCl; lead(II) chloride, $PbCl_2$
(b) Zinc carbonate, $ZnCO_3$; zinc sulfide, ZnS
(c) Iron(II) carbonate, $FeCO_3$; iron(II) oxalate, FeC_2O_4

17.39 (a) and (b) are soluble, (c) and (d) are insoluble.

17.41 (a) $AgCN(s) \rightarrow Ag^+(aq) + CN^-(aq)$, $K_{sp} = [Ag^+][CN^-]$
(b) $NiCO_3(s) \rightarrow Ni^{2+}(aq) + CO_3^{2-}(aq)$, $K_{sp} = [Ni^{2+}][CO_3^{2-}]$
(c) $AuBr_3(s) \rightarrow Au^{3+}(aq) + 3\,Br^-(aq)$, $K_{sp} = [Au^{3+}][Br^-]^3$

17.43 $K_{sp} = (1.9 \times 10^{-3})^2 = 3.6 \times 10^{-6}$

17.45 $K_{sp} = 4.37 \times 10^{-9}$

17.47 $K_{sp} = 1.4 \times 10^{-15}$

17.49 (a) 9.2×10^{-9} M; (b) 2.2×10^{-6} g/L

17.51 (a) 2.4×10^{-4} M; (b) 0.018 g/L

17.53 Only 2.1×10^{-4} g dissolves.

17.55 (a) $PbCl_2$; (b) FeS; (c) $Fe(OH)_2$

17.57 Solubility in pure water = 1.0×10^{-6} mol/L; solubility in 0.010 M SCN^- = 1.0×10^{-10} mol/L

17.59 (a) Solubility in pure water = 2.2×10^{-6} mg/mL
(b) Solubility in 0.020 M $AgNO_3$ = 1.0×10^{-12} mg/mL

17.61 $[Fe^{2+}] = 4.9 \times 10^{-3}$ M

17.63 (a) PbS
(b) Ag_2CO_3
(c) $Al(OH)_3$

17.65 $Q < K_{sp}$, so no precipitate forms.

17.67 $Q > K_{sp}$; $Zn(OH)_2$ will precipitate.

17.69 $[OH^-]$ must exceed 1.0×10^{-5} M.

17.71 Using K_{sp} for $Zn(OH)_2$ and K_f for $[Zn(OH)_4]^{2-}$, K_{net} for

$$Zn(OH)_2(s) + 2\,OH^-(aq) \rightleftharpoons [Zn(OH)_4]^{2-}(aq)$$

is 1×10^1. This indicates that the reaction is definitely product-favored.

17.73 K_{net} for $AgCl(s) + 2\,NH_3(aq) \rightleftharpoons [Ag(NH_3)_2]^+(aq) + Cl^-(aq)$is 2.0×10^{-3}. When all the AgCl dissolves, $[Ag(NH_3)_2^+] = [Cl^-] = 0.050$ M. To achieve these concentrations, $[NH_3]$ must be 1.12 M. Therefore, the amount of NH_3 added must be 2×0.050 mol/L (to react with the AgCl) plus 1.12 mol/L (to achieve the proper equilibrium concentration). The total is 1.22 mol/L NH_3.

17.75 (a) Solubility in pure water = 1.3×10^{-5} mol/L or 0.0019 g/L.
(b) K_{net} for $AgCl(s) + 2\,NH_3(aq) \rightleftharpoons [Ag(NH_3)_2]^+(aq) + Cl^-(aq)$ is 2.0×10^{-3}. When using 1.0 M NH_3, the concentrations of species in solution are $[Ag(NH_3)_2]^+ = [Cl^-] = 0.041$ M and so $[NH_3] = 1.0 - 2(0.041)$ M or about 0.9 M. The amount of AgCl dissolved is 0.041 mol/L or 5.88 g/L.

17.77 (a) $NaBr(aq) + AgNO_3(aq) \rightarrow NaNO_3(aq) + AgBr(s)$
(b) $2\,KCl(aq) + Pb(NO_3)_2(aq) \rightarrow 2\,KNO_3(aq) + PbCl_2(s)$

17.79 $Q > K_{sp}$, so $BaSO_4$ precipitates.

17.81 $[H_3O^+] = 1.9 \times 10^{-10}$ M; pH = 9.73

17.83 $BaCO_3 < Ag_2CO_3 < Na_2CO_3$

17.85 Original pH = 8.62; dilution will not affect the pH.

17.87 (a) 0.100 M acetic acid has a pH of 2.87. Adding sodium acetate slowly raises the pH.
(b) Adding $NaNO_3$ to 0.100 M HNO_3 has no effect on the pH.
(c) In part (a), adding the conjugate base of a weak acid creates a buffer solution. In part (b), HNO_3 is a strong acid, but its conjugate base (NO_3^-) is so weak that the base has no effect on the complete ionization of the acid.

17.89 (a) pH = 4.13
(b) 0.6 g of $C_6H_5CO_2H$
(c) 8.2 mL of 2.0 M HCl should be added

17.91 $K = 2.1 \times 10^6$; yes, AgI forms

17.93 (a) 0.030 L (30. mL)
(b) 0.48 g CaC_2O_4

17.95 (a) $[F^-] = 1.3 \times 10^{-3}$ M
(b) $[Ca^{2+}] = 2.9 \times 10^{-5}$ M

17.97 (a) $PbSO_4$ will precipitate first.
(b) $[Pb^{2+}] = 5.1 \times 10^{-6}$ M

17.99 When $[CO_3^{2-}] = 0.050$ M, $[Ca^{2+}] = 6.8 \times 10^{-8}$ M. This means only 6.8×10^{-4} % of the ions remain, or that essentially all of the calcium ions have been removed.

17.101 (a) Add H_2SO_4, precipitating $BaSO_4$ and leaving Na^+(aq) in solution.
(b) Add HCl or another source of chloride ion. $PbCl_2$ will precipitate, but $NiCl_2$ is water-soluble.

17.103 (a) $BaSO_4$ will precipitate first.
(b) $[Ba^{2+}] = 1.8 \times 10^{-7}$ M

17.105 (a) pH = 2.81
(b) pH at equivalence point = 8.72
(c) pH at the midpoint = pK_a = 4.62
(d) Phenolphthalein
(e) After 10.0 mL, pH = 4.39.
After 20.0 mL, pH = 5.07.
After 30.0 mL, pH = 11.84.
(f) A plot of pH versus volume of NaOH added would begin at a pH of 2.81, rise slightly to the midpoint at pH = 4.62, and then begin to rise more steeply as the equivalence point is approached (when the volume of NaOH added is 27.0 mL). The pH rises vertically through the equivalence point, and then begins to level off above a pH of about 11.0.

17.107 The K_b value for ethylamine (4.27×10^{-4}) is found in Appendix I.
(a) pH = 11.89
(b) Midpoint pH = 10.63
(c) pH = 10.15
(d) pH = 5.93 at the equivalence point
(e) pH = 2.13
(f) Titration curve

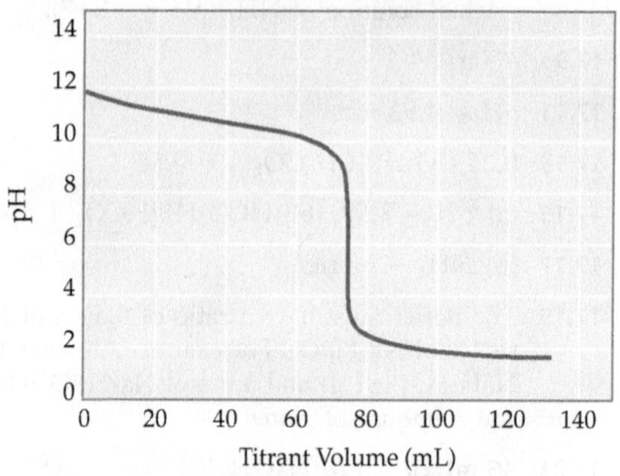

(g) Alizarin or bromcresol purple (see Figure 17.10)

17.109 110 mL NaOH

17.111 Add dilute HCl, say 1 M HCl, to a solution of the salts. Both AgCl and $PbCl_2$ will precipitate, but Cu^{2+} ions will stay in solution (as $CuCl_2$ is water-soluble). Decant off the copper-containing solution to leave a precipitate of white AgCl and $PbCl_2$. Lead(II) chloride ($K_{sp} = 1.7 \times 10^{-5}$) is much more soluble than AgCl ($K_{sp} = 1.8 \times 10^{-10}$). Warming the precipitates in water will dissolve the $PbCl_2$ and leave the AgCl as a white solid.

17.113 $Cu(OH)_2$ will dissolve in a nonoxidizing acid such as HCl, whereas CuS will not.

17.115 When Ag_3PO_4 dissolves slightly, it produces a small concentration of the phosphate ion, PO_4^{3-}. This ion is a strong base and hydrolyzes to HPO_4^{2-}. As this reaction removes the PO_4^{3-} ion from equilibrium with Ag_3PO_4, the equilibrium shifts to the right, producing more PO_4^{3-} and Ag^+ ions. Thus, Ag_3PO_4 dissolves to a greater extent than might be calculated from a K_{sp} value (unless the K_{sp} value was actually determined experimentally).

17.117 (a) Base is added to increase the pH. The added base reacts with acetic acid to form more acetate ions in the mixture. Thus, the fraction of acid declines and the fraction of conjugate base rises (i.e., the ratio $[CH_3CO_2H]/[CH_3CO_2^-]$ decreases) as the pH rises.
(b) At pH = 4, acid predominates (85% acid and 15% acetate ions). At pH = 6, acetate ions predominate (95% acetate ions and 5% acid).
(c) At the point the lines cross, $[CH_3CO_2H] = [CH_3CO_2^-]$. At this point pH = pK_a, so pK_a for acetic acid is 4.74.

17.119 (a) C—C—C angle, 120°; O—C=O, 120°; C—O—H, 109°; C—C—H, 120°
(b) Both the ring C atoms and the C in CO_2H are sp^2 hybridized.
(c) $K_a = 1 \times 10^{-3}$
(d) 10%
(e) pH at half-way point = pK_a = 3.0; pH at equivalence point = 7.3

Chapter 18

Case Study

Thermodynamics and Living Things

1. Creatine phosphate + $H_2O \rightarrow$ creatine + HP_i

   $\Delta_r G° = -43.3$ kJ/mol

   Adenosine + $HP_i \rightarrow$ adenosine monophosphate + H_2O

   $\Delta_r G° = +9.2$ kJ/mol

   Net reaction (sum of the two reactions):

   Creatine phosphate + adenosine $\rightarrow$ creatine + adenosine monophosphate

   For this, $\Delta_r G° = -43.3$ kJ/mol + 9.2 kJ/mol = −34.1 kJ/mol. The negative value indicates that the transfer of phosphate from creatine phosphate to adenosine is product-favored.

2. $\Delta_r G°' = \Delta_r G° + RT \ln[C][H_3O^+]/[A][B] = \Delta_r G° + (8.31 \times 10^{-3}$ kJ/mol · K)(298 K) $\ln[1][1 \times 10^{-7}]/[1][1]$

   $\Delta_r G°' = \Delta_r G° - 39.9$ kJ/mol

Check Your Understanding

18.1 (a) O_3; larger molecules generally have higher entropies than smaller molecules.
(b) $SnCl_4(g)$; gases have higher entropies than liquids.

18.2 (a) $\Delta_r S° = \Sigma nS°(\text{products}) - \Sigma nS°(\text{reactants})$

$\Delta_r S° = (1 \text{ mol/mol-rxn})\ S°[NH_4Cl(aq)]) - (1 \text{ mol/mol-rxn})\ S°[NH_4Cl(s)]$

$\Delta_r S° = (1 \text{ mol/mol-rxn})(169.9 \text{ J/mol} \cdot \text{K}) - (1 \text{ mol/mol-rxn})(94.85 \text{ J/mol} \cdot \text{K})$
$= 75.1 \text{ J/K} \cdot \text{mol-rxn}$

A gain in entropy for the formation of a mixture (solution) is expected.

(b) $\Delta_r S° = (2 \text{ mol } CO_2\text{/mol-rxn})\ S°(CO_2) + (3 \text{ mol } H_2O\text{/mol-rxn})\ S°(H_2O) - [(1 \text{ mol } C_2H_5OH\text{/mol-rxn})\ S°(C_2H_5OH) + (3 \text{ mol } O_2\text{/mol-rxn})\ S°(O_2)]$

$\Delta_r S° = (2 \text{ mol/mol-rxn})(213.74 \text{ J/mol} \cdot \text{K}) + (3 \text{ mol/mol-rxn})(188.84 \text{ J/mol} \cdot \text{K}) - [(1 \text{ mol/mol-rxn})(282.70 \text{ J/mol} \cdot \text{K}) + (3 \text{ mol/mol-rxn})(205.07 \text{ J/mol} \cdot \text{K})]$

$\Delta_r S° = +96.09 \text{ J/K} \cdot \text{mol-rxn}$

An increase in entropy is expected because there is an increase in the number of moles of gases.

18.3 $\Delta S°(\text{system}) = \Delta_r S°$
$= \Sigma nS°(\text{products}) - \Sigma nS°(\text{reactants})$

$\Delta_r S° = (2 \text{ mol HCl/mol-rxn})\ S°[HCl(g)] - \{(1 \text{ mol } H_2\text{/mol-rxn})\ S°[H_2(g)] + (1 \text{ mol } Cl_2\text{/mol-rxn})\ S°[Cl_2(g)]\}$

$= (2 \text{ mol HCl/mol-rxn})(186.2 \text{ J/K} \cdot \text{mol HCl}) - \{(1 \text{ mol } H_2\text{/mol-rxn})(130.7 \text{ J/K} \cdot \text{mol } H_2) + (1 \text{ mol } Cl_2\text{/mol-rxn})\ (223.08 \text{ J/K} \cdot \text{mol } Cl_2(g)\}$

$= 18.6 \text{ J/K} \cdot \text{mol-rxn}$

$\Delta_r H° = \Sigma n\Delta_f H°(\text{products}) - \Sigma n\Delta_f H°(\text{reactants})$

$\Delta_r H° = (2 \text{ mol HCl/mol-rxn})\ \Delta_f H°[HCl(g)] - \{(1 \text{ mol } H_2\text{/mol-rxn})\ \Delta_f H°[H_2(g)] + (1 \text{ mol } Cl_2\text{/mol-rxn})\ \Delta_f H°[Cl_2(g)]\}$

$= (2 \text{ mol HCl/mol-rxn})(-92.31 \text{ kJ/mol HCl}) - \{(1 \text{ mol } H_2\text{/mol-rxn})(0 \text{ kJ/mol } H_2) + (1 \text{ mol } Cl_2\text{/mol-rxn})\ (0 \text{ kJ/mol } Cl_2(g)\}$

$= -184.62 \text{ kJ/mol-rxn}$

Both $\Delta_r H°$ (< 0) and $\Delta_r S°$ (> 0) are favorable, so this reaction is predicted to be spontaneous under standard conditions.

$\Delta S°(\text{surroundings}) = -\Delta_r H°/T = -(-184.62 \text{ kJ/mol-rxn})/298.15 \text{ K} = 0.61922 \text{ kJ/K} \cdot \text{mol-rxn} = 619.22 \text{ J/K} \cdot \text{mol-rxn}$

$\Delta S°(\text{universe}) = \Delta S°(\text{system}) + \Delta S°(\text{surroundings}) = 18.6 \text{ J/K} \cdot \text{mol-rxn} + 619.22 \text{ J/K} \cdot \text{mol-rxn} = 637.8 \text{ J/K} \cdot \text{mol-rxn}$

$\Delta S°(\text{universe}) > 0$, so the reaction is spontaneous under standard conditions.

18.4 For the reaction $N_2(g) + 3\ H_2(g) \rightarrow 2\ NH_3(g)$:

$\Delta_r H° = (2 \text{ mol/mol-rxn})\ \Delta_f H°$ for $NH_3(g) = (2 \text{ mol/mol-rxn})(-45.90 \text{ kJ/mol}) = -91.80 \text{ kJ/mol-rxn}$

$\Delta_r S° = (2 \text{ mol/mol-rxn})\ S°(NH_3) - [(1 \text{ mol/mol-rxn})\ S°(N_2) + (3 \text{ mol/mol-rxn})\ S°(H_2)]$

$\Delta_r S° = (2 \text{ mol/mol-rxn})(192.77 \text{ J/ mol} \cdot \text{K}) - [(1 \text{ mol/mol-rxn})(191.56 \text{ J/mol} \cdot \text{K}) + (3 \text{ mol/mol-rxn})(130.7 \text{ J/mol} \cdot \text{K})]$

$\Delta_r S° = -198.1 \text{ J/K} \cdot \text{mol-rxn}$
$(= -0.1981 \text{ kJ/K} \cdot \text{mol-rxn})$

$\Delta_r G° = \Delta_r H° - T\Delta_r S° = -91.80 \text{ kJ/mol-rxn} - (298 \text{ K})(-0.1981 \text{ kJ/K} \cdot \text{mol-rxn})$

$\Delta_r G° = -32.8 \text{ kJ/mol-rxn}$

18.5 $SO_2(g) + \frac{1}{2}\ O_2(g) \rightarrow SO_3(g)$

$\Delta_r G° = \Sigma n\Delta_f G°(\text{products}) - \Sigma n\Delta_f G°(\text{reactants})$

$\Delta_r G° = (1 \text{ mol/mol-rxn})\Delta_f G°[SO_3(g)] - \{(1 \text{ mol/mol-rxn})\Delta_f G°[SO_2(g)] + (0.5 \text{ mol/mol-rxn})\Delta_f G°[O_2(g)]\}$

$\Delta_r G° = -371.04 \text{ kJ/mol-rxn} - (-300.13 \text{ kJ/mol-rxn} + 0 \text{ kJ/mol-rxn})$
$= -70.91 \text{ kJ/mol-rxn}$

18.6 $HgO(s) \rightarrow Hg(\ell) + \frac{1}{2}\ O_2(g)$; determine the temperature at which $\Delta_r G° = \Delta_r H° - T\Delta_r S° = 0$.
T is the unknown in this problem.

$\Delta_r H° = [-\Delta_f H°$ for $HgO(s)] = 90.83 \text{ kJ/mol-rxn}$

$\Delta_r S° = S°[Hg(\ell)] + \frac{1}{2}\ S°[O_2(g)] - S°[HgO(s)]$

$\Delta_r S° = (1 \text{ mol/mol-rxn})(76.02 \text{ J/mol} \cdot \text{K}) + [(0.5 \text{ mol/mol-rxn})(205.07 \text{ J/mol} \cdot \text{K}) - (1 \text{ mol/mol-rxn})(70.29 \text{ J/mol} \cdot \text{K})]$
$= 108.27 \text{ J/K} \cdot \text{mol-rxn}$

$\Delta_r H° - T(\Delta_r S°) = 0 = 90{,}830 \text{ J/mol-rxn} - T(108.27 \text{ J/K} \cdot \text{mol-rxn})$

$T = 839$ K (566 °C)

18.7 $CaCO_3(s) \rightleftharpoons CaO(s) + CO_2(g)$
$\Delta_r G° = \Sigma n\Delta_f G°(\text{products}) - \Sigma n\Delta_f G°(\text{reactants})$
$\Delta_r G° = \Delta_f G°(CaO) + \Delta_f G°(CO_2) - \Delta_f G°(CaCO_3)$
$\Delta_r G° = (1 \text{ mol CaO/mol-rxn})(-603.42 \text{ kJ/mol CaO}) + (1 \text{ mol } CO_2\text{/mol-rxn})(-394.359 \text{ kJ/mol } CO_2) - (1 \text{ mol } CaCO_3\text{/mol-rxn})(-1129.16 \text{ kJ/mol } CaCO_3)$
$\Delta_r G° = 131.38$ kJ/mol-rxn
$\Delta_r G° = -RT \ln K$
131,380 J/mol-rxn = $-(8.3145$ J/mol-rxn · K)(298.15 K)(ln K)
$K_p = 9.62 \times 10^{-24}$

18.8 $C(s) + CO_2(g) \rightleftharpoons 2\ CO(g)$
$\Delta_r G° = \Sigma\ n\Delta_f G°(\text{products}) - \Sigma\ n\Delta_f G°(\text{reactants})$
$\Delta_r G° = 2\ \Delta_f G°(CO) - \Delta_f G°(CO_2)$
$\Delta_r G° = (2 \text{ mol/mol-rxn})(-137.17 \text{ kJ/mol}) - (1 \text{ mol/mol-rxn})(-394.36 \text{ kJ/mol})$
$\Delta_r G° = 120.02$ kJ/mol-rxn
$\Delta_r G° = -RT \ln K$
120,020 J/mol-rxn = $-(8.3145$ J/mol-rxn · K)(298.15 K)(ln K)
$K = 9.41 \times 10^{-22}$

18.9 (a) $\Delta_r G° = 2\ \Delta_f G°(NO) = 2$ mol/mol-rxn × 86.58 kJ/mol = 173.2 kJ/mol-rxn
The reaction is reactant-favored at equilibrium.
(b) $\Delta_r G = \Delta_r G° + RT \ln Q = 173.2$ kJ/mol-rxn + (0.0083145 kJ/K · mol-rxn)(298.15 K) $\ln[P(NO)]^2/[P(N_2)][P(O_2)]$
$\Delta_r G = 173.2$ kJ/mol-rxn − 11.4 kJ/mol-rxn = 161.8 kJ/mol-rxn. The reaction is not spontaneous.

Review & Check

Section 18-1

1. (b) toward equilibrium
2. (b) false
3. (b) sometimes spontaneous

Section 18-2

1. (c) > 0
2. (c) dispersed
3. (b) 3.19 J/K

Section 18-3

1. (b) increases
2. (c) 2.5×10^{-23} J/K

Section 18-4

1. (c) $NaCl(s) < H_2O(\ell) < NH_3(g)$
2. (c) $\Delta_r S° > 0$
3. (a) −326.6 J/K · mol-rxn

Section 18-5

1. (b) −121.6 J/K · mol-rxn
2. (d) 1320 J/K · mol-rxn
3. (b) at higher temperatures

Section 18-6

1. (d) less, less
2. (a) product-favored at equilibrium

Section 18-7

1. (c) −2155 kJ/mol-rxn
2. (a) −225 kJ/mol-rxn
3. (c) 23 kJ/mol-rxn

Applying Chemical Principles: Are Diamonds Forever?

1. C(diamond) → C(graphite)
   (a) $\Delta_r G° = -2.900$ kJ/mol-rxn; $K = 3.22$
   (b) $\Delta_r H° = -1.8$ kJ/mol-rxn; $\Delta_r S° = 3.2$ J/K · mol-rxn = 0.0032 kJ/K · mol; $\Delta_r G° = -5.0$ kJ/mol-rxn; $K = 1.8$
   Though still favoring graphite, the equilibrium has shifted more toward diamond.
   (c) Greater pressures favor the formation of diamond, which is more dense than graphite.
   (d) The rate of reaction is negligibly slow at room temperature.

Study Questions

18.1 (a) For a given substance at a given temperature, a gas always has a greater entropy than the liquid. Matter and energy are more dispersed.
(b) Liquid water at 50 °C
(c) Ruby
(d) One mole of N_2 at 1 bar

18.3 (a) $\Delta_r S° = +12.7$ J/K · mol-rxn. Entropy increases.
(b) $\Delta_r S° = -102.56$ J/K · mol-rxn. Significant decrease in entropy.
(c) $\Delta_r S° = +93.3$ J/K · mol-rxn. Entropy increases.
(d) $\Delta_r S° = -129.7$ J/K · mol-rxn. The solution has a smaller entropy (with H^+ forming H_3O^+ and hydrogen bonding occurring) than HCl in the gaseous state.

18.5 (a) $\Delta_r S° = +9.3$ J/K · mol-rxn
(b) $\Delta_r S° = -294.0$ J/K · mol-rxn

18.7 (a) $\Delta_r S° = -507.3$ J/K · mol-rxn; entropy declines as a gaseous reactant is incorporated in a solid compound.
(b) $\Delta_r S° = +313.25$ J/K · mol-rxn; entropy increases as five molecules (three of them in the gas phase) form six molecules of products (all gases).

18.9 $\Delta S°(\text{system}) = -134.2$ J/K · mol-rxn; $\Delta H°(\text{system}) = -662.75$ kJ/mol-rxn; $\Delta S°(\text{surroundings}) = +2222.9$ J/K · mol-rxn; $\Delta S°(\text{universe}) = +2088.8$ J/K · mol-rxn. The reaction is spontaneous under standard conditions.

18.11 $\Delta S°$(system) = +163.3 J/K · mol-rxn; $\Delta H°$(system) = +285.83 kJ/mol-rxn; $\Delta S°$(surroundings) = −958.68 J/K · mol-rxn; $\Delta S°$(universe) = −795.4 J/K · mol-rxn

The reaction is not spontaneous because the overall entropy change in the universe is negative. The reaction is disfavored by energy dispersal.

18.13 (a) Type 2. The reaction is enthalpy-favored but entropy-disfavored. It is more favorable at low temperatures.
(b) Type 4. This endothermic reaction is not favored by the enthalpy change nor is it favored by the entropy change. It is not spontaneous under standard conditions at any temperature.

18.15 (a) $\Delta_r H°$ = −438 kJ/mol-rxn; $\Delta_r S°$ = −201.7 J/K · mol-rxn; $\Delta_r G°$ = −378 kJ/mol-rxn. The reaction is product-favored at equilibrium and is enthalpy-driven.
(b) $\Delta_r H°$ = −86.61 kJ/mol-rxn; $\Delta_r S°$ = −79.4 J/K · mol-rxn; $\Delta_r G°$ = −62.9 kJ/mol-rxn. The reaction is product-favored at equilibrium. The enthalpy change favors the reaction.

18.17 (a) $\Delta_r H°$ = +116.7 kJ/mol-rxn;
$\Delta_r S°$ = +168.0 J/K · mol-rxn;
$\Delta_f G°$ = +66.6 kJ/mol
(b) $\Delta_r H°$ = −425.93 kJ/mol-rxn;
$\Delta_r S°$ = −154.6 J/K · mol-rxn;
$\Delta_f G°$ = −379.82 kJ/mol
(c) $\Delta_r H°$ = +17.51 kJ/mol-rxn;
$\Delta_r S°$ = +77.95 J/K · mol-rxn;
$\Delta_f G°$ = −5.73 kJ/mol

The reactions in (b) and (c) are predicted to be product-favored under standard conditions.

18.19 (a) $\Delta_r G°$ = −817.54 kJ/mol-rxn; product-favored
(b) $\Delta_r G°$ = +256.6 kJ/mol-rxn; reactant-favored
(c) $\Delta_r G°$ = −1101.14 kJ/mol-rxn; product-favored

18.21 $\Delta_f G°$ [$BaCO_3$(s)] = −1134.4 kJ/mol

18.23 (a) $\Delta_r H°$ = +66.2 kJ/mol-rxn;
$\Delta_r S°$ = −121.62 J/K · mol-rxn;
$\Delta_r G°$ = +102.5 kJ/mol-rxn

Both the enthalpy and the entropy changes are unfavorable. There is no temperature at which the reaction will be product-favored at equilibrium. This is a case like that in the right panel in Figure 18.11 and is a Type 4 reaction (Table 18.1). As the temperature increases, the reaction becomes even more reactant-favored (the value of $\Delta_r G°$ becomes more positive).

(b) $\Delta_r H°$ = −221.05 kJ/mol-rxn;
$\Delta_r S°$ = +179.1 J/K · mol-rxn;
$\Delta_r G°$ = −274.45 kJ/mol-rxn

The reaction is favored by both enthalpy and entropy and is product-favored at all temperatures. This is a case like that in the left panel in Figure 18.11 and is a Type 1 reaction. As the temperature increases, the reaction becomes even more product-favored (the value of $\Delta_r G°$ becomes more negative).

(c) $\Delta_r H°$ = −179.0 kJ/mol-rxn;
$\Delta_r S°$ = −160.2 J/K · mol-rxn;
$\Delta_r G°$ = −131.23 kJ/mol-rxn

The reaction is favored by the enthalpy change but disfavored by the entropy change. The reaction becomes less product-favored as the temperature increases; it is a case like the red line in the middle panel of Figure 18.11.

(d) $\Delta_r H°$ = +822.2 kJ/mol-rxn;
$\Delta_r S°$ = +181.28 J/K · mol-rxn;
$\Delta_r G°$ = +768.19 kJ/mol-rxn

The reaction is not favored by the enthalpy change but favored by the entropy change. The reaction becomes more product-favored as the temperature increases; it is a case like the blue line in the middle panel of Figure 18.11.

18.25 (a) $\Delta_r S°$ = +174.75 J/K · mol-rxn;
$\Delta_r H°$ = +116.94 kJ/mol-rxn
(b) $\Delta_r G°$ = +64.84 kJ/mol-rxn. The reaction is not product-favored under standard conditions at 298.15 K.
(c) As the temperature increases, $\Delta_r S°$ becomes more important, so $\Delta_r G°$ can become negative at a sufficiently high temperature and the reaction is product-favored.

18.27 $K_p = 6.8 \times 10^{-16}$. Note that K_p is very small and that $\Delta G°$ is positive. Both indicate a process that is reactant-favored at equilibrium.

18.29 $\Delta_r G°$ = −100.24 kJ/mol-rxn and $K_p = 3.6 \times 10^{17}$. Both the free energy change and K indicate a process that is product-favored at equilibrium.

18.31 (a) $\Delta_r G°$ = −32.74 kJ/mol-rxn. The reaction is product-favored at equilibrium.
(b) $\Delta_r G$ = −21.33 kJ/mol-rxn. The reaction is spontaneous in the forward direction.

18.33 (a) HBr(g)
(b) NH_4Cl(aq)
(c) C_2H_4(g)
(d) NaCl(g)

18.35 $\Delta_r G°$ = −98.9 kJ/mol-rxn. The reaction is product-favored at equilibrium. It is enthalpy-driven.

18.37 $\Delta_r H°$ = −1428.66 kJ/mol-rxn; $\Delta_r S°$ = +47.1 J/K · mol-rxn; $\Delta S°$(universe) = +4840 J/K · mol-rxn. Combustion reactions are spontaneous, and this is confirmed by the sign of $\Delta S°$(universe).

18.39 (a) The reaction occurs spontaneously and is product-favored. Therefore, $\Delta S°$(universe) is positive and $\Delta_r G°$ is negative. The reaction is likely to be exothermic, so $\Delta_r H°$ is negative, and $\Delta S°$(surroundings) is positive. $\Delta S°$(system) is expected to be negative because two moles of gas form one mole of solid. The calculated values are as follows:

$\Delta S°$(system) = −284.1 J/K · mol-rxn
$\Delta_r H°$ = −176.34 kJ/mol-rxn

$\Delta S°$(surroundings) = +591.45 J/K · mol-rxn

$\Delta S°$(universe) = +307.4 J/K · mol-rxn

$\Delta_r G°$ = −91.64 kJ/mol-rxn

(b) $K_p = 1.1 \times 10^{16}$

18.41 $K_p = 1.3 \times 10^{29}$ at 298 K ($\Delta G°$ = −166.1 kJ/mol-rxn). The reaction is already extremely product-favored at 298 K. A higher temperature would make the reaction less product-favored because $\Delta_r S°$ has a negative value (−242.3 J/K · mol-rxn).

18.43 At the boiling point, $\Delta G° = 0 = \Delta H° - T\Delta S°$.

Here $\Delta S° = \Delta H°/T$ = 112 J/K · mol-rxn at 351.15 K.

18.45 $\Delta_r S°$ is +137.2 J/K · mol-rxn. A positive entropy change means that raising the temperature will increase the product favorability of the reaction (because $T\Delta S°$ will become more negative).

18.47 The reaction is exothermic, so $\Delta_r H°$ should be negative. Also, a gas and an aqueous solution are formed, so $\Delta_r S°$ should be positive. The calculated values are $\Delta_r H°$ = −183.32 kJ/mol-rxn (with a negative sign as expected) and $\Delta_r S°$ = −7.7 J/K · mol-rxn

The entropy change is slightly negative, not positive as predicted. The reason for this is the negative entropy change upon dissolving NaOH. Apparently the OH^- ions in water hydrogen-bond with water molecules, an effect that also leads to a small, negative entropy change.

18.49 $\Delta_r H°$ = +126.03 kJ/mol-rxn; $\Delta_r S°$ = +78.2 J/K · mol-rxn; and $\Delta_r G°$ = +103 kJ/mol-rxn. The reaction is not product-favored at equilibrium.

18.51 $\Delta_r G°$ from K value = 4.87 kJ/mol-rxn

$\Delta_r G°$ from free energies of formation = 4.73 kJ/mol-rxn

18.53 $\Delta_r G°$ = −2.27 kJ/mol-rxn

18.55 (a) $\Delta_r G°$ = +141.82 kJ/mol-rxn, so the reaction is not product-favored at equilibrium.

(b) $\Delta_r H°$ = +197.86 kJ/mol-rxn; $\Delta_r S°$ = +187.95 J/K · mol-rxn

$T = \Delta_r H°/\Delta_r S°$ = 1052.7 K or 779.6 °C

(c) $\Delta_r G°$ at 1500 °C (1773 K) = −135.4 kJ/mol-rxn

K_p at 1500 °C = 1×10^4

18.57 $\Delta_r S°$ = −459.0 J/K · mol-rxn;
$\Delta_r H°$ = −793 kJ/mol-rxn; $\Delta_r G°$ = −657 kJ/mol-rxn

The reaction is product-favored at equilibrium. It is enthalpy-driven.

18.59 (a) $\Delta_r G°$ at 80.0 °C = +0.14 kJ/mol-rxn

$\Delta_r G°$ at 110.0 °C = −0.12 kJ/mol-rxn

Rhombic sulfur is more stable than monoclinic sulfur at 80 °C, but the reverse is true at 110 °C.

(b) T = 370 K or about 96 °C. This is the temperature at which the two forms are at equilibrium under standard conditions.

18.61 $\Delta_r G°$ at 298 K = 22.64 kJ/mol; reaction is not product-favored at equilibrium. It does become product-favored above 469 K (196 °C).

18.63 $\Delta_f G°$ [HI(g)] = −10.9 kJ/mol

18.65 (a) $\Delta_r G°$ = +194.8 kJ/mol-rxn and $K = 6.7 \times 10^{-11}$

(b) The reaction is reactant-favored at equilibrium at 727 °C.

(c) Keep the pressure of CO as low as possible (by removing it during the course of the reaction).

18.67 $K_p = P_{Hg(g)}$ at any temperature

K_p = 1 at 620.3 K or 347.2 °C when $P_{Hg(g)}$ = 1.000 bar

T when $P_{Hg(g)}$ = (1/760) bar is 398.3 K or 125.2 °C.

18.69 (a) True

(b) False. Whether an exothermic system is spontaneous also depends on the entropy change for the system.

(c) False. Reactions with $+\Delta_r H°$ and $+\Delta_r S°$ are product-favored at higher temperatures.

(d) True

18.71 Dissolving a solid such as NaCl in water is a product-favored process. Thus, $\Delta G° < 0$. If $\Delta H° = 0$, then the only way the free energy change can be negative is if $\Delta S°$ is positive. Generally the entropy change is the important factor in forming a solution.

18.73 $2\ C_2H_6(g) + 7\ O_2(g) \rightarrow 4\ CO_2(g) + 6\ H_2O(g)$

(a) Not only is this an exothermic combustion reaction, but there is also an increase in the number of molecules of gases from reactants to products. Therefore, we would predict a positive value for $\Delta S°$ for both the system and the surroundings and thus for the universe as well.

(b) The exothermic reaction has $\Delta_r H° < 0$. Combined with a positive $\Delta S°$(system), the value of $\Delta_r G°$ is negative.

(c) The value of K_p is likely to be much greater than 1. Further, because $\Delta S°$(system) is positive, the value of K_p will be even larger at a higher temperature. (See the left panel of Figure 18.11.)

18.75 Reaction 1: $\Delta_r S°_1$ = −80.7 J/K · mol-rxn

Reaction 2: $\Delta_r S°_2$ = −161.60 J/K · mol-rxn

Reaction 3: $\Delta_r S°_3$ = −242.3 J/K · mol-rxn

$\Delta_r S°_1 + \Delta_r S°_2 = \Delta_r S°_3$; entropy is a state function.

18.77 (a) $\Delta_r H°$ = −352.88 kJ/mol-rxn and $\Delta_r S°$ = +21.31 J/K · mol-rxn. Therefore, at 298 K, $\Delta_r G°$ = −359.23 kJ/mol-rxn.

(b) 4.8 g of Mg is required.

18.79 (a) $N_2H_4(\ell) + O_2(g) \rightarrow 2\ H_2O(\ell) + N_2(g)$

O_2 is the oxidizing agent and N_2H_4 is the reducing agent.

(b) $\Delta_r H°$ = −622.29 kJ/mol-rxn and $\Delta_r S°$ = +4.87 J/K · mol-rxn. Therefore, at 298 K, $\Delta_r G°$ = −623.74 kJ/mol-rxn.

(c) 0.0027 K

(d) 7.5 mol O_2

(e) 4.8×10^3 g solution

(f) 7.5 mol $N_2(g)$ occupies 170 L at 273 K and 1.0 atm of pressure.

18.81 Iodine dissolves readily, so the process is product-favored and $\Delta G°$ must be less than zero. Because $\Delta H° = 0$, the process is entropy-driven.

18.83 $CH_3OH(g) \rightarrow C(s, \text{graphite}) + 2\ H_2(g) + 1/2\ O_2(g)$

(a) The reaction becomes more product-favored at equilibrium as temperature increases.

(b) There is no temperature between 400 K and 1000 K at which the decomposition is product-favored at equilibrium.

18.85 (a) For the electrolysis of water: $\Delta_r G° = 474.3$ kJ. For the formation from methane: $\Delta_r G° = 142.2$ kJ.

(b) For the electrolysis of water: $\Delta_r G° = 237.2$ kJ/mol H_2
For the formation from methane: $\Delta_r G° = 47.4$ kJ/mol H_2

(c) The free energy change for the formation of H_2 from methane is clearly less than that to obtain H_2 from water electrolysis.

18.87 (a, b)

Temperature (K)	$\Delta_r G°$ (kJ/mol)	K
298.0 K	−32.74	5.5×10^5
800.0 K	+72.9	2×10^{-5}
1300. K	+184.0	4.0×10^{-8}

(c) The largest mole fraction of NH_3 in an equilibrium mixture will be at 298 K.

Chapter 19

Case Study

Manganese in the Oceans

1. Cathode reaction: $Mn^{3+} + e^- \rightarrow Mn^{2+}$
Anode reaction: $Mn^{3+} + 2\ H_2O \rightarrow MnO_2 + 4\ H^+ + e^-$
Net reaction: $2\ Mn^{3+} + 2\ H_2O \rightarrow MnO_2 + Mn^{2+} + 4\ H^+$
$E°_{cell} = E°(\text{cathode}) - E°(\text{anode}) = 1.50\ V - 0.95\ V = 0.55\ V$
The cell potential associated with this disproportionation is positive, indicating a product-favored reaction at equilibrium.

2. (a) $MnO_2 + HS^- + 3\ H^+ \rightarrow Mn^{2+} + S + 2\ H_2O$
(b) $2\ Mn^{2+} + O_2 + 2\ H_2O \rightarrow 2\ MnO_2 + 4\ H^+$

3. Cathode reaction: $O_2 + 4\ H^+ + 4\ e^- \rightarrow 2\ H_2O$ ($E° = 1.229$ V)
Anode reaction: $Mn^{2+} + 2\ H_2O \rightarrow MnO_2 + 4\ H^+ + 2\ e^-$ ($E° = 1.23$ V, from Appendix M)
$E°_{cell} = E°(\text{cathode}) - E°(\text{anode}) = 1.229\ V - 1.23\ V = 0\ V.$

Check Your Understanding

19.1 Oxidation half-reaction: $Al(s) \rightarrow Al^{3+}(aq) + 3\ e^-$
Reduction half-reaction: $2\ H^+(aq) + 2\ e^- \rightarrow H_2(g)$
Overall reaction: $2\ Al(s) + 6\ H^+(aq) \rightarrow 2\ Al^{3+}(aq) + 3\ H_2(g)$
Al is the reducing agent and is oxidized; $H^+(aq)$ is the oxidizing agent and is reduced.

19.2 (1) $2\ VO^{2+}(aq) + Zn(s) + 4\ H^+(aq) \rightarrow Zn^{2+}(aq) + 2\ V^{3+}(aq) + 2\ H_2O(\ell)$
$2\ V^{3+}(aq) + Zn(s) \rightarrow 2\ V^{2+}(aq) + Zn^{2+}(aq)$

(2) Oxidation (Fe^{2+}, the reducing agent, is oxidized):
$Fe^{2+}(aq) \rightarrow Fe^{3+}(aq) + e^-$
Reduction (MnO_4^-, the oxidizing agent, is reduced)
$MnO_4^-(aq) + 8\ H^+(aq) + 5\ e^- \rightarrow Mn^{2+}(aq) + 4\ H_2O(\ell)$
Overall reaction:
$MnO_4^-(aq) + 8\ H^+(aq) + 5\ Fe^{2+}(aq) \rightarrow Mn^{2+}(aq) + 5\ Fe^{3+}(aq) + 4\ H_2O(\ell)$

19.3 (a) Oxidation half-reaction:
$Al(s) + 3\ OH^-(aq) \rightarrow Al(OH)_3(s) + 3\ e^-$
Reduction half-reaction:
$S(s) + H_2O(\ell) + 2\ e^- \rightarrow HS^-(aq) + OH^-(aq)$
Overall reaction:
$2\ Al(s) + 3\ S(s) + 3\ H_2O(\ell) + 3\ OH^-(aq) \rightarrow 2\ Al(OH)_3(s) + 3\ HS^-(aq)$

(b) Aluminum is the reducing agent and is oxidized; sulfur is the oxidizing agent and is reduced.

19.4 Construct two half-cells, the first with a silver electrode and a solution containing $Ag^+(aq)$, and the second with a nickel electrode and a solution containing $Ni^{2+}(aq)$. Connect the two half-cells with a salt bridge. When the electrodes are connected through an external circuit, electrons will flow from the anode (the nickel electrode) to the cathode (the silver electrode). The overall cell reaction is $Ni(s) + 2\ Ag^+(aq) \rightarrow Ni^{2+}(aq) + 2\ Ag(s)$. To maintain electrical neutrality in the two half-cells, negative ions will flow from the $Ag|Ag^+$ half-cell to the $Ni|Ni^{2+}$ half-cell, and positive ions will flow in the opposite direction.

19.5 $Zn(s)|Zn^{2+}(aq)||SO_4^{2-}|PbSO_4(s)|Pb(s)$

19.6 (a) Using Appendix M, the order determined for these metals from least strong reducing agent to strongest reducing agent is Hg < Pb < Sn. (The further down the table, the stronger the metal is as a reducing agent.)

(b) F_2, Cl_2, and Br_2 all can oxidize mercury to mercury(II); Hg is located "southeast" of them on the table. I_2 cannot oxidize mercury to mercury(II); mercury is located "northeast" rather than "southeast" of it.

19.7 Overall reaction: $2\ Al(s) + 3\ Fe^{2+}(aq) \rightarrow 2\ Al^{3+}(aq) + 3\ Fe(s)$
($E°_{cell} = 1.22$ V, $n = 6$)
$E_{cell} = E°_{cell} - (0.0257/n) \ln \{[Al^{3+}]^2/[Fe^{2+}]^3\}$
$= 1.22 - (0.0257/6) \ln \{[0.025]^2/[0.50]^3\}$
$= 1.22\ V - (-0.023)\ V = 1.24\ V$

19.8 Overall reaction: $Fe(s) + 2\ H^+(aq) \rightarrow Fe^{2+}(aq) + H_2(g)$
($E^\circ_{cell} = 0.44$ V, $n = 2$)
$E_{cell} = E^\circ_{cell} - (0.0257/n) \ln \{[Fe^{2+}]P_{H_2}/[H^+]^2\}$
$= 0.44 - (0.0257/2) \ln \{[0.024]1.0/[0.056]^2\}$
$= 0.44\ V - 0.026\ V = 0.41\ V$

19.9 $\Delta_r G^\circ = -nFE^\circ$
$= -(2 \text{ mol e}^-)(96{,}500 \text{ C/mol e}^-)(-0.76 \text{ V})(1 \text{ J/1 C} \cdot \text{V})$
$= 146{,}680 \text{ J} = 150 \text{ kJ}$
The negative value of E° and the positive value of ΔG° both indicate a reactant-favored reaction at equilibrium.

19.10 $E^\circ_{cell} = E^\circ_{cathode} - E^\circ_{anode} = 0.799\ V - 0.855\ V = -0.056\ V$; $n = 2$
$E^\circ = (0.0257/n) \ln K$
$-0.056 = (0.0257/2) \ln K$
$K = 0.013$

19.11 Cathode: $2\ H_2O(\ell) + 2\ e^- \rightarrow 2\ OH^-(aq) + H_2(g)$
$E^\circ_{cathode} = -0.83$ V
Anode: $4\ OH^-(aq) \rightarrow O_2(g) + 2\ H_2O(\ell) + 4\ e^-$
$E^\circ_{anode} = 0.40$ V
Overall: $2\ H_2O(\ell) \rightarrow 2\ H_2(g) + O_2(g)$
$E^\circ_{cell} = E^\circ_{cathode} - E^\circ_{anode} = -0.83\ V - 0.40\ V = -1.23\ V$
The minimum voltage needed under standard conditions to cause this reaction to occur is 1.23 V.

19.12 (1) O_2 is formed at the anode, by the reaction
$$2\ H_2O(\ell) \rightarrow 4\ H^+(aq) + O_2(g) + 4\ e^-.$$
$(0.445 \text{ A})(45 \text{ min})(60 \text{ s/min})(1 \text{ C/1 A} \cdot \text{s})(1 \text{ mol e}^-/96{,}500 \text{ C})(1 \text{ mol } O_2/4 \text{ mol e}^-)(32 \text{ g } O_2/1 \text{ mol } O_2) = 0.10 \text{ g } O_2$
(2) The cathode reaction (electrolysis of molten NaCl) is
$$Na^+(\text{melt}) + e^- \rightarrow Na(\ell).$$
$(25 \times 10^3 \text{ A})(60 \text{ min})(60 \text{ s/min})(1 \text{ C/1 A} \cdot \text{s})(1 \text{ mol e}^-/96{,}500 \text{ C})(1 \text{ mol Na/mol e}^-)(23 \text{ g Na/1 mol Na}) = 21{,}450 \text{ g Na} = 21 \text{ kg}$

Review & Check

Section 19-1

1. (a) CuS
2. (d) $4\ H^+ + 3\ e^- + NO_3^- \rightarrow NO + 2\ H_2O$
3. (b) $12\ OH^- + Br_2 \rightarrow 2\ BrO_3^- + 6\ H_2O + 10\ e^-$

Section 19-2

1. (b) Electrons transfer from Cd to Ni.
2. (a) Cd is the anode and is negative.
3. (b) NO_3^- ions move from the Ni half-cell to the Cd half-cell, and K^+ ions move from the Cd half-cell to the Ni half-cell.

Section 19-3

1. (b) Lead(IV) oxide is reduced.
2. (b) Sulfuric acid is consumed.

Section 19-4

1. (a) 1.562 V
2. (d) Mg
3. (a) ii and iv

Section 19-5

1. (a) 0.47 V

Section 19-6

1. (b) 6.3×10^{16}

Section 19-7

1. (d) Ag^+

Section 19-8

1. (d) 1450 seconds

Applying Chemical Principles: Sacrifice!

1. An insulator will prevent the flow of electrons from the zinc to copper, preventing zinc from keeping the copper reduced.
3. (e) chromium
5. (a) $Cu(OH)_2(s) + 2\ e^- \rightarrow Cu(s) + 2\ OH^-(aq)$
   (b) $Zn(s) + 2\ OH^-(aq) \rightarrow Zn(OH)_2(s) + 2\ e^-$
   (c) $Cu(OH)_2(s) + Zn(s) \rightarrow Cu(s) + Zn(OH)_2(s)$
   (d) $E = 0.89$ V

Study Questions

19.1 (a) $Cr(s) \rightarrow Cr^{3+}(aq) + 3\ e^-$
Cr is a reducing agent; this is an oxidation reaction.
(b) $AsH_3(g) \rightarrow As(s) + 3\ H^+(aq) + 3\ e^-$
AsH_3 is a reducing agent; this is an oxidation reaction.
(c) $VO_3^-(aq) + 6\ H^+(aq) + 3\ e^- \rightarrow V^{2+}(aq) + 3\ H_2O(\ell)$
$VO_3^-(aq)$ is an oxidizing agent; this is a reduction reaction.
(d) $2\ Ag(s) + 2\ OH^-(aq) \rightarrow Ag_2O(s) + H_2O(\ell) + 2e^-$
Silver is a reducing agent; this is an oxidation reaction.

19.3 (a) $Ag(s) \rightarrow Ag^+(aq) + e^-$
$e^- + NO_3^-(aq) + 2\ H^+(aq) \rightarrow NO_2(g) + H_2O(\ell)$
$Ag(s) + NO_3^-(aq) + 2\ H^+(aq) \rightarrow Ag^+(aq) + NO_2(g) + H_2O(\ell)$
(b) $2[MnO_4^-(aq) + 8\ H^+(aq) + 5\ e^- \rightarrow Mn^{2+}(aq) + 4\ H_2O(\ell)]$
$5[HSO_3^-(aq) + H_2O(\ell) \rightarrow SO_4^{2-}(aq) + 3\ H^+(aq) + 2\ e^-]$
$2\ MnO_4^-(aq) + H^+(aq) + 5\ HSO_3^-(aq) \rightarrow 2\ Mn^{2+}(aq) + 3\ H_2O(\ell) + 5\ SO_4^{2-}(aq)$

(c) $4[Zn(s) \rightarrow Zn^{2+}(aq) + 2\ e^-]$

$2\ NO_3^-(aq) + 10\ H^+(aq) + 8\ e^- \rightarrow N_2O(g) + 5\ H_2O(\ell)$

$4\ Zn(s) + 2\ NO_3^-(aq) + 10\ H^+(aq) \rightarrow 4\ Zn^{2+}(aq) + N_2O(g) + 5\ H_2O(\ell)$

(d) $Cr(s) \rightarrow Cr^{3+}(aq) + 3\ e^-$

$3\ e^- + NO_3^-(aq) + 4\ H^+(aq) \rightarrow NO(g) + 2\ H_2O(\ell)$

$Cr(s) + NO_3^-(aq) + 4\ H^+(aq) \rightarrow Cr^{3+}(aq) + NO(g) + 2\ H_2O(\ell)$

19.5 (a) $2[Al(s) + 4\ OH^-(aq) \rightarrow Al(OH)_4^-(aq) + 3\ e^-]$

$3[2\ H_2O(\ell) + 2\ e^- \rightarrow H_2(g) + 2\ OH^-(aq)]$

$2\ Al(s) + 2\ OH^-(aq) + 6\ H_2O(\ell) \rightarrow 2\ Al(OH)_4^-(aq) + 3\ H_2(g)$

(b) $2[CrO_4^{2-}(aq) + 4\ H_2O(\ell) + 3\ e^- \rightarrow Cr(OH)_3(s) + 5\ OH^-(aq)]$

$3[SO_3^{2-}(aq) + 2\ OH^-(aq) \rightarrow SO_4^{2-}(aq) + H_2O(\ell) + 2\ e^-]$

$2\ CrO_4^{2-}(aq) + 3\ SO_3^{2-}(aq) + 5\ H_2O(\ell) \rightarrow 2\ Cr(OH)_3(s) + 3\ SO_4^{2-}(aq) + 4\ OH^-(aq)$

(c) $Zn(s) + 4\ OH^-(aq) \rightarrow [Zn(OH)_4]^{2-}(aq) + 2\ e^-$

$Cu(OH)_2(s) + 2\ e^- \rightarrow Cu(s) + 2\ OH^-(aq)$

$Zn(s) + 2\ OH^-(aq) + Cu(OH)_2(s) \rightarrow [Zn(OH)_4]^{2-}(aq) + Cu(s)$

(d) $3[HS^-(aq) + OH^-(aq) \rightarrow S(s) + H_2O(\ell) + 2\ e^-]$

$ClO_3^-(aq) + 3\ H_2O(\ell) + 6\ e^- \rightarrow Cl^-(aq) + 6\ OH^-(aq)$

$3\ HS^-(aq) + ClO_3^-(aq) \rightarrow 3\ S(s) + Cl^-(aq) + 3\ OH^-(aq)$

19.7 Electrons flow from the Cr electrode to the Fe electrode. Negative ions move via the salt bridge from the Fe/Fe^{2+} half-cell to the Cr/Cr^{3+} half-cell (and positive ions move in the opposite direction).

Anode (oxidation): $Cr(s) \rightarrow Cr^{3+}(aq) + 3\ e^-$

Cathode (reduction): $Fe^{2+}(aq) + 2\ e^- \rightarrow Fe(s)$

19.9 (a) Oxidation: $Fe(s) \rightarrow Fe^{2+}(aq) + 2\ e^-$
Reduction: $O_2(g) + 4\ H^+(aq) + 4\ e^- \rightarrow 2\ H_2O(\ell)$
Overall: $2\ Fe(s) + O_2(g) + 4\ H^+(aq) \rightarrow 2\ Fe^{2+}(aq) + 2\ H_2O(\ell)$

(b) Anode, oxidation: $Fe(s) \rightarrow Fe^{2+}(aq) + 2\ e^-$
Cathode, reduction: $O_2(g) + 4\ H^+(aq) + 4\ e^- \rightarrow 2\ H_2O(\ell)$

(c) Electrons flow from the negative anode (Fe) to the positive cathode (site of the O_2 half-reaction). Negative ions move through the salt bridge from the cathode compartment in which the O_2 reduction occurs to the anode compartment in which Fe oxidation occurs (and positive ions move in the opposite direction).

19.11 (a) Reduction of Fe^{3+} ions by copper.

Reduction: $Fe^{3+}(aq) + e^- \rightarrow Fe^{2+}(aq)$

Oxidation: $Cu(s) \rightarrow Cu^{2+}(aq) + 2\ e^-$

Overall: $2\ Fe^{3+}(aq) + Cu(s) \rightarrow 2\ Fe^{2+}(aq) + Cu^{2+}(aq)$

(b) Reduction of Fe^{3+} ions by lead

Reduction: $Fe^{3+}(aq) + e^- \rightarrow Fe^{2+}(aq)$

Oxidation: $Pb(s) + SO_4^{2-}(aq) \rightarrow PbSO_4(s) + 2\ e^-$

Overall: $Pb(s) + SO_4^{2-}(aq) + 2\ Fe^{3+}(aq) \rightarrow PbSO_4(s) + 2\ Fe^{2+}(aq)$

19.13 $Cu(s)|Cu^{2+}(aq)||Cl^-(aq)|Cl_2(g)|Pt$

19.15 (a) All are primary batteries, not rechargeable.
(b) Dry cells and alkaline batteries have Zn anodes and are primary batteries. Ni-Cd batteries have a cadmium anode and are rechargeable.
(c) Dry cells have an acidic environment, whereas the environment is alkaline for alkaline and Ni-Cd cells.

19.17 (a) $E°_{cell} = -1.298$ V; not product-favored
(b) $E°_{cell} = -0.51$ V; not product-favored
(c) $E°_{cell} = -1.023$ V; not product-favored
(d) $E°_{cell} = +0.028$ V; product-favored

19.19 (a) $Sn^{2+}(aq) + 2\ Ag(s) \rightarrow Sn(s) + 2\ Ag^+(aq)$
$E°_{cell} = -0.94$ V; not product-favored
(b) $3\ Sn^{4+}(aq) + 2\ Al(s) \rightarrow 3\ Sn^{2+}(aq) + 2\ Al^{3+}(aq)$
$E°_{cell} = +1.81$ V; product-favored
(c) $2\ ClO_3^-(aq) + 10\ Ce^{3+}(aq) + 12\ H^+(aq) \rightarrow Cl_2(aq) + 10\ Ce^{4+}(aq) + 6\ H_2O(\ell)$
$E°_{cell} = -0.14$ V; not product-favored
(d) $3\ Cu(s) + 2\ NO_3^-(aq) + 8\ H^+(aq) \rightarrow 3\ Cu^{2+}(aq) + 2\ NO(g) + 4\ H_2O(\ell)$
$E°_{cell} = +0.62$ V; product-favored

19.21 (a) Al
(b) Zn and Al
(c) $Fe^{2+}(aq) + Sn(s) \rightarrow Fe(s) + Sn^{2+}(aq)$; reactant-favored at equilibrium
(d) $Zn^{2+}(aq) + Sn(s) \rightarrow Zn(s) + Sn^{2+}(aq)$; reactant-favored at equilibrium

19.23 Best reducing agent, Cr(s) (Use Appendix M.)

19.25 Ag^+

19.27 See Example 19.6
(a) F_2, most readily reduced
(b) F_2 and Cl_2

19.29 $E°_{cell} = +0.3923$ V. When $[Zn(OH)_4^{2-}] = [OH^-] = 0.025$ M and $P(H_2) = 1.0$ bar, $E_{cell} = 0.345$ V.

19.31 $E°_{cell} = +1.563$ V and $E_{cell} = +1.58$ V

19.33 $E°_{cell} = +1.563$ V. When $E_{cell} = 1.48$ V, $n = 2$, and $[Zn^{2+}] = 1.0$ M, the concentration of $Ag^+ = 0.040$ M.

19.35 (a) $\Delta_rG° = -29.0$ kJ; $K = 1 \times 10^5$
(b) $\Delta_rG° = +89$ kJ; $K = 3 \times 10^{-16}$

19.37 $E°_{cell}$ for $AgBr(s) \rightarrow Ag^+(aq) + Br^-(aq)$ is -0.7281.
$K_{sp} = 4.9 \times 10^{-13}$

19.39 $K_{formation} = 2 \times 10^{25}$

19.41 See Figure 19.19. Electrons from the battery or other source enter the cathode where they are transferred to Na^+ ions, reducing the ions to Na metal. Chloride ions move toward the positively charged anode where an electron is transferred from each Cl^- ion, and Cl_2 gas is formed.

19.43 O_2 from the oxidation of water is more likely than F_2. See Example 19.11.

19.45 See Example 19.11.
(a) Cathode: $2\ H_2O(\ell) + 2\ e^- \rightarrow H_2(g) + 2\ OH^-(aq)$
(b) Anode: $2\ Br^-(aq) \rightarrow Br_2(\ell) + 2\ e^-$

19.47 Mass of Ni = 0.0334 g

19.49 Time = 2300 s or 38 min

19.51 Time = 250 h

19.53 (a) $UO_2^+(aq) + 4\ H^+(aq) + e^- \rightarrow U^{4+}(aq) + 2\ H_2O(\ell)$
(b) $ClO_3^-(aq) + 6\ H^+(aq) + 6\ e^- \rightarrow Cl^-(aq) + 3\ H_2O(\ell)$
(c) $N_2H_4(aq) + 4\ OH^-(aq) \rightarrow N_2(g) + 4\ H_2O(\ell) + 4\ e^-$
(d) $ClO^-(aq) + H_2O(\ell) + 2\ e^- \rightarrow Cl^-(aq) + 2\ OH^-(aq)$

19.55 (a, c) The electrode at the right is a magnesium anode. (Magnesium metal supplies electrons and is oxidized to Mg^{2+} ions.) Electrons pass through the wire to the silver cathode, where Ag^+ ions are reduced to silver metal. Nitrate ions move via the salt bridge from the $AgNO_3$ solution to the $Mg(NO_3)_2$ solution (and Na^+ ions move in the opposite direction). A salt bridge is needed to maintain electrical neutrality in each half-cell and to complete the electrical circuit.
(b) Anode: $Mg(s) \rightarrow Mg^{2+}(aq) + 2\ e^-$
Cathode: $Ag^+(aq) + e^- \rightarrow Ag(s)$
Net reaction: $Mg(s) + 2\ Ag^+(aq) \rightarrow Mg^{2+}(aq) + 2\ Ag(s)$

19.57 (a) For 1.7 V:
Use chromium as the anode to reduce $Ag^+(aq)$ to Ag(s) at the cathode. The cell potential is +1.71 V.
(b) For 0.5 V:
(i) Use copper as the anode to reduce silver ions to silver metal at the cathode. The cell potential is +0.46 V.
(ii) Use silver as the anode to reduce chlorine to chloride ions. The cell potential would be +0.56 V. (In practice, this setup is not likely to work well because the product would be insoluble silver chloride.)

19.59 (a) $Zn^{2+}(aq)$ (c) Zn(s)
(b) $Au^+(aq)$ (d) Au(s)
(e) Yes, Sn(s) will reduce Cu^{2+}.
(f) No, Ag(s) can only reduce $Au^+(aq)$.
(g) Cu^{2+}, Ag^+ and Au^+
(h) $Ag^+(aq)$ can oxidize Cu, Sn, Co, and Zn.

19.61 (a) The cathode is the site of reduction, so the half-reaction must be $2\ H^+(aq) + 2\ e^- \rightarrow H_2(g)$. This is the case with the following half-reactions: $Cr^{3+}(aq) \rightarrow Cr(s)$, $Fe^{2+}(aq) \rightarrow Fe(s)$, and $Mg^{2+}(aq) \rightarrow Mg(s)$.
(b) Choosing from the half-cells in part (a), the reaction of Mg(s) and $H^+(aq)$ would produce the most positive potential (2.37 V), and the reaction of H_2 with Cu^{2+} would produce the least positive potential (+0.337 V).

19.63 8.1×10^5 g Al

19.65 (a) $E°_{anode} = -0.268$ V
(b) $K_{sp} = 2 \times 10^{-5}$

19.67 $\Delta_r G° = -409$ kJ

19.69 6700 kWh; 820 kg Na; 1300 kg Cl_2

19.71 Ru^{2+}, $Ru(NO_3)_2$

19.73 9.5×10^6 g Cl_2 per day

19.75 Anode: $2\ H_2O(\ell) \rightarrow O_2(g) + 4\ H^+(aq) + 4\ e^-$
Cathode: $Cu^{2+}(aq) + 2\ e^- \rightarrow Cu(s)$

19.77 The rate of the reaction with H_2O is more rapid than the rate of the reaction with NO_3^-.
Products formed at anode: $O_2(g)$ and $H^+(aq)$
Anode half-reaction: $2\ H_2O(\ell) \rightarrow O_2(g) + 4\ H^+(aq) + 4\ e^-$

19.79 Under standard conditions, the spontaneous reaction is $Hg^{2+}(aq) + 2\ Fe^{2+}(aq) \rightarrow Hg(\ell) + 2\ Fe^{3+}(aq)$ with $E° = 0.084$ V.
Under the conditions present, $E = -0.244$ V. The reaction is not spontaneous in the same direction as under standard conditions but in the opposite direction: $Hg(\ell) + 2\ Fe^{3+}(aq) \rightarrow Hg^{2+}(aq) + 2\ Fe^{2+}(aq)$. Under these conditions, the anode for the spontaneous reaction is the $Hg(\ell)|Hg^{2+}(aq, 0.020\ M)$ electrode and the measured voltage will be 0.244 V.

19.81 $E° = 0.771$ V. When $[H^+] = 1.0 \times 10^{-7}$ M, $E = 1.185$ V. The reaction is more favorable at a lower $[H^+]$ (higher pH). The reaction is thus less favorable at lower pH.

19.83 (a) See Figure 19.5
In this case, both electrodes are made of silver metal. On one side, the solution contains 1.0×10^{-5} M Ag^+ and on the other the solution contains 1.0 M Ag^+. The cathode is the electrode on the side that has the 1.0 M Ag^+ solution [half-reaction: $Ag^+(aq) + e^- \rightarrow Ag(s)$], and the anode is the electrode on the side that has the 1.0×10^{-5} M Ag^+ solution [half-reaction: $Ag(s) \rightarrow Ag^+(aq) + e^-$]. Connecting the two electrodes is a wire. Electrons flow through the wire from the anode to the cathode. A salt bridge also connects the two compartments.
(b) $E = 0.30$ V

19.85 (a) $K = 3.4 \times 10^{-10}$; reactant-favored at equilibrium
(b) $K = 3.0$; product-favored at equilibrium

19.87 (a) $\Delta_r G° = -3.6 \times 10^2$ kJ/mol-rxn
(b) $\Delta_r G° = -79$ kJ/mol-rxn

19.89 (a) $2[Ag^+(aq) + e^- \rightarrow Ag(s)]$
$C_6H_5CHO(aq) + H_2O(\ell) \rightarrow C_6H_5CO_2H(aq) + 2\ H^+(aq) + 2\ e^-$
$2Ag^+(aq) + C_6H_5CHO(aq) + H_2O(\ell) \rightarrow C_6H_5CO_2H(aq) + 2\ H^+(aq) + 2\ Ag(s)$
(b) $3[CH_3CH_2OH(aq) + H_2O(\ell) \rightarrow CH_3CO_2H(aq) + 4\ H^+(aq) + 4\ e^-]$
$2[Cr_2O_7^{2-}(aq) + 14\ H^+(aq) + 6\ e^- \rightarrow 2\ Cr^{3+}(aq) + 7\ H_2O(\ell)]$
$3\ CH_3CH_2OH(aq) + 2\ Cr_2O_7^{2-}(aq) + 16\ H^+(aq) \rightarrow 3\ CH_3CO_2H(aq) + 4\ Cr^{3+}(aq) + 11\ H_2O(\ell)$

19.91 (a) 0.974 kJ/g
(b) 0.60 kJ/g
(c) The silver-zinc battery produces more energy per gram of reactants.

19.93 (a) $2\ NO_3^-(aq) + 3\ Mn^{2+}(aq) + 2\ H_2O(\ell) \rightarrow 2\ NO(g) + 3\ MnO_2(s) + 4\ H^+(aq)$
$3\ MnO_2(s) + 4\ H^+(aq) + 2\ NH_4^+(aq) \rightarrow N_2(g) + 3\ Mn^{2+}(aq) + 6\ H_2O(\ell)$
(b) $E°$ for reduction of NO_3^- with Mn^{2+} is −0.27 V.
$E°$ for oxidation of NH_4^+ with MnO_2 is +1.50 V.

19.95 (a) $Fe^{2+}(aq) + 2\ e^- \rightarrow Fe(s)$
$2[Fe^{2+}(aq) \rightarrow Fe^{3+}(aq) + e^-]$
$3\ Fe^{2+}(aq) \rightarrow Fe(s) + 2\ Fe^{3+}(aq)$
(b) $E°_{cell} = -1.21$ V; not product-favored
(c) $K = 1 \times 10^{-41}$

19.97 (a) + 4 in CoO_2 and +3 in $LiCoO_2$
(b) Cathode reaction:
$CoO_2(s) + Li^+(Solv) + e^- \rightarrow LiCoO_2(s)$
Anode reaction: Li(on carbon) $\rightarrow Li^+(solv) + e^-$
(c) No, because Li, an alkali metal, would react directly with water (giving H_2 and LiOH)

19.99 (a)

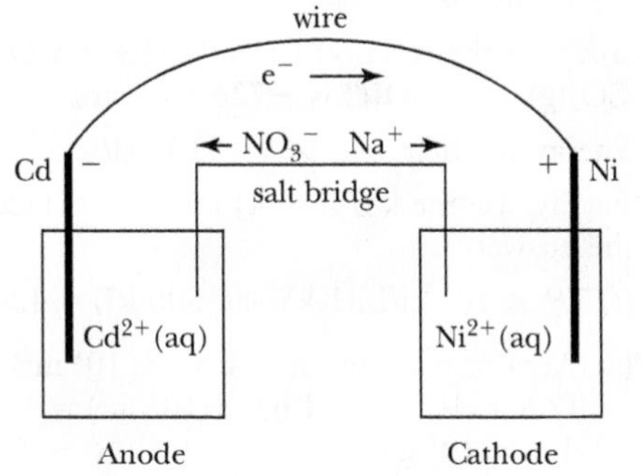

(b) Anode: $Cd(s) \rightarrow Cd^{2+}(aq) + 2\ e^-$
Cathode: $Ni^{2+}(aq) + 2\ e^- \rightarrow Ni(s)$
Net: $Cd(s) + Ni^{2+}(aq) \rightarrow Cd^{2+}(aq) + Ni(s)$
(c) The anode is negative and the cathode is positive.
(d) $E°_{cell} = E°_{cathode} - E°_{anode} = (-0.25\ V) - (-0.40\ V) = +0.15\ V$
(e) Electrons flow from anode (Cd) to cathode (Ni).
(f) Positive ions move from the anode compartment to the cathode compartment. Anions move in the opposite direction.

(g) $K = 1 \times 10^5$
(h) $E_{cell} = 0.21$ V; yes, the net reaction is still the same.
(i) 480 h

19.101 0.054 g Au

19.103 I^- is the strongest reducing agent of the three halide ions. Iodide ion reduces Cu^{2+} to Cu^+, forming insoluble CuI(s).
$2\ Cu^{2+}(aq) + 4\ I^-(aq) \rightarrow 2\ CuI(s) + I_2(aq)$

19.105 (a) 92 g HF required; 230 g CF_3SO_2F and 9.3 g H_2 isolated
(b) H_2 is produced at the cathode.
(c) 48 kWh

19.107 290 h

19.109 (a) 3.6 mol glucose and 22 mol O_2
(b) 86 mol electrons
(c) 96 amps
(d) 96 watts

Chapter 20

Case Study

What to Do with All of That CO_2? More on Green Chemistry

1. $(9.1 \times 10^9$ g C)(1 mol C/12.01 g C)(1 mol CO_2/1 mol C)(44.01 g CO_2/1 mol CO_2) = 3.3×10^{10} g CO_2

2. $(1.0 \times 10^6$ g CO_2)(1 mol CO_2/44.01 g CO_2)(1 mol $(NH_4)_2CO_3$/1 mol CO_2)(96.09 g $(NH_4)_2CO_3$/1 mol $(NH_4)_2CO_3$) = 2.2×10^6 g $(NH_4)_2CO_3$

Review & Check

Section 20-1

1. (b) CH_4
2. (a) The O—O bond in O_2

Section 20-2

1. (d) $Al_2(SO_4)_3$
2. Melting of the polar ice cap will result in a rise in sea levels.

Section 20-3

1. (b) hydroelectric power
2. (c) nuclear
3. (a) Light-emitting diodes

Section 20-4

1. (d) H_2
2. (c) Oxygen gas is a component of some sources of natural gas.
3. (a) biofuels

Section 20-5

1. (c) Hydrogen is explosive.
2. (c) Petroleum is a mixture of hydrocarbons.

Section 20-6

1. (d) O_2

Applying Chemical Principles: Alkalinity of Water Supplies

1. (a) At pH = 7.0: from the alpha plot $[CO_3^{2-}]$ is almost zero and $[OH^-] = 1.0 \times 10^{-7}$ M

   $[Alk] = 1.00 \times 10^{-3} = [HCO_3^-] + 2\,(0) + (1.00 \times 10^{-7})$

   Therefore, $[HCO_3^-] = 1.00 \times 10^{-3}$ M

   To find $[H_2CO_3]$ use $K_{a1} = 4.2 \times 10^{-7}$ for

   $H_2CO_3(aq) + H_2O(\ell) \rightleftharpoons HCO_3^-(aq) + H_3O^+(aq)$

   which gives $[H_2CO_3] = 2.4 \times 10^{-4}$ M

   (b) At pH = 10.0

   $[Alk] = 1.00 \times 10^{-3} = [HCO_3^-] + 2\,[CO_3^{2-}] + [OH^-]$

   Here $[OH^-] = 1.00 \times 10^{-10}$ M and $[CO_3^{2-}] = K_{a2}[HCO_3^-]/1.0 \times 10^{-10}$

   Solving for $[HCO_3^-]$ gives 4.6×10^{-4} M

   Now use $K_{a2} = 4.8 \times 10^{-11} = [CO_3^{2-}][H_3O^+]/[HCO_3^-]$

   and find $[CO_3^{2-}] = 2.2 \times 10^{-4}$ M

2. Dissolved carbon at pH = 7.0

   $[C] = 2.4 \times 10^{-4}\text{ M} + 1.00 \times 10^{-3}\text{ M} + 0 = 1.24 \times 10^{-4}$ M

   Dissolved carbon at pH = 10.0 (at this pH all CO_2 is in the form of CO_3^{2-} or HCO_3^- ions).

   $[C] = 0 + 4.6 \times 10^{-4}\text{ M} + 2.2 \times 10^{-4}\text{ M} = 6.8 \times 10^{-4}$ M

Study Questions

20.1 For gases, ppm refers to numbers of particles, and hence to mole fractions. Gas pressure exerted is directly proportional to mole fraction. Thus, 40,000 ppm water vapor would exert a pressure of 40,000/1,000,000 of one atmosphere, or 30.4 mm Hg (0.040 × 760 mm Hg). This would be the case at a little over 29 °C, at 100% humidity.

20.3 (a) H—O—N=O

Electron-pair geometry around N is trigonal planar and around O (between H and N) is tetrahedral.

(b) 5.95×10^{-7} m (or 595 nm)

20.5 0.0115 mg/L of air; 9.7 ppm

20.7 $[HCO_3^-]/[CO_3^-] = 170$

20.9 The amount of NaCl is limited by the amount of sodium present. From a 1.0-L sample of seawater, a maximum of 0.460 mol NaCl could be obtained. The mass of this amount of NaCl is 26.9 g [(0.460 mol/L) (1.00 L)(58.43 g NaCl/1 mol NaCl) = 26.9 g].

20.11 $Ca(OH)_2(s) + Mg^{2+}(aq) \rightarrow Mg(OH)_2(s) + Ca^{2+}(aq)$
$Mg(OH)_2(s) + 2\,H_3O^+(aq) \rightarrow Mg^{2+}(aq) + 4\,H_2O(\ell)$
$MgCl_2(\ell) \rightarrow Mg(s) + Cl_2(g)$

20.13 $NH_4^+(aq) + NO_2^-(aq) \rightarrow N_2(g) + 2\,H_2O(\ell)$
$2\,NH_4^+(aq) + 3\,O_2(g) \rightarrow 2\,NO_2^-(aq) + 2\,H_2O(\ell) + 4\,H^+(aq)$

20.15 (a) From methane: $H_2O(g) + CH_4(g) \rightarrow 3\,H_2(g) + CO(g)$

37.7 g of H_2 produced

(b) From petroleum: $H_2O(g) + CH_2(\ell) \rightarrow 2\,H_2(g) + CO\,(g)$

28.7 g H_2 produced

(c) From coal: $H_2O(g) + C(s) \rightarrow H_2(g) + CO(g)$

16.8 g H_2 produced

20.17 70. lb (453.6 g/lb)(33 kJ/g) = 1.0×10^6 kJ

20.19 Assume burning oil produces 43 kJ/g (the value for crude petroleum in Table 20.3)

7.0 gal(3.785 L/gal)(1000 cm³/L)(0.8 g/cm³)(43 kJ/g) = 0.9×10^6 kJ. Uncertainty in the numbers is one significant figure. This value is close to the value for the energy obtained by burning from 70 kg of coal (calculated in Question 20.17).

20.21 (a) Isooctane:

$C_8H_{18}(\ell) + 25/2\,O_2(g) \rightarrow 8\,CO_2(g) + 9\,H_2O(\ell)$

$\Delta_rH° = -5461.2$ kJ/mol-rxn (or −47,809 kJ/kg C_8H_{18})

Ethanol:

$C_2H_5OH(\ell) + 3\,O_2(g) \rightarrow 2\,CO_2(g) + 3\,H_2O(\ell)$

$\Delta_rH° = -1367.5$ kJ/mol-rxn (or −29,684 kJ/kg C_2H_5OH)

Isooctane releases more energy per kilogram.

(b) Isooctane = 70.0 mol CO_2 and ethanol = 43.4 mol CO_2. Ethanol produces less CO_2 per kilogram.

(c) On the basis of this simplistic comparison, there is not a clear winner. Isooctane releases more energy per kilogram but also releases more CO_2 per kilogram.

20.23 $\Delta_rH°$ for the reaction $CH_3OH(\ell) + 1.5\,O_2(g) \rightarrow CO_2(g) + 2\,H_2O(\ell)$ is −726.8 kJ/mol-rxn.

Energy per liter = -17.9×10^3 kJ/L.

Finally, use the kW-h to kJ conversion factor to obtain the answer.

[(17.9×10^3 kJ/L)(1 kW-h/3600 kJ) = 4.96 kW-h/L].

20.25 (a) Area of parking lot = 1.63×10^4 m²

(2.6×10^7 J/m²)(1.63×10^4 m²) = 4.2×10^{11} J

(b) 1.3×10^7 g C

20.27 Energy per gallon of gas = 1.34×10^5 kJ/gal

Energy to travel 1 mile = 2430 kJ

20.29 (a) The cage is a dodecahedron, so it has 20 vertices, each of which is the O atom of a water molecule (the red spheres in the model are O atoms).

(b) 30 hydrogen bonds. (This estimate is made by assuming there is an H bond on each of the edges.)

(c) A dodecahedron has 12 faces.

20.31 (a) $C_{13}H_{27}CO_2CH_3(\ell) + 43/2\ O_2(g) \rightarrow 15\ CO_2(g) + 15\ H_2O(g)$

(b) $\Delta_r H° = -8759.1$ kJ/mol-rxn

(c) Hexadecane ($\Delta H° = -9951.2$ kJ/mol) provides more energy per mole of fuel than methyl myristate ($\Delta H° = -8759.1$ kJ/mol).

Hexadecane ($\Delta H° = -3.4 \times 10^4$ kJ/L) also provides more energy per liter of fuel than methyl myristate ($\Delta H° = -3.1 \times 10^4$ kJ/L).

20.33 (a)

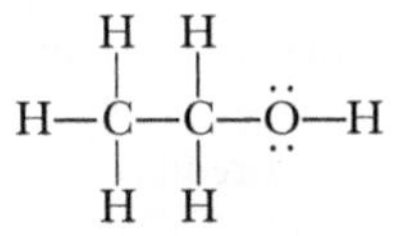

Ethanol

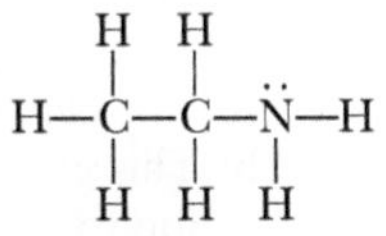

Ethylamine

Both carbon atoms are tetrahedral; oxygen atom is bent.

Both carbon atoms are tetrahedral. Nitrogen atom is pyramidal.

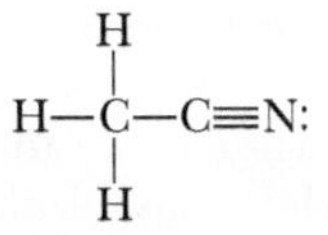

Acetonitrile

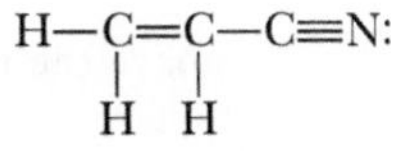

Acrylonitrile

CH_3 carbon atom is tetrahedral. Carbon atom of CN group is linear.

CH_2 and CH carbon atoms are trigonal planar. Carbon atom of CN group is linear.

(b) $CH_3CH_2OH + NH_3 \rightarrow CH_3CH_2NH_2 + H_2O$
$CH_3CH_2NH_2 + O_2 \rightarrow CH_3CN + 2\ H_2O$

(c) Reactants (CH_3CH_2OH, NH_3, and O_2) have 2 C, 9 H, 1 N, and 3 O; molar mass = 95. Product (CH_3CN) has 2 C, 3 H, and 1 N; molar mass = 41. Atom economy = (41/95) × 100% = 43%

20.35 Using a C—Cl bond energy of 339 kJ/mol, the wavelength of the required radiation is 3.53×10^{-7} m or 353 nm. This is in the ultraviolet region.

20.37 $NH_4^+(aq) + 2\ H_2O(\ell) \rightarrow NO_2^-(aq) + 8\ H^+(aq) + 6\ e^-$
$NO_2^-(aq) + H_2O(\ell) \rightarrow NO_3^-(aq) + 2\ H^+(aq) + 2\ e^-$

20.39 3.1×10^{13} atoms gold

20.41 (a) Only 92% of the ice is submerged, and the water displaced by ice (the volume of ice under the surface of water) is 23 cm^3 (0.92×25 cm^3 = 23 cm^3). Thus, the liquid level in the graduated cylinder will be 123 mL.

(b) Melting 25 cm^3 of ice will produce 23 mL of liquid water [25 cm^3 ice (0.92 g H_2O/cm^3 ice) (1.0 cm^3 liquid H_2O/g H_2O) = 23 cm^3 liquid H_2O]. The water level will be 123 mL (the same as in (a); that is, the water level won't rise as the ice melts).

20.43 Non-renewable resources are not replenished when used. Renewable resources are, for the foreseeable future, not depleted when used. Non-renewable: coal, natural gas; renewable: solar, geothermal energy, wind power.

20.45 Troposphere: ozone is toxic and a health hazard, particularly with regard to respiratory problems. Stratosphere: The presence of O_3 is beneficial. Ozone shields the planet from harmful ultraviolet radiation.

20.47 Mercury: from coal burning power plants

Lead: paint residues (before 1970), soil (from the use of tetraethyllead in gasoline), water supplies (from use of lead in pipes and plumbing

Arsenic: some ground water sources, residual from some common chemicals (use in wood treatment, for example)

20.49 (a) Fracking: Positive; greatly increased supply and decreased cost of this energy resource. Negative: contamination of water supplies, excessive water use, release of CH_4 into the atmosphere.

(b) Ethanol in gasoline: Positive: this is a renewable resource. Negative: serious questions about energy balance (energy required to produce ethanol versus energy generated with its use.) Diverts foodstuff from human consumption.

(c) Cars powered by electricity and natural gas: Positive: energy efficiency, zero or low air pollution. Negative: high relative costs even with government subsidies, lack of energy distribution network (electrical distribution stations, natural gas).

20.51 The main pollutant is SO_2, arising from the burning of coal. Some SO_3 in the atmosphere arises from oxidation of SO_2, and this combines with water to give H_2SO_4, a primary component of acid rain. Removing SO_2 is best done at the source, by extracting it from the flue gases of coal burning plants. This can be done by passing the gases from of coal oxidation through a scrubber containing a $CaCO_3$ slurry.

Chapter 21

Case Studies

Hard Water

1. For Mg^{2+}: (50. mg)(1 mmol Mg^{2+}/24.31 mg) (1 mmol CaO/mmol Mg^{2+})(56.08 mg CaO/1 mmol CaO) = 120 mg CaO

For Ca^{2+}: (150 mg)(1 mmol Ca^{2+}/40.08 mg) (1 mmol CaO/mmol Ca^{2+})(56.08 mg CaO/1 mmol CaO) = 210 mg CaO

Total CaO = 120 mg + 210 mg = 330 mg (two significant figures)

We get 2 mol $CaCO_3$ per mole Ca^{2+} and 1 mol each of $CaCO_3$ and $MgCO_3$ per mole Mg^{2+}

$CaCO_3$ from Ca^{2+} reaction: (0.15 g Ca^{2+}) (1 mol/40.08 g Ca^{2+})(2 mol $CaCO_3$/1 mol Ca^{2+}) (100.1 g $CaCO_3$/1 mol $CaCO_3$) = 0.75 g

$CaCO_3$ from Mg^{2+} reaction: (0.050 g Mg^{2+}) (1 mol/24.31 g Mg^{2+})(1 mol $CaCO_3$/1 mol Mg^{2+}) (100.1 g $CaCO_3$/1 mol $CaCO_3$) = 0.21 g

$MgCO_3$ from Mg^{2+} reaction: (0.050 g Mg^{2+}) (1 mol/24.31 g Mg^{2+})(1 mol $MgCO_3$/1 mol Mg^{2+}) (84.31 g $MgCO_3$/1 mol $MgCO_3$) = 0.17 g

Total mass of solids = 0.75 g + 0.21 g + 0.17 g = 1.1 g (two significant figures)

2. $CaCO_3(s) + 2\ CH_3CO_2H(aq) \rightarrow Ca(CH_3CO_2)_2(aq) + H_2O(\ell) + CO_2(g)$

This is a gas-forming reaction.

Lead, Beethoven, and a Mystery Solved

1. 50 ppb is 50 g in 1×10^9 g of blood. Assume the density of blood is 1.0 g/mL. In 1.0×10^3 mL (i.e., 1.0 L) of blood, there will be 50×10^{-6} g of Pb. From this:

   $(50 \times 10^{-6}$ g) (1 mol Pb/207.2 g Pb) (6.022×10^{23} atoms Pb/mol Pb) = 1.5×10^{17} atoms Pb

2. (750 mL wine)(1.0 g wine/mL wine) (2000 g Pb/1,000,000 g wine) = 1.5 g Pb

A Healthy Saltwater Aquarium and the Nitrogen Cycle

1. $2\ NH_4^+(aq) + 4\ OH^-(aq) + 3\ O_2(aq) \rightarrow 2\ NO_2^-(aq) + 6\ H_2O(\ell)$

2. Reduction half-reaction:

   $2\ NO_3^-(aq) + 6\ H_2O(\ell) + 10\ e^- \rightarrow N_2(g) + 12\ OH^-(aq)$

   Oxidation half-reaction:

   $CH_3OH(aq) + 6\ OH^-(aq) \rightarrow CO_2(aq) + 5\ H_2O(\ell) + 6\ e^-$

   Net: $6\ NO_3^-(aq) + 5\ CH_3OH \rightarrow 3\ N_2(g) + 5\ CO_2(aq) + 6\ OH^-(aq) + 7\ H_2O(\ell)$

3. HCO_3^- is the predominant species. Recall that when acid and base concentrations are equal, pH = pK_a. If H_2CO_3 and HCO_3^- are present in equal concentrations, the pH would be about 6.4. If HCO_3^- and CO_3^{2-} are present in equal concentrations, the pH would be 10.3. For the pH to be about 8 (in a salt water aquarium), [HCO_3^-] would have to be higher than either of the other carbonate species.

4. Concentration of N in mg/L = [(1.7×10^4 kg NO_3^-) (10^6 mg NO_3^-/kg NO_3^-)(14.0 mg N/62.0 mg NO_3^-)]/ (2.2×10^7 L) = 1.7×10^2 mg/L

   Concentration of NO_3^- in ppm (mg/L) = (1.7×10^4 kg) (10^6 mg/kg)/(2.2×10^7 L) = 770 mg/L

   Concentration of NO_3^- in mol/L = [(1.7×10^4 kg)(10^3 g/kg)(1 mol/62.0 g)]/(2.2×10^7 L) = 0.012 mol/L

Check Your Understanding

21.1 (a) $2\ Na(s) + Br_2(\ell) \rightarrow 2\ NaBr(s)$
(b) $Ca(s) + Se(s) \rightarrow CaSe(s)$
(c) $2\ Pb(s) + O_2(g) \rightarrow 2\ PbO(s)$

Lead(II) oxide, a red compound commonly called *litharge,* is the most widely used inorganic lead compound. Maroon-colored lead(IV) oxide is the product of lead oxidation in lead-acid storage batteries. Other oxides such as Pb_3O_4 also exist.

(d) $2\ Al(s) + 3\ Cl_2(g) \rightarrow 2\ AlCl_3(s)$

21.2 (a) H_2Te
(b) Na_3AsO_4
(c) $SeCl_6$
(d) $HBrO_4$

21.3 (a) NH_4^+ (ammonium ion)
(b) O_2^{2-} (peroxide ion)
(c) N_2H_4 (hydrazine)
(d) NF_3 (nitrogen trifluoride)

21.4 (a) In Na_2Cl, chlorine would have the unlikely charge of 2− (to balance the two positive charges of the two Na^+ ions).
(b) This compound would require either the calcium ion to have the formula Ca^+ or the acetate ion to have the formula $CH_3CO_2^{2-}$. In all of its compounds, calcium occurs as the Ca^{2+} ion. The acetate ion, formed from acetic acid by loss of H^+, has a 1− charge.
(c) In Mg_2O, the magnesium ions would need to have the incorrect charge of 1+ to balance charge of the O^{2-} ion or else the oxygen would need to have the incorrect charge of 4− to balance the charge of the two Mg^{2+} ions. Neither of these possibilities is acceptable.

Review & Check

Section 21-2

1. (d) Ca_2O_3
2. (d) tetraphosphorus decaoxide
3. (b) +3
4. (d) +5

Section 21-3

1. (a) neon
2. (c) the high temperature reaction of methane and water

Section 21-4

1. (c) has a high melting point (>400 °C)
2. (a) Li^+
3. (c) two Na^+ ions and one O_2^{2-} ion

Section 21-5

1. (c) gypsum, $CaSO_4 \cdot 2\ H_2O$
2. (c) converting slaked lime, $Ca(OH)_2$, to lime

Section 21-6

1. (c) third
2. (d) dissolve in acid and in base

Section 21-7

1. (c) SiO_2
2. (c) +4

Section 21-8

1. (c) between 2 and 3
2. (b) Aqueous solutions of ammonia are acidic.
3. (c) +3

Section 21-9

1. (c) +3
2. (d) All electrons in O_2 are paired.

Section 21-10

1. (b) Cl_2
2. (c) F_2 is prepared industrially by electrolysis of aqueous NaF.

Section 21-11

1. (c) XeF_3^+
2. (e) octahedral

Applying Chemical Principles: van Arkel Triangles and Bonding

1. (a) CuZn is metallic.
   (b) GaAs and BP are semiconductors. As and B are metalloids; Ga and P are not. In both compounds, only one element is a metalloid.
   (c) Mg_3N_2 and $SrBr_2$ are ionic. Both are composed of a metal combined with a nonmetal.
   (d) Covalent bonding
   (e) SBr_2 and C_3N_4 are covalent. Both elements in the compounds are nonmetallic.

Study Questions

21.1 $4\ Li(s) + O_2(g) \rightarrow 2\ Li_2O(s)$
$Li_2O(s) + H_2O(\ell) \rightarrow 2\ LiOH(aq)$
$2\ Ca(s) + O_2(g) \rightarrow 2\ CaO(s)$
$CaO(s) + H_2O(\ell) \rightarrow Ca(OH)_2(s)$

21.3 These are the elements of Group 3A: boron, B; aluminum, Al; gallium, Ga; indium, In; and thallium, Tl.

21.5 $2\ Na(s) + Cl_2(g) \rightarrow 2\ NaCl(s)$
The reaction is exothermic and the product is ionic (see Figure 1.2).

21.7 The product, NaCl, is a colorless solid and is soluble in water. Other alkali metal chlorides have similar properties.

21.9 Calcium will not exist in the Earth's crust because the metal reacts with water.

21.11 Increasing basicity: $CO_2 < SiO_2 < SnO_2$

21.13 (a) $2\ Na(s) + Br_2(\ell) \rightarrow 2\ NaBr(s)$
(b) $2\ Mg(s) + O_2(g) \rightarrow 2\ MgO(s)$
(c) $2\ Al(s) + 3\ F_2(g) \rightarrow 2\ AlF_3(s)$
(d) $C(s) + O_2(g) \rightarrow CO_2(g)$

21.15 $2\ H_2(g) + O_2(g) \rightarrow 2\ H_2O(g)$
$H_2(g) + Cl_2(g) \rightarrow 2\ HCl(g)$
$3\ H_2(g) + N_2(g) \rightarrow 2\ NH_3(g)$

21.17 $CH_4(g) + H_2O(g) \rightarrow CO(g) + 3\ H_2(g)$
$\Delta_r H° = +206.2$ kJ; $\Delta_r S° = +214.7$ J/K;
$\Delta_r G° = +142.2$ kJ (at 298 K).

21.19 Step 1: $2\ SO_2(g) + 4\ H_2O(\ell) + 2\ I_2(s) \rightarrow 2\ H_2SO_4(\ell) + 4\ HI(g)$
Step 2: $2\ H_2SO_4(\ell) \rightarrow 2\ H_2O(\ell) + 2\ SO_2(g) + O_2(g)$
Step 3: $4\ HI(g) \rightarrow 2\ H_2(g) + 2\ I_2(g)$
Net: $2\ H_2O(\ell) \rightarrow 2\ H_2(g) + O_2(g)$

21.21 $2\ Na(s) + F_2(g) \rightarrow 2\ NaF(s)$
$2\ Na(s) + Cl_2(g) \rightarrow 2\ NaCl(s)$
$2\ Na(s) + Br_2(\ell) \rightarrow 2\ NaBr(s)$
$2\ Na(s) + I_2(s) \rightarrow 2\ NaI(s)$
The alkali metal halides are white, crystalline solids. They have high melting and boiling points, and they are soluble in water.

21.23 (a) $2\ Cl^-(aq) + 2\ H_2O(\ell) \rightarrow Cl_2(g) + H_2(g) + 2\ OH^-(aq)$
(b) If this were the only process used to produce chlorine, the mass of Cl_2 reported for industrial production would be 0.88 times the mass of NaOH produced (2 mol NaCl, 117 g, would yield 2 mol NaOH, 80 g, and 1 mol Cl_2, 70 g). The amounts quoted indicate a Cl_2 to NaOH mass ratio 0.96. Chlorine is presumably also prepared by other routes than this one.

21.25 $2\ Mg(s) + O_2(g) \rightarrow 2\ MgO(s)$
$3\ Mg(s) + N_2(g) \rightarrow Mg_3N_2(s)$

21.27 $CaCO_3$ is used in agriculture to neutralize acidic soil, to prepare CaO for use in mortar, and in steel production.
$CaCO_3(s) + H_2O(\ell) + CO_2(g) \rightarrow Ca^{2+}(aq) + 2\ HCO_3^-(aq)$

21.29 1.4×10^6 g SO_2

21.31

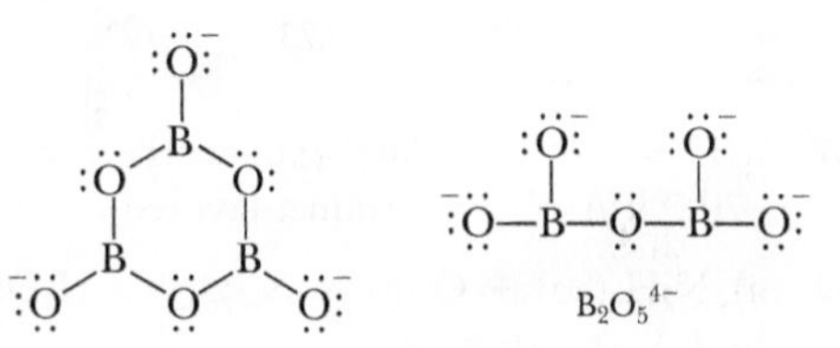

$B_3O_6^{3-}$ $B_2O_5^{4-}$

21.33 (a) $2\ B_5H_9(g) + 12\ O_2(g) \rightarrow 5\ B_2O_3(s) + 9\ H_2O(g)$
(b) Enthalpy of combustion of $B_5H_9 = -4341.2$ kJ/mol. This is more than double the enthalpy of combustion of B_2H_6.
(c) Enthalpy of combustion of $C_2H_6(g)$ [to give $CO_2(g)$ and $H_2O(g)$] $= -1428.7$ kJ/mol. C_2H_6 produces 47.5 kJ/g, whereas diborane produces much more (73.7 kJ/g).

21.35 $2\ Al(s) + 6\ HCl(aq) \rightarrow 2\ Al^{3+}(aq) + 6\ Cl^-(aq) + 3\ H_2(g)$
$2\ Al(s) + 3\ Cl_2(g) \rightarrow 2\ AlCl_3(s)$
$4\ Al(s) + 3\ O_2(g) \rightarrow 2\ Al_2O_3(s)$

21.37 $2\ Al(s) + 2\ OH^-(aq) + 6\ H_2O(\ell) \rightarrow 2\ Al(OH)_4^-(aq) + 3\ H_2(g)$

Volume of H_2 obtained from 13.2 g Al = 18.4 L

21.39 $Al_2O_3(s) + 3\ H_2SO_4(aq) \rightarrow Al_2(SO_4)_3(s) + 3\ H_2O(\ell)$

Mass of H_2SO_4 required = 860 g and mass of Al_2O_3 required = 298 g.

21.41 Pyroxenes have as their basic structural unit an extended chain of linked SiO_4 tetrahedra. The ratio of Si to O is 1:3.

21.43 This structure has a six-member ring of Si atoms with O atom bridges. Each Si also has two O atoms attached. The basic unit is SiO_3^{2-}, and the overall charge is −12 in $[(SiO_3)_6]^{-12}$. (Electron lone pairs are omitted in the following structure.)

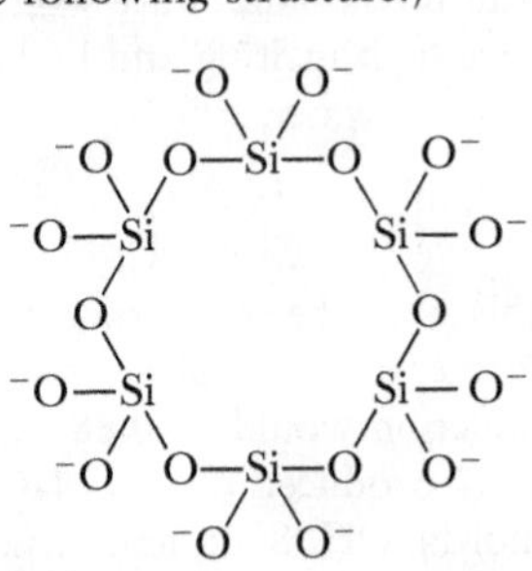

21.45 Consider the general decomposition reaction:

$$N_xO_y \rightarrow {}^{x}/_{2}\ N_2 + {}^{y}/_{2}\ O_2$$

The value of $\Delta G°$ can be obtained for all N_xO_y molecules because $\Delta_rG° = -\Delta_fG°$. These data show that the decomposition reaction is spontaneous for all of the nitrogen oxides. All are unstable with respect to decomposition to the elements.

Compound	$-\Delta_fG°$ (kJ/mol)
NO(g)	−86.58
NO_2	−51.23
N_2O	−104.20
N_2O_4	−97.73

21.47 $\Delta_rH° = -114.4$ kJ/mol-rxn; exothermic $\Delta_rG° = -70.7$ kJ/mol-rxn, product-favored at equilibrium

21.49 (a) $N_2H_4(aq) + O_2(g) \rightarrow N_2(g) + 2\ H_2O(\ell)$
(b) 1.32×10^3 g

21.51 (a) Oxidation number = +3
(b) Diphosphorous acid ($H_4P_2O_5$) should be a diprotic acid (losing the two H atoms attached to O atoms).

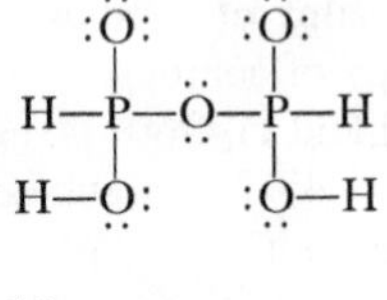

21.53 (a) 3.5×10^3 kg SO_2
(b) 4.1×10^3 kg $Ca(OH)_2$

21.55

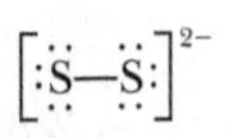

disulfide ion

21.57 $E°_{cell} = E°_{cathode} - E°_{anode} = +1.44\ V - (+1.51\ V) = -0.07\ V$

The reaction is not product-favored under standard conditions.

21.59 $Cl_2(aq) + 2\ Br^-(aq) \rightarrow 2\ Cl^-(aq) + Br_2(\ell)$

Cl_2 is the oxidizing agent, Br^- is the reducing agent; $E°_{cell} = 0.28$ V.

21.61 The reaction consumes 4.32×10^8 C to produce 8.51×10^4 g F_2.

21.63 Xe-F bond dissociation energy = 132 kJ/mol

21.65 0.015 g/L of argon; 2.6×10^3 L for 1.0 mol of argon.

21.67

Element	Appearance	State
Na, Mg, Al	Silvery metal	Solids
Si	Black, shiny metalloid	Solid
P	White, red, and black allotropes; nonmetal	Solid
S	Yellow nonmetal	Solid
Cl	Pale green nonmetal	Gas
Ar	Colorless nonmetal	Gas

21.69 (a) $2\ K(s) + Cl_2(g) \rightarrow 2\ KCl(s)$
$Ca(s) + Cl_2(g) \rightarrow CaCl_2(s)$
$2\ Ga(s) + 3\ Cl_2(g) \rightarrow 2\ GaCl_3(s)$
$Ge(s) + 2\ Cl_2(g) \rightarrow GeCl_4(\ell)$
$2\ As(s) + 3\ Cl_2(g) \rightarrow 2\ AsCl_3(\ell)$
($AsCl_5$ has been prepared but is not stable.)
(b) KCl and $CaCl_2$ are ionic; the other products are covalent.
(c) The electron-pair and molecular geometries of $GaCl_3$ are both trigonal-planar; the electron-pair geometry of $AsCl_3$ is tetrahedral, and its molecular geometry is trigonal-pyramidal.

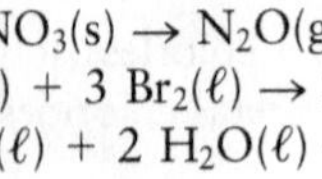

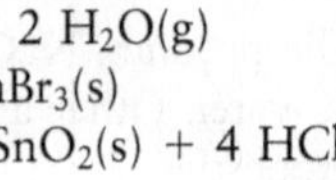

21.71 (a) $2\ KClO_3(s) \rightarrow 2\ KCl(s) + 3\ O_2(g)$
(b) $2\ H_2S(g) + 3\ O_2(g) \rightarrow 2\ H_2O(g) + 2\ SO_2(g)$
(c) $2\ Na(s) + O_2(g) \rightarrow Na_2O_2(s)$
(d) $P_4(s) + 3\ KOH(aq) + 3\ H_2O(\ell) \rightarrow PH_3(g) + 3\ KH_2PO_2(aq)$
(e) $NH_4NO_3(s) \rightarrow N_2O(g) + 2\ H_2O(g)$
(f) $2\ In(s) + 3\ Br_2(\ell) \rightarrow 2\ InBr_3(s)$
(g) $SnCl_4(\ell) + 2\ H_2O(\ell) \rightarrow SnO_2(s) + 4\ HCl(aq)$

21.73 1.4×10^5 metric tons

21.75 Mg: $\Delta_rG° = +64.9$ kJ
Ca: $\Delta_rG° = +131.40$ kJ
Ba: $\Delta_rG° = +219.4$ kJ

Relative tendency to decompose: $MgCO_3 > CaCO_3 > BaCO_3$

21.77 (a) $\Delta_fG°$ should be more negative than $(-95.1\ kJ) \times n$.
(b) Ba, Pb, Ti

21.79 O—F bond energy = 190 kJ/mol

21.81 (a) N_2O_4 is the oxidizing agent (N is reduced from +4 to 0 in N_2), and $H_2NN(CH_3)_2$ is the reducing agent.
(b) 1.3×10^4 kg N_2O_4 is required. Product masses: 5.7×10^3 kg N_2; 4.9×10^3 kg H_2O; 6.0×10^3 kg CO_2.

21.83 $\Delta_r H° = -257.78$ kJ. This reaction is entropy-disfavored, however, with $\Delta_r S° = -963$ J/K because of the decrease in the number of moles of gases. Combining these values gives $\Delta_r G° = +29.19$ kJ, indicating that under standard conditions at 298 K the reaction is not spontaneous. (The reaction has a favorable $\Delta_r G°$ at temperatures less than 268 K, indicating that further research on this system might be worthwhile. Note that at that temperature water is a solid.)

21.85 A = B_2H_6; B = B_4H_{10}; C = B_5H_{11}; D = B_5H_9; E = $B_{10}H_{14}$

21.87 48.6 kiloamps

21.89

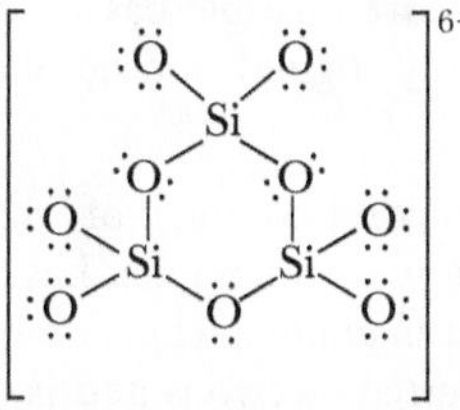

The ring is not expected to be planar because a tetrahedral electron-pair geometry is predicted for each atom in the ring.

21.91 $\Delta_r G° = -834.28$ kJ/mol-rxn, therefore the reaction is product-favored at equilibrium at 298 K.

$\Delta_r S° = -149.9$ J/K · mol-rxn at 298 K. Because this is negative, the reaction will be less product-favored at high temperatures.

21.93 (a) $2\ CH_3Cl(g) + Si(s) \rightarrow (CH_3)_2SiCl_2(\ell)$
(b) 0.823 atm
(c) 12.2 g

21.95 $5\ N_2H_5^+(aq) + 4\ IO_3^-(aq) \rightarrow 5\ N_2(g) + 2\ I_2(aq) + H^+(aq) + 12\ H_2O(\ell)$

$E°_{net} = 1.43$ V

21.97 (a) Br_2O_3
(b) The structure of Br_2O is reasonably well known. Several possible structures for Br_2O_3 can be imagined, but experiment confirms the structure below.

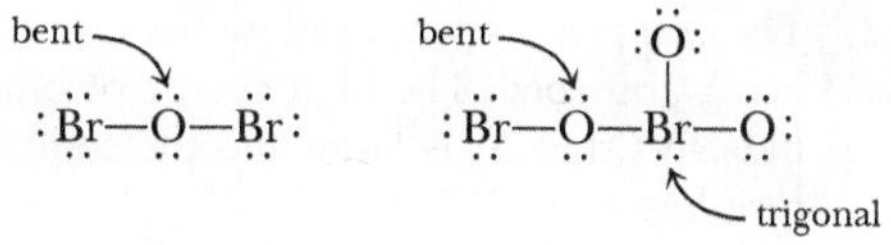

21.99 (a) The NO bond with a length of 114.2 pm is a double bond. The other two NO bonds (with a length of 121 pm) have a bond order of 1.5 (as there are two resonance structures involving these bonds).

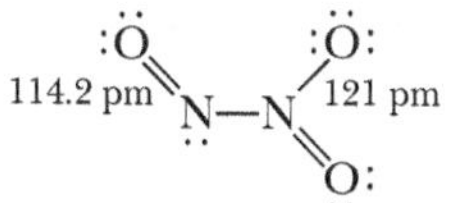

(b) $K = 1.90$; $\Delta_r S° = 141$ J/K · mol-rxn
(c) $\Delta_f H° = 82.9$ kJ/mol

21.101 The flask contains a fixed number of moles of gas at the given pressure and temperature. One could burn the mixture because only the H_2 will combust; the argon is untouched. Cooling the gases from combustion would remove water (the combustion product of H_2) and leave only Ar in the gas phase. Measuring its pressure in a calibrated volume at a known temperature would allow one to calculate the amount of Ar that was in the original mixture.

21.103 Generally, a sodium fire can be extinguished by smothering it with sand. The worst choice is to use water (which reacts violently with sodium to give H_2 gas and NaOH).

21.105 Nitrogen is a relatively unreactive gas, so it will not participate in any reaction typical of hydrogen or oxygen. The most obvious property of H_2 is that it burns, so attempting to burn a small sample of the gas would immediately confirm or deny the presence of H_2. If O_2 is present, it can be detected by allowing it to react as an oxidizing agent. There are many reactions known with low-valent metals, especially transition metal ions in solution, that can be detected by color changes.

21.107 3.5 kW-h

21.109 The reducing ability of the Group 3A metals declines considerably on descending the group, with the largest drop occurring on going from Al to Ga. The reducing ability of gallium and indium are similar, but another large change is observed on going to thallium. In fact, thallium is most stable in the +1 oxidation state. This same tendency for elements to be more stable with lower oxidation numbers is seen in Groups 4A (Ge and Pb) and 5A (Bi).

21.111 (a) $CH_4(g) + 2\ H_2O(\ell) \rightarrow CO_2(g) + 4\ H_2(g)$

$SiH_4(g) + 2\ H_2O(\ell) \rightarrow SiO_2(s) + 4\ H_2(g)$

(b) Reaction of CH_4:

$\Delta_f G° = \Delta_f G°(CO_2) - \Delta_f G°(CH_4) - 2\ \Delta_f G°(H_2O) = +130.7$ kJ

Reaction of SiH_4:

$\Delta_f G° = \Delta_f G°(SiO_2) - \Delta_f G°(SiH_4) - 2\ \Delta_f G°(H_2O) = -439.51$ kJ

The reaction of silane with water is product-favored at equilibrium. This is an important difference between methane and silane.

(c) Electronegativities: C = 2.5, Si = 1.9, H = 2.2. Polarities are in opposite directions: in CH_4, $C^{\delta-}H^{\delta+}$ (H is positive); in SiH_4, $Si^{\delta+}H^{\delta-}$ (H is negative).

(d) Si prefers to form four single bonds, rather than form a double bond to O, similar to what is seen in acetone. We predict that a molecular species Si_2H_4, analogous to ethane, will not exist; a compound of this formula will be a polymer —$(SiH_2SiH_2)_x$—

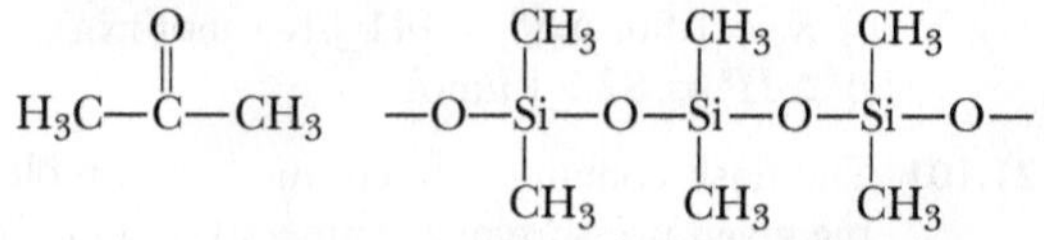

Acetone $[(CH_3)_2SiO]_n$ polymer

21.113 (a) $HXeO_4^-$ (Xe oxidation number = +6) is both oxidized (to XeO_6^{4-}, Xe oxidation number = +8) and reduced (to Xe). In addition, O is oxidized to O_2.

(b) One Xe atom in $HXeO_4^-$ loses 2 electrons to give the Xe atom in XeO_6^{4-}. A second Xe atom in $HXeO_4^-$ gains 6 electrons to give Xe. Thus, 2 $HXeO_4^-$ ions require a net of 4 electrons. These electrons can be supplied by the oxidation of 2 O^{2-} ions to give O_2.

Chapter 22

Case Studies

High-Strength Steel

1. Ferrite has a body-centered cubic unit cell.
2. Austenite has a face-centered cubic unit cell of iron atoms with a carbon atom embedded in the body of the cell.
3. The face-centered unit cell of austenite transforms into a body-centered unit cell, but this unit cell is not cubic because it is longer in one dimension than the other two (this is called a *body-centered tetragonal unit cell*). The carbon atoms remain embedded in the lattice.

Cisplatin: Accidental Discovery of a Chemotherapy Agent

$k = 0.693/t_{1/2} = 0.28\ \text{hr}^{-1}$

$\ln(\text{fraction remain}) = -(0.28\ \text{hr}^{-1})(24\ \text{hr}) = -6.7$

$\text{fraction remain} = e^{-6.7} = 0.0013$

Mass remaining = 0.013 mg

The Rare Earths

1. Nd: [Xe] $4f^4\,6s^2$; Eu: [Xe] $4f^7\,6s^2$
2. Ce^{3+}: [Xe] $4f^1$
   Nd^{3+}: [Xe] $4f^3$
3. $Fe^{2+}(aq) + [Ce(NO_3)_6]^{2-}(aq) \rightarrow Fe^{3+}(aq) + Ce^{3+}(aq) + 6\ NO_3^-(aq)$

   $C = [0.181\ \text{g Fe}(1\ \text{mol Fe}/55.85\ \text{g Fe})(1\ \text{mol [Ce]/mol Fe})]/0.03133\ \text{L} = 0.103\ \text{M}$
4. $2\ CeO_2(s) + CO(g) \rightarrow Ce_2O_3(s) + CO_2(g)$

   $2\ Ce_2O_3(s) + O_2(g) \rightarrow 4\ CeO_2(s)$

Check Your Understanding

22.1 (a) $Co(NH_3)_3Cl_3$
(b) $Fe(H_2NCH_2CH_2NH_2)_2Br_2 = Fe(en)_2Br_2$

22.2 (a) (i) $K_3[Co(NO_2)_6]$: a complex of cobalt(III) with a coordination number of 6
(ii) $Mn(NH_3)_4Cl_2$: a complex of manganese(II) with a coordination number of 6
(b) $NH_4[Co(EDTA)]$: a complex of cobalt(III) with a coordination number of 6

22.3 (a) hexaaquanickel(II) sulfate
(b) dicyanobis(ethylenediamine)chromium(III) chloride
(c) potassium amminetrichloroplatinate(II)
(d) potassium dichlorocuprate(I)

22.4 (a) Geometric isomers are possible (with the NH_3 ligands in *cis* and *trans* positions).
(b) Only a single structure is possible.
(c) Only a single structure is possible.
(d) This compound is chiral; there are two optical isomers.
(e) Only a single structure is possible.
(f) Two structural isomers are possible based on coordination of the NO_2^- ligand through oxygen or nitrogen.

22.5 (a) $[Ru(H_2O)_6]^{2+}$: an octahedral complex of ruthenium(II) (d^6). A low-spin complex has no unpaired electrons and is diamagnetic. A high-spin complex has four unpaired electrons and is paramagnetic.

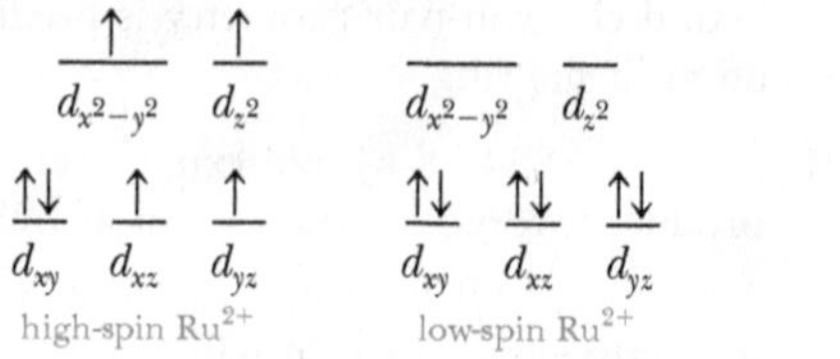

(b) $[Ni(NH_3)_6]^{2+}$: an octahedral complex of nickel(II) (d^8). Only one electron configuration is possible; it has two unpaired electrons and is paramagnetic.

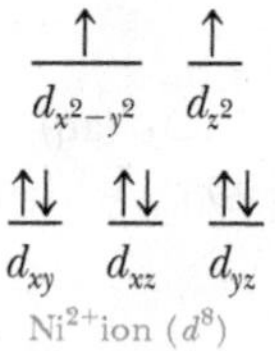

22.6 1. A wavelength of 500 nm corresponds to green light being absorbed. The complex ion will appear magenta.
2. The complex appears yellow because blue light is being absorbed. The high energy of blue light indicates that Δ_o is large and the complex is therefore low spin.

Review & Check

Section 22-1

1. (e) +7
2. (b) Atomic radii that are similar to the 5th period transition elements.

Section 22-2

1. (b) Copper is reduced; sulfur is oxidized.
2. (b) iron oxide

Section 22-3

1. (b) 6
2. (d) +3
3. (b) $Na_4[Fe(C_2O_4)_3]$
4. (b) pentaamminehydroxochromium(III) chloride

Section 22-4

1. (b) $Ni(H_2O)_4(C_2O_4)$
2. (b) $Fe(en)_2(CN)_2$
3. (b) There are two geometric isomers, one of which has an optical isomer.
4. (d) 3

Section 22-5

1. (b) high-spin $[Mn(NH_3)_6]^{2+}$
2. (a) square-planar $[PtCl_4]^{2-}$

Section 22-6

1. (c) $[CrF_6]^{3-}$

Applying Chemical Principles: Green Catalysts

1. Coordination number = 5
3. tetradentate
5. Square-planar

Study Questions

22.1 (a) Cr^{3+}: [Ar]$3d^3$, paramagnetic
(b) V^{2+}: [Ar]$3d^3$, paramagnetic
(c) Ni^{2+}: [Ar]$3d^8$, paramagnetic
(d) Cu^+: [Ar]$3d^{10}$, diamagnetic

22.3 (a) Fe^{3+}: [Ar]$3d^5$, isoelectronic with Mn^{2+}
(b) Zn^{2+}: [Ar]$3d^{10}$, isoelectronic with Cu^+
(c) Fe^{2+}: [Ar]$3d^6$, isoelectronic with Co^{3+}
(d) Cr^{3+}: [Ar]$3d^3$, isoelectronic with V^{2+}

22.5 (a) $Cr_2O_3(s) + 2\ Al(s) \rightarrow Al_2O_3(s) + 2\ Cr(s)$
(b) $TiCl_4(\ell) + 2\ Mg(s) \rightarrow Ti(s) + 2\ MgCl_2(s)$
(c) $2\ [Ag(CN)_2]^-(aq) + Zn(s) \rightarrow 2\ Ag(s) + [Zn(CN)_4]^{2-}(aq)$
(d) $3\ Mn_3O_4(s) + 8\ Al(s) \rightarrow 9\ Mn(s) + 4\ Al_2O_3(s)$

22.7 Monodentate: CH_3NH_2, CH_3CN, N_3^-, Br^-
Bidentate: en, phen (see Figure 22.12)

22.9 (a) Mn^{2+}; (b) Co^{3+}; (c) Co^{3+}; (d) Cr^{2+}

22.11 $[Ni(en)(NH_3)_3(H_2O)]^{2+}$

22.13 (a) $Ni(en)_2Cl_2$ (en = $H_2NCH_2CH_2NH_2$)
(b) $K_2[PtCl_4]$
(c) $K[Cu(CN)_2]$
(d) $[Fe(NH_3)_4(H_2O)_2]^{2+}$

22.15 (a) Diaquabis(oxalato)nickelate(II) ion
(b) Dibromobis(ethylenediamine)cobalt(III) ion
(c) Amminechlorobis(ethylenediamine)cobalt(III) ion
(d) Diammineoxalatoplatinum(II)

22.17 (a) $[Fe(H_2O)_5OH]^{2+}$
(b) Potassium tetracyanonickelate(II)
(c) Potassium diaquabis(oxalato)chromate(III)
(d) $(NH_4)_2[PtCl_4]$

22.19

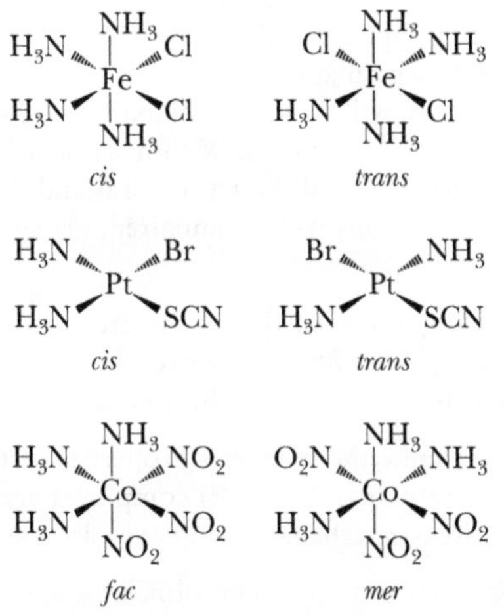

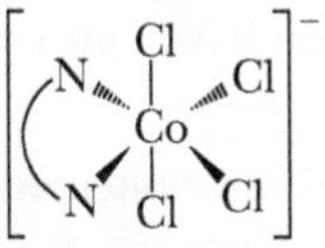

Only one structure possible. (N—N is the bidentate ethylenediamine ligand.)

22.21 (a) Fe^{2+} is a chiral center.
(b) Co^{3+} is not a chiral center.
(c) Co^{3+} is not a chiral center.
(d) No. Square-planar complexes are never chiral.

22.23 (a) $[Mn(CN)_6]^{4-}$: d^5, low-spin Mn^{2+} complex is paramagnetic (one unpaired electron).

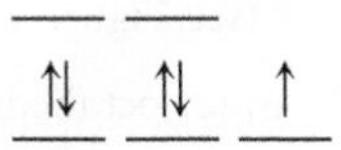

(b) $[Co(NH_3)_6]^{3+}$: d^6, low-spin Co^{3+} complex is diamagnetic.

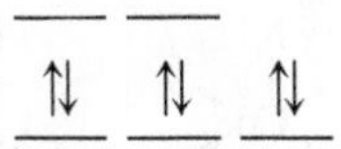

(c) $[Fe(H_2O)_6]^{3+}$: d^5, low-spin Fe^{3+} complex is paramagnetic [one unpaired electron; same as part (a)].
(d) $[Cr(en)_3]^{2+}$: d^4, Cr^{2+} complex is paramagnetic (two unpaired electrons).

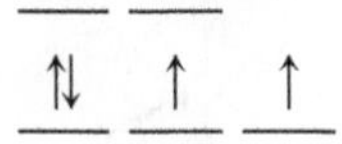

22.25 (a) Fe^{2+}, d^6, paramagnetic, four unpaired electrons
(b) Co^{2+}, d^7, paramagnetic, three unpaired electrons
(c) Mn^{2+}, d^5, paramagnetic, five unpaired electrons
(d) Zn^{2+}, d^{10}, diamagnetic, zero unpaired electrons

22.27 (a) 6
(b) Octahedral
(c) +2
(d) Four unpaired electrons (high spin)
(e) Paramagnetic

22.29 With four ligands, complexes of the d^8 Ni^{2+} ion can be either tetrahedral or square-planar. The CN^- ligand is at one end of the spectrochemical series and leads to a large ligand field splitting, whereas Cl^- is at the opposite end and often leads to complexes with small orbital splitting. With ligands such as CN^- the complex will be square-planar (and for a d^8 ion it will be diamagnetic). With a weak field ligand (Cl^-) the complex will be tetrahedral and, for the d^8 ion, two electrons will be unpaired, giving a paramagnetic complex.

22.31 The light absorbed is in the green region of the spectrum (page 888). Therefore, the light transmitted—which is the color of the solution—is magenta.

22.33 Determine the magnetic properties of the complex. Square-planar Ni^{2+} (d^8) complexes are diamagnetic, whereas tetrahedral complexes are paramagnetic.

22.35 Fe^{2+} has a d^6 configuration. Low-spin octahedral complexes are diamagnetic, whereas high-spin octahedral complexes of this ion have four unpaired electrons and are paramagnetic.

22.37 Square-planar complexes most often arise from d^8 transition metal ions. Therefore, it is likely that $[Ni(CN)_4]^{2-}$ (Ni^{2+}) and $[Pt(CN)_4]^{2-}$ (Pt^{2+}) are square planar. (See also Study Question 22.29.)

22.39 Two geometric isomers are possible.

22.41 Absorbing at 425 nm means the complex is absorbing light in the blue-violet end of the spectrum. Therefore, red and green light are transmitted, and the complex appears yellow (see Figure 22.27).

22.43 (a) Mn^{2+}; (b) 6; (c) octahedral; (d) 5; (e) paramagnetic; (f) *cis* and *trans* isomers exist.

22.45 Name: tetraamminedichlorocobalt(III) chloride

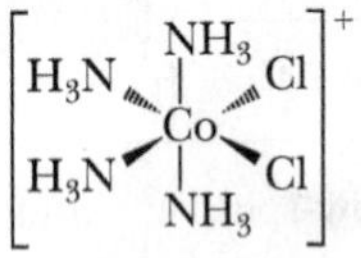

cis

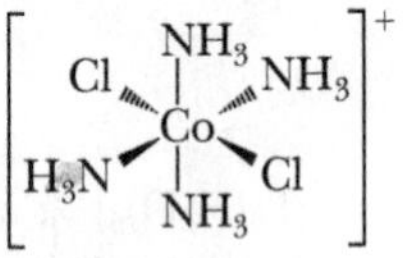

trans

22.47 $[Co(en)_2(H_2O)Cl]^{2+}$

22.49

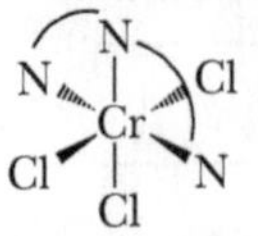

mer

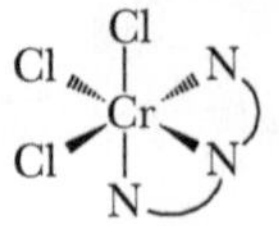

fac

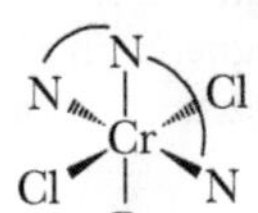

trans chlorides

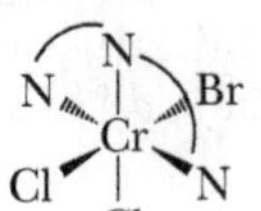

cis chlorides

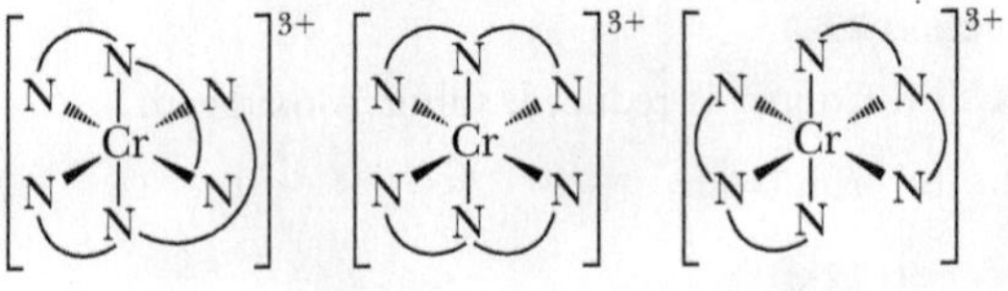

22.51

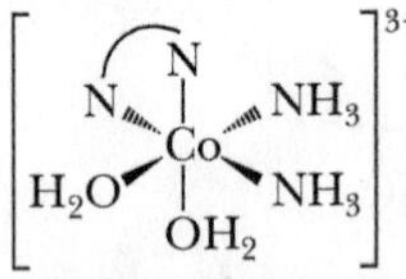

H_2O and NH_3 *cis*, chiral

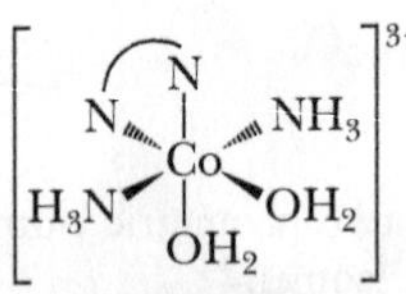

H_2O *cis* and NH_3 *trans*, not chiral

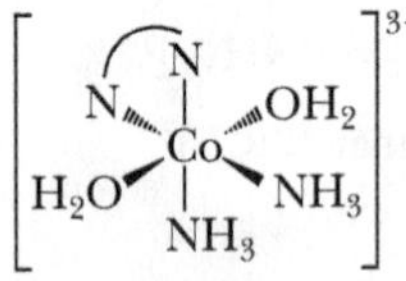

H_2O *trans* and NH_3 *cis*, not chiral

22.53 In $[Mn(H_2O)_6]^{2+}$ and $[Mn(CN)_6]^{4-}$, Mn has an oxidation number of +2 (Mn is a d^5 ion).

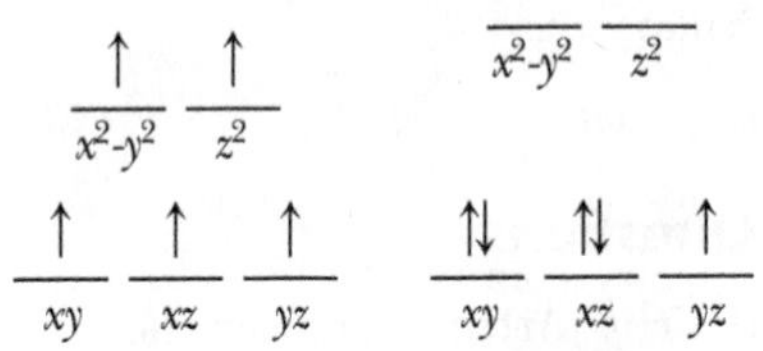

$[Mn(H_2O)_6]^{2+}$ paramagnetic, 5 unpaired e^-

$[Mn(CN)_6]^{4-}$ paramagnetic, 1 unpaired e^-

This shows that Δ_o for CN^- is greater than for H_2O.

22.55 (a) Ammonium tetrachlorocuprate(II)
(b) $[Cr(H_2O)_4Cl_2]Cl$
(c) $[Co(H_2O)(NH_2CH_2CH_2NH_2)_2(SCN)](NO_3)_2$

22.57 (a) The light absorbed is in the orange region of the spectrum (page 888). Therefore, the light transmitted (the color of the solution) is blue or cyan.
(b) Using the cobalt(III) complexes in Table 22.3 as a guide, we might place CO_3^{2-} between F^- and the oxalato ion, $C_2O_4^{2-}$.
(c) Δ_o is small, so the complex should be high spin and paramagnetic.

22.59

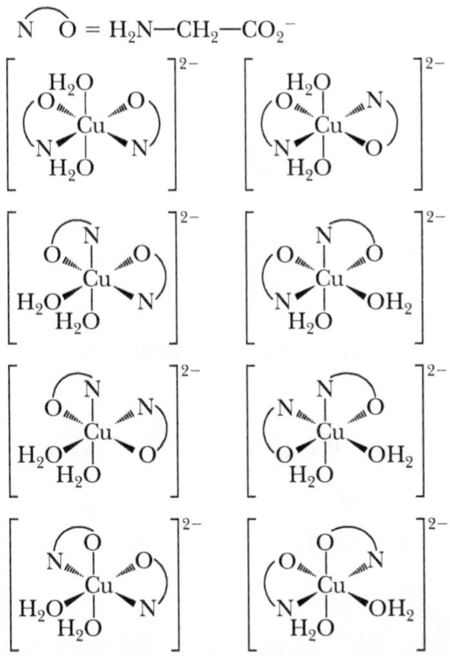

22.61 (a) In complexes such as $M(PR_3)_2Cl_2$ the metal is Ni^{2+} or Pd^{2+}, both of which are d^8 metal ions. If an Ni^{2+} complex is paramagnetic it must be tetrahedral, whereas the Pd^{2+} must be square planar. (A d^8 metal complex cannot be diamagnetic if it has a tetrahedral structure.)

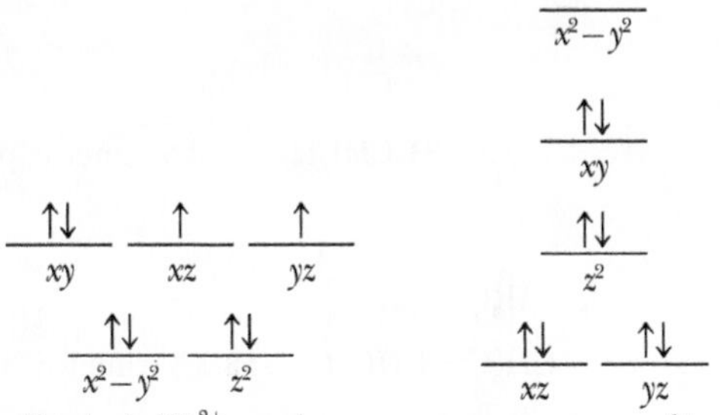

Tetrahedral Ni^{2+} complex, paramagnetic

Square-planar Pd^{2+} complex, diamagnetic

(b) A tetrahedral Ni^{2+} complex cannot have isomers, whereas a square-planar complex of the type $M(PR_3)_2Cl_2$ can have *cis* and *trans* isomers (see page 878.)

22.63 (a) Ce [Xe] $4f^1\ 5d^1\ 6s^2$
Ce^{3+} [Xe] $4f^1$
Ce^{4+} [Xe] diamagnetic

(b) Ce^{3+} is paramagnetic with 1 unpaired electron. Ce^{4+} is diamagnetic.

(c) A unit cell of CeO_2 consists of Ce^{4+} ions as a face-centered cube (4 Ce^{4+} ions) with O^{2-} ions in all of the tetrahedral holes (8 O^{2-} ions).

22.65 A, dark violet isomer: $[Co(NH_3)_5Br]SO_4$

B, violet-red isomer: $[Co(NH_3)_5(SO_4)]Br$

$$[Co(NH_3)_5Br]SO_4(aq) + BaCl_2(aq) \rightarrow [Co(NH_3)_5Br]Cl_2(aq) + BaSO_4(s)$$

22.67 (a) There is 5.41×10^{-4} mol of $UO_2(NO_3)_2$, and this provides 5.41×10^{-4} mol of U^{n+} ions on reduction by Zn. The 5.41×10^{-4} mol U^{n+} requires 2.16×10^{-4} mol MnO_4^- to reach the equivalence point. This is a ratio of 5 mol of U^{n+} ions to 2 mol MnO_4^- ions. The 2 mol MnO_4^- ions require 10 mol of e^- (to go to Mn^{2+} ions), so 5 mol of U^{n+} ions provide 10 mol e^- (on going to 5 UO_2^{2+} ions, with a uranium oxidation number of +6). This means the U^{n+} ion must be U^{4+}.

(b) $Zn(s) \rightarrow Zn^{2+}(aq) + 2\ e^-$

$$UO_2^{2+}(aq) + 4\ H^+(aq) + 2\ e^- \rightarrow U^{4+}(aq) + 2\ H_2O(\ell)$$

$$UO_2^{2+}(aq) + 4\ H^+(aq) + Zn(s) \rightarrow U^{4+}(aq) + 2\ H_2O(\ell) + Zn^{2+}(aq)$$

(c) $$5[U^{4+}(aq) + 2\ H_2O(\ell) \rightarrow UO_2^{2+}(aq) + 4\ H^+(aq) + 2\ e^-]$$

$$2[MnO_4^-(aq) + 8\ H^+(aq) + 5\ e^- \rightarrow Mn^{2+}(aq) + 4\ H_2O(\ell)]$$

$$5\ U^{4+}(aq) + 2\ MnO_4^-(aq) + 2\ H_2O(\ell) \rightarrow 5\ UO_2^{2+}(aq) + 4\ H^+(aq) + 2\ Mn^{2+}(aq)$$

22.69

Ion	$K_{formation}$ (ammine complexes)
Co^{2+}	1.3×10^5
Ni^{2+}	5.5×10^8
Cu^{2+}	2.1×10^{13}
Zn^{2+}	2.9×10^9

The data for these hexaammine complexes do, indeed, verify the Irving-Williams series. In the book *Chemistry of the Elements* (N. N. Greenwood and A. Earnshaw: 2nd edition, p. 908, Oxford, England, Butterworth-Heinemann, 1997), it is stated: "the stabilities of corresponding complexes of the bivalent ions of the first transition series, irrespective of the particular ligand involved, usually vary in the Irving-Williams order, . . . , which is the reverse of the order for the cation radii. These observations are consistent with the view that, at least for metals in oxidation states +2 and +3, the coordinate bond is largely electrostatic. This was a major factor in the acceptance of the crystal field theory."

22.71 (a) Define length of the side of the cube as x, then the length of the diagonal across the cube is $x\sqrt{3}$. This is set equal to:
$2\ r_{Ti} + 2\ r_{Ni}$, i.e., $x\sqrt{3} = 2\ r_{Ti} + 2\ r_{Ni} = 540$ pm;
$x = 312$ pm ($a = b = c = 3.12 \times 10^{-8}$ cm)

(b) Calculated density:

Mass of one unit cell is the mass of one Ti and one Ni atom = (47.87 g/mol)(1 mol/6.022×10^{23} atoms Ti) + (58.69 g/mol)(1 mol/6.022×10^{23} atoms Ti) = 1.77×10^{-22} g

Volume of the unit cell is $x^3 = (3.12 \times 10^{-8}\ cm)^3 = 3.04 \times 10^{-23}\ cm^3$

Calculated density = 1.77×10^{-22} g/$3.04 \times 10^{-23}\ cm^3$ = 5.82 g/cm^3

The agreement is not very good, probably because atoms don't pack together as tightly as is assumed.

(c) As free atoms, both Ti and Ni are paramagnetic.

Chapter 23

Case Studies

An Awakening with L-DOPA

1. L-DOPA is chiral. Its chiral center is indicated in the following structural formula.

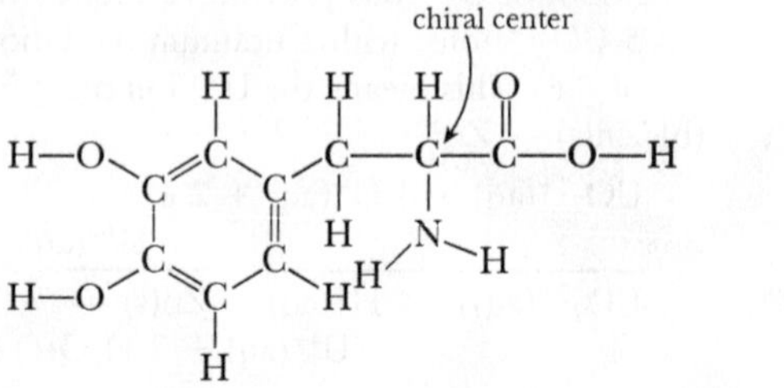

2. Dopamine is not chiral. Epinephrine is chiral. Its chiral center is indicated in the following structural formula.

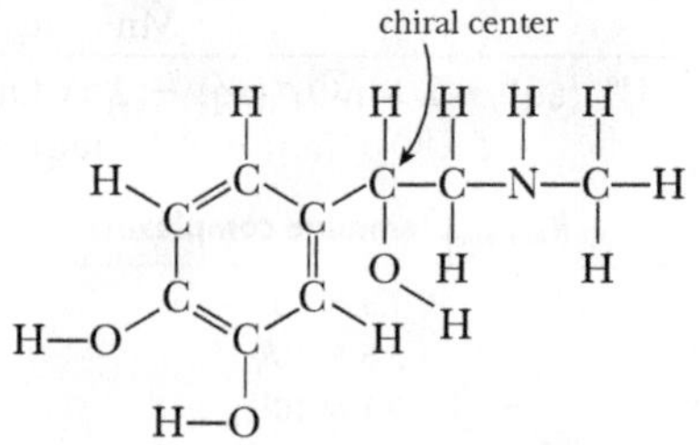

3. 5.0 g L-DOPA (1 mol L-DOPA/197.2 g L-DOPA) = 0.025 mol L-DOPA

Green Adhesives

1. Structural formulas:

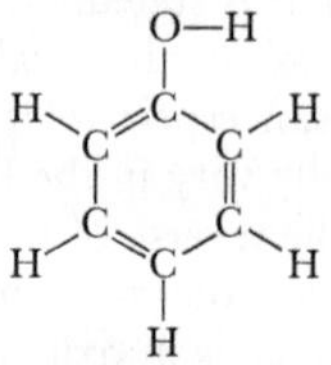
phenol

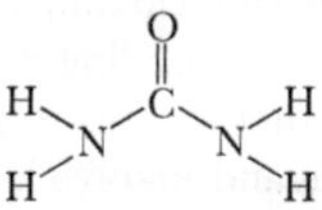
urea

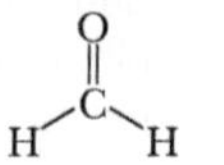
formaldehyde

2. The electron-pair and molecular geometries are both trigonal-planar. The C—H σ bonds are each formed by the overlap of an sp^2 hybrid orbital on the C atom with the 1*s* orbital of the H atom. The σ bond between the C and O is formed by the overlap of an sp^2 hybrid orbital on the C with an sp^2 hybrid orbital on the O. The π bond between the C and O is formed by the overlap of a 2*p* orbital on C with a 2*p* orbital on O.
3. Similarity: Both nylon-6,6 and proteins are polyamides.

   Differences:

   1. In proteins there is one direction for the amide linkage: CONH. In nylon-6,6 two orientations are present: CONH and NHCO.
   2. In proteins there is only one C between the amide linkages. In nylon-6,6 there are four or six carbons between amide linkages.
   3. Proteins have numerous R groups that can be attached to the carbon in between the amide groups, whereas nylon-6,6 has only hydrogen atoms attached to the carbons in between the amide groups.
   4. Proteins are chiral, whereas nylon-6,6 is not.

Check Your Understanding

23.1 (a) Isomers of C_7H_{16}

$CH_3CH_2CH_2CH_2CH_2CH_2CH_3$ heptane

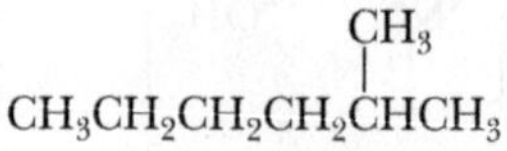
2-methylhexane

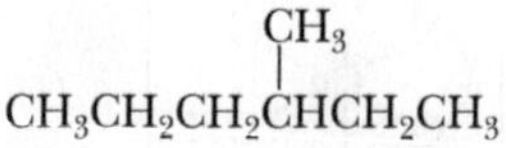
3-methylhexane

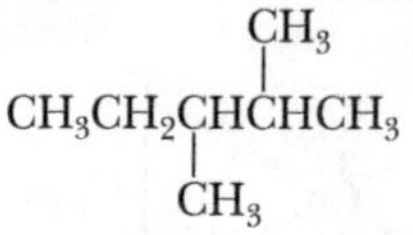
2,3-dimethylpentane

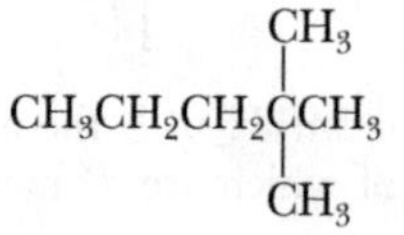
2,2-dimethylpentane

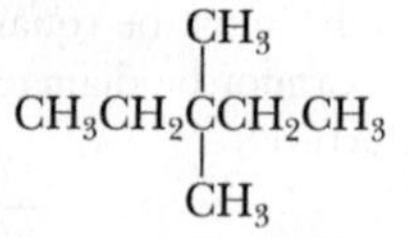
3,3-dimethylpentane

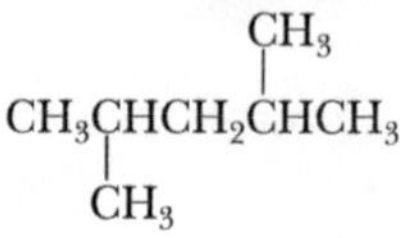
2,4-dimethylpentane

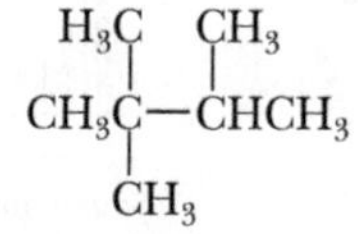
2,2,3-trimethylbutane

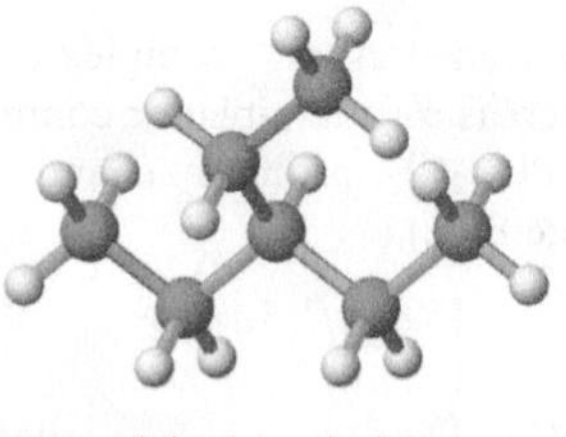

A model of 3-ethylpentane

(b) Two isomers, 3-methylhexane and 2,3-dimethylpentane, are chiral.

23.2 The names accompany the structures in the "Check Your Understanding" answer in Example 23.1.

23.3 Isomers of C_6H_{12} in which the longest chain has six C atoms:

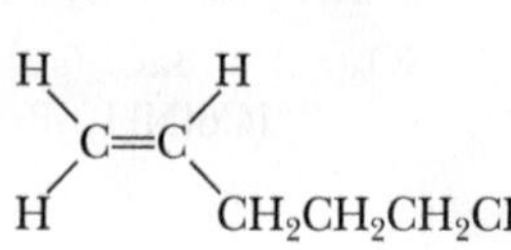

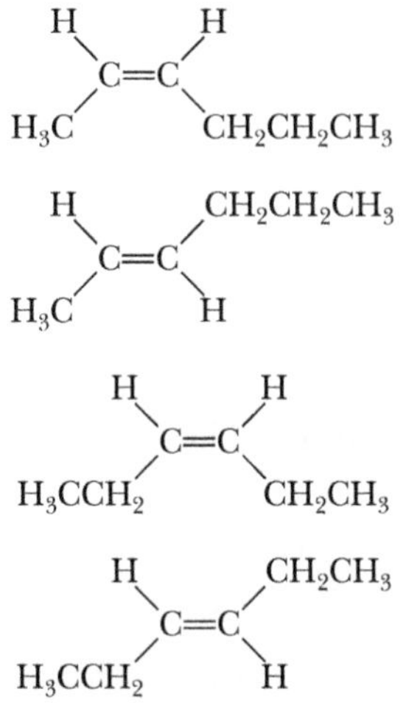

Names (in order, top to bottom): 1-hexene, *cis*-2-hexene, *trans*-2-hexene, *cis*-3-hexene, *trans*-3-hexene. None of these isomers is chiral.

23.4 (a)

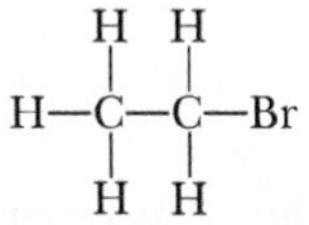

bromoethane

(b)

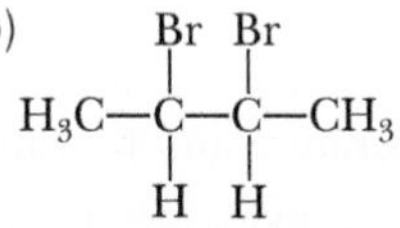

2,3-dibromobutane

23.5 1,4-diaminobenzene

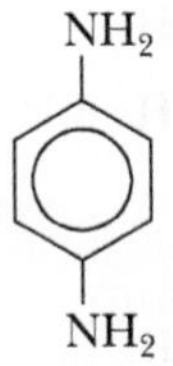

23.6

$CH_3CH_2CH_2CH_2OH$ 1-butanol

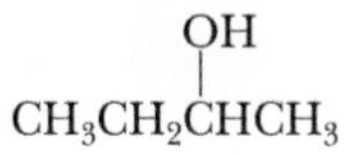

2-butanol

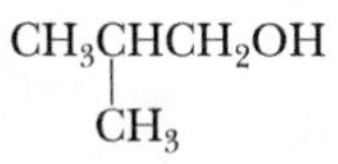

2-methyl-1-propanol

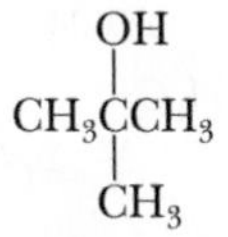

2-methyl-2-propanol

23.7 (a) $CH_3CH_2CH_2OH$: 1-propanol, has an alcohol (—OH) group

CH_3CO_2H: ethanoic acid (acetic acid), has a carboxylic acid (—CO_2H) group

$CH_3CH_2NH_2$: ethylamine, has an amino (—NH_2) group

(b) 1-propyl ethanoate (propyl acetate)

(c) Oxidation of this primary alcohol first gives propanal, CH_3CH_2CHO. Further oxidation gives propanoic acid, $CH_3CH_2CO_2H$.

(d) N-ethylacetamide, $CH_3CONHCH_2CH_3$

(e) The amine is protonated by hydrochloric acid, forming ethylammonium chloride, $[CH_3CH_2NH_3]Cl$.

23.8 Kevlar is a condensation polymer, prepared by the reaction of terephthalic acid and 1,4-diaminobenzene.

$$n\ H_2NC_6H_4NH_2 + n\ HO_2CC_6H_4CO_2H \rightarrow$$
$$-\!\!\left(HNC_6H_4NHCOC_6H_4CO\right)\!\!-_n + 2n\ H_2O$$

Review & Check

Section 23-1

1. (c) b and c
2. (a) a and b
3. (c) 2

Section 23-2

1. (c) 2,5-dimethylheptane
2. (c) The compound is an isomer of hexane, is not chiral, and is named 2,2-dimethylbutane.
3. (i) (c) only 3
   (ii) (c) 1 and 2
4. (a) 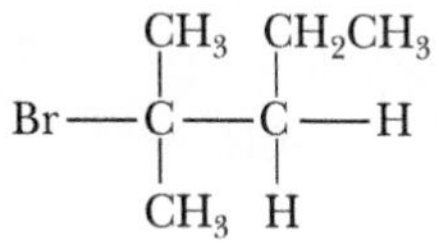
5. (c) 3

Section 23-3

1. (d) more than 4
2. (a) 2-propanol
3. (a) sp^3
4. (d) NaOH

Section 23-4

1. (d) 1 aldehyde and 2 ketones
2. (b) 2-butanone
3. (d) 120°, sp^2 hybridized
4. (c) ethyl ethanoate

Section 23-5

1. (c) 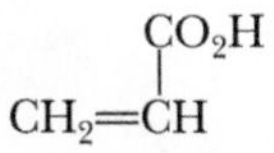

Applying Chemical Principles: Bisphenol A (BPA)

1. Reactants: 15 C, 18 H, 3 O, molar mass = 246; Products: 15 C, 16 H, 2 O, molar mass = 228.
   Atom economy = (228/246) × 100% = 92.7%
3. (15 lb)(1 kg/2.2 lb)(13 μg/kg) = 89 μg, more than 50 g recommended.
5. Volume of base needed = (0.300 g BPA) (1 mol BPA/228 g BPA)(2 mol NaOH/1 mol BPA) (1.00 L/0.050 mol NaOH) = 0.0526 L (or 52.6 mL)

Study Questions

23.1 Heptane

23.3 C_5H_{12} and $C_{14}H_{30}$ are alkanes.

23.5 3-Ethyl-2-methylhexane

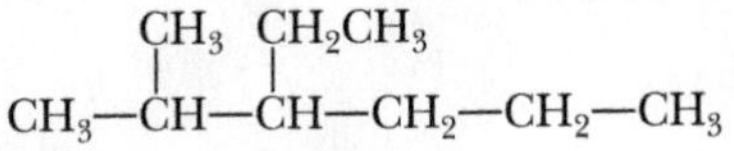

2,3,3,4-Tetramethylpentane

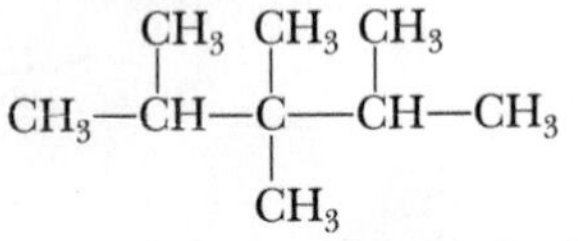

Other possibilities include 2,2,3,4-tetramethylpentane, 3-ethyl-2,2-dimethylpentane, 3-ethyl-2,3-dimethylpentane, and 3-ethyl-2,4-dimethylpentane.

23.7 2,3-Dimethylbutane

23.9 (a) 2,3-Dimethylhexane

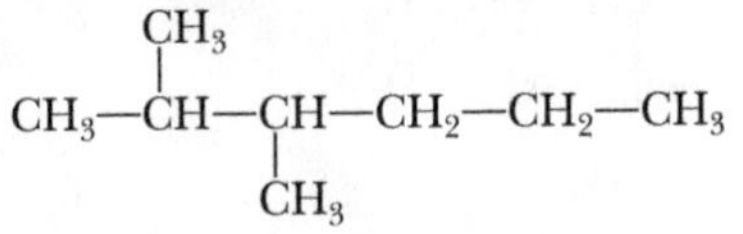

(b) 2,3-Dimethyloctane

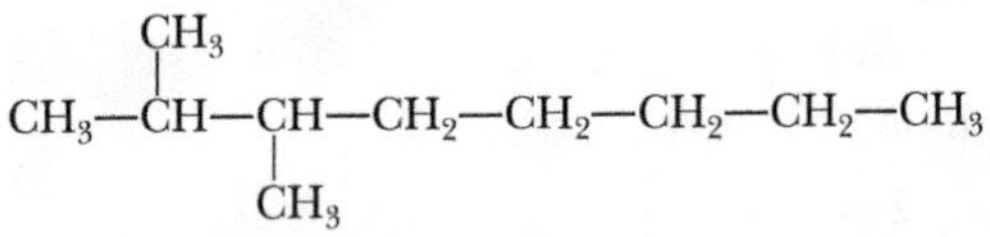

(c) 3-Ethylheptane

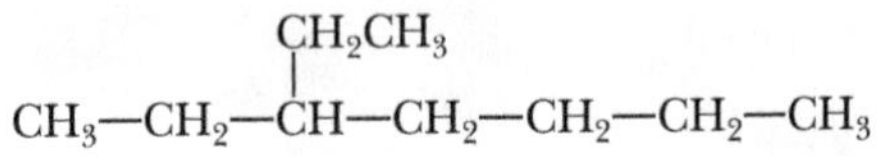

(d) 3-Ethyl-2-methylhexane

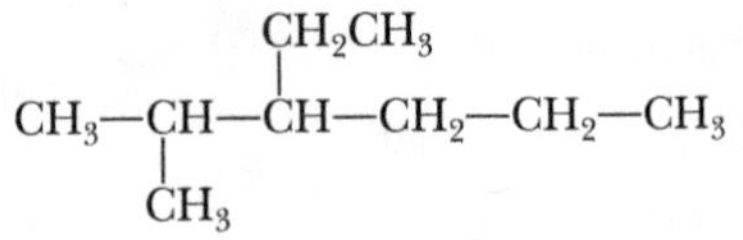

23.11

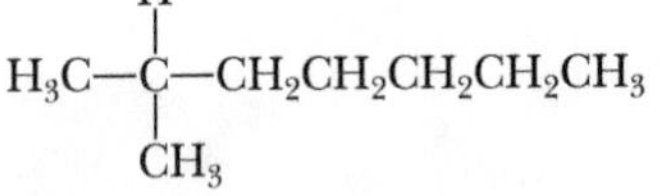

2-methylheptane

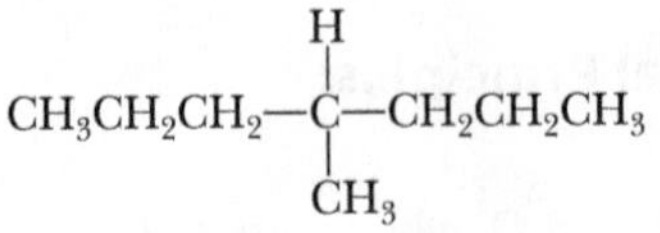

4-methylheptane

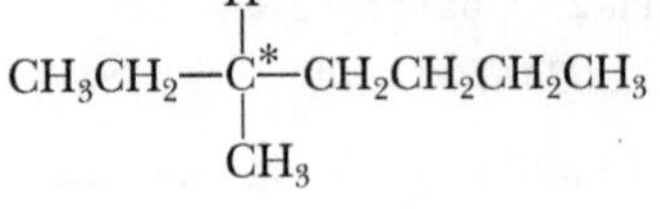

3-methylheptane. The C atom with an asterisk is chiral.

23.13 Chair form of cyclohexane:

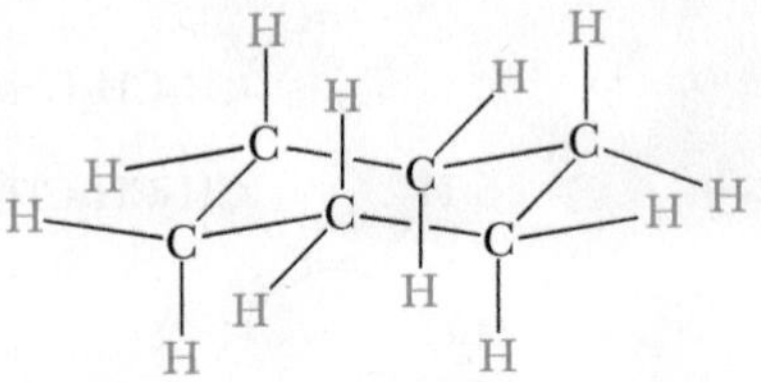

Axial hydrogens are shown in red; equatorial hydrogens are shown in blue.

23.15

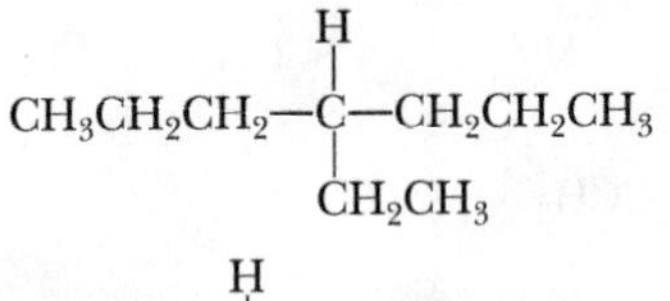

4-ethylheptane. The compound is not chiral.

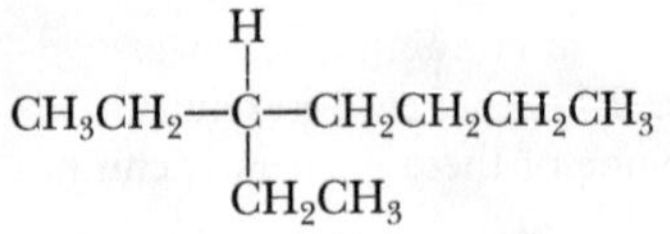

3-ethylheptane. Not chiral.

23.17 C_4H_{10}, butane: a low-molar-mass fuel gas at room temperature and pressure. Slightly soluble in water.

$C_{12}H_{26}$, dodecane: a colorless liquid at room temperature. Expected to be insoluble in water but quite soluble in nonpolar solvents.

23.19

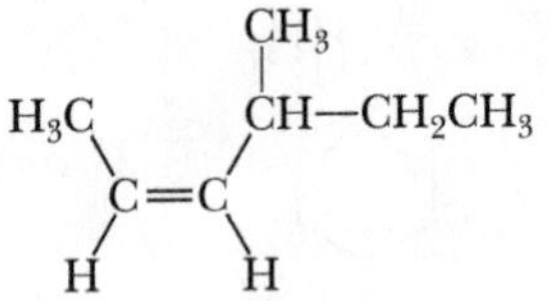

cis-4-methyl-2-hexene

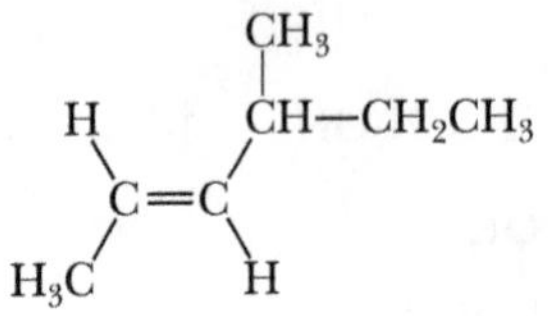

trans-4-methyl-2-hexene

23.21 (a)

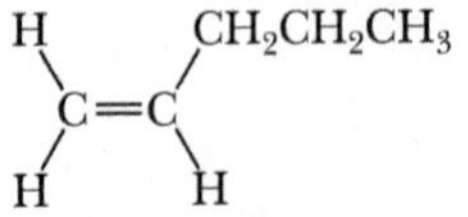

1-pentene

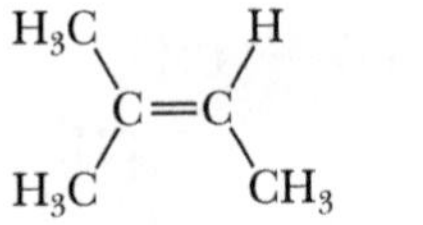

2-methyl-2-butene

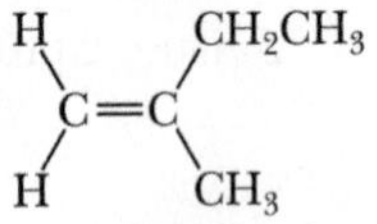

2-methyl-1-butene

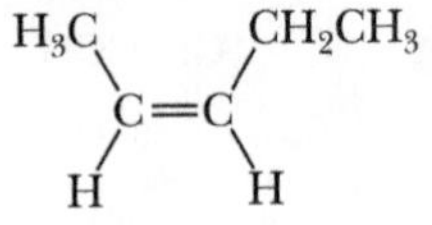

cis-2-pentene

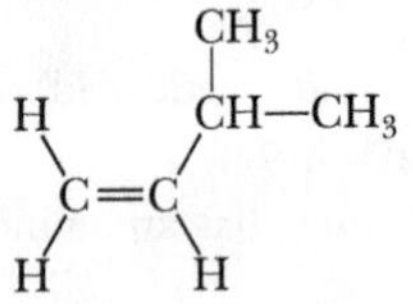

3-methyl-1-butene

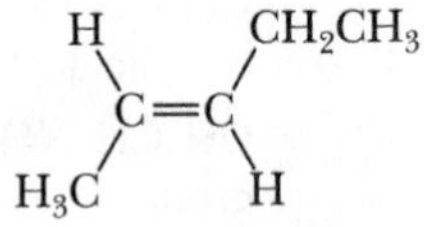

trans-2-pentene

(b)

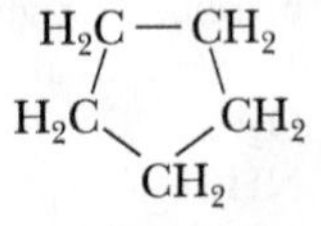

cyclopentane

23.23 (a) 1,2-Dibromopropane, $CH_3CHBrCH_2Br$
(b) Pentane, C_5H_{12}

23.25 The three alkenes are 1-butene, *cis*-2-butene, and *trans*-2-butene. The reaction with 1-butene is shown below:

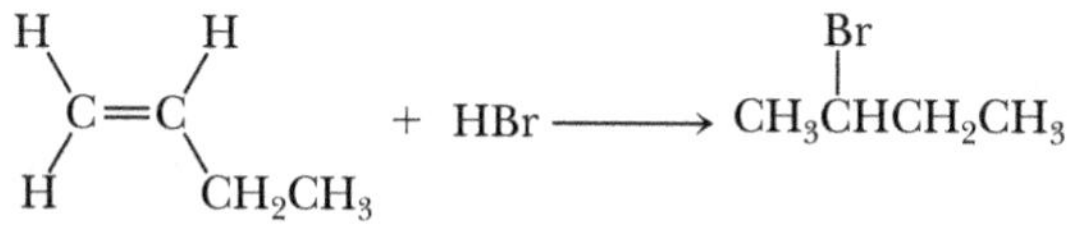

23.27 Four isomers are possible.

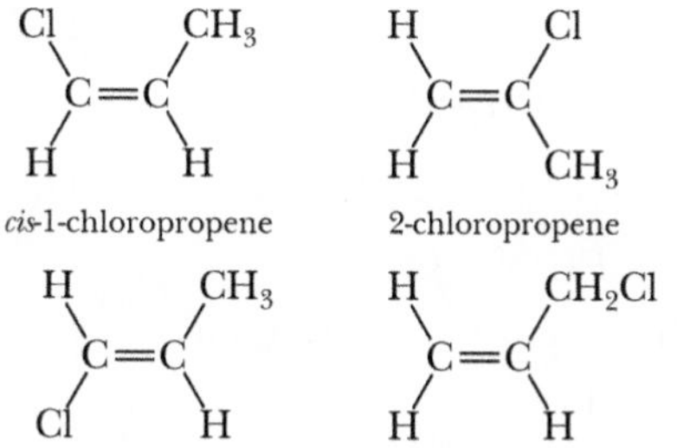

cis-1-chloropropene; 2-chloropropene; *trans*-1-chloropropene; 3-chloro-1-propene

23.29

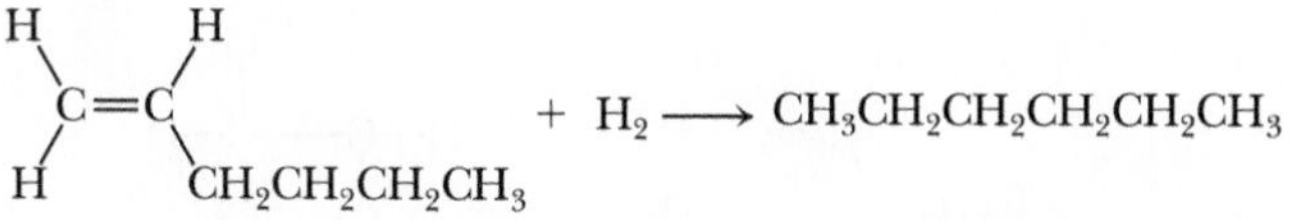

Hydrogenation is often carried out in the presence of a metal catalyst (Pt, Pd, Rh). Hydrogenation is used in the food industry to convert liquid oils to solids and to make them less susceptible to spoilage.

23.31

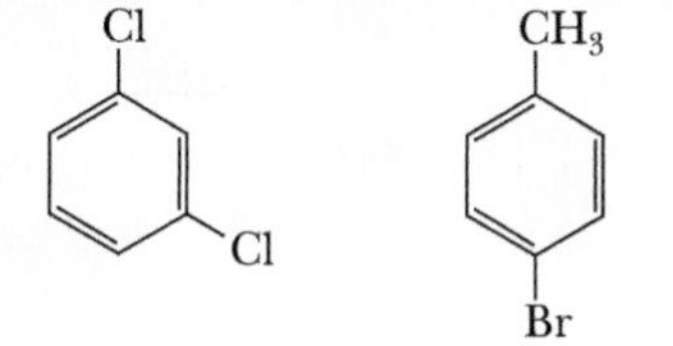

m-dichlorobenzene; *p*-bromotoluene

23.33

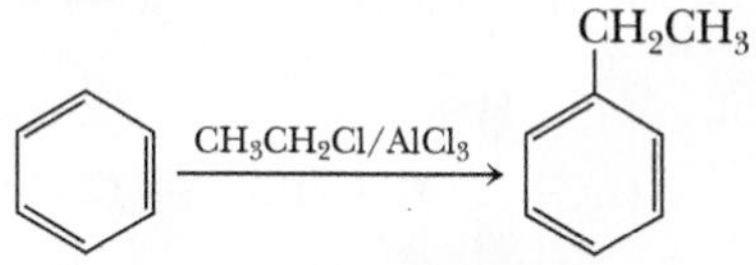

ethylbenzene

23.35

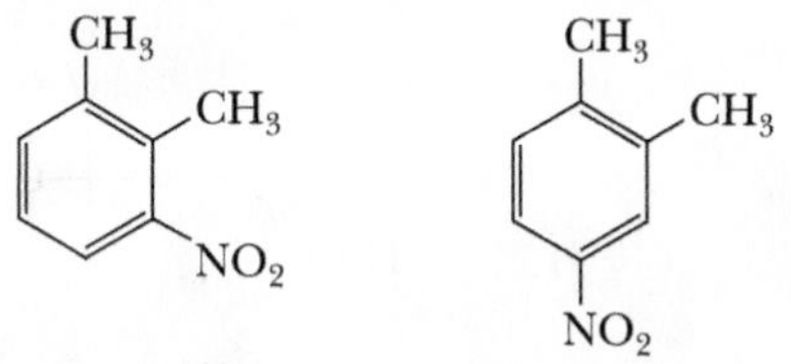

1,2-dimethyl-3-nitrobenzene; 1,2-dimethyl-4-nitrobenzene

23.37 (a) 1-Propanol, primary
(b) 1-Butanol, primary
(c) 2-Methyl-2-propanol, tertiary
(d) 2-Methyl-2-butanol, tertiary

23.39 (a) Ethylamine, $CH_3CH_2NH_2$
(b) Dipropylamine, $(CH_3CH_2CH_2)_2NH$

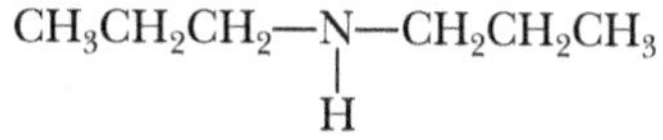

(c) Butyldimethylamine

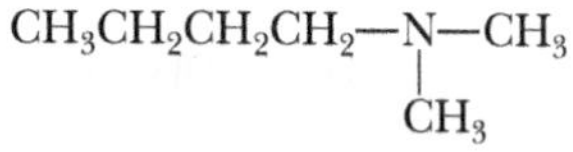

(d) Triethylamine

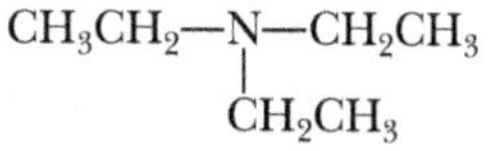

23.41 (a) 1-Butanol, $CH_3CH_2CH_2CH_2OH$
(b) 2-Butanol

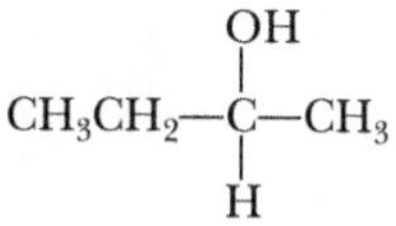

(c) 2-Methyl-1-propanol

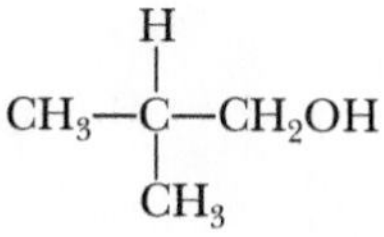

(d) 2-Methyl-2-propanol

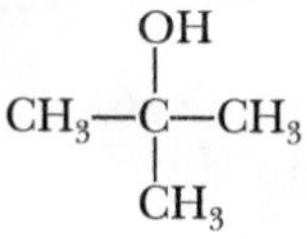

23.43 (a) $C_6H_5NH_2(\ell) + HCl(aq) \rightarrow (C_6H_5NH_3)Cl(aq)$
(b) $(CH_3)_3N(aq) + H_2SO_4(aq) \rightarrow [(CH_3)_3NH]HSO_4(aq)$

23.45

(a)

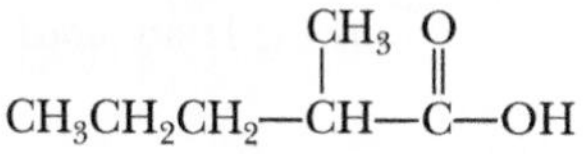

(b)

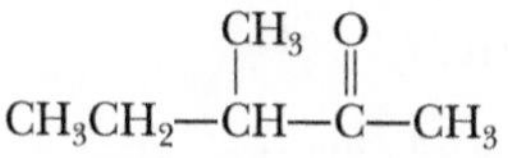

(c)

(d)

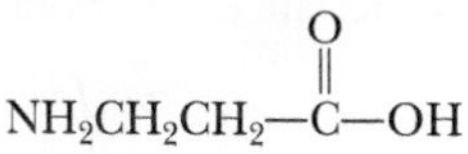

23.47

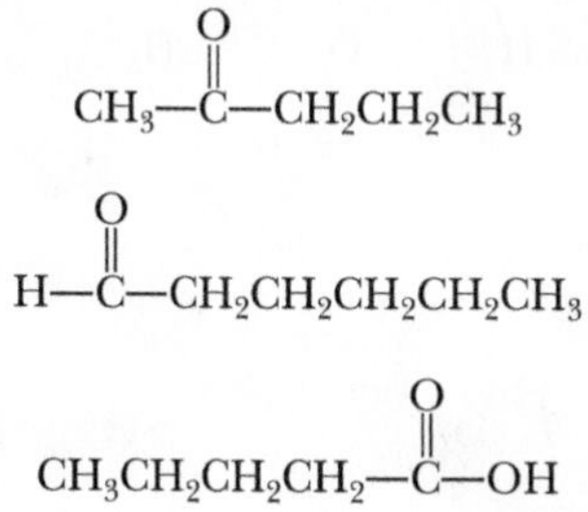

23.49 (a) Acid, 3-methylpentanoic acid
(b) Ester, methyl propanoate
(c) Ester, butyl acetate (or butyl ethanoate)
(d) Acid, *p*-bromobenzoic acid

23.51 (a) Pentanoic acid

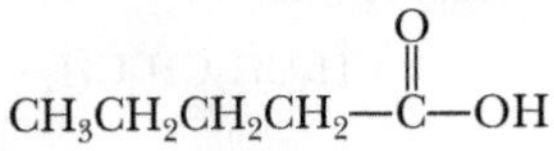

(b) 2-Octanol

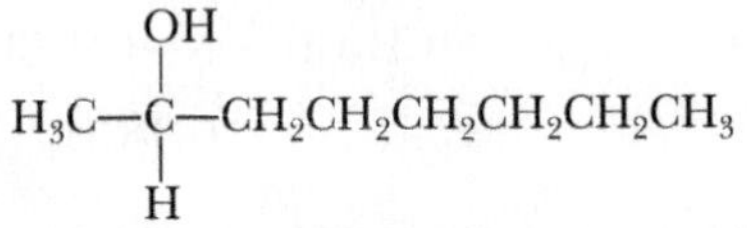

23.53 Step 1: Oxidize 1-propanol to propanoic acid.

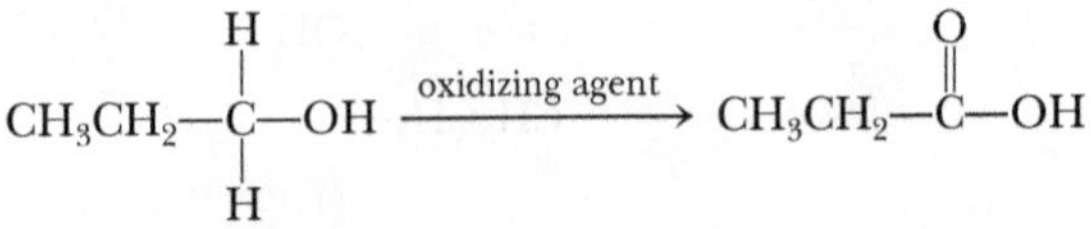

Step 2: Combine propanoic acid and 1-propanol.

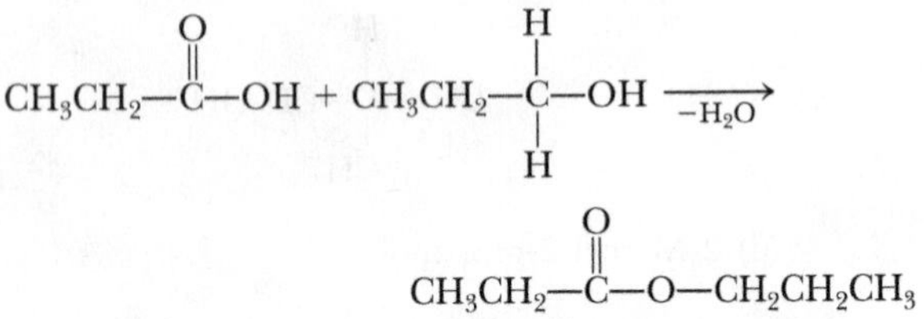

23.55 Sodium acetate, $NaCH_3CO_2$, and 1-butanol, $CH_3CH_2CH_2CH_2OH$

23.57 (a) Trigonal-planar
(b) 120°
(c) The molecule is chiral. There are four different groups around the carbon atom marked 2.
(d) The acidic H atom is the H attached to the CO_2H (carboxyl) group.

23.59

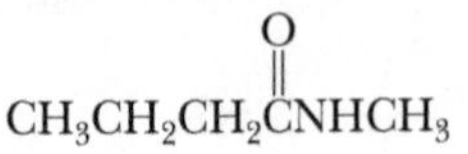

This compound is an amide.

$CH_3CH_2CH_2CO_2H + CH_3NH_2 \rightarrow CH_3CH_2CH_2CONHCH_3 + H_2O$

23.61 (a) Alcohol (b) amide (c) acid (d) ester

23.63 (a) Prepare polyvinyl acetate (PVA) from vinylacetate.

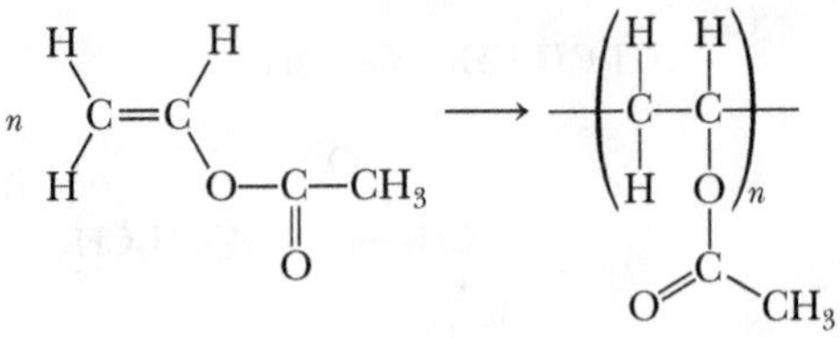

(b) Three units of PVA:

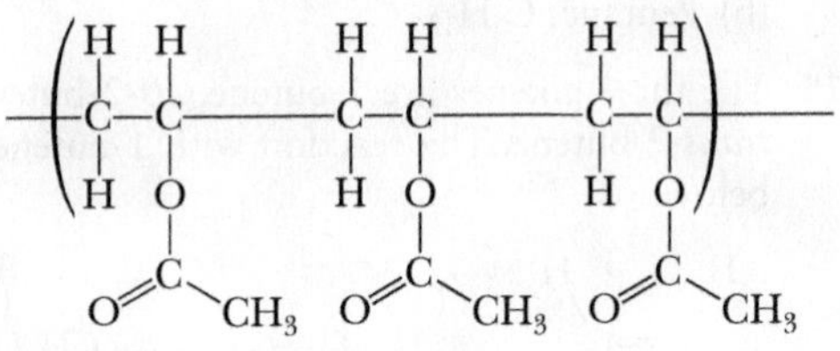

(c) Hydrolysis of polyvinyl acetate will yield polyvinyl alcohol.

23.65 Polyacrylonitrile from acrylonitrile.

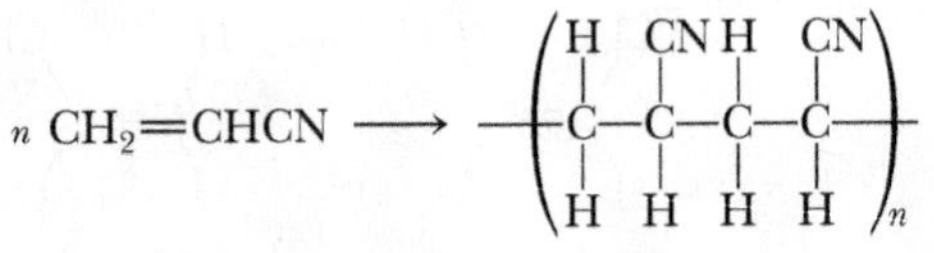

23.67

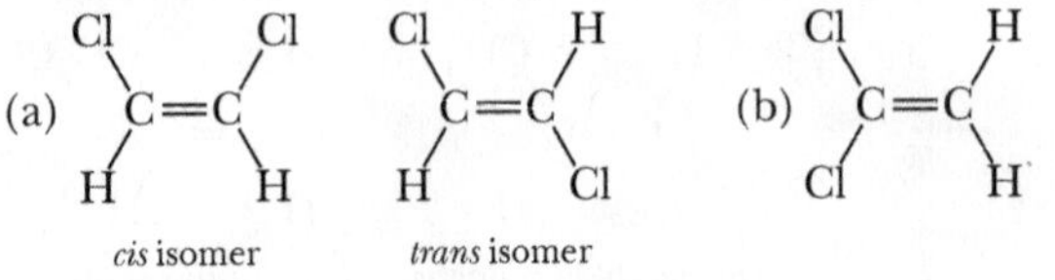

23.69 Five isomers: 1-hexene, *cis*- and *trans*-2-hexene, and *cis*- and *trans*-3-hexene.

23.71

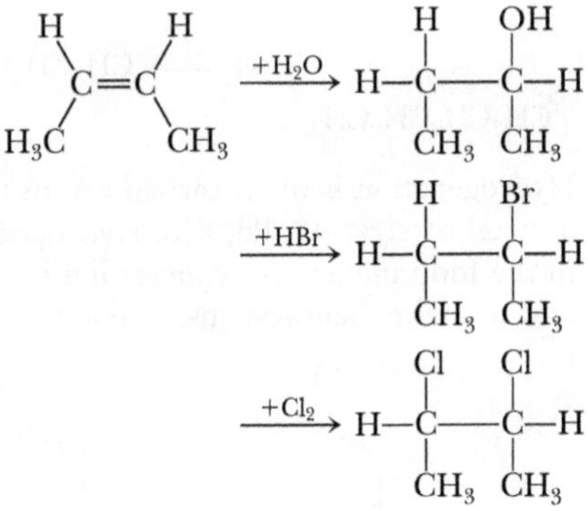

23.73 (a)

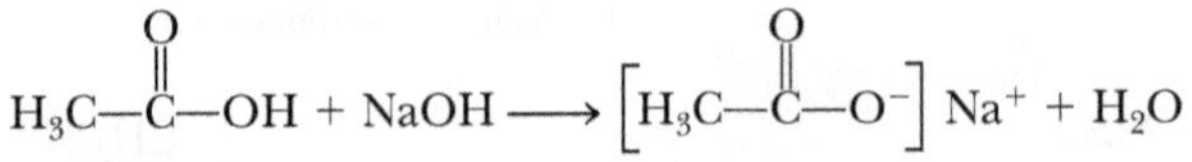

(b)

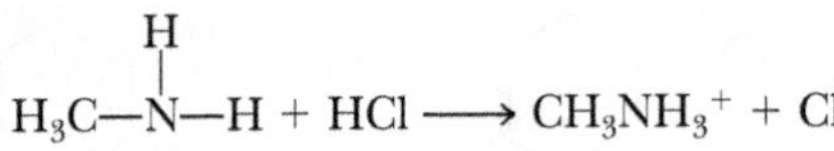

23.75

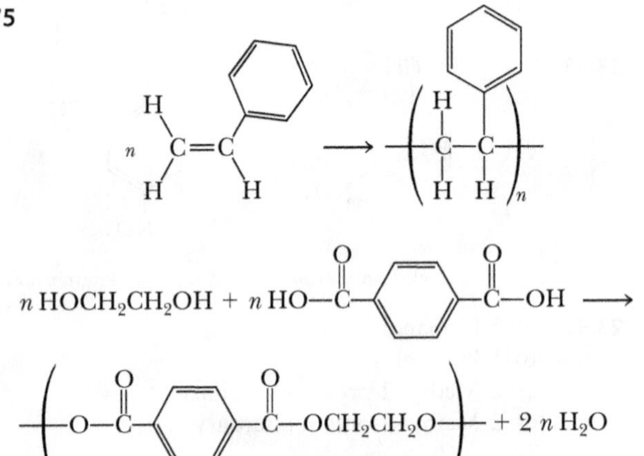

23.77 (a) 2, 3-Dimethylpentane

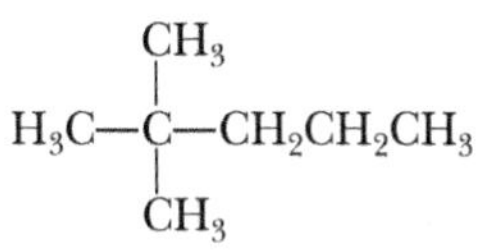

(b) 3, 3-Diethylpentane

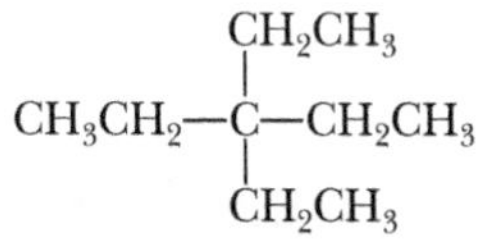

(c) 3-Ethyl-2-methylpentane

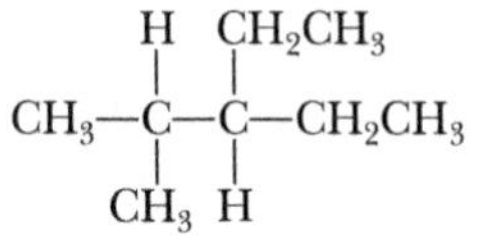

(d) 3-Ethylhexane

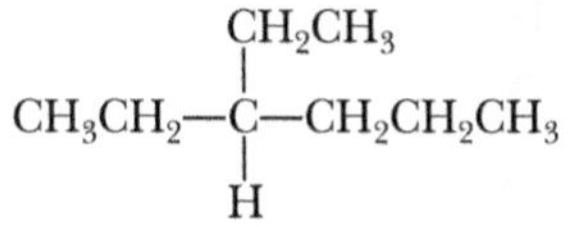

23.79

1,1-Dichloropropane

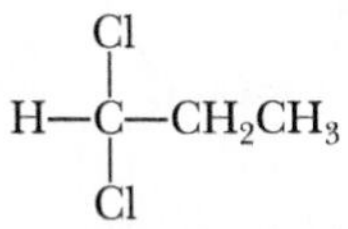

1,2-Dichloropropane

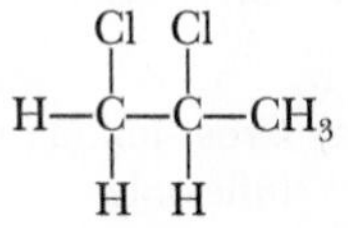

1,3-Dichloropropane

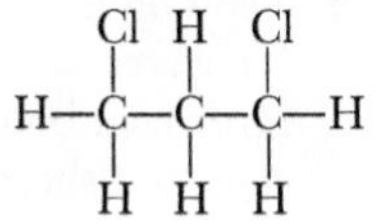

2,2-Dichloropropane

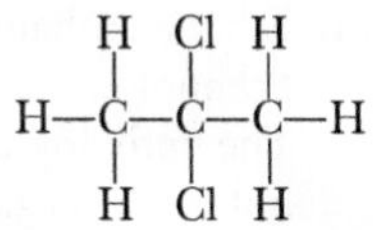

23.81

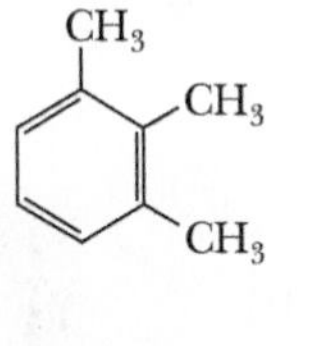

1,2,3-trimethylbenzene

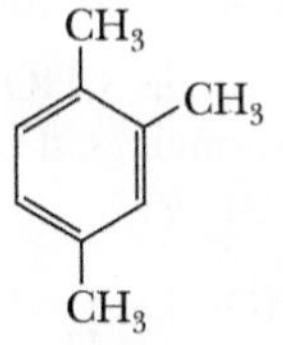

1,2,4-trimethylbenzene

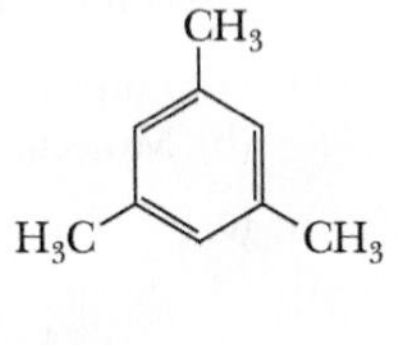

1,3,5-trimethylbenzene

23.83 Replace the carboxylic acid group with an H atom.

23.85 (a)

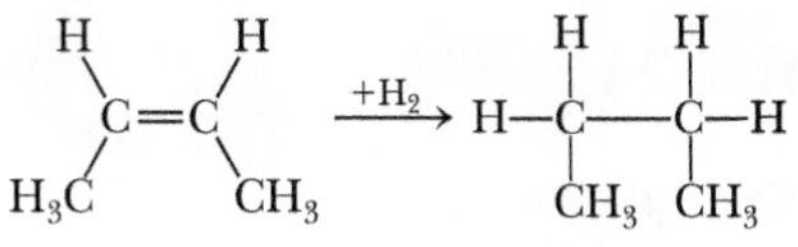

butane (not chiral)

(b)

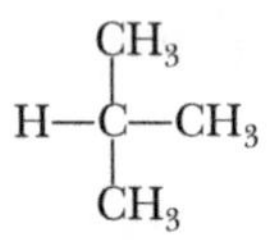

23.87

(a)

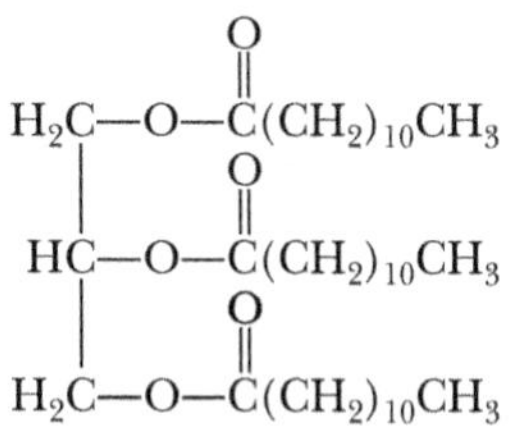

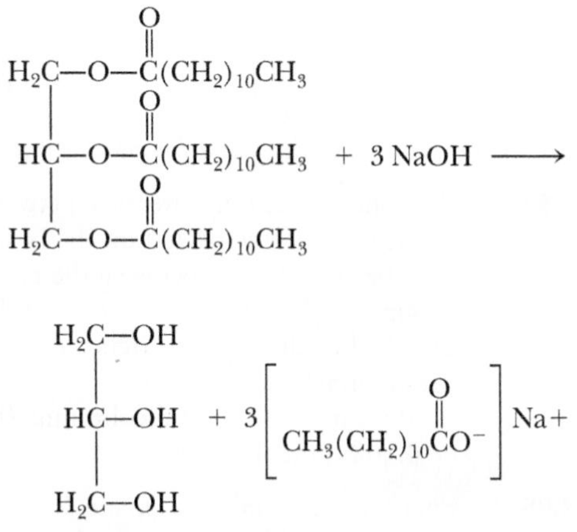

(b)

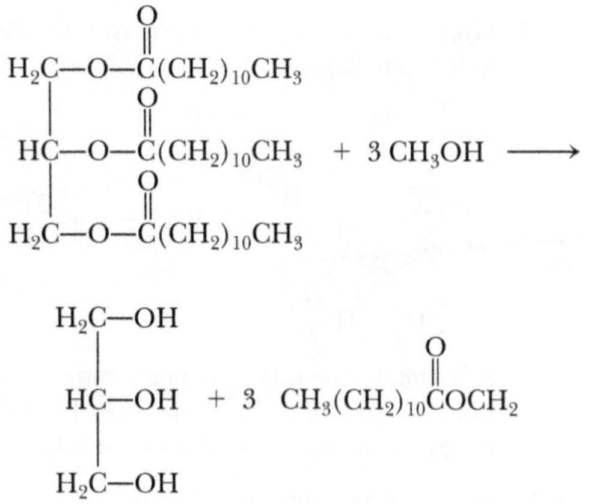

23.89

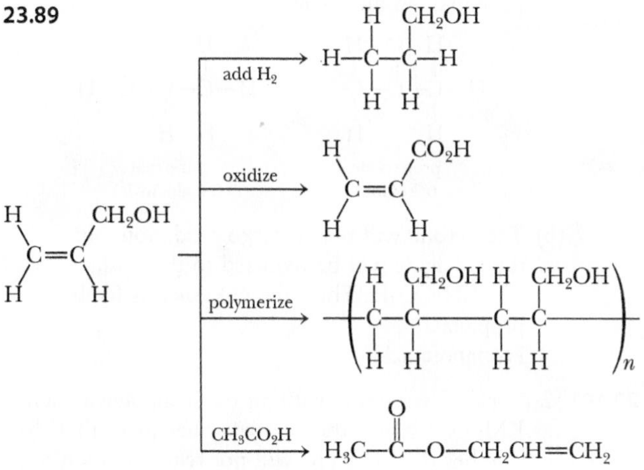

23.91 (a)

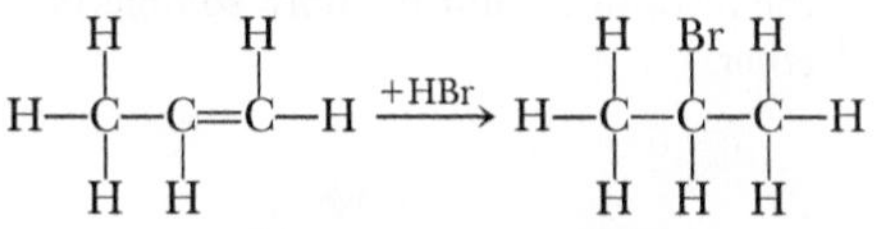

2-bromopropane

(b)

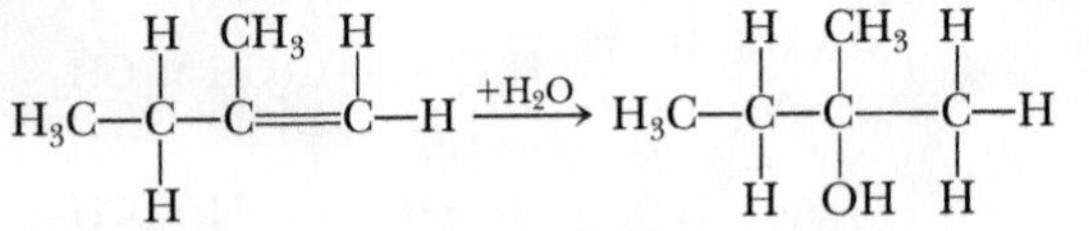

2-methyl-2-butanol

(c)

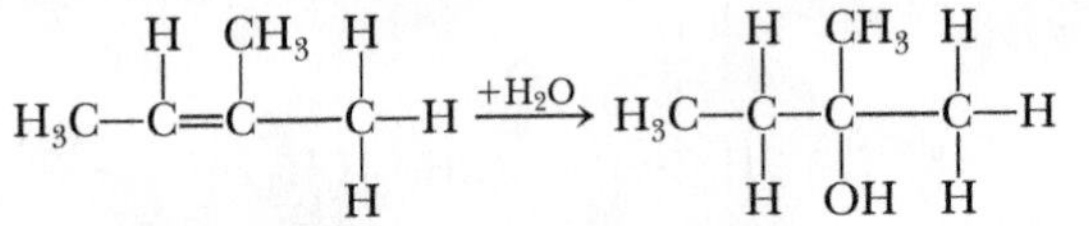

The product is the same for parts (b) and (c).

23.93 (a) The only structural difference between theobromine and caffeine occurs on the N in the six-member ring that is between the two C=O groups. In theobromine, there is an H atom attached to this N. In caffeine, there is a CH_3 group attached.

(b) 5.00 g sample (2.16 g theobromine/100 g sample) = 0.108 g theobromine

23.95 Compound (b), acetaldehyde, and (c), ethanol, produce acetic acid when oxidized.

23.97 Cyclohexene, a cyclic alkene, will add Br_2 readily (to give $C_6H_{10}Br_2$).

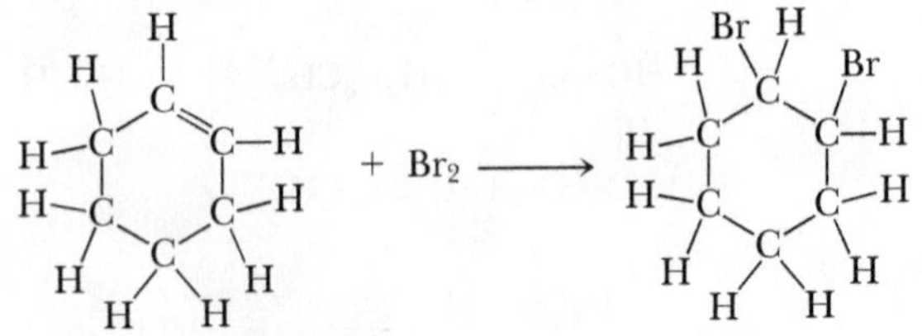

Benzene, however, needs much more stringent conditions to react with bromine; then Br_2 will substitute for H atoms on benzene and not add to the ring.

23.99 (a) The compound is either propanone, a ketone, or propanal, an aldehyde.

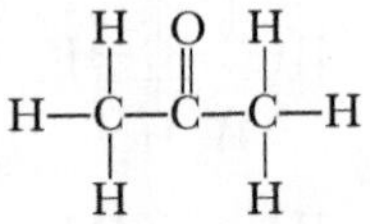

propanone (a ketone)

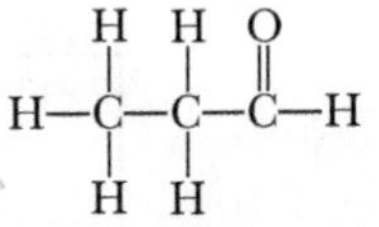

propanal (an aldehyde)

(b) The ketone will not undergo oxidation, but the aldehyde will be oxidized to the acid, $CH_3CH_2CO_2H$. Thus, the unknown is likely propanal.

(c) Propanoic acid

23.101 2-Propanol will react with an oxidizing agent such as $KMnO_4$ (to give the ketone), whereas methyl ethyl ether ($CH_3OC_2H_5$) will not react. In addition, the alcohol should be more soluble in water than the ether.

23.103

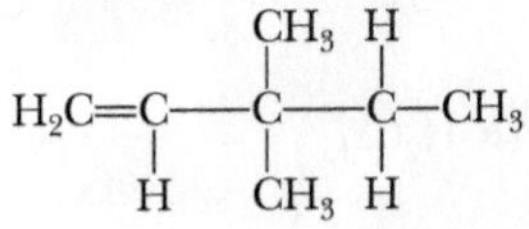

X = 3,3-dimethyl-1-pentene

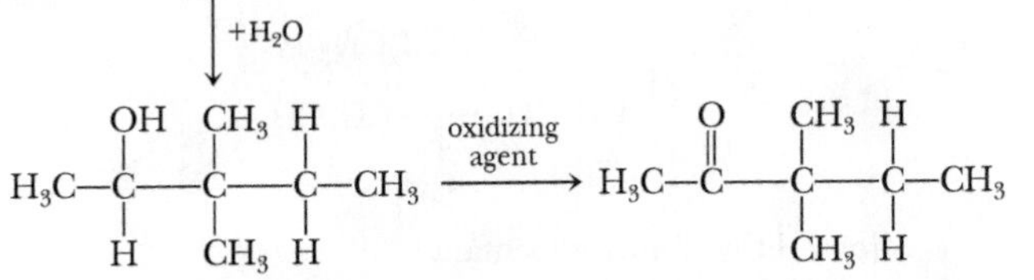

Y = 3,3-dimethyl-2-pentanol   3,3-dimethyl-2-pentanone

23.105 The ^{18}O label will be found in dimethyl terephthalate.

23.107

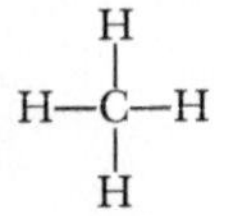	methane	four single bonds
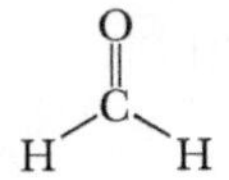	formaldehyde	one double bond and two single bonds
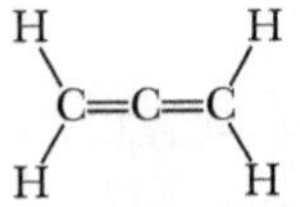	allene	two double bonds
H—C≡C—H	acetylene	one single bond and one triple bond

23.109 (a) Cross-linking makes the material very rigid and inflexible.

(b) The OH groups give the polymer a high affinity for water.

(c) Hydrogen bonding allows the chains to form coils and sheets with high tensile strength.

23.111 (a) Ethane enthalpy of combustion = −47.51 kJ/g
Ethanol enthalpy of combustion = −26.82 kJ/g

(b) The enthalpy change for the combustion of ethanol is less negative than for ethane, so partially oxidizing ethane to form ethanol decreases the amount of energy per gram available from the combustion of the substance.

23.113 (a) Empirical formula, CHO

(b) Molecular formula, $C_4H_4O_4$

(c)

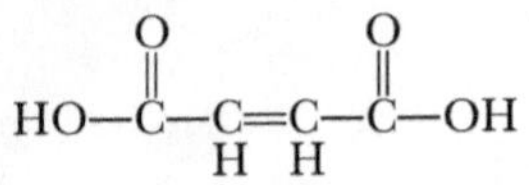

(d) All four C atoms are sp^2 hybridized.

(e) 120°

Chapter 24

Case Study

Antisense Therapy

1. 5′-GGUGCGAAGCAGACUGAGGC-3′
2. 7595 g/mol
3. tetrahedral

Check Your Understanding

24.1

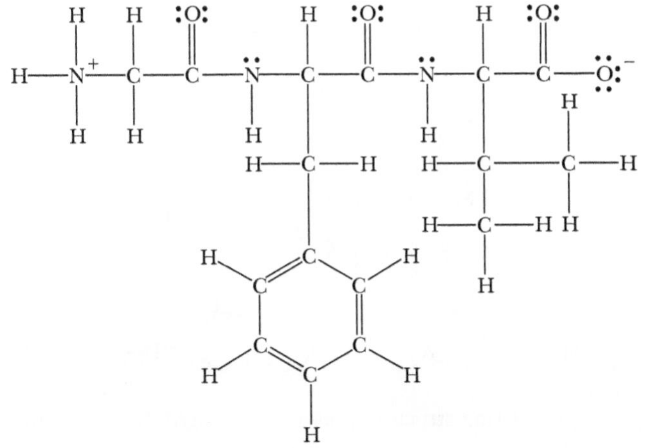

24.2 5′-GTACGTATCG-3′

24.3 mRNA: 5′-AAA GCA CAA-3′
amino acid sequence: lysine-alanine-glutamine

Review & Check

Section 24-1

1. (a) amino acids
2. (c) zwitterionic
3. (b) structures built from the hydrogen bonding network of the amide linkages in the protein's backbone

Section 24-2

1. (c) $C_3H_6O_3$
2. (b) glucose and fructose
3. (c) cellulose

Section 24-3

1. (b) RNA
2. (c) 5′-CAU-3′
3. (b) glutamic acid

Section 24-4

1. (b) ethanol
2. (c) polar heads pointing to both the extracellular fluid and the intracellular fluid

Section 24-5

1. (c) exothermic and product-favored at equilibrium
2. (d) NADH

Applying Chemical Principles: Polymerase Chain Reaction

1. $2^{20} = 1{,}048{,}576$

3. (a) Cytosine and guanine bind with three hydrogen bonds per base pair, whereas adenine and thymine (uracil) bind with only two. Sequences with a high number of cytosines and guanines will thus bind more strongly.
(b) This sequence could fold over and base pair to itself instead of to the target strand.
(c) Using a large excess of primers ensures that the target strands will bind to the primers instead of having the complementary target strands bind to each other.

Study Questions

24.1 (a)

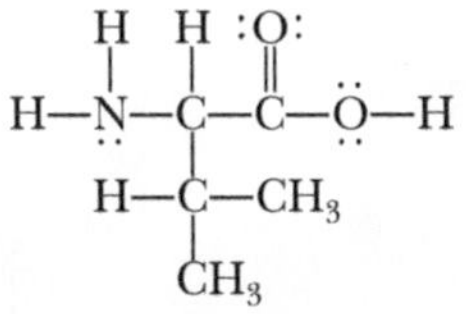

(b)

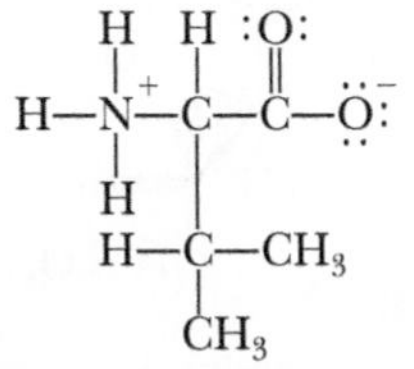

(c) The zwitterionic form is the predominant form at physiological pH.

24.3 Polar: serine, lysine, aspartic acid
Nonpolar: alanine, leucine, phenylalanine

24.5

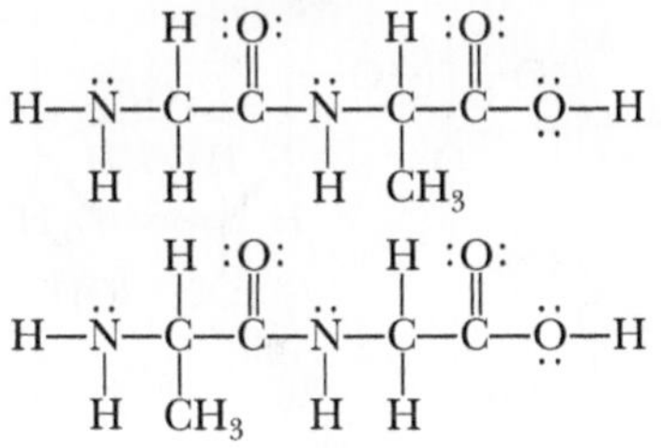

24.7

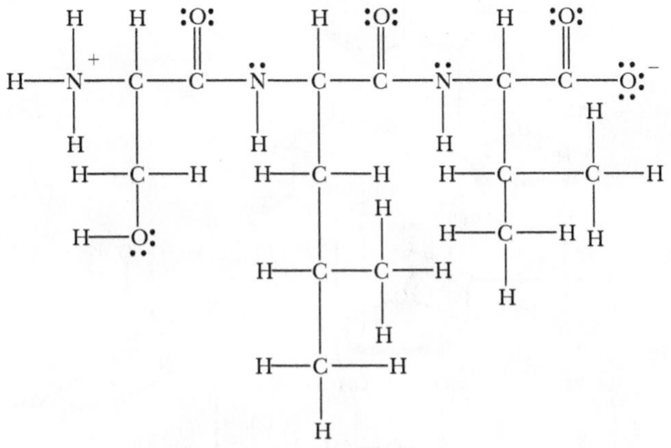

24.9 (a) primary
(b) quaternary
(c) tertiary
(d) secondary

24.11

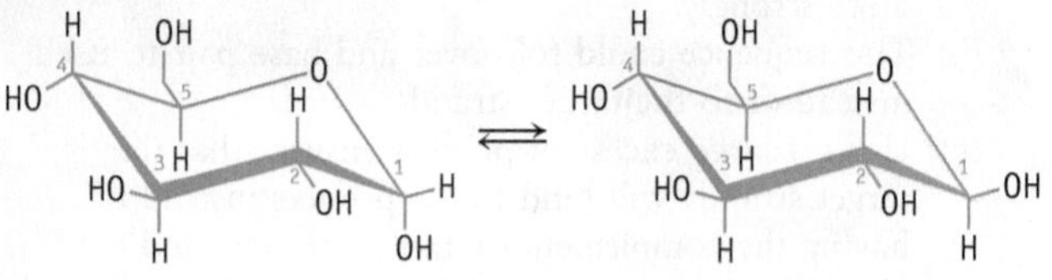

α-D-glucose ⇌ β-D-glucose

24.13 (a) The structure of ribose is given on p. 957.

(b) **Adenosine**

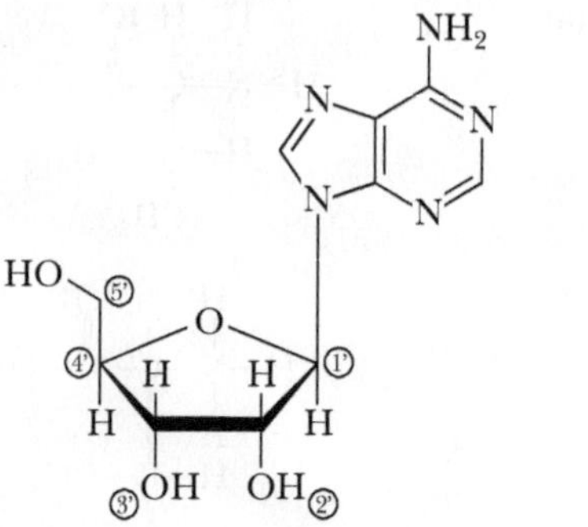

(c) **Adenosine-5′-monophosphate**

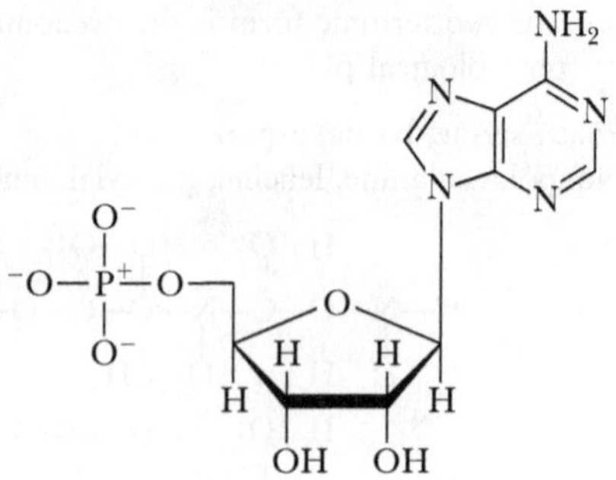

24.15

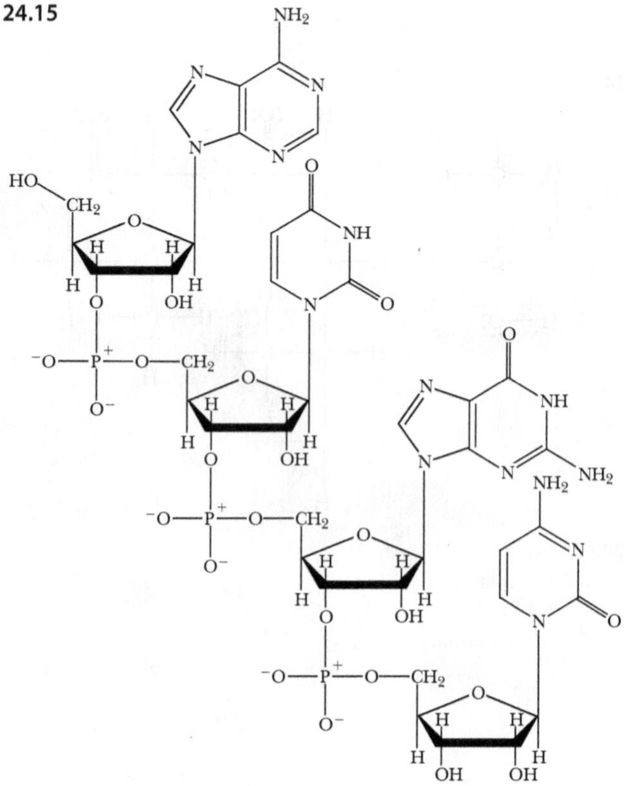

24.17 (a) 5′-GAATCGCGT-3′
(b) 5′-GAAUCGCGU-3′
(c) 5′-UUC-3′, 5′-CGA-3′, and 5′-ACG-3′
(d) glutamic acid, serine, and arginine

24.19

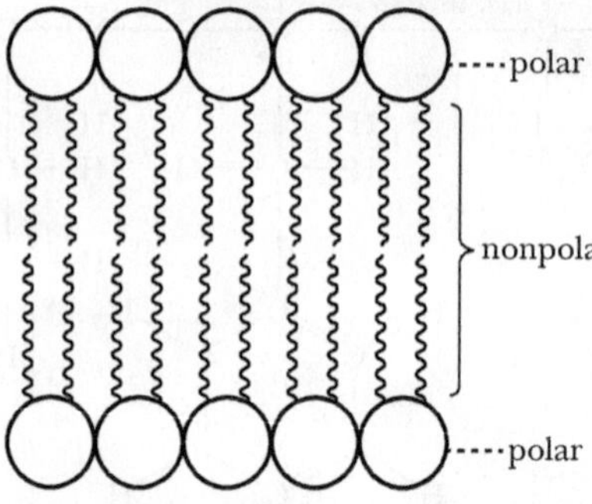

24.21 The 4-ring structure present in all steroids is given in Figure 24.20.

24.23 $C_6H_{12}O_6(s) + 6\ O_2(g) \rightarrow 6\ CO_2(g) + 6\ H_2O(\ell)$

$\Delta_rH° = \Sigma n\Delta_fH°(\text{products}) - \Sigma n\Delta_fH°(\text{reactants})$

$\Delta_rH° = (6\text{ mol } CO_2/\text{mol-rxn})[\Delta_fH°(CO_2)] + (6\text{ mol } H_2O/\text{mol-rxn})[\Delta_fH°(H_2O)] - (1\text{ mol } C_6H_{12}O_6/\text{mol-rxn})[\Delta_fH°(C_6H_{12}O_6)]$

$\Delta_rH° = (6\text{ mol } CO_2/\text{mol-rxn})(-393.5\text{ kJ/mol } CO_2) + (6\text{ mol } H_2O/\text{mol-rxn})(-285.8\text{ kJ/mol } H_2O) - (1\text{ mol } C_6H_{12}O_6/\text{mol-rxn})(-1273.3\text{ kJ/mol } C_6H_{12}O_6)$

$\Delta_rH° = -2{,}803\text{ kJ/mol-rxn}$

24.25 (a) NADH
(b) O_2
(c) O_2
(d) NADH

24.27

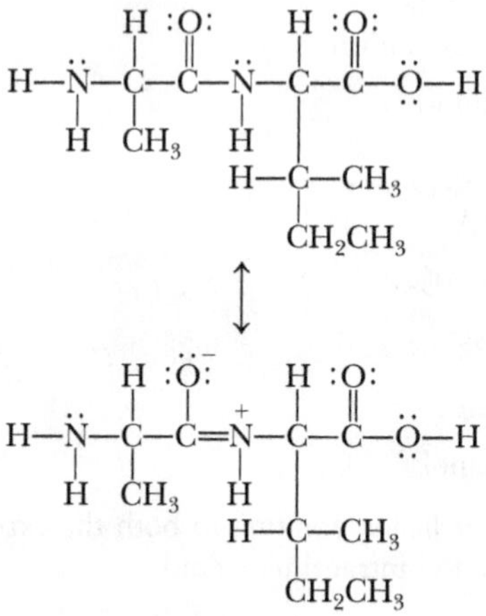

24.29 (a) $6\ CO_2(g) + 6\ H_2O(\ell) \rightarrow C_6H_{12}O_6(s) + 6\ O_2(g)$

$\Delta_rH° = \Sigma n\Delta_fH°(\text{products}) - \Sigma n\Delta_fH°(\text{reactants})$

$\Delta_rH° = (1\text{ mol } C_6H_{12}O_6/\text{mol-rxn})[\Delta_fH°(C_6H_{12}O_6)] - (6\text{ mol } H_2O/\text{mol-rxn})[\Delta_fH°(H_2O)] - (6\text{ mol } CO_2/\text{mol-rxn})[\Delta_fH°(CO_2)]$

$\Delta_rH° = (1\text{ mol } C_6H_{12}O_6/\text{mol-rxn})(-1273.3\text{ kJ/mol } C_6H_{12}O_6) - (6\text{ mol } H_2O/\text{mol-rxn})(-285.8\text{ kJ/mol } H_2O) - (6\text{ mol } CO_2/\text{mol-rxn})(-393.5\text{ kJ/mol } CO_2)$

$\Delta_rH° = +2{,}803\text{ kJ/mol-rxn}$

(b) (2803 kJ/mol)(1 mol/6.022 × 10^{23} molecules)(1000 J/1 kJ) = 4.655 × 10^{-18} J/molecule

(c) $\lambda = 650$ nm(1 m/10^9 nm) = 6.5 × 10^{-7} m

$E = hc/\lambda = (6.626 \times 10^{-34}\ J \cdot s)(3.00 \times 10^8\ m \cdot s^{-1})/(6.5 \times 10^{-7}\ m) = 3.1 \times 10^{-19}$ J

(d) The energy per photon is less than the amount required per molecule of glucose, therefore multiple photons must be absorbed.

24.31 There are four nucleotide bases, and each codon is three nucleotides long, so there are $4^3 = 64$ codons possible. Some amino acids have more than one codon.

24.33 oxidation: $C_6H_{12}O_6$
reduction: O_2

24.35 A graph of $y = 1/\text{Rate}$ and $x = 1/[S]$ yields a straight line with the equation $y = 1.5x + 9200$. The y-intercept corresponds to $1/\text{Rate}_{max}$, so $\text{Rate}_{max} = 1/9200 = 1.1 \times 10^{-4}$ mol/L · min.

24.37 glycine

24.39 The sequences differ in the positions of attachments of the phosphate to deoxyribose on adjacent units. Consider the A-T attachments. In ATGC, the phosphate links the 3′ position on A to the 5′ position on T. In CGTA, the phosphate links the 5′ position on A to the 3′ position on T.

24.41 (a) In transcription, a strand of RNA complementary to the segment of DNA is constructed.
(b) In translation, an amino acid sequence is constructed based on the information in an mRNA sequence.

Chapter 25

Case Study

Technetium-99m and Medical Imaging

1. $^{99}_{42}Mo \rightarrow ^{99}_{43}Tc + ^{0}_{-1}\beta$

2. Oxidation number = 7

   Tc^{7+} electron configuration = [Kr]

   Diamagnetic

3. Amount $NaTcO_4$ = (1.0 μg)(1 g/10^6 μg)(1 mol/184.9 g) = 5.4 × 10^{-9} mol

   Mass Tc = (5.4 × 10^{-9} mol $NaTcO_4$)(1 mol Tc/mol $NaTcO_4$)(97.9 g Tc/mol) = 5.3 × 10^{-7} g Tc

4. 24 hours is 4 half-lives for ^{99m}Tc. Thus, mass remaining is 1/16th of 1.0 μg, or 0.063 μg.

5. Beta particle

6. The attractive forces binding an anion to the column are related to the anion charge. The anion MoO_4^{2-} has a higher charge than TcO_4^-.

Check Your Understanding

25.1 (a) Emission of six α particles leads to a decrease of 24 in the mass number and a decrease of 12 in the atomic number. Emission of four β particles increases the atomic number by 4 but doesn't affect the mass. The final product of this process has a mass number of 232 − 24 = 208 and an atomic number of 90 − 12 + 4 = 82, identifying it as $^{208}_{82}Pb$.

(b) Step 1: $^{232}_{90}Th \rightarrow ^{228}_{88}Ra + ^{4}_{2}\alpha$
Step 2: $^{228}_{88}Ra \rightarrow ^{228}_{89}Ac + ^{0}_{-1}\beta$
Step 3: $^{228}_{89}Ac \rightarrow ^{228}_{90}Th + ^{0}_{-1}\beta$

25.2 (a) $^{0}_{+1}\beta$ (b) $^{41}_{19}K$ (c) $^{0}_{-1}\beta$ (d) $^{22}_{10}Ne$

25.3 (a) $^{32}_{14}Si \rightarrow ^{32}_{15}P + ^{0}_{-1}\beta$
(b) $^{45}_{22}Ti \rightarrow ^{45}_{21}Sc + ^{0}_{+1}\beta$ or $^{45}_{22}Ti + ^{0}_{-1}e \rightarrow ^{45}_{21}Sc$
(c) $^{239}_{94}Pu \rightarrow \alpha + ^{235}_{92}U$
(d) $^{42}_{19}K \rightarrow ^{42}_{20}Ca + ^{0}_{-1}\beta$

25.4 $\Delta m = 0.03435$ g/mol
$\Delta E = (3.435 \times 10^{-5}\ kg/mol)(2.998 \times 10^8\ m/s)^2 = 3.087 \times 10^{12}$ J/mol (= 3.087 × 10^9 kJ/mol)
$E_b = 5.146 \times 10^8$ kJ/mol nucleons

25.5 (a) 49.2 years is exactly four half-lives; quantity remaining = 1.5 mg$(1/2)^4$ = 0.094 mg
(b) Three half-lives, 36.9 years
(c) 1% is between six half-lives, 73.8 years (1/64 remains), and seven half-lives, 86.1 years (1/128 remains). [Using the integrated first-order rate equation with $[R]/[R]_0 = 0.010$ and $k = (\ln 2)/t_{1/2} = 0.0564\ y^{-1}$, the amount of time is calculated to be 81.7 years.]

25.6 (a) $\ln([A]/[A_o]) = -kt$
$\ln([3.18 \times 10^3]/[3.35 \times 10^3]) = -k(2.00\ d)$
$k = 0.0260\ d^{-1}$
$t_{1/2} = 0.693/k = 0.693/(0.0260\ d^{-1}) = 26.7$ d
(b) $k = 0.693/t_{1/2} = 0.693/200\ y = 3.47 \times 10^{-3}\ y^{-1}$
$\ln([A]/[A_o]) = -kt$
$\ln([3.00 \times 10^3]/[6.50 \times 10^{12}]) = -(3.47 \times 10^{-3}\ y^{-1})t$
$\ln(4.62 \times 10^{-10}) = -(3.47 \times 10^{-3}\ y^{-1})t$
$t = 6190$ y

25.7 $\ln([A]/[A_o]) = -kt$
$\ln([9.32]/[13.4]) = -(1.21 \times 10^{-4}\ y^{-1})t$
$t = 3.00 \times 10^3$ y
This compares quite well with the estimated date.

25.8 $^{98}_{42}Mo + ^{1}_{0}n \rightarrow ^{99}_{42}Mo + \gamma$
$^{99}_{42}Mo \rightarrow ^{99}_{43}Tc + ^{0}_{-1}\beta$

25.9 4.17 × 10^{-5}(0.0100 g Pb^{2+}) = 4.17 × 10^{-7} g Pb^{2+}
Solubility = [4.17 × 10^{-7} g Pb^{2+} (1 mol Pb^{2+}/207.2 g Pb)(1 mol $PbCrO_4$/1 mol Pb^{2+})]/0.01000 L = 2.01 × 10^{-7} mol $PbCrO_4$/L

Review & Check

Section 25-2

1. (a) alpha radiation
2. (b) 7 α and 4 β
3. (c) ${}^{90}_{38}Sr \rightarrow {}^{90}_{39}Y + \beta$

Section 25-3

1. (c) ${}^{56}_{26}Fe$

Section 25-4

1. (a) 20%
2. (d) 1/32

Section 25-5

1. (c) electrons

Section 25-6

1. (a) ${}^{93}_{37}Rb$

Applying Chemical Principles: The Age of Meteorites

1. ${}^{87}_{37}Rb \rightarrow {}^{87}_{38}Sr + {}^{0}_{-1}\beta$
3. $k = 1.42 \times 10^{-11}\ y^{-1}$
5. Age of meteorite $= 2.80 \times 10^9$ y

Study Questions

25.1 Each answer is in the format: person(s); experiment; significance.

(a) Becquerel; potassium uranyl sulfate caused an image to appear on a photographic plate; this opened up a new area of study.

(b) Marie and Pierre Curie; separated these elements from pitchblende; discovery of new elements based on radioactivity.

(c) Rutherford; bombarded ^{14}N with α particles and found protons and ^{17}O among products; human-caused transmutation of one element into another.

(d) Fermi; absorption of a neutron by a nucleus with subsequent release of a γ ray; production of more nuclei and the use of this process to produce many of the radioisotopes used in medicine.

(e) Hahn and Strassman, experiment explained by Meitner; bombarded a sample of uranium with neutrons and detected barium in products; nuclear fission is used in atomic bombs and in nuclear energy plants.

25.3 Binding energy per nucleon is determined by first calculating the mass defect for an isotope, converting the mass defect to binding energy (using $E = mc^2$) and then dividing the binding energy by the mass number of the nucleus.

25.5 Nuclear reactions are carried out in a laboratory by hitting a nucleus with a particle. Various particles have been used: α particles, protons, neutrons, and the nuclei of other atoms. In producing transuranium elements, this last method is used; the particles are usually accelerated to high energy in a particle accelerator.

25.7 While an organism lives, the percentage of carbon that is ^{14}C in the organism will equal the percentage in the atmosphere. When the organism dies, it no longer replenishes the ^{14}C. By measuring the activity of ^{14}C in the organism, comparing it to the ambient ^{14}C activity, and using first-order kinetics, it is possible to determine how long ago the organism stopped taking in ^{14}C (died). Limitations: (1) The method assumes that the amount of ^{14}C in the atmosphere has remained constant, whereas it has varied by as much as 10%. (2) ^{14}C dating cannot be used to date an object less than 100 or more than about 40,000 years old. (3) The accuracy of ^{14}C dating is about ± 100 years.

25.9 A radioactive decay series occurs when a radioactive isotope decays to form another radioactive isotope. The series continues until a nonradioactive isotope is formed. Uranium ore contains radium and polonium because these elements are formed in the radioactive decay series of uranium.

25.11 (a) ${}^{56}_{28}Ni$; (b) ${}^{1}_{0}n$; (c) ${}^{32}_{15}P$; (d) ${}^{97}_{43}Tc$; (e) ${}^{0}_{-1}\beta$; (f) ${}^{0}_{1}e$ (positron)

25.13 (a) ${}^{0}_{-1}\beta$; (b) ${}^{87}_{37}Rb$; (c) ${}^{4}_{2}\alpha$; (d) ${}^{226}_{88}Ra$; (e) ${}^{0}_{-1}\beta$; (f) ${}^{24}_{11}Na$

25.15
${}^{235}_{92}U \rightarrow {}^{231}_{90}Th + {}^{4}_{2}\alpha$
${}^{231}_{90}Th \rightarrow {}^{231}_{91}Pa + {}^{0}_{-1}\beta$
${}^{231}_{91}Pa \rightarrow {}^{227}_{89}Ac + {}^{4}_{2}\alpha$
${}^{227}_{89}Ac \rightarrow {}^{227}_{90}Th + {}^{0}_{-1}\beta$
${}^{227}_{90}Th \rightarrow {}^{223}_{88}Ra + {}^{4}_{2}\alpha$
${}^{223}_{88}Ra \rightarrow {}^{219}_{86}Rn + {}^{4}_{2}\alpha$
${}^{219}_{86}Rn \rightarrow {}^{215}_{84}Po + {}^{4}_{2}\alpha$
${}^{215}_{84}Po \rightarrow {}^{211}_{82}Pb + {}^{4}_{2}\alpha$
${}^{211}_{82}Pb \rightarrow {}^{211}_{83}Bi + {}^{0}_{-1}\beta$
${}^{211}_{83}Bi \rightarrow {}^{211}_{84}Po + {}^{0}_{-1}\beta$
${}^{211}_{84}Po \rightarrow {}^{207}_{82}Pb + {}^{4}_{2}\alpha$

25.17 (a) ${}^{198}_{79}Au \rightarrow {}^{198}_{80}Hg + {}^{0}_{-1}\beta$

(b) ${}^{222}_{86}Rn \rightarrow {}^{218}_{84}Po + {}^{4}_{2}\alpha$

(c) ${}^{137}_{55}Cs \rightarrow {}^{137}_{56}Ba + {}^{0}_{-1}\beta$

(d) ${}^{110}_{49}In \rightarrow {}^{110}_{48}Cd + {}^{0}_{1}e$

25.19 (a) ${}^{80}_{35}Br$ has a high neutron/proton ratio of 45/35. Beta decay will allow the ratio to decrease:

${}^{80}_{35}Br \rightarrow {}^{80}_{36}Kr + {}^{0}_{-1}\beta$.

(b) Alpha decay is likely: ${}^{240}_{98}Cf \rightarrow {}^{236}_{96}Cm + {}^{4}_{2}\alpha$

(c) Cobalt-61 has a high *n/p* ratio, so beta decay is likely:

${}^{61}_{27}Co \rightarrow {}^{61}_{28}Kr + {}^{0}_{-1}\beta$

(d) Carbon-11 has only five neutrons, so K-capture or positron emission may occur:

$^{11}_{6}C + {}^{0}_{-1}e \rightarrow {}^{11}_{5}B$

$^{11}_{6}C \rightarrow {}^{11}_{5}B + {}^{0}_{1}e$

25.21 Generally beta decay will occur when the *n/p* ratio is high, whereas positron emission will occur when the *n/p* ratio is low.

(a) Beta decay: $^{20}_{9}F \rightarrow {}^{20}_{10}Ne + {}^{0}_{-1}\beta$

$^{3}_{1}H \rightarrow {}^{3}_{2}He + {}^{0}_{-1}\beta$

(b) Positron emission

$^{22}_{11}Na \rightarrow {}^{22}_{10}Ne + {}^{0}_{1}\beta$

25.23 Binding energy per mole of nucleons for ^{11}B = 6.70×10^8 kJ

Binding energy per mole of nucleons for ^{10}B = 6.26×10^8 kJ

25.25 8.256×10^8 kJ/mol nucleons

25.27 7.700×10^8 kJ/mol nucleons

25.29 0.781 micrograms

25.31 (a) $^{131}_{53}I \rightarrow {}^{131}_{54}Xe + {}^{0}_{-1}\beta$

(b) 0.075 micrograms

25.33 9.5×10^{-4} mg

25.35 (a) $^{222}_{86}Rn \rightarrow {}^{218}_{84}Po + {}^{4}_{2}\alpha$

(b) Time = 8.87 d

25.37 (a) 15.8 y; (b) 88%

25.39 $^{239}_{94}Pu + {}^{4}_{2}\alpha \rightarrow {}^{240}_{95}Am + {}^{1}_{1}H + 2\,{}^{1}_{0}n$

25.41 $^{48}_{20}Ca + {}^{242}_{94}Pu \rightarrow {}^{287}_{114}Fl + 3\,{}^{1}_{0}n$

25.43 (a) $^{115}_{48}Cd$; (b) $^{7}_{4}Be$; (c) $^{4}_{2}\alpha$; (d) $^{63}_{29}Cu$

25.45 $^{10}_{5}B + {}^{1}_{0}n \rightarrow {}^{7}_{3}Li + {}^{4}_{2}\alpha$

25.47 Time = 4.4×10^{10} y

25.49 If $t_{1/2}$ = 14.28 d, then $k = 4.854 \times 10^{-2}$ d^{-1}. If the original disintegration rate is 3.2×10^6 dpm, then (from the integrated first order rate equation), the rate after 365 d is 0.065 dpm. The plot will resemble Figure 25.5.

25.51 (a) $^{238}_{92}U + {}^{1}_{0}n \rightarrow {}^{239}_{92}U + \gamma$

(b) $^{239}_{92}U \rightarrow {}^{239}_{93}Np + {}^{0}_{-1}\beta$

(c) $^{239}_{93}Np \rightarrow {}^{239}_{94}Pu + {}^{0}_{-1}\beta$

(d) $^{239}_{94}Pu + {}^{1}_{0}n \rightarrow 2\,{}^{1}_{0}n$ + energy + other nuclei

25.53 (a) Calcium-48. Possible reaction is

$^{248}_{96}Cm + {}^{48}_{20}Ca \rightarrow {}^{296}_{116}Lv$

(b) Three neutrons

25.55 About 2700 years old

25.57 Plot ln(activity) versus time. The slope of the plot is $-k$, the rate constant for decay. Here, $k = 0.0050$ d^{-1}, so $t_{1/2}$ = 140 d.

25.59 Time = 1.9×10^9 y

25.61 Energy obtained from 1.000 lb (452.6 g) of $^{235}U = 4.1 \times 10^{10}$ kJ

Mass of coal required = 1.6×10^3 ton (or about 3 million pounds of coal)

25.63 The percentage of tagged fish in the lake is (27/5250)100% = 0.51%. Therefore, 1000 tagged fish is 0.51% of the total or approximately 190,000 fish.

25.65 (a) The mass decreases by 4 units (with an $^{4}_{2}\alpha$ emission) or is unchanged (with a $^{0}_{-1}\beta$ emission), so the only masses possible are 4 units apart.

(b) ^{232}Th series, $m = 4n$; ^{235}U series $m = 4n + 3$

(c) ^{226}Ra and ^{210}Bi, $4n + 2$ series; ^{215}At, $4n + 3$ series; ^{228}Th, $4n$ series

(d) Each series is headed by a long-lived isotope (in the order of 10^9 years, the age of the Earth). The $4n + 1$ series is missing because there is no long-lived isotope in this series. Over geologic time, all the members of this series have decayed completely.

25.67 (a) ^{231}Pa isotope belongs to the ^{235}U decay series (see Question 25.65b).

(b) $^{235}_{92}U \rightarrow {}^{231}_{90}Th + {}^{4}_{2}\alpha$

$^{231}_{90}Th \rightarrow {}^{231}_{91}Pa + {}^{0}_{-1}\beta$

(c) Pa-231 is present to the extent of 1 part per million. Therefore, 1 million grams of pitchblende need to be used to obtain 1 g of Pa-231.

(d) $^{231}_{91}Pa \rightarrow {}^{227}_{89}Ac + {}^{4}_{2}\alpha$

25.69 Pitchblende contains $^{238}_{92}U$ and $^{235}_{92}U$. Thus, both radium and polonium isotopes must belong to either the $4n + 2$ or $4n + 3$ decay series. Furthermore, the isotopes must have sufficiently long half-lives in order to survive the separation and isolation process. These criteria are satisfied by ^{226}Ra and ^{210}Po.

Additional AP Content

O-1 Metals and Alloys

Metals: The Electron Sea Model

We have described the solid-state structures of metals as consisting of a regular lattice of atoms (Figure 12.5, page 440). The fact that most metals have high melting and boiling points tells us that the forces of attraction between atoms in the lattice, that is, the bonding between metal atoms, must be very strong.

The classical picture of bonding in metals is the **electron sea model**. This is a qualitative model in which metal ions formed by the loss of one or more valence electrons are arranged in their lattice positions. The electrons from ionization of the metal atoms make up an electron sea surrounding the metal ions (Figure O.1). The "bond" between particles in this model is associated with the coulombic forces of attraction between the electrons and the positively charged metal ions.

The significant feature of this model is that the electrons are *delocalized*, that is, the electrons in the electron sea are not associated with the individual metal ions. Based on this model, the electrons are free to move throughout the lattice. This is the key to explaining the properties of metals. In other types of bonding (*A Closer Look: A Triangular View of Chemical Bonding,* page 284), bonding electrons are localized. In covalent bonding, electrons are placed as bonds between atoms. In ionic bonding, the electrons are firmly attached in the individual ions. With both ionic and covalent bonding, a significant expenditure of energy would accompany changes in the electronic structure.

The high electrical conductivity of metals arises because the electrons are free to move throughout the lattice under the influence of an applied electric potential. There is no large energy barrier to the movement of the electrons in the metal. Thermal conductivity is also a direct consequence of the mobility of the electrons in the electron sea, allowing rapid dispersion of heat within a sample of metal. Malleability and ductility (characteristics in which metals can be pounded into sheets or drawn

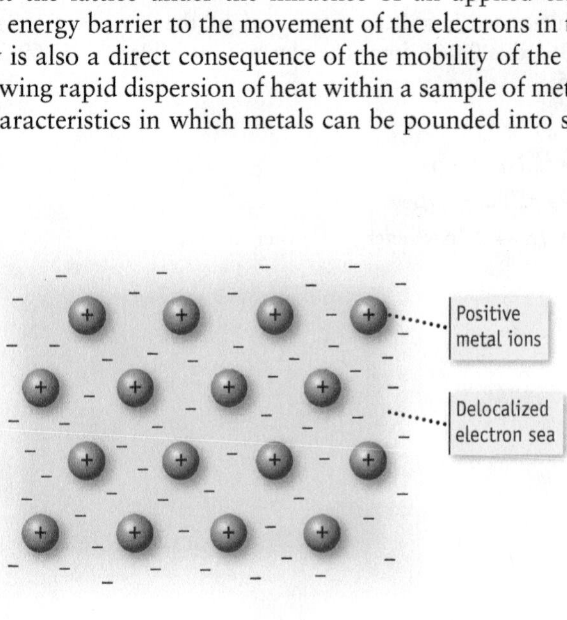

FIGURE O.1 Electron Sea Model for Metal Bonding. Coulombic forces of attraction exist between metal ions and delocalized electrons.

out into wires) are facilitated because moving metal ions in the lattice in these procedures doesn't require the breaking of chemical bonds.

Alloys: Mixtures of Metals

Pure metals often do not have the ideal properties needed for many typical uses. Mixing one or more elements with metals to form alloys is done with the aim of improving the properties of the metal but still retaining the characteristics of a metal. There are many familiar examples in everyday life: bronze, brass, stainless steel, and pewter, to name a few.

Alloys are among the earliest materials made by humans. The Bronze Age, dating back to around 3300 BC, is well established in history, and the use of this alloy of copper and tin for tools and decorations is well known. Bronze was favored over copper because it was harder and stronger than pure copper. Gold amalgams (liquid mixtures of mercury and gold) were used for centuries to plate the surface of an object; the amalgam would be placed on the surface of a metal object, which when heated, vaporizes the mercury and leaves a surface coating of gold.

In fact, most "metals" we use are alloys. Iron in its various forms is an alloy of this element with small amounts of carbon and other elements. Stainless steel, made from iron, chromium, and several other elements, is much more corrosion resistant than iron, and aluminum used in the aerospace industry contains about 5% magnesium to improve its hardness. Common magnets used in stereo speakers are made from Alnico, a strongly magnetic alloy mainly containing iron, aluminum, nickel, and cobalt. Sterling silver, commonly used in jewelry and which one might mistakenly think of as pure silver, is an alloy composed of 92.5% Ag and 7.5% Cu. Pure silver is soft and easily damaged, and the addition of copper makes the metal more rigid. You can confirm that an article of jewelry is sterling silver by looking for the stamp that says either "sterling" or "925," which means 92.5% silver. Gold used in jewelry is rarely pure (24 karat) gold. More often, you will find 18 K, 14 K, or 9 K stamped in a gold object, referring to alloys that are 18/24, 14/24, or 9/24 gold. The 18 K "yellow" gold is 75% gold, and the remaining 25% is copper and silver. As with sterling silver, the added metals lead to a harder and more rigid material (and one that is less costly).

There are three general classes of alloys: solid solutions, which are homogeneous mixtures of two or more elements; heterogeneous mixtures; and intermetallic compounds. In solid solutions, the element in larger amount is usually considered the "solvent" and the other the "solute." As with solutions in liquids, the solute atoms are dispersed throughout the solvent such that the bulk structure is homogeneous. Unlike liquid solutions, however, there are limitations based on the size of solvent and solute atoms. For a solid solution to form, the solute atoms must be incorporated in such a way that the original crystal structure of the solvent metal is preserved. This can be achieved in two ways: with solute atoms as interstitial atoms or with solute atoms as substitutional atoms in the crystalline lattice. In interstitial alloys, the solute atoms occupy the interstices, the small holes in the crystal lattice between solvent atoms (Figure O.2a). The solute atoms must be substantially smaller than the metal atoms making up the lattice to fit into these positions. In substitutional alloys, the solute atoms replace solvent atoms in the original crystal structure (Figure O.2b). For this to occur, the solute and solvent atoms must be similar in size.

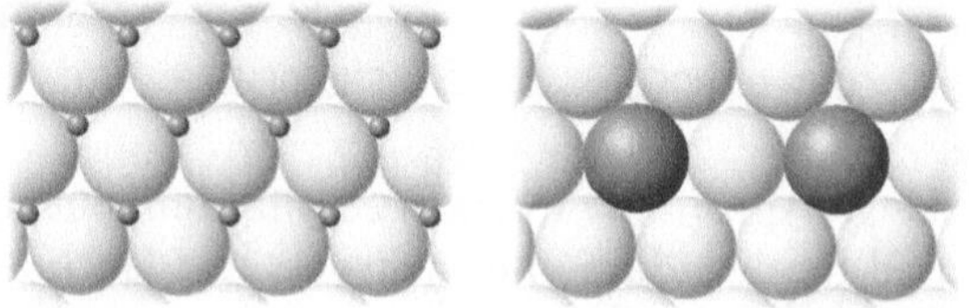

(a) Interstitial atoms (b) Substitutional atoms

FIGURE O.2 **Alloys. (a)** The solute atoms may be interstitial atoms, fitting into holes in the crystal lattice. **(b)** The solute atoms can also substitute for one of the lattice atoms.

FIGURE O.3 A photomicrograph of the surface of a heterogeneous mixture of lead and tin.

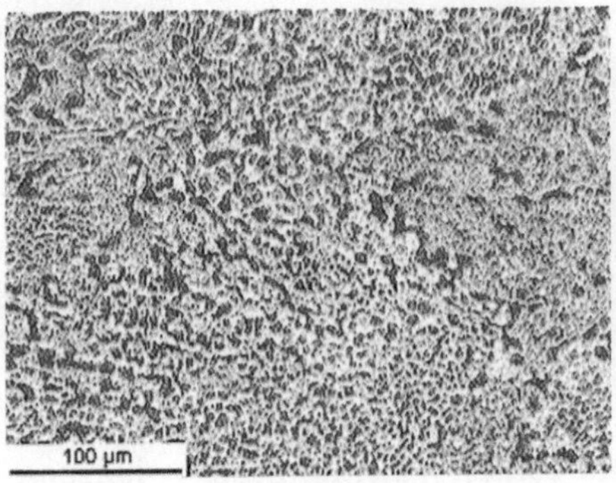

If the size constraints are not met, then a mixture of the two component elements will likely be a heterogeneous alloy. If such a mixture is viewed under a microscope, regions of different composition and crystal structure are seen (Figure O.3).

The macroscopic properties of an alloy will vary, depending on the ratio of the elements in the mixture. Melting point, electrical resistance, thermal conductivity, ductility, and other properties can be similarly adjusted by changing the composition of the alloy. This allows scientists and engineers to prepare materials for use with optimal properties.

Intermetallic alloys are actually compounds. They have a definite stoichiometry and formula. Examples of intermetallic compounds include $CuAl_2$, Mg_2Pb, and $AuCu_3$. In general, intermetallic compounds are likely to form if there is a substantial difference in the electronegativity of the two elements. In Mg_2Pb, for example, the electronegativities of Mg and Pb are 1.3 and 2.3, respectively.

On occasion, the formation of an intermetallic alloy will be undesirable. In microelectronics, for example, intermetallic compounds such as Au_5Al_2 and $AuAl_2$ can form if these metals are in contact. The result is a poor electrical connection because neither intermetallic compound is a good conductor.

It is interesting to note how the general chemical parameters such as atom size and electronegativity can be used to understand alloys. Metals and their alloys are good examples of how changes in the atomic composition and structure of a crystalline substance can have profound effects on its macroscopic chemical and physical characteristics.

O-2 Acid Catalysts

In Section 14-2, you learned that catalysts are substances that accelerate chemical reactions without being consumed themselves. Heterogeneous catalysts exist in a different phase from the reactants. For example, finely ground MnO_2 catalyzes the decomposition of hydrogen peroxide (Figure 14.4). Homogeneous catalysts, on the other hand, exist in the same phase as the reactants. Acids and bases are two common types of homogeneous catalysts.

Acid catalysts are often used in the synthesis of organic molecules, and an example is an esterification reaction. An ester is produced from the condensation reaction of a carboxylic acid and an alcohol (Section 23-4). For example, the reaction of acetic acid with methanol produces methyl acetate and water.

$$CH_3\overset{\overset{\displaystyle O}{\|}}{C}OH + HOCH_3 \rightleftharpoons CH_3\overset{\overset{\displaystyle O}{\|}}{C}OCH_3 + H_2O$$

Without a catalyst, the system is slow to reach equilibrium, but the rate of the process is greatly increased by the addition of a strong acid (such as HCl or H_2SO_4).

The acid catalyzes two steps in the reaction mechanism. First, the acid protonates the carbonyl oxygen (the O atom of the C=O group) on the acetic acid molecule.

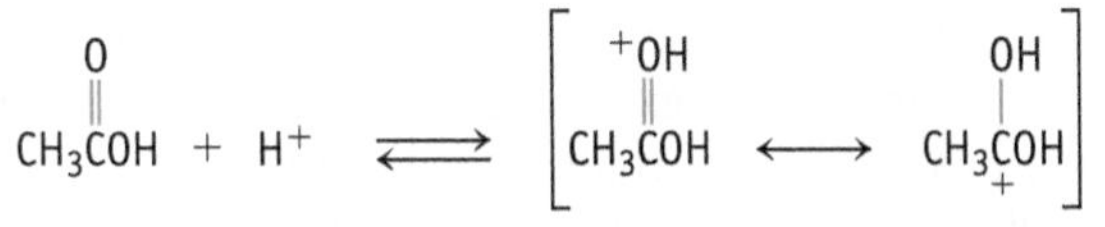

Protonation weakens the carbon-oxygen double bond, increasing the positive character of the carbon atom. The carbon atom bonds to the oxygen atom of methanol, producing a tetrahedral intermediate, and a proton is returned to the solution.

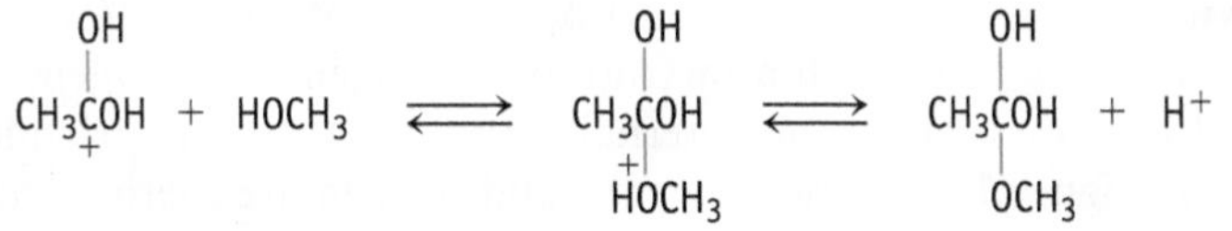

In the second catalyzed part of the reaction, a hydroxide group is protonated, then removed as water.

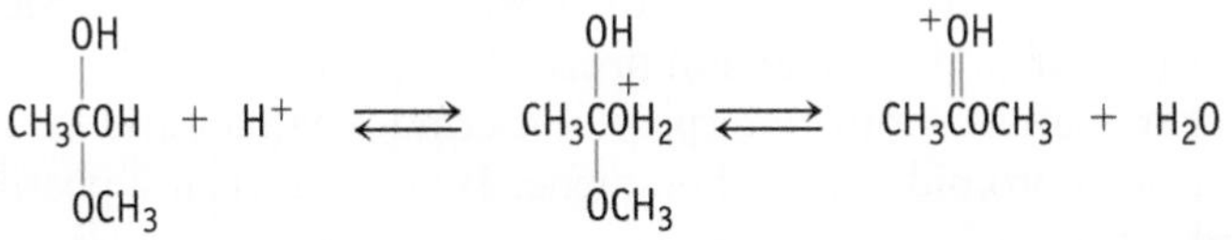

Finally, a proton is lost, resulting in the formation of methyl acetate.

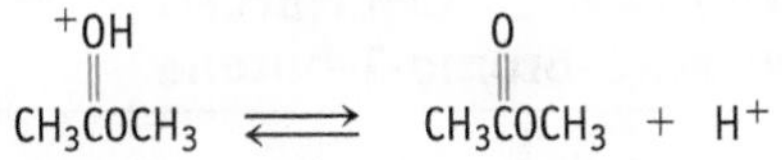

Remember, catalysts are not consumed in chemical reactions. Although protons appear twice in the mechanism as reactants, they also appear twice as products. Overall, there is no net production or consumption of protons in the reaction.

An ester can be decomposed by hydrolysis (i.e., reaction with water). This process is also acid catalyzed. The mechanism for acid catalyzed hydrolysis is exactly the reverse of the esterification reaction.

It is important to know that although a catalyst increases the rate of a chemical reaction, it does not influence whether a reaction is product-favored or reactant-favored at equilibrium. A catalyst simply enables a reaction to reach equilibrium more quickly. However, many reactions can be made to favor either the formation of reactants or the formation of products by controlling the concentrations of reactants and products. In the esterification reaction, removing water from the system favors formation of the ester; adding water favors hydrolysis. This is an application of Le Chatelier's principle (Section 15-6).

O-3 The Interplay of Kinetics and Thermodynamics

In the main text, you have learned about both thermodynamics and kinetics. Thermodynamics tells you *whether* a chemical reaction can occur on its own. Kinetics tells you how *fast* a reaction occurs. Just because a reaction is product-favored at equilibrium, that is, thermodynamically favored, does not mean that it will necessarily proceed quickly. For example, at 25 °C and atmospheric pressure, $\Delta_r G°$ for the conversion of diamond to graphite has a value of -2.9 kJ/mol-rxn.

Thermodynamics favors the transformation. Because it has a lower free energy, graphite is more **thermodynamically stable** than diamond under these conditions. But the activation energy for this process, a kinetics parameter, is very large. This causes the reaction to be so slow that we do not have to worry about it on an ordinary timescale. A diamond's long existence under normal conditions is due to the slow kinetics of the process, rather than to its thermodynamics. Although diamond is thermodynamically unstable compared to graphite, diamond is said to be **kinetically stable** due to the large activation energy for the process.

Likewise the transformation of hydrogen gas and oxygen gas to water

$$2\ H_2(g) + O_2(g) \rightarrow 2\ H_2O(g)$$

is thermodynamically very favored with a $\Delta_r G°$ value of −457 kJ/mol-rxn at 25 °C. Yet a balloon can be filled with a mixture of hydrogen and oxygen and float in a room for a long time until some external source of energy is provided such as a lighted candle (Figure 1.15). The hydrogen and oxygen are thermodynamically unstable with respect to water at this temperature but are kinetically stable due to the activation energy for the reaction being large enough that ambient conditions do not provide enough energy to overcome this barrier to reaction. Once some energy is provided, the reaction of some molecules proceeds; the energy released in the reaction of this small number of molecules then provides the energy needed for more of the reaction to occur, and the reaction proceeds explosively.

Yet another example of the interplay of thermodynamics and kinetics is the addition of hydrogen bromide to 1,3-butadiene. Two products are possible: 3-bromo-1-butene and 1-bromo-2-butene.

$H_2C{=}CHCH{=}CH_2 + HBr \rightarrow$	$H_2C{=}CHCHBrCH_3$ 3-bromo-1-butene	+	$BrCH_2CH{=}CHCH_3$ 1-bromo-2-butene
Yield at −80 °C	81%		19%
Yield at 45 °C	15%		85%

Depending on the temperature, different ratios of these two products are obtained. At a low temperature, such as −80 °C, 3-bromo-1-butene predominates, whereas at a higher temperature, such as 45 °C, 1-bromo-2-butene is the major product. Why is this so?

The reaction coordinate diagram for this reaction is shown in Figure O.4. Butadiene first forms an intermediate, called an allylic carbocation, by the addition of a hydrogen ion from the hydrogen bromide. This carbocation can then form either of the two products by addition of the bromide ion.

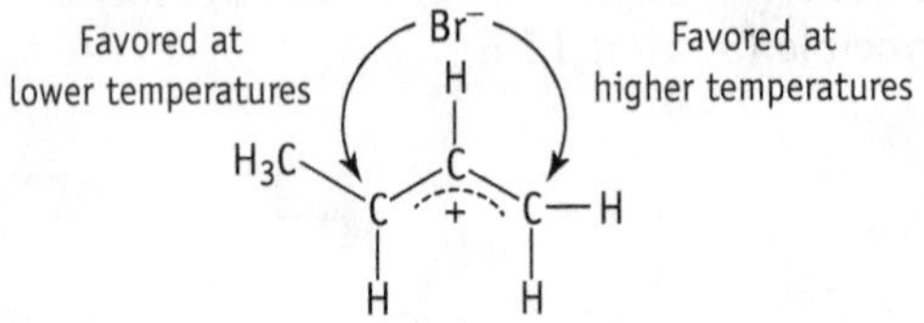

The point of attack of Br⁻ on the allylic carbocation depends on temperature.

At −80 °C, the product ratio is influenced by the rates of the chemical reactions and is said to be under **kinetic control**. The activation energy for the formation of 3-bromo-1-butene is smaller, so this product forms faster and is thus present in a larger amount.

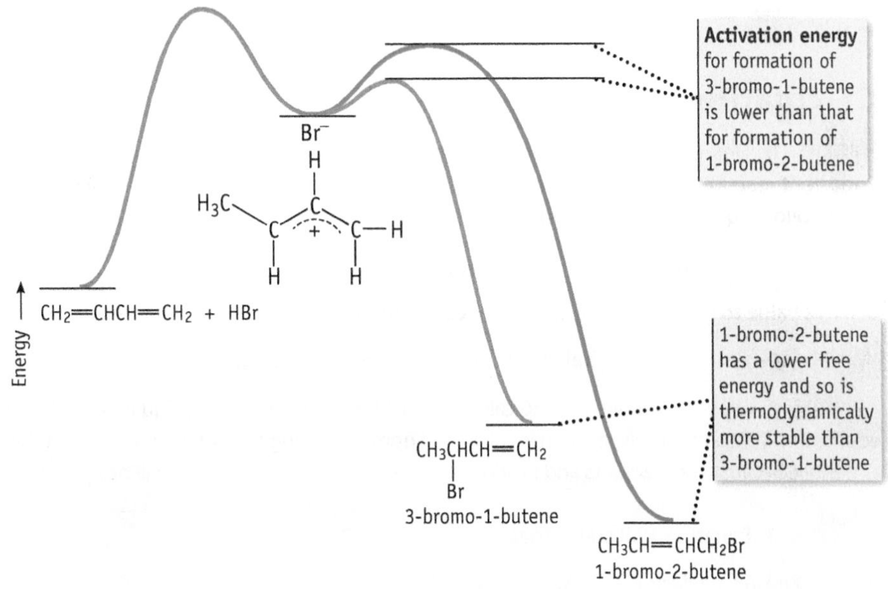

FIGURE O.4 Reaction coordinate diagram for the addition of HBr to 1,3-butadiene

As the temperature is raised, the number of molecules following the two paths is increased, and the ratio of products changes. More molecules have sufficient energy to form both products. In addition, reformation of the allylic carbocation and Br^- from the two product molecules (the reverse of the second step of this reaction) also occurs. This provides a mechanism allowing the two products to reach equilibrium.

$$\text{3-bromo-1-butene} \rightleftharpoons \text{1-bromo-2-butene}$$

At 45 °C, the ratio of the two products is established by this equilibrium. A reaction run under these conditions, in which the ratio of products is defined by the equilibrium between the species, is said to be under **thermodynamic control**, that is, thermodynamics is controlling the ratio of products.

In studying chemical reactions, therefore, both kinetics and thermodynamics play important roles. It is important that you learn about both in your study of general chemistry.

O-4 The Relationship of the Equilibrium Constant and the Standard Gibbs Free Energy Change

In the main text, you learned about the following relationship between the equilibrium constant, K, and the standard Gibbs free energy change, $\Delta_r G°$

$$\Delta_r G° = -RT \ln K$$

We can solve this equation for K by the following steps. We first divide both sides of the equation by $-RT$

$$-\frac{\Delta_r G°}{RT} = \ln K$$

and then take the antilog of both sides of the equation.

$$K = e^{-\frac{\Delta_r G°}{RT}}$$

This equation can be used to calculate the value of K if the value of $\Delta_r G°$ is known.

EXAMPLE

Calculating K_p from $\Delta_r G°$

Problem Determine the standard free energy change, $\Delta_r G°$, for the environmentally important reaction of nitrogen monoxide and oxygen to form nitrogen dioxide, according to the following chemical equation at 25.0 °C

$$2\ NO(g) + O_2(g) \rightleftharpoons 2\ NO_2(g)$$

Use this value to calculate the equilibrium constant for this reaction at this temperature.

What Do You Know? Values of $\Delta_f G°$ are given in Appendix L.

Strategy Values of $\Delta_f G°$ are used to calculate $\Delta_r G°$ for the reaction using Equation 18.8. The equilibrium constant for this reaction is calculated from $\Delta_r G°$ using the equation derived in this appendix. Because the reactants and products are gases, the calculated value will be K_p.

Solution Equation 18.8 states that

$$\Delta_r G° = \Sigma n\Delta_f G°(\text{products}) - \Sigma n\Delta_f G°(\text{reactants})$$

$$= (2\ \text{mol NO}_2(g)/\text{mol-rxn})\ \Delta_f G°[NO_2(g)]$$
$$- \{(2\ \text{mol NO(g)/mol-rxn})\ \Delta_f G°[NO(g)] + (1\ \text{mol O}_2(g)/\text{mol-rxn})\ \Delta_f G°[O_2(g)]\}$$

$$= (2\ \text{mol NO}_2(g)/\text{mol-rxn})(51.23\ \text{kJ/mol})$$
$$- [(2\ \text{mol NO(g)/mol-rxn})(86.58\ \text{kJ/mol}) + (1\ \text{mol O}_2(g)/\text{mol-rxn})(0\ \text{kJ/mol})]$$

$$= -70.70\ \text{kJ/mol-rxn}$$

This is then used in the equation derived in this appendix to solve for K_p.

$$K_p = e^{-\frac{\Delta_r G°}{RT}}$$

$$= e^{-\frac{-70.70\ \text{kJ/mol-rxn}}{(0.0083145\ \text{kJ/K}\cdot\text{mol})(298.2\ \text{K})}}$$

$$K_p = 2.4 \times 10^{12}$$

Think about Your Answer The value of $\Delta_r G°$ is less than zero, indicating that this reaction is product-favored at equilibrium. The value of K_p calculated is greater than 1 as it should be for such a process.

Check Your Understanding

Determine the value of the equilibrium constant, K_p, for the decomposition of water according to the following equation at 25.0 °C

$$2\ H_2O(g) \rightleftharpoons 2\ H_2(g) + O_2(g)$$

Answer: $K_p = 8 \times 10^{-81}$

Index / Glossary

Italicized page numbers indicate pages containing illustrations, and those followed by "t" indicate tables. Glossary terms, printed in boldface, are defined here as well as in the text.

Periodic Table of the Elements

- MAIN GROUP METALS
- TRANSITION METALS
- METALLOIDS
- NONMETALS

Key: Uranium — 92 (Atomic number) — U (Symbol) — 238.0289 (Atomic weight)

Period	1A (1)	2A (2)	3B (3)	4B (4)	5B (5)	6B (6)	7B (7)	8B (8)	8B (9)	8B (10)	1B (11)	2B (12)	3A (13)	4A (14)	5A (15)	6A (16)	7A (17)	8A (18)
1	Hydrogen 1 H 1.0079																	Helium 2 He 4.0026
2	Lithium 3 Li 6.941	Beryllium 4 Be 9.0122											Boron 5 B 10.811	Carbon 6 C 12.011	Nitrogen 7 N 14.0067	Oxygen 8 O 15.9994	Fluorine 9 F 18.9984	Neon 10 Ne 20.1797
3	Sodium 11 Na 22.9898	Magnesium 12 Mg 24.3050											Aluminum 13 Al 26.9815	Silicon 14 Si 28.0855	Phosphorus 15 P 30.9738	Sulfur 16 S 32.066	Chlorine 17 Cl 35.4527	Argon 18 Ar 39.948
4	Potassium 19 K 39.0983	Calcium 20 Ca 40.078	Scandium 21 Sc 44.9559	Titanium 22 Ti 47.867	Vanadium 23 V 50.9415	Chromium 24 Cr 51.9961	Manganese 25 Mn 54.9380	Iron 26 Fe 55.845	Cobalt 27 Co 58.9332	Nickel 28 Ni 58.6934	Copper 29 Cu 63.546	Zinc 30 Zn 65.38	Gallium 31 Ga 69.723	Germanium 32 Ge 72.63	Arsenic 33 As 74.9216	Selenium 34 Se 78.96	Bromine 35 Br 79.904	Krypton 36 Kr 83.798
5	Rubidium 37 Rb 85.4678	Strontium 38 Sr 87.62	Yttrium 39 Y 88.9059	Zirconium 40 Zr 91.224	Niobium 41 Nb 92.9064	Molybdenum 42 Mo 95.96	Technetium 43 Tc (97.907)	Ruthenium 44 Ru 101.07	Rhodium 45 Rh 102.9055	Palladium 46 Pd 106.42	Silver 47 Ag 107.8682	Cadmium 48 Cd 112.411	Indium 49 In 114.818	Tin 50 Sn 118.710	Antimony 51 Sb 121.760	Tellurium 52 Te 127.60	Iodine 53 I 126.9045	Xenon 54 Xe 131.293
6	Cesium 55 Cs 132.9055	Barium 56 Ba 137.327	Lanthanum 57 La 138.9055	Hafnium 72 Hf 178.49	Tantalum 73 Ta 180.9479	Tungsten 74 W 183.84	Rhenium 75 Re 186.207	Osmium 76 Os 190.23	Iridium 77 Ir 192.22	Platinum 78 Pt 195.084	Gold 79 Au 196.9666	Mercury 80 Hg 200.59	Thallium 81 Tl 204.3833	Lead 82 Pb 207.2	Bismuth 83 Bi 208.9804	Polonium 84 Po (208.98)	Astatine 85 At (209.99)	Radon 86 Rn (222.02)
7	Francium 87 Fr (223.02)	Radium 88 Ra (226.0254)	Actinium 89 Ac (227.0278)	Rutherfordium 104 Rf (265)	Dubnium 105 Db (268)	Seaborgium 106 Sg (271)	Bohrium 107 Bh (270)	Hassium 108 Hs (277)	Meitnerium 109 Mt (276)	Darmstadtium 110 Ds (281)	Roentgenium 111 Rg (280)	Copernicium 112 Cn (285)	Ununtrium 113 Uut Discovered 2004	Flerovium 114 Fl (289)	Ununpentium 115 Uup Discovered 2004	Livermorium 116 Lv (292)	Ununseptium 117 Uus Discovered 2010	Ununoctium 118 Uuo Discovered 2002

Lanthanides	Cerium 58 Ce 140.116	Praseodymium 59 Pr 140.9076	Neodymium 60 Nd 144.242	Promethium 61 Pm (144.91)	Samarium 62 Sm 150.36	Europium 63 Eu 151.964	Gadolinium 64 Gd 157.25	Terbium 65 Tb 158.9254	Dysprosium 66 Dy 162.50	Holmium 67 Ho 164.9303	Erbium 68 Er 167.26	Thulium 69 Tm 168.9342	Ytterbium 70 Yb 173.054	Lutetium 71 Lu 174.9668
Actinides	Thorium 90 Th 232.0381	Protactinium 91 Pa 231.0359	Uranium 92 U 238.0289	Neptunium 93 Np (237.0482)	Plutonium 94 Pu (244.664)	Americium 95 Am (243.061)	Curium 96 Cm (247.07)	Berkelium 97 Bk (247.07)	Californium 98 Cf (251.08)	Einsteinium 99 Es (252.08)	Fermium 100 Fm (257.10)	Mendelevium 101 Md (258.10)	Nobelium 102 No (259.10)	Lawrencium 103 Lr (262.11)

Note: Atomic masses are 2009 IUPAC values (up to four decimal places). Numbers in parentheses are atomic masses or mass numbers of the most stable isotope of an element.

Standard Colors for Atoms in Molecular Models

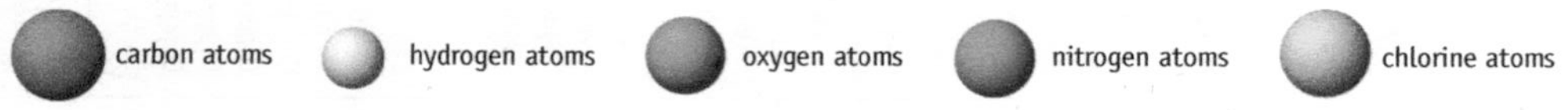

STANDARD ATOMIC WEIGHTS OF THE ELEMENTS 2009 Based on relative atomic mass of $^{12}C = 12$, where ^{12}C is a neutral atom in its nuclear and electronic ground state.†

Name	Symbol	Atomic Number	Atomic Weight
Actinium*	Ac	89	(227)
Aluminum	Al	13	26.9815386(8)
Americium*	Am	95	(243)
Antimony	Sb	51	121.760(1)
Argon	Ar	18	39.948(1)
Arsenic	As	33	74.92160(2)
Astatine*	At	85	(210)
Barium	Ba	56	137.327(7)
Berkelium*	Bk	97	(247)
Beryllium	Be	4	9.012182(3)
Bismuth	Bi	83	208.98040(1)
Bohrium	Bh	107	(270)
Boron	B	5	10.811(7)
Bromine	Br	35	79.904(1)
Cadmium	Cd	48	112.411(8)
Cesium	Cs	55	132.9054519(2)
Calcium	Ca	20	40.078(4)
Californium*	Cf	98	(251)
Carbon	C	6	12.0107(8)
Cerium	Ce	58	140.116(1)
Chlorine	Cl	17	35.453(2)
Chromium	Cr	24	51.9961(6)
Cobalt	Co	27	58.933195(5)
Copernicium	Cn	112	(285)
Copper	Cu	29	63.546(3)
Curium*	Cm	96	(247)
Darmstadtium	Ds	110	(281)
Dubnium	Db	105	(268)
Dysprosium	Dy	66	162.500(1)
Einsteinium*	Es	99	(252)
Erbium	Er	68	167.259(3)
Europium	Eu	63	151.964(1)
Fermium*	Fm	100	(257)
Flerovium	Fl	114	(289)
Fluorine	F	9	18.9984032(5)
Francium*	Fr	87	(223)
Gadolinium	Gd	64	157.25(3)
Gallium	Ga	31	69.723(1)
Germanium	Ge	32	72.63(1)
Gold	Au	79	196.966569(4)
Hafnium	Hf	72	178.49(2)
Hassium	Hs	108	(277)
Helium	He	2	4.002602(2)
Holmium	Ho	67	164.93032(2)
Hydrogen	H	1	1.00794(7)
Indium	In	49	114.818(3)
Iodine	I	53	126.90447(3)
Iridium	Ir	77	192.217(3)
Iron	Fe	26	55.845(2)
Krypton	Kr	36	83.798(2)
Lanthanum	La	57	138.90547(7)
Lawrencium*	Lr	103	(262)
Lead	Pb	82	207.2(1)
Lithium	Li	3	6.941(2)
Livermorium	Lv	116	(292)
Lutetium	Lu	71	174.9668(1)
Magnesium	Mg	12	24.3050(6)
Manganese	Mn	25	54.938045(5)
Meitnerium	Mt	109	(276)

Name	Symbol	Atomic Number	Atomic Weight
Mendelevium*	Md	101	(258)
Mercury	Hg	80	200.59(2)
Molybdenum	Mo	42	95.96(2)
Neodymium	Nd	60	144.242(3)
Neon	Ne	10	20.1797(6)
Neptunium*	Np	93	(237)
Nickel	Ni	28	58.6934(4)
Niobium	Nb	41	92.90638(2)
Nitrogen	N	7	14.0067(2)
Nobelium*	No	102	(259)
Osmium	Os	76	190.23(3)
Oxygen	O	8	15.9994(3)
Palladium	Pd	46	106.42(1)
Phosphorus	P	15	30.973762(2)
Platinum	Pt	78	195.084(9)
Plutonium*	Pu	94	(244)
Polonium*	Po	84	(209)
Potassium	K	19	39.0983(1)
Praseodymium	Pr	59	140.90765(2)
Promethium*	Pm	61	(145)
Protactinium*	Pa	91	231.03588(2)
Radium*	Ra	88	(226)
Radon*	Rn	86	(222)
Rhenium	Re	75	186.207(1)
Rhodium	Rh	45	102.90550(2)
Roentgenium	Rg	111	(280)
Rubidium	Rb	37	85.4678(3)
Ruthenium	Ru	44	101.07(2)
Rutherfordium	Rf	104	(265)
Samarium	Sm	62	150.36(2)
Scandium	Sc	21	44.955912(6)
Seaborgium	Sg	106	(271)
Selenium	Se	34	78.96(3)
Silicon	Si	14	28.0855(3)
Silver	Ag	47	107.8682(2)
Sodium	Na	11	22.98976928(2)
Strontium	Sr	38	87.62(1)
Sulfur	S	16	32.065(5)
Tantalum	Ta	73	180.94788(2)
Technetium*	Tc	43	(98)
Tellurium	Te	52	127.60(3)
Terbium	Tb	65	158.92535(2)
Thallium	Tl	81	204.3833(2)
Thorium*	Th	90	232.03806(2)
Thulium	Tm	69	168.93421(2)
Tin	Sn	50	118.710(7)
Titanium	Ti	22	47.867(1)
Tungsten	W	74	183.84(1)
Ununoctium	Uuo	118	(294)
Ununpentium	Uup	115	(288)
Ununseptium	Uus	117	(294)
Ununtrium	Uut	113	(284)
Uranium*	U	92	238.02891(3)
Vanadium	V	23	50.9415(1)
Xenon	Xe	54	131.293(6)
Ytterbium	Yb	70	173.054(5)
Yttrium	Y	39	88.90585(2)
Zinc	Zn	30	65.38(2)
Zirconium	Zr	40	91.224(2)

†The atomic weights of many elements can vary depending on the origin and treatment of the sample. This is particularly true for Li; commercially available lithium-containing materials have Li atomic weights in the range of 6.939 and 6.996. The uncertainties in atomic weight values are given in parentheses following the last significant figure to which they are attributed.

*Elements with no stable nuclide; the value given in parentheses is the atomic mass number of the isotope of longest known half-life. However, three such elements (Th, Pa, and U) have a characteristic terrestrial isotopic composition, and the atomic weight is tabulated for these. **http://www.chem.qmw.ac.uk/iupac/AtWt/**